INTEGRATED PRINCIPLES OF ZOOLOGY

INTEGRATED PRINCIPLES OF ZOOLOGY

FOURTH EDITION

Cleveland P. Hickman, Ph.D.

Department of Zoology, DePauw University,
Greencastle, Indiana

With 751 illustrations

The C. V. Mosby Company

Saint Louis 1970

Fourth edition

Previous editions copyrighted 1955, 1961, 1966

Printed in the United States of America

Standard Book Number 8016-2183-6

Library of Congress Catalog Card Number 78-106146

Distributed in Great Britain by Henry Kimpton, London

To

Cleve, Jr., Mary Lee, Betty Jeanne, Clifford, and Janice

who have made my life worthwhile

• PREFACE

● In this revision the text has been reorganized into nine parts. Part 1 deals with an approach to the major concepts and principles that compose and influence life in all its aspects. In Part 2 the student is introduced to the fundamental molecular plan and structure that is the basis of all life. This part may be called a refinement of the classic morphologic structure that follows logically in Part 3. This part naturally stresses the structure and physiology of cells and the way they are put together to form the architecture of the living body. Part 4 shows the diverse types or patterns of animal life and how they are classified. This part indicates how the various biomolecular combinations that make up life are arranged in a logical evolutionary relationship so far as is known. Part 5 leads the student into an understanding of how animals have met the requirements of life in their body systems and how they have specialized for survival. How life continues from one generation to another is the theme of Part 6, which shows how patterns develop and are transmitted with a fair degree of stability and uniformity. Part 7 treats of one of the greatest concepts in the life sciences—the evolutionary doctrine that tries to explain the origin of the great diversity of life and how the variety of organisms have arisen by modifications from preexisting species. This part also shows how life may have arisen from inanimate matter and how primitive conditions could ultimately have led to the existence of life. Stress is placed upon the appearance of man in evolution and the significance of his role in the evolutionary process. Part 8 shows how life is related to and is dependent upon environmental conditions. The concept of the ecosystem and man's relation to it emphasizes the important role the ecosystem plays in shaping the conditions to which every animal is subjected throughout its existence. This part explains how man, above all other animals, bears the responsibility for directing the factors that will make for the most beneficial adjustments to the totality of environmental relations. For an understanding of the animal's reactions to its environment, stress is placed upon animal behavior and how a basic understanding of the animal's reactions can aid in interpreting the psychic foundation of the life process. In Part 9 the development of the science of zoology is considered. Its major aim is to perceive how man in his long quest for an understanding of the meaning of life has arrived at certain basic concepts. It is my hope that the student will gain some appreciation of the laborious work of dedicated scholars in seeking scientific truth. The student should also see from the evidence at hand that the study of life is an ever-continuing process and that new facets of understanding are continually appearing as breakthroughs are made. Perhaps above everything else the student will realize the basic unity of all scientific disciplines that are marshaled together in working out the meaning of that unique matter and energy which make up life.

In a more specific way I have tried in the present edition to incorporate the latest developments in the zoologic field. In this day and time new breakthroughs in the life sciences are commonplace and many aspects of knowledge are quickly outdated. New chapters have been added and some of the older ones entirely rewritten. For the clarification of certain concepts nearly a hundred new illustrations have been inserted and several old ones have been redrawn or replaced. More emphasis has been given to the molecular aspects of biology, and a more extensive background of chemical knowledge is presented. The enormous problems of the ecosystem have merited an entirely new chapter. Only in recent years has man become conscious of the sad plight of his environment. This awakening to the problems of pollution and wasted resources has demanded urgent action. These and other problems of his surroundings will require all of man's skills to resolve.

This edition is a continuation of certain basic concepts of zoologic knowledge that were started more than fifteen years ago and that have been retained with such variations as new knowledge demands. Beginning with the first edition many professional zoologists have read and have given suggestions and criticisms to the various editions. I wish to acknowledge especially the aid furnished by the following individuals: J. T. Bagnara, C. L. Bieber, C. J. D. Brown, W. H. Brown, E. L. Cockrum, P. A. Dehnel, R. W. Dexter, C. J. Ellis, F. D. Fuller, J. Heath, D. Heyneman, C. P. Hickman, Jr., W. D. Ivey, C. H. Lowe, Jr., G. O. Mackie, W. E. Martin, R. Rector, A. E. Reynolds, H. W. Schoenborn, W. L. Shapeero, and J. F. Vernberg. I am especially indebted to Professor J. T. Crofts of the Chicago City Junior College for his keen eye in detecting typographic errors and for his helpful suggestions.

Scores of professors using the various editions have written in suggestions and helpful hints that have been incorporated in the present edition. It is impossible to mention the names of all these professors, but their suggestions have been gratefully received. I hope that those who use this edition will continue this policy.

For copyrighted photographs, line illustrations, and electron micrographs I am indebted to Dr. Warren Andrew of the Indiana University Medical School, Dr. Jan Gibbons of Harvard University, Dr. George E. Palade of the Rockefeller University, the Encyclopaedia Britannica, the McGraw-Hill Book Company, the Natural Science Museum of Cleveland, Ohio, Dr. W. L. Shapeero of the University of Washington, and others whose names are indicated in the pertinent legends.

For the technical aspects of the revision a few need special mention. The artistic skill of Clifford M. Hickman has been employed in making most of the new illustrations for this edition. The new text material has been typed by Janice H. Thatcher. My wife, Frances M. Hickman, has assumed much of the burden of checking details of organization and helping with the photography, illustrations, and proofreading of all the editions.

Finally, I assume the responsibility for all errors that may appear in the text.

Cleveland P. Hickman

• CONTENTS

PART ONE

BASIC CONCEPTS OF LIFE

● The study of the life sciences is in a period of transition. Many of its basic concepts are recent and many of the older ones are being revised. Much of this advancement is due to newer techniques that have opened up a whole new world of insights never dreamed of by biologists a few years ago. More and more the study of the life sciences has become central in all sciences. This revolution in the biologic sciences has come with dramatic suddenness. One fundamental discovery follows another, or, it may be stated in another way, that one discovery opens up new vistas for other discoveries. It is as though the background of the life sciences has produced over a long period of time an extensive accumulation of facts that are now fitted into conceptional schemes that actually explain what has seemed so mysterious before.

The basic problem of life is still unsolved, but a firm foundation for understanding it is being laid. The concepts of traditional biology, which have been so long in emerging as man with his mind stumbled through the maze of life's complicated nature, have paved the way for the reception of new ideas that have developed from molecular biology. But an application of the principles and laws of all scientific disciplines is called into action to unravel the secret of our greatest mystery—life itself. The sciences of physics and chemistry are useful at every step of advancement. The physical laws that apply to the nonliving world should also apply to the living, for it is the firm belief of biologists that living matter is made up of the same elements found in inorganic material, except that they are differently organized. As scientific evidence accumulates, the basic differences between the living and nonliving tend to disappear.

However, there are some intrinsic distinctions between the living and the nonliving. If we consider only individual phenomena, we find no fundamental difference between the two. But the distinctive differences lie in the specific arrangements of the life units. Life represents a higher level in the hierarchy of matter. This level has events not shared by the nonliving. The chief task of the student of life sciences is to establish the laws and principles governing the order and organization of living matter. He will discover that life's patterns (organic units) are transient units through which basic matter is continually flowing and that these patterns are continually changing under the impact of environmental influences. Since life represents a higher and unique level of organization with chemical molecules in more complicated forms, it is evident that biologic order surpasses the laws applying to the nonliving because each new level of matter has its own properties and laws.

CHAPTER 1

• SOME ASPECTS OF LIFE

WHAT IS LIFE?*

● The concept that living things on this planet came from the nonliving is rather firmly established in the minds of biologists, even though it is highly speculative regarding how this phenomenon occurred. In recent years many scientists have advanced theories to explain the origin of life. Some of these theories have experimental evidence to back them up to some degree. Although it is difficult to define life, the difference between the living and the nonliving is becoming clearer as scientists understand more about the basic substance of life. Both the living and the nonliving share the same kind of chemical elements, and both follow the law of the conservation of energy. The essential difference between the two appears to be organization. The living organism has combined atoms and molecules into patterns that have no counterparts in the nonliving. Examples of these patterns are the complex macromolecules of proteins and nucleic acids that give rise to the properties of life. Such combinations have dynamic systems of coordinated chemical or physical functions or activities that, taken as a whole, distinguish the living from the nonliving. The living differ from the nonliving not so much in qualities as in the way its substance is organized into unique patterns of position and shape. The organism is a system of interwoven and overlapping hierarchies of organization.

Almost any single criterion one may take of the living has its counterpart in the nonliving. Most characteristics of life are found to some extent in the inanimate world, which may indicate the close relationship of the two. Only animate things, however, have combined these properties into unique functional and structural patterns. One of the most fundamental properties of living matter is perhaps its uniqueness in reproducing itself, but there are other important aspects that deserve attention. Life illustrates a unique integrity under the impact of the environment so that it can adjust itself by its own energy.

Another important difference that the living possess is the intimate relationship between life and its environment. The evolutionary history of the organism has placed it specifically in certain environments and has determined its physical properties and different capabilities. Life and the environment are part and parcel of each other, and its innate behavior patterns and physiologic capabilities determine how well it gets along and adjusts itself to changing environmental conditions. This relationship between organism and environment is well shown by the behavior adjustments of correlative rhythms it must make to fluctuating surroundings. In other words, the interaction between the living and the nonliving has determined the character of life and to a certain extent the character of the earth planet on which we live. At all times in its daily living the organism is inseparable from its environment.

NATURE OF MATTER

Matter is the substance that comprises entities perceptible to the senses. The chief properties of matter are gravitation and inertia. Mass, which all material bodies have, is a measure of inertia. Matter and energy make up the universe, and these two components are interconvertible according to Einstein's theory of relativity, which is expressed in the equation Energy $= MC^2$, where M equals the mass and C equals the speed of light. This equation represents the theoretic basis for converting matter to energy. As we commonly understand matter and energy, they are separate. Matter in whatever form it may be (solid, liquid, or gas) occupies space and has weight. Energy has the ability

*Refer to Chapter 2, Principle 2.

to produce change or motion or the ability to perform work.

Matter is made up of atoms, which are the simplest form of matter possessing specific chemical properties. Chemistry recognizes 92 different atoms from the smallest (hydrogen) to the largest (uranium). About a dozen others are man made in a cyclotron and nuclear reactor. All atoms, natural or artificial, are extremely small, and their structures and properties are known by indirect physicochemical methods.

Atoms are composed of elementary particles such as electrons, protons, neutrons, photons. No one knows how many elementary particles there are, but some appear to be more elementary than others. If there is a basic stuff (elementary particle?) of the universe, no one knows what it is. The whole of atomic structure and the interaction of radiation with matter as well as the concepts of chemistry can be explained by the elementary particles of proton, electron, photon, and neutron. By electromagnetic forces these elementary particles interact with each other and produce the characteristic properties of atoms.

Both the living and the nonliving are made up of atoms. As will be pointed out later, living matter is more selective and has fewer kinds of atoms (although the same kinds are also found in the nonliving). An analysis of living matter after death shows no change in its atoms or elements. Living matter varies according to the general type of animal. Terrestrial animals have more nitrogen and sodium but less potassium, silicon, and aluminum than do aquatic forms. Marine organisms have more chloride and more water than do terrestrial organisms.

But the presence or absence of atoms alone cannot explain the fundamental difference between the living and the nonliving. The chief difference is the arrangement of atoms into huge organic macromolecules that are able to display the basic properties of life.

LEVELS OF COMPLEXITY

Life is made up of a hierarchy of structure and function, ranging all the way from the atom and molecule to the highly developed and complex community, or even to levels of the ecosystem. This concept involves the nonliving as well as the living and is commonly divided into the following levels of organization: atom, molecule, organelle, cell, tissue, organ, organism, community, and ecosystem. Starting with the atom, it is seen that each level furnishes the building stones for the units of the next higher level. Of course, one can start with a lower level than the atom, the elementary particle, of which about 70 have been found. At each level are properties that are more or less unique for that level. Molecules of water have different properties from separate hydrogen and oxygen atoms. The large macromolecules may be considered as the lowest biologic level.

It will be noted that any given level contains all the lower levels as components. All the structural levels up to and including the molecular components are common to both the animate and the inanimate.

Cells are made up of organelles, and since cells are the lowest levels that can be considered alive, it follows that an organism must have at least one cell (unicellular). Organisms other than the unicellular ones are the multicellular organisms (metazoa). A level between the unicellular and the multicellular is the protistan colony, in which the cells are more or less alike. It is thus possible for the organism as a whole to have one or the other of five levels of organization complexity—the unicellular form, the colonial form, the cell-tissue level organism, the tissue-organ level, and the organ-system level.

Levels other than those already mentioned may be distinguished in the grouping of organisms, such as species, genera, families, populations, and communities. This structural hierarchy may represent the evolutional history of matter, both the living and the nonliving. This would indicate that, level by level, matter has become organized progressively to form the hierarchy as we now have it.

It will be noted that each level has fewer units than lower levels. For instance, there are fewer tissues than cells and fewer cells than organelles. Each level also has, in addition to its own complexity, the complexities of all the lower levels. In the shift from one organization level to another, energy is expended, and when a higher level has been attained, energy is necessary to maintain that level. A price in energy is required for the new properties that are acquired by having a higher level and the environmental advantages such a level confers.

This hierarchically organized matter reveals one of the basic aspects of life in that it provides the great concept of the evolution of matter from the nonliving to the living and gives a meaningful interpretation to the whole problem of the origin of life.

COMPARISON OF THE LIVING WITH THE NONLIVING*

If one were to summarize the chief differences between living and nonliving matter, one would find certain criteria that stand out more than others do. One of the characteristics of life is that it is an action-performing system of definite boundary, undergoing a continual interchange of materials with the environment, requiring energy to run the system and matter to repair it whenever needed. This may be called a metabolic criterion, which is actually made up of three vital processes; nutrition, respiration, and synthesis. It is true that some inanimate objects could very well simulate this metabolic criterion. A steady flame, such as that of an oil lamp, has a definite boundary and continually takes up oxygen, and gives off carbon dioxide and water, just as an organism would do. The similarity, however, is superficial, as the student will discover when he studies cellular metabolism and the complex metabolic pathways of enzymatic action. The metabolic criterion is almost nonexistent in suspended animation or in seeds and spores.

The metabolic mechanism by which chemical changes are brought about is made up of teams of enzymes. Although enzymes are biologic catalysts and catalysts exist in the chemical reactions of the nonbiologic world, the enzymes have an entirely different structure, being essentially proteins. Some enzymes have in addition a prosthetic group of a metal or a coenzyme of an organic compound. Indeed, all living matter may be considered an organized system of enzymes dispersed in an aqueous solution.

Metabolism has two types—anabolism and catabolism. Anabolism is a chemical process in which simpler substances are built up into more complex ones for storage and growth and also to produce new cellular substances. On the other hand, catabolism is the breaking down of complex substances for releasing energy and the natural wear and tear on bodily structures by living processes. These two types are so woven together and so interdependent that it is difficult to separate them in the living process. As the student will see later, the body parts are in a state of flux by which interconversion of the basic substances is continuously occurring. Catabolism breaks down complex compounds for the release of energy that is needed in every aspect of life. Living matter is never the same at any two instances.

*Refer to Chapter 2, Principle 19.

Another fundamental difference between the living and the nonliving is the specific organization of the former. In general, the organism has an upper size limit and a characteristic shape, whereas such factors are variable among nonliving substances. More basic still is the specialization of parts in the organism as expressed in the hierarchy described above. Organization, as we have seen, is one of the key criteria, and this involves different parts, each with its special function. Cells, tissues, and organs, so characteristic of life, have no counterparts in the nonliving world. Furthermore, a living system is a highly permanent form of matter, and its basic pattern was laid down perhaps in the first cells.

All living matter has certain basic properties of irritability, conductivity, movement, excretion, secretion, absorption, respiration, reproduction, and growth. As will be explained later, these functions form the basis for the development of the specialized tissues that are characteristic of all organisms. Each of these tissues is made up of the basic structures of cells, intercellular substances, and body fluids of various kinds that bathe the cells. Of all these properties, that of reproduction must be considered the most fundamental property distinguishing a living thing. This property of reproduction and its mutant types, or variables under the influence of natural selection, have made possible the course of evolution by which present living forms are found as they are.

WHERE IS LIFE FOUND?

At present there is no convincing evidence that life exists elsewhere than on our planet Earth. Nor is there evidence that the physical conditions, which made life possible on this planet, are also duplicated elsewhere in the universe. But the immensity of the universe with its countless billions of stars and other bodies is beyond man's comprehension, and that similar conditions might be found elsewhere is within the realm of possibility. Matter is found within the universe as gas cloud, dust, rocky bodies, and stars. Stars are gathered together to form galaxies. According to astronomic calculations, stars are vast reservoirs where there are conversions of matter and energy. Within stars there has occurred the evolution of the elements with which we are acquainted here on our planet. Stars apparently have life histories. Some are young and others old. Their properties change with time in their life history. Some stars die and return their matter and energy to interstellar space; others are born, probably from the same substances released by the disintegration of the older stars. Cosmic evolution is as real as is organic evolution on a smaller scale. But it is impossible to think of life within a star because of temperature and other conditions. If life is present elsewhere in the universe, it must be on satellites of stars. Only there would one find temperature and density conditions that might support life.

The old theory of the origin of life on earth from spores or similar bodies carried to this planet is not worthy of consideration. Such bodies could not withstand cosmic radiation, and it is simply "passing the buck" as far as explaining the origin of living matter is concerned.

It is possible that life may exist under different conditions from those under which it does on earth. All such matters are highly speculative and are not backed up by a shred of evidence. In recent years some study has been made of certain meteorites that contain a variety of hydrocarbons. Carbonaceous meteorites are not common, and the view that they may carry evidence of life from extraterrestrial sources has aroused some interest. Investigation has shown that organic material (hydrocarbons, fatty and aromatic acids, water, etc.) is found as microstructures embedded in the meteorite matrix. It is not known with certainty just where these meteorites originated—whether they are of lunar, comet, or solar nebula origin. At present it is impossible to determine whether or not such substances are abiologic or of extraterrestrial biologic origin. It is possible that such substances are merely contaminations from our own planet and therefore without significance in speculating about life beyond our planet.

BIOCHEMICAL BASIS OF LIFE*

Enough has been discussed in previous topics to indicate that living matter is made up of molecules that have biochemical roles. Although this aspect of life will be discussed more fully later, it will suffice here to point out the significance of the biochemical background in a resume of the general features of life. An understanding of modern biology requires an understanding of certain basic biochemical and biophysical principles. Both unity and diversity are found in the biochemical plan of animals. There are striking similarities and also striking diversities in the biochemical plans of living matter. Organisms have different ways and patterns of arriving at the same end in biochemistry, just as they have divergent bodily processes.

Animals have only a fractional part of the chemical atoms found in nature. Hydrogen, oxygen, nitrogen, and carbon make up 98% to 99% of living substance (protoplasm). Some 25 to 30 other atoms are also found, many of which have been assigned restricted roles in the life process. But others, such as calcium, iron, and sodium, have wider and more general roles, yet are far less common than the "big four." The predominant elements of animals—C, N, O, H, P, and S—make up most of the molecules of life. The importance of life's constituents will be evaluated in a later section. The smaller life molecules are amino acids, sugars, fatty acids, the purine and pyrimidine bases, and the nucleotides. These smaller molecules are also constituents of the larger macromolecules of proteins, nucleic acids, glycogen, starch, and fats. The basic building blocks of all the macromolecules contain hydrogen, carbon, and oxygen. Some also have phosphorus, nitrogen, and sulfur.

Diversity in biochemical process is found especially in the metabolic functions and pathways of biosynthesis and other functions. This diversity is particularly striking in the different macromolecules used for the transportation of oxygen. Some organisms use copper-containing proteins and others iron-containing proteins, yet the different molecules perform the same task. Anaerobic breakdown of glucose may yield alcohol (yeast) or lactic acid (muscular contraction). Diversity is also shown in the ability to synthesize the various amino acids. Man cannot synthesize certain amino acids (essential amino acids). Rats require even more essential amino acids. Animals also vary in the ability to synthesize other molecules necessary for life.

Even though there is diversity, there is also unity or repetitious performance in metabolic patterns. The genetic code for DNA and RNA appears to be universal in all organisms. Proteins, nucleic acids, and amino acids are practically the same throughout the animal kingdom. Krebs citric acid cycle, as well as other metabolic pathways, is found in most cells and the great energy package, ATP, is common to all.

*Refer to Chapter 2, Principle 2.

ENERGY RELATIONS

The reactions of living systems to make energy available represent a large part of their total activities. We have already mentioned the two fundamental components of the universe, energy and matter, and have indicated that under certain conditions they are interconvertible. There may be diversity in the different directions of their metabolisms, but all living systems require energy. Plants (autotrophic) use the energy from sunlight to construct organic substances such as carbohydrates, proteins, fats, and nucleic acids from carbon dioxide, water, nitrogen, and other compounds. Certain bacteria (chemosynthetic autotrophs) use reducible inorganic substances such as iron or sulfur as energy sources. Multicellular animals are heterotrophic and must depend on preformed organic food compounds for their energy. Some lower forms, such as the protozoa, some bacteria, algae, and others, must depend on preformed compounds for energy purposes.

Even though photosynthesis is lacking in animals, their biochemical reactions are similar to those in plants. As will be seen under **cellular metabolism,** each biochemical reaction is involved in each level of energy transfer and conversion, although such reactions may not produce or utilize energy-rich substances. As far as animals are concerned, there are many energy transformations in cells, such as chemical to electrical energy in nervous processes, light to electrical in the retina of the eye, chemical to osmotic in the kidney and cell membranes, chemical to radiant in luminescence, sound to electrical in the ear, and chemical to mechanical in muscles and cilia.

Two kinds of energy are recognized by physicists: potential energy, as stored energy or energy of position, and kinetic, or the energy of motion. A familiar example of the two kinds is illustrated by a stone on an elevation where it has potential energy while at rest and kinetic energy when it rolls down to a lower level. Energy is stored as potential energy in the bonds that hold the atoms together in molecules of food. This potential energy can become kinetic energy when the animal transforms this food in its biochemical activities. Nearly all forms of energy are interconvertible, and animals in their living processes are constantly transforming one kind of energy into another.

Thermodynamics, which is concerned with energy and its transformation, has two basic laws: the law of the conservation of energy, according to which energy can be transformed but not destroyed, and the law of entropy, which states that during any reaction or process there is a decrease in free energy in that some energy is dissipated to the environment as heat and unavailable energy.

The energy relations of the organism give a basic understanding of the true nature of an animal or organism. The numerous interacting systems of an animal can be maintained only by the continuous expenditure of energy. The biochemical interactions found in the transformation of the energy of oxidation necessary for physiologic work are complex, and the animal must be viewed as a highly adaptable dynamic system that is in continuous exchange of energy relations with its environment.

PROTOPLASM AS THE LIFE SUBSTANCE*

The substance making up the organism is often termed living matter, or protoplasm. The term protoplasm is less used by biologists than it was formerly. Instead of the concept that protoplasm is chiefly a colloid, the intrinsic meaning of the life substance is placed on a physicochemical appraisal of the types of forces and the chemical bonds that give living matter its rigidity and its fluidity. Protoplasm is often now regarded as a vague and nebulous term because it has lost its meaning in the light of more knowledge about its organization. The cell's compartmented organelles and their functions afford the basis for the dynamic structure, since an attempt has been made to form a molecular concept for each cell organelle from its chemical constituents and the part it plays in life as a whole.

Protoplasm is not homogeneous matter, and no drop of it can be called truly representative of the whole. From a physicochemical standpoint, it is a complex colloidal system, represented by phases of particles of widely varying sizes, physical natures, and chemical constitution. Some of its constituents are in molecular or other physicochemical systems. The modern concept of a netlike arrangement of an unstable fibrous framework of long threadlike molecules with junctional connections has been widely accepted. There is little to be learned by superficial examination of protoplasm from any source, and before the electron microscope and the era of molecular biology such descriptions are to a great extent worthless. Its organization, according to our present knowledge is not static but dynamic. It main-

*Refer to Chapter 2, Principle 1.

tains itself by a continuous building up and breaking down of the substances that compose it. Much further investigation will have to be done before a rational evaluation of living matter can be made.

UNDERSTANDING THE NATURE OF LIFE

Much has been learned about the nature of life within the past few decades. How has this understanding come about? To understand living matter and the processes of life is difficult, for the life sciences do not lend themselves as easily to analytical methods as do the physical sciences. Any attempt to understand the nature of life involves a careful study of the processes by which the animal acquires the characteristics of living matter. If one selected an animal at random and attempted to learn all that is known about the basic principles of life from it and others like it, he would find that there would be many gaps in his final understanding. During the past few years the frontier of life sciences has been pushed more and more toward the molecular level. Biochemistry has come into greater prominence. Biophysical methods loom up at every step in analytical interpretation. Biologic investigation requires the methods and techniques from all scientific disciplines. This signifies that no one person has all the skills necessary to master all the analytical procedures necessary in most biologic investigations, even those of a modest scope.

One of the most outstanding advances made in the life sciences in recent years has been the development of our knowledge of the genetic code, or the manner in which the chromosomal genes carry the information for protein synthesis. Up to the present, practically all of this revealing work has been performed with microorganisms, especially with bacteriophages (viruses that parasitize bacteria). This material is unusually favorable for such study because the genetic arrangement is at an elementary level and experimental types are numerous. With analytical techniques and recombination of genetic factors, the genetic constitution of an organism has been broken down into its constituent elements. By precise analytical methods it has been possible to determine that genetically controlled forms of a protein can be produced by changes in single amino acids. As the students will see in the discussion of the genetic code, an alteration in a tiny subunit of a gene is responsible for a different kind of amino acid. It is thus possible for information to be carried in the nucleotide sequence of the deoxyribonucleic acid (DNA) molecule and to be transformed into the amino acid sequence of a definite protein. The amount of work done by numerous investigators to prove how this process operates has been tremendous and includes many years of work.

Someone has said that science is the search for simplicity. Complex problems in the life sciences may actually involve simple explanations when it is possible to attack them at an elementary level.

MOLECULAR BIOLOGY AND ITS LIMITATIONS

The concept of organization levels helps in understanding the broader unity of all matter. Biologic organization may be considered a unique aggregation of chemical structures that fit into a unified pattern of physical constitution. The distinction between the life sciences and physical sciences is rapidly being broken down. Recent advances in molecular biology are linking the natural and physical sciences closer together. No longer is the world of the zoologist set apart from the world of the physical scientist, nor are the phenomena of animal life considered to exist outside the realm of the inanimate. Living substance is a certain arrangement of chemical molecules of greater complexity than is found in the nonliving world, but nonetheless it is basically a chemical organization.

This change in animal study has been so spectacular and so radical as compared with the classic study of zoology that the new approach has been called the "new biology." This innovation in zoologic study has had a revolutionary impact on methods of study and on the training of zoologists. Many persons who are not zoologists are now active in this field because the disciplines of biochemistry, physical chemistry, and physics are now considered by many to be necessary prerequisites for zoologic study. This has resulted in a tendency to exclude from the training of zoologists anything not directly related to the physical sciences.

Although this trend in zoologic study is marked, many zoologists regard it as extreme and altogether inadequate for an effective understanding of the life disciplines. Molecular biology is an important level of study, but there are also many others. The major aim of biology is to understand all aspects of life organization, not merely the molecular structure. Another criticism of molecular biology is that its investigation has been concentrated on organisms of simple structure that may have different organization patterns from those of higher forms. The various disciplines of the life sciences cannot be arranged in a hierarchy of importance. One discipline may arouse a greater interest at one time, and much progress may be made in its development, for example, cytology in the last quarter of the last century and genetics and evolution in the first half of the present century; but for true biologic understanding, other disciplines such as taxonomy, ecology, and paleontology must make their contributions.

The true zoologist is interested in the whole organism, both functionally and structurally at all levels of organization. The functions of biologic molecules with which the biochemist is now so concerned can be understood and appreciated only in the light of their relations to the whole organism, its environment, its population structure, and its past history.

The major aim of most competent biologists is to discover facts and to establish biologic generalizations that can be applied to an understanding of the phenomena of life. Most scientific discoveries are not far removed from their practical applications. The rapid advance of biologic investigation and its exciting discoveries have already aroused many enthusiastic biologists to believe that man will soon be able to control his destiny in ways never dreamed of before. The possibility of directing mutations in certain microorganisms by means of specific agents, the genetic alteration or chemical hybridization of bacteria by the processes of transformation and transduction, the wide use of animal tissue cultures (including human) for analysis of genetic constitutions at the cellular level, and the development of techniques for extracting the major substance (DNA) of the gene have all been responsible for the belief that man will be able in the near future to remake or alter his own hereditary constitution. Similar enthusiastic beliefs have been advanced before when a major breakthrough in scientific achievement occurred, but in every case a cooling-off period followed under the impact of a more sober and realistic realization of scientific limitations.

However, certain aspects about the scope and future direction of biology can be predicted with reasonable assurance. Molecular biology will, of course, unfold more information of the inner working of the cell, such as the synthesizing processes of the many complex systems of the cell, under the impact of the decoding mechanisms of genetics. A breakthrough of great significance may be expected in the fields of development, differentiation, and growth of organisms. At the higher levels of community and population ecology, the application of the preceding studies as well as those of other biologic disciplines will no doubt contribute materially to the adaptation of animals (including man) to their physical and biotic environments. Much of man's efforts will have to be expended in correcting or redressing his mistakes in upsetting natural communities. Out of these and other advancements, there are gradually emerging a keener recognition and analysis of man's cultural evolution, a more basic understanding of man as a biologic unit, and an effective motivating sense of his social responsibility.

It may be stated in summary that students of the life sciences have two major objectives at the present time. The first objective is to probe into all aspects of life and to understand how the biologic organization of matter fits into the scheme of all matter, both living and inanimate. This means that a thorough understanding must be achieved of nucleic acids, proteins, nature of membranes, molecular elements of cells, and the way these units fit into the pattern of life. The second objective is to explore and to explain how the immense diversity of life has arisen, the varied evolutionary patterns that have been responsible for this diversity, the structure of populations and the way species interact with each other in populations, and how group relations have evolved—in short, the concept of the ecosystem, or the functional relationship of the living and nonliving environment.

WHAT IS AN ANIMAL?

The simple dictionary definition of an animal is not satisfactory to a biologist who appraises the living organism from its organization, properties, and historic character. The more we know about an animal the greater the difficulty in defining it. A definition of an animal that would exclude all plants cannot be made within the limits of a short, logical statement. Perhaps we should confine ourselves to defining any living organisms and thus avoid debatable grounds that arise when different organic types are considered. For instance, certain basic differences between higher animals and higher plants are apparent and distinctive, but among the lower forms of both the plant and animal kingdoms the members grade imperceptibly into each other. The acellular or single-celled forms of both are now often lumped together under the Protista (Gr. *protistos,* first of all), a term proposed long ago by

Haeckel. In general, plants are characterized by cellulose cell walls, synthesis of complex organic foodstuffs by photosynthesis (holophytic nutrition), inconstant body form, limited movement, and external organs; and animals are characterized by absence of cellulose cell walls, fairly constant body form, holozoic nutrition (ingestion and digestion of organic matter), mostly internal organs, pronounced movement, and definite irritability.

On the basis of what was stated about the living and the nonliving, we may tentatively define an organism as a **physicochemical system of specific and varying levels of organization patterns, self-regulative, self-perpetuating, and in continuous adjustment with its environment.**

DEFINITION OF ZOOLOGY

Zoology (Gr. *zoon*, animal, + *logos*, study) is the branch of the life sciences that deals with the animal organism as contrasted to botany, the science of the plant organism. Both zoology and botany make up the science of biology (Gr. *bios*, life, + *logos*, study), or the study of living things. The distinction between animals and plants is mainly one of convention rather than of basic differences. The biologic sciences are empirical; that is, knowledge about them is acquired by observation and experimentation. Theories and hypotheses must be testable and must be verified in a life science, as in any other science. At present a life science may be considered a descriptive science, in contrast to an exact science such as physics, but progress in molecular biology and the effective application of mathematics, biochemistry, biophysics, and other disciplines to biologic problems are providing the life sciences with a more exact status.

HOW INFORMATION ABOUT ANIMALS IS FOUND

Knowledge about animals is acquired by the same methods used by other sciences, that is, by close observation, by controlled experiments, by careful analysis and arrangement of facts, by determining relationships between facts, and by the formulation of concepts that have wide application to other problems in that field of study. Almost anyone with ordinary abilities and skills plus lively curiosity and patience can make new discoveries in an extensive field such as the biologic sciences, but it is a different matter to fit these facts into conceptual schemes that have fruitful meanings. Perhaps the greatest shortcoming in scientific investigation is the inability to think things through to logical conclusions.

Not all scientists follow the same procedures in their investigations any more than they follow the same pattern of thinking. In general, however, good scientists formulate hypotheses from their accumulated facts; they test out their theories and reject those that do not apply; they repeat their experiments; they are cautious about generalizations; and they do not hesitate to seek the advice and observations of others competent in that field. Above all, they have a great curiosity. Finally, they are eager to communicate their findings to the world of science, not necessarily through pride of personal achievements but that others may profit thereby and that the frontiers of knowledge in that particular field may be advanced.

MAJOR SUBDIVISIONS OF ZOOLOGY

Systematic zoology. This group includes taxonomy or classification, ecology, distribution, and evolution of animals.

Morphology. Structural aspects are stressed in this group, which includes comparative anatomy, histology, cytology, embryology, and paleontology.

Physiology. This group has to do with the functional considerations of the organism. It includes general physiology, physiologic chemistry, and animal behavior or psychology.

Experimental zoology. This group is a broad one and includes those subdivisions that are concerned with experimental alterations of the patterns of organisms. It includes genetics, experimental morphology, and embryology.

Molecular biology. This is the study of the ultimate, or ultramicroscopic, structure and function of living matter. At present it emphasizes the four fields of biochemistry, genetics, chemistry of macromolecules, and chemical physics.

• • •

Such groupings cannot be arbitrary, for there is much overlapping and interrelation among the various fields of zoologic investigation. For example, cytogenetics represents the close dependence of two branches of study, cytology and genetics, which were formerly considered more or less separately. As specialization increases, branches of study become more and more restricted in their scope. We thus have protozoology, the study of protozoans; entomology, the study of insects; parasitology, the study of parasites; and many others.

Some other subdivisions of zoology

anatomy (Gr. *ana,* up, + *tome,* cutting) The study of animal structures as revealed by gross dissection.

anatomy, comparative The study of various animal types from the lowest to the highest, with the aim of establishing homologies and the origin and modifications of body structures.

biochemistry (Gr. *bios,* life, + *chemos,* fluid) The study of the chemical makeup of animal tissues.

cytology (Gr. *kytos,* hollow vessel) The study of the minute parts and functions of cells.

ecology (Gr. *oikos,* house) The study of animals in relation to their surroundings.

embryology (Gr. *embryon,* embryo) The study of the formation and early development of the organism.

endocrinology (Gr. *endon,* within, + *krinein,* to separate) The science of hormone action in organisms.

entomology (Gr. *entomon,* insect) The study of insects.

genetics (Gr. *genesis,* origin) The study of the laws of inheritance.

helminthology (Gr. *helmins,* worm) The study of worms, with special reference to the parasitic forms.

herpetology (Gr. *herpein,* to creep) The study of reptiles, although the term sometimes includes both reptiles and amphibians.

histology (Gr. *histos,* tissue) The study of structure as revealed by the microscope.

ichthyology (Gr. *ichthys,* fish) The study of fishes.

morphology (Gr. *morphe,* form) The study of organic form, with special reference to ideal types and their expression in animals.

ornithology (Gr. *ornis,* bird) The study of birds.

paleontology (Gr. *palaios,* ancient, + *onto,* existing) The study of past life as revealed by fossils.

parasitology (Gr. *para,* beside, + *sitos,* foods) The study of parasitic organisms.

physiology (Gr. *physis,* nature) The study of animal functions.

taxonomy (Gr. *taxis,* organization, + *nomos,* law) The study of the classification of animals.

zoogeography (Gr. *zoon,* animal, + *ge,* earth, + *graphein,* to write) The study of the principles of animal distribution.

METHODS AND TOOLS OF THE BIOLOGIST

The higher level of material organization represented by life is made up of properties that are the most difficult to understand in the universe. Protoplasm consists of very large molecules, but the organization of these molecules into particular patterns has given life many of its unique qualities. There are so many variables that reactions cannot always be predicted with certainty. Another difficulty of biologic investigation is that the whole is more than the sum of its parts. The mere study of one part of the living organism affords a restricted idea of the working of the whole integrated organism.

Biologic investigation was at first purely descriptive, but the trend is now toward experimental biology. The controlled experiment using a single variable factor is becoming commonplace in investigations in the life sciences. However, in several fields such as evolution and taxonomy little has been done beyond the descriptive phase.

Biologists rely heavily upon the methods of the physical sciences because they assume that living organisms obey the physical laws and because they consider living matter a higher (but also very complex) level in the hierarchy of all matter. The great advances in molecular biology or biophysics have resulted from research into atomic and molecular structure, which was the primary investigation of physicists a few decades ago. Living matter may be governed by other laws not known to physicists and chemists that, when formulated, may well widen the sciences of physics and chemistry. The unity of all science is a basic assumption of scientists.

Biologists employ whatever available methods they deem necessary in doing their experimental problems. As their science widens, the nature of their problems changes. New insights reveal new vistas to be explored. Some of the problems of greatest interest revolve around cellular biochemistry, energy relationships of metabolic pathways and processes, integrative relationships of physiologic processes, controlling factors of development, the basis of hereditary transmission, neuromuscular phenomena, and behavior patterns in animals. Most of these problems require complex techniques and apparatus drawn from physical and chemical sources. However, ingenious biologists often modify such borrowed instrumentation to fit their particular purposes.

The microscope, with all its types and modifications, has contributed more to biologic investigation than any other instrument developed by man. Its major objectives are magnification, resolution, and definition. The following represents the chief advances in the improvement of the microscope.

1. First compound microscope (Janssen, 1590; Galileo, 1610)
2. Microscope with condenser (1635)
3. Huygenian ocular (Huygens, 1660)
4. Substage mirror (Hertzel, 1712)
5. Achromatic lens (Dolland, 1757; Amici, 1812)
6. Polarizing microscope (Talbot, 1834)
7. Binocular miscroscope (single objective with double oculars) (Riddell, 1853)
8. Water immersion objective (Amici, 1840)
9. Oil immersion objective (Wenham, 1870)
10. Compensating oculars (1886)
11. Apochromatic objectives (1886)
12. Iris diaphragm (Bausch and Lomb, 1887)
13. Abbé condenser (Abbé, 1888)
14. Double objective binocular microscope (Greenough, 1892)
15. Ultramicroscope (dark-field) (Zsigmondy, 1900)
16. Electron microscope (Knoll and Ruska, 1931)
17. Phase-contrast microscope (Zernicke, 1935)
18. Reflecting microscope (Burch, 1943)
19. Fluorescence microscope (Coons, 1945)

The compound light microscope has been justified in a thousand ways, but the spectacular advances in molecular biology of the past decade or so have been due in large measure to the electron microscope. This microscope makes use of a beam of electrodes in a vacuum instead of a beam of light as an optical system. The electrons produced by a heated filament are focused by a magnetic coil and pass through the object, where they are scattered in accordance with the nature of the object. The electrons have a very short wavelength and their resolving power is much greater than that of the light microscope. After passing through a magnetic objective lens and a projector lens, the transmitted electrons form an image on a photographic plate or fluorescent screen and thus can be made visible to the eye. The chief limitations of the electron microscope are that the biologic material must be dead and arranged in very thin layers. The resolving power of a microscope is its ability to distinguish adjacent objects. In the light microscope this resolution is about 2,000 Å*; in the electron microscope it is about 5 to 10 Å. Anything smaller will merge and cannot be seen as a discrete particle. The magnifica-

*An angstrom (Å) = 1/10,000 micron (μ), or 1/100,000,000 cm.; 1 inch = 2.54 cm.

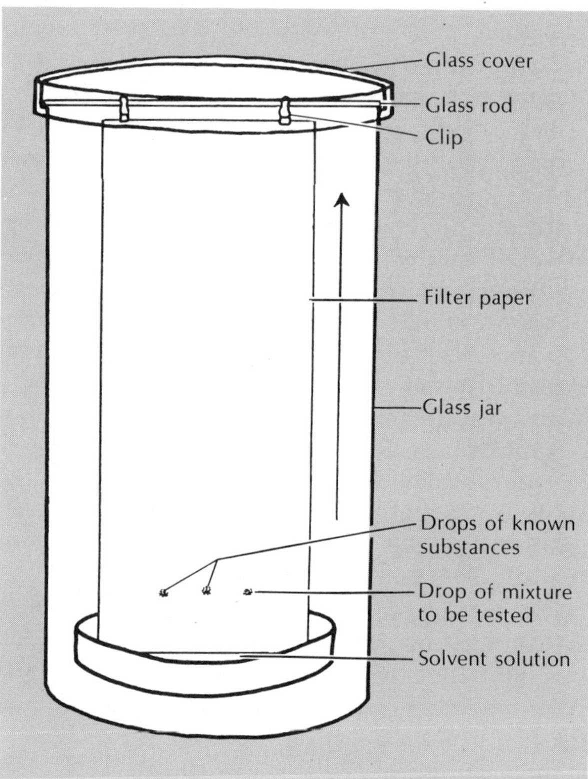

FIG. 1-1

Method of ascending paper chromatography. Similar materials such as amino acids or pigments in solvent will separate from each other by flowing at different rates over surface of porous solid material such as special filter paper. To identify amino acids in mixture, drop of mixture may be placed near bottom of strip of filter paper, along with drops of known amino acids, and allowed to dry. Strip is then placed in cylinder, with its lower end dipping into organic solvent saturated with water. By capillary action, solvent flows along paper over spots, carrying substances up paper with it. Depending upon their relative solubility, various amino acids will each move specific distance up paper. Paper is then developed to cause resulting spots to show up. By comparing relative heights of unknown amino acids of mixture with heights of known ones, identification can be made. Various modifications of method are employed and have been applied to many biologic materials, such as plant pigments, sugars, sugar derivatives, and many extracts from living cells.

tions produced by the electron microscope are enormous compared with those produced by the light microscope.

Other useful methods are (1) isotopic tracers, in which a radioactive isotope of an element can be substituted in a chemical compound and can then be detected by some method (Geiger tube, photographic plate, etc.) so that the chemical pathway or other information can be acquired; (2) chromatography, which involves the separation of organic or inorganic components by allowing a solution of a mixture to flow over a porous surface such as filter paper (Fig. 1-1); (3) centrifugation, which separates materials of different densities from each other and which can be employed for many analytical purposes; and (4) colorimetry and related methods, which measure and identify materials by determining the differential absorption of radiant energy of different concentrations.

A relatively new technique is the rearing of animals in the absence of all microorganisms (**gnotobiotics**). This may be done by the use of sterile and aseptic methods, or by the use of mechanical barriers that keep out contaminating organisms. Gnotobiotics may prove a useful research tool in determining the effects of microbiota upon the host in health and disease, for example, dietary and vitamin studies on intestinal tracts of germ-free animals, the complex relationships that exist between hosts and their microbiotic populations, experimental dental caries, the virus theory of cancer, the use of antibiotics, and many other problems.

The phase-contrast microscope has proved useful in studying living cells. If two cell components transmit the same amount of light, it is difficult with the light microscope to distinguish differences between them. If there is a difference in refractive index between the components, the phase-contrast microscope will show a difference in their brightness. This microscope is especially useful in the study of mitochondria and chromosomes in the living cell.

In biochemistry the spectrophotometer is widely used to determine different chemical substances. Ultraviolet light is absorbed by different chemicals of characteristic wavelengths. By determining the wavelength absorbed by an unknown substance and comparing it with a table of known absorbances, identification can be made. Variant forms of this mechanism are in use, but all are based on the selective powers of light absorption of components when traversed by a beam of light.

HOMEOSTASIS AS THE IDEAL ADAPTATION*

Homeostasis is one of the most important concepts in biology. It may be described as the tendency of an organism to maintain a constancy of the internal fluid environment that surrounds the cells and tissues of the body. The concept was first developed by the famous French physiologist Claude Bernard over a period of years, beginning about 1857. Bernard emphasized what he called the *milieu intérieure,* which served as a medium for the exchange of foods and waste. He thought that all vital mechanisms within the body had only the one object of preserving constancy in the conditions of life in the internal environment within the range suitable for continued normal functioning. The concept has been broadened by many others such as W. B. Cannon to include regulatory devices and feedback mechanisms. Cannon stressed the coordinated physiologic processes that promote steady states. To Bernard the idea of the internal environment, to which he constantly added new facets of meaning over many years, meant a new approach to experimental physiology and medical problems as well as a basic understanding of the whole organization of living organisms.

Homeostasis in its broader sense is the most important adaptation of all organisms. It involves the self-regulatory mechanisms for functional stability that an organism must maintain to survive in a constantly changing external environment. The concept may be considered a broad, goal-directed, functional regulation that applies to all processes having to do with normal adjustments to the conditions of life. Regulatory controls are found in all systems of the body. To appreciate the significance of the general concept, one has only to mention a few of these homeostatic control mechanisms, such as the pH (acid-base balance), the maintenance of carbon dioxide levels in the blood, the constant temperature controls of birds and mammals, the control of hormone functioning, the glucose balance in the blood, and the regulation of water by the kidneys. Indeed, it is difficult to think how our bodily processes could function without such regulatory mechanisms. In population studies in the ecosystem, homeostasis is implicit at all stages in the ecologic organization of the community. Biochemical

*Refer to Chapter 2, Principle 17.

control mechanisms operate in protein and enzyme synthesis. In reversible chemical reactions the products of a series of biochemical reactions may accumulate and tend to shift the reaction in the opposite direction.

In any feedback mechanism, homeostasis is particularly evident. For instance, sugar (glucose) is a major source of energy for body activities and is found as a normal constituent in blood, with the excess stored as glycogen in the liver. When the blood supply falls to a level below normal, the adrenal medulla is stimulated to secrete epinephrine (a hormone) into the blood by the hypothalamus. One of the effects of epinephrine is to convert glycogen into blood glucose in the liver by enzymatic action. More glucose in the blood stimulates the islets of Langerhans to secrete insulin, which indirectly causes more glucose to be stored as glycogen. The amount of glucose in the blood acts as a feedback mechanism in each case. A feedback is the output of a product of a system that, when fed back into the system, influences further production of that product. The above effect is called negative feedback and aims to produce a condition of equilibrium. Positive feedback can occur when there is a lack of normal control mechanisms; for example, a fever tends to increase metabolism and to bring about still higher temperatures, producing a vicious circle.

Homeostatic mechanisms show an evolutionary development, as indicated by the differences between lower and higher animals. Less specialized animals have a much wider range of internal environmental conditions than the more specialized. Regulatory mechanisms are much more precise in higher than in lower vertebrates. However, temperature control in a warm-blooded form such as a mammal, for instance, is a gradual development from the young to maturity. Young mammals fluctuate between the ectothermic (cold-blooded) and endothermic (warm-blooded) conditions.

CONCEPT OF THE ECOSYSTEM*

Every animal is part of a group of similar individuals that interbreed and share common factors of the environment. They are organized into populations, communities, and ecosystems. The individuals of a particular species make up a population. When a population coexists with other populations of different species but with similar requirements and all adapted to a certain complex of environmental conditions, a community is formed. A community is a localized association of several populations of different species. This aggregation of population is so organized that it is more or less independent of other communities and so constituted that it is self-sufficient in its energetics, or energy transformations. Within its organization are different strata of populations, each adapted for a particular role in the maintenance of the community. One stratum may be the producers, such as plants, which can convert solar energy to chemical energy in plant products. A second stratum is the consumers, which eat plants and other animals that live on plants. A third stratum contains the decomposers (bacteria and fungi chiefly), which decompose dead organisms and organic debris, etc. and release basic chemical substances to be used again by plants. The community and the nonliving environment interact to form an ecologic system, or **ecosystem.** An ecosystem therefore is the sum total of the physical and biologic factors operating within an area that includes living organisms and abiotic substances interacting in an ecologic system in which the exchange of materials between the living and nonliving occurs in a circular path. Such a system usually consists of a few species with large populations and many species with small populations.

The ecosystem is the basic functional unit in ecology. It may be large or small, provided it meets the requirements of major components that operate together to form a functional stability. Life cycles result from the interactions between the biotic and abiotic components of the system. A forest region, a meadow, a lake, a desert, or even an ocean are examples of ecosystems. If the system is well balanced, no supporting materials are ever exhausted. An ecosystem is characterized by self-regulation, balanced energetics, functional and interspecies diversity, and independence except for a solar energy source.

All animals are faced with a dependence on environment. The organism derives from it the source of its food and energy, elements used in the construction of its body, and oxygen from the air for its respiration. At every instance of its existence it is exposed to environmental temperatures, heat, light, and other physical factors. These factors determine where an animal shall live—its habitat. Every animal must have a special range of tolerance for every factor in its en-

*Refer to Chapter 2, Principle 33.

vironment. This "internal environment" of which Claude Bernard speaks is not entirely one sided, for the physical environment is influenced or modified by animals. Deposits of the hard skeletons of microorganisms have been impressive in most parts of the world. Soil changes are produced by overgrazing, and decomposers in the chain of life add to the fertility and chemical value of soil, to mention just a few influential factors.

But in another sense, the ecosystem looms as man's greatest problem. The dominant role he plays in controlling the factors of the environment has placed an enormous responsibility on his shoulders. His failure to live up to this responsibility has produced serious disturbances in the homeostasis of his surroundings, and it has only been within recent decades that he has made much of an attempt to face this challenge. Man has largely ignored the basic principles of ecologic organization as he has expanded his technologic skills and has increased his numbers so rapidly. He has made advancements in his industrial use of resources and in medical knowledge of a sound and rational management of his environment. Despite warnings by ecologists and conservationalists, man has suddenly been brought up with a jolt as he has begun to realize the enormity of his mistakes.

These problems will be discussed in greater detail in Chapter 42.

CYCLE OF EXISTENCE*

Most animals have a more or less definite life-span of existence. Some biologists consider the protozoans as immortal because the parent loses its identity when its substance passes directly to the daughter cells in binary fission. As all biologists know, the life-span of animals varies enormously in the different species of the animal kingdom. Why animals grow old and die is not known, although many facts about senescence and other aspects of aging have been studied in recent years. There may be a buildup of insoluble materials within the cells of an animal, or the wear and tear on the machinery of life cannot be replaced as quickly or as efficiently as in the younger periods of the life-span. However, many tissue cells in the body are constantly being shed (perhaps 1% to 2% daily in man) so that the material in an animal's body is constantly in a state of flux and transformation, even though the individuality may be the same. M. Rubner had a theory of aging that has not been wholly discredited. He considered that various mammals during their lifetime used up about the same number of calories per unit of body weight. A mouse, for instance, lives about 3 to 4 years and an elephant about 70 years. He showed that there is a more rapid tempo, or physiologic time, in the mouse than in the elephant. A mouse's heart beats from 520 to 780 times per minute and that of an elephant from 25 to 28. He concluded that the 3 years or so of a mouse's life corresponded, on a physiologic time scale, to the much longer life of the elephant. There are many obscure points in his theory, but it can be concluded that the attainable length of life of a mammal is dependent partly on its rate of energy dissipation.

There are a number of correlations between the length of the life-span and certain factors. In general, mammals with a longer gestation period have a longer life-span. Among homoiothermic animals the larger forms tend to live longer than smaller ones. The smaller the animal, the greater its surface in proportion to its weight and thus the more rapid is its heat loss. To preserve a constancy of body temperature, small mammals and birds must have a higher unit rate of metabolism. The larger the animal, the longer it takes to grow to maturity; also, the larger it is, the more complex it is. Increased complexity requires time for the various divisions of labor to occur. When a bacterium divides, only half an animal needs to be regenerated, but most metazoans start with a single cell (as the zygote) and must build a complete, complex body from there.

Some animals seem to have more definite life-spans than others. There is far more uniformity of length of life in mammals, birds, and insects than in most other metazoans. However, data about the length of life-spans are very unreliable. Length of life of various animals has often been acquired from zoological gardens, where animals living in captivity have constant diet, little or no exercise, little exposure to seasonal change, and lack of other conditions found in the wild. It is difficult to draw valid conclusions from such sources. Perhaps most animals living under natural conditions in the wild state have little or no opportunity to live a normal life-span because as they grow older they weaken and fall prey to predators.

Since animals that live more rapidly have a shorter

*Refer to Chapter 2, Principle 22.

life, cold-blooded forms that hibernate, or are very inactive, may have a longer life-span. Certain reptiles are known to live longer when the temperature is colder. Dietary restrictions often add to the life-span of experimental animals.

The complete life cycle, which includes development, adult equilibrium, and senescence, has a central position in the life sciences. It is the essential unit (rather than merely the adult animal). J. T. Bonner has recently emphasized the importance of the life cycle as the unit of evolution; not only adults are adapted to ecologic conditions, but all stages of the life cycle are also. He considers the life sciences as steps in the chemical reactions that occur in definite sequence in time within living animals. All steps of the life cycle must be adaptive to ensure the survival of the animal. From an evolutionary viewpoint natural selection operates at each step of the life cycle. Innovations or variations are introduced during the early stages (especially in the nuclear genes of the zygote by mutation and recombination), and later unfavorable ones are eliminated by differential reproduction. Genes do not restrict their expressions to the formation of the adult but throughout the course of development.

Annotated references

Arber, A. 1954. The mind and the eye. New York, Cambridge University Press. *This small work is a general analysis of the nature of biologic research.*

Bates, M. 1960. The forest and the sea. New York, Random House. *Written in a popular style, this revealing book will give the inquisitive student much to think about regarding man's relations to the world around him.*

Bonner, J. T. 1962. The ideas of biology. New York, Harper & Row, Publishers.

Bonner, J. T. 1965. Size and cycle: an essay on the structure of biology. Princeton, N. J., Princeton University Press. *The author considers the whole life-span of animals rather than the adult animal as the fundamental unit in the understanding of the various disciplines concerned with biology.*

Calder, R. 1954. Science in our lives. East Lansing, Michigan State College Press. *The author stresses the fact that the essentials of a great scientific discovery depend upon three factors—the method, the man, and the moment. Is not this last factor mainly responsible for independent discovery by more than one worker? All students should read this little book.*

Cannon, W. B. 1945. The way of an investigator. New York, W. W. Norton & Co., Inc.

Conant, J. B. 1951. Science and common sense, New Haven, Conn., Yale University Press. *This masterly treatise deals with all science, but Chapters 8 and 9 are devoted to the living organisms. The nature of the control experiment and the methods biologists have employed are explained. The history of the investigations on spontaneous generation is used as an example.*

Elsasser, W. M. 1966. Atom and organism. Princeton, N. J., Princeton University Press. *A theoretical physicist presents his views on the nature of life. He believes that the laws of biology are more or less unique and not altogether deducible from the laws of physics and chemistry. He presents arguments against both a mechanistic and vitalistic view of life.*

Gray, P. (editor). 1961. Encyclopedia of the biological sciences. New York, Reinhold Publishing Corp. *A reference work of great importance to all majors in the life sciences.*

Gray, P. 1967. The dictionary of the biological sciences. New York, Reinhold Publishing Corp. *A useful reference work for biology students. Genera and species are not found among the main entries.*

Grobstein, C. 1964. The strategy of life. San Francisco, W. H. Freeman & Co., Publishers. *An excellent paperback on the revolution of present day biology.*

Haggis, G. H. (editor). 1964. Introduction to molecular biology. New York, John Wiley & Sons, Inc. *Traces the exciting discoveries in this discipline. The Appendix includes a concise version of the "Origin of Life."*

Hall, T. S. 1951. A source book in animal biology. New York, McGraw-Hill Book Co. *An excellent biologic anthology of great selections from the leading biologists of all times. Suitable for the beginning student.*

Jaeger, E. C. 1955. A source-book of biological names and terms, ed. 3. Springfield, Ill., Charles C Thomas, Publisher. *This is a useful book for all students who are interested in the meaning and derivation of biologic terms. It is perhaps the best in the field.*

Johnson, W. H., and W. C. Steere (editors). 1962. This is life. New York, Holt, Rinehart & Winston, Inc. *This is an anthology of essays in modern biology.*

Kendrew, J. C. 1966. The thread of life. Cambridge, Mass., Harvard University Press. *A simple introductory account of the exciting development of molecular biology and its possibilities in the future.*

Lanham, U. 1968. The origins of modern biology. New York, Columbia University Press.

Lenhoff, E. S. 1966. Tools of biology. New York, The Macmillan Co. *A description of the numerous instruments biologists use in their investigations. Refinement and sophisticated instruments have been responsible for many breakthroughs in biology.*

Pennak, R. W. 1964. Collegiate dictionary of zoology. New York, The Ronald Press Co. *An extremely useful reference work for all students of zoology.*

Wischnitzer, S. 1962. Introduction to electron microscopy. New York, Pergamon Press, Inc.

CHAPTER 2

• SOME IMPORTANT BIOLOGIC PRINCIPLES AND CONCEPTS

● A principle or generalization is a statement of fact that has a wide application and can be used to formulate other principles and concepts. The physical sciences, such as physics and chemistry, would be difficult to master without clear-cut formulas and rules. The biologic sciences do not lend themselves to the mathematical exactness of the physical sciences, and few generalizations of universal application can be made. However, certain well-formulated principles are indispensable for clear thinking; they help the student see important relationships and form basic conclusions. Principles in biology, as in other sciences, are based on observation and experimentation and have been tested by many workers over long periods of time. Biologic principles are always subject to revision and new interpretation in the light of new knowledge.

The following list of basic concepts is not intended to be exhaustive. References to some of these principles have already been made. Further references will be made in later chapters where they will have significant application and will be better understood. These principles demonstrate the essential unity of the organism and the integration of all biologic systems.

1. ***All organisms are composed of protoplasm, which is the physical basis of life.*** Wherever there is life there is protoplasm. Not everything found in protoplasm, however, is alive, for many lifeless materials such as yolk granules, waste materials, etc. may be scattered through it. The elements in protoplasm are shared with nonliving matter, but protoplasm is highly selective and many of the elements in inanimate matter are not found in it. Protoplasm is always enclosed by a thin plasma membrane, which is a specialized part of protoplasm. The mystery of protoplasm does not lie in its chemical elements but in the way they are linked together into compounds and are organized into the complex substance to which we ascribe the phenomenon of the life process. (Chapters 1, 3, and 4.)

2. ***Many biologic phenomena are now explained at the molecular level.*** Ultimately it is thought that living processes can be understood by the interactions of molecules, atoms, and electrons. Molecular biology thus stresses the physicochemical aspects of life. By such means it has been possible to understand more about energy transformations and the enzymes responsible for such reactions. Throughout the biologic kingdom the basic metabolic processes are similar. The basic principles of this biochemical unity are also similar to those found in the inanimate world. (Chapters 3 and 4.)

3. ***The property of replication may be considered as the most unique life feature.*** The power to make exact copies of its patterns as well as innovations or mutations has made possible the evolution and development of the biologic units (organisms) as we now know them. This property, together with the directive forces of evolution (natural selection, etc.), has gradually led to higher and higher levels of organization, complexity, and adaptation. (Chapters 35 and 37.)

4. ***Most of the unique and distinctive features of protoplasm are due to the presence and composition of certain large molecules (macromolecules).*** These macromolecules are the polysaccharides, the nucleic acids, the proteins, and the fats. Polysaccharides are made up of subunits (glucose) and are the chief sources of energy. Nucleic acids, deoxyribonucleic acid (DNA) and ribonucleic acid (RNA), form the hereditary duplicating mechanisms of the genes and are composed of subunits—the nucleotides. The proteins consist of subunits (amino acids); they form the framework of protoplasmic units (cells) and enzymes, which are basic for all the phenomena of the life process. (Chapters 4 and 35.)

5. ***Protoplasm has a unique physicochemical organization, which varies to produce the potentialities of each particular group of organisms.*** Superficially, protoplasm appears much the same in all organisms,

but its submicroscopic organization and chemical characteristics vary widely with different species and with different cells in the same organism. This organization accounts for functional and morphologic differences between organisms. That of man, for instance, is not the same as that of the ameba. Because of these facts and others, protoplasm, as seen under the light microscope, reveals little of its intrinsic makeup. Its true fundamental nature seems to be ultramicroscopic and hence a fruitful source of investigation in the relatively new and immature field of molecular biology. (Chapters 3, 4, and 5.)

6. ***In all protoplasmic systems the ground substance is differentiated into a superficial region (ectoplasm) and an inner region (endoplasm).*** Because of its position the ectoplasm serves as the boundary between the external environment and the inner part of the protoplasmic system. The ectoplasm is specialized to perform many roles, such as exchange between the environment and the protoplasmic system, conduction, respiration, differentiation of development, fertilization, and general integration of the system. Classification in protozoa is based on ectoplasmic differentiation, such as pseudopodia, cilia, and flagella. This distinction between ectoplasm and endoplasm may be seen best in some eggs and ameboid cells; body cells in general do not show it clearly. (Chapters 5, 6, and 10.)

7. ***All protoplasm has certain general properties that are the basic expressions of life.*** These characteristics distinguish the living from the nonliving and are the criteria by which we measure the dynamic aspects of the protoplasmic system. They also represent the adaptive nature of living systems, as revealed in their mechanisms of survival. One fundamental property of protoplasm is its power to respond to its environment (irritability). Another is the ability to perform such essential physiologic functions as ingestion and digestion of food, absorption, circulation, excretion, and reproduction. Although all protoplasm has these properties, in multicellular organisms the protoplasm in cells or groups of cells (tissues) tends to be specialized to carry on these functions. Thus we have nerve cells for receiving and transmitting stimuli, muscle cells for contraction, etc. (Chapters 6 and 7.)

8. ***Protoplasmic systems are differentiated and organized into compartment units.*** This concept implies some kind of partition between the various units that go to make up living systems, from the lowest to the highest. Integration of whatever kind takes place through membranes, films, ectoplasmic-endoplasmic differentiations, etc. Diffusion and osmosis of bodily fluids and what they carry occur along concentration gradients through membranes. A single cell is made up of many unitary compartments, such as the nucleus, food vacuoles, and cytoplasmic inclusions. Even nervous transmission occurs through membranes from one compartment to another (synaptic junctions). Some compartments (blood vessels and gut) are large and extensive to facilitate internal transport and to overcome the limitations of diffusion and osmosis. (Chapters 5 and 6.)

9. ***Specialization and division of labor are correlated with the organization level of the organism.*** The evolutionary trend is toward more specialized organs and division of labor. In Protozoa, specialized cytoplasmic structures (organelles) illustrate division of labor. Among Metazoa there is a progressive sequence of specialization, ranging from the cell-tissue level of coelenterates to the organ-system level of the higher forms. Whenever structures become differentiated or specialized, they are always accompanied by physiologic divisions of labor. (Chapters 6, 7, and 10.)

10. ***All organisms come from preexisting organisms.*** This concept means that all protoplasmic units have come from similar units. This is the principle of **biogenesis,** in contrast to the principle of **abiogenesis** (spontaneous generation), which has been discredited. The principle of biogenesis has been broadened to include the various units of protoplasmic systems, such as "all nuclei from previous nuclei," "all chromosomes from previous chromosomes," and "all centrosomes from previous centrosomes." Just how far this concept can be carried is a debatable point. It may be well to point out that biogenesis does not include the first beginning of life itself. If the animate has come from the inanimate, this fact would be difficult to reconcile with the principle. (Chapters 5, 7, and 34.)

11. ***Reproduction involves the division of parental material to form offspring.*** All new organisms are formed at the expense of the old. Whatever the nature of reproduction, whether of one-celled or many-celled animals, there is division of the parent or parents. This division may be equal or unequal and may or may not involve the destruction of the parental organism. In one-celled and some multicellular animals, there is a simple division of the parent into two daughter cells

or organisms. In sexual forms the egg and sperm are the real offspring, and fertilization can be considered as a restorative process for the new parental body. (Chapters 5, 6, and 34.)

12. *All organisms develop, within limits, a characteristic form.* Within variable limits all organisms develop a particular and predictable size and shape. This generalization emphasizes the science of **morphogenesis,** which is concerned with the developmental concepts of hormones, axial gradients, organizers, and specific patterns of embryologic development. Many biologists have been interested in the interpretation of form in organisms on the basis of physical forces and causes. In some cases, shapes and forms of animals can be explained by physical factors. For instance, the form of some of the low organisms such as Protozoa can be explained on the basis of surface tension forces according to the principle of maxima and minima of surface films. Closely allied to the principle of form is that of organic symmetry. (Chapters 7 and 34.)

13. *Animals have a diversity of body plans.* These plans are not infinitely diverse, but most animals follow one or the other of a few major types that correspond in certain ways to the evolutionary unity of the ancestral form. A basic similarity of body plan is expected from common ancestors. Specialization, however, for a certain way of life has produced some modification in the evolutionary history of all major groups of animals. Chief among these major plans are the flatworm type, the tube-within-a-tube type, the segmented type, and the vertebrate type. (Chapters 7 and 38.)

14. *The final form (morphology) of an animal is the result of the interactions between basic structural features and functions.* In the early development of an animal structural features precede function. A certain genetic pattern may be inherited, but what this pattern actually becomes depends to a great extent on the functional experience of the animal. This functional modification is especially marked in the vertebrate body. The size of a muscle, the structure and nature of bone, tendons, and ligaments, the elaboration and distribution of blood vessels, and the detailed patterns of nervous systems are all dependent on functional modifications. (Chapters 7, 35, and 38.)

15. *All organisms have the capacity for growth.* Growth can be accomplished in two ways—by cell division and by cell expansion. In all true growth the increase in size is an actual increase in protoplasm and not merely a swelling induced by water or some other agent. This involves a distinction between volume (wet weight) increase and dry weight increase. In early cleavage stages of embryologic development the cells become smaller with successive divisions so that there is no actual increase in the whole structure. For true growth to occur, new material must be built up into protoplasm. Mere cell division is a preliminary to actual growth, however, for such division increases the total surface area of cell membranes, which facilitates diffusion of the minerals, proteins, etc. that go into the makeup of protoplasm. Growth within the protoplasmic structure (intussusception) must also be distinguished from accretionary growth, which involves the addition of materials externally. Examples of accretion are the growth of crystals, the shells of clams and snails, teeth, etc. These substances cause an increase in size but not necessarily in living matter. Patterns of growth are inherited so that certain proportions are usually constant from generation to generation. Other factors such as vitamins and hormones also play a part. (Chapter 34.)

16. *All patterns of life are rhythmic in nature.* The activities of the living organism fluctuate around some mean that best promotes physiochemical equilibrium. Cycles and rhythms are involved in practically every phase of the life process. This principle ranges from the ordinary physiologic cyclic patterns of heartbeat, respiration, metabolism, reproduction, etc. to those larger cycles that include the external influences of light and temperature, such as the rhythms of day and night, sun and moon, and seasonal changes. The best-adapted organism is one that can adjust its own cycles of activity to those imposed by its surroundings. For such adjustments animals have evolved precise timing mechanisms (internal clocks) that enable them to synchronize their own activities with those of their external environment. (Chapters 41 and 43.)

17. *All organisms tend to maintain a constancy of conditions within their internal media.* This is commonly known as the principle of **homeostasis.** It refers to the stabilization of internal conditions for which all organisms strive. External environmental factors tend to upset internal conditions in the organism; the organism is constantly trying to counteract these influences. There is an evolutionary progression in the development of this principle. Lower forms are more restricted in their activities because they have not evolved a control of stabilization to the same degree as higher ones. As an example, the temperature of warm-blooded animals is more easily regulated than that of cold-blooded animals so that the former enjoy greater freedom of activity under more varied environmental temperatures. Organisms must also maintain stable fluid conditions of salt, acids, alkalines, foods, and oxygen within the body. (Chapters 1, 6, and 31.)

18. ***All organisms use energy in their living processes.*** All aspects of life require energy in some form. Energy is the capacity to do work and can be measured in calories. The energy potentialities of most food substances can be measured, although some required substances are not energy giving. The ultimate source of all energy is the sun. Plants utilize this energy directly by using the process of photosynthesis to form carbohydrates. Energy made and stored in plants is used by animals that eat plants. These animals may be eaten by other animals that get energy this way. According to their type of nutrition, organisms may be divided into holophytic, or those that carry on photosynthesis; holozoic, or those that ingest and digest organic materials; and saprophytic, or those that absorb decayed organic matter through their body surface. Organisms that make their own food are also called autotrophic; those that depend on other organisms for their nutrition are called heterotrophic. (Chapters 4, 31, and 41.)

19. ***All the basic activities of animals are mediated by enzymes.*** All metabolic processes involve series of enzymes, each of which controls a specific chemical reaction. In this process a substance undergoing a chemical reaction unites with an enzyme of a specific configuration to form a specific enzyme-substrate complex. By such means, enzymes can control the speed and particular nature of the reaction. Enzymes are large protein molecules with or without other chemical groups. (Chapters 4 and 6.)

20. ***All organisms are fundamentally alike in their basic requirements.*** Life processes are about the same everywhere in the animal kingdom. Animals carry on similar metabolic processes such as nutrition, digestion, respiration, and excretion. They must adjust to their environment and must develop adaptations for doing so. They must reproduce. This uniformity is to be expected, for all organisms are composed of protoplasm and the requirements of protoplasm are much the same wherever found. Organisms do show some differences in their basic requirements. Some can synthesize food elements that others cannot; some require different vitamins; some must even get along without oxygen and must get their energy by anaerobic processes. (Chapters 7, 31, 33, and 41.)

21. ***The parts of any one organism are so closely connected that the character of one part must receive its pattern from the character of all the rest.*** This may be referred to as correlation of growth. A single tooth may indicate whether the animal was carnivorous or herbivorous, whether it was a mammal or other vertebrate, etc. Certain structural features always coexist. This principle is helpful to paleontologists in the reconstruction of an organism from fossil parts. Thus, if a fossil lower jaw is strengthened inside by a shelf of bone, it belonged to an ape; if strengthened outside, it belonged to a human being. (Chapter 34.)

22. ***All organisms pass through a characteristic life history.*** This principle is concerned with the life cycle, which is more or less characteristic for each species of organisms. It involves the life-span and the various phases of the cycle, such as the period of development, the reproductive span, and the postreproductive period. It also includes other factors, such as litter size, frequency of litters, age differential of reproductive capacity, and population relations. (Chapters 1, 33, and 34.)

23. ***Existing organisms have developed by a process of gradual change from previously existing organisms.*** This is the **evolutionary concept,** better known as organic evolution. It is based on the belief that present-day forms have descended with modifications from primitive forms that may have been radically different in structure and behavior. This principle is the key to our modern interpretation of animal origins and relationships. It gives us an explanation of phylogeny, or racial relationships, and helps in the taxonomic groupings of animals. Much fundamental evidence is still lacking because more specific ancestral forms are needed for understanding the exact relationships of animal groups. The idea that there has been direct evolutionary progression from simple to complex forms is only partly true, for it is not always possible to suggest what ancestral forms may have been like. This does not, however, invalidate the concept of evolution. (Chapters 37 and 38.)

24. ***Each major group of animals usually has a certain basic adaptive pattern that may have determined its evolutionary divergence.*** Such basic adaptive features are often obscure in a widespread group that

has undergone marked evolutionary diversity. Moreover, a basic adaptation may be retained by certain taxa of a group and may be lost by others. Good examples of basic adaptive features are shown by rodents (gnawing), by bats (flight), and by primates (arboreal). Such original adaptiveness may have arisen early in the evolution of a group and thereafter may have determined the degree of specialization and adaptive radiation. (Chapters 7, 9, and 43.)

25. ***Animals that have many morphologic characters in common have a common descent.*** The more characters organisms have in common, the more closely they are related. This phylogenetic scheme forms the basis for modern classification of animals. A few common characters shared by two groups may have limited significance because of the possibility of convergent evolution; in other words, the characters may have originated independently. When these common characters are homologous, or similar in origin, the evidence for relationships is considered fundamental. (Chapters 7, 8, and 38.)

26. ***Organisms of higher levels may repeat in their embryonic development some of the corresponding stages of their ancestors.*** This is better known as the **biogenetic law**, which was formerly interpreted to mean that the embryonic stages of an animal are similar to the adult stages of its phylogenetic ancestors. This was the principle of **recapitulation,** or the idea that ontogeny (the life history) repeats phylogeny (the ancestral history). The modern interpretation is merely that some of the corresponding embryonic stages of the early ancestor are repeated. The earlier viewpoint would assume that all evolutionary advancements were added to the terminal stages of the life histories of organisms, but early embryonic stages have also undergone evolution. Evolution has produced many ontogenies in the phylogeny of an animal. Some biologists have suggested that **paleogenesis** is a better term to express the tendency for early developmental patterns to become more or less stabilized in successive ontogenies of later descendants. In early stages this tendency is more marked than it is in later stages because the developmental adjustments produced by the evolution of animals may involve embryonic adaptations (**caenogenesis**) and other changes that may appear in the terminal or adult stages. The principle must be considered generalized and not absolute, for some animal ontogenies do not repeat ancestral ontogenies at all. (Chapters 34 and 38.)

27. ***All organisms inherit a certain pattern of structural and functional organization from their progenitors.*** This generalization involves the laws of **heredity** and applies to all living things. The highest and lowest types of animals have the capacity for reproducing their kind and transmitting their characteristics to their offspring. Hereditary transmission is much the same in all organisms. What is inherited by an offspring is not necessarily the exact traits as expressed by the parents because heredity is not as simple as this. What is inherited is a certain type of organization that, under the influence of developmental and environmental forces, gives rise to a certain visible appearance. Many potentialities may be inherited, but only one of these may express itself visibly. Heredity is the transmission of a sequence code (in DNA molecules) of amino acids for the formation of varied protein patterns or enzymes characteristic for each organism. (Chapter 35.)

28. ***Patterns of organization can be changed suddenly by mutation.*** Sudden changes in the appearance of an animal or plant different from anything inherited from the parents do appear in nature. Some of these changes are not transitory but are transmitted to the offspring. Mutations that occur in somatic (body) cells disappear with that generation. Mutations in the germ cells can be inherited by future generations. The latter usually involve changes in the genes. Mutations may be induced by artificial means, such as x-rays, radium, and mustard gas, but their natural causes are largely obscure. Although most mutations are considered harmful, some may be useful under favorable environmental conditions. Mutations play an important role in the evolutionary process. (Chapters 35 and 38.)

29. ***All organisms are sensitive to changes in their environment.*** No organism could survive long without mechanisms for responding to the environment. This is a basic reaction of all protoplasmic units. Specialization and division of labor have resulted in sensory organs that are especially sensitive to changes in the environment. Most of an animal's activities are directed toward finding a favorable ecologic environment and avoiding unpleasant stimuli. (Chapters 10, 32, and 41.)

30. ***There is a definite gradient of physiologic activities in the body, from the anterior region of high activity to the posterior region of low activity.*** This is the principle of **axial gradients.** Metabolic rates vary

within an animal, being greater at the anterior end and progressively smaller toward the posterior end. This rate is correlated with the regeneration of lost parts. The anterior end of a fragment of an animal may regenerate a new head, whereas the posterior end with a lower metabolism will form a tail. What a regenerating part becomes is determined mainly by its relation to the animal as a whole. Some forms such as flatworms and coelenterates seem to demonstrate the principle better than most groups. (Chapters 13 and 34.)

31. ***All organisms are adapted in some way to their environment.*** To survive, an organism must adapt to the conditions imposed by its environment. Universal adaptations by which animals can adjust to all conditions are nonexistent. Adaptations are always special adjustments to particular conditions and are always relative. Some animals are better adjusted to their environment than others. Most animals have become specialized in their adaptive relations so that the more perfectly they are adapted to one environment, the less they are fitted for adjustment to a different environment. Adaptations are either inherited or acquired. Inherited adaptations are present from birth, such as the sense organs; acquired adaptations originate in response to definite stimuli, such as the formation of antibodies against a particular disease. (Chapters 41 and 43.)

32. ***All organisms have some capacity to adjust themselves to changes in their environment.*** This is the principle of **acclimatization,** which refers to the process by which an organism, within the limits of its life history, is able to become inured to conditions that are normally harmful or injurious to it, such as extremes of heat, cold, salinity of water medium, oxygen pressure, toxins, and many others. The process must be distinguished from adjustments that are made over many generations, such as the accumulation of mutant genes that may favor the new adjustment in an organism over a long period of time. Acclimatization also does not refer to the routine and rapid adjustments that physiologic organs are able to make in their normal functioning, such as the ability to adapt to dim and strong light or the ability to detect differential sensitivity. (Chapters 40, 41, and 43.)

33. ***All organisms fit into a scheme of interrelationships between themselves and their environment.*** No animal can live apart from its environment. All animals are influenced by environmental forces, but the interrelationship is mutual, for each organism also influences its environment. The factors of the environment may be **biotic,** which includes interrelations between the animal and other animals within its range, or **physical,** which involves such forces as temperature, moisture, soil, air, light, and many others. Biotic factors may involve members of the same or different species. The interrelationships are often different in the two groups, because competition between members of the same species includes the search for the same food, shelters, and water; those of different species include such problems as food chains, population pressures, and other general community relations. Through the operation of these environmental factors a balance of nature is worked out. (Chapter 41.)

34. ***In all group organizations, individuals profit mutually from an unconscious cooperation.*** No animal lives to itself throughout its life history, for it either comes in contact with other members of the same species or with other species of the animal community to which it belongs. In animals with definite social organizations there are optimal population sizes that determine their success. Definite hazards appear when there are too few or too many organisms within a population. The rate of evolution appears to bear a definite relationship to an optimal-sized population. Many biologic processes are dependent upon an optimum factor of numbers involved in any particular process. It is easy to see that overcompetition for mates, for food, and for shelter may result in a decrease rather than an increase. (Chapters 41 and 43.)

35. ***In metazoan forms the segregation of germ plasm and somaplasm represents the first specialization of cells.*** This principle stresses the separation of **somatic cells,** which take care of the general bodily functions of locomotion, nutrition, etc., from the **germinal cells,** which are responsible for reproduction. In general the principle holds true, but there are cases in which sex cells have come directly from soma cells in some animals. In colonial Protozoa, which are intermediate between the Protozoa and the Metazoa, the first differentiation is that between nutritive and reproductive cells. (Chapters 9, 33, and 34.)

36. ***Embryonic germ layers are the forerunners of adult organs and structures.*** The differentiation of the early embryo into three germs layers is an important event in the embryology of most metazoans, for these germ layers give rise to the future body structures.

Some lower metazoans are diploblastic; that is, they have only two germ layers, **ectoderm** and **endoderm,** so that their capacity for developing complex organs is restricted. In higher metazoans (triploblastic animals) the third germ layer, **mesoderm,** is added, which forms most of the body organs. The importance of germ layers in animal development gave rise to the **germ layer theory,** which states that germ layers have been formed in much the same way throughout all metazoans and that each layer is destined to form certain specific organs. For example, the skin and nervous system are derived from ectoderm and muscle and skeleton from mesoderm. Modern embryologists, however, have found many exceptions to this theory. Muscle usually comes from mesoderm, but lower animals with only the two germ layers also have muscle, which must come from ectoderm or endoderm. (Chapters 7 and 34.)

37. ***A body cavity of some form is characteristic of most bilateral animals.*** Body cavities are varied in form. Coelenterates and other radially symmetric forms have only a digestive cavity. In flatworms and some others the space between ectoderm and endoderm is filled with mesenchyme or its derivatives. The roundworms have a form of cavity known as the **pseudocoel.** The true **coelom,** a space that appears in the mesoderm, is characteristic of the higher phyla that have a **tube-within-a-tube** arrangement. **The coelom** encloses most of the internal organs, and its development has made possible the differentiation of many systems in the evolution of the animal. (Chapters 7, 14, and 15.)

38. ***An organism is a biologic system whose parts are organized into a functional whole.*** An organism is not a mere summation of its constituent parts. It is a self-sufficient unit, and its parts, whether they are cells, tissues, or organs, cannot survive apart from the whole. The organism as a whole has properties that cannot be explained merely by considering the sum of the properties of its individual parts. It is impossible to understand the whole organism by analyzing its parts, for such a procedure destroys the organization that is the basic part of life. This, then, refutes much of the mechanistic interpretation of life; although physics and chemistry may be able to explain the parts, they cannot as yet explain the life process as a whole. (Chapters 1, 4, and 7.)

PART TWO

MOLECULAR REQUIREMENTS OF LIFE

● One of the greatest advancements in biologic study is the idea that the life process is an expression of chemical reactions. Present-day biology is founded on the concept that life consists of chemical elements organized into complex compounds that display successively higher levels of organization and reaction. Where the animal exists is determined by the interactions of the organism's chemical machinery with those of the environment. Whatever may be the nature of biologic phenomena, they must operate under the laws that regulate all aspects of the nonliving environment. These laws find their best expression in the sciences of chemistry and physics. There is thus a biochemical approach to all biologic problems. Chemicophysical techniques are the chief tools for revealing insights into what goes on in the process of living. Yet biologic phenomena are not synonymous with chemistry. Certain chemical properties are uniquely associated with animals and plants. Although the life process shows the same chemical elements as that of the physical world, many of these elements in the organism are combined into far more complicated combinations, or compounds, than are found in the inanimate world. Among these unique molecules are two that stand out—proteins and nucleic acids. Out of these two types of molecules the various units or patterns of organic matter are built. Despite the many patterns making up the diversity of life, they are unified by the way proteins and nucleic acids are organized to form their individual structures.

What is commonly called the "alphabet" of living matter consists of the elementary or subatomic particles (protons, neutrons, photons, and electrons), some 20 bioelements (C, H, O, N, S, P, and others in tiny amounts, or traces), and about 36 important organic molecules (amino acids, nucleotides, glucose, ribose, neutral fats, and phospholipids). There are no unique elements in the alphabet of organic matter, but with few exceptions nature has been highly selective in choosing those elements and combining them in unique molecules for her organic patterns.

The key element in most organic compounds is carbon because of its versatility in forming complex molecules. This element, however, is not restricted to organic substances. Its atomic weight (C^{12}) has replaced oxygen (O^{16}) as the basis for computing the atomic weights of all the other elements. It has the power to act chemically both as a metal and as a nonmetal. With hydrogen it forms the extensive class of hydrocarbons, and with oxygen and hydrogen together it gives rise to the great carbohydrate group. Study of both its synthetic and natural compounds is called organic chemistry.

Molecular biology in a sense is a complement of classic biology. It seeks to understand the nature of biologic molecules and how they are organized to form the level of life. Therefore it is concerned with the structures of proteins, nucleic acids, and other large biologic molecules as well as with the basic structures of chromosomes, myofilaments, membranes, and whatever makes up the cell. Moreover, it tries to explain how the interactions of these constituents constitute the life process.

CHAPTER 3

• BASIC STRUCTURE OF MATTER*

THE MOLECULAR WORLD

● As pointed out in Part One, the world is composed of tiny units called **molecules**, which in turn are made up of simpler units (**atoms**). The molecular architectural structure of the substances around us—window glass, clothing, leather, iron, foodstuffs, etc.—determines the behavior and character of these substances and the uses we make of them. Although molecules and atoms are too small to be seen, there are various ways in which scientists can learn about them. The spectroscope, which measures the wavelength of the light emitted and absorbed by molecules and atoms, reveals a great deal of information about the way atoms are joined to form molecules and about their behavior. On photographic plates it is possible to record the deflected beams of x-rays or electrons, and by such means physicists and chemists have learned the size of molecules and the arrangement of the atoms within the molecules.

Some molecules have few atoms, and others are huge with complicated patterns of atoms. They vary not only in size but also in their properties. Some are elastic, with long threadlike molecules (rubber), and others are solid and rigid (steel). Many are arranged in compact three-dimensional patterns, and others form long chains of interconnected atoms. Molecules are found in all three states of matter—gas, liquid, and solid. Molecules are attracted to each other by electric and gravitational forces. They are also in a constant state of motion. Heat gives us an indication of their motion. In a cold substance the molecules move sluggishly; in a warm substance they move rapidly. At low temperatures, molecules are in well-ordered arrays, as in a crystal; at high temperatures the molecular pattern of a crystal becomes highly distorted. Hot temperatures tear the molecules asunder, as when a liquid is transformed into a gas.

As the student will see, living matter is also made up of atoms and molecules displaying higher and higher levels of organization. But to appreciate the organization and behavior of living matter, it is necessary to learn something about the general principles of chemistry and chemical processes, to which this chapter is devoted.

HISTORIC BACKGROUND OF THE ATOM

Although the ancient Greeks had certain conceptions of the composition of matter, such as the universe being composed of the four elements—fire, air, earth, and water—our present concepts of the nature of matter have originated within the past two centuries. A. L. Lavoisier, the great French scientist of the eighteenth century, compiled the first list of elements, a total of 28, and explained the precise nature of respiration (1778). J. Dalton, the English chemist, conceived (1808) that matter was composed of atoms, which combine in definite proportions to form chemical compounds. The Italian investigator A. Avogadro showed how many atoms of each kind make up each compounded atom and gave the concept of the molecule (1811). By 1869 no fewer than 92 kinds of atoms had been ascertained, and D. I. Mendeléeff worked out his periodic table of the elements. In this table he arranged the elements into 8 groups on the basis that a relation of the chemical elements can be expressed by their properties, which are periodic functions of their atomic weights. If the elements are in a group of elements that have similar properties and relations, they follow a regular progression in the individual differences of their members.

For many years the atom was considered solid and indivisible. In 1911 Lord Rutherford showed that every

*Refer to Chapter 2, Principle 2.

atom consists of a positively charged nucleus surrounded by a negatively charged planetary system of electrons. It was thus seen that atoms consisted of smaller particles (elementary particles). New elementary particles have been discovered from time to time, but the three of the most importance in understanding the nature of the atom are protons, neutrons, and electrons.

NATURE OF ATOMS AND MOLECULES

There are 92 naturally occurring elements in the universe and perhaps a dozen or so man-made ones that have been formed in the cyclotron or nuclear reactor. An atom is the smallest structural unit of an element that has all the chemical properties of that element. Most of the atom is empty space, but the atom consists of a **nucleus** and **electrons.** The nucleus is the center that contains most of the atom's mass. It is made up of two kinds of particles, **protons** and **neutrons** (Fig. 3-1). These two particles have about the same weight, each being about 1,800 times heavier than an electron. The protons bear positive charges, and the neutrons have no charges (neutral). Although there is the same number of protons in the nucleus as there are electrons revolving around the nucleus, the number of neutrons may vary. For every positively charged proton in the nucleus there is a negatively charged electron. The total charge of the atom is thus neutral.

FIG. 3-1

Two lightest atoms. Since first shell closest to atomic nucleus can hold only 2 electrons, helium shell is closed so that helium is chemically inactive.

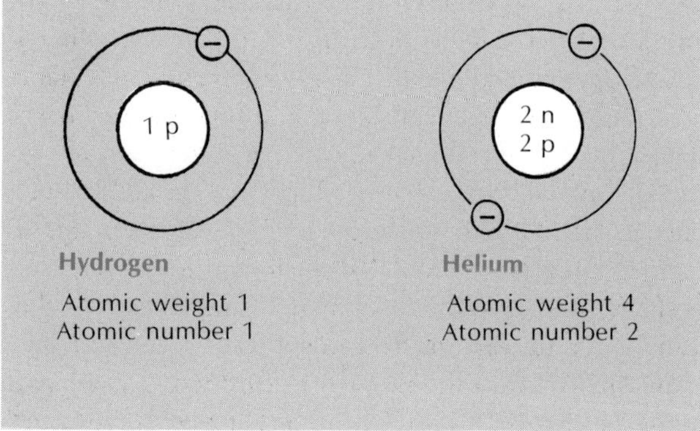

The electrons revolve around the nucleus in orbits, or shells. These shells are identified as (from inside to out) K, L, M, N, O, P, and Q. Some of the heavier atoms have all seven shells, but others have fewer. The shells are often called electron clouds because the rapid motion of the electrons give such an effect. Electrons are considered to be indivisible and therefore may be called fundamental, or elementary, particles. In all neutral atoms there are enough electrons to balance the positive charges on the nucleus. An atomic nucleus consists of protons and neutrons, and the total number of these two kinds of particles make up the **atomic weight** (the small weight of the electron is negligible). The nucleus of an oxygen atom contains 8 protons and 8 neutrons. It therefore has an atomic weight of 16. The heavy molecule, uranium, has a nucleus of 92 protons and 146 neutrons, and so its atomic weight is 238. A common isotope, uranium 235, has 143 neutrons. Although almost the whole weight of an atom is in the nucleus, the latter is only 1/10,000 of the diameter of the atom. The atomic weight of oxygen was formerly used as a base for the comparison of the weight of other atoms, but in 1961 physicists changed this standard to the carbon atom (C^{12}) (Fig. 3-2) because this element is frequently used in mass spectroscopy in determining atomic weights. Its atomic weight is arbitrarily assigned 12.000. Thus the atomic weight of other atoms may be defined as their relative weight compared with that of carbon. In the periodic table many natural elements are not whole numbers because the proportion of their isotopes is included in their atomic weights.

The **atomic number** of an element is the number of protons in the nucleus of its atom, or the number of electrons in the shells. The number of protons determines the number of electrons that govern the chemicophysical properties of the atom. It is the electrons, for instance, that determine that 1 atom of oxygen will unite with 2 atoms of hydrogen to form water.

The number of concentric shells, or the paths of the electrons in their orbits, naturally varies with the element. Each shell can hold up to a maximum number of electrons. The first shell (K) next to the atomic nucleus can hold a maximum of 2 electrons (hydrogen has only 1) (Fig. 3-1); the second shell (L) can hold 8; in other shells there is also a maximum number, but no atom can have more than 8 electrons in its outermost shell. In order of atomic number the inner shells are filled first, and if there are not enough

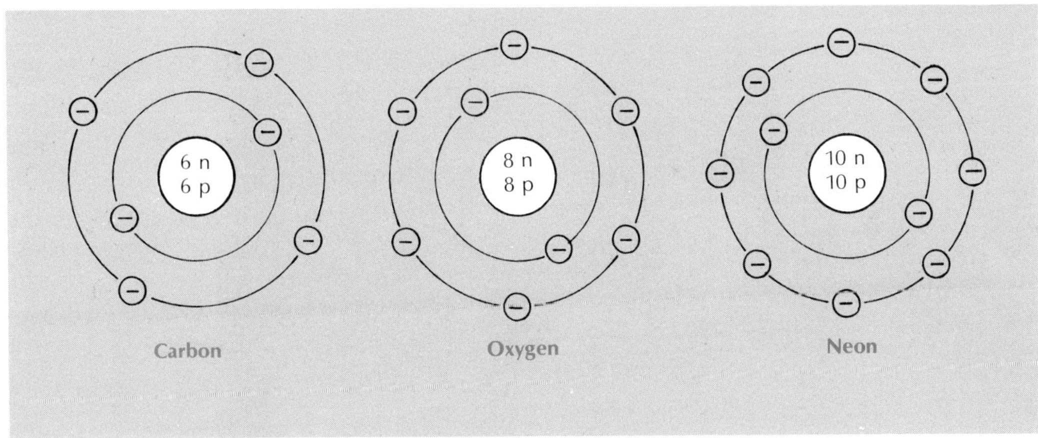

FIG. 3-2

Electron shells of 3 common atoms. Since no atom can have more than 8 electrons in its outermost shell and 2 electrons in its innermost shell, neon is chemically inactive. However, second, or L, shells of carbon and oxygen, with 4 and 6 electrons, respectively, are open so that these elements are electronically unstable and react chemically whenever appropriate atoms come into contact. Chemical properties of atoms are determined by their outermost electron shells.

electrons to fill all the shells, the outer shell is left incomplete. Hydrogen has 1 proton and 1 electron in its single orbit but no neutron. Its atomic number (and atomic weight) is therefore 1. Since its shell can hold 2 electrons, it has an incomplete shell. Helium (Fig. 3-1) has 2 electrons in its single shell, and its nucleus is made up of 2 protons and 2 neutrons. Its atomic number is 2 and its atomic weight is 4. Since its 2-electron arrangement in its shell is the maximum number for this shell, it is closed and precludes all chemical activity. There are no known compounds of helium. Neon is another inert gas because its outer shell (L) contains 8 electrons, the maximum number, and cannot be chemically active. Lithium has a new outer orbit. Its nucleus consists of 3 protons and 4 neutrons; its atomic weight is 7 and its atomic number is 3. The 3 revolving electrons are distributed as follows: 2 in the inner shell (K) and 1 in the outer orbit (L). It is thus an active element. Oxygen (Fig. 3-2) has an atomic number of 8. Its 8 electrons are arranged with 2 in the K shell and 6 in the L shell. It is very active chemically, forming compounds with almost all the elements except the inert gases.

The number of electrons in the outer shell varies from 0 to 8. With either 0 or 8 in this shell the element is chemically inactive. When there are fewer than 8 electrons in the outer shell, the atom will tend to lose or gain some electrons to have an outer shell of 8. This can result in an **ion** because the number of protons remains the same. Atoms with 1 to 3 in the outer shell tend to lose them to other atoms and to become positively charged ions because of the excess protons in the nucleus. Atoms with 5 to 7 electrons in the outer orbit tend to gain electrons from other atoms and to become negatively charged ions because of excess electrons over the protons. Positive and negative ions tend to unite.

Isotopes of atoms

It is possible for 2 atoms of the same chemical element to have the same number of protons in their nuclei but to have a different number of neutrons. Such atoms have different atomic masses and are called **isotopes** (Figs. 3-3 and 3-4). The nuclei of isotopes have identical numbers of protons but different numbers of neutrons. Thus isotopes of an element are composed of atoms that differ from each other in weight. All the isotopes with the same atomic number have the same chemical properties. Twenty of the elements have no isotopes, each of these elements having only one type of atom. The other elements possess isotopes ranging in number from 2 to 9. At present there are about 270 natural isotopes. Tin with 10 isotopes has the most. The atomic weight of an element is therefore the average atomic weight of a group of atoms with the same properties. This explains, as already mentioned, why the atomic weights are not always whole numbers. Thus oxygen is a mixture of 3 isotopes. Oxygen 16 makes up 99.76% of the atoms. Oxygen 17 and oxygen 18 account for about 0.24% of the atoms. Since atomic weights are based on protons and neu-

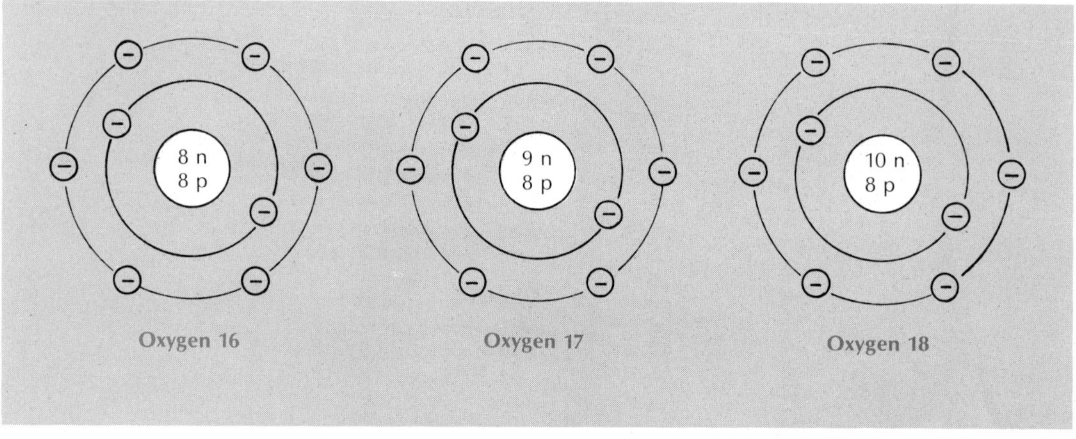

FIG. 3-3

Three isotopes of oxygen. Oxygen 16 makes up about 99.76% and the other two about 0.24% of all oxygen. The numbers indicate atomic weights.

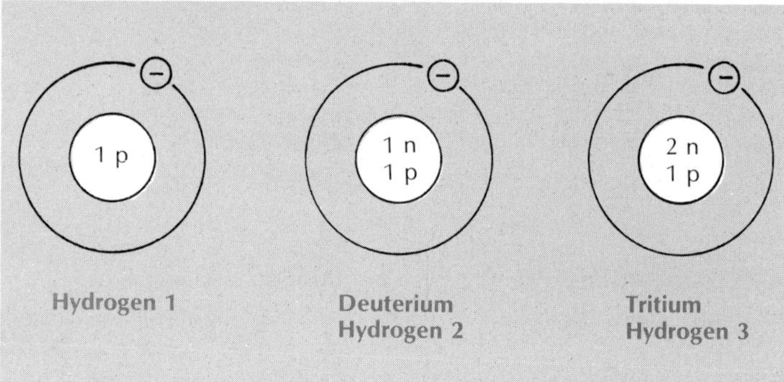

FIG. 3-4

Three isotopes of hydrogen. Of the 3 isotopes, hydrogen 1 makes up about 99.98% of all hydrogen and deuterium makes up about 0.02%. Tritium is found only in traces in water. Numbers indicate atomic weights. Most elements are mixtures of isotopes. Some elements (for example, tin) have as many as 10 isotopes.

trons in the nuclei, the atomic weight of oxygen is a little more than 16 and is so indicated in some periodic tables.

For most elements both stable and radioactive isotopes are known. In radioactive, or unstable, isotopes the number of neutrons is altered and thus a part of its mass or energy is given off by radiation. **Electromagnetic radiation** is given off in the form of short-wave, high-energy gamma waves. Another type of radiation, **particulate radiation,** emits actual subatomic particles with lower energy in the form of **alpha** particles, **beta** particles, and **neutrons.** Different radioactive isotopes give off different forms of these radiations. For instance, widely used carbon 14 gives off only beta particles of single electrons. The time it takes for a radioactive substance to reach stability follows the pattern of **half-life,** which means that at the end of a predictable time, one half of the radioactive isotope has decayed; and one half of the remainder will decay in the same length of time, and so on, repeatedly. The half-life of different radioactive atoms varies anywhere from a fraction of a second to millions of years. The half-life of radioactive iodine 13 is 8 days and of uranium 238, about 4.5 billion years. The stable end product is usually a nonradioactive isotope of another element. For instance, radium 226 decays to lead 200, uranium 238 to lead 206, etc.

Radioactive isotopes have wide practical use in biologic and medical studies. Many are employed as tracer agents, making it possible to follow the action and reaction of organic and inorganic substances within the body. Radioactive iodine is used in the diagnosis of thyroid function and in the treatment of hyperthyroidism. The naturally occurring isotope C^{14} has a half-life of 5760 years. A compound synthesized with C^{14} is "tagged." By using a Geiger counter, C^{14} can be followed through biochemical studies of the utilization of foods in animal nutrition, the age of archaeologic specimens, and in many other ways.

With various devices (cyclotron, nuclear reactor, atomic pile) it has been possible to make artificially many new isotopes. Some of these are radioactive and can be detected with a Geiger counter by the rays they emit. Oak Ridge and other places make many isotopes for the use of scientists.

MOLECULES AND COMPOUNDS

Atoms rarely exist by themselves. The atoms of most elements tend to combine with atoms of other elements. A combination of 2 or more elements forms a **compound.** A molecule is the smallest particle of an element or compound that can exist by itself. Compounds always contain different elements, but the term molecule is often applied to compounds. Molecules of most elementary gases are made up of 2 atoms. Thus a molecules of oxygen is O_2 and that of hydrogen, H_2. In such cases the 2 atoms are always found together. Carbon dioxide and CH_4 are true compounds because they consist of different elements, each of which is present in definite proportions.

The properties of compounds are different from the properties of their single elements. Hydrogen and oxygen separately have certain properties that are different from water when the 2 elements are combined into H_2O. Water is not simply a mixture of hydrogen and oxygen, but a chemical change has occurred between the 2 elements involved. When oxygen and hydrogen combine to form water, there has been a change in electronic structure. A molecule is too small to be visible, but large protein molecules can be detected with an electron microscope. Compounds may occur in one or more of the three forms, as a gas, liquid, or solid. A given phase is largely a matter of the interactions between the attractive forces of the involved molecules and their kinetic energy. In a gas the vigorous vibrations of the molecules, determined by temperature, enable the kinetic energy to overcome the attractive forces so that a gas completely fills whatever contains it. The larger the space in which the gas is found, the greater the distance between its molecules. In solids the molecules are held together as crystals by strong mutual attraction. Liquid molecules are midway between the gaseous and solid phases in their ability to move, although they have stronger mutual attraction but less molecular velocity than do those of the gaseous state.

The kinetic energy of molecules increases with temperature. This phenomenon often determines the phase of the substance. At 0° C. water is a liquid, and above 100° C. it is a vaporous gas. Water is the only liquid that expands on freezing.

Chemists have been able to put their investigations of molecular structure to practical applications in many ways. Studies of molecular structure have contributed directly to the solution of many technical problems. For instance, the determination of the precise arrangement of the atoms in the molecules of various drugs is necessary to learn their physiologic action, which lies in their molecular architecture.

Chemists have represented elements by symbols, a type of shorthand. For simplicity they use the capitalized first letter wherever this is possible. For instance, the symbol for oxygen is O; for hydrogen, H; for nitrogen, N; for phosphorus, P; for sulfur, S; and for carbon, C. When more than 1 element begins with the same letter, a second small letter is added. Thus the symbol for cobalt is Co; for chromium, Cr; for calcium, Ca; for chlorine, Cl; and for copper, Cu. Some common elements have arbitrarily two-letter symbols, as aluminum, Al; magnesium, Mg; zinc, Zn; manganese, Mn; radium, Ra; bromine, Br; and helium, He. Some elements have symbols derived from their corresponding Latin names, as iron, Fe (ferrum); lead, Pb (plumbum); silver, Ag (argentum); mercury, Hg (hydrargyrum); sodium, Na (natrium); and potassium, K (kalium).

GRAM ATOMIC AND GRAM MOLECULAR WEIGHTS

To appreciate the quantitative expression of compounds, the student should be familiar with the terms **gram atomic weight** and **gram molecular weight.** This information is useful in computing the composition of compounds. A gram atomic weight of an element is its atomic weight expressed in grams. The number of atoms in a gram atomic weight is 6.02×10^{23} (Avogadro's number). This means that the gram atomic weight of all elements has the same number of atoms. The atomic weight of hydrogen is 1 and that of oxygen, 16. Therefore, 1 gram of hydrogen has the same number of atoms as does 16 grams of oxygen or 12 grams of carbon. If in carbon monoxide (CO) 1 atom of carbon combines with 1 atom of oxygen, 12 grams of carbon will react with 16 grams of oxygen. A gram molecular weight, or **mole,** is the sum of the atomic weights of the atoms in a molecule. This also means that the same number of moles of all substances have the same number of molecules. Thus 18 grams of water (H_2O) has the same number of molecules as does 32 grams of oxygen (O_2) or 28 grams of carbon monoxide (CO).

VALENCE AND BONDS

Valence is the relative combining power of one chemical element with another and represents the bonding forces between atoms and ions. The valence of an element can be more specifically defined as its ability to combine with or to replace hydrogen in forming compounds. Chemical reactions occur because every atom tends to complete its outer shell. This outermost shell has from 1 to 8 electrons (valence electrons). To attain a stable condition by filling its outer shell, the atom is bonded to another atom by taking or giving up valence electrons. This is called electrovalence and is determined by the number of electrons gained or lost by the atom. Metals usually lose electrons; their electrovalence is the number of electrons they give up and is called positive. On the other hand, nonmetals usually take up electrons, and the number taken up represents their electrovalence, which is negative. It is also called an ionic bond when a compound is formed this way. In an **ionic bond** (Fig. 3-5), oppositely charged ions are attracted to one another, and a strong electrostatic force binds them together.

Valence is shown by an element only when it combines with another. By itself it has 0 valence. Although certain elements do not combine with hydrogen, the number of hydrogen atoms that these elements replace from a compound shows their valences. Thus

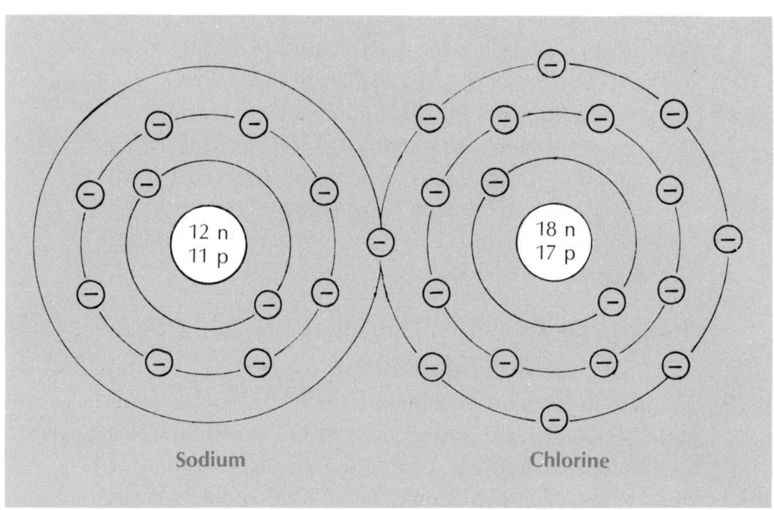

FIG. 3-5

Ionic bond. When an atom of sodium and one of chlorine react to form a molecule, single electron in outer shell of sodium is transferred to third or outer shell of chlorine. This causes outer or second shell (third shell is empty) of sodium to have 8 electrons and also chlorine to have 8 electrons in its outer or third shell. The compound thus formed is called sodium chloride (NaCl). By losing 1 electron, sodium becomes a positive ion, and by gaining 1 electron, chlorine (chloride) becomes a negative ion. This ionic bond is held together by a strong electrostatic force.

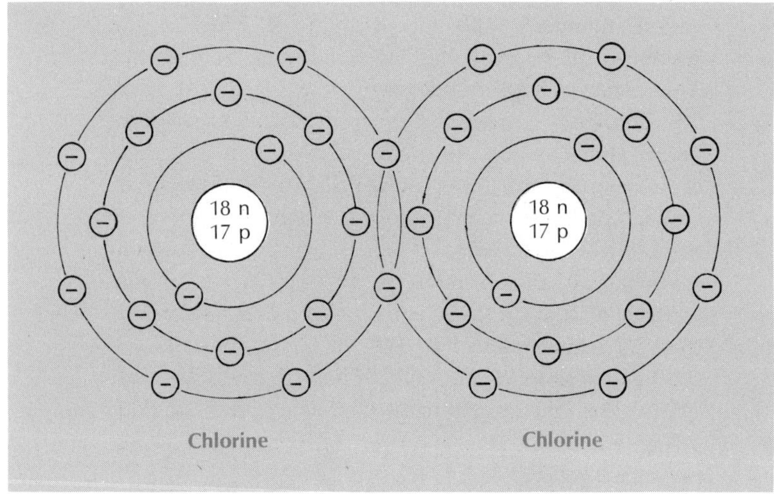

FIG. 3-6

Covalent bond. Each chlorine atom has 7 electrons in its outer shell, and by sharing one pair of electrons, each atom acquires a complete outer shell of 8 electrons, thus forming a molecule of chlorine (Cl_2). Such a reaction is called a molecular reaction, and such bonds are called covalent bonds.

the zinc atom replaces 2 hydrogen atoms in the sulfuric acid molecule when zinc sulfate is formed. Zinc therefore has a valence of 2. Some elements have variable valences. Iron has valences of 2 and 3 and phosphorus of 3 and 5. Many elements have only one valence. Oxygen has two and carbon, four.

Other types of bonds are known besides the ionic (electrostatic) bond just described. The **covalent** bond (Fig. 3-6) involves the sharing of a pair of electrons by 2 adjacent atoms. For instance, in methane (CH_4) each hydrogen atom shares a pair of electrons with the carbon atom. These bonds are common in the formation of organic compounds. The **hydrogen bond,** biologically considered, holds a more or less unique role because of its low energy and the part it played in the early formation of molecules that were the antecedents of complex biologic macromolecules. The hydrogen bond is formed when 2 atoms are joined by sharing of a hydrogen atom. It involves an interaction between a hydrogen atom attached to a negatively charged atom in one molecule and another negatively charged atom in the same or in a different molecule. This bond often determines the properties of proteins and nucleic acids in living organisms. It determines also the uniqueness of water as an environmental component.

In many compounds, for example, sodium sulfate, there may be more than one kind of bonding.

BONDS AND ENERGY

Every compound has a greater or lesser energy content. Forces of mutual attraction between atoms or their ions form the chemical bonds of a compound. Every molecule has stored, or potential, energy. This chemical energy is found in the bonding forces that hold the atoms or ions together. The greater the attraction between 2 atoms or ions, the greater is the bond energy. **Bond energy** is the amount of work necessary to break a chemical bond. The forcible separation of 2 bonded atoms or ions (breaking bonds) requires energy from some source, and the amount of energy required must be great enough to overcome the attraction between the atoms or ions. Thus the energy required to break a bond is equal to the bond energy. The total potential energy of a compound is the energy required to break all the bonds.

In chemical reactions there are also energy changes. When heat is liberated, as when hydrogen and oxygen combine to form water, heat is given off (exothermic or exergonic reaction). In other reactions heat is absorbed. This energy gain by a chemical reaction is called endothermic or endergonic reaction, and can occur when water is degraded into hydrogen and oxygen by some process. To do so, it requires as much energy as was released when hydrogen and oxygen combined to form water.

To start a chemical reaction, the compounds reacting must be sufficiently activated to react properly. The molecules must be brought close enough together to overcome the repulsive action of their electrons. It is necessary for molecules and ions to collide with each other to break and remake chemical bonds. This energy necessary for starting a reaction is called the **activation energy.** Heat is one of the most common activation energies because it greatly intensifies the motion of the reacting atoms or ions and thus causes them to collide. Other kinds of external energy that will activate reactions are electricity, light, mechanical pressure, etc.

OXIDATION-REDUCTION

All **oxidations** are energy-liberating chemical reactions. The reverse process is **reduction;** oxygen is reduced and energy is bound into the chemical that is reduced. Oxidation as defined today is a loss of electrons, whereas reduction is a gain of electrons. The two processes occur simultaneously and in chemically equivalent quantities. The meanings of the two terms also include a large number of reactions that do not involve loss or gain of oxygen. For instance, the removal of hydrogen is an oxidation and its addition is a reduction. Also, in the formation of magnesium chloride, for every magnesium atom oxidized by a loss of 2 electrons, 2 chlorine atoms are reduced by a gain of 1 electron each. Either the removal of oxygen (oxidation) or the addition of hydrogen (reduction) to a compound adds an electron and thus binds energy. In energy terminology, oxidations are exergonic and reductions are endergonic. In balanced oxidation-reduction reactions the substance losing electrons (oxidation) is considered an electron donor (reductant) because its lost electrons are given to and reduce the other substance. On the other hand, the substance gaining electrons (reduction) is an electron acceptor (oxidant). In electrolysis, oxidation occurs at the anode pole and reduction at the cathode pole.

Oxidation-reduction processes occur in most biologic energy transfers. Most of them involve the removal of hydrogen (dehydrogenation) from a compound. The oxygen used in the decomposition of sugar in the cell acts as a hydrogen acceptor and not as an oxygen donor. In this way sugar releases energy by the removal of hydrogen from the sugar molecule and not by the addition of oxygen to it.

IONIZATION OF MOLECULES

Molecules often tend to dissociate into their constituent ions. An ion is an electrically charged atom or group of atoms. Ionization may occur by dissociation, by collision of matter with radiant energy, or by application of heat. The original molecule is electrically neutral, but each individual ion has an electric charge. Thus, when NaCl is dissolved in water, the salt breaks down into particles below molecular size, the sodium and chlorine atoms. The sodium atom is positively charged (Na^+) and the chlorine atom is negatively charged (Cl^-). An ion differs from an atom in having more or fewer electrons than protons. When NaCl breaks down into Na^+ and Cl^-, the chlorine atom carries with it 1 of the electrons from the sodium ion, thus leaving the sodium ion positive. The H^+ ion, when water dissociates, consists only of its nucleus (proton) because its single electron is given to the OH^- ion.

Negatively charged ions are called **anions** and positively charged ones, **cations.** Ions with multiple charges (for example, Ca^{++}) are uncommon. Negative ions rarely carry more than two charges, although some positive ions may have three or four charges. All common ions are produced by the gain or loss of 1, 2, or 3 electrons.

In biologic processes the occurrence of certain ions, Na^+, K^+, and Cl^-, plays a great part in the physical chemistry of life activities. Cell membrane phenomena involve especially the behavior of the Na^+ and K^+ atoms. Cell membrane permeability, nervous conduction, sodium pumps, and other processes involve the activities of ions. Moreover, the Ca^{++} ion is essential in the construction of bone. Calcium phosphate is precipitated when sufficient concentrations occur together in solution.

ACIDS, BASES, AND SALTS

Every ionic compound is either an acid, a base, or a salt. An **acid** is any compound that dissociates to yield hydrogen ions. An acid is classified as strong or weak, depending upon the extent to which an ionic compound is dissociated. Those that dissociate completely in water (H_2SO_4, HNO_3, and HCl) are called strong acids. In these practically all ionic bonds are broken. In a weak acid, such as acetic acid (CH_3COOH), only a few of the ionic bonds are broken. A solution of acetic acid will contain the whole ionic compound (CH_3COOH) along with a few acetate and hydrogen ions that have been freed by dissociation. Acids in aqueous solutions have a sour taste, turn litmus red, react with bases, and conduct electricity.

A **base** contains negative ions called hydroxyl ions. It may be defined as a molecule or ion that will combine with a proton. They are produced when compounds containing them are dissolved in water. Thus NaOH (sodium hydroxide) will dissociate completely

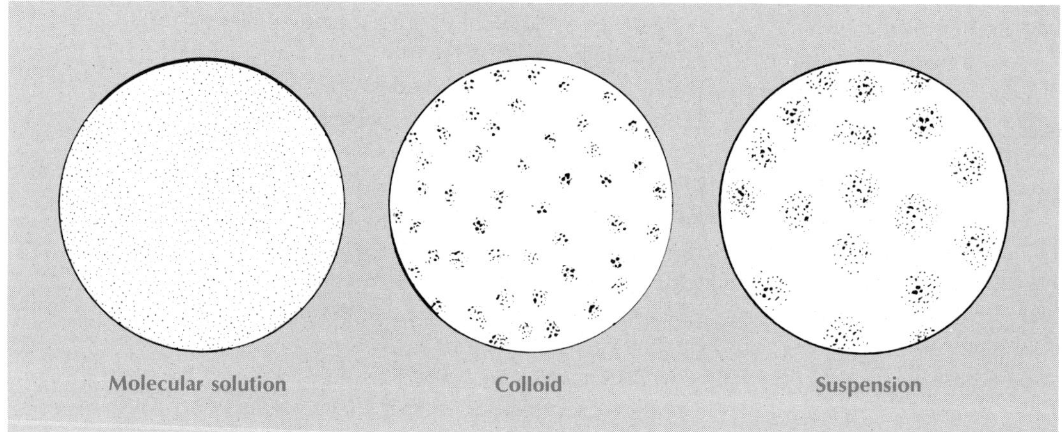

FIG. 3-7

Diagrams of three types of solutions or mixtures.

in water into sodium (Na^+) and hydroxyl (OH^-) ions. Among the characteristics of a base is its ability to combine with a hydrogen ion. Like acids, bases vary in the extent to which they dissociate in aqueous solutions into hydroxyl ions. Bases turn litmus blue, react with acids, and conduct electricity.

A **salt** is a compound resulting from the chemical interaction of an acid and a base. The common salt sodium chloride (NaCl) is formed by the interaction of hydrochloric acid (HCl) and sodium hydroxide (NaOH). In water the HCl is dissociated into H^+ and Cl^- ions. The hydrogen and hydroxyl ions combine to form water (H_2O) and the sodium and chloride ions to form salt:

$$\underset{\text{Acid}}{HCl} + \underset{\text{Base}}{NaOH} = \underset{\text{Salt}}{NaCl} + H_2O$$

The significance of acid and basic conditions in the animal will be discussed in a later section.

Organic acids are usually characterized by having in their molecule the carboxyl radical (—COOH). The common organic acids are acetic, citric, formic, lactic, and oxalic. The student will encounter many of these later in discussions of cellular metabolism, etc.

MIXTURES AND THEIR PROPERTIES

Whenever masses of different kinds are thrown together, we have what is called a mixture. All the different states of matter (solids, liquids, gases) may be involved in these mixtures. The mixtures we are mainly interested in here are those in which water or other fluid is one of the states of matter. When something is mixed with a liquid, any one of three kinds of mixtures is formed.

Molecular solutions. If crystals of salts or sugars are added to water, the molecules or ions (in the case of salts) are uniformly dispersed through the water, forming a **true solution** (Fig. 3-7). Such solutions are transparent. In such a case the water is the **solvent** and the dissolved salt or sugar the **solute.** Other solutions may be formed by adding acids and bases to water. The freezing point of solutions is lower and the boiling point is higher than those of pure water.

Suspensions. If solids added to water remain in masses larger than molecules, the mixture is a suspension. Muddy water is a good example. When allowed to stand, the particles in suspension will settle out to the bottom. Suspensions have a turbid appearance and have the same boiling and freezing points as pure water.

Colloids. Whenever the dispersed particles are intermediate in size between the molecular state and the suspension, a third mixture is the result—the colloidal solution. Colloidal particles are rather arbitrarily considered to be between 1 and 100 millimicrons in size. If the particles are smaller, the solution is classified as a true solution; if larger, they are suspensions or emulsions. Colloids consist of two phases—an internal, or discontinuous, phase and an external, or continuous, phase. These phases may be represented by the same states of matter or different ones. Some familiar examples are as follows:

Internal phase	External phase	Example
Solid	Liquid	Ink
Liquid	Liquid	Emulsion
Liquid	Solid	Gel
Solid	Solid	Stained glass
Gas	Liquid	Foam, carbonated water
Liquid	Gas	Fog
Solid	Gas	Smoke

A true colloidal solution is stable (that is, will not settle out), has about the same boiling point and freezing point as pure water, and is either transparent or somewhat cloudy.

Proteins, which are important constituents of protoplasm, form colloidal solutions because their large molecules are well within the size range of colloidal particles and behave like colloids. Since protein molecules also dissolve as molecules in solution, such solutions may also be called molecular.

One special form of colloidal solution is the **emulsion** in which both phases are immiscible liquids (Fig. 3-8). Cream is a good example. Here, droplets of oil, or fat, are dispersed in water. This type of colloidal solution has considerable significance in the makeup of protoplasm.

Colloidal emulsions also well illustrate the property of some (but not all) colloids to reverse their phases. When gelatin is poured into hot water, the gelatin particles (internal phase) are dispersed through the water (external phase) in a thin consistency which is freely shakable (Fig. 3-9). Such a condition is called a **sol.** When the solution cools, gelatin now becomes the external or continuous phase and the water is in the discontinuous phase. Moreover, the solution has stiffened and become semisolid and is called a **gel.** Heating the solution will cause it to become a sol again, and the phases are reversed. Some colloidal emulsions are not reversible. Heating egg white, for example, will change the egg albumin from a sol into an irreversible gel. In such cases the coagulated particles may collect into larger particles and settle out.

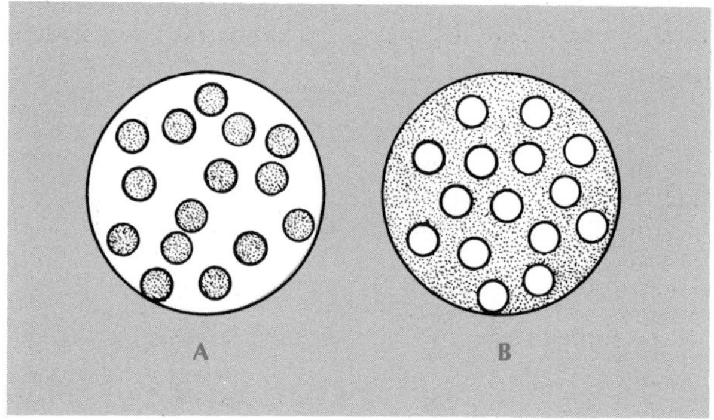

FIG. 3-8

Diagram of colloidal solution in which each phase is a liquid. **A,** Oil-in-water emulsion, water being the continuous, or external, phase, oil the discontinuous or internal phase. **B,** Water-in-oil emulsion, water being the discontinuous, or internal, phase, oil the continuous or external phase. Certain agents can bring about this phase reversal.

FIG. 3-9

Diagram of sol and gel. **A,** Sol condition in which gelatin particles are the internal phase, water the external phase. **B,** Gel condition in which gelatin particles form external phase (network), enclosing water as internal phase.

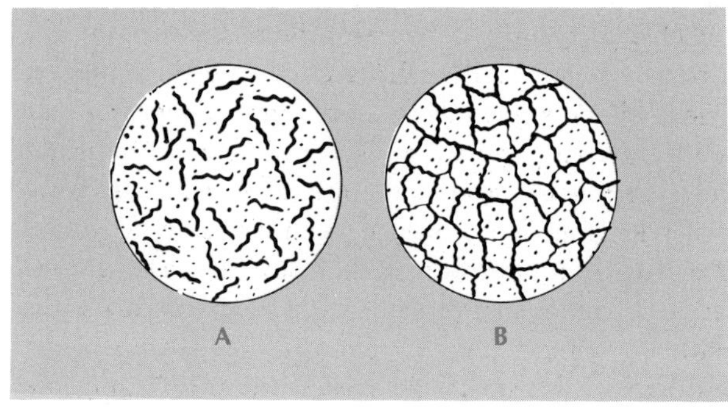

Within a given colloidal system, the particles usually bear the same electric charge and thus repel each other. This, together with a phenomenon known as **brownian movement** (the movement induced by the bombardment of the particles by water molecules), is mainly responsible for keeping colloidal solutions stable.

Behavior of colloidal solutions as contrasted with molecular solutions. In solid forms, substances such as salts and sugars are indefinite shapes known as crystals; hence, they are called **crystalloids.** In solutions, as we have seen, they form molecular solutions. There are two classes of crystalloids: **nonelectrolytes,** which do not ionize or carry electric charges (sugars and starches are examples), and **electrolytes,** which do ionize and carry positive or negative charges. Salts, acids, and bases are examples of this class. As a group, crystalloids diffuse easily through membranes, have low freezing points, and have relatively high osmotic pressures.

In contrast to these properties of the crystalloids, colloids do not go through membranes readily, do not crystallize readily, have little effect on freezing point, and have relatively low osmotic pressures. Many of the properties of colloids depend on the surface area between the dissolved particles and the surrounding medium.

Why do colloids play such an important role in the structure of protoplasm? There are several reasons, among which may be mentioned the following:

1. Great surface exposure, which allows for many chemical reactions.
2. The property of phase reversal, which helps explain how protoplasm can carry on diverse functions and change its appearance during metabolic activities.
3. The property of undergoing gelation or solation, which enables the protoplasm to contract, thus explaining the movements such as ameboid movement.
4. The inability of colloids to pass through membranes, which promotes the stability and organization of the cellular system, such as cell and nuclear membranes and cytoplasmic inclusions.
5. The selective absorption or permeability of the cell membrane, which is largely dependent on the phase reversal of its colloidal structure.

HYDROGEN ION CONCENTRATION (pH)

Solutions are classified as acid, base, or neutral according to the proportion of hydrogen (H^+) and hydroxyl (OH^-) ions they possess. In acid solutions there is an excess of hydrogen ions; in alkaline, or basic, solutions the hydroxyl ion is more common; whereas in neutral solutions both hydrogen and hydroxyl ions are present in equal numbers.

To express the acidity or alkalinity (or pH concentration) of a substance, a logarithmic scale, a type of mathematical shorthand, is employed that uses the numbers 1 to 14. In this scale, numbers below 7 indicate an acid range; numbers above 7 indicate an alkaline range. The number 7 indicates neutrality, that is, the presence of equal numbers of H^+ and OH^- ions. The smaller the number within the acid range, the greater the acidity; the larger the number within the alkaline range, the greater the alkalinity. According to this logarithmic scale, a pH of 3 is ten times as acid as one of 4; a pH of 9 is ten times as alkaline as one of 8.

In protoplasmic systems pH plays an important role, for, in general, slight deviations from the normal usually result in severe damage. Most substances and fluids in the body hover closely around the point of neutrality, that is, a pH of around 7. Blood, for instance, has a pH of 7.35, or just slightly on the alkaline side. Lymph is slightly more alkaline than blood. Saliva has a pH of 6.8, on the acid side. A 24-hour sample of urine gives an acid reaction of pH 6. Gastric juice is the most acid substance in the body, about pH 1.6. The regulation of the pH of the body tissue fluids involves many important physiologic mechanisms, one of the most important of which is the buffer action of certain salts.

BUFFER ACTION

In living animals the pH of the body fluids as indicated in the previous section hovers around the point of neutrality. The reason for regulating the hydrogen ion concentration in the extracellular fluids is to maintain a constancy of the pH so that metabolic reactions in the cell will not be adversely affected by a constantly changing hydrogen ion concentration. For this regulation the body has certain substances that resist any change in the pH when acids or alkalies are added to the body fluids. These are called **buffers.** The hydrogen ion concentration within the cells is probably greater than the hydrogen ion concentration in the extracellular fluids because of the metabolic production of CO_2, which reacts with the cellular water to form carbonic acid (H_2CO_3). There are also certain phosphates, sulfates, and organic acid radicals that add to the acidic nature of the intracellular fluids. Within the cells the high content of protein serves as a buffer and thus tends to keep the pH from going too low.

The buffer function of the blood is dependent on both the plasma and red blood corpuscle buffer mechanisms. The chief buffer of the plasma and tissue fluid is sodium bicarbonate ($NaHCO_3$). This salt dissociates into sodium ions (Na^+) and bicarbonate ions (HCO_3^-). When a strong acid (for example, HCl) is added to the fluid, the H^+ ions of the dissociated acid will react with the bicarbonate ion (HCO_3^-) to form a very weak acid, carbonic acid, which dissociates very slightly. Thus the H^+ ions from the HCl are removed and the pH is little altered. There are also many other buffer mechanisms in the blood.

The chief buffer of the red blood corpuscle is hemoglobin (Hb). Reduced Hb is a weak acid and exists in the red blood cell as HHb. Oxygenated Hb is a stronger acid than reduced Hb and is found in the corpuscle in the form of $KHbO_2$, which tends to ionize into K^+ and HCO_3^- ions. Potassium cannot pass out of the cell membrane but HCO_3^- can. When the bicarbonate ion enters the plasma, it reacts with the Na^+ ion (from the dissociation of NaCl) to form $NaHCO_3$. To offset the loss of anions from the red blood cell, Cl^- anions enter the corpuscle as part of the chloride shift.

CHAPTER 4

• BIOCHEMISTRY OF LIFE*

CHEMICAL EVOLUTION OF LIFE

● The origin of life must involve a gradual increase of complexity from lower levels to higher grades of organization. It is agreed that life emerged as the result of a sequence of chemical reactions that led to molecular organizations of biochemical potentialities of life. One aspect is the fitness of the chemical elements and molecules that make up biochemical mechanisms. A living system is more than the molecules it contains; of greater importance is the manner in which chemical reactions occur. A logical explanation of the origin of life must trace the emergence of these chemical mechanisms: the origin of organic compounds from inorganic ones, the polymerization of large macromolecules, the formation of enzyme systems, and the energetics of chemical reactions and cellular metabolism. Of primary importance also is the creation of a self-duplicating mechanism that could synthesize its components and energy requirements.

BASIC STRUCTURE OF LIVING SYSTEMS

An analysis of living organisms today reveals that there are about 20 bioelements that make up their structure. The major elements are C, H, N, O, S, P, Na, K, Ca, and Mg. Besides these there are certain trace elements such as Zn, Mn, Fe, Co, Cu, I, V, Al, Mo, and B. Some other elements are also found, but whether they are in living substance by accident or form functional constituents has never been satisfactorily resolved. There are some 35 chief organic molecules, which include the sugars (glucose, ribose, deoxyribose), phospholipid, neutral fat, 21 amino acids, 5 nucleotides, and assorted molecules of small structure. Variations occur in the distribution of these molecules in living organisms. Some amino acids, for instance, occur only in particular types of protein.

There are four main types of inorganic compounds in living systems—water, salts, acids, and bases—but these compounds, with the exception of water, are present in smaller amounts than the organic ones. All these can decompose into inorganic ions, the chief of which are cations (Na^+, H^+, K^+, NH_4^+, Ca^{++}, Mg^{++}) and anions (Cl^-, NO_3^-, HCO_3^-, OH^-, $SO_4^=$, $PO_4^{\equiv}$). Water is formed by the union of H^+ and OH^- ions, acids by the union of an H^+ ion with any anion except OH^-, bases by the union of OH^- with any cation except H^+, and salts by the union of any cation except H^+ with any anion except OH^-.

All organisms also contain dissolved gases in their structure. Cellular membranes are usually very permeable to atmospheric gases that are soluble in both protoplasm and water. Free nitrogen is one of the most abundant of these gases in the atmosphere, but its inert nature prevents its participation in cellular metabolism to any extent. Oxygen, of course, is a basic requirement in cell metabolism, and carbon dioxide as a metabolite is mostly found in cells in the form of carbonic acid.

Any theory of the origin of life must take into account the appearance and relation of most of the constituents just mentioned in the patterns of living systems.

COMPARISON OF EARTH'S CRUST COMPOSITION WITH THAT OF LIVING SYSTEMS

It will be noted from a comparison of Tables 4-1 and 4-2 that there is no single element entirely peculiar to living substance. All the elements found in protoplasm (Table 4-2) are relatively abundant in nonliving matter, although protoplasm is highly selective. With the exception of oxygen, the chief elements (oxygen, hydrogen, carbon, nitrogen), which make up about 98% of protoplasm, are relatively much more abundant in living than in nonliving substance.

FITNESS OF BIOELEMENTS

Carbon, hydrogen, oxygen, and nitrogen make up about 98% of living substance and therefore occupy a

*Refer to Chapter 2, Principle 2.

TABLE 4-1

Abundance of elements in terrestrial material ½ mile deep, including earth's crust, oceans, and atmosphere

Element	Atomic number*	Parts per thousand
Oxygen	8 (1)	495
Silicon	14	257
Aluminum	13	75
Iron	26	47
Calcium	20	34
Sodium	11	26
Potassium	19	24
Magnesium	12	19
Hydrogen	1 (9)	8.8
Titanium	22	5.8
Chlorine	17	1.9
Phosphorus	15	1.2
Carbon	6 (13)	0.9
Manganese	25	0.8
Sulfur	16	0.5
Barium	56	0.5
Nitrogen	7 (17)	0.3
Fluorine	9	0.3
Chromium	24	0.3
Strontium	38	0.2
Remaining elements		1.5

*The figures in parentheses indicate the occurence rank in the earth's crust of the four major elements in protoplasm.

TABLE 4-2

Abundance of elements in average protoplasm

Element	Percent by weight
Oxygen	66
Carbon	17
Hydrogen	10
Nitrogen	2.5
Magnesium	1.5
Phosphorus	0.9
Potassium	0.3
Calcium	0.3
Sulfur	0.2
Chlorine	0.1
Sodium	0.04
Iron	0.01
Copper	Trace
Zinc	Trace
Cobalt	Trace
Manganese	Trace
Others	Trace in special cases

unique position in the chemical patterns of the organism. These elements are peculiarly fitted for their functions in the protoplasmic system. As far as is known, living things anywhere can arise only when these elements are common. They represent the backbone of all organic compounds, and although they are found in both organic and inorganic matter, some, such as carbon and nitrogen, are more abundant in living things.

Hydrogen is one of the most unique of all the elements. It is the lightest of all the elements in the periodic table and its comparative weight represents unity. It is very reactive and can form more chemical combinations than any other element. Since it is small it can be squeezed into molecular structures not possible with other elements. Its lightness caused much of it to be lost to outer space in the early formation of the earth, and the part that remained was saved mainly by combining with other elements. The hydrogen bond is a small energy bond and little energy is involved in its formation and rupture. It also forms bonds in reactions at normal temperatures. Much of the uniqueness of water can be attributed to the hydrogen bond. Water is the most abundant single compound in living systems, and it usually makes up 60% to 90% of the weight of protoplasm. It has high solvent properties and favors the reactions of dissolved substances within it, which are so necessary for the life processes. Its high-heat capacity tempers the drastic action of abrupt environmental changes, and its high heat of vaporization is important in the regulation of body temperature. Dissociation and ionization are promoted when substances are dissolved in water.

Carbon, with its great combining power (it has a valence of 4), plays an important role in the formation of organic compounds. Present in all organic compounds, it is the basis of organic chemistry. Its central position in the periodic table enables it to combine with either electropositive or electronegative atoms. It can form 4 bonds with other elements by gaining, losing, or sharing the 4 valence electrons. Carbon can form strong carbon-to-carbon bonds and can produce long chains or rings. It is uniquely fitted to produce the large molecules characteristic of living substance. The enormous number of compounds carbon can form not only permits wide variations of compounds, but also precision in forming nearly identical compounds with nearly identical properties so that a working basis for the evolutionary process of selection can operate.

Oxygen is the most abundant element both in living matter and in the crust of the earth. Its unique role in biologic oxidations and in making energy available for the living organism gives it a special position among the bioelements. Its part in the formation of water and carbon dioxide are other important roles of this ubiquitous element. Not all organisms make use of oxygen in energy metabolism, however. Some organisms are anaerobic and do not need it. As a part of water, oxygen is used in photosynthesis, but some photosynthetic bacteria make use of hydrogen sulfide in place of water. Oxygen forms many oxides, which are usually formed slowly at low temperatures or rapidly at high temperatures. Ordinary decay is a slow oxidation brought about with the aid of microorganisms.

Nitrogen is an essential component (about 3%) of all living animal and plant matter. It makes up an important part of all amino acids. Enzymes are nitrogen-containing compounds, as are all nucleoproteins. Not only does the protein part of nucleoproteins contain nitrogen but so also do the purine and pyrimidine bases. Although there is a great store of nitrogen in the atmosphere, no animals and few plants can make use of it. For most plants to use nitrogen it must be in the form of various inorganic compounds, such as ammonia (NH_3) nitrates (salts with NO_3), and nitrites (salts with NO_2). Animals get their nitrogen by consuming compounds (proteins) that they get from plants or other animals. Most nitrogen is taken from the air by nitrogen-fixing bacteria in the roots of legumes and by some fungi and algae. When they decay, few organisms decompose nitrogen compounds completely (although some denitrifying bacteria do so), but the end products of nitrogen metabolism are usually compounds, such as urea, uric acid, and ammonia. One unique property of nitrogen is that it is available for long periods of time and can be used over and over through many different organisms.

Some other elements, which make up a smaller percentage of living substance than the preceding, should be mentioned here. Phosphorus, which makes up about 0.9% of the total weight of protoplasm, is of the utmost importance in life processes. It is never found in the free state in nature because of its ready affinity for other elements, but because of its high energy bonds, it plays a role in all major energy exchanges in the life process. In combination with lipids it forms the phospholipids that are found in all cell membranes. It also forms a part of bone and plays a part in the phosphate buffer system. Calcium (1.5%) is closely associated with phosphorus in the formation of bone. It functions in regulation of the heartbeat, blood clotting, and other functions. Sulfur (0.2%) is part of two essential amino acids and is used by certain bacteria as a source of chemical energy in the synthesis of food molecules by combining CO_2 and water.

Besides the more common elements described, living substance has certain metallic elements that are far less abundant. A few of these "trace elements" are known to be important in body functions, but the presence of others may be accidental.

As a group these rarer elements have diverse functions to perform. Two of them, iron (Fe) and copper (Cu), aid in the transport of oxygen in the blood. Iron is a constituent of the hemoglobin molecule and copper of hemocyanin in some invertebrates. Both are also members of the cytochrome electron system. Many are involved in enzymatic activities, such as zinc (Zn), cobalt (Co), molybdenum (Mo), and magnesium (Mg).

RADICALS

In many chemical reactions certain groups of atoms remain intact as a definite unit and are called **radicals.** A radical therefore may be defined as a group of atoms that goes through chemical changes without any change in structure or composition. Some of the radical ions involved in dissociation and ionization have already been mentioned, such as NH_4^+ and $SO_4^{=}$. In reactions that do not involve dissociation, such as the displacement of OH^- from methyl alcohol (CH_3–OH), the OH is called the **hydroxyl group,** or hydroxyl radical, and the CH_3 is referred to as the methyl radical. Some of the common groups found in biomolecules are the **carboxyl radical** (–COOH), which can be represented by the following structural formula:

$$-\underset{\underset{\displaystyle O}{\|}}{C}-OH$$

This carboxyl radical represents an acid compound, such as those found in fatty acids and amino acids. Another radical is the **carbonyl group** (C=O), which is one of the most common radicals in organic compounds, including the proteins, amino acids, and sugars. It is the product of the oxidation of a hydrocarbon unit or an alcohol group. In most carbonyl groups it is attached to one or more organic groups. Two common types of compounds in which the carbonyl group is found are the aldehydes and ketones. In an aldehyde, C=O is bound to an H atom and to a C atom:

```
  |
—C—C—H
  |  ||
     O
```

In a ketone, C=O is bound on both sides to C atoms:

```
  |     |
—C—C—C—
  |  ||  |
     O
```

An important group in the formation of proteins is the **amino group** ($-NH_2$). On hydrolysis, proteins yield amino acids in which the NH_2 group is mainly on the carbon atom next to the COOH group:

```
    R
    |
H—C—NH2
    |
    C
```

The *R* represents the body of the amino acid molecule that varies with the different amino acids. Two important groups (radicals) are found in an amino acid—the carboxyl (—COOH) and the amino ($-NH_2$).

The alcohol group is found in alcoholic compounds, some sugars, and other carbohydrates. The addition or removal of an alcoholic group may completely change the chemical nature of an organic compound:

```
   H
   |
—C—OH
   |
```

Another group, the sulfhydryl, is fairly common in enzymes. It consists of a sulfur atom bonded to a hydrogen atom: —S—H.

These radicals occur repeatedly in carbon compounds and perform important roles. Radicals occur only as parts of organic compounds; they do not exist by themselves. All are found in cellular metabolism as intermediary or end products.

ORGANIC MOLECULES*

The inorganic components of living matter are obtained directly or indirectly in finished form from the external physical environment. Besides water the other inorganic substances are the mineral solids that commonly form the ash of the body after incineration. It usually makes up 1% to 5%, depending on the kind of animal. This mineral solid may consist of hard deposits on the outside of animal cells, for example, the external shells of protozoa, claws, and the calcium phosphate of bone. Several minerals are in solution within the cell, either as free ions or in combination with organic compounds. Most of these ions are hydrogen (H^+), calcium (Ca^{++}), potassium (K^+), sodium (Na^+), magnesium (Mg^{++}), hydroxyl (OH^-), carbonate ($CO_3^=$), bicarbonate (HCO_3^-), chlorine (Cl^-), sulfate ($SO_4^=$), and phosphate ($PO_4^{\equiv}$). The animal obtains these from the earth's crust when these minerals are dissolved in water.

All **organic compounds** contain carbon, and they represent a great variety of compounds that share many characteristics. As a group they often contain hydrogen and oxygen and may contain nitrogen, salts, sulfur, phosphorus, and other elements. Organic compounds are those compounds in which the principal bonds are carbon-to-carbon and carbon-to-hydrogen.

Organic compounds are usually insoluble in water, except those of alcohol, acetic acid, sugar, amino acids, and perhaps a few others. The number of carbon compounds is immense. Other elements may bond to other atoms of like kind but only to a restricted number. Carbon's valency of 4 enables it to have a great bonding potential. The carbon atoms may be combined one to another in the form of a chain:

```
  |   |   |   |
—C—C—C—C—
  |   |   |   |
```

When hydrogen is joined to each of the free bonds, an aliphatic hydrocarbon is produced:

```
    H  H  H  H
    |   |   |   |
H—C—C—C—C—H
    |   |   |   |
    H  H  H  H
```

It will be noted that at each end carbon uses 3 valences. Alternately types of atoms other than hydrogen may also be bonded to such chains.

In aromatic hydrocarbons there are ring compounds containing a number of double bonds per molecule. The most notable ring is the **benzene ring:**

```
        H
        |
        C
      //  \
H—C        C—H
    |        ||
H—C        C—H
      \\  /
        C
        |
        H
```

*Refer to Chapter 2, Principle 4.

The benzene ring is thus a hexagon of 6 carbon atoms, each bearing 1 hydrogen atom and joined to the adjacent carbon atoms by alternate single and double bonds. Carbon chains also may be branched with other configurations.

Both aliphatic and aromatic hydrocarbons are the end product of plant and animal remains buried in the earth in the form of coal and petroleum oil. Ring compounds that have one or more of their ring atoms made up of atoms other than carbon are called **heterocyclic.** The purine and pyrimidine rings found in nucleic acid are examples.

FIG. 4-1

Glucose exists in these two forms in equilibrium with each other, but straight-chain type is less common than the other.

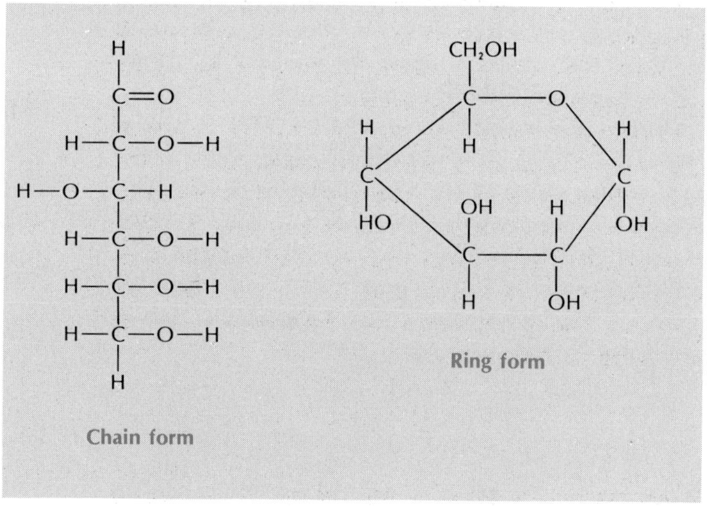

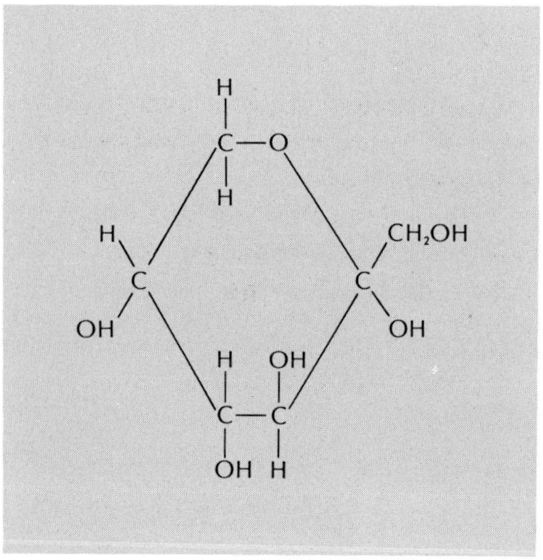

Chain form

Ring form

The great versatility of the carbon atoms makes possible the enormous complexity of many organic molecules. The large number of organic constituents found in living organisms have many underlying principles and patterns of biochemical structure and function that bear out the idea of a unity of biochemistry in the great diversity of animal life.

Carbohydrates. Carbohydrates are compounds made up of carbon, hydrogen, and oxygen and are usually present in the ratio of 1C:2H:1O. This ratio between hydrogen and oxygen gives carbohydrates their name (hydrates of carbon) because this ratio is the same as that of water. Some carbohydrates, however, are exceptions to the rule. Familiar examples of carbohydrates are sugars, starches, and cellulose. They comprise about 1% of protoplasm. Carbohydrates are made synthetically from water and the carbon dioxide of the air by green plants and leaves with the aid of the sun's energy. This process is called **photosynthesis** and has never been duplicated by man. It is a reaction on which all life depends, for it is the starting point in the formation of food. Some bacteria such as *Nitrosomonas* have the power to synthesize complex organic substances from carbon dioxide and water (chemosynthesis) with the energy supplied by the oxidation of ammonium and other compounds.

Carbohydrates are usually divided into three classes: (1) **monosaccharides,** or simple sugars; (2) **disaccharides,** or double sugars; and (3) **polysaccharides,** or complex sugars. Simple sugars, such as glucose, galactose, and fructose, have the formula $C_6H_{12}O_6$ (hexoses) (Figs. 4-1 and 4-2). The atoms in these molecules differ in arrangement, which confers on them different chemical properties. Another simple sugar is the rare pentose ($C_5H_{10}O_5$), which has only 5 carbon atoms.

A disaccharide is formed from 2 molecules of simple sugar by the loss of a molecule of water in this way:

$$\underset{\text{Glucose}}{C_6H_{12}O_6} + \underset{\text{Fructose}}{C_6H_{12}O_6} \longrightarrow H_2O + \underset{\text{Sucrose}}{C_{12}H_{22}O_{11}}$$

FIG. 4-2

Structure of fructose. Fructose has same empirical formula as glucose ($C_6H_{12}O_6$) but has a different arrangement of its hydrogen and oxygen atoms. These compounds are thus isomers, each with distinctive physicochemical properties. Fructose, for instance, is much sweeter than glucose.

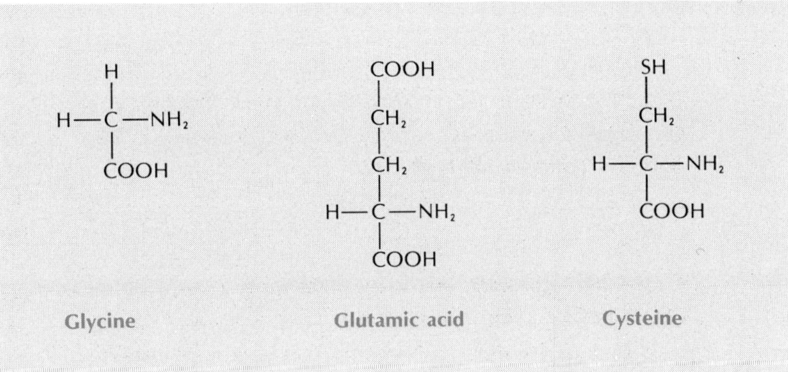

FIG. 4-3

Three amino acids. Glycine is simplest of amino acids and R is represented by a single hydrogen atom. Cysteine is the principal amino acid carrying a sulphydryl group (—S—H).

Besides sucrose or cane sugar two other common disaccharides are maltose (malt sugar), formed by the linkage of 2 molecules of glucose, and lactose (milk sugar), composed of 1 molecule of glucose and 1 of galactose.

Polysaccharides are made up of many molecules of a simple sugar (usually glucose). It is not known exactly how many molecules are found in these complex sugars, and since they are made up of a multiple number of molecules of the same substance, they are referred to by the chemist as polymers. The formula for them is usually written $(C_6H_{10}O_5)^n$ where *n* stands for the unknown number of simple sugar molecules of which they are composed. Starch is very common in most plants and is an important food constituent. **Glycogen,** or animal starch, is found mainly in the liver and muscle cells. When needed, glycogen is converted into glucose and is delivered by the blood to the tissues. A more complex polymer is **cellulose,** which is an important part of the cell walls of plants. Cellulose cannot be digested by man, but some animals, such as the herbivores with the aid of bacteria and termites with the aid of flagellates, can do so. Sugars are soluble in water, but the polysaccharides are far less so and thus are ideal for storage, since their large molecules will not pass through plasma membranes.

The main role of carbohydrates in protoplasm is to serve as a source of chemical energy. Protoplasm requires energy for its activities, and the oxidation of carbohydrates furnishes much of this energy. Glucose is the most important of these energy carbohydrates, and other carbohydrates are transformed into glucose before they are utilized as a source of energy. Some carbohydrates become basic components of protoplasmic structure, such as the pentoses that form constituent groups of nucleic acids and of nucleotides. The lipid compounds of nervous tissue known as cerebrosides also contain a simple sugar component, and certain sugars are found in the coenzymes of enzymatic systems.

Proteins. Proteins are organic compounds that contain carbon, hydrogen, oxygen, nitrogen, and sometimes sulfur, iodine, and phosphorus. The unique properties of proteins center mainly around nitrogen. Since proteins bear such an intimate relationship to protoplasm, they are often referred to as its foundation substance.

They are colloidal by nature and form large and complex molecules. The molecular weight of certain representative proteins are as follows: insulin (a pancreatic hormone), 12,000; egg albumin, 40,000; and hemoglobin, 68,000. Others are far more complex, with molecular weights reckoned in millions. There are many different forms of proteins in animal tissues, and different species of animals have different kinds of proteins. The protein molecule is made up of many thousands of atoms, but when broken down it always yields simpler components known as **amino acids** (Fig. 4-3). At least 25 of these amino acids are recognized by biochemistry, and a dozen others of doubtful status are known to occur in nature. Few proteins contain all the different kinds of amino acids, but considering all the possible combinations of amino acids in protein molecules, it is easy to see that an almost infinite variety can be produced, just as by combining the 26 different letters of the alphabet we can get thousands of different words.

The structural formulas of all the amino acids are known to scientists. The distinctive formula for any amino acid is as follows:

$$\begin{array}{l} R—CH—COOH \\ \quad\;\; | \\ \quad\; NH_2 \end{array}$$

In this formula the symbol *R* may represent any one of about 20 different atomic groupings. One of the simplest amino acids is glycine:

$$\begin{array}{c} H{-}CH{-}NH_2 \\ | \\ COOH \end{array}$$

R here represents the single hydrogen atom, but in other amino acids *R* could stand for a methyl group ($-CH_3$) or a variety of carbon radicals. Another amino acid, alanine, is represented thus:

$$\begin{array}{c} CH_3{-}CH{-}COOH \\ | \\ NH_2 \end{array}$$

Here the group CH_3 stands for *R*.

The various amino acids are chiefly distinguished from each other by what constitutes the *R*.

It will be seen, therefore, that amino acids contain an amino group (NH_2) and an acid group (COOH). In solution, amino acids can dissociate into ions that can act both as base and as acid. The NH_2 group is basic and will combine with acids; the COOH group is acid and will combine with bases. Proteins can thus serve as buffers against excess acids or bases that may harm the protoplasm. Also, by having both groups, proteins are very active chemically and can form large molecules. In forming a simple protein, the amino acids are linked together by a bond between the NH_2 group of one and the COOH group of the other; this is called a peptide linkage (Fig. 4-4). A combination of two amino acids is called a dipeptide; of three amino acids a tripeptide, etc. If many amino acids are combined, a polypeptide is formed. Proteins are built up of polypeptide chains of the amino acids of great diversity in sequence. A simple protein such as albumin or egg white contains at least 300 amino acids. The exact arrangement of the amino acids in a protein molecule is known in only a few proteins; insulin is one of these.

FIG. 4-4

Linkage of amino acids by a peptide bond. Adjacent amino acids are so linked that amino group of one acid is united to carboxyl group of another with loss of 1 molecule of water. Dipeptide so formed has peptide bond encircled in this figure. When large number of amino acids are so linked together, they constitute a polypeptide chain and may form a protein. Since a protein may consist of several polypeptide chains, there are other types of bonds (for example, hydrogen, disulfide, and ionic bonds) that may hold polypeptide chains together. Polypeptide chains are held in coiled (helical) shape chiefly by hydrogen bonds that share electrons with 2 other atoms. In polypeptide chain, hydrogen bonds are located chiefly in nitrogen and double-bonded oxygen of peptide bonds.

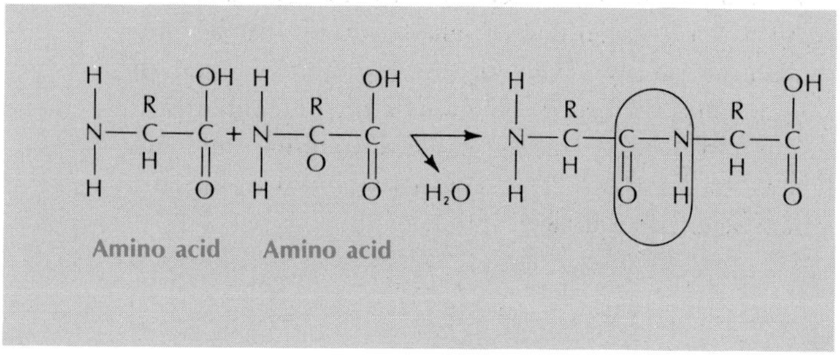

$$\begin{array}{ccccccc} H & & OH\ H & & OH & & H \qquad\qquad\qquad OH \\ |\ \ R & & |\ \ \ | & R & | & & |\ \ R \qquad\qquad R\ \ | \\ N{-}C{-}C & + & N{-}C{-}C & & & \longrightarrow & N{-}C{-}C{-}N{-}C{-}C \\ |\ \ H & & \|\ \ \ | & O & \| & \searrow & |\ \ H\ \ \|\ \ \ |\ \ H\ \ \| \\ H & & O\ \ H & & O & H_2O & H\qquad O\ \ H\qquad O \end{array}$$

Amino acid   Amino acid

Proteins are usually classified into three major groups: (1) **simple,** such as the albumins and globulins, which are represented in all cells, in blood plasma, in enzymes, and in muscle; (2) **compound** or **conjugated,** which are made up of a nonprotein group attached to a protein molecule and represented by the nucleoproteins and the chromoproteins (hemoglobin and visual purple); and (3) **derived,** which are obtained from the breakdown of natural proteins by digestion or otherwise are represented by proteoses, peptones, etc. There are many other subdivisions under each of these classes.

Since the amino acid molecules are relatively small, all of them can diffuse through the cellular membrane, and in the amino acid form they are transported in the blood.

Proteins serve as the chief structural pattern of protoplasm and also form enzymes, hormones, chromosomes, and other cell components; they may release energy when utilized as food. The uniqueness of different cells is mainly due to the unique proteins they possess, and different species of organisms have certain proteins different from those of other species. The more closely two organisms are related, the more their proteins are alike; conversely, the more they are unlike, the more their proteins differ. Proteins thus serve as evidence for evolutionary relationship (species specificity). This generalization has practical application in grafting tissues from one animal to another because grafts are more likely to succeed in closely related animals that have similar protein patterns; in distantly related species these grafts will not "take" and so they degenerate.

Some amino acids can be made in the body from other amino acids, but others must always be supplied in the food. These latter are called essential amino acids and include tryptophan, phenylalanine, and five or six others. Therefore, a diet composed of these essential amino acids in pure form would supply the protein needs of the body. Most tissues have a 15% content of protein, and next to water, proteins are the most abundant constituent of protoplasm.

Nucleic acids and nucleoproteins. These complex substances of high molecular weight are universal in living systems and are considered to represent life at the most fundamental level. They contain the elements carbon, hydrogen, oxygen, nitrogen, and phosphorus. They can be broken down into structural units (nucleotides) of which there are nine known at present. Each nucleotide is composed of a nitrogenous base (Fig. 4-5), a pentose sugar, and phosphoric acid. When nucleic acids are conjugated with simple proteins, nucleoproteins are formed. According to the kind of pentose sugar present in the molecule, nucleic acids are divided into two classes (there may be more). One kind contains the sugar deoxyribose and is called deoxyribonucleic acid (DNA). This one is found chiefly in the nucleus and is supposed to make up the chief part of the hereditary genes. Some authorities believe that each gene is a single molecule of nucleoprotein. The other kind contains the sugar ribose and is called ribonucleic acid (RNA). It is found mainly in the cytoplasm and nucleoli and is directly concerned in the cellular synthesis of proteins.

The reaction of substances in the cell to dyes depends on the relative amount of nucleic acid in nucleoproteins. Chromatin, for instance, is highly basophilic because of its high content of nucleic acid. Viruses also consist of nucleoproteins, some viruses containing DNA and others RNA. They have the power of reproduction in the cells of a living host. On this account viruses are often referred to as "naked genes." The quantity of DNA in a cell is constant under nearly all conditions; that of RNA fluctuates with nutritional states, type of tissue, etc. (See discussion on genetic code, Chapter 35.)

Lipids. Fats and fatlike substances are known as lipids. They include the true fats, oils, compound lipids, and steroids. As a group they make up about 3% of protoplasm. The true fats, or simple lipids, are sometimes called the neutral fats. They consist of oxygen, carbon, and hydrogen and are formed by the combination of 3 fatty acid molecules and 1 glycerol molecule. True fats are therefore esters, that is, a combination of an alcohol (glycerol [Fig. 4-6]) and an acid. They also bear the term "triglyceride" because the glycerol radical is combined with three radicals from fatty acid

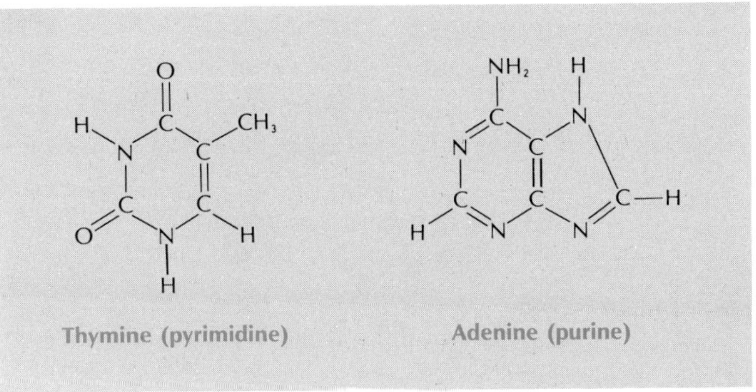

FIG. 4-5

Nucleic acid nitrogenous bases. Nucleic acids contain the organic bases, pyrimidines and purines. Nucleic acids are composed of long chains of nucleotides, each of which is made up of an organic base (two are shown), a pentose sugar, and a phosphate. Nucleic acids control cell activity and store genetic information.

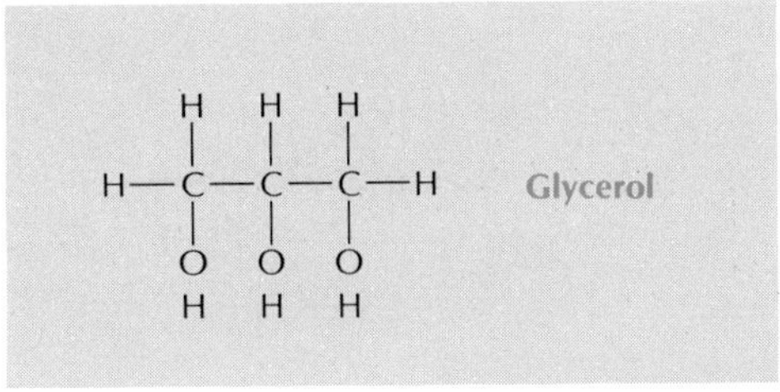

$$\begin{array}{ccccccc} & H & & H & & H & \\ & | & & | & & | & \\ H- & C & - & C & - & C & -H \\ & | & & | & & | & \\ & O & & O & & O & \\ & H & & H & & H & \end{array}$$

Glycerol

FIG. 4-6

Structural formula of glycerol (glycerin). This substance chemically is a type of alcohol and is obtained from fats and oils. Each fat molecule consists of 3 fatty acid molecules combined with 1 molecule of glycerol with elimination of 3 water molecules. The 3 fatty acid molecules may be same, or they may be different.

groups. A chemically pure fat such as stearin is an ester of glycerol and 3 molecules of a single fatty acid (stearic acid) (Fig. 4-7). Most natural fats, however, such as lard and butter are mixtures of chemically pure fats, for they usually have two or three different fatty acids attached to the three hydroxyl groups of glycerol. The production of a typical fat by the union of glycerol and stearic acid is shown by the following formula:

$$\begin{array}{lcllcl} C_{17}H_{35}CO|OH & & H|O-CH_2 & & C_{17}H_{35}OCO-CH_2 & \\ & & & & \quad\quad\quad\quad\quad | & \\ C_{17}H_{35}CO|OH & + & H|O-CH & \longrightarrow & C_{17}H_{35}OCO-CH & + 3H_2O \\ & & & & \quad\quad\quad\quad\quad | & \\ C_{17}H_{35}CO|OH & & H|O-CH_2 & & C_{17}H_{35}OCO-CH_2 & \\ \text{Stearic acid} & & \text{Glycerol} & & \text{Stearin} & \\ \text{(3 mols.)} & & \text{(1 mol.)} & & \text{(1 mol.)} & \end{array}$$

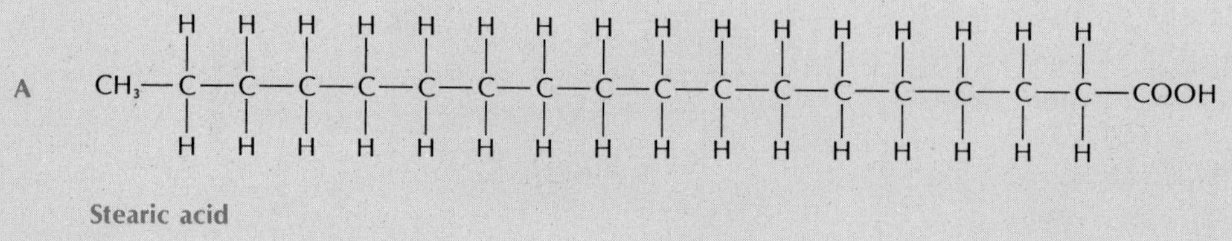

A

Stearic acid

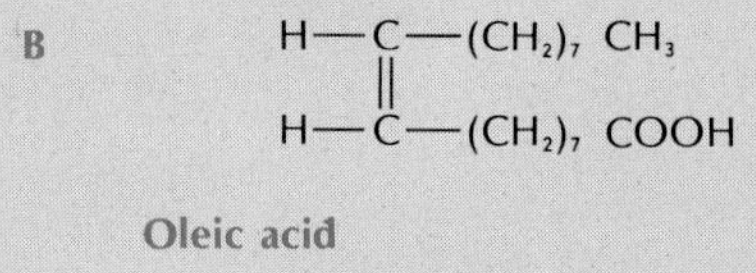

B

H—C—$(CH_2)_7$ CH_3

H—C—$(CH_2)_7$ COOH

Oleic acid

FIG. 4-7

Saturated and unsaturated fatty acids. When all available bonds of carbon chain are filled with hydrogen ions, as in stearic acid, **A,** such fatty acids are called saturated. Unsaturated fats, such as oleic acid, **B,** have 1 or more double bonds (C=C) in their molecules because all available bonds of carbon are not filled with hydrogen atoms. Unsaturated fats tend to be oily liquids in contrast to more solid saturated fats.

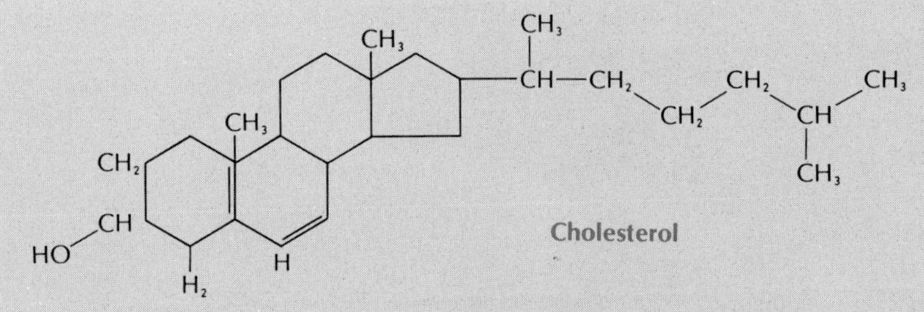

Cholesterol

FIG. 4-8

Cholesterol, one of parent steroids. Steroids are a group of lipid compounds with carbon atoms arranged in four rings, three of 6 carbon atoms and a fourth ring of 5. Steroids are represented by vitamin D, male and female sex hormones, adrenocortical hormones, and bile salts. Cholesterol is a structural component of nervous tissue. Consumption of saturated fats in animal flesh and dairy products can raise blood cholesterol level; unsaturated fats (vegetable oils and fish) can lower blood level of cholesterol.

In this formula it will be seen that the 3 fatty acid molecules have united with the OH group of the glycerol to form stearin (a neutral fat), with the production of 3 molecules of water. Other common fatty acids in nature are palmitic and oleic acids (Fig. 4-7).

Most true fats are solid at room temperatures, but plant oils (linseed, cottonseed, etc.) and animal oils (fish and whale) are liquid because of the nature of their fatty acids. Waxes such as beeswax are secreted by certain glands and differ from true fats in having an alcohol other than glycerol in their molecular structure. Some waxes may also have hydrocarbons.

Compound lipids are fatlike substances that, when broken down, will yield glycerol (or some other alcohol), fatty acids, and some other substances, such as a nitrogenous base (for example, choline), phosphoric acid, or a simple sugar. Among these lipids are the phospholipids (lecithin) found in egg yolk and probably every living cell and the cerebrosides (glycolipid) that are common in nervous tissue. The steroids, or solid alcohols, are not chemically related to fats but are included among the lipids because they have fatlike properties. Cholesterol ($C_{27}H_{45}OH$) is a common example of a steroid (Fig. 4-8). Ergosterol, a plant steroid, becomes vitamin D (calciferol) when activated by ultraviolet rays. Male and female sex hormones and the adrenal gland hormones are other examples of steroids. Some of these steroids are derived from cholesterol by oxidation or reduction.

Lipids have many functions in protoplasm. The true fats furnish a concentrated fuel of high-energy value and represent an economic form of storage reserves in the body. Excess carbohydrates can be transformed into fat, and to a limited extent fatty acids can be changed into glucose. Some phospholipids form part of the basic protoplasmic structure, such as lecithin, which gives a constant characteristic pattern to all cells. Phospholipids also share with proteins the basic structure of the plasma membrane and of the myelin sheaths or nerve fibers. Cholesterol is a component of bile and of gallstones, which are bile precipitates.

Annotated references

Allen, J. M. (editor). 1966. Molecular organization and biological function. New York, Harper & Row, Publishers. *A paperback by several specialists dealing with a number of aspects of molecular biology. Subjects dealt with are protein structure, mitochondria, cell membranes, light receptors, and others. An excellent up-to-date discussion of these timely topics.*

Baldwin, E. 1962. The nature of biochemistry. New York, Cambridge University Press. *This little text is intended as a starting point for a basic understanding of the biochemical background of biologic study. A careful study of this treatise will be a fruitful reward for any biology student.*

Barry, J. M. 1964. Molecular biology: genes and the control of living cells. Englewood Cliffs, N. J., Prentice-Hall, Inc. *A paperback dealing with the structure of chemical molecules and the way they are formed.*

Bennett, T. P., and E. Frieden. 1966. Modern topics in biochemistry. New York, The Macmillan Co. *A paperback that will enable the beginning student to appreciate the role chemical compounds play in molecular biology.*

Clark, B. F. C., and K. A. Marcker. 1968. How proteins start. Sci. Amer. **218**:36-42 (Jan.). *Their investigations (in Escherichia coli) showed that the initiation of a protein chain occurred when a variant form of a particular amino acid (formylated methionine) was delivered to a particular site on the ribosome by a specific tRNA. Only two polynucleotides (poly-UAG and poly-UG) were found in the synthetic messenger RNA to have this power of delivery.*

Watson, J. D. 1965. Molecular biology of the gene. New York, W. A. Benjamin, Inc. *Of the numerous works that have appeared on molecular biology, this is one of the clearest written and most comprehensive. All students starting the study of molecular biology should read this one first.*

PART THREE

ANIMAL ORGANIZATION AND CELLULAR FUNCTION

● The cell is the basic morphologic and functional unit of all living things. The cell doctrine states that all organisms are composed of cells or cell products. There are some exceptions to this statement, such as certain slime molds in which cell organization is not definitely found. The cell, however, may be considered the minimum organization that shows the proper ties and processes of what we know as life. Here the chemical actions of great variety occur and make up the expression of life. A similarity of composition and structure exists among all cells so that a cell can be recognized as such because of the uniformity of these properties. Each animal cell consists of a cell boundary or plasma membrane and a discrete nucleus made up of a nuclear membrane that encloses the all-important chromatin with its hereditary code. Some cells are multinuclear and some have no nuclei at all. Many new interpretations of cell structure and function are due to the development of the electron microscope and other technical sophistications.

The discussion of cells necessarily includes cell structure, specialization of cells, their reproduction, and how they perform in the life process. Each cell part is involved in some specific function, the totality of which expresses life. One of the main characteristics of life is the capacity of self-reproduction. All cells are formed from preexisting cells. The precision of this process of replication indicates how important it is in the transmission of life from one generation to another. Specifically, it involves the genes, commonly called the basic units of heredity. But the gene concept also includes the formation of the structural and functional characteristics of cells and the properties of individual distinctions between organic units at cell levels. Within the past decade or so it has been possible to analyze in detail the organization of the gene and how it performs its functions.

Cellular processes depend on the taking in of energy-rich compounds from the environment and the release of the energy from them. Cellular respiration is responsible for the release of this energy. This occurs in an oxidation-reduction reaction within the cell, in which electrons play a great part in the energy transfers. The loss of electrons is called oxidation; the gain of electrons is reduction. Enzymatic activity is involved at every step of cellular metabolism. Within the cell the enzymes are sometimes localized within cell organelles such as mitochondria. All enzymes are protein and usually have a specific activity for a particular molecular structure.

There are many architectural patterns among organic forms. Even though there is much uniformity in their makeup, these patterns reflect many styles in the structure and shaping-up of the diverse animals. There are also many grades of structures within the organization of protoplasmic matter. The cell as the basic unit of all animal structure may persist simply as an entire organism (protozoans), or they may be grouped into specialized masses (tissues) to form the multicellular animals (metazoans). Size in animal form depends mainly on the number of cells involved and not on the quantitative values among all the animals, large or small.

CHAPTER 5

• THE CELL AS THE UNIT OF LIFE*

THE CELL CONCEPT

● Although the idea that the cell represents the basic unit of living forms and functions is still often referred to as the cell theory, it has long passed the status of theory and should be known as the cell concept or doctrine. Perhaps no principle of biology is more accepted or is considered more important. It is virtually the chief cornerstone for biologic study and understanding.

As is the case with all important concepts, the cell concept has had an extensive background of development. The English scientist R. Hook is often credited with seeing and naming the first cells when he observed the small boxlike cavities in the surface of cork and leaves. The classic microscopist A. van Leeuwenhoek, the Dutch lens-maker, described many kinds of cells in addition to his famous protozoan discoveries. M. Malpighi, the Italian microscopist who described capillary circulation among many other discoveries no doubt observed cellular units. The French biologist R. Dutrochet gave some basic ideas about cells in 1824. In 1831 R. Brown discovered and described the nuclei of cells. J. Purkinje (1839) not only described cells as being the structural elements of plants and animals but also coined the term **protoplasm** for the living substance of cells. M. J. Schleiden and T. Schwann, German biologists, are often given credit for the cell theory formulation (1838) because of their rather extensive descriptions and diagrams, although they had erroneous ideas about how cells originate. In 1858 R. Virchow stressed the role of the cell in disease, or pathology, and stated that all cells came from preexisting cells. M. Schultze (1864) gave a clear-cut concept of protoplasmic relations to cells and its essential unity in all organisms.

It may be said in summarizing the main features of the cell doctrine that all plants and animals are composed of cells or cell products, that a basic unity exists in their physical construction, and that all cells come from preexisting cells. These cell aspects lead to the fundamental idea that the total processes and activities of life can be interpreted on the basis of the cellular components of the organism. This statement does not contradict the belief that the whole organism behaves as a unit in its development and in its integration of cell activities or that the action of cells is determined in accordance with the physiologic behavior of the organism at all stages of its existence. This limitation of the cell doctrine is often expressed as the "inadequacy of the cell theory."

METHODS OF STUDYING CELLS

Since cells are small and mostly invisible, it follows that the microscope has been the tool of choice in studying them. But the microscope alone was unable to fulfill its function without the aid of staining methods. Fortunately the discovery and development of the aniline dyes by W. H. Perkin and others gave the investigators of the last half of the nineteenth century the opportunity to work out the details of cellular structures and cell division within the limits of the light microscope. It was at this time that cytology, the study of cells, developed into a flourishing science—a study that has greatly broadened under the impact of the electron microscope.

Cytologic techniques have constantly widened in every generation of investigators. Among these advances are the careful histologic techniques of fixing the tissues to preserve them as naturally as possible, the art of preparing and slicing tissues with microtome, and proper staining methods for differential staining of cell constituents, or the selective affinity of the different cell components for the various stains. More precise physicochemical methods for locating specific entities within cells and for identifying them are con-

*Refer to Chapter 2, Principles 8 and 9.

stantly being sought. Ultraviolet light is employed because different chemical substances absorb rays of characteristic wavelengths. Some of the histochemical techniques for demonstrating inorganic or organic substances in cells and tissues are (1) the periodic acid–Schiff (PAS) reaction for showing carbohydrates, (2) the fluorescent antibody method that injects antibodies conjugated with a fluorescent substance into an animal, determining where the antibodies are localized in the cells, and (3) injecting tagged atoms that have been labeled with a radioactive isotope (tritium [H^3], iodine 131, and many others), and then photographing the desired specimen of tissue on a special photographic emulsion plate that will record the beta or other particles from the radioactive isotope.

ORGANIZATION OF THE CELL

Protoplasm is usually found in small discrete bodies or microscopic droplets known as cells. (An exception is the plasmodium of the noncellular slime molds [myxomycetes]. Plasmodia are slow creeping, jellylike structures with thousands of nuclei and without cell walls.) The cell is the unit of biologic structure and function, and it is the minimum biologic unit capable of maintaining and propagating itself.

To see a living cell, scrape the inside of your cheek with a blunt instrument, put the scrapings on a slide in a drop of physiologic salt solution, and examine, unstained, with a microscope. The flat circular cells with small nuclei that you see are the squamous epithelial cells that line the mouth region.

Cells vary greatly in both size and form. Some of the smallest animal cells are certain parasites that may be 1 μ (1/25,000 inch) or less in diameter. At the other extreme we have the fertilized eggs of birds, some of which, including the extracellular material, are several inches in diameter. A red blood corpuscle in man has a diameter of about 7.5 μ. The longest cells are the nerve cells because the fibers, which are parts of the cells, may be up to several feet long. Some striped muscle cells or fibers are several inches long.

The evolutionary pattern of life from the unicellular to the multicellular forms of life has increased in complexity as new qualities arise at each level. The various functions of the life process carried on at the unicellular stages tend to be allotted to specialized cells in multicellular organisms. Functional specialization is accompanied by structural specialization or division of labor, and the hierarchy of tissues, organs, and organ systems

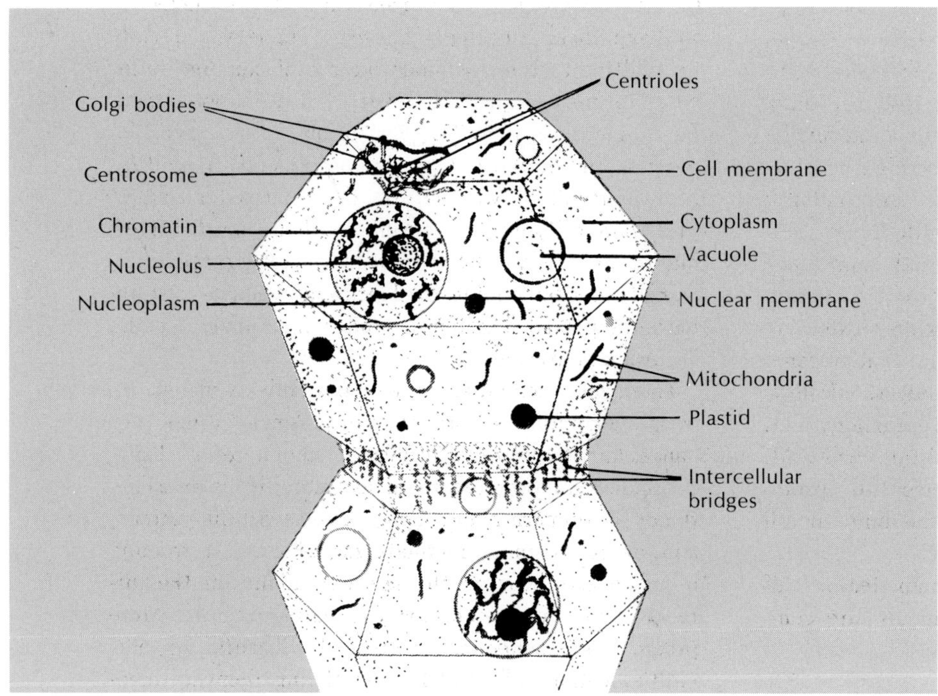

FIG. 5-1

Scheme of generalized cell as revealed by light microscope showing principal constituents commonly found in most cells. Shape of cells is correlated with function and with mechanical pressure of adjacent cells. Pressure often produces fourteen-faceted surface that appears hexagonal in cross section. Constituents vary with types of cells and phases of activity. Protoplasmic processes (intercellular bridges) may connect cells in some tissues such as epithelia. Smallest cells, probably bacteria, are less than 1 μ in diameter; ostrich eggs may be several inches around.

arise as a consequence in the evolutionary development of life. Although each cell is integrated with the functioning of the body as a whole, it retains the capacity to act independently of the others. One cell of a group may divide, secrete, or die, while adjacent cells may be in a different physiologic state.

A cell includes both its outer wall, or membranes, plus its contents (Fig. 5-1). Typically, it is a semifluid mass of microscopic dimensions, completely enclosed within a thin, differentially permeable **plasma membrane.** It usually contains two distinct regions—the nucleus and cytoplasm. (A few unicellular organisms, such as bacteria and blue-green algae, do not show a distinctive separation of nuclear and cytoplasmic constituents but have the chromatin material scattered through the cytoplasm.) Cells without nuclei are called prokaryotic in contrast to those with nuclei called karyotic. The **nucleus** is enclosed by a **nuclear membrane** and contains the **chromatin** and one **nucleolus** or more. Within the **cytoplasm** are many **organelles,** such as mitochondria, Golgi complex, centrioles, and endoplasmic reticulum. Plant cells may contain in addition plastids, or chloroplasts.

The variety of different shapes assumed by cells is mostly correlated with their particular function (Fig. 5-2). Although many cells, because of surface tension forces, will assume a spherical shape when freed from restraining influences, there are others that retain their shape under most conditions because of their characteristic cytoskeleton, or framework.

The electron microscope reveals small cytoplasmic **microtubules** that may serve as cytoskeletal elements in maintaining the shape of cells. These tubules are straight, are of indefinite length, and have a diameter of about 200 to 270 Å. Their walls are made up of ten or more filamentous subunits. They appear to be most common near the cell center and may be closely related to the centriole. They form the spindle apparatus of dividing cells, the caudal sheath of spermatids, the marginal bands of nucleated erythrocytes, and the axoplasm of neurons. Their power to contract may be involved in the movements of the cytoplasm and the alterations in cell shape.

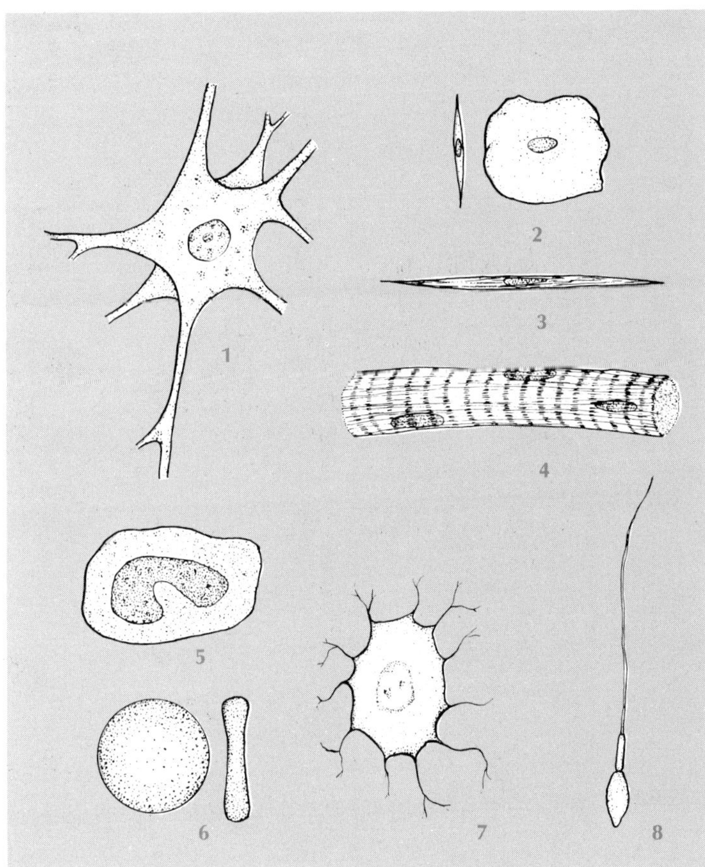

FIG. 5-2

Some common examples of cells. **1,** Nerve cell from spinal cord; **2,** epithelial cell from lining of mouth, with side view on left; **3,** smooth muscle cell from intestinal wall; **4,** striated muscle cell from gross muscle; **5,** white blood corpuscle; **6,** red blood corpuscle, with side view on right; **7,** bone cell; **8,** human spermatozoan. (Not drawn according to size.)

Components of the cell and their function*

All structures, or organelles, of the cell have separate, important functions. The **nucleus** (Fig. 5-3) has two important roles: (1) to store and carry hereditary information from generation to generation of cells and individuals and (2) to translate genetic information into the kind of protein characteristic of a cell and thus determine the cells' specific role in the life process. A component of the nucleus, the **nucleolus,** contains ribonucleic acid (RNA) and may act as an intermediate between the code of the chromosomes and the execution of the code in the cytoplasm. In the **mitochondria** (Figs. 5-3 and 5-6 to 5-8) the energy-yielding oxidations from the breakdown of complex organic compounds are localized. This energy is stored in high-energy phosphate bonds to be used in biologic activities as needed.

*Refer to Chapter 2, Principles 5 and 9.

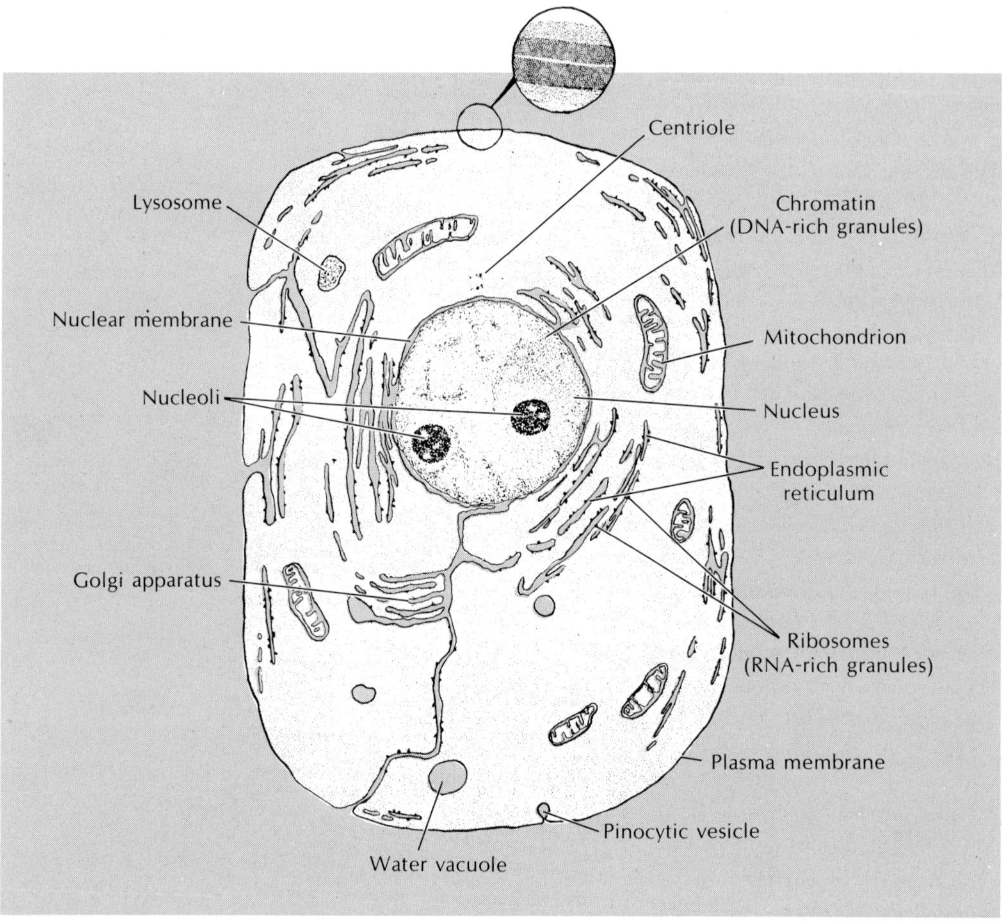

FIG. 5-3

Diagram of generalized cell with principal organelles, as might be seen with electron microscope. Small drawing at top is enlargement of plasma membrane (about 70 to 100 Å thick) thought to consist of a double layer of lipid molecules between two layers of protein. Cell is made up of many organelles, or self-contained compartments, in which biochemical reactions of cell occur. Membranes of organelles are believed to be continuous with, or derived from, plasma membrane by infolding process. Structure of other membranes (of nucleus, endoplasmic reticulum, mitochondria, etc.) is probably similar to that of plasma membrane. Such a system of membranes may afford network of canaliculi for rapid communication in synthesis of specific compounds.

The double-layered membranous **endoplasmic reticulum** (ergastoplasm) (Figs. 5-3, 5-6, and 5-7) is supposed to contain enzymes that synthesize cholesterol and other nonproteins. Often associated with the endoplasmic reticulum are **granules (ribosomes)** (Fig. 5-3) that are the sites of protein syntheses under the influence of RNA, which receives its coded genetic information from deoxyribonucleic acid (DNA) of the chromosomes. The **centrioles** (Fig. 5-3) determine the orientation of the plane of cell division and probably supply the **basal granules,** or **kinetosomes,** which are concerned with the formation of motile fibrillar structures, such as cilia and flagella at the surface of cells. Another type of granules, **lysosomes,** are somewhat larger than ribosomes and are the sites of certain hydrolytic enzymes.

The Golgi complex is the primary site for the packaging of the secretory products that are synthesized on the ribosomes and migrate to the saccules, or stacks of flattened sacs, making up the Golgi complex. Here also carbohydrate molecules formed by the Golgi complex are added to the protein secretions to form glycoproteins before they are discharged for their various functions. **Plastids,** found in plants, serve as sites of synthesis of complex organic compounds from simpler substances, such as the formation of sugar from carbon dioxide and water.

Although the vast majority of cells contain these basic structures, there are some organisms that lack conformity to this cellular structure.

The structure of every cell consists of chemical compounds; whatever function a cell may have depends on the properties of cellular compounds. With the electron microscope, it has been possible in recent years to learn a great deal about subcellular organization and to explain the relations between structure and function in terms of the interactions of macromolecules. Among the exciting discoveries are (1) information concerning the submicroscopic membrane systems of the cytoplasm and their roles in the synthesis, storage, and transport of metabolic products and (2) the structure and function of cellular constituents involved in the energy transformations of cells, such as the changing of oxidation energy into usable and packaged energy by mitochondria and the changing of light energy into chemical energy by plant chloroplasts.

Plasma membrane. The electron microscope has also revealed much about the plasma membrane that surrounds the cell. The membrane is now known not merely to enclose the cell but also to form the organelles within the cytoplasm. Organelles are specialized parts of a cell that have specific functions, just as organs have in higher forms. The plasma membrane therefore serves as a partition to subdivide the cell space into self-contained compartments in which biochemical reactions may take place for the living process. As seen with the electron microscope, the plasma membrane appears as two black lines with a space between and is about 70 to 100 Å thick (an angstrom is 1/100,000,000 cm.). Its structure suggests a lipid-protein membrane made up of two lipid monolayers between two protein monolayers (Fig. 5-4). Phospholipid molecules are long, with elongated hydrophobic organic compounds and a hydrophilic polar group at one end. Such molecules tend to be absorbed at an air-water or water-oil interface because the lipid end enters the oil or air and the polar end enters the water. The molecules also tend to be tightly packed and oriented in parallel layers at interfaces. Many aspects of this phosphoprotein membrane are obscure. It serves to regulate the molecular traffic in and out of the cell.

Plasma membranes have **selective permeability** that is quite necessary to maintain a proper balance of organic and inorganic substances on which life depends. See Chapter 6 for a description of selective permeability.

Mechanisms derived from chemical reactions within the cell (active transport) are often referred to as pumping devices. Thus by **phagocytosis** the membrane forms pockets in which food particles are engulfed. These pockets with the enclosed substance are pinched off and form a vesicle within the cytoplasm. Another pumping device is **pinocytosis,** or cell drinking, which is similar to phagocytosis except that drops of liquid are taken up discontinuously and sucked in to form vesicles within the cell. The concept has been broadened to include the uptake of dissolved substances as well as liquids. By this method it is thought that ions, sugars, and proteins can be pumped into the cell. The average diameter of a pinocytosis vacuole is about 1 to 2 μ but often they coalesce. About 30 minutes is required for the formation of a pinocytosis vacuole. Besides these methods of substance transfer across membranes, there are many instances that cannot be explained by any known method of permeability.

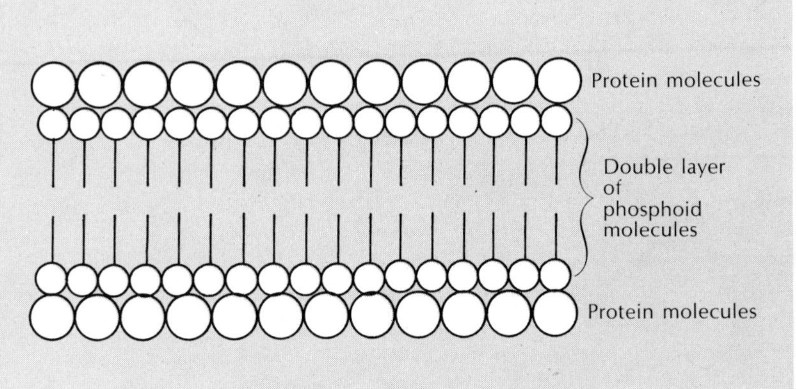

FIG. 5-4

Diagram of plasma membrane. Thickness of membrane varies with kind of cell—as much as 200 Å units in a red blood cell—but in most cells it is about 75 Å. Electron microscope shows membrane 4 molecules thick. Fatty acids of lipid layer have their —COOH groups facing outward and form a barrier against passage of water-soluble contents of cell. Membrane appears to have pores about 3 to 7 Å in size.

Mention has been made earlier of the formation of cytoplasmic organelles from the infolding of the plasma or similar membranes. These internal membranes, invisible with the optical microscope, give rise to a characteristic cytoskeleton that is revealed to some extent by the electron microscope. Some investigations seem to reveal that the internal membranes of the cell are continuous with the external membrane, so that there is a deeply invaginated surface area for communication with the outside fluid. The present concept of the membrane originated when the nature of the Schwann cell was investigated. These satellite cells accompany the axons of nerve cells and have their membrane surfaces wrapped concentrically around the axons to form a multilayered myelin sheath. The sheath, which is part of the cell of Schwann (Fig. 5-5), is formed after the cell wraps itself around the axon and then unfolds its membrane that surrounds the axon many times. In cross section each layer is about 100 to 140 Å thick. The function of the sheath is obscure, but it may facilitate the passage of energy waves along the nerve. The mem-

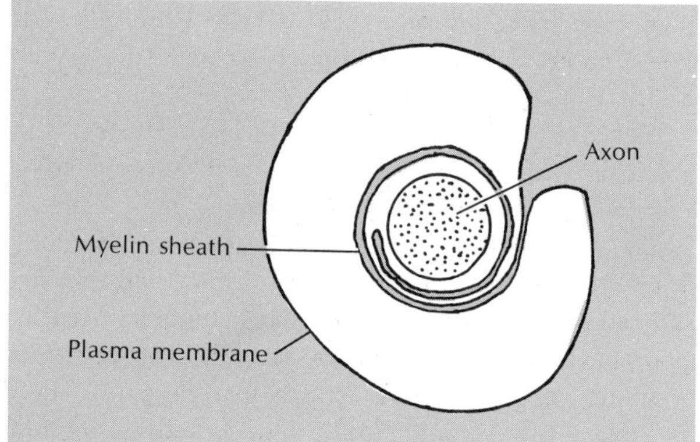

FIG. 5-5

Myelin sheath of cell of Schwann. The way plasma membrane envelops axon may indicate how internal membranes (cytoskeleton) are continuous with external membrane of cells in general, permitting intimate communication with outside fluid.

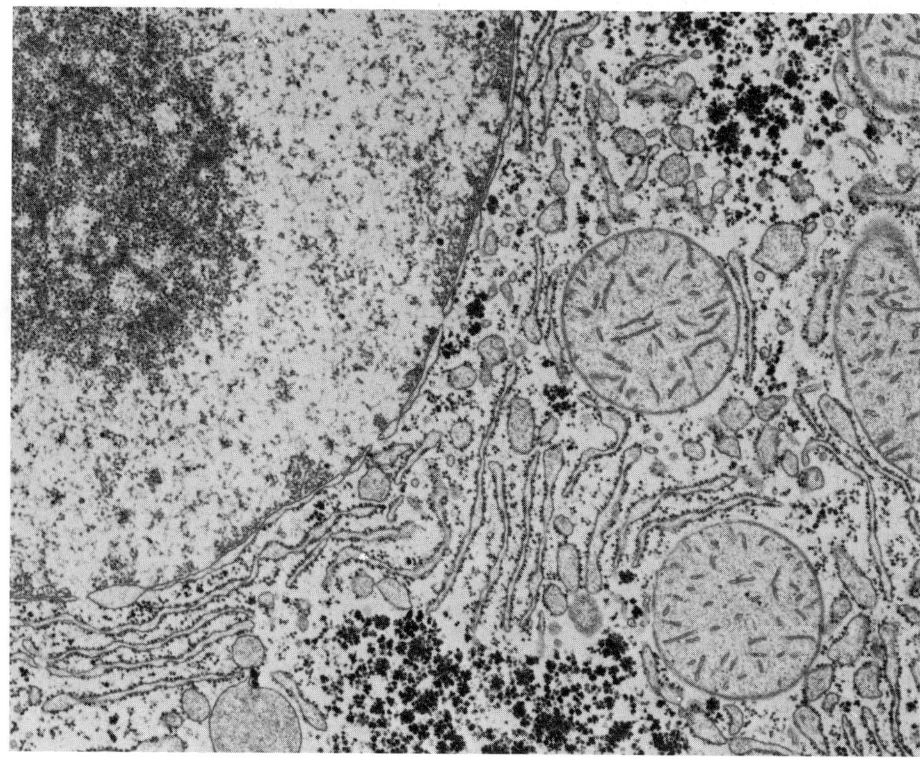

FIG. 5-6

Electron micrograph of part of hepatic cell of rat showing portion of nucleus (left) and surrounding cytoplasm. Endoplasmic reticulum and mitochondria are visible in cytoplasm, and pores are seen in nuclear membrane. (×14,000.) (Courtesy G. E. Palade, The Rockefeller University, New York.)

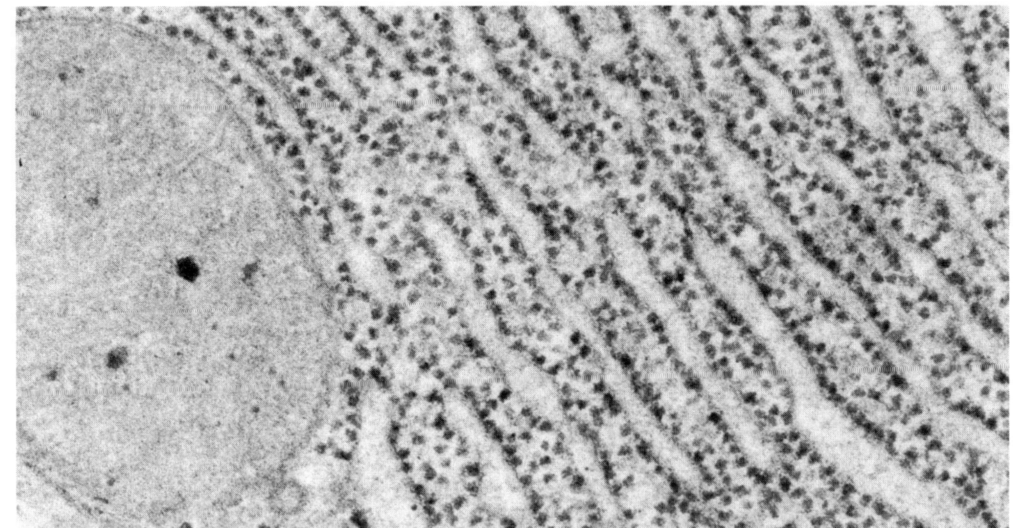

FIG. 5-7

Electron micrograph of portion of pancreatic exocrine cell from guinea pig showing endoplasmic reticulum with ribosomes (small dark granules). Oval body (upper left) is mitochondrion. (×66,000.) (Courtesy G. E. Palade, The Rockefeller University, New York.)

brane involved appears to be double and is about 75 Å thick.

Endoplasmic reticulum. Within recent years it has been found that most cells are filled with membranes folded in complicated ways. The focal point of investigation has been directed toward a complex membrane system called the endoplasmic reticulum (Figs. 5-3 and 5-7). This system has been closely associated with the storage and transport of products of cellular mechanisms. The nuclear membrane is formed from parts of this membrane system, and it is so arranged that there is direct continuity between nucleus and cytoplasm by openings in the nuclear membrane (Fig. 5-6). The double-walled endoplasmic reticulum is a highly variable morphologic structure consisting of vesicles and tubules, and it often has the power to fragment and reform its structural features. There are two types: rough- and smooth-surfaced. The rough-surfaced type has on its outer surface small granules called **microsomes** (the dense granules are often called **ribosomes** [Fig. 5-7] because they contain ribonucleic acid). These ribosomes are important sites of protein synthesis. In some cases the granules can function without being attached to the membrane. The endoplasmic reticulum is also important as an intracellular transport system for the products synthesized by the ribosomes. Among the substances transported by this system are the zymogen bodies that give rise to digestive enzymes and that are carried to the smooth-surfaced Golgi vesicles. Later these zymogen granules are discharged as enzymes through openings at the surface of the cell.

By this relationship of the endoplasmic reticulum to the surface membrane of the cell, the cell is a three-phase structure consisting of cytoplasm, cavities of the endoplasmic reticulum, and membranes separating the other two phases. The concept also includes the idea that there is really a one-membrane unit from the cell surface membrane to the system of interior membranes.

Mitochondria. Another important cytoplasmic organelle is the mitochondrion (Figs. 5-3 and 5-8). Mitochondria are found in all cells and can be detected by the light microscope. They show considerable diversity in shape, size, and number. Many of them are rodlike and are about 0.2 to 5 μ in greatest diameter. About two thirds of their structure is protein and one third is lipid. They are capable of altering their form in accordance with the physiologic condition of the cell. They may be scattered more or less uniformly through the cytoplasm or they may be localized near cell surfaces and other regions where there is unusual metabolic activity. Investigation of the fine structure of the mitochondrion with the electron microscope and centrifuge microscope reveals that it is a double membrane system that may be formed from detached pockets of the cell membrane. The inner layer of the double membrane is much folded and forms prosections (cristae) that extend into the interior fluid or matrix. There are thus two structural systems—the membrane system and the homogenous fluid matrix.

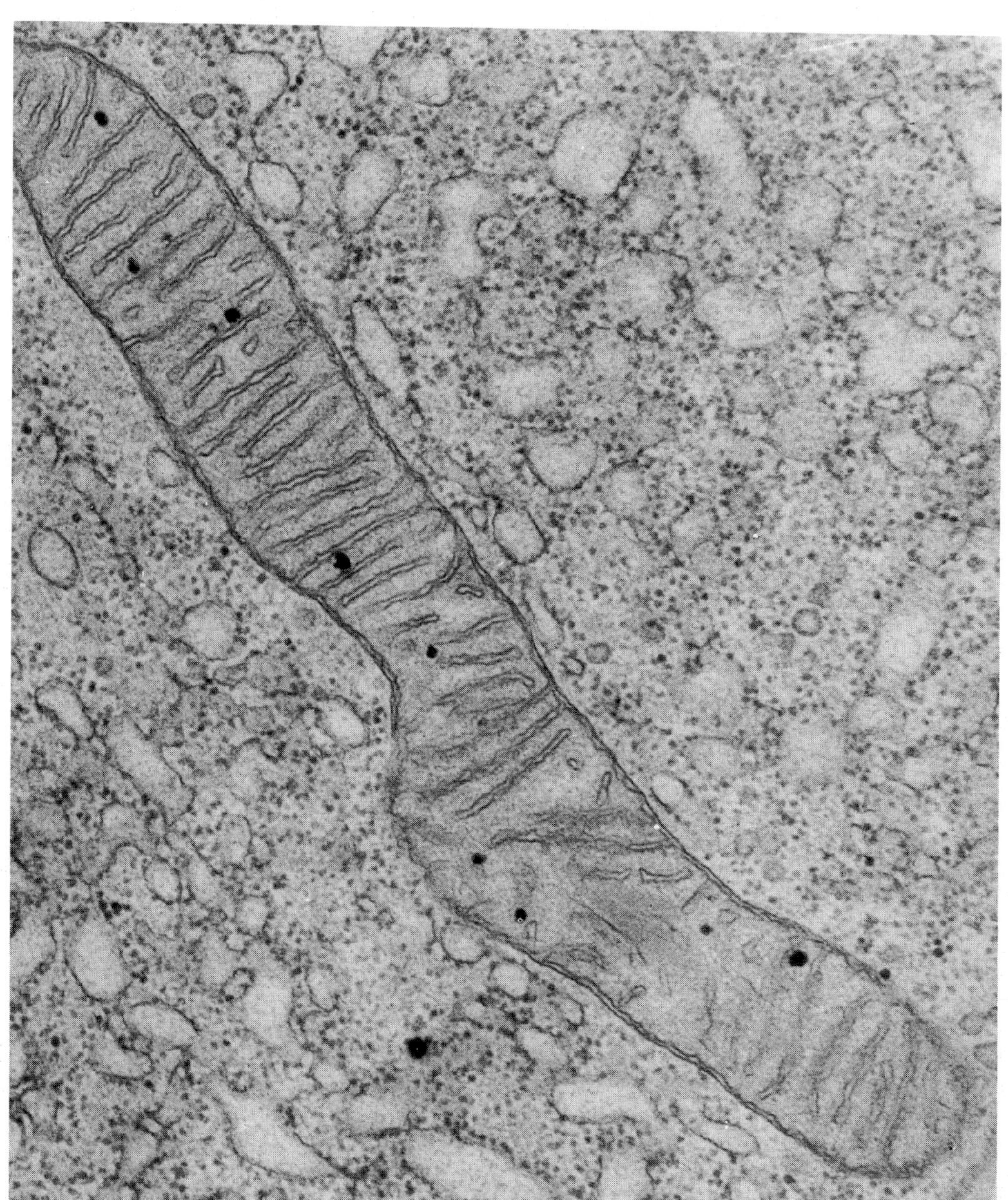

FIG. 5-8

Electron micrograph of elongated mitochondrion in pancreatic exocrine cell of guinea pig. (×50,000.)
(Courtesy G. E. Palade, The Rockefeller University, New York.)

Research during the past few years shows that the mitochondria are the principal chemical sites for cellular respiration. They contain highly integrated systems of enzymes for providing energy in cell metabolism. Among these systems is the important tricarboxylic acid cycle and its respiratory enzymes that produce the energy-rich adenosine triphosphate (ATP) so essential for many vital activities. The complete Krebs cycle (p. 87) is probably carried out in the mitochondria. DNA has been found recently in mitochondria.

CELL DIVISION (MITOSIS)*

All cells of the body arise from the division of preexisting cells. Indeed, all the cells found in most multicellular organisms have originated from the division of a single cell, the **zygote,** formed from the union of an **egg** and **sperm** (fertilization). This is one of the basic principles of biology. This division provides the basis for one form of growth, for both sexual and asexual

*Refer to Chapter 2, Principles 3 and 10.

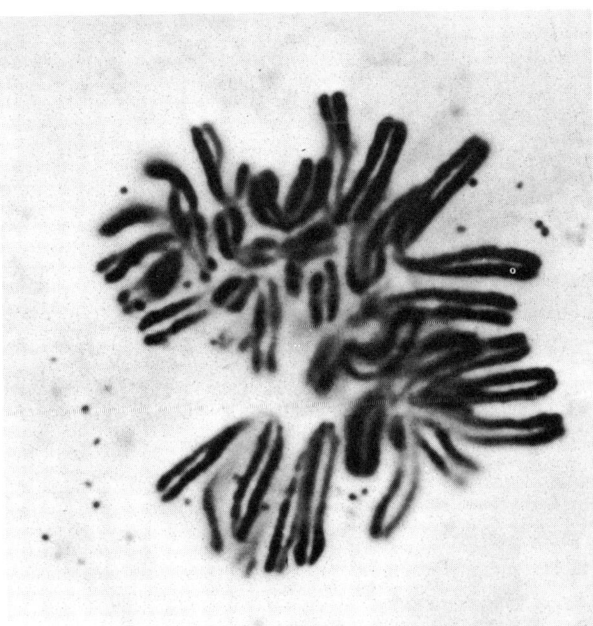

FIG. 5-9

Chromosome in tail epidermis of salamander *Ambystoma* shown arranged on equatorial plate in metaphase stage of mitosis. (Courtesy General Biological Supply House, Inc., Chicago.)

FIG. 5-10

Life cycle of chromosome in mitotic division. History of chromosome is based primarily on life cycle of coiled filaments called chromonemata, which are basic units of chromosome. In interphase, chromosome has reached its maximum length and consists of two chromatids (two chromonemata). In prophase, two chromatids shorten by coiling. During prometaphase, chromonemata become duplicated so that each chromatid contains two chromonemata. At anaphase, each daughter chromosome still has two chromonemata and remains so during telophase and interphase. Structure of chromosome is still in process of analysis and not all details are fully known. (Modified from De Robertis, Nowinski, and Saez: General cytology, W. B. Saunders Co.)

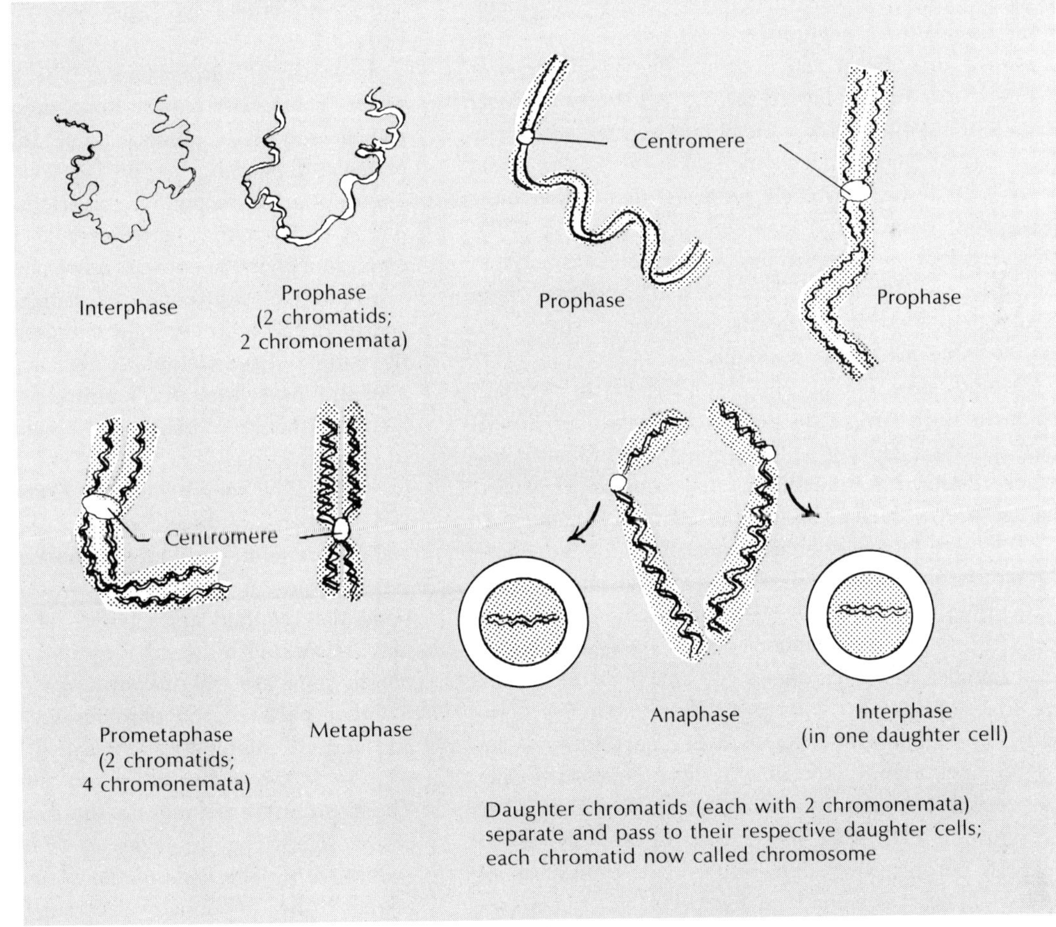

reproduction, and for the transmission of hereditary qualities from one cell generation to another cell generation.

In the formation of **body cells** (somatic cells) the process of cell division is referred to as **mitosis** and is the method of cell division to be described in this section. However, **germ cells** (egg and sperm) have a somewhat different type of cell division all their own known as **meiosis.** Meiosis will be described in Chapter 33.

There are two distinct phases of mitosis: the division of the nucleus and the division of the cytoplasm. These two phases ordinarily occur at the same time, but there are occasions when the nucleus may divide a number of times without a corresponding division of the cytoplasm. In such a case the resulting mass of protoplasm containing many nuclei is referred to as a **multinucleate** cell. Skeletal muscle is an example. A many-celled mass formed by fusion of cells that have lost their cell membranes is called a **syncytium.**

Mitosis or indirect cell division. The whole process of mitosis has been followed through all stages in living cells. As long ago as 1878 Flemming observed it in the skin cells of young salamanders. However, the usual study is made from specially prepared tissues that have been fixed, stained, and mounted on slides (Fig. 5-9). The sequence is observed by finding cells caught in the various stages by the fixatives and arranging them in the proper order. Naturally, on stained slides one cannot follow all stages in one cell.

Chromosomes. The nucleus bears **chromatin** material, which in turn carries the **genes** responsible for hereditary qualities. During cell division this chromatin becomes arranged into definite **chromosomes** of varied shapes. These shapes are constant within a species. It is customary to consider the metaphase or anaphase chromosomes as most typical of their morphology, for at this time they have reached their maximum contraction (Fig. 5-10). Each animal within a species has the same number of chromosomes in each body cell. Man has 46 in each of his body cells (but not in his germ cells). The number of chromosomes a species possesses has no basic significance nor is there necessarily any relationship between two different species that have the same number. Both the guinea pig and the onion have 16 chromosomes. Since there are thousands of different species of animals, many species must of necessity have the same number. The range is usually between 8 and 50 chromosomes, although numbers in the hundreds are known (crayfish, for example). Some worms have as few as 2, the least number an organism can have.

Chromosomes are always arranged in pairs, or two of each kind. Of each pair, one has come from one parent and the other from the other parent. Thus in man there are twenty-three pairs. Each pair usually has certain characteristics of shape and form that aid in identification. It will be seen that a biparental organism begins with the union of two gametes, each of which furnishes a **haploid** set of chromosomes (23 in man) to produce a somatic or **diploid** number of chromosomes (46 in man). The chromosomes of a haploid set are also called a **genome.** Thus, a fertilized egg (zygote) consists of a paternal genome and a maternal genome.

The purpose of mitosis is to ensure an equal distribution of each kind of chromosome to each daughter cell. A cell becomes highly abnormal in its reactions if it fails to receive its proper share of chromosomes, as the great German cytologist Boveri showed many years ago.

Structure of chromosomes. The shape of the metaphase or anaphase chromosome, although constant for a specific species of animals, is of different types among animals, depending on the location of the centromere, length of arms, secondary constrictions, etc. Some chromosomes have the **centromere** at the midpoint, with equal limbs (metacentric); other chromosomes have the centromere closer to one end, with unequal arms (acrocentric). The ordinary light microscope may reveal only the outline of the metaphase chromosome, with two parallel strands (chromatids) united at one point (centromere) within it. With special techniques and the electron microscope, finer details are found, such as the presence of a coiled multiple filament (**chromonema**) along which are beadlike, dark-staining enlargements called **chromomeres.** The chromomeres, which may represent superimposed coils or nucleoprotein condensations, may contain aggregations of genes, or the genes may be located between them. Many details about the chromosome are still unknown.

Other parts of the chromosome include condensed and variable staining regions called **heterochromatin,** in contrast to the rest of the chromosome or **euchromatin.** The centromere belongs to the heterochromatin. Most chromosomes contain segments of heterochromatin and euchromatin. The ends of the chromosomes, **telomeres,** appear to be functionally different from the rest of the chromosome.

The chemical nature of the chromosome consists of two nucleic acids (deoxyribonucleic acid, or DNA, and ribonucleic acid, or RNA), together with certain proteins (histones, protamines, etc.). How the nucleic acids are arranged in the chromosome is not yet known. (See the discussion on genes, Chapter 35.)

Process of cell division

It is not known what triggers cells to divide, although many theories have been proposed. A common theory held by biologists is that division depends on the attainment of a critical mass (for example, when the cell has doubled its mass), but some cells are known to divide without growth. There are also ways to prevent cells from dividing, and thus they become giant cells much larger than normal. Examples of such agencies are growth hormones, x-rays, and colchicine. Other agencies are known to promote cell division. In certain instances many factors are known to influence the process, such as nutrition and cellular specialization. Specialized cells, such as neurons, lose their power to divide, as do red blood corpuscles that have no nuclei. Certain preparations must be completed before cell division can actually occur. These include the chemical duplication of the chromosomes, the doubling of the centrioles, the synthesis of the protein material out of which mitotic figures are formed, and adequate metabolism to furnish energy for the process.

The essential plan of cell division is not involved, but its various steps are known only in part. Briefly, the centrioles double to form two poles, and a mitotic apparatus is established. The chromosomes are exactly duplicated—sister chromosomes migrate to sister poles, the cytoplasm cleaves into two parts, and two cells are formed. In most organisms cell division really consists of two separate processes—nuclear division by mitosis and cytokinesis or cleavage of the cytoplasm. These two processes usually take place simultaneously. There are, however, variations of this binary fission plan. In some cases nuclear duplication without cytokineses may occur and form a multinucleated cell, or cytokinesis of a binucleate cell may occur without nuclear duplication. In some unicellular organisms a single cell may also give rise to many daughter cells by multiple fission.

Although the term "mitosis" is often used loosely as a synonym for cell division, the two terms are not the same. Mitosis refers to a particular kind of nuclear duplication that involves a precise doubling of the chromosomes and their genes. Each chromosome set so formed is distributed to one of the daughter nuclei. Bacteria and blue-green algae do not have true nuclei or chromosomes, but they have gene duplication. There are several different types of mitosis, especially among many unicellular forms, or Protista. In some Protista mitosis may be **intranuclear** or **extranuclear.** In the intranuclear type the process occurs wholly within the intact nuclear membrane until the nucleus divides at the same time as the cytoplasm. In the extranuclear type the mitotic process occurs throughout the cell, and two nuclei are formed with their membranes when cell cleavage takes place. Other aberrant forms of mitosis may be found, such as **acentric** mitosis, in which the centriole is either inside the nucleus or lacking altogether, and **anastral** mitosis, in which the cell has no aster. Anastral types are always present when there is no centriole. These unusual types are in contrast to the common **extranuclear, centric, astral** types found in metazoans.

The process of mitosis is arbitrarily divided for convenience into four successive stages or phases, although one stage merges into the next without sharp lines of transition. These phases are prophase, metaphase, anaphase, and telophase. When the cell is not actively dividing, it passes through the "resting" stage or **interphase.** Before the first visible active phase appears, the chromosome threads and their component genes become chemically duplicated. Genetically, the DNA content of the nucleus is the important constituent that is duplicated between divisions. Thus when the cell begins mitosis, it has a double set of chromosomes.

The mechanism by which the chromosomes of a pair are separated and pushed or pulled to opposite poles ensures that each daughter cell always receives a complete set of hereditary units or genes. For this separation, a special mechanism or mitotic apparatus is required. In animal cells one of the requirements for mitosis is the presence of centrioles that are permanent, self-duplicating, small, dotlike bodies (they have not been found in higher plant cells). Centrioles are generally found in pairs, with the members of a pair lying at right angles to each other. The finer structure of a centriole, as revealed by the electron microscope, shows that it is a cylindrical body with walls made up of nine groups of tubulelike bodies, each group containing three tubules. The structure of the centrioles is similar to that of the granules (kinetosomes) found at the bases of cilia and flagella. Each cell inherits one set of centrioles and produces another set.

At the start of **prophase** the centrioles, as soon as they have reproduced, migrate toward opposite sides of the nucleus. At the same time portions of the cytoplasm are attracted to the regions of the centrioles and are transformed into fine gel fibrils. Some of these fibrils run between the two centriole complexes to form a **spindle,** and some radiate out from each centriole or pole to form **asters.** The whole structure is called a **mitotic apparatus,** and it increases in size as the centrioles move farther apart. In higher animals the cells at mitosis have two large asters, one at each end of the spindle. At the center of each aster there is a spherical **centrosome** within which is the centriole. These asters are especially large at telophase. Some plants do not have asters, but spindles are formed. During this process the nuclear membrane disappears, and the nucleolus disintegrates or becomes invisible. The mitotic apparatus is composed mainly of a single type of protein and some RNA nucleotides.

After the mitotic apparatus is formed, the chromosomes begin to move under the control of the poles of the spindle. Each chromosome is made up of a double filament and has condensed into visible units. The finer analysis of the chromosome reveals that it is composed of tight coils. Each longitudinal half-chromosome (chromatid) has the identical nucleic acids of the chromosome before duplication occurred. The paired chromatids of a chromosome are joined at a single point by the **centromere.** The position of the centromere varies for different chromosome pairs. From each pole of the spindle a fibril makes connection with the centromere of each double chromosome. The centromere seems to be all important in guiding the sequence of events in mitosis.

During early **metaphase** the chromosomes are somewhat scattered, but they quickly migrate into the equatorial plane set at right angles to the spindle axis. It is actually the centromeres that come to occupy a precise position within the equatorial plane, and the chromosomes to which they are attached trail behind, often in various shapes. When they line up in one plane, the centromeres form the **metaphase plate.** It is thought that the centromeres are pulled into position by the equal tension of the two fibrils that connect each centromere to each pole at this stage.

The two chromatids of each double chromosome now separate. Up to this time each double chromosome has a single centromere that holds the two chromatids together. Now the centromere splits so that two independent chromosomes, each with its centromere, are formed. The same tension of their pole-attached fibrils that pulled the double chromosome into the equatorial plate now pulls the two chromatids (now called chromosomes) of a pair toward opposite poles at a speed of about 1 μ per minute. The chromosomes move in straight lines, and at this **anaphase** stage two sets of chromosomes are plainly visible, one set moving toward one pole and the other set moving toward the other pole. Sometimes the poles move farther apart during this stage and carry the chromosomes with them. At the anaphase, interzonal fibrils connect the separated chromosomes and lie peripheral to the continuous fibrils of the spindle. These interzonal fibrils may be attached to the centromeres of the originally paired chromosomes. They lengthen as the chromo-

FIG. 5-11

Diagram of mitotic spindle (anaphase). It is not yet clear how chromosomes are moved apart. Spindle fibers may act as guides, along which chromosomes move toward poles. Mechanism may involve pushing produced by swelling between two sets of separating chromosomes, or chromosomes may be pulled to poles by folding of protein chains of fibers that produce traction on attached chromosomes. Fibers are tubes, not threads.

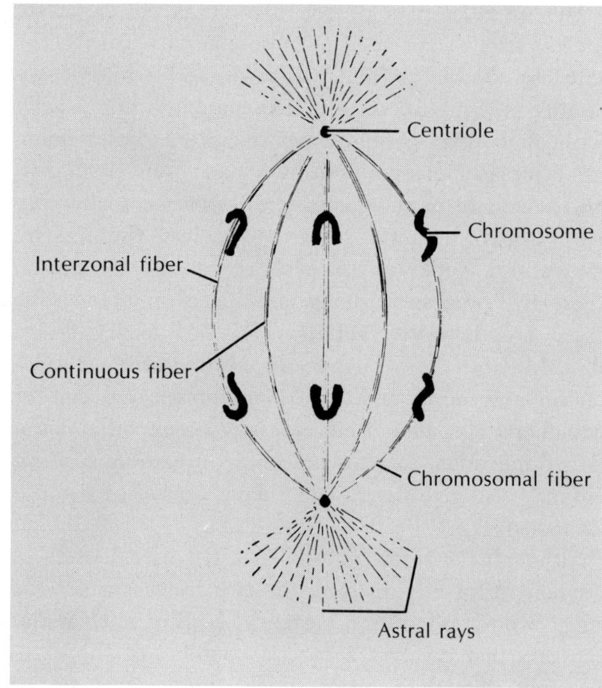

somes move farther apart, while the chromosomal fibrils between chromosomes and spindle poles shorten (Fig. 5-11).

When the daughter chromosomes reach their respective poles, the **telophase** has begun. The daughter chromosomes are crowded together and stain intensely. Two other events also occur—the appearance of a **cleavage furrow** encircling the surface of the cell (Fig. 5-12) and a **cell plate** (in plants) that originates from the central portions of the interpolar spindle fibers. Eventually the cleavage furrow deepens and constricts the cell into two daughter cells (Fig. 5-13). Other changes that terminate the telophase period are the disappearance of the spindle fibrils that revert to a sol from a gel condition, the gradual assumption of a chromatin network as the chromosomes lose their identity, the formation of a new nuclear membrane, and the manufacture of new nucleoli by the chromosomes.

The duration of the mitotic process varies in different cells. In some cases investigated (tissue cultures) it took from ½ to 3 hours for the complete process, prophase and telophase being the longest. The interphase in cells that regularly divide usually last from 10 to 20 hours.

What are the biophysical forces involved in cell division? No definite answer can be given to this question at present, although many theories have been proposed. Mitosis is mainly a chemical affair, and chemical syntheses must be involved throughout. The feat of removing the entire mitotic apparatus from the living cell (D. Mazia) has made it possible to study its chemical nature. By digesting the cytoplasm away with a detergent to leave only the chromosomes and mitotic apparatus, Mazia was able to find sulfur-to-sulfur chemical bonds in the fibrils and other chemical information. The high-energy bond ATP seems to be involved as an energy source. The fibrils, so easily seen with the light microscope, are known to be real and appear to exert a positive pull in the movement of chromosomes, but the fibrils shorten to the point of vanishing, as E. B. Wilson showed long ago, and they do not become thicker when they shorten or thinner when they lengthen.

To explain furrowing or constriction of the cell into two cells, some investigators (D. A. Marsland and others) think it is due to a contraction of a gelated layer of cytoplasm around the equator and the diffusion of nuclear and cytoplasmic materials to the polar regions of the cell cortex. Other investigators think it is actually due to an expansion of the cell surface. Whatever its cause, furrowing does not depend on the chromosomes.

The result of cell division is the formation of two cells, each with an identical gene set, so that each daughter cell is potentially the same as the mother cell. Cell division is important for growth and replacement, wound healing, etc. Muscle cells rarely divide, and nerve cells never divide after birth. The more specialized the cell the less frequently it divides. However, some tissues continually divide because the body loses a percentage of its cells daily and these must be replaced. Cell reproduction is faster in the embryonic state and slows down with age, a condition that may be due to metabolic checks brought on by larger cell populations.

THE CELL AS THE BASIC UNIT OF LIFE*

A cell is usually considered a combination of organelles and is organized completely enough to have all the necessary materials and apparatus for performing metabolism and self-replication. A cell, therefore, is considered to be the minimum unit that manifests the vital phenomena of life. However, the boundary between the living and the nonliving is not as sharply drawn as formerly. Some particles smaller than cells, for example, viruses, are regarded by some as living. All viruses, however, are associated with cells from which they derive their energy. Although viruses have the initial genetic mechanisms and multiply, they do so at the expense of the host's cells.

Many features or aspects of life can be produced in the test tube without cellular organization. Genetic investigations make use of strands of nucleic acid that can synthesize duplications of DNA and proteins. Life must have originated from the nonliving world in much simpler units than the complex cell. Some present cells are simpler than others. Bacterial cells as well as those of blue-green algae lack such organelles as mitochondria, lysosomes, and a definite nucleus. Motile bacteria have a flagellum of a single fibrous protein molecule instead of the ninefold symmetry of higher forms. There must have been many precellular forms in the long evolution of the cell because the properties of life did not arise all at once. Many intermediate forms represent a continuity from the nonliving to the living. Whether

*Refer to Chapter 2, Principles 6 and 10.

or not some of these precellular units still exist has never been satisfactorily settled, but the consensus of opinion is that the whole spectrum of the origin of life from inorganic matter could have occurred only once in this planet's history. The cell as representing a combination of all the vital phenomena may logically be considered the basic unit of life.

In the light of these factors a living organism must consist of at least one cell. If one considers all **unicellular** organisms—bacteria, fungi, algae, protozoans, etc.—it is probable that they constitute the majority of all living forms. This level of complexity, or of hierarchy, may still be considered the favorite one of nature despite the attention we give to multicellular forms. Even in the simplest multicellular types or cellular colonies, the cells of the aggregation are very much alike, and therefore each ranks more or less as an independent cell.

A technical distinction is thus made between a unicellular organism and a cell of a metazoan. A cell of a unicellular form may be considered homologous only with the multicellular organism as a whole and not with the individual cells of that organism. On this account, many biologists consider the unicellular organism as **acellular.** Since the unicellular organisms must carry on all the vital properties, it must have within the boundary of its limiting membrane organelles analogous to the organ systems of the multicellular forms. Differentiations and division of labor occur in protozoans, for instance, but some ciliates possess in their morphologic features and correlated functions the same general complexity of higher animals.

Cellular differentiation has many advantages over the unicellular condition. For example, it gives the large development of surfaces on which exchange of material occurs. It also promotes functional differentiation and size increase. In all higher organization the principle of cellular construction has been retained because nature has evolved no better method to meet the requirements of the environmental factors.

CELL NUMBER AND CELL CONSTANCY

Among multicellular animals, one of the chief causes (but not the only one) of variation in body size is difference in cell numbers. Large animals have many cells; smaller animals have fewer cells. Although most organisms have an indefinite number of cells, depending on

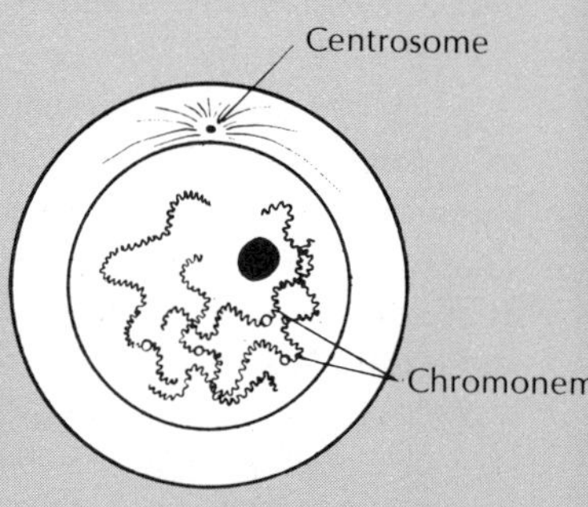

1. Interphase
Each chromosome reaches its maximum lengt and minimum thickness; each chromosome composed of coiled thread of genes (chromonema) and centromere; duplication of chromosome occurs at this state

5. Prometaphase
Nuclear membrane disintegrates or changes structure

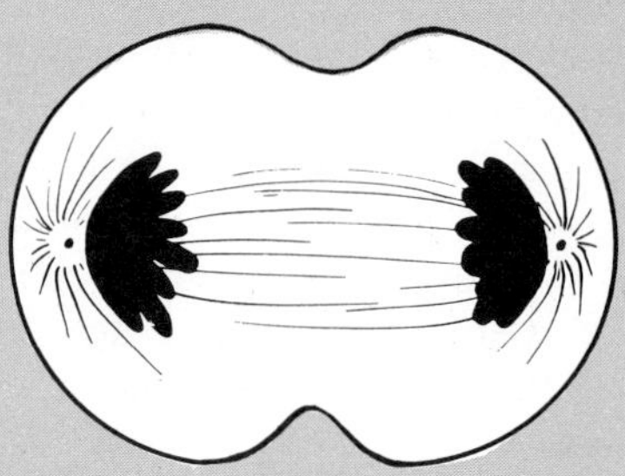

9. Early telophase
Chromosomes lie close together and form a clump; nuclear reorganization begins

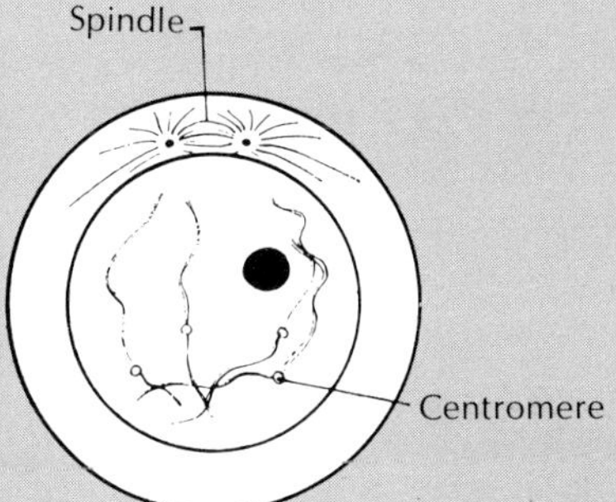

2. Early prophase
Each elongated chromosome now consists of 2 chromatids attached to single centromere; double nature of chromosome not apparent; centrosome divides and spindle starts development

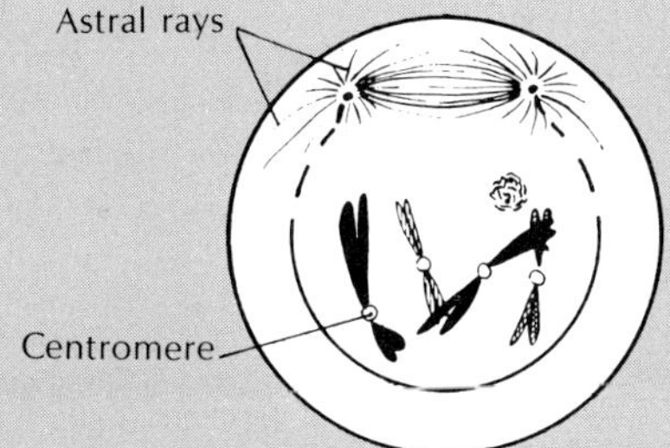

3. Middle prophase
Each chromosome may be visibly double; coils of chromonemata increase and make chromosome shorter and thicker

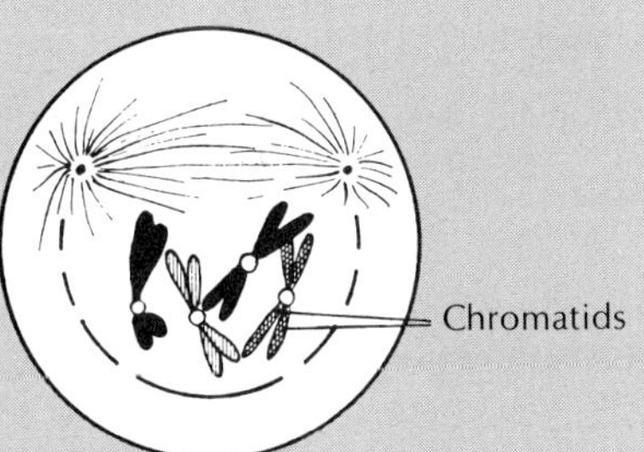

4. Late prophase
Double nature of short, thick chromosome more apparent; each chromosome made up of 2 half-chromosomes or sister chromatids; nucleolus usually disappears

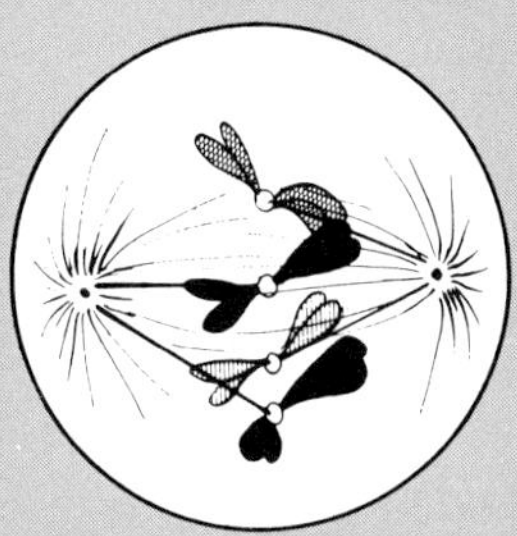

6 Metaphase
Chromosomes arranged on equatorial plate; centromeres (not yet divided) anchored to equator of spindle

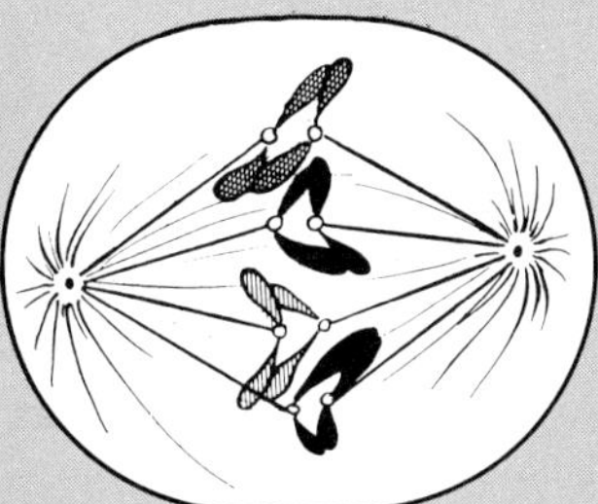

7. Early anaphase
By splitting of centromere each chromatid has its own centromere, which lies on equator and is attached to spindle fiber

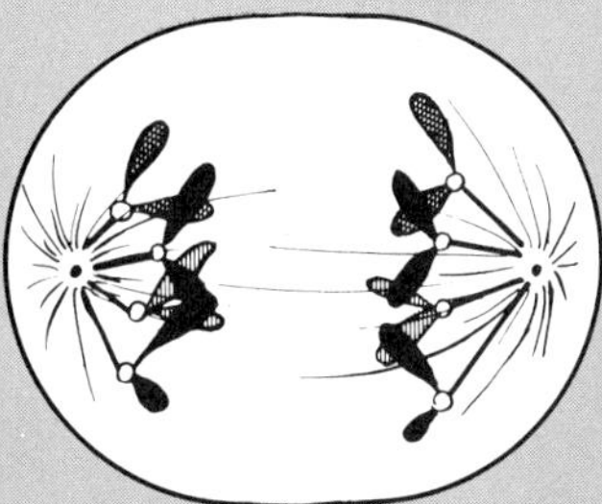

8. Anaphase
Chromatids, now called daughter chromosomes are in 2 distinct groups; daughter centromeres which may be attached at various points on different chromosomes, move apart and drag daughter chromosomes toward respective poles

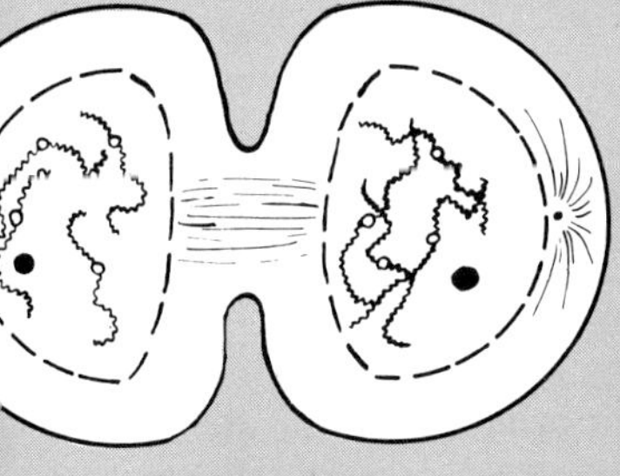

10. Late telophase
Chromonemata lose major coils and chromosomes become longer and thinner; chromosomes may lose identity; nuclear membrane reappears and spindle-astral fibers fade away; cell body divides into 2 daughter cells, each of which now enters interphase

FIG. 5-12
Diagrams of mitotic stages.

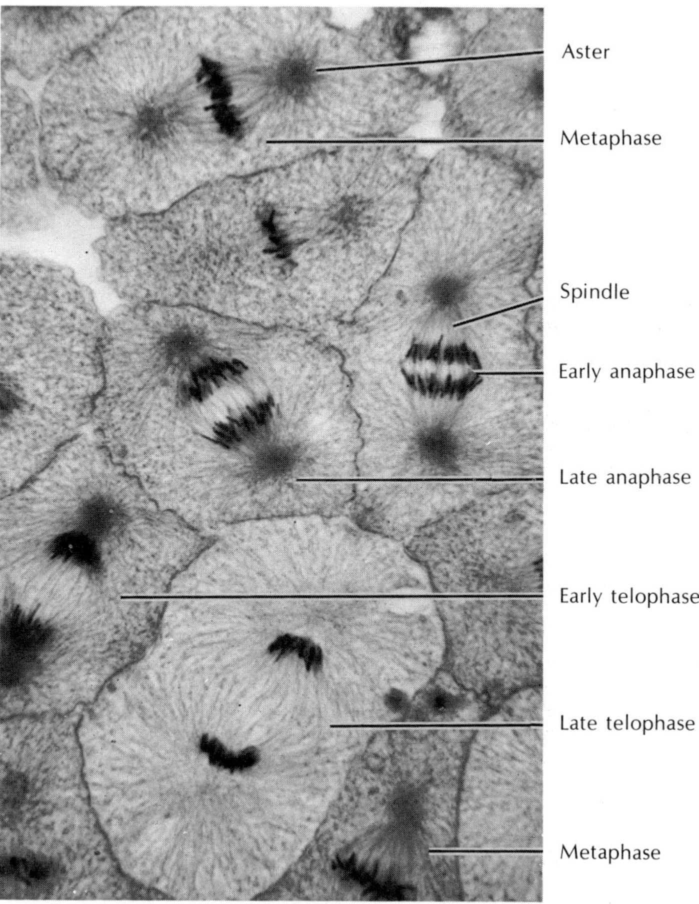

FIG. 5-13

Stages of mitosis in whitefish. (Courtesy General Biological Supply House, Inc., Chicago.)

the ultimate size the organism reaches at maturity, there are some examples of cell constancy (**eutely**) in the animal kingdom. This constancy in the number of cells may be characteristic of the entire animal or it may be restricted only to certain tissues or organs. Interest in eutely is focused upon the mechanism that terminates cell division with such precision at a definite point in development. Some protistan colonies have long been known to have a constant number of cells. *Pandorina morum* (a green alga) has 8 to 16 cells; *Pandorina charkowiensis* has 16 or 32 cells; and certain species of *Eudorina* have 64 cells. Many roundworms show the trait. *Epiphanes* (a rotifer) has 958 nuclei (syncytial patterns are common in the aschelminths). In this animal the nuclei or cells are distributed as follows: skin, 301; pharynx, 167; digestive system, 76; urogenital system, 43; muscles, 120; and nervous system, 247. Cell constancy does not apply to the gonads that form eggs and sperm continuously.

Even in higher forms, certain tissues undergo no increase in number of cells after birth. In man there appears to be no cell division in nervous and muscle tissue after the fetal stages. The number of glomeruli in the kidneys of some animals is fixed at birth.

FLUX OF CELLS

In many organisms, certain tissues continually shed their cells because of wear and tear or other causes. The epidermis of the skin, the lining of the alimentary canal, and the blood-forming tissues lose large numbers of cells daily. There must be a constant replacement of the cells that are lost, for there is no net loss or gain in the overall picture. In man it has been estimated that the number of cells shed daily is about 1% to 2% of all the body cells.

In its contact with the environment the organism is usually subject to a constant attrition of physical and chemical forces. Mechanical rubbing wears away the outer cells of the skin, and emotional stresses destroy many cells. Food in the alimentary canal rubs off lining cells, the restricted life cycle of blood corpuscles must involve a renewal of enormous numbers of replacements, and during active sex life many millions of sperm are produced each day. This loss is made up by a chain reaction of binary fission or mitosis.

At birth the child has about 2,000 billion cells. This immense number has come from a single fertilized egg (zygote). Such a number of cells could be attained by a chain reaction in which the cell generations had divided about 42 times, with each cell dividing once about every 6 to 7 days. In about five more cell generations by the chain reaction, the cells have increased to 60,000 billion at maturity (in an individual of 170 pounds). However, not all cells divide at the same rate and some cells (nervous and muscular), as we have seen, stop dividing altogether at birth. The growth of an organism is not merely an increase in number of cells but it also involves some molecular reproduction or increase in cell size.

The life span of different cells varies with the tissue, the animal, and the conditions of existence. Nerve cells and muscle cells, to some extent, persist throughout the life of the higher animal. Red blood corpuscles live about 120 days. The normal process of metamorphosis found in many animals involves a great loss of cells. Many cells are removed in the shaping of organs during morphogenesis.

Cells undergo a senescence with aging. At some point

in the life cycle of most cells there is a breakdown of cell substance, the formation of inert material, a slowing down of metabolic processes, and a decrease in the synthetic power of enzymes. These factors lead eventually to the death of the cell. In certain cases, parts of the cell such as scales, feathers, and bony structures, may persist after the death of the cell.

Annotated references

Bonner, J. T. 1955. Cells and societies. Princeton, N. J., Princeton University Press. *The author emphasizes the sameness of the basic biologic requirements of the organisms, but the methods of meeting these requirements are highly varied. It is an excellent review of some of the chief functions of organisms.*

Bonner, J. T. 1959. The cellular slime molds. Princeton, N. J., Princeton University Press. *One group of slime molds, Myxomycetes, forms a multinucleate mass of protoplasm called a plasmodium; but another unrelated group, called the simple slime molds (Acrasiales), form aggregations of multicellular individuals, not a concentration of protoplasm in one spot. The latter pose some interesting problems in development and differentiation.*

De Robertis, E. D. P., W. W. Nowinski, and F. A. Saez. 1960. General cytology, ed. 3. Philadelphia, W. B. Saunders Co. *Chapter 3 in this excellent work deals with the morphologic organization of the cell. A good description of mitosis is given.*

Freeman, J. A. 1964. Cellular fine structure. New York, McGraw-Hill Book Co. *This revealing book on the interpretation of electron micrographs introduces the student to molecular biology from the structural point of view. Basic techniques of electron microscopy are given considerable emphasis. One of the best accounts of some of the revealing structures found with the electron microscope.*

Hoffman, J. C. 1957. The life and death of cells. New York, Doubleday & Co., Inc. *An up-to-date account of the cell cycle in the light of the development of modern methods in biology. One of the best elementary treatises in the field.*

Jensen, W. A., and R. B. Park. 1967. Cell ultrastructure. Belmont, Calif., Wadsworth Publishing Co., Inc. *A collection of electron micrographs and illustrated cells and their components from both plants and animals.*

Marsland, D. 1957. Temperature-pressure studies on the role of sol-gel relations in cell division. Washington, D. C., American Physiological Society, pp. 111-126.

Mazia, D. 1961. How cells divide. Sci. Amer. **205**:100-120 (Sept.).

Mercer, E. H. 1962. Cells: their structure and function. (Paperback.) New York, Doubleday & Co., Inc. *This compact little book should be read by all biologists for it clearly describes the latest concepts of the cell as revealed by molecular biology.*

Neutra, M., and C. P. Lebiond. 1969. The Golgi apparatus. Sci. Amer. **220**:100-107 (Feb.). *Explains how the Golgi apparatus packages secretion and synthesizes large carbohydrates.*

Palay, S. L. (editor). 1958. Frontiers in cytology. New Haven, Yale University Press. *This work is based on a series of lectures delivered at Yale University by many eminent specialists on current problems of cytology. It is a work for the serious student of zoology for it deals with the latest concepts of molecular biology.*

Porter, K. R., and M. A. Bonneville. 1963. An introduction to the fine structure of cells and tissues. Philadelphia, Lea & Febiger. *This work gives one an insight into what the electron microscope means to the modern study of histology.*

Racker, E. 1968. The membrane of the mitochondrion. Sci. Amer. **218**:32-39 (Feb.). *Describes how the inner membrane of the mitochondrion is involved in the process of oxidative phosphorylation. The attempt has been made to analyze step by step by fragmentation the various sites and enzymes necessary for the complicated process of oxidation and energy formation.*

Ramsey, J. A., and V. B. Wigglesworth (editors). 1961. The cell and the organism. Cambridge, Cambridge University Press. *A great variety of biologic phenomena are treated in the light of recent advances in this revealing volume.*

Robertson, J. D. 1962. The membrane of the living cell. Sci. Amer. **206**:65-72 (April).

Rustad, R. C. 1961. Pinocytosis. Sci. Amer. **204**:121-130 (April).

Solomon, A. K. 1960. Pores in the cell membrane. Sci. Amer. **203**:146-156 (Dec.). *Pores are too small to be measured by electron microscope, but can be measured indirectly by experimental methods. One measurement found the pore to have a diameter of 8.4 Å units.*

Stern, H., and D. L. Nanney. 1965. The biology of cells. New York, John Wiley & Sons, Inc. *This introductory textbook in cell biology stresses the cell doctrine, the chromosome and gene, and the physicochemical basis of life.*

Swanson, C. P. 1964. The cell, ed. 2. Englewood Cliffs, N. J., Prentice-Hall, Inc. *One of a series of biologic monographs. An excellent account of the modern concept of the cell.*

Wyckoff, R. W. G. 1958. The world of the electron microscope. New Haven, Yale University Press. *This work explains the principles of this important tool of research and its practical application.*

Zirkle, R. E. (editor). 1959. A symposium on molecular biology. Chicago, University of Chicago Press. *Molecular biology is the most active branch of biologic investigation at the present time, and the papers in this symposium summarize many of the studies made in this field. There is an interesting chapter on the widely used electron microscope and its possibilities in molecular biology.*

CHAPTER 6

• PHYSIOLOGY OF THE CELL*

DIFFERENTIATION OF CELL FUNCTIONS

● In previous chapters the principal organelles and their functions were described. In this chapter some of the more general physiologic processes are studied in relationship with the physical structure and chemical organization of the cell. Two related aspects of cellular physiology will be emphasized—how things get into the cell and the metabolic changes that explain how the cell gets its energy to stay alive. Both of these processes involve complicated and highly differentiated cellular structures that represent the very key to the major functions of the cell.

As already explained, the cell is a highly organized entity. Its various organelles are adapted to carry on the life processes. But there is far more involved than the separate functions of the organelles. The cells of the body are integrated to form a whole individual. This may be accomplished by two levels of reactions. In the first place there is a regulation of cellular behavior in response to stimuli from the environment. Messages from the environment may be sent through neural pathways and hormones of the bloodstream. A second level of integration may be an intrinsic regulation of cells from within. Cells by evolutionary experience have acquired certain basic behavior patterns and mechanisms, transmitted by inheritance, which regulate cell size and control cellular multiplication. These behavior mechanisms must be flexible enough to adjust to an ever-changing environment. No cell type has evolved in a completely constant environment. In the long evolution of animals they have tended toward constancy of internal conditions, for example the temperature regulation and fluid homeostasis of higher forms. The larger the animal the greater opportunity for certain cells to be free from direct external influences. Security varies with different cells. Those in the epidermis are on the frontier; bone marrow cells are deep and protected.

In most of the principal organs there are many more cells available than are needed for the services of that organ. Thus a man could get along very well with one half of his lung tissue, one third of his kidneys, one fourth of his liver, and one fifth of his pancreas. Activities of an organ's units are spread fairly evenly so that they will have alternate rest and active periods. Cardiac muscle cells, for instance, rest more every 24 hours than they work, although each rest and activity period is necessarily very short.

When necessary, this general discussion on physiology will consider the revelation of cell structure and function as seen by the electron microscope. Only by considering the working of cell parts at the molecular level can the student appreciate or understand what goes on in this microcosm. All parts seen with the light microscope (and some that cannot be seen at all) can be observed in greater detail with the electron microscope. But with the vast development of the knowledge that has emerged about the cell in the past few decades, a whole new world of discovery yet remains. Every problem solved produces additional ones that await solution.

Surface of cells and their relations

Cell surfaces vary depending on many factors. Several cell types are free and can move throughout the animal. These free cells have no direct junctional arrangements with other cells and include such types as leukocytes, red blood corpuscles, coelomocytes, amebocytes, macrophages, thigmocytes, and many others. Interstitial cells are undifferentiated, are located on epithelial structures, and often migrate to injured regions for repair. They also have other functions in some animals. Pigment cells (chromatophores) have a

*Refer to Chapter 2, Principle 8.

certain amount of freedom to move about. Chloragogue cells in annelids, and similar cells in other animals, carry waste among other functions.

Every cell is bounded by a cell or plasma membrane that has been described previously. All living systems have membranes of some type because they are basic to the compartment organization. Viruses apparently lack them, but these organisms grow only within a host. Cell membranes have been subjected to microchemical analysis. An erythrocyte, for instance, on hemolysis liberates hemoglobin and the ghost of the erythrocyte that is left is made up apparently of only the cell membrane. Analysis of this membrane shows that it consists of lipids (mainly cholesterol and phospholipids) and protein. Nucleic acid has been found in the egg membrane of *Arbacia* (an echinoderm) and may be present in similar situations in other animals. Carbohydrates may be conjugated with the protein constituent. Membranes, wherever found, have both dynamic qualities of regulation (self-repair, mechanisms of transport, etc.) and static qualities of fixed arrangements of molecular structures. Pores are seen, but their exact status is unknown.

Cells are usually packed close together and their cell contours may be smooth, or they may have projections that interlock more or less with similar ones from adjacent cells. External animal cells may not be naked, but they are provided with pellicles or cuticles (protozoan and others). The chitinous coat of the arthropods is distinctive as is the limy shell of mollusks. Some animals have films of mucus and tunicates have cellulose in their outer layers. Vertebrates as a group have made great use of keratin, a protein substance.

The surface cells of many types throughout the animal kingdom bear specialized structures of locomotion called cilia and flagella (Figs. 10-16 and 10-17). These are vibratile extensions of the cell surface and their covering membrane is continuous with the plasma membrane. Internally cilia and flagella have the same structure of nine fibrils surrounding a pair of fibrils. Cilia are usually short and numerous on a cell surface; flagella are usually few and long. They may be modified to form undulating membranes, sensory processes, or cirri. Nematodes and arthropods are supposed to be lacking in cilia and flagella, but they have recently been found in certain sensory receptors in nematodes and they may occur in the gonoducts of arthropods. At the base of flagella and cilia where they are anchored in the cell cytoplasm, they are attached to a granule, a **kinetosome.** The kinetosome is similar to the cilia and flagella, but has nine triplet filaments and no double central filaments. In *Euglena* and some others the flagellum is connected to a centriole by a fibril, the rhizoplast. Flagella and cilia have numerous functions such as propelling individual cells (protozoans), multicellular animals (planarians and ctenophores), or fluids or entities through tubular organs (sponges and gonoducts). Most animal sperm are provided with them for propulsion.

The surfaces of contiguous cells, or those packed together, have junction complexes between them that give a different picture with the electron microscope than with the light microscope. There are several types of these specializations. Cells are held very firmly together, especially in epithelial tissues, as in the lining of the esophagus. The surface of contiguous cells are attached or sealed only in restricted areas. They are not cemented together as extensively as the light microscope indicates. A small amount of intercellular substance of mucopolysaccharide with a high content of calcium may act as cement. The so-called intercellular bridges, of the stratum spinosum of the skin, have been shown by the electron microscope to have no continuity between cells. Present in these cells are cytoplasmic filaments, the **tonofibrils,** which were formerly thought to pass in the bridges between adjacent cells. Instead, at these zones are **desmosomes** that are small ellipsoidal disks scattered between the epithelial cells. Desmosomes are electron dense, discontinuous thickenings of apposing plasma membranes or two apposed plates. They measure about 250 to 410 millimicrons in their greatest diameter (J. A. Freeman). From the cell cytoplasm tufts of fine filaments, which made up the tonofibrils, converge onto the desmosomes. Between the two apposed plates of a desmosome is a narrow intercellular space (200 to 240 Å wide). This space may be obliterated in some zones by fusion of adjacent plasma membranes.

Terminal bars are found at the distal junctions of adjacent columnar epithelial cells. They appear as dark lines near the free surface of the cells when viewed in flat sections. The electron microscope shows that they are produced by thickened areas of apposing plasma membranes in which adjacent cell membranes are apposed closely or fused. They form a complete beltlike junction just beyond the luminal or apical portion of the plasma membrane.

Other specializations of the cell surface are the interdigitations of confronted cell surfaces. These are complexities of the lateral cell interfaces where the plasma membranes of the cells infold and interdigitate very much like a zipper. They are especially common in the epithelium of kidney tubules. The distal or apical boundaries of some epithelial cells show regularly arranged **microvilli,** as seen with the electron microscope. They are small, fingerlike projections consisting of tubelike evaginations of the plasma membrane, with a core of cytoplasm. They are well seen in the lining of the intestine where they greatly increase the absorptive or digestive surface. Such specializations are seen as striated and **brush borders** by the light microscope. The spaces between the microvilli are continuous with tubules of the endoplasmic reticulum that may facilitate the movement of materials into the cells.

Passage of materials through membranes: exchange between cell and environment*

The general metabolism of living cells requires a continuous supply of food materials and oxygen for the energy of the life process. Cells give off, in turn, by-products to the surrounding medium. These substances must all pass through the plasma membrane of the cell, whether they are entering or leaving the cell. Most cells are surrounded by an aqueous solution of some kind. The ameba is surrounded by the fresh water in which it lives. In many-celled animals the cell lives in a medium composed of blood, lymph, or tissue fluid. Before a substance can enter a cell, it must be soluble to some degree in the surrounding medium. The plasma membrane, then, acts as a doorkeeper for the entrance and exit of the substances involved in cell metabolism. Some things can pass through with ease; others enter slowly and with difficulty; and still others cannot enter at all. Biologic membranes have three methods of transfer: (1) **semipermeable,** which allows certain substances to pass through and blocks others as though the membrane had pores that restricted the size of the molecules passing through; (2) **selective permeability,** which allows certain types of molecules to pass through almost regardless of molecular size (fat-soluble and uncharged molecules and ions); and (3) **active transport,** in which a specific mechanism involving energy carries the molecules through the membrane regardless of the concentrations on the different sides of the membrane. The first two methods are diffusion phenomena from the more concentrated to the less concentrated side of the membrane and are energy yielding; active transport is an energy demanding process and may involve the transfer of substances from a lower to a higher concentration. The mechanism of active transport is not well understood, but it will be referred to later.

*Refer to Chapter 2, Principle 8.

Diffusion. All molecules are in a state of motion because of the energy within them. In solids the molecules are so restricted that they merely vibrate; within a liquid the molecules have more freedom of movement; but in gases the freedom to move is restricted only by containing vessels. When free, molecules will move in a straight line until they meet another molecule, then bounce off and take a different direction, producing a zigzag path (**brownian movement**).

The total molecular activity of a substance in a par-

FIG. 6-1

Diagram of diffusion and osmosis through a membrane permeable to both water and sugar molecules. When lump of sugar is placed in left compartment of beaker, its molecules will diffuse through water of that compartment and through permeable membrane into right compartment until, as shown in right beaker, molecules are evenly dispersed.

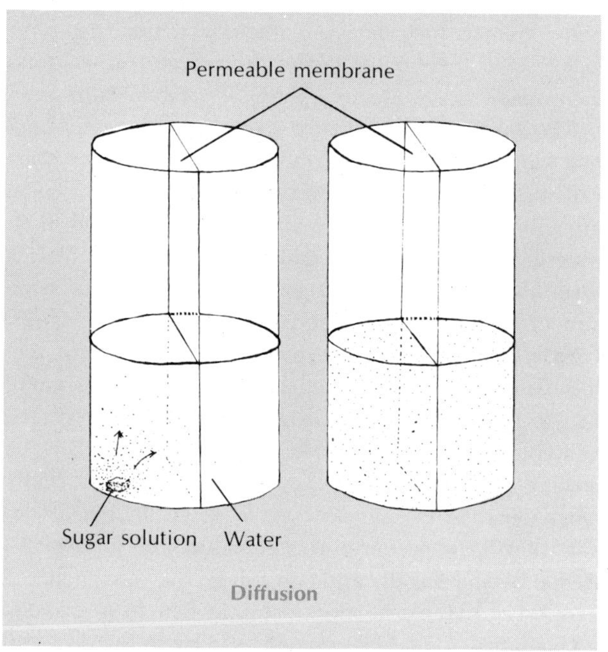

ticular region results in a **diffusion pressure.** This activity depends on the concentration of molecules, the velocity of the molecules (faster at high temperatures), and any pressure on the molecules from the outside. **Diffusion** may be defined as the movement of molecules or ions (brought about by their kinetic energy) from a region of greater to a region of lesser diffusion pressure (even against gravity) because there is less collision with other particles in the region of lesser concentration. Diffusion ceases when an equilibrium is established and the molecules are uniformly distributed, but molecular movement still continues.

If some salt is dropped in a beaker of water, salt molecules and ions will spread through the water until the concentration of salt is uniform throughout. The salt particles, as well as the water molecules, are in a continuous state of movement, and through mass movement every component in the solution will diffuse until it reaches equal concentration everywhere in the solution (Fig. 6-1).

Diffusion will occur in all states of matter but is fastest in gases and slowest in solids. The rate of diffusion depends on a number of factors. The greater the concentration differences of the substance diffusing and the higher the temperature of the solution, the faster the particles diffuse. Also, small particles diffuse much faster than larger particles, and solutions with low viscosity diffuse faster than those with high viscosity. Agitation also hastens it.

Osmosis. Osmosis is essentially a diffusion process. Whenever a semipermeable membrane is placed between two unequal concentrations of dissolved substances, that is, two different diffusion pressures, water will pass from the higher to the lower diffusion pressure until equilibrium is established. Thus we may define **osmosis** as the diffusion of water (or gas) through a differentially permeable membrane. A **semipermeable** or **differentially permeable membrane** refers to a membrane that allows some molecules to pass through and prevents others. A membrane is **permeable** when it permits any molecule to get through and **impermeable** if it allows none to pass. In an osmotic system each substance will pass from the solution where its concentration is greater to the one where its concentration is lesser. This is the same law as that of diffusion except in this case a membrane has been introduced through which molecules must pass to bring about equilibrium (Fig. 6-2).

A familiar example of osmosis is shown by the following experiment. A collodion membrane bag is filled with a strong sugar solution. A glass tube is tied in the open end of the bag, paraffined to waterproof it, and the bag is placed in a beaker of pure water so that the water levels inside and outside the bag are identical. In a short time the water level in the glass tube will be seen to rise, indicating that water is passing through the collodion bag into the sugar solution. The explanation lies in the difference between the concentrations inside and outside the bag. Inside the bag are sugar molecules as well as water. In the beaker outside there are only water molecules. Thus the concentration of water is greater on the outside because some of the space inside is taken up with sugar molecules. The water therefore will go from the greater concentration (outside) to the lesser (inside).

Actually, water molecules go in both directions, but the conditions favor the inflow rather than the outgo.

FIG. 6-2

Diagram of diffusion and osmosis with semipermeable membrane. When sugar is placed in left compartment of beaker, concentration of water molecules is lower than it is in pure water on right, and so water passes through semipermeable membrane and column of water in left compartment will rise, as shown by beaker on right.

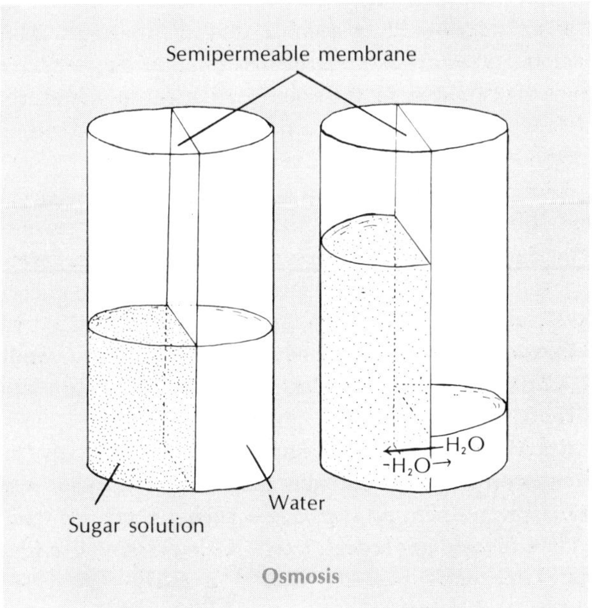

Two forces may operate here. On the inside of the membrane sac there is less surface or fewer pores for the passage of the water molecules since part of the surface is occupied with sugar molecules. In addition, many water molecules are loosely bound or absorbed to sugar molecules, so that there are fewer diffusible water molecules. Eventually the water in the tube will go no higher. This indicates that the hydrostatic pressure of the column of water is sufficient to drive the water molecules back through the membrane as fast as they come in. This force produces a **turgor pressure,** often called osmotic pressure, but osmotic pressure may be reserved for the possible pressure any substance exerts in a solution whether or not it is an osmotic system. A salt or sugar solution in a container has osmotic pressure; it develops a turgor pressure when the solution is separated by a differentially permeable membrane from another solution of lesser concentration. Turgor pressure is caused by the influx of water molecules through a semipermeable membrane to equalize the concentration of water molecules on both sides of the membrane. However, this collodion membrane allows sugar molecules to pass through as well as water, but they do so slowly; hence the total osmotic pressure, or **osmotic value,** of this sugar solution is never realized, for the osmotic pressure of a solution is proportional to the number of solute particles that will not pass through the membrane. It is not the size of the particles but their number that is important. The osmotic pressure of a particular solution depends on the concentration of the solute particles, temperature, electric charges (if any) on the particles, and other factors.

Dialysis is another form of osmosis and applies to the diffusion of solutes through a differentially permeable membrane. This process is often useful in separating salts from colloids or proteins because the membrane allows salt molecules to pass through into a low concentration, but the membrane pores are too small to allow the colloid particles to pass, and they are left behind.

Substances of biologic importance vary greatly in their power to pass through cell membranes that are selective in their action. Gases such as oxygen and carbon dioxide go through freely. Glucose, amino acids, and fatty acids pass through at a fairly slow rate. Strong electrolytes and most inorganic salts penetrate membranes very slowly, whereas polysaccharides, fats, and proteins will not pass through at all. Cell membranes can also alter their permeability and thus influence the substances that enter and leave cells. In any case only substances in solution can pass through cell membranes.

Filtration. Filtration is a mechanical process by which molecules under an external pressure are forced or filtered through a membrane. Blood pressure created by heart action is an outstanding example in the body. Not only is the blood propelled around the vascular system, but also the force of blood pressure tends to drive water and solutes through capillary walls and membranes.

Application to zoology. In biologic processes, osmosis, osmotic pressure, and filtration play an important role. The colloidal substance of the cell does not pass through plasma membranes readily, if at all, but water can. Water is, therefore, the important component in establishing osmotic equilibria between the cell and its surrounding medium. The ideal surrounding for the cells would be a fluid of the same osmotic pressure as that of the protoplasm in the cell. Such a surrounding fluid is called **isotonic.** Blood and lymph are usually isotonic to the cells they carry or bathe. **Hypotonic** solutions contain less dissolved material than the protoplasm of the cell. In this case more water will enter the cell than leaves it because the greater concentration of water is on the outside. **Hypertonic** solutions contain a higher proportion of nonpenetrating solute than does the protoplasm of the cell, and more water leaves the cell than enters it. A physiologic saline solution (0.9% sodium chloride) is isotonic to blood cells of mammals and is employed when blood is studied on the slide (Fig. 6-3). Lower concentrations of salt (0.5%) will cause the blood corpuscles to rupture (**hemolysis**); higher concentrations will shrink the cell (**crenation**).

Osmosis naturally plays a part in the diffusion of food and oxygen into the tissue cells and, in return, the giving off of waste products.

An illustration of osmosis and osmotic pressure is seen in the use of Epsom salts (magnesium sulfate) as a laxative. When a solution of this salt is taken into the intestine, water is drawn into the intestine from the surrounding blood and body fluids because the magnesium salt solution has a higher osmotic pressure. Magnesium salts are largely nondiffusible, however, and will not leave the intestine to enter the blood.

Filtration is employed in the kidneys when urinary

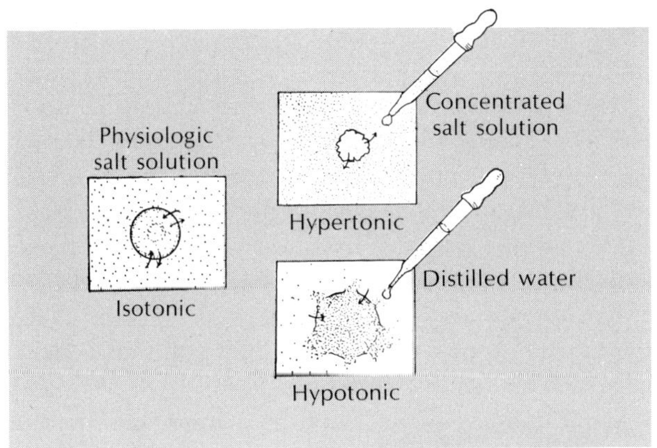

FIG. 6-3

Diagram showing effect of osmosis and osmotic pressure on red blood corpuscle. In isotonic solution there is no change in volume of cell; in hypertonic solution cell shrinks, and in hypotonic solution cell swells and bursts.

constituents are separated from the blood because this process is largely a filtering device.

Freezing point as expression of osmotic pressure.* Physiologists often use the freezing point of a solution as a convenient way to determine its osmotic pressure. Compared with pure water, which freezes at 0° C., a watery solution, that is, containing particles in solution, will freeze at a lower temperature, depending on its osmotic pressure or concentration. The greater the number of solutes, the further the lowering of the freezing point. All solutions having the same freezing point have the same osmotic pressure. The freezing point is represented by the Greek letter Δ (delta) and is determined by a method called cryoscopy. For example, human blood will freeze at about −0.56° C., or in other words, its Δ is equal to −0.56° C. The blood of other mammals has a similar Δ that tends to remain remarkably constant. Other body fluids such as urine often show a great variation in their freezing points over a period of time.

How aquatic animals meet problems of osmosis. Terrestrial animals such as reptiles, birds, and mammals have a skin that is largely impermeable to water and are adapted to their air environment. Such problems of water balance and composition of body fluids as they may have are regulated by their kidneys. It is difficult with aquatic animals that are surrounded all the time by a watery medium. Even though their skins may be more or less water impermeable, parts of their body such as the gills represent semipermeable membranes that can and do form osmotic systems. Water is thus free to pass into or out of the body in accordance with the laws of diffusion and osmosis. If the water outside has a higher concentration of solutes, the body fluids will lose water; the reverse will happen if the surrounding osmotic pressure is lower than that of the body fluids. In lower forms of fish such as the cartilaginous ones (Chondrichthyes), the Δ of the body fluids is about the same as that of sea water (about −2.25° C.). To keep their osmotic concentration equal to that of sea water, these fish retain urea and other organic compounds normally excreted by other animals.

On the other hand, most marine bony fish have body fluids of a lower osmotic pressure than that of the surrounding sea water (3.5%) and tend to lose water through the gills. Their Δ is around −1° C. To keep themselves from drying out, such fish drink much water and excrete little through the kidneys. The excess salt they take in with the sea water is excreted through the gills by an active secretory process requiring energy. Anadromous fish (marine fish that return to fresh water to breed) are able to retain about the same osmotic pressure of their body fluids in both fresh water and sea water. Marine mammals such as whales and porpoises have body fluids of the same osmotic pressure as terrestrial mammals. They get their water by eating fish and excrete excess salt by a concentrated urine.

The osmotic pressure of the body fluids of freshwater fish is higher than that of fresh water (hypertonic). Their problem, then, is to get rid of excess water that tends to enter them all the time. To compensate, they drink little water, excrete freely through the kidneys, absorb salts through the gills, and carefully salvage most of the salt that enters the body, leaving free water available for urine formation.

Role of enzymes in the living process*

The whole life process involves many chemical reactions within the cells. It is the chemical breakdown of large molecules that release energy for the activities

*Refer to Chapter 2, Principles 31 and 32.

*Refer to Chapter 2, Principle 19.

of any organism. Food to furnish potential energy must be taken into the body because all organisms literally use themselves up as their molecules are oxidized in these energy-yielding reactions. **Enzymes** make these chemical activities possible. An enzyme is a biologic catalyst produced by living protoplasm and regulating the speed and specificity at which these numerous reactions occur. A catalyst is any organic or inorganic substance that accelerates a chemical reaction without affecting the end products of the reaction and without being destroyed as a result of the reaction. Inorganic catalysts are common in the chemical industry, such as manganese dioxide in the liberation of oxygen from peroxide and the use of finely divided metals (iron, platinum, nickel, etc.) in surface catalysis. Water may be considered a catalyst because many substances that are inert when mixed together in a dry condition will quickly react when a little water is added. Catalysts furnish no energy, and the reactions they promote would probably occur slowly without the presence of the catalysts.

There must be thousands of enzymes in the animal body because physiologic processes are mainly enzymatic. Enzymes are involved in every aspect of life phenomena. They control the reactions by which food is digested, absorbed, and metabolized. They promote the synthesis of structural materials to replace the wear and tear on the body. They determine the release of energy used in respiration, growth, muscle contraction, physical and mental activities, and a host of others. A few protoplasmic activities may not involve enzymes, such as the secretion of milk by the mammary glands. Much of our knowledge about enzymes may be summarized as follows.

Chemical nature of enzymes. All the enzymes so far isolated and crystallized are proteins. They are complex with large molecular weights, that of urease being 483,000. No enzyme has been artificially created in the laboratory. Most of them are colorless, but some are brown, red, green, etc. Many of them, such as pepsin, are pure proteins made up of chains of amino acids. Others, such as certain vitamins, are made up of proteins joined to chemical groups. Still others (cytochrome) contain a metal such as iron. Most of them are soluble in water, but those with lipoprotein are insoluble in water. All are insoluble in absolute alcohol. Most are destroyed or made inactive by temperatures over 65° C., some at lower temperatures. The rate of reaction increases up to about 35° C. and then decreases.

Where enzymes are found. All enzymes are made in cells. Some are found dissolved in cytoplasm. Extracts made from groundup liver cells have the team of enzymes necessary to convert glucose to lactic acid. Some enzymes may be found in small differentiated parts of the cells, such as microsomes and mitochondria. Enzymes may be precipitated or thrown down from their natural sources by dilute alcoholic solutions, mercuric chloride solutions, acetone solutions, and others. Enzymes are colloidal in nature and behave like colloids with a precipitation agent. All cells do not necessarily produce the same enzymes. Certain cells only in the stomach wall manufacture pepsin; other cells in the pancreas make trypsin. What product a cell makes is determined mainly by the kind of enzymes the cell has. Some enzymes normally act only within the cell (intracellular) and are represented by such an enzyme as cytochrome oxidase; others (extracellular) perform their work in secretions such as the digestive enzymes.

How enzymes are named. The most common method of naming enzymes is to add the suffix **-ase** to the root word of the substance or substrate on which the enzyme works. A substrate is the substance that is altered by the influence of the enzyme. Thus sucrase (an enzyme) acts upon sucrose, lipase upon lipids, protease upon proteins, etc. Some enzymes have special names, such as pepsin, ptyalin, and trypsin. Sometimes the suffix **-lytic** is used in naming enzymes. Proteolytic (protein-splitting) is a general term for an enzyme that digests protein and amylolytic (starch-splitting) for an enzyme that digests starch.

How enzymes are activated. Some enzymes are first produced in cells as inactive forms (**zymogens**) without enzymatic properties. Thus the zymogen of pepsin is pepsinogen, that of trypsin is trypsinogen, etc. Zymogens have entirely different properties from the enzymes they produce because they are less sensitive to acids and alkalies. Zymogens can be demonstrated in gland cells as granules by proper techniques of fixation and staining. They are activated by various agents such as by hydrogen ions that change pepsinogen to pepsin, or by a special enzyme, enterokinase, that is supposed to convert trypsinogen into trypsin, although there is some doubt on this point. Other enzymes are activated by their **coenzymes** (usually vitamins). When separated by filtration or other means,

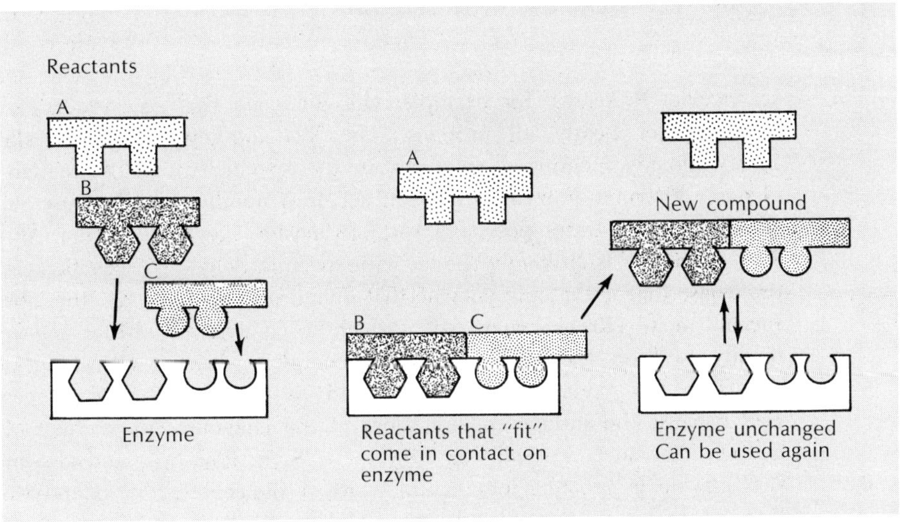

FIG. 6-4

Enzyme action and specificity. Enzymes are thought to have surface configurations that "fit" specific substrates. Here molecules **B** and **C** fit into enzyme surface, but **A** does not. Reactions involving **B** and **C** are speeded up by coming in contact briefly with enzyme. When reaction is complete, the enzyme, still unchanged, can dissociate from the substrate and is free to aid in further reactions. Molecule **A** and others not specific to this enzyme are unaffected by it.

neither enzymes nor coenzymes will produce enzymatic effect but will do so when brought together.

How enzymes act. Enzymes perform their action by combining with some particular part of the substrate molecule. This may be due to the unique shape of an enzyme molecule that can fit only a certain niche in the molecule of the substrate (the lock-and-key theory) (Fig. 6-4). When the enzyme-substrate combination has been formed, what happens depends on the nature of the enzyme, substrate, and other factors. In some cases there is a transfer of electrons from the substrate to the enzyme (enzyme-substrate complex), or in other cases the enzyme simply brings a substrate molecule and a water molecule into closer association so that hydrolysis can be facilitated. When the substrate molecule is changed, the enzyme is freed and is ready to combine with another substrate molecule. Enzymes rarely work singly but in teams. Whenever the end products of one enzyme-catalyzed reaction are produced, they become involved in other enzyme-controlled reactions. One enzyme carries out one step, and other enzymes carry on from there in succession. In this way the metabolism of cells becomes a continuous sequence of reactions, each of which is controlled by specific enzymes. One important aspect of enzymatic action is the so-called **coupled reaction.** This occurs whenever certain chemical reactions require the expenditure of energy and others release energy at the same time, to furnish this energy. This is well illustrated in muscular physiology when certain energy-yielding reactions produce the synthesis of high-energy substances, such as adenosine triphosphate (ATP), which are used to contract the muscle.

Apoenzymes and coenzymes. Digestive enzymes such as pepsin and trypsin are made up entirely of protein, but many others have two parts—a protein and a nonprotein component. It is customary in such cases to call the protein part **apoenzyme** and the nonprotein, **coenzyme.** The combination of the two can be referred to as an enzyme system. Since the smaller molecules of the coenzymes may be able to pass through a dialyzing membrane, it has been possible to separate the two components from each other in many cases. Others have been separated by hydrolysis. When analyzed, coenzymes are found to consist of vitamins such as niacin in coenzymes I and II, riboflavin in the yellow vitamin, and thiamine in many enzyme systems. It is as coenzymes that so many microconstituents or "trace" substances, such as the ions of magnesium, chloride, phosphate, iron, and copper, are absolute requirements for complete nutrition. Only when both components, apoenzyme and coenzyme, are combined can there be enzymatic activity; neither can produce catalytic action by itself.

Specificity of enzymes. Enzymes are usually highly specific among the molecules of protoplasm. Some will cause reaction only in certain substrates, even to the point of making subtle distinctions between isomers, that is, molecules of the same atoms but of different structural arrangements. Specificity is demonstrated by the different enzymes that split the double sugars—sucrose, lactose, and maltose. Other enzymes are not so specific. Proteases, for example, will influence the hydrolysis of nearly all proteins. The lock-and-key theory already mentioned may explain the specificity of many enzymes. Enzymes that can act on a number of different substrates possess a sort of "master" key. This specificity is strikingly shown with succinic dehydrogenase that is the only enzyme that dehydrogenates succinic acid (Krebs cycle) with which it combines readily to form the enzyme-substrate complex. This results in the oxidation of succinic acid to fumaric acid because the surface configurations of the enzyme is such that succinic acid can fit into it. Sometimes the enzyme is brought into contact with a molecule that resembles its normal substrate. Malonic acid is such a molecule and when succinic dehydrogenase combines with it, the active site is blocked and the enzyme is inhibited or poisoned (Fig. 6-5). Malonic acid (which undergoes no chemical transformation) thus acts as a competitive inhibitor.

Reversibility of enzyme action. A particular enzyme is effective in accelerating a reaction in either direction because it does not determine the direction of a reaction. All enzymes simply accelerate the rate at which reactions reach that equilibrium that would be attained in the absence of the enzymes. The same enzymes that convert glucose to starch are equally effective in breaking down starch to glucose in the body. However, reversion may be prevented by removing the products of enzymatic action as fast as they are formed and also by other factors.

Catalytic power of enzymes. Enzymes are very effective in small amounts. For instance, a single molecule of catalase, the enzyme that splits hydrogen peroxide into hydrogen and water, can effectively transform more than 5 million hydrogen peroxide molecules a minute at certain temperatures. Other enzymes are not as effective, but many of them can split up to 500,000 molecules of the substrate per minute.

How enzyme activity is influenced. Besides the higher temperatures already referred to, enzymatic action can be affected by a number of factors. Freezing will slow or stop their action, but their activity is resumed when the temperature rises. As a general rule,

FIG. 6-5

Blocking enzymatic action. Enzyme action is sometimes inhibited by a molecule that resembles the normal specific substrate. Succinic dehydrogenase, for example, catalyzes dehydrogenation of succinic acid to fumaric acid, one of the steps of Krebs cycle. Malonic acid is so similar to succinic acid that, when present, it can temporarily occupy enzyme's active site, thus competing with succinic acid. Some enzyme inhibitors, such as carbon monoxide, nerve gas, or cyanide, remain permanently in the active site, thus putting the enzyme out of commission and poisoning the system.

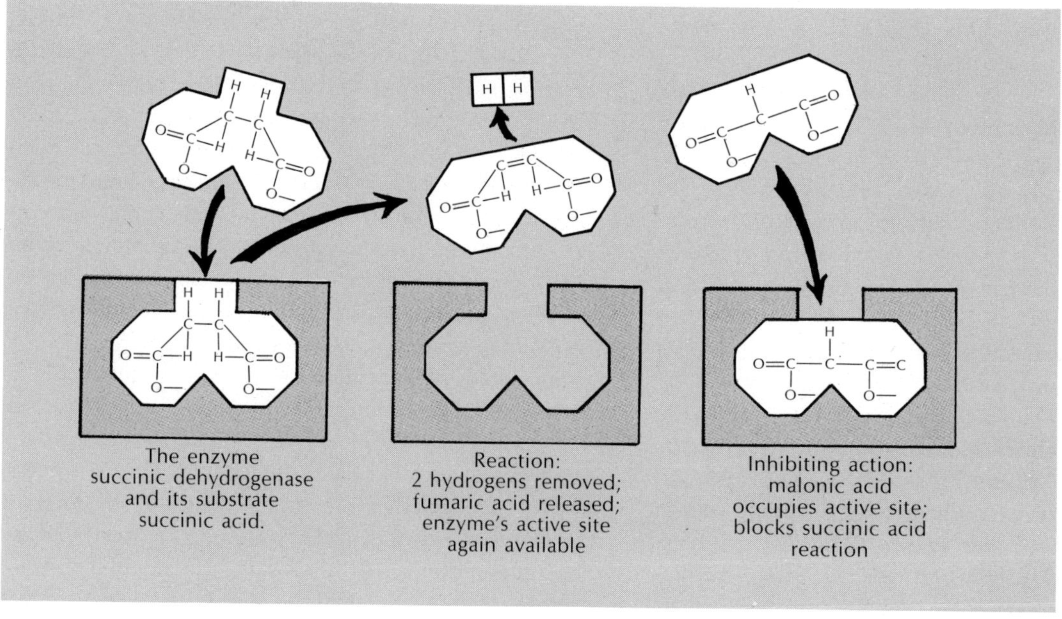

enzymes accelerate chemical reactions with rise of temperature but will do so only within certain limits. Moreover, this increase in velocity is not proportional to the rise in temperature. Usually the rate is doubled with each 10° C. rise, but a change from 20° to 30° C. is greater than one from 30° to 40° C. The optimum temperature for animal enzymes is about body temperature. Above 40° C. most enzymes are slowed down or inactivated altogether.

Enzymes are also sensitive to hydrogen ion (pH) activity. Each enzyme usually works best within a certain range of acidity or alkalinity. Pepsin of the acid gastric juice is most active at about pH 1.8; trypsin of the alkaline pancreatic juice is most active at about pH 8.2. Many work best when the pH is around neutrality. In strong acid or alkaline solutions, enzymes lose irreversibly their catalytic power.

An enzyme will do its maximal work when there is enough substrate to combine with all of the enzyme present. In such a case no further increase in the substrate can increase the amount of reaction because all of the enzyme is being used. Conversely, the initial rate of reaction (within the limits just stated) is proportional to the amount of enzyme present (at constant pH and temperature) if there is an excess of substrate.

Enzymes can be destroyed or their action can be inhibited by a number of agents besides those already mentioned. Enzymes placed in water without a substrate lose their catalytic power rapidly because they themselves are hydrolyzed. Some of them are very sensitive to poisons, such as cyanide and iodoacetic acid, which tend to inactivate the enzymes. Cyanide poisoning is caused by the destruction of the respiratory cytochrome enzymes by the cyanide. On the other hand, enzymes are little affected by antiseptics (chloroform, alcohol, etc.) in concentrations strong enough to kill protoplasm.

Relation of hormones to enzyme systems

Considerable progress has been made in determining the part hormones play in enzyme activity. It has been found, for instance, that the balance between the sugar of the blood and the liver glycogen is influenced by the action of the diabetogenic hormone secreted by the pituitary gland. This hormone tends to inhibit the action of the enzyme hexokinase, which promotes the storage of sugar as glycogen. If the diabetogenic hormone is secreted in excess, sugar will not be stored in the liver as glycogen but will remain in the blood and thus cause the sugar level of the blood to be elevated. The diabetogenic hormone is itself controlled by the hormone of the pancreatic islets—insulin. But if insulin is deficient, the pituitary hormone is free to inhibit the action of hexokinase. From this standpoint, sweet diabetes may be caused in either of two ways —by an underproduction of the hormone insulin or an overproduction of the diabetogenic hormone. When the two hormones are well balanced, such a diabetic condition does not occur. Other relationships of this kind between enzymes and hormones are probably common, but much additional work will be necessary to confirm this. It appears that hormones work hand in hand with vitamins in enzymatic systems. Indeed, some biochemists refer to all three substances as members of one family.

CELLULAR METABOLISM*

Cellular metabolism refers to the sum total of the chemical processes that are necessary for all the phenomena of life such as the synthesis of new cell materials, the replacement of that which is destroyed during wear and tear, and whatever is needed by the cell to grow, reproduce, move, etc. For these processes cells require a continuous supply of nutrients that they obtain from the surrounding fluid. These nutrients form the food substances commonly known as proteins, fats, carbohydrates, water, vitamins, and minerals. Some of these nutrients become a part of the cell structure, and others are broken down to release chemical energy that is needed for all aspects of the life process.

How cell structure is adapted to cellular metabolism

The metabolism of the cell is not identical to that of the whole animal because the latter involves a wider range of processes such as elimination, circulation of food molecules in blood and body fluids, respiratory devices of gas exchange in lungs or gills, transportation of gas in circulation, and, of course, much more extensive synthetic processes for construction and repairs. Basically, cellular metabolism and whole body metabolism are the same because the two are intertwined and involve the same requirements of nutrition, respiration, and synthesis.

Animals are heterotrophic in contrast to the auto-

*Refer to Chapter 2, Principles 18 and 19.

trophic green plants. The cell of the heterotrophic organism requires preformed, ready-made fuels of macromolecules such as carbohydrates, proteins, and fats. Heterotrophic cells receive their energy by oxidizing those complex molecules in the respiratory process that makes use of molecular oxygen from the atmosphere. The energy the cells obtain in this process is used for whatever is needed to live. In return the cells give off carbon dioxide as an end product, which is used by autotrophic cells in making glucose and the more complex molecules. In this way the cellular energy cycle of life involves the acquiring of sunlight energy by autotroph (green plants) directly and by animal cells indirectly.

The problem of the cell is to collect this energy from the complex molecules and package it in convenient units for efficient use. This requires intricate processes of many steps, as summarized below. This is not done in a random, hodge-podge manner by throwing the constituents together and extracting their energy. Enzymes so necessary for every step of the process are not randomly distributed within the cell but are located in various cell compartments and isolated regions. This intracellular differentiation is made possible by intracellular membranes that dispose the compartments in orderly fashion within the macromolecular framework of the cell and among the cell organoids.

The four phases of cellular respiration of carbohydrates are as follows:

1. **Glucose phosphorylation**—formation of glucose-6-phosphate synthesized by the combination of ATP with glucose molecules
2. **Glycolysis**—changes in which glucose phosphate undergoes a series of chemical reactions resulting in the formation of pyruvic acid and the release of energy
3. **Krebs cycle**—oxidation of pyruvic acid and the splitting off of hydrogen and carbon dioxide with the release of energy
4. **Hydrogen and electron transfer**—removal of hydrogen atoms and their electrons and their transport by a metabolic pathway to their union with oxygen and the formation of water and the release of energy

There are three basic mechanisms to be considered in the overall picture of cellular metabolism: (1) enzyme activity, (2) the sequence coding of proteins and enzymes, and (3) the absorption (diffusion) and distribution of nutrients, or metabolites. To a certain extent these three basic mechanisms are spatially distributed within the cell. Since enzymes are involved in every cell activity, whether it be the decomposition of macromolecules or their synthesis, changes in chemical bonding, etc., they have a wide distribution in the cell. Certain enzyme systems have localized regions in which they operate, but most of them are wherever the action is. Krebs citric acid cycle, the great biochemical machine for recovering energy contained in foodstuffs, is located in the mitochondria. Many aspects of enzyme localization, however, have not gone beyond the speculative stage.

Sequence coding involves the nucleic acid of the nucleus, but only the gene transcription is so located, since the protein or enzyme synthesis is located mainly in the cytoplasmic ribosomes. The site of transfer and ribosomal RNA synthesis appears to be the nucleolus. Messenger RNA is a specific coding assembly formed in the transcription of the code.

Nutrients are absorbed from the cellular environment that is usually the body fluids. Such metabolites are almost always individual molecules or ions, and their diffusion is controlled by membranes. Absorption takes place in different ways. It may be partly osmosis, as is the case with water; some compounds dissolved in water are absorbed partly by simple diffusion, or absorption may involve energy-consuming active transport. Respiratory gases (O_2 and CO_2) are exchanged by diffusion due to the pressure or tension gradient of the gas involved, that is, oxygen into the cell and CO_2 from the cell. Another important site in cellular metabolism is the place where phosphorylation occurs. This is the chemical addition of a phosphate or high energy group to a molecule, that is, glucose, which is a convenient means of storing and distributing energy in cells. This important process may occur at the cell surface and give rise to glucose-6-phosphate. After a metabolite has entered a cell, its intracellular distribution takes place by diffusion and enables the organic nutrients to reach the mitochondria where the Krebs cycle and respiratory pathway are located.

It is thus seen that the nutrients we take into our cells must have two requirements. One of these is the oxidative destruction of carbon—carbon bonds for producing utilizable forms of energy; the other is the formation of carbon—carbon bonds in the synthesis of cell constituents. One tears down and the other builds up. At present, our atmosphere favors oxidation, but in the early history of our planet, according to present ideas about the origin of life, the atmosphere was highly reducing and organic molecules that must now be synthesized by cells were formed spontaneously.

Historic background of cellular metabolism

The phenomenon of metabolism is so complex that an immense amount of background development of ideas over long periods of time was necessary. No one individual could comprehend the vast range of the metabolic concept because it involved an understanding of life itself, a problem that is far from being resolved at present. A whole host of investigators in many disciplines have been involved in unraveling this great mystery, which with its related problem, the genetic transcription of inheritance, may be considered the greatest achievement of man's mind and activity. All of this amazing discovery has been worked out little by little. Here one investigator worked out one aspect and there another. In the end the ideas were put together into a unified concept, a single system that seems to bear out the great Newtonian maxim, "Nature is simple enough." But to work out the details of this process was not simple and many hypotheses were formulated and demolished before facts began to fall into place.

Many concepts had to be worked out and understood on the long road to an understanding of metabolism. There had to be explained, first of all, just what was involved in chemical reactions, the thermodynamic laws of matter, the concept of energy, the ability to transform one kind of energy into another, the course of physicochemical change, the chemical exchanges between cell and environment, the nature of catalytic action, how organic reactions released free energy only in living organisms, and especially the processes of respiration, fermentation, and photosynthesis. Full explanations of many of these concepts are still forthcoming, but vital progress has been made. Those who contributed to the structural foundation of this master concept are legion, but certainly such names as Lavoisier, von Liebig, Wöhler, Berzelius, Bernard, von Helmholtz, and Pasteur will rank high in the development of biochemistry, the science concerned with chemical processes in living matter and with the organic products of organisms. In a more specific way, studies on putrefaction and fermentation, with their relations to spontaneous generation, were fundamental in initiating basic concepts about the whole problem of metabolism. L. Pasteur's outstanding investigation (1860-1876) on the relationship between yeast cells and fermentation and the kind of microorganism determining the formation of lactic acid or alcohol enabled him to generalize that the maintenance of life required either respiration or fermentation. E. Buchner (1896) and later A. Harden extended Pasteur's work by showing that cell-free extracts of yeast, or zymase (enzymes), were nonliving and how the phosphorylation of the glucose molecule occurs. In the meantime, work on biologic catalysts by such investigators as J. J. Berzelius (1837) and M. Berthelot had shown them to be definite biologic entities. They were called "enzymes" by W. Kühne (1878) and J. B. Sumner isolated the first enzyme (urease) in 1926.

That muscle contraction as well as fermentation produces lactic acid was shown by F. G. Hopkins (1907). The relation between the amount of lactic acid produced and the amount of glycogen used up was worked out by O. Meyerhof, who also indicated that the first stage of energy metabolism of muscle was anaerobic (without oxygen) (1920). Oxygen is later used to oxidize the accumulated lactic acid (Fig. 6-6). With G. Embden, Meyerhof (1920-1940) worked out the sequence of reactions that can operate anaerobically in what is now called the Embden-Meyerhof pathway of glycolysis. The actual enzymes in the sequence of steps in the pathway was largely the work of C. Cori (1945).

FIG. 6-6

Lactic acid accumulates in a working muscle (anaerobic glycolysis or Embden-Meyerhof glycolytic pathway) and is also produced by certain bacteria, as in souring of milk. Part of lactic acid remaining after aerobic respiration in muscle contraction is oxidized to release energy for reconversion of remaining lactic acid to glycogen.

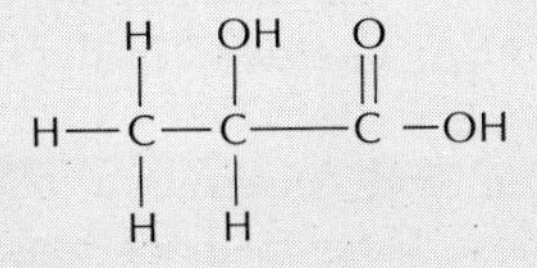

The aerobic part of respiration received a tremendous impetus when H. Krebs announced the citric acid cycle (Krebs cycle) (1937). This is an oxygen-requiring continuation of the Embden-Meyerhof pathway. It carries to completion the lactic acid and pyruvic acid, the end products of anaerobic glycolysis, to CO_2 and water. F. Lipmann (1945), who discovered acetyl-coenzyme A, was the one who linked the glycolytic pathway and the citric acid cycle together. O. Warburg (1926) discovered the nature and mode of action of Warburg's yellow respiratory enzyme, an iron-containing enzyme involved in the oxidation of foodstuffs in the presence of free oxygen. He devised the helpful respirometer (Warburg apparatus) that measures the pressure of gas at constant volume and temperature (1923). The respiratory pigments, cytochromes, were rediscovered by D. Keilin (1925). The work of both Warburg and Keilin is chiefly concerned with the respiratory chain, or electron transfer system, that is normally coupled to the Krebs cycle. Along this chain a series of oxidations and reductions occurs on the waste hydrogen and its electrons, and the final energy of the food molecule is locked in the high-energy bonds of ATP.

How extensive the investigation on this concept of metabolism has been is indicated by the awarding of some fifteen Nobel prizes to those who gave key insights into its nature.

Methods used for metabolic discovery

Biochemists use a variety of methods in their investigations. Some fields of investigations lend themselves to special types of methods. New methods in histochemistry and bioanalysis are constantly advanced as the researcher becomes familiar with the material on which he is working. Whatever method he employs, he must constantly be on the guard against the introduction of artifacts or contaminations of his material from unrelated sources. Checking and rechecking must constantly be done, not only by himself, but by comparisons with the work of others interested in the same field of investigation.

The precise identification and localization of enzymes is absolutely necessary. Here methods must be employed that will not inactivate enzymatic action because enzymes are very sensitive to many kinds of reagents. The right kind of substrate must also be determined. Unfixed frozen sections are made in a cryostat, and techniques for identifying and localizing enzymes are made by specific analytical methods. Incubation of tissue sections with a given substrate is found useful for some enzymes. Many cell components can be separated by differential centrifugation, and the spectroscope will reveal characteristic bands in the substance examined. Many cell components will absorb ultraviolet light specifically. The absorption range, for instance, for nucleic acid is different from that of proteins.

The tracer method of using radioactive isotopes is a favorable one in many investigations. Traceable atoms commonly used are C^{14}, H^3 (tritium), S^{35}, K^{42}, Zn^{65}, and others. Such radioactive atoms have been used successfully in recent years when they are tagged to certain molecules and their distribution determined in the intermediate products of a pathway.

These methods and many others will give the student some idea of the immense work that must be done to find the intermediate steps in such complicated series of reactions involved in glycolysis and the citric acid cycle of Krebs.

The metabolic process*

Although ordinary combustion or burning of fuels is similar in some ways to the respiratory process of metabolism, there are certain fundamental differences. In combustion many chemical bonds are broken simultaneously, releasing the energy with a great deal of heat. In respiration, on the other hand, the energy is released gradually by breaking bonds one after another (Fig. 6-7). Temperatures can thus be kept low. Furthermore, respiration consists of a series of enzymatic reactions that control each step of the process. Most of the energy of combustion is dissipated as heat, whereas metabolic energy creates new chemical bonds and loses little energy as heat. By placing the energy in small packages (chemical bonds), cellular metabolism can transfer energy to wherever the cell needs it. However, in the two processes of combustion and cellular oxidation, the potential energy within a given amount of an organic compound will always yield the same amount of energy, whether by one process or the other. This is in accordance with the first law of thermodynamics.

When chemical bonds are broken, this energy is removed from a bond by the process of dehydrogenation,

*Refer to Chapter 2, Principles 2 and 19.

in which 2 electrons and 2 protons, or 2 hydrogen atoms, are removed together. A common hydrogen acceptor is oxygen. Other substances also serve as hydrogen acceptors. These electrons are transferred to oxygen by a system of enzymes that form an electron transmitter system (Fig. 6-8). Hydrogenation in cellular metabolism is effected and continued throughout life by enzymatic reactions and not by heat, which initiates ordinary combustion by breaking bonds. The electron transmitter system is made up of several components, each of which passes the electrons along from the primary hydrogen acceptors to oxygen, which is the final acceptor. Dehydrogenation involves the common chemical processes of oxidation and reduction. Whenever oxidation occurs, there must also be reduction because electrons do not exist in a free state. Thus electrons pass in the transmitter system by a series of oxidation-reduction reactions. In this way, as a result of oxidation, the fuel molecules are broken down into smaller fragments and energy is released step by step. Most of the energy is converted to chemical bond energy in particular molecules. In general the energy is transferred to adenosine triphosphate (ATP), where it can be converted to other forms of energy as needed. ATP is a high-energy molecule and is the chief product of the respiratory process.

The chemical reactions of metabolism may take place in the absence of oxygen (fermentation) or in its presence (respiration). In fermentation, yeast cells, or the zymase enzymes from them, will ferment glucose, producing alcohol and carbon dioxide ($C_6H_{12}O_6 \rightarrow 2C_2H_5OH + 2CO_2$). Early organisms lived without free oxygen, as do some bacteria and others today (anaerobic respiration) (Fig. 6-9). Most animals, however, are aerobic and require oxygen for their survival, although some of the tissues and cells of aerobes can tolerate a lack of oxygen for a time. Whether or not oxygen is present has a bearing on cellular metabolism because oxygen is the normal outlet for hydrogen; but when it is not available, another final acceptor, such as pyruvic acid (Fig. 6-10), is used, as in glycolysis to be described later.

The rate of respiration is influenced by a number of factors. In cold-blooded animals at least, the rate increases with a rise of environmental temperature, usually by a factor of two respirations for each 10° C. rise in temperature within the viable range of the animal. Environmental temperature has little effect on

FIG. 6-7

How energy is released gradually in respiration instead of all at once, as in a fire.

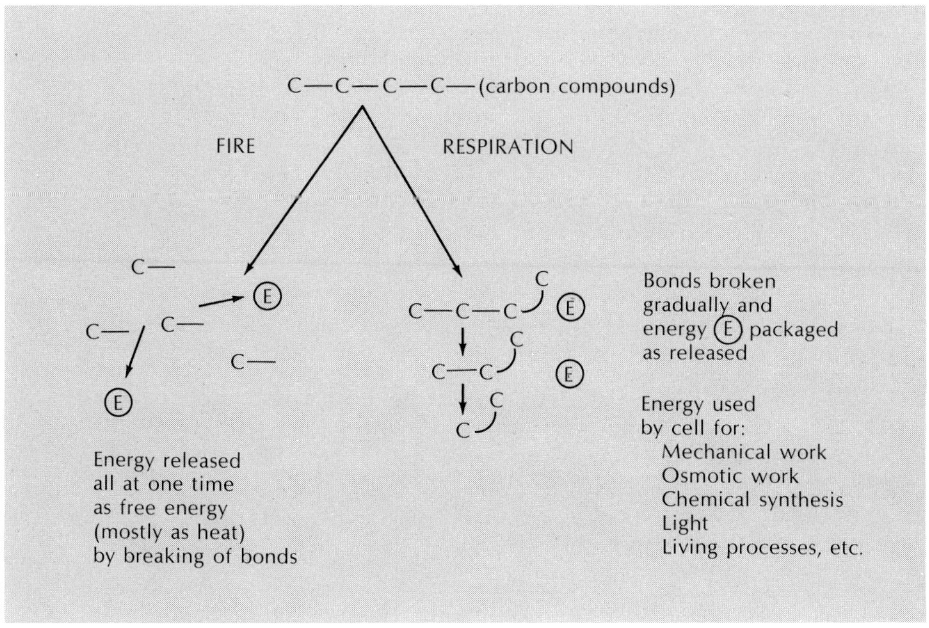

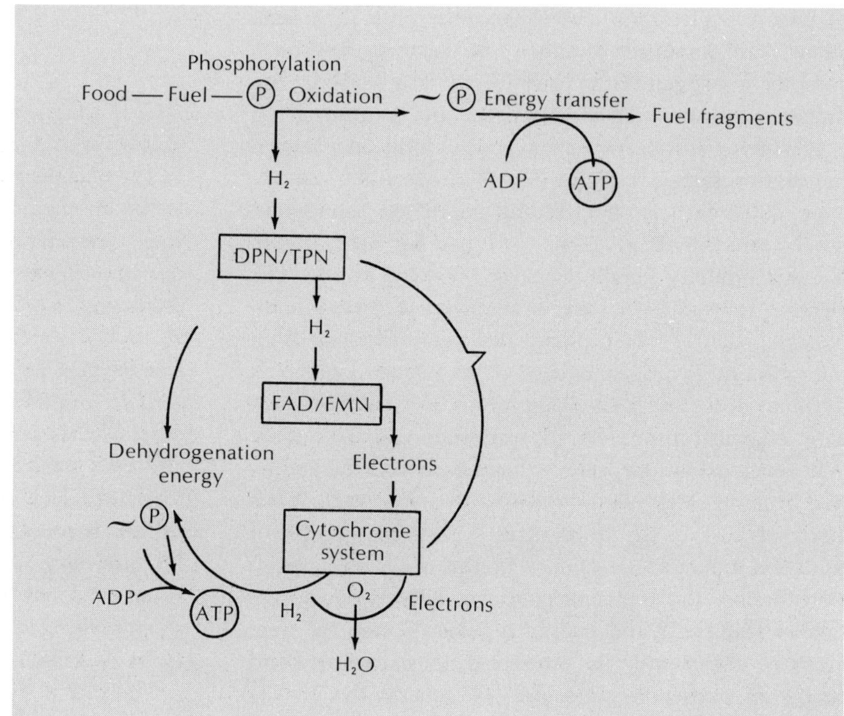

FIG. 6-8

Aerobic respiration showing scheme of hydrogen or electron transport system and trapping of energy-rich phosphate bonds. Actual hydrogen carriers consist of three series—pyridine nucleotides (DPN/TPN), flavins (FAD/FMN), and cytochromes. There are two sources of ATP formation. One is oxidation of food —fuel by H_2 removal; the other is dehydrogenation energy from hydrogen transfer.

FIG. 6-9

Anaerobic respiration showing scheme of hydrogen transport and trapping of high-energy ATP molecules. Anaerobic respiration is same up to DPN hydrogen acceptor, but without oxygen (fermentation) it uses alternate hydrogen acceptor (pyruvic acid) instead of FAD/FMN, the normal outlet of hydrogen. When pyruvic acid reacts with hydrogen, kind of end products (lactic acid, alcohol, CO_2) depends upon enzymes involved. Anaerobic respiration or fermentation produces little energy gain (only about 5%) compared with aerobic respiration (95%), because there is no oxygen acceptor for hydrogen, and fermentation does not continue beyond lactic acid or alcohol stage that still contains great deal of energy.

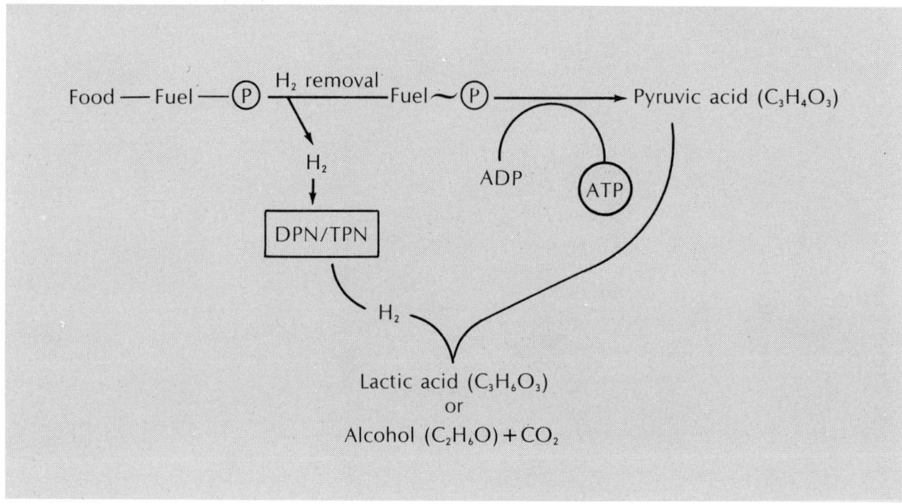

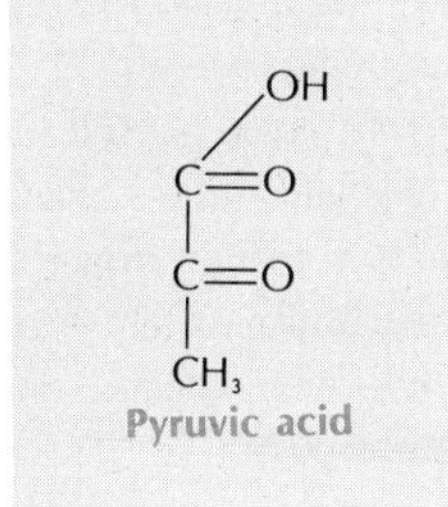

FIG. 6-10

Pyruvic acid is important in metabolic reactions. Three radicals, keto (—C=O), methyl (—CH_3), and carboxyl (—COOH), enable it to react in many ways. When no oxygen is present, it can, with the aid of enzymes, be converted into lactic acid or some alcohol, etc. In presence of oxygen and certain enzymes, pyruvic acid unites with coenzyme A to form acetyl-CoA. When this compound loses a molecule of CO_2, it enters the Krebs cycle.

regulated temperature, such as that of warm-blooded forms. The rate of respiration increases as the size of the animal decreases because the animal loses heat through its surface, and the smaller it is the larger is its surface in proportion to its volume.

A discussion of the general nature of enzymes has already been given, but a few other particulars may be pointed out here. Since oxidations perform most of the energy of the cell, the oxidases and other oxidative enzymes represent a unique group of the utmost importance. These enzymes consist of a protein carrier and a prosthetic group (often called a coenzyme). The prosthetic group is of special interest because it usually contains one of the members of the vitamin B group, such as thiamine, niacin, and pantothenic acid. Such enzymes usually have a high degree of specificity and act only on a certain substrate. They are very sensitive and easily inactivated by other molecules that differ slightly from their normal substrate as well as by strong acids and bases. The specificity of the relationship of an enzyme to its substrate was explained by E. Fisher as being similar to a lock-and-key mechanism, and mechanical models were formulated to account for the reaction. A more fruitful idea, enzyme-substrate complex, was advanced in 1913 by L. Michaelis who, by mathematical and inductive reasoning, calculated the relationship that existed between enzyme concentration, substrate concentration, and velocity of the reaction. That such an enzyme-substrate complex does exist for a fleeting instant has been verified by the direct evidence of D. Keilin and B. Chance who demonstrated its presence by color changes. According to the scheme proposed, the intermediate enzyme-substrate complex decomposes quickly to release the free enzyme. This intermediate complex is thought to promote the reactivity of the substrate.

Stages of cellular metabolism

The whole process in the utilization of fuel foods may be divided into three major stages. In the first or preparatory stage, complex molecules are broken down into a simple, common unit by special enzymes. The second stage, called glycolysis or anaerobic (fermentation) process, and the third stage, or citric acid cycle of Krebs (aerobic) (Fig. 6-11), are concerned primarily with the liberation and trapping of energy.

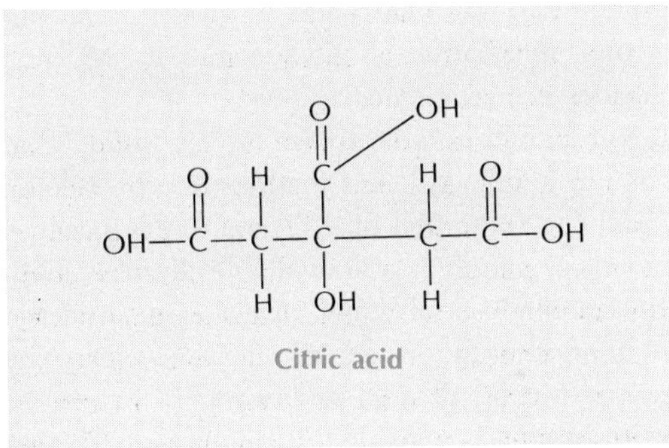

FIG. 6-11

Citric acid plays important part in energy-releasing processes in cells. It is found in citrus fruits. Another name for the Krebs cycle is the citric acid cycle.

Since carbohydrates are the chief respiratory fuels, their metabolism may be taken as the type example of the process (Fig. 6-13). If the fuel material is glycogen (starch), these complex molecules are broken down into glucose that is energy rich to start with. Although glycogen may be phosphorylated directly, it is usually in the form of glucose that is converted to glucose-phosphate, the phosphate being drawn from the mineral of the cell or from ATP. This glucose-phosphate molecule is a low-energy compound, and the process by which it is formed is called phosphorylation. Then in a series of several steps, each with a specific enzyme, the glucose-phosphate molecule is broken down into a series of compounds terminating in pyruvic acid. In some of these steps, energy is liberated and trapped in the energy-rich phosphate bonds of ATP (Fig. 6-12). However, in glycolysis the amount of energy released per mole (molecular weight of the glucose in grams) is much less than the original glucose. The total amount of energy in a mole of glucose is about 690,000 calories, but only about 20,000 to 50,000 calories per mole are released in this second stage, which is commonly represented as the Embden-Meyerhof system of glycolysis. Most of the energy released in this metabolic stairway of glucose-phosphate to pyruvic acid is trapped in the high-energy bonds of ATP. Altogether, about 4 ATP molecules are formed during glycolysis, but 2 of these are expended for energy in the chemical reactions of the pathway. Thus there is a net gain of 2 ATP molecules in this breakdown of glucose to pyruvic acid, a process that involves the phosphorylation of glucose and its splitting into 2 molecules of pyruvic acid.

The student should be able to see, at this point, that glycolysis is not a very efficient method for the release of energy and the formation of ATP molecules because a great amount of energy is still available. Pyruvic acid, the oxidative metabolism of which furnishes most of the phosphate bond energy in aerobic animals, may be metabolized to carbon dioxide and water if oxygen is present; if no oxygen is available, it might then be metabolized to alcohol, acetic acid, lactic acid, or other products, depending on the enzyme present. These anaerobic or fermentation products still contain a great deal of energy.

The next stage in the metabolism of glucose is known as the Krebs citric acid cycle, which is the major energy-yielding process (Fig. 6-14). It is also the stage in which other routes of cellular metabolism converge because it also handles the products of amino acids and fatty acids. The intermediate pyruvic acid molecule is oxidized in this stage, which is presided over by a series of enzymes mostly furnished by the mitochondria of the cell. It has been possible to separate mitochondria from other cell components and to study their chemical properties. The rat liver cell, a common object of study, contains about 1,000 mitochondria. They contain many enzymes and coenzymes that appear to be arranged on the infolded membranes that are found in the interior of each mitochondrion. In the Krebs cycle the pyruvic acid (by losing CO_2) is first converted to acetic acid (2 carbons) that reacts with coenzyme A (from the vitamin pantothenic acid) to form acetyl coenzyme A (2 carbons). The latter then unites with oxaloacetic acid (4 carbons), which is a normal constituent of cells, to form citric acid (6 carbons). Then in a cyclic series of steps, each controlled by a special enzyme or enzymes, the citric acid undergoes a series of rearrangements and degradations, involving at least eight different organic acids, back to oxaloacetic acid, which then can continue the cycle again. The energy released in the Krebs cycle is trapped in the high-energy bonds of ATP. Indeed, the Krebs cycle is an endless cyclic process into which acetic acid from glucose is continually poured and degraded into H, CO_2, and energy. As already mentioned, the process of glycolysis produced only a net gain of 2 ATP molecules, but the various reactions of the Krebs cycle yields 36 more ATP molecules, totaling 38 molecules per mole of glucose. Thus the respiratory cycle is by far the chief source of energy conversion because 38 molecules of ATP represent about 456,000 calories or about 66% of the potential energy of a mole of glucose. This indicates that respiration has an efficiency of 66% in salvaging energy in high-energy phosphate bonds. This efficiency, however, is somewhat lessened when ATP is degraded to ADP in performing useful work. However, man-made machines lose a far greater amount of energy as heat instead of in useful work.

In glycolysis and especially in the citric acid cycle there are many energy-releasing oxidations in which the hydrogen atoms are stripped off the glucose fragments (dehydrogenation) and carbon dioxide is formed. Excess water and CO_2 pass into the cytoplasm, but the hydrogen atoms are carried by the flavoprotein and cytochrome systems of enzymes to oxygen, which is the final hydrogen acceptor. The dehydrogenation reactions in the metabolic cycle are actually oxidations in which electrons are released from a molecule. Such electrons cannot exist in a free state and must be received at once by the hydrogen or electron acceptors. When hydrogen is removed from a fuel molecule, the first hydrogen acceptors are diphosphopyridine nucleotide (DPN) and triphosphopyridine nucleotide (TPN) (Fig. 6-9). These contain the vitamin niacin as part of their structure. From these acceptors the hydrogens are passed on to the flavin nucleotides (flavin adenine dinucleotide, or FAD) and flavin mononucleotide (FMN) (Fig. 6-15). These acceptors are also derived from another vitamin B—riboflavin. In the absence of oxygen the

DPN/TPN may pass the hydrogen to any available acceptor such as acetaldehyde to form alcohol (yeast cells) or to pyruvic acid to form lactic acid (muscle) (Fig. 6-9). In such cases no high-energy phosphates are formed. When oxygen is present, the flavoproteins liberate hydrogen ions into the cytoplasm and electrons to the cytochrome system, a series of four or more cell pigments. The cytochromes are red tetrapyrol pigments containing iron and are also found in the electron-carrying system of photosynthesis. In the presence of free oxygen and the enzyme cytochrome oxidase, the cytochrome passes its hydrogen or electrons to oxygen to form water as a by-product of respiration. Thus oxygen acts as the final hydrogen acceptor. At each step during the passage of the electrons through the flavoprotein and cytochrome systems, high-energy phosphate bonds (ATP) are formed and added to the total ATP molecules.

It is well at this point to note that the high-energy phosphate storage system of the cell is made up of three major compounds: adenosine disphosphate (ADP), with one low-energy and one high-energy phosphate; adenosine triphosphate (ATP), with an additional high-energy phosphate; and phosphagens (phosphocreatine and phosphoarginine), with one high-energy phosphate (Fig. 6-12). Phosphocreatine is formed by the reaction of the organic base creatine with ATP and is primarily characteristic of vertebrate muscle. Phosphoarginine is formed when arginine and ATP react and is more characteristic of invertebrate muscle. However, evolutionary significance of the phosphagens is not stressed at present. Phosphagens make up about 0.5% of muscle and furnish a reserve of high-energy phosphates for ADP

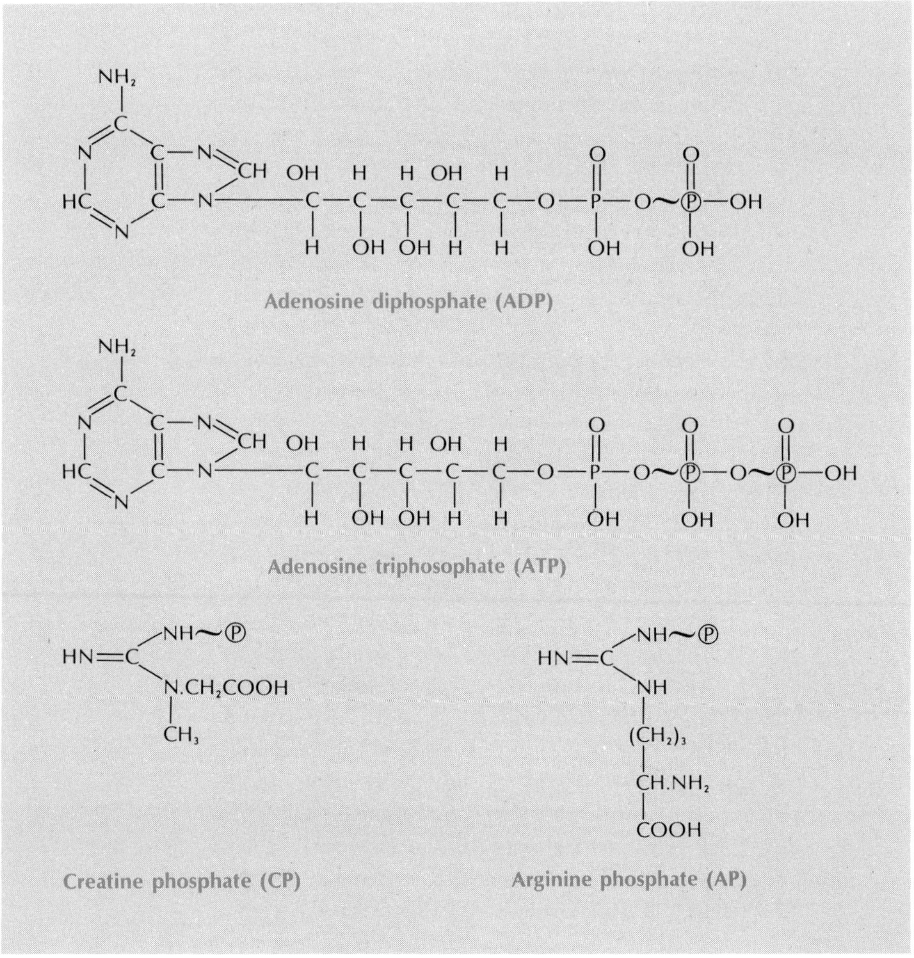

Adenosine diphosphate (ADP)

Adenosine triphosophate (ATP)

Creatine phosphate (CP)

Arginine phosphate (AP)

FIG. 6-12

High-energy phosphate storage system of cell. The ~Ⓟ represents high-energy phosphates. Phosphogens (CP or AP) furnish reserve for high-energy phosphates when ADP is converted to ATP.

when the latter is converted to ATP in muscular contraction.

What is the advantage of such a complicated mechanism of energy release and the many chemical reactions associated with it? Many aspects of the process and the varied pathways are still unknown. New facets are added each year. Only the general overall pattern has been presented in this brief outline. Energy is needed in every cellular process for the maintenance of the cell. It will be noted that ATP serves as the chief source of work. As it gives up its energy, it is degraded to ADP and inorganic phosphate. In return the ADP picks up high-energy phosphate from the phophagens or metabolic reactions. The process of releasing and storing the energy in the breakdown of a fuel molecule is done with amazing speed. The more obvious advantages and general significance of biologic oxidation are the efficient conversion of the energy into small-change currency for cellular utilization, the relative small amount of heat loss by the stepwise character of the process, and the production of intermediate raw materials of simpler structures than the original fuel molecules for the cell's general economy. It is evident that these factors would be impossible if the energy was released by a one-step combustion. Moreover, the method not only supplies energy in a usable form, but it is able to rapidly regulate its production to the activity of the organism.

Summaries of the glycolytic pathway, Krebs cycle, and the electron transport chain as involved in cellular metabolism are herewith presented.

Summary of glycolytic pathway (Fig. 6-13)

Glycogen is broken down into glucose that undergoes phosphorylation with the addition of a phosphate group (H_2PO_3) from ATP. In this process the third phosphate group of ATP is transferred to the glucose to form glucose phosphate and is reduced to ADP with one high-energy bond. Glucose phosphate thus becomes the activated form of glucose. Another molecule of ATP adds another phosphate group to form fructose diphosphate that splits into two 3-carbon molecules (phosphoglyceraldehyde and dihydroxyacetone phosphate), each with a phosphate group and interconvertible. Each of these molecules has the same fate, so only phosphoglyceraldehyde is followed in the scheme, but all reactants and products are doubled for the rest of the process. Each phosphoglyceraldehyde molecule has a phosphate group from inorganic phosphoric acid (H_3PO_4) added and by the removal of two H ions becomes diphosphoglyceric acid. When a high-energy phosphate is transferred to ATP, 3-phosphoglyceric acid is formed. The phosphate group in the latter molecule is shifted to another position to form 2-phosphoglyceric acid. An H and an OH ion are removed (oxidative dehydration) at this stage so that 4 H's altogether are given off in glycolysis. Phosphopyruvic acid is formed as a result. Since phosphopyruvic acid has a high-energy

FIG. 6-13

Glycolytic pathway.

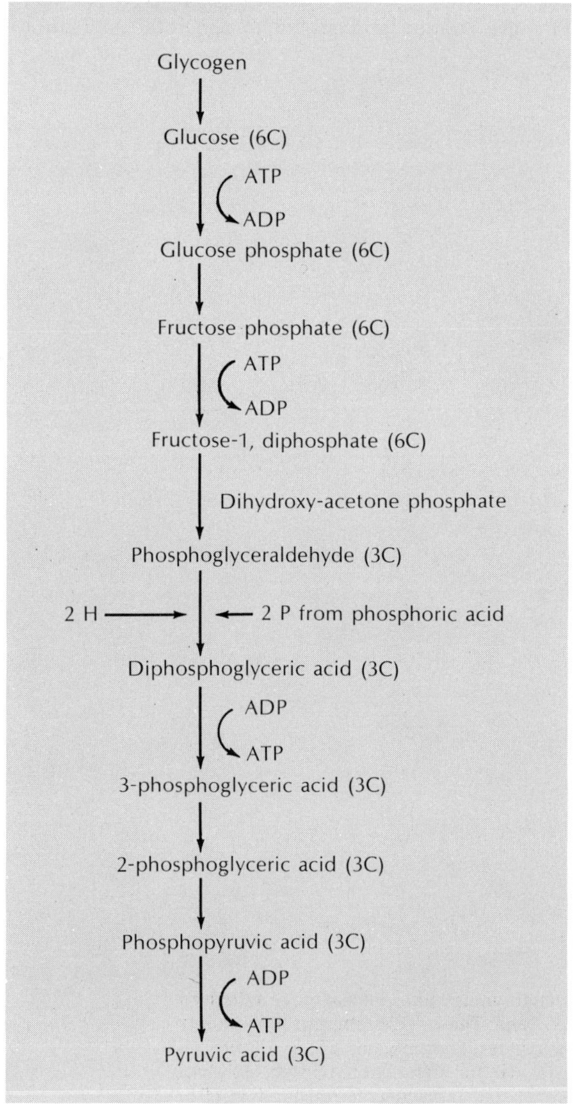

phosphate group when this latter is transferred to ADP, the end products are ATP and pyruvic acid—the termination of the glycolytic path. Note that 2 ATP molecules are used up and 4 ATP molecules are produced with a net gain of 2 ATP molecules in this pathway.

Summary of Krebs cycle (Fig. 6-14)

Only part of the energy of the glucose molecule is released by glycolysis that takes place in the cytoplasm. The end product of glycolysis is pyruvic acid that becomes the most important source of energy in all aerobic cells. The 3-carbon pyruvic acid passes from the cytoplasm into the mitochondria that have enzyme systems for utilizing molecular oxygen and pyruvic acid. Pyruvic acid now undergoes an oxidation reaction in which both hydrogen and CO_2 are removed, leaving the remnant acetyl. The latter joins with coenzyme A to form acetyl-CoA. Acetyl-CoA occupies a central position in intermediary metabolism and is the principal mechanism for building carbon chains in cells. It is also involved in the breakdown of fatty acids and amino acids. Acetyl-CoA (2C) enters the Krebs citric acid cycle by combining with oxaloacetic acid (4C) to form citric acid (6C). The citric acid cycle is a circular pattern of sequential reactions that yields energy in the transformation of pyruvic acid, during which many intermediate products are formed. In these reactions the potential energy of pyruvic molecules is given up in small amounts in the formation of ATP. The citric acid cycle consists of nine consecutive steps, consisting of four 6-carbon acids, one 5-carbon acid, and four 4-carbon acids. In the course of these reactions (each under a specific enzyme), two molecules of CO_2 are released, and four pairs of hydrogen removed for each molecule of acetyl-CoA that enters the cycle at the start. The last of the 4-carbon molecules is oxaloacetic acid, which is free to combine with more acetyl-CoA to start the cycle over. For every mole of glucose (180 grams per liter) that enters the cycle as pyruvic acid, there are 36 moles of ATP produced.

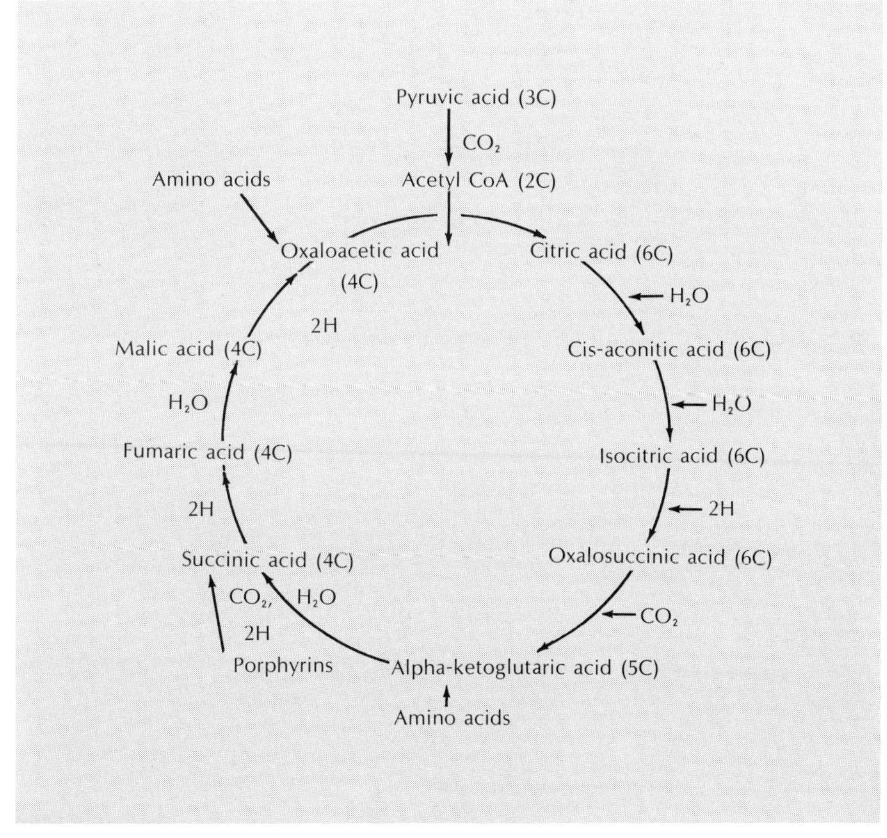

FIG. 6-14
Krebs citric acid cycle.

Summary of electron transport system

FIG. 6-15

Processes of glycolysis and Krebs citric acid cycle involve removal of hydrogen atoms and their electrons from a food substance, resulting in release of energy and elimination of carbon dioxide as a waste. Process of releasing hydrogen is dehydrogenation, which involves enzymes—dehydrogenases. Hydrogen ions and their electrons are now channeled into a metabolic pathway (stages 1 to 9) that eventually leads to their union with oxygen to form water. Before hydrogen combines with oxygen to form water, it reacts with a number of compounds embracing transfer of a pair of electrons and hydrogen atoms from donor to acceptor in chain with help of an enzyme.

In stage 1 a pair of hydrogen ions already released by glycolysis is transferred to a hydrogen acceptor, coenzyme NAD, or nicotinamide adenine dinucleotide, which is reduced to form $NADH_2$.

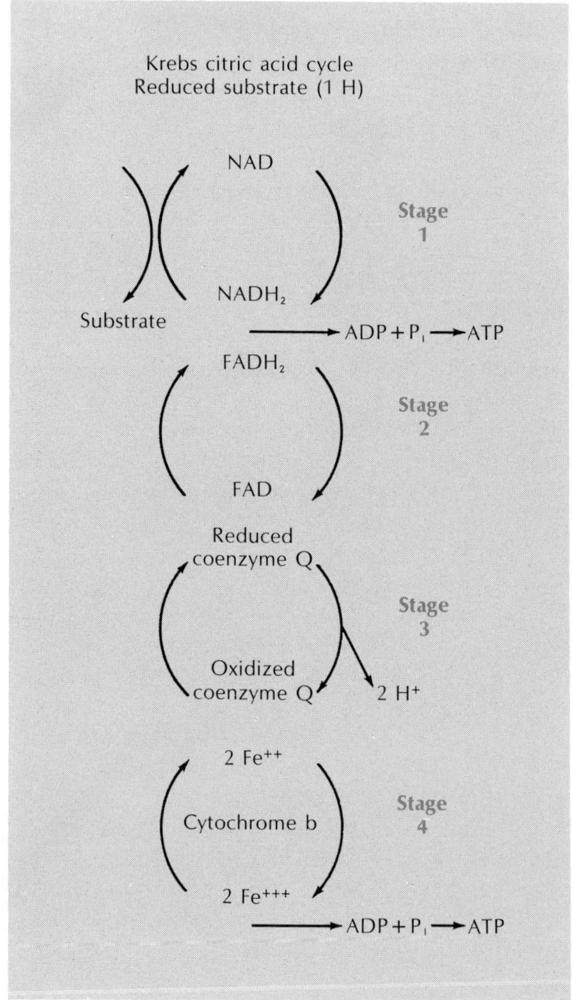

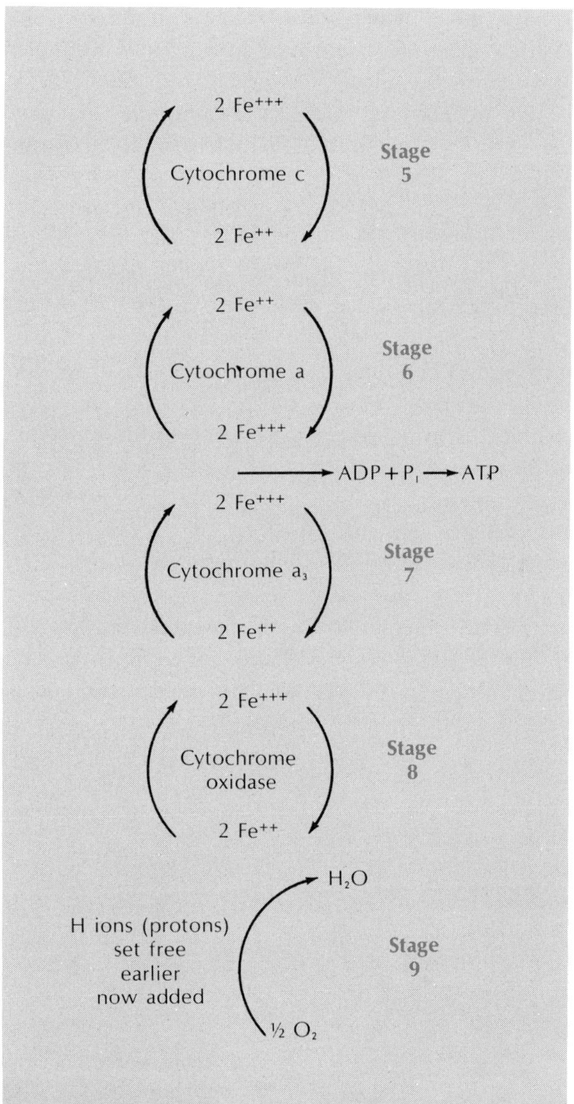

Next stage (2) is oxidation of $NADH_2$ and passing of its hydrogens to flavoproteins that contain vitamin riboflavin. From the flavoprotein (FAD, or flavine adenine dinucleotide), hydrogen (protons) is passed to cell cytoplasm as hydrogen ion (H^+), while electrons are sent to coenzyme Q (a quinone) (stage 3).

Electrons are now passed through a series of cytochromes that are iron-containing proteins (stages 4 to 7). Iron is center of porphyrin group. During electron transfer, iron changes its valence from Fe^{++} (electron added) to Fe^{+++} (electron removed). Several cytochromes are involved, since iron atom shifts from one valence to another.

Electrons are finally passed to cytochrome oxidase (stage 8), which transfers them to acceptor oxygen. Oxygen then unites with hydrogen atoms (protons) set free earlier in cytoplasm, to form water (stage 9).

In this transfer pathway, 3 additional molecules of ATP are produced at sites indicated by arrows (following stages 1, 4, and 6).

Annotated references

Baldwin, E. 1957. Dynamic aspects of biochemistry, ed. 3. New York, Cambridge University Press. *One of the best texts for the general zoology student. The most recent work on the highly important subject of enzymes is dealt with in a clear, well-balanced manner.*

Brachet, J. 1957. Biochemical cytology. New York, Academic Press, Inc. *An advanced work on the morphology and biochemistry of the cell. The author summarizes in admirable fashion the great strides made in this field during the past few decades but also warns that many of our concepts will no doubt be radically changed in the future.*

Brachet, J., and A. E. Mirsky. 1959. The cell: biochemistry, physiology, morphology. New York, Academic Press, Inc. *This is the first volume of a planned three-volume work on the various aspects of the cell and deals with the methods used in cytology and with some of the problems of cell biology. It is an ambitious work and should be a useful tool to many generations of biologists.*

Butler, J. A. V. 1964. Inside the living cell. Some secrets of life, ed. 2. New York, Basic Books, Inc. *This little volume will appeal to any ambitious zoology student who is interested in the scientist's present knowledge of the fundamental processes of life. "Multum in parvo" should be the subtitle of this revealing book.*

Giese, A. C. 1962. Cell physiology, ed. 2. Philadelphia, W. B. Saunders Co. *An account of the latest concepts in cell physiology for students who have had good introductory courses in chemistry and physics.*

Guthe, K. F. 1968. The physiology of cells. (Paperback.) New York, The Macmillan Co.

Levine, L. (editor). 1962. The cell in mitosis. New York, Academic Press, Inc. *The more complicated aspects of cell division are treated by various specialists in this field.*

McElroy, W. D. 1964. Cell physiology and biochemistry. (Paperback.) ed. 2. Englewood Cliffs, N. J., Prentice-Hall, Inc.

Scientific American. 1961. The cell, vol. 205, pp. 50-137. *Articles by many specialists on the various aspects of the cell from present knowledge.*

Swanson, C. P. 1964. The cell, ed. 2. Englewood Cliffs, N. J., Prentice-Hall, Inc. *A good introduction to the amazing concepts that have arisen in recent years from the study of molecular biology.*

Trumbore, R. H. 1966. The cell: chemistry and function. St. Louis, The C. V. Mosby Co. *A good basic, well-organized text, with summaries, on all aspects of the cell.*

CHAPTER 7

• ARCHITECTURAL PATTERN OF AN ANIMAL

FUNDAMENTAL UNIFORMITY AMONG ANIMALS*

● All animals have the same general plan, differing only in modification. There is a principle of uniformity throughout all biologic organization. Of course there is a vast range of complexity between a protozoan and man, but the same life processes are found in each. Although structural plans among animals vary, the organs are concerned with the same functions. Tracheal tubes, gills, and lungs, for instance, are all devices for breathing. The form of an animal determines how it meets its environment. Nearly every structure in an animal has a functional or adaptational connotation. The student must not, however, think that structural adaptations are caused by the environment; rather the adaptations arose when, by natural selection, beneficial variations were preserved. This concept will be clearer when evolution is discussed.

GRADES OF STRUCTURE AMONG ANIMALS

There are many grades of structure among animals. Through long geologic periods of time, organic evolution has produced functional and structural adaptations that enable animals to fill a great variety of niches. The fossil record shows that some animals such as lamp shells have persisted unchanged for hundreds of millions of years because they were well adapted to an environmental niche that has changed little during that long time.

The first grade of structure is that between the acellular (protozoa) and the cellular (metazoa). The **acellular** or single-celled forms are complete organisms and carry on all the functions of higher forms. Within the confines of their cell, they often show complicated organization and division of labor, such as skeletal elements, locomotor devices, fibrils, beginnings of sense organs, and many others.

On the other hand, the **metazoan** or multicellular animal has cells differentiated into tissues and organs that are specialized for different functions. The metazoan cell is not the equivalent of a protozoan cell; it is only a specialized part of the whole organism and usually cannot exist by itself.

How has complexity arisen in the animal kingdom? In general, it is a matter of difference in organization, but certain principles are involved. One of these is size, which will be discussed later in this chapter. Another is specialization and division of labor. An ameba can move without muscles, digest food without an alimentary canal, and breathe without gills or lungs. But higher forms have specialized organs for these functions. The more complicated a device becomes, the more necessary it is to have accessory organs to help out. An alimentary canal is not a mere epithelial tube for secretion and absorption but has muscles to manipulate and nerves to control it. Specialization and division of labor have many advantages for adjustments to specific niches, but they require complicated machinery and more energy.

Does this mean that life is progressing toward higher and higher types, such as man? In the evolutionary picture the first animals were small and relatively simple, but there is no reason to believe that more recent animals are better adjusted to their environments than were their ancient ancestors. Nor is there any evidence that evolution has led in man's direction, for many lines definitely have not.

ORGANIZATION OF THE BODY

The body consists of three different elements—body cells, extracellular structural elements, and body fluids. The body fluids include the blood, tissue or intercellular fluid between the cells, and lymph within the lymphatics. An endothelial barrier separates the tissue fluid outside the lymphatics and the lymph within them. There is an exchange of materials between the blood

*Refer to Chapter 2, Principles 7 and 20.

within its cavities and channels and the intracellular (tissue) fluid between the cells. Body fluids fill continuous spaces and are responsible for diffusion and convection.

Intercellular or extracellular substance is the material that lies between the cells. It affords mechanical stability, protection, storage, and exchange agents. It is mainly responsible for the firmness of tissues and gives support to the cells. Two types of intercellular tissue are recognized—formed and amorphous. The formed type includes collagen (white fibrous tissue). This is the most abundant protein in the animal kingdom and makes up the major part of the fibrous constituent of the skin, tendon, ligaments, cartilage, and bone. Elastin, which gives elasticity to the tissues, also belongs to the formed type. Amorphous intercellular substance (ground substance) is composed of mucopolysaccharides arranged in long chain polymers.

The above description applies especially to vertebrates and higher invertebrates. Modifications of this basic plan may be found in the animal kingdom. Unity of pattern is characteristic of the structure of animals, but structural variations do occur in comparative morphology throughout the gamut of animal life. For example, blood and tissue fluid may be identical in arthropods, hemichordates, tunicates, and some others. Some mollusks have the same pattern, but cephalopods have blood and tissue fluid separated by membranes.

PRINCIPLE OF INDIVIDUALITY

All organisms, however simple, are composed of **units** with coordinated interreactions. The smallest units capable of independent existence are the **cells.** Among some biologists the **gene** is considered the chief biologic unit; but many other units are recognized in both acellular and many-celled forms. Protozoans contain such units as the **contractile vacuole, nucleus,** and other organelles. In the metazoans units of different levels are **tissues, organs,** and **systems.** In some phyla **metamerism,** or the serially repeated division of the body into successive segments (as in the earthworm, for example), represents another grade of individuality. In **polymorphism,** there is more than one form of the same species; these may consist of united individuals (Portuguese man-of-war) or they may be separate (certain ant colonies). Individuality is difficult to define because there are many gradations between separate organic entities and those of colonies whose members are attached together in some way. The organism is a historic entity that is made up of many stages in a life cycle, some of which may be very different, for example, the tadpole and frog, the caterpillar and butterfly, etc. Is each stage a separate individual or should the combined stages of a life cycle be considered an individual?

Within the cell itself are many other units. Whether there is an ultimate living unit, biologists do not know.

GRADES OF ORGANIZATION*

An animal is an organization of units differentiated and integrated for carrying on the life processes, but this organization goes from one level to another as we ascend the evolutionary path.

Protoplasmic grade of organization. This type is found in protozoans and other acellular forms. All activities of this level are confined to the one mass called the cell. Here the protoplasm is differentiated into specialized organelles that are capable of carrying on definite functions.

Cellular grade of organization. Here aggregations of cells are differentiated, involving division of labor. Some cells are concerned with reproduction and others with nutrition. The cells have little tendency to become organized into tissues. Some protozoan colonial forms having somatic and reproductive cells might be placed in this category. Many authorities also place the sponges at this level.

Cell-tissue grade of organization. A step beyond the preceding is the aggregation of similar cells into definite patterns of layers, thus becoming a tissue. Sponges are considered by some authorities to belong to this grade, although the jellyfish are usually referred to as the beginning of the tissue plan. Both groups are still largely of the cellular grade of organization because most of the cells are scattered and not organized into tissues. An excellent example of a tissue in coelenterates is the **nerve net,** in which the nerve cells and their processes form a definite tissue structure, with the function of coordination.

Tissue-organ grade of organization. The aggregation of tissues into organs is a further step in advancement. Organs are usually made up of more than one kind of tissue and have a more specialized function than tissues.

*Refer to Chapter 2, Principle 5.

The first appearance of this level is in the flatworms (Platyhelminthes), in which there are a number of well-defined organs such as eyespots, proboscis, and reproductive organs. In fact, the reproductive organs are well organized into a reproductive system.

Organ-system grade of organization. When organs work together to perform some function we have the highest level of organization—the organ system. The systems are associated with the basic bodily functions—circulation, respiration, digestion, etc. Typical of all the higher forms, this type of organization is first seen in the nemertean worms in which a complete digestive system, separate and distinct from the circulatory system, is present.

PRELIMINARY SURVEY OF ANIMAL EMBRYOLOGY*

A brief summary of embryology is necessary for understanding the pattern of an animal and also for understanding some of the basic concepts used in describing animal groups and their classification. Broader problems in this field and those of experimental embryology will be discussed in Chapter 34.

Embryology deals with the development of the organism from the zygote to the completion of its bodily structure. An embryo is the stage of an organism before birth or hatching.

All animals have a characteristic life history. This may be very simple but is often involved in the Metazoa. Many protozoans such as the ameba are potentially immortal and come from an ancestral line that has never experienced natural death from old age because their method of asexual binary reproduction is simply the dividing of the parent organism into two daughter cells, each essentially a continuation of the parent. Early in the life history of all metazoans, however, there occurs a differentiation of the germ cell from the body or soma cells. It is the uniting of the germ cells (male sperm and female ova) that gives rise to a new generation (sexual reproduction), while the body (soma) cells die. The real life history of a metazoan starts with the union of an ovum (egg) with a spermatozoan, a process called fertilization.

Sexual reproduction may be of two types. If the egg develops without fertilization, it is called **parthenogenesis;** if both egg and sperm are involved, it is called **biparental reproduction.** If only one kind of sex cell (egg or sperm) is produced in a single individual, such a condition is called **dioecious;** if both kinds are in the same individual, it is called **monoecious** or **hermaphroditic.**

The fertilized egg, called a **zygote,** is really a one-celled organism, and from it develops a complete animal with all its structures and functions. The major process that makes this possible is **differentiation,** by which the various cells become unlike. How this occurs is only partly known. When a zygote divides into cells (**cleavage**), there is a distribution of different structures and functions to the cells. Both morphologic differentiation and physiologic division of labor thus take place. Some structures and functions are present in the zygote, but many new ones arise from new combinations, for embryology is synthetic. What determines the final animal pattern? Heredity stabilizes the pattern; variation makes evolutionary changes possible.

*Refer to Chapter 2, Principles 9, 22, and 26.

GENERAL PATTERN OF DEVELOPMENT

Ontogeny is the sequence of developmental events in an organism. It should include both the embryonic life and the finished individual. Every animal has its own course of development within the limits of a normal and predictable sequence of morphologic forms from the zygote to the end of life. No one member of a species has a life history exactly like that of others of its species. However, the range of variation within one species is small, since the potentialities of an individual are inherited from the parents with restricted alterations by external forces. The individual characters are coded into the DNA molecule from the start of development.

During development of every species, certain basic characteristics of the phylum appear before the specific qualities of the species appear. Such basic qualities may be symmetry, a longitudinal axis, and if a vertebrate, a notochord, dorsal tubular nerve cord, three major pairs of sensory organs, paired pharyngeal pouches, a chambered heart, a liver, paired kidneys, paired pectoral and pelvic appendages, etc. There are overlappings of some of these characteristics in both vertebrates and invertebrates. As development continues the individual acquires the morphologic characters of its lower taxa (class, order, family, and genera) and finally of his own species. This indicates that development proceeds from the general to the specific in gross morphologic characters. Species-specific characteristics as far as minor features are concerned, on the other hand, may appear quite early.

Mutations or changes in genes are reflected in the developmental patterns of animals. How these changes affect the animal depends on the time in development when they occur. If they occur early in the developmental sequence, they are usually lethal and the animal fails to mature. If they occur later, they may be incorporated into the genotype and produce permanent changes. This may be reflected in longer embryologic sequences of the various stages and produce marked differences in the phylogeny of animals.

Types of eggs and the zygote

Differences in embryonic development depend partly on the type of egg involved. Some eggs have much food material (**yolk**) for the growing embryo; others have little yolk. It is an embryonic principle that the speed of cleavage (the cell division by which the embryo is formed) is inversely proportional to the amount of yolk in the egg.

Eggs may be classified as follows with respect to yolk distribution (Fig. 7-1):

The **isolecithal egg** (also called alecithal or homolecithal) is small, and the small amount of yolk (deutoplasm) and cytoplasm is uniformly distributed through the egg, with the nucleus near the center. Cleavage is usually **holoblastic** (total) and the cells (blastomeres) are nearly equal in size. Such eggs are found in the protochordates (such as sea squirts and *Amphioxus*) and the echinoderms (sea stars and sea urchins).

In the **telolecithal egg** the large amount of yolk (50% to 90%) tends to be concentrated toward one pole (the vegetal pole) where metabolism is lower. The protoplasm and nucleus are found mainly at the opposite (animal) pole where metabolic activity is greater. There are two classes of this type: (1) Yolked eggs with **holoblastic** cleavage, in which the later cleavages produce unequal cells—small cells, or micromeres, at the animal pole and large cells, or macromeres, at the vegetal pole. Amphibians and bony fish have this kind of egg. (2) Yolked eggs (megalecithal) with **meroblastic** (partial or discoidal) cleavage, in which the small amount of protoplasm is concentrated at the animal pole in the germinal disk, or blastoderm, where cleavage occurs. These eggs are usually large, contain a great deal of albumin (egg white) derived from the oviducts, and have a hard or soft shell. Bird and reptile eggs are good examples.

In the **centrolecithal egg** the nucleus and the surrounding layer of protoplasm are at first in the center of the egg, but as cleavage occurs, most of the nucleated masses of cytoplasm migrate to the periphery and form a cellular layer (blastoderm), leaving the yolk in the center of the egg. From the blastoderm the embryo develops. These eggs are characteristic of the arthropods.

Eggs may also be classified with respect to their environment into **freshwater eggs,** with much salt and yolk (amphibians); **marine eggs,** with little salt and yolk (fish); **terrestrial eggs,** with much yolk and more or less free from environmental dependence (birds); and **intrauterine eggs,** with little yolk and largely dependent on the maternal organism for nourishment (mammals).

In addition to the plasma membrane universally present in eggs, there are in the various animal groups many kinds of protective membranes or envelopes around the eggs. These include the **vitelline,** or fertilization membrane, secreted by the egg, the **zona pellucida** formed

FIG. 7-1

Types of eggs. **A,** Isolecithal (echinoderms and *Amphioxus*); small yolk evenly distributed. **B,** Telolecithal with holoblastic cleavage (amphibians and bony fish); yolk concentrated at vegetal pole. **C,** Telolecithal with meroblastic cleavage (birds and reptiles); protoplasm concentrated in germinal disk at animal pole. **D,** Centrolecithal (insects and other arthropods); protoplasm centered but migrates out at cleavage, leaving yolk centered.

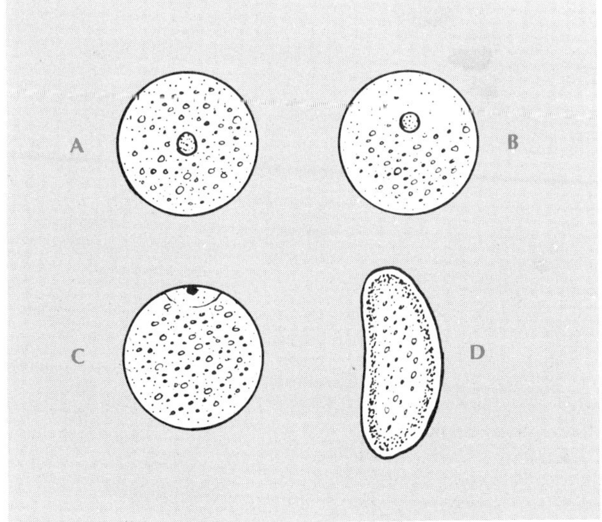

by ovarian follicle cells of mammals, the **egg jelly** from the oviducts of bony fish and amphibians, and the **chitinous shell** (chorion) from the ovarian tubules of insects.

Major stages of development

The individual animal's entire life is one of progressive developmental changes. Although in a technical sense developmental stages are restricted to certain phases in the life history, even after mature development has been attained, morphology is a relative thing and there is no such thing as structural stability. We are concerned with the embryonic stages that are preparatory to the definite form the animal reaches by birth or hatching.

Fertilization and formation of the zygote. The fusion of the pronuclei of sperm and egg is really the starting point of embryonic development. Specifically, the process restores the diploid number of chromosomes, combines the maternal and paternal genetic traits, and activates the egg to develop. This will be treated in more detail in later sections.

Cleavage. This is the initial phase of development; by cell division this stage increases the number of cells (blastomeres) by which differentiation occurs among the cells. The process of cell division involved in cleavage is often called mitosis; however, in ordinary mitosis the cells undergo a period of growth between successive divisions, whereas in cleavage the divisions occur so rapidly that with each division the blastomeres become smaller (Fig. 7-2). After the cleavage stage, ordinary division takes over and the cells no longer become smaller. Blastomeres and ordinary mitotic cells are similar in that each has the diploid number of chromosomes.

There are a number of different types of cleavage, depending on the amount of yolk in the egg. **Holoblastic cleavage** is complete, and the early blastomeres are approximately equal in size (*Amphioxus* and mammals). **Meroblastic cleavage** planes are restricted to a small disklike area on the surface (birds and many invertebrates). **Superficial cleavage** is restricted to a layer around the yolk (insects) (Fig. 7-3).

Radial and spiral cleavage. Holoblastic cleavage is also classified on the basis of radial and spiral types (Fig. 7-4). In **radial cleavage** the cleavage planes are symmetrical to the polar axis and produce tiers, or layers, of cells on top of each other. Radial cleavage is **indeterminate,** that is, there is no definite relation between the position of any blastomere and the specific tissue it will form in the embryo. Very early blastomeres, if separated, may each be capable of giving rise to a complete embryo (Fig. 34-14). In **spiral cleavage** the cleavage planes are diagonal to the polar axis and produce alternate clockwise and counterclockwise quartets

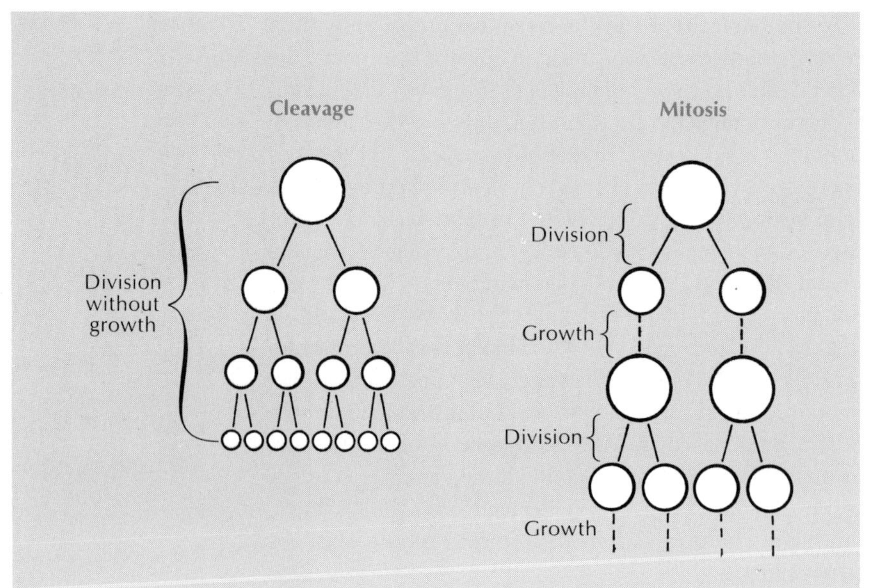

FIG. 7-2

Comparison of cell division in cleavage and mitosis. In cleavage, cells become progressively smaller with no interdivisional growth; in mitosis a period of growth follows each division so that daughter cells become as large as parent cell. Both types retain diploid hereditary constitution.

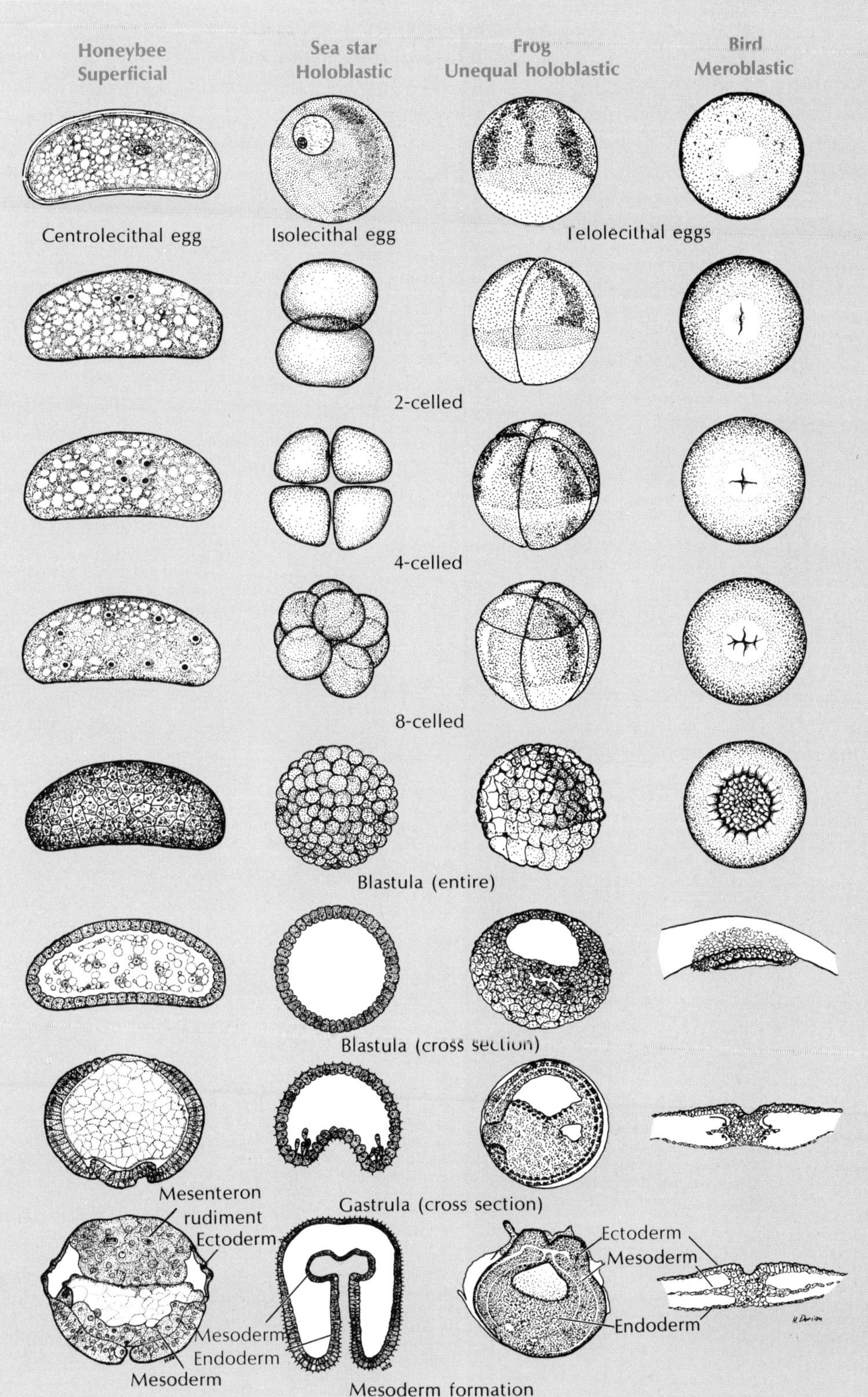

FIG. 7-3

Examples of different types of cleavage. Note that all stages of honeybee egg shown are sections, except for whole blastula; first four stages are shown in sagittal section and last two in cross section.

of unequal cells around the axis of polarity. Spiral cleavage is **determinate** and the fate of each blastomere can be foretold. All blastomeres must be present to form a whole embryo (Fig. 34-14). With few exceptions, radial cleavage is found in the deuterostomes and spiral cleavage in the protostomes. See Chapter 34 for further discussion.

Blastula and gastrula. These stages vary markedly with the type of egg involved. Cleavage is considered to be terminated on the establishment of the blastula. The **blastula** stage typically is characterized by having the blastomeres in a single layer (**blastoderm**) toward the peripheral part of the developing egg. The inner

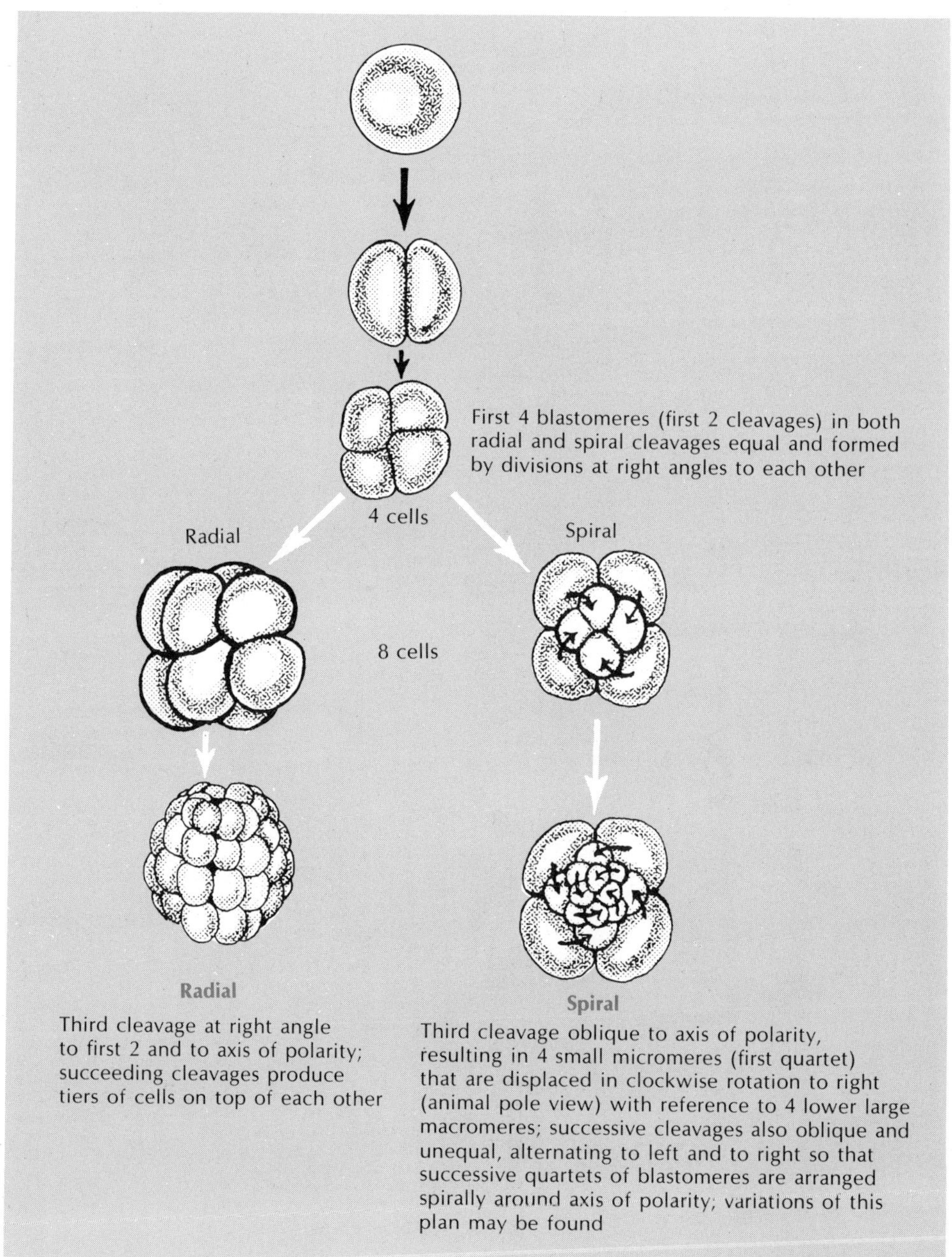

FIG. 7-4

Comparison of spiral and radial changes in holoblastic cleavage. Spiral cleavage (Annelida, Mollusca, Rhyncocoela, Platyhelminthes, certain minor phyla) produces definite pattern of development so that fate of early blastomeres can be foretold (determinate cleavage). In radial cleavage (Echinodermata, Chordata, and a few others), differentiation of early blastomeres is delayed and each one is equipotent; that is, each can give rise to a whole embryo (indeterminate cleavage). Nematodes have neither radial nor spiral cleavage.

cavity thus formed is called the **blastocoel** (Fig. 7-5). This arrangement of the blastomeres into a blastula may facilitate the migration of the cells in gastrulation.

During gastrulation an inpushing of one side of the blastula occurs, partially obliterating the blastocoel and forming a two-layered cuplike state—the **gastrula.** The new cavity so formed is the **archenteron** (primitive gut), with its opening to the outside—the **blastopore** (Figs. 7-5 and 7-6). Modifications of this process are found in yolk-laden eggs. The gastrula represents the initial establishment of what is going to be the pattern of development.

Formation of germ layers. Gastrulation gives rise to two layers of cells called **germ layers**—an outer **ectoderm** and an inner **endoderm** (Fig. 7-5). In certain simple metazoans such as some of the coelenterates, these are the only germ layers and the animals are called **diploblastic.** In higher forms a middle germ layer, the **mesoderm,** develops either from pouches of the archenteron or from other cells, and such animals are called **triploblastic** (Figs. 7-6 and 7-7). Most bilateral animals derive their mesoderm from both of the other layers; however, it is possible for some animals to acquire their mesoderm chiefly from either the ectoderm (ectomesoderm), or from the endoderm (endomesoderm).

Formation of coelom. The coelom, or true body cavity that contains the viscera, may be formed by one of two methods—**schizocoelous** or **enterocoelous** (Fig. 7-6). In schizocoelous formation the coelom arises from the splitting of mesodermal bands that originate from the blastopore region and grow between the ectoderm and endoderm; in enterocoelous formation the coelom comes from the fusion and expansion of outfolding pouches of the archenteron, or primitive gut.

Among the lophophoral phyla the coelom may be developed schizocoelously by some and enterocoelously by others; other methods of coelom formation are not unknown in this group. As will be pointed out later, the deuterostomes are supposed to follow the enterocoelous and the protostomes the schizocoelous method of coelom production.

Neurula stage. Differentiation started in previous

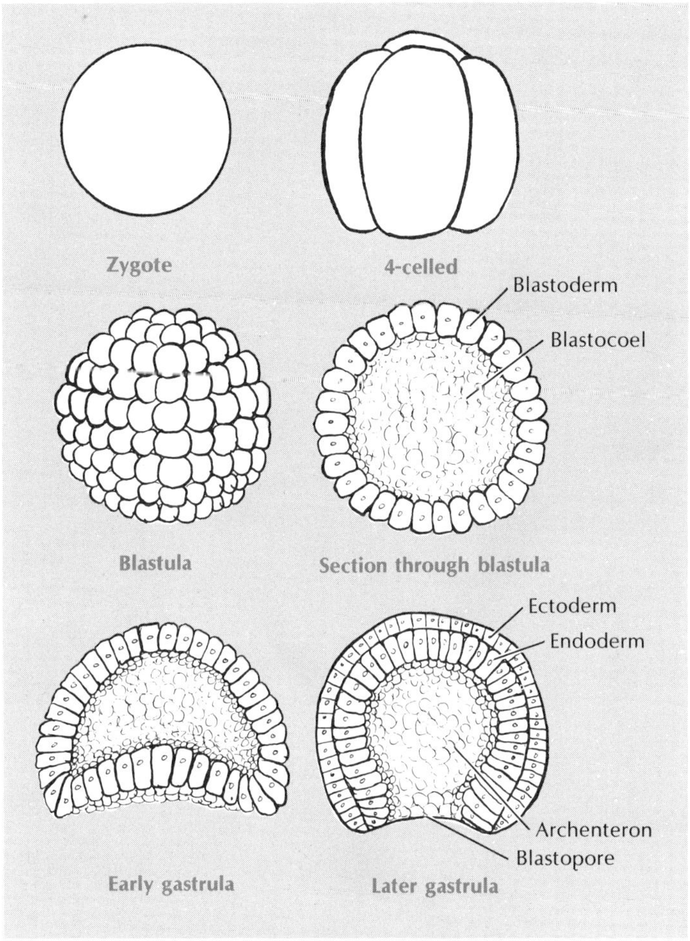

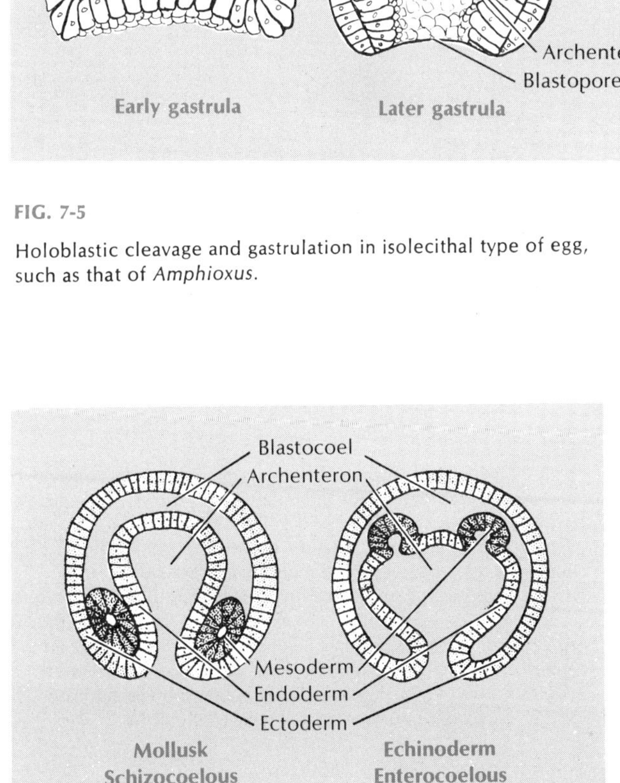

FIG. 7-5

Holoblastic cleavage and gastrulation in isolecithal type of egg, such as that of *Amphioxus*.

FIG. 7-6

Two types of mesoderm and coelom formation. Schizocoelous, in which mesoderm originates from wall of archenteron near lips of blastopore, and enterocoelous, in which mesoderm and coelom develop from endodermal pouches.

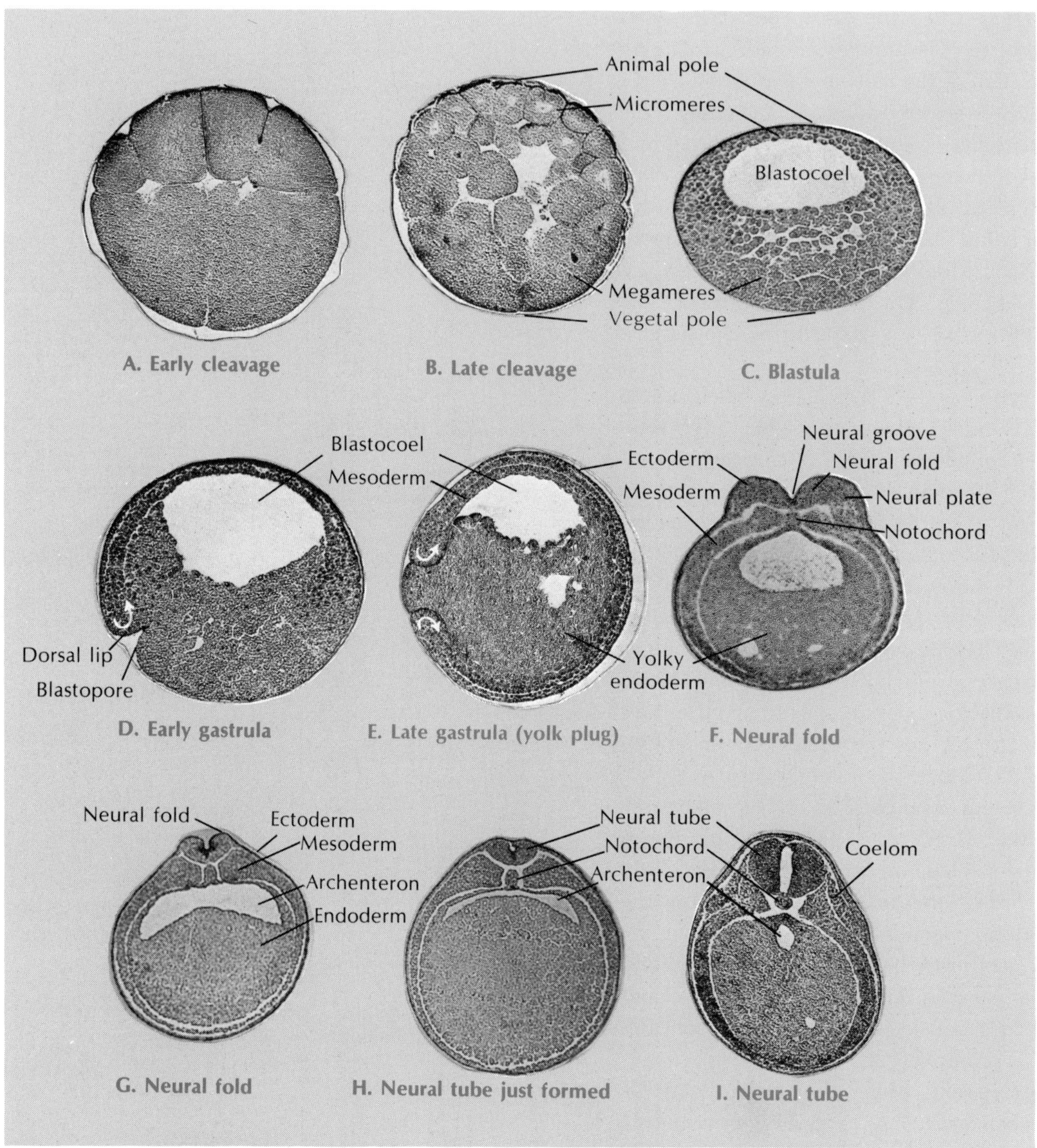

FIG. 7-7

Early embryology of frog. All views are sections through developing embryos. **A,** Beginning of fourth cleavage division, which will result in 16-cell stage. **B** to **C,** Unequal division of cells results in hollow blastula, small cells at animal pole, and yolk cells at vegetal pole. **D,** Gastrulation begins; multiplying animal cells overgrow vegetal cells and turn in, forming dorsal lip of blastopore. **E,** Involution continues until vegetal hemisphere is covered by ectodermal overgrowth (epiboly) leaving plug of yolk at blastopore. Mesoderm forms inside ectoderm, proliferated from dorsal lip of blastopore. Blastopore will become external opening of gut. **F,** Gastrulation completed. Germ layers are present, with gut forming in endoderm. Dorsal ectoderm thickens to form neural plate, which begins to fold. Notochord differentiates from mesoderm. **G** to **H,** Neural fold closes to form neural tube. **I,** Mesoderm spreads between ectoderm and endoderm and splits to form coelomic cavity. Triploblastic body plan is now established. Neural tube will become brain and spinal cord; other organs and systems will differentiate.

stages now begins to emerge in the formation of definite patterns of morphology. The most significant organ rudiment to appear at this stage is the central nervous system, which gives the name to the stage. The neural canal with the notochord, somites, and germ layers in place constitute the embryonic axis.

Pharyngula stage. This stage takes its name from the structural feature of the pharynx with its lateral walls arranged in segments, separated from each other by pharyngeal clefts or grooves. This stage, just beyond the neurula, represents the basic pattern of vertebrate morphology and varies with different classes. This stage serves as the pivotal point from which the various organs differentiate along their lines of unique specializations. It represents a period during which structure is evolving rapidly. It has been said that the pharyngula stage represents the primitive plan of the vertebrate before divergent trends of various class characteristics start to appear. This stage will be understood better when Chapter 34 on principles of development is studied.

Early embryology of the frog

In the telolecithal egg of the frog the holoblastic cleavage is unequal because of the large amount of yolk (Fig. 7-7). The cleavage divisions at the lower or vegetal pole are slowed down by the inert yolk so that the resulting blastula consists of many small cells at the animal pole and a few large cells at the vegetal pole. Actually, the yolk-filled part of the egg never undergoes cleavage. The cavity of the blastula, or blastocoel, is relatively small, and the type of gastrulation described for the isolecithal egg, as shown by *Amphioxus* (Fig. 7-5), is impossible.

In the frog, gastrulation begins by an invagination of the cells of the vegetal pole and a turning in of the cells at the dorsal lip of the blastopore (involution). Those cells from the animal hemisphere that pass over the dorsal lip help form the wall of the archenteron. The process of involution continues so that a growth of ectodermal cells down over the cells of the vegetal pole (epiboly) occurs, leaving only a yolk plug of endodermal cells visible.

Before gastrulation is completed with the formation of the blastopore, mesoderm is being formed between the ectoderm and endoderm in the dorsal region of the embryo. Eventually, by further growth, the mesoderm spreads between ectoderm and endoderm and splits to form the coelomic cavity.

After gastrulation, differentiation of the organs and organ systems starts. This is accomplished by thickenings, invaginations, evaginations, etc. In this way, the neural tube, which forms the brain and spinal cord, is laid down, as shown in Fig. 7-7, *F* to *I*.

Fate of germ layers

Following are some of the structures that normally arise from certain layers of the three germ layers:

Ectoderm

Epidermis of skin
Lining of mouth, anus, nostrils
Sweat and sebaceous glands
Epidermal coverings such as hair, nails, feathers, horns, epidermal scales, enamel of teeth
Nervous system, including sensory parts of eye, nose, ear

Endoderm

Lining of alimentary canal
Lining of respiratory passages and lungs
Secretory parts of liver and pancreas
Thyroid, parathyroid, thymus
Urinary bladder
Lining of urethra

Mesoderm

Skeleton and muscles
Dermis of skin
Dermal scales and dentin
Excretory and reproductive systems
Connective tissue
Blood and blood vessels
Mesenteries
Lining of coelomic cavity

The idea that each germ layer can give rise to certain tissues and organs only, and to no others, is no longer held. It is now known that the interactions of cells play a part in determining their differentiation in vertebrate animals. The precise position of a cell with relation to other cells and tissues during early development often controls the real fate of that cell. Under some conditions a certain germ layer may give rise to structures normally arising from a different germ layer. Experiments have demonstrated that a presumptive ectodermal structure, when grafted into appropriate regions, will form organs that normally come from a different germ layer. The topographic position, therefore, of cells in their development must play a significant role in their final fate and destiny. Embryologic development must be considered quite flexible. The biologic system cannot be restricted to a definite pattern even though normally it appears to be. Are there any organs or structures that do not come from any germ layer?

In a strict sense the germ cells do not originate from any of the three germ layers because they come directly from cells that were segregated in the early cleavage stages of the fertilized egg.

Recognition of cells

During the developmental stages the cells of a type characteristic of a particular tissue may not be easy to recognize. One must know the location of cells and their relation to each other. The problem is more difficult if cells have migrated some distance from their places of origin. In the adrenal gland the medullary cells originate in the neural crest of the spinal cord and then migrate into the cortical region in which cells have originated from the dorsal wall of the coelomic cavity. In such cases the embryologist traces the cells in sections through the embryo from place of origin to final location.

In primordial germ cells the problem is more pronounced because the cells migrate before they are fully differentiated. These cells probably originate in the dorsal mesentery of the gut and then at an early stage migrate to the developing gonads. It is impossible to distinguish these cells when they are in the mesentery, but chemically they have a high concentration of alkaline phosphatase that the other cells around them do not have. Stage by stage they can be traced by this enzyme.

A specific activity of a cell may occur before it reaches cellular maturity. The embryonic heart of a rat will beat on the tenth day of development before the cross striations and myofibrils, characteristic of cardiac muscle, actually appear. The onset of a function in a differentiating cell may afford a clue to its recognition. A liver cell, for example, may be recognized in a chick embryo about a week after incubation by the presence of glycogen.

Differentiation of tissues, organs, and systems

The different types of tissues originate from the basic properties of protoplasm (Fig. 7-8). These are irritability and conductivity (nervous), contractility (muscle), supportive and adhesive (connective tissue), absorptive and secretion (epithelial), and fluidity and conductivity (vascular). These five tissues are specializations of the various protoplasmic properties, and with their varied structures and functions they are able to meet the basic requirements of morphologic patterns, as in organogenesis.

The processes by which germ layers give rise to tissues and organs vary. The germ layers, by budding and folding, first form a tubular embryo. Then by a process called **histogenesis**, the five major tissues are differ-

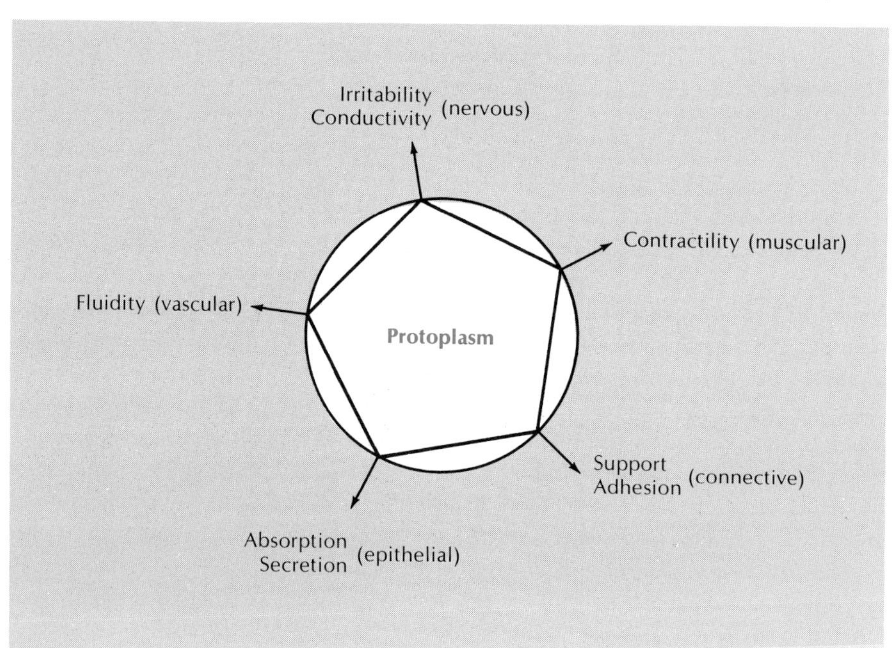

FIG. 7-8

Origin of tissues. The four or five basic tissues of body are manifestations of properties found in all protoplasm. Tissues are variously specialized to perform functions, as listed in diagram.

entiated (Fig. 7-9): (1) epithelial tissue, from all three germ layers; (2) connective or supporting tissue, from mesoderm; (3) muscular or contractile tissue, from mesoderm; (4) nervous tissue, from ectoderm; and (5) vascular tissue, from mesoderm. A **tissue** is a group of similar cells (together with associated cell products) specialized for the performance of a common function. The study of tissues is called **histology.** All cells in metazoan animals take part in the formation of tissues. Sometimes the cells of a tissue may be of several kinds, and some tissues have a great many intercellular materials.

Epithelial tissue. An **epithelium** is a tissue that covers an external or internal surface. It also includes hollow or solid derivatives from this tissue. Epithelial tissues (Figs. 7-10 and 7-11) are made up of closely associated cells, with some intercellular material between the cells. Some cells are bound together by **intercellular bridges** of cytoplasm. Most of them have one surface free and the other surface lying on vascular connective tissue. A noncellular **basement membrane** is often attached to the basal cells. Epithelial cells are often modified to produce secretory glands that may be unicellular or multicellular. Some free surfaces (joint cavities, bursae, brain cavity) are not lined with typical epithelium.

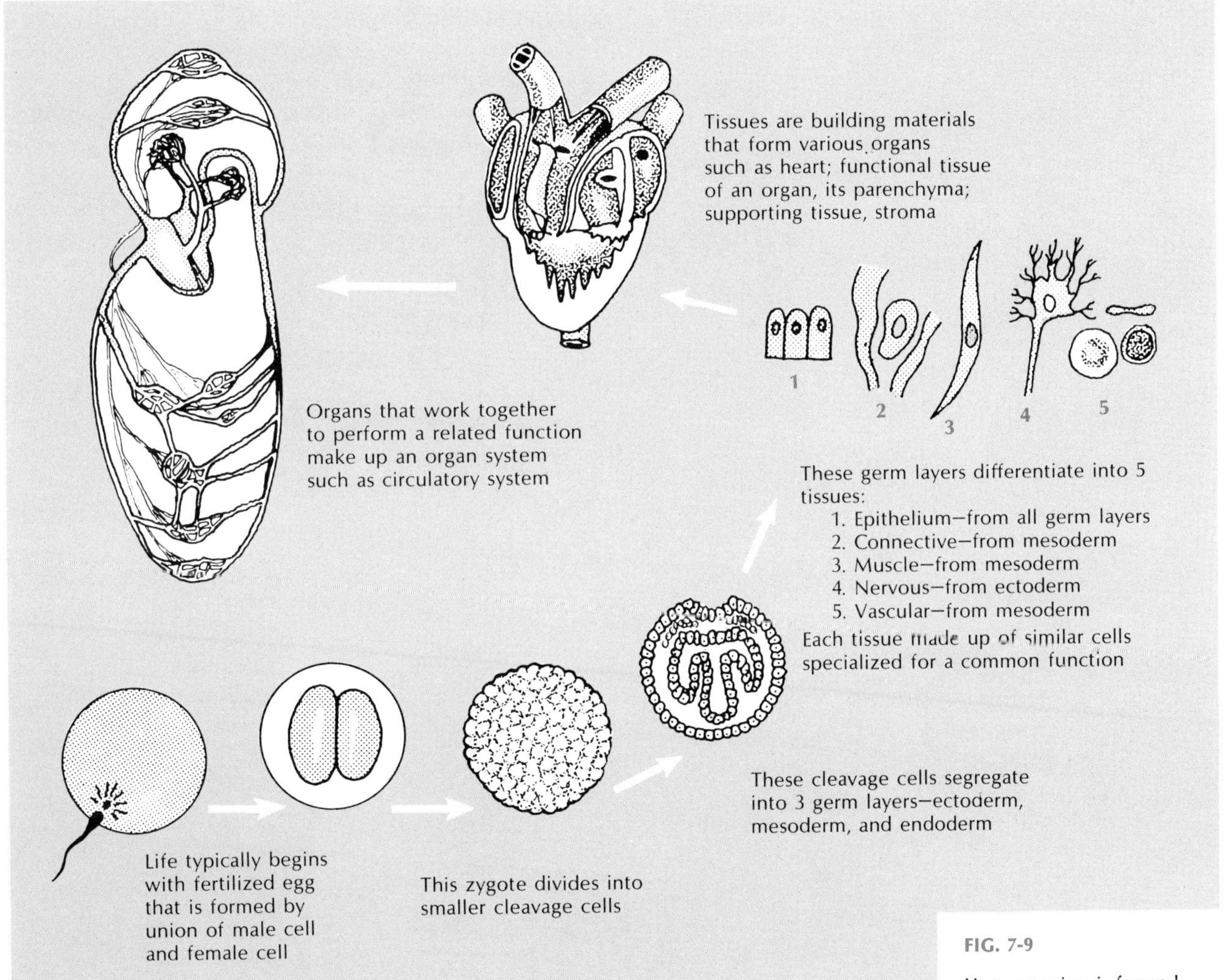

FIG. 7-9

How organism is formed.

Epithelia are classified on the basis of cell form and number of cell layers. **Simple epithelium** is one layer thick (Fig. 7-10), and its cells may be flat or **squamous** (endothelium of blood vessels), short prisms or **cuboidal** (glands and ducts), and tall or **columnar** (stomach and intestine). Any of these three forms of cells may occur in several layers as a **stratified epithelium** (skin, sweat glands, urethra) (Fig. 7-11). Some stratified epithelia can change the number of their cell layers by movement (**transitional**—bladder). Others have cells of different heights and give the appearance of stratified epithelia (**pseudostratified**—trachea). Many epithelia may be **ciliated** at their free surfaces (oviduct). Epithelia serve to protect, secrete, excrete, lubricate, etc.

Connective tissue (supporting). Connective tissues bind together and support other structures. They are so common that the removal of other bodily components would still leave the gross outlines of the body distinguishable. Connective tissue is made up of scattered cells and a great deal of formed materials such as **fibers** and ground substance (**matrix**) secreted by the cells. There are three types of fibers; white or collagenous, yellow or elastic, and branching or reticular. Connective tissue may be classified in various ways, but all the types fall under either **loose connective tissue** (reticular, areolar, adipose) or **dense connective tissue** (sheaths, ligaments, tendons, cartilage, bone) (Figs. 7-12 and 7-13). Adipose stresses cells, ligaments stress fibers, and cartilage stresses ground substance (matrix).

Connective tissues are derived from the **mesenchyme,** a generalized embryonic tissue that can differentiate also into vascular tissue and smooth muscle. Mesenchyme may also be considered the most primitive connective tissue. When its cells are closely packed to-

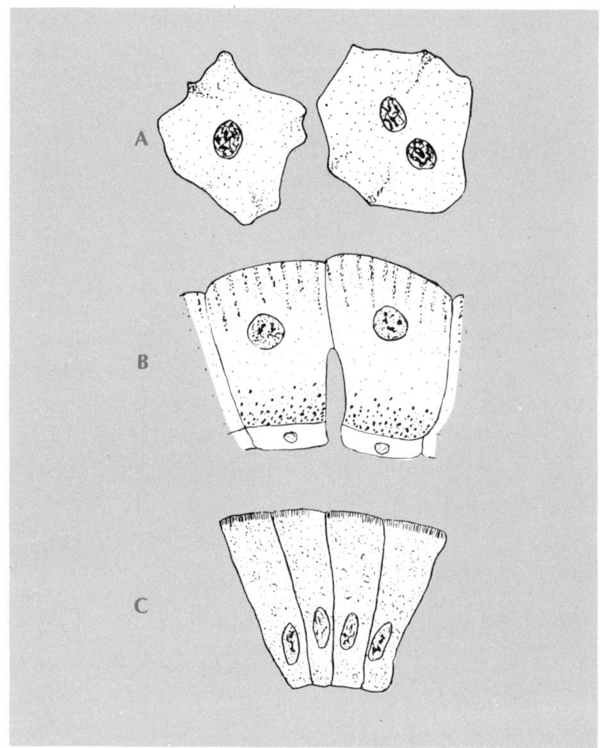

FIG. 7-10

A, Simple squamous epithelial cells from lining of mouth. **B,** Simple cuboidal epithelium. **C,** Simple columnar epithelium.

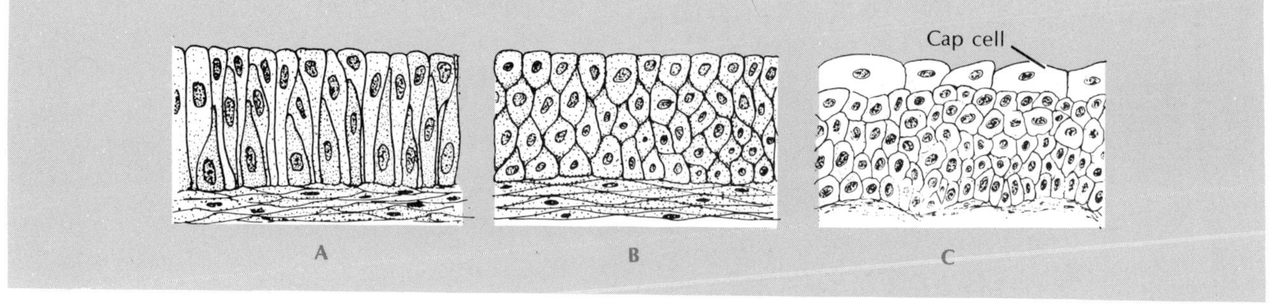

FIG. 7-11

Types of epithelial tissue. **A,** Pseudostratified epithelium. **B,** Stratified columnar epithelium. **C,** Transitional epithelium.

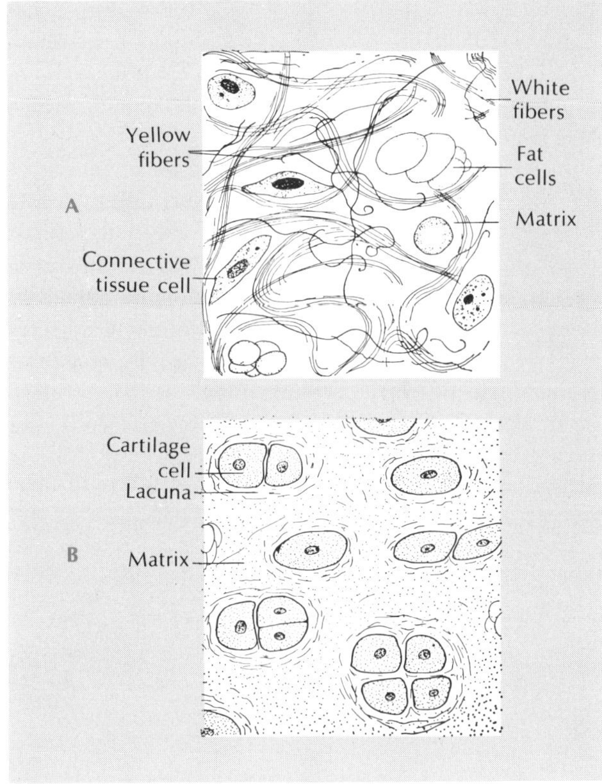

FIG. 7-12

A, Areolar connective tissue. **B,** Hyaline cartilage, most common form of cartilage in body.

FIG. 7-13

Photomicrograph of section through bone showing haversian systems.

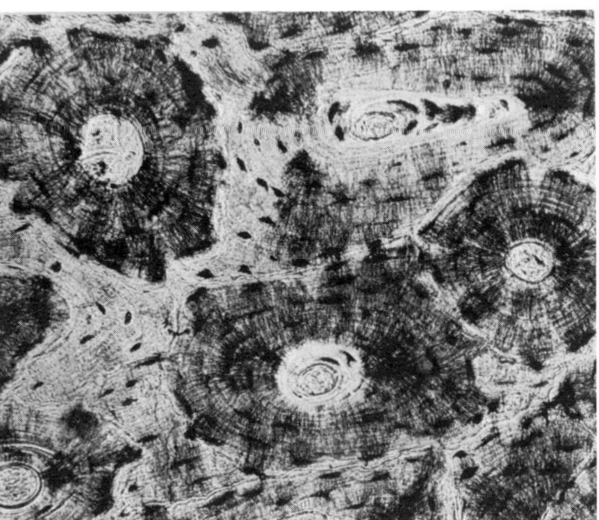

gether, it is called **parenchyma;** when loosely arranged with gelatinous material, it is called **collenchyma.**

Muscular tissue. Muscle is the most common tissue in the body of most animals. It is made up of elongated cells or fibers specialized for contraction. It originates (with few exceptions) from the mesoderm, and its unit is the cell or **muscle fiber.** The unspecialized cytoplasm of muscles is called **sarcoplasm,** and the contractile elements within the fiber (cell) are the **myofibrils.** Functionally, muscles are either **voluntary** (under control of will) or **involuntary.** Structurally, they are either **smooth** (fibers unstriped) or **striated** (fibers cross-striped). The three kinds of muscular tissue (Figs. 7-14 and 7-15) are **smooth involuntary** (walls of viscera and walls of blood vessels), **striated involuntary** or **cardiac** (heart), and **striated voluntary** or **skeletal** (limb and trunk). Another type of muscular tissue is made up of the **myoepithelial** cell. Myoepithelial cells are found in sweat, salivary, and mammary glands between the epithelium and connective tissue. They extend branching processes around the secretory cells of the glands. Their function may be to squeeze secretions from the acini toward the surface openings of the larger ducts.

Nervous tissue. Nervous tissue is specialized for irritability and conductivity. The structural and functional unit of the nervous system is the **neuron** (Fig. 7-16), a nerve cell made up of a body containing the nucleus and its processes or fibers. It originates from an embryonic ectodermal cell called a **neuroblast.** (Part of the nervous system of echinoderms may be mesodermal in origin.) In most animals the bodies of nerve cells are restricted to the central nervous system and ganglia, but the fibers may be very long and ramify through the body. Neurons are arranged in chains, and the point of contact between neurons is a **synapse.** Some of the fibers bear a sheath (medullated or myelin); in others the sheath is absent (nonmedullated).

Sensory neurons are concerned with picking up impulses from sensory **receptors** in the skin or sense organs and transmitting them to nerve centers (brain or spinal cord). **Motor neurons** carry impulses from the nerve centers to muscles or glands (**effectors**) that are thus stimulated to act. **Association neurons** may form various connections between other neurons.

Vascular tissue. Vascular tissue is a fluid tissue composed of **white blood cells, red blood cells, platelets,** and a liquid—**plasma.** Traveling through blood vessels,

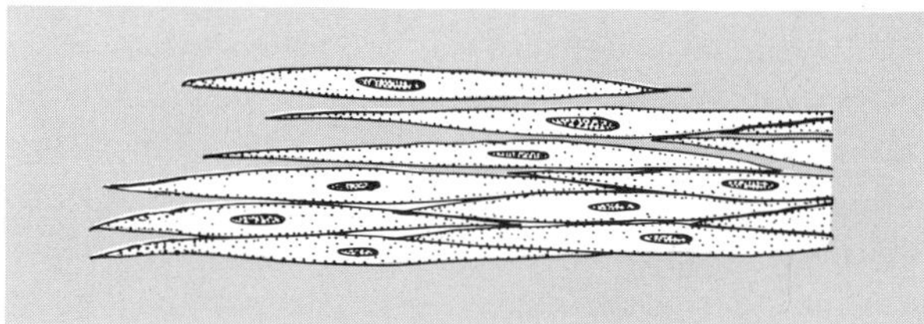

FIG. 7-14

Group of smooth muscle cells.

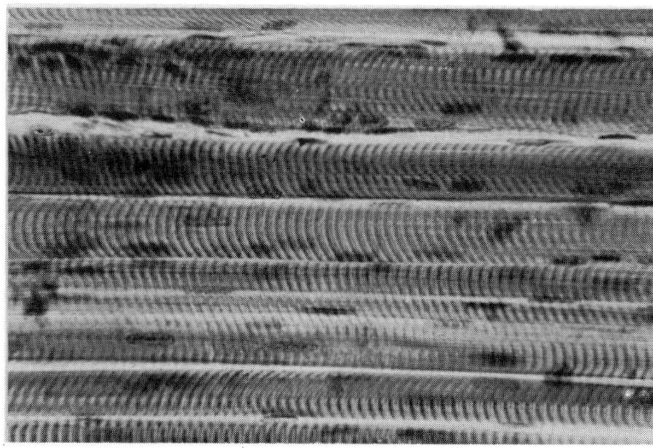

A

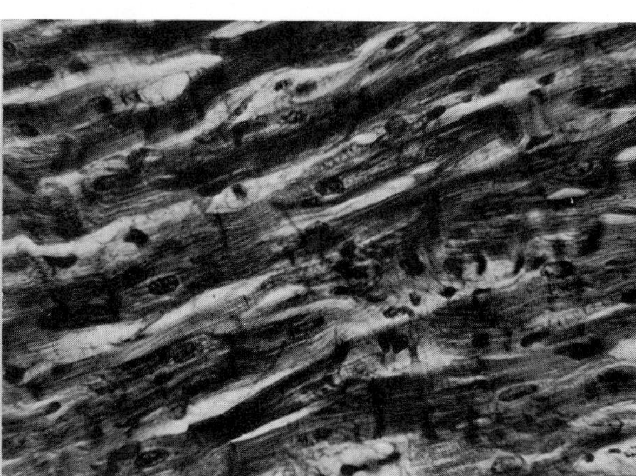

B

FIG. 7-15

A, Photomicrograph of skeletal muscle showing several striated fibers lying side by side. **B,** Photomicrograph of heart, or cardiac, muscle. Arrangement of fibers can be seen. (Courtesy Joseph W. Bamberger.)

the blood carries to the tissue cells the materials necessary for their life processes. **Lymph** and tissue fluids, which arise from blood by filtration and serve in the exchange between cells and blood, also belong to vascular tissue.

MOIST MEMBRANES

Important functional structures of the body are the moist mucous and serous membranes. These membranes are modified from epithelium and connective tissue and are kept moist by either thin watery secretions or thick mucous secretions. **A mucous membrane** is made up of a layer of epithelium (simple or stratified) resting upon a bed of connective tissue. Its sur-

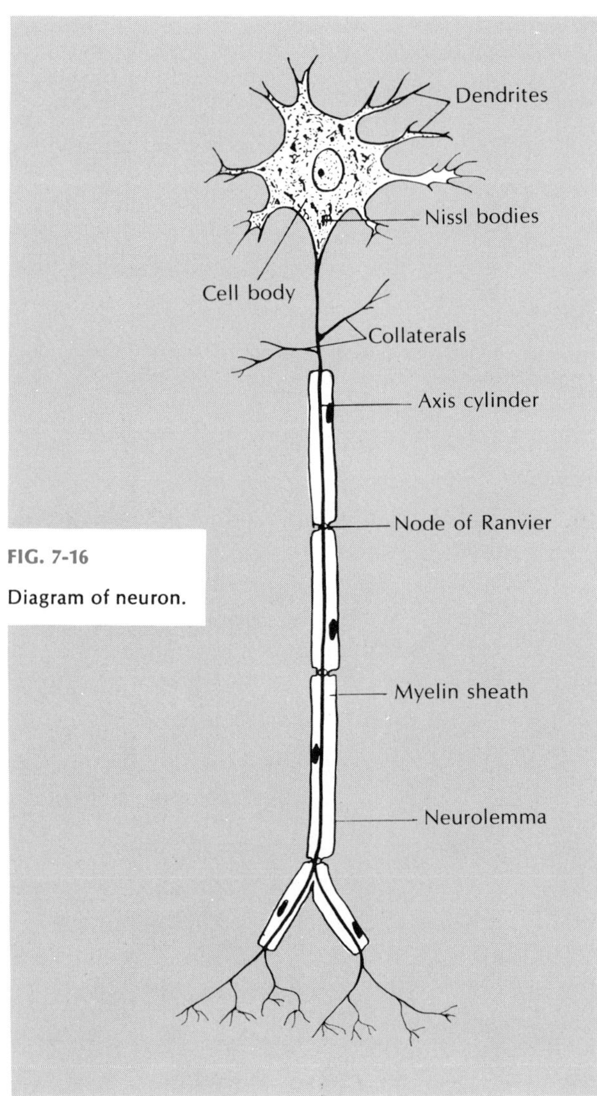

FIG. 7-16

Diagram of neuron.

face is kept moist by goblet cells or multicellular glands. Mucous membranes have a wide distribution in the lining of hollow organs that communicate with the outside of the body, such as the alimentary canal, urinary and genital tracts, sinuses, and respiratory passageways. A **serous membrane** consists of a flat mesothelium (sometimes cuboidal or columnar cells in lower vertebrates) that is supported by a thin layer of connective tissue. This membrane is kept moist by a scanty fluid and contains various free cells from the mesothelium and the blood. Serous membranes are usually divided into a parietal portion, which lines the external walls of the cavities, and a visceral portion, which is reflected over the exposed surfaces of organs. The pericardium, pleura, and peritoneum are all serous membranes.

Both mucous and serous membranes perform important functions of lubrication, protection, support, and defense against bacterial infection.

ORGANS AND SYSTEMS*

Definitions. An **organ** is a group of tissues that performs a certain function. In higher forms many organs may have most of the various tissues in their makeup (Fig. 7-17). The heart has (Fig. 7-18) epithelial tissue for covering and lining, connective tissue for framework, muscular walls for contraction, nervous elements for coordination, and vascular tissue for transportation.

The science of the arrangement of tissues to form organs is called **organology.** All organs have a characteristic structural plan. Usually one tissue carries the burden of the organ's chief function, as muscle does in the heart; the other tissues are of secondary importance. The chief functional cells of an organ are called its **parenchyma;** the supporting tissues are its **stroma.** For instance, in the pancreas the secreting cells are the parenchyma; the capsule and connective tissue framework represent the stroma.

Organs are, in turn, associated in groups to form **systems,** each system concerned with one of the basic functions. Only the higher metazoans have all eleven organ systems. However, all living organisms perform the same basic functions. The need for procuring and utilizing food and for movement, protection, perception, and reproduction are as important to an ameba,

*Refer to Chapter 2, Principle 9.

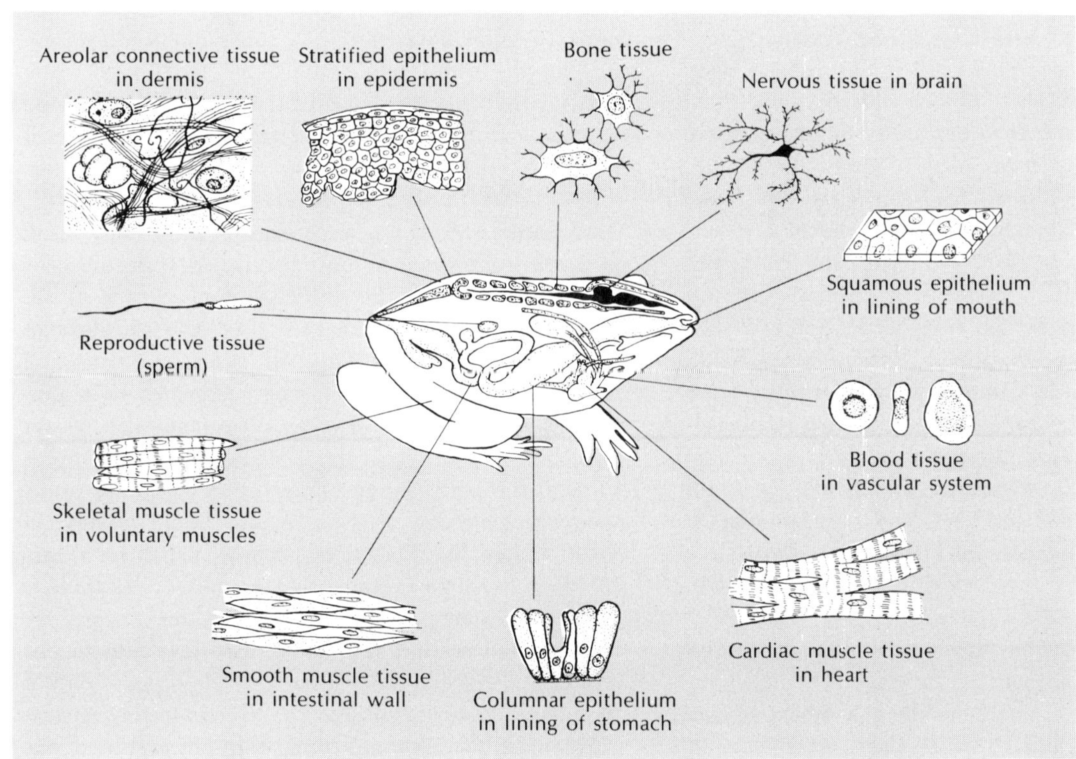

FIG. 7-17

Diagram of frog showing various types of tissues.

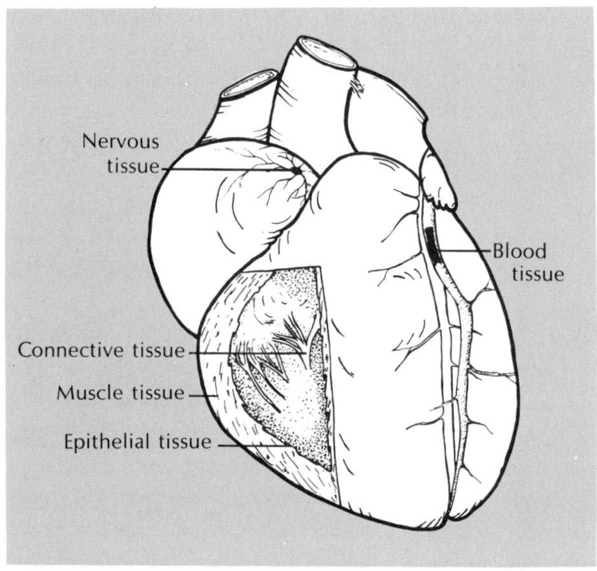

FIG. 7-18

Heart showing various types of tissue in its structure.

a clam, or an insect as to a man. Obviously, because of differences in size, structure, and environment, each must meet these problems in a different manner.

Following is a brief résumé of the eleven basic body functions or systems.

Digestive processes. Ingestion is the intake of food. In most animals this takes place through the mouth, although in most protozoans and some parasitic forms it occurs directly through the body surface.

Digestion is the process of transforming food substances into a solution of small molecules that can readily be absorbed by the body cells. Some of this breakdown may occur by physical means—teeth, rough surfaces, or muscular action—but much of it must occur by chemical action. Chemical digestion may occur inside cells (**intracellular digestion**) or outside cells in a digestive cavity (**extracellular digestion**). In protozoans food is taken in and retained in a droplet of water (food vacuole) into which digestive enzymes are secreted to digest the food. Most multicellular animals, however, have digestive systems of some kinds that may vary from a simple saclike gastrovascular cavity with a mouth but no anus to an elaborate alimentary canal consisting of a mouth, esophagus, stomach, and intestine, together with the accessory salivary glands, liver, and pancreas that secrete enzymes and bile into the digestive tract.

Egestion is the elimination of unused or unusable food products. In most protozoans this process, like ingestion, occurs directly through the cell membrane. In most metazoans egestion occurs through the anus, if there is one, or through the mouth if there is no anus.

Respiration. Energy is bound up in food products and must be released by oxidation for cellular use. Oxygen is obtained from the air or from the water in which the animal lives. Respiration is the process of taking in oxygen and giving off carbon dioxide. In some animals this exchange of gases takes place by diffusion through the plasma membrane (protozoans) or through the cells of the body wall (lower metazoans). In most metazoans, however, there are specialized respiratory organs in which the diffusion of gases occurs between the environment and the animal's body fluids or blood. Such respiratory organs include gills, lungs, air passages, and others concerned with breathing.

Circulation. Regardless of the size or structure of an organism, substances must be able to move about within it. Nourishment and oxygen must reach all cells, and waste products must be carried away. Transportation of products varies from the simple streaming of protoplasm within the walls of an ameba, or the movement of body fluids within a small multicellular animal, to the complicated circulatory systems of vertebrates, which include blood, a muscular heart, blood vessels, and lymphatics. In a circulatory system it is the blood that transports the products of digestion, respiratory gases, waste products, and hormones.

Excretion. Metabolic processes of body cells result in waste products that must be carried from the cells and removed from the body. Carbon dioxide is removed by respiratory processes, but it is the duty of the excretory organs to get rid of excess water and nitrogenous wastes (urea, purine bodies, etc.). In protozoans and a number of lower metazoans such wastes may be diffused through the plasma membrane or through the body surface. In most multicellular forms special devices are used to remove liquid wastes. In invertebrates these devices include flame cells, nephridia, malpighian tubules, etc. In vertebrates there is a complex excretory system of kidneys, ureters, urinary bladder, and urethra. The kidneys remove nitrogenous wastes and excess water from the blood and send it through a system of tubules and ureters to the outside.

Nervous coordination. Both the physical and the

physiologic activities of the body must be skillfully coordinated and integrated to be effective. Such coordination is under the control of both the nervous system and the endocrine system. A fundamental principle of protoplasm is irritability; each living cell responds to stimuli. But even in protozoans some parts of the protoplasm may be more sensitive to stimuli than others, for example, the light-sensitive eyespots of certain flagellates and the neuromotor apparatus that coordinates the beating of cilia. In even the lowest of metazoans, there are specialized nerve cells for transmission of stimuli. In other metazoans these cells are organized into nerves and nerve centers that regulate the transmission of stimuli from special receptor cells to effectors such as muscles and glands. In still higher forms these nerve cells are organized into a complex central nervous system of brain, ganglia, nerve cord, and peripheral connections. In vertebrates the nervous system comprises two major parts, the cerebrospinal and the autonomic systems.

Sensory perception. The nervous system is involved in handling information about the environment and coordinating the animal's responses to changes in that environment. To gain information about the environment, various sensory cells are receptive to certain kinds of outside stimuli—light, sound, touch, taste, chemical, heat, and cold, to name a few. Protozoans and sponges, which have no specialized sense organs, are nevertheless sensitive to light, touch, and certain chemicals. Many invertebrates have developed simple sensory organs such as light-sensitive eyes, statocysts for balance, tactile hairs, and chemoreceptors. In a few invertebrates and most vertebrates we find not only the simple receptors for touch, taste, and temperature, but also highly specialized and complicated organs of sight, smell, and hearing.

Endocrine regulation. Along with the nervous system, the endocrine glands are physiologic coordinators. Whereas the nervous regulation is rapid, with the messages being carried over a network of nerves, the hormones produced by the endocrine glands are carried by the blood to their targets. Thus they react more slowly, but the reaction lasts much longer. Endocrine glands are ductless glands that secrete their products directly into the bloodstream. In arthropods there are hormones that control the darkening or lightening of skin pigmentation and others that control molting and metamorphosis. Much more is known about the endocrine glands in vertebrates. These include the pituitary, adrenal, thyroid, parathyroid, and others, and they control or integrate such body functions as growth, metabolism, sexual development, reproduction, and many others.

Reproduction. Reproduction may be either asexual or sexual. Asexual reproduction, found among the lower forms, includes fission (the dividing of an animal into two parts), budding of outgrowths that develop into young, and fragmentation into several parts (sporulation). Sexual reproduction is more common and involves the production of eggs and sperm. Although some invertebrates possess only simple gonads that shed their gametes into the surrounding water, many invertebrates have reproductive systems as complex as those of vertebrates. The reproductive system typically includes gonads (ovaries or testes) that produce the eggs and sperm; ducts and special organs for transporting, transferring, or receiving the gametes; accessory glands; and organs for storage before and after fertilization. There is a close coordination between the reproductive and endocrine systems.

Integument. The integument is the skin and its modifications. Most invertebrates are covered with a single layer of epidermis. In some forms the epidermis secretes an outer noncellular cuticle, and in other forms it secretes an exoskeleton. The vertebrate integument consists of the skin and its derivatives such as hair, scales, feathers, nails, and hoofs. Besides being an outer protective covering, the integument is provided with sensory cells and glands. In some forms it has secretory and respiratory functions, and in warm-blooded animals it helps regulate the body heat.

Skeletal support. Skeletal structures serve as a framework for the animal body and give it support and protection. They also serve for the attachment of muscles and therefore are intimately involved in the movement of animals. Some animals carry their skeletons outside (exoskeletons). These may be calcareous or siliceous tests (protozoans), hard calcareous shells (mollusks), or tough but flexible chitinous coverings (insects and other arthropods). Such skeletons are secreted by the epidermis, are nonliving, and cannot grow. Mollusks continuously add to their shells as they grow; arthropods must shed (molt) their exoskeletons as they outgrow them. A few invertebrates and all chordate animals have internal skeletons (endoskeletons). These are composed of bone or cartilage that are live tissues and can grow as the animal grows.

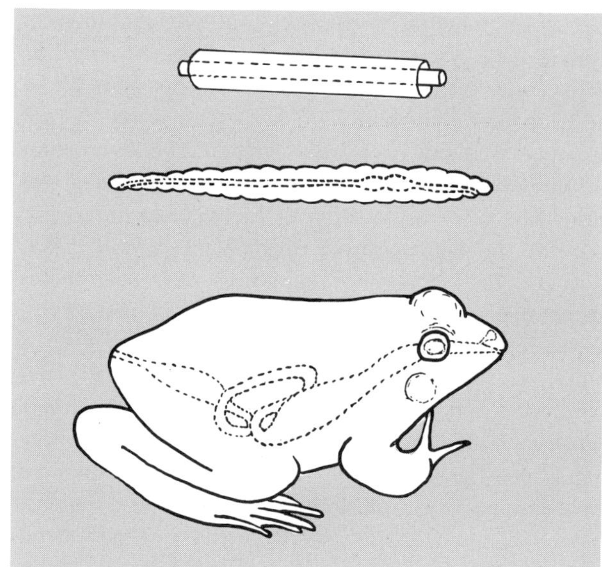

FIG. 7-19

Tube-within-a-tube arrangement.

FIG. 7-20

Schematic drawings of types of body cavity organizations. **A,** Longitudinal sections; **B,** cross sections. In acoelomate type, space between epidermis and gastrodermis is filled with mesenchymal parenchyma, which may contain small spaces; in pseudocoelomate type, space between body wall and digestive tract is remnant of blastocoel and is not lined with mesodermal peritoneum; and in eucoelomate, or true coelomate, type, body cavity is lined with mesodermal peritoneum, which also covers digestive tract. Mesenteries are made up of two peritoneal layers.

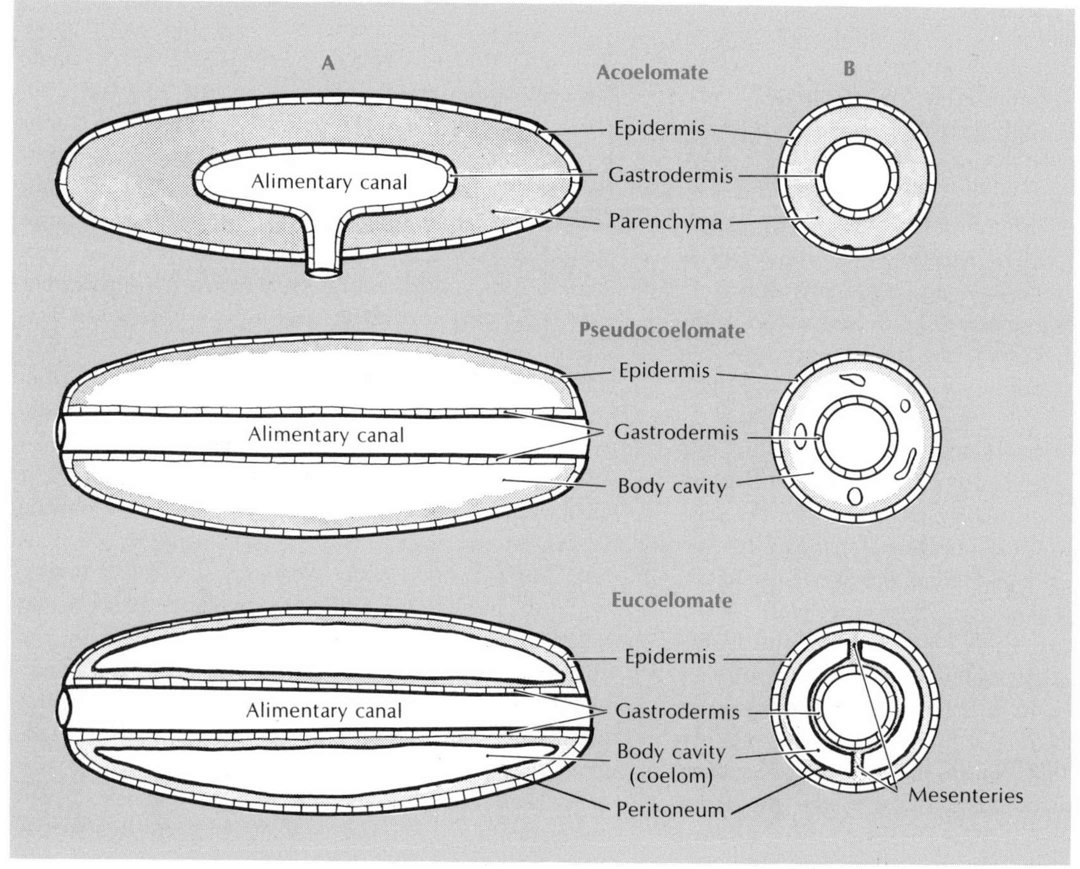

Muscular movement. Most movement in animals is produced by the shortening of muscles or muscle fibers. Special contractile fibers called myonemes are found in some of the lower forms. In higher forms, muscles are arranged in antagonistic pairs or groups. They contract or shorten when stimulated by motor nerves and thus move the part to which they are attached. Most animals have muscular body walls in which antagonistic muscles run circularly and longitudinally or diagonally. This same pattern of circular and longitudinal muscles is found in many of the body organs. Attached to skeletal parts, muscles serve as levers.

INSTABILITY OF TISSUES AND ORGANS

Instead of being fixed or static, most tissues, according to the new view, are continually undergoing change and remain constant only in their general pattern. There is a ceaseless ebb and flow of their constituents. Molecules are being shifted from one region to another. There is a steady interchange of substances and a constant release and uptake from cellular tissues. Some substances are broken down; others are synthesized. Much of this dynamic state is influenced or controlled by hormones, vitamins, and enzymes. Much of the evidence for this has been based on tagging suitable compounds by the isotope tracer method and introducing them into the biologic system. Later, the location and fate of these labeled substances are determined.

BODY CAVITY, OR COELOM

The coelom is the true body cavity. It is the space between the digestive tube and the outer body wall; it contains the visceral organs. Not all animals have a coelom, for example, the jellyfish and flatworms. Animals that do have one have a "tube-within-a-tube" arrangement (Fig. 7-19). The outer tube is the body wall; the inner tube is the digestive tract, and the space between is the coelom. A true coelom develops between two layers of mesoderm—an outer somatic layer and an inner visceral layer—and is lined with mesodermal epithelium called the **peritoneum.**

The coelom is of great significance in animal evolution because it provides spaces for visceral organs, permits greater size and complexity by exposing more cells to surface exchange, and contributes directly to the development of certain systems such as excretory, reproductive, and muscular. This fluid-filled cavity also serves as a hydrostatic fluid skeleton in some primitive forms, aiding them in movement, rapid change of shape, or burrowing. One has only to compare the locomotion of a planarian worm (without a coelom) with that of an annelid worm (with a coelom) to see this advantage.

In roundworms and some others the body cavity is not lined with mesoderm and so is given the name **pseudocoel** (Fig. 7-20).

BODY PLAN AND SYMMETRY

Convenient terms for locating regions of an animal body are **anterior** for the head end, **posterior** for the opposite or tail end, **dorsal** for the back side, and **ventral** for the front or belly side. **Medial** refers to the midline of the body, **lateral** to the sides. **Distal** parts are farther from a point of reference; **proximal** parts are nearer. **Pectoral** refers to the chest region or the area supporting the forelegs, and **pelvic** refers to the hip region or the area supporting the hind legs.

Symmetry refers to balanced proportions, or the

FIG. 7-21

Types of symmetry.

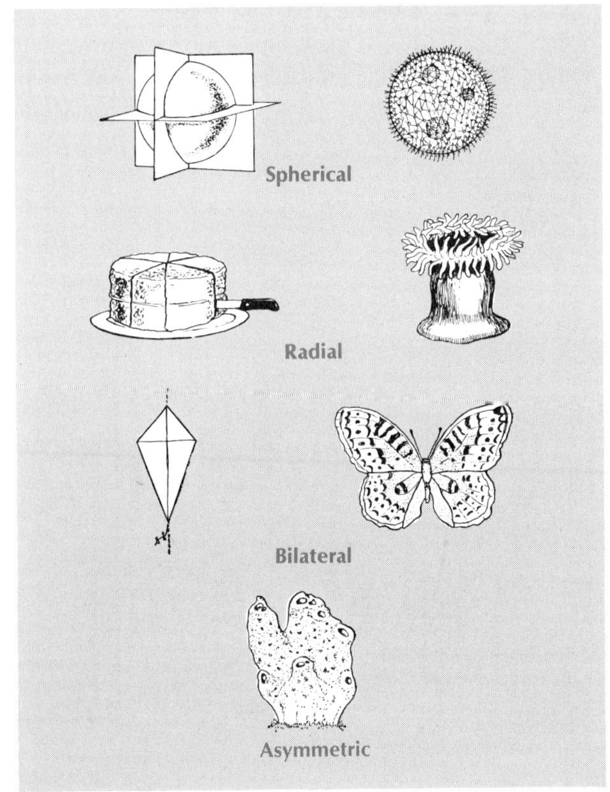

correspondence in size and shape of parts on opposite sides of a median plane (Fig. 7-21). A symmetrical body can be cut into two equivalent or mirrored halves. **Spherical symmetry** is found in a few organisms, chiefly protozoans. Such a form, like a ball, could be divided equally by any plane that passed through the center. These are usually floating or rolling forms. **Radial symmetry** applies to a few sponges, most coelenterates, and adult echinoderms that, like bottles or wheels, can be divided into similar halves by any plane passing through the longitudinal axis. In such forms one end of the longitudinal axis is usually the mouth or oral end and the other is the aboral end. A variant form is **biradial symmetry** in which, because of the presence of some part that is single or paired rather than radial, only one or two planes through the longitudinal axis divides the form into mirrored halves. Examples are the comb jellies, which are basically radial forms but have a pair of arms or tentacles, and sea stars, which have a sieve plate located between two of their radially arranged arms. Radial animals are usually well suited to a sessile existence, for they react equally well on all sides.

Most other animals have **bilaterally symmetrical** bodies (Fig. 7-22). In these types only a **sagittal plane** divides the animal into equivalent right and left halves. A sagittal plane passes through the anteroposterior axis and through the dorsoventral axis. A **frontal plane** divides a bilateral body into dorsal and ventral halves by running through the anterior-posterior axis and the right-left axis at right angles to the sagittal plane. A **transverse plane** would cut through a dorsoventral and a right-left axis at right angles to both the sagittal and frontal planes and would result in anterior and posterior portions. Along with bilateral symmetry, we find differentiation of a head end, which has greater perception than the tail end. These forms are suited for forward movement, which is an asset in the search for food and protection.

Most of the sponges lack any symmetry at all and are called **asymmetrical.**

CEPHALIZATION AND POLARITY*

The differentiation of a definite head end is called **cephalization** and is found chiefly in bilaterally symmetrical animals. Cephalization involves the concentration of nervous tissue (brain and sense organs) in the head. This arrangement in an actively moving animal makes possible the most efficient reaction with the environment. Cephalization is always accompanied by a differentiation along an anteroposterior axis (**polarity**). Polarity usually involves gradients of activities between limits, such as between anterior and posterior ends (see axial gradient theory in Chapter 13).

*Refer to Chapter 2, Principle 30.

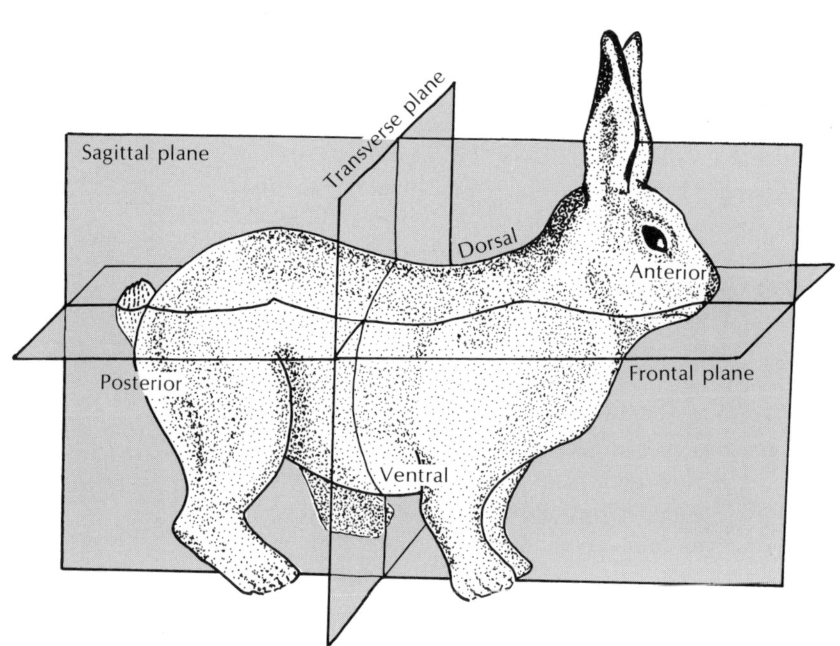

FIG. 7-22
Diagram of bilaterally symmetrical animal showing three planes of symmetry—frontal, transverse, and sagittal.

METAMERISM

Metamerism is a condition in animals in which the body is composed of a linear series of similar body segments. Each segment is called a **metamere,** or **somite.** In forms, such as the earthworm and other annelids, in which metamerism is best represented, the segmental arrangement includes both external and internal structures of several systems. There is repetition of muscles, blood vessels, nerves, and the setae of locomotion. Some other organs, such as those of sex, are repeated in only a few somites. In higher animals much of the segmental arrangement has become obscure.

When the somites are similar, as in the earthworm, the condition is called **homonomous metamerism;** if they are dissimilar, as in the lobster and insect, it is called **heteronomous metamerism.**

Segmentation often shows up in embryonic stages in forms in which metamerism is not so evident in the adult. Muscles of vertebrate animals show a marked metamerism in the embryo but little in the adult. In adult vertebrates the arrangement of the vertebrae is metameric.

True metamerism is found in only three phyla: Annelida, Arthropoda, and Chordata (Fig. 7-23), although superficial segmentation of the ectoderm and the body wall may be found among many diverse groups of animals.

Tagmatization (tagmosis). In connection with segmentation as found in the annelids and arthropods, the segments may be united into functional groups of two or

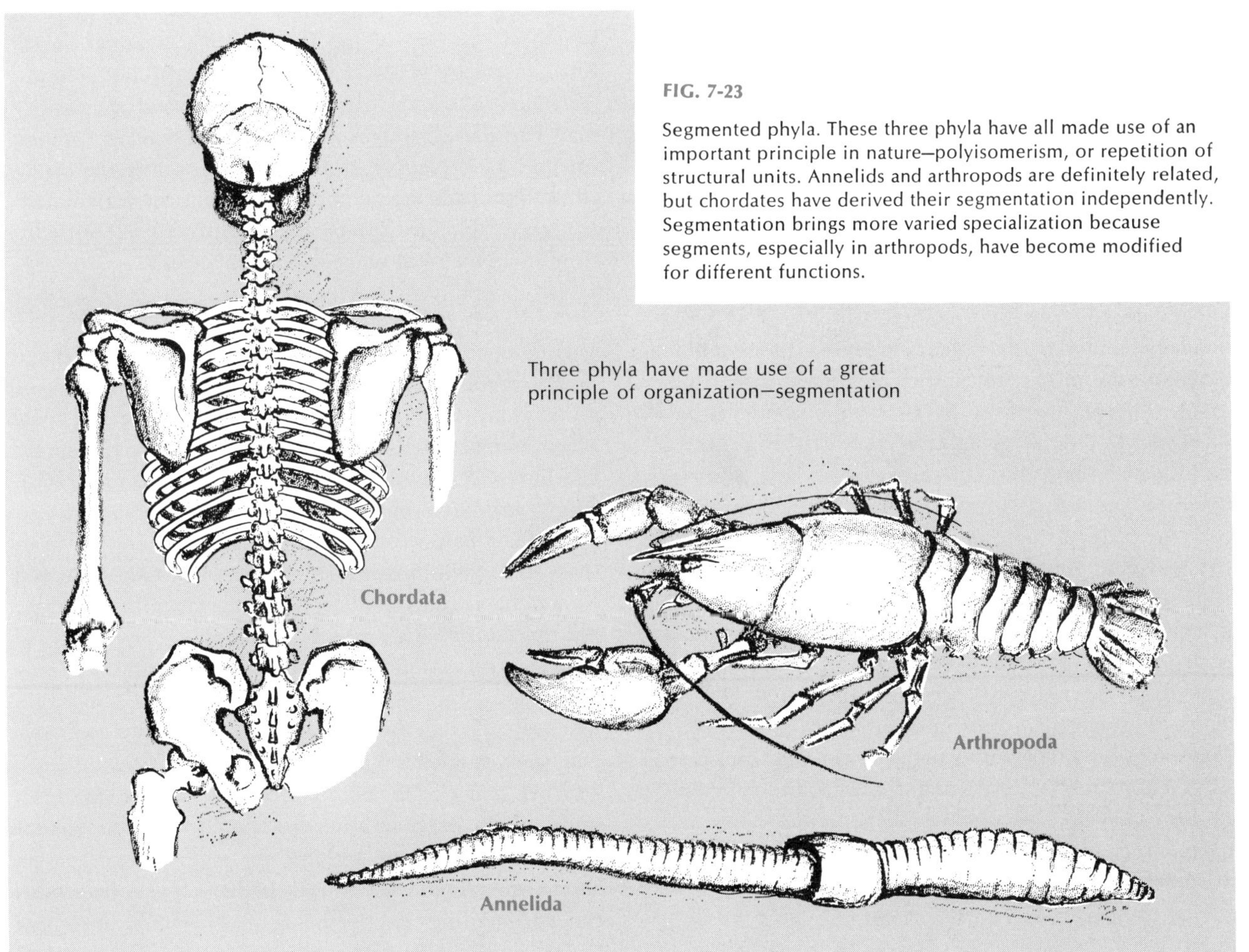

FIG. 7-23

Segmented phyla. These three phyla have all made use of an important principle in nature—polyisomerism, or repetition of structural units. Annelids and arthropods are definitely related, but chordates have derived their segmentation independently. Segmentation brings more varied specialization because segments, especially in arthropods, have become modified for different functions.

more somites, each group being structurally separated from other groups and specialized to perform a certain function for the whole animal. In the primitive forms of both annelids and arthropods the general pattern for the entire organism is a serial succession of identical somites. As will be seen later, tagmosis is more common among the arthropods than in the annelids because the soft-bodied annelid requires the fluid-filled body somite in its locomotion. A good example of tagmosis is the familiar insect that has three tagmata: head, thorax, and abdomen. Each tagma in this animal has a certain number of segments and each is specialized for a general function.

HOMOLOGY, HOMOPLASY, AND ANALOGY*

In comparative studies of animals the concepts of **homology** (similarity in origin), **homoplasy** (similarity in appearance but not in origin), and **analogy** (similarity in function) are frequently used to express relationship of animals, the basic patterns of morphology, and the way these patterns have varied. Two main types of homology are recognized by embryologists—that within a single individual, or **general homology**, and that dealing with structures of two different individuals, or **special homology.** Examples of general homology are the ribs or vertebrae, often called serial homology, and the resemblance between the forelimb and hind limb or the left and right hand, bilateral homology. Special homology refers to correspondence between parts of different animals such as the arm of a man, the wing of a bird, the foreleg of a dog, and the pectoral fin of a fish—all of which are homologous in a broad meaning of the term.

However, homology is a relative term and an absolute meaning has to be guarded against. If one always insists on criteria of similarity of structure and development for strict homology, then many structures that are called homologous do not meet these requirements. For instance, the wing of a bird and the wing of a bat are homologous only in so far as both are derived from pentadactyl forelimbs. Their structures are quite different, but they may be regarded as homoplastic. They are analogous, however, for they have the same function. In examining homologous structures it is best to keep in mind the question: To what extent or degree are they homologous? Convergent evolution, or the independent origin of two similar structures, is caused by independent mutations that are favored under similar environments. Horns have appeared independently many times in mammals, but should they be considered homologous? Perhaps the best criterion for homology would be homologous genes, but this is impossible at our present state of knowledge. Embryologists deal with phenotypes, or the visible expressions, which is not the same thing as the genotypes, or hereditary constitution.

Analogy denotes similarity of function. The wing of a bird is analogous to the wing of a butterfly because they have the same function, but they are not homologous because they are formed from different sources. The term analogy in its usage may or may not denote similarity of origin.

The principle of homology, despite the shortcomings mentioned above, has a wide application in zoology. It is used as an argument for evolution because it is based on the idea of inheritance from common ancestors. Homology is also important in classifying animals. As more is known about animals, chemical identity may become an important aspect of homology among organisms. A plan of archetype with which the structures of animals are compared may thus be formulated, not only from gross morphologic structures, but also from their chemical makeup resemblances.

*Refer to Chapter 2, Principle 25.

SIZE OF ORGANISM

Different species of animals show an enormous range in size, from the tiny protozoan weighing a fraction of a milligram to the whale weighing more than 100 tons. Many animals such as birds and mammals have definite age limits to growth, but in reptiles and fishes growth may continue throughout life, although at a reduced pace. Mammals vary from forms as small as shrews to those as large as whales. One may get the idea that the evolutionary trend has been from the small to the large, but this has not always been the case.

It is a general principle that every organism is distinguished by a characteristic size. Of course, many factors may modify the dimensions of an individual animal, such as nutrition and hormone imbalance.

When unicellular animals reach a certain size they divide, for a size limitation is imposed upon the animal by its surface-volume ratio. Every cell depends on its surface membrane for the exchange of materials with the surrounding environment. The volume increases as the cube of the radius; the surface, as the square of the radius. Since the volume increases much faster than the surface, as the size of the cell increases, the rate of exchange of food and waste decreases. Protozoans can solve the problem by simply dividing when they reach a certain size. Large animals are made up of cells. By keeping their cells small there is a morphologic increase in surface.

The ratio between the nucleus and cytoplasm may be a controlling factor in determining the size of cells, for these two units must be in a certain balance for the efficient functioning of the cell. The importance of cell size as a regulative force in metabolism is strikingly demonstrated by the fact that the volume is very much the same for any cell type and is independent of the animal's size. The cells found in a mouse are about the same size as those found in the largest mammals.

Annotated references

Andrew, W. 1959. Textbook of comparative histology. New York, Oxford University Press. *An excellent comparative histology, with good treatment of the invertebrate groups.*

Arey, L. B. 1968. Human histology. A textbook in outline form, ed. 3. Philadelphia, W. B. Saunders Co. *An excellent summary of histology.*

Ballard, W. W. 1964. Comparative anatomy and embryology. New York, The Ronald Press Co. *An excellent fusion of the two disciplines that form an integrated unit of study.*

Holmes, R. L. 1965. Living tissue. New York, Pergamon Press, Inc. *This little book is an excellent introduction to functional histology.*

Manner, H. W. 1964. Elements of comparative vertebrate embryology. New York, The Macmillan Co. *This clearly-written textbook stresses the general principles that underlie all vertebrate development. Illustrations are simple, but explain well the description involved. This text is highly recommended for all beginning students in embryology.*

Maximow, A. A., and W. Bloom. 1968. A textbook of histology, ed. 9. Philadelphia, W. B. Saunders Co. *An authoritative text for medical students but of great value to all students of biology.*

Montagna, W. 1956. The structure and function of skin. New York, Academic Press, Inc. *A good account of the most versatile organ in the body. Read especially the revealing chapters on the sweat glands, including the apocrine glands. Mainly for the advanced student, but others can profit from its reading.*

Montagna, W., and R. A. Ellis (editors). 1958. The biology of hair growth. New York, Academic Press, Inc. *A book by many eminent scientists on the most modern research of the growth and development of hair.*

Page, I. H. (editor). 1959. Connective tissue, thrombosis, and atherosclerosis. New York, Academic Press, Inc. *Aside from the clinical aspects of this work, there is much general information about the properties of connective tissue found here.*

Romer, A. S. 1962. The vertebrate body, ed. 3. Philadelphia, W. B. Saunders Co. *Good descriptions of body tissues and organs. Will give the beginning student a good knowledge of body structures.*

PART FOUR

MAJOR TYPES OF ANIMAL PATTERNS IN THE ANIMAL KINGDOM

● There are about 1½ million species of animals classified and perhaps far more to be classified in time. Why so much diversity? Species differ in the adaptations that have evolved for diversified environmental niches. Evolution teaches that from the most primitive type of organism all the present species and those of past geologic times have originated. The marked chemical similarities between all living things indicate that they are all part of a single evolutionary process. Evolution implies variations are partly produced by specific changes (mutations) in the genes or by the recombination of genes to form different types of gene pools.

On the basis of evolutionary relationships, classification is laid down. This is the only way that the great diversity of life is truly understood. One of the great problems of zoology is to arrange this diversity so that it may be studied in an orderly and understandable manner. What is involved is to show that nature's structural phylogenies of biomolecular combinations are a natural arrangement. Accidental and superficial similarities must be carefully distinguished from significant ones. A good classification system should furnish valid information about the fundamental body structures and their evolutionary history. Functional differences play more of a minor part in classifying animals because these factors may be more adapted for certain environmental niches, even though the animals concerned may be closely related. Basic functions may also be similar in remotely unrelated forms. The historic record (fossils) is very much restricted and in its overall picture is far from satisfactory. A comparison of genetic codes is a suggested study toward a fruitful understanding of evolutionary relationships, but that line of evidence seems to be far in the future.

All animals have a specific architectural plan or form. As one descends from the higher taxa of a group to the lower, there is an increasing resemblance of design and a more common history. Species of a group (for example, a genus) resemble each other in many ways; classes of a phylum far less so. Architectural patterns are generalized in higher taxa; they become more specialized in adaptive radiation in lower ones. The basic generalized body plan of an animal may be difficult to determine because it is impossible to know all the particulars about its earliest ancestral conditions. Embryologic forms may give significant insights into the early patterns. If one studies a display of representative embryos of each of the vertebrate classes, he will find their resemblances most striking in the early stages but far less so in the later ones.

CHAPTER 8

• HOW ANIMALS ARE CLASSIFIED

DIVERSITY OF ANIMAL LIFE*

● Whatever their differences, all animals fall into certain groups of similar organisms called species. More than 1½ million species of animals have been named, and thousands more are added to the list each year. The fossil record indicates that there has been a vast change in most animal forms in geologic ages. In general the evidence shows that the organic world has passed progressively from simpler to more complex forms. There are excellent reasons for believing that variants have been arising since the beginning of life. If all evolutionary lines of animals that have ever existed were now present, the diversity of animals would have assumed ponderous proportions. Some evolutionists think that present species make up less than 1% of those that have existed in the past. Extinction has been, therefore, a major feature in the development of life.

Why extinction has occurred can only be guessed and may never be known. Inability to adapt to changing environments, invasion of new diseases into a biotic community, failure of heredity to respond to selection pressures, and overspecialization may be possible causes for extinction. Recently a cause of mass extinction has been proposed by K. D. Terry and W. H. Tucker, who based their theory on the calculated explosion of a supernova (super giant variable star) every 50 million years that releases 500 roentgens of radiation to the earth. It is known that doses of 200 to 700 roentgens are lethal to many animals, and it is thus possible that large populations could be eliminated. Many stocks of animals in the past developed into highly specialized groups and then became extinct. One group has often supplanted another group in the long evolution of life. Some lines, within a relatively short time, have given rise to numerous species; others have remained virtually unchanged for millions of years and few species have evolved. However, diversity of life in general seems to have been greatest in high and constant temperatures, as far as terrestrial evolution is concerned. Biotic diversity depends on a time factor in which plants and animals have an opportunity to evolve in an uninterrupted fashion. Tropical regions have been least affected by climatic fluctuations.

The student no doubt wonders about this diversity of life. What produced it? Why do some groups have more variations than others? What has been the role of the environment in this diversity? If our concept about the origin of life is correct, why is not life the same the world over? No outright answers can be given to all these questions, but the student in his study of the many evolutionary patterns may arrive at some of the answers on his own.

CONCEPT OF SPECIES

Although the species concept is of the utmost importance in biology, most biologists do not agree on a single rigid definition that applies to all cases. The species is fundamental to any form of classification, and in the light of the new biology it must be considered a significant level of integration in the structure of matter. In early concepts the species were considered static units, convenient merely for classification. Evolution later showed that these arbitrary divisions of living matter were ever changing and not fixed, and that they were integrated on the basis of common ancestry and relationship. Genetics changed the concept further by stressing population equilibrium with the environment and the sharing of common gene (hereditary unit) pools. Morphologic characters have always been given high priority in the diagnosis of species, but careful analysis clearly shows that other characteristics, such as physiologic reactions, behavior patterns, chemical constituents, and ecologic requirements, also afford a basis for classifying organisms into species units.

The criteria for diagnosing a species naturally vary

*Refer to Chapter 2, Principles 5 and 9.

with those characteristics that are being stressed. The term "species characters" usually refers to those attributes that distinguish one species from all other species. Criteria commonly employed deal with morphologic characters, reproductive characteristics, range of population, ecologic segregation, genetic composition, and isolating mechanisms. The property that maintains the integrity of a species more than any other property, especially among biparental organisms, is interbreeding. The members of a species can interbreed freely with each other, produce fertile offspring, and share in a common genetic pool. Interbreeding of different species is usually either physically impossible or produces sterile offspring. There are, of course, exceptions, but it is mainly a matter of degree of frequency in these instances because such cases are rare compared with the general population of species. Species are thus usually considered genetically closed systems, whereas races within a species are open systems and can exchange genes.

In defining a species most biologists have shunned purely morphologic distinctions. In contrast, genetic implications are stated or implied in the definitions. A **species thereore may be defined as a group of organisms of interbreeding natural populations that are reproductively isolated from other groups and that share in common gene pools** (Mayr and Dobzhansky).

CRITERIA USED IN CLASSIFYING ANIMALS

Early taxonomists classified animals into groups according to anatomic and physiologic characters common to the group in question. Species were regarded as fixed, unchanged units. Any slight variations among the members were largely ignored or were considered accidental. A species was a type of primeval pattern or archetype divinely created. The concept of archetype was also applied to taxa higher than the species, in which the common characters were broader and fewer but revealed an archetypal pattern of a higher degree.

When the evolutionary concept evolved and it was found that species were not fixed units but have evolved one from another and often grow into each other, the criteria of taxonomy used by the systemist underwent a gradual change. At first each species was supposed to have a type that was used as a standard, and all individuals were fitted into that type which they most nearly resembled. Thus the typologic specimen was by the taxonomists duly labeled and deposited in some prestigious center such as a museum. Anyone classifying a particular group would always take the pains to compare his specimens with the available typologic specimens. Since variations from the type specimen nearly always occurred, these differences were supposed to be due to imperfections that naturally happened and were considered of minor significance.

This method of classifying persisted for a long period of time (and still does to some extent), although the broad basis of evolutionary descent as the foundation of classification was becoming more firmly established. The development of ecologic principles with the emphasis placed on population studies no doubt was responsible for the modern interpretation of the species. Anatomic and physiologic characters must be considered in their total distribution within the individuals of a population. No one pattern can be taken as truly representative nor can be thought of as an idealized abstraction of the characters of an individual. The species must be regarded as a population made up of individuals of common descent within a similar environment of a definite region and uniquely set apart from other species by a distinct evolutionary role. The test of determining the species status of an individual animal is to ascertain just where it fits into a definite population group.

PROBLEMS OF CLASSIFICATION

There are many complications in the taxonomy of animals, and only a few need be mentioned here. In the first place, the totality of the genes of a species is coadapted with each other, but its gene complex may be polluted by invasion of foreign genes, and such hybridization could produce striking changes in systematic relations that are often difficult to figure out. Such hybridization is common among plants and throws confusion into systematics. It is not known how common this process may be among animals, but it may be said that a complex of coadapted genes is a protection against pollution from other genes.

In polytypic species or a species with several subspecies over an extensive geographic range, each population can breed successfully with an adjacent population, but those at the ends of the range are intersterile. The leopard frog, *Rana pipieus,* represents such a species. This species has an extensive range, covering a large part of North America. The frogs of Wisconsin can interbreed with those of Iowa or Nebraska, but not with those in Mexico. Polytypic species are found in many populations of animals. However, these two subspecies (from Wisconsin and Mexico) meet one of the fundamental requirements of a species, that is, inability to interbreed successfully. Are these subspecies actually true species?

Also, conclusions about common ancestries are not always valid because of lack of information about their fossil history, etc. Two structural patterns may have similar adaptive responses to survival requirements, but they may have developed these similar patterns independently without the benefit of common ancestry. Evolutionary knowledge is more precise with lower taxa, but with higher ones ancestral information is largely speculative, or it may be based on structural resemblances among the animals that now exist. This explains why classification of a group may vary from one generation of zoologists to another as new knowledge is acquired.

EARLY HISTORY OF TAXONOMY

Although Aristotle, the great Greek philosopher and student of zoology, attempted to classify animals on the basis of their structural similarities, little was done about the grouping of animals until the English naturalist John Ray (1627-1705) brought forth his system of classification. He employed structural likenesses as the basis of his classification and worked out a number of groups. He seems to have been the first biologist to have a modern concept of species and paved the way for the work of Carolus Linnaeus (1707-1778), who gave us the modern scheme of classification. Linnaeus was a Swedish botanist connected with the University of Uppsala. He had a great talent for collecting and classifying objects, especially flowers. Through the collaboration of workers in all parts of the world, Linnaeus worked out a fairly extensive system of classification for both plants and animals. His scheme of classification was published in his great classic work *Systema Naturae,* which had gone through ten editions by 1758. Linnaeus emphasized structural features of plants and animals in his methods of classification. His classification at first was largely arbitrary and artificial, and he believed strongly in the fixity of species. He divided the animal kingdom down to species, and according to his scheme each species was given a distinctive name. He recognized four classes of vertebrates and two classes of invertebrates. These classes were divided by him into orders, the orders into genera, and the genera into species. Since his knowledge of animals was limited, his lower groups, such as the genera, were very inclusive and included animals now placed in several orders or families. As a result of this, much of his classification has been drastically altered, yet the basic principle of his scheme is followed at the present time.

Although Linnaeus recognized four units, or taxa, in classification—class, order, genus, and species—since his time other major units of grouping have been added, such as the phylum and the family, so that the units now used are **phylum, class, order, family, genus,** and **species.** The major units can be subdivided into finer distinctions, such as subphylum, subclass, suborder, subfamily, subgenus, and subspecies.

BINOMIAL NOMENCLATURE AND THE NAMING OF ANIMALS

Linnaeus early adopted the use of two names for each species: the genus name and the species name. These words are from Latin or in Latinized form, because Latin was the language of scholars and universally understood. The generic name is usually a noun and the specific name an adjective. For instance, the scientific name of the common robin is *Turdus migratorius* (L. *turdus,* thrush; *migratorius,* of the migratory habit). This usage of two names to designate a species is called **binomial nomenclature.** There are times when a species is divided into subspecies, in which case a **trinomial nomenclature** is employed. Thus to distinguish the southern form of the robin from the eastern robin, the scientific term *Turdus migratorius achrustera* (duller color) is employed for the southern type. Taxa lower than subspecies are sometimes employed when four words are used in the scientific name, the last one usually standing for **variety.** In this latter case the nomenclature is **quadrinomial.** The trinomial and quadrinomial nomenclatures are really additions to the linnaean system, which is basically binomial.

BASIS FOR FORMATION OF TAXONOMIC UNITS (TAXA)

Taxonomy, as already mentioned, emphasizes the natural relationships among the various animal types. Descent from a common ancestor makes for similarity in character, and the more recent this descent the closer the animals are grouped in taxonomic units. For instance, the genera of a particular family show less diversity than do the families of an order. Families must take more time to become diverse, and thus their common ancestor must have been more remote than that of the genera. The same principle applies to the higher categories, and therefore we should expect the common ancestors of the various phyla to be much older than those of classes. This principle, however, cannot be applied too rigidly to all groups of animals, for some have been much faster in their evolution than others. As we shall see later, some mollusks have taxa that have changed little in the course of millions of years. Some of their genera are actually much older than orders and classes in other groups.

As an illustration, one may use the following criteria to distinguish the phyla of the animal kingdom:

1. Unicellular or multicellular
2. Body saclike or tube-within-a-tube
3. Diploblastic or triploblastic
4. Segmented or nonsegmented
5. Presence or absence of a digestive system
6. Type of symmetry—asymmetry, bilateral, or radial
7. Presence or absence of appendages
8. Jointed or nonjointed appendages
9. Type of skeleton—exoskeleton or endoskeleton
10. Presence or absence of a notochord
11. Presence or absence of a coelom

IMPORTANCE OF TAXONOMY

Taxonomy aims to apply a name tag to every species of animal in the animal kingdom. Since each species has a universal specific name, students of all languages know what animal is meant when the scientific name is designated. Common names vary with the different languages or even in different parts of one country, but the scientific ones are universal. The woodpecker *Colaptes auratus luteus,* for instance, is called the golden-winged woodpecker, the flicker, the high-hole, etc., depending on the part of the United States in which it is found. But it has only one valid scientific name wherever it is found.

WHY CLASSIFICATION VARIES AMONG DIFFERENT AUTHORITIES

Taxa are the outcome of changing concepts of classification and therefore are subject to man's diverse judgments. One may expect differences of opinion among taxonomists.

1. It is very difficult to appraise all the fine distinctions among animals. The fact that two animals have similar characteristics does not establish their relationship. The similar characteristics may have developed entirely independently of each other, by convergent evolution, with no common ancestry involved. Taxonomists do not always agree about these lines of descent.

2. Many thousands of new species are named each year. Not all of these are well defined and more will have to be found out about them before they are firmly established in animal classification. For this reason much of the work of the taxonomist consists of revising what has already been described rather than describing new species.

3. There is some diversity of opinion among zoologists about subdivision of groups. Some are "splitters," inclined to much subdivision; others are "lumpers," preferring to lump together minor groups.

4. The **law of priority** also brings about frequent changes. The first name proposed for a taxonomic unit that is published and meets other proper specifications has priority over all subsequent names proposed. The rejected duplicate names are called **synonyms.** It is amazing sometimes to find that species that have been well established for years must undergo a change in terminology when some industrious systematist discovers that on the basis of priority, or for some other reason, the species are misnamed.

RULES OF SCIENTIFIC NOMENCLATURE

To prevent confusion in the field of taxonomy and to lay down a uniform code of rules for the classification of animals, there was established in 1898 an International Commission on Zoological Nomenclature. This Commission meets from time to time to formulate rules and to make decisions in connection with taxonomic work.

The *Basic Rules of Nomenclature* laid down by the International Commission on Zoological Nomenclature are as follows:

1. The system of nomenclature adopted is the binomial system as described by Linnaeus in the tenth edition of his *Systema Naturae* (1758). This system is modified in some cases to include a trinomial nomenclature when a subspecific name is used.

2. Zoological nomenclature is independent of botanical nomenclature and may employ the same names for taxonomic units, but this procedure is not recommended.

3. The scientific names of animals must be either Latin or Latinized in form.

4. The genus name is a single word, nominative singular, and begins with a capital letter.

5. The species name may be a single or compound word, is printed with an initial lower case letter, and is usually an adjective in grammatical agreement with the generic name. In case the species name is derived from a personal name, it may be written with a capital initial letter. When a subspecies name is used, it also has an initial small letter.

6. The author of a scientific name is the one who first definitely published the name in connection with a description of the animal. The author's name should follow the species name and should rarely be abbreviated.

7. The law of priority states that the first published name in connection with a genus, species, or subspecies is the one recognized. All duplicate names are called synonyms.

8. When the genus name is not the one under which a species is placed by the original author, or if the generic name is changed, the original author's name is placed in parentheses. For instance, the name *Rana gryllus* was given by Le Conte to the common cricket frog, but since the generic name has been changed, it is now often written *Acris gryllus* (Le Conte).

9. A type specimen is the particular specimen or specimens on which the name of the species was established. It is customary for taxonomists to place such types in public museums or other places where they can be available to those who are interested. Such types must retain their original name even if the species is later divided. Whenever a new genus is described, one species is taken as the type of the genus and also retains the original name in case the genus is later divided into two or more genera. No two genera of animals may have the same name.

10. The name of a family is formed by adding *idae* to the stem of the name of the type genus; the name of a subfamily, by adding *inae*.

RECENT TRENDS IN TAXONOMY

Since the concept of organic evolution, biologic units have been classified mainly on the basis of common descent. But it has not always been clear just what this evolutionary relationship is in all cases. Only the fossil record can supply convincing evidence, and that is often lacking. One of the problems is to determine the exact nature of characters by which organisms are classified. Another is the lack of agreement regarding what constitutes a species. The taxon of the species must always represent a central role in all schemes of classification, but the current interest in population studies has changed the widely held biologic concept of species. To determine the nature, properties, and genetic variations of species, data from many disciplines, such as genetics, cytology, ecology, behavior, and physiology, are brought to bear on the problem. The old concept of species as distinct and set apart by definite criteria is being replaced by the concept that a species is an intrabreeding, reproductively isolated gene pool, with the variations found within a dynamic population.

In systematics it is necessary to recognize the characters that have taxonomic value and to make a proper analysis of the data (characters) before assigning them to the proper taxon. Often the analysis of the data involves a statistical approach. In 1763 the Frenchman M. Adanson proposed a scheme of classification that involved the grouping of individuals into a particular species according to the number of shared characteristics. Thus each member of a species would have a majority of the total characteristics of the taxon, even though some of its characters are not shared with others of the same taxon. Such a classification has quantitative rather than qualitative significance. This classification lacks the phyletic relationship of evolutionary taxonomy (Adanson lived long before Darwin's time). However, this scheme has been revived (especially by plant taxonomists) in recent years and has given rise to **numerical taxonomy,** which makes use of the computer method for ascertaining calculations of similarity. Similar and dissimilar characteristics are simply fed into a computer and an analysis is made of its calculations for determining the taxon of a group.

Many other techniques are now being developed in systematics that offer great promise in solving problems of phylogenetic relationships, evolution, and taxonomic proceedings. Refinements of analytical methods are now being employed in electrophoresis, protein and genetic homology, blood groups, chromosomal analysis, etc. with this in view.

In recent years the investigators B. H. Hoyer, B. J. McCarthy, and E. T. Bolton have presented a molecular approach to the systematics of higher forms. They have presented evidence to show that there were certain homologies among polynucleotide sequences in the

DNA molecules of such different forms as fish and man. These sequences appear to be genes that have been retained with little change throughout vertebrate evolution. Possible phenotypic expressions of these homologous sequences are bilateral symmetry, notochord, hemoglobin, etc. By using a single strand of DNA from one species, short radioactive pieces of a DNA strand from another species, and mixing the strands together, it was found that some of the smaller strands paired with similar regions on the large strand, indicating that the paired parts had common genes. As more information is acquired, this process may well be used as another criterion of relationship.

SOME EXAMPLES OF SCIENTIFIC NOMENCLATURE

The examples listed in Table 8-1 will give you some idea of how animals are classified on the basis of relationship and likeness. Of all animals the anthropoid apes are generally agreed to be nearest man in relationship and structural features. In contrast to man and the gorilla are the frog, also a vertebrate like the others but diverging from them much earlier, and the little katydid, which is not a chordate but belongs to a lower phylum.

Annotated references

Blair, W. F., et al. 1968. Vertebrates of the United States, ed. 2. New York, McGraw-Hill Book Co. *An up-to-date description and classification of American vertebrates. Extremely valuable to all zoologists.*

Manville, R. H. 1952. The principles of taxonomy. Turtox News **30**: nos. 1 and 2. *A concise account of classification procedures.*

Mayr, E., E. G. Linsley, and R. C. Usinger. 1953. Methods and principles of systematic zoology. New York, McGraw-Hill Book Co. *The present status of the rules and regulations of taxonomy is well discussed.*

Mayr, E. (editor). 1957. The species problem. Washington, D. C., American Association for the Advancement of Science. *This is a symposium by many authorities on the problems of species.*

Rothschild, L. 1961. A classification of living animals. New York, John Wiley & Sons, Inc.

Schenk, E. T., and J. H. McMasters. 1948. Procedures in taxonomy, including a reprint of the International Rules of Zoological Nomenclature with summaries of opinions rendered, ed. 2. Stanford, Calif., Stanford University Press.

Simpson, G. G. 1945. The principles of classification and a classification of mammals. Bull. Amer. Museum Natural History, vol. 85. *A well-presented account of the bases of taxonomic procedures.*

Simpson, G. G. 1961. Principles of animal taxonomy. New York, Columbia University Press. *An outstanding contribution of the basic principles of systematics and morphologic diversity.*

TABLE 8-1

Examples of classification of animals

	Man	Gorilla	Grass frog	Katydid
Phylum	Chordata	Chordata	Chordata	Arthropoda
Subphylum	Vertebrata	Vertebrata	Vertebrata	
Class	Mammalia	Mammalia	Amphibia	Insecta
Subclass	Eutheria	Eutheria		
Order	Primates	Primates	Salientia	Orthoptera
Suborder	Anthropoidea	Anthropoidea		
Family	Hominidae	Simiidae	Ranidae	Tettigoniidae
Subfamily			Raninae	
Genus	*Homo*	*Gorilla*	*Rana*	*Scudderia*
Species	*sapiens*	*gorilla*	*pipiens*	*furcata*
Subspecies			*pipiens*	*Brunner*

CHAPTER 9

• PHYLOGENY OF ANIMALS

THE FIRST ANIMALS*

● The origin of life from nonliving beginnings may have taken more than 2 billion years. During this time there occurred the preliminary synthesis of organic compounds, and later of macromolecular systems that were the forerunners of the first living things. This biopoesis therefore included the abiotic synthesis of macromolecular systems, followed by biogenesis, or the transformation of the macromolecular systems into the first living things.

The nature of the first life is purely speculative. It is generally agreed that such primitive forms could not now survive in the face of stronger competitors such as bacteria and fungi. It must have been very simple of construction, judged by biogenetic standards of the present day. The earliest form of life must have had the basic characteristics of a living form, such as self-duplication and some capacity of metabolism and adaptive adjustments to its environment.

One naturally thinks of viruses as giving some insight into what early life must have been like. Viruses are the smallest biologic structures that have all the information needed for their own reproduction. They consist of a shell of protein enclosing a core of nucleic acid (DNA or RNA). The protein shell is not only protective but may serve for entrance into the walls of living cells that are attacked by the virus. Leaving the protein coat behind, the nucleic acid enters the cell, which it causes to produce large numbers of virus particles. In time the cell ruptures and the viruses are set free to attack other cells. Viruses require an electron microscope to be seen for their size is smaller (100 to 2000 Å) than one-half the wavelength of violet light, which is the minimum size for the light microscope. But viruses are not cells and not organisms. Some viruses have the power to arise as mere fragments broken off from the nucleic acid material of a donor cell. These fragments have the power to direct the cell to form the protective mantle around the virus. Viruses are inactive in the free state and become reactivated when they enter a new cell.

Since plants and animals cannot be separated by biologic criteria, it is a moot question to state whether or not the earliest organisms were unicellular plants or animals. The first true animals were probably metazoans and heterotrophic by nature, although they could have been parasitic. They were undoubtedly simpler than the bacteria and were able to live an independent existence with the simplest of requirements for duplication, metabolism, and environmental adjustments.

*Refer to Chapter 2, Principles 23 and 24.

ORIGIN OF METAZOA

The origin of the multicellular animals (Metazoa) has posed many problems to zoologists. It is generally believed that both plant and animal traits evolved gradually from the Protista. It has been customary to pick out flagellates as the ancestors of the many-celled animals. Some of the primitive flagellates had both ameboid and flagellate methods of locomotion, which could explain the types of gametes found among present metazoans. Many flagellates have tendencies to form colonies of few to many cells, and it is possible to pick out a progressive series of such aggregations of gradual complexity from simple to complex (Fig. 9-1). Thus *Chlamydomonas* (1 cell), *Gonium* (4 to 16 cells), *Pandorina* (16 cells), *Eudorina* (32 cells), *Pleodorina* (32 to 128 cells), and *Volvox* (many thousand cells). The zooids, or cells, may be loosely connected or may be held together in a mucilaginous jelly. *Pleodorina* has its cells differentiated into a few somatic cells (sterile) and those capable of reproduction. This differentiation is carried further in *Volvox,* in which the majority of cells cannot reproduce. In all the others each zooid is capable of both asexual and sexual reproduction. These examples merely show phases of development as arbitrarily arranged but do not afford evidence that one gave rise to another. It is thought by some zoologists that it is unlikely flagellates evolved beyond the colony.

The Metazoa are often considered a diphyletic group, with sponges (Parazoa) as one separate line and the Eumetazoa as the other. Sponges probably arose from Protozoa and represent complex flagellate colonies at a differentiated cellular level, with a tendency toward a tissue level of construction. Their digestive collar cells are similar to the protozoan collar flagellates. Sponges also have many other differences in construction and embryonic development.

FIG. 9-1

Some flagellates live in clumps or colonies, joined at their outer surfaces or enclosed in gelatinous envelope. In *Gonium* all cells are alike and each may divide to form new colony. Some colonies have division of labor, possessing both somatic and reproductive cells. *Pleodorina illinoisensis* has 4 somatic and 28 reproductive cells; *Volvox* has hundreds of somatic and only a few reproductive cells. *Chlamydomonas* is solitary and does not form colonies.

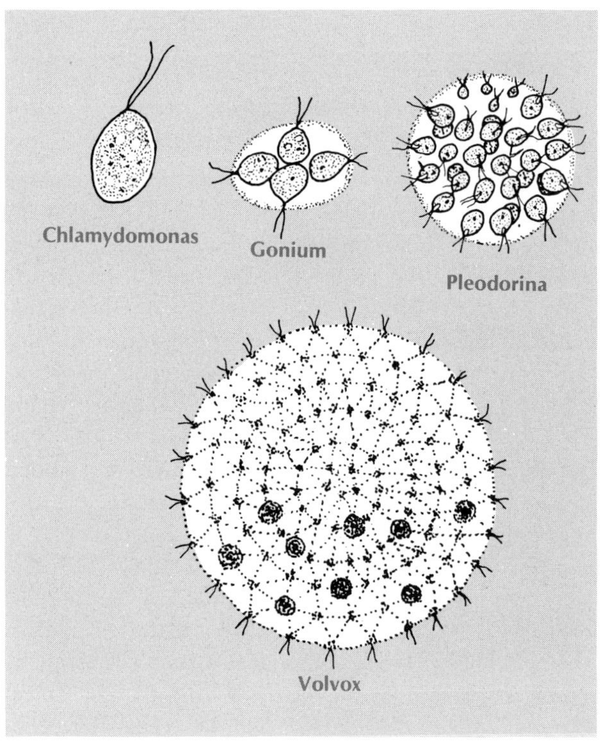

There is also a theory of metazoan origin from **syncytial ciliates.** This theory differs from the colonial theory just described in that the whole animal (a ciliate) is at first a syncytium (multinucleated) and later becomes multicellular by the development of internal cell boundaries. According to this theory, the first true metazoans were the flatworms resembling the acoel flatworms that are considered to be the most primitive bilateral animals. The chief advantage of the syncytial theory is that some syncytial ciliates have an established bilateral symmetry and an anteroposterior axis. But there are many objections to the theory because it implies that coelenterates with radial symmetry are derived from flatworms and not the reverse. This theory also fails to account for the flagellate sperm cell so characteristic of the metazoan pattern.

A third theory favors the origin of the Metazoa from plantlike protozoans (the Metaphyta theory). According to this theory, it is easy to explain the transformation of plantlike protozoans to cellular metaphytes because each group absorb nutriment from each side equally. However, the metazoan has a mouth and a different method of nutrition; although some ciliates do have a mouth and gullet, such specialized requirements were later developments, and it is difficult to think that metazoans could be derived from such specialized forms.

Other theories have been proposed for the origin of the Metazoa, but objections can be urged against all of them. Some seem more logical than others, but all are purely speculative, and definite evidence is lacking in every case. It is possible that metazoans had a polyphyletic origin, that is, the major groups may have evolved independently of each other and in different ways. Evolution may have been channeled in certain ways because of particular physicochemical conditions of the environment, and relationships may have played little or no definite roles in the process.

PHYLOGENY AND ONTOGENY

As we have seen in the discussion on embryology earlier, all eumetazoans in their embryonic development pass through certain common stages. These are in succession the zygote, cleavage, blastula, gastrula, and pharyngula. The German evolutionist E. Haeckel of the last century thought that these successive stages of individual development corresponded to an adult form of an ancestral form. Thus the zygote would represent the protozoan or protistan stage; the blastula, the hollow colonial protozoans; and the gastrula, the adult coelenterate of the present. The human embryo with gill depressions in the neck was believed to represent the stage when our adult ancestors were fishes. On this basis he gave his generalization; ontogeny (individual development) repeats phylogeny (evolutionary descent).

This hypothesis of Haeckel is often called the **gastrea** hypothesis. It is based primarily on coelenterate development that occurs in a different way from what Haeckel supposed. For instance, he considered embolic gastrulation to be the primitive pattern, although it is now known that such gastrulation is rare in coelenterates. Moreover, he thought that the gastrea to have been the common ancestor of all eumetazoans.

K. E. von Baer, the embryologist, had noticed long before Haeckel the general similarity between the embryonic stages and the adults of certain animals, but arrived at a more correct interpretation. According to his view, the earlier stages of all embryos tend to look alike, but as development proceeds, the embryos become more dissimilar. There are exceptions to this generalization because the young of related species differ more than do the adults, for example, the feeding larvae (caterpillars) compared with the reproducing adults (butterflies).

The recapitulation of Haeckel would be correct only when changes in development were added on as new stages at the end of development, but the addition of new stages at ontogeny is not the usual course of development. When changes in ontogeny that have evolutionary significance do happen, they are more evident in later stages. Often there are special adaptations to embryonic life that are not found in the adult condition, such as the fetal membranes of the amniotes, and are of evolutionary importance because similar structures are absent in lower vertebrates. New development usually occurs by **developmental divergence,** by which a new path of embryonic development diverges away from a preexisting path. This is strikingly shown in neoteny, in which larval or embryonic characters are retained and the organism does not develop into the customary adult. Instead, it develops sex organs and functions as a new type of animal. It may be stated in conclusion that ontogeny repeats ontogeny, with variations, and that phylogeny consists of a series of ontogenies. In whatever ways animals have evolved, they have in general followed four important guidelines in their morphogenesis:

1. Development of germ layers from diploblastic to triploblastic conditions
2. Formation of a body cavity
3. Emergence of adaptations suitable for land and air existence from aquatic ancestral life
4. Grouping of higher metazoans into the great divisions of protostomes and deuterostomes

Much of our future discussion of the nature of the various animal groups will center around the adaptability of these guidelines.

PHYLOGENY OF ANIMALS

Phylogeny is the science of ancestral history and racial relationships. Exact relationships of the members of the animal kingdom are often vague or nonexistent according to our present knowledge. This is especially the case with the large major groups (phyla), regarding which there is much disagreement among authorities. Within smaller taxonomic units (species, genera, orders, etc.) relationships have been more definitely established. The student should therefore remember that the sequence in which zoologists present the various groups does not indicate that each group has arisen directly from the one that has preceded it. Most existing forms are related indirectly to each other through common ancestors that are now extinct. Most common ancestors were sufficiently generalized in structure to give rise to many divergent groups, but such ancestors have either undergone evolution or else have become extinct because of their inability to adapt to a changing environment. The closing of the gaps in relationships is very much like supplying the missing parts of a jigsaw puzzle. If many parts are gone, the problem becomes complicated. However, if similarity of structure and development mean anything in an evolutionary interpretation, then it is obvious that certain groups are closely connected because the evidence stands out clearly. It is a generalization widely accepted in biology that if two different organisms share many common traits, it is logical to assume that there is a relationship basis for this similarity and that it has not been due to convergent or coincidental evolution.

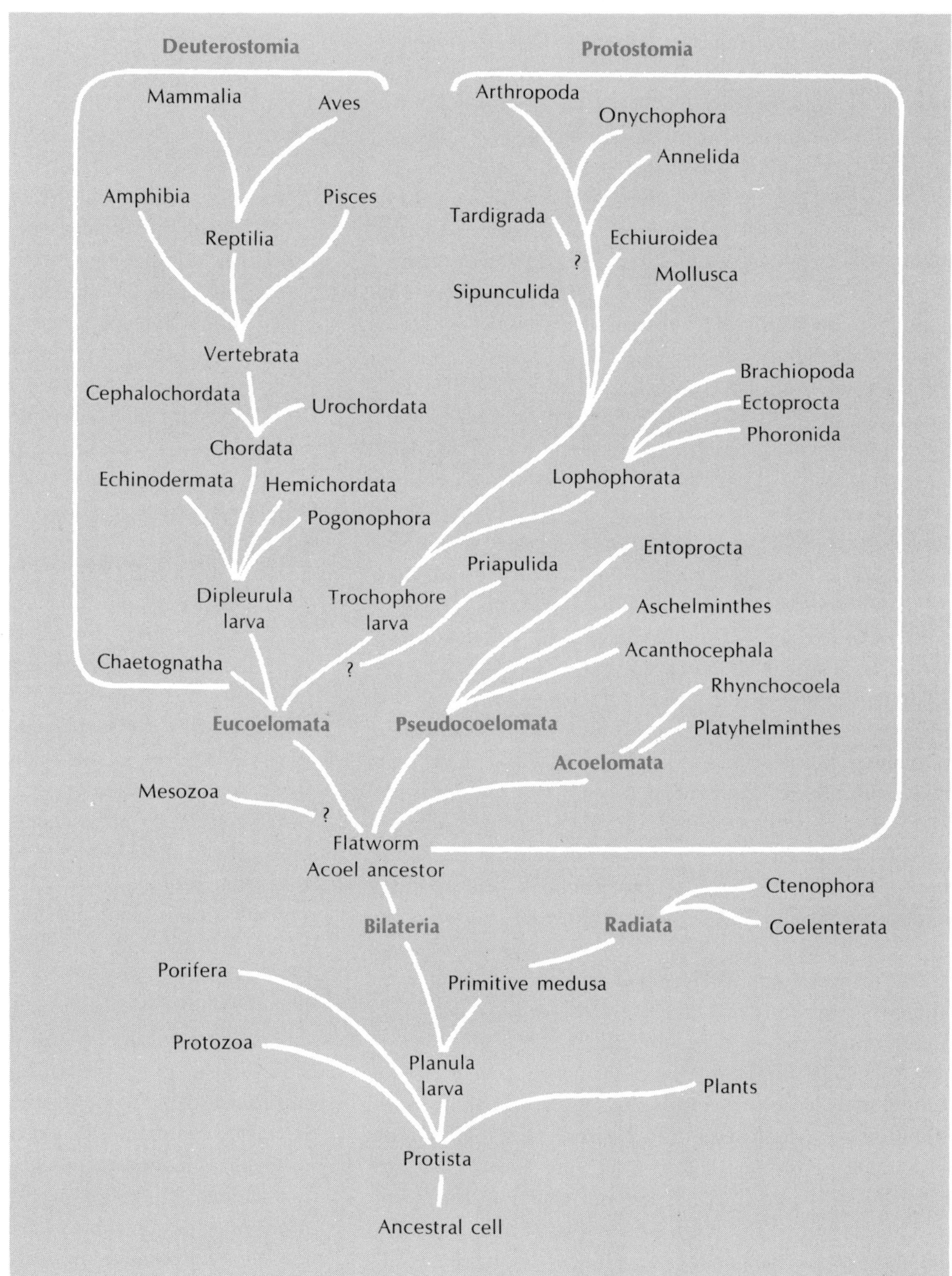

FIG. 9-2

Diagram of animal phylogeny (hypothetical). The basis for such a tree phylogeny is evolutionary relationship, or common ancestry, but such information is scanty. In general, time is represented by vertical levels—the higher the branch, the more recent the taxon—but this is also uncertain because fossil record is incomplete. Interpretations of relationship are based on common characters, similarity of embryologic development, basic structural patterns, fossils, etc.

With all the shortcomings any phylogenetic tree (Fig. 9-2) must possess, such a scheme of hypothetical relations has some value in visualizing the evolutionary picture, provided it is not stressed too dogmatically. Many lines of evidence will be pointed out in the discussions of the various invertebrate phyla. The phylogenetic tree here presented on the basis of these evidences may serve to tie the phyla together in the evolutionary blueprint. A better way, perhaps, to represent phylogeny is by a fan-shaped scheme because there is little difference in the age of most phyla from a geologic viewpoint (Simpson).

LARGER DIVISIONS OF ANIMAL KINGDOM

Although the phylum is often considered to be the largest and most distinctive taxonomic unit, zoologists often find it convenient to combine phyla under a few large groups because of certain common embryologic and anatomic features. Such large divisions may have a logical basis, for the members of some of these arbitrary groups are not only united by common traits, but evidence also indicates some relationship in phylogenetic descent.

Subkingdoms, branches, and grades. Hyman has proposed a scheme for some of these larger groupings that should give the student a more comprehensive view of animal classification.

- Subkingdom Protozoa (acellular)—phylum Protozoa
- Subkingdom Metazoa (cellular)—all other phyla
  - Branch A (Mesozoa)—phylum Mesozoa
  - Branch B (Parazoa)—phylum Porifera
  - Branch C (Eumetazoa)—all other phyla
    - Grade I (Radiata)—phyla Coelenterata (Cnidaria), Ctenophora
    - Grade II (Bilateria)—all other phyla
      - Acoelomata—phyla Platyhelminthes, Rhynchocoela
      - Pseudocoelomata—phyla Acanthocephala, Aschelminthes, Entoprocta
      - Eucoelomata—all other phyla

Protostome and deuterostome—divisions of bilateral animals. The largest group of animals, the Bilateria, may be arranged into two major divisions—Protostomia and Deuterostomia. The characteristics and the phyla of each are as follows:

Protostomia—Mouth usually formed from blastopore; schizocoelous formation of body cavity (coelom); mostly spiral cleavage; determinate or mosaic pattern of egg cleavage; ciliated larva (when present) a trochophore or trochosphere type. Examples: phyla Platyhelminthes, Aschelminthes, Rhynchocoela, Annelida, Mollusca, Arthropoda, and others.

Deuterostomia—Anus formed from blastopore; enterocoelous formation of coelom; mostly radial cleavage; indeterminate or equipotential pattern of egg cleavage; ciliated larva (when present) a pluteus type. Examples: phyla Echinodermata, Hemichordata, Pogonophora, and Chordata.

These divisions form the two main lines of evolutionary ascent in the animal kingdom and are often referred to as the diphyletic theory of phylogeny.

Annotated references

Anfinson, C. B. 1959. The molecular basis of evolution. New York, John Wiley & Sons, Inc. *This book has made a great impact on all serious students of the life sciences. Chapter 1, although brief, will give the student a good phylogenetic orientation.*

De Beer, G. R. 1940. Embryos and ancestors. New York, Oxford University Press. *An excellent evaluation of the biogenetic law.*

Hyman, L. H. 1940-1967. The invertebrates, vols. 1-6. New York, McGraw-Hill Book Co. *Informative discussions on the phylogenies of most of the invertebrates are treated in this outstanding series of monographs.*

Kerkut, G. A. 1960. The implications of evolution. New York, Pergamon Press, Inc. *Many long-established concepts are rather rudely upset in this informative treatise.*

Marcus, E. 1958. On the evolution of animal phyla. Quart. Rev. Biol. 33:24-58.

Moore, J. A. (editor). 1965. Ideas in modern biology. New York, The Natural History Press. *Includes papers of the Plenary Symposia of the XVI International Congress of Zoology held at Washington, D. C., August 20-27, 1963. Papers deal with genetics, cell biology, development, evolution, phylogeny, and behavior.*

Romer, A. S. 1968. The procession of life. Cleveland, The World Publishing Co., Inc. *An excellent summary of the evolutionary development of the structure, physiology, and habits of the major groups of animals.*

CHAPTER 10

• PHYLUM PROTOZOA* (UNICELLULAR OR CELLULAR ANIMALS)

BIOLOGIC PRINCIPLES

Protoplasmic level of animal organization

1. The life activities are all carried on within the limits of a single plasma membrane.
2. The protozoan is thus a complete organism and functionally and structurally is not the same as a metazoan cell.
3. By tradition, protozoans are considered as single cells, but by the concept of the organism they may be regarded as a protoplasmic mass that is not divisible into cells and is therefore **acellular.**

Biologic contributions

1. Specialization in Protozoa is mainly confined to the cytoplasm where certain areas are organized into **organelles,** but nuclear material may also undergo specialization (macronuclei and micronuclei).
2. Asexual reproduction involving the behavior of the nuclear elements of chromosomes and genes is first developed in Protozoa (and probably bacteria) and is the method of division (mitosis) in all cell bodies of Metazoa.
3. In certain protozoans the behavior of conjugant mates may indicate the early **differentiation of sex.** True sexual reproduction with zygote formation is found in some.
4. The **taxes** or responses of Protozoa to stimuli represent the early beginnings of **reflexes** and **instincts** as we know them in Metazoa.
5. The first appearance of an **exoskeleton,** so well developed in Metazoa, is indicated by certain shelled Protozoa.
6. In colonial Protozoa we have the first indication of **division of labor** among cells. These may be considered the transition links between the protozoan and the metazoan.

Position in animal kingdom

1. Metazoans may not have come directly from protozoans as we now know them but may have been derived from organisms similar to protozoans. Protozoans are often placed close to the beginning of the genealogic tree.
2. The flagellates are considered to be nearest the ancestral stem of both the plant and animal kingdoms.
3. Protozoa may furnish types that fit into a logical sequence for the development of Metazoa.
4. Their evolution has been guided chiefly by the basic adaptive features of their cortex or ectoplasm. They have exploited most of the known possibilities of the unicellular type of existence. Within a single cell body plan they have undergone division of labor and specialization of morphologic structures (organelles) that have enabled them to meet the requirements of particular habitats. Within the group are found evolutionary novelties and specializations characteristic of the metazoans. They are thus fitted to occupy most of the ecologic niches in the ecosystem, and perhaps because of their small size, some niches denied to higher forms. All types of heterotrophism are found among them, and no known source of energy supply is withheld from them. All modes of living, whether free-living or symbiotic, are represented among them.

POSITION IN ANIMAL KINGDOM

Sometimes it is difficult to tell whether noncellular organisms are plants or animals. Some have the characteristics of animals, some of plants, but between these categories are intermediate forms that possess both animal and plant characteristics. Many biologists now use the term **Protista** for all acellular organisms. This grouping of Protista includes such forms as bacteria, slime molds (Mycetozoa), and Protozoa.

CHARACTERISTICS

1. **Acellular** (or one cell), some colonial
2. **Mostly microscopic,** although some large enough to be seen with the unaided eye
3. All symmetries represented in the group; shape variable or constant (oval, spherical, etc.)
4. **No germ layer present**
5. No organs or tissues, but **specialized organelles** found; nucleus single or multiple
6. Free living, mutualism, commensalism, parasitism all represented in the group
7. Locomotion by **pseudopodia, flagella, cilia,** and direct cell movements; some sessile
8. Some provided with a **simple protective exoskeleton,** but mostly naked
9. Nutrition includes all types: holozoic (on other organisms), holophytic (own food by pho-

*Pro'to-zo'a (Gr. *protos,* first, + *zoon,* animal).

tosynthesis), saprozoic (on dead animal matter), and saprophytic (on dissolved substances)
10. Habitat: aquatic, terrestrial, or parasitic, with or without locomotor organoids
11. Reproduction asexually by fission, budding, and cysts and sexually by conjugation of gametes

HABITAT

Most Protozoa live in water or damp soil, although many are parasitic in other forms. Free-living species are found in both fresh water and marine water. Pond scums and cesspools often yield large numbers of them. They prefer quiet pools in which aquatic plants are growing but usually are scarce if the water tends toward the acid side.

NUMBER OF SPECIES

The number of named species of Protozoa lies somewhere between 15,000 and 50,000, but this figure probably represents only a fraction of the total number of species. Some protozoologists think that there may be more protozoan species than all other species together because each species of the higher phyla may have its own unique protozoan parasites, and many protozoans bear parasites themselves. There are probably more parasitic species than free-living ones.

LEVEL OF ORGANIZATION

Protozoans are sometimes called single-celled animals. Strictly, however, they should be called **acellular** animals, for they do not correspond to the cells of metazoans, although some protozoans that have a single nucleus and chromosomal patterns similar to metazoans may be called unicellular.

A protozoan, then, may be defined as an organism that is made up of a mass of protoplasm not divided into cells and that carries on all the life processes. It has specialization and division of labor within its cytoplasmic mass. It is altogether erroneous to think of protozoans as simple animals, for many have complicated structures and are physiologically complex. Their organelles have some resemblance to cell differentiations among the Metazoa and may be quite complex, such as skeletons, sensory systems, conducting mechanisms, contractile system, organs of locomotion, defense mechanisms, and others.

Inasmuch as Protozoa are not made up of cells, they represent what is called the **protoplasmic level of organization.** From this standpoint and others, many biologists place them close to the common ancestor of the many-celled forms. Some protozoans are quite close to the plants and may be considered as connecting links between animals and plants. (See Chapter 37.) In the early evolution of animals holophytic flagellates may have lost their chloroplasts to become colorless animals. Most Protozoa are small or microscopic, usually from 3 to 300 μ long. The largest are among the Foraminifera, some of which have shells 4 to 5 inches in diameter. Certain amebas may be 4 to 5 mm. in diameter. Some of them are found in colonies in which each individual carries on its functions independent of the others, although in a few colonies there is a small amount of differentiation.

The distinction between colonial Protozoa and Metazoa is mainly a matter of degree of division of labor. If the cells are dependent on each other for such functions as nutrition, movement, excretion, and reproduction, the colony belongs properly to the Metazoa; if only certain cells are for reproduction and the rest can perform all other bodily functions, the grouping is a protozoan colony. *Volvox,* for instance, is difficult to appraise this way. Those protozoans with many nuclei may be considered analogous to the syncytial tissues of metazoans.

BRIEF CLASSIFICATION

Four main groups of protozoans are commonly recognized—the mastigophorans or flagellates, the ameboid, the spore-forming, and the ciliates. Traditionally, each of these groups has been represented as a taxonomic class under a single phylum (Protozoa). However, in recent years there have been many changes in the taxonomic arrangement of such an extensive group and many authorities assign subphylum or even phylum rank to each of the groups. In some cases the term Protozoa has been given superphylum rank. No system of protozoan taxonomy has become stabilized, and the following brief classification follows a conservative plan of retaining the familiar names of groupings, with their distinctive characteristics.

Subphylum Plasmodroma (plas′mo-dro″ma) (Gr. *plasma,* anything formed, + *dromos,* course). With locomotor organelles of flagella or pseudopodia, or absent; monomorphic nuclei.

Class Mastigophora (mas′ti-gof″o-ra) (Gr. *mastix,* whip, + *pherein,* to bear) (**Flagellata**). Move by flagella or by pseudopodia.

Subclass Phytomastigina (fi-to-mas′ti-ji″na) (Gr. *phyto,* plant, + *mastix,* whip, + *ina,* pl. suffix meaning belonging to). Usually with chromatophores. Examples: *Dinobryon, Euglena, Ceratium, Volvox.*

Subclass Zoomastigina (zo-o-mas'ti-ji"na) (Gr. *zoon,* animal, + *mastix,* whip). No chromatophores. Examples: *Trypanosoma, Leishmania, Trichomonas.*

Class Sarcodina (sar'ko-di"na) (Gr. *Sarkos,* flesh, + *ina,* belonging to) (**Rhizopoda**). Locomotion by pseudopodia; no definite pellicle; free-living or parasitic; uninucleate or multinucleate; mostly holozoic.

Subclass Actinopoda (ak'ti-nop"o-da) (Gr. *aktino,* ray, + *podos,* foot). With radiating axopodia or filopodia; floating or sessile. Examples: *Actinophrys, Thalassicolla.*

Subclass Rhizopoda (ri-zop"o-da) (Gr. *rhizo,* root, + *podos,* foot). No axopodia: variety of pseudopodia. Examples: *Amoeba, Entamoeba, Arcella, Globigerina.*

Class Sporozoa (spor'o-zo"a) (Gr. *sporos,* seed, + *zoon,* animal). No locomotor organelles; asexual and sexual phases; saprozoic; parasitic.

Subclass Telosporidia (tel'o-spor"i-de-a) (Gr. *telos,* end, + *sporos,* seed). Spores with no polar capsules; infective sporozoite; complex life histories. Examples: *Monocystis, Gregarina, Eimeria, Plasmodium.*

Subclass Cnidosporidia (ni'do-spor"i-de-a) (Gr. *knide,* nettle, + *sporos,* seed). Spore with one to four filaments in polar capsule; sexual and asexual phases; spore often of many cells. Examples: *Nosema, Myxidium.*

Subclass Acnidosporidia (ak-ni'do-spor"i-de-a) (Gr. *knide,* nettle, + *sporos,* seed). Simple spores without polar filaments; spore with single sporozoite. Examples: *Sarcocystis, Haplosporidium.*

Subphylum Ciliophora (sil'i-of"o-ra) (L. *cilium,* eyelid, + *pherein,* to bear). Cilia in adult or young stages; tentacle in adults of some; usually two kinds of nuclei (macronucleus and micronucleus); reproduction usually involves conjugation.

Class Ciliata (L. *cilium,* eyelid, + *ata,* group suffix). Cilia present at some or all stages; nuclei of two kinds.

Subclass Holotricha (ho-lot"ri-ka) (Gr. *holo,* entire, + *trichos,* hair). Body surface usually covered with cilia; usually lack highly specialized ciliary organelles. Examples: *Paramecium, Colpoda, Tetrahymena, Vorticella, Podophrya.*

Subclass Spirotricha (spi-rot"ri-ka) (L. *spiro,* coil, + Gr. *trichos,* hair). Adoral zone of membranelles on buccal region; membranelles winding clockwise toward cytostome; cirri often on ventral surface of body. Examples: *Stentor, Halteria, Epidinium, Euplotes.*

EVOLUTION

It is not known just what were the ancestors of Protozoa. With the exception of certain shell-bearing Sarcodina, such as Foraminifera and Radiolaria, Protozoa have left no fossil records. Mastigophorans are considered to be the oldest of all protozoans and may have arisen from bacteria and spirochetes. This group also includes members that are chlorophyll bearing and resemble the plant algae. This may indicate a common origin for both plants and animals. Sporozoa, which are all parasitic, are somewhat degenerate in structure and may have come from Sarcodina and Mastigophora. Evidence for the origin of Sarcodina from Mastigophora is shown by the fact that both flagellate and ameboid stages are found in some forms. However, the evidence strongly indicates that the different orders of Sarcodina may have arisen independently from different kinds of flagellates (Mastigophora). The orders of Sporozoa may also have had separate origins. The origin of the most highly specialized protozoan forms, ciliates, is somewhat obscure, but there is some evidence that they, too, have come from flagellates.

PROTOZOA IN THE ECONOMY OF NATURE

Protozoans have both a theoretical and a practical importance. In a theoretical sense these organisms afford a great deal of speculation on the problems of phylogeny and of evolution. Biologists do not agree on where the protozoans fit into the pattern of animal evolution. That some of them are ancient cannot be doubted, but many are certainly far from primitive.

Protozoans have been extensively studied with the hope that the basic problems of the life process may be determined. Many believe that generalizations that apply to these small forms also apply to higher animals. But the more we learn about protozoans, the more complicated they appear to be. The extensive work now being done on mating types and extranuclear inheritance in *Paramecium* illustrates this. It is too optimistic to regard them as the key to the solution of all biologic problems.

From the practical standpoint, protozoans have played an important role in building up soil and forming earth deposits; they have important roles in food chains; they have formed important symbiotic relationships; they have been responsible for much of the contamination of water; and, above all, many of them as parasites have been responsible for serious diseases in man and other animals.

Role in building earth deposits

In the class Sarcodina (to which the common ameba belongs) there are two orders, Foraminifera and Radiolaria, which have existed since Precambrian times, or the Proterozoic era. They have left excellent

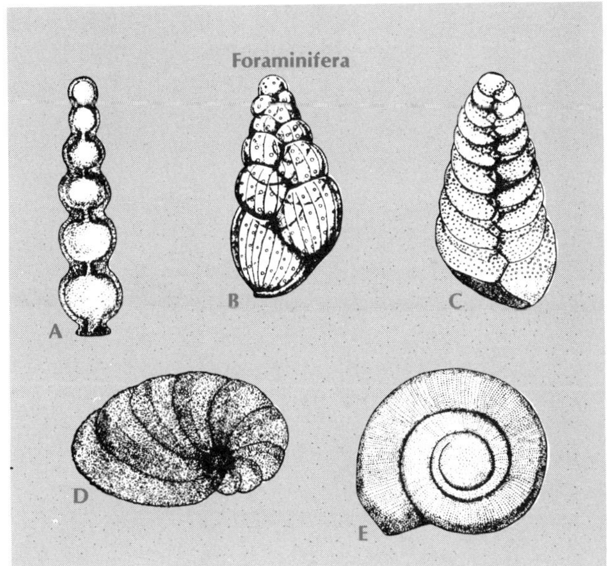

FIG. 10-1

Foraminifera shells. Millions of square miles of thick ocean ooze is made up of tests of forams. **A,** *Nodosaria vigula* Brady (fossil, Brunn, Moravia). **B,** *Textularia fucosa* Reiss (recent, Antillen Island). **C,** *Bolivina punctata* d'Orb (fossil, Santa Monica, U.S.A.). **D,** *Monionina scapha* Ficht (recent, Samoa). **E,** *Spirillina vivipara* Ehrenberg (recent, Samoa). (Courtesy General Biological Supply House, Inc., Chicago.)

fossil records, for their hard shells have been preserved unaltered. Many of the extinct species are identical to present ones. These ancient forms were especially abundant during the Cretaceous and Tertiary periods of geologic history. Some of them were among the largest of protozoans. Living forams range from 0.02 to 50 mm. in diameter, whereas some fossil forms may measure up to 100 mm. or more in diameter.

For untold millions of years the tests, or shells, of dead Foraminifera have been sinking to the bottom of the ocean, building up a characteristic ooze rich in lime and silica (Fig. 10-1). Most of this ooze is made up of the shells of the genus *Globigerina* (Fig. 10-2). About one third of all sea bottom (50 million square miles) is covered with *Globigerina* ooze. This ooze is especially abundant in the Atlantic Ocean, where sediment may be several thousand feet thick.

The Radiolaria, with their less soluble siliceous shells (Fig. 10-3), are usually found at greater depths (15,000 to 20,000 feet), mainly in the Pacific and Indian Oceans. Radiolarian ooze probably covers about 2 to 3 million square miles. Under certain conditions, radiolarian ooze forms rocks (chert). Many fossil Radiolaria are found in the Tertiary rocks of California. In northern seas, diatom (a plant) ooze is also abundant, covering around 12 million square miles of sea bottom.

The thickness of these deep-sea sediments has been estimated to be from 2,000 to 12,000 feet. Although the average rate of sedimentation must vary greatly, it is always very slow. *Globigerina* ooze probably forms from 0.04 to 0.5 inch in a thousand years. When one considers that as many as 50,000 shells of Foraminifera may be found in a single gram of sediment, one can form some idea of the magnitude of numbers of these microorganisms and the length of time it has taken them to form the sediment carpet on the ocean floor.

Of equal interest and of greater practical importance are the limestone and chalk deposits on land that were laid down when a deep sea covered the continents.

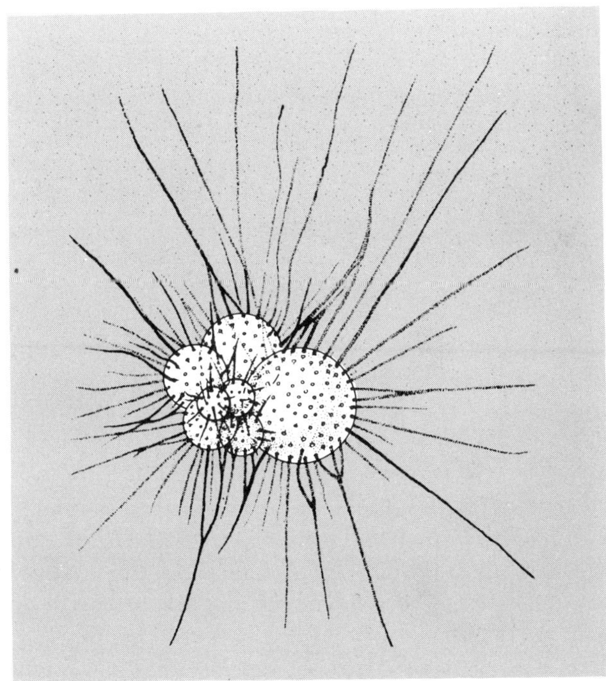

FIG. 10-2

Globigerina alive showing pseudopodia of streaming cytoplasm. Order Foraminifera. (Courtesy General Biological Supply House, Inc., Chicago.)

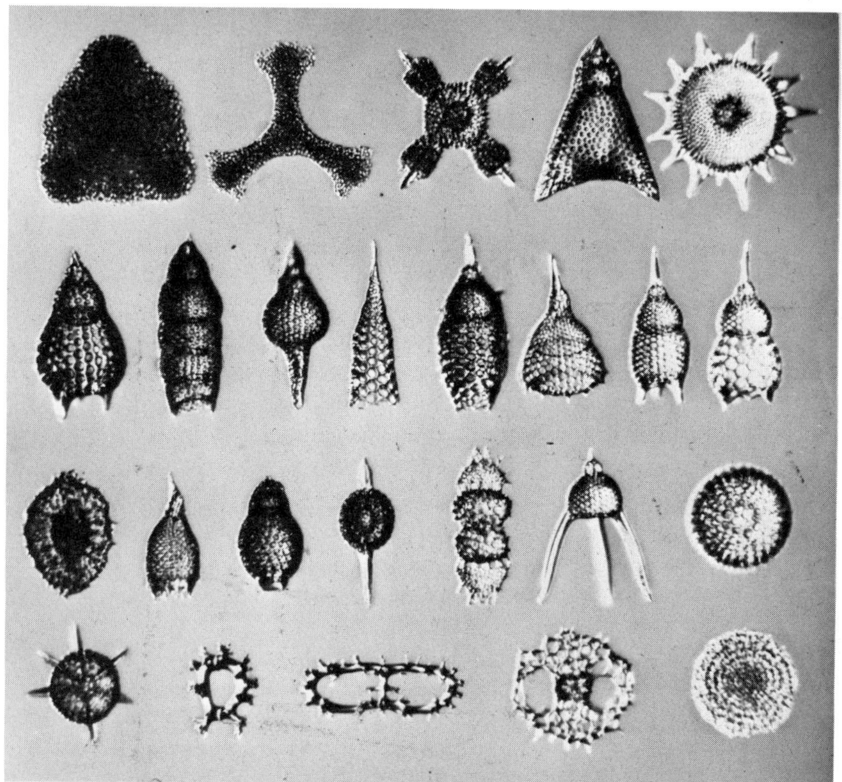

FIG. 10-3

Types of radiolarians. In his study of these beautiful forms collected on famous *Challenger* expedition, Haeckel worked out our present concepts on symmetry. (Courtesy General Biological Supply House, Inc., Chicago.)

Later, through a rise in the ocean floor and other geologic changes, this sedimentary rock emerged as dry land. Many years ago Professor Thomas H. Huxley wrote a classic essay, "On a Piece of Chalk," in which he described how the chalk deposits of many areas of England, including the White Cliffs of Dover, were laid down by the accumulation of these small microorganisms. The great pyramids of Egypt were made from limestone beds that were formed by a very large foraminiferan that flourished during the early Tertiary period. Since petroleum oil is of organic origin, the presence of fossil Foraminifera (and also Radiolaria) in oil-bearing rock strata may be significant to oil geologists. For this reason, borings from test wells are carefully examined, rock strata compared, and contour plotting of the various layers done. From this and other knowledge it is possible to predict the location of oil with a fair degree of accuracy.

Protozoan fauna of plankton

Plankton is a general term for those organisms that passively float and drift with the wind, tides, and currents of both fresh water and marine water. It is composed mostly of microscopic animals and plants, of which protozoans form an important part. Some foraminiferans and almost all radiolarians are represented among the fauna of ocean plankton. Although members of the classes Sarcodina and Mastigophora make up the most important protozoan members of plankton, the class Ciliata are also represented. Even members of the parasitic class Sporozoa are found in the bodies of certain plankton animals.

Plankton is important as food. Many fish such as the herring and mackerel and even the largest of all animals, the whalebone whales, feed directly upon plankton. As the animals of the surface plankton die, they sink to deeper layers of the ocean to serve as food for animals at lower levels.

Symbiotic relationships

The term **symbiosis** refers to the intimate interrelationships between two organisms of different species for the purpose of deriving energy or for some other benefit. This special relationship may be beneficial to both (mutualism) or beneficial to only one but not harmful to the other species (commensalism), or the

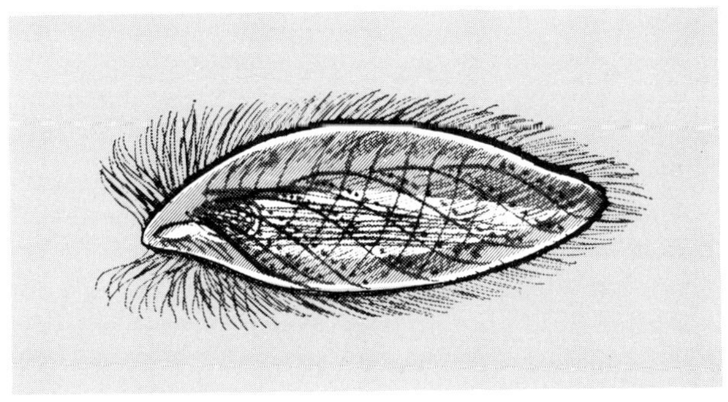

FIG. 10-4

Intestinal flagellate *Spirotrichonympha* from gut of termite. Many individuals or species found in same host. Their relations to termite represent classic case of mutualism in animal kingdom. Note large number of flagella.

relationship may be forced so that one receives benefit and the other furnishes all the energy and may actually be harmful (parasitism). These relationships are not always clear cut, and there are intermediate grades that are difficult to distinguish. Such relationships are not limited to protozoans, but protozoans are represented by all three major types of symbiosis.

Mutualism. *Paramecium bursaria* harbors green algae (zoochlorellae) that manufacture carbohydrates (by photosynthesis) for the benefit of the paramecium and receive a safe shelter in return. Zoochlorellae are also found in other protozoans, such as *Stentor,* certain amebas, and heliozoans. Zooxanthellae (yellow or brown algae) are found in certain ectoparasitic ciliates such as *Trichodina.*

Another example of mutualism is the relation between certain flagellates and termites and cockroaches (Fig. 10-4). These flagellates (many belonging to the genus *Trichonympha*) live in the intestines of termites and wood-feeding roaches *(Cryptocercus),* where they secrete enzymes for digesting the cellulose that is thus made available to their hosts. The Protozoa cannot live outside the host; the termite or roach would starve without the flagellates. The protozoans ingest the wood after the insects have chewed it up into small bits. When termites lose their protozoan fauna (by high oxygen exposure, high temperatures, or prolonged starvation), they can survive only a short time even when fed an abundance of wood, unless they are reinfected with the flagellates.

Commensalism. Commensal protozoans may live on the outside (ectocommensals) or, more commonly, on the inside (endocommensals) of another organism. Common ectocommensals are the ciliates *Kerona* and *Trichodina,* which are often seen on hydra. Some *Vorticella* and suctorians are also found attached to hydroids as ectocommensals. Endocommensals are especially common in the digestive tubes of higher forms, including man. Ruminants and other herbivorous mammals contain great numbers of ciliates and also a few flagellates and amebas. The commensal ciliates belong to the subclass Spirotricha (order Entodiniomorphina). Instead of body cilia they often have tufts or rows of cirri (fused cilia). In ruminants such as cattle and sheep they are found in the first two stomach compartments, where they digest bacteria and foodstuffs in the host's food. Eventually they pass into the other compartments of the stomach and intestine, where they are destroyed and digested so that the host gets all the nutrition after all. Estimates are given of as many as 100,000 to 1 million ciliates per cubic millimeter of gut contents and a total number in a mature cow of 10 to 50 billion. The number is influenced by the kind of food, acidity, starvation, and so on. Apparently Protozoa are not essential to the cattle, which can live and grow normally when the commensals are removed.

Parasitism. Parasitism is the most common form of symbiosis among Protozoa. Ectoparasites live on the outside of the body and endoparasites live within the host. Most animals, especially higher ones, have one or more kinds of protozoan parasites. Protozoa, even protozoan parasites, are often parasitized by other Protozoa. For instance, the opalinid mastigophoran that lives in the frog's intestine is parasitized by a certain ameba. Parasitic species are found among all classes of Protozoa; class Sporozoa is entirely parasitic. Every vertebrate species probably harbors a parasitic or endocommensal ameba. Protozoan parasites have different ways of infecting the host. Some are transferred by contact of bodily parts *(Entamoeba histolytica);* by arthropod or other vectors *(Trypanosoma* and *Plasmodium);* by placenta (blood parasites); and by invasion of ovary or egg *(Babesia).*

Protozoan parasites may differ little in structure from free-living forms, but they undoubtedly have physiologic adaptations. Some protozoans have acquired structures adapted for parasitism, such as the organelles of attachment in *Gregarina.* Host specificity varies. Some protozoan parasites, such as *Trypanosoma, Entamoeba,* and *Eimeria,* are adapted to a wide range of hosts and parasitize many species; others, such as the Coccidia of mammals, are restricted to a few species.

Many other examples of protozoan parasites will be mentioned later under the classes to which they belong.

Contamination of water

Many protozoan parasites are transmitted in water and may give rise to serious diseases such as amebic dysentery. But protozoans also affect the taste and odor of water and often determine its drinking qualities. Water derived from surface sources and stored in large reservoirs is most likely to suffer this way. Other factors, such as algae and decomposing organic matter, also cause bad odors and taste. The chief cause of fishy, aromatic, or other odors is the production of aromatic oils by the disintegration of microscopic organisms. Some odors are characteristic of certain organisms. The worst protozoan offenders are certain flagellates, such as *Dinobryon* and *Uroglena,* that impart a pronounced fishy odor, not unlike cod-liver oil, to water. *Synura,* another flagellate, gives a bitter and spicy taste to water. Other flagellates also produce odors.

Much attention has been given to certain dinoflagellates that are responsible for the so-called "red or poisonous tides" that have destroyed so many fish and other marine forms. In 1946 along the west coast of Florida the sea water was viscid and yellowish from the enormous swarms of these microorganisms. Dead fish piled up along the coast for many miles. Similar outbreaks have been reported in many other parts of the world. It is thought that the upwellings of nutrient-laden, cold waters along coasts may explain the outbreaks of the dinoflagellates, and the consequent decay of dead fish may increase the nutrients of the protozoans. A toxic alkaloid, which acts on the synaptic regions of the nervous systems of animals, is responsible for the harm the dinoflagellate does. Only a few species of naked dinoflagellates seem to be involved; *Gymnodinium* on the Florida coast and *Gonyaulax* on the Pacific coast have caused the American outbreaks (Fig. 10-5).

FIG. 10-5

Gonyaulax polyhedra, a dinoflagellate responsible for "red tides" along coast of southern and lower California. This organism produces toxic alkaloidal substance that is very destructive to fish. Similar dinoflagellate, *Gymnodium brevis,* causes frequent "red tides" along Florida coast. Shellfish that feed on these organisms may be source of food poisoning in man.

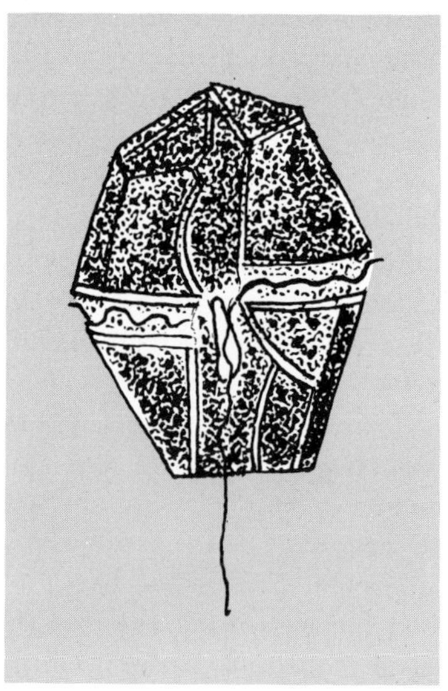

REPRODUCTION AND LIFE CYCLES

Reproduction

Reproduction in most Protozoa is primarily by cell division (asexual). It is comparable in some respects to cell division in the multicellular animals. The protozoan, however, has certain structural specializations (organelles), such as flagella, cilia, contractile vacuole, and gullet, that may be divided equally or unequally to the two daughter cells, so that a certain amount of differentiation or regeneration may be necessary to make the new animal complete. Some of these organelles are self-reproducing, but others are lost by resorption (dedifferentiation), then differentiated anew in each of the daughter organisms. The method of reproduction varies. Some Protozoa simply undergo binary fission, budding, or sporulation. All of these are basically asexual processes. In others, however, asexual reproduction is often followed at certain periods by some form of sexual reproduction that may or may not be necessary for the continued existence of the organism.

Most Protozoa will fall under one or more of the following types, although there are many variations.

Binary fission. This process, the most common among Protozoa, involves the division of the organism, both nucleus and cytoplasm, into two essentially equal daughter organisms. Binary fission may be transverse (most ciliates) or longitudinal (Mastigophora). The nucleus divides by mitosis, and in many cases the chromosomes found in it are similar in structure to and behave much like metazoan chromosomes; in other cases the chromosomes are granular and highly atypical. Chromosome numbers appear to be constant for a species; for example, *Zelleriella intermedia* (Ciliata) has 24, *Entamoeba histolytica* (Sarcodina), 6; *Oxytricha fallax* (Ciliata) (Fig. 10-37), 24; and *Euglena viridis* (Mastigophora), 30.

Budding. Budding involves unequal cell division in which usually the parent organism retains its identity while forming one or more small cells, each of which assumes the parent form after it becomes free. In some cases the bud may be as large as the parent. Budding may be either external (certain suctorians and ciliates) or internal (suctorians and sporozoans). In internal budding the young cells are formed inside of the parent, from which they escape.

Multiple division (sporulation). In multiple division the nucleus divides a number of times, followed by the division of the cytoplasm of the organism into as many parts as there are nuclei. It is a method of rapid multiplication and is characteristic of such parasitic forms as the Sporozoa. It is often found in protozoans with complicated life cycles, including asexual and sexual phases.

Protozoan colonies. Protozoan colonies are formed when the daughter zooids remain associated together instead of moving apart and living a separate existence. Protozoan colonies vary from individuals embedded together in a gelatinous substance to those that have protoplasmic connections among them. The spatial relations of the individuals also serve as the basis for certain types of colonies, such as **linear** (daughter cells attached endwise), **spherical** (grouped in a ball shape), **discoid** (platelike arrangement), and **arboroid** (treelike branches). All the individuals of a colony are usually structurally and physiologically the same, although there may be a minor degree of division of labor among some of them, such as differentiation of reproductive and somatic zooids. Simple colonies may have only a few zooids *(Pandorina)* or they may have thousands of zooids *(Volvox)*. Division of labor, however, may be carried so far that it is difficult to distinguish between a protozoan colony and a metazoan individual.

Sexual phenomena. Sex is found in certain Protozoa but is absent in others. When sex is found in Protozoa, it may involve the formation of male and female gametes (similar or unlike in appearance) that unite to form a zygote (synkaryon), or there may be variant forms of this, such as the complete union of two mature sexual individuals that merge their cytoplasm and nuclei together to form the zygote. By division the zygote may give rise to many individuals or to a new colony. Many other kinds of sexual phenomena have been described for Protozoa, such as **autogamy,** in which gametic nuclei arise and fuse to form a zygote in the same organism that produces the gametes; **endomixis,** which involves nuclear reorganization without fusion of micronuclei; **parthenogenesis,** or the development of an organism from a gamete without fertilization (syngamy); and **conjugation,** in which there is an exchange of gametic nuclei of micronuclear origin between paired organisms (conjugants).

Some of these processes are described under the discussion of the paramecium.

Life cycles

Many Protozoa have very complex life cycles; others have simple ones. A simple life cycle may consist of an active phase and a cyst. In some cases the cyst may be lacking. *Amoeba* has a relatively simple life cycle. The more complex life cycles include two or more stages in the active phase and a reproductive phase that may include sexual as well as asexual phenomena. Some protozoans, for example, have both a ciliated and a nonciliated stage in the same organism; others have ameboid and flagellate stages; and still others, free-swimming and sessile stages, etc. The most complex life cycles among the Protozoa are found in the parasitic class Sporozoa, a good example of which is *Plasmodium*, the malarial parasite, described in a later section.

Encystment is common among protozoans, helping them withstand drought and extreme weather (Fig. 10-6). There is usually a complex series of events when free-living forms encyst. The organism becomes quiescent and many organelles (cilia, flagella, contractile vacuole, etc.) may disappear. A cyst wall is secreted over the surface so that the animal can withstand desiccation, temperature changes, and other harsh conditions. Reproductive cycles, such as budding, fission, and syngamy, may also occur in the

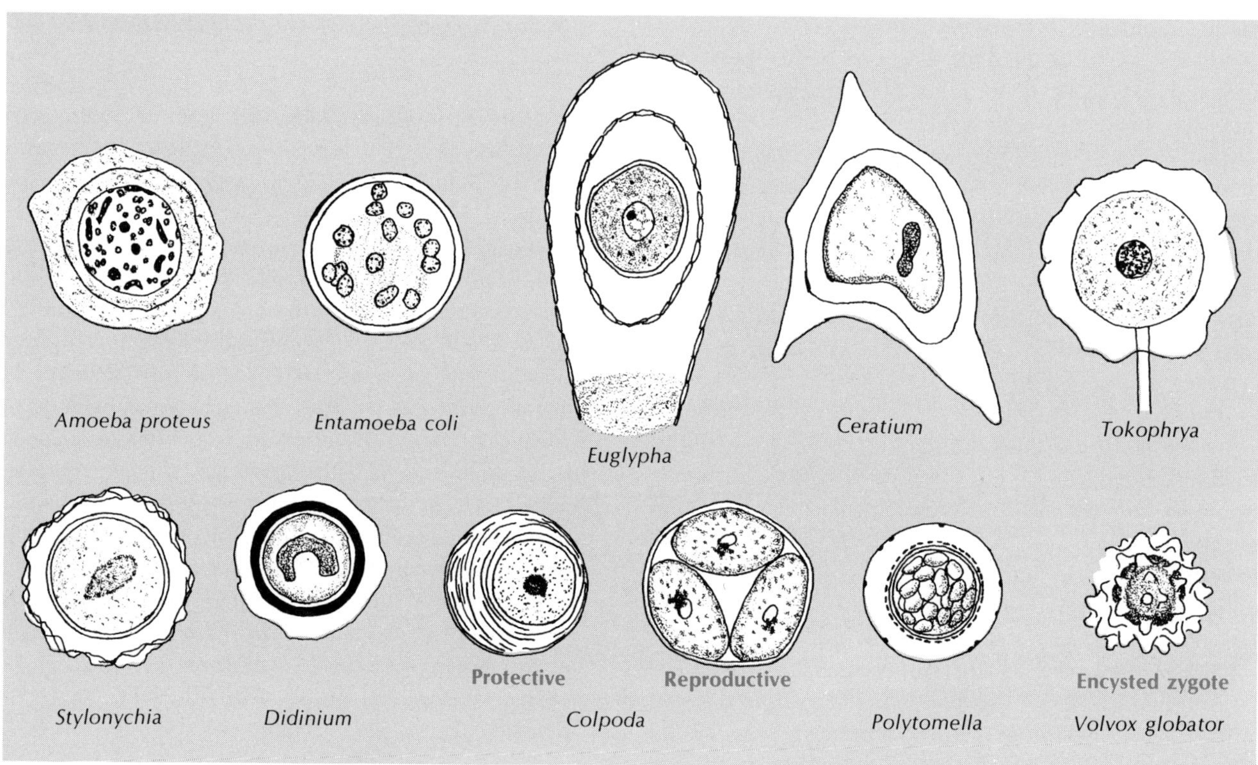

FIG. 10-6

Some protozoan cysts. Many protozoans have encystment at some stage in their life cycle. Process (which varies) may involve accumulation of reserve food, loss of water, rounding up of organism, loss of organelles, etc., and secretion of an enclosing wall of chitin, salts, keratin and other materials. (From Hickman: Biology of the invertebrates, The C. V. Mosby Co.)

encysted condition of some protozoans. The cysts of some protozoans may be viable for many years.

REPRESENTATIVE TYPES

In the following section, descriptions are given of types from each class of Protozoa. Those presented here are usually the ones the student studies in the laboratory and are therefore Protozoa with which he will become most familiar. Forms such as *Amoeba* and *Paramecium* offer some advantages for study because they are large and easy to obtain, but they cannot be called truly representative, for their life histories are somewhat simple compared with other members of their respective classes. More or less the same plan of presentation will be given in each case so that the student may have some basis for comparison.

CLASS SARCODINA

Amoeba proteus

Habitat. *Amoeba proteus* is widely distributed. It lives in slow streams and ponds of clear water, often in shallow water on the underside of lily pads and other aquatic vegetation, or on the sides of dams, in watering troughs, and in the sides of ledges where the water runs slowly from a brook or spring. They are rarely found free in water, for they require a substratum on which to glide. In cultures they are somewhat more difficult to grow than are other protozoans.

Structure. The ameba is irregular in shape because of its power to thrust out **pseudopodia** or false feet at any point on its body (Fig. 10-7). It is a mass of clear, colorless jelly about 250 to 600 μ in greatest diameter. The ameba is continually changing its shape by sending out and withdrawing its pseudopodia. Sometimes its shape is almost spherical when all its pseudopodia are withdrawn. Although it possesses no cell wall, it has a thin delicate outer membrane called the **plasmalemma** (Fig. 10-7). Just beneath this is a nongranular layer, the **ectoplasm,** which encloses the granular **endoplasm.** The endoplasm is made up of an outer, relatively stiff **plasmagel** and a more fluid inner **plasmasol,** which exhibits flowing or streaming movements. In the gel layer the crystals and granules keep their distance (fixed) from each other; in the sol they bump and move over each other.

A number of **organelles** are found within the endoplasm. One of these is the disk-shaped **nucleus,** which is somewhat difficult to see. When the streaming movements are vigorous, the nucleus can sometimes be seen carried along with the current. The nucleus is granular and refractive to light. Another organelle is the **contractile vacuole,** a bubblelike body that grows to a maximum size and then contracts to expel its fluid contents to the outside. Scattered through the endoplasm are **food vacuoles,** which are drops of water enclosing food particles. There are also other vacuoles, **crystals,** and **granules** of various shapes and forms. Foreign substances such as sand and bits of debris may also be in the protoplasm, where they have been picked up accidentally.

Metabolism. The ameba lives upon algae, protozoans, rotifers, and even other amebas. It shows some selection in its food, for it will not ingest everything that comes its way. Food may be taken in at any part of the body surface. When the ameba engulfs food, it thrusts out pseudopodia to enclose the food particle completely (Fig. 10-8). Along with the food, some water in which the food is suspended is also taken in. These food vacuoles are carried around by the streaming movements of the endoplasm. A lysosome with enzymes fuses with each food vacuole, and digestion proceeds within the vacuole. At first the vacuoles give acid reaction because of digestive enzymes that kill the prey and start digestion, but later they become alkaline. As digestion proceeds, the vacuoles decrease in size because of loss of water and the passage of the digested material into the surrounding cytoplasm. Finally, only indigestible material is left, which is eliminated by the animal simply flowing away from the mass as the latter passes out through the plasmalemma.

The ameba is able to live for many days without food but decreases in volume during this process. The actual time necessary for the completion of the digestion of a food vacuole varies with the kind of food, but the usual time is around 15 to 30 hours.

The ameba needs and utilizes energy like any other animal. It gets this energy by oxidation, which results in waste products such as carbon dioxide, water, and urea. Some of these waste substances are eliminated through the body surface, but some are discharged through the contractile vacuole. The contractile vacuole also gets rid of excess water that the ameba is continually taking in. It is thus responsible for regulating

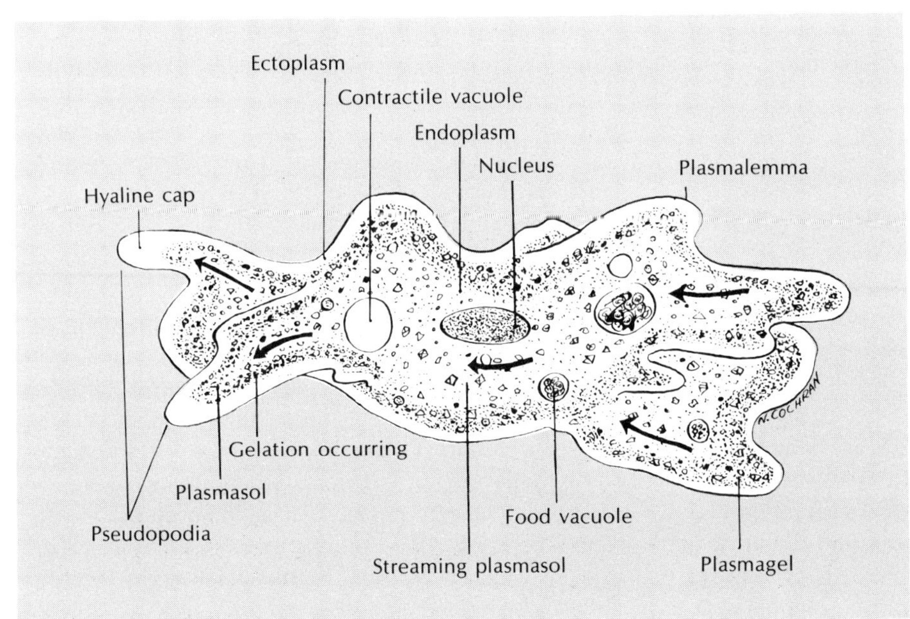

FIG. 10-7

Structure of *Amoeba* in active locomotion. Arrows indicate direction of streaming plasmasol. There is no entirely satisfactory theory of ameboid movement. First sign of formation of new pseudopodium is thickening of ectoplasm to form clear hyaline cap. Into this hyaline region flow granules from fluid endoplasm (plasmasol), forming a type of tube with walls of plasmagel and core of plasmasol. As plasmasol flows forward it is converted into plasmagel, which may involve contraction that squeezes pseudopodium in a definite direction. Substratum is necessary for ameboid movement, but only tips of pseudopodia touch it. See text for explanation of ameboid movement.

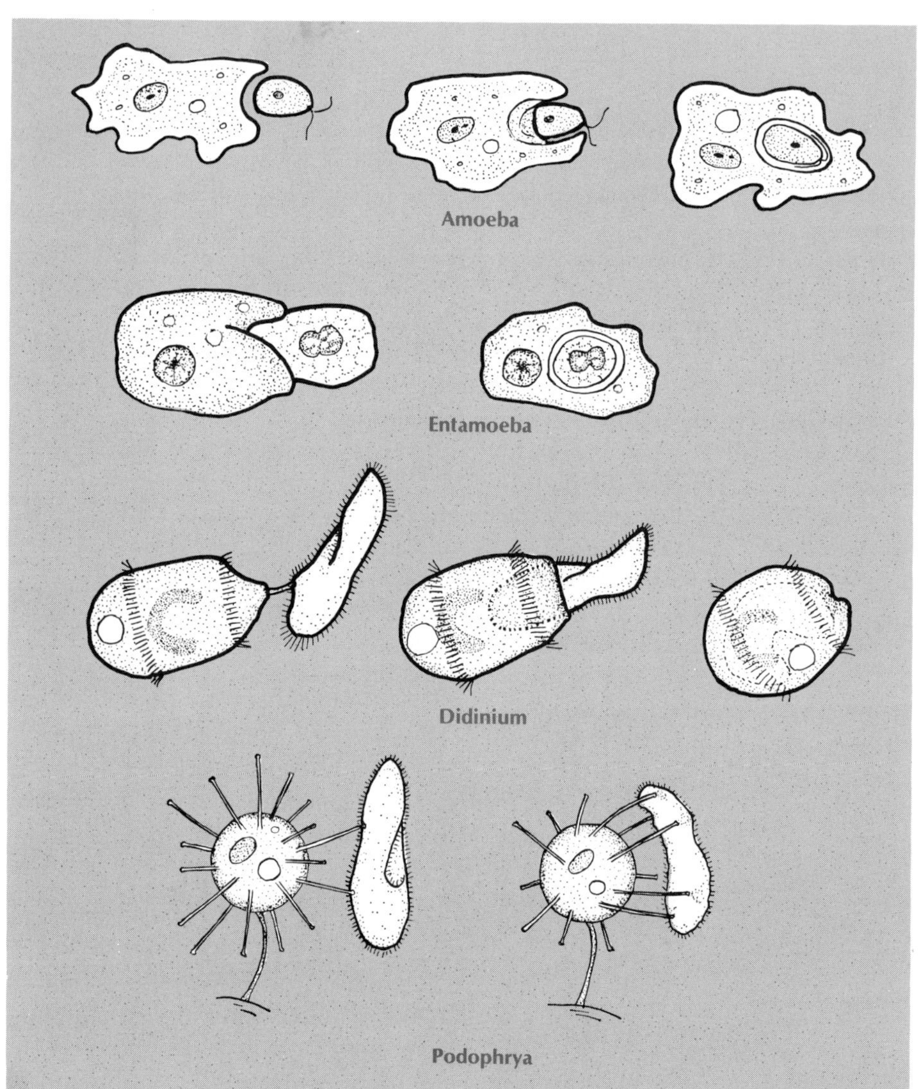

FIG. 10-8

Some typical methods of ingestion among protozoans. *Amoeba* ingests small flagellate. *Entamoeba,* a parasite, engulfs leukocyte. *Didinium,* a holotrich, eats only paramecia. It pierces prey before swallowing it whole. Suctorians such as *Podophrya* have protoplasmic tentacles with funnel ends that suck protoplasm from prey.

the osmotic pressure of the body. The ameba has a certain amount of salt in its protoplasm that makes it hypertonic to the surrounding fresh water. Water will therefore enter the ameba by osmosis through its plasmalemma. It is interesting to note that marine amebae do not have contractile vacuoles because they are immersed in isotonic sea water (but when placed in fresh water they will form them).

Respiration occurs directly through the body surface by diffusion. Oxygen is dissolved in the water, which is everywhere in contact with the cell membrane so that the gas is easily accessible and diffuses into the ameba.

Locomotion. Locomotion takes place by the formation of temporary locomotor structures, the pseudopodia, which are thrust out on any part of the body surface and into which the cytoplasm flows. This characteristic movement is called **ameboid movement** (Fig. 10-9). When a pseudopodium is beginning to form, a blunt, fingerlike projection called the **hyaline cap,** composed only of ectoplasm, first appears. A little later the granular plasmasol flows into this projection as it extends forward. Usually the ameba forms several small pseudopodia at the start of the movement; one of these gradually becomes larger, while the others disappear.

Theories to account for ameboid movement are far from satisfactory. One theory stresses changes in surface tension, which is lessened at the point where pseudopodia are formed. Another widely accepted theory

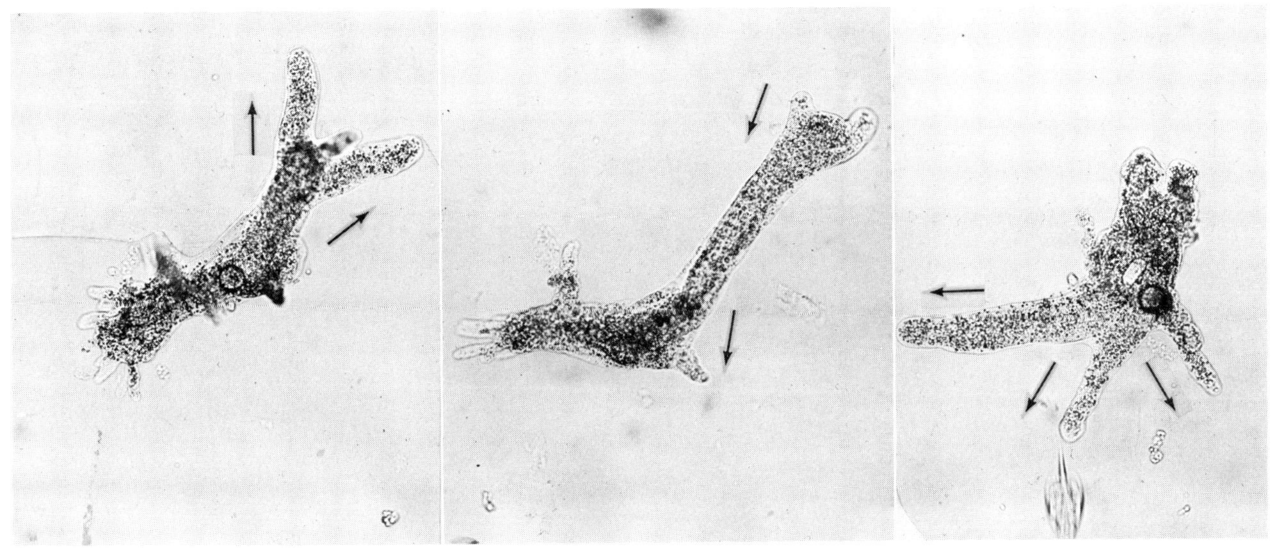

FIG. 10-9

Ameboid movement. Series photographed at intervals of about half a minute. In view at right, pseudopodium is extending toward escaping rotifer.

(Mast's) is based upon a reversible transformation of the cytoplasm from a sol (fluid) to a gel (solid). According to this theory, the forward movement of the solated endoplasm is caused by the contraction of the plasmagel or ectoplasmic tube in the posterior (tail) end of the ameba. This pressure pushes out the solated anterior end, forming a pseudopodium. As the fluid, or sol, endoplasm reaches the plasmalemma at the tip of the advancing pseudopod, it fountains (just back of the hyaline cap) to the sides, undergoes gelation, and forms a plasmagel sleeve, or tube. Contraction of the posterior gel ectoplasm is immediately followed by solation to replenish the internal plasmasol.

This tail-contraction theory is now considered too simple by some investigators, who maintain that the ameba pulls itself forward by contraction in the endoplasm at the anterior end (front-contraction theory) (Fig. 10-10). Evidence indicates that the endoplasmic axial core has a viscosity about the same as that of the ectoplasmic tube, instead of being much less, as in Mast's theory. The only regions with low viscosity and rapid movement of cytoplasm are the zone around the axial endoplasm and the region where the endoplasm is being formed from the posterior ectoplasm. Strands of free-moving cytoplasm stream forward in the axial endoplasm to the anterior fountain zone, where they di-

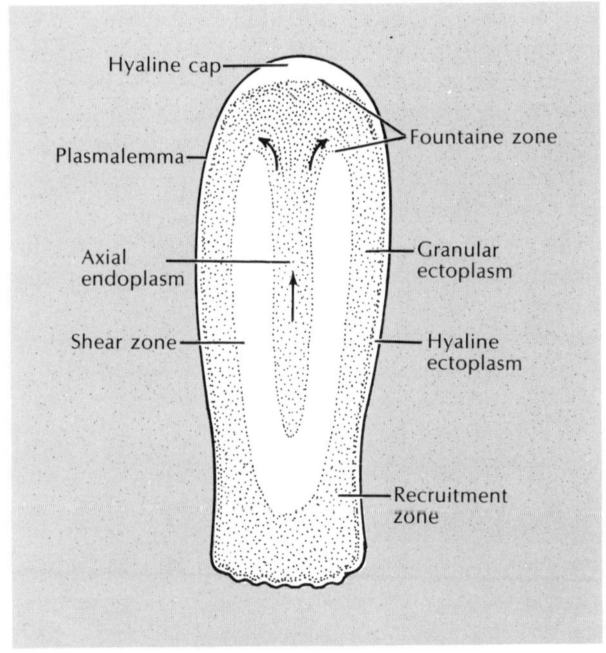

FIG. 10-10

Mechanism of ameboid movement. Tail contraction theory of Mast and others is now considered unsatisfactory by many biologists. There is now evidence that cytoplasm is pulled forward by contractile force operating near tips of pseudopodia. But there may be more than one mechanism of ameboid movement. For details of mechanism of forward contraction theory see text. (After Allen, 1962.)

verge outward and join the ectoplasmic tube. The endoplasm anchored to the ectoplasmic tube contracts, everts, and pulls the axial endoplasm forward. Continuous streaming movements are kept up by the propagated contraction along the ectoplasm. The hyaline cap is formed from water squeezed from the endoplasm. This water eventually moves backward to the tail in the channel just beneath the plasmalemma. A necessary feature of ameboid movement is the attachment of the ameba (at the tips of pseudopodia) to a substratum during the act of moving.

Ameboid movement is also found elsewhere in the animal kingdom, notably in the white corpuscles of blood, in amebocytes of sponges, etc.

Reproduction. When the ameba reaches full size, it divides into two animals by the process of **binary fission.** A series of nuclear changes accompanies this process. Typical mitosis (Fig. 10-11) occurs with all the phases—prophase, metaphase, anaphase, and telophase. It takes about 30 minutes. During the process of division the shape of the ameba is spherical, with a number of small pseudopodia. The nuclear membrane disappears during the metaphase and the body elongates and separates by fission into two daughter cells. Under ordinary conditions the ameba attains a size for division about every three days.

Sporulation and budding may occur in the ameba under favorable conditions. Binary fission seems to be the only regular method employed.

Behavior. The ameba reacts to stimuli just as any other animal does. Its reactions center around food getting, locomotion, changes in shape, avoidance of unfavorable environments, etc. Its responses to different forms of stimuli vary. In a positive reaction the ameba goes toward the stimulus; in a negative reaction it moves away. If touched with a needle it will draw back and move away, but when floating it will respond in a positive way to a solid object. It moves away from a strong light and may change its direction a number of times to avoid it, but it may react positively to a weak light. The ameba's rate of locomotion is lessened by colder temperatures and may cease entirely near the freezing point. Its rate increases up to 90° F., but it ceases to move at temperatures higher than this.

Its response to chemicals varies with the nature of the chemical. Although indifferent to most normal constituents in its medium, the ameba will react positively toward substances of a food character.

Other members of class Sarcodina

There are a number of other species of *Amoeba,* such as *A. verrucosa,* with short pseudopodia; *Pelomyxa carolinensis (Chaos chaos)* (Fig. 10-12), which is several times as large as *A. proteus;* and *A. radiosa,* with many slender pseudopodia.

Most parasitic members of Sarcodina are amebas (order Amoebina, or Lobosa) that live in the intestine of man and other animals. There are two common genera—*Endamoeba* and *Entamoeba. Endamoeba blattae* is common in the intestine of cockroaches. This form may be an endocommensal rather than a parasite. Related species are also found in the gut of termites. The only serious rhizopod parasite of man is *Entamoeba histolytica,* which is responsible for amebic dysentery. This species lives in the connective tissues and muscular lay-

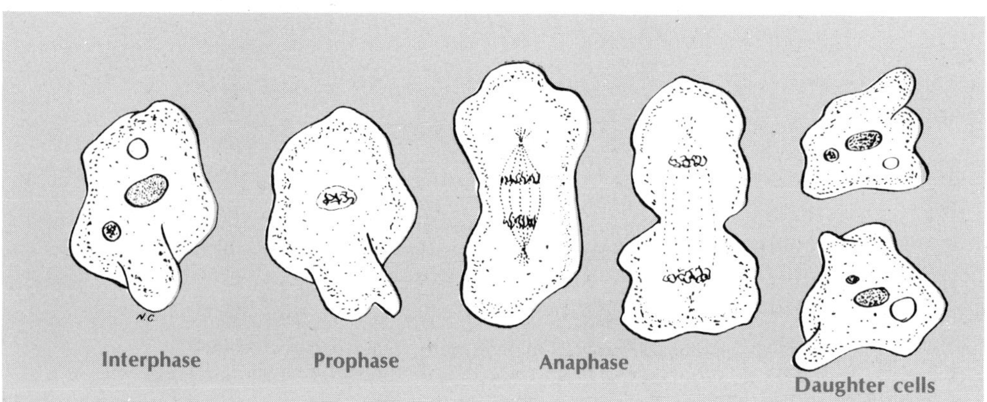

FIG. 10-11

Mitosis in nucleus of *Amoeba*. There are many mitotic patterns among protozoans. In most cases nuclear membrane persists throughout mitosis, and division bodies of centrioles, centrosphere, and spindle are of nuclear rather than of cytoplasmic origin. Sometimes one of these division bodies may be absent. In many cases, chromosomes behave as in metazoans. In others, chromatin mass splits and passes to poles without forming chromosomes. Amitosis in protozoans is restricted mainly to macronucleus of ciliates.

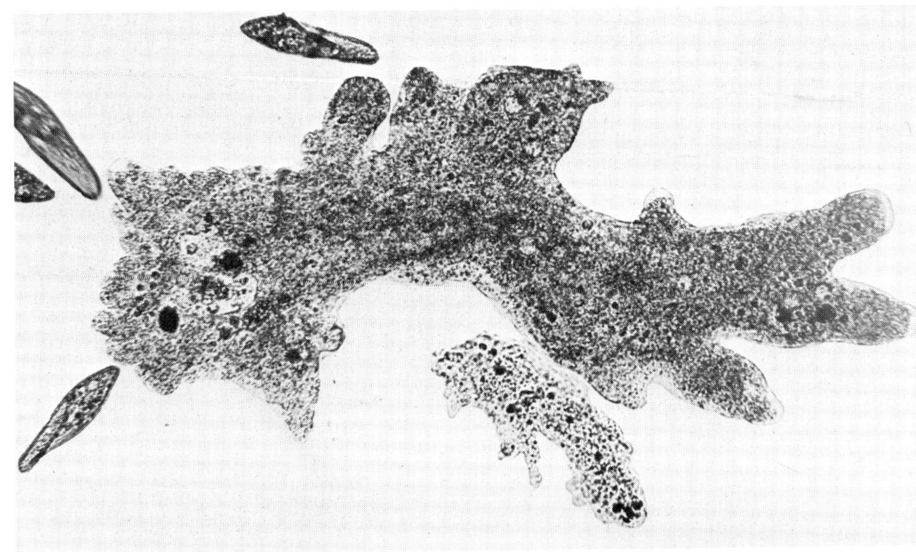

FIG. 10-12

Comparison in size of *Pelomyxa* (larger) and *Amoeba*. The former may attain length of 5 mm. Several paramecia also shown. (Courtesy Carolina Biological Supply Co., Burlington, N. C.)

ers of the intestinal wall, which it enters by secreting a substance that dissolves away the intestinal lining. They often produce severe lesions and abscesses and may spread to the liver, lungs, brain, and other organs. Not all infected persons show severe symptoms, but they may become carriers. Contaminated water or food containing the cysts discharged through the feces are the chief methods of spreading the infection. *E. histolytica* or a closely related form is also found in monkeys, rats, and other animals. Among other species of *Entamoeba* found in man are *Entamoeba coli,* which is usually considered to be nonpathogenic but may cause intestinal disturbances, and *E. gingivalis,* found in the mouth and causing pyorrhea by dissolving away the cement that holds the teeth to the bone. Many species of *Entamoeba* are found in all classes of vertebrates.

The **Foraminifera** are found in all oceans and a few live in fresh and brackish water. They are mostly bottom living, but a few live in open water. Most forms are invested with shells or tests, which are of numerous types (Figs. 10-1 and 10-13). Most tests are many-chambered and are made of calcium carbonate, although silica, silt, and other foreign materials are sometimes used. Slender pseudopodia extend through openings in the test, then branch and run together to form a protoplasmic net in which they ensnare their prey. Here the captured prey is digested and the digested products are carried into the interior by the flowing protoplasm. Their life cycles are complex, for they have multiple division and alternation of generations.

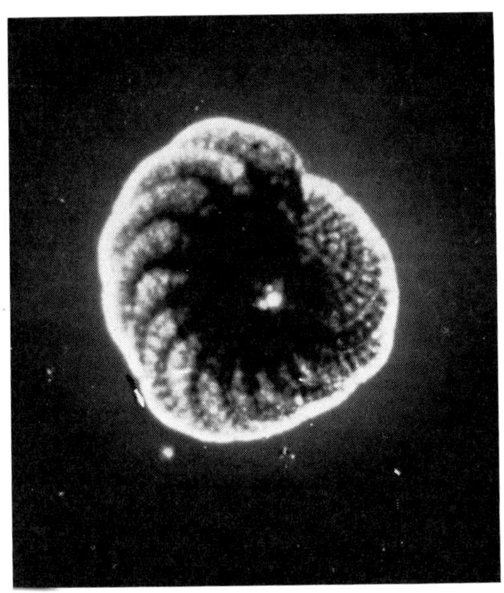

FIG. 10-13

Foraminiferan shell.

The **Radiolaria** are the oldest known group of animals. They live in open water, both surface and deep. Their highly specialized skeletons are intricate in form and of unimaginable beauty. The body is divided by a central capsule that separates inner and outer zones of cytoplasm. The central capsule, which may be spherical, ovoid, or branched, is perforated to allow cytoplasmic continuity. The skeleton is made of silica or strontium sulfate and usually has a radial arrangement of spines that extend through the capsule from the center of the body. At the surface a shell may be fused with the spines. Around the capsule is a frothy mass of cytoplasm from which stiff pseudopodia arise. These are sticky for catching the prey that are carried by the streaming protoplasm to the central capsule to be digested. Radiolaria may have one or many nuclei. Their life history is not completely known, but binary fission, budding, and sporulation have been observed in them (Figs. 10-3 and 10-14).

Arcella and *Difflugia* (order Testacea) are two common members of Sarcodina that have shells for protection (Fig. 10-14). Their shells may be secreted or built of sand. They move by pseudopodia that project from openings in the shell.

CLASS MASTIGOPHORA

Euglena viridis

Habitat. The normal habitat of *Euglena viridis* is freshwater streams and ponds where there is considerable vegetation. Lily ponds in well-kept parks are often a good source for them. They are sometimes so numerous as to give a distinctly greenish color to the water. Although light is necessary for their metabolism,

FIG. 10-14

Some examples of Sarcodina showing wide variety of forms.

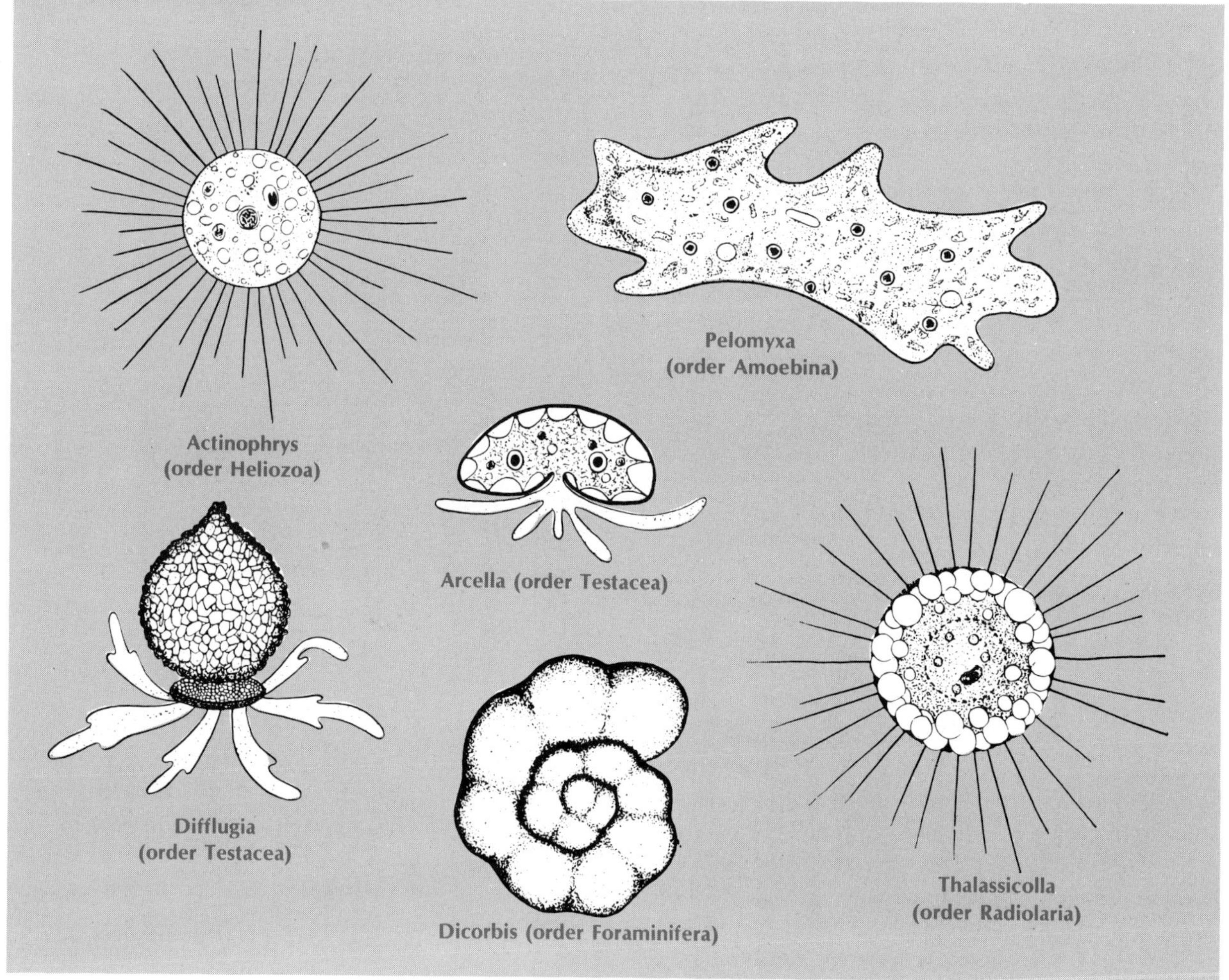

they are often found at various depths below the surface of water, for they are fairly active forms. In the laboratory they thrive best in a jar exposed to indirect sunlight.

Structure. The euglena's spindle-shaped body is about 60 μ (0.06 mm.) long, with a rather pointed posterior end. It is covered by a **pellicle** flexible enough to permit movement (Figs. 10-15 and 10-16). Inside the pellicle is the clear **ectoplasm** that surrounds the mass of **endoplasm.** A flask-shaped **reservoir** dips into the anterior end of the euglena. In the posterior end of the reservoir a **flagellum** originates as the union of two delicate threads, or **axonemes,** each of which ends as a tiny granule, or **blepharoplast,** on the floor of the reservoir. A tiny fibril, or **rhizoplast,** extending from one of the blepharoplasts to the nuclear membrane suggests that the flagellum is under nuclear control. A swelling of the flagellum associated with the eyespot suggests a possible mechanism by which the organism reacts to light changes. The blepharoplast may function as a centriole in division.

The electron microscope reveals that a flagellum consists of eleven fibrils arranged with nine of them in a circle and two in the center and all contained in an elastic outer sheath (Fig. 10-17). It is thought that contraction of fibrils on one side causes the flagellum to bend and that the elasticity of the outer layer causes it to return. Each of the fibrils is in turn made up of

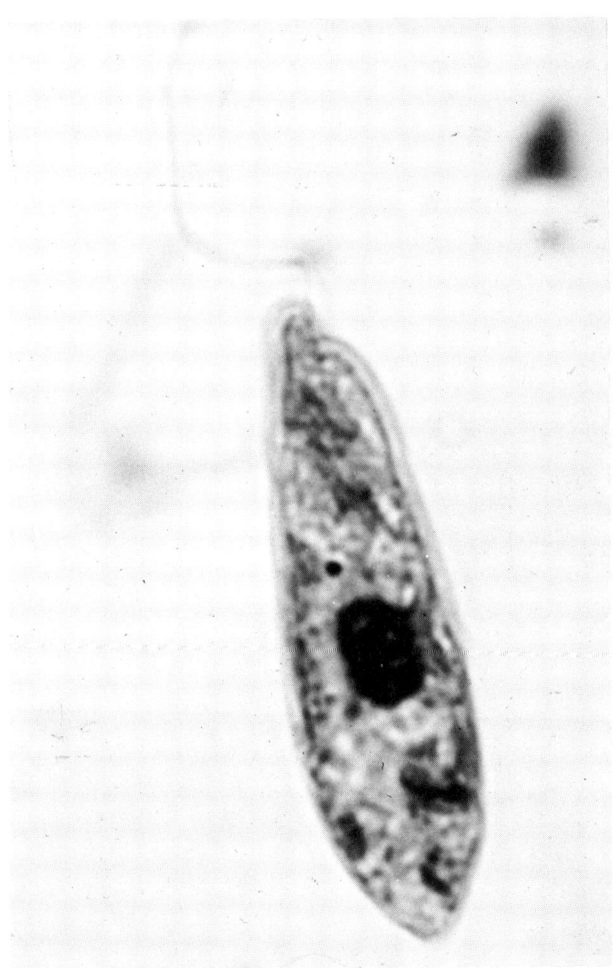

FIG. 10-15

Photograph of *Euglena viridis* showing flagellum. (Courtesy Ward's Natural Science Establishment, Inc., Rochester, N. Y.)

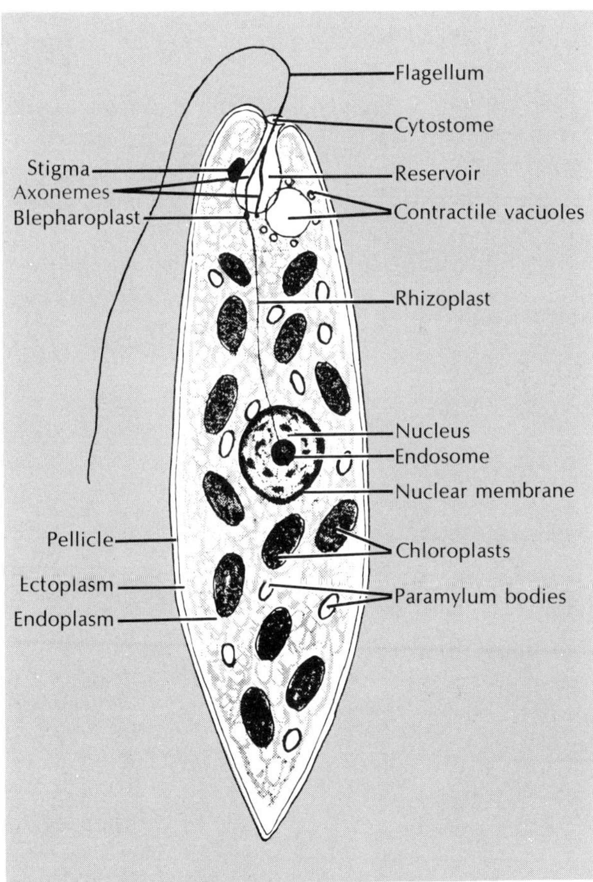

FIG. 10-16

General structure of *Euglena.* Features shown are combination of those visible in living and stained preparations.

two microfibrils within a sheath. This same pattern is true of cilia and of the tail or flagellum of the spermatozoa of higher animals. This pattern appears to have a significant evolutionary sequence because the flagellum of bacteria has only two or three closely wound fibrils instead of eleven (Dillon).

A large **contractile vacuole**, which is formed by fusion of smaller vacuoles, empties wastes and excess water into the reservoir, the anterior opening of which (called the cytostome) is an exit.

Near the reservoir is a red **eyespot,** or **stigma.** This is a shallow cup-shaped spot of pigment that allows light from only one direction to strike a light-sensitive receptor located as a swelling near the base of the flagellum. When the euglena is moving toward the light, the receptor is illuminated; when it changes direction, the shadow of the pigment falls on the receptor. Thus the animal, which depends upon sunlight for its photosynthesis, can orient itself toward the light.

The **nucleus,** a slightly oval body near the center of the cell, has a prominent center body, the **endosome.**

Within the cytoplasm are the oval **chromatophores** (chloroplasts) that bear chlorophyll and give the euglena its greenish color. They function as in plants in the manufacture of carbohydrates. **Paramylum bodies** of various shapes are masses of starch, a means of food storage.

Metabolism. The euglena derives its food mainly through **holophytic** nutrition, which makes use of photosynthesis, a process that takes place within the chromatophores through the action of chlorophyll. This form also makes use of **saprozoic nutrition,** which is the absorption of dissolved nutrients through the body surface. It is doubtful whether the euglena ingests solid food particles through its mouth region (**holozoic nutrition**), although some flagellates such as *Paranema* ingest other organisms. Respiration and excretion are carried out by diffusion through the body wall.

Locomotion. The euglena swims freely by the movement of its flagellum, which moves in a whiplike manner or with rotary motion, with the undulation passing from base to tip. This motion pulls the animal forward in a straight course while the body rotates spirally. Flagellates can travel from a few tenths to 1 mm. per second, according to their size, the speed increasing

FIG. 10-17

Cross section of flagella. Each flagellum has nine peripheral and two central fibrils, each made up of two microfibrils enclosed in a sheath. (Electron micrograph courtesy I. R. Gibbons, Harvard University.)

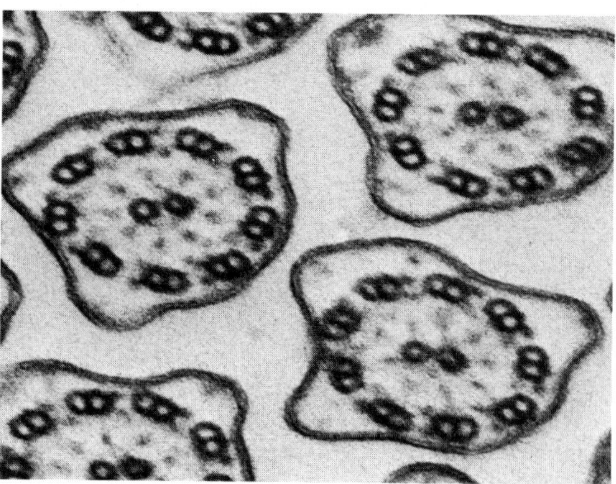

FIG. 10-18

Changes of shape in mastigophorans such as *Euglena* are called "euglenoid movement."

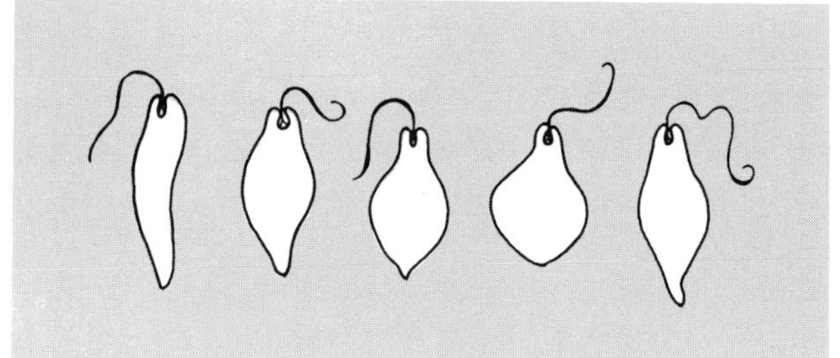

FIG. 10-19

Reproduction in *Euglena* occurs by longitudinal fission, beginning at anterior end.

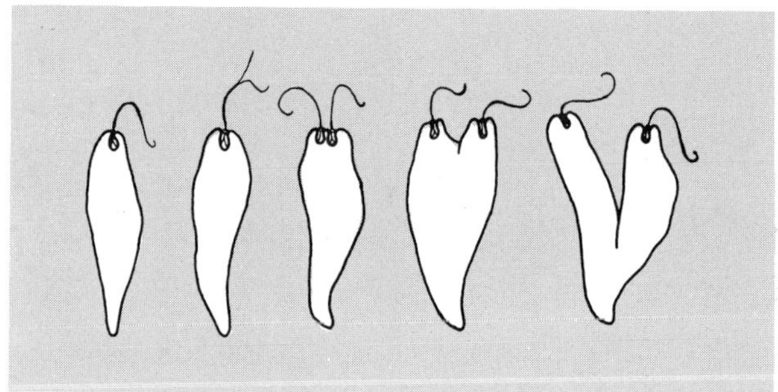

with the larger flagellates. Some flagellates use the flagella to push rather than to pull themselves along. *Euglena* can also move by a squirming, peristalsis-like action called "euglenoid" movement or metabolic changes of shape (Fig. 10-18).

Reproduction. *Euglena* reproduces by longitudinal **binary** division. The nucleus undergoes mitotic division, while the body, beginning at the anterior end, divides in two lengthwise (Fig. 10-19). This division may involve a splitting of the flagellum, blepharoplast, reservoir, and eyespot, or else there is a duplication of these organelles. During inactive periods and for protection the euglena assumes a spherical shape surrounded with a gelatinous covering, thus becoming encysted. In this condition it can withstand drought and can become active when it is again in water. Encysted euglenae usually divide so that each cyst may contain two or more euglenae.

Behavior. The euglena is sensitive to light and will swim toward light if it is not too bright. If given the choice, it will avoid shady areas and regions of bright light. The eyespot seems to be responsible for determining its reactions to light.

Volvox globator

The group (order Phytomonadina) to which *Volvox* belongs includes many freshwater flagellates that have

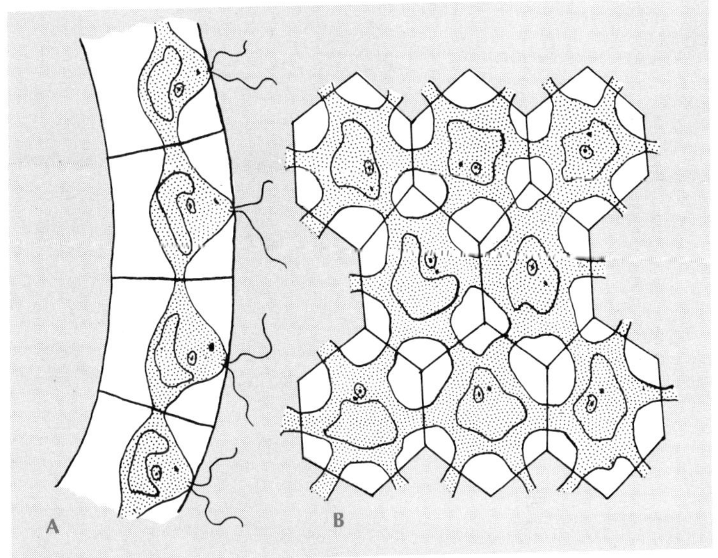

FIG. 10-20

Portion of colony of *Volvox globator*. **A,** Side view. **B,** Surface view. Zooids are embedded in a gelatinous matrix and adjacent cells have cytoplasmic connections between them. (From Hickman: Biology of the invertebrates, The C. V. Mosby Co.)

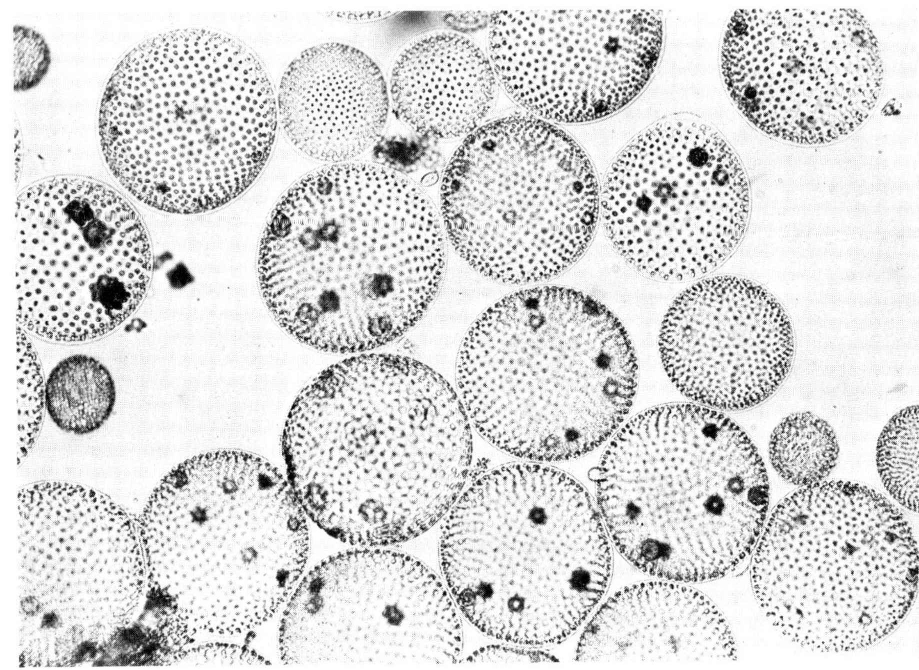

FIG. 10-21

Colonies of *Volvox* in various stages of reproduction. Larger ones contain small daughter colonies. Class Mastigophora.

a close resemblance to algae. Their cells, or zooids, are usually enclosed in a cellulose membrane through which two short flagella project. Most of them are provided with green chromatophores. Many are colonial forms. *Volvox* is a green hollow sphere that may reach a diameter of 0.5 to 1 mm. It is a colony of many thousands of zooids (up to 50,000) embedded in the gelatinous surface of a jelly ball. Each cell is much like a euglena, with a nucleus, a pair of flagella, a large chloroplast (a type of chromatophore), and a red stigma. Adjacent cells are connected with each other by cytoplasmic strands (Fig. 10-20). At one pole (usually in front as the colony moves), the stigmata are a little larger. Coordinated action of the flagella causes the colony to move by rolling over and over. Here we have the beginning of division of labor to the extent that most of the zooids (somatic) are concerned with nutrition and locomotion, and a few others (germ cells), located in the posterior half, are responsible for reproduction.

Reproduction is asexual or sexual. In either case only certain zooids located around the equator or posterior half take part. **Asexual reproduction** occurs by the repeated mitotic division of one of the germ cells, to form a hollow sphere of cells, with the flagellate ends of the cells inside. It then invaginates, or turns itself wrong side out, to form a daughter colony like the parent colony (Fig. 10-21). Several daughter colonies are formed inside the parent colony before they escape by rupture of the parent.

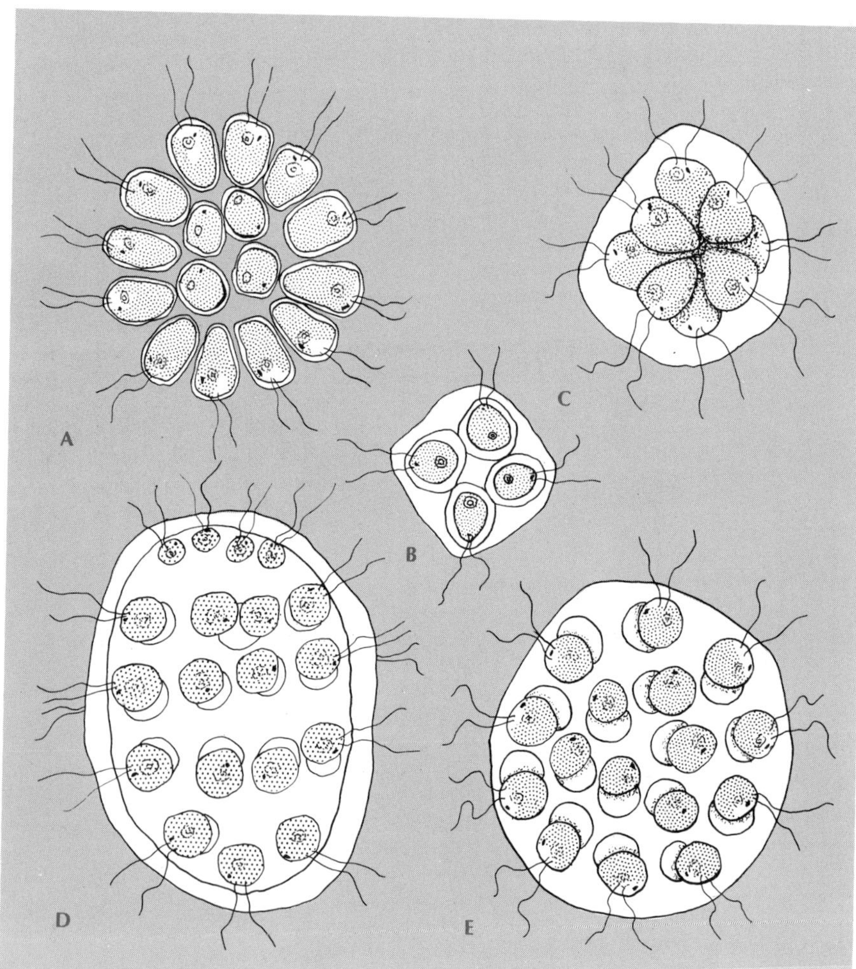

FIG. 10-22

Some colonial protozoans. Such colonies may have been the forerunners of the metazoans. **A,** *Gonium pectorale,* usually of 16 zooids. **B,** *G. sociale* 4 zooids, each of which may give rise to a daughter colony by cell division or may serve as an isogamete. **C,** *Pandorina morum,* 16 zooids, each of which divides four times to form new colony. **D,** *Pleodorina illinoisensis,* 32 zooids, of which the four anterior are sterile and the others are capable of both sexual and asexual reproduction. **E,** *Eudorina elegans,* 32 zooids, each of which forms a new colony. (From Hickman: Biology of the invertebrates, The C. V. Mosby Co.)

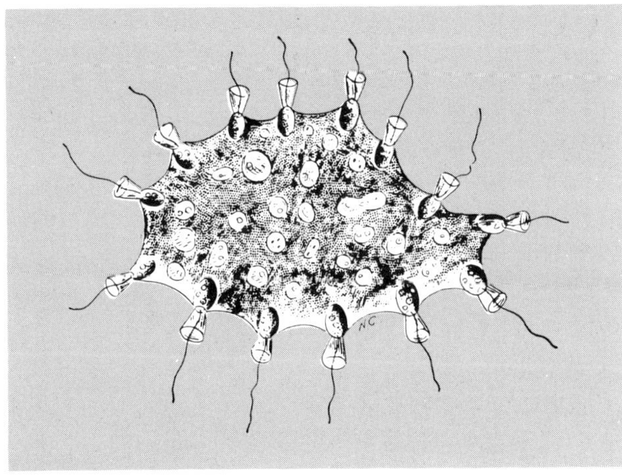

FIG. 10-23

Proterospongia, a colonial choanoflagellate. In gelatinous mass, collared zooids are embedded on outside and collarless ameboid zooids on inside. Collared cells resemble choanocytes of sponges. Only choanoflagellates and sponges have these peculiar cells.

FIG. 10-24

Some common types of Mastigophora, both solitary and colonial.

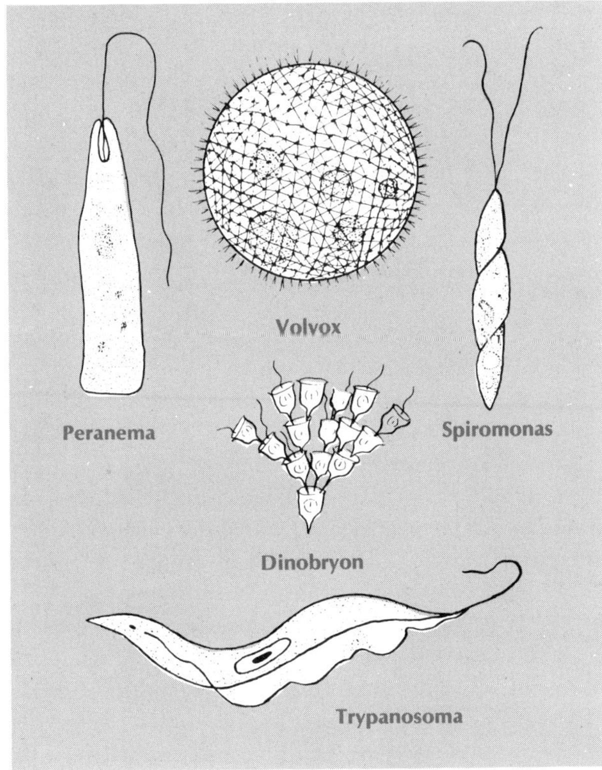

In **sexual reproduction** some of the zooids differentiate into **macrogametes** (ova) and **microgametes** (sperm). The macrogametes are fewer and larger and are loaded with food for nourishment of the young colony. The microgametes, by repeated division, form bundles or balls of small flagellated sperm that, when mature, leave the mother colony and swim about to find a mature ovum. When a sperm enters or fertilizes an egg, the zygote so formed secretes a hard, spiny, protective shell around itself. When released by the breaking up of the parent colony, the zygote remains quiescent during the winter. Within the shell the zygote undergoes repeated division until a small colony is produced that is released in the spring. A number of asexual generations may follow before sexual reproduction occurs again.

Other members of class Mastigophora

The class Mastigophora is divided into two groups; those that have chlorophyll, such as the euglena, and those without chlorophyll. The second group may be holozoic, saprozoic, or **entozoic** (living within another animal). The class is a large one with many types (Figs. 10-22 to 10-24). *Noctiluca,* a marine form, is luminescent and produces a striking greenish light at night. Another common form is *Chilomonas,* which has two flagella at the anterior end and is used as food by the ameba. There are also other species of *Euglena,* such as *E. spirogyra,* with marked spiral striations and often seen in mixed cultures; *E. oxyuris,* with sharp-pointed posterior ends; and *E. gracilis,* which is similar to *E. viridis.* Another flagellate, *Ceratium,* found in both fresh water and marine water, has a body of plates and horns.

The colorless flagellates (order Protomonadina) are represented by *Proterospongia* (Fig. 10-23), a gelatinous mass of collar zooids at the surface and internal collarless ameboid zooids. *Proterospongia* has been suggested as a possible link between the choanoflagellates and the sponges.

Some of the worst of the protozoan parasites are flagellates. Many of these belong to the genus *Trypanosoma* and live in the blood of fishes, amphibians, reptiles, birds, and mammals. Some are nonpathogenic, but those that infect the mammals produce severe diseases. Important to man are *T. gambiense,* which causes African sleeping sickness (Figs. 10-24 and 10-25), and

T. rhodesiense, which causes the similar but more virulent Rhodesian sleeping sickness. *T. brucei* causes nagana in domestic cattle but does not infect man. The three are indistinguishable morphologically, and all are transmitted by the tsetse fly (*Glossina*). Their natural reservoirs (antelope and other wild mammals) are apparently not harmed by harboring these parasites. *T. cruzi* causes Chagas' disease in man in Central and South America. It is transmitted by the bite of a "kissing bug" (*Triatoma*). *T. lewisi,* a parasite of rats, is transmitted by the rat flea and is probably nonpathogenic. *T. rotatorium,* which occurs in the blood of frogs, is transmitted by the bite of the leech. Three species of another flagellate *(Leishmania)* causes severe diseases in man. *L. donovani* causes a disease of the spleen and liver, *L. tropica* causes a peculiar type of skin lesion, and *L. braziliense* produces lesions in the mucous membranes of the nose and throat. These are transmitted by sandflies or by direct contact and are common in Africa, around the Mediterranean, in Asia, and in Central and South America. Several species of the genus *Trichomonas* (order Polymastigina) are commensals. *T. hominis* is found in the cecum and colon of man, transmitted by trophozoites; *T. vaginalis* is sometimes found in the vagina of women when secretions are acid and may cause vaginitis; and other species of Trichomonas are widely distributed through all classes of vertebrates and many invertebrates. A common flagellate of the small intestine of man is *Giardia intestinalis* (*G. lamblia*), which is often blamed for a severe diarrhea. It is transmitted through fecal contamination. Species are found in all classes of vertebrates.

FIG. 10-25

Trypanosoma gambiense scattered among human red blood cells. These blood parasites cause sleeping sickness (trypanosomiasis) in tropical Africa. One part of their life history is passed in tsetse flies, which distribute the parasites to man and wild game animals. Class Mastigophora.

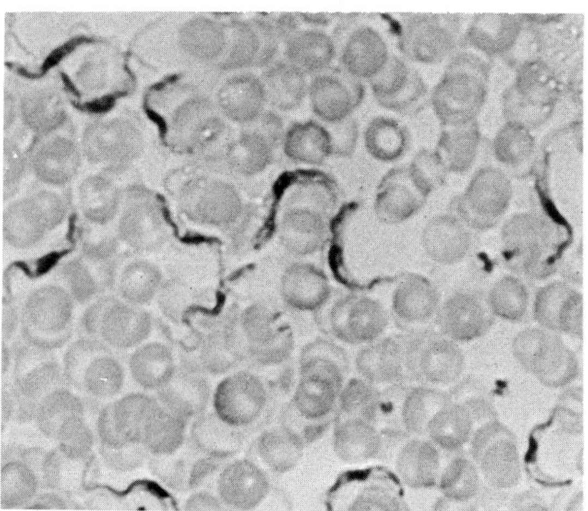

CLASS SPOROZOA

Plasmodium

Malaria is caused by a protozoan parasite, *Plasmodium,* which belongs to order Haemosporidia of class Sporozoa. All known members of this class are parasitic. They have rather simple bodies, no well-defined organelles for locomotion, and no contractile vacuoles. They reproduce by spore formation, which may involve both asexual and sexual methods. Malaria is one of the most widespread diseases in the world. It is mainly a disease of tropical and subtropical countries but is also common in the temperate zones. The vectors of the parasites are female mosquitoes of the genus *Anopheles.* Four species of *Plasmodium* are known to infect man—*P. vivax, P. malariae, P. falciparum,* and *P. ovale.* Each produces its own peculiar clinical picture, although all malarial parasites have similar cycles of development in the host (Fig. 10-26).

Man acquires malaria from the bite of the mosquito, which introduces the parasites from its salivary glands into the blood in the form of sporozoites. It was found in 1948 that the sporozoites first enter the cells of the liver. Here, as **cryptozoites,** they pass through a process of multiple division (**schizogony**). The products of this division, **merozoites,** then enter the red corpuscles. This period when the parasites are in the liver is called the incubation period. During this time antimalarial drugs may have little effect upon the parasites. When they enter the red blood corpuscles (usually only one to a cell), they become amebalike **trophozoites.** These feeding forms then develop into **schizonts,** which have granules of black pigment. Each schizont, by multiple fission (schizogony), divides into many daughter asexual merozoites (6 to 36 in number, according to the species of *Plasmodium*); these break out of the red cells to enter other red corpuscles and repeat the asexual cycle. In a few days the number of parasites is so great that the characteristic chills and fever occur; these symptoms are caused mainly by the toxins released by the parasites. The time elapsing between the fever-chill stages of the cycle depends upon the type of malaria. In *P. vivax* (benign tertian) the chills and fever occur every 48 hours; in *P. malariae* (quartan), every 72 hours; in *P. falciparum* (malignant tertian), usually every 24 to 48 hours, although it may be irregular; and in *P. ovale,* every 48 hours.

After a period of this asexual reproduction, or schizogony, the merozoites become sexual forms, **gametocytes.** When these gametocytes are sucked up into the stomach of the mosquito, they become **microgametocytes** (male) and **macrogametocytes** (female) A zygote is formed by the union of two gametes from opposite sexes and develops into the mobile **ookinete.** The ookinetes penetrate into the stomach walls of the mosquito to lie under the covering epithelium. Later the ookinetes enlarge to form **oocysts.** Each oocyst then divides in a few days into thousands of sporozoites that rupture the cyst and migrate to the salivary glands, whence they are transferred to man by the bite of the mosquito. The developmental cycle in the mosquito requires from 7 to 18 days but may be longer in cool weather. After being inoculated by the mosquito, man usually manifests the symptoms of the disease 10 to 14 days later.

Some forms of malaria may persist for some years without showing clinical symptoms. It is thought that this latent malaria is due to the small number of parasites in the blood. The body gradually acquires an immunity to the disease; this causes malaria to subside. However, this immunity does not prevent relapses.

The time-honored treatment for malaria has been quinine, which was found effective 300 years ago; but Atabrine and Plasmochin are also employed. The elimination of mosquitoes and their breeding places (by

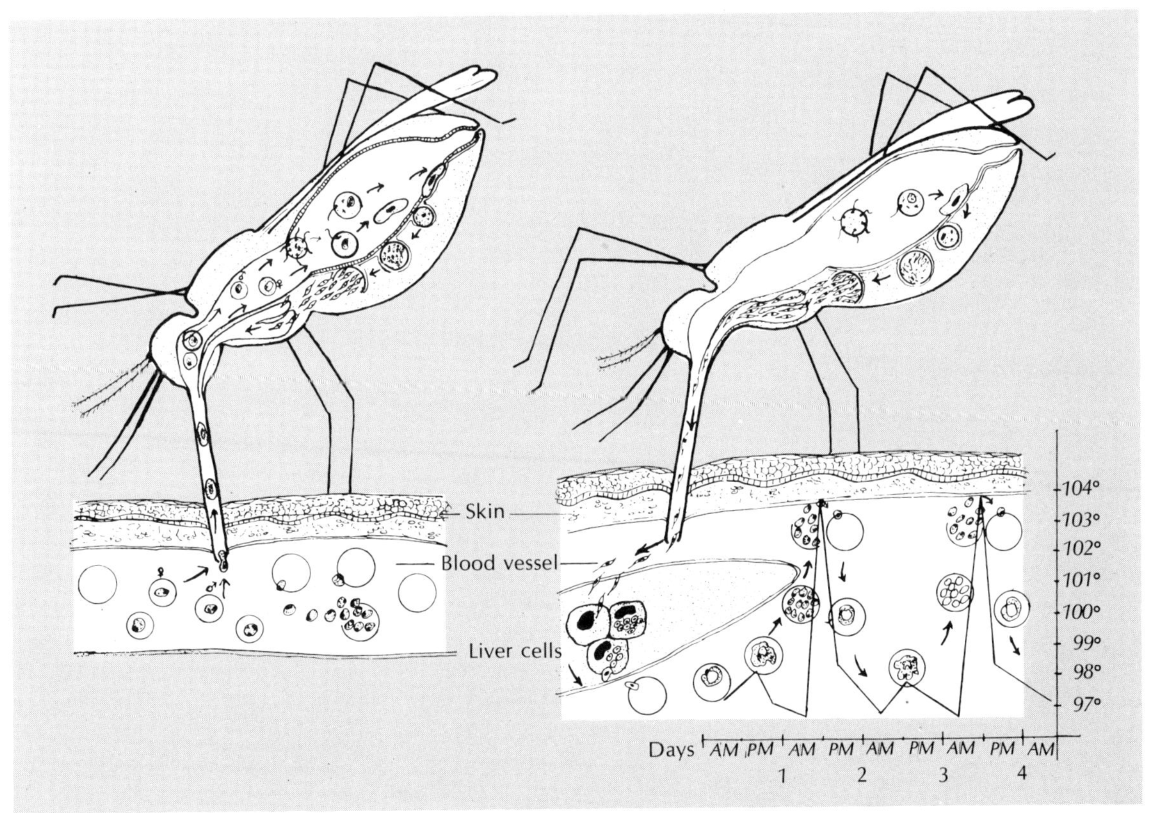

FIG. 10-26

Life cycle of *Plasmodium vivax,* malarial parasite. At left, mosquito, *Anopheles,* ingests infected blood; at right, sporozoites injected into man by mosquito. Fever cycle of infected patient is shown in lower right-hand corner.

DDT, drainage, etc.) has been effective in controlling malaria.

Other species of *Plasmodium* parasitize birds, reptiles, and mammals. Those of birds are transmitted chiefly by the *Culex* mosquito.

Gregarinida

The order Gregarinida of Sporozoa consists of parasites that live mainly in the digestive tract and body cavity (sometimes in tissue cells) of certain invertebrates such as arthropods and annelids. A familiar example is *Monocystis lumbrici* (Fig. 10-27), which lives in the seminal vesicles of earthworms. They may cause sterility in the parasitized worm, for they destroy the sperm. Earthworms are infected by spores, each of which contains 8 sporozoites. Each sporozoite enters a bundle of immature sperm cells and becomes a trophozoite, which lives on the sperm cells. Two trophozoites (gametocytes) come together and are surrounded by a cyst wall. Each divides a number of times to produce gametes. Two of these from different trophozoites unite to form the zygote, which forms a hard case around itself. This is the spore case, or oocyst. The zygote nucleus divides into 2, 4, and then 8 daughter nuclei. Each of these nuclei, with a small amount of cytoplasm, becomes a sporozoite, and the cycle is ready to start over.

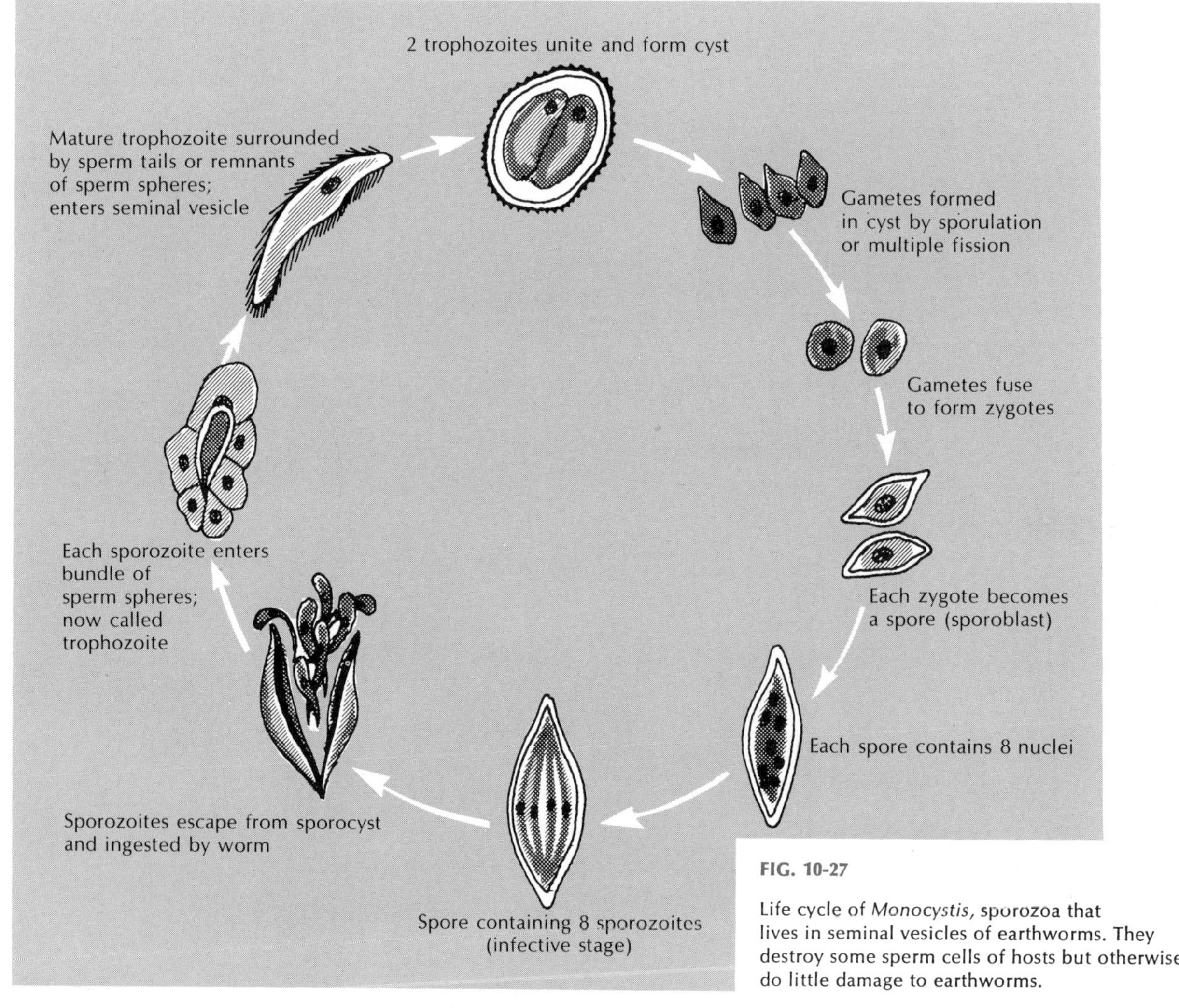

FIG. 10-27

Life cycle of *Monocystis,* sporozoa that lives in seminal vesicles of earthworms. They destroy some sperm cells of hosts but otherwise do little damage to earthworms.

Coccidia

The order Coccidia are Sporozoa whose life cycle (which involves both schizogony and sporogony) is passed in a single host. They are parasites that infect epithelial tissues in both invertebrates (annelids, arthropods, mollusks) and vertebrates. They are found chiefly in the epithelial lining of the coelom, alimentary canal, bile duct, blood vessels, etc. The disease produced is called coccidiosis and may be serious. The symptoms are usually severe diarrhea or dysentery. Infection is by the ingestion of oocysts and sometimes by separate sporozoites. *Eimeria* (Fig. 10-28) is a common genus found in rabbits and chickens. *E. magna* and *E. stiedae* infect the intestine and liver of rabbits. Their life history is briefly indicated in Fig. 10-28. Oocysts usually pass in the feces of the rabbit. Later each zygote divides into four sporoblasts, each of which forms a sporocyst enclosing two sporozoites. When ingested, the life cycle is repeated.

CLASS CILIATA

Paramecium caudatum

Habitat. Paramecia are usually abundant in fresh water that contains a great deal of decaying organic matter. A good place for them is in ponds or sluggish streams containing aquatic plants such as *Ceratophyllum* ample is *Monocystis lumbrici* (Fig. 10-27), which lives

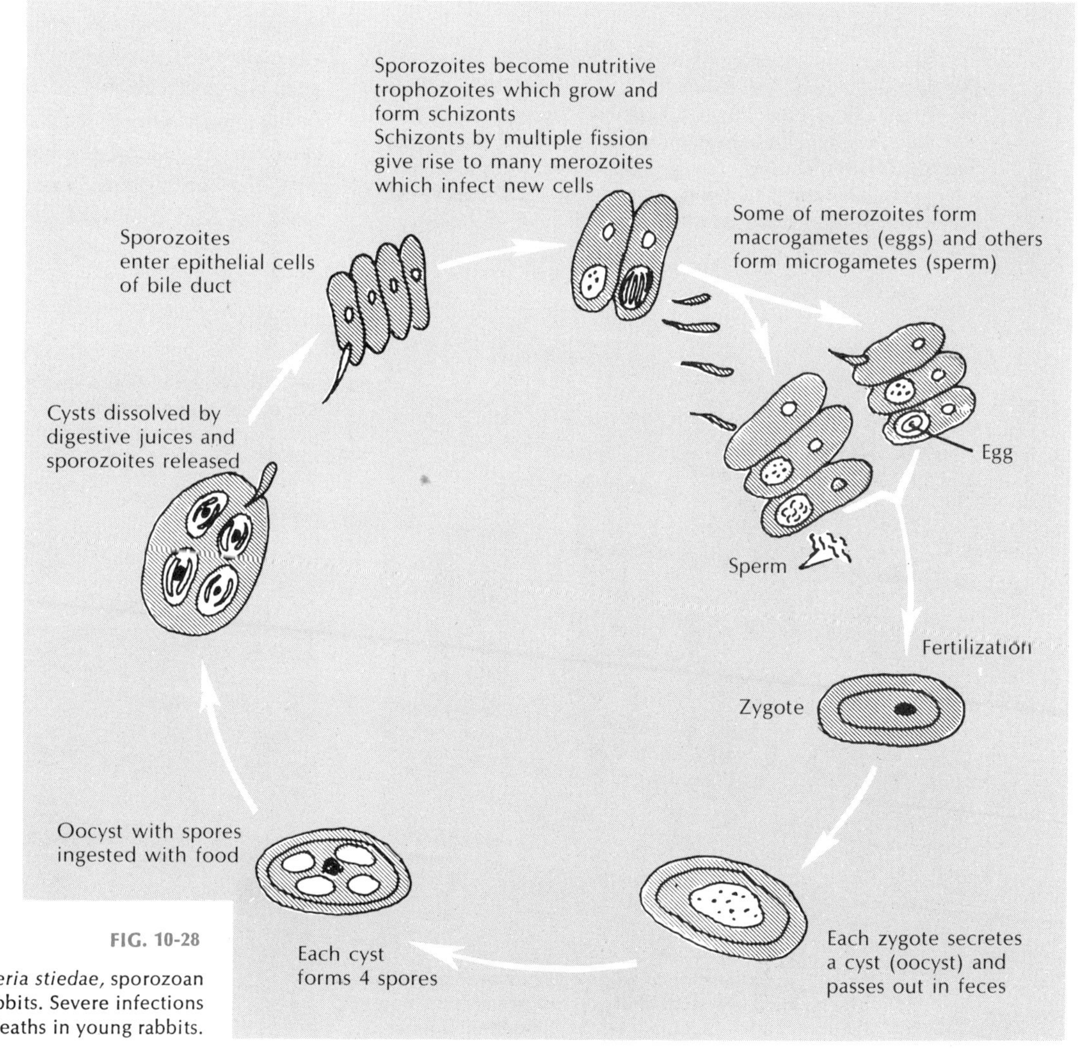

FIG. 10-28

Life cycle of *Eimeria stiedae*, sporozoan (Coccidia) parasite of rabbits. Severe infections may cause many deaths in young rabbits.

found at sewage disposal plants, are excellent places for them. A jar of contaminated water allowed to stand for a day or so will yield them in abundance. They gather in scum near the surface but are active and free swimming and may be found throughout the water in which they live.

Structure. The paramecium is often described as slipper shaped. *Paramecium caudatum* is from 150 to 300 μ (0.15 to 0.3 mm.) in length.* It is blunt at the anterior end and somewhat pointed at the posterior end, with the greatest width behind the center of the body (Fig. 10-29). The animal has an asymmetric appearance because of the **oral groove,** a depression that runs obliquely backward, ending just behind the middle of the body. Viewed from the anterior end, the groove usually runs clockwise, but in some individuals it runs in a counterclockwise direction. The **oral** or **ventral** side is the side containing the oral groove; the opposite side is called the **aboral** or **dorsal** side.

Over the entire surface is a clear, elastic membrane —the **pellicle,** or **cuticle.** This membrane is divided into small hexagonal areas by tiny elevated ridges (Fig. 10-30). The pellicle is covered over its entire surface by fine cilia, which are characteristic of the class to which *Paramecium* belongs. The cilia are arranged in lengthwise rows, and in some species, *P. caudatum* among them, they are longer at the posterior end, producing a caudal tuft.

Just below the pellicle is the thin clear **ectoplasm** that surrounds the larger mass of granular **endoplasm.** Embedded in the ectoplasm just below the surface are spindle-shaped cavities, known as **trichocysts,** filled with a semifluid substance that may be discharged as long threads for attachment and defense. The trichocysts alternate with the bases of the cilia.

At the posterior end of the oral groove is the **mouth** (**cytostome**), which leads into the tubular **gullet,** or **cytopharynx.** Along the gullet are two rows of fused cilia—the **undulating membrane.** When discharging fecal material, the **anal pore** can be seen posterior to

*Within each species of *Paramecium* the individuals exhibit morphologic and physiologic differences. Since these differences are usually more minor and more superficial than those that distinguish species, the groups within a species are referred to as strains, biotypes, or varieties. Most species of Protozoa can be divided into a number of these groups.

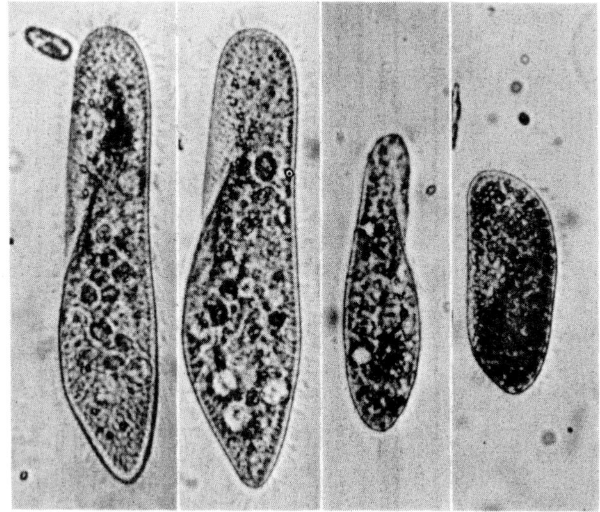

FIG. 10-29

Comparison of four common species of *Paramecium* photographed at same magnification. Left to right: *P. multimicronucleatum, P. caudatum, P. aurelia,* and *P. bursaria.* (Courtesy Carolina Biological Supply House, Burlington, N. C.)

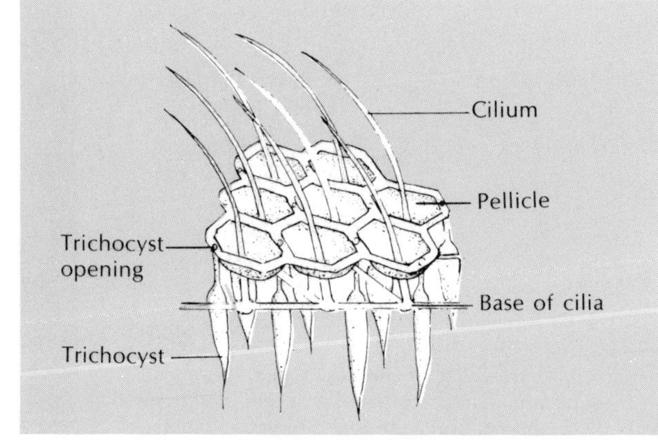

FIG. 10-30

Section of pellicle of *Paramecium* showing arrangement of cilia, trichocysts, and neuromotor system. (Modified from Lund.)

the oral groove (Fig. 10-31). The endoplasm contains **food vacuoles,** with food in various stages of digestion. Toward each end of the cell body and near the surface is a **contractile vacuole.** Each contractile vacuole is made up of a central space surrounded by several **radiating canals.** There are two **nuclei:** a large kidney-shaped **macronucleus** and a smaller **micronucleus** fitted into a depression of the former. These can usually be seen only in stained specimens. The macronucleus is concerned chiefly with vegetative activities and with regeneration after injury. The micronucleus has only genetic functions. The number of nuclei may vary in different species. *Paramecium multimicronucleatum* may have 3 or 4, or as many as 7, micronuclei.

Paramecia are complex little animals. Special fixing and staining methods show that the cilia are connected to **basal granules,** which in turn are linked to each other by longitudinal fibers, the whole comprising the **neuromotor system** concerned with the coordination of ciliary action (Fig. 10-30). The structure of a cilium is very similar to that of a flagellum, and the basal granules are thought to be homologous to the blepharoplasts of flagella.

Metabolism. Paramecia do not have chlorophyll for forming their own food. They are holozoic, living upon other Protozoa, bacteria, algae, and other small organisms. They are selective in choosing their food, for some items are taken in and others rejected. The cilia in the oral groove sweep food particles in the water into the cytostome, whence they are carried into the cytopharynx by the undulating membrane. At the posterior part of the cytopharynx the food is collected into a food vacuole, which is constricted off and dropped into the endoplasm. The food vacuoles take a definite course in their circulation, first posteriorly, then forward near the dorsal surface to the anterior end. During this course the food is digested by enzymes from the endoplasm, and the vacuoles become smaller. By the use of indicator dyes it is possible to demonstrate that vacuoles are first acid and later alkaline. The indigestible part of the food is ejected through the anal pore. Digestion in ciliates is fairly rapid. A *Didinium* can digest a whole paramecium in about 20 minutes.

Respiration takes place through the body surface by diffusion, oxygen dissolved in the surrounding water passing in and the waste, including carbon dioxide, passing out.

The two contractile vacuoles regulate the water content of the body and may also serve to get rid of the nitrogenous waste. The vacuoles lie close to the dorsal surface and drain fluid from the cytoplasm by means of radiating canals that are easily seen when the vacuole is forming. When the vacuole reaches a certain size, it discharges to the outside through a pore. The two vacuoles contract alternately at intervals of about 10 to 20 seconds. They contract more frequently at higher temperatures and in the mature animal. Since the contents of the paramecium are hypertonic to the surrounding fresh water, osmotic pressure would cause water

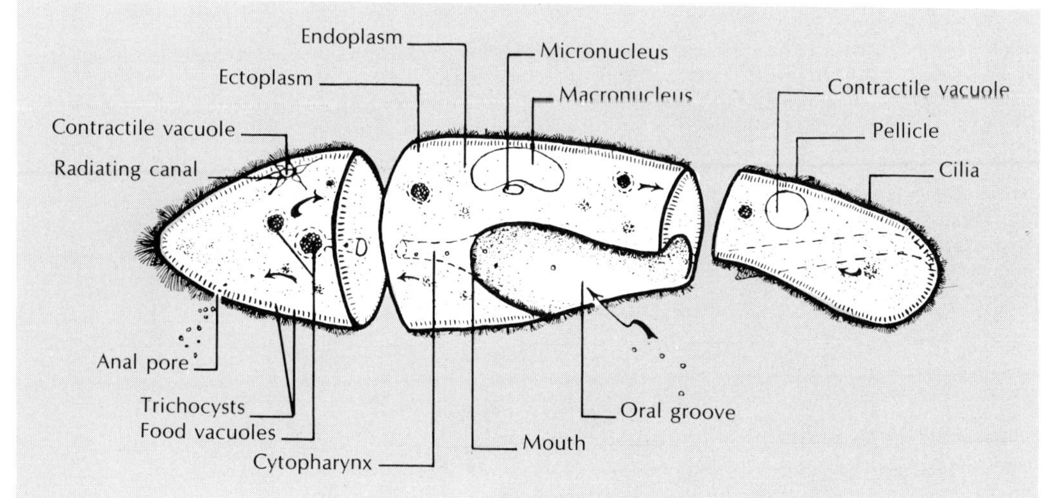

FIG. 10-31

General structure of *Paramecium caudatum.* (Shown cut into three sections.)

to diffuse into the cell, and thus one of the main functions of the contractile vacuoles is to get rid of the excess water.

Locomotion. The body of the paramecium is elastic, for it can squeeze its way through a narrow passage. Its cilia can beat either forward or backward, so that the animal can swim in either direction. The cilia beat obliquely, thus causing the animal to rotate on its long axis. In the oral groove the cilia are longer and beat more vigorously than the others so that the anterior end swerves aborally. As a result of these factors, the animal follows a spiral path in order to move directly forward (Fig. 10-32). In swimming backward the beat and path of rotation are reversed.

When the paramecium comes in contact with a disturbing chemical stimulus, it performs the **avoiding reaction** (Fig. 10-33). In this process it reverses its cilia, backs up a short distance, and swerves the anterior end aborally as it pivots on its posterior end. While it is doing this, samples of the surrounding medium are brought into the oral groove. When the sample no longer contains the unfavorable stimulus, the animal moves forward.

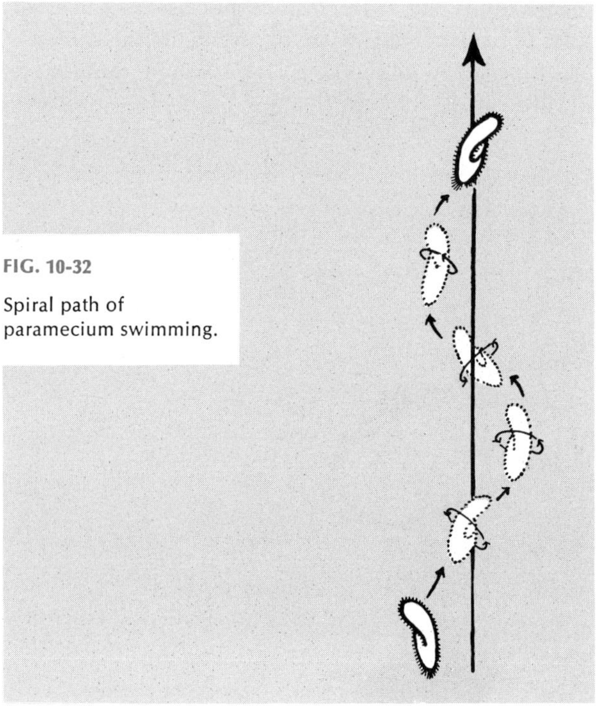

FIG. 10-32

Spiral path of paramecium swimming.

Reproduction. Paramecia reproduce only by **transverse binary fission** but have certain forms of nuclear reorganization called **conjugation** and **autogamy.**

In **binary fission** the micronucleus divides mitotically into 2 daughter micronuclei, which move to opposite ends of the cell (Fig. 10-34). The macronucleus elongates and divides amitotically. Another cytopharynx is budded off and two new contractile vacuoles appear, one near the anterior end and another posteriorly. In the meantime a constriction furrow appears near the middle of the body and deepens until the cytoplasm is completely divided. The process of binary fission requires from ½ to 2 hours. The division rate usually varies from

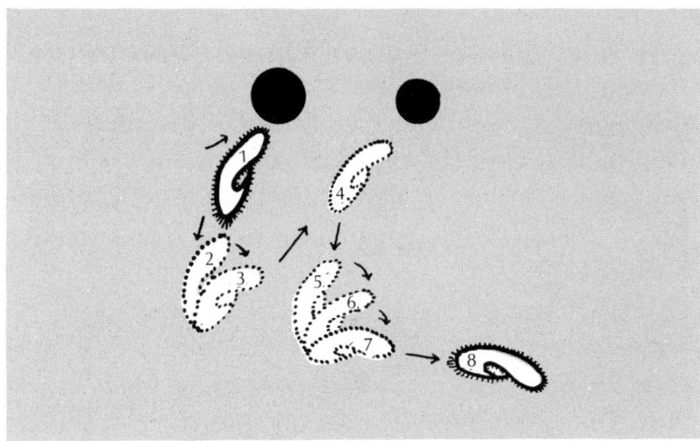

FIG. 10-33

Avoiding reaction of paramecium.

FIG. 10-34

Binary fission in paramecium.

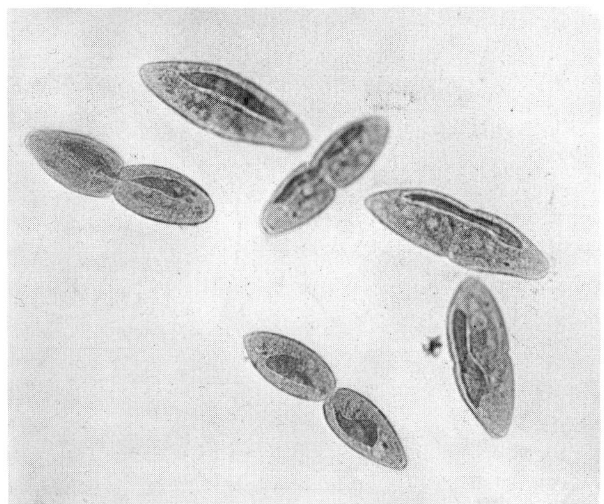

one to four times each day. About 600 generations are produced in a year. If all descendants were to live and reproduce, the number of paramecia produced would soon equal the volume of the earth! The term **clone** is used to refer to all the individuals that have been produced from one individual by binary fission. All the members of a clone are hereditarily alike.

The process known as **conjugation** (Fig. 10-35) occurs in ciliates and a few other Protozoa. This phenomenon happens only at intervals. It is more frequent in *P. caudatum* than it is in *P. aurelia.* It is the temporary union of two individuals that mutually exchange micronuclear material. Conjugating individuals come together and attach by their oral surfaces, and a protoplasmic bridge forms between them. In thriving cultures one may see a number of these conjugating pairs swimming about. A series of nuclear changes now occurs. The micronucleus of each member moves from its recess in the macronucleus, while the latter starts to disintegrate and finally disappears. The micronucleus enlarges, forms a spindle, and divides by meiosis, resulting in daughter nuclei with only half the usual number of chromosomes (haploid). After a second division of each micronucleus, 3 of the resulting micronuclei degenerate, leaving only 1. This remaining micronucleus divides unequally into 2 micronuclei, the smaller of which in each animal moves across the protoplasmic bridge into the other animal. Each of these exchanged micronuclei fuses with the larger micronucleus of the other animal, thus restoring the normal (diploid) number of chromosomes in the micronucleus of each animal.

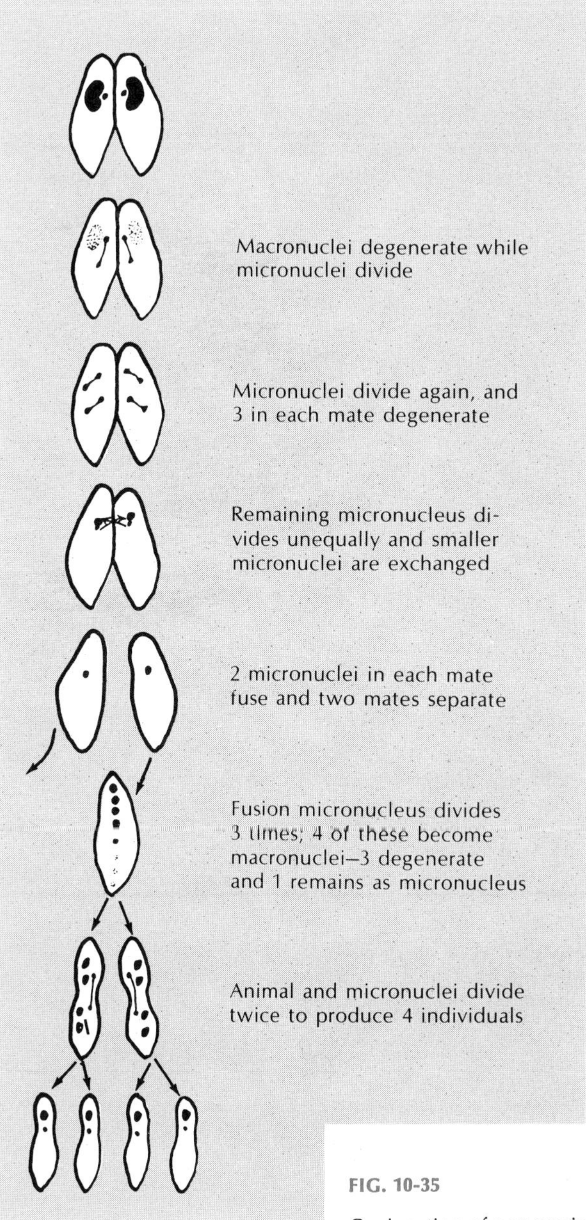

FIG. 10-35

Conjugation of paramecia.

The two paramecia now separate, and in each the fused micronucleus, which in comparable to a zygote in higher forms, divides by mitosis into 2, 4, and 8 micronuclei. Four of these enlarge and become macronuclei, and 3 of the other 4 disappear. The paramecium now divides twice, resulting in four paramecia, each with 1 micronucleus and 1 macronucleus. After this complicated process, the animal continues its binary fission reproduction.

What is the meaning of this unique phenomenon? There is first of all an exchange of hereditary material so that each conjugant profits from a new hereditary constitution. It is not the same as the union of the gametes in higher forms (zygote formation), in which direct progeny is the result, for in conjugation the animals still continue asexual division. However, about the same result is attained because the nucleus of each exconjugant contains hereditary material from two individuals. The process does not seem necessary for rejuvenation, for experiments have been conducted that show that cultures can be maintained for many years without undergoing conjugation.

In 1937 it was discovered that not every paramecium

would conjugate with any other paramecium of the same species. Sonneborn found that there were physiologic differences between individuals that set them off into **mating types.** Ordinarily conjugation will not occur between individuals of the same mating type but only with an individual of another (complementary) mating type. It was also found that within a single species there are a number of varieties, each of which has mating types that conjugate among themselves but not with the mating types of other varieties. In *Paramecium aurelia,* for instance, each of six varieties has two mating types; conjugation, however, will occur only between members of opposite or complementary mating types within their own variety. Mating types are usually designated by Roman numerals. Thus in variety 1 of *P. aurelia,* the mating types are called mating types I and II; in variety 2, mating types III and IV, etc. New varieties of this species have been described from time to time until sixteen were known in 1957. Their wide and sporadic distribution pose interesting evolutionary problems. With few exceptions, each variety has only two interbreeding mating types. There is no morphologic basis for distinguishing mating types within a variety; such differences that exist must be physiologic. Some varieties, however, can be distinguished from each other morphologically. Mating types are found in other species of paramecia as well as among other ciliates. *Paramecium bursaria* has six varieties, but only one variety has a system of two mating types; the others have multiple (four to eight) mating types. Each mating type can conjugate with all the others in the same variety but not with individuals of its own mating type. Genetically each variety may be considered a separate species, since they do not interbreed, but this taxonomic scheme has not yet been adopted.

As an example of how conjugation occurs, the mating types of three varieties of *P. aurelia* are shown in Table 10-1.

Autogamy refers to a process of self-fertilization. After the disintegration of the macronucleus and the division of the 2 micronuclei to form 8 micronuclei, 2 of the haploid gametic nuclei that result from this division enter a small bulge (paroral cone), fuse together, and restore the diploid number of chromosomes in the synkaryon, or zygote. The other 6 micronuclei degenerate, and the synkaryon divides twice to produce

TABLE 10-1

Examples of conjugation in three varieties of *Paramecium aurelia*

		Variety					
		1		2		3	
	Mating type	I	II	III	IV	V	VI
1	I	−	+	−	−	−	−
	II	+	−	−	−	−	−
2	III	−	−	−	+	−	−
	IV	−	−	+	−	−	−
3	V	−	−	−	−	−	+
	VI	−	−	−	−	+	−

\+ indicates conjugation will occur.
− indicates conjugation will not occur.

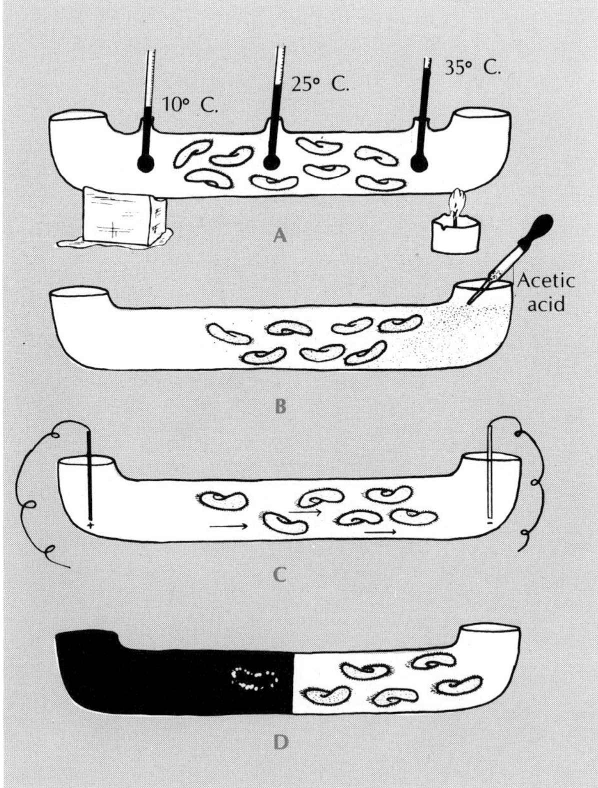

FIG. 10-36

Certain typical taxes of paramecia. **A,** Temperature. **B,** Acid. **C,** Electric current. **D,** Light.

2 macronuclei and 2 micronuclei. At the first binary fission each daughter cell will receive 1 of the macronuclei and by division of the micronuclei also 2 micronuclei. This process is similar to conjugation but does not involve two individuals.

A variant form of conjugation and autogamy is **cytogamy,** in which two ciliates become fused along their oral surfaces and three pregametic divisions occur. Two of the gametic nuclei then form a synkaryon as in autogamy. However, there is no exchange of nuclear material between the two fused members.

Behavior.* The avoiding reaction already described serves as a key in the interpretation of the various reactions of paramecia to stimuli. In its responses a paramecium uses the "trial-and-error" method to make its adjustments. In this method the animal attempts many directions until it finds one that is favorable and then makes its escape from the injurious environment.

Paramecia do not always respond in the same manner to the same stimuli. Their physiologic states vary with conditions. A hungry animal will react in a different way from one that it well fed. In general its behavior is conditioned by factors that favor or hinder the normal life processes.

The responses of paramecia and other Protozoa are often called **taxes.** A taxis is an orientation of the body either toward or away from a stimulus (Fig. 10-36). If the response is toward the stimulus, it is called a **positive response;** if the animal avoids the stimulus, it is termed a **negative response.**

With respect to the kind of stimuli, taxes are classified as follows:

thermotaxis Response to heat. For the paramecium, the optimum temperature lies between 24° and 28° C.

phototaxis Response to light rays. The optimum for paramecia is subdued light; it will try to avoid total darkness or bright light.

thigmotaxis Response to contact. Response to this stimulus is varied. When the anterior end is touched lightly, the animal will usually back up, but if some other part is touched, it may be indifferent.

chemotaxis Response to chemical substances. Paramecia react negatively to most chemicals, yet to mildly acid solutions they often respond in a positive way. They are partial to carbon dioxide solutions.

rheotaxis Response to currents of air or water. The paramecium will swim toward a current of water if it is not too swift, or it will head upstream.

galvanotaxis Response to constant electric current. Paramecia will move toward the negative (cathode) pole. This response is supposed to be due to the effect of the electrons upon the action of the cilia.

geotaxis Response to gravity. The response of paramecia is mostly negative; they tend to gather close to the surface film with their anterior ends uppermost.

Since no nervous system is found in Protozoa (except perhaps the neuromotor system in ciliates), these responses must be due to the innate irritability of protoplasm. The complex responses of higher forms are thought to have developed from these simple mechanical responses.

*Refer to Chapter 2, Principle 29.

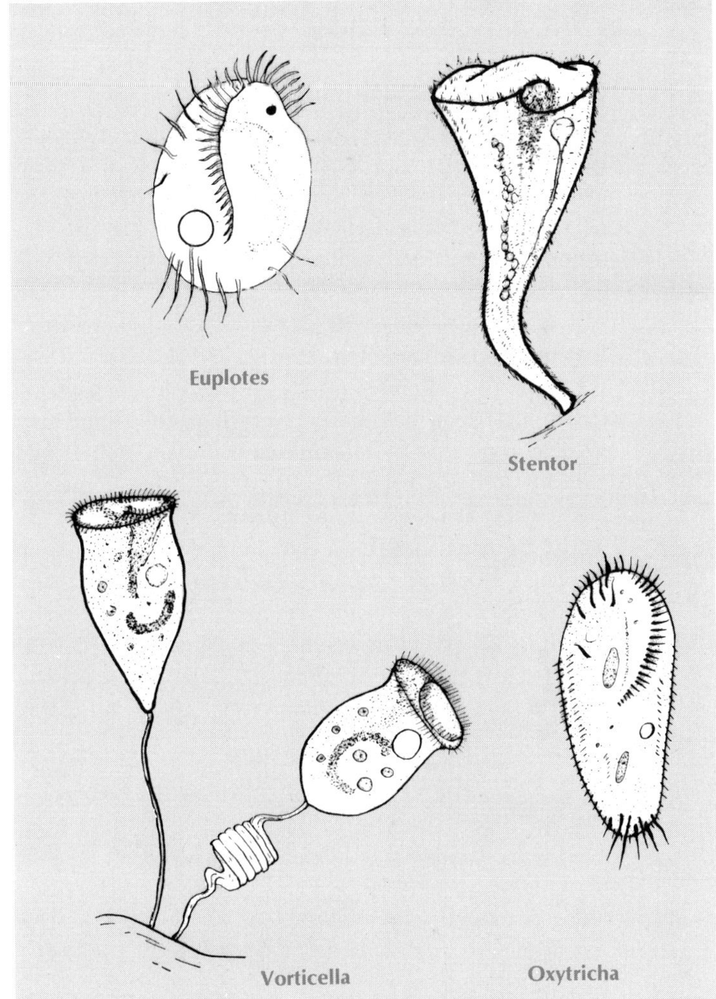

FIG. 10-37

Some representative ciliates. *Euplotes* and *Oxytricha* can use stiff cirri for crawling about. Contractile myonemes in ectoplasm of *Stentor* and in stalks of *Vorticella* allow great expansion and contraction.

Other members of class Ciliata

Ciliata is an interesting class, with many forms in both fresh water and marine water. There is a great diversity of shape and size among them. Among the more striking forms of ciliates are *Stentor* (Fig. 10-37), trumpet shaped and solitary; *Vorticella,* inverted bell form and solitary (Figs. 10-37 and 10-38); and *Euplotes,* flattened body with groups of fused cilia (cirri) that function as legs (Fig. 10-37).

Ciliates are represented by a number of parasitic forms, most of which are not very harmful. Some may even be commensals. *Balantidium coli* is the only ciliate parasite in man (Fig. 10-39). It is often found in hogs, where it usually does no harm. Man becomes infected by water and food contaminated by cysts from the hog's feces. The parasite enters the intestinal submucosa and causes ulcers and severe and even fatal dysentery. It is not as common in America as it is in Europe, Asia, and Africa. Other similar species are found in cattle and horses—*Epidinium* (Fig. 10-40) in cattle, for example. Some ciliate parasites such as *Nyctotherus* also occur in the colon of frogs and toads. Frogs in captivity, however, tend to lose parasites rapidly. Tadpoles are infected when they eat the feces of frogs containing the cysts.

ORDER SUCTORIA (CLASS CILIATA)

Suctorians are found in both fresh water and marine water. The young possess cilia and are free swimming. As adults they grow a stalk for attachment to animal or nonliving matter and lose their cilia. As young they are often mistaken for ciliates, and some authorities consider them as a subdivision of the class Ciliata. The body, covered with a pellicle, may be spherical, branched, or another form. Nutrition is holozoic. They have no cytostome but have protoplasmic processes that serve as tentacles. Some of these have rounded knobs for capturing their prey—usually ciliates; some are sharp for piercing and for sucking up the protoplasm. The tentacles in some are scattered over the body; in others they are arranged in clusters. Reproduc-

FIG. 10-38

Living *Vorticella* attached by its stalk to debris in pond water culture. Class Ciliata, subclass Holotricha.

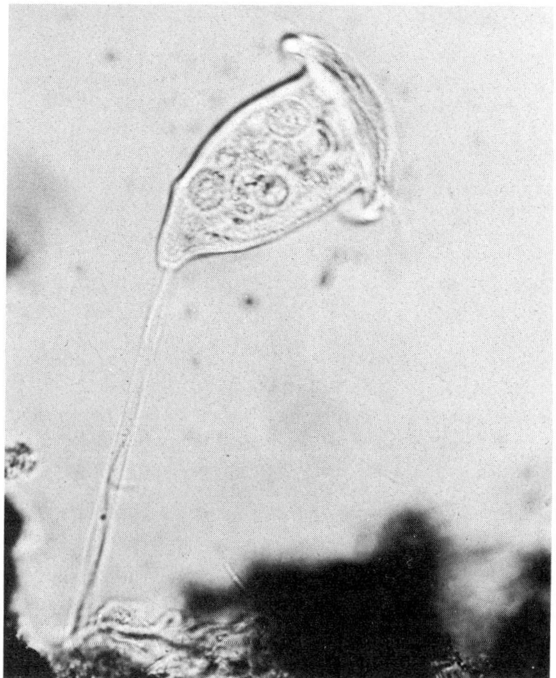

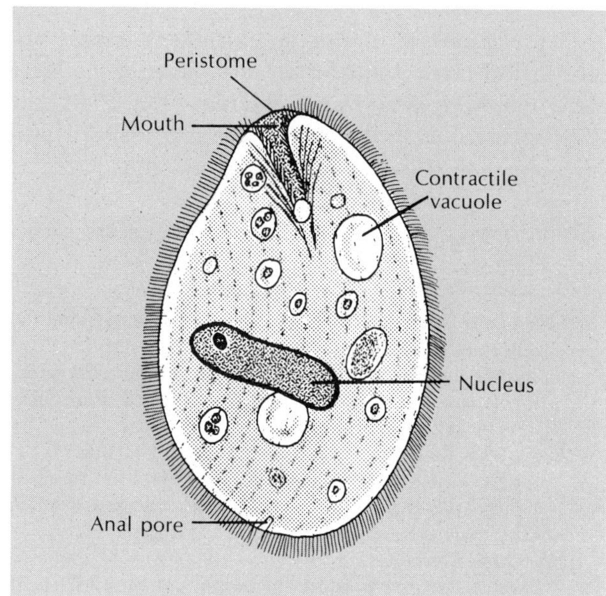

FIG. 10-39

Balantidium coli, ciliate parasitic in man. Ciliate is common in hogs in which it does little damage; man becomes infected by food or water contaminated by cysts from hog feces or by handling intestines. In man it lives in cecum or colon, in which it produces ulcers and severe chronic dysentery. Cysts formed by ciliate are protective; no multiplication occurs within them. Infections common in parts in Europe, Asia, and Africa; rare in United States.

tion, mostly asexual, includes both fission and budding. In sexual reproduction two individuals undergo a complete fusion, which is a type of conjugation.

One of the best places to find suctorians is in the algae that grows on the carapace of turtles, such as the snapping turtle (*Chelydra serpentina*) and the western painted turtle (*Chrysemys picta belli*). Common genera of suctorians found there are *Anarma* (without stalk or test) and *Squalorophrya* (with stalk and test).

Suctorian parasites include the *Trichophrya,* which is parasitic on the gills of the small-mouthed black bass and may cause serious damage to the fish; *Allantosoma,* which occurs in the intestine of certain mammals; and *Sphaerophrya,* which is found in *Stentor.*

Among freshwater representatives are *Podophrya* (Fig. 10-8) and *Dendrosoma.* Some saltwater forms are *Acinetopsis* and *Ephelota.*

VALUE IN BIOLOGIC INVESTIGATION

Protozoans are widely studied by biologists everywhere. Geneticists have long given consideration to the problem of heredity and variation in Protozoa. The rapid multiplication of protozoans and the many generations one can produce in a short time make these animals ideal for this study. The more some of these are studied, the more complex they turn out to be. The discovery of mating types in paramecia gives a hint or

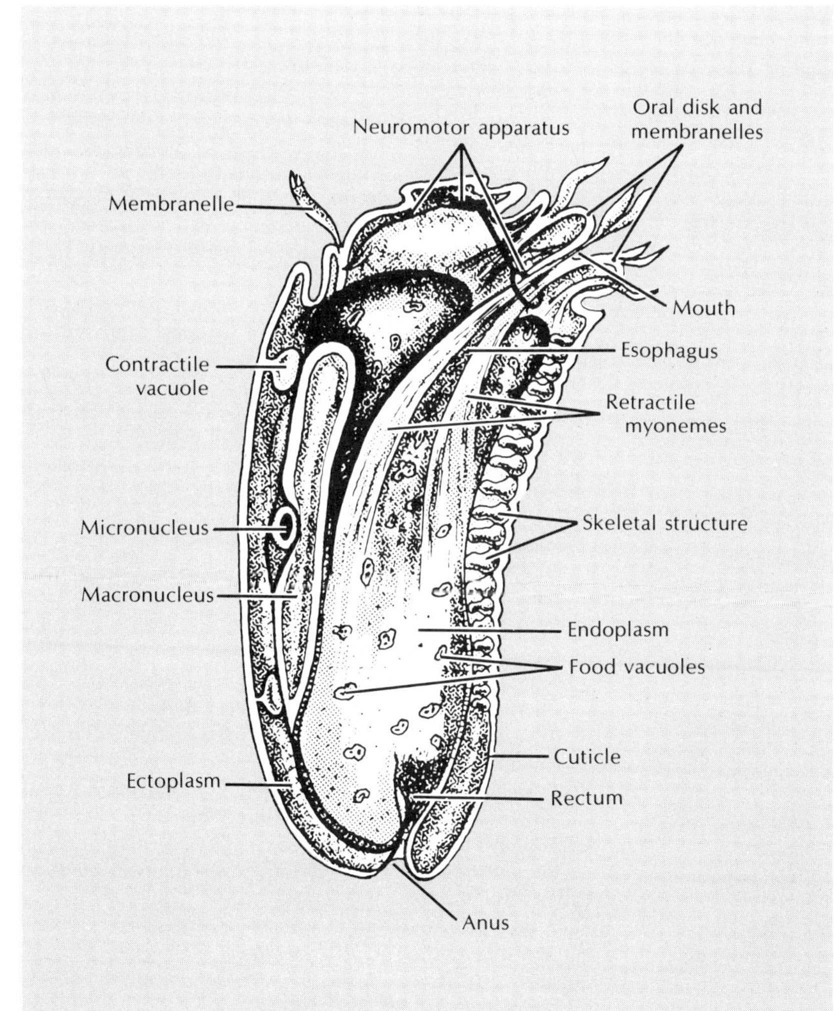

FIG. 10-40

Epidinium. This ciliate, which lives in stomach of ruminants, shows how complex a protozoan can be. It was with this ciliate that Sharp made his classic demonstration of neuromotor apparatus. He showed how organelles are controlled by neurofibrils connected anteriorly with motor mass (brain). Note that this so-called single cell has organelles specialized for coordination, ingestion and digestion, support, contraction, food storage, egestion, and hereditary continuity. (Modified from Sharp.)

suggestion of sex. Although individual paramecia cannot be labeled male or female, there is definitely a physiologic difference between individuals, just as there is in well-established sexual forms. In recent years much interest has centered upon the role *Paramecium aurelia* plays in explaining the phenomena of cellular transformations, that is, the changing of one type of cell into another type. Sonneborn made use of two hereditary strains of paramecia that he called "killers" and "sensitives." The killer strain contained in its cytoplasm certain visible particles (kappa particles) that liberated into the culture fluid a chemical substance (paramecin) that had the effect of destroying the other strain—the sensitive. Kappa particles, or killer substances, are transmitted directly by cytoplasmic genes (plasmagenes) from the cytoplasm of the parent cell to the daughter cells and not by nuclear genes as in ordinary heredity. This is often used as an example of cytoplasmic inheritance. Sonneborn was also able to change, experimentally, killers into sensitives and the reverse, thus producing a form of cellular transformation. Work by Beale and Gibson indicates that the killer substance is dependent upon a special particle (metagon) that acts as an intermediary between the killer particles and nuclear genes. There are many problems in this interesting phenomenon still unsolved.

Many other studies of Protozoa of current interest involve their nutritional needs, population crowding, permeability, and problems of serology and immunity.

Derivation and meaning of basic terminology

Amoeba (Gr. *amoibe,* change). Genus (Sarcodina).

Arcella (L. *arca,* box). Genus (Sarcodina); with a box-like test.

aurelia (L. *aurum,* gold). Species of *Paramecium.*

autogamy (Gr. *autos,* self, + *gamos,* marriage). Conjugation without exchange of micronuclei.

axopodia (L. *axis,* an axis, + Gr. *podos,* foot). Long, thin projections of cytoplasm, but not for locomotion.

blepharoplast (Gr. *blepharon,* eyelid, + *plastos,* formed). Granule connected with a flagellum.

caudatum (L. *caudata,* tail). Species of *Paramecium.*

cilium (L. eyelash). Threadlike organ of locomotion.

Coccidia (Gr. *kokkos,* kernel or berry). Order (Sporozoa).

conjugation (L. *conjugare,* to yoke together). Temporary union of two protozoans while they are exchanging chromatin material; may be a complete fusion in Suctoria.

cytopharynx (Gr. *kytos,* cell, + *pharynx,* throat). Short tubular gullet in protozoans.

cytostome (Gr. *kytos,* cell, + *stoma,* mouth). Mouth of a unicellular animal.

Difflugia (L. *diffluo,* flow apart). Genus (Sarcodina); refers to the flowing out of the pseudopodia.

Eimeria (after Eimer, German zoologist). Genus (order Coccidia of Sporozoa).

endomixis (Gr. *endon,* within, + *mixis,* mixing). Reorganization of the nuclear material in the protozoan.

Entamoeba (Gr. *entos,* within, + *amoibe,* change) ***histolytica*** (Gr. *histo,* tissue, + *lysis,* dissolve). Genus and species (Sarcodina).

Euglena (Gr. *eu,* true, + *glene,* eyeball or eye pupil). Refers to the stigma, or eyespot.

Euplotes (Gr. *eu,* good, + *ploter,* swimmer). Genus (Ciliata).

flagellum (L. *a whip*). Whiplike organ of locomotion.

Foraminifera (L. *foramen,* hole, + *fero,* bear). The tests are frequently perforated.

holozoic (Gr. *holos,* whole, + *zoikos,* of animals). That type of nutrition that involves ingestion of solid organic food.

Infusoria (L. *infusus,* crowded). So-called because of their abundance in a culture.

Leishmania (Leishman, who discovered it). Genus of a parasite (Mastigophora).

macronucleus (Gr. *makros,* large, + L. *nucleus,* kernel). Larger of the two types of nuclei in a ciliate.

micronucleus (Gr. *mikros,* small, + L. *nucleus,* kernel). Smaller of the two types of nuclei in a ciliate.

Monocystis (Gr. *monos,* single, + *kystis,* bladder). Parasitic genus (Sporozoa).

Noctiluca (L. *nox,* night, + *luceo,* shine). Genus (Mastigophora). Their luminescence is most apparent at night.

Opalina (L. *opalus,* opal). Genus (Mastigophora).

organelle (Gr. *organon,* organ, + L. *ell,* dim.). Specialized part of a cell; literally, a small organ.

Paramecium (Gr. *paramekes,* oblong). Genus (Ciliata).

paramylum (Gr. *para,* beside, + *mylos,* mil). Starch inclusions in certain protozoans.

Pelomyxa (Gr. *pelos,* mud, + *myzo,* suck in). Refers to the black and brown inclusions in body. Genus (Sarcodina).

proteus (*Proteus,* Greek mythology, sea god who could change shape). Species of *Amoeba.*

pseudopodium (Gr. *pseudes,* false, + *podos,* foot). Protrusion of part of cytoplasm of an ameba.

Radiolaria (L. *radius,* ray). Order (Sarcodina). The axopodia radiate in all directions.

Rhizopoda (Gr. *rhiza,* root, + *podos,* foot). Many pseudopodia may be extended at one time.

saprophytic (Gr. *sapros,* rotten, + *phyton,* plant). Type of nutrition by which the organism lives on decayed organic matter.

schizogony (Gr. *schizo,* to split, + *gonos,* seed). Asexual reproduction by multiple fission.

Stentor (Gr. Grecian herald with loud voice). Genus (Ciliata). Shaped like a megaphone.

stigma (Gr. *stigma,* a point). Eyespot in certain protozoans.

Suctoria (L. *suctus,* sucking). Food is sucked in by the tentacles.

symbiosis (Gr. *symbios,* a living together). Includes mutualism, commensalism, and parasitism.

taxis (Gr. arrangement). Response of animal organisms to sources of stimuli.

trichocyst (Gr. *thrix,* hair, + *kystis,* bladder). Saclike organelle in the ectoplasm of ciliates, which discharges a threadlike weapon of defense.

Trichomonas (Gr. *thrix,* hair, + *monas,* single). Genus (Mastigophora).

Trypanosoma (Gr. *trypanon,* auger, + *soma,* body). Genus (Mastigophora). The body with undulating membrane is twisted.

viridis (L. *viridis,* green). This species of Euglena bears chloroplasts.

Volvox (L. *volvo,* roll). Genus (Mastigophora). Refers to their characteristic movement.

Vorticella (L. *vortex,* a whirlpool). Genus (Ciliata). Movement of their cilia creates a spiral movement of water.

Annotated references

Allen, R. D. 1962. Amoeboid movement. Sci. Amer. **206:** 112-122 (Feb.).

Barrington, E. J. W. 1967. Invertebrate structure and function. Boston, Houghton Mifflin Co. *Stresses the importance of animal organization in the light of molecular and ultrastructural studies. Invertebrate study is considered to be a fundamental need to understand the basic principles of animal life at higher levels.*

Brieger, E. M. 1963. Structure and ultrastructure of microorganisms. New York, Academic Press, Inc. *Molecular biology has been focused for some time upon microorganisms in studying the basic organization of the cell at submicroscopic levels, but this treatise attempts to show that the bacterial cell is not a replica of the cell of higher organisms.*

Corliss, J. O. 1961. The ciliated Protozoa: characterization, classification and guide to the literature. New York, Pergamon Press, Inc. *This treatment of the largest and most difficult group of protozoans has received well-deserved recognition.*

Cushman, J. A. 1948. Foraminifera, their classification and economic use, ed. 4. Cambridge, Mass., Harvard University Press. *A definitive treatise on this important group of Protozoa. The student will appreciate how important these animals, small in size but abundant in numbers, are in the building of geologic formations.*

Edmondson, W. T. (editor). 1959. Ward and Whipple's fresh-water biology, ed. 2. New York, John Wiley & Sons, Inc. *In this handbook there are useful keys of the major groups of Protozoa.*

Gojdics, Mary. 1953. The genus *Euglena*. Madison, University of Wisconsin Press. *A comprehensive and technical account of this group. Much attention is given to taxonomy, but there are also good descriptions of morphology.*

Grasse, P. P. 1953. Traité de zoologie, vol. I. Paris, Masson & Cie, Editeurs.

Hall, R. P. 1953. Protozoology. Englewood Cliffs, N. J., Prentice-Hall, Inc. *A standard text on Protozoa. Good accounts of the morphology and physiology as well as taxonomy. There is an excellent chapter on reproduction and life cycles.*

Hardy, A. C. 1956. The open sea, its natural history: the world of plankton. Boston, Houghton Mifflin Co. *This fine work shows the role Protozoa and other forms play in the natural history of plankton. Good descriptions are given of the Radiolaria and other protozoans in Chapter 6. Beautiful color illustrations add much to the book.*

Hickman, C. P. 1967. Biology of the invertebrates. St. Louis, The C. V. Mosby Co.

Hyman, L. H. 1940. The invertebrates: Protozoa through Ctenophora, vol. 1. New York, McGraw-Hill Book Co. *In this first volume of a highly technical project on invertebrates, an extensive and exhaustive section is devoted to the morphology and physiology of protozoans. Some attention is given to classification, but this ambitious work summarizes in an admirable way many concepts in this field.*

Jahn, T. L., and F. F. Jahn. 1949. How to know the Protozoa. Dubuque, Iowa, William C. Brown Co., Publishers. *A valuable manual on the identification and description of protozoan forms. There is an excellent introductory account of the general features of Protozoa. All students of Protozoa will find this little book useful.*

Jennings, H. S. 1906. Behavior of the lower organisms. New York, Columbia University Press. *A classic work on the tropisms (taxes) of protozoan forms. This treatise has had a profound influence on all subsequent investigations along this line.*

Manwell, R. D. 1961. Introduction to protozoology. New York, St. Martin's Press, Inc.

Mayr, E. (editor). 1957. The species problem. Washington, D. C., American Association for the Advancement of Science. *This is a symposium by the authorities on the problems of species. The paper entitled "Breeding Systems, Reproductive Methods, and Species Problems in Protozoa" by Professor T. M. Sonneborn is a masterly analysis of the present status of mating types and the new concept of syngen as applied to the varieties found within the traditional species of Protozoa.*

Pennak, R. W. 1953. Fresh-water invertebrates of the United States. New York, The Ronald Press Co. *A very complete reference work with considerable attention devoted to Protozoa.*

Pettersson, H. 1954. The ocean floor, New Haven, Conn., Yale University Press. *The role the Foraminifera and*

Radiolaria have played in building up the sediment carpet of the ocean floor is vividly described in this little book. The author thinks the time of accumulation of deep-sea deposits to be 2 billion years and the rate of sedimentation of Globigerina ooze to be 0.4 inch in a thousand years.

Pitelka, D. R. 1963. Electron-microscopic structure of Protozoa. New York, The Macmillan Co. *A fine account of the ultrastructure of this basic group by one of the greatest authorities in the field.*

Sleigh, M. A. 1962. The biology of cilia and flagella. New York, The Macmillan Co. *Cilia and flagella have posed a challenge to biologists for more than a century, and this work is an excellent summary of their present status.*

Tartar, V. 1961. The biology of *Stentor*. New York, Pergamon Press, Inc.

Wichterman, R. 1953. The biology of *Paramecium*. New York, McGraw-Hill Book Co. *Those who think Protozoa are "simple animals" will be disillusioned by this well-written treatise on one genus of protozoans. A bibliography of more than 2,000 references gives an idea of the impressive amount of work performed on an animal that must meet all the basic physiologic functions of animal life (with all of its variations and complications) within the confines of a single-cell membrane.*

CHAPTER 11

• PHYLA MESOZOA (DICYEMIDS AND ORTHONECTIDS) AND PORIFERA (SPONGES)

BIOLOGIC PRINCIPLES

1. The Metazoa, or multicellular animals, are typically divided into three branches—Mesozoa, Parazoa (the poriferans), and Eumetazoa (all other phyla).
2. Two phyla (Mesozoa and Porifera) have in common the status of being separate branches of the metazoans in contrast to the Eumetazoa, or true metazoans.
3. Neither phylum fits into the general organization of other metazoans, but both groups are multicellular animals that have integrated morphologic structures.
4. The metazoan body is composed of layers of cells, but the basis of division into branches is based upon unique differences in structural organization and embryologic development.
5. The phylum Mesozoa has the simplest pattern of organization of all the branches, being composed of an outer layer of somatic cells that enclose one or more reproductive cells.
6. On the other hand, the branch Parazoa, or sponges, are more complex, with incipient tissues that are organized into low levels of integration. They have some differentiation of cells for various functions, and these cells have enough integration to produce a functional whole.
7. Although the Parazoa are far more complex in their structural pattern, they are more simple in their reproductive cycle than the Mesozoa, which have amazingly complicated life histories.
8. In development sponges have patterns different from those found in the Eumetazoa, and their embryonic layers are not homologous to those in other animals.
9. The body layers of the Mesozoa are also not homologous to those in higher metazoans. The mesozoan outside layer, the so-called ectoderm, has digestive functions whereas the inside layer, "endoderm," is entirely reproductive.

Position in animal kingdom

1. Both phyla have unknown phylogenetic relations. Some consider the Mesozoa as degenerate trematodes; others regard them as primitive. If they are primitive, this may indicate that the first metazoans had a solid blastula (stereoblastula) instead of a hollow one. Hyman thinks that they have affinities with the protozoans because of the widespread cilia in the group and the differentiation of only somatic and reproductive cells, as in certain colonial protozoans.
2. The origin of the sponges is equally mysterious. Their unique structural pattern makes it difficult to relate them to other groups. The evidence that they may have evolved from choanoflagellates such as *Proterospongia* has not met with much favor because larval sponges do not acquire collars until late in development. Sponges also show relationships to the Protozoa in the phagocytic method of nutrition and of the resemblance of their flagellated larvae to colonial protozoans. Sponges have some resemblances to coelenterates by their calcareous skeletons, mesenchyme, and amebocytes as gamete-forming cells.
3. The mesozoans are adapted to a parasitic existence. Parasites often have complicated life histories, and this may explain some of their evolutionary development. The small size and small number of mesozoan species (50) would indicate a modest adaptive radiation.
4. The Porifera of many thousand species have been a highly successful group. In their evolutionary diversification their unique water-current system has been largely responsible for their degree of complexity from simple to the more complicated. The leuconoid pattern of sponge structure, for example, favors a larger size because it has more chambers for capturing food and for gaseous exchange over the asconoid and syconoid types.

Phylum Mesozoa*

The members of phylum Mesozoa probably have the simplest structure of any metazoan form. They are minute wormlike forms composed of an outer layer of somatic cells (somatoderm), often ciliated, and a syncytium enclosing one or more reproductive cells (axial cells). This two-layered pattern does not corre-

*Mes′o-zo″a (Gr. *mesos*, middle, + *zoon*, animal).

spond to the ectoderm and endoderm of other Metazoa, for the inner layer (often of 1 cell) is concerned with reproduction and not digestion. They are endoparasites, with a life cycle involving both asexual and sexual generations.

There are two orders—the Dicyemida and the Orthonectida. The dicyemids are found only in the renal organs of cephalopods. Their body is made up of a long, axial reproductive cell surrounded by a single layer of large, ciliated somatic cells (not more than 24). The anterior somatic cells form a polar cap by which the dicyemid clings to the renal organ of its host. The germ cells, called agametes, are formed by the repeated division of the axial reproductive cell without maturation. Embryos in all stages of development are found inside the axial cell. In young cephalopods the dicyemids are called **nematogens** (Fig. 11-1) and their larvae are called **vermiform larvae,** which are similar to the parents; in mature cephalopods the dicyemids are called **rhombogens** and their larvae are called **infusoriform larvae,** which are short and rounded. Vermiform larvae escape from the parent nematogen

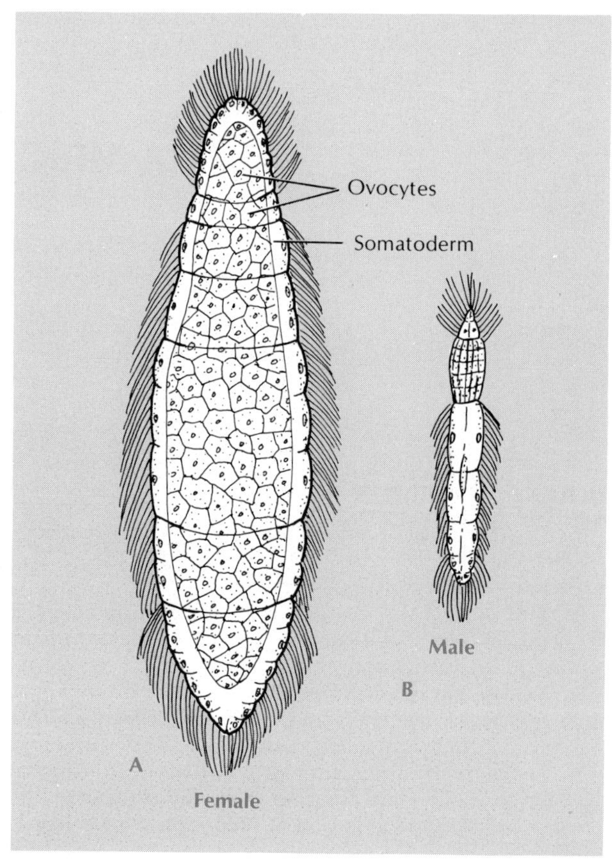

FIG. 11-2

A, Female and, **B,** male orthonectid *(Rhopalura).* This mesozoan parasitizes such forms as flatworms, mollusks, annelids, and brittle stars. Note that structure consists of single layer of ciliated epithelial cells surrounding inner mass of sex cells. (From Hickman: Biology of the invertebrates, The C. V. Mosby Co.)

FIG. 11-1

Primary nematogen stage of *Dicyema* (phylum Mesozoa), common endoparasite of squids and octopuses. Mesozoans are considered simplest of multicellular animals (about 25 cells). Their complicated life history involves asexual and sexual generations. In nematogen stage, agametes (germ cells without maturation) are formed by division of axial cell nucleus, and each agamete forms a nematogen. After leaving mother and giving rise to other generations, each nematogen is transformed into rhombogen stage. Phylogenetic status of phylum is obscure. Some think they are degenerate flatworms; others consider them primitive and related to protozoans.

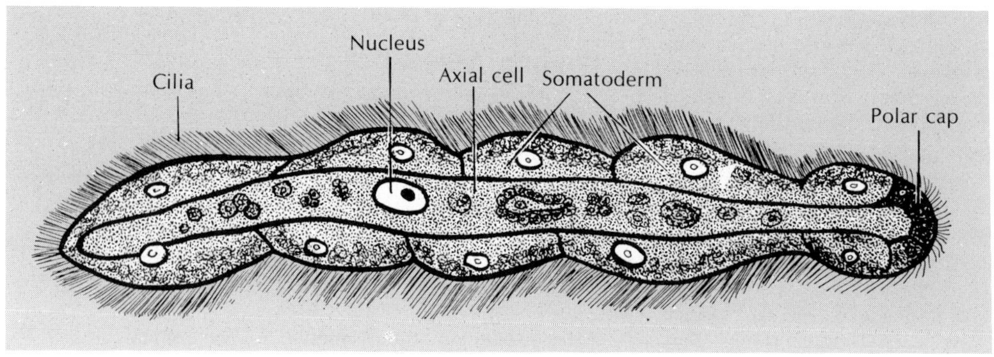

and attach to the renal tissue; infusoriform larvae escape from the parent rhombogen, are discharged with the urine, and probably infect new hosts. Evidence exists that there is a sexual as well as an asexual stage in the life history of dicyemids, but many aspects are still speculative.

Orthonectids parasitize many invertebrate hosts, such as rhynchocoels, bivalve mollusks, and polychaetes. Their minute body is made up of a central multinucleated mass, which forms male and female reproductive cells, surrounded by a single layer of ciliated surface cells arranged in rings (Fig. 11-2). The sexes are separate, but the females are much larger than the males. When the sexual forms escape from the host, fertilization occurs, and the zygotes develop inside the female into ciliated larvae, which escape to infect new hosts.

Common forms of Mesozoa are represented by *Dicyema, Pseudicyema, Microcyema,* and *Rhopalura.* Some authorities consider Mesozoa to be degenerate flatworms or coelenterates, with the evidence perhaps stronger in favor of the flatworms. This affinity to Platyhelminthes is based largely upon the resemblance between life cycles of the two groups, both of which produce ciliated larvae. Another view emphasizes the primitive nature of their organization as intermediate between Protozoa and Metazoa.

Phylum Porifera*

POSITION IN ANIMAL KINGDOM

Sponges belong to phylum Porifera, which means "to bear pores." All the members of this group have bodies containing tiny pores that are basic structures in their functional activity. Most biologists consider the group to be aberrant, that is, deviating widely from standard patterns. Sponges are not in the direct line of evolution of other animals and are placed as an offshoot from the main line of animal descent. They may have come from a flagellate or similar Protozoa because of the flagella-bearing **choanocytes** that line their cavities. One family of colorless flagellate protozoans (Craspedomonadidae) is made up of choanoflagellates, or cells provided with transparent collars that enclose the single flagellum. The collar (which may have come from the fused axopods of Heliozoa) catches food, which is passed down the outside of the collar to the cytosome. The colonial choanoflagellate *Proterospongia,* which consists of a gelatinous mass of collared zooids at the surface and collarless ones in the center, is probably not an ancestor of the sponges. Less than 100 years ago sponges were thought to be plants, for they cannot move about in the adult stage, and there is a considerable diversity of form and size in some of the species. Because they do vary so much from other Metazoa, they are often called **Parazoa,** which means "beside the animals."*

Organization in sponges goes little further than the cellular level. There is some indication in sponges to show grouping and coordination of cells to form tissues. However, sponges are said to have **cellular level of organization.** This particular type of organization would logically follow the protoplasmic level of organization characteristic of Protozoa. It has been shown that sponges have a primitive nervous system, with only slight coordination, although physiologic evidence is lacking on this point.

There is no evidence to indicate that any of the higher Metazoa arose from sponges. The latter may be considered as "dead ends" as far as evolutionary descent is concerned. Within the group, however, there has been considerable variation, which has resulted in about 5,000 distinct species, although classification of sponges within the group is difficult.

The fossil record of sponges is very incomplete. Sponges with exclusively spongin skeletons are not preserved as fossils. Class Calcispongiae have been poorly preserved. The best sponge fossils are those of class Hyalospongiae that occurred from the Cambrian period to the present.

Sponges have many unique features. One of these oddities is their complicated system of canals and

*Po-rif'e-ra (L. *porus,* pore, + *ferre,* to bear).

*Some evidence, both pro and con, has been advanced with respect to this point. Biochemical investigations show that sponges have about the same nucleic acids and amino acids as metazoans. They have both phosphoarginine (an invertebrate phosphagen) and phosphocreatine (a chordate phosphagen). Embryologically they have two types of larvae, the amphiblastula in calcareous sponges and the parenchymula in Demospongiae. In the amphiblastula the flagellated half invaginates into the inside to become the collar cell lining; in the parenchymula the flagellate cells on the outside may move in by ameboid movement and transform into choanocytes, or new choanocytes may be provided by transformation of cells already present there. In either case the embryologic development is different from that of metazoans.

chambers. Another is their lack of a metazoan type of digestive system, for they rely entirely on **intracellular** digestion, as do Protozoa.

CHARACTERISTICS

1. Mostly marine, although a few freshwater forms; all aquatic
2. All sponges **attached** and with a variety of body forms, such as **vaselike, globular**, and **many-branched**
3. Radial symmetry or none
4. **Multicellular;** body a loose aggregation of cells of mesenchymal origin; body surface or dermal epithelium simply a colloid with freely movable cells or a syncytium; mesenchyme usually with skeletal spicules or horny fibers and free ameboid cells
5. Body with many **pores (ostia), canals,** and **chambers** that serve for the passage of water
6. Most of the inner chambers and interior surfaces lined with **choanocytes,** or **flagellate collar cells**
7. No organs or definite tissues
8. Digestion intracellular and no excretory or respiratory organs; contractile vacuoles in some freshwater sponges
9. Primitive nervous system of neurons arranged in a diffuse network of bipolar or multipolar cells may be found in some, but is of doubtful status
10. **Skeleton usually of calcareous** or **siliceous crystalline spicules** or of **protein spongin**
11. Asexual reproduction by **buds** or **gemmules** and sexual reproduction by eggs and sperm; free-swimming, ciliated larva

HABITAT

Sponges are found in both fresh water and sea water, although the greater number are found in the latter. They are abundant everywhere in the sea, from the shallow water of the shore to the abysmal depths. The common bath sponge is found in warm, tropical, fairly shallow waters. All adult sponges are sessile and are attached to rocks and other solid objects.

The glass sponges (class Hyalospongiae) are mostly deep-sea inhabitants and have rarely been seen alive, for most specimens have been dredged from great depths. They are especially abundant in the waters off the coasts of Japan and the Philippines.

Most sponges form colonies that often attain great size (1 to 2 meters in diameter); others are small (1 to 2 mm.). They vary greatly in color, ranging from dull gray and brown to brilliant scarlet and orange.

CLASSES

There are three classes of sponges, classified mainly by the kinds of skeletons they possess.

Class Calcispongiae (cal′si-spon″ji-e) (L. *calcis,* lime, + Gr. *spongos,* sponge) (**Calcarea**). Have spicules of carbonate of lime that often form a fringe around the osculum. Spicules are single or three- or four-branched. All three types of canal systems represented. All marine. Examples: *Scypha, Leucosolenia.*

Class Hyalospongiae (hy′a-lo-spon″ji-e) (Gr. *hyalos,* glass, + *spongos,* sponge) (**Hexactinellida**). Have six-rayed siliceous spicules in three dimensions; often cylindric or funnel shaped. Choanocytes limited to certain chambers. Habitat mostly in deep water; all marine. Examples: Venus's flower basket *(Euplectella), Hyalonema.*

Class Demospongiae (de′mo-spon″ji-e) (Gr. *demas,* frame, + *spongos,* sponge). Have siliceous spicules, spongin, or both. One family found in fresh water; all others marine. Examples: *Thenea, Cliona, Spongilla, Meyenia,* and all bath sponges.

STRUCTURE

Sponges vary enormously in their structure and other features. Most dry sponges we see consist only of skeletal framework. In the living condition many of them appear as slimy gelatinous masses resembling masses of liver. The common bath sponge has this appearance, and only when the protoplasmic mass is removed in the method of preparing them do we see the commercial sponge with its skeleton of fibers.

The surface of sponges possesses many small pores (**ostia**) for the inflow of water. The ostia open into **canals,** simple or complex, which run into a central cavity, the **spongocoel** (cloaca). The opening of the spongocoel to the outside is known as the **osculum.** Colonial sponges have many oscula. The sponge has no mouth and no organs. The outer surface and the incurrent canals are covered with a thin layer of dermal epithelium composed of flat, highly contractile **pinacocyte** cells. The term "layer of cells" must be used with certain reservations, for the cells in sponges are loosely arranged in a gelatinous **mesenchyme;** in some cases even cells may be lacking, and only a spongin sheet or syncytium is present.

In simple sponges the spongocoel is lined with characteristic flagella-bearing cells, the **choanocytes,** commonly called "collar cells" because each has a little collar around the base of the flagellum. In more complex sponges the collar cells are confined to the radial canals and chambers and are not present in the spongocoel. In these sponges the spongocoel is lined with a thin epithelium derived from the epidermis. Another type of cell is the **amebocyte,** many kinds of which wander around in the mesenchyme.

Among the different sponges are a great variety of canals (Fig. 11-3). Most sponges fall into one or the other of three principal types.

1. *Asconoid type.* The canals pass directly from the ostia to the spongocoel, which is lined with collar cells. *Leucosolenia* has this type of canal.

2. *Syconoid type.* The incurrent canals (from the outside) lie alongside of the radial canals that empty into the spongocoel. Both types of canals end blindly in the body wall but are connected by minute pores. Only the radial canals are lined with collar cells. *Scypha* is an example of this type.

3. *Leuconoid or rhagon type.* The canals of this type are much branched and complex, with numerous chambers lined with collar cells. The spongocoel lacks collar cells. The larger sponges, including the bath sponge, are all this type.

These three types of canals are correlated with the evolution of sponges, from the simple to the complex forms. It has been mainly a matter of increasing the surface in proportion to the volume, so that there may be enough collar cells to meet the food demands. This problem has been met by the outpushing of the spongocoel of a simple sponge such as the asconoid type to form the radial canals (lined with choanocytes) of the syconoid type. The formation of incurrent canals between the blind outer ends of the radial canals completes this type. Further increase in the body wall foldings produces the complex canals and chambers (with collar cells) of the leuconoid type.

SKELETONS

The skeleton serves as the basis for classifying sponges (Figs. 11-4 to 11-7). In sponges such as *Scypha*

FIG. 11-3

Three types of sponge structure. Degree of complexity from simple asconoid type to complex leuconoid type has involved mainly the water and skeletal systems, accompanied by outfolding and branching of collar cell layer. Leuconoid type considered major plan for sponges, for it permits greater size and more efficient water circulation.

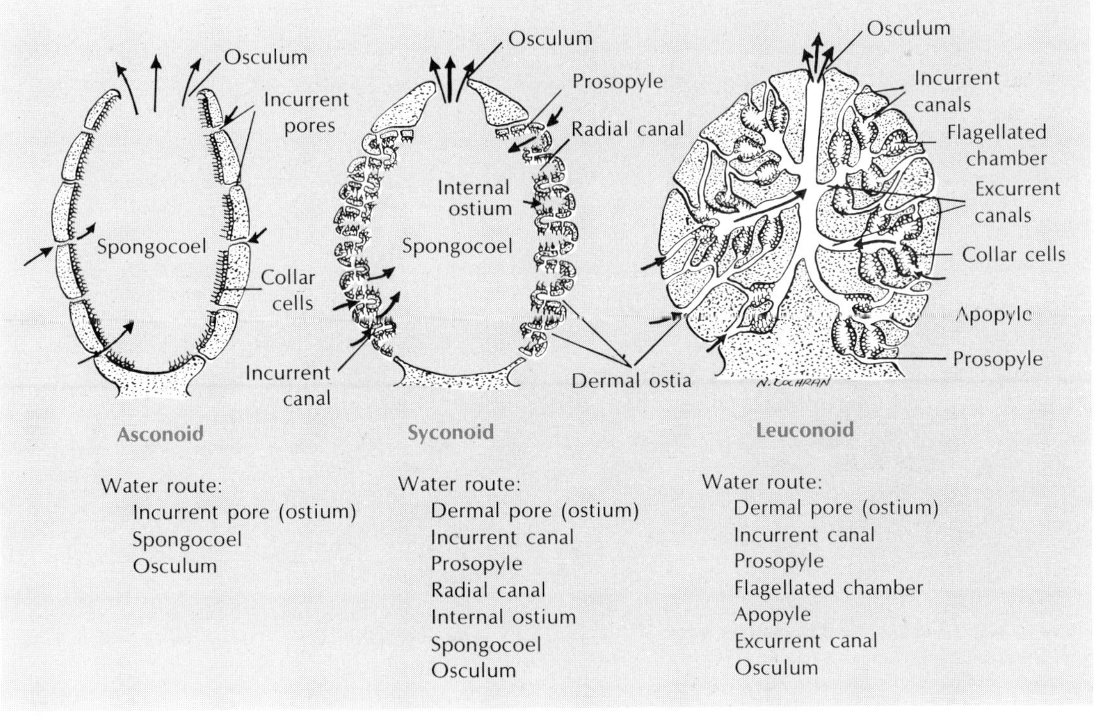

the skeleton consists of spicules of calcium carbonate; glass sponge spicules are formed of siliceous material. These spicules are of many different forms and shapes. The straight ones are called the **monaxons;** those of three rays in one plane are **triradiates;** those of four rays in four planes are **tetraxons;** and those of many rays are **polyaxons.** Some sponges have the spicules arranged in regular order, others in a haphazard arrangement. Spicules are formed by **scleroblasts,** special ameboid cells. In some sponges the larger spicules are called **megascleres;** the smaller ones are called **microscleres.**

Sponges, such as the bath sponge, freshwater sponges, and others, contain **spongin** (Fig. 11-6), a proteinlike substance. This type of skeleton is a branch-

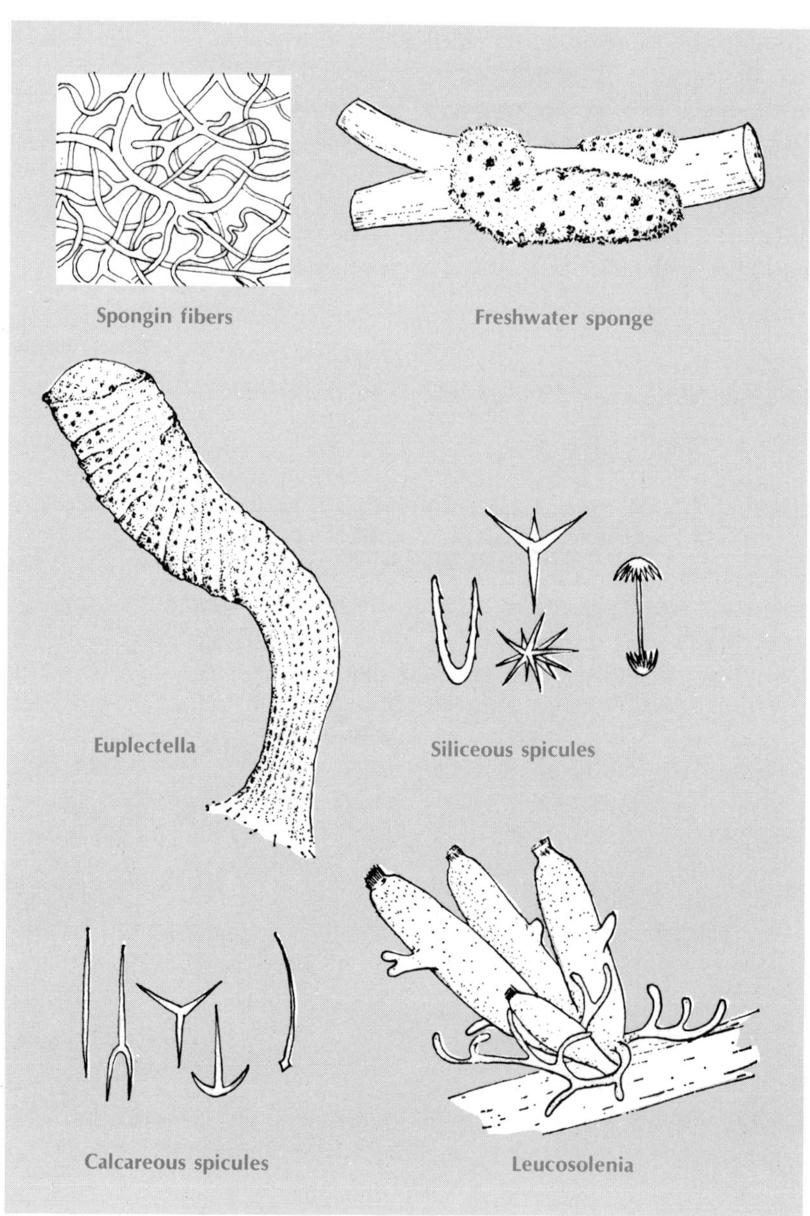

FIG. 11-4

Types of skeletal structure found in sponges, with example of each. There is amazing diversity, complexity, and beauty of form among the many types of spicules.

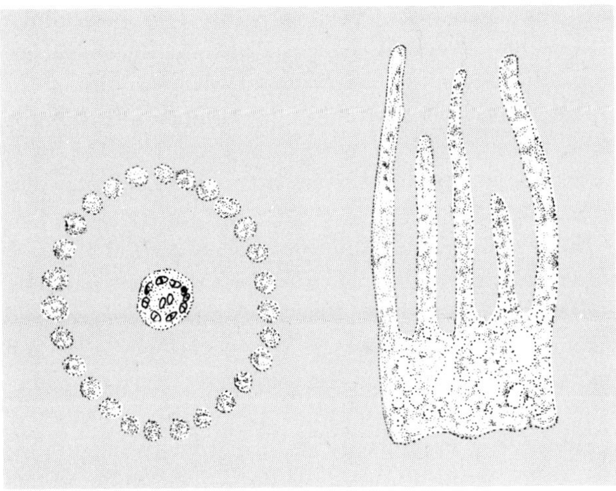

FIG. 11-5

Structure of collar cell based on electron microscope studies. Left, transverse section through collar showing ring of protoplasmic tentacles and flagellum (center). Right, longitudinal section showing portion of cell with protoplasmic tentacles. (From Hickman: Biology of the invertebrates, The C. V. Mosby Co.)

ing, fibrous network that supports the soft, living cells of the sponge. Special cells from the mesenchyme, called **spongioblasts,** form this type of skeleton.

TYPES OF CELLS

Although there are many types of cells in sponges (Fig. 11-8), none of them are actually arranged with the regularity of tissues. Perhaps the nearest approach to tissues in the sponges are the flat protective cells (**pinacocytes**) of the dermal and gastral epithelium and the collar cells (**choanocytes**) wherever these are found (Fig. 11-5). The pinacocytes are contractile and help regulate the surface area of the sponge. Choanocytes create water currents and engulf and digest food. **Gland cells** provide a means of attachment for the animal; tubular **porocytes** form the ostia in asconoid sponges; and **myocytes,** or muscle cells, form sphincters around the pores and oscula.

FIG. 11-6

Spongin fibers.

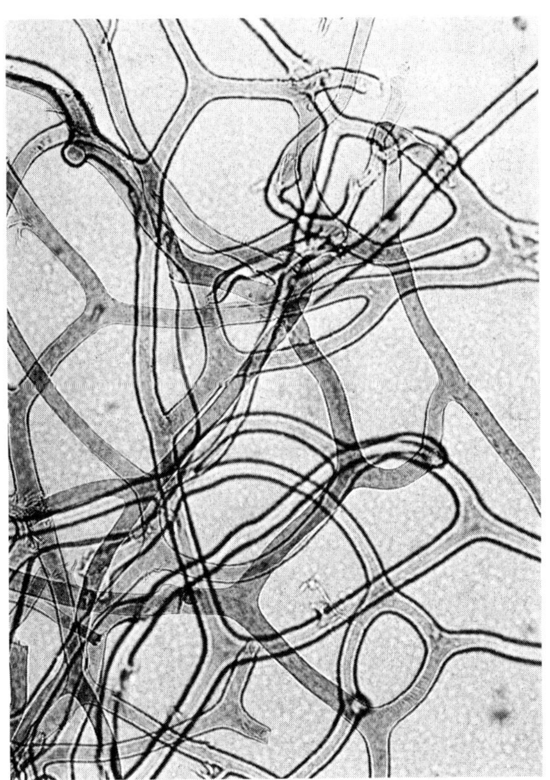

FIG. 11-7

Calcareous spicules.

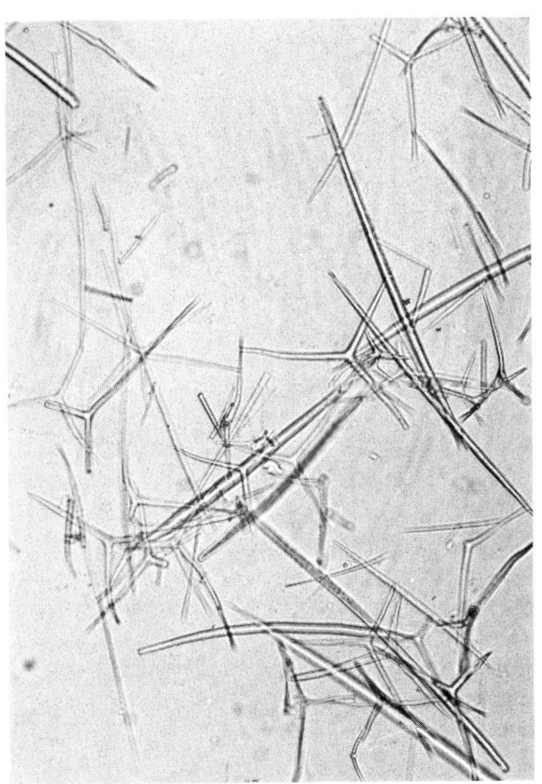

The middle layer, or mesenchyme, contains ameboid cells, known as **scleroblasts,** which form the spicules; **spongioblasts,** which form spongin; **archeocytes,** which have a variety of functions, such as the digestion of food and the formation of eggs and sperm, and collencytes (Fig. 11-8).

Sponges have great power of regeneration. H. V. Wilson discovered many years ago that when sponge cells were sifted through bolting cloth into small groups upon a surface under water, each group of cells would grow into a separate sponge.

METABOLISM

Metabolism in sponges is mainly a matter of individual cellular function. Their food consists of small organic substances, both plant and animal, which are drawn into the ostia and through the canal system by currents of water induced by the waving of the flagella on the choanocytes. As the flagella undulate spirally from base to tip, water currents are set up that bring particles of food to the outer surface of the collars, where the food adheres. Later the food reaches the base of the cells and passes into the cytoplasm, where food vacuoles are formed. Digestion is therefore **intracellular** in sponges. Digestive enzymes aid in digestion, just as we have seen in the Protozoa. Amebocytes in the mesenchyme layer may aid in digestion and distribution of food from the choanocytes to other parts of the body. Absorption of food substances from cell to cell may also occur.

FIG. 11-8

Four types of sponge cells. Some authorities have suggested a nervous function for collencytes. (From Hickman: Biology of the invertebrates, The C. V. Mosby Co.)

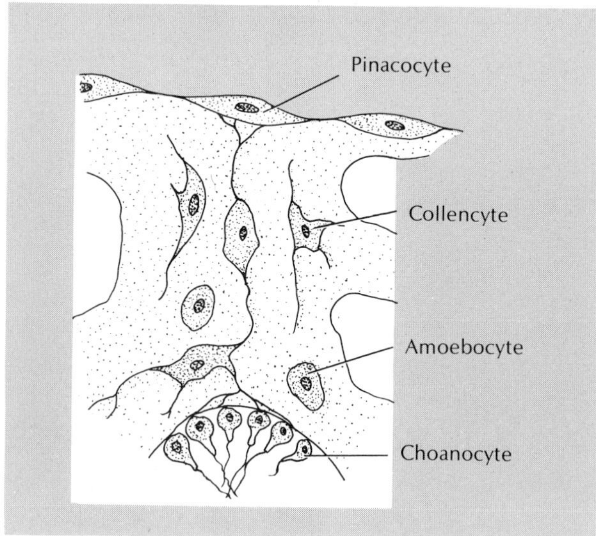

Excretion and respiration are taken care of by each individual cell by simple diffusion processes. Contractile vacuoles have been found in the amebocytes and choanocytes of freshwater sponges (*Spongilla* and *Ephydatia*). Undigested food is ejected by the amebocytes into outgoing currents.

Since water currents are of such primary importance to sponges, many studies have been made to determine the mechanics, rate of flow, amount of water discharged, and other aspects of these currents. In the synconoid type of sponge such as *Scypha* the route of the water current is through the dermal pores, incurrent canals or spaces, prosopyles, radial canals, internal ostia, spongocoel, and osculum. As the result of the movement of the many flagella of the collar cells, the water is sucked through the route mentioned, but the rate of flow is different in the various parts of the passageway. One investigator found in a certain sponge that the velocity of discharge through the osculum was 8 cm. per second, but in the flagellate chambers it was only 2 to 4 cm. per hour, because only one osculum (or relatively few oscula) must carry away the water that enters many chambers or canals of a sponge. The hydraulic pressure of the water current in the flagellate chambers of some sponges studied was equivalent to a column of water 4 mm. in height. The amount of water passing through a sponge depends upon its size; a large sponge with many oscula was found by Parker to filter more than 1,500 liters of water a day. It is to the advantage of the sponge to discharge the current of water from its oscula as far away as possible to prevent reusing water containing its own waste and carbonic acid. The water flow is regulated by contraction and relaxation of the pores and oscula.

Adult sponges have very limited motion, although the ciliated larval forms move freely about. In the adult condition, **myocytes** around the ostia can contract or relax, thus regulating the size of the openings. Several factors may influence these contractile cells. Still water tends to close them; moving water, to open them. The drug atropine in weak solutions will cause them to open, whereas injurious agents will cause the pores to close.

REPRODUCTION

Sponges reproduce both asexually and sexually. **Asexual** reproduction is mainly a matter of bud formation. After reaching a certain size, these buds may become detached, or they may remain to form colonies. Internal buds, or **gemmules,** are formed in freshwater and some marine sponges (Fig. 11-9). Here, archeocytes are collected together in the mesenchyme and become surrounded by a siliceous shell, or sometimes by a cluster of spicules. When the animal dies, the gemmules survive and preserve the life of the animal during periods of severe drought or freezing. Later the cells in the gemmules escape through a special opening and develop into new sponges.

In **sexual** reproduction ova and sperm develop from archeocytes or from choanocytes. The ova are fertilized in the mesenchyme, develop there, and finally break out into the spongocoel and then out the osculum. Some sponges are monoecious (having both male and female sex organs in one individual) and others are dioecious (having separate sexes).

During development the zygote undergoes cleavage and differentiation of cells in the mesenchyme of the sponge, and finally a flagellated larva, **amphiblastula** (calcareous sponges), emerges (Fig. 11-12). This larval form is made up of flagellate cells at one end and nonflagellate at the other. In time the flagellate cells are invaginated into or overgrown by the nonflagellate group and become the choanocytes; in the parenchymula (Demospongiae) the flagellate cells migrate into the interior. In both larvae what is ectoderm in other metazoans becomes internal cells. The larval form, after swimming around, soon settles down and becomes attached to some solid object, where it grows into an adult.

REPRESENTATIVE TYPES

CLASS CALCISPONGIAE

Scypha

Scypha is a marine form, living in shallow water where it is usually attached to rocks. It may be free living or it may form a cluster or colony by budding.

The animal is vase shaped and is from ½ to 1 inch in length (Fig. 11-10). At the unattached end is the opening, or **osculum,** with a fringe of straight spicules that discourage small animals from entering. Spicules also project from other parts of the body so that the animal has a hairy appearance. There is no outer covering or cortex in *Scypha,* the common form studied in America; a European genus called *Grantia,* often confused with *Scypha,* does have such a cortex. The entire outside of the body is full of tiny pores, or **ostia.** These ostia are the openings into the so-called **incurrent canals** (actually spaces) (Fig. 11-11) that end blindly near the central cavity, or **spongocoel** (sometimes called the cloaca, or gastral cavity). From the spongocoel, **radial canals,** or flagellated chambers, run toward the outer surface and end blindly and nakedly. Their openings into the spongocoel are called **apopyles,** or **internal ostia.** The incurrent and the radial canals are connected by small pores called **prosopyles,** which are intercellular spaces and not canals through tubular porocytes, as in the asconoid type.

The incurrent canals are lined with spicules and a few pinacocytes, whereas radial canals are lined mainly with **choanocytes,** or flagellate collar cells. The spongocoel is lined by a thin epithelium from the epidermis.

FIG. 11-9

Gemmule and colony formation in *Spongilla,* freshwater sponge. **A,** Sponge in winter showing cluster of gemmules. **B,** Greatly enlarged cross section of gemmule showing cells, some emerging from pore. **C,** Cells from gemmule that will develop into new colony.

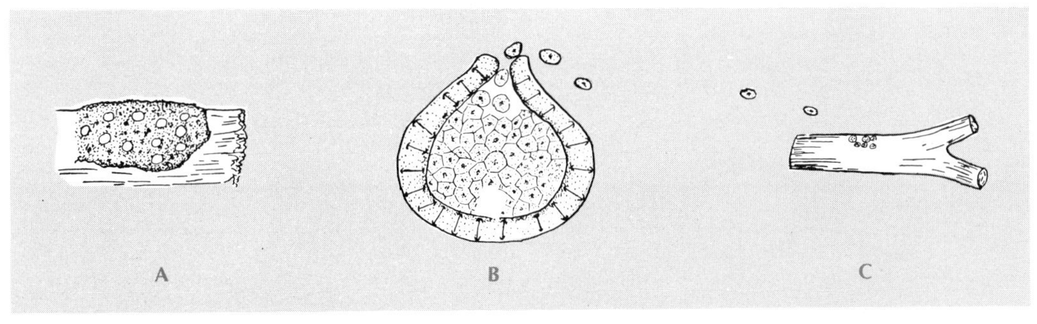

The body wall contains a large number of interlacing spicules of carbonate of lime that support and protect the soft parts of the body. About four types of spicules are recognized: **short monaxons, long monaxons, triradiates,** and **polyaxons.** All spicules originate from **scleroblasts.** The body substance between the epithelium and the choanocytes is an indefinite gelatinous mass called the **mesenchyme.** It contains skeletal spicules and the **ameboid** wandering cells that have a great variety of functions to perform, such as the digestion of food, the formation of skeleton, and the origin of the reproductive cells.

FIG. 11-10

Cluster of sponges, *Scypha.* About natural size.

Scypha lives upon minute organisms and bits of organic matter in the water. Water containing these is drawn into the incurrent canals by the beating of the flagella of the collar cells and thence is passed through the prosopyles into the radial canals, which carry it to the spongocoel and finally discharge it through the osculum. The rate of water flow is determined by the diameter of the osculum and the dermal ostia, which are regulated by myocyte sphincters and by the action of the encircling pinacocytes. This action is more pronounced in the Demospongiae. Digestion is **intracellular** by the choanocytes, which engulf the food and form food vacuoles. Distribution of the digested food from cell to cell takes place by diffusion and by the wandering ameboid cells of the mesenchyme layer. Respiration occurs by direct absorption of oxygen from the water and the giving off of carbon dioxide to the water as it flows through the canal system (Fig. 11-11). Excretory products and other waste substances are also carried by the water out through the osculum.

Reproduction in *Scypha* is by two methods—asexual

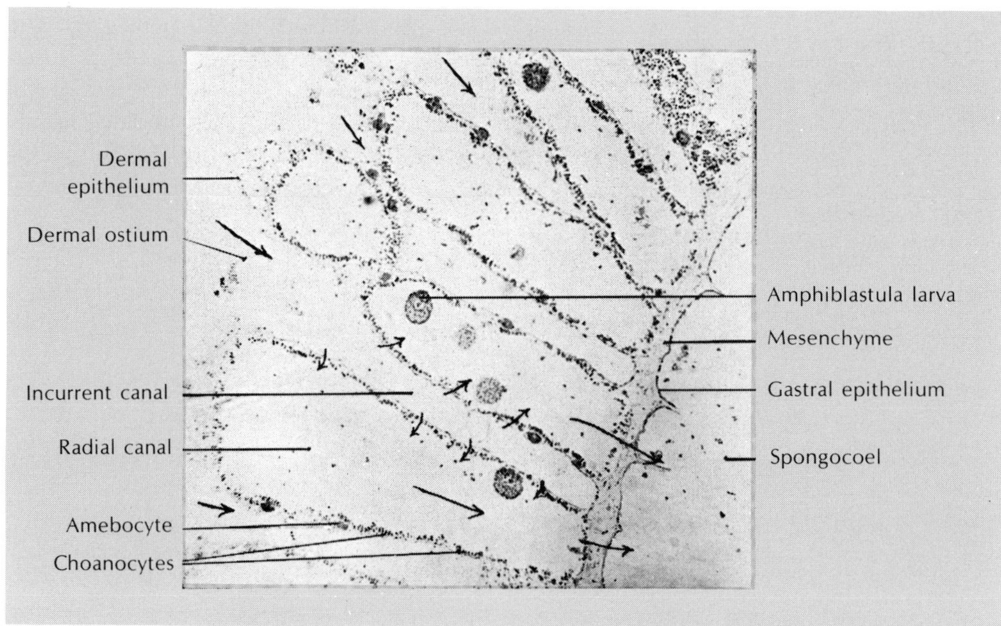

FIG. 11-11

Cross section through wall of sponge *Scypha* showing canal system. Photomicrograph of stained slide.

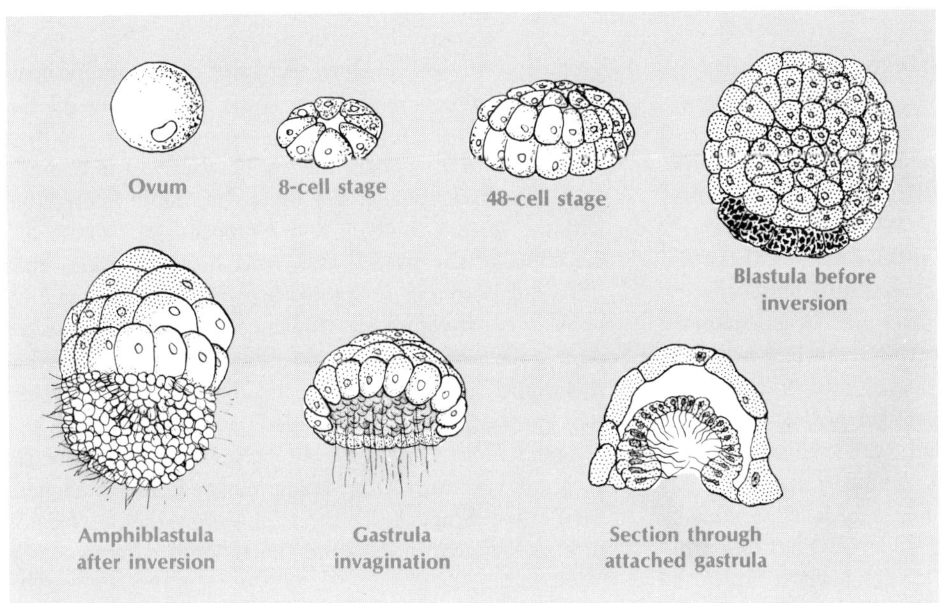

FIG. 11-12

Development of calcareous sponge *Scypha*. (From Hickman: Biology of the invertebrates, The C. V. Mosby Co.)

and sexual. The **asexual** method involves **budding;** that is, a small bud appears at the base of an adult sponge and grows into full size. It may adhere to the parent and thus help form a colony, or it may break free and form a new attachment.

Sexual reproduction occurs by the formation of eggs and sperm that develop from **archeocytes** or choanocytes. Both types of sex cells are formed in the same individual and thus *Scypha* is **monoecious.** The zygote, or fertilized egg, develops into an embryo while in position in the mesenchyme and later in a radial canal (Fig. 11-12). The flagellated larval form finally escapes from the parent, swims around a while, settles down, becomes attached, and grows into an adult.

CLASS HYALOSPONGIAE

Glass sponges

The glass sponges are nearly all deep sea forms that are collected by dredging. Most of them are radially symmetric, with vase- or funnel-shaped bodies that are usually attached by stalks of root spicules to a substratum (Fig. 11-4). In size they range from 3 or 4 inches to more than 4 feet in length. Their distinguishing features are the skeleton of six-rayed siliceous spicules that are commonly bound together into a network forming a glasslike structure, and the **trabecular net** of living tissue produced by the fusion of the pseudopodia of many types of amebocytes. Within the trabecular net are elongated finger-shaped chambers lined with choanocytes and opening into the spongocoel. The osculum is unusually large and may be covered over by a sievelike plate of silica. There is no epidermis or gelatinous mesenchyme, and both the external surface and spongocoel are lined with the trabecular net. Because of the rigid skeleton and lack of contractility, muscular elements (myocytes) appear to be absent. The general arrangement of their chambers fits glass sponges into both syconoid and leuconoid types. Their structure is adapted to the slow constant currents of sea bottoms, for the channels and pores of the sponge wall are relatively large and uncomplicated and permit an easy flow of water. Little, however, is known about their physiology.

Glass sponges can reproduce asexually by buds and sexually by germ cells, which are developed from archeocytes. The fertilized egg develops into a flagellated larva that swims around and finally settles down into a sessile existence.

The framework or latticelike network of spicules found in many glass sponges is of exquisite beauty, such as that of *Euplectella*, or Venus's flower basket, a classic example of the Hyalospongiae. Many fossil sponges, especially of the Cretaceous and Jurassic periods, are members of this class.

CLASS DEMOSPONGIAE

Freshwater sponges

Class Demospongiae contains the majority of sponge species, including the once common bath sponge and most of the familiar North American sponges. All of them are marine except one family, the Spongillidae, which because of its wide distribution over the country has been chosen as the type for this class.

Freshwater sponges are of special interest because they are the only living sponges most students ever see. They have a wide distribution and are not uncommon if one knows where to look. Most of them live in clear, well-oxygenated water of ponds, lakes, and slow streams where they may be found encrusting twigs, plant stems, old pieces of submerged wood, sluiceways, etc. In standing water they are usually found where there is some wave action. They look like a type of wrinkled, irregular scum, pitted with some pores. They are yellowish or brownish, although some have a greenish tinge from the presence of the symbiotic algae (zoochlorellae). They may grow to several inches in diameter (Fig. 11-4).

They all belong to the family Spongillidae, of which the most common genera are *Spongilla* and *Myenia*. *S. lacustris*, the commonest freshwater sponge, develops fingerlike branches and is usually green. Another common species is *S. fragilis*, which is unbranched. *Myenia* may be found either in still or running water. Freshwater sponges are most common in midsummer, although some are more easily found in the fall. They die and disintegrate in late autumn, leaving the gemmules (already described), which are able to survive drying and freezing for many months.

When examined closely, freshwater sponges reveal a thin dermis underneath composed of large subdermal spaces (separated by columns of spicules) with many water channels. There are usually several oscula, each of which (at least in *Myenia*) is mounted on a small chimneylike tube. Their spiculation also includes a spongin network. Their cells include a variety of amebocytes.

Although the gemmule method of asexual reproduction is common among freshwater sponges, sexual reproduction also occurs.

ECONOMIC IMPORTANCE

The skeletons of sponges have long been used by man, mostly for washing, bathing, and mopping. Although many artificial sponges are made out of rubber or other materials, natural sponges are still in demand, and sponge fisheries are a profitable industry in many parts of the world. The best commercial sponges are found in the warm shallow waters of the Mediterranean Sea, the Gulf of Mexico, the West Indies, and off the coast of Florida. In the latter place more than a million dollars worth of sponges have been collected in a single year. The bath sponges belong to the family Spongiidae and the genera *Spongia* and *Hippospongia*. These are members of the group, known as horny sponges, that have only spongin skeletons. Sponges are collected by hooks, by dredging or trawling, or by divers. After their collection they are exposed out of water to kill them and are then placed in shallow water, where they are squeezed or treaded upon to remove the softened animal matter until only the horny, spongin skeleton remains. After being cleaned and bleached, they are trimmed and sorted for the market. A fungus disease has greatly depleted the sponge industry in the West Indies.

Sponges are often cultured by cutting out pieces of the individual animals, fastening them to concrete or rocks, and dropping them into the proper water conditions. It takes many years for sponges to grow to market size.

They are used for sound absorption and for packing material, as well as for cleaning in glass manufacturing.

The taste of sponges is so unpleasant that few animals eat them. However, many small animals, such as shrimp, fish, and crab, take advantage of the canals and cavities in sponges to make their homes. This relationship is probably commensal, for these tenants do the sponges no harm in return for a safe hiding place from enemies.

One sponge, *Cliona*, bores into mollusk shells by employing a dissolving secretion and destroys the animal within the shell.

PROBLEMS STILL TO BE SOLVED

The fact that sponges have been a blind branch in the evolutionary blueprint and have not led to other forms may be responsible for a certain lack of interest in their study by zoologists. There are many aspects of their morphology and physiology that have not been satisfactorily explained. One of these problems is how the flagellate chambers are formed during development. There is still much to learn about the integration of the various cells, their primitive nervous system, and how cells aggregate again after being dissociated. Little is known about the relationships of the three sponge classes. Experimental modifications of sponge morphology is still in its infancy. Not least among the many unsolved problems is their complicated taxonomy.

Derivation and meaning of basic terminology

amebocyte (Gr. *amoibe,* change, + *kytos,* cell). Free cells in the mesenchyme.

amphiblastula (Gr. *amphi,* double, + *blastos,* germ). Larval stage in sponges, so called because one half bears flagella cells and the other half does not.

apopyle (Gr. *apo,* away from, + *pyle,* gate). Opening of the radial canal into the spongocoel.

archeocyte (Gr. *archi,* chief or beginning, + *kytos,* cell). Ameboid cells of varied function in sponges.

ascon (Gr. *askos,* bladder). Simplest form of canal in sponges, leading directly from the outside to the interior.

Calcarea (L. *calcarius,* limy). Synonym of class Calcispongiae.

choanocyte (Gr. *choane,* funnel, + *kytos,* cell). Flagellate collar cells that line cavities and canals.

Dicyemida (Gr. *di,* two, + *kyema,* embryo). An order of the Mesozoa.

gemmule (L. *gemma,* bud). Asexual reproductive unit in certain sponges.

Hexactinellida (Gr. *hex,* six, + *aktino,* ray, + *ell,* dim., + *ida,* suffix). Synonym of class Hyalospongiae.

infusoriform (L. *infusoria,* similar to Infusoria [ciliates], + form). A larval stage in dicyemids.

Leucosolenia (Gr. *leukos,* white, + *solen,* pipe). Genus of sponges (Calcispongiae).

mesenchyme (Gr. *mesos,* middle, + *enchyme,* infusion). Gelatinous middle layer in sponges.

myocyte (Gr. *myos,* mouse [muscle], + *kytos,* cell). A contractile cell.

nematogen (Gr. *nema,* thread, + *gene,* produced). The vermiform embryo of a dicyemid.

Orthonectida (Gr. *orthos,* straight, + *nektos,* swimming). An order of the Mesozoa.

ostium (L. door). Opening to the incurrent canal in sponges.

Parazoa (Gr. *para,* beside, + *zoon,* animal). Sponges are so called because they do not appear to be closely related to any group of the Metazoa.

parenchymula (Gr. *para,* beside, + *enchyma,* infusion, + *ula,* diminutive). A stereogastrula larva of class Demospongiae.

pinacocyte (Gr. *pinako,* plank, + *kytos,* cell). Flat cell found on surface and lining of sponge cavities.

prosopyle (Gr. *pros,* near, + *pyle,* gate). Connection between the incurrent and radial canal.

rhagon (Gr. *rhagos,* berry). Stage in leuconoid type of canals; contains small chambers lined with collar cells.

scleroblast (Gr. *skleros,* hard, + *blastos,* germ). Mesenchyme cell that secretes spicules.

Scypha (Gr. *skyphos,* cup). This genus is often incorrectly called *Grantia* or *Sycon.*

spicule (L. *spica,* point). Skeletal element found in certain sponges.

spongocoel (Gr. *Spongos,* sponge, + *koilos,* hollow). Cloaca or central cavity in sponges.

sycon (Gr. *sykon,* fig). Sometimes called syconoid. A type of canal system.

Annotated references

deLaubenfels, M. W. 1936. Sponge fauna of the dry Tortugas with material for a revision of the families and orders of the Porifera. Carnegie Institute, Washington, D. C., Tortugas Laboratories, pub. 30. *An important work in resolving many of the difficulties of sponge classification.*

deLaubenfels, M. W. 1945. Sponge names. Science (n.s.) **101**:354-355. *The author points out the confusion resulting from the incorrect usage of the genus name Grantia, a European sponge, for Scypha, the form commonly used in American laboratories.*

Hyman, L. H. 1940. The invertebrates: Protozoa through Ctenophora. New York, McGraw-Hill Book Co.

Jewell, M. 1959. Porifera (section 11). In W. T. Edmondson (editor): Ward and Whipple's fresh-water biology, ed. 2. New York, John Wiley & Sons, Inc. *A taxonomic key to the freshwater sponges of the United States.*

Jones, W. C. 1962. Is there a nervous system in sponges? Biol. Rev. **37**:1-150. *The author refutes the idea that sponges have sensory and ganglionic cells.*

McConnaughey, B. H. 1951. The life cycle of the dicyemid Mesozoa. Univ. Calif. Pub. Zool. **55**:295-336.

McConnaughey, B. H. 1963. The Mesozoa. In E. C. Dougherty (editor): The lower Metazoa: comparative biology and phylogeny. Berkeley, University of California Press. *A recent account of this enigmatic group by the foremost American student of the phylum. The author stresses the resemblance between the Mesozoa and the parasitic flatworms.*

Minchin, E. A. 1900. Porifera. In Lankester's treatise on zoology, part II. *A detailed account of the general morphology of sponges, invaluable to the student who wishes to know the basic structure of sponges.*

Stunkard, H. W. 1954. The life history and systematic relations of the Mesozoa. Quart. Rev. Biol. **29**:230-244. *Presents evidence that the Mesozoa are degenerate flatworms.*

Van Beneden, E. 1876. Recherches sur les Dicyemides. Bruxelles Acad. Roy. Belg. Bull. Cl. Sci. **41**:1160-1205, **42**:35-97. *One of the first investigations on the group that was discovered in 1839. He considered them intermediate between the Protozoa and the Metazoa.*

Wilson, H. V. 1907. On some phenomena of coalescence and regeneration in sponges. J. Exp. Zool. **5**:245-258. *This classic experimental work on siliceous sponges first showed the phenomenon of regeneration after dissociation. A new sponge is formed by aggregation and fusion out of the cells of an old sponge, which have been separated by squeezing through a piece of gauze. This phenomenon also occurs in forms other than the Porifera.*

CHAPTER 12

• PHYLA COELENTERATA (CNIDARIA) AND CTENOPHORA (RADIATE ANIMALS)

BIOLOGIC PRINCIPLES

1. These two groups make up the radiate phyla, which are characterized by primary radial or biradial symmetry and represent the lowest eumetazoans. All other Eumetazoa have bilateral symmetry.

2. This type of symmetry is composed of an oral-aboral axis, with the parts arranged concentrically around it. Arrangement of bodily parts may be indefinite or may be built around a definite number—four or six or a multiple thereof.

3. In general structure their body is cylindric, globular, or spherical in shape, with the body wall composed of two distinct layers—epidermis and gastrodermis (from the embryonic ectoderm and endoderm, respectively). Between these two layers there may be only a structureless, gelatinous mesoglea (mostly of ectodermal origin) or there may be the beginning of a third germ layer, the mesoderm, consisting of a mesenchyme made up of amebocytes, connective tissue fibers, and muscle fibers.

4. The only internal space is the gastrovascular cavity, which is an epithelial sac with a single opening, the mouth, which also serves as an anus. Throughout the coelenterates and to a greater extent in the ctenophores, there is a tendency for this gastrovascular cavity to send out branches in the form of canals and outpocketings, or it may be divided into compartments by projections. In many coelenterates the epidermis and gastrodermis meet at the mouth rim, but in other coelenterates and in all ctenophores the epidermis is turned into the gastrovascular cavity to form a pharynx, or gullet.

5. Most coelenterates have tentacles or extensible projections around the oral end, often in considerable numbers. In ctenophores the two tentacles are each situated at opposite ends of the transverse or tentacular axis, and each is provided with a sheath into which the tentacle may be retracted. Some members of each phylum lack tentacles.

6. The radiate phyla have digestive, muscular, nervous, and sensory systems but lack the respiratory, excretory, and vascular systems. Skeletal systems in some form are common among the coelenterates but are lacking among the ctenophores. Neither phylum has a definite reproductive system. They have sex cells that develop from interstitial cells in either epidermis or gastrodermis. Asexual multiplication is common in both phyla.

7. Both phyla have not advanced beyond the tissue grade of organization, although refinements that might be called incipient organs occur here and there. In general, the ctenophores are considered to have a higher structural grade than that of coelenterates. The former have mesenchymal muscles (they originate from ectoderm and endoderm in coelenterates), a more differentiated digestive system, and more highly developed sensory organs.

8. Each phylum has certain unique features. The coelenterates have stinging organoids, or nematocysts, which are entirely lacking (with a single exception) among the ctenophores. The latter have colloblasts (adhesive organoids) on their tentacles instead of nematocysts. Polymorphism, so common among coelenterates, is not found in ctenophores, which are monomorphic. Ctenophores have eight meridional rows of ciliary or comb plates for which the coelenterates have no counterpart.

9. Aside from their unique features, certain important contributions are made by the radiate phyla. Among these are well-defined germ layers, ectoderm and endoderm, with the beginnings of the third, or mesoderm. The saclike body plan is typical of the gastrula stage in the embryonic development of higher forms. The first true nerve cells (protoneurons) in their nerve net arrangement is an advancement toward the centralized nervous system of higher eumetazoans. Biradial symmetry in some members is a step toward the bilateral Metazoa.

PHYLOGENY AND ADAPTIVE RADIATION

1. Although nearest to the ancestral stock of the eumetazoans, the origin of the radiate phyla is obscure. The coelenterates may have come from a ciliated, free-swimming, gastrula-type animal similar to the planula larva found throughout the group. The trachyline medusae (Hydrozoa) are considered to be the most primitive of modern coelenterates because of their direct development from planula and actinula to medusa stages and because their ontogeny repeats the phylogenetic history of coelenterates better than does that of other members of the phylum. On this basis the coelenterates may have come from a primitive medusa, as most trachylines lack a polyp stage.

In the light of their many resemblances to the coelenterates, the ctenophores should have originated from the same ancestral stock, such as the trachyline medusa, but evidence of relationships are not forthcoming. It has been possible to derive biradial symmetry from tetramerous radial symmetry of the hydromedusae. The ancestral form of this phylum was supposed to be a more or less spherical animal with a concentration of cilia along eight meridional rows, which later developed into the comb plates.

2. In their evolution both radiate phyla have never deviated from their basic plan of structure as already described. In polymorphic forms (coelenterates) both the polyp and medusa are constructed on the same scheme. Likewise, the ctenophores have adhered to the arrangement of the comb plates and their biradial symmetry. Each phylum has stuck to its pattern in whatever modification it has undergone in its adaptive radiation into different environments. Polymorphism, especially the dimorphism of the polyp and medusa, has made possible both a benthonic (bottom) as well as a pelagic (open-water) existence. To overcome the restriction imposed by a body structure that has little space for specialized organs, the coelenterates to some extent compensate by the evolutionary development of different individuals specialized for performing different functions in their life cycle.

Phylum Coelenterata (Cnidaria)*

POSITION IN ANIMAL KINGDOM

This large and interesting group of animals takes its name from the large cavity in the body that serves as an intestine. The name "coelenteron" means "hollow intestine." Of the more than 9,000 species, some are found in fresh water, but the greater number are marine. There are no terrestrial forms. Because of the aberrant nature of the sponges, coelenterates may be considered the first phylum of Metazoa. They include the jellyfish, sea anemones, corals, and some other forms.

Evidence indicates that the coelenterates arose from protozoans, probably by way of a free-swimming ciliated planula larva. Such a form, pushed inward to form a double-layered gastrula form, would correspond roughly to a coelenterate with an outer ectoderm having sensory and protective functions and an inner endoderm specialized for digestion and absorption. Between these two layers the mesoglea would provide an elastic framework of support. The addition of tentacles and other modifications would transform this ancestor into a coelenterate. This theory is supported by the fact that most forms in this group have such a larva somewhere in their life cycle.

Of the two types of individuals (polyps and medusae), one view holds that polyps are the ancestral type. By attachment to its aboral pole the ancestral form developed into a polyp similar to hydra. By asexual budding hydroid colonies emerged with specialization among the polyps, some of which were modified into medusae. An alternative view is that the ancestral coelenterate was a medusa and that the polyp arose as a larval stage, later becoming established in its own right as an important phase of the life cycle and, in some groups becoming sexually mature so that the medusa—the original adult—was no longer necessary.

In coelenterates the main central cavity (gastrovascular) opens to the outside by a mouth, whereas sponges use their main opening, the osculum, for an exit. Here the coelenterates show that they probably have come from the same ancestors as higher forms.

Coelenterates have a tendency for cells to be arranged into **tissues.** The epidermis includes many types of cells and cannot be called a tissue in the strictest sense. However, the nerve net is a well-defined tissue, for its nervous elements are similar and are in intimate contact with each other.

Coelenterata is the best example of the radiate phyla, animals that have primary radial symmetry or some modification of it. They consist of a solid body wall enclosing a gastrovascular cavity. The body wall consists of two well-defined epithelial layers, **epidermis** (ectodermal) and **gastrodermis** (endodermal), and an intermediate layer, **mesoglea**, which is somewhat gelatinous in structure and contains cellular elements or connective tissue (in Scyphozoa and Anthozoa). Because of the nature of its origin, the mesoglea is sometimes called **ectomesoderm** (Hyman). It is not an epithelium and is the only mesoderm present in coelenterates. In higher phyla most mesoderm is endodermal (endomesoderm) in origin and may be in the form of mesenchyme or epithelium.

CHARACTERISTICS

1. Entirely aquatic, some in fresh water but mostly marine
2. **Radial symmetry** or biradial symmetry around a longitudinal axis with **oral** and **aboral ends;** no definite head
3. Two types of individuals—**attached polyps** and **free medusae**
4. Exoskeleton (perisarc) of chitin or lime in some
5. Body with two layers, epidermis and gastroder-

*Se-len'te-ra"ta (Gr. *koilos*, hollow, + *enteron*, gut, + *ata*, pl. suffix meaning characterized by). Ni-da're-a (Gr. *knide*, nettle, + *aria*, pl. suffix meaning like or connected with).

mis, with mesoglea between; mesoglea with cells and connective tissue (ectomesoderm) in some

6. **Gastrovascular cavity** (often branched or divided with septa) with a single opening that serves as both mouth and anus; extensible tentacles often encircling the mouth or oral region
7. Special stinging cell organoids called **nematocysts** in either or both epidermis and gastrodermis; nematocysts abundant on tentacles, where they may form batteries or rings
8. **Nerve net** of synaptic and nonsynaptic patterns; with some sensory organs; diffuse conduction
9. Muscular system (epitheliomuscular type) of an outer layer of longitudinal fibers at base of epidermis and an inner one of circular fibers at base of gastrodermis; modifications of this plan in higher coelenterates, such as separate bundles of independent fibers in the mesoglea
10. Reproduction by asexual budding (in polyps) or sexual reproduction by gametes (in all medusae and some polyps). Sexual forms monoecious or dioecious; **planula larva**; holoblastic cleavage; mouth from blastopore
11. No excretory or respiratory system
12. No coelomic cavity

FIG. 12-1

Comparison of polyp and medusa types of individuals.

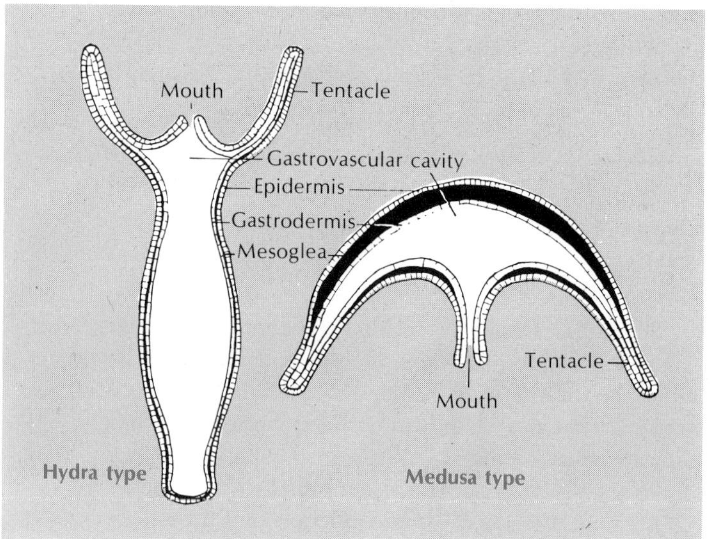

TWO TYPES OF INDIVIDUALS

Coelenterates may be single or in colonies. Two morphologic types of individuals are recognized in the group.

1. **Polyps** with tubular bodies having a mouth surrounded by tentacles at one end. The other end is blind and usually attached by a pedal disk or other device to substratum.

2. **Medusae,** or free-swimming jellyfish with umbrella-shaped bodies, having a mouth centrally located on a projection of the concave side. Around the margin of the umbrella are the tentacles, which are provided with stinging cells.

Some species have both types of individuals in their life history *(Obelia);* others have only the polyp stage (hydra and Anthozoa); and still others have only the jellyfish, or medusa, stage (certain Scyphozoa).

Though polyps and medusae seem superficially to be different from each other, actually this difference is not marked. If a polyp form such as that of the hydra were inverted, broadened out laterally to shorten the oral-aboral axis, the hypostome lengthened to form a manubrium, and mesoglea greatly increased, the result would be a structure similar to a medusa, or jellyfish (Fig. 12-1). The great amount of mesoglea in the medusae makes it more buoyant so that it can float easily. It also necessitates a system of ring and radial canals in the jellyfish to carry nourishment from the gastrovascular cavity to other parts of the body.

In the evolution of the two types, polyps and medusae, it is thought that the jellyfish represents the complete and typical coelenterate, whereas the polyp is merely a persistent larval stage.

The view formerly held, that coelenterates having both polyp and medusa stages in their life histories represented metagenesis or alternation of asexual and sexual generations, is no longer considered valid by many authorities. The polyp may be considered as an asexual juvenile stage in the development of a complete coelenterate and merely fits into the plan of a general life cycle.

CLASSES

Class Hydrozoa (hy'dro-zo"a) (Gr. hydra + *zoon,* animal). Solitary or colonial; asexual polyps and sexual medusae, although one type may be suppressed; hydranths with no mesenteries; medusae (when present) with a velum; both fresh water and marine. Examples: hydra, *Obelia, Physalia.*

Class Scyphozoa (si'fo-zo"a) (Gr. *skyphos,* cup, + *zoon,* animal). Solitary; polyp stage reduced or absent; bell-shaped medusae without velum; gelatinous mesoglea much enlarged; margin of bell or umbrella typically with eight notches that are provided with sense organs; all marine. Examples: *Aurelia, Cassiopeia.*

Class Anthozoa (an'tho-zo"a) (Gr. *anthos,* flower, + *zoon,* animal). All polyps; no medusae; solitary or colonial; enteron subdivided by at least eight mesenteries or septa with nematocysts; gonads endodermal; all marine. Examples: sea anemone *(Metridium),* corals, sea pens.

HABITAT

Most coelenterates are marine, although there are a few freshwater forms such as the hydra found in quiet streams, lakes, and ponds attached to the underside of aquatic plants. Colonial polyp coelenterates are found along the coast, usually in shallow water, where they may be attached to mollusk shells, rocks, and wharves, Corals are found in reefs along the shallow waters of the southern seas.

The free-swimming medusae are found in the open sea and lakes, often a long distance from the shore. Floating colonies, such as Portuguese man-of-war (Fig. 12-2) and *Velella,* have floats or sails (pneumatophores) by which they are carried in the wind. Hydroids have been found at great ocean depths.

REPRESENTATIVE TYPES

CLASS HYDROZOA

Hydra

The common freshwater hydra is a solitary polyp and one of the few coelenterates found in fresh water. Its normal habitat is the underside of aquatic leaves and lily pads in cool, clean fresh water of pools and streams. The hydra family is found throughout the world, with ten species occurring in the United States. Two common species are the green hydra (*Chlorohydra viridissima*), which owes its color to symbiotic algae (zoochlorella) in its cells, and the brown hydra *(Pelmatohydra oligactis).* With the exception of a few minor details, a description of one of the species will apply to all.

Structure. The body of the hydra can extend to a length of 25 to 30 mm. (Fig. 12-3) or can contract to a tiny mass of jelly. It is a cylindric tube with the lower (aboral) end drawn out into a slender stalk *(Pelmatohydra),* on the end of which is the basal or pedal disk for attachment. This pedal disk is provided with gland cells to enable the hydra to adhere to a substratum and also to secrete a gas bubble for floating. In the center of the disk there may be an excretory pore. The opposite or oral end contains a **mouth** located on a conical elevation, the **hypostome,** which is encircled by six to ten hollow tentacles. Like the body, the tentacles can be greatly extended and may stretch out for several millimeters when the animal is hungry. In some of the larger species the extension is much longer; in fact, as much as 8.5 cm. has been reported in one species. The mouth opens into the **gastrovascular cavity,** or **enteron,** which communicates with the cavities in the

FIG. 12-2

Representative coelenterates. Class Hydrozoa: **1,** *Physalia;* **2,** *Gonionemus;* **3,** *Obelia.* Class Scyphozoa: **4,** *Aurelia;* **5,** *Chrysaora.* Class Anthozoa: **6,** *Metridium;* **7,** *Astrangia;* **8,** *Gorgonia;* **9,** staghorn coral *(Acropora).* (Not sized to scale.)

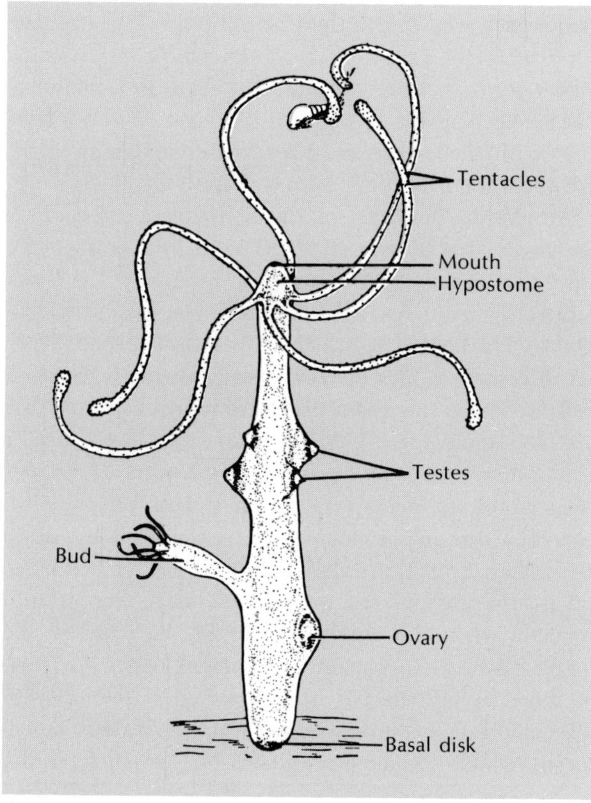

FIG. 12-3

General structure of hydra. Although specimen shown is hermaphroditic, most species are dioecious.

tentacles. In some individuals **buds** may project from the sides, each with a mouth and tentacles like the parent. Testes or ovaries, when present, appear as rounded projections on the surface of the body.

Cross sections of the body and tentacles reveal a body wall surrounding the gastrovascular cavity (Fig. 12-4). The wall consists of an outer **epidermis** (ectodermal) and an inner **gastrodermis** (endodermal) with **mesoglea** between them.

Epidermis. The epidermis is made up of small cubical cells and is covered with a delicate cuticle. This layer contains several types of cells—epitheliomuscular, interstitial, gland, cnidoblast, and sensory and nerve cells.

1. Epitheliomuscular cells. These cells make up most of the epidermis and serve both for epithelial covering and for muscular contraction. Each cell has an outer portion extending to the body surface and a basal part made up of one or more stalks that are drawn out into longitudinal muscle fibers (**myonemes**) fastened to the surface folds of the mesoglea. Contraction of the fibers shortens the body or tentacles. Each fiber is made up of minute fibrils.

2. Interstitial cells. These are small, oval, undifferentiated cells that lie among the bases of the epitheliomuscular cells. Really a form of mesenchyme, they can transform into cnidoblasts, sex cells, or buds.

3. Gland cells. These are tall cells found chiefly on the pedal disk and around the mouth region. They produce a secretion by which the animal can attach itself and sometimes a gas bubble by which the animal can rise and fasten onto the surface of the water to float.

4. Cnidoblasts. Cnidoblasts are found throughout

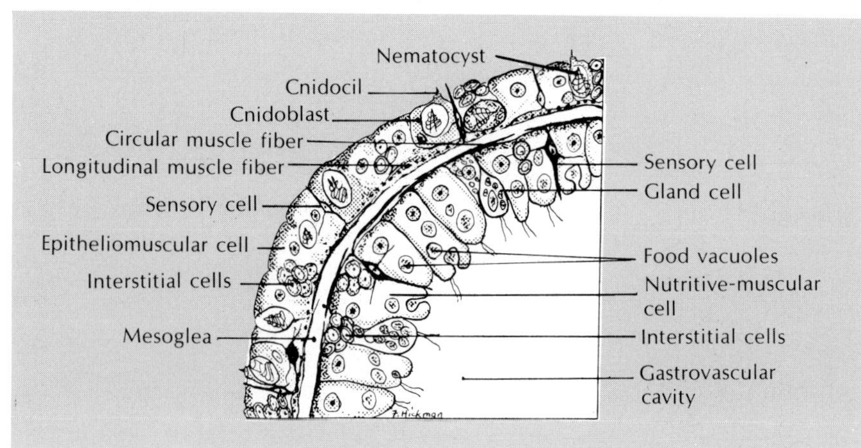

FIG. 12-4

Portion of cross section through body of hydra to show cellular detail. Semidiagrammatic.

the epidermis but especially on the tentacles. These somewhat oval-shaped cells contain the cell organoid—the **nematocyst,** or stinging cell. The nematocyst is made up of a rounded capsule that encloses a coiled tube or thread that is continuous with the capsular wall to which it is attached.

5. Sensory and nerve cells. Sensory cells are long, slender cells scattered among the other epidermal cells, especially around the mouth, on the tentacles, and on the pedal disk. Each sensory cell terminates near the body surface in a flagellated point or bulb. The other end of the cell branches into fine fibrils attached to the nerve plexus found in the epidermis next to the mesoglea. They serve as receptors for touch, temperature, and other stimuli.

The many nerve cells of the epidermis are either bipolar with two processes or multipolar with many processes. These processes or neurites will conduct impulses in either direction. They lie in the epidermis near the level of the nuclei of the epidermal cells, although they may occupy a position adjacent to the mesoglea. There is no evidence that they lie in the mesoglea. Their processes connect with sensory cells, with the longitudinal fibers of the epitheliomuscular cells, and with other nerve cells. The latter connections are usually continuous in the hydra, but synaptic junctions may be present.

Gastrodermis. The inner gastrodermis, a layer of cells lining the coelenteron, has a plan similar to the epidermis. It is made up chiefly of large columnar epithelial cells with irregular flat bases. The free ends of the cells give a jagged and uneven contour to the coelenteron in cross section. The cells of the gastrodermis include nutritive-muscular, interstitial, and gland cells.

1. Nutritive-muscular cells. These are similar to the epitheliomuscular cells and have their bases drawn out into muscles or myonemes that run circularly around the body or tentacles. When the myonemes contract, they lengthen the body by decreasing its diameter. Some of them serve as sphincters to close the mouth. Myonemes may be lacking in some cells. The cell is highly vacuolated and often filled with food vacuoles. The free end of the cell usually bears two flagella. Gastrodermal cells in the green hydra *(Chlorohydra)* bear green algae (zoochlorella), which give the hydrae their color. This is probably a case of symbiotic mutualism, for the algae utilize the carbon dioxide and waste to form organic compounds useful to the host and receive shelter and other advantages in return. Nutritive-muscular cells may also secrete digestive enzymes into the coelenteron for the digestion of foods.

2. Interstitial cells. There are a few of these small cells scattered among the bases of the nutritive cells. They may transform into other types of cells when the need arises.

3. Gland cells. Gland cells both in the hypostome and in the column secrete digestive enzymes. Mucous glands about the mouth apparently aid in ingestion. Gland cells are often club shaped, with the larger end facing the coelenteron.

Cnidoblasts are not found in the gastrodermis, for nematocysts are lacking in this layer.

Mesoglea. The mesoglea lies between the epidermis and gastrodermis and is attached to both layers. It is gelatinous, or jellylike, and has no fibers or cellular elements. It is a continuous layer that extends over both body and tentacles, thickest in the stalk portion and thinnest on the tentacles. This arrangement allows the pedal region to withstand great mechanical strain and gives the tentacles more flexibility. The mesoglea supports and gives rigidity to the body, acting as a type of elastic skeleton.

Nematocyst as characteristic structure of Coelenterata. One of the most characteristic structures in the entire coelenterate group is the stinging organoid called the **nematocyst** (Fig. 12-5). Seventeen different types of nematocysts have been described in the coelenterates so far; they are important in taxonomic determinations. The nematocyst is a tiny capsule composed of material similar to chitin and containing a coiled tubular "thread" or filament, which is a continuation of the narrowed end of the capsule. This end of the capsule is covered by a little lid, or **operculum.** The inside of the undischarged thread may bear little barbs or spines. The nematocyst is found in a modified interstitial cell called a **cnidoblast,** which is provided with a projecting triggerlike **cnidocil.** When the cnidocil is stimulated by food, prey, or enemies, the coiled thread turns inside out with explosive force, the spines unfolding to the outside as the tube everts. Many chemicals (for example, weak acetic acid or methyl green) will cause discharge of nematocysts. Neither touch alone nor the presence of animal fluids (food) alone causes discharge, but touch combined with the presence of food does. The exploding force is probably pressure caused by the increase of water in the capsule, a result of osmotic changes, plus contraction of the cnidoblast that forces the operculum open. The nematocysts may occur singly

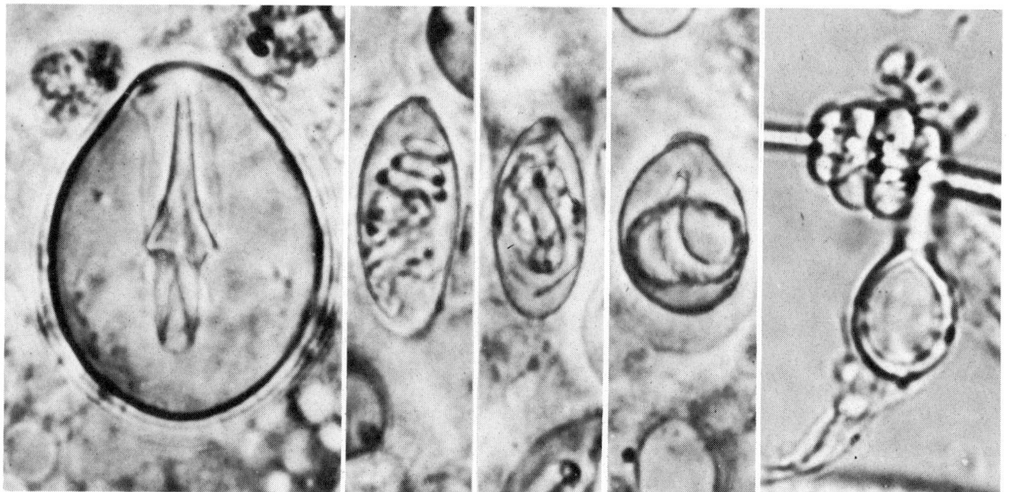

FIG. 12-5

Nematocysts of *Hydra littoralis,* swift-water hydra. Left to right: penetrant, streptoline glutinant, stereoline glutinant, volvent, and discharged volvent attached to copepod bristle. Largest and most familiar type is the penetrant, provided with barbed spines and long threadlike tube. Nematocysts used to immobilize prey and to aid in locomotion. (Courtesy Carolina Biological Supply Co., Burlington, N. C.)

or in batteries, each consisting of one large and many small ones. They are found everywhere except on the basal disk but are especially abundant on the tentacles. Four kinds of nematocysts are found in the hydra:

1. The **penetrant** is long and threadlike with spines and thorns. When discharged, it is capable of entering the bodies of small animals that happen to touch the tentacles, paralyzing them with the druglike hypnotoxin that it secretes. The hydra may then seize its prey with its tentacles and draw it into the mouth.
2. The **streptoline glutinant** is a long barbed thread that usually coils when discharged. It produces an adhesive secretion used in locomotion and attachment.
3. The **volvent** is a short thread that coils in loops around the prey.
4. The **stereoline glutinant** is a straight unbarbed thread also used for attachment.

Nervous connections play no direct part in the discharge of nematocysts, for they are indirect effectors. However, nerves could affect the threshold of discharge: a full hydra ceases to discharge nematocysts at prey, and so does an overstimulated one.

When a nematocyst is discharged, the cnidoblast is digested and replaced from the interstitial cells. Cnidoblasts do not originate on the tentacles. There is a zone of growth near the base of the tentacles. From here the maturing cnidoblasts are carried out along the tentacles by normal growth of the whole epidermis (Fig. 12-13).

The nematocysts of most coelenterates are not harmful to man, but the stings of the Portuguese man-of-war and certain large jellyfish such as *Cyanea* are quite painful and may even be dangerous to life. Some small freshwater worms that feed on hydrae digest all the body except the nematocysts; they migrate to the surface of the predator, where they serve for defense.

Nerve net and sensory mechanisms. The nerve net of the coelenterates is one of the best examples of a diffused nervous system in the animal kingdom. This plexus of nerve cells (protoneurons) connected with nerve fibers is found both at the base of the epidermis and at the base of the gastrodermis, because there are two interconnected nerve nets. In the hydra the net appears to be continuous. However, evidence* exists that in some coelenterates there are two nervous systems—one continuous and one discontinuous, or synaptic (Fig. 12-6). Impulses can pass in all directions over the net. Although the nerve net of coelenterates is generally unpolarized and is characterized by diffuse transmission, unrestricted spreading of excitation is found only in those parts specialized for through conduction. The nerve cells of the net are connected to slender sensory cells that receive external stimuli and to epitheliomuscular cells that react by contracting. The only localization of nervous function in the hydra is found around the hypostome and on the pedal disk where sensory and other nerve cells are more numerous. Separated bodily parts, when stimulated, often react just as they do in an intact animal.

*Mackie (1960) reports that in *Velella* there is evidence of two nervous systems—one continuous and one discontinuous. The continuous one would seem comparable to the syncytial giant nervous system in squids, annelids, and some arthropods, being specialized for rapid conduction to all parts for, say, an escape response.

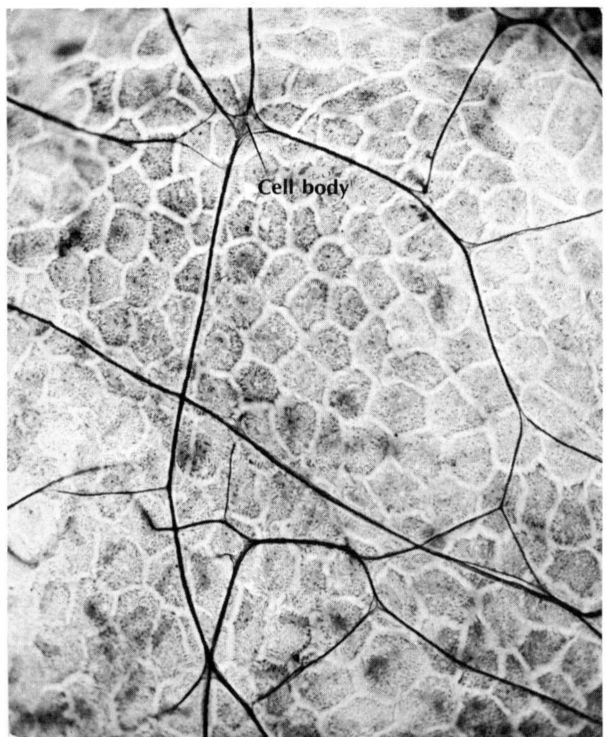

FIG. 12-6

Portion of syncytial giant fiber nervous system of *Velella*. *Velella* is provided with two nervous systems—one of syncytial (continuous) giant fibers and one of nonsyncytial (discontinuous) neurons. (Courtesy G. O. Mackie, University of Alberta.)

Together with the contractile fibers of the epitheliomuscular cells, the sensory-nerve cell net combination is often referred to as a **neuromuscular system,** the first important landmark in the evolution of the nervous system. The nerve net is never completely lost from higher forms. Annelids have it in their digestive systems. In the human digestive system it is represented by the plexus of Auerbach and the plexus of Meissner. The rhythmic peristaltic movements of the stomach and intestine are coordinated by this counterpart of the coelenterate nerve ring.

Metabolism. The hydra feeds upon a variety of small crustaceans, insect larvae, and annelid worms. It is especially fond of *Cyclops* and *Daphnia,* which are small crustaceans. A hungry hydra waits for its food to come to it. It may, if necessary, shift to a more favorable location, but once attached to its chosen substratum, it waits motionless, its tentacles fully extended. Any small organism that brushes against one of its tentacles is immediately stopped, harpooned by dozens of tiny nematocyst threads; some penetrate the prey's tissues to inject a poisonous paralyzing fluid, while some coil themselves about bristles, hairs, or spines for holding. The hapless prey may be many times as large as its captor. Now the tentacles begin to move; some of them become attached to the prey and then move slowly toward the hydra's mouth. The mouth slowly opens and the prey slides slowly in. It is not pushed in or swallowed by muscular action; the mouth simply extends and widens and, well moistened with mucus, glides over and around the prey (Fig. 12-7).

The stimulus that actually causes the mouth to open is now known to be a chemical (glutathione) that is found in all living cells. Glutathione is released from the prey through the wounds made by the nematocysts, but only those animals that release enough of the chemical are eaten by the hydra. This explains how a hydra distinguishes between *Daphnia* that it relishes and some other forms that it refuses. When commercial glutathione is placed in water containing hydrae, the hydra will go through all the motions of feeding even though no prey is present.

Inside the gastrovascular cavity contraction of the body wall forces the food downward. Gland cells in the gastrodermis discharge extracellular enzymes and digestive juices on the food. The digestion started in the gastrovascular cavity is called **extracellular digestion,** but many of the food particles are drawn by pseudopodia into the nutritive-muscular cells of the gastrodermis, where **intracellular digestion** occurs. Indigestible particles are forced back out of the mouth, for there is no anus. Digested food products may be stored in the gastrodermis or distributed by diffusion to other cells, including the epidermis.

Respiration and **excretion** are carried on individually by each cell. There are no special organs for these processes, although it is thought that the gastrodermis of the pedal disk does accumulate some excretory matter, which may be discharged through a pore.

Locomotion. A hydra has several ways of moving from one region to another (Fig. 12-8). One is a gliding movement, with the basal disk sliding slowly over the substratum, aided by secretions from mucous glands. A second method is a "measuring-worm" type of movement, in which the hydra bends over and attaches its tentacles, slides its basal disk up close to the tentacles, and then releases its tentacles and straightens up. Another method is like a handspring, in which the animal attaches its tentacles, then suddenly releases its basal disk, carries it completely over, and attaches it to a new position. The hydra may move from one place to another in an inverted position by using its tentacles as legs. To rise to the surface of the water it often forms a gas bubble on its basal disk and floats up.

Reproduction. The hydra uses both asexual and sexual methods of reproduction. Asexual reproduction is by **budding,** in which projections grow out from the body wall by a proliferation of cells (Figs. 12-3 and 12-9). Several buds may be found on the same animal, and

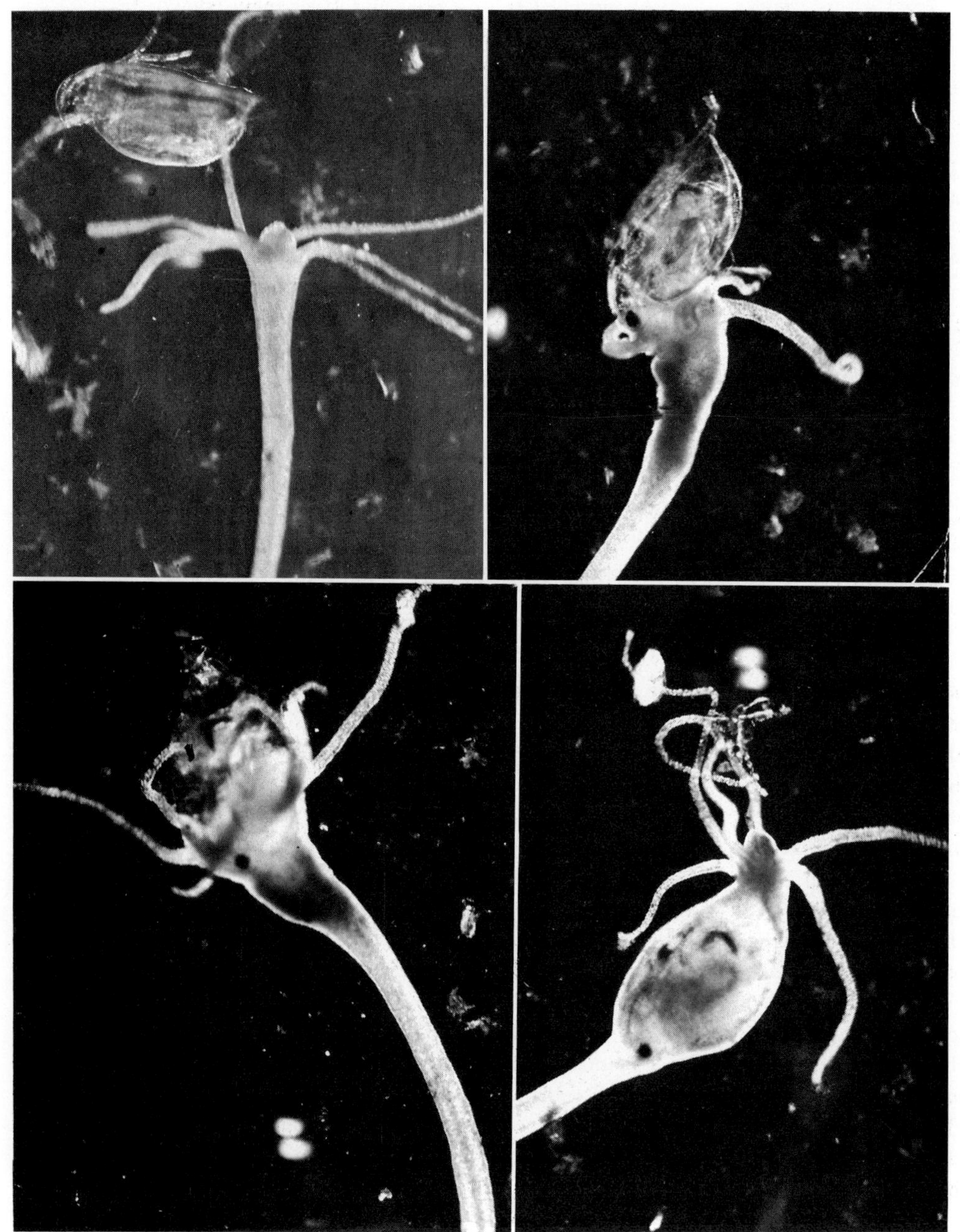

FIG. 12-7

Lunch for hungry hydra. **A,** Unwary daphnid gets too close to waiting tentacle. Still kicking, he is drawn into widening mouth of captor. **B,** Swallowing process is slow but odds are against daphnid. Mission accomplished, hydra settles down to digest lunch.

FIG. 12-8

Methods of behavior in hydra. **1,** Contracted; **2,** extended; **3,** rising to surface by bubble; **4** to **8,** steps in "somersaulting"; **9** to **11,** steps in "measuring-worm" movements; **12,** ingesting food by aid of tentacles; **13,** floating while suspended by air bubble.

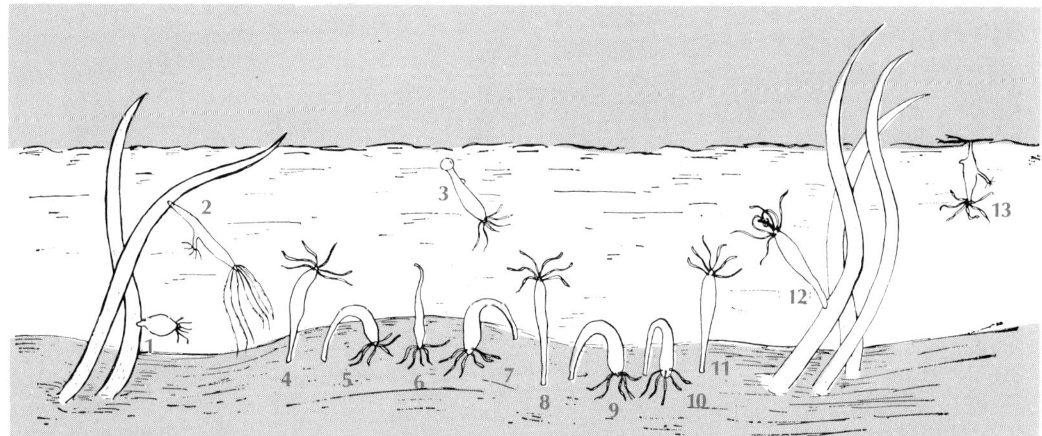

these may bear secondary buds of their own. Buds represent outpocketings of the entire body wall, the gastrovascular cavity of the bud being in communication with the cavity of the parent. The bud acquires a hypostome with a mouth and a ring of tentacles. Eventually it constricts at its base and detaches to lead a separate existence. Buds are formed at the junction of the gastric region and stalk (budding zone).

In sexual reproduction some species are **dioecious** and others are **monoecious,** or hermaphroditic. Most hydra species are dioecious. Sexual reproduction involves the formation of gonads, which are more common in the autumn. Reduction of water temperature will promote their formation, but work by Loomis has shown that high pressures of free carbon dioxide and reduced aeration in stagnant water may be a factor responsible for sexuality in the hydra. Gonads are temporary structures formed from interstitial cells that have accumulated at certain points, multiply, and undergo all stages of gametogenesis. In monoecious species the several **testes** form rounded outgrowths near the oral end, whereas the **ovaries,** nearer the basal end, are larger and more conical (Fig. 12-10). In dioecious species the testes or ovaries may be spread throughout the gastric region. Gonads are never found in the stalk region. Many sperm are produced and set free in the water, although only one egg is found in an ovary. In the development of the egg one centrally located egg cell enlarges by the union of other interstitial cells and eventually occupies most of the space in the ovary. In some species the eggs ripen one at a time, in succession; in others, several may ripen at once. The egg undergoes two maturation divisions, produces two polar bodies, and reduces its chromosome number from 30 to 15 *(Pelmatohydra).* The sperm also has 15 chromosomes, and thus the zygote will have 30 chromosomes.

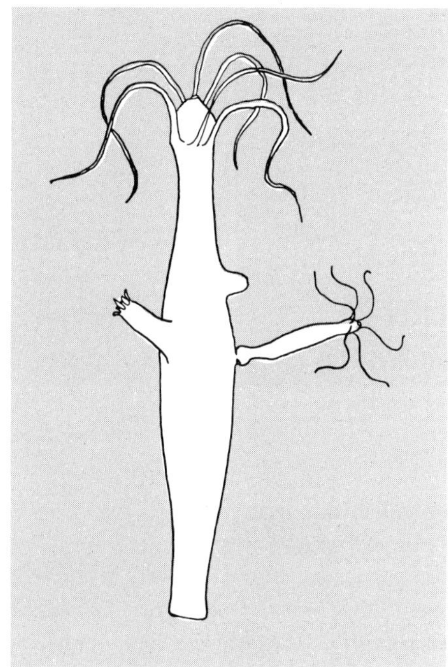

FIG. 12-9

Asexual reproduction in hydra showing buds in three stages.

While the fertilized egg or zygote is still in the ovary, it undergoes holoblastic **cleavage** and forms a hollow **blastula.** The outer part of the blastula becomes the **ectoderm,** which later forms the epidermis; the inner part of the blastula delaminates to form an inner solid mass, the **endoderm** (gastrodermis in the adult). The **coelen-**

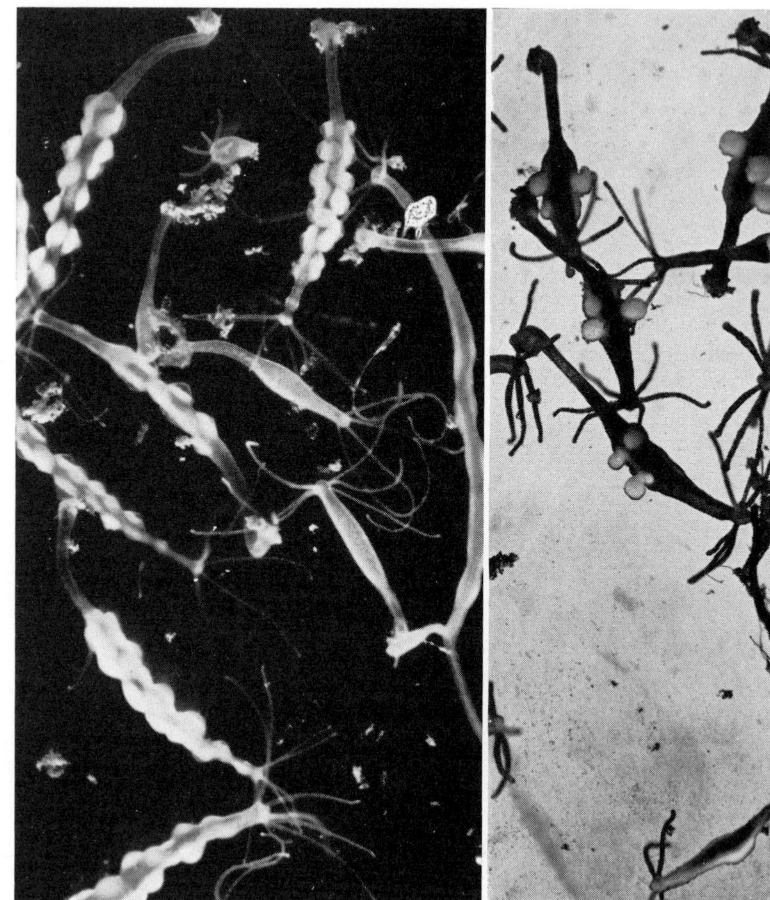

FIG. 12-10

A, Living hydras, mostly males with testes. **B,** Living hydras, mostly females with ovaries and eggs. (Courtesy General Biological Supply House, Inc., Chicago.)

teron is later formed in this mass, and the mesoglea is laid down between the ectoderm and endoderm (Fig. 12-11). At about this time a shell, or cyst, is secreted about the embryo, which breaks loose from the parent. In the encysted condition the embryo may pass the winter and complete its development when weather conditions are more favorable. After a resting period, which varies according to weather conditions, the shell ruptures, and a young hydra with tentacles hatches out and soon grows into the adult condition without a larval stage.

When testes and ovaries appear together, self-fertilization may occur, but when the gonads are produced at different times, cross-fertilization is the procedure.

Regeneration. The power of the hydra to restore lost parts is pronounced, as Trembley long ago discovered (about 1745). When the hydra is cut into several pieces, each fragment will give rise to an entire animal (Fig. 12-12). If the hypostome and the tentacles are cut off, they also will give rise to a new individual. It is also possible to produce a two-headed hydra by splitting it through the mouth. Parts of individuals of the same species (and sometimes of different species) may be grafted together, even though these fragments are too small to grow independently. The endodermal layer appears to be responsible for fusion, for cells of this layer project out ameboid processes that produce an interlacing effect. It has been found in regeneration experiments that the middle region of the hydra is in an indeterminate state and carries the potentialities of oral and aboral region simultaneously. A section of the middle region transplanted to the hypostome region will form a basal disk; transplanted to the posterior part of the body, it forms a hypostome at the aboral end.

Investigations by Brien and others on the growth patterns of the hydra indicate that the hydra may be considered immortal (Fig. 12-13). When a stained graft is inserted at the growth zone just below the tentacles,

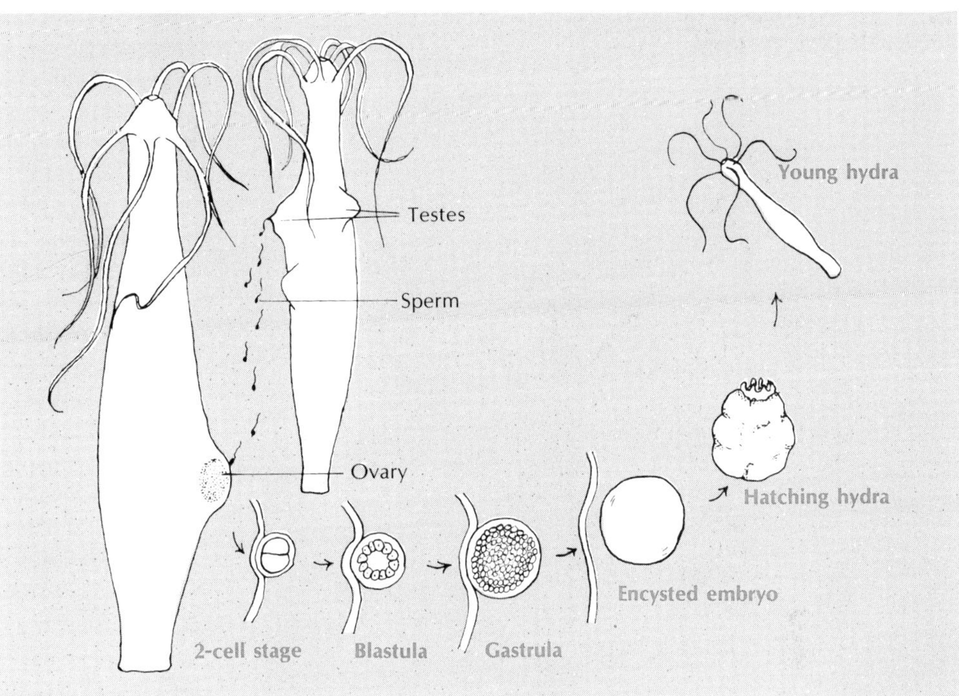

FIG. 12-11

Sexual reproduction and life cycle of hydra.

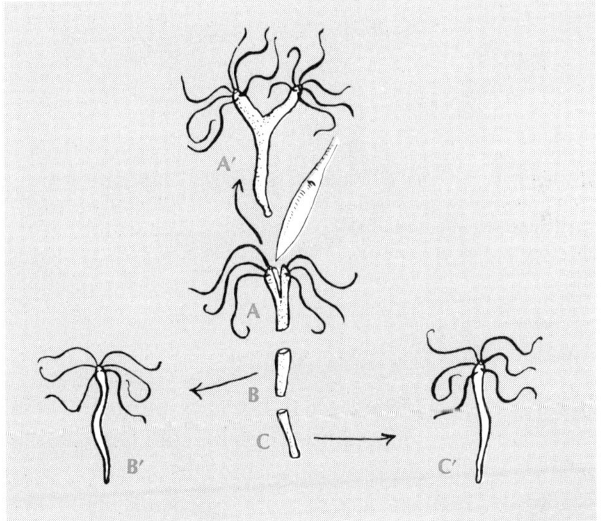

FIG. 12-12

Regeneration in hydra. Splitting hydra part way through mouth and hypostome, **A**, will give rise to two-headed polyp, **A′**. When pieces are cut off below head, **A**, **B**, and **C**, each will give rise to whole individual. **A′**, **B′**, and **C′**.

colored cells are seen to move gradually toward the base, where dead or worn out cells are shed. In this way the various cells that arise at the growth zone occupy successively different levels of the hydra as they make their way toward the base (or toward the tip of the tentacles, where a similar renewing is taking place). This active renewing of all the cells in the hydra is believed to take about forty-five days and appears to continue indefinitely. If the interstitial cells (which transform into the various types of cells) are destroyed by x-rays, the hydra will live for only a few days.

When a hydra is turned inside out, either by natural or artificial means, it was once thought (Trembley) that the epidermal cells became gastrodermal cells and the gastrodermal cells became epidermal cells in their new positions. Many investigations, however, have shown that in some cases the hydrae turn themselves right side out, and in other cases they switch their layers by the migration of the inside cells to the outside and of the outside cells to the inside, thus restoring the original arrangement of the cells.

Behavior. The hydra will respond to various stimuli, both internal and external. Spontaneous movements of body and tentacles occur while the animal is attached. If the individual is well fed, its movements are slow,

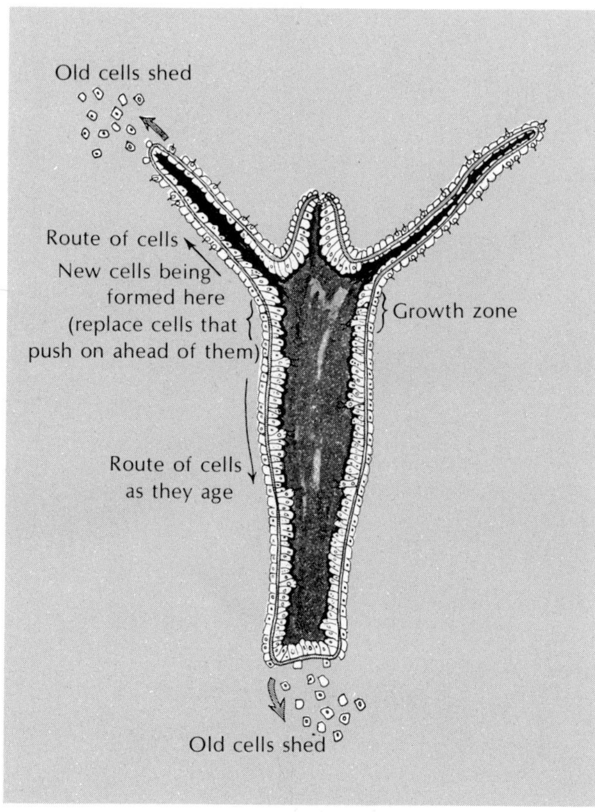

FIG. 12-13

Why hydra is considered immortal. New cells, continually being formed in growth zone below tentacles, force older cells basally and distally. Eventually old cells are shed at base or tip of tentacles as they are replaced by newer cells.

but they step up whenever it becomes hungry. These movements are produced by the contractile fibers in the wall when they are stimulated through the nerve net.

How the hydra reacts to stimuli depends upon the intensity and kind of the stimuli. If the stimulus is strong, the animal usually responds negatively. A slight jar will cause the whole animal to contract rapidly. The same effect may be produced by a localized stimulus, such as touching one of the tentacles with a sharp needle, in which case all the tentacles and body may contract. The explanation for this probably lies in the widespread transmission of the nerve impulse over all the nerve net. If such a localized stimulus is mild, there may be a more or less localized response, such as the contraction of a single tentacle or the pulling away of that part of the body touched.

A unique behavior pattern called the **contraction burst** has been described in some hydras under constant conditions (C. B. McCullough). At 5- to 10-minute intervals a hydra suddenly assumes a ball shape by contracting its longitudinal muscles. After a few seconds the individual usually extends itself again. It is thought that this behavior pattern enables the hydra to sample its environment intermittently, and the pattern may play a part in movement and light orientation. A neuronal pacemaker located in the subhypostome region may initiate the impulse for the action.

To light stimuli, hydras respond in an optimum way, tending to avoid very strong light but seeking lighted regions of moderate intensity. By trial and error they find the situation that best suits them. When subjected to a weak **constant electric current,** they become oriented so that the oral end is toward the anode and the basal end toward the cathode. Water currents produce little or no response in them. They are partial to cold water and quickly disappear from surface water when it reaches 20° to 25° C. They will avoid strong and injurious chemicals.

The **physiologic** state of the hydra determines to a great extent the nature of its responses to stimuli. When the hydra is not hungry, it is sluggish to most stimuli, but the hungry hydra will react to the same stimuli in a more vigorous manner.

The student will frequently note small protozoans crawling over the body surface of a live hydra, particularly on the tentacles. Most of these are ciliates, *Kerona* and *Trichodina.* Certain work (H. C. Yeatman) indicates *Kerona* is an ectoparasite and not a commensal on the hydra.

Obelia and Gonionemus as examples of hydroid and medusa stages

Both *Obelia* and *Gonionemus* are strictly marine and have polyp and medusa stages in their life histories. *Obelia* has a prominent hydroid (juvenile) stage but an inconspicuous medusa (adult) stage (Fig. 12-14). The reverse conditions are found in *Gonionemus,* in which the medusa is large and the hydroid small.

Obelia may be considered a typical colonial hydroid. Its habitat is both the Atlantic and Pacific coasts, where it is found attached to stones and other objects by a rootlike base called **hydrorhiza,** from which arise branching stems (**hydrocauli**). On these stems are large

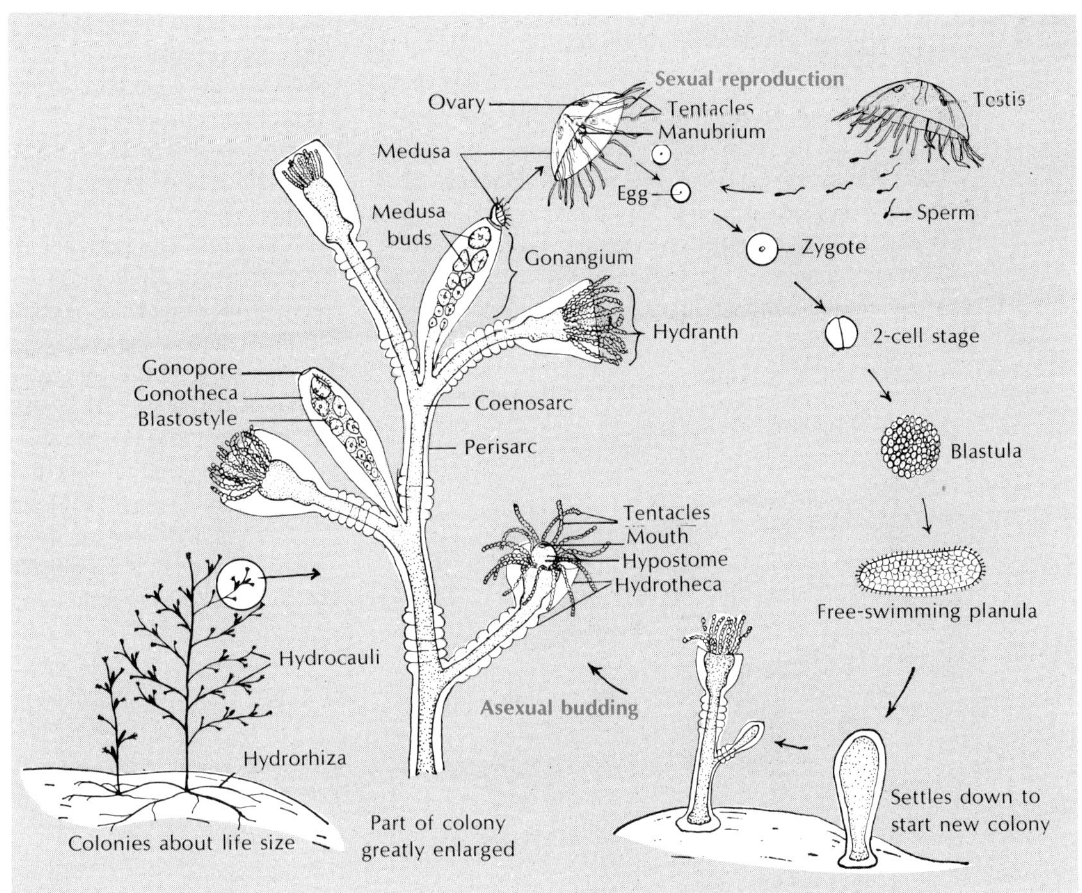

FIG. 12-14

Life cycle of *Obelia* showing alternation of polyp (asexual) and medusa (sexual) stages.

numbers of polyps, which are of two types: **hydranths,** which are nutritive, and **gonangia,** which are reproductive. The hydranths furnish nutrition for the colony; the gonangia produce young medusae by budding. The medusae (Fig. 12-15) are sexual, giving rise to sperm and eggs. When zygotes are formed, they develop through a series of stages, terminating in a polyp form, thus completing the life cycle. In this way the polyps represent the asexual phase and the medusae represent the sexual phase.

The **hydrocaulus,** or stem that bears the polyps, is a hollow tube composed of a cellular **coenosarc** surrounding the **gastrovascular cavity** and covered by a transparent chitinous **perisarc.** The coenosarc, like the body of the hydra, has an outer epidermis, an inner gastrodermis, and mesoglea between them. The gastrovascular cavity is continuous throughout the colony so that nourishment can be distributed from polyps to hydrorhiza. The perisarc is also continuous, being modified to cover the polyps.

The nutritive polyp or **hydranth,** is much like a miniature hydra, with a **hypostome** and **mouth** surrounded by many **tentacles.** By means of the tentacles and **nematocysts,** these feeding polyps capture their prey. They are strictly carnivorous, eating any small crustaceans, worms, or insect larvae that come their way. Within the gastrovascular cavity food is reduced by digestive enzymes to a broth containing small particles. This is driven throughout the colony by convulsive peristaltic contractions of the hydranth. Cells of the gastrodermis pick up the food and complete digestion in food vacuoles. As far as is known, starches, cellulose, and chitin are not digested by hydroids. The hydranth is protected by a cuplike **hydrotheca,** a continuation of the perisarc, into which the tentacles can contract.

The reproductive **gonangium** is club shaped. In it the coenosarc continues as a **blastostyle** on which the **medusae** develop as lateral buds, **gonophores.** The gonangium is surrounded by the transparent **gonotheca**—a protective sheath with an opening, the **gonopore,** through which the medusae escape.

The cellular structure of the colony is much like that of the individual hydra. Myonemes from the epitheliomuscular and nutritive-muscular layers provide movement, stimulated through a **nerve net. Sensory cells** are most abundant around the mouth and tentacles. Digestion, as in the hydra, is both extracellular and intracellular, with distribution being effected by both bodily contractions and ciliary movement within the digestive cavity.

Gonionemus is frequently studied as a type of jellyfish, since the medusa is much larger than that of *Obelia* (Fig. 12-16). It is fairly typical of the medusae of this class. The polyp of this form is extremely small. *Gonionemus* is bell shaped and about ½ inch in diameter. The convex, or aboral, side is called the **exumbrella,** whereas the concave, or oral, side is the **subumbrella.** Around the margin of the bell are a score or more of **tentacles** with nematocysts, each tentacle with a bend near the tip bearing an **adhesive pad.**

Inside the margin is a thin muscular membrane, the **velum,** which partly closes the open side of the bell. The velum distinguishes the hydrozoan from the scyphozoan jellyfish. It is used in swimming movements. Contractions in the velum and body wall bring about a

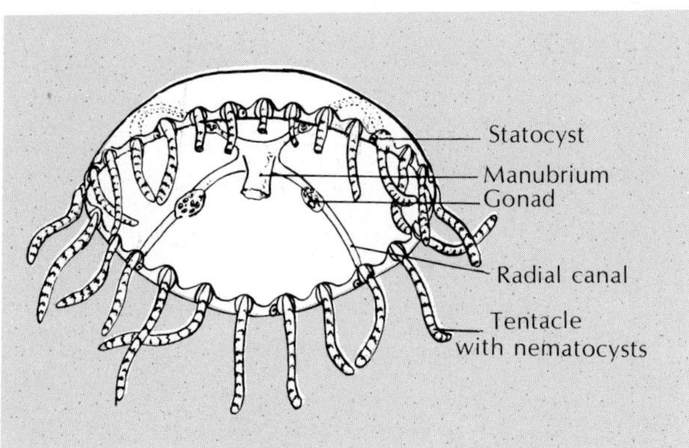

FIG. 12-15

Medusa of *Obelia* is only 1 to 2 mm. in diameter. Note that velum is rudimentary, although *Obelia* belongs to Hydrozoa. Compare with *Gonionemus*, Fig. 12-16.

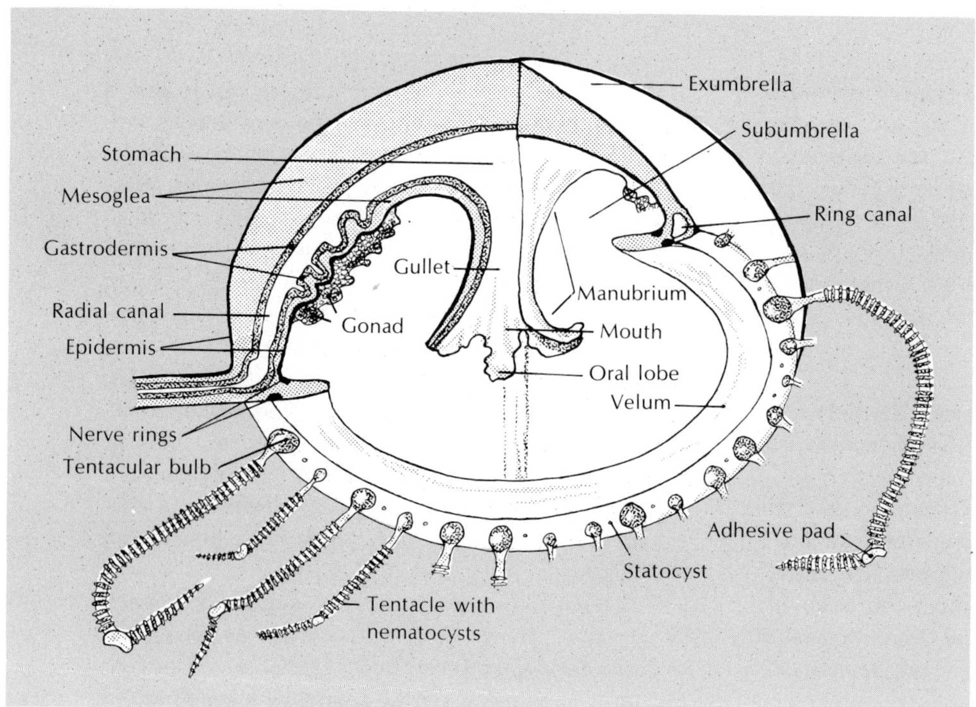

FIG. 12-16

Medusa of *Gonionemus*, partly cut away to show internal structures and relations of parts.

pulsating movement that alternately fills and empties the subumbrellar cavity. As the animal contracts, forcing water out of the cavity, it is propelled forward, aboral side first, with a sort of "jet propulsion." The animal swims upward, turns over, and floats lazily downward, tentacles outspread to capture unwary prey. It rests while attached to vegetation by its adhesive pads.

Hanging down inside the bell is the **manubrium,** at the tip of which is the **mouth** surrounded by four **oral lobes.** From the mouth a **gullet** leads to the **stomach** at the base of the manubrium. Four **radial canals** lead out from the stomach to a **ring canal** around the margin, which connects with all the tentacles. The entire continuous cavity from the gullet to the tips of the tentacles makes up the **gastrovascular cavity,** in which food is partly digested by enzymes and is distributed to all parts of the body. Digestion is completed in the cells of the gastrodermis. Worms, crustaceans, and small fish are favorite foods.

Medusae are dioecious. In *Gonionemus* the **gonads** are suspended under each of the radial canals. The eggs or sperm break through the epidermis into the water outside. The fertilized egg develops into a ciliated **planula** larva, which swims about for a time, then settles down, attaches to some object, loses its cilia, and develops into a minute polyp. The cycle begins again with the young polyp budding off additional polyps that finally produce tiny medusae by asexual budding.

Since free-swimming medusae are more active than the polyps, they need a little more elaborate nervous system. The **nerve net** is concentrated into two **nerve rings** at the base of the velum, one in the exumbrellar and one in the subumbrellar epithelium. **Statocysts** around the margin provide a sense of balance. Each statocyst is a small sac with a hard mass inside that

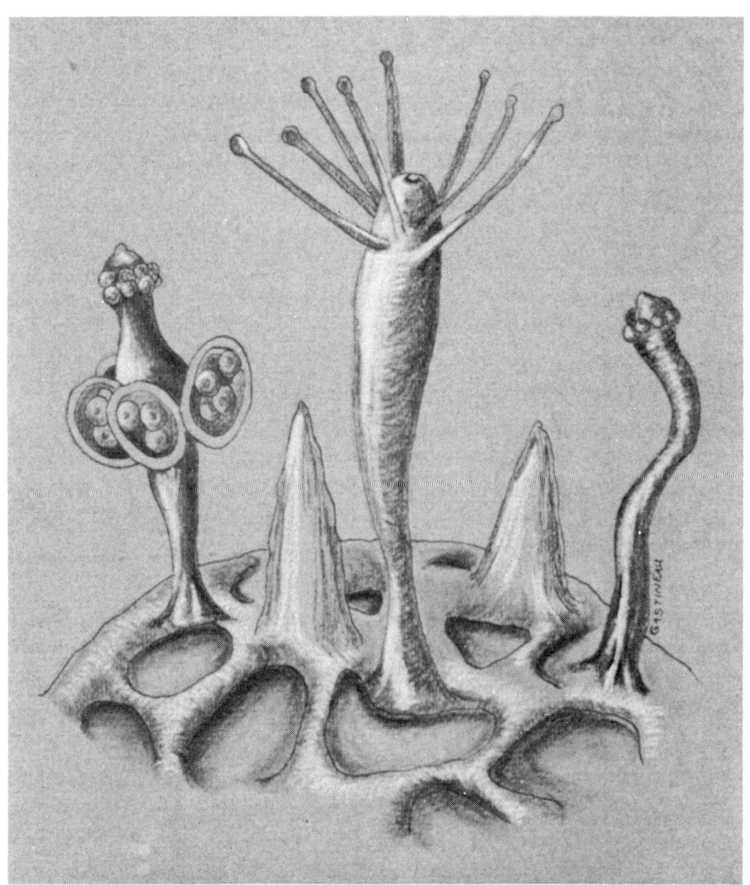

FIG. 12-17

Portion of colony of *Hydractinia* (enlarged view), with three types of individuals connected at base by network of stolons. Left, gonozooid for reproduction; center (between two spines), gastrozooid for nutrition; and right, dactylozooid with nematocysts for defense. Sensory zooids, resembling the dactylozooids, are not shown. (From Hickman: Biology of the invertebrates, The C. V. Mosby Co.)

moves about as the animal moves, acting as a stimulus to direct the movements. **Tentacular bulbs** are enlargements located at the base of the tentacles. Within the bulbs nematocysts are formed and migrate out to the batteries on the tentacles. The bulbs may also help in intracellular digestion. The entire animal seems to be photosensitive.

A life cycle composed of both sexual and asexual generations is typical of this group, although there are interesting exceptions. The freshwater hydra, which has no medusoid stage, is, of course, an exception, as is also the marine *Hydractinia* (Fig. 12-17). Other forms such as the marine jellyfish *Liriope* have no hydroid stage. The larvae of *Liriope* develop directly into medusae (Fig. 12-18). Still other forms (*Sarsia*), besides reproducing sexually, also **bud off medusae** from the manubrium or from the base of the tentacles.

Polymorphism

Coelenterates such as *Obelia,* which have only two types of zooids (individuals) in the hydroid colony, are called **dimorphic.** Some coelenterates have more than two kinds of individuals and are called **polymorphic.** Polymorphism is, then, a condition in which the hydroid colony of a species has a variety of forms so that individuals have different functions. It is a division of labor involving several zooids instead of several organs in the same individual.

Members of order Siphonophora are polymorphic

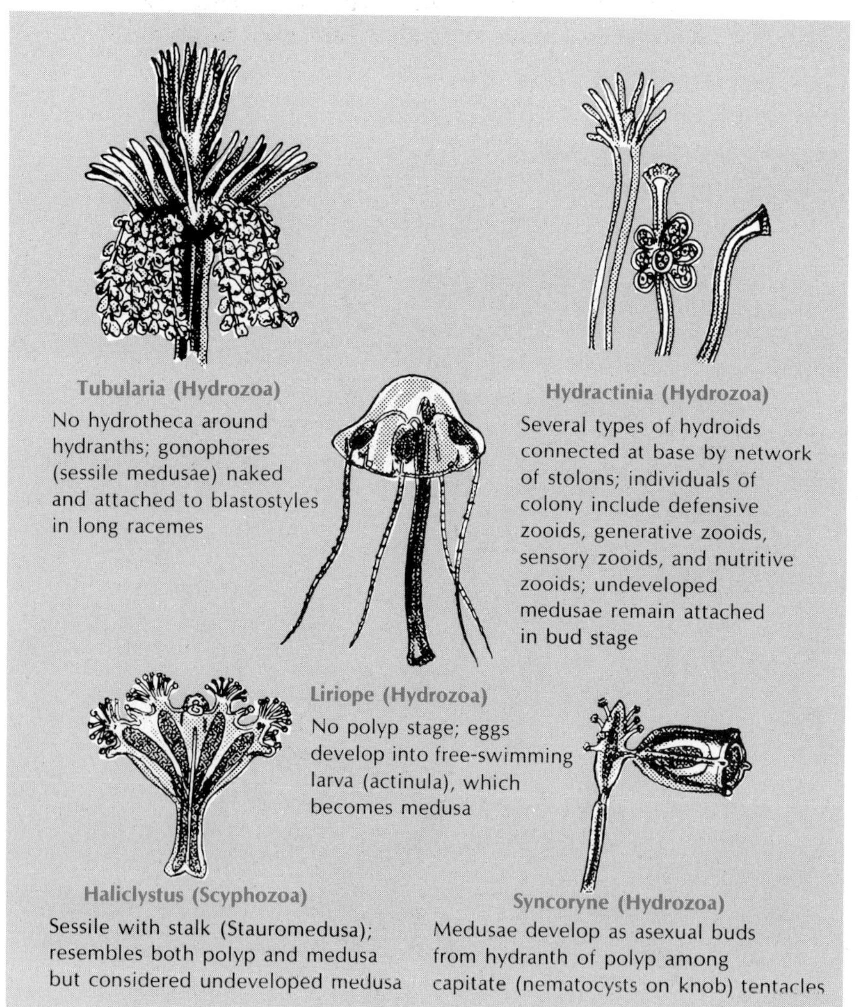

FIG. 12-18

Types of coelenterates showing diversity of life histories and structures.

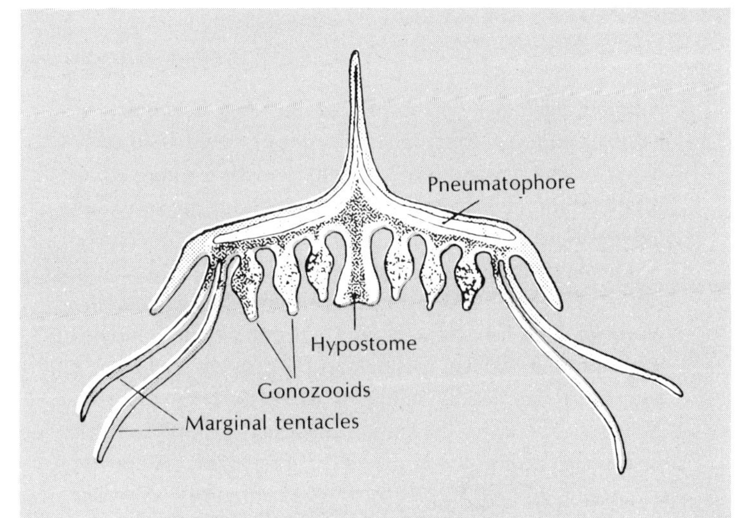

FIG. 12-19

Diagrammatic section through *Velella,* thought to be essentially an expanded hydranth. Gonozooids are reproductive polyp individuals. The hypostome is considered by some to be a gastrozooid and the tentacles, dactylozooids. Vertical extension forms "sail" by which colony is carried about by wind.

swimming or floating colonies made up of a number of modified medusa and polyp types. The gonophores do not develop into complete and freed medusae as in the dimorphic forms such as *Obelia. Velella,* the "sailor," and *Physalia,* the Portuguese man-of-war, are well-known forms (Figs. 12-19 and 12-20). Siphonophora is a very ancient group, as revealed by fossils and other evidence.

Physalia is a colony of incredible beauty, with a rainbow-hued float of bright blues and pinks that carries it along on the surface waters of the southern seas. Many of them are carried northward by the Gulf Stream and are blown to shore on our eastern coast. Bathers frequently find that the long graceful tentacles (sometimes as much as 60 feet long) are laden with nematocysts and are capable of painful and sometimes dangerous stings.

The **pneumatophore,** or float, of *Physalia* (Fig. 12-20) is considered to be the vastly expanded body of the original larval polyp, hatched from a fertilized egg (Totton). It contains an air sac that is an invagination of the aboral body wall and is filled with a gas similar to air. This larval body acts as a type of nurse-carrier (paedophore) for future generations of individuals that bud from it and hang suspended in the water. There are several types of polyp individuals that include the **gastrozooids** (also called siphons). These are the only members that can ingest food; they have the usual polyp form, but instead of the hypostomal tentacles they have one long tentacle arising from the base. Some of them are separated from their tentacles. The separated

FIG. 12-20

Portuguese man-of-war *Physalia physalis* (order Siphonophora, class Hydrozoa) eating fish. This colony of medusa and polyp types is integrated to act as one individual. As many as a thousand zooids may be found in one colony. They often drift upon southern ocean beaches, where they are a hazard to bathers. Although a drifter, the colony has restricted directional movement. Their stinging organoids secrete a powerful neurotoxin. (Courtesy New York Zoological Society.)

stinging tentacles are often called **dactylozooids,** or fishing tentacles. There are two types of medusoid individuals: the **gonophores,** which are little more than sacs containing either ovaries or testes, and the so-called **jelly polyps.**

An interesting symbiotic relationship is found between *Physalia* and a small minnowlike fish called *Nomeus.* This fish swims in and out among the tentacles with perfect safety. Other larger fish, however, are caught by the deadly tentacles when they try to catch *Nomeus.* The latter lives upon pieces of the prey, which is broken up in the process of digestion. However, according to another theory, the immunity *Nomeus* enjoys is due to its habit of eating the zooids and the nematocysts of the tentacles, thus becoming immune to the poison of the stinging organoids. A more recent explanation involves the release by the fish of ectocrines (external hormones) that give *Physalia* precise recognition of its commensal partner.

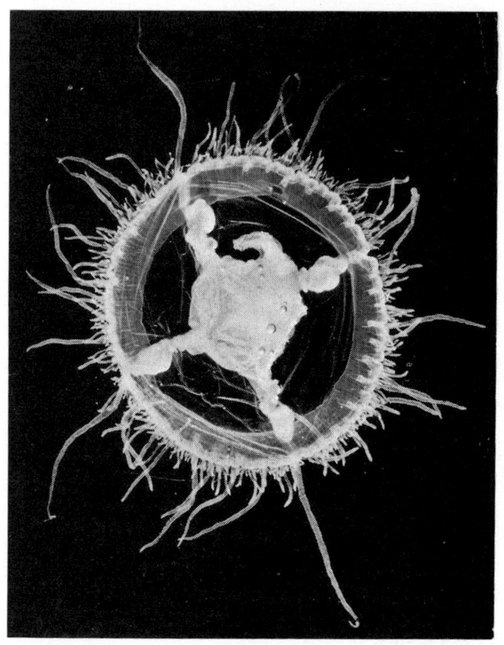

FIG. 12-21

Freshwater jellyfish *Craspedacusta sowerbyi.* Although closely resembling *Gonionemus,* tentacles are more varied in length and have no adhesive pads. (Courtesy Carolina Biological Supply Co., Burlington, N. C.)

Freshwater medusae

The freshwater medusa *Craspedacusta sowerbyi* (class Hydrozoa, order Trachylina) may have evolved from marine ancestors in the Yangtze River of China. This interesting form has been found in many parts of Europe and the United States. At one time it was considered extremely rare, and its discovery in any new region was published usually without delay. It is still not a common animal but has been found all over the United States and in parts of Canada, usually in artificial ponds. (Figs. 12-21 to 12-23.)

This animal has a hydroid phase, but for a long time its relation to the medusa was not recognized, and thus the hydroid was given a name of its own, *Microhydra ryderi.* This hydroid is tiny (2 mm.) and hard to find and appears to be more or less degenerate, for it has no perisarc and no tentacles. It occurs in colonies of a few polyps. On the basis of its relationship to the jellyfish and the law of priority, both the hydroid (polyp) and the medusa should be called *Craspedacusta.* This hydroid gives rise to the tiny medusae by budding.

FIG. 12-22

Polyp of freshwater jellyfish *Craspedacusta.* Only 2 mm. long, this polyp has no tentacles, and its nematocysts are restricted to mouth region. Polyp can creep around on a substrate and feed on small organisms. (Photomicrograph courtesy Charles F. Lytle.)

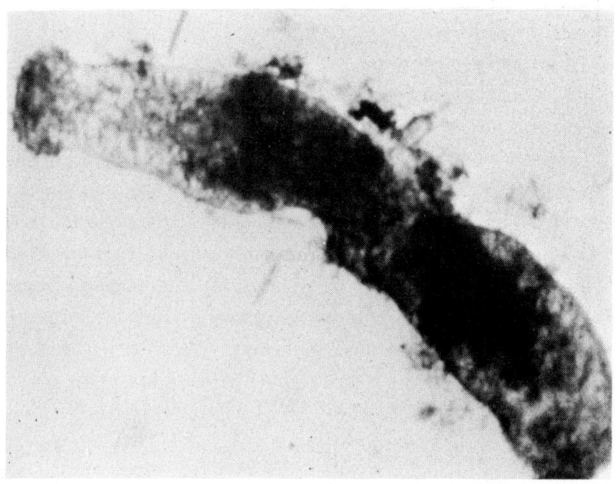

This polyp has three methods of asexual reproduction: (1) by budding off new individuals, which may remain attached to the parent (colony formation); (2) by constricting off nonciliated planula-like larvae (frustules), which can move around and give rise to new

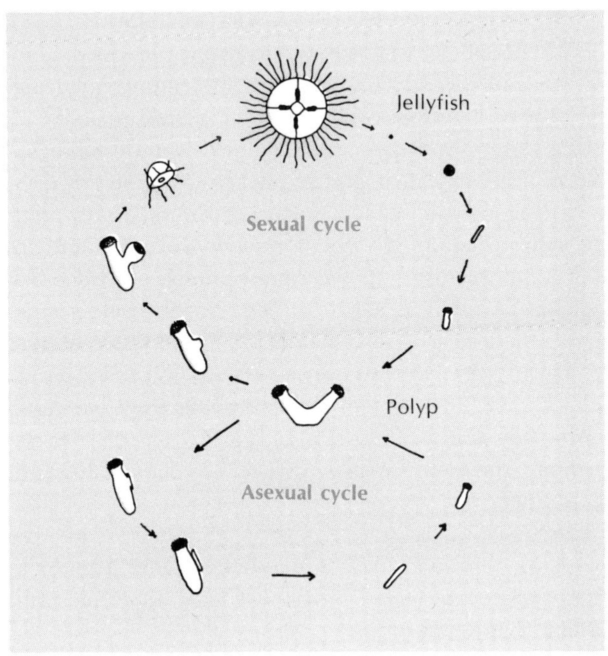

FIG. 12-23

Life history of freshwater jellyfish *Craspedacusta* showing both sexual and asexual cycles. Polyp may bud off planula-like larvae (frustules), which grow into polyps, or it may produce medusa buds, which develop into sexual jellyfish whose zygotes develop into polyps. (Courtesy Charles F. Lytle.)

polyps; and (3) by producing medusa buds, which develop into sexual jellyfish. Monosexual populations (that is, male or female) are characteristic of this species; both sexes are rarely found together. This may be due to environmental causes (temperature of water), or the polyps in a particular habitat may be either male-producing or female-producing individuals (Payne).

The jellyfish, which may attain a diameter of 20 mm. when mature, has some odd features. The tentacles are numerous and are arranged in three or more sets. Unlike *Gonionemus* and many other jellyfish, the tentacles of this freshwater jellyfish are unequal in length and are not provided with adhesive pads. Only one kind of nematocyst is found. The gonads are enlarged sacs that hang down inside the subumbrella, and the manubrium extends down almost to the level of the velum. Although the medusae are dioecious, usually all the jellyfish of a habitat are of the same sex.

CLASS SCYPHOZOA

Class Scyphozoa contains most of the large jellyfish and can be distinguished from the jellyfish of class Hydrozoa by the absence of a velum and the presence of a notched margin of the umbrella. Most of them have polyp and medusa stages, but the polyp stage is insignificant. Both polypoid and medusoid states have tetramerous radial symmetry (in parts of four). Some of these jellyfish are several feet in diameter, with tentacles more than 75 feet long (*Cyanea*) (Fig. 12-24). Others, however, are quite small. Most are found floating in the open sea, although others are attached. Although constructed on the coelenterate plan, this class shows some advancements over class Hydrozoa. It has in its middle layer (mesoglea) ameboid cells and fibers embedded in jelly so that this stratum is now called a **collenchyme.** Other differences from the Hydrozoa are the location of the gonads in the gastrodermis, the more complicated sense organs, the presence of gastrodermic tentacles, and the division of the gastrovascular cavity by septa.

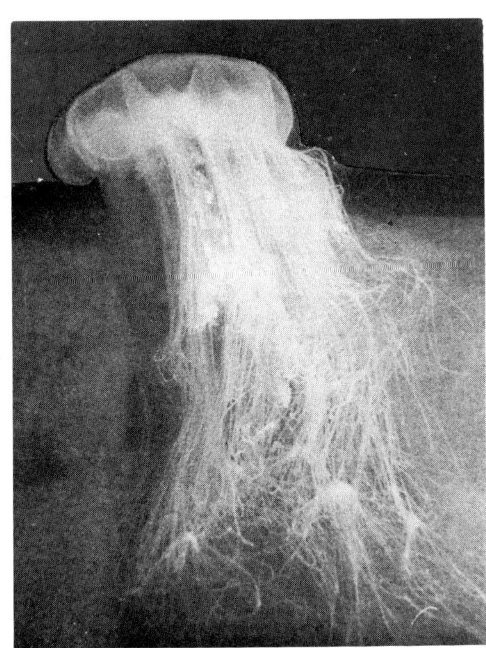

FIG. 12-24

Large jellyfish *Cyanea*. Some may attain diameter of more than 6 feet in Arctic waters but are smaller in warmer waters. Its many hundred tentacles may reach length of 75 feet or more. It is one of the most striking of all jellyfish. (Courtesy C. P. Hickman, Jr.)

Aurelia

Aurelia is 3 or 4 inches in diameter and is found in the coastal waters from Maine to Florida. Its general form is similar to that of *Gonionemus*, for it has **exumbrella** (aboral) and **subumbrella** (oral) surfaces (Fig. 12-25). In the margin of the umbrella are eight indentations and many small tentacles. In each of the marginal notches there is a sense organ, **tentaculocyst,** which is flanked by marginal lappets. Each sense organ consists of a pigmented eyespot sensitive to light and a hollow statocyst for equilibrium. Mineral particles enclosed in cells near the tip of the tentaculocyst act as weights, causing the structure to bend up and down at its base when the animal tilts to one side or the other. This bending is recorded by sensory cells near the base of the organ and provides a sense of equilibrium. Two olfactory pits are near the tentaculocyst. In the oral surface is the **mouth** at the end of a short **manubrium.** From each corner of the square mouth an **oral lobe** or arm hangs down. Nematocysts in the lobes paralyze small prey, which are then conveyed by ciliated grooves in the lobes up to the mouth and the digestive cavity. Flagella in the gastrodermis keep a current of water moving to bring in food and oxygen and to carry away wastes. Extending out from the central digestive cavity are four **gastric pouches** in which the gastrodermis extends down in little tentacle-like projections called **gastric filaments.** These are covered with nematocysts to further quiet any prey that are still struggling. Gastric filaments are not found in hydrozoan medusae. **Radial canals** branch out from the pouches to a **ring canal** in the margin. In each gastric pouch there is a C-shaped **gonad.** As in many of the syphomedusae and anthozoans, *Aurelia* has two nerve nets—a giant fiber system for controlling the swimming contraction and a diffuse one for local reactions such as feeding. The two systems, however, communicate with each other.

The jellyfish is covered with epidermis, and the mesoglea (collenchyme) is unusually thick. The bulk of the jellyfish is water. Movement is by rhythmic pulsations of the umbrella.

The sexes are separate, and fertilization is internal, the sperm of the male being carried into the gastric cavity where the eggs are (Fig. 12-26). The zygotes then lodge on the oral lobes, where they develop into ciliated planula larvae. After swimming about, the

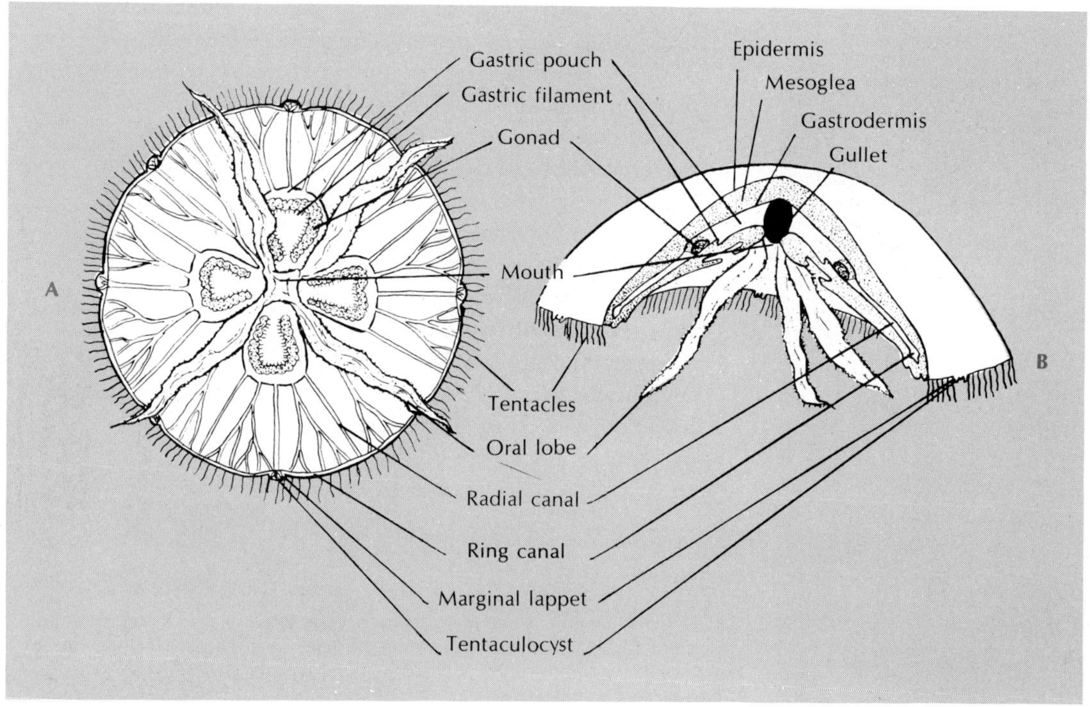

FIG. 12-25

Structure of jellyfish *Aurelia.* **A,** Oral view. **B,** Side view with part of body cut away to show internal structure.

larva becomes fixed and develops into a **scyphistoma,** a hydralike form. By a process of **strobilation** the scyphistoma forms a series of saucerlike buds, **ephyrae,** and is now called a **strobila.** When the ephyrae break loose, they become inverted and grow into mature jellyfish.

CLASS ANTHOZOA

Class Anthozoa includes the sea anemones, the stony corals, the horny, black, and soft corals, the sea pens, sea pansies, sea feathers, and others. Some of them are provided with an external or internal skeleton, and they may be solitary or colonial. They have a flowerlike appearance and are strictly polyps, for no medusa stages are found. They are found in deep as well as in shallow marine water and in polar seas as well as in the tropics. They vary greatly in size and are firmer in texture than are the polyps of other coelenterates.

The class Anthozoa differs from the other classes of Coelenterata in a number of particulars (some of which may be considered advancements), such as an exclusively polypoid form, a tendency toward biradial and even bilateral symmetry, the presence of a mesoglea made up of a mesenchyme of ameboid cells, the formation of a true stomodaeum (lined with invaginated ectoderm), and the presence of a disk-shaped oral end.

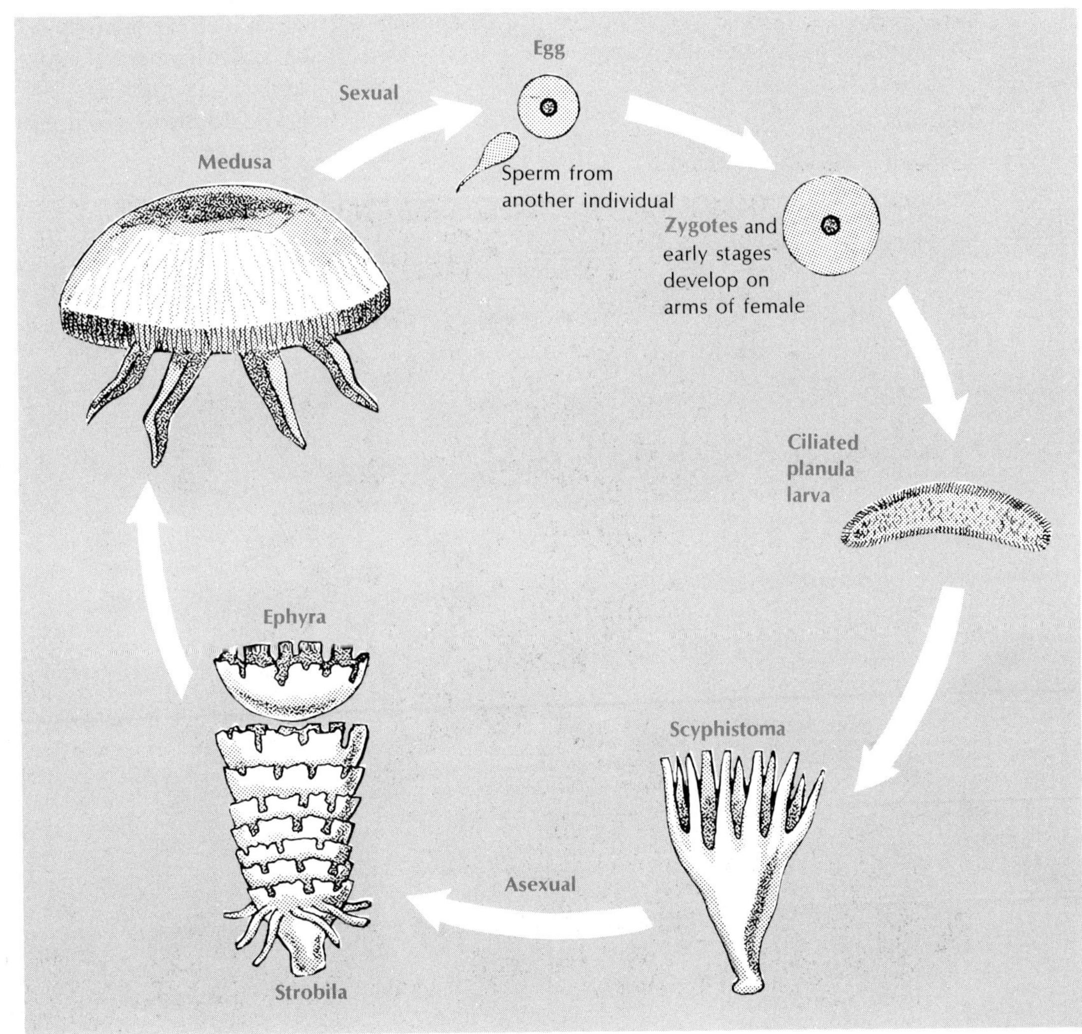

FIG. 12-26

Life cycle of jellyfish *Aurelia* (class Scyphozoa). Eggs and sperm from separate sexes form zygotes, which develop on oral arms of female. After early stages of development (not shown on diagram), ciliated planula larva swims away and becomes attached to form a scyphistoma. The latter by transverse fission or strobilation develops into strobila stage, made up of saucerlike ephyrae. Ephyrae separate and float off as small jellyfish. Life cycle is thus made up of sexual and asexual phases.

Metridium

Metridium, a sea anemone, which is one of the types of the class, is 2 to 3 inches long and is commonly found on wharves, piers, and rocky bottoms along the North Atlantic coast. It is cylindric in form, with a crown of hollow tentacles arranged in circlets around the **mouth** on the flat **oral disk** (Figs. 12-27 and 12-28). The base, or **pedal disk,** serves for attachment. The mouth leads into a **gullet,** or pharynx, on either side of which is a **ciliated groove** called the **siphonoglyph** (single in some species). These grooves create water currents to carry in oxygen, whereas the cilia on the rest of the gullet carry water and waste products out. The gullet leads into the **gastrovascular** cavity, which is divided into six **radial** chambers by six pairs of **septa,** or **mesenteries,** that extend vertically from the body wall to the gullet (Fig. 12-29). These chambers communicate with each other by means of **ostia** in the mesenteries and are open below the gullet. Smaller mesenteries partially subdivide the larger chambers but do not reach the gullet. Attached to the base of the mesenteries are the threadlike **acontia,** which bear nematocysts and gland cells. The acontia can be protruded through the mouth or pores in the body wall and help overcome prey. The pores (cinclides) in the body wall also aid in the rapid discharge of water from the body when the endangered animal contracts to a very small size.

The sexes are separate, and the gonads are arranged on the margins of the mesenteries. The zygote develops into a ciliated larva. Asexual reproduction sometimes occurs by budding and fragmentation. (Fig. 12-30.)

Sea anemones are muscular, having muscle fibers not only in the epidermis and gastrodermis but also in the collenchyme as well. There are definite muscle bands in the mesenteries. Anemones can glide along slowly on their pedal disks. They can expand and

FIG. 12-27

Cluster of sea anemones, *Metridium.*

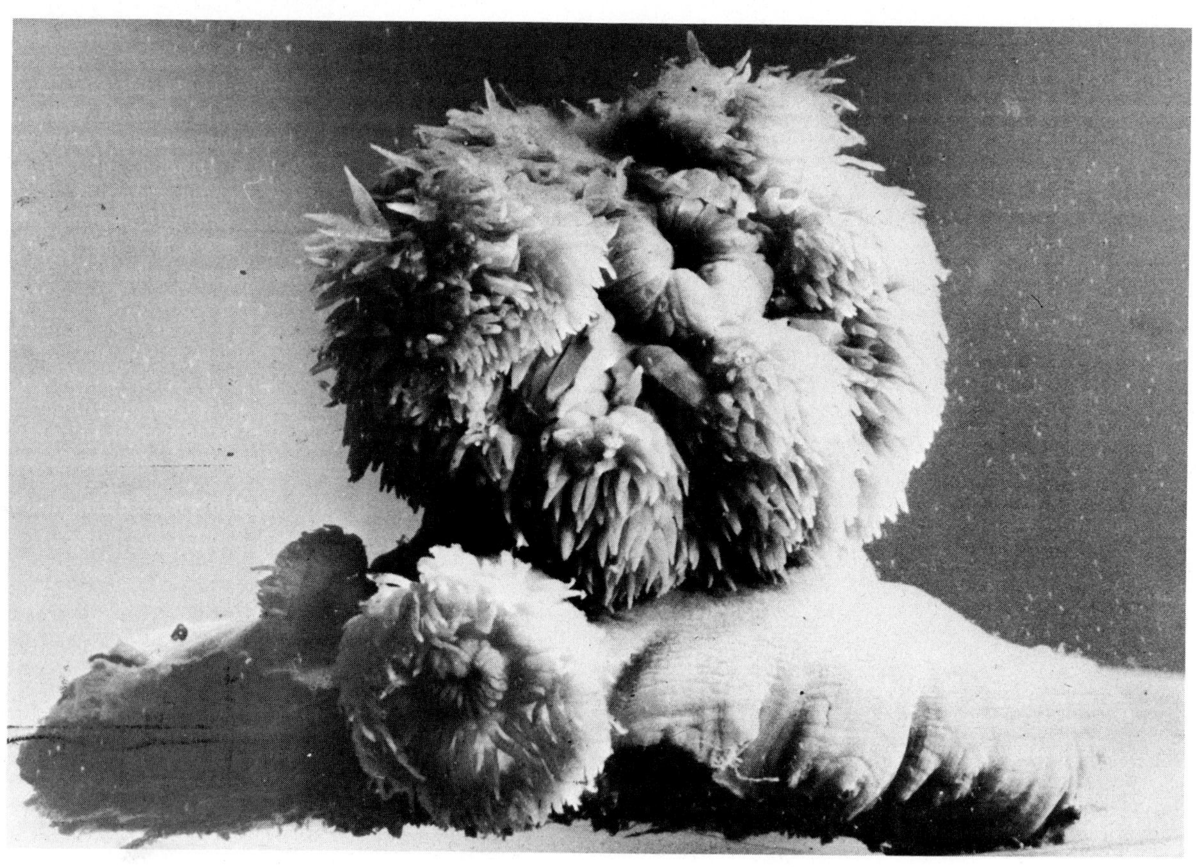

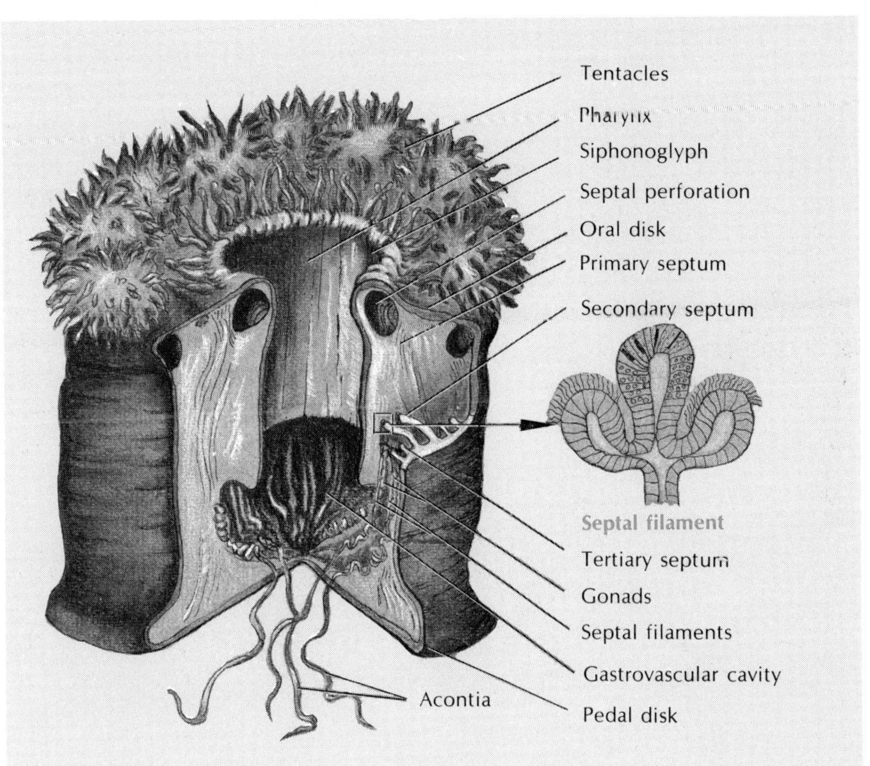

FIG. 12-28

Structure of *Metridium* cut to show pharynx, or gullet, and septal arrangement. Insert, section through septal filament. (From Hickman: Biology of the invertebrates, The C. V. Mosby Co.)

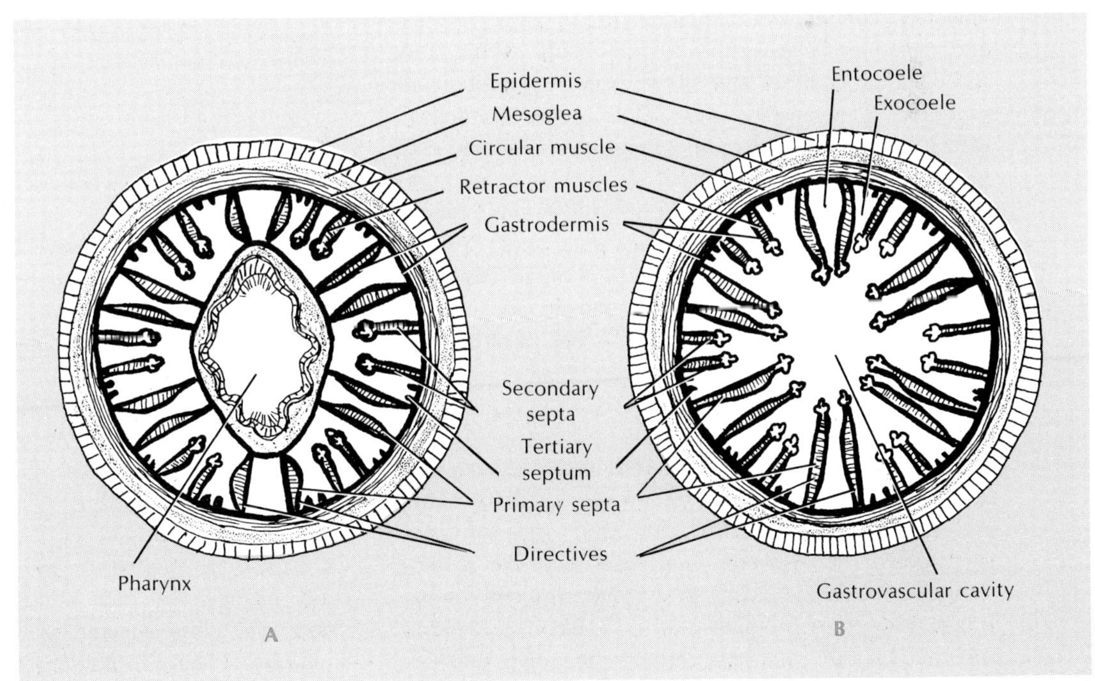

FIG. 12-29

Transverse section through actiniarian polyp such as *Metridium*. **A,** Through pharynx, or gullet. **B,** Below pharynx or gullet. (From Hickman: Biology of the invertebrates, The C. V. Mosby Co.)

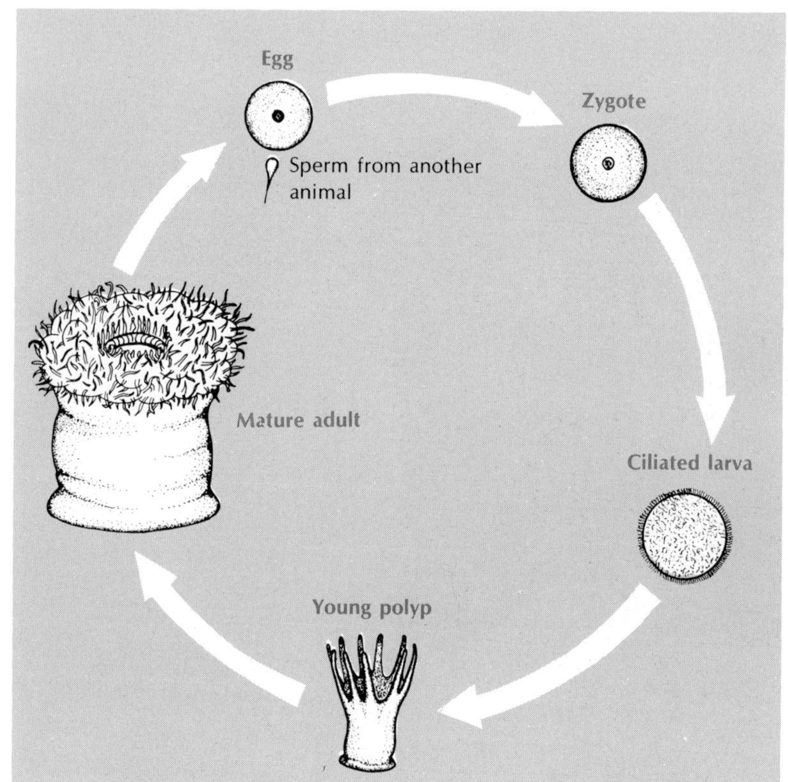

FIG. 12-30

Life history of sea anemone, Anthozoa. This class has only polyp type, no medusa.

FIG. 12-31

Group of coral polyps, *Astrangia danae,* protruding from their shallow cups. This is a common coral of Atlantic coast. (Courtesy General Biological Supply House, Inc., Chicago.)

stretch out their tentacles in search of small vertebrates and invertebrates, which they overpower with tentacles and nematocysts and carry to the mouth. When disturbed, they contract and draw in their tentacles and oral disks. Some anemones are able to swim, to a limited extent, by rhythmic bending movements, which may be an escape mechanism from enemies such as nudibranchs. Extracts (ectocrines) given off by nudibranchs will provoke the reaction in the sea anemones. Respiration and excretion are by diffusion through the body walls and cells. Some of these animals are colorful when open and look like incredibly beautiful aquatic flowers.

Corals

Most corals belong to class Anthozoa, although one or two are from Hydrozoa. Many species, both living and fossil, are recognized. The coral organism is a small polyp (about ½ inch long) that looks like a miniature sea anemone living in a stony cup with radial ridges (Fig. 12-31). The cup is a limy exoskeleton secreted by the epidermis around the polyp and between its mesenteries. Living polyps can withdraw into these cavities when not feeding. Although some are solitary, most are in colonies, which assume a great variety of forms, such as multiple branching and rounded masses. Living polyps are found only on the surface layers of coral masses (Fig. 12-32). Thus there is deposited over long periods of time large amounts of calcareous coral.

Most corals (especially shallow-water and true reef corals) have an interesting symbiotic relationship with microscopic plants (zooxanthellae) that are found in the animal coral tissue. These photosynthetic plants are not used as food by the corals, but they render a service to the corals by removing carbon dioxide and nitrogenous and other wastes and make possible the close spacing of the polyps in reef communities. They also assist in the formation of the coral framework.

Reef-building corals are mainly restricted to shallow water of tropic seas (Fig. 12-33). They are rarely found in water below 100 to 150 feet in depth and flourish best in temperatures between 22° and 28° C. They are most common in the coastal waters of Florida and the West Indies, the east coast of Africa and Madagascar, the East Indies, Australia and the islands of the Coral Sea, and a few other places. Three kinds of coral reefs are commonly recognized, depending on how they are formed. One of these is the **fringing reef,** which may extend out to a distance of a quarter mile from the shore, with the most active zone of coral growth facing the sea. A **barrier reef** differs from a fringing reef in being separated from the shoreland by a lagoon of varying width and depth. The Great Barrier Reef off the northeast coast of Australia is more than 1,200 miles long and up to 90 miles from the shore. A third type of reef is the **atoll,** which is a reef that encircles a lagoon but not an island. Of the many theories advanced to explain coral reef formation, none are entirely satisfactory. Darwin's theory assumed that fringing reefs were first formed on a sloping shore, and by subsidence of the sea floor in the regions of the reefs and the simultaneous upward and outward growth of the coral, these fringing reefs became barrier reefs. In places an entire volcanic island may have become submerged, leaving only the coral atoll, which in time acquired a growth of vegetation. Another theory (Daly) stresses the lowering of the ocean level by the withdrawal of water for glacial formation. Wave action then produced flat areas. When the glaciers melted and the temperature became favorable, the corals began to grow on these surfaces, building higher as the ocean level rose. Borings to great depths on certain atolls confirm a belief that atolls developed on volcanic tops or mountains as they became submerged. Most reefs grow at the rate of 10 to 200 mm. each year. Most of the existing reefs could have been formed in 15,000 to 30,000 years.

Some solitary sea corals that do not form reefs have been found at depths of 4 or 5 miles, and a few have been collected from the waters of northern latitudes.

Coral reefs have great economic importance, for they serve as habitats for a large variety of organisms, such as sponges, worms, echinoderms, mollusks, many kinds of fish, and man. Nearly every phylum of marine life is found among their crevices and chasms.

Besides the stony corals there are many other types of corals such as the sea fans and sea plumes (Fig. 12-

FIG. 12-32

Stony coral *Oculina* showing cups in which polyps once lived.

FIG. 12-33

Organ-pipe coral *Tubipora*. These often build extensive reefs.

34). Some of these have horny skeletons instead of calcareous ones. Horny skeletons consist chiefly of rods that pass through stems and branches, with the polyps arranged around the rods.

In recent years J. W. Wells has stressed the importance of corals in determining a relative chronology for geologic deposits and a time scale of events. In some corals it was possible to count the daily striations of calcium carbonate deposits within the annual bands of growth. On the basis of astronomic calculations the Earth's present rotation on its axis is decreasing at the rate of 2 seconds per 100,000 years. However, at the beginning of the Cambrian period (600 million years ago) a day was less than 21 hours long and there were 424 days in the year. Some Devonian corals had as many as 410 striations per year instead of 360 in recent (Quaternary period) corals. These values are in agreement with the age of the Earth based upon the isotope dating of geophysics and the rotation-time variations of astronomy.

ECONOMIC IMPORTANCE

As a group, coelenterates have little economic importance. Some animals use them as food, although this is rarely done by man. Precious coral serves for jewelry and ornaments. Corals also are important in building the coral reefs and islands, some of which are used as habitations by man and other animals. In places where it is available, coral rock serves for building purposes. Some mollusks and flatworms eat hydroids bearing nematocysts and utilize these stinging cells for their own defense. Planktonic medusae may be of some importance as food for fish that are of commercial value; on the other hand, the reverse is true—the young of the fish fall prey to coelenterates.

FIG. 12-34

Gorgonian soft corals, dried. **A,** Sea fan *Gorgonia.* **B,** Sea plume. These horny corals have exoskeletons of calcareous spicules or hornlike gorgonin (an organic substance) and are often in fanlike or featherlike colonies. (From Hickman: Biology of the invertebrates, The C. V. Mosby Co.)

Derivation and meaning of basic terminology

acontia (Gr. *akontion,* dart). Threads with nematocysts on mesenteries of sea anemone.

Aurelia (L. *aurelia,* gold-colored). Genus (Scyphozoa).

Chlorohydra (Gr. *chloros,* green, + hydra). Genus (Hydrozoa).

cinclide (Gr. *kinklis,* opening or lattice). Small pores in the external body wall of sea anemones.

cnidoblast (Gr. *knide,* nettle, + *blastos,* germ). Modified interstitial cell that holds the nematocyst.

cnidocil (Gr. *knide,* nettle, + *cilium,* hair). Triggerlike spine on nematocyst.

collenchyme (Gr. *kolla,* glue, + *enchyma,* infusion). A gelatinous mesenchyme that forms the third layer in the wall of coelenterates.

Craspedacusta (Gr. *kraspedon,* border, + *acusta,* pointed). Genus (Hydrozoa).

ephyra (Gr. *Ephyra,* Greek city). Refers to castlelike appearance. Stage in development of Scyphozoa.

gonangium (Gr. *gonos,* seed, + *angeion,* dim. of vessel). Reproductive zooid of hydroid colony.

Gonionemus (Gr. *gonia,* angle, + *nema,* thread). Genus (Hydrozoa).

Hydra (Greek mythology, water serpent).

hydranth (Gr. hydra + *anthos,* flower). Nutritive zooid of hydroid colony.

interstitial (L. *inter,* among, + *sistere,* to stand). Refers to one of the totipotent cells in the body wall of coelenterates.

medusa (*Medusa,* Greek mythology, female monster with snake-entwined hair). Jellyfish stage in coelenterates.

mesoglea (Gr. *mesos,* middle, + *glea,* glue). Jellylike noncellular layer between epidermis and gastrodermis.

Metridium (Gr. *metridios,* fruitful). This animal has symmetric parts.

nematocyst (Gr. *nema,* thread, + *kystis,* bladder). Stinging organoid of coelenterates.

Nomeus (Gr. herdsman). Refers to the habits of this commensal fish in inducing larger fish to chase it into the grasping tentacles of the Portuguese man-of-war.

Obelia (Gr. *obelias,* round cake). Genus (Hydrozoa).

Pelmatohydra (Gr. *pelmato,* stalk or sole, + hydra). Genus (Hydrozoa). These hydras have a stalk at the basal disk end of body.

perisarc (Gr. *peri,* around, + *sarx,* flesh). Sheath covering the stalk and branches of a hydroid.

Physalia (Gr. *physallis,* bladder). Genus (Hydrozoa).

polymorphism (Gr. *poly,* many, + *morpha,* form). A condition in which there are two or more types of individuals within a single species.

polyp (L. *polypus,* many-footed). Sedentary form of coelenterates.

scyphistoma (Gr. *skyphos,* cup, + *stoma,* mouth). A stage in the development of scyphozoan jellyfish just after the larva becomes attached.

siphonoglyph (Gr. siphon + *glyphe,* carving). Ciliated furrow in the gullet of sea anemones.

Siphonophora (Gr. siphon + *phoros,* bearing). An order of Hydrozoa. Refers to the gastrozooid polyp with a single hollow tentacle in these polymorphic hydrozoan colonies.

strobila (Gr. *strobilos,* anything twisted). A stage in the development of the scyphozoan jellyfish.

tentacle (L. *tentare,* to feel). Flexible processes about the mouth and margin of the umbrella in coelenterates.

tentaculocyst (L. *tentaculum,* feeler, + *kystis,* bladder). A sense organ on the margin of the jellyfish umbrella.

Trachylina (L. *trachy,* rough, + *linum,* flax). An order of hydrozoa. Refers to the appearance produced by the long-haired sensory cells and lithostyles or sense clubs.

velum (L. veil). A membrane on the subumbrella surface of jellyfish of class Hydrozoa.

Phylum Ctenophora*

GENERAL RELATIONS

Many zoologists have placed ctenophores in phylum Coelenterata. The tendency at present is to consider them as a separate phylum. They comprise a small group of fewer than 100 species, and they are strictly marine forms. They take their name from the eight comblike plates they bear for locomotion. Common names for them are "sea walnuts" and "comb jellies." They are widely distributed, especially in warm waters, and are extensively used in biologic investigations. With coelenterates, they represent the only two phyla with basic radial symmetry in contrast to other Metazoa, which have developed bilateral symmetry. In contrast to coelenterates, nematocysts are lacking in ctenophores, except in one species (*Euchlora rubra*) that is provided with nematocysts on certain regions of its tentacles but lacks colloblasts. These nematocysts are a part of this ctenophore and are not obtained by eating hydroids. In common with the coelenterates, ctenophores have not advanced beyond the tissue grade of organization. There are no definite organ systems in the strict meaning of the term.

Although they have some common characteristics, there is no convincing evidence that ctenophores were derived from coelenterates, although there may be some kinship. The ancestral ctenophore seems to have been a spherical form, with eight radially arranged nerves that represented a concentrated form of advancement over the nerve net of the coelenterates. In time the eight meridional rows of comb plates developed over the regions of these nerves.

*Te-nof'o-ra (Gr. *ktenos,* comb, + *phoros,* bearing).

Ctenophores have some resemblance to the Trachylina and may have diverged very early from that coelenterate stem. The flat creeping ctenophores *Ctenoplana* and *Coeloplana,* formerly thought to show affinities between the flatworms and the Radiata, are now considered to be highly modified ctenophores that have acquired a creeping mode of life.

The ctenophores must be considered as a blind offshoot that gives rise to no higher form. They are thus not in direct evolutionary line with the pattern of animal life.

CHARACTERISTICS

1. Symmetry **biradial;** arrangement of internal canals and the opposite position of the tentacles change the radial symmetry into a combination of the two (**radial + bilateral**)
2. Usually ellipsoidal or spherical in shape, **with eight rows of comb plates on the external surface**
3. Ectoderm, endoderm, and a mesoglea (ectomesoderm) with scattered cells and muscle fibers; ctenophores may be considered **triploblastic**
4. Nematocysts absent (except in one species) but **adhesive cells (colloblasts)** present
5. Digestive system consisting of a mouth, pharynx, stomach, and a series of canals
6. Nervous system consisting of an aboral sense organ (**statocyst**), with a subepidermal plexus arranged into eight strands beneath the eight comb plate rows
7. No polymorphism or attached stages
8. Reproduction monoecious; gonads (endodermal origin) on the walls of the digestive canals, which are under the rows of paddle plates; cydippid larva

COMPARISON WITH COELENTERATA

Ctenophores resemble the coelenterates in the following ways:

1. Form of radial symmetry; with the coelenterates, they form the group Radiata
2. Aboral-oral axis around which the parts are arranged
3. Well-developed gelatinous ectomesoderm (collenchyme)
4. No coelomic cavity
5. Diffuse nerve plexus
6. Lack of organ systems

They differ from the coelenterates in the following ways:

1. No nematocysts except in *Euchlora*
2. Development of muscle cells from mesenchyme
3. Presence of comb plates and colloblasts
4. Mosaic, or determinate, type of development
5. Presence of pharynx general

HABITAT

The ctenophores are strictly marine, and all are free swimming. They are feeble swimmers and are carried by tides and currents. Storms may drive them in concentrated numbers onto beaches and sea bays and inlets. Although they are more common in surface waters, they also occur at great depths in the sea.

CLASSES

Class Tentaculata (ten-tac′u-la″ta) (L. *tentaculum,* feeler, + *ata,* group suffix). With tentacles. Tentacles may or may not have sheaths into which they retract. Some types of this class flattened for creeping; others compressed to a bandlike form. In some the comb plates may be confined to the larval form. Examples: *Pleurobrachia, Cestum.*

Class Nuda (nu′da) (L. *nudus,* naked). Without tentacles; conical form; wide mouth and pharynx; gastrovascular canals much branched. Example: *Beroë.*

REPRESENTATIVE TYPE

CLASS TENTACULATA

Pleurobrachia

Structure. *Pleurobrachia* is a ctenophore commonly studied in zoologic laboratories. Its transparent, whitish body is a little less than 1 inch in diameter and is ovoid in shape (Fig. 12-35). The oral pole bears the mouth opening, and the aboral pole has a sensory organ, the **statocyst.**

On the surface are eight equally spaced bands called comb rows that extend as meridians from the aboral pole and end before reaching the oral pole (Fig. 12-36). Each band is made up of short transverse plates of long fused cilia (**comb plates**). On opposite sides, near the aboral end, are the two **tentacle sheaths,** blind sacs that contain the bases of the tentacles. The two tentacles are long and solid and very extensible and are provided with muscle fibers and lateral branches. They can be fully retracted into the sheaths, and when completely extended, they may be 6 inches long. The surface of the tentacles bear **colloblasts,** or glue cells (Fig. 12-37), which secretes a sticky substance for catching small animals.

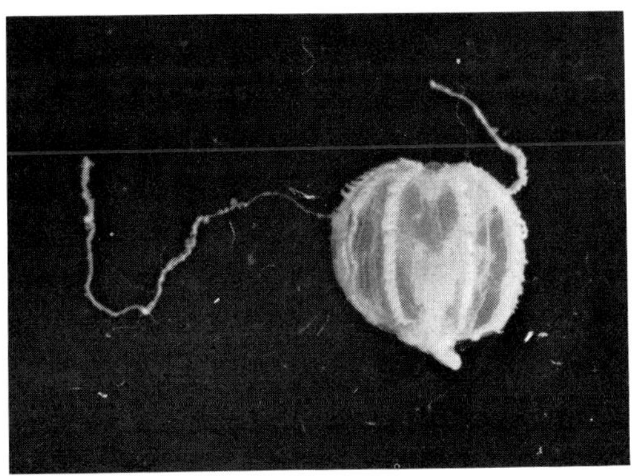

FIG. 12-35

Pleurobrachia, common ctenophore, about ¾ inch in diameter. The paired tentacles are shown extended. Note rows of ciliated comb plates. (Photograph of preserved specimen.)

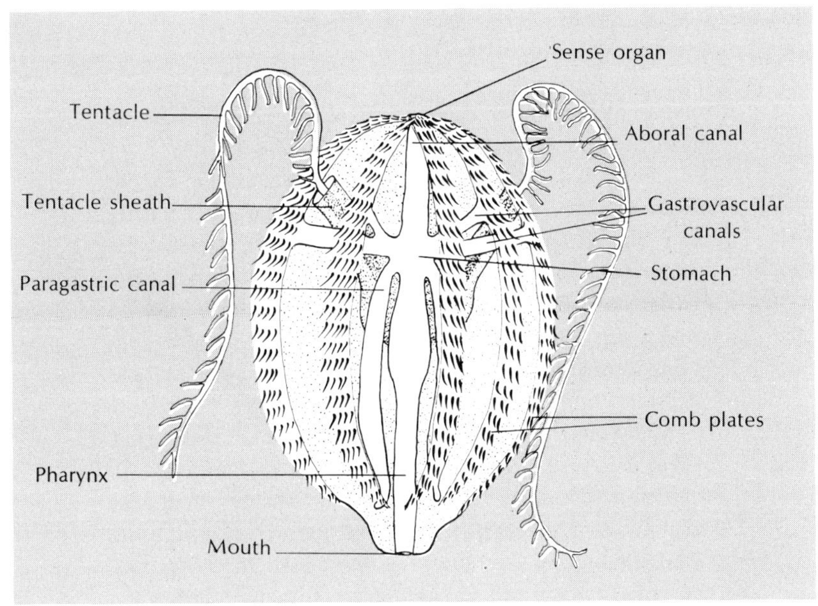

FIG. 12-36

Structure of *Pleurobrachia.* Diagrammatic.

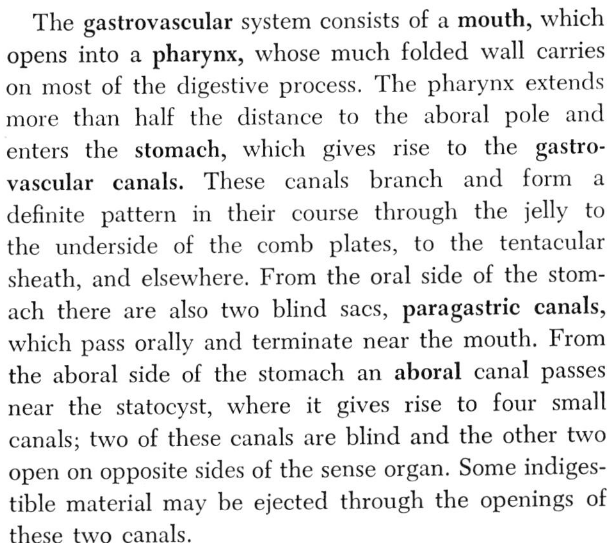

The **gastrovascular** system consists of a **mouth,** which opens into a **pharynx,** whose much folded wall carries on most of the digestive process. The pharynx extends more than half the distance to the aboral pole and enters the **stomach,** which gives rise to the **gastrovascular canals.** These canals branch and form a definite pattern in their course through the jelly to the underside of the comb plates, to the tentacular sheath, and elsewhere. From the oral side of the stomach there are also two blind sacs, **paragastric canals,** which pass orally and terminate near the mouth. From the aboral side of the stomach an **aboral** canal passes near the statocyst, where it gives rise to four small canals; two of these canals are blind and the other two open on opposite sides of the sense organ. Some indigestible material may be ejected through the openings of these two canals.

The **sense organ** at the aboral pole consists of four tufts of cilia that support a calcareous **statolith,** the whole being enclosed in a bell-like container. This is an organ of equilibrium, for alterations in the position of the animal would change the pressure on the tufts of cilia so that a differential discrimination would be possible. It is also concerned in the coordination of the beating of the comb rows.

Pleurobrachia has a nervous system similar to that of the coelenterates. It is made up of a subepidermal plexus of multipolar ganglion cells and neurites that may or may not anastomose. There is a concentration of the

FIG. 12-37

Colloblast. This is one of characteristic organelles of ctenophores. (From Hickman: Biology of the invertebrates, The C. V. Mosby Co.)

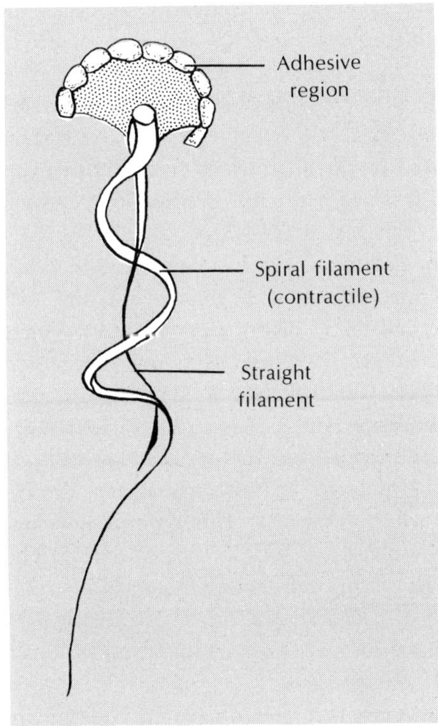

nerve plexus under each comb plate, but there is no central control such as is found in higher forms.

The cellular layers of ctenophores are similar to those of the coelenterates. On the exterior of the body is a ciliated **epidermis** of ectodermal origin. Most of the gastrovascular cavity is lined with **gastrodermis.** Between the two layers is the jellylike **collenchyme,** which makes up most of the interior of the body and contains muscle fibers of mesenchymal origin and ameboid cells.

Metabolism. Ctenophores live on small organisms, such as marine eggs, crustaceans, and mollusks. In catching their prey they make use of the two tentacles that hold onto the prey with the glue cells and bring it to the mouth. Digestion is extracellular in the gastrovascular cavity and its numerous branches, but some intracellular digestion also occurs in the gastrodermis. Most indigestible material is voided through the mouth and through the anal pores on each side of the sense organ. Respiration and excretion occur through body surface.

Locomotion. Ctenophores are propelled by the beating of the cilia on the comb or paddle plates (Fig. 12-38). The beat in each row starts at the aboral end and proceeds successively along the combs to the oral end. The animal is thus driven forward, with the mouth in advance. The animal can swim backward by reversing the direction of the wave. The beat of the comb plates is under nervous control of the diffuse nervous system but is not initiated by the aboral sense organ. However, the sense organ is concerned with coordination between the comb rows.

Reproduction. *Pleurobrachia,* in common with other ctenophores, is monoecious. The gonads are arranged on the gastrodermal lining of the gastrovascular canals under the comb plates. Fertilized eggs are discharged through the epidermis into the water. Cleavage in ctenophores is determinate (mosaic), for the various parts of the animal are mapped out in the cleavage cells. If one of the cells is removed in the early stages, the resulting embryo will be deficient. This type of development is just the opposite of that of coelenterates. The free-swimming larval form of ctenophores, which is different from that of coelenterates, develops directly into an adult. The larval form is called cydippid and is characteristic of most ctenophores.

Behavior. Not much is known about the reactions of ctenophores to various types of stimuli. They seem to avoid bright light, which causes them to seek a lower level in water. Whenever the surface of the sea is agitated by a storm, they will also swim rapidly downward. Much of their activity has been studied with reference to their locomotion, and experiments on their comb plates have been carried out.

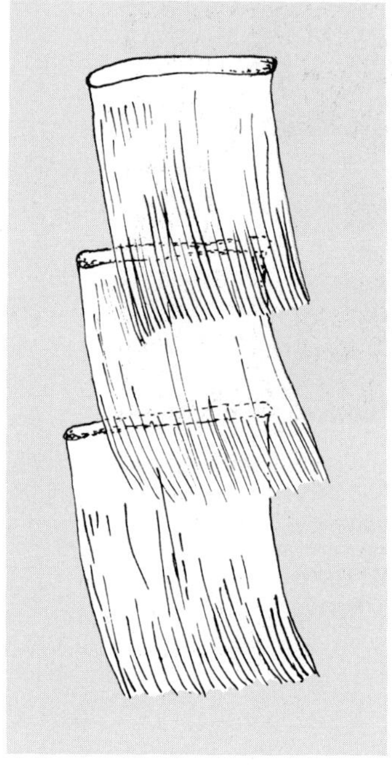

FIG. 12-38

Portion of comb row showing three plates, each composed of transverse rows of long fused cilia. (From Hickman: Biology of the invertebrates, The C. V. Mosby Co.)

The epidermis is abundantly supplied with sensory cells so that they are sensitive to chemical and other forms of stimuli. When a ctenophore comes in contact with an unfavorable stimulus, it often reverses the beat of its comb plates and backs up. The comb plates themselves are very sensitive to touch, which often causes them to be withdrawn into the jelly.

Other ctenophores

Ctenophores are among the most beautiful of all creatures. Their transparent bodies glisten like fine glass, brilliantly iridescent during the day and luminescent at night.

One of the most striking ctenophores is *Beroë,* which may be more than 100 mm. in length and 50 mm. in breadth. Its shape is conical or ovoid, and it is provided with a large mouth but no tentacles. It is pink colored, and the body wall is covered with an extensive network of canals formed by the union of the paragastric and meridional canals. Venus's girdle *(Cestum)* is compressed and bandlike, may be more than a yard long, and presents a graceful appearance as it swims. The highly modified *Ctenoplana* and *Coeloplana* are very rare but are interesting because they have flattened disk-shaped bodies and are adapted for creeping rather than swimming. Both have unusually long tentacles. A common ctenophore along the Atlantic coast is *Mnemiopsis,* which has a laterally compressed body with two large oral lobes and unsheathed tentacles.

Nearly all ctenophores give off flashes of luminescence at night, especially such forms as *Mnemiopsis.* The vivid flashes of light seen at night in southern seas are often due to members of this phylum.

ECONOMIC IMPORTANCE

Ctenophores have little economic importance. They are used as a food by many marine forms, but their main interest to man is their position in the phylogeny of animals and their divergence from the coelenterates, the other great phylum of the division Radiata.

Derivation and meaning of basic terminology

Cestum (Gr. *kestos,* girdle). Genus (Tentaculata). The body is compressed into a ribbonlike form.

colloblasts (Gr. *kolla,* glue, + *blastos,* germ). Glue-secreting cells on the tentacles.

comb plate One of the plates of fused cilia that are arranged in rows for ctenophore locomotion.

Pleurobrachia (Gr. *pleuron,* side, + *brachia,* arms). Genus (Tentaculata). Refers to the tentacles, one on each side.

statocyst (Gr. *statos,* standing, + *kystis,* bladder). Sense organ concerned with orientation.

statolith (Gr. *statos,* standing, + *lithos,* stone). Small calcareous body resting on the tufts of cilia in the statocyst.

Annotated references

Berrill, N. J. 1957. The indestructible hydra. Sci. Amer. **197**:48-58 (Nov.). *Summarizes in a clearly written manner the many facets of the hydra's structure and regenerative behavior.*

Bourne, G. C. 1900. Ctenophora, In E. R. Lankester: A treatise on zoology. London, A. & C. Black, Ltd. *Good, detailed descriptions of the morphology of ctenophores; taxonomy only briefly considered.*

Brown, F. A., Jr. 1950. Selected invertebrate types. New York, John Wiley & Sons, Inc. *Good for certain representative marine forms.*

Buchsbaum, R. 1948. Animals without backbones. Chicago, University of Chicago Press. *Many excellent illustrations of coelenterates.*

Bullough, W. S. 1950. Practical invertebrate anatomy. London, The Macmillan Co. *An excellent practical manual of certain selected types.*

Burnett, A. L. 1959. Hydra: an immortal's nature. Natural History **68**:498-507 (Nov.). *Describes among other aspects of the hydra's nature the experiments of P. Brien on the renewal of cells.*

Dougherty, E. C. (editor). 1963. The lower Metazoa. Berkeley, University of California Press. *Deals with comparative biology and phylogeny of the lower metazoan phyla.*

Fraser, C. M. 1937. Hydroids of the Pacific coast of Canada and the United States. Toronto, University of Toronto Press. *This monograph and a similar one on the hydroids of the Atlantic coast are the most comprehensive taxonomic studies yet made on the American group.*

Hardy, A. C. 1956. The open sea. Boston, Houghton Mifflin Co. *Many beautiful plates of medusae and other coelenterates in this outstanding treatise on sea life.*

Hickman, C. P. 1967. Biology of the invertebrates, St. Louis, The C. V. Mosby Co.

Hyman, L. H. 1940. The invertebrates: Protozoa through Ctenophora. New York, McGraw-Hill Book Co. *Extensive accounts are given of the coelenterates (Cnidaria) and the ctenophores in the last two chapters of this authoritative work.*

Lane, C. E. 1960. The Portuguese man-of-war. Sci. Amer. **202**:158-168 (March). *The author considers this jellyfish to be made up of a colony of four kinds of polyps —the float, the fishing tentacles, the gastrozooids, and the reproductive polyps. A revealing article on the morphology and physiology of this remarkable form.*

Loomis, W. F. 1959. The sex gas of hydra. Sci. Amer. **200**:145-156 (April). *Describes the factors that induce sexual reproduction in the hydra.*

Mackie, G. O. 1960. The structure of the nervous system in *Velella.* Quart. J. Micr. Sci. **101**:119-131.

Pennak, R. W. 1953. Freshwater invertebrates of the United States. New York, The Ronald Press Co. *A complete reference work on this group. Chapter 4 is devoted to the freshwater coelenterates, including a good description of the rare freshwater jellyfish.*

Rees, W. J. (editor). 1966. The Cnidaria and their evolution. New York, Academic Press, Inc. *A symposium devoted entirely to the coelenterates of Great Britain. A discussion of many aspects by authorities on this group, which has been a favorite for investigations ever since Trembley.*

Russell, F. S. 1953. The medusae of the British Isles. Cambridge, Cambridge University Press. *In this magnificent monograph the many species of British medusae are described fully in text and by beautiful plates, many in color. An excellent account of the structural characters of medusae as well as methods for rearing and preserving them is included.*

Smith, F. G. W. 1948. Atlantic reef corals. Miami, University of Miami Press. *Describes with diagrams the manner of formation of coral reefs and an account of the western Atlantic reefs.*

Totton, A. K., and G. O. Mackie. 1960. Studies on *Physalia physalis* (L.). Discovery Reports **30**:301-407. Cambridge, Cambridge University Press. *This excellent monograph is an exhaustive treatment of the natural history and morphology (Totton) and the behavior and histology (Mackie) of the Portuguese man-of-war. It is a superb work of interest to both the specialist and all serious students of zoology.*

Uchida, T. 1963. Two phylogenetic lines in the coelenterates from the viewpoint of their symmetry. Proceedings of the Sixteenth International Congress of Zoology (Washington), vol. 1, p. 24. The author believes that a planuloid ancestor gave rise to those with radial symmetry (Hydrozoa and Scyphozoa) and those with bilateral symmetry (Anthozoa).

Yeatman, H. C. 1965. Ecological relationship of the ciliate *Kerona* to its host hydra. Turtox News **43**:226-227.

Yonge, C. M. 1949. The sea shore. London, William Collins Sons & Co., Ltd. *Many descriptions of coelenterates are scattered throughout this fascinating work. Some superb colored photographs of sea anemones.*

CHAPTER 13

• PHYLA PLATYHELMINTHES AND RHYNCHOCOELA (ACOELOMATE BILATERAL ANIMALS)

BIOLOGIC PRINCIPLES

1. These two phyla represent the most primitive groups of bilateral animals, a type of symmetry assumed by all animals that have reached the highest stage of evolutionary advancement.

2. These phyla have only one internal space, the digestive cavity, with the region between the ectoderm and endoderm filled with mesoderm in the form of muscle fibers and mesenchyme. Since they lack a coelom of any kind, they are termed acoelomate animals.

3. The acoelomates may be considered in direct or indirect evolutionary line of higher invertebrate phyla and have given the basic organization plan widely exploited in the animal kingdom.

4. Acoelomates have also shown more specialization and division of labor, resulting in a higher grade of organization. The flatworms (Platyhelminthes) have arranged more definite layers of tissues into organs and have attained the tissue-organ level. Ribbon worms (Rhynchocoela) have advanced to the organ-system level by collecting organs into systems.

5. By developing the mesoderm into a well-defined embryonic germ layer, the two phyla have made possible a great source of tissues, organs, and systems in the future evolution of animals, thus pointing the way to greater complexity.

6. Both phyla have made contributions to the evolutionary blueprint. Besides the mesoderm they have established bilateral symmetry and cephalization. Along with the subepidermal musculature there is also a mesenchymal system of muscle fibers. There is some centralization of the nervous systems so well shown in the ladder pattern found in flatworms. An excretory system now appears for the first time. Rhynchocoela have given the first circulatory system with blood and the first one-way alimentary canal. Although not stressed by zoologists, the rhynchocoel cavity in ribbon worms is actually a true coelom, but as part of the unique proboscis mechanism it cannot be of evolutionary significance in the future development of the coelomic cavity.

7. Unique and specialized structures occur in both phyla. The parasitic habit of many flatworms has produced many modifications of the basic free-living plan of the worms. Organs of adhesion such as hooks and suckers are common, and some may be modifications of free-living structures.

PHYLOGENY AND ADAPTIVE RADIATION

1. Both phyla appear to be closely related, with the flatworms the more primitive. The order Acoela is thought to have originated from a planuloid ancestor and in turn gave rise to the other members of the phyla. The Rhynchocoela could have arisen from the flatworms because the body construction of ciliated epidermis, muscles and mesenchyme-filled spaces, etc. are similar in both groups. But the former are more advanced than the flatworms in having a complete digestive system, a vascular system, and a more highly organized nervous system.

2. The flatworm body plan with its creeping adaptation facilitates the development of bilateral symmetry, cephalization, ventral-dorsal region, and caudal differentiation. It was adapted in many ways for a parasitic existence into which its adaptive radiation led many of the more common parasites of man and beast. All its numerous species are variations on the same theme of body structure and functional behavior. The ribbon worms have stressed the proboscis apparatus in their evolutionary diversity. Its use in capturing prey may have been secondarily evolved from its original function as a highly sensitive organ for exploring the environment. Being free living and active, the ribbon worms have advanced beyond the flatworms in their evolution. Perhaps the possession of a proboscis was a deterrent to a parasitic habit but highly efficient as predator tool.

Phylum Platyhelminthes*

GENERAL RELATIONS

The term "worm" has been loosely applied to elongated invertebrate animals without appendages and with bilateral symmetry. At one time zoologists considered worms (Vermes) to be a group in their own right. Such a group included a highly diverse assortment of forms. Modern classification has broken up this group into phyla and reclassified them. By tradition, however, zoologists still refer to these animals as "flatworms," "roundworms," "segmented worms," etc.

*Plat'y-hel-min"thes (Gr. *platys*, flat, + *helmins*, worm).

The term Platyhelminthes, "flatworms," was first proposed by Gegenbaur (1859) and was applied to the animals now included under that heading. At first nemertines and some others were included but later were removed to other groups. The phylum is now restricted to three classes: Turbellaria, Trematoda, and Cestoda. These classes show enough similarity in body pattern to indicate a common origin.

According to Hyman's classification, the phyla of the animal kingdom may be placed in three great divisions: **Acellular** (Protozoa), **Radiata** (Porifera, Coelenterata or Cnidaria, Ctenophora), and **Bilateria** (other phyla). The emphasis placed upon bilateral symmetry by Hyman is indicated by the name she has given to the higher division. The bilateral condition may be considered a basic morphologic plan for all animals that have advanced far in complexity of organization.

Most zoologists believe the flatworms came from a coelenterate-like ancestor that had acquired a creeping habit and a transformation of radial into bilateral symmetry, a differentiation of circular and longitudinal muscles, sensory emphasis of the anterior end (cephalization), and the formation of mesoderm. The transformation of a radially symmetric animal into a bilateral one involves many modifications in body form. There would be a dorsoventral flattening of the animal, with the oral end becoming the ventral surface and the aboral end becoming the dorsal surface. The ventral surface would become specialized for locomotion with the aid of cilia and muscles. Directional movement would result in an elongated body and the development of anterior and posterior ends. No doubt the advantages of cephalization put a premium on the natural selection of the best type of head development. The change to a bilateral form would also involve the appearance of the three axes: dorsoventral, anteroposterior, and mediolateral. The small flatworms (order Acoela) seem to meet many of the requirements of an early ancestor of Platyhelminthes. They have many characteristics of the planula larva (coelenterate), such as no epidermal basement membrane, no digestive cavity, a centroventrally located mouth, no excretory system, a nerve plexus under the epidermis, and no distinct gonads.

True mesoderm (endomesoderm) originating from endoderm laid the basis for a higher type of organization with well-defined tissues and the beginnings of organs and organ systems. Structures already present in coelenterates have become more specialized in flatworms. The gastrovascular cavity is more efficient and complex; the nervous system, with its anterior ganglia (brain), together with the sensory eyespots, indicates cephalization. An entirely new system, the excretory, with its characteristic network of tubes and the flame cells provides for the efficient removal of waste.

CHARACTERISTICS

1. Three germ layers (**triploblastic**)
2. **Bilateral symmetry**; definite polarity of anterior and posterior ends
3. **Body flattened dorsoventrally**; oral and genital apertures mostly on ventral surface
4. Body segmented in one class (Cestoda)
5. No definite coelom (acoelomate)
6. Epidermis may be cellular, syncytial, or absent (ciliated in some); **rhabdites in epidermis or mesenchyme** of some Turbellaria; thick cuticle with suckers or hooks in parasitic forms, cuticle or tegument a syncytial living tissue
7. Digestive system incomplete (gastrovascular type); absent in some
8. Muscular system of a sheath form and of mesenchymal origin; layers of circular, longitudinal, and oblique fibers beneath the epidermis
9. Spaces between organs filled with **parenchyma,** a form of connective tissue or mesenchyme
10. **Nervous system consisting of a pair of anterior ganglia with longitudinal nerve cords connected by transverse nerves and located in the mesenchyme** in most forms; similar to coelenterates in primitive forms
11. Simple sense organs; eyespots in some
12. Excretory system of two lateral canals with branches bearing **flame cells (protonephridia)**; lacking in some primitive forms
13. Respiratory, circulatory, and skeletal systems lacking; lymph channels with free cells in some trematodes
14. Most forms monoecious; reproductive system complex with well-developed gonads, ducts, and accessory organs; internal fertilization; development direct; usually indirect in internal parasites in which there may be a complicated life cycle often involving several hosts
15. One class (Turbellaria) mostly free living; others (Trematoda and Cestoda) parasitic

Class Turbellaria (tur'bel-la"re-a) (L. *turbella,* a stirring, + *aria,* like or connected with). Usually free-living forms with soft flattened bodies; covered with ciliated epidermis containing secreting cells and rodlike bodies (rhabdites); mouth usually on ventral surface, sometimes near center of body; no body cavity except intercellular lacunae in parenchyma; mostly hermaphroditic, but some have asexual fission. Examples: *Dugesia* (planaria), *Microstomum, Planocera.*

Class Trematoda (trem'a-to"da) (Gr. *trematodes,* with holes, + *eidos,* form). Body covered with thick living cuticle without cilia; leaflike or cylindric in shape; presence of suckers and sometimes hooks; alimentary canal usually with two main branches; nervous system similar to turbellarians; mostly monoecious; development direct in external parasites but usually indirect in case of internal parasites with alternation of hosts; all parasitic. Examples: *Fasciola, Opisthorchis, Schistosoma.*

Class Cestoda (ses-to'da) (Gr. *kestos,* girdle, + *eidos,* form). Body covered with thick, nonciliated, living cuticle; scolex with suckers or hooks and sometimes both for attachment; body divided into series of proglottids; no digestive or sense organs; general form of body tapelike; usually monoecious and self-fertilizing; many organs reduced; all parasitic, usually with alternate hosts. Examples: *Diphyllobothrium, Taenia, Echinococcus.*

REPRESENTATIVE TYPES

CLASS TURBELLARIA

Class Turbellaria is made up of a number of orders (Fig. 13-1). *Dugesia* belongs to order Tricladida, which is chiefly characterized by a three-branched enteron. Some members of this order are marine, such as *Bdelloura,* an ectoparasite on the gills of *Limulus,* the horseshoe crab. Another member of this order is a terrestrial form, *Bipalium,* which is common in greenhouses.

Closely related to order Tricladida is order Alloeocoela, with irregular saclike intestines.

Another order is Acoela, comprised of animals that are small and have a mouth but no gastrovascular cavity or excretory system. Food is merely passed through the mouth or pharynx into temporary spaces that are surrounded by a syncytial mesenchyme where gastrodermal phagocytic cells digest the food intracellularly. This order has syncytial epidermis and a diffuse nervous system. It is thought that this group has changed little from the ancestral form from which all flatworms have come. Some members of this order, such as *Otocelis,* live as commensals in the digestive system of echinoderms (sea urchins and sea cucumbers).

Order Rhabdocoela is characterized by a straight, unbranched gastrovascular cavity. One representative (*Microstomum*) of this order has the habit of feeding on hydrae and taking over the nematocysts for its own defense.

Another order, Polycladida, is comprised of animals that have many intestinal branches from the central digestive cavity and are leaflike marine forms. Some are ectoparasites such as *Planocera,* which lives in the mouth of certain marine snails. One feature of some polyclads is the presence of a ciliated free-swimming larval form. One of these, called Müller's larva, is provided with ciliated projecting lobes and eyespots.

Dugesia tigrina—common planaria

Habitat. A well-known representative of the triclad turbellarians is the common freshwater planarian (*Dugesia tigrina*) (Figs. 13-2 and 13-3). This species is found on the underside of rocks and debris in brooks or ponds of cold running water—but not in springs or in water immediately fed by springs. They are small and flat and their dark mottled color blends perfectly with the rocks or plants to which they cling. Three other species of *Dugesia* are known to occur in the United States. One of these, *D. dorotocephala,* a dark, almost black form, is found in springs or spring-fed water. This species has sharp-pointed auricles in contrast to the more rounded lobes of *D. tigrina.* Two other species, *D. agilis* and *D. microbursalis,* are more restricted in their distribution and have been found in spring-fed swamps and under stones in streams.

Structure. *Dugesia* is flat and slender and about ¾ inch or less in length. The head region is triangular, with two lateral lobes known as **auricles.** These are not ears but olfactory organs. Two **eyespots** on the dorsal side of the head near the midventral line give the animal a cross-eyed appearance. Dark pigment in the body gives it a mottled or streaked look that accounts for the species name. Its background color may range from a dark yellow to olive, brown, or blackish brown. The ventral side is lighter or white, with no pigment pattern. Near the center of the ventral side is the **mouth,** through which the muscular **pharynx (proboscis)** can be extended for the capture of prey. Posterior to the mouth on the ventral surface is the **genital pore,** the external opening of the reproductive system.

The **skin** is ciliated epidermis resting on a basement membrane (Fig. 13-4). It contains rod-shaped **rhabdites** that, when discharged into water, swell and form a protective gelatinous sheath around the body. Single-

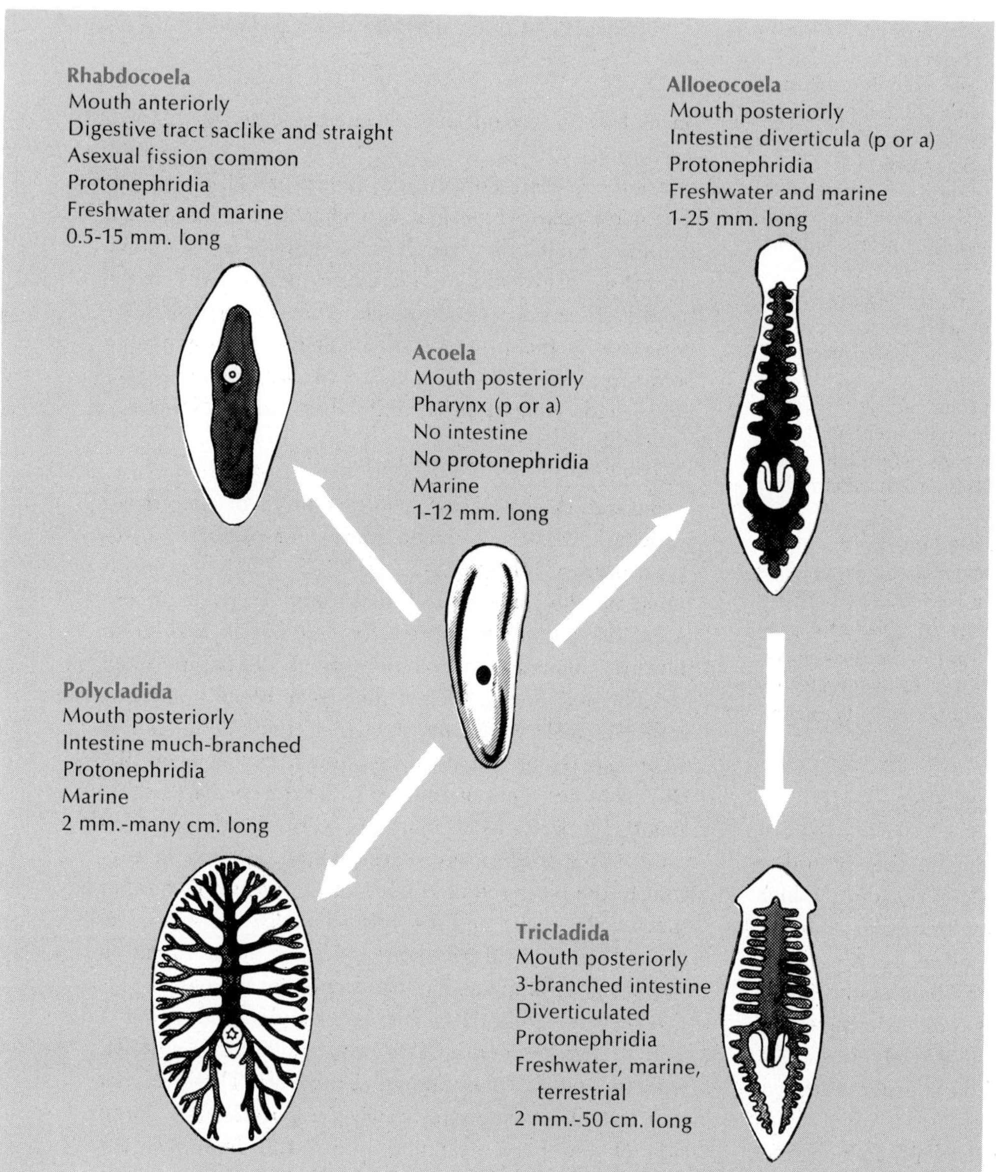

FIG. 13-1

Orders of class Turbellaria, with chief diagnostic characteristics. Arrows indicate possible phylogenetic relationships. Structures marked **"p or a"** may be present or absent.

cell mucous glands open on the surface of the epidermis. In the body wall below the basement membrane are layers of **muscle fibers** that run circularly, longitudinally, and diagonally. A meshwork of **parenchyma** cells, developed from mesoderm, fills the spaces between muscles and visceral organs.

Digestion. The digestive system includes a mouth, pharynx, and **intestine (enteron).** The pharynx lies in a **pharyngeal sheath,** to which it is attached at the anterior end. The pharynx opens posteriorly just inside the mouth, through which it can extend. The intestine has three main trunks, one anterior and two posterior, each with many lateral **diverticula.** The whole forms a **gastrovascular cavity** lined with columnar epithelium (Fig. 13-5).

Planarians are mainly carnivorous, feeding upon injured, intact, or dead prey, such as small crustaceans, nematodes, rotifers, and insects. In the laboratory they are often fed liver or chopped up animals. By their chemoreceptors they can detect food from some distance. They capture ther prey by entangling them in

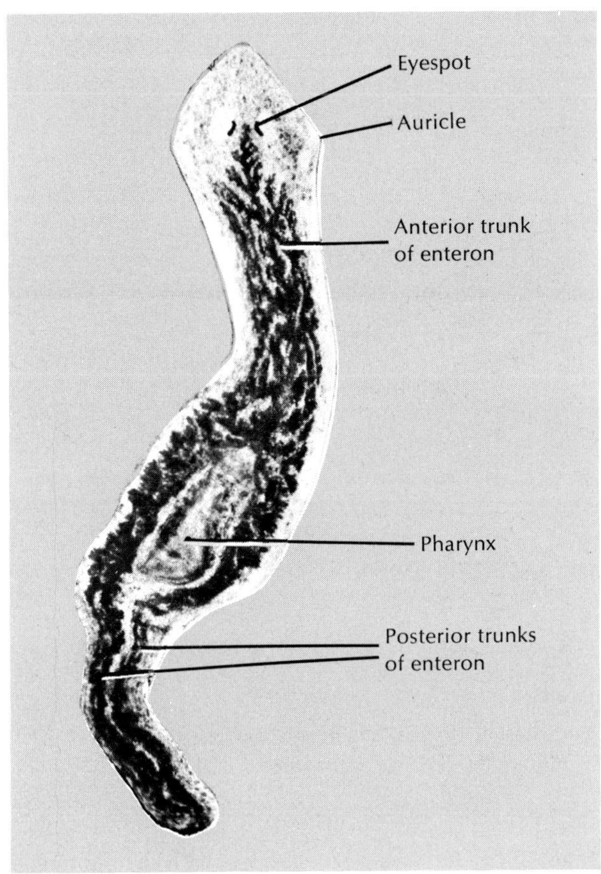

mucous secretions from the mucous glands and rhabdites. The planarian grips its prey with its anterior end, wraps its body around the prey, extends its proboscis, and sucks up minute bits of the food. When one animal feeds, others are soon attracted by the juices from the food. It is now known that intestinal secretions contain proteolytic enzymes for some extracellular digestion. Bits of food are sucked up into the intestine, where the phagocytic cells of the gastrodermis complete the digestion (**intracellular**). The gastrovascular cavity, which ramifies to most parts of the body, distributes the food that is absorbed through its walls into the cells. Since these forms have no anus, undigested food is egested through the pharynx. Planarians can go a long time without feeding, for they can draw food from the parenchyma cells back into the intestinal cells where it is digested. During starvation they literally eat themselves, sacrificing first the reproductive organs, then the parenchyma, muscles, etc. as they grow smaller

FIG. 13-2

Photograph of living planarian.

FIG. 13-3

Living planarians. Small amount of chloroform in culture water has caused them to contract and thrust out tubular pharynxes.

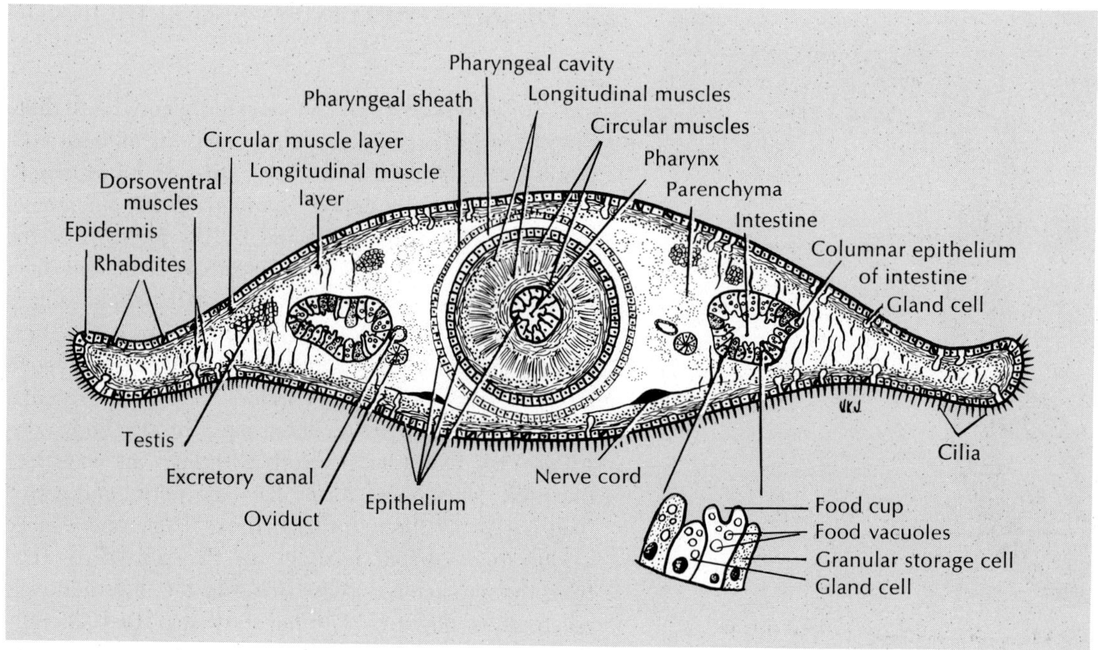

FIG. 13-4

Cross section of planarian through pharyngeal region showing relations of body structures.

in size. When they feed again they regenerate the missing parts.

Excretion. The excretory system consists of two longitudinal canals with a complex network of tubules that branch to all parts of the body and end in **flame cells** (protonephridia). The flame cell is hollow and contains a tuft of cilia which prevents stagnant layers of fluid on the inner surface of tubules. The two main canals open on the dorsal body surface by excretory pores. The excretory system is concerned largely with water regulation as well as excretion of organic wastes. Excretion of metabolic wastes takes place not only through these tubes but also through the epidermis and probably through the gastrodermis (Figs. 13-6 and 13-7, *A*).

Respiration. There are no respiratory organs. Exchange of gases takes place through the body surface.

Nervous system. Two **cerebral ganglia** beneath the eyespots serve as the "**brain.**" Two ventral longitudinal **nerve cords** extend from the brain to the posterior end of the body. Transverse nerves connect the nerve cords, and short nerves extend from the brain to the anterior end and to the eyespots. This arrangement is often called a "ladder-type" nervous system (Figs. 13-5 and 13-8).

The **eyespots** (Fig. 13-9) are made up of pigment cups located in a nonpigmented area in such a manner as to look cross-eyed. Retinal cells extend from the brain to dip into the pigment cups, with the photosensitive ends of the cells inside of the cup. They are sensitive to light intensities and can distinguish the direction of a light source, but they can form no images. The pigment cups serve as shields that allow light to reach the light-sensitive ends of the cells through the openings of the cups only, thus permitting the animal to ascertain the exact direction of the light source. Planaria are negatively phototactic and are most active at night. The auricular sense organs on the side of the head are concerned with taste, smell, and touch. If the auricles are removed, the animal cannot locate food.

Reproduction. Triclad turbellarians reproduce both sexually and asexually. Asexually the animal merely constricts behind the pharyngeal region and separates into two animals. Each new animal regenerates its missing parts—the anterior piece growing a new tail end; the posterior piece, a new head. Sexually the worm is monoecious; each individual is provided with both male and female organs (Fig. 13-6).

In the **male** system two rows of **testes** produce sperm. Each of the testes in a row empties its sperm by a tiny tube (**vas efferens**) into a common duct (**vas deferens**), which enlarges posteriorly to form a **seminal vesicle,**

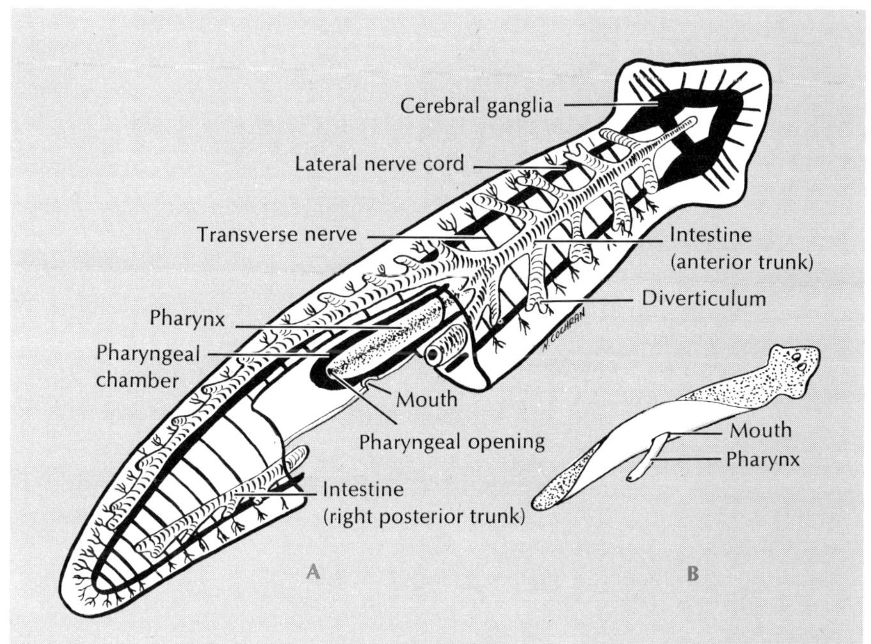

FIG. 13-5

A, Diagrammatic view of digestive system and ladder-type nervous system of planaria. Cut section shows relation of pharynx, in resting position, to digestive system and mouth on ventral surface. **B,** Pharynx extended through ventral mouth.

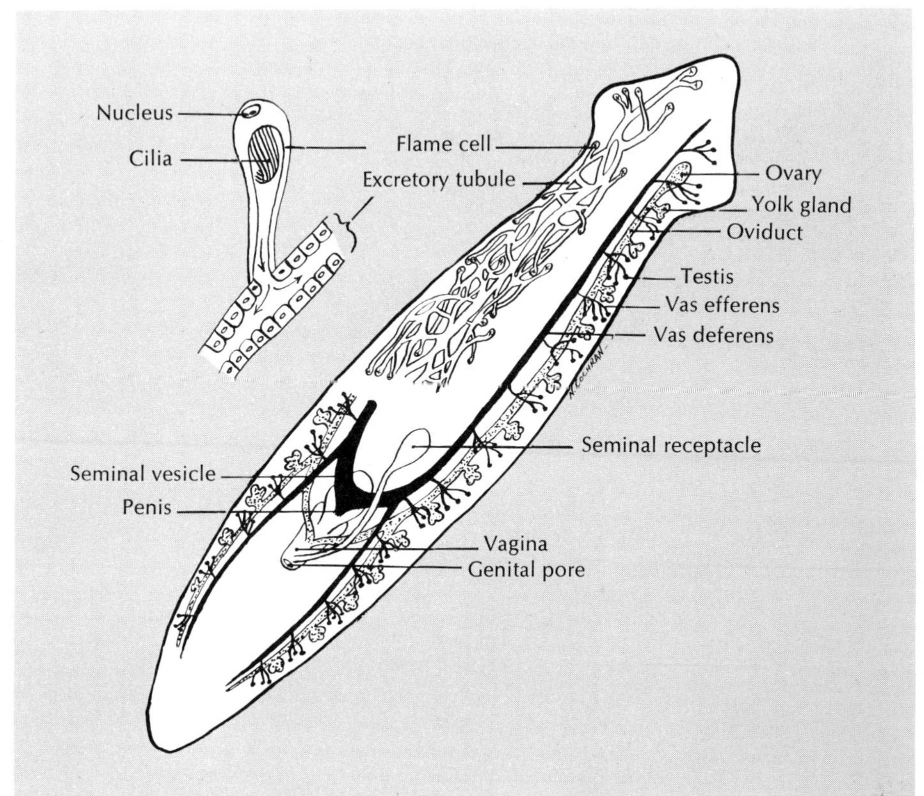

FIG. 13-6

Reproductive and excretory systems in planaria. Portions of male and female organs omitted to show part of excretory system. Insert at left is enlargement of flame cell.

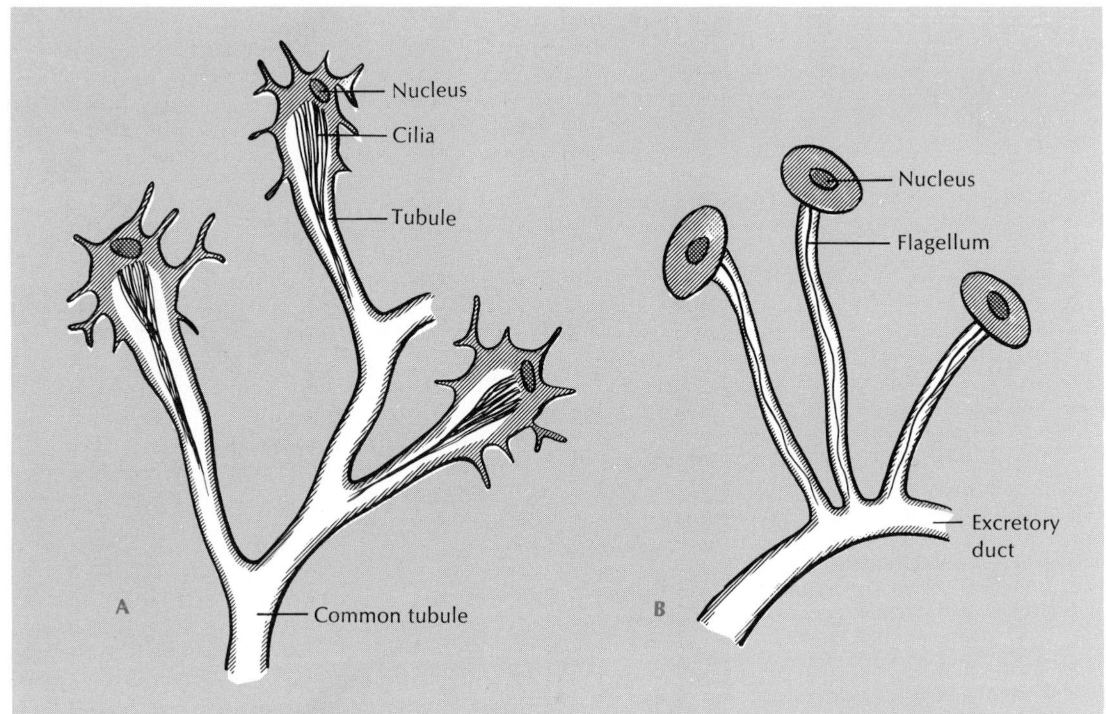

FIG. 13-7

Two types of protonephridia. **A,** Flame cells, typical of flatworms. Each flame cell has one or more nuclei and tuft of cilia projecting into bulb cavity. Beating of cilia (flame) produces water diffusion currents into blind tubule or prevents stagnant layers of fluid from accumulating in tubule. **B,** Solenocytes, found in polychaetes and protochordates *(Amphioxus).* Single long flagellum produces current. Solenocytes, often found in clusters, have thin walls and are well supplied with blood vessels. Thought to have evolved from flame bulbs.

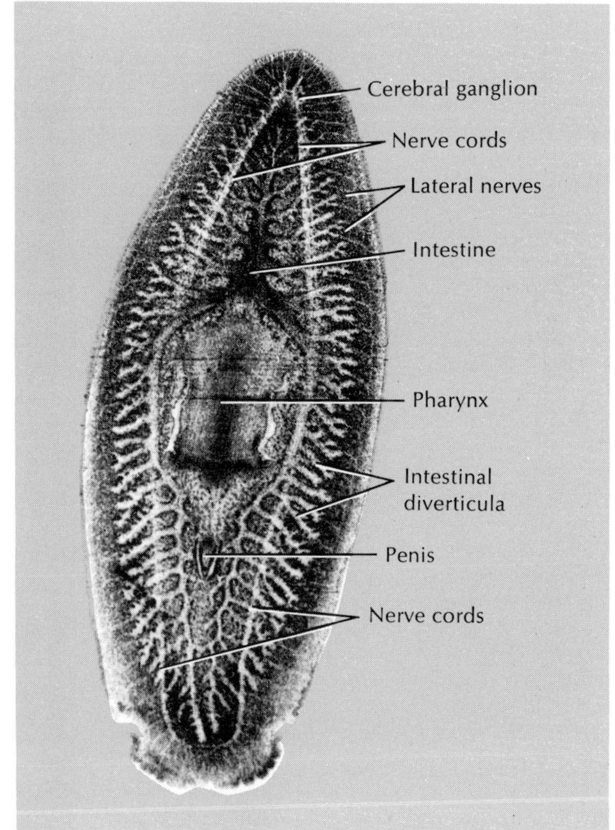

FIG. 13-8

Ladder-type nervous system shows up clearly in this photomicrograph of stained preparation of *Bdelloura,* marine triclad.

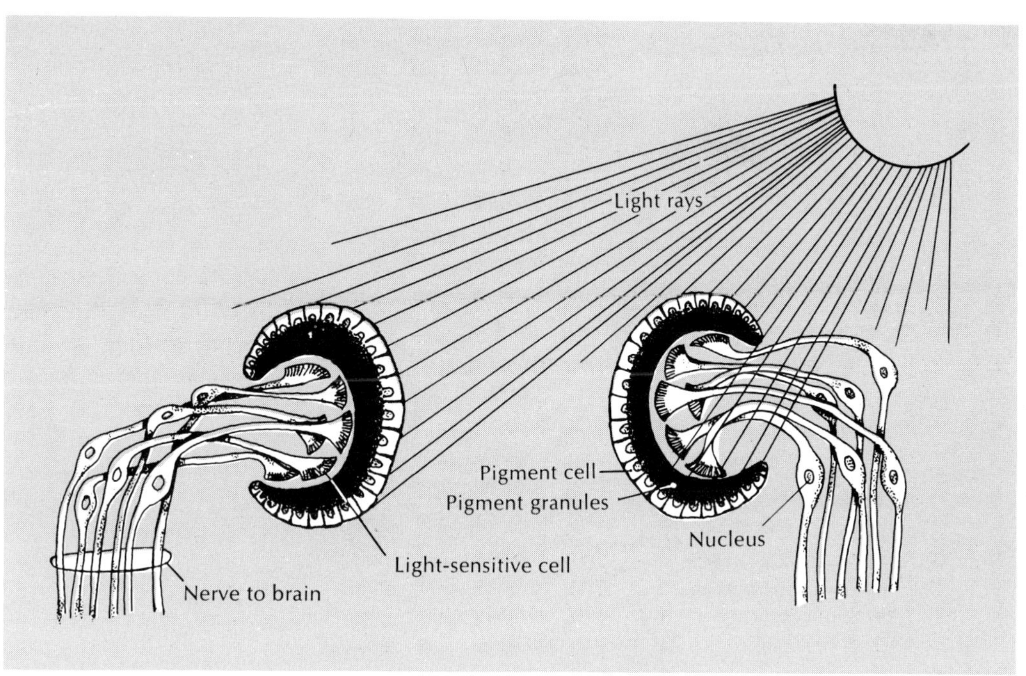

FIG. 13-9

Ocelli, or eyes, of planarian. Pigment cup lets light enter open side, parallel to long axis of retinal (light-sensitive) cells. Planarian determines light direction from stimulation of light-sensitive cells.

where the sperm are stored until discharged through the muscular **penis.** The penis opens into a **genital atrium,** a cavity that terminates in the **genital pore** through which the penis extends during **copulation** (the mating act).

The **female** system contains two ovaries near the anterior end of the body, which discharge eggs into two tubular **oviducts,** one along each side. **Yolk glands** empty into the oviducts, which join to form a median **vagina.** The vagina opens into the genital atrium, which also receives the penis. Connected to the vagina is a rounded **seminal receptacle,** which receives and stores the sperm from the mating partner. Each spermatozoan is long and filamentous and is provided with a flagellum. Planarians have a reproductive system only during the breeding season, from early spring to late summer; at other times the system disappears and the worms reproduce by fission (Fig. 13-10).

Although turbellarians are hermaphroditic, they practice cross-fertilization. Two animals in copulation bring their posterior ventral surfaces together and each inserts

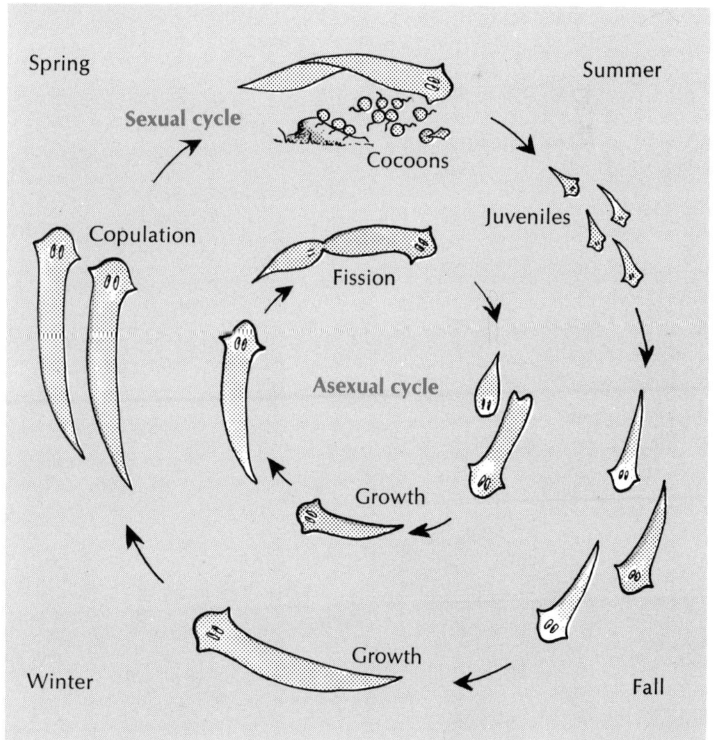

FIG. 13-10

Life cycles of planarian *Dugesia tigrina* showing asexual cycle (inner circle) and sexual cycle (outer circle).

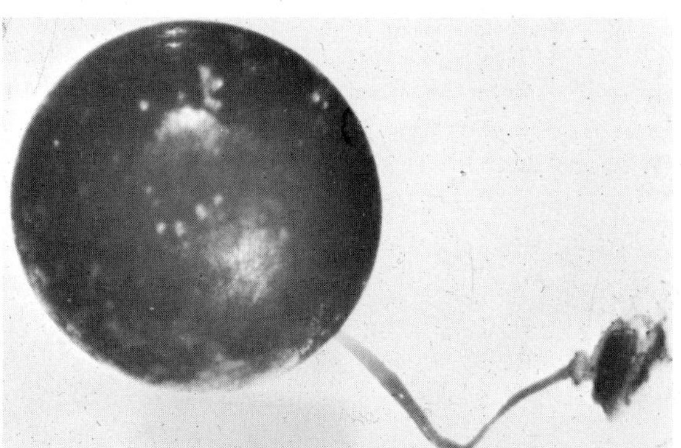

FIG. 13-11

Egg capsule, or cocoon, of planarian with stalk for attachment to rock. Capsule containing many eggs and yolk cells is formed in male atrium. In two or three weeks eggs hatch into small, fully formed worms. (Courtesy Carolina Biological Supply Co., Burlington, N. C.)

FIG. 13-12

Regeneration in planarian. When cut transversely into three separate pieces (left), each piece develops into planarian. If head is split (right), a double-headed animal results.

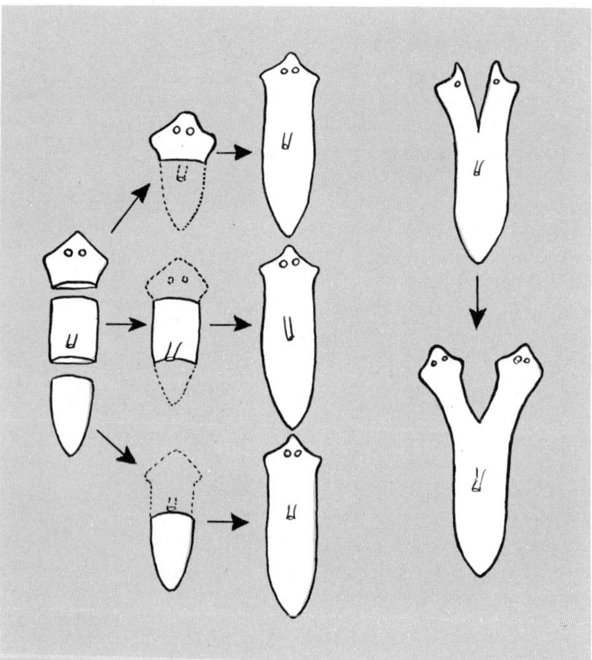

its penis into the genital pore of the other. Sperm from the male seminal vesicle passes through the penis to the female seminal receptacle of the other so that sperm are mutually exchanged between the two partners. Self-fertilization does not occur, probably because the sperm are not activated until they are injected by the penis into another animal or because the dilated penis blocks the oviducts and prevents its own sperm from entering and fertilizing the eggs. After the worms separate, the sperm pass up the oviducts to fertilize the eggs as they are discharged from the ovaries. As the zygotes move down the oviducts, the yolk cells are added from the yolk glands. Several eggs (from two to a dozen), together with their yolk cells, become enclosed in a proteinaceous capsule, or cocoon (Fig. 13-11). After a short development in the atrium the cocoons pass to the outside and in many species become attached by little stalks, usually to the underside of stones. The embryos finally emerge as little planarians (**juveniles**).

Locomotion. Freshwater planarians move in two ways. The usual way is by gliding, head slightly raised, over a slime tract secreted by its marginal adhesive glands. The beating of the epidermal cilia in the slime tract drives the animal along. Rhythmic waves of movement can be seen passing backward from the head as it glides. A less common method is crawling. The worm lengthens, anchors its anterior end with mucus or by its special adhesive organ, and by contracting its longitudinal muscles pulls up the rest of its body. By means of its oblique muscles it can change its direction.

Regeneration.* Planarians have great power to regenerate lost parts (Fig. 13-12). When an individual is cut in two, the anterior end will grow a new tail and the posterior end a new head. Regeneration in these organisms is used as evidence for the **axial gradient theory.** According to this theory there are different metabolic rates in different regions of the body. The rate is greatest at the anterior end of the gradient and decreases gradually to the posterior end. The metabolic activity of any fragment will depend upon its position with respect to this axial gradient. Metabolic activity is measured by the amount of oxygen consumed and the amount of carbon dioxide given off. In any fragment a head will develop where metabolic activity is greatest, whereas a tail will develop from that part in which the rate is lowest.

In addition to regenerating lost parts, planarians

*Refer to Chapter 2, Principle 30.

may be grafted or cut in ways that produce freakish designs such as two heads or two tails.

Recent work on regeneration reveals that, when a planarian is cut across, free cells (**neoblasts**) from the mesenchyme migrate to the cut surface and aggregate there to form a blastema, which develops into the new part. X-radiation of a worm will destroy these neoblasts and no regeneration will occur. It has been suggested that the neoblasts are attracted to the cut region by chemical emanations, which cease when the blastema is formed.

Behavior. Planarians respond to the same kinds of stimuli mentioned in the discussion of other animals. Their ventral surfaces are positively thigmotactic, whereas their dorsal surfaces are negatively thigmotactic. Flowing-water planarians are positively rheotactic; pond-dwelling forms usually do not react to water currents. Weak mechanical or chemical stimuli applied to the head will cause the animal to react positively by turning toward the stimulus. When a strong stimulus is applied to the posterior parts of the body, it moves rapidly forward. Planarians also respond in a positive way to the juices of foods, especially those of meat or liver. They avoid strong light and will seek out dark or dimly lighted regions. With their eyespots they can detect light and the direction it comes from. They are more active at night than during the day. The auricular lobes appear to be sensitive to both water currents and chemical stimuli. In general their reactions to water currents depends upon their normal habitats. Those from flowing water are usually positively rheotactic; those from still water will not react or else are positively rheotactic to weak currents only.

The behavior patterns of flatworms have been the subject of numerous investigations all over the world,

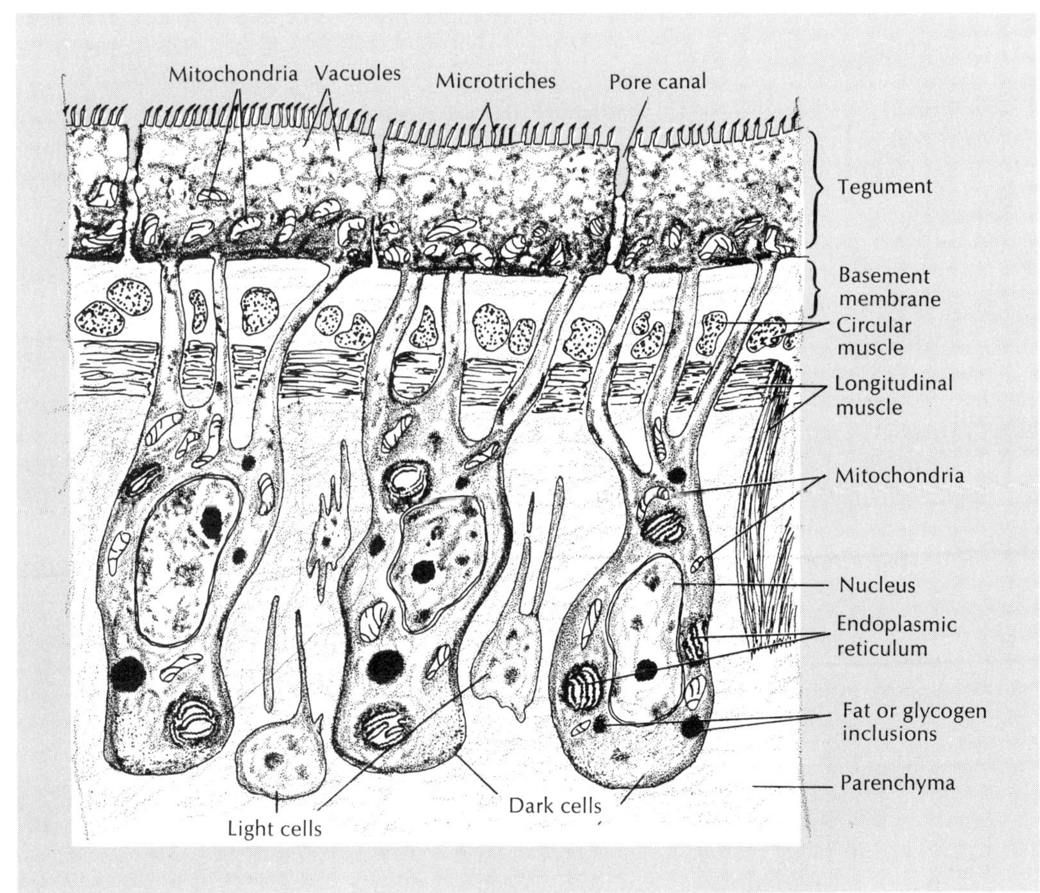

FIG. 13-13

Section through tegument of cestode, as revealed by electron microscope, showing so-called "cuticle" composed of syncytial, living protoplasm rather than lifeless secretion, as formerly believed. Trematode tegument shows similar structure. (From Hickman: Biology of the invertebrates, The C. V. Mosby Co.)

for animal behaviorists have considered them to be the lowest group that show any capacity for learning in response to simple conditioned changes. In the evolution of nervous systems those in higher forms may be mostly a variation on the planarian theme of nervous integration.

CLASS TREMATODA

The flukes or trematodes are all parasitic (usually in vertebrates), are chiefly leaflike in form, and do not have cilia in the adult condition. Although parasitic, they are not, as a rule, much different structurally from the nonparasitic turbellarians. Some of their parasitic adaptations are the lack of an epidermis, the presence of a cuticle resting directly on mesenchyme, and the development of special adhesive organs for clinging to their host, such as glandular or muscular disks, hooks, and true suckers. In the Trematoda (and also Cestoda) the electron microscope shows that the cuticle, or tegument, consists of a syncytial, living protoplasm that represents extensions of deeper-lying nucleated cells (Fig. 13-13). The outer surface of the tegument has many small extensions (microtriches) and pore canals. They retain also some of the turbellarian characteristics, such as a well-developed alimentary canal (but with the mouth at the anterior, or cephalic, end) and similar reproductive, excretory, and nervous systems, as well as a musculature and mesenchyme that are only slightly modified from those of the Turbellaria. Sense organs are poorly developed in flukes and occur only in larval stages and in a few adults (eyespots in order Monogenea). Just as in Turbellaria, the body shows many variations among the different groups. Although basically they all have the flattened form of flatworms, some are round, some are elongated and oval, and others are slender.

According to their parasitic habits, class Trematoda is divided into two main orders or subclasses—the Monogenea and the Digenea. The monogenetic flukes require only one host for their life history, whereas the digenetic ones require two to four hosts.

The members of the order Monogenea are mostly ectoparasites. They live on the gills or skin or in cavities that open to the exterior (nose, mouth, urinary bladder) of vertebrates, such as fish, amphibians, reptiles, and rarely mammals. Some are found on invertebrates, such as crustaceans and cephalopods. Only one or two species are endoparasites. All of them develop directly on one host. Adhesive structures are found at both ends of the worm, but the posterior adhesive organ is usually a complex of hooks and suckers. Unlike the order Digenea, the mouth is rarely encircled by a sucker. Their reproductive system is similar to the turbellarians, especially that of rhabdocoeles. Their eggs are few in number and frequently only one egg is present in the uterus. The egg hatches a ciliated larva that attaches itself to the host to develop, or the larva may in some cases swim around in the water before its attachment. The best-known monogenetic genera are *Polystoma,* which is found in the urinary bladder of frogs, and *Gyrodactylus,* which lives on the skin and gills of freshwater fish. Monogenetic flukes damage fish by feeding on epithelial cells and blood, often producing fatal injury to the gills. They move by leechlike or measuring-worm methods, alternately attaching their anterior and posterior adhesive organs.

The order Digenea is almost exclusively endoparasitic, having two or more hosts in the life cycle. They rarely have more than two suckers and are without hooks. The anterior, or oral, sucker surrounds the mouth; the ventroposterior sucker is commonly called the **acetabulum.** The latter is quite large in some flukes and may be important in taxonomic determinations. Internal structures are similar to those of the turbellarians, with certain modifications. The pharynx is anterior, with two long branches of the intestine that end blindly. Digenetic trematode development involves a succession of forms that live in certain organs of different hosts. These different hosts have probably been added to their life cycle as new groups of animals have emerged in evolution. When vertebrates arose and became definitive hosts, the trematodes still retained their early invertebrate hosts for the larval stages. Their life cycle may be described as the alternation of a bisexual generation (chiefly in vertebrates), with parthenogenetic generations (in invertebrates). The adults are found mainly in terrestrial, freshwater, and marine vertebrates. Various species are found only in certain organs, such as the intestine, lungs, bile passages, kidneys, urinary bladder, coelom, and head cavities. It is an extensive group, and new species are described frequently. They have the most complicated life histories in the animal kingdom. They usually have four larval stages (Fig. 13-14): miracidium, sporocyst, redia, and cercaria. Another stage, the metacercaria (or adolescaria), is considered a juvenile fluke with the general

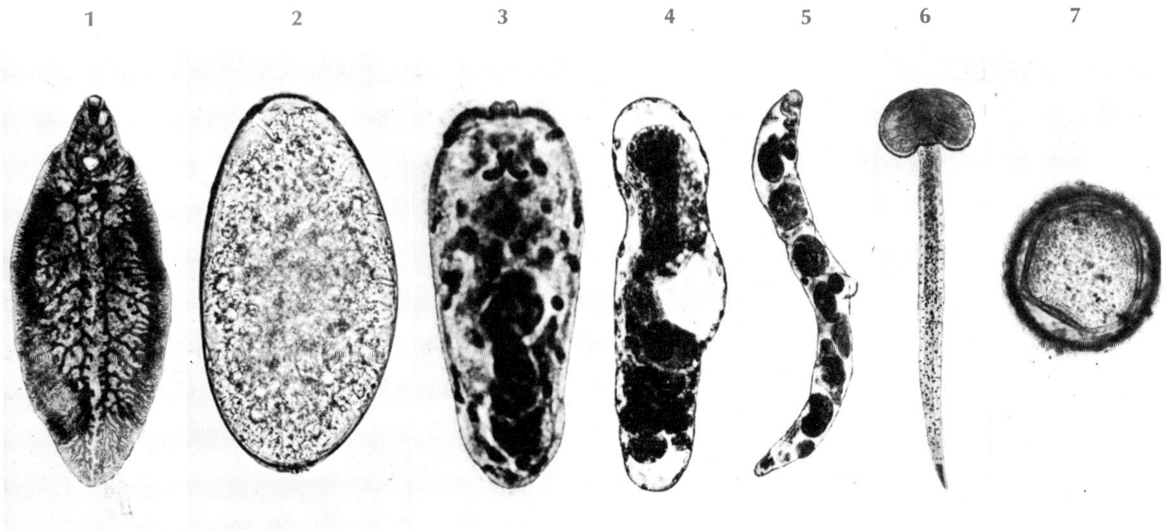

FIG. 13-14

Stages in life cycle of sheep liver fluke *Fasciola hepatica* (class Trematoda, order Digenea). **1,** Adult; **2,** egg; **3,** miracidium; **4,** sporocyst; **5,** redia; **6,** cercaria; **7,** metacercaria. (Not shown according to relative size.) (Courtesy Carolina Biological Supply Co., Burlington, N. C.)

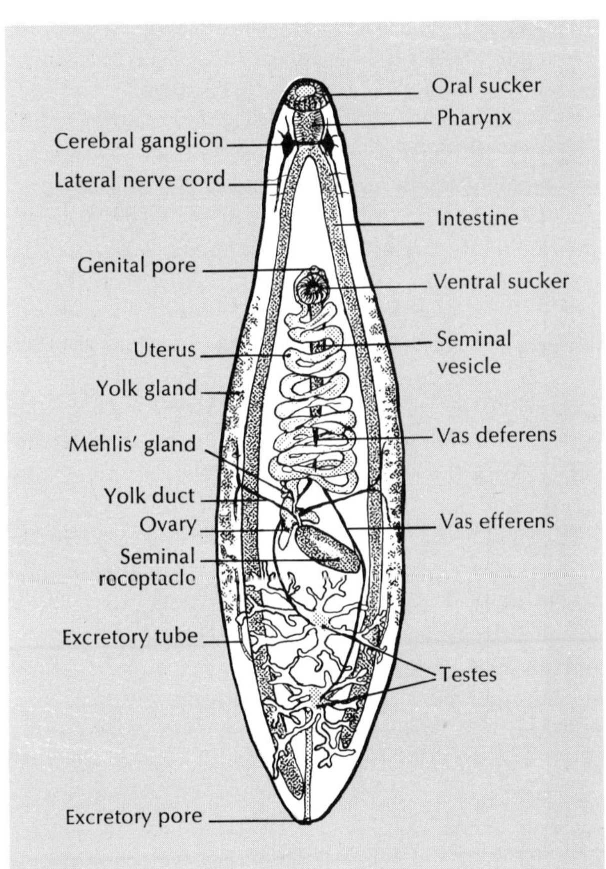

FIG. 13-15

Human liver fluke *Opisthorchis (Clonorchis) sinensis.* General structure of adult (dorsal view).

structural features of the adult. Of the larval stages, the miracidium nearly always enters a mollusk (bivalve or snail) as the first intermediate host. However, in 1944 the American investigator Martin found the rare exception—the sporocysts and cercaria of a certain fluke developed in a polychaete annelid (*Eupomatus*) instead of a mollusk. The larval stages may also be abbreviated, as when cercariae arise directly from sporocysts without the intervention of the redia stage.

Examples of Digenea are often studied because of their complicated life histories and their economic importance. Some of our most serious parasites belong to this group. One of the first digenetic forms to be worked out was the sheep liver fluke *Fasciola hepatica,* which is often used as a type for study. However, other flukes that attack man are of more practical importance and are more easily studied than the sheep liver fluke.

Opisthorchis (Fig. 13-15) is the most important liver fluke of man and is very common in many regions of the Orient, especially in China, southern Asia, and Japan. In addition to man, cats, dogs, and pigs are often infected. This fluke has two intermediate hosts for the larval stages and a final host for the adult.

Opisthorchis (Clonorchis) sinensis—liver fluke of man

Structure. The worms vary from 10 to 20 mm. in length and from 2 to 4 mm. in width (Fig. 13-15). They have two small suckers, an anterior **oral sucker** and a ventral **acetabulum** about one third of the distance from the anterior end. They are covered externally by a rough cuticle (cuticula). The **digestive system** consists of a globular pharynx and a muscular esophagus, followed by two long, unbranched intestinal ceca that extend almost to the posterior end of the body. The **excretory system** consists of two protonephridial tubules, with branches provided with flame cells or bulbs. The two tubules unite to form a single median tubule that opens to the outside. The **nervous system,** like that of turbellarians, is made up of two cerebral ganglia connected to longitudinal cords that have transverse connectives. The **muscular system** also is like that of the planarian type—an outer circular, a middle longitudinal, and an inner diagonal layer. The **reproductive system** is hermaphroditic and complicated. The **male system** is made up of two much-branched testes, from each of which runs a vas efferens. The two vasa efferentia unite to form a single vas deferens, which widens into a seminal vesicle. To the seminal vesicle a protrusible penis or a cirrus sac is attached within the genital opening. The **female system** contains a branched ovary with a short oviduct, which is joined by ducts from the seminal receptacle and from yolk glands that supply yolk and shell material. The bulblike enlargement (ootype) of the oviduct is surrounded by Mehlis' gland of unknown function. From Mehlis' gland the much-convoluted uterus runs to the genital pore. Cross-fertilization is the usual method of fertilizing the eggs. Two flukes in copulation bring their genital pores in opposition and fertilize each other's ova. After the ova have received yolk and a shell, they pass through the genital pore.

Life cycle. The normal habitat of the adults is in the bile passageways of man (Fig. 13-16). The eggs, each containing a complete **miracidium,** are shed into the water with the feces but do not hatch until they are ingested by the snail *Bythinia* or related genera. The eggs, however, may live for some weeks in water. In the snail the miracidium enters the tissues and is transformed into the **sporocyst** (a baglike structure with embryonic germ cells), which produces one generation of **rediae.** The redia is elongated, with an alimentary canal, a nervous system, an excretory system, and many germ cells in the process of development. The rediae pass into the liver of the snail where, by a process of internal budding, they give rise to the tadpolelike **cercariae.** The cercariae escape into the water, swim about until they meet with fish of the family Cyprinidae, and then bore into the muscles or under the scales. Here the cercariae lose their tails and encyst as **metacercariae.** If man eats raw infected fish, the metacercarial cyst dissolves partially in the stomach and completely in the intestine, and the metacercariae are free to migrate up the bile duct, where they become adults. Here the flukes may live for 15 to 30 years. The effect of the flukes on man depends mainly upon the extent of the infection. A heavy infection may cause a marked cirrhosis of the liver and result in death. Cases are diagnosed through fecal examinations. One interesting diagnostic aspect is the high eosinophil (white corpuscle of the blood) count in those infected. To avoid infection, all fish used as food should be thoroughly cooked. Destruction of the snails that carry larval stages would be a method of control.

Schistosoma—blood flukes

Three important species of blood flukes belong to genus *Schistosoma.* Infection by these flukes is called **schistosomiasis,** a disorder very common in Africa, China, southern Asia, and parts of South America. The old generic name was *Bilharzia,* and the infection was called **bilharziasis.** The blood flukes differ from most other flukes in being dioecious and having the two branches of the digestive tube united into a single tube in the posterior part of the body. The male is usually broader and encloses the very slender female (Fig. 13-17) in his gynecophoric canal, a ventral fold on the body.

The plan of the life history of blood flukes is similar in all species (Fig. 13-18). Eggs are discharged in human feces or urine; if they get into water, they hatch out as ciliated **miracidia** which must contact a certain kind of snail within 24 hours to survive. When they find the right snail, they burrow into the soft flesh and transform into **sporocysts,** which develop **cercariae** directly, without the formation of rediae. These cercariae have two suckers, a forked enteron, an excretory system with flame cells, and a forked tail. They escape from the snail and swim about in the water until they come in contact with the bare skin of a human being bathing or wading. They penetrate through the skin into a blood vessel, which they follow to the blood

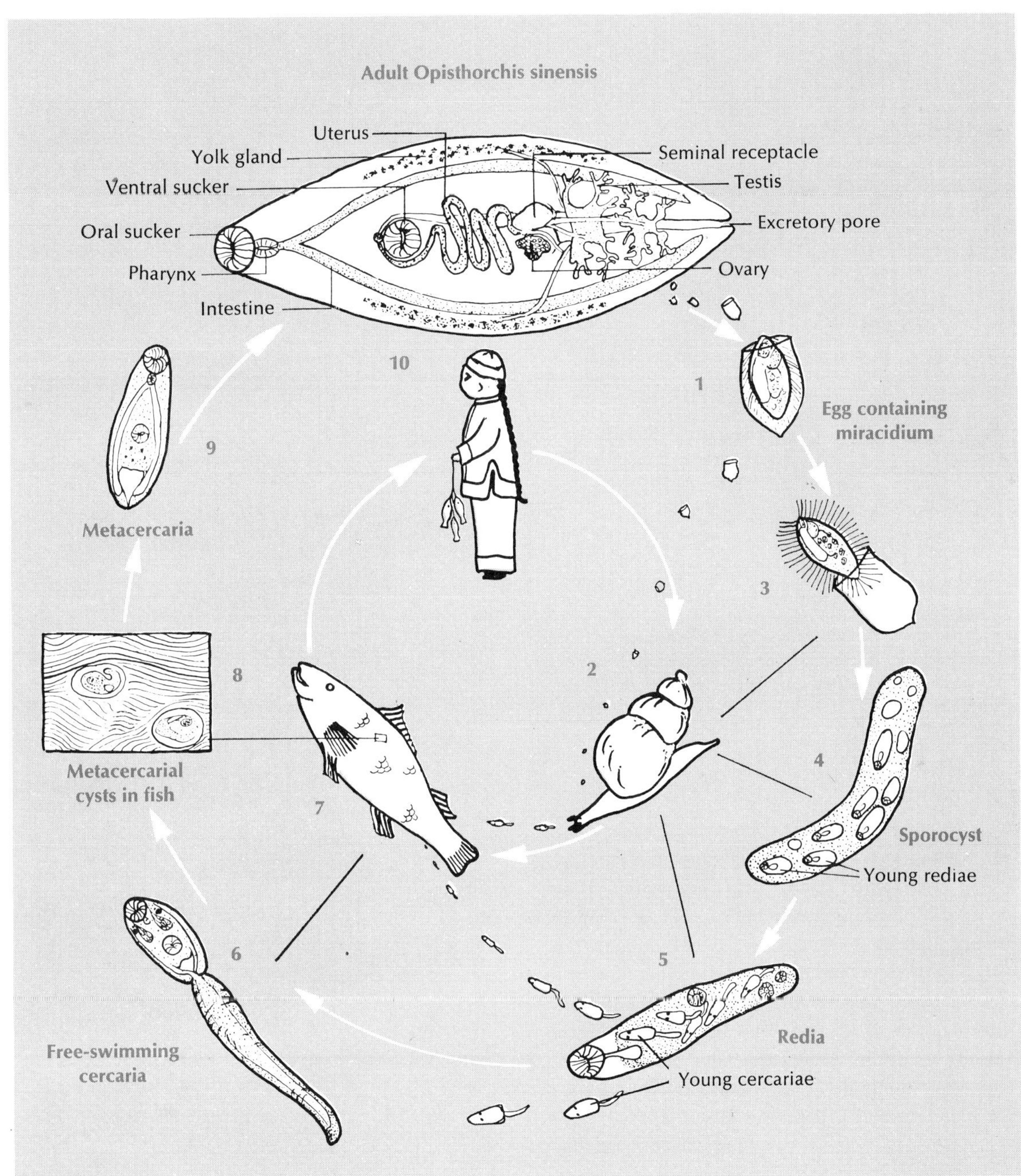

FIG. 13-16

Life cycle of human liver fluke *Opisthorchis sinensis*. Egg, **1,** shed from adult trematode, **10,** in bile ducts of man, is carried out of body in feces and is ingested by snail (*Bythinia*), **2,** in which miracidium, **3,** hatches and becomes mother sporocyst. **4,** Young rediae are produced in sporocyst, grow, **5,** and in turn produce young cercariae. Cercariae now leave snail, **6,** find a fish host, **7,** and burrow under scales to encyst in muscle. **8,** When raw or improperly cooked fish containing cysts is eaten by man, metacercaria is released, **9,** and enters bile duct, where it matures, **10,** to shed eggs into feces, **1,** thus starting another cycle.

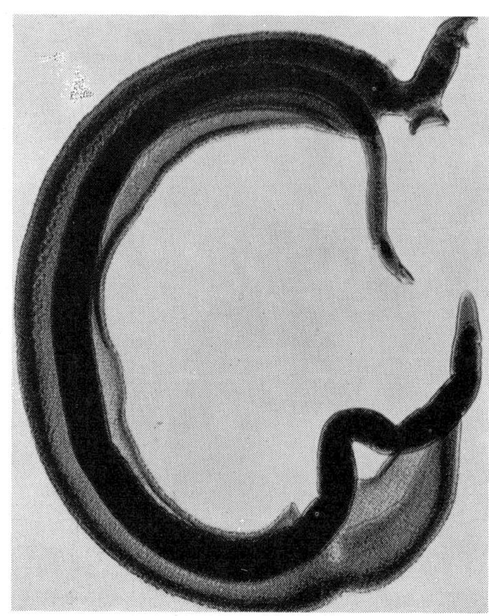

FIG. 13-17

Adult male and female *Schistosoma mansoni* in copulation. Male has long sex canal that holds female (the darkly stained individual) during insemination and oviposition. Man is usually host of adult parasites, found mainly in Africa but also in South America and elsewhere. Man becomes infected by wading or bathing in cercaria-infested waters. (AFIP No. 56-3334.)

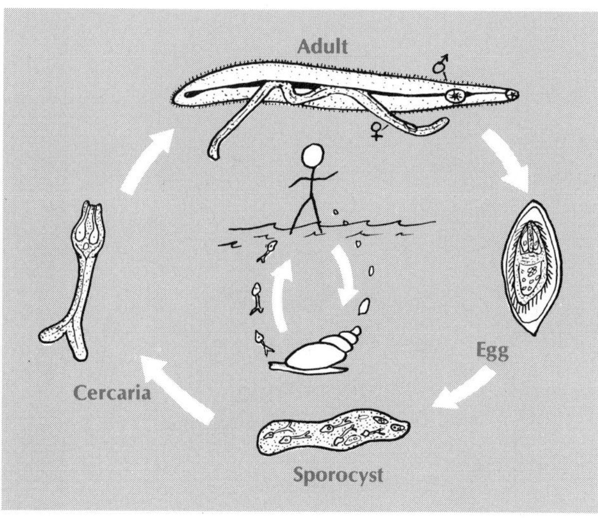

FIG. 13-18

Life history of blood fluke. An egg discharged in human feces passes into water and hatches into miracidium (shown enclosed in egg), which enters a snail and transforms into a sporocyst. Cercariae escape from snail and penetrate exposed skin of man to enter bloodstream.

FIG. 13-19

Egg of *Schistosoma mansoni*. (Courtesy Ward's Natural Science Establishment, Inc., Rochester, N. Y.)

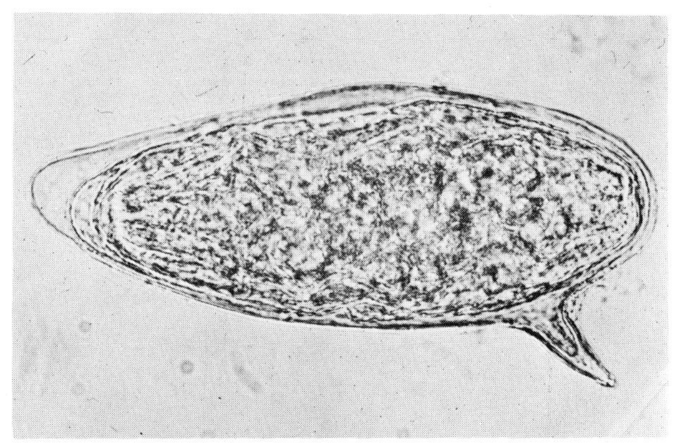

vessels of certain regions, depending upon the kind of fluke. When they enter with drinking water, they may bore through the mucous membrane of the mouth or throat, but they do not survive in the stomach.

No encysted metacercarial stage is found, for the cercariae lose their tails as they enter the host, and by the time they settle down, they have transformed into the adult condition. When the eggs are fertilized, the female leaves the male gynecophoric canal and goes into small blood vessels where she lays the eggs. The ova may be provided with spines (Fig. 13-19) that facilitate their penetration into the intestine or urinary bladder. By the time these ova reach the exterior, they have within them fully formed miracidia.

Following is a comparison of the three species—*S. haematobium, S. mansoni,* and *S. japonicum.*

Schistosoma haematobium. This species is found chiefly in Africa and is one of the most dangerous of the blood flukes. The adults (the male being about 10 to 15 mm. long) live in the blood vessels of the bladder and urinary tract. The eggs have sharp spines that enable them to pass through the walls of the blood vessels into the urine. Lacerations of the mucous membrane of the bladder are caused by the passage of these eggs, and bloody urine results. Inflammation of the bladder also frequently occurs, and the ova may also serve as nuclei for kidney stones. The eggs escape in

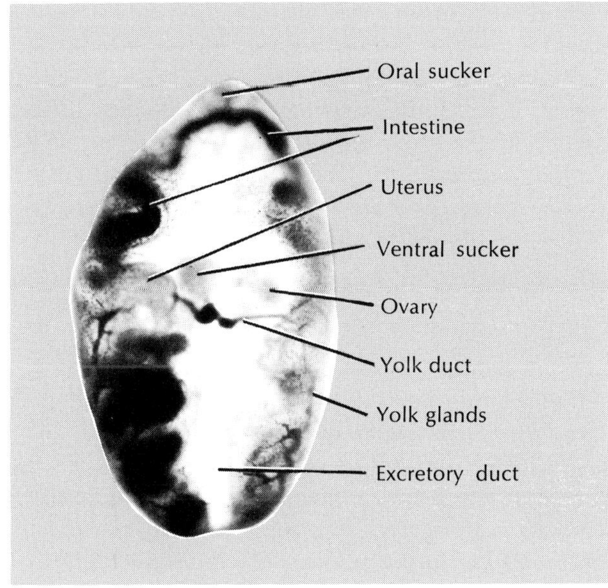

FIG. 13-20

Pulmonary fluke *Paragonimus westermani* infects human lung, producing paragonimiasis. Adults are up to ½ inch long. Eggs discharged in sputum or feces hatch into free-swimming miracidia that enter snails. Cercariae from snail enter freshwater crabs and encyst in soft tissues. Man is infected by eating poorly cooked crabs or by drinking water containing larvae freed from dead crabs. (AFIP No. 52-1862.)

the urine, and if snails of genus *Bulinus* are available, the miracidia will enter them and start the life cycle. Infections with these flukes are very common, for in the regions where they are found, the poor hygienic conditions of the people promote the spread of *Schistosoma.*

Schistosoma mansoni. This species is common in the West Indies, parts of South America, and Africa. The adults live chiefly in branches of the portal and mesenteric veins. The ova have sharp lateral spines and escape into the intestine, from which they are discharged with the feces. A number of different kinds of snails, including the common genus *Planorbis,* seem to be the intermediate host. Symptoms of this form of **schistosomiasis** are severe dysentery and anemia.

Schistosoma japonicum. These flukes often cause a lot of trouble in Japan, China, and the Philippines. The life history is similar to that of the other blood flukes. The adults live in the small veins of the superior and inferior mesenteric vessels. Infection causes liver enlargement, formation of ulcers, and disturbances in the spleen. The chief intermediate host is the snail *Oncomelania.*

Schistosoma dermatitis (swimmer's itch). Bathers in northern lakes, such as those of Michigan, Wisconsin, and Canada, often suffer from a skin irritation that is now known to be caused by cercariae of *Schistosoma.* It is detected soon after the bather leaves the water and is felt as a prickling sensation. After an hour or so the irritation subsides, to return as severe itching with edema and pustules. The reaction reaches its climax by the second or third day, but the infection may last longer. Infection is most common in July and August. Summer resorts in some regions have had to close because of these infections.

Several species of cercariae are known to cause these infections. Infections of man are purely accidental attempts of the flukes to penetrate man's skin and use him as a host, but it is a "dead end" for the cercariae, for none are known to survive. Many species of snails serve as intermediate hosts and aquatic birds are the final hosts. Destroying the snails near beaches by copper sulfate helps control infections. Soothing applications are helpful in treating this type of dermatitis. Wiping the body thoroughly and quickly after leaving the water has been recommended, for some authorities think the cercariae enter the skin as the water evaporates, but the efficacy of this preventive treatment has been disputed by some parasitologists.

Paragonimus westermani—lung flukes

Lung flukes are found in many parts of the Orient and to some extent in America. One of the most common is *Paragonimus westermani* (Fig. 13-20), which uses the carnivorous mammals, such as mink, cats, and dogs, as the definitive host. It is also the only species of lung fluke known to infect man. In China, Korea, and Japan human infection may reach 40% to 50% in some regions. In the United States it appears to be most common in the Great Lakes area. The life history involves snails, freshwater crabs, and crayfish as intermediate hosts and man and mammals as the final hosts. Ova are coughed up in the sputum, and under moist conditions the miracidia develop in three weeks. After entering certain species of snails they develop a sporocyst and two generations of rediae. The cercariae, after leaving the snail, crawl about and encyst in freshwater crabs and crayfish. Whenever man eats poorly cooked crustaceans, the ingested flukes pass through the intestinal walls into the abdominal cavity, then through the diaphragm into the lungs. Here they exist as adults, which may be about 20 mm. long.

Other trematodes

Fasciola hepatica (liver fluke of sheep). This fluke (Fig. 13-14) is responsible for "liver rot" in sheep and other ruminants. It lives in the liver and bile passageways and may attain a length of 30 mm. Although often used as a type for studying the Digenea, it must be considered somewhat atypical because of the much-branched intestine and other structural differences. The undeveloped eggs are shed in the feces in damp surroundings and in the course of some weeks develop into ciliated miracidia. If the miracidia find a certain snail (*Lymnaea*) within 8 hours, they penetrate into the soft tissues. The miracidium is transformed into a sporocyst that produces two generations of rediae. The rediae give rise to cercariae, which burrow out of the snail and swim in the water. In a short time the cercariae encyst on aquatic vegetation as metacercariae. When the infested vegetation is eaten by the definitive host (sheep or other ruminant), the cysts hatch into young flukes, which burrow through the intestinal wall and body cavity to the liver. There have been some cases of human infection.

Fasciolopsis buski (intestinal fluke of man). This fluke is a common parasite of man and pigs in India and China. The leaflike adult may be 70 mm. long. Larval stages occur in snails of the genera *Planorbis* and *Segmentina*. The cercariae encyst on certain nutlike fruits of aquatic vegetation (water chestnut) that are eaten raw by man.

The genus Leucochloridium is noted for its remarkable sporocysts, as shown in Fig. 13-21.

FIG. 13-21

Leucochloridium, trematode found in birds and snails. Snails, *Succinea,* eat vegetation infected with capsules from bird droppings. Capsules hatch into miracidia, followed by generations of sporocysts. Sporocysts branch and enter snail's head and tentacles, where they enlarge, become brightly colored with orange and green bands, and pulsate at frequent intervals. This attracts attention of birds, which eat them. Thus color and movement combine to ensure complete life history.

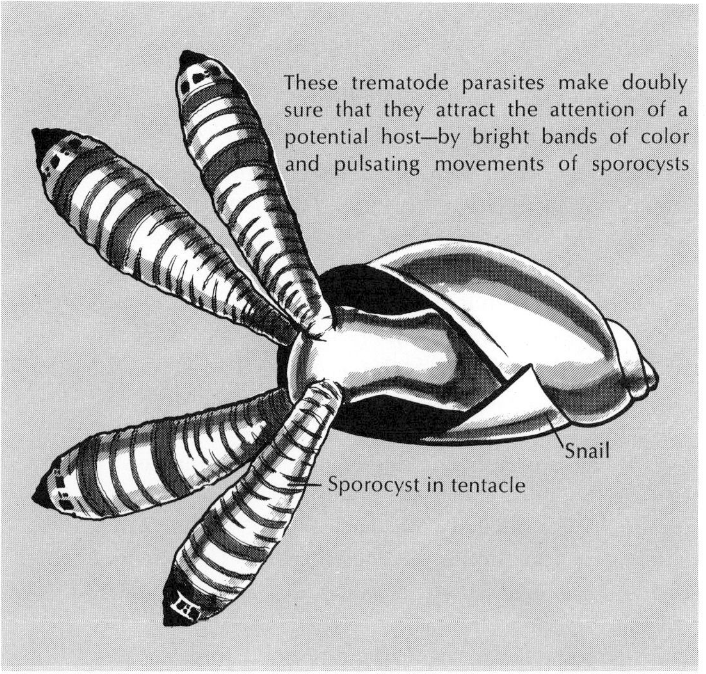

CLASS CESTODA

The third class of Platyhelminthes is Cestoda, the tapeworms. The members of this class differ in many respects from those of the preceding classes: their long flat bodies are usually made up of many sections, or **proglottids,** and there is a complete lack of a digestive system. They have no cilia, are covered with a modified epidermis, or tegument, and possess well-developed muscles. They have an excretory system and a nervous system somewhat similar to those of other flatworms. They are all monoecious, with the exception of four or five genera. They have no special sense organs but do have free sensory nerve endings. One of their most specialized structures is the **scolex,** or holdfast, which is the organ of attachment. It is provided with a varying number of suckers and, in some cases, also with hooks.

All members of this class are endoparasites, and all, with a few exceptions, involve at least two hosts of different species. The adults are always found in vertebrates; other stages may be found in either vertebrates or invertebrates.

Class Cestoda is divided into two subclasses: Cestodaria and Eucestoda.

Subclass Cestodaria is made up of forms that have undivided bodies and no scolices but are provided with some organ of attachment such as a rosette or proboscis. They have only one set of reproductive organs and give

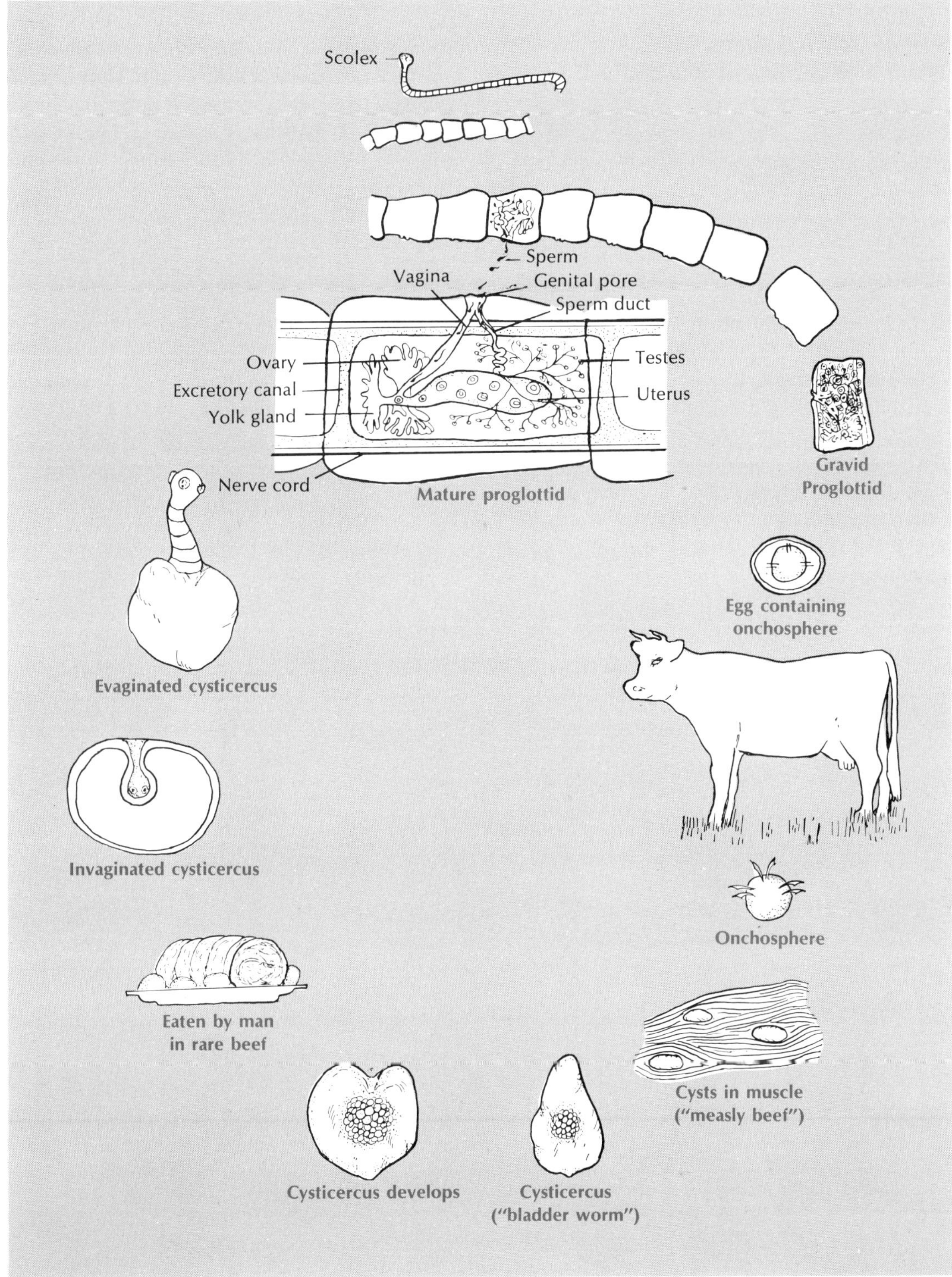

FIG. 13-22

Life cycle of beef tapeworm *Taenia saginata*. Ripe proglottids break off in man's intestine, pass out in feces, and are ingested by cows. Eggs hatch in cow's intestine, freeing onchospheres which penetrate into muscles and encyst, developing into "bladder worms." Man eats infected rare beef and cysticercus is freed in intestine where it develops, forms a scolex, attaches to intestine wall, and matures.

rise to ten-hooked larvae. Most of them are found as parasites in lower fish. *Amphilina foliacea* is a common type.

Subclass Eucestoda is composed of members that have the body divided (rarely undivided) into proglottids and are provided with a scolex. Their larval forms have only six hooks. This subclass contains the typical tapeworms, of which the beef tapeworm (*Taenia saginata*) is an example (Fig. 13-22).

Is the tapeworm a single animal with subdivided parts (proglottids), or it is a series of separate individuals loosely held together like a colony? Is it a true segmented animal like the annelids or arthropods? Zoologists differ in their interpretation of these points. Although the tapeworm forms its segments from the proliferation of the scolex and the true segmented animals from the proliferation of the region just in front of the anal segment, this difference is considered unimportant by some zoologists. From this viewpoint, cestodes would be considered segmented rather than colonial.

The scolex may be regarded as the ancestral individual that gives rise by strobilation to daughter individuals—the proglottids. The scolex, or holdfast organ, is not a head specialized for perceiving or food handling, and some zoologists think it is really the original posterior end that has been modified for attachment, but embryology does not support this view. As long as the scolex is present, it is impossible to get rid of a tapeworm, for new proglottids will be formed as the old ones are shed. A proglottid is a sexually complete unit, for it is hermaphroditic. Its chief function is the production of ova, and its structure is specialized toward this end.

Taenia saginata—beef tapeworm

Structure. The beef tapeworm lives as an adult in the alimentary canal of man, whereas the larval form

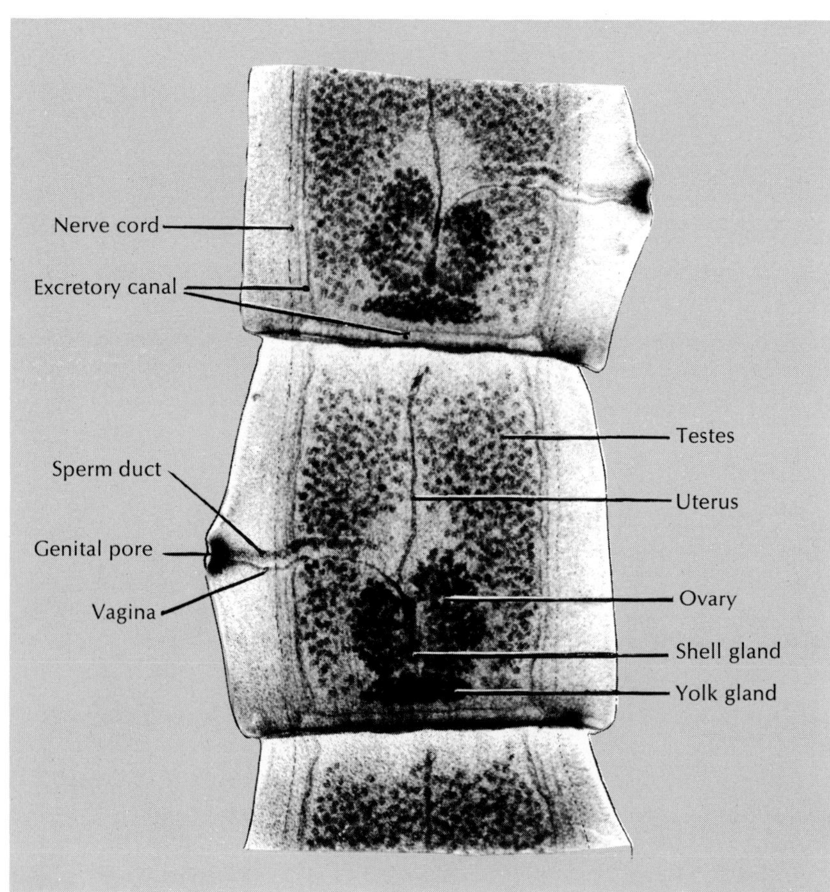

FIG. 13-23

Photomicrograph of mature proglottid of *Taenia pisiformis*, dog tapeworm. Portions of two other proglottids also shown. (Courtesy General Biological Supply House, Inc., Chicago.)

is found primarily in the intermuscular tissue of cattle. The mature adult may reach a length of 30 feet or more. Its **scolex** has four **suckers** but no hooks. Back of the suckers is a short neck, which connects the scolex to the body, or **strobila**, which may be made up of as many as 2,000 **proglottids.** The scolex is the attachment organ and by means of the suckers is firmly fastened to the intestinal wall. New proglottids are formed by **transverse budding** of the neck region. As they move backward, the proglottids increase in size, so that the proglottids are narrow near the scolex and broader and larger toward the posterior end, where they are finally detached and shed in the feces. The youngest and smallest proglottid is therefore nearest the scolex and the oldest one is at the posterior end.

The tapeworm shows some unity in its organization (Fig. 13-23), for **excretory canals** in the scolex are also connected to the canals, two on each side, in the proglottids, and two **longitudinal nerve cords** from a **nerve ring** in the scolex run back into the proglottids also. Attached to the excretory ducts are the **flame cells.** Each proglottid also contains **muscles** and **parenchyma** as well as a complete set of **male and female organs** similar to those of a trematode. Ova may be fertilized by the sperm of the same proglottid, from other proglottids of the same individual, or from other tapeworms if more than one should be present. When the terminal **gravid proglottids** with their eggs break off and pass out with the feces, the proglottids disintegrate, and the eggs with the embryos may be scattered on the soil, grass, dust, etc., where they may be picked up by grazing cattle.

Life cycle. When cattle swallow the eggs or proglottids, the eggshells are dissolved off in the intestine, and the six-hooked larvae (**oncospheres**) burrow through the intestinal wall into the blood or lymph vessels and finally reach voluntary muscle, where they encyst to become **bladder worms** (**cysticerci**). Here in a period of ten to twenty weeks the larvae develop an invaginated scolex with suckers and remain quiescent until the uncooked muscle is eaten by man or another suitable host. Such infected meat is known as "measly" meat (Fig. 13-24). When the cyst wall is dissolved off by the digestive juices of the host, the bladder disappears, the scolex evaginates and becomes attached to the intestinal mucosa, and new proglottids begin to develop. It takes two or three weeks for a mature worm to form. When man is infected with one of these tapeworms, many single proglottids are expelled daily from his intestine. Usually only one tapeworm infects a host; an immunity against others is apparently established. Man usually becomes infected by eating rare steaks and hamburgers. In the southwest (Arizona and New Mexico), where barbecued meat is popular, a considerable percentage of the people may be infected. About 1% of American cattle are infected, and since a great deal of meat is consumed without government in-

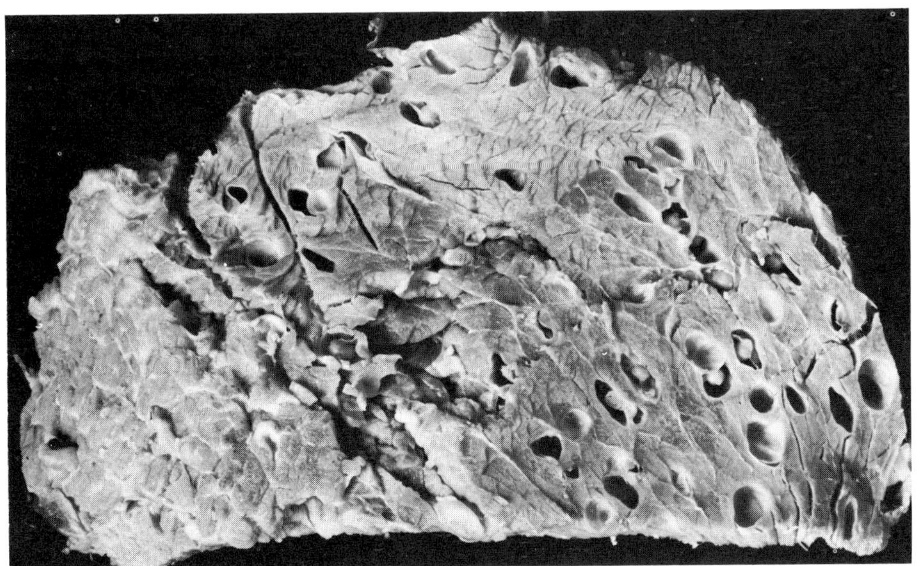

FIG. 13-24

"Measly" pork showing cysts of bladder worms, *Taenia solium.* Beef infected with beef tapeworm has similar appearance.

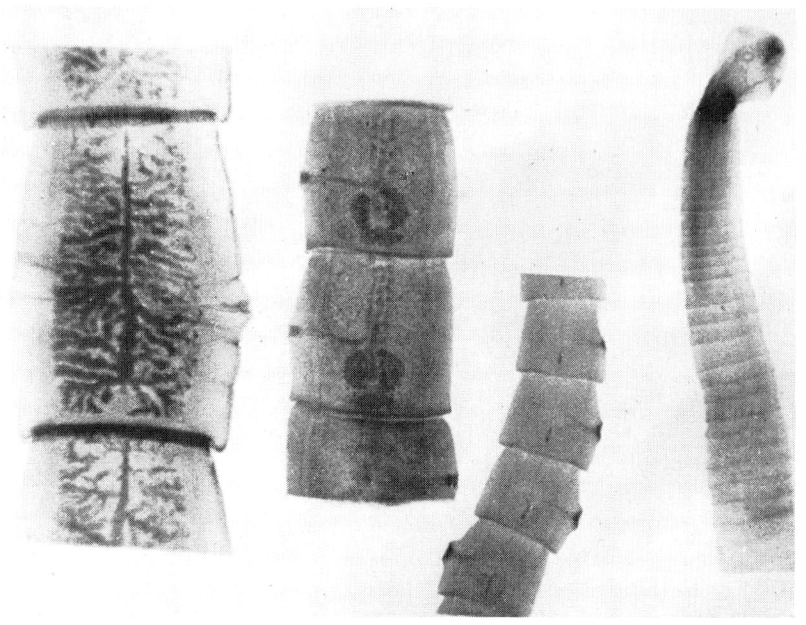

FIG. 13-25

Pork tapeworm, *Taenia solium.* Left to right: gravid (terminal) proglottids with uterus distended with eggs; mature proglottids with male and female reproductive organs; immature proglottids found just back of neck region; and at right, scolex, neck, and very young proglottids. (Photograph of stained preparation.)

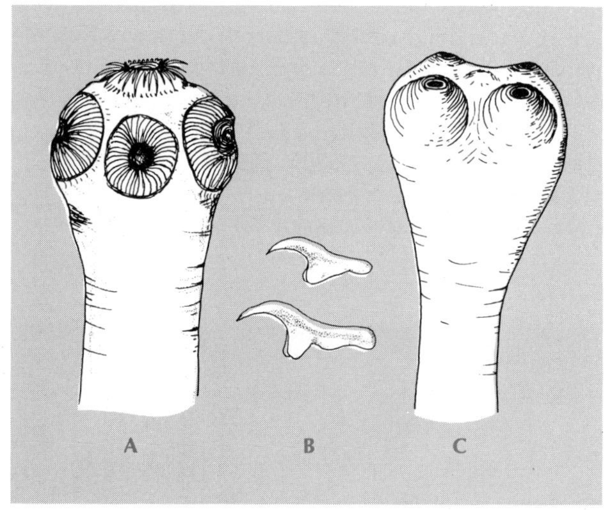

FIG. 13-26

Comparison of scolex (holdfast) of pork, **A,** and beef, **C,** tapeworms. **A,** Scolex of *Taenia solium* with apical hooks and suckers. **B,** Hooks of *T. solium.* **C,** Scolex of *T. saginata,* with suckers only. (From Hickman: Biology of the invertebrates, The C. V. Mosby Co.)

spection, a certain amount of tapeworm infection must be expected.

Other tapeworms

More than 1,000 species of tapeworms are known to parasitologists. Almost all vertebrates are infected. Nearly all tapeworms have an intermediate host and a final host that is infected by preying upon the former. Some of these tapeworms do considerable harm to the host by absorbing nourishment and by secreting toxic substances, but unless present in large numbers, they are rarely fatal.

Some of the more common ones are *T. solium, Diphyllobothrium latum, Dipylidium caninum, Hymenolepis nana, Echinococcus granulosus, Moniezia expansa,* and *T. pisiformis.*

Taenia solium (pork tapeworm). The adult lives in the small intestine of man, whereas the larvae live in the muscles of the pig. Adults may be 20 feet or longer. The scolex (Fig. 13-25) of *T. solium* differs from that of *T. saginata* in having both suckers and hooks arranged on its tip (Fig. 13-26), the **rostellum.** More than 1,000 proglottids may be in a single tapeworm. The life history of this tapeworm is similar to that of the beef tapeworm. Man becomes infected by eating improperly cooked pork. The incidence of infection is much lower than that of the beef tapeworm.

It is also possible for the larvae or bladder worms to develop in man, although this is not the normal procedure. If eggs or proglottids are ingested by man or broken-up proglottids from an adult tapeworm are carried back by reverse peristalsis to the stomach, the liberated embryos may migrate into any of several organs, including the brain. Disorders from these causes are called **cysticercosis.** One form of this may cause epilepsy.

Diphyllobothrium latum (fish tapeworm). The adult tapeworm is found in the intestine of man, dog, and cat; the immature stages are in crustaceans such as *Cyclops* and in fish. This tapeworm, often called the broad tapeworm of man, is the largest and most destructive of the cestodes that infect man. It sometimes reaches a length of 60 feet and may have more than 3,000 proglottids. After the eggs are discharged in water by the human host, they hatch into a ciliated **coracidium** that is swallowed by the first intermediate host, a crustacean (*Cyclops*). The coracidium loses its cilia in this host and undergoes other changes. When the crustacean is eaten by the second intermediate host, a fish, the larva penetrates the stomach walls and migrates to the muscles, where it develops into a **plerocercoid** larva about 1 inch long. Usually the larva encysts in the muscle. When raw or poorly cooked fish is eaten by man or another suitable host, the larva is liberated and grows into adult form. It has been known to live in man for many years. Broad tapeworm infections are found all over the world; in the United States infections are most common in the Great Lakes region.

Dipylidium caninum (dog tapeworm). This tapeworm is very common in pet dogs and cats and sometimes in children. It may be 1 foot or more in length and has about 200 proglottids. The larval form is found in the louse and flea of dogs. The dog or cat becomes infected by licking or biting these ectoparasites. It takes about two weeks for the worm to mature.

Hymenolepis nana (dwarf tapeworm). The dwarf tapeworm is the smallest of human tapeworms and is very common in the United States. In some parts of the country the incidence runs as high as 5%. No intermediate host is necessary. The adults are ½ to 2 inches long and have 100 to 200 proglottids. After the eggs have been ingested, the larval forms (**oncospheres**) are liberated and penetrate the intestinal mucosa, where they are transformed into cysticercoid larvae. After a few days they reenter the lumen of the intestine, evaginate their heads, become attached, and mature. Unsanitary toilet habits will cause superinfection. The tapeworm is also found in rats and other rodents.

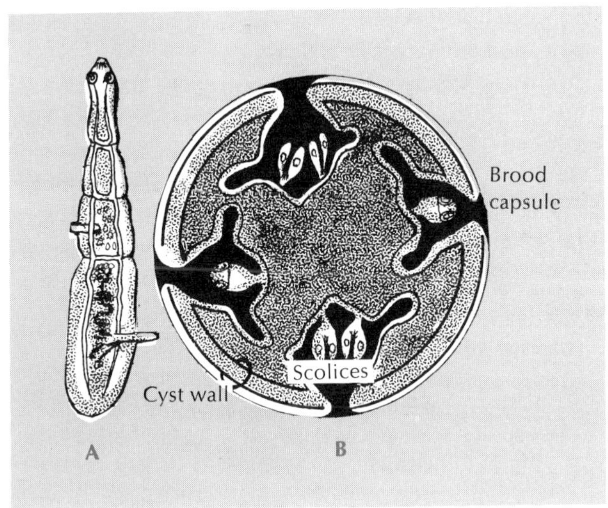

FIG. 13-27

Echinococcus granulosus, dog tapeworm that may be dangerous to man. **A,** Adult tapeworm. **B,** Early cyst. Small adult (5 to 10 mm.) lives in intestine of dogs and some other carnivores. Bladder worm stage found in cattle, sheep, hogs, and sometimes man, producing hydatid disease. Man acquires disease by unsanitary habits in association with dogs. Human cases reported from central Europe, Australia, South Africa, and Argentina and some 500 cases in the United States. When eggs are ingested by intermediate host, liberated larvae usually encyst in liver. Brood capsules containing scolices are formed from inner layer of each cyst. Cyst enlarges, developing other cysts with brood pouches. May grow for years, to size of orange, necessitating surgery.

Echinococcus granulosus (hydatid worm) (Fig. 13-27). The adult is found in the dog, wolf, and a few other animals; the larvae, in more than 40 species of mammals, including man, monkeys, cat, sheep, and cattle. Man thus serves as an intermediate host in the case of this tapeworm. The adults are only 5 to 10 mm. long and are composed of a scolex and four proglottids. The larval stages do most of the harm in the life cycle, for the cysticercus forms what is known as a **hydatid cyst.** These cysts are usually formed in the liver but may be found in other organs. Some of them are 2 or 3 inches in diameter in man and may produce death by their pressure and other effects. Wherever a cyst is formed, it slowly enlarges by the continuous formation of brood capsules, each of which buds off many scolices internally. Many cases of hydatid cysts are reported each year in the United States. Man probably gets his infections from ingesting the eggs of a tapeworm eliminated by a dog.

Moniezia expansa (sheep tapeworm). The adult is found in sheep and goats (Fig. 13-28); the larva in a small mite (*Galumna*).

Taenia pisiformis (dog tapeworm). *T. pisiformis* is widely used as a type for study in the laboratory (Fig. 13-23). The larvae occur in the mesenteries and liver of rabbits; the adults are found in cats and dogs.

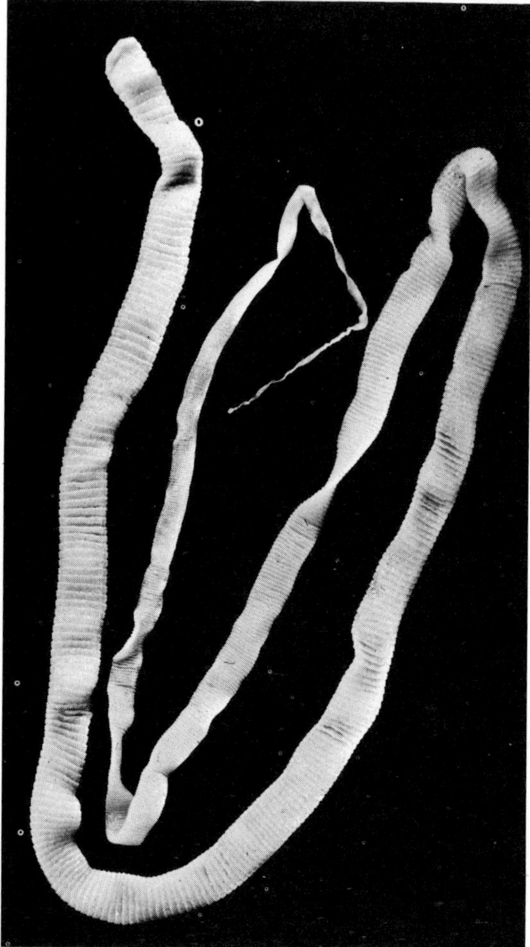

FIG. 13-28

Section of sheep tapeworm *Moniezia expansa*. Note progressive increase in size. Young proglottids are budded from scolex and neck (center); oldest (gravid) proglottids shown at upper left.

Derivation and meaning of basic terminology

Acoela (Gr. *a,* without, + *koilos,* hollow). Order of Turbellaria. These worms have no enteron.

Alloeocoela (Gr. *alloios,* different, + *koilos,* hollow). Order of turbellarians.

cercaria (Gr. *kerkos,* tail, + *aria,* like or connected with). Tadpolelike larva of trematodes.

Digenea (Gr. *dis,* double, + *genos,* race). Subclass (Trematoda). These flukes require two or more hosts for their complete development.

Diphyllobothrium (Gr. *dis,* double, + *phyllon,* leaf, + *bothrion,* hole). Genus (Cestoda). The scolex of this tapeworm has only two suckers instead of four, which is the number commonly found.

Dugesia (formerly called *Euplanaria* but changed by priority to *Dugesia* after Dugès, who first described the form in 1830). Genus (Turbellaria).

Echinococcus (Gr. *echinos,* spiny, + *coccus,* berry). Genus (Cestoda). The multiple scolices give a spiny and berrylike appearance to the dangerous tapeworm larval cysts.

fluke (AS. *floc,* flat). A member of class Trematoda.

Monogenea (Gr. *monas,* single, + *genos,* race). Subclass (Trematoda). Only one host required for development.

Opisthorchis (Gr. *opistho,* behind, + *orchis,* testis). Genus (Trematoda). Testes are located in the posterior part of the body.

Paragonimus (Gr. *para,* beside, + *gonimos,* generative). Genus (Trematoda). Refers to the position of the reproductive organs. Testes lie side by side and the ovary lies opposite the uterus.

Polycladida (Gr. *poly,* many, + *klados,* branch). Order of turbellarians that have intestines of many branches.

proglottid (Gr. *pro,* before, + *glotta,* tongue, + *id,* suffix). A section of a tapeworm. Dujardin (1843) gave this derivation because of its resemblance to the tip of the tongue.

protonephridium (Gr. *protos,* first, + *nephros,* kidney). Primitive excretory organ of tubule with terminating flame tube or solenocyte.

redia (after Francesco Redi, Italian microscopist). Larva stage in the development of trematodes.

rhabdite (Gr. *rhabdos,* rod, + *ite,* suffix). Ectodermal rodlike structures in certain turbellarians. May function in slime formation.

Rhabdocoela (Gr. *rhabdos,* rod, + *koilos,* cavity). Order of turbellarians that have a straight intestine of smooth contour.

rosette (L. *rosa,* rose, + *ette,* dim.) An organ for attachment in the subclass Cestodaria.

rostellum (L. little beak). Hook-bearing tip of the tapeworm scolex.

saginata (L. *saginare,* to fatten, + *ata,* characterized by). Species name of the beef tapeworm. The proglottids have a plump appearance.

Schistosoma (Gr. *schistos,* divided, + *soma,* body). Genus (Trematoda). Male canal in which the female is held gives a split appearance to the body.

scolex (Gr. *skolex,* worm). Term restricted to the so-called head of the tapeworm.

sporocyst (Gr. *sporos,* seed, + *kystis,* bladder). One of the larval stages of trematodes.
Taenia (Gr. *tainia,* band, ribbon). Genus (Cestoda).
Tricladida (Gr. *tria,* three, + *klados,* branch). Order of turbellarians with 3-branched intestines.

Phylum Rhynchocoela (Nemertina)*

GENERAL RELATIONS

The nemertine worms are commonly known as ribbon worms. They derive their name from a long, muscular tube, known as the **proboscis,** which can be thrust out to grasp the prey and which is supposed to be unerring in its aim (Nemertina, Gr. *nemertes,* unerring one). They were formerly classed under Platyhelminthes, but most zoologists now consider them a separate phylum. They are mostly marine forms, and there are about 570 species in the group. Some are less than an inch long, and others are several feet in length. Their colors are often bright, and almost all hues are represented among the various species. In the odd genus *Gorgonorhynchus* (1931) the proboscis is divided into many proboscides, which appear as a mass of wormlike structures in the everted proboscis. This form may have arisen suddenly as a new genus, but this interpretation has been questioned.

With few exceptions, the general body plan of the nemertines is similar to that of Turbellaria. Like the latter, their epidermis is covered with numerous short cilia and many gland cells. Another striking line of evidence in favor of their flatworm affinities is the presence of flame cells in the excretory system. Recently rhabdites have been found in several nemertines, including *Lineus.* However, they differ from Platyhelminthes with respect to their reproductive system. In the marine forms there is a ciliated larva, the **pilidium larva.** This larva has a ventral mouth but no anus—another flatworm characteristic. It also has some resemblance to the trochophore larva that is found in several higher phyla such as annelids and mollusks. Other flatworm characteristics are the presence of bilateral symmetry, mesoderm, and lack of coelom. All in all, the present evidence seems to indicate that the nemertines came from an ancestral form closely related to Platyhelminthes and Ctenophora.

The nemertines show some advances over the flatworms. One of these is the retractile **proboscis** and its sheath, for which there are no counterparts among Platyhelminthes. Another difference is the presence of an **anus** in the adult. Thus these forms have a complete digestive system, the first to be found in the animal kingdom. They are also the simplest animals to have a **blood vascular** system, which usually consists of a medium dorsal and two lateral trunks. Most of them are dioecious, and their reproductive systems are much simpler than that of Platyhelminthes.

CHARACTERISTICS

1. Bilateral symmetry; highly contractile body that is cylindric anteriorly and flattened posteriorly
2. Three germ layers
3. Epidermis with cilia and gland cells; rhabdites in some
4. Body spaces with parenchyma, which is partly connective tissue and partly gelatinous
5. An **eversible proboscis,** which lies free in a cavity (rhynchocoel) above the alimentary canal
6. **Complete digestive system**
7. Body-wall musculature of outer circular and inner longitudinal layers with diagonal fibers between the two; sometimes another circular layer inside the longitudinal layer
8. **Blood vascular system with three longitudinal trunks**
9. No regular coelom; rhynchocoel may be considered true coelom
10. Nervous system usually a four-lobed brain connected to paired longitudinal nerve trunks or, in some, middorsal and midventral trunks
11. Excretory system of two coiled canals, which are branched with flame cells
12. Sexes separate with simple gonads; asexual reproduction by fragmentation; few hermaphrodites; pilidium larva in some
13. No respiratory system
14. Sensory **ciliated pits** or **head slits on each side of head,** which communicate between the outside and the brain; tactile organs and ocelli (in some)
15. In contrast to Platyhelminthes, few nemertines are parasitic

HABITAT

A few of the nemertines are found in moist soil and fresh water, but by far the larger number are marine.

*Ring′ko-se″la (Gr. *rhynchos,* beak, + *koilos,* hollow). Nem′er-ti″na (Gr. *nemertes,* unerring one, + *ina,* belonging to).

At low tide they are often coiled up under stones. It seems probable that they are active at high tide and quiescent at low tide. Some nemertines such as *Cerebratulus* frequent empty mollusk shells. The small species live among seaweed, or they may be found swimming near the surface of the water. Nemertines are often secured by dredging at depths of 15 to 25 feet or deeper. In a few instances they are commensals or parasites. *Prostoma rubrum,* which is less than an inch long, is a well-known freshwater species.

CLASSES

Class Enopla (en'o-pla). (Gr. *enoplos,* armed). Proboscis armed with stylets; muscular layer of outer circular and inner longitudinal muscles; no nerve plexus; intestinal ceca; mouth opens in front of brain. Example: *Amphiporus.*

Class Anopla (an'o-pla). (Gr. *anoplos,* unarmed). Proboscis lacks stylets; muscular layer of inner and outer longitudinal and middle circular muscles; nerve plexus present; mouth opens behind brain; intestinal pouches absent or rudimentary. Example: *Cerebratulus.*

REPRESENTATIVE TYPE
CLASS ENOPLA

Most nemertines have a close resemblance to each other, and almost any one of them, with few exceptions, can be taken as a type. Some are very long and difficult to study in the laboratory because their internal organs are not easily seen. They are slender worms and are fragile. No group of worms shows a greater diversity in size than do nemertines. *Amphiporus* (Fig. 13-29), which is taken as the type for description here, is one of the smaller ones.

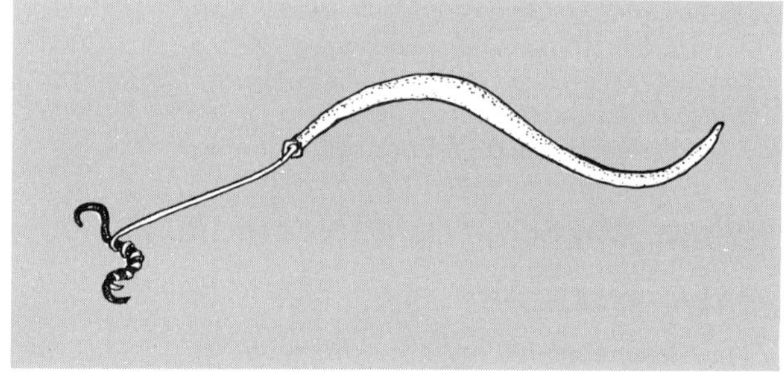

FIG. 13-29

Amphiporus, with proboscis extended to catch prey.

FIG. 13-30

Diagrammatic cross section of female nemertine worm.

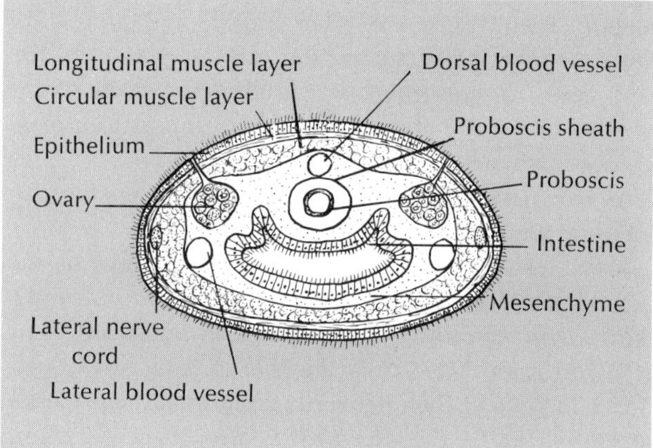

Amphiporus ochraceus—ribbon worm, or bandworm

Structure. This worm is from 1 to 3 inches long, with a width of about $\frac{1}{10}$ inch. It is dorsoventrally flattened (Fig. 13-30), with both anterior and posterior ends rounded. The body is composed first of an epidermis of ciliated columnar cells, with some of the cells specialized for sensory and mucous functions and all resting on a basement membrane of connective tissue. Just underneath the basement membrane is the **muscle** layer, composed of an **inner longitudinal** and an **outer circular** layer. Some nemertines have both an outer and inner circular layer of muscle. Eyes, or **ocelli,** are found on each side of the anterior end. Beneath the body wall and surrounding the visceral organs is the **parenchyma,** which consists partly of connective tissue and partly of a gelatinous substance, or **mesenchyme.** On the ventral surface near the front end of the body is the **mouth** with thick tumid lips.

Just above the mouth is a small terminal pore, the external opening of the **proboscis** (Fig. 13-31). The proboscis pore opens into a short cavity, the rhynchodeum, to the inner end of which is attached the anterior end of the proboscis (Fig. 13-32). The proboscis, which has no connection with the digestive tract, is an eversible organ that can be protruded and retracted through the above-mentioned pore. It serves for defense and for catching prey. The proboscis is made up of three parts—a thick-walled tube, a middle bulbous sac with stylets, and a blind tube. It is contained within a sheath to which it is attached at its anterior end by strong muscles inside the sheath. The proboscis sheath is made up of a muscular wall and a cavity (rhynchocoel) which encloses the proboscis. The rhynchocoel is filled with fluid, and by muscular pressure on this fluid the anterior part of the tubular proboscis is everted or turned inside out. The proboscis apparatus is an invagination of the anterior body wall, and its structure therefore duplicates that of the body wall. The retractor muscles attached at the end are used to retract the everted proboscis, much like everting the tip of a finger of a glove by a string attached to its tip. The proboscis is armed with a sharp-pointed stylet. A frontal gland also opens at the anterior end by a pore.

The **digestive system** is complete and extends straight through the length of the body to the terminal **anus.** The **esophagus** is straight and opens into a dilated part of the tract, the **stomach.** The blind anterior end of the intestine as well as the main intestine is provided with paired **lateral ceca.** Throughout its course the alimentary tract is lined with ciliated epithelium, and in the wall of the esophagus there are glandular cells. The digestive system lies ventral to the proboscis sheath.

The **blood vascular system** is simple and enclosed, with a single dorsal vessel and two lateral vessels (Fig. 13-33). Both dorsal and lateral vessels are connected together by regularly arranged transverse vessels. All three longitudinal vessels join together anteriorly to

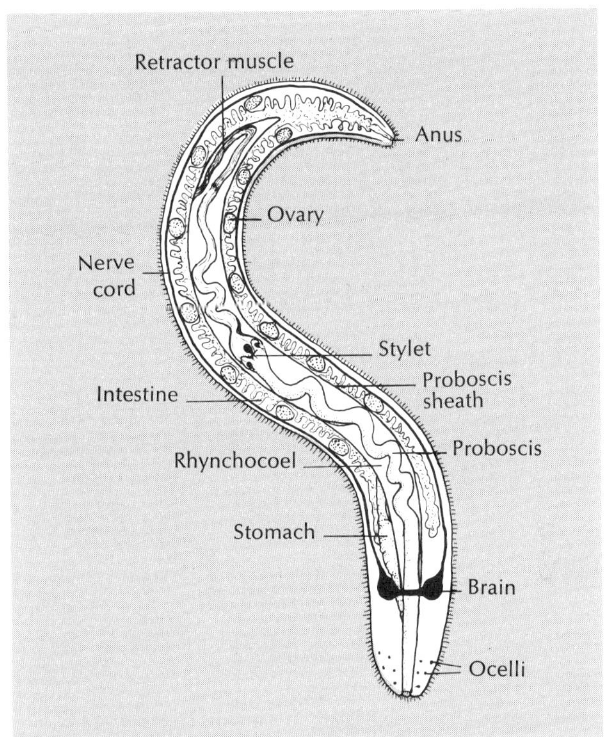

FIG. 13-31

Structure of female nemertine worm *Amphiporus* (diagrammatic). Dorsal view to show proboscis.

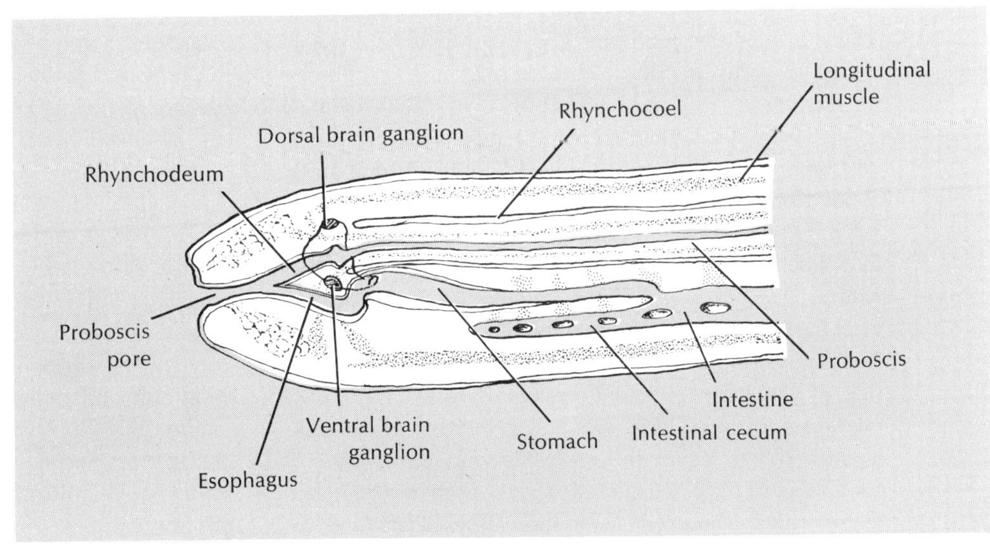

FIG. 13-32

Longitudinal section through anterior region of nemertine worm. This type has a common anterior pore for both proboscis and mouth, but others have separate openings for each. (From Hickman: Biology of the invertebrates, The C. V. Mosby Co.)

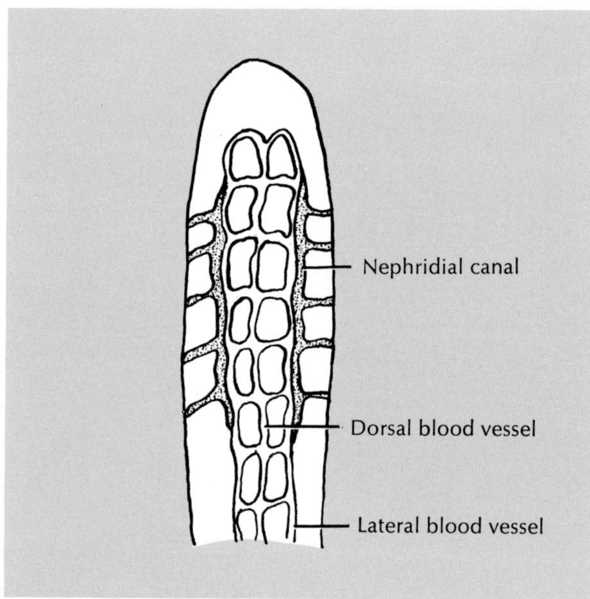

FIG. 13-33

Excretory and circulatory systems of anterior region of nemertine worm. Flame bulbs along nephridial canal are closely associated with lateral blood vessels. (From Hickman: Biology of the invertebrates, The C. V. Mosby Co.)

form a type of collar. The blood is colorless, containing nucleated corpuscles, although in some nemertines the blood is red because of the presence of hemoglobin. There is no heart, and the blood is propelled by the muscular walls of the blood vessels and by bodily movements.

The **excretory system** contains a pair of lateral tubes with many branches and flame cells. Each lateral tube opens to the outside by one or more pores.

The **nervous system** includes a brain composed of four fused ganglia, one pair lying dorsal and one pair ventral to the rhynchodeum, united by commissures that pass around it. Five longitudinal nerves extend from the brain posteriorly—a large lateral trunk on each side of the body, paired dorsolateral trunks, and one middorsal trunk. These are connected by a network of nerve fibers. From the brain anterior nerves run to the proboscis; and peripheral nerves, both sensory and motor, run to the ocelli and other sense organs and to the mouth and esophagus. In addition to the eyes, or ocelli, already mentioned, there are other sense organs, such as tactile papillae, sensory pits and grooves, and probably auditory organs.

In common with most nemertines, the **reproductive system** in *Amphiporus* is dioecious. The gonads in either sex are sacs that lie between the intestinal ceca, where they have developed from lateral mesenchyme. From each gonad a short duct (gonopore) runs to the dorsolateral body surface to discharge the sex products to the outside.

Metabolism. The nemertines are carnivorous and very voracious, eating either dead or living prey. In seizing their prey they thrust out the slime-covered proboscis, which quickly ensnares the prey by wrapping around it (Fig. 13-29). The stylet also pierces and holds the prey. Then by retracting the proboscis, the prey is drawn near the mouth and is engulfed by the esophagus that is thrust out to meet it. Nemertines do not hesitate to eat each other when they are confined together. Digestion is largely extracellular in the intestinal tube, and when the food is ready for absorption, it passes through the cellular lining of the intestinal tract into the blood vascular system. The indigestible material passes out the anus (Fig. 13-34), in contrast to Platyhelminthes, in which it leaves by the mouth. Waste is picked up from the mesenchyme spaces and blood by the flame cells and carried by the excretory ducts to the outside. Respiration occurs through the body surface.

Locomotion. *Amphiporus* can move with considerable rapidity by the combined action of its well-developed musculature and its cilia. It glides mainly against a substratum; some make use of muscular waves in crawling. Some nemertines have the interesting method of protruding the proboscis, attaching themselves by means of the stylet, and then drawing the body up to the attached position.

Reproduction. Eggs and sperm are discharged into the water, where fertilization occurs. Egg production in the females is usually accompanied by degeneration of the other visceral organs. From the zygote there develops a pilidium larva, which is helmet shaped and bears a dorsal spike of fused cilia and a pair of lateral lobes. The entire larva is covered with cilia and has a mouth and alimentary canal but no anus. In some nemertines the zygote develops directly without undergoing metamorphosis. The freshwater species, *Prostoma rubrum*, is hermaphroditic. A few nemertines are viviparous.

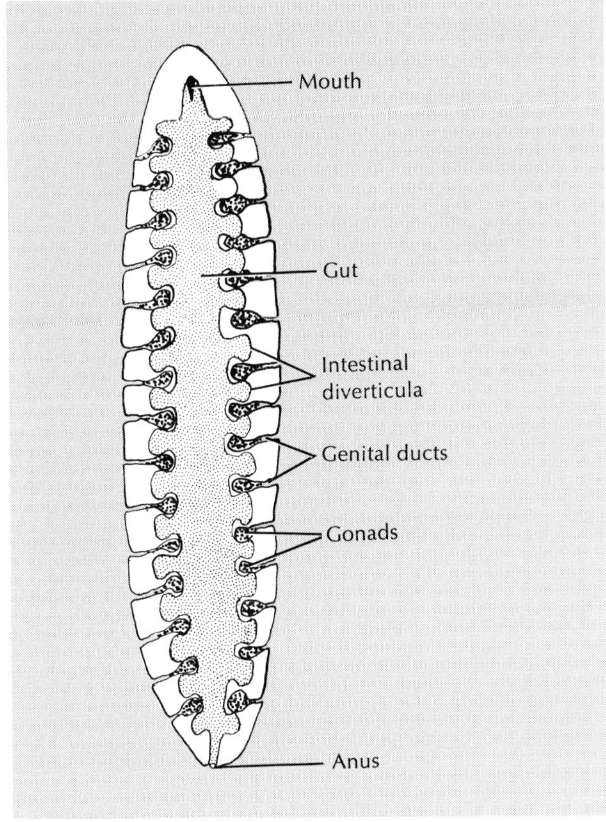

FIG. 13-34

Digestive and reproductive systems of nemertine worm. Note that digestive system is complete with mouth and anus and that each genital sac has its own duct to exterior—a simple, primitive arrangement. (From Hickman: Biology of the invertebrates, The C. V. Mosby Co.)

Regeneration. Nemertines have great powers of regeneration. At certain seasons some of them fragment by autotomy, and from each fragment a new individual develops. This is especially noteworthy in the genus *Lineus*. Fragments from the anterior region will produce a new individual more quickly than will one from the posterior part, in accordance with the principle of the axial gradient. Sometimes the proboscis is shot out with such force that it is broken off from the body. In such a case a new proboscis is developed within a short time. The severed proboscis behaves very much like an individual worm for some time before it dies. The abundant nerve plexus it possesses may account for this behavior.

Derivation and meaning of basic terminology

Amphiporus (Gr. *amphi,* double, + *poros,* pore). Genus (Enopla). Refers to the mouth and proboscis pores at the anterior end.

Cerebratulus (L. *cerebrum,* brain, + *ulus,* dim.) Genus (Anopla). Refers to the relatively prominent cerebral ganglia.

pilidium (Gr. *pilidion,* dim. of felt cap). Refers to the shape of the larva.

proboscis (Gr. *pro,* before, + *bosko,* feed). The sensory, offensive, and defensive organ at the anterior end of the nemertine.

rhynchodeum (Gr. *rhynchos,* beak, + *daio,* divide). Short tubular cavity to which the proboscis is attached in Rhynchocoela. It opens anteriorly by a small pore. It must not be confused with the rhynchocoel in which the proboscis lies.

stylet (Gr. *stylos,* stake). Sharp-pointed defense organ on the proboscis.

Annotated references

Böhmig, L. 1929. Art. Nemertini. In W. Kükenthal and T. Krumbach: Handbuch der Zoologie, vol. 2, part 1, sec. 3. Berlin, Walter de Gruyter & Co. *One of the best detailed accounts in German.*

Chang, T. C. 1964. The biology of animal parasites. Philadelphia, W. B. Saunders Co.

Chandler, A. C. 1949. Introduction to parasitology. New York, John Wiley & Sons, Inc. *Emphasizes many flatworms that infect man. A good and authoritative presentation by one of America's foremost parasitologists.*

Coe, W. R. 1943. Biology of the nemerteans of the Atlantic Coast of North America. Hartford, Transactions of Connecticut Academy of Arts and Science. *This is only one of many valuable papers on Rhynchocoela by this author.*

Craig, C. F., and E. C. Faust. 1945. Clinical parasitology, ed. 4. Philadelphia, Lea & Febiger. *A good account of those flatworms that are most often seen in clinical examinations.*

Dawes, B. 1946. The trematoda with special reference to British and other European forms. New York, Cambridge University Press. *A rather comprehensive review of the group. An excellent bibliography is included.*

Grasse, P. P. (editor). 1961. Traité de zoologie, anatomie, systematique, biologie, vol. IV, Platyhelminthes, Mesozairies, Acanthocephales, Nemertiens (first fascicule). Paris, Masson & Cie. *An authoritative treatise on these groups.*

Hickman, C. P. 1967. Biology of the invertebrates, St. Louis, The C. V. Mosby Co.

Hyman, L. H. 1951. The invertebrates: Platyhelminthes and Rhynchocoela. The acoelomate bilateria. New

York, McGraw-Hill Book Co. *The most comprehensive account of this group yet published.*

Karling, T. G. 1963. Some evolutionary trends in turbellarian morphology. In E. C. Daugherty (editor): The lower Metazoa: comparative biology and phylogeny. Berkeley, University of California.

Martin, W. E. 1952. Another annelid first intermediate host of a digenetic trematode. J. Parasit. **38**:1-4. *This report, together with an earlier one, describes the rare exceptions in which a group other than mollusks acts as the first intermediate host.*

Pennak, R. W. 1953. Fresh-water invertebrates of the United States. New York, The Ronald Press Co. *An excellent description of the structure and life history of the freshwater nemertine, Prostoma rubrum.*

Swellengrebel, N. H., and M. N. Sterman. 1961. Animal parasites in man. New York, D. Van Nostrand Co., Inc. *An English edition of a well-established Dutch text. This work is of great interest to all students of human parasitology.*

Thomas, A. P. 1883. The life history of the liver fluke (*Fasciola hepatica*). Quart. J. Micr. Sci. (ser. 2) **23**: 99-133. *This classic work is justly famous, for it represents the first life history of a digenetic trematode to be worked out. The work is also noteworthy because there are simpler trematode life histories than that of Fasciola. It gave a great impetus to work in the field of parasitology.*

Threadgold, L. T. 1963. The tegument and associated structures of *Fasciola hepatica*. Quart. J. Micr. Sci. **104**:505-512. *The cuticle is considered to be surface layer of protoplasm that is an extension of flasklike, nucleated cells of the interior.*

Wardle, R. A., and J. A. McLeod. 1952. The zoology of tapeworms. Minneapolis, University of Minnesota Press. *A comprehensive account of these highly specialized parasites. It is an indispensable work for investigators in this field.*

CHAPTER 14

• PHYLA ASCHELMINTHES, ACANTHOCEPHALA, AND ENTOPROCTA (PSEUDOCOELOMATE BILATERAL ANIMALS)

BIOLOGIC PRINCIPLES

1. In these three phyla, the original blastocoel of the blastula makes up a space, or pseudocoel, between enteron and body wall without a peritoneal lining.
2. The pseudocoelomates represent a heterogeneous assemblage of animals, many of which share few common features except that of a pseudocoel. Many are small, even microscopic in size, and others are fairly large. Taxonomic distinctions are still uncertain with some pseudocoelomates. There are so many different groups that several diverse structural features are found among them.
3. The pseudocoel of the three phyla vary in characteristics. In some it is filled with fluid; in others it may contain a gelatinous substance and mesenchyme cells. In all there is usually space enough, or the contained substance is so loosely arranged, that there is room for differential organ development and freedom of movement within the body.
4. The advantages of a body cavity are many. It affords space for the differentiation of the digestive system and other organs or systems. It can also act as a storage place for waste products, which can be discharged to the outside by excretory ducts. It can also furnish space for the gonads and sex cells.
5. The basic body plan of the group is that of a roundworm, or a tube-within-a-tube arrangement. Even this organization is found in those without a digestive system (for example, the Acanthocephala), in which the ligament sacs or strands represent the endoderm. Modifications of the tube-within-a-tube plan may be caused by parasitism.
6. In such a diversified grouping of forms there are certain characteristics that are shared to some extent. Many have radial symmetry at the anterior end. The epidermis is chiefly syncytial and secretes a hard cuticle, which undergoes specializations (spines, bristles, etc.). Longitudinal muscles are emphasized in many. Constancy of cells (or nuclei) is common in some groups. Likewise, there are unique characteristics, such as the lacunar system of the Acanthocephala, the corona of rotifers, and the zonites of the Kinorhyncha.

PHYLOGENY AND ADAPTIVE RADIATION

1. Affinities are difficult to establish within such a varied assemblage. Acanthocephala seem to have relations with both the flatworms and the roundworms. The flattened shape of the body, the lack of a digestive system (as in cestodes), and a body wall of both circular and longitudinal muscles as well as some other features may indicate a relationship with the Platyhelminthes. The nuclear constancy and superficial segmentation, on the other hand, show Aschelminthes affinities. The Aschelminthes themselves are thought to have been derived from rhabdocoel flatworms, according to some students of the group. The Entoprocta have often been included with the Ectoprocta, or moss animals, but the latter are true coelomate animals and the former are much simpler in their structure. Entoprocta may have come from an early offshoot of the same line that led to the Ectoprocta.
2. Each group of this vast assemblage of pseudocoelomates may have its own unique basic adaptive pattern in determining its evolutionary history. The most numerous group of all, the nematodes, have been able to adapt to almost every ecologic niche available to animal life. Their viability under the most harsh environmental conditions may be due to a wide range of physiologic response. Longitudinal muscles have restricted their undulations to a dorsoventral plane. Their constant activity within the range of their restricted movement has enabled them to move into many niches. Being wholly parasitic, the Acanthocephala have undergone those modifications characteristic of parasitic forms. Their invaginable proboscis has evolved some changes in spine patterns and in a few other ways, but the size range from 1 or 2 mm. to almost 2 feet represents their chief evolutionary diversification. Variations in the evolutionary patterns of ciliary feeding and general structural organization are found in the modest group of Entoprocta.

Phylum Aschelminthes*

GENERAL RELATIONS

Phylum Aschelminthes has been classified in different ways by many authorities. Until recently some of the classes under Aschelminthes were considered as separate phyla. For instance, the rotifers were once

*As'kel-min"thes (Gr. *askos*, cavity, + *helmins*, worm).

included in a phylum of their own (Trochelminthes) and the horsehair worms (Nematomorpha) were placed as a class under phylum Nemathelminthes. The recent tendency is to drop the names of phyla Nemathelminthes and Trochelminthes and to combine them under one phylum—Aschelminthes. This is not altogether arbitrary, for there are evidences of relationship among the varied forms that make up this new phylum.

The proposed name Aschelminthes is derived from the Gr. *askos,* cavity, + *helmins,* worm. The animals that make up the group all have some form of pseudocoel, bilateral symmetry, and a wormlike form or a modification of it. Most of them are small, even microscopic, although some of the parasitic nematodes may reach a length of more than a meter. The body is often round or cylindric, although it is distinctly flattened in some. One of their striking characteristics is the almost universal presence of a thick, tough cuticle that is often molted. With few exceptions, only the longitudinal layer of muscle is present. Aschelminthes occupy a wide range of habitat distribution. Many are aquatic in both fresh water and marine water; others occupy terrestrial habitats. Although most are free living, some are among the most common of all parasites. Probably all vertebrates and most of the invertebrates are parasitized by one or more kinds of aschelminths. The number of species in this phylum must be very great, although only a relatively few in some of its classes have been named to date such as the nematodes.

The relations of the Aschelminthes to other major phyla are very obscure. Rotifers and gastrotrichs have often been grouped together because of the similarity between their muscular and excretory systems, but Gastrotricha seems to be more closely related to nematodes in other particulars. Hyman suggests that all three groups may stem from a turbellarian-like ancestor. Within the phylum certain relationships from structural similarities are more revealing. Radial symmetry of the anterior end is pronounced in nematodes and kinorhynchs. Superficial segmentation, especially of the cuticle, is common among most classes. The epidermal cords, one of the characteristic features of nematodes, are also found in modified form in the kinorhynchs, nematomorphs, and priapulids (Chapter 16). Nearly all members of Aschelminthes have emphasized longitudinal muscles in their muscular systems.

CHARACTERISTICS

1. Symmetry bilateral; unsegmented; triploblastic (three germ layers)
2. Size mostly small; some microscopic; a few a meter or more in length
3. Body usually vermiform, cylindric, or flattened; body wall a **syncytial** or cellular **epidermis** with thickened cuticle; cuticle often ringed with spines and bristles, sometimes molted; **cilia** mostly absent
4. Muscular layers of the body mostly of **longitudinal fibers,** with few exceptions
5. Body cavity an unlined **pseudocoel**
6. Digestive system complete with mouth, enteron, and anus; pharynx muscular and well developed; **tube-within-a-tube arrangement;** digestive tract usually only an epithelial tube with **no definite muscle layer**
7. Circulatory and respiratory organs lacking
8. Excretory system of canals and protonephridia (in some); cloaca that receives excretory, reproductive, and digestive products present in some
9. Nervous system of cerebral ganglia or of a circumenteric nerve ring connected to anterior and posterior nerves; sense organs of **ciliated pits,** papillae, bristles, and eyespots (few)
10. Reproductive system of gonads and ducts that may be single or double; sexes nearly always separate, with the male usually smaller than the female; eggs microscopic with chitinous shell
11. Development may be direct or with a complicated life history; cleavage mostly determinate; **cell or nuclear constancy common**

CLASSES

Class **Rotifera** (ro-tif'e-ra) (L. *rota,* wheel, + *ferre,* to bear). Aquatic and microscopic; shell-like cuticle (lorica); anterior end with ciliary organ (corona); forked foot with cement gland; digestive system usually complete with grinding organ (mastax); body cavity without lining; excretory system of protonephridia and two canals that empty into a bladder; nervous system of a ganglion with nerves; eyespots; separate sexes, males much smaller than females; parthenogenesis and sexual reproduction; no larval stages; about 1,500 species. Examples: *Asplanchna, Epiphanes (Hydatina), Philodina.*

Class **Gastrotricha** (gas-trot'ri-ka) (L. *gaster,* stomach, + *trichos,* hair). Aquatic microscopic animals of about the same size as rotifers; no corona; cilia present; cuticle often covered with short, curved, dorsal spines; body usually posteriorly forked with adhesive tubes and glands for attachment; excretory system (when present) of a pair of protonephridia; digestive system complete with mouth surrounded with bristles; nervous system of a ganglion with two main longitudinal nerves; females found only in some species, eggs develop parthenogenetically; some species hermaphroditic; about 140 species. Examples: *Chaetonotus, Macrodasys.*

Class **Kinorhyncha** (kin'o-ring"cha) (Gr. *kineo,* move, + *rhyncos,* beak) (**Echinodera**). Marine, microscopic animals; body of 13 or 14 rings (zonites); spiny cuticle but no cilia; retractile head with circlet of spines; digestive system complete with distinct lining epithelium in pharynx; pseudocoel with fluid containing amebocytes; excretory system of a pair of tubes and protonephridia; nervous system of a dorsal ganglion in epidermis with a ventral ganglionated nerve cord; eyespots in some; sexes separate with gonads in the form of tubular sacs; penial spicules in males; metamorphosis of several larval stages; about 100 species. Examples: *Centroderes, Echinoderella.*

Class **Nematoda** (nem'at-o"da) (Gr. *nema,* thread, + *eidos,* form). Aquatic, terrestrial, or parasitic worms; body cylindric, unsegmented, and elongated; body wall of thick cuticle, syncytial epithelium, longitudinal muscles, which are divided into four sections by four longitudinal epidermal cords; no cilia; body cavity an unlined pseudocoel; circulatory and respiratory systems absent; digestive system complete without muscles and glands; excretory system of one or two glandular organs or of canals or of both; nervous system of a circumenteric ring with anterior and posterior nerves; sense organs simple; sexes usually separate, with female generally larger than male; gonads single or double; male duct enters cloaca, female duct with separate opening (vulva); penial spicules in male; fertilization internal; development usually direct but life history may be intricate; a few thousand species named, but their number has been estimated to be at least 500,000. Example: *Ascaris* (intestinal roundworm), *Necator* (hookworm), *Wuchereria* (filarial worm), *Dioctophyma* (giant kidney worm), *Trichinella* (trichina worm), *Enterobius* (pinworm).

Class **Nematomorpha** (nem'a-to-mor"pha) (Gr. *nema,* thread, + *morphe,* shape) (**Gordiacea**). Long, slender worms with cylindric bodies; size from a few millimeters to a meter in length; larval forms parasitic, adults free living; body wall of cuticle bearing small papillae, one-layered epithelium, and longitudinal muscles; no lateral cords; digestive system degenerate in both juveniles and adults; pseudocoel mostly filled with parenchyma; no circulatory, respiratory, or excretory system; nervous system of a circumenteric ring with a single midventral nerve cord; separate sexes with paired gonads; paired ducts; cloaca in both sexes; development mostly direct. Example: *Paragordius.*

REPRESENTATIVE TYPES

CLASS ROTIFERA

Rotifers are microscopic animals about 0.5 to 1.5 mm. in length. They are found mostly in fresh water, although a few are marine and some are even parasitic. Their common habitats are sluggish waters, such as that found in ponds, ditches, and gutters, and wet mosses and similar places. They derive their name from the beating of the cilia on the anterior end (corona) of the body, which gives one the impression of rotating wheels. The more than 1,500 species have a worldwide distribution. Some of the rotifers have beautiful colors and odd, bizarre shapes. They may be free swimming, colonial, or sessile. Because of their structure and interesting behavior, they have been extensively studied.

Among the many species, *Philodina roseola* and *Epiphanes* (*Hydatina*) *senta* are among the best known and have been most studied. As a type description of a rotifer, *Philodina* (Fig. 14-1) may be selected (although there are many variable types), and the following account is based largely on this form.

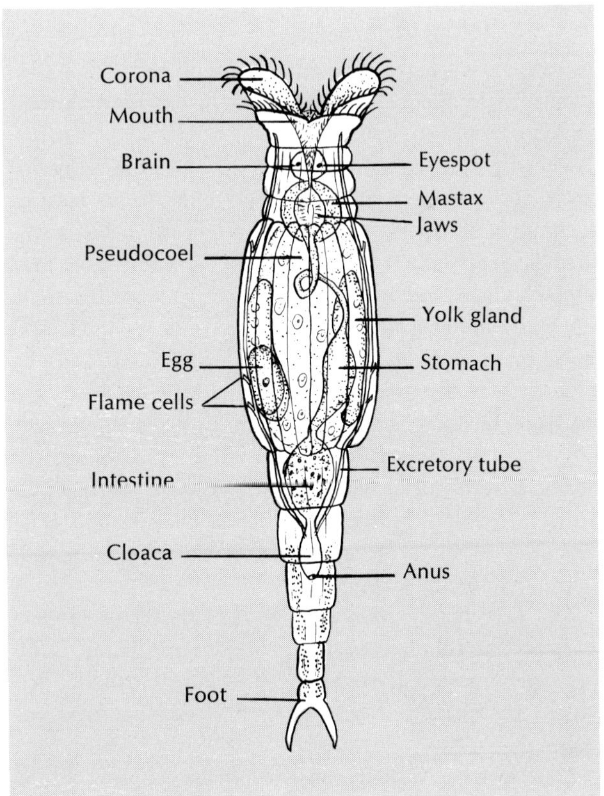

FIG. 14-1

Structure of *Philodina,* common rotifer.

Philodina

Structure. The body of the rotifer is elongated and cylindric and is divided into three regions: the broad anterior head provided with two retractile trochal disks (**corona**) with cilia; an elongated and enlarged trunk; and the slender posterior tail, or **foot,** which bears four toes. The body and foot are superficially segmented, the joints of the foot being telescopically retractile. The toes have **cement glands** that enable the rotifer to cling to objects. The **cuticle** (scleroproteins) is ringed to simulate segmentation, but there is no lorica in this form. It is fairly easy to see the internal structures of the animal, for it is transparent. Underneath the cuticle is the syncytial **epidermis** with scattered nuclei, which secretes the cuticle. Adjacent to the epidermis are the **subepidermal muscles.** These muscles are arranged in a variety of muscle bands that run in different directions, some of them through the pseudocoel. There are no definite muscle layers. Muscles serve to contract the body and to move the foot. The **pseudocoel** is large and occupies the space between the body wall and the viscera. It is filled with a fluid, some of the longitudinal muscle bands, and a network of ameboid or mesenchymal cells.

The **digestive system** is made up of the **mouth,** just below the corona; a **buccal tube;** a **pharynx** or **mastax,** a complex muscular, elongated organ that bears the hard **jaws** (trophi) with **teeth** for grinding the food (mainly algae and microscopic forms); a short **esophagus;** an enlarged **stomach** made up of a syncytial wall and provided with circular and longitudinal muscles and a pair of gastric glands; a short **intestine;** the **cloaca,** which receives the intestine and the oviducts; and the **anus,** which is the external opening of the cloaca at the dorsal side of the posterior end of the trunk. Most of the digestive tract is ciliated and is of endodermal origin. Enzymes from the gastric glands help in extracellular digestion.

The **excretory system** is made up of a pair of protonephridial tubules, each provided with flame bulbs and opening into a common ventral **urinary bladder,** which, by pulsating, discharges its contents into the cloaca.

The **nervous system** consists of the bilobed **brain,** dorsal to the mastax, which sends nerves to the sensory organs, to the muscles, and to the wall of the mastax. **Sensory** organs are well represented by the paired **eyespots,** the various ciliated pits and papillae, and the fingerlike **dorsal antennae.**

Although they are dioecious, no males are known in *Philodina* and the females are parthenogenetic. The female **reproductive system** consists of paired **ovaries,** yolk glands (vitellaria), and paired **oviducts** that open into the cloaca. When the eggs are laid, they are fastened to some object and hatch in about two days. At hatching the female has the adult form and reaches sexual maturity in a few days.

In some rotifers, but not in *Philodina,* three kinds of eggs are produced: thin-shelled amictic eggs (diploid number of chromosomes), which always develop parthenogenetically into females; smaller thin-shelled mictic eggs (haploid), which can develop parthenogenetically into males; and thick-shelled dormant eggs, which are fertilized mictic eggs (diploid), which hatch into amictic females. Amictic eggs are produced only by one kind of female and mictic eggs only by another kind of female. However, both kinds of females look alike and are diploid. The fertilized dormant egg is often called the winter egg, for it does not hatch until after the winter season. Winter eggs can also be dispersed by wind or on the feet of wading birds, a fact that may account for the peculiar distribution of some species of rotifers.

Most rotifers can withstand extreme desiccation and freezing. Some have even been found in hot springs where nothing else can live.

Cell or nuclear constancy in rotifers

Most structures in rotifers are syncytial, but the nuclei in the various organs show a remarkable constancy in number in any given species. One German investigator reports that one species, *Epiphanes* sp., always recorded 958 nuclei. Another investigator (Martini) has reported on the number of nuclei in the different organs in the same species of rotifer. He found 183 nuclei in the brain, 172 in the corona epidermis, 108 in the trunk and foot epidermis, 91 in the mastax epithelium, 39 in the stomach, etc. Other zoologists, however, are not convinced that cell constancy is as absolute as these investigations appear to show.

CLASS GASTROTRICHA

The organisms of class Gastrotricha (Fig. 14-2) are found in both fresh water and salt water, and their habitats are about the same as those of rotifers. They are common in protozoan cultures, where they are found creeping along on a substratum and feeding on

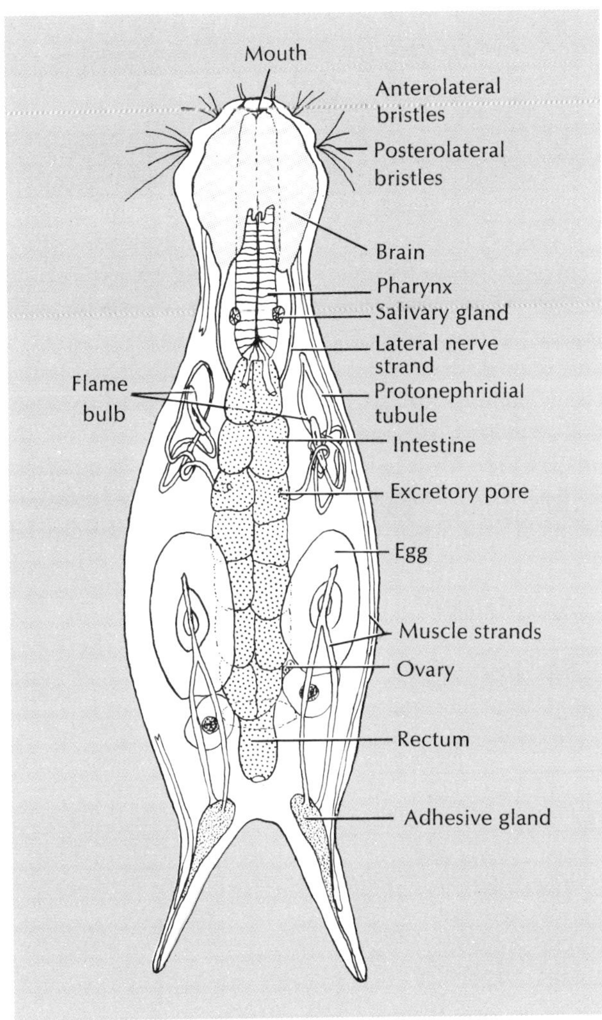

FIG. 14-2

Dorsal view of female *Chaetonotus*, a common gastrotrich, showing internal structures. Note general resemblance to rotifers. (From Hickman: Biology of the invertebrates, The C. V. Mosby Co.)

microscopic organisms. They are ventrally flattened with dorsal spines and can glide by means of bands of cilia on the ventral side. The body of some species is forked posteriorly. The head is in the form of a lobe and bears cilia and, in some species, long bristles. The body structures have some resemblance to the rotifers. A syncytial epidermis is found beneath the cuticle. Longitudinal muscles are better developed than are circular ones, and in most cases they are unstriped. Adhesive tubes, which secrete a substance for attachment, are also found. The pseudocoel is somewhat reduced and contains no amebocytes. The digestive system is complete and is made up of an anterior mouth surrounded by bristles; a long muscular pharynx, which is lined with a cuticle; a stomach-intestine, which lacks a cuticular lining; and an anus, which may be located dorsally or ventrally. Protonephridia are restricted to certain species. The nervous system contains a brain near the pharynx and a pair of lateral nerve trunks through the body. Sensory structures are similar to those in rotifers, except the eyespots are generally lacking. Only females occur in freshwater species, and the eggs all develop parthenogenetically. The female reproductive system consists of one or two ovaries, a uterus, an oviduct, and an opening (gonopore), which may open anteriorly to, or in common with, the anus. Eggs are laid on some substratum such as weeds and hatch in a few days. Development is direct and the larvae have the same form as the adults. Species of *Chaetonotus* are common freshwater gastrotrichs.

Gastrotrichs are assumed to be closely related to rotifers. They resemble the rotifers in having cilia, protonephridia, and a similar pattern of muscles. They differ from rotifers in their digestive system, cuticular spines, and presence of adhesive tubes. Some of their structures are similar to those of nematodes.

CLASS KINORHYNCHA

The class Kinorhyncha (Echinodera) gets its name from the Greek words *kineo,* move, + *rhynchos,* beak, and refers to retractile proboscis that these animals possess. They are marine worms about 1 mm. long and are found in the bottom muck of shallow or deep water. Their cylindric body is divided into thirteen or fourteen rings (zonites), which bear spines that may be quite long in the tail region, but they have no cilia. The retractile head has a circlet of spines with a small retractile proboscis. The body is flat underneath and arched above, with the posterior end more or less tapering. Their body wall is made up of a cuticle, a syncytial epidermis, and longitudinal epidermal cords much like those of nematodes. The arrangement of the muscles is correlated with the zonites, and circular, longitudinal, and diagonal muscle bands are all represented. By means of these muscles the animal can contract and extend its body and head. The digestive system is complete, with a mouth at the tip of the proboscis, a pharynx, an esophagus, a stomach-intestine, and an anus in the terminal zonite. The pseudocoel is filled with fluid-bearing amebocytes. The excretory system contains a pair of flame cells, each provided with an excretory canal that opens on the eleventh zonite. In close contact with the epidermis is the nervous system, with a brain encircling the pharynx, from which extends a ventral ganglionated cord throughout the body. Sense organs are represented by eyespots in some and by the sensory bristles. Sexes are separate, with the gonads in the form of elongated sacs. From each ovary an oviduct extends to the genital pore in the female; in the male a vas deferens runs from each testis to the genital pore, which has penial spicules.

The members of this strange group are not easy to find, although some 100 species have been reported. They cannot swim, but they move by squirming and by wormlike contraction and relaxation of their longitudinal muscles.

Among the most widely known of the genera of the Kinorhyncha are *Echinoderes, Echinoderella, Pycnophyes* (Fig. 14-3), and *Trachydemus.*

Class Kinorhyncha shares anatomic features with a number of other groups without being closely related to any. The segmental arrangement of kinorhynchs makes them somewhat intermediate between annelids and arthropods, but the development of their segmentation is not as basically tied in with the mesoderm formation as it is in the case of annelids and arthropods. In other words, segmentation in kinorhynchs is more superficial and secondary to the body plan. They have, in common with such forms as rotifers and gastrotrichs,

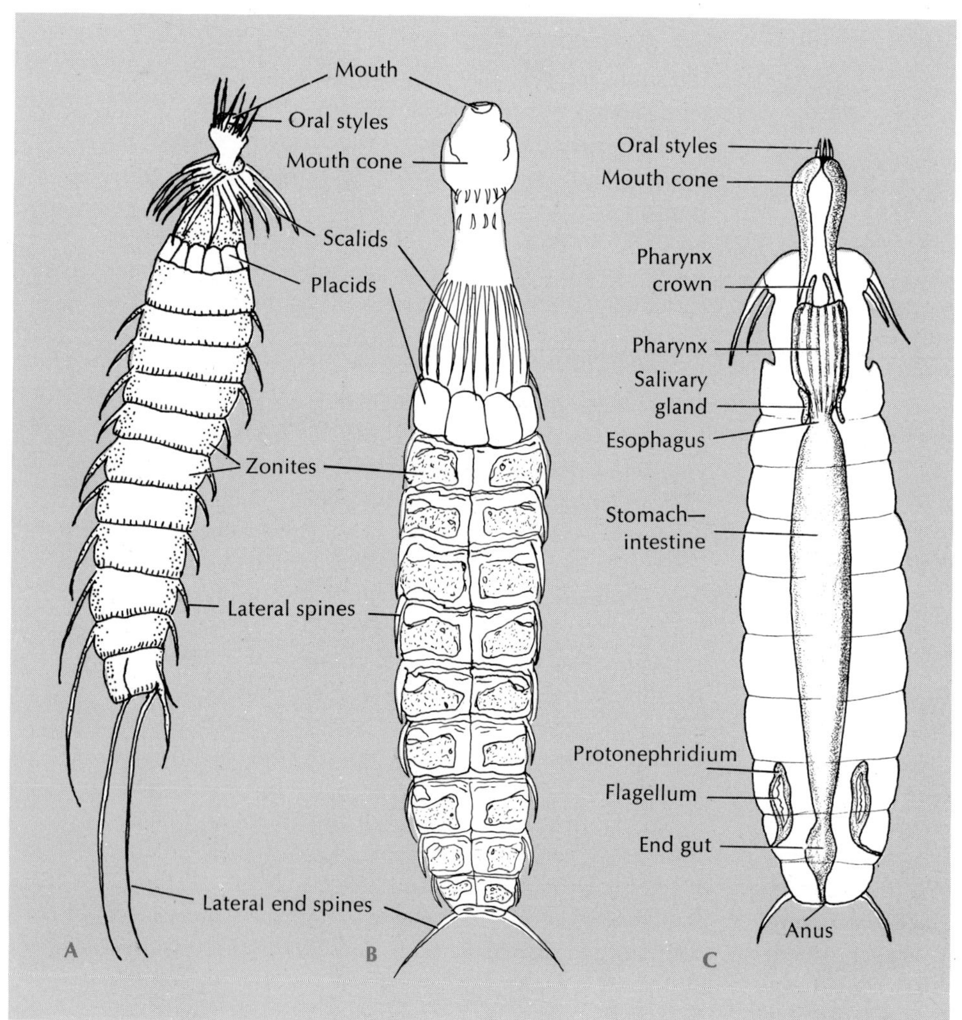

FIG. 14-3

Two kinorhynchs. **A,** *Echinoderella.* **B,** *Pycnophyes.* In **C** digestive system and protonephridia of *Pycnophyes* are shown. Note circles of spines (scalids) in head region and superficial segmentation of zonites. (From Hickman: Biology of the invertebrates, The C. V. Mosby Co.)

spines, flame cells, and retractile head ends; with the nematodes they share a similar pattern of the nervous system, longitudinal cords, and copulatory spicules. Authorities, such as Hyman, for instance, think Kinorhycha represents an offshoot from a common stem that also gave rise to the nematodes and the gastrotrichs. However, K. Lang thinks that the Kinorhyncha and the Priapulida are related because they both have an eversible proboscis, spiny pharynx, similar nervous system, etc.

CLASS NEMATODA

The members of class Nematoda are among the most numerous of any phylum. There are thousands of them in every fistful of soil; water, whether fresh or salt, contains them in great numbers. Some of them are parasitic, but more of them are free living. Many also live in the tissue fluids of plants, where they do considerable damage. It has been estimated that when all the species of nematodes are properly classified, they will outnumber the arthropods.

The distinctive characteristics of this extensive group of animals (which now number more than 12,000 named species) are their cylindric wormlike shape; their flexible but inelastic cuticle, which prevents them from changing length and thickness; and their unique manner of thrashing around, forming patterns of C's and S's. Other more or less unique features are (1) the pharynx, which is three-angled, lined with cuticle and a syncytial epithelium, highly muscular, and often bears differentiated parts, such as glands, swellings (bulbs), and ceca, and (2) the excretory system, consisting either of one or more large gland cells (the renette) opening by an excretory pore in the midventral line, or a canal system (without protonephridia) formed by outgrowth from the renette cells, or both renette and canals together.

Nematodes are now commonly divided by some authorities into two subclasses, Phasmidia and Aphasmidia. Subclass Phasmidia bears a pair of unicellular pouches (**phasmids**) near the posterior tip, a pair of porelike sense organs (**amphids**) at the anterior end, and an excretory system of lateral canals. Most of the common parasitic forms as well as many free-living ones, such as *Rhabditis, Ascaris,* and *Enterobius,* belong to this group. Subclass Aphasmidia lacks phasmids and lateral excretory canals and has spiral or disk-shaped amphids and special caudal glands. Most members of this subclass are free living, but a few parasitic ones include the trichina worm and the giant kidney worm.

The various members of the nematodes are very much alike, although there are some structural differences here and there as well as striking diversities in their life histories. Because of the simplicity of their structure and life history as well as their availability, some member of genus *Ascaris* is usually selected as a type for study in zoology. There are many species of this genus or closely related ones. One of the most common species *(A. megalocephala)* is found in the intestines of horses. *Neoascaris vitulorum* is another species found in cattle. The common roundworm of the cat is *Toxocara cati;* that of the dog, *Toxocara canis.*

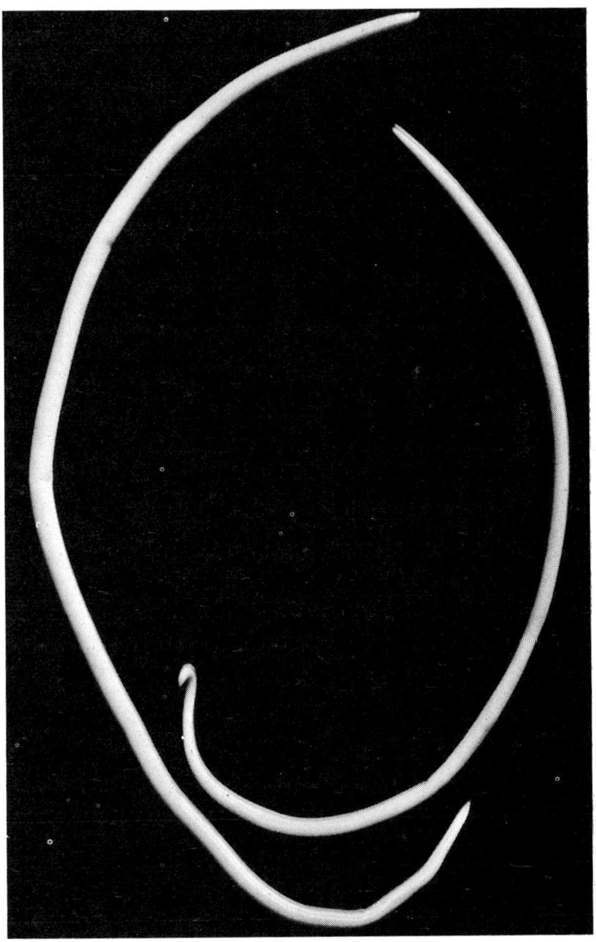

FIG. 14-4

Intestinal roundworm *Ascaris lumbricoides,* male and female. Male (right) has sharp kink in end of tail.

Infection with *Toxocara* is rare in man. The roundworm *A. lumbricoides suilla* found in pigs is morphologically similar to *A. lumbricoides* found in man, but the two species or subspecies seem to be physiologically distinct, for it is rare for the larval form of the one found in man to grow to maturity in the pig and vice versa.

Ascaris lumbricoides—intestinal roundworm

A. lumbricoides is found in man and, according to some authorities, in the pig. It is one of the most common parasites found in man. In some communities of the southern states its incidence may run as high as 5% to 10%, sometimes higher in children. Infection normally occurs by swallowing embryonated ova. Unsanitary habits in which contaminated food and vegetables containing the ova are conveyed to the mouth represent one of the most frequent methods of infection.

Structure. The females of this species are about 20 to 33 cm. long; the males, about 15 to 30 cm. *A. lumbricoides* is pointed at both ends and whitish yellow in color (Fig. 14-4). The body is covered with a tough elastic **cuticle,** and four brownish or whitish lines (dorsal, ventral, and two lateral), thickenings of the subcuticular region, extend the length of the body. The head end bears three lips, a dorsal and two lateroventral, provided with papillae. Between these lips is the mouth. The male can be distinguished from the female by the smaller size and by the sharply curved posterior end that bears two **penial spicules** in the genital pore. In the female the posterior end is straight, and the **vulva,** or genital pore, is found on the ventral surface about one third of the distance from the head end. The **anus** is a ventral slit near the posterior end.

The body wall (Fig. 14-5) is made up of the noncellular cuticle of many layers, formed from the epidermis, a syncytial **epidermis** or hypodermis with many nuclei, and a layer of **longitudinal muscles.** There are no circular muscles. The longitudinal muscles are divided into four bandlike parts by the four longitudinal

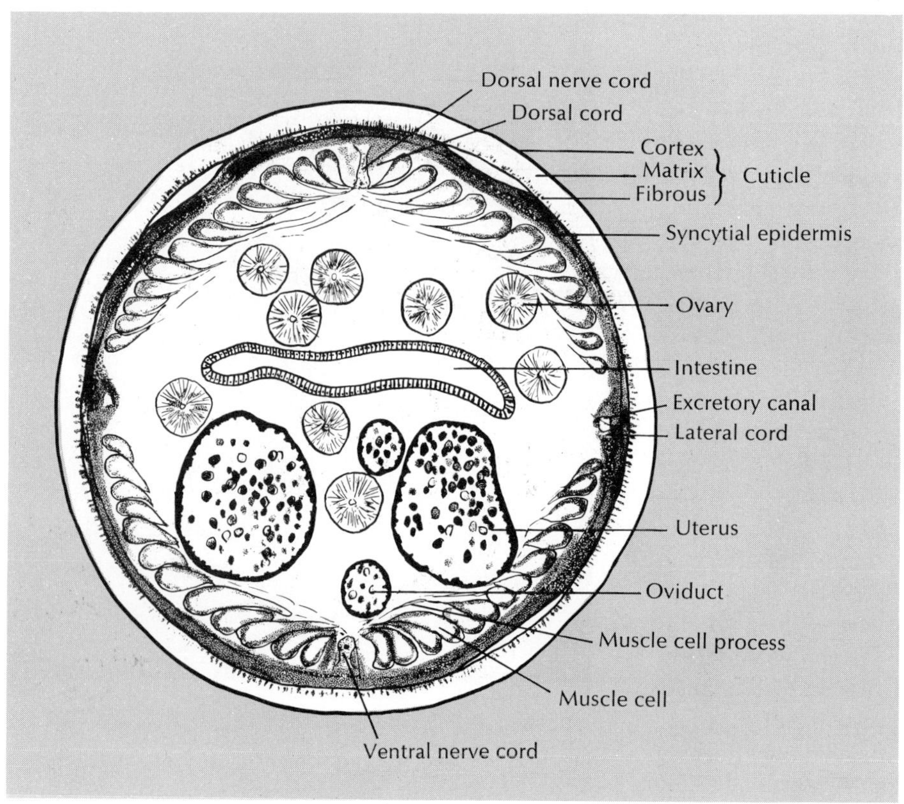

FIG. 14-5

Cross section of female *Ascaris.* Semidiagrammatic.

cords that represent epidermal bulges into the pseudocoel. Two of them are lateral, one middorsal, and one midventral in position. These cords are usually better developed in the anterior regions of the body, and they divide the muscular coat into four quadrants. Each muscle cell is large and spindle shaped. In cross section it shows two portions or zones; an outer U-shaped contractile or fibrillar zone that partly surrounds an inner or protoplasmic zone containing a nucleus. The protoplasmic zone also gives off a process that bends inward and runs to a nerve trunk in either the dorsal or ventral longitudinal cord. In this way the muscle receives its nerve supply. Each muscle quadrant is assumed to have about 150 muscle cells. The **body cavity,** in which the visceral organs lie, is called a **pseudocoel** and is not lined with mesoderm. It is filled with fluid and contains fibers and giant cells (a nematode characteristic).

The alimentary canal consists of a **mouth** (Fig. 14-6), a short muscular sucking **pharynx,** a long nonmuscular **intestine** lined with endodermal cells for absorption, and a short **rectum** with an **anus.**

The excretory system consists of a lateral **excretory canal** in each lateral cord, with a transverse network connecting the two lateral canals anteriorly and a common tube from the transverse network to the ventral **excretory pore** just behind the mouth. There are no flame cells.

There are no special organs for respiration and circulation.

A ring of nerve tissue and ganglia around the pharynx gives rise to several small nerves to the anterior end and two main nerve cords, dorsal and ventral and several small ones to the tail end. Sense organs are poorly developed. The chief ones are the papillae of the lips. Amphids, lateral chemoreceptors characteristic of free-living nematodes, are greatly reduced in *Ascaris.*

The **reproductive organs** are tubular, with many coils in the body cavity, and are attached only at the genital pore (female) or cloaca (male) (Fig. 14-6).

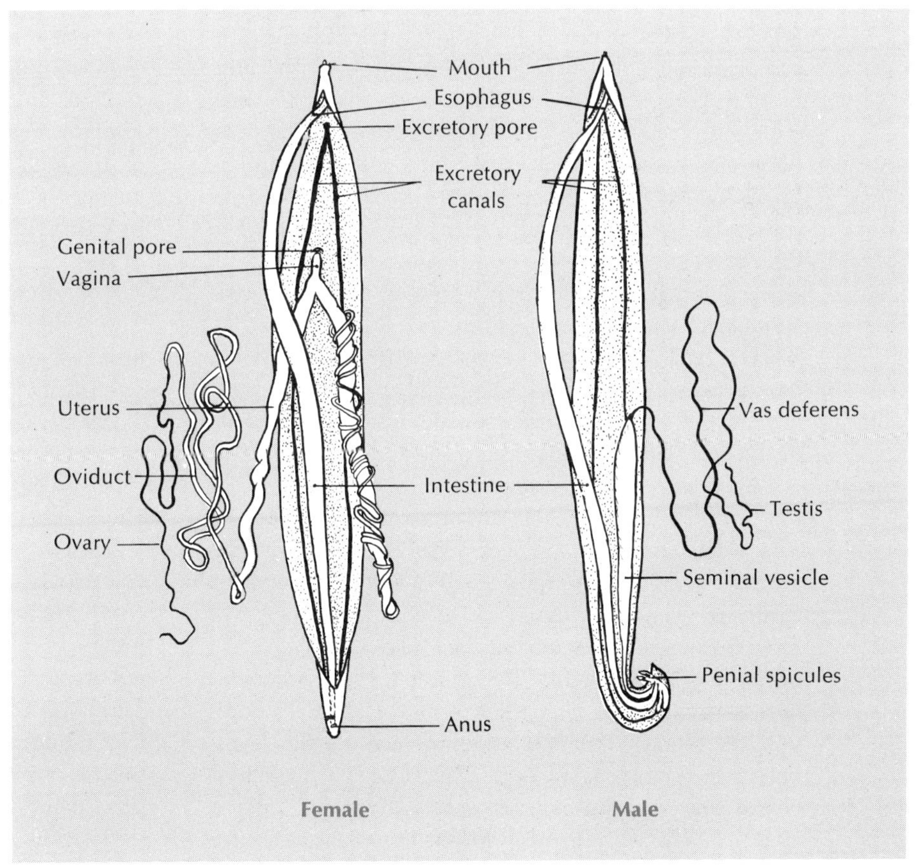

FIG. 14-6

Internal structure of *Ascaris* showing digestive and reproductive systems.

The male system is single and consists of a coiled **testis** for producing sperm, a **vas deferens** for conducting sperm, a **seminal vesicle** for storing sperm, an **ejaculatory tube** for discharging sperm into the **rectum** or cloaca, and the two **penial spicules** for attachment into the female genital pore during copulation. The whole reproductive system is a single, continuous, much-coiled tubule and is unattached, except where it connects with the digestive tract. The various divisions show certain structural differences, such as a gradually increased diameter from the testes to the ejaculatory duct.

Instead of a single reproductive system the female has a partly paired one. It contains two **ovaries** for producing eggs, two **oviducts** for carrying eggs, and two **uteri,** which unite into a common **vagina** that opens to the outside at the genital pore.

Metabolism. Since the ascaris is parasitic in the intestine of man, its food is the partly digested and semi-fluid material found there. Food is sucked into the worm's digestive tract by its muscular esophagus, and after digestion is completed, the soluble food is absorbed through the walls of the intestine and the indigestible part is eliminated through the anus. A thick cuticle protects against the digestive juices of the host. Such oxygen as it needs is obtained mainly from the breakdown of glycogen within its own body. Waste is picked up by the excretory canals and is discharged to the outside.

Locomotion. The ascaris is restricted to dorsoventral bending of its body produced by the alternate contractions of the dorsal and ventral longitudinal muscles. Nevertheless, it can thrash about and, by taking advantage of the friction afforded by the intestinal contents of the host, manages progressive locomotion.

Life cycle. A female ascaris may produce millions of eggs, which she lays at the daily rate of about 200,000. The eggs pass with the feces, are deposited on the ground, and develop into small worms inside their shells. If taken into the body in this form they will grow into mature worms, but they have many hazards. In the first place, a too dry or too cold environment may be fatal to the young worm in the shell. In addition, the sanitary habits of man may prevent the ingestion of the embryonated eggs. Also, if eggs are ingested before they develop embryo worms, they will not be infective. This development within the egg usually requires two to three weeks. When such eggs are swallowed, they pass to the intestine and hatch into tiny larvae (0.2 mm.), which burrow through the intestinal wall into the veins or lymph vessels. In the blood they pass through the heart to the pulmonary capillaries of the lungs, break through into the air passageways, move up the trachea, cross over into the esophagus, and then go down the alimentary canal to the intestine, where they grow to maturity in about two months. Here the two sexes copulate and the female begins her egg laying.

Thus only one host is involved in the life cycle. They do their greatest damage to the host while the juvenile worms are migrating, especially through the lung sacs, where they may cause inflammation. Ordinarily the adult worms live in the upper small intestine, but when numerous, they will wander to other parts of the body, such as the appendix, bile ducts, nose, and sinuses. In very large numbers they are known to cause intestinal obstructions. In its life history the ascaris undergoes four molts before becoming sexually mature. One of these molts occurs in the egg, two in the lungs, and the last one in the intestine of the host.

Other nematodes

In addition to the parasitic nematodes already described, there are many others, some resembling *A. lumbricoides* and others differing in minor details. Most of these differences are found in the mouth regions and in the reproductive system. Nearly all vertebrates, as well as many invertebrates, are parasitized by nematodes.

Not all nematodes are parasites; most are actually free living. Many feed on plant juices, algae, and bacteria; others feed on small live forms; or some may be scavengers that feed upon dead animals and plants. Those parasitic in plants cause galls or nodular growths on roots and leaves. The vinegar eel *Turbatrix,* often found in cider, is a good example of a free-living nematode.

Hookworm. Three common forms of hookworms infect man. *Ancylostoma duodenale* is common in Europe, Asia, Africa, and a few places in North and South America. A closely related species, *A. braziliense,* is restricted to certain regions in Brazil. *Necator americanus* is the common American form, although it was introduced from Africa. These worms are called hookworms because the male has a hook-shaped body; they actually have no hooks. The adult worms are 10 to 15 mm. long, the females being longer than the males. They have cutting plates or teeth in their mouths by which the worms cut holes into the intestinal mucosa (Fig. 14-7). By means of the sucking pharynx they draw blood, fluids, etc. into their intestines. To facilitate their feeding they have an anticoagulant in their mouth secretions to prevent blood clotting. They often take more blood into their bodies than they can digest, and they leave a bleeding wound after feeding.

The life cycle is similar in some ways to that of the ascaris. The sexes copulate in the intestine, after which the female lays several thousand eggs daily. The eggs pass out with the host's feces and hatch in about a day on warm moist soil. The larvae feed on bacteria or organic matter and undergo two molts.

They are now about 0.5 mm. long and are infective. If opportunity does not present itself, they may live (without feeding) in warm, moist soil four to eight weeks; in a cool, moist environment they have been known to live six months. If infected soil touches the skin, the larvae burrow through the skin into the blood. In warm countries the bare foot is the most common point of entry. That entrance causes a mild irritation known as "ground itch." One can also become infected by swallowing larvae. After entering, their subsequent journey is the same as that described for the ascaris. In their journey to the intestine they undergo a third molting, and then after reaching the intestine, a fourth molting. They may live for several years in the host, and an infection of 25 to 50 worms may cause pronounced anemia. Infection with 1,500 worms is known. The results of infection are, in addition to anemia, retarded mental and physical growth and general loss of energy.

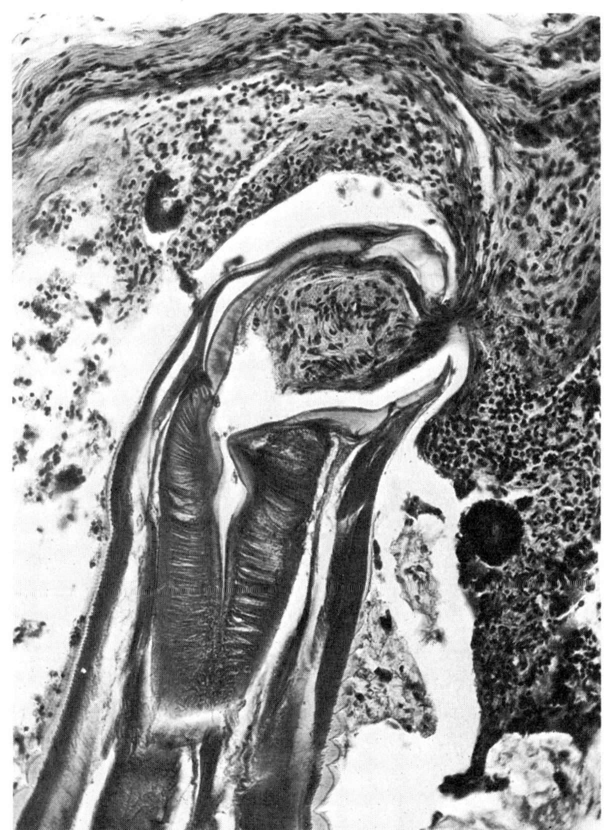

FIG. 14-7

Hookworm attached to human intestine. Note cutting plates of mouth pinching off bit of mucosa from which thick muscular pharynx will suck blood. Mouth secretes anticoagulant to prevent blood clotting. (AFIP No. 33810.)

In the United States hookworm disease is common in the rural areas of the southern states. In certain countries such as China and India the incidence of infection is much higher. Sanitary disposal of feces and the wearing of shoes are excellent preventives. Worms can be gotten rid of in infected persons by treatment with certain drugs.

Trichina worm. *Trichinella spiralis* is a nematode worm 1.5 to 4 mm. long and is responsible for the serious disease **trichinosis.** The adults live in the small intestine, where the female burrows into the intestinal mucosa and for several weeks produces living larvae about 0.1 mm. long. These larvae penetrate into the lymphatics or veins and are carried to the skeletal muscles, especially those of the diaphragm, tongue, eye, and neck. Here they coil up and form a cyst that becomes calcified (Fig. 14-8). Each cyst measures 0.25 to 0.5 mm. in diameter. In the cyst the worm may live for 10 to 20 years if undisturbed, but eventually the worms die. When the cysts are swallowed in the ingestion of infected meat, the larvae are liberated in the intestine and develop in a few days into mature worms and die within a few months, after releasing many living larvae into the blood of the host.

Besides man the worms infect many mammals, such as hogs, rats, cats, and dogs. Man becomes infected by eating raw or improperly cooked pork. Hogs usually get their infection by eating garbage containing pork scraps infected with the cysts. Hogs may also get infected from eating rats. Rats can get the worms from infected pork

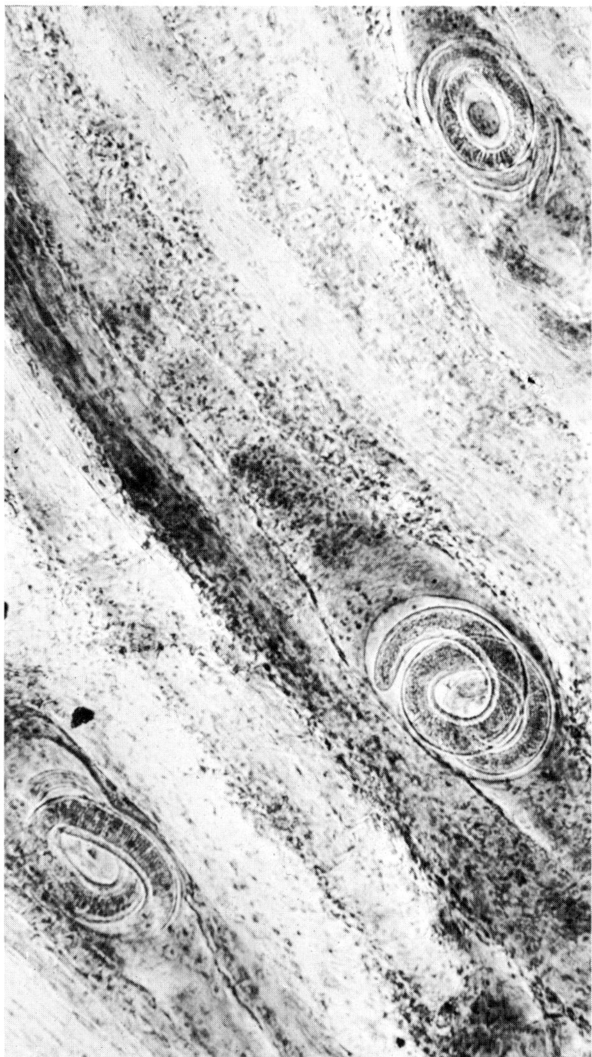

FIG. 14-8

Muscle infected with trichina worm *Trichinella spiralis*. Larvae may live 10 to 20 years in these cysts. If eaten in poorly cooked meat, larvae are liberated in intestine. They quickly mature and release many larvae into blood of host.

scraps or from eating each other. Nearly 75% of all rats are infected. As far as man is concerned, the infection of man is a "dead-end alley" for the worms, unless human flesh should be eaten, which is rare.

In the United States 18% to 20% of the people are infected, but this infection is usually mild and gives rise to no pronounced symptoms. Heavy infections, however, cause trichinosis, the symptoms of which vary greatly. Some of these symptoms are intestinal disturbances, muscular pains, fever, mental conditions, and edema. The disease often terminates fatally. There is no effective treatment for trichinosis. Trichinosis is common among arctic natives from eating poorly cooked meat of polar bears that are heavily infected.

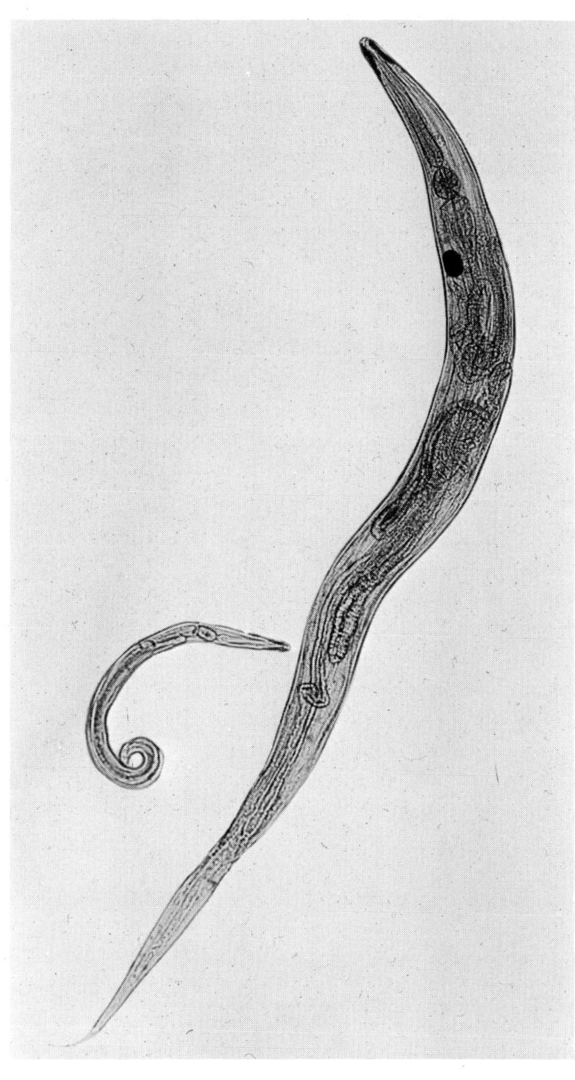

FIG. 14-9

Male and female (larger) pinworms, *Enterobius vermicularis*. Infestation in up to 40% of school children has been found in some communities; this worm may be most common and most widely distributed of human helminth parasites. (Courtesy Indiana University School of Medicine, Indianapolis.)

The simplest preventive measure is the thorough cooking of all pork; a pink color indicates insufficient cooking. Cooking garbage before it is fed to hogs is required in many communities, a practice that keeps down the incidence of infected pork.

Pinworms. The pinworm *Enterobius* or *Oxyuris vermicularis* is also very common, especially in warm countries. In some communities nearly 40% of the children are infected (Fig. 14-9). The adult worms live in the cecum and adjacent parts of the large intestine with their heads attached to the mucosa. The female is the larger, being about 12 mm. long and about the thickness of a thread. Females with eggs often migrate to the anal region at night and deposit their eggs (Fig. 14-10). Since they cause irritation, scratching often contaminates fingers as well as bedclothing with the ova, and reinfection can occur if the person is unsanitary. Each generation lasts about three to four weeks, and if reinfection does not occur, the infection will die out. When the ova are swallowed, they are carried to the duodenum, where they hatch. They then pass through the small intestine, molt, and become adults in the upper part of the large intestine. No intermediate host is necessary. Infection through inhalation of dust containing the ova is known to occur.

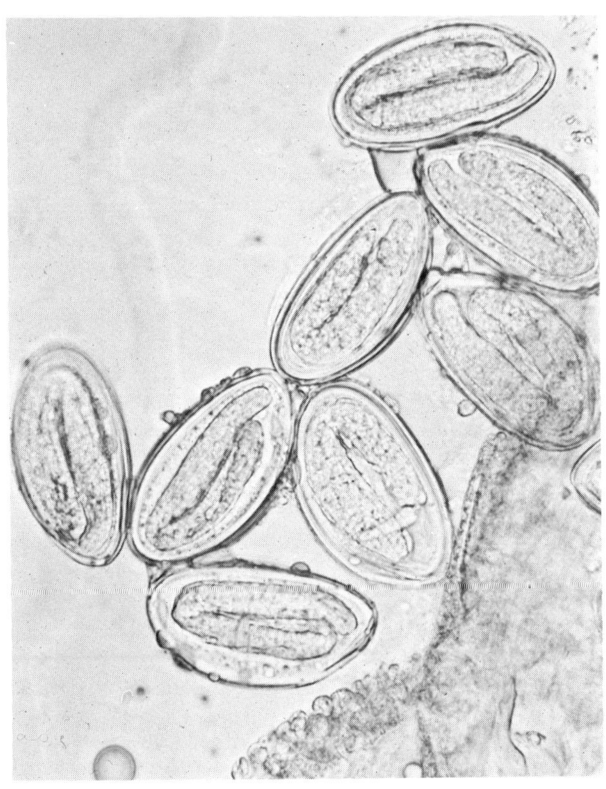

FIG. 14-10

Group of pinworm eggs containing embryos. These eggs are usually discharged by female just outside of anus of infected persons. By scratching, fingernails and clothing are contaminated with eggs, which serve as immediate source of future reinfections. No intermediate host required, and life cycle is about a month. (Courtesy Indiana University School of Medicine, Indianapolis.)

The widespread distribution of pinworm infection has been revealed by the better development of diagnostic techniques. The older fecal examinations have been found to be unreliable in giving a true picture of the state of this infection. Present-day methods of diagnosis emphasize perianal and perineal scrapings and show a much higher incidence of pinworm infection than was shown by the older methods. These newer diagnoses reveal that in some communities there may be 100% infection. Authorities are agreed that there may be ways by which infection is disseminated that are not fully known. An interesting fact is that incidence is higher among white persons than among Negroes. Children also have a higher incidence than do adults. Surgically removed appendices reveal, in many cases, the presence of pinworms. Pinworms in small numbers cause few symptoms, but heavy infections are nearly always marked by intestinal disturbance and intense pruritus. Injuries are caused in the intestinal wall where the worms are attached, and these sites may be invaded by bacteria. In some cases pinworms are thought to cause appendicitis. Extreme nervousness and irritability may be manifested in persons who are heavily infected. The worms may also give off toxic substances, which add to the clinical picture.

Whipworms. These nematodes (*Trichuris trichiura*) are about 1 inch long, with the anterior part of the body prolonged into a narrow, whiplike structure. They are parasites in the intestine of children in the tropics, and they fasten themselves to the mucosa wall. Eggs are passed in the feces into the soil, where they embryonate in about three weeks. When eggs are ingested, the larvae hatch, develop into adults in two months, and live in the colon. Infection may be acquired by eating contaminated food or earth (geophagy). Heavy infestation produces a wasting diarrhea or even anemia because they may suck blood.

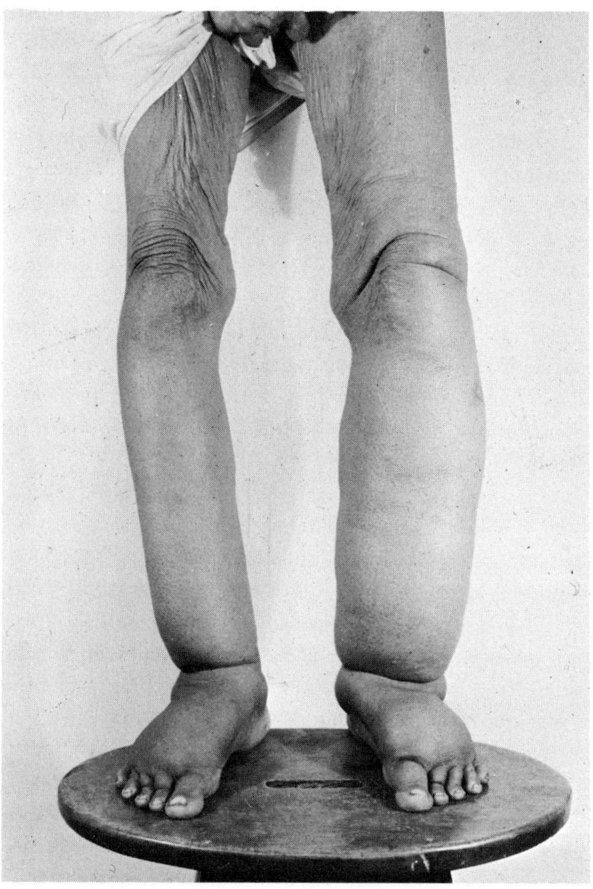

FIG. 14-11

Elephantiasis of leg. Condition produced by adult filarial worms of *Wuchereria bancrofti,* which live in lymph passages and block flow of lymph. Females give birth to microfilariae, which circulate in blood, are picked up by a biting mosquito (female of several genera of mosquitoes), and are transmitted to another individual bitten by infected mosquito. Larvae are not infective until they have passed through this part of their life cycle in mosquito. (AFIP No. A-44430-1.)

Filarial worms. Filarial worms (*Wuchereria bancrofti*) are found in tropical and subtropical countries. The adult worms (2 to 4 inches long) live in the lymphatic glands where they often obstruct the flow of lymph, producing in severe infections **elephantiasis,** which involves an excessive growth of connective tissue and enormous swelling of the affected parts, such as the scrotum, legs, or arms (Fig. 14-11). The females give birth to microscopic larvae, known as **microfilariae,** which are discharged into the lymph and are carried to the blood. Here they undergo no further development unless sucked up by a mosquito of the right kind (usually some species of *Culex* or *Aëdes*). During the night the larvae are found in the surface blood vessels but are in the deeper vessels during the day. In places where there are diurnal mosquitoes, the larvae reverse this periodicity. In the mosquito they pass from the stomach to the thoracic muscles, where they metamorphose, and then migrate to the proboscis. When a mosquito bites a person, the larvae crawl out on the skin, enter it, and pass to the lymph vessel. In the lymph glands they coil up and mature.

In a large percentage of cases filarial infection is not injurious to man. When there are repeated reinfections, the condition of elephantiasis is built up in time.

Guinea worms. Guinea worms (*Dracunculus medinensis*) are long worms, the females being from 2 to 4 feet long and 1/25 inch in diameter (Fig. 14-12). They are found in Africa, Arabia, India, and other places in the East. They are also found in South America, the West Indies, and in dogs and mink in the United States. The female adult worm (the males are small and rarely found) lies near the surface of the skin, where it has the appearance of an elongated and much-coiled varicose vein. The anterior end of the worm protrudes through an ulcer in the skin, and the living young are discharged to the outside when the ulcer comes in contact with water. If the larvae are ejected into water and come in contact with *Cyclops,* a crustacean, they enter its body and undergo development (Fig. 14-13). When a human being swallows infected *Cyclops* in drinking water, the worms pass to the intestine and then migrate to the subcutaneous tissue, where they develop into mature worms in about a year.

The time-honored method of removing the worm is by winding it out on a stick, a little each day. If the worm is ruptured by winding too rapidly, serious consequences may result. It is interesting to note that the "fiery serpent" of Biblical times is thought to have been this worm.

Giant kidney worms. The giant kidney worm (*Dioctophyma renale*) may attain a length of 1 meter (female) and is perhaps the longest nematode. It is a bright red color and is a parasite of dogs, minks, and other mammals. They live awhile in the abdominal cavity, but the adults are found mostly in the kidneys (usually the right one), where they digest away the kidney substance during a period of one to three years.

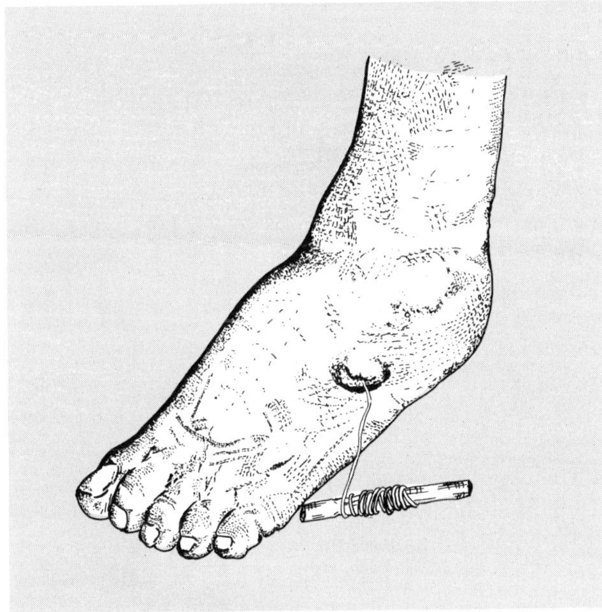

FIG. 14-12

Guinea worm *Dracunculus* is slowly extracted from body of its host by making one turn of stick each day to prevent rupturing worm and causing bacterial infection. If not removed, the worm would die in time and become calcified.

Infection may be without symptoms or it may be fatal. Eggs are passed in the urine and are swallowed by branchiobdellid annelid worms (attached to crayfish), where they hatch in six to twelve months. After encystment in the annelid, which is eaten by a certain fish, they develop further and encyst in the fish. The cycle of two years is completed when the fish is eaten by a mammal (Woodhead).

Ecology and economic relations of nematodes

A great student of nematodes once said that if the earth were to disappear, leaving only the nematode worms, the general contour of the earth's surface would be outlined by the worms, for their presence is indicated in nearly every conceivable kind of ecologic niche. They are the most highly adaptable of all metazoans, for the same species may be found in arctic as well as tropical habitats. They are not common in extremes of dry and wet soils, but many can live in either freshwater or terrestrial habitats if the latter have water films. They have been found in the soil to a depth of 25 feet. Rich agricultural lands may have as many as five billion nematodes per acre in the few inches of topsoil.

Although many nematode species are cosmopolitan, some are restricted to special habitats, such as *Turbatrix* in the felt mats of beer mugs in Germany. Many nematodes, especially the microscopic ones, live in or around the roots of plants. Larval forms feed extensively on root tissues, which react by forming galls. Excessive gall formation causes the death of the plant. Plant parasitic nematodes do extensive damage to many crops because several generations of worms each year are possible in warm soil. Recently the golden potato nematode (*Heterodera rostochiensis*) has damaged potato crops to an alarming extent in many parts of the country. Nematodes occur wherever decaying animal or plant food is found. Many species can withstand great extremes of temperature and desiccation. Nema-

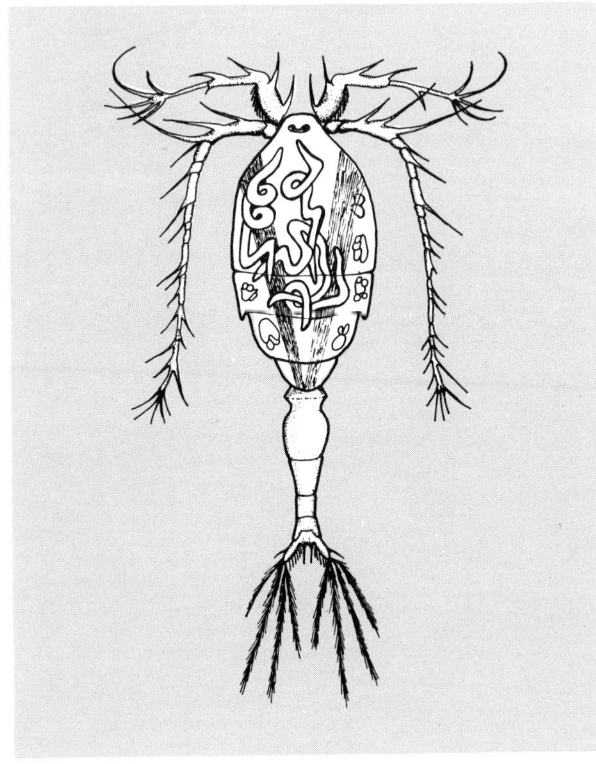

FIG. 14-13

Cyclops copepod with four larvae of *Dracunculus* in its body cavity. Man becomes infected by drinking contaminated water containing infected *Cyclops*. These larvae are about 500 μ long. (Modified from many sources.)

tode eggs are especially resistant and are easily transported long distances by animals and winds.

CLASS NEMATOMORPHA

The popular name for class Nematomorpha is "horsehair worms," based on the superstition that they arise from horsehairs that happen to fall into the water. They have a wide distribution and are found in aquatic habitats in both the temperate and tropical zones. These animals are interesting in that in the adult condition they never feed, for their digestive system is degenerate, and they are free living. The larval stages, however, are parasitic in some arthropod host. The different species vary in length from a few millimeters to about a meter, and many of them have the habit of coiling themselves into a knot, often around an aquatic plant or other object.

Structure. The worms are long and slender, with a cylindric body (Fig. 14-14). With one or two exceptions, the females are longer than the males, in which the posterior ends are slightly curved as in nematodes. The diameter of the body rarely exceeds 1 or 2 mm. and is usually uniform throughout except at the ends, which are rounded or slightly tapered. The coloration is usually a dirty brown, although brighter hues are occasionally found. The surface of the body may bear small papillae (areoles), which give a rough appearance to the cuticle. Small bristles or pores may also be found on these areoles. The body wall consists of a cuticle of a fibrous nature, an epidermis, and a musculature of longitudinal fibers only. Dorsal and ventral longitudinal cords (thickenings) of the epidermis may also be present. A pseudocoel of some form is found, which in some nematomorphs is filled with parenchyma.

The digestive system appears to be more or less incomplete in both the adult and larval forms, although the latter absorb food from their hosts through the body wall. When present, the mouth is located at the anterior end, followed by a pharynx, an elongated intestine, a cloaca, and an anus at the terminal end. Circulatory, respiratory, and excretory systems are lacking. The nervous system contains a nerve ring around the pharynx

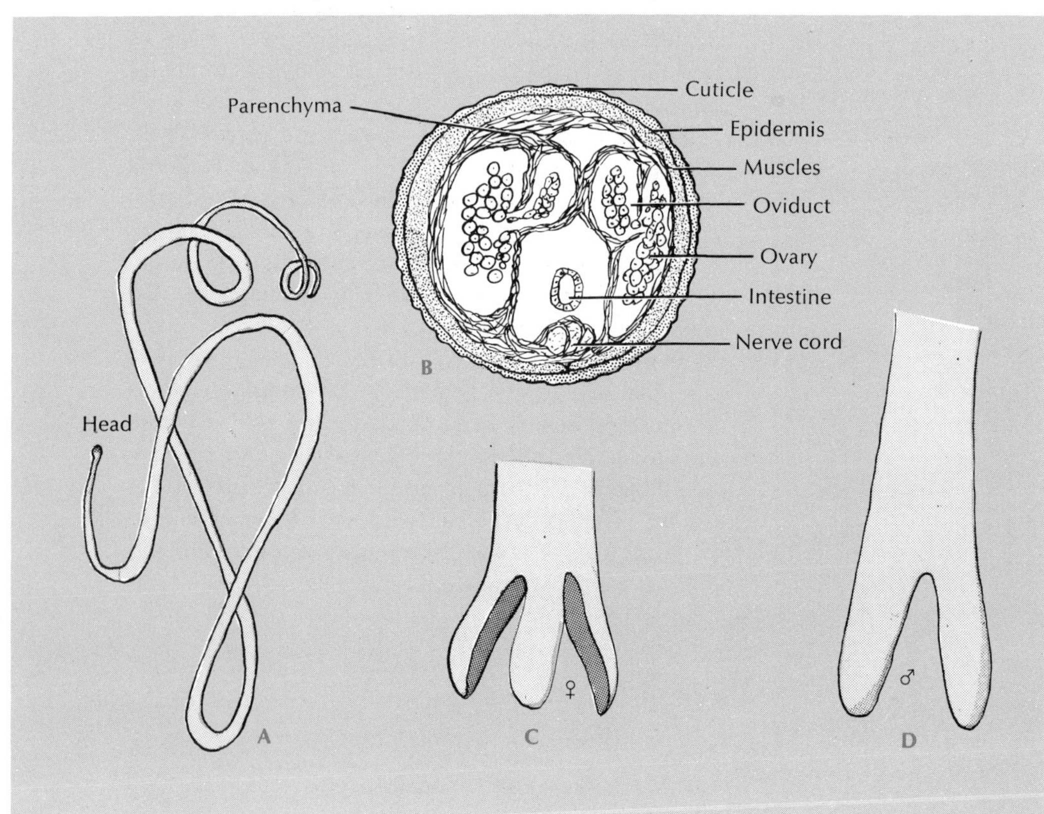

FIG. 14-14

A, A nematomorph. **B,** Cross section of female nematomorph. Posterior end of female *Paragordius,* **C,** and of male *Paragordius,* **D.** (From Hickman: Biology of the invertebrates, The C. V. Mosby Co.)

and a single midventral cord. Sensory structures are represented by various sensory cells located on the epidermis and by eyespots in some.

Each sex has a pair of gonads that run through much of the body in some species. The female system on each side contains an ovary and an oviduct that enters into the cloaca. In the male system each testis discharges its sperm through a short sperm duct into the cloaca, which may bear some spines but no copulatory spicules. The female lays strings of eggs, which develop into the larvae. These swim around and may enter the body of an aquatic host, although they must find the right host before they can complete their development. This is usually a grasshopper, beetle, or cricket that may happen to come to aquatic habitats. Only one host is involved in the parasitic existence of horsehair worms. The larval worm remains in the body cavity of the host for several months, grows in size until it reaches the adult condition, leaves its host, and molts. As an adult it leads a free existence in the water until it dies.

Common species of Nematomorpha are represented by *Gordius robustus, G. aquaticus, Paragordius varius,* and *Nectonema agile*. Of these, only the last-named is marine.

The nematomorphs were long included with the nematodes, with which they have many common characters, such as the structure of the cuticle, presence of epidermal cords, longitudinal muscles only, and pattern of nervous system. However, the early larval form of some species has a striking resemblance to the priapulid so that it is impossible to state to just what group in the Aschelminthes they are most closely related.

Derivation and meaning of basic terminology

amictic (Gr. *a,* without, + *miktos,* mixed or blended). Pertains to diploid egg of rotifers or the females that produce such eggs.

amphid (Gr. *amphi,* double). One of a pair of anterior sense organs in certain nematodes.

Ascaris (Gr. *askaris,* intestinal worm).

Dioctophyma (Gr. *di,* double, + *okto,* eight, + *phyma,* swelling). Refers to the papillae around the mouth, 6 to 18 in number.

Dracunculus (L. *draco,* dragon, + *unculus,* small).

elephantiasis (Gr. *elephas,* elephant, + *osis,* state of). A condition of enormous swelling and connective tissue growth induced by filarial worms.

Enterobius (Gr. *enteron,* intestine, + *bios,* life).

Gordius (Greek mythologic king who tied an intricate knot).

mictic (Gr. *miktos,* mixed or blended). Pertains to haploid egg of rotifers or the females that lay such eggs.

Necator (L. *necator,* killer).

Oxyuris (Gr. *oxys,* sharp, + *oura,* tail).

phasmid (Gr. *phaskolos,* pouch). One of a pair of glands found in the posterior end of certain nematodes.

pseudocoel (Gr. *pseudes,* false, + *koilos,* hollow). Body cavity in the roundworms is so called because it is not a true coelom.

solenocyte (Gr. *solen,* pipe, + *kytos,* cell). Special type of protonephridium in which the end bulb bears a flagellum instead of a tuft of cilia, as in Platyhelminthes.

Trichinella (Gr. *trichos,* hair).

trichinosis (Gr. *trichos,* hair, + *osis,* suffix meaning state of). Parasitized condition produced by heavy infection of the trichina worm.

Phylum Acanthocephala*

GENERAL RELATIONS

The acanthoceph group of parasitic worms was formerly included as a class under Nemathelminthes but is now considered as a separate phylum in its own right. These worms are endoparasitic, living as adults in the intestines of vertebrates and as larval forms in arthropods. The worm derives its name from one of its most distinctive characters, a cylindric invaginable proboscis bearing rows of recurved spines, by which it attaches itself to the intestine of its host. When inverted into the proboscis sheath by special muscles, the proboscis has its spines pointed anteriorly; when everted, the spines point posteriorly. The origin of the term is thus derived from the Gr. *akantha,* spine or thorn, + *kephale,* head. The group is commonly known as the spiny-headed worms. They possess several peculiar features that make it difficult to determine their relations to other animal groups. Their totally parasitic habits have no doubt been responsible for many of their distinctive characters. None of them has a free-living stage, and neither the larvae nor adults have a digestive system at any stage of their existence. In their affinities they resemble in some ways platyhelminths and in other ways aschelminths, in which group they were once included. They differ from most aschelminths in having no digestive system, in having circular muscles, and in having certain peculiarities of the reproductive system. On the other hand, they show some resemblances to aschelminths in possessing a pseudocoel and a syncytial nu-

*A-kan′tho-sef″a-la (Gr. *akantha,* spine or thorn, + *kephale,* head).

cleated epidermis. They resemble platyhelminths in their reproductive system and their method of development.

About 300 species of acanthocephs have been named, most of which parasitize fish, birds, and mammals. They are worldwide in their distribution. In size the various species show a wide range from less than 2 mm. to 650 mm. in length. Sexual dimorphism is usually quite marked, the females being much larger than the males of the same species. The shape of the body also shows considerable difference among the various species. In some forms the body is long, slender, and cylindric; in others it may be laterally flattened or short and plump. The body surface may be smooth, but often it is wrinkled. In most cases the body is capable of considerable extension and contraction because of the muscular arrangement. The color of worms is often determined by the kind of food they absorb from their hosts, ranging all the way from a dirty brown to brighter colors.

Acanthocephs share with rotifers, nematodes, and tunicates the condition of cell or nuclear constancy. Van Cleve found in five different species of *Eorhynchus* the same number of nuclei in each of several organs, such as the lemnisci (3 nuclei), the cement glands (8 nuclei), the uterus (2 nuclei), the retractor muscles of hooks (4 nuclei), and the selective apparatus (2 nuclei). On this account, increase in size of the worm is correlated with a definite increase in cell size rather than in cell or nuclei number. Some theories consider such a constancy a barrier to evolutionary development and progress.

CHARACTERISTICS

1. Anterior end with **spiny retractile proboscis** and **sheath**
2. Body cylindric in form, in three sections—proboscis, neck and trunk
3. **Epidermis syncytial in structure** and covered with cuticle and containing **fluid-filled lacunae;** cell or nuclei constancy pronounced
4. Body wall with circular and longitudinal muscle layers
5. Body cavity fluid filled, without epithelial lining
6. **No digestive tract**
7. Excretory system (when present) with two branched ciliated protonephridia, which are connected to a common excretory duct
8. No circulatory or respiratory organs
9. Nervous system with a central ganglion on the proboscis sheath and nerves to the proboscis and posterior parts of the body
10. Sensory papillae near male genital orifice and on the proboscis
11. Separate sexes; male organs of paired testes formed in cordlike ligament, vas deferens, cement glands, and penis; female organs of paired ovaries formed in a ligament and breaking down into ova; young develop in body cavity of female; special selector apparatus in female system
12. **Parasitic in the intestine of vertebrates**

CLASSIFICATION

The acanthocephs have been classified in various ways by different authorities who have worked with this group. The most recent classification is that of Hyman, who has divided the phylum into three orders but into no classes. The classification is based upon the arrangement of the proboscis spines and a few other characteristics.

Order 1. Archiacanthocephala (ar″ki-a-kan′tho-sef″a-la) (Gr. *arch,* chief, + *acantha,* spine or thorn, + *kephale,* head). Acanthocephs with an excretory system of protonephridia; median lacunar channels; proboscis spines in a concentric arrangement. Example: *Macracanthorhynchus hirudinaceus* (intestinal worm of pigs).

Order 2. Palaeacanthocephala (pa″le-a-kan′tho-sef″a-la) (Gr. *palaios,* old, + acanthocephala). Acanthocephs without excretory system; with lateral lacunar channels; with the proboscis spines in alternating radial rows. Example: *Leptorhynchoides thecatus* (a common fish parasite).

Order 3. Eocanthocephala (e″o-kan′tho-sef″a-la) (Gr. *eos,* dawn, + acanthocephala). Acanthocephs without an excretory system; with median lacunar channels; with proboscis spines radially arranged. Example: *Neoechinorhynchus emydis* (a common parasite of turtles).

REPRESENTATIVE TYPE

The acanthoceph that is used as a type description of the phylum is *Macracanthorhynchus hirudinaceus,* which occurs in the small intestine of the pig throughout the world. It has also been found occasionally in other mammals. Its common occurrence and large size have caused it to be extensively studied from every aspect, and its life cycle has been known for a long time.

Macracanthorhynchus hirudinaceus—intestinal spiny-headed worm of pigs

Structure. The cylindric body of *Macracanthorhynchus* is widest near the anterior end and tapers to the posterior end. At the anterior end is the **proboscis**

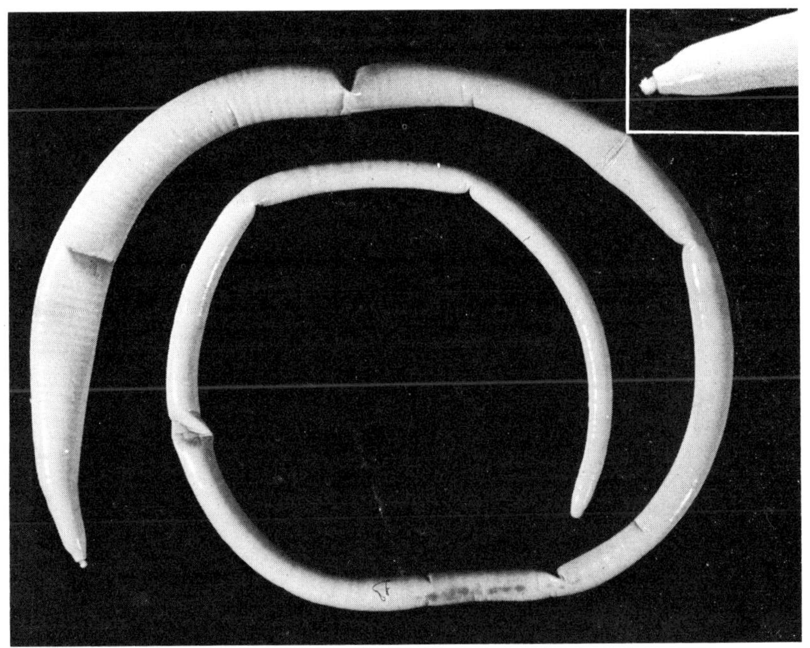

FIG. 14-15

Spiny-headed worm of pigs, *Macracanthorhynchus hirudinaceus* (female), shown about life size. Inset is enlarged view of head showing proboscis.

(Fig. 14-15) and at the posterior end is the **genital pore.** The **body** is covered by a thin **cuticle,** beneath which is the syncytial **epidermis.** The epidermis or hypodermis contains the lacunar system of ramifying fluid-filled canals, which do not communicate with anything outside the epidermis. This system, unique in the Acanthocephala, absorbs and distributes food from the host. The proboscis bears six rows of recurved hooks for clinging to the intestine and is attached to the neck region (Fig. 14-16). In size the female is from 10 to 65 cm. in length and usually less than 1 cm. in thickness. The male is only about one-fourth the size of the female and is provided with a **genital bursa,** which is partly everted through the terminal genital pore (Fig. 14-17).

The **body cavity** (which is not a true coelom) is lined with **longitudinal muscles; circular muscles** are found outside of the longitudinal fibers. At the anterior end is the **proboscis sheath,** which receives the proboscis when the latter is retracted by the **invertor** and **retractor** muscles (Fig. 14-18). Attached to the neck region are two elongated **lemnisci** (extensions of the epidermis and lacunar system), which may act as reservoirs for the fluid of the neck region when the proboscis is invaginated. Tubular **genital ligaments** or ligament sacs run back to the posterior end of the worm. The **excretory system,** which is difficult to distinguish,

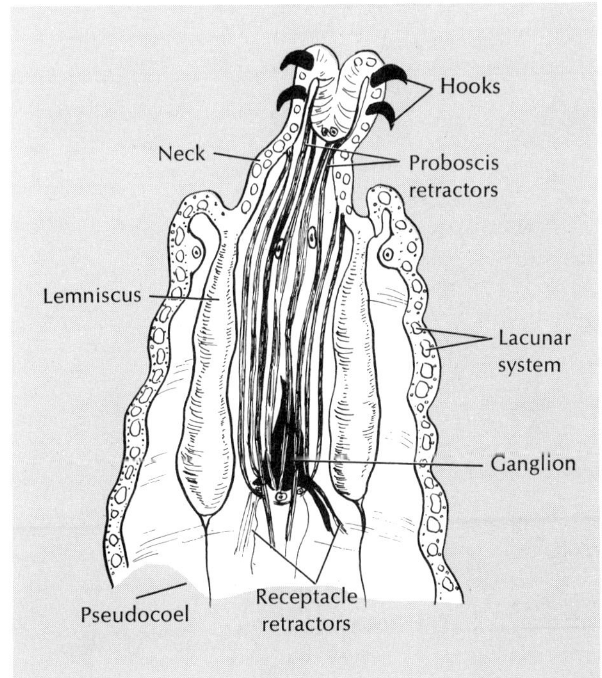

FIG. 14-16

Longitudinal section through anterior end of acanthoceph with proboscis partially everted. Recurved spines, or hooks, are numerous and their arrangements have taxonomic significance. (After Hamann, modified from Hyman; from Hickman: Biology of the invertebrates, The C. V. Mosby Co.)

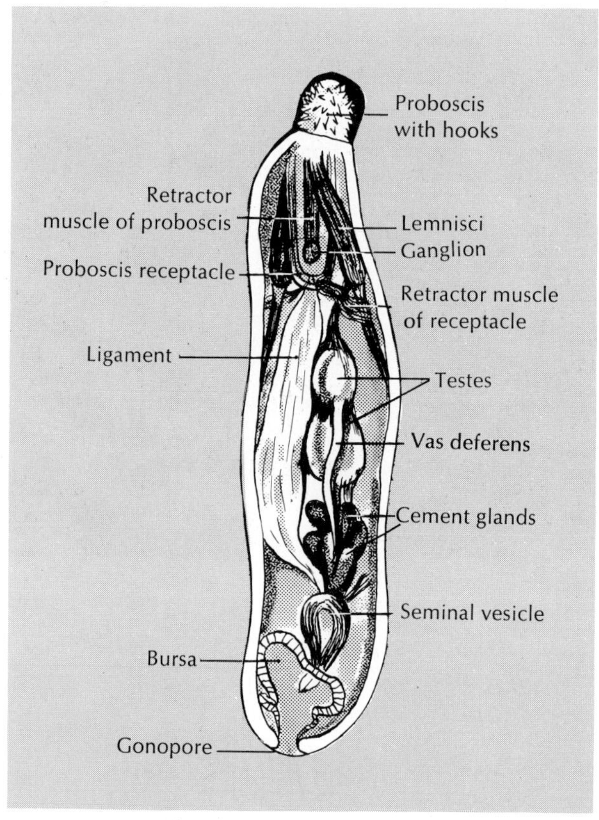

FIG. 14-17

Diagram of internal structure of male acanthoceph.

consists of paired protonephridia lying dorsal to the reproductive ducts and ligament. Each protonephridium is much branched with flame cells, and the two unite to form a common tube that opens into either the sperm duct or the uterus.

In the **female** the genital ligament bears a whitish ovarian tissue with masses of eggs scattered over it as well as in the body cavity. A single funnel-shaped oviduct is modified at its posterior end into a **uterus** and **vagina.** A special selective apparatus (Fig. 14-19) forms the anterior part of the genital tract or oviduct and is provided with a rejection pore through which eggs and immature embryos are returned to the pseudocoel or to one of the ligament sacs; the mature embryos pass on into the uterus and vagina. The latter opens through the genital pore, which also receives the male penis during copulation. The **male** organs consist of paired **testes** on the genital ligament and a **vas deferens** from the anterior end of each testis, running side by side with the common **ejaculatory duct,** which ends in a small penis or cirrus at the posterior end of the body. The penis projects into a copulatory bursa, which grips the posterior end of the female during copulation. **Ce-**

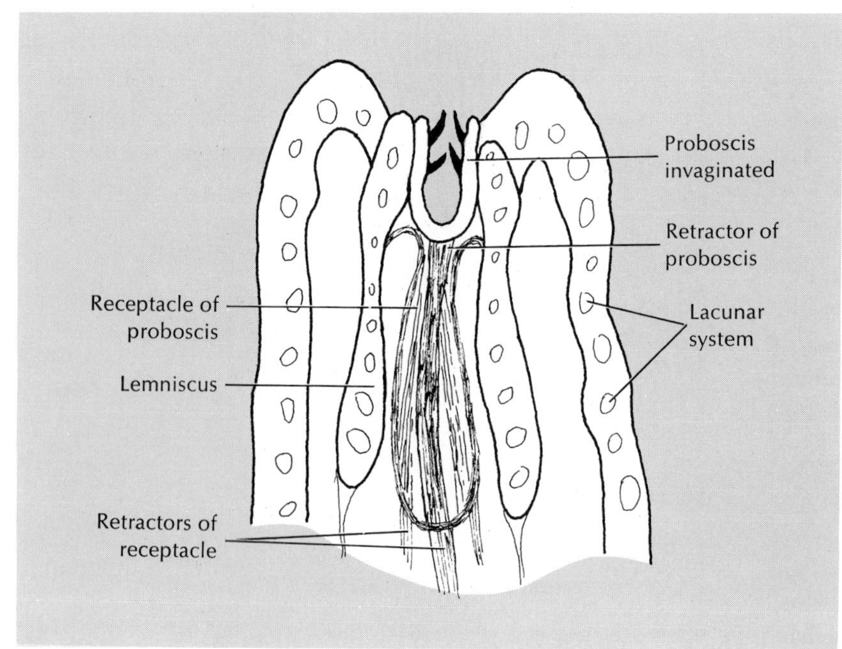

FIG. 14-18

Diagram of longitudinal section through anterior end of acanthoceph showing relations of invaginated proboscis and other structures. Note spines, or hooks, pointed forward in this position. (From Hickman: Biology of the invertebrates, The C. V. Mosby Co.)

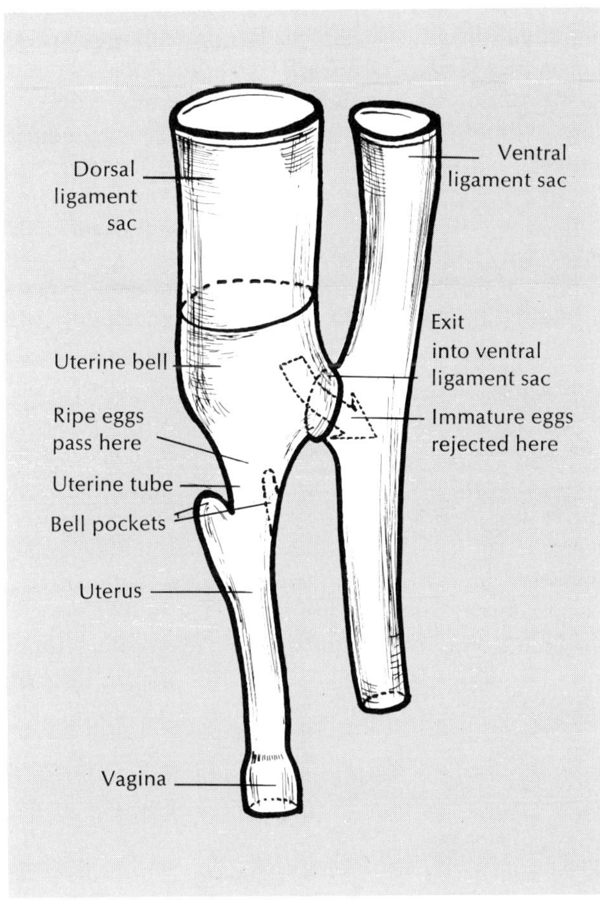

FIG. 14-19

Genital selective apparatus of female Acanthocephala (diagrammatic). This is unique device for separating immature from mature fertilized eggs. Uterine bell draws in developing eggs through dorsal ligament sac and passes them toward uterine tube. Immature eggs are shunted by special aperture into ventral ligament sac or pseudocoel; mature ones continue through uterus and vagina to outside.

ment glands pour their secretions into the vasa deferentia and the copulatory bursa for binding the bodies of the two sexes together during copulation.

The **nervous system,** also difficult to distinguish, consists of an oval, flat ganglion on the proboscis and a number of nerves running anteriorly to the proboscis and posteriorly to other parts of the body. The few tactile sense organs are found on the proboscis and the male bursa.

Life cycle. This worm, which is common in pigs, has for its intermediate host the larva, or grub, of the June beetle *(Lachnosterna).* The eggs that are discharged from the female worm contain embryos provided with hooks and are eliminated in the feces of the primary host. The eggs have several coats or shells and do not hatch until eaten by the intermediate host. In this host the first larva (acanthor) burrows through the intestine and encysts as a juvenile. Pigs become infected by eating the grubs. Man rarely becomes infected, although cases have been reported from south Russia, where the natives sometimes eat raw beetles.

Members of this phylum are the most harmful of all parasites, for great damage is done mechanically by the spiny head. Multiple infection may do considerable damage to the pig's intestine and perforation may occur.

Metabolism. Acanthocephala with their parasitic habits derive their nourishment from the host by absorption through the thin, delicate cuticle. The actual digestion of their food is done for them by their host. This power of absorption is strikingly shown when they are placed in water, for their bodies become swollen in a short time. After absorption into the body of the worms, the food products are distributed by the fluid-filled lacunar canal system and the body cavity.

Derivation and meaning of basic terminology

acanthor (Gr. *akantha,* spine or thorn). First larval form of acanthocephs in the intermediate host.

cement gland One of a cluster of unicellular glands near the testes in acanthocephs, which furnishes secretions for binding the sexes together during copulation.

lacunar system (L. *lacuna,* channel). Epidermal canal system peculiar to acanthocephs.

lemniscus (L. ribbon). One of a pair of internal projections of the epidermis from the neck region of Acanthocephala, which functions in fluid control in the protrusion and invagination of the proboscis.

Leptorhynchoides (Gr. *leptos,* slender, + *rhynchos,* beak, + *eidos,* form).

Macracanthorhynchus (Gr. *makros,* long, + *akantha,* thorn, + *rhynchos,* beak).

Neoechinorhynchus (Gr. *neos,* new, + *echinos,* hedgehog, + *rhynchos,* beak).

Phylum Entoprocta*

The members of Entoprocta were once included in the phylum Bryozoa. However, a number of zoologists consider them sufficiently different to be placed in a

*En′to-prok″ta (Gr. *entos,* inside, + *proktos,* anus).

phylum of their own. The rest of the bryozoans are now placed in a phylum called Ectoprocta, although the ectoprocts are still frequently referred to as bryozoans.

Entoprocts are stalked sessile animals, solitary or colonial, that are found in both fresh water and sea water. They are small forms that do not exceed 5 mm. in length and have some superficial resemblances to the hydroids of the coelenterates. The body is made up of the **calyx,** which bears a circlet of tentacles and contains the visceral organs, a slender **stalk,** and an **attachment disk** with adhesive glands. The crown of the calyx bearing the tentacles is retractile and can be contracted inward when the animal is disturbed. The tentacles may vary in the same species, although the number is usually between eight and thirty. They are ciliated on their inner surfaces, and each can move individually.

The digestive system is complete and U shaped. Unlike ectoprocts, in which only the mouth is found within the circle of tentacles, members of Entoprocta have both the mouth and the anus opening inside the tentacles. The system consists of mouth, esophagus, stomach, and rectum and is ciliated throughout. The body wall contains a cuticle, a cellular epidermis, and a longitudinal musculature. Between the body wall and the digestive system and also in the interior of the tentacles and stalk is the pseudocoel. A gelatinous parenchyma fills most of it. The excretory system consists of a pair of protonephridia, each of which is provided with a canal. These canals unite and open to the outside by a single pore near the mouth. Circulatory and respiratory organs are absent. The nervous system contains a mass of ganglia on the ventral side of the stomach, from which nerves pass to various parts of the body. Sense organs are represented by surface bristles and sensory pits and are chiefly tactile in function. Some members of this phylum are monoecious and others are dioecious. Some also appear to be protandric—that is, the gonad at first produces sperm and later eggs. The paired gonads are found near the ventral side of the stomach. Each

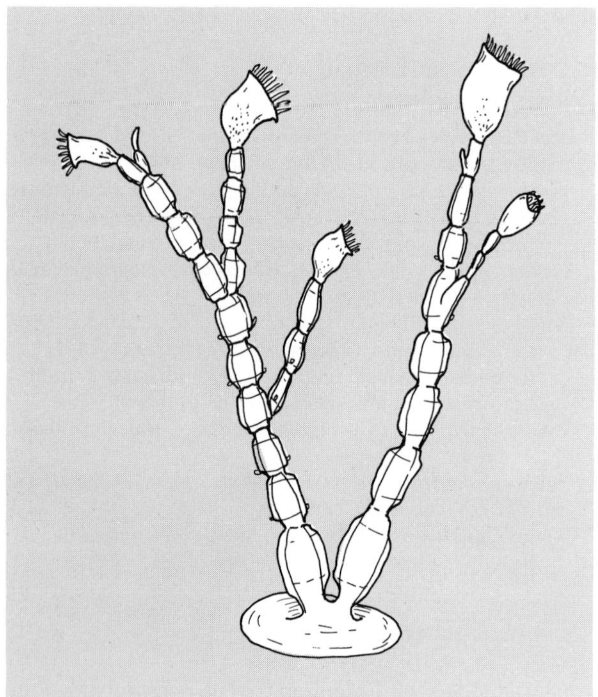

FIG. 14-20

The only freshwater entoproct *Urnatella.* (From Hickman: Biology of the invertebrates, The C. V. Mosby Co.)

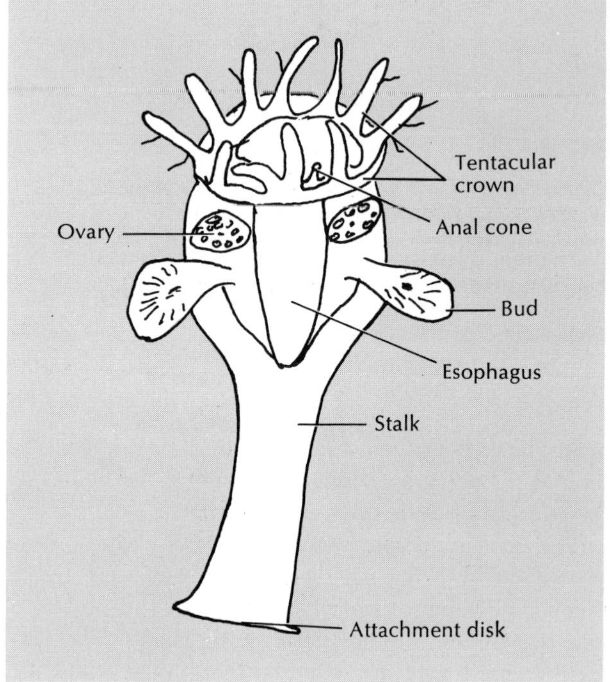

FIG. 14-21

The common marine entoproct *Loxosoma.* This is one of most primitive forms of Entoprocta. (From Hickman: Biology of the invertebrates, The C. V. Mosby Co.)

gonad is provided with a duct that unites with the other duct to open by the common gonopore on the ventral surface of the calyx.

Urnatella gracilis (Fig. 14-20) is the only common freshwater species in North America, where it is found growing under stones in running water; *Loxosoma* (Fig. 14-21) is one of the more familiar marine forms and has a wide distribution along the coastlines of America, Europe, Asia, and Africa. Many marine species are found attached to other animals such as sponges and various worms.

Although entoprocts have some form of a pseudocoel, whereas ectoprocts are higher in organization because they have a true coelom and because of other features, it is thought that the closest affinity of Entoprocta is to the Ectoprocta through an early offshoot from a common line.

Annotated references

Baer, J. G. 1952. Ecology of animal parasites. Urbana, University of Illinois Press. *Excellent account of the ways parasites have adapted themselves.*

Cori, C. 1936. Kamptozoa. In H. G. Bronn (editor): Klassen und Ordnungen des Tierreichs, vol. 4, part 2. Leipzig, Akademische Verlagsgesellschaft.

Dougherty, E. C. (editor). 1963. The lower Metazoa. Berkeley, University of California Press. *This is a comparative phylogeny, morphology, and physiology of the invertebrates below the annelids. More than 30 specialists have contributed monographs to this highly important work.*

Hyman, L. H. 1951. The invertebrates: Acanthocephala, Aschelminthes, and Entoprocta, vol. 3. New York, McGraw-Hill Book Co. *The newest classification of the invertebrates is presented in this series, of which this volume is one. Aside from the logical taxonomy, Miss Hyman has also described with great accuracy the many types of these phyla.*

Lapage, G. 1951. Parasitic animals. New York, Cambridge University Press. *Good descriptions of the life histories of many nematodes, including Ascaris and Trichina.*

Meyer, A. 1933. Acanthocephala. In H. G. Bronn (editor): Klassen und Ordnungen des Tierreichs, vol. 4, part 2, sec. 2. Leipzig, Akademische Verlagsgesellschaft. *The definitive German account.*

Nickerson, W. 1901. On *Loxosoma davenporti*. J. Morph. **17**:357-376.

Pennak, R. W. 1953. Fresh-water invertebrates of the United States. New York, The Ronald Press Co. *This excellent work deals with the free-living, freshwater invertebrates and omits the parasitic forms. Many of the sections describe various types of Aschelminthes under the old classification. The treatment of Gastrotricha, among the rarer types, is especially noteworthy.*

Rogick, M. D. 1948. Studies on marine Bryozoa. Part II. *Barentsia laxa*. Biol. Bull. **94**:128-142. *The author considers the Endoprocta as a class under the Bryozoa, not a separate phylum (Hyman).*

Sasser, J. N., and W. R. Jenkins (editors). 1960. Nematology. Chapel Hill, University of North Carolina Press. *An important work by more than a score of eminent authorities in this difficult field.*

Van Cleve, H. J. 1941. Relationships of Acanthocephala. American Naturalist **75**:1-20. *In this and many other articles the most active American investigator of this group has attempted to appraise the position of the Acanthocephala in the animal kingdom. Read also his revealing article, "Expanding Horizons in the Recognition of a Phylum," Journal of Parasitology, vol. 34, pp. 1-20, 1948.*

CHAPTER 15

• PHYLA PHORONIDA, ECTOPROCTA (BRYOZOA), AND BRACHIOPODA (LOPHOPHORATE EUCOELOMATE BILATERAL ANIMALS)

BIOLOGIC PRINCIPLES

1. These three phyla of coelomate animals have a crown of ciliated, hollow tentacles on a ridge, the lophophore, which is specialized for sedentary filter feeding.

2. The lophophore is an extension of the distal part of the body and bears numerous tentacles surrounding the mouth but not the anus. The body of lophophorates consists of the divisions mesosome and metasome (the protosome is absent because of the lack of a head), and each of these two parts encloses a coelomic cavity, the mesocoel and metacoel, which are separated by a peritoneal septum. That part of the coelom in the lophophore is the mesocoel. The lophophore is variously shaped in the different members, although horseshoe and spiral or coiled shapes are common.

3. Lack of a true coelom and the inclusion of the anus within the circle of tentacles excludes the Entoprocta and some other tentaculated groups.

4. The lophophore serves as a type of trough for the food stream. The alimentary canal is mainly U shaped, and besides serving as ciliary feeding organs, the tentacles assist in respiration by providing a large surface area for gaseous exchange. In some lophophorates there are blood vessels that run up and down the tentacles. Food is carried to the mouth in currents of water driven by the ciliary tracts on the tentacles, and the plankton is filtered off in the process.

PHYLOGENY AND ADAPTIVE RADIATION

1. The three phyla apparently have a close relationship because of the common possession of a lophophore of similar construction. They occupy a unique position between the protostomes and the deuterostomes, and may be a connecting link between the two groups. Although classed as protostomes, one phylum (Brachiopoda) has an enterocoelous formation of the coelom, which is a deuterostome characteristic. Both lophophorates and deuterostomes have the same body regionalization of three divisions (protostome, mesosome, and metasome), except that the protostome is chiefly suppressed in the lophophorates. A common ancestry of the two groups is indicated by the evidence at hand. The lophophorates are considered to have a common trochophore larva, but it is highly modified in each of the phyla. The lack of a head in the lophophorates may be correlated with their ciliary method of feeding.

2. Since all lophophorates are filter-feeders, it may be supposed that their evolutionary diversification has been guided to a great extent by this function. Each phylum has had structural modifications in this and other respects. Phoronids have varied their tubes according to the nature of their habitats. Ectoprocts have a tendency toward an evolutionary development of a gelatinous zooecium from a chitinous one to have more flexibility. Primitive forms had rigid calcareous skeletons, for they have fossilized well. Some calcareous ectoprocts overcame rigidity by developing flexible, chitinous joints. The brachiopods have been guided in their evolution by their shells and lophophores. The primitive form of the lophophore in these animals was a short tentacle-bearing ridge, which has gradually increased in length in its subsequent evolution. This increased length may take the form of lobulations, arm formations, or spiral coils. Many brachiopods have undergone little change because their environment has remained fairly constant over long periods of time.

Phylum Phoronida*

Phylum Phoronida is made up of wormlike animals that live in tubes on the bottom of shallow seas (Fig. 15-1). Most are small (1 mm. or less), but some are more than 1 foot long. They have some resemblance to bryozoans and in the past have been included in that group. Some species are more or less solitary, but other species are found in associations of many individuals. Each worm is enclosed in a leathery or chitinous tube that it has secreted and from which its tentacles are extended. As in the ectoprocts, the ciliated tentacles are borne on a lophophore that may be spirally coiled. When disturbed, the animal draws back into its tube with its tentacles completely hidden. The body is well advanced, for it has a body wall of cuticle, epidermis, and both longitudinal and circular muscles. The coelomic cavity is a true coelom, being lined with

*Fo-ron′i-da (Gr. *phoros,* bearing, + L. *nidus,* nest).

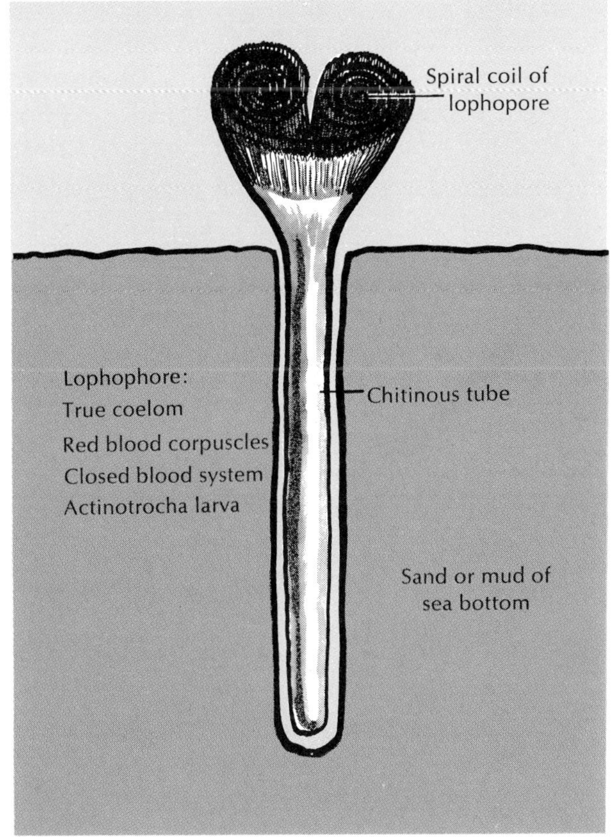

FIG. 15-1

Phoronid *Phoronis* in its habitat.

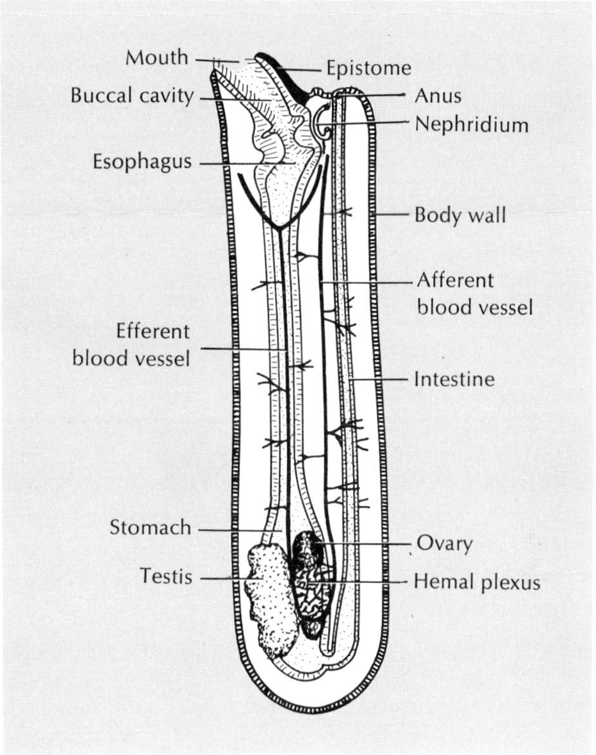

FIG. 15-2

Chief internal structures of a phoronid. Lophophore has been omitted. (From Hickman: Biology of the invertebrates, The C. V. Mosby Co.)

peritoneal epithelium. It is subdivided by mesenteric partitions into compartments.

The alimentary canal is U shaped, as in ectoprocts; is made up of esophagus, stomach, and intestine; and is ciliated most of its length. Although there is no respiratory system (since respiratory gases diffuse through surfaces), the circulatory system is a closed system of blood vessels, which have contractile walls, but a heart is absent. Red blood corpuscles are found also. The nervous system just below the epidermis consists of a nerve ring around the mouth, with nerves running to various parts of the body. The members of this phylum are monoecious; a testis and ovary are found in each individual near one of the large blood vessels (Fig. 15-2). When the sex cells are released, they pass through the paired nephridia to the space enclosed by the tentacles, where fertilization occurs. The larva, which is characterized by a large hoodlike lobe over the mouth, is called an actinotrocha and is commonly considered a type of the trochophore larva.

Two of the common species of the phylum are *Phoronopsis californica,* a large form found along the Pacific coast, and *Phoronis kowalevskii,* which has a wide distribution.

Phylum Ectoprocta (Bryozoa)*

The name Ectoprocta applies to bryozoans because the anus opens outside the lophophore, whereas in phylum Entoprocta the anus, like the mouth, opens inside the circle of tentacles. Bryozoans took their name from the Greek word *bryon,* moss, and were commonly called the moss animals.

*Ek'to-prok"ta (Gr. *ektos,* outside, + *proktos,* anus). Bry'o-zo"a (Gr. *bryon,* moss, + *zoon,* animal).

Ectoprocts have a more advanced structure than do hydroids, which they resemble. Most of them live in marine waters, although a few are found in fresh water. They are forms that one is likely to overlook, for they are microscopic and form colonies that resemble thin, matlike debris on rocks, shells, or stems of plants. Some of the colonies, however, may attain considerable size. Although most colonies are attached, there are some that float around free. Since these have plant-like characteristics, they are often confused with seaweeds.

Characteristics. Bilateral symmetry; unsegmented; form colonies by budding; each individual in a cup-shaped shell (zoecium); coelom; U-shaped alimentary canal; ciliated lophophore around mouth; anus outside lophophore; no excretory or vascular systems; nerve ganglion between mouth and anus; monoecious or dioecious reproduction; brood pouch (ooecium); a form of trochophora larva.

Structure and behavior. Ectoprocta are ordinarily found in shallow water. Their food consists of small plants and animals caught by the lophophore, which is also used for respiration. This ridge, the lophophore, bears a circle of ciliated tentacles and tends to be circular in marine forms and U shaped in freshwater Ectoprocta. The entire crown can be drawn into the protective shell, or zoecium, by retractor muscles. The digestive system is U shaped, consisting of a mouth within the ring of tentacles, an enlarged pharynx, a slender esophagus, a V-shaped stomach, and an intestine that terminates in the anus outside of the lophophore. Digestion is extracellular. The true coelom is filled with a coelomic fluid, which distributes the food in the absence of a circulatory system. Most members of the phylum go through a periodical renewal process, when the tentacles and internal organs degenerate into a compact mass called the "brown body." When new organs are regenerated from the body wall, the brown body is discharged through the anus. Since there is no excretory system, the brown body may have some relation to excretion. The muscular system consists mainly of the body-wall muscles and the retractor muscles referred to earlier. The nervous system is composed of a single ganglion between the lophophore and anus and many nerves to the tentacles, digestive system, muscles, and a few other places. No sense organs have been detected.

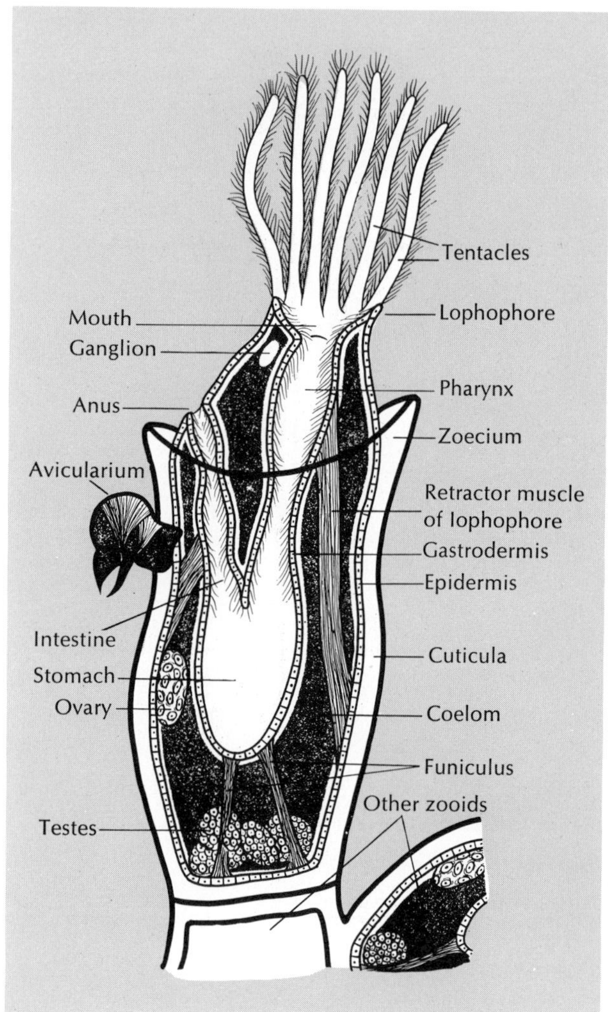

FIG. 15-3

Semidiagrammatic structure of zooid of *Bugula* (phylum Ectoprocta). This phylum has external fossil record dating back to Ordovician period. Its nearest relatives seem to be members of phylum Phoronida.

The colonies grow by asexual reproduction. Some of the individuals (zooids) (Fig. 15-3) are provided with an interesting structure, the **avicularium,** which resembles the beak of a bird and is used to keep other animals away as well as to remove debris that might settle on the colonies. When living zooids are observed, these avicularia are seen constantly opening and snapping closed. In sexual reproduction the eggs are fertilized in the coelom and develop in the ooecium, which is a modified portion of the body cavity. The testis is formed on a special mesentery (funiculus) that extends

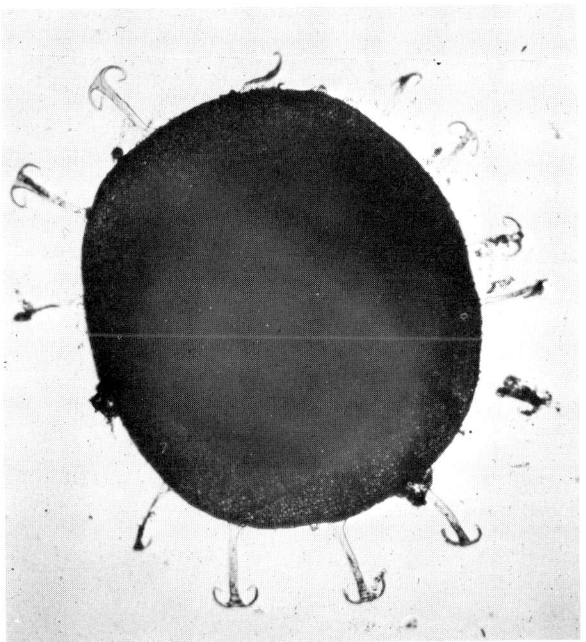

FIG. 15-4

Statoblast of *Pectinatella*. (Photomicrograph, greatly enlarged.)

from the stomach to the posterior body wall; the ovary is formed on the peritoneum of the coelom.

Freshwater ectoprocts form interesting mosslike colonies on the stems of plants or on sticks. They are usually found in shallow water of ponds or pools; the colonies as a whole may have the power of sliding along the object on which they are supported. Freshwater ectoprocts also have a peculiar type of asexual reproduction by which internal buds known as **statoblasts** (Fig. 15-4) are formed. When the members of a colony die in late autumn, these statoblasts are released and in the spring can produce new colonies.

The most common marine form of the ectoprocts is *Bugula* (Figs. 15-3 and 15-5); the most common freshwater ones are *Plumatella* (Fig. 15-6) and *Pectinatella*. Altogether there are more than 2,000 species recognized in this phylum.

Phylum Brachiopoda*

The animals of phylum Brachiopoda resemble the mollusks in having two valves (shells), but in this phylum the valves are dorsal and ventral instead of lateral, as in the mollusks. The name is derived from the Greek words *brachion,* arm, and *podos,* foot. Formerly these animals were classified with the Mollusca, but they differ from that phylum not only in the arrangement of the valves but also in internal details. Because brachiopods resemble the lamps of the ancients, they are often referred to as lamp shells. The ventral valve is larger than the dorsal one and is provided with a fleshy peduncle that is used for attaching the animal to the sea bottom or to some object. All members of the phylum are marine and solitary. They represent a very ancient group, and in the past they were far more abundant than they are now. Some have undergone few changes since early geologic periods. They have left an excellent fossil record. About 200 living species are found in the group.

*Bra'ki-op"o-da (Gr. *brachion,* arm, + *podos,* foot).

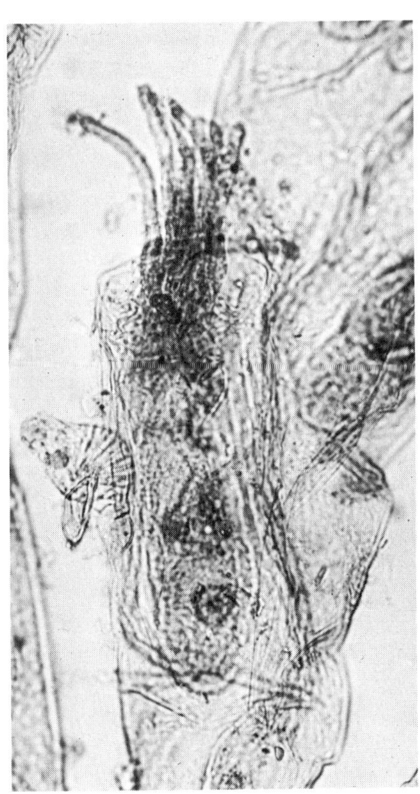

FIG. 15-5

Part of a colony of *Bugula*. Zooid is seen with tentacles above, an avicularium, looking like a bird's beak, on left. See Fig. 15-3 for detailed structure.

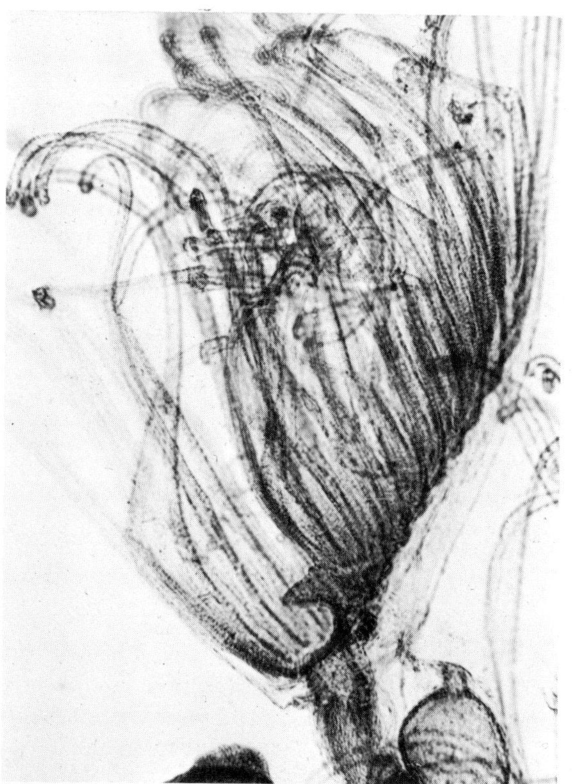

FIG. 15-6

Zooid of *Plumatella,* colonial freshwater bryozoan.

Characteristics. Bilateral symmetry; no segmentation; dorsal and ventral calcareous shells; peduncle as an attachment organ; true coelom; lophophore of two coiled ridges; heart and blood vessels; one or two pairs of nephridia; nerve ring; separate sexes; digestive system complete or incomplete; a form of trochophore larva.

Structure and behavior. The body is enclosed between the two valves, but most of it is in the posterior region (Fig. 15-7). Two flaps, the dorsal and ventral mantle lobes, are formed from the body wall. The horseshoe-shaped lophophore bears long ciliated tentacles, which are used for food getting and respiration. The mouth is in the middle of the lophophore and leads into a gullet, which opens into the stomach provided with digestive glands. The intestine usually ends blindly in most lamp shells. There are well-developed muscles for opening and closing the valves. The nephridia have one opening in the coelom and the other in the mantle cavity. A contractile heart, blood vessels, and nerve ring are also present. The paired gonads in each sex discharge their products through the nephridia. Development is by metamorphosis, and the free-swimming larval form has a resemblance to the trochophore larva before it becomes attached.

The most common species are *Terebratulina transversa* (Fig. 15-8) and *Megellania leticularis.*

The phyla Brachiopoda, Ectoprocta, and Phoronida are all lophophorate coelomates and may be related.

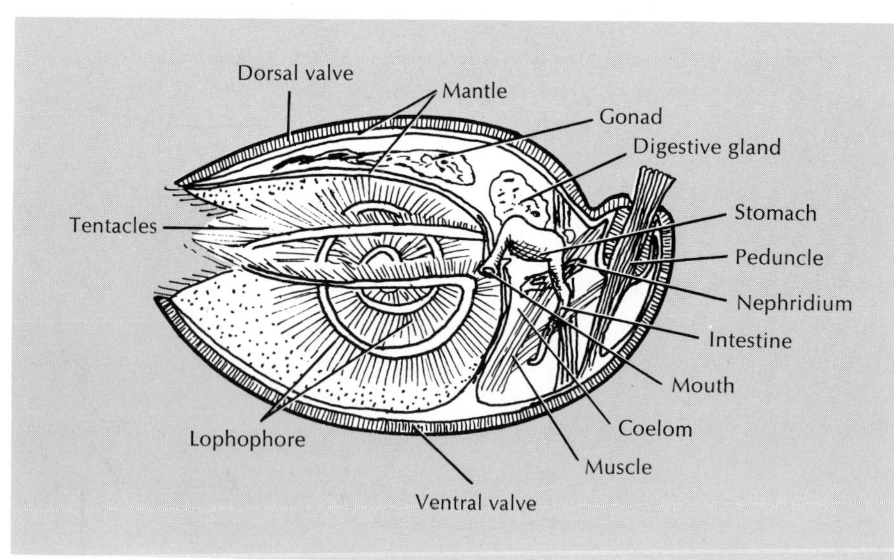

FIG. 15-7

Internal structure of articulate brachiopod (longitudinal section). (From Hickman: Biology of the invertebrates, The C. V. Mosby Co.)

FIG. 15-8

Shell of *Terebratulina,* common brachiopod, or lamp shell. Note how shell is covered with skeletons of other invertebrates, including another brachiopod.

Derivations and meaning of basic terminology

avicularium (L. *avis,* bird, + *aria,* like or connected with). Modified zooid that is attached to the surface of the major zooid in Ectoprocta and resembles a bird's beak.

Bugula (L. *bugulus,* bunch of flowers). A common marine genus of Ectoprocta.

lophophore (Gr. *lophos,* crest, + *phoros,* bearing). A ridge about the mouth region bearing tentacles.

ooecium (Gr. *oion,* egg, + *oikos,* house). Brood pouch.

trochophore (Gr. *trochos,* wheel, + *phoros,* bearing). A ciliated marine larva, characteristic of many schizocoelomate animals.

zoecium (Gr. *zoon,* animal, + *oikos,* house). Cuticular sheath or shell of Ectoprocta.

Annotated references

Barnes, R. D. 1968. Invertebrate zoology, ed. 2. Philadelphia, W. B. Saunders Co.

Barrington, E. J. W. 1967. Invertebrate structure and function. New York, Houghton Mifflin Co. *An excellent up-to-date account.*

Bronn, H. G. (editor). 1939. Phoronidea. Klassen und Ordnungen des Tierreichs, vol. 4, part 4. Leipzig, Akademische Verlagsgesellschaft. *An authoritative monograph.*

Chuang, S. 1959. Structure and function of the alimentary canal in *Lingula unguis.* Proc. Zool. Soc. (London) **132**:293-311. *An account of the digestive system.*

Edmondson, W. T. (editor). 1959. Ward and Whipple's fresh-water biology, ed. 2. New York, John Wiley & Sons, Inc. *The section on freshwater Bryozoa (which includes both entoprocts and ectoprocts) is by the late M. D. Rogick, foremost authority on the group.*

Hickman, C. P. 1967. Biology of the invertebrates. St. Louis, The C. V. Mosby Co.

Hyman, L. H. 1959. The invertebrates: smaller coelomate groups, vol. 5. New York, McGraw-Hill Book Co. *Up-to-date accounts of Chaetognatha, Phoronida, Ectoprocta, Brachiopoda, and Sipunculida. This volume maintains the high traditions of the others in this outstanding modern treatise of zoology.*

Meglitsch, P. A. 1967. Invertebrate zoology. New York, Oxford University Press.

Rogick, M. D. 1935. Studies on fresh-water Bryozoa. II. The Bryozoa of Lake Erie. Trans. Amer. Micr. Soc. **54**:245-263. *This and other papers on Bryozoa by the same author represent the best available accounts of American freshwater species.*

Russell-Hunter, W. D. 1969. A biology of higher invertebrates. (Paperback.) New York, The Macmillan Co. *With the author's companion volume, A Biology of Lower Invertebrates, the student can get a fine evaluation, within the limits of paperback editions, of the extensive group of invertebrates.*

CHAPTER 16

• PHYLA SIPUNCULIDA, PENTASTOMIDA, ECHIUROIDEA, ONYCHOPHORA, PRIAPULIDA, AND TARDIGRADA (MINOR EUCOELOMATE BILATERAL GROUP)

BIOLOGIC PRINCIPLES

1. These phyla are more or less distinct groups that present puzzling affinities to each other and to other groups. Some have been appended to other phyla in various classifications, but many zoologists at present are inclined to regard them as sufficiently different to be listed as independent phyla.

2. The actual evolutionary development of these (and other) phyla are so hidden in the past that taxonomic divisions and relations of them are based upon what embryologic and morphologic features yield, such as symmetry, coelomic formation, metamerism, egg-type cleavage, and other criteria. Such information is often inconclusive, although certain relationships appear to be fairly clear.

3. All these phyla have relatively minor economic and ecologic importance. All have undergone modest evolutionary diversification so that they are represented in most cases at present by few species (probably fewer than 800 altogether).

4. They also have much in common. All are coelomates and protostomes, although one or two have deuterostome characteristics in their embryologic development. In spite of their lack of numbers and evolutionary diversity, they have survived in the competition with the more successful protostomes to which they are related in some degree.

5. Although the members of these phyla are assigned obscure roles in the animal kingdom, they take a fairly high rank in their morphologic and function levels among the invertebrates. Organ systems, with few exceptions, are well represented. Respiratory systems in general are lacking, although the onychophorans have a tracheal system. The same may be said for the circulatory system, which is absent in some and present in others. Many of them burrow in the sand and mud and have ingenious methods for securing their food.

6. The group has many odd morphologic devices for performing their functions. For example, one may mention the introvert of the Sipunculida and the proboscis of the Echiuroidea for burrowing and feeding, the complex feeding apparatus of the Tardigrada, the stumpy, clawed legs of the Onychophora for locomotion, and the caudal appendages of the Priapulida of questionable function but maybe for respiration.

PHYLOGENY AND ADAPTIVE RADIATION

1. Such an odd assortment of phyla must have many puzzling phylogenetic affinities. Most are apparently developed from the annelid-arthropod stem line at different times. The Priapulida have long been considered a class under the phylum Aschelminthes because of their supposed pseudocoelomate condition, and were given a close relationship to the class Kinorhyncha of that phylum. Present investigations consider them true coelomates, although many zoologists think that their exact status is debatable. Sipunculida have a typical trochophore larva and are related to the annelids, as are also the Echiuroidea, because of their similar embryologic development and for other reasons. The three phyla—Pentastomida, Onychophora, and Tardigrada—have been often placed together as a group called Pararthropoda, or Oncopoda, because they have unjointed limbs with claws (at some stage) and a cuticle that undergoes molting.

2. The small number of species in most of these phyla indicates fairly stable ecologic conditions, low mutation rates, or other causes for few modifications. In their evolutionary development the Sipunculida, the Priapulida, and the Echiuroidea have been guided mainly by their varied proboscis devices, which they have stressed in burrowing and food getting. The Onychophora show the greatest structural diversity in the number of their stump legs, which vary from 14 to 44 pairs in the different species. Tardigrades have varied their mechanisms of claws and feeding apparatus among their species, whereas the pentastomidan adaptations have been chiefly those having to do with attachments to their hosts.

Phylum Sipunculida*

Sipunculids are marine worms that live in the sand or among the rocks of the seashore. Some are small, slender worms, but generally they are more robust and may reach a length of 1 foot or more. They have no segmentation or setae. The anterior part of the body is

*Si-pun′kyu-li″da (L. *sipunculus,* little siphon, + *ida,* pl. suffix).

called the **introvert** and is retractile. The body wall is made up of a cuticle, an epidermis of a single layer of cells, a dermis of connective tissue containing several kinds of glands and sense papillae, and a musculature of three layers—circular, oblique, and longitudinal. The ciliated **coelom** is large and contains connective tissue, muscle fibers, and coelomic fluid. The mouth region is surrounded by tentacles, and the alimentary canal is a uniform tube that turns to the posterior end and then doubles back on itself to end in the anus near the base of the introvert. Two groups of rectal glands open into the rectum near the anus. Usually there is a single pair of nephridia, which are brown tubes that open into the coelom and to the outside anterior of the anus.

There are no circulatory or respiratory systems, but the coelomic fluid contains red corpuscles which bear a pigment, hemerythrin, containing iron. This pigment is used in the transportation of oxygen. The coelomic fluid also contains other formed elements such as amebocytes. The nervous system has a bilobed cerebral ganglion just behind and dorsal to the tentacles, which sends connectives to a ventral nerve cord extending the length of the body. Although it has no ganglionic enlargements, the cord gives off many lateral nerves. The sexes are separate, but definite gonads are lacking, for the ovaries or testes develop seasonally in the connective tissue covering of the retractor muscles. When released, the sexual elements are carried from the coelomic fluid to the outside through the nephridia. The larval form is usually a trochophore, and no trace of segmentation is found in it. Of the 200 or 300 species, the best known genera are *Sipunculus* (Fig. 16-1),

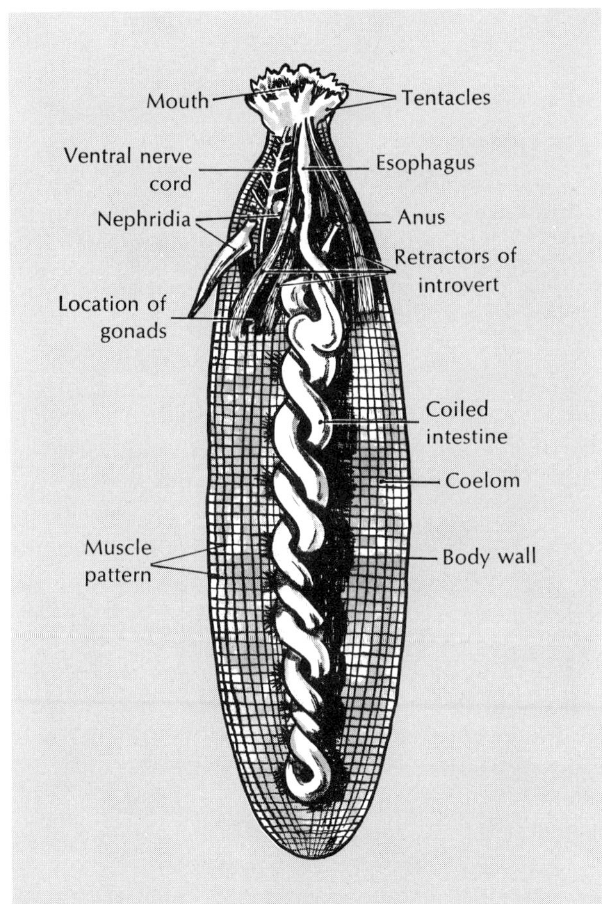

FIG. 16-1

Internal structure of *Sipunculus*. Although not segmented, phylum Sipunculida shows many close affinities to annelid worms, having same type of cleavage, same method of coelom formation, same type of nervous system, and other similarities.

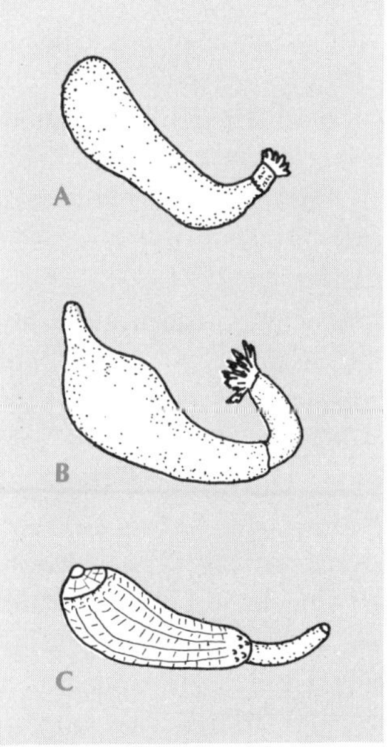

FIG. 16-2

Some types of sipunculids. **A,** *Phascolosoma,* most common genus along Pacific coast. **B,** *Dendrostomum*. **C,** *Aspidosiphon*. (From Hickman: Biology of the invertebrates, The C. V. Mosby Co.)

Dendrostomum (Fig. 16-2), and *Phascolion*. *Golfingia* is the largest genus.

Many authorities have placed the sipunculids and echiuroids together under the group Gephyrea as a class of the Annelida, but aside from some similarities the groups differ in many important respects, such as the anterior end, the position of the anus, and the presence or absence of the setae.

Phylum Pentastomida*

The wormlike Pentastomida are internal parasites of carnivorous vertebrates. They are found in the lungs and nasal passageways, where they live by sucking blood. They occur mostly in tropical reptiles, but they are also found in birds and mammals. Human infection is known in Africa and Europe, but so far none have been reported from North America. Most adult worms parasitize snakes and lizards.

Their life history usually includes an intermediate host for the larval stages, although they may complete their entire life cycle in the same host. Their intermediate hosts are usually vertebrates that are eaten by the final host. *Linguatula taenioides* may be taken as an example of a typical life history of one that lives in the nasal passageways of carnivorous mammals. The eggs of the adult worm are discharged in the mucus secretions, or the feces, and hatch into larvae that have a remarkable resemblance to four-legged tardigrades or mites having stumpy legs with claws on the ends. The larvae climb on vegetation that may be eaten by rabbits. In the rabbit the larvae encyst in the liver or another vital organ. Here the larvae undergo several molts in their development, and if the rabbit is eaten, the larvae complete their development in the gut and find their way to the nasal passageways of the final host.

The adults are vermiform and usually vary in length from 1 to 5 inches. They have hooks in both larva and adult for attachment. Their bodies are cylindric or flattened with transverse rings that give the appearance of superficial segmentation (Fig. 16-3). The kind of hooks and body rings have diagnostic value in the determination of species. The hooks are secreted by glands. Frontal glands secrete an anticoagulant for the

*Pen'ta-stom"i-da (Gr. *penta*, five, + *stoma*, mouth).

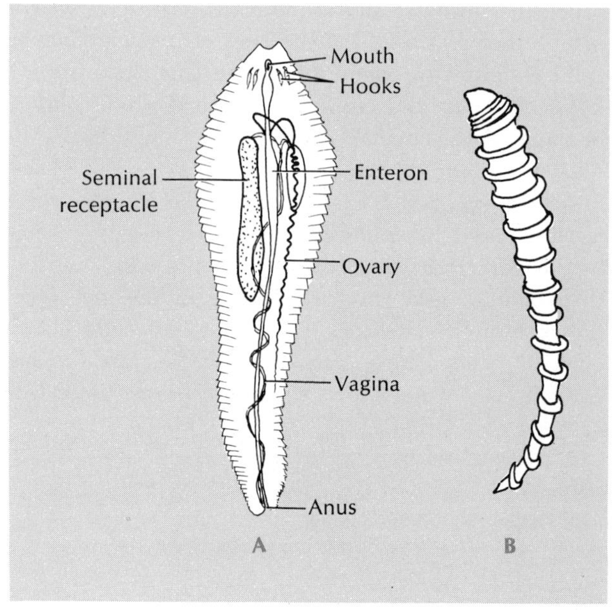

FIG. 16-3

Two common pentastomids. **A,** *Pentastomum,* found in lungs of snakes and other vertebrates. Female is shown with some internal structures. **B,** Female *Armillifer,* a pentastomid with pronounced body rings. In Africa man is parasitized by immature stages; adults (4 inches long or more) live in lungs of snakes. Human infection may occur from eating snakes or from contaminated food and water. (From Hickman: Biology of the invertebrates, The C. V. Mosby Co.)

blood of the host and join the hook glands. The straight digestive system is adapted at the mouth end for sucking blood. Their anus opens on the ventral side in most species. Their nervous system is of the annelid, or ladder, type with three pairs of ganglia along the ventral nerve cord. They have no excretory or circulatory systems, and a definite respiratory system is lacking, except for breathing pores (stigmata) over the body surface. The sexes are separate, with the female much larger than the male. The genetic pore in each sex is located on the ventral side, usually toward the head end. Fertilization is internal, and zygotes reach the external aquatic environment either by way of the mouth or by nasal secretions or sometimes by way of the feces.

Parasitic modifications have made phylogenetic affinities difficult. The worms show several arthropod characters, such as jointed appendages in the larva, stigmata in the skin, a molting cuticle, and in other ways. The larvae also show resemblances to the tardigrades, and a great student of the group (R. Heymons) believed that they may have evolved from the polychaetes because they show features of the Myzostomidae, a polychaete parasite or commensal.

Phylum Echiuroidea*

The members of phylum Echiuroidea have often been a taxonomic puzzle, and many zoologists have included them as a class under the annelids. It seems best, however, to assign them phylum rank, for they logically do not belong to any other group. They are unsegmented worms that are found in the mud and sand in shallow coast waters of warm and temperate seas. Many of them dwell in burrows, from which they feed by means of a proboscis. Their general body shape is cylindric or ovoid, and most of them have a long nonretractile proboscis with a ciliated groove. The body wall consists of a thin cuticle; an epidermis with glandular cells and papillae arranged in rings; and a muscular layer of both longitudinal and circular muscles. A pair of ventral anterior setae is characteristic of most species, and some have a row of chitinous bristles around the posterior end of the body near the anus.

The coelom is well developed and crossed by muscular strands that help support the alimentary canal. The alimentary canal contains a mouth at the base of the proboscis, a muscular pharynx, a coiled intestine, a slightly enlarged rectum, with a pair of long anal vesicles, and the terminal anus. The anal vesicles have ciliated openings into the body cavity and may help control the amount of fluid in the body cavity and the excretory process. The closed circulatory system consists of a contractile dorsal vessel on the alimentary canal and proboscis and a ventral vessel, which is found on the dorsal surface of the nerve cord. The two vessels unite at the tip of the proboscis. There may be two or three pairs of nephridia that serve mainly to carry the sex products. The nervous system is made up of a nerve ring around the pharynx and an unsegmented ventral nerve cord, which gives off paired lateral nerves to the skin. There are no special sense organs. The sexes are separate, with a single gonad in each sex. The mature sex cells break loose from the gonads and leave the body cavity by way of the nephridia, and fertilization is usually outside. In some species sexual dimorphism is marked, the female being much the larger of the two.

Bonellia (Fig. 16-4) is noteworthy for the way sex is differentiated in this genus. At first most of the larvae are sexually indifferent and can develop either into males or females. Those larvae that come into contact with the female proboscis become males in the larval

*Ek'i-u-roi"de-a (Gr. *echis,* adder, + *oura,* tail, + *eidos,* form, + *ea,* pl. suffix meaning characterized by).

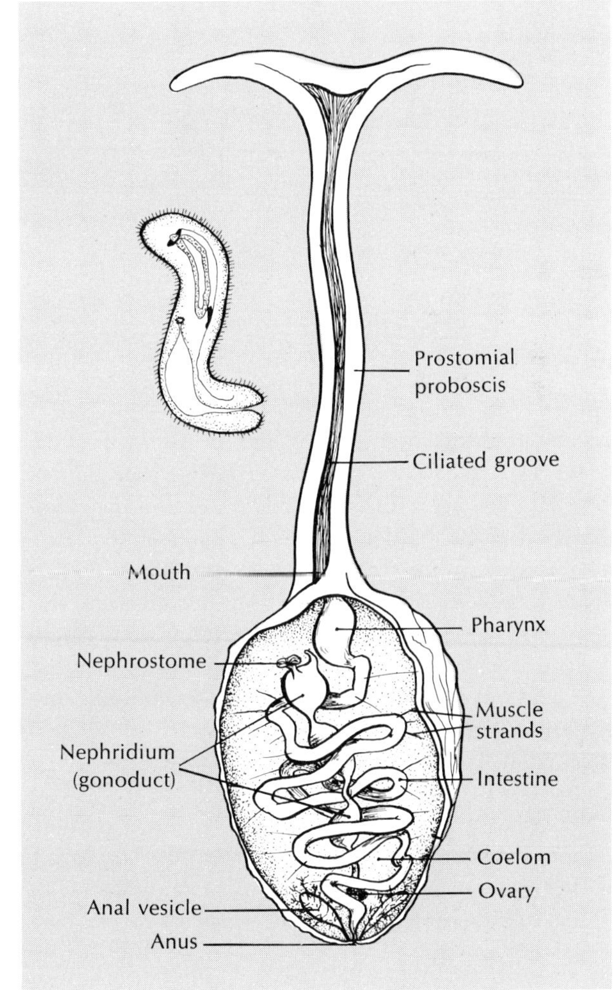

FIG. 16-4

Chief internal organs of female *Bonellia* (phylum Echiuroidea). This form is famed for extreme sexual dimorphism and peculiar sex determination. Larva has potentialities of both sexes. If larva attaches to body of female, it metamorphoses into minute male with a gonad but with other organs degenerated. It migrates to female nephridium to fertilize eggs for a season. If larva develops in sea water, it becomes a female.

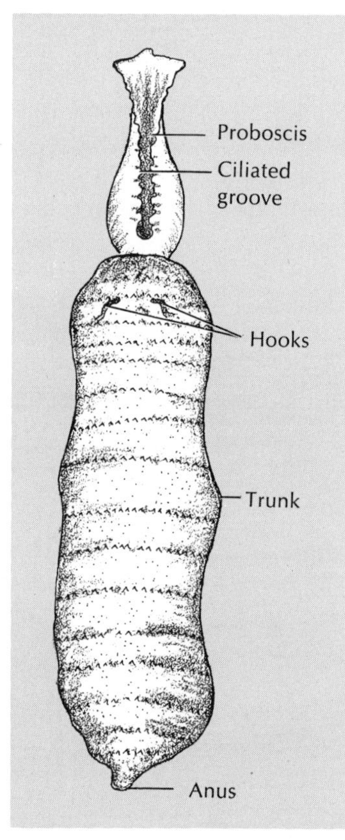

FIG. 16-5

Echiurus, an echiurid common on both Atlantic and Pacific coasts. (From Hickman: Biology of the invertebrates, The C. V. Mosby Co.)

FIG. 16-6

Peripatus in its natural habitat, usually moist places under logs, bark, or other rubbish. Phylum Onychophora. (Courtesy Ward's Natural Science Establishment, Inc., Rochester, N. Y.)

stages and spend most of their lives in the nephridium of the female as parasites. Those larvae that do not come into contact with the female undergo a metamorphosis into females. The stimulus for the male development appears to be a chemical one from the proboscis of the female. Baltzer was able to get various degrees of intersexuality by removing larvae at various stages of male transformation.

Besides *Bonellia* other common echiuroids are *Echiurus* (Fig. 16-5), *Urechis, Hamingia,* and *Saccosoma.* Altogether there are more than 60 species.

Peripatus

From the standpoint of phylogenetic relationship between two groups as different as two phyla, few animals are more interesting than a small wormlike form called *Peripatus* (Figs. 16-6 and 16-7). This animal is a type of a small phylum—Onychophora. There are about 70 species in this phylum widely distributed over the world—Africa, Australia, New Zealand, Central America, Mexico, and other localities. Their wide distribution in local habitats, an example of discontinuous distribution, may indicate that once they were common and widespread over the world but are now disappearing. This phylum shows characteristics of two phyla, Annelida and Arthropoda, and its members are often referred to as "missing links." If this phylum is primitive, which is denied by some zoologists, then its members must be considered similar to the ancestors of Arthropoda.

The various species of Onychophora live in moist places in crevices of rock, under logs and bark, and other dark places. They are nocturnal in their habits and avoid light at all times. When annoyed, they eject slime from their peculiar oral papillae.

External structure. *Peripatus* is about 2 to 3 inches long and resembles a caterpillar. It is cylindric in body

*On'y-kof"o-ra (Gr. *onyx,* claw, + *pherein,* to bear).

FIG. 16-7

Ventral view of anterior end of *Peripatus,* which combines annelid-like and arthropod-like structures. Note antennae, eyes, ventral mouth with small horny jaws and short oral papilla, small skin papillae all over body, and legs with claws. Segmentation apparent only by number of legs. Seventy species (2 to 3 inches long) have wide, tropical, discontinuous distribution. It may be a link between annelids and arthropods, or it may be independent branch from a form common to all segmented groups. (Courtesy Ward's Natural Science Establishment, Inc., Rochester, N. Y.)

form but shows no external segmentation. The integument is soft and velvety and is thrown into fine transverse wrinkles with many conical papillae, which bear chitinous spines. The head, which is not well marked off from the rest of the body, bears two short antennae, a pair of dorsal eyes, a pair of short, fleshy oral papillae, and a midventral mouth with a pair of chitinous jaws. On the oral papillae are the openings of the slime glands. Both the jaws and oral papillae represent modified limbs. The legs, which are not jointed, are ringed with ridges bearing rows of papillae. Each leg is short and stocky and bears a pair of claws. In some species there are seventeen pairs of legs, but other species contain more. The Onychophora represent the first group of animals that walk with the body raised upon stiffened but not flexible legs. Locomotion is slow, with waves of body contractions in which the legs of a few segments are lifted and moved forward in succession from the anterior to posterior end. At the posterior end of the body are the anus and a ventral genital opening.

Internal structure (Fig. 16-8). The **body wall** consists of a cuticle, epidermis, dermis, and layers of unstriped circular and longitudinal muscles. Special muscles are used to manipulate the jaws. The **body cavity** (hemocoel) is lined with epithelium, which also invests the organs within the cavity, and is imperfectly divided by muscular partitions into a few compartments. The slime glands that open on the oral papillae are found on either side of the body cavity. Secretions from these glands are ejected a considerable distance and adhere to the objects they hit. In this way the animal can capture its prey. The slime glands are modified from the paired coxal glands (excretory glands that open at the base of the leg in some insects and arachnids).

The **digestive system** is made up of the mouth, the tongue with rows of small spines, the muscular pharynx into which open two large salivary glands, the short esophagus, the long intestine, and the rectum. The **excretory system** consists of a pair of nephridia in each segment. Each nephridium has a vesicle, ciliated funnel, and duct, which has an opening at the base of the leg. A dorsal blood vessel forming a contractile heart lying within the pericardial space and receiving blood from each segment by a pair of ostia forms an open **circulatory system.** Respiration is carried on by a **tracheal system** that ramifies to all parts of the body and communicates to the outside by openings, or stigmata. These trachea, however, are not homologous with those of insects. The **nervous system** contains a pair of cerebral ganglia with two circumpharyngeal connectives to two widely separated ventral nerve cords. The two nerve cords are connected by transverse commissures. Slight enlargements of the nerve cords opposite each pair of legs represent the only signs of ganglia. The nerve cords, however, are made up of continuous layers of ganglionic cells. Nerves are given off from the nerve cords to the legs and from the dorsal brain to anterior regions. Sensory organs are represented by the two simple eyes on top of the head and by the conical papillae (tactile) of the integument.

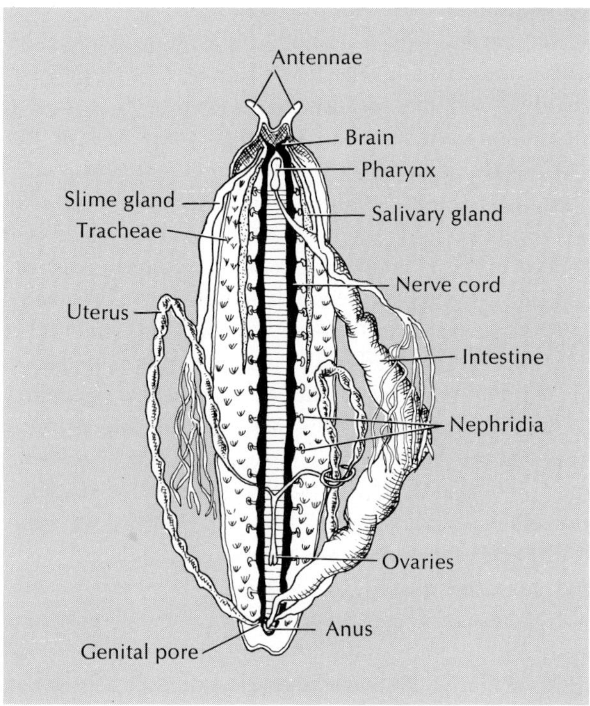

FIG. 16-8

Internal anatomy of female *Peripatus.* (From Hickman: Biology of the invertebrates, The C. V. Mosby Co.)

The sexes are distinct in *Peripatus.* **Female** organs are two tubular ovaries, a pair of oviducts, and paired uteri that join to form a vaginal opening. The **male** system has paired testes, seminal vesicles, vasa deferentia, and genital opening to the outside. The male in some species deposits its spermatophores, or bundles of sperm, on the body of the female, from whence the sperm penetrate the thin skin to fertilize the eggs in the oviducts. Thirty or more young, each about ½ inch long, are produced each year by the female, but all are not born at the same time. In some there is a definite placenta by which the young are attached to the uterus, where nutrition and other exchanges between mother and young are carried on. The young resemble the adults.

Evolutionary status of Peripatus. The phylum Onychophora seems to have a structure intermediate between a generalized annelid type and the common ancestor of such arthropods as centipedes and insects. According to Gregory, *Peripatus* is more primitive than insects and agrees somewhat with centipedes in the arrangement of its internal metamerism. Its morphologic pattern has not changed in 400 million years and represents a stage in the long evolutionary road between annelids and insects. It has remained the same because it has been restricted to narrow ecologic niches where selective mutations did not have a chance to operate. A fossil form, *Aysheaia,* discovered in the mid-Cambrian shale of British Columbia, is so much like *Peripatus* that it is considered a direct ancestor.

Comparison of Onychophora with Annelida

Onychophorans have both arthropod and annelid features. They show a resemblance to the annelids as follows:

1. Segmentally arranged nephridia
2. Ciliated reproductive ducts
3. Muscular body wall
4. Structure of the eyes

They resemble the arthropods as follows:

1. Tubular heart with ostia
2. Presence of tracheae
3. Mouth parts modified from appendages
4. Hemocoel for body cavity
5. Large size of brain

Their own unique characters are as follows:

1. Scanty metamerism
2. Structure of the jaws
3. Separate arrangement of the nerve cords with no well-defined ganglia

Phylum Priapulida*

The Priapulida are a small group of vermiform marine animals that are found chiefly in the colder waters of both northern and southern hemispheres, although some species have been found at great depths in tropical waters. They have been reported in the New World from Massachusetts to Greenland on the Atlantic coast, from California to Point Barrow, Alaska, on the Pacific coast, and from the coast of Uruguay to the Falkland Islands and other islands of the Antarctic region. In the Old World, specimens have been collected from the coasts of northern regions and as far south as Belgium. They live in the bottom muck of mud and sand on the sea floor and range from intertidal zones to

*Pri′a-pu″li-da (Gr. *priapos,* phallus, + *ida,* pl. suffix).

depths of several thousand meters. Although they can plow through the bottom muck by means of alternate invagination and evagination of the proboscis, aided by wall movements, they usually remain quietly in a vertical position with the mouth on a level with the surface.

Taxonomically the Priapulida have been linked in the past with various other groups such as the Echiuroidea and the Sipunculida because of the radial symmetry of their anterior end and supposed pseudocoel organization. Hyman emphasized their resemblance to the Kinorhyncha and placed them as a class in the phylum Aschelminthes. More recently Shapeero (1961) and other investigators report that the body cavity is lined with a thin, nucleated peritoneum and thus class them as true eucoelomate animals. Because of this and their indefinite relationship to other groups, the priapulids are now assigned the rank of a separate phylum.

The phylum is made up of two genera, *Priapulus* and *Halicryptus*, and eight species, seven of which are in the genus *Priapulus*. Although a solitary animal, many individuals are sometimes collected in the same locality.

Basic adaptations. Priapulida have undergone little evolutionary divergence, as evidenced by the few species in the phylum. The eversible proboscis, with its numerous recurved teeth surrounding the mouth and lining the pharynx, is well adapted for its predaceous habits. Their restricted movements fit them to capture only slowly moving prey. Their stable ecologic niche has afforded them little opportunity for evolutionary diversification within the group.

Morphologic features. Priapulida are mostly medium-sized animals, the largest being 5 to 6 inches long (Fig. 16-9). The cylindric body includes a proboscis, trunk, and caudal appendage (lacking in *Halicryptus*). The trunk is annulated but not segmented. Scattered over the trunk are many tubercles and spines that give it a distinctly warty appearance. The eversible proboscis, which may be larger in diameter than the trunk, bears rows of teeth that lead toward the mouth. The proboscis is used both in capturing prey and sampling surroundings. The mouth, at the terminal end of the proboscis, is surrounded with concentric rows of teeth, which, when this region is everted, point forward in capturing prey. The anus and two urogenital pores are located at the posterior end of the trunk. *Priapulus* has one or two caudal appendages, which are hollow stems with many soft, hollow vesicles.

The body wall is thick and muscular. It consists of a two-layered cuticle, a single layer of epidermis of

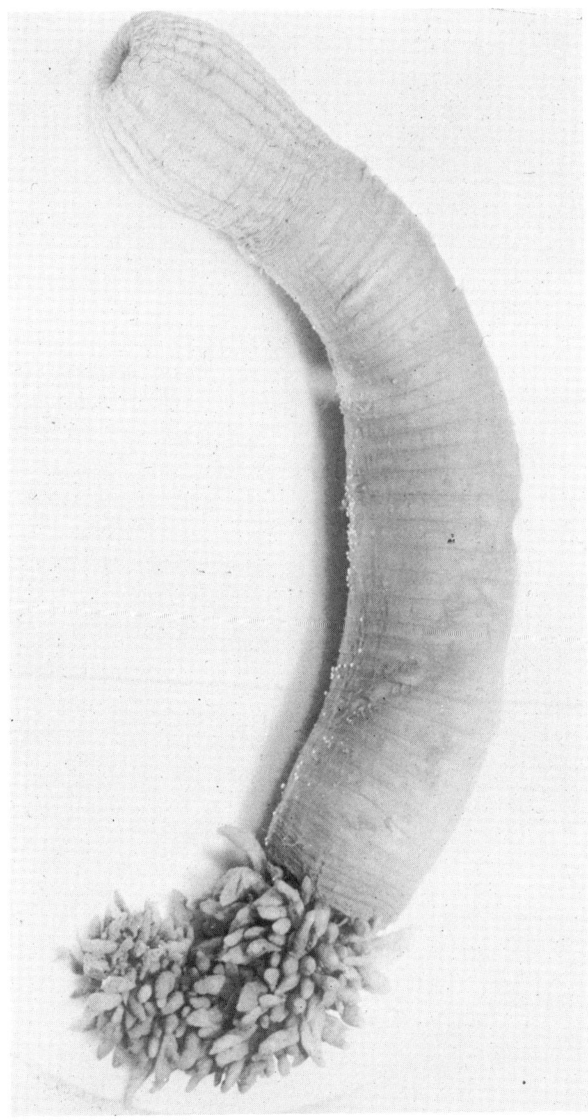

FIG. 16-9

Priapulus caudatus Lamarck. Proboscis (top) is partially withdrawn. Note longitudinal rows of papillae on proboscis, superficial segmentation along trunk, and bushy caudal appendage. When fully expanded, some specimens may attain length of 145 mm. (Courtesy W. L. Shapeero, University of Washington, Seattle.)

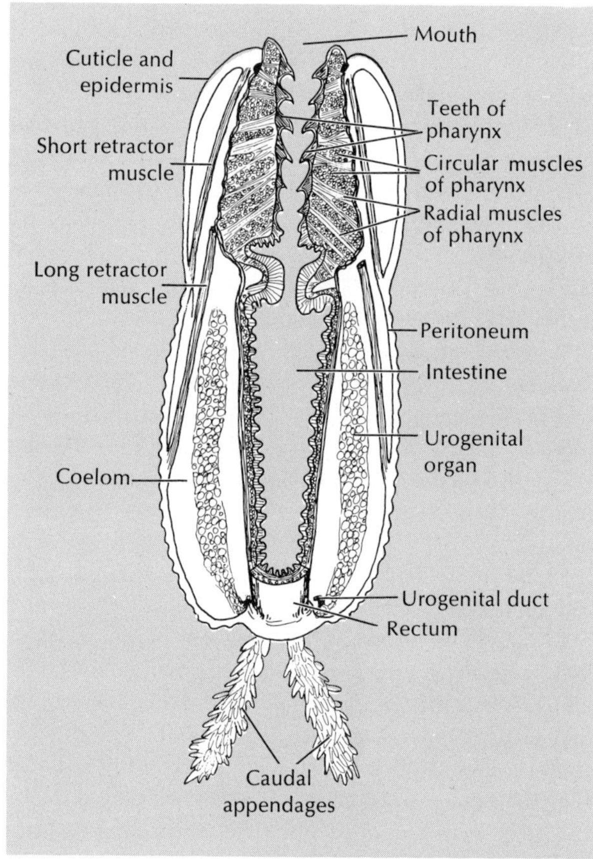

FIG. 16-10

Major internal structures of *Priapulus*. (From Hickman: Biology of the invertebrates, The C. V. Mosby Co.)

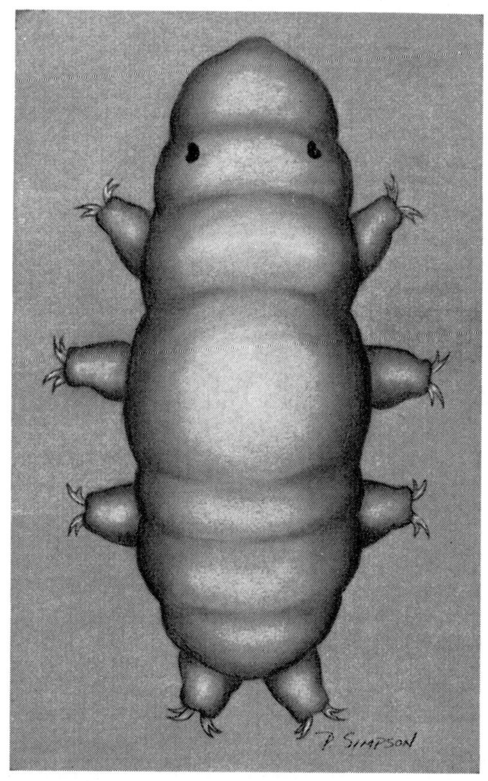

FIG. 16-11

Dorsal view of water bear (phylum Tardigrada). They live in terrestrial mosses, lichens, aquatic plants, debris of ponds, blanket algae of ponds and lakes, and other places. Although dioecious, most specimens collected are females that produce two kinds of eggs similar to summer and winter eggs of rotifers. Unique characteristics are four pairs of unjointed legs and complicated buccal apparatus for sucking liquid food.

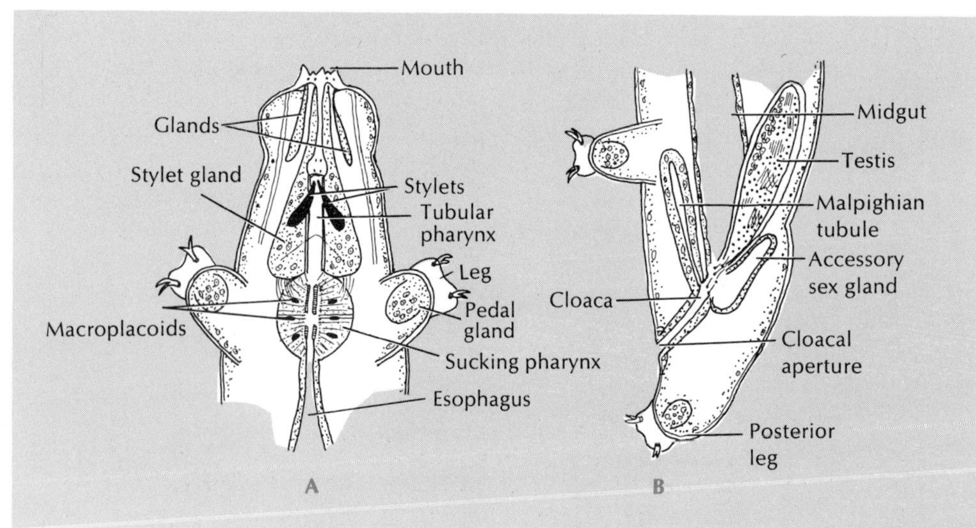

FIG. 16-12

Major structural features of a tardigrade. **A,** Buccal apparatus and pharynx. **B,** Side view of internal anatomy of posterior region of male. (From Hickman: Biology of the invertebrates, The C. V. Mosby Co.)

cuboidal or columnar cells, layers of circular and longitudinal muscles, and a thin peritoneum. The body cavity and spaces are filled with a fluid containing coelomocytes.

The digestive system (Fig. 16-10) consists of a muscular, invaginable pharynx lined with epidermis and cuticle-bearing teeth, a straight intestine with muscular walls and a lining of epithelium, and a short rectum lined with epithelium and cuticle. Priapulids live on polychaetes, small crustaceans, and even other priapulids, which they swallow whole.

The nervous system consists of a ring around the pharynx and a midventral cord. The paired urogenital organs are each made up of a gonad on one side and clusters of solenocytes on the other. Each urogenital organ has a urinary tube that passes genital as well as excretory products to the outside. The separate sexes shed their sex cells into the sea, where fertilization occurs. The egg hatches into a simple postgastrula (stereogastrula), which, in later stages, develops into a loricated larva similar to that of a rotifer. Little else is known about their embryology.

Phylum Tardigrada*

Water bears, or tardigrades (Fig. 16-11), are minute forms, usually less than 1 mm. in length, and are found in both fresh water and salt water, wet moss, sand, damp soils, pond debris, liverworts, and lichens. The body is elongated, cylindric, or a long oval and is unsegmented. The head is merely the anterior part of the trunk. It bears four pairs of short, stubby, unjointed legs armed with four single or two double claws, which may be unequal in size and are used for clinging to its substrate. The last pair of appendages lies at the posterior end of the body. The body is covered by a cuticle secreted by the hypodermis, which may be smooth or ornamented with spines or plates. Cilia are absent. The cuticle is shed (ecdysis) four or more times in its life history.

The mouth is at the anterior end and opens into a tubular pharynx, which is adapted for sucking by radial muscle fibers (Fig. 16-12, *A*). The pharynx is supplied with two needle-like stylets that can be protruded through the mouth or withdrawn by muscular action. These stylets are used for piercing the cellulose walls of the plants they live upon, and the liquid contents are sucked in by the pharynx. The rest of the digestive tube is made up of a short esophagus, a stomach, a short rectum, and a cloacal aperture or anus that opens between the posterior pair of legs. Glands empty into both the pharynx and the intestinal tract. At the junction of the stomach and rectum, two paired ventral malpighian tubes and a single dorsal gland empty into the digestive system and may be excretory in function. Most of the body cavity is a hemocoel, with the true coelom restricted to the gonadal cavity. There are no circulatory or respiratory systems, as fluids freely circulate through the body spaces and gaseous exchange can occur through the body surface.

The muscular system consists of a number of long muscle bands, each of which is composed of a single fibrillar cell that may be a syncytium. These muscles have most of their origins and insertions on the body wall and manipulate body movements and the legs. Circular muscles are absent, but the hydrostatic pressure of the body fluid may act as a type of skeleton.

The brain is large and covers most of the dorsal surface of the pharynx. It connects by way of circumpharyngeal connectives to the subpharyngeal ganglion, from which the double ventral nerve cord extends posteriorly as a chain of four ganglia. Sense organs consist usually of a pair of pigmented eyespots and various tactile organs.

Tardigrades are dioecious, but usually females are more common than males and may make up an entire population. Parthenogenesis is common. The ovary or testis lies dorsal to the intestine and opens by a single oviduct or two sperm ducts into the cloaca or through a separate gonopore (Fig. 16-12, *B*). Both thin-shelled and thick-shelled eggs, similar to the summer and winter eggs of rotifers, occur. Eggs are often found in the shed cuticle.

Like rotifers, tardigrades have great ability to withstand harsh environmental conditions (desiccation, freezing, etc.). Under such conditions the tardigrade loses water, shrivels, and contracts into a more or less rounded condition with low metabolism (anabiosis). When placed in water, it becomes normal again, even after being in the anabiotic state for years.

Only 40 to 50 species of tardigrades have been found in North America, but 300 to 400 species occur in other parts of the world.

The affinities of tardigrades are among the most puzzling of all animal groups. They are coelomate ani-

*Tar′di-gra″da (L. *tardus,* slow, + *grad,* walk).

mals and their mesoderm is enterocoelous like that of deuterostomes, although they may be highly modified protostomes. Various authorities have placed them near the arthropods, annelids, nematodes, or chaetognaths.

Common American genera of tardigrades are *Macrobiotus, Echiniscus,* and *Hypsibius.*

Derivation and meaning of basic terminology

avicularium (L. *avicula,* dim. of *avis,* bird, + *aria,* like). Modified zooid attached to the surface of the major zooid in Ectoprocta.

introvert (L. *intro,* inward, + *vertere,* to turn). In the sipunculid the anterior narrow portion that can be withdrawn into the trunk.

lophophore (Gr. *lophos,* crest, + *phoros,* bearing). Anterior ridge bearing ciliated tentacles in Ectoprocta, Brachiopoda, and Phoronida.

ooecium (Gr. *oion,* egg, + *oikos,* house). Brood pouch.

trochophore (Gr. *trochos,* wheel, + *phoros,* bearing). A ciliated marine larva characteristic of many schizocoelomate animals.

zoecium (Gr. *zoon,* animal, + *oikos,* house). Cuticular sheath or shell of Ectoprocta.

Annotated references

Barrington, E. J. W. 1967. Invertebrate structure and function. Boston, Houghton Mifflin Co. *The minor phyla are well considered in this outstanding work on the invertebrates.*

Dawydoff, C. 1959. Echiuroidea. In P. P. Grasse (editor): Traitè de zoologie, vol. 5, part 1. Paris, Masson & Cie, pp. 855-907. *One of the best general treatments of the echiurids. Extensive bibliography.*

Hickman, C. P. 1967. Biology of the invertebrates. St. Louis, The C. V. Mosby Co. *General treatment and descriptions of all the minor coelomate phyla.*

Hill, H. R. 1960. Pentostomida. In McGraw-Hill encyclopedia of science and technology, vol. 9. New York, McGraw-Hill Book Co., pp. 623-624.

Hyman, L. H. 1959. The invertebrates: smaller coelomate groups. New York, McGraw-Hill Book Co.

Manton, S. M. 1950. The locomotion of *Peripatus.* J. Linn. Soc. Zool. **41**:529-539.

Marcus, E. 1928. Zur vergleichenden Anatomie und Histologie der Tardigraden. Zool. Jahrb. Abt. Allg. Zool. **45**:99-192.

McCinitic, C. E., and N. McGinitie. 1967. Natural history of marine animals, ed. 2. New York, McGraw-Hill Book Co. *Describes the physiology and behavior of Echiurus and Urechis.*

Pennak, R. W. 1953. Fresh-water invertebrates of the United States. New York, The Ronald Press Co. *A good general account of the tardigrades and keys to the common species.*

Pickford, G. 1947. Sipunculida. Encyclopaedia Britannica, vol. 20. *A concise, well-written account.*

Russell-Hunter, W. D. 1969. A biology of higher invertebrates. New York, The Macmillan Co.

Shapeero, W. 1961. Phylogeny of Priapulida. Science **133**:879-880.

Shapeero, W. 1962. The epidermis and cuticle of *Priapulus caudatus* Lamarck. Trans. Amer. Micr. Soc. **81**:352-355.

Shipley, A. E. 1920. Tardigrada and Pentastomida. In S. F. Harmer and A. E. Shipley (editors): The Cambridge natural history, vol. 4. London, Macmillan Co., Ltd.

CHAPTER 17

• PHYLUM ANNELIDA*
(MAJOR EUCOELOMATE BILATERAL GROUP)

BIOLOGIC PRINCIPLES

Organ-system level of organization

1. The organs having related functions are now grouped into definite **systems.**
2. The appearance of **metamerism** for the first time lays the groundwork for a more highly organized type of animal.
3. Annelids as a group show a primitive metamerism but with few differences between different somites, but some do show the beginning of such differentiation.
4. Annelids belong to the protostome branch, or schizocoelous coelomates, of the animal kingdom and have spiral and determinate cleavage.

Biologic contributions

1. The introduction of **metamerism** by the group represents the greatest advancement.
2. A true coelomic cavity reaches a high stage of development, necessitating development of various systems to carry out its functions, such as a separation of the circulatory from the digestive system.
3. Specialization of the head region into differentiated organs, such as the tentacles, palps, and eyespots of the polychaetes, is carried further in some annelids than in other invertebrates so far considered.
4. The tendency toward **centralization of the nervous system** is more developed, with cerebral ganglia (brain), two closely fused ventral nerve cords with unique giant fibers running the length of the body, and various ganglia with their lateral branches.
5. The well-developed **nephridia** in most of the somites have reached a differentiation that involves a removal of waste from the blood as well as from the coelom.
6. The circulatory system is much more complex than any we have so far considered. It is a closed system with muscular blood vessels and **aortic arch** ("hearts") for propelling the blood.
7. The appearance of the fleshy **parapodia,** with their respiratory function, introduces a suggestion of the specialized gills in higher forms.
8. Annelids are the most highly organized animals capable of complete regeneration.

*An-nel'i-da (L. *annellus,* ring, + *ida,* pl. suffix).

Position in animal kingdom

1. The segmented worms share with the flatworms similar larval forms, such as the trochophore larva, which is used as a basis of relationship between the two.
2. Phylum Onychophora has both annelid and arthropod characteristics and is often considered a transitional link between the two phyla.
3. In their embryonic patterns annelids have much in common with the mollusks.
4. In the genealogic tree Annelida are usually placed between Mollusca and Arthropoda, all three coming from the same common stem.
5. The septal arrangement and coelomic fluid compartments for precise movements of burrowing and swimming represent basic adaptive features in their evolution.

GENERAL RELATIONS

The Annelida are worms whose bodies are divided into similar rings or segments. The origin of the name of the phylum describes this basic characteristic, for it comes from the Latin word *annellus,* meaning little ring. This biologic principle of body segmentation is commonly called **metamerism,** and the divisions are known as **segments, somites,** or **metameres.** Worms previously considered do not possess this property of body segmentation, although a hint here and there in the form of transverse grooves may be found. This metamerism in Annelida is manifested not only in external body features but also in the internal arrangement of organs and systems. Circulatory, excretory, nervous, muscular, and reproductive organs all show a segmental arrangement, and there are internal partitions between the somites.

The phylum is an extensive one and is divided into several classes. Annelids are found in the soil, in fresh water, and in the sea. Many are free living, but some are parasitic in whole or in part of their life cycles.

The annelids show some striking relations to certain other phyla. Their larval stages are similar to those of

Platyhelminthes, and their marine representatives have trochophore larvae. One view holds that the adult forms of segmented worms and of flatworms have come from a common ancestor. The gap between the annelids and flatworms is the metamerism. However, the annelids also have many arthropod characteristics, such as a hypodermis-secreted cuticle and a nervous system fundamentally similar to that of arthropods.

One phylum (Onychophora) is a classic example of an intermediate or transition form, for it has both annelid and arthropod characters. Also, there is some similarity of the parapodia in the annelid class Polychaeta to the foliaceous appendages of certain arthropods. In embryonic development Annelida have a pattern not much different from Mollusca and thus have some features in common with that group. Within the phylum, it is supposed that Polychaeta gave rise to Oligochaeta and Archiannelida and that Oligochaeta gave rise to Hirudinea.

SIGNIFICANCE OF METAMERISM

No satisfactory reason can be given for the origin of metamerism. One theory is that chains of subzooids formed by asexual fission in flatworms, instead of separating into distinct individuals, may have held together and developed structural and functional unity with the passage of time. This theory would take into account the axial gradient idea that the anterior individuals would become the dominant part of the chain in determining the coordination of the whole. It is well known that in some platyhelminths the daughter individuals formed by asexual division cling together for some time before separating. Another theory stresses the secondary origin of metamerism by the repetition of body parts, such as muscles, nerves, nephridia, coelom, and blood vessels, in a single individual. Later, partitions were interposed to form definite segments. It is also possible that segmentation may have started in the musculature of an elongated, swimming animal, for the breaking up of the body into segments would facilitate swimming movement.

The locomotion produced by metamerism in conjunction with a fluid-filled coelomic cavity and powerful body-wall musculature represents an advancement over the ciliary and creeping methods of the lower Metazoa. The coordination of muscular action and the fluid-filled septal compartments have made possible efficient swimming and creeping over a substratum by undulatory body movements. Fluid-filled coelomic cavities also provide hydrostatic skeletons for burrowing. Differential turgor (especially if the coelom is subdivided by septa) can be effected by shifting the coelomic fluid from one part of the body to the other so that precise movements can occur. Another advancement of metamerism is the possibility for each metamere to become specialized for particular functions. This would indicate that metamerism is not unlike the formation of cells in a metazoan body in which each cell or group of cells is differentiated for some definite purpose. This specialization, not marked in the Annelida but well developed in the Arthropoda, has made possible a rapid evolution of high organization in animals.

Although three phyla—Annelida, Arthropoda, and Chordata—are outstanding examples of metamerism, some other groups have tendencies toward a segmental arrangement, wholly or in part, such as one group (Monoplacophora) of the mollusks and the proglottid arrangement of the cestodes. True segmentation has arisen at least twice independently—in the Annelida-Arthropoda groups and in the Chordata. However, there may be many types of metamerism for different adaptive reasons, such as swimming (chordates), burrowing (annelids), reproduction (cestodes), and repetition of organs in elongated animals for effective control (rhynchocoels).

The whole evolutionary potential of the Annelida has been guided to a great extent by the morphologic organization of metamerism and its varied patterns of related structures.

CHARACTERISTICS

1. Body **metamerically segmented;** symmetry bilateral; three germ layers
2. Body wall with outer circular and inner longitudinal muscle layers; transparent moist cuticle secreted by columnar epithelium (hypodermis) covers body
3. **Chitinous setae,** often present on fleshy **parapodia** for appendages; absent in some
4. Coelom (schizocoel) well developed in most and usually divided by septa; coelomic fluid for turgidity
5. **Blood system closed** and segmentally arranged; respiratory pigments (erythrocruorin and chlorocruorin) with amebocytes in blood plasma
6. Digestive system complete and not metamerically arranged

7. Respiration by skin or **gills**
8. Excretory system typically a **pair of nephridia for each metamere**
9. Nervous system with a double ventral nerve cord and a pair of ganglia with lateral nerves in each metamere; brain a pair of dorsally located cerebral ganglia
10. Sensory system of tactile organs, taste buds, statocysts (in some), photoreceptor cells, and eyes with lenses (in some)
11. Hermaphroditic or separate sexes; larvae, if present, are trochophore type; asexual reproduction by budding in some; spiral and determinate cleavage

CLASSES

The annelids are classified primarily on the basis of the presence or absence of parapodia, setae, metameres, and other morphologic features.

Class Clitellata (cli'tel-la"ta) (L. *clitellae,* packsaddle, + *ata,* group suffix). Body with clitellum; segmentation conspicuous; segments with or without annuli; segments definite or indefinite in number; parapodia absent; hermaphroditic; eggs usually in cocoons; mostly freshwater and terrestrial.

Order Oligochaeta* (ol'i-go-ke"ta) (Gr. *oligos,* few, + *chaite,* hair, bristle). Body with conspicuous segmentation; setae few per metamere; head absent; coelom spacious and usually divided by intersegmental septa; development direct, no larva; chiefly terrestrial and freshwater. Examples: *Lumbricus, Allolobophora, Aelosoma, Tubifex.*

Order Hirudinea (hir'u-din"e-a) (L. *hirudo,* leech, + *ea,* characterized by). Body with definite number of segments (33 or 34) with many annuli; body with anterior and posterior suckers usually; setae usually absent; coelom closely packed with connective tissue and muscle; terrestrial, freshwater, and marine. Examples: *Hirudo, Placobdella, Macrobdella.*

Class Polychaeta* (pol'y-ke"ta) (Gr. *polys,* many, + *chaite,* hair, bristle). Body of numerous segments with lateral parapodia bearing many setae; head distinct, with eyes and tentacles; clitellum absent; sexes usually separate; gonads transitory; asexual budding in some; trochophore larva usually; mostly marine.

Subclass Errantia (er-ran'she-a) (L. *errare,* to wander, + *ia,* pl. suffix). Body of many segments, usually similar except in head and anal regions; parapodia alike and with acicula; pharynx usually protrusible; head appendages usually present; free living, tube dwelling, pelagic, mostly marine. Examples: *Neanthes, Aphrodite, Glycera.*

Subclass Sedentaria (sed'en-ta"ri-a) (L. *sedere,* to sit, + *aria,* like or connected with). Body with unlike segments and parapodia and with regional differentiation; prostomium small or indistinct; head appendages modified or absent; pharynx without jaws and mostly nonprotrusible; parapodia reduced and without acicula; gills anterior or absent; tube dwelling or in burrows. Examples: *Arenicola, Chaetopterus, Amphitrite.*

[**Class Archiannelida** (old classification) is now considered an unnatural order under class Polychaeta. Their organization, formerly considered primitive, is the result of reduction. Parapodia and setae are reduced or absent. A trochophore larva is present in some. *Polygordius* is a common example.]

*Since Oligochaeta and Polychaeta are both provided with setae, both these classes are sometimes assigned to a group called Chaetopoda (ke-top'o-da) (Gr. *chaite,* hair, bristle, + *podos,* foot).

REPRESENTATIVE TYPES

ORDER OLIGOCHAETA

Lumbricus terrestris—earthworm

Habitat. Nearly everyone is familiar with the common earthworm, for it is almost worldwide in distribution. One cannot spade the soil without coming in contact with these worms. Moreover, they crawl out on the sidewalks after a heavy rain and are easily seen there. The German name for them is Regenwürmer (rainworms). Earthworms like moist, rich soil for their burrows. Golf courses are excellent places to see these holes because there the same burrow may be used for a long period of time and the castings of the worms are much in evidence. *Eisenia foetida,* the brandling, a smaller worm and often studied in zoology, is found in manure piles. Sandy, clay, and acid soils deficient in humus are unfavorable for earthworms. At night they emerge from their burrows to explore their surroundings, often keeping their tails in their burrows into which they rapidly withdraw when disturbed. During very dry weather the earthworm may coil up in a slime-lined chamber several feet underground and pass into a state of dormancy.

External features. The body of the earthworm is elongated, cylindric in form, and tapered at each end. The body is divided into 100 to 175 **metameres,** or somites (500 to 600 in giant earthworms), which are separated from each other by grooves. Few metameres are added after hatching. The usual length of the common earthworm is from 5 to 12 inches. On the anterior side of the first metamere is the **mouth,** overhung by the fleshy **prostomium** (regarded by some as the first segment). The **anus** is located on the last segment, or

pygidium. Straddled over the back like a saddle (in somites 31 to 37) is the swollen, whitish, glandular **clitellum** (Fig. 17-1), which is important in the reproductive process. Both prostomium and clitellum are useful in taxonomic determinations.

The external surface of the worm is covered by a thin, transparent **cuticle** (cuticula) bearing cross striations, which give it an irridescent appearance. The cuticle is secreted by the epidermal cells, which lie just beneath it. The **epidermis** contains **unicellular glands** whose secretions reach the surface through pores in the cuticle. There are also sensory and small basal cells in the epidermis. Beneath the epidermis is the **basement membrane,** which rests upon the muscle layers that make up most of the body wall. Certain pigments such as protoporphyrin are also found in the body wall.

Openings. Many external openings are found for taking in food, for discharging feces and waste products, and for the exit and entrance of the reproductive cells. They may be enumerated as follows: (1) **mouth;** (2) **anus;** (3) openings of the paired **vasa deferentia** on somite 15; easily recognized on the ventral surface of this somite by their swollen lips; serve for the exit of the sperm; (4) openings of the paired **oviducts** on the ventral side of somite 14; are small and serve for the exit of the eggs; (5) openings of the two pairs of **seminal receptacles** in the grooves between somites 9 and 10 and 10 and 11; serve to pick up sperm from a mate during copulation; (6) paired excretory openings (**nephridiopores**) on the lateroventral side of each segment except the first three and the last; (7) **dorsal pores,** one of which is located in the middorsal line at the anterior edge of each somite from 8 or 9 to the last one; are openings into the coelomic cavity. Coelomic fluid of a malodorous nature may be ejected through these pores for defense.

Locomotion. With the exception of the first and last somites, each segment bears four pairs of chitinous **setae,** which are located on the ventral and lateral surfaces. Each seta (Fig. 17-2) is a bristlelike rod set in a sac within the body wall. It is moved by retractor and protractor muscles attached to the sac. The setae project through small pores in the cuticle to the outside. When an earthworm is moving forward, the setae anchor the somites of a part of the body and prevent backward slipping. The contraction of the circular muscles in the anterior end pushes the body forward and is followed by the contraction of the longitudinal muscles which pulls the posterior part of the body anteriorly. By the repetition of this process the worm is able to advance with speed. Rarely do worms use the setae as levers while moving, for this is usually too slow for them. Setae are also used by the worm to hold fast in the

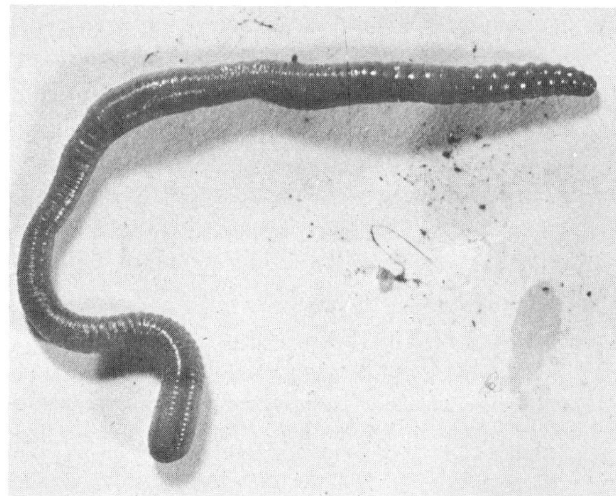

FIG. 17-1

Common earthworm *Lumbricus terrestris.* Head at upper right. Swollen region about one third of distance from anterior end is clitellum.

FIG. 17-2

Seta with its muscle attachments showing relation to adjacent structures. Setae lost by wear and tear are replaced by new ones, which develop from formative cell. (Modified from Stephenson and others.)

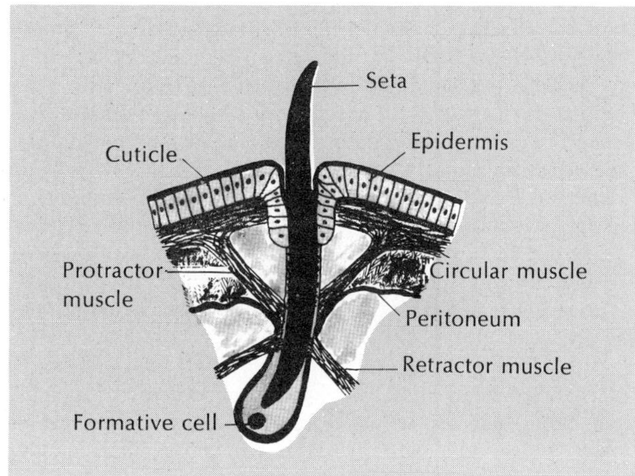

burrow, as all robins well know. When a seta is lost, a new one is formed in a reserve follicle to replace it.

Body plan. The earthworms have a tube-within-a-tube arrangement. There is a body wall of external **circular** muscles and a thicker internal layer of **longitudinal** muscles lying just underneath the epidermis and its basement membrane. This body wall surrounds the **coelomic cavity. Coelomic fluid** within the cavity gives rigidity to the body by maintaining turgor. The fluid contains two main types of coelomic cells: **leukocytes,** which are phagocytic ameboid cells, and **eleocytes,** which come from the chlorogogue cells of the digestive tract and carry nutritive granules to all parts of the body. The coelomic cavity is divided by **septa,** which mark the boundaries of the somites. These septa are not always complete and may be absent between certain somites. The inner surface of the coelom as well as the outer surface of its organs is lined with **peritoneum.** Through the center of the coelom runs the alimentary canal from the first to the last segment. The septa help hold it in place. The metameric arrangement is noticeable in the distribution of certain visceral organs; for instance, a pair of nephridia and a pair of nerve ganglia are located in each of the somites. Other visceral organs—reproductive apparatus and the main circulatory vessels—are closely located around the alimentary canal, which serves as a type of body axis.

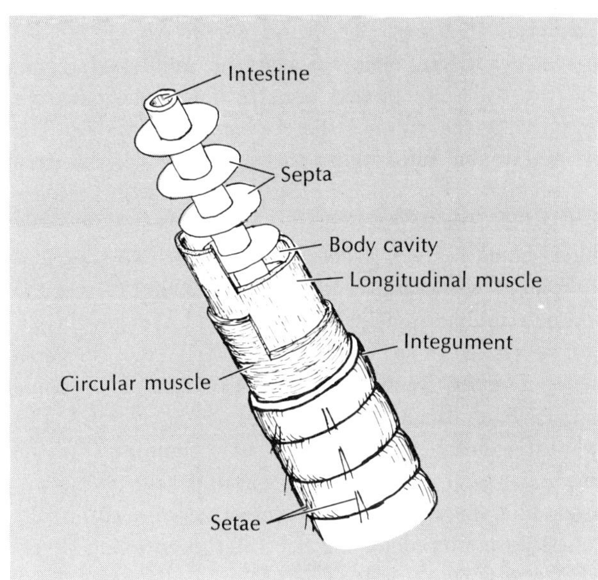

FIG. 17-3

Part of earthworm showing arrangement of muscle layers in body wall and septa. (Modified from Parry.)

FIG. 17-4

Chief internal features of anterior portion of earthworm, as shown by removal of left body wall.

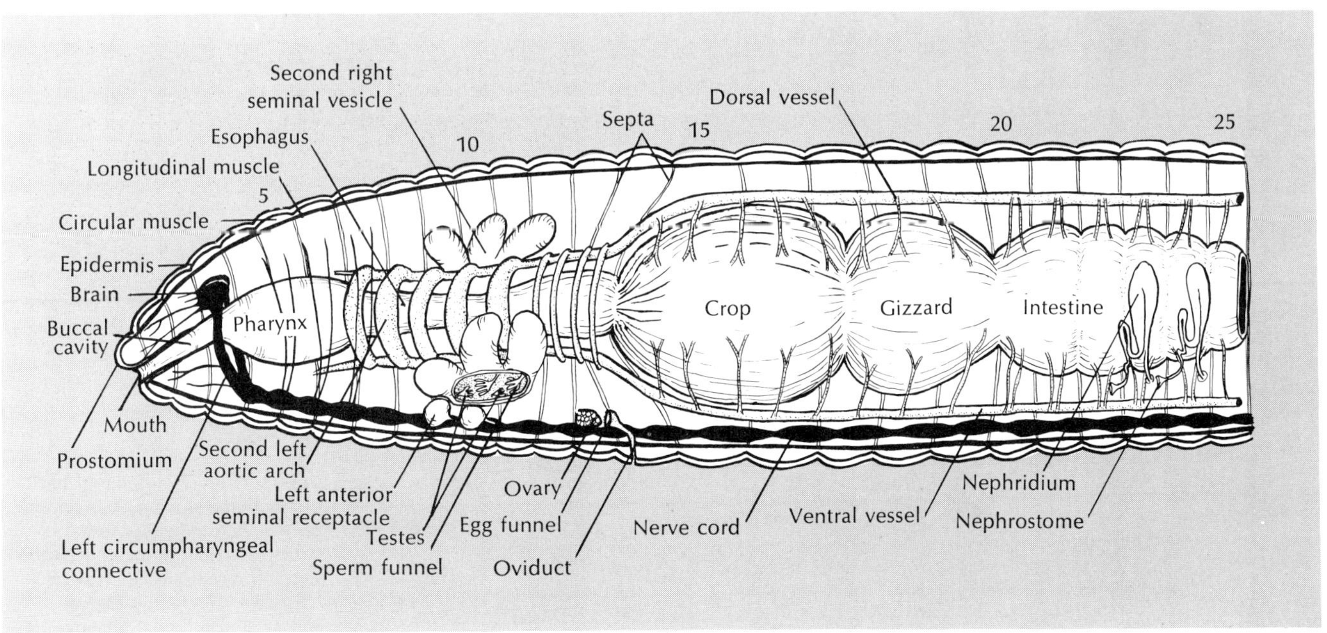

Internal features. When an earthworm is placed in water and cut open through the middorsal region and the walls are pinned out, the internal organs are revealed to the view of the student (Fig. 17-3). The visceral organs and systems that are easily seen in such a dissection are as follows (Fig. 17-4): (1) the alimentary canal, running straight through the worm, (2) the dorsal blood vessel just dorsal to the digestive tract and the paired aortic arches in segments 7 to 11, (3) the white, glandlike seminal vesicles folded over on the digestive system in segments 9 to 12, (4) the thin partitions of septa (with pores for passage of coelomic fluid), which divide the coelom into compartments, (5) the little fluffy nephridia in each somite, (6) the cerebral ganglia (brain) on the dorsal side of the anterior pharynx, and (7) the ventral nerve cord and its ganglia, running along the floor of the coelomic cavity when the alimentary canal is pushed aside.

Digestive system. The alimentary canal of the earthworm is divided into a large number of compartments, each with certain special functions to perform. The parts of the system are (1) the **mouth** and **buccal cavity** in somites 1 to 3, (2) the muscular **pharynx** in somites 4 and 5, (3) the straight **esophagus,** with three pairs of **calciferous glands** in somites 6 to 14, (4) the thin-walled, enlarged **crop** in somites 15 to 16, (5) the thick, muscular **gizzard** in somites 17 to 18, and (6) the long **intestine,** with slight bulges in each somite, from somite 19 to the last somite, where it ends in the **anus.** When seen in section, the intestine reveals on its dorsal wall a peculiar infolded **typhlosole** (Fig. 17-5), which greatly increases the absorptive and digestive surface. The lining of the digestive system is made up of simple columnar epithelium, which is ciliated. Longitudinal and circular muscles are found in the wall of the system, and curious yellow **chlorogogue cells** from the peritoneum surround the digestive tract and fill much of the typhlosole. The chlorogogue cells store foodstuffs and may convert protein into fat. When a cell is ripe (full of fat), its nucleus divides mitotically and the fat-containing portion of the cell constricts off as an eleocyte. The eleocytes, or wandering cells, apparently contribute their fat to other body cells. The chloragogue cells also function in excretion.

The food is mainly decayed organic matter, bits of leaves and vegetation, refuse, and animal matter. After being moistened by secretions from the mouth, food is drawn in by the sucking action of the pharynx controlled by the numerous muscles extending from pharynx to body wall. The liplike prostomium aids in manipulating the food into position. The calciferous glands, by secreting calcium carbonate, may neutralize the acidity of the food, or they may simply excrete calcium as a metabolic product. Food is stored temporarily in the crop before being passed on into the gizzard, which grinds the food into small pieces. Digestion and absorption take place in the intestine. The digestive system secretes various enzymes to break down the food: pepsin, which acts upon protein; amylase, which acts upon

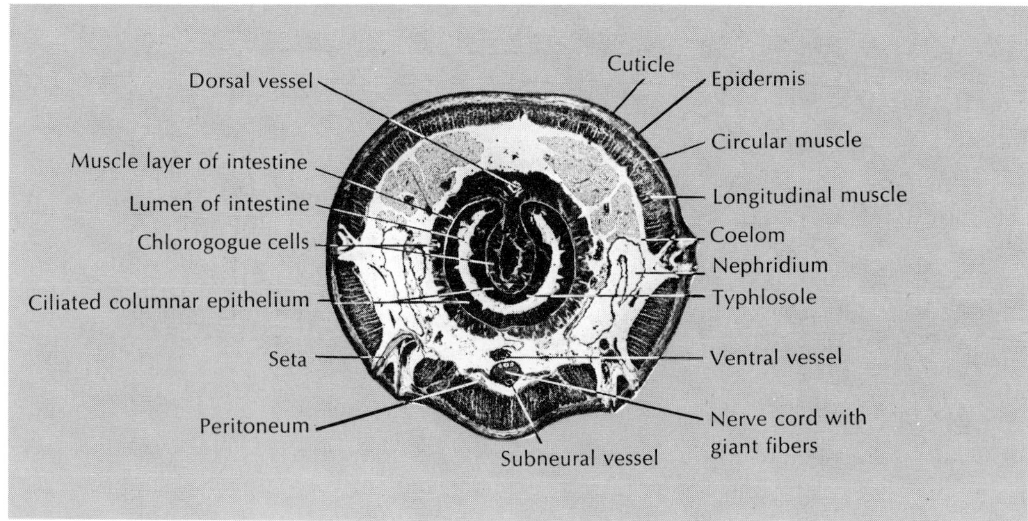

FIG. 17-5

Cross section of earthworm back of clitellum showing arrangement of setae and general internal structures. Section made between septa to reveal muscular bands. (Courtesy General Biological Supply House, Inc., Chicago.)

carbohydrates; cellulase, which acts upon cellulose; and lipase, which acts upon fats. The indigestible residue is discharged through the anus. Naturally, earthworms take in a great deal of soil, sand, and other indigestible matter along with their food. In hard, firm soil, worms literally eat their way through the soil in their burrowing; this accounts for their numerous castings. The food products are absorbed into the blood, which carries them to the various parts of the body for assimilation. Some of the food is absorbed into the coelomic fluid, which also aids in food distribution.

Circulatory system. The circulatory system of the earthworm (Fig. 17-6) is a "closed system" consisting of a complicated pattern of blood vessels and capillaries that ramify to all parts of the body. There are five main blood trunks, all running lengthwise through the body. These may be described as follows:

1. The **dorsal vessel** (single) runs above the alimentary canal from the pharynx to the anus. It is a pumping organ provided with valves and functions as the true heart. This vessel receives blood from the **parietal vessels,** the **dorsointestinal vessels,** and the **lateral esophageal vessels** and pumps the blood by peristalsis anteriorly into the five pairs of **aortic arches** (formerly called hearts), pharyngeal wall, and **afferent vessel to the typhlosole.** The chief function of the aortic arches is to maintain a steady pressure of blood into the subintestinal vessel.

2. The **ventral (subintestinal) vessel** (single) lies between the alimentary canal and the nerve cord. This vessel may be considered the real aorta of the earthworm. It receives blood from the aortic arches and delivers it anteriorly to the brain and other regions and posteriorly to the tail region. As the subintestinal vessel passes backward it gives off (a) one pair of **segmental vessels** in each segment to the body-wall musculature, nephridia, and lateral neural vessels, and (b) one pair of **ventrointestinal vessels** in each segment to the alimentary canal.

3. The **lateral neural vessels** (paired) lie one on each side of the nerve cord. These receive the blood from the segmental vessels and carry it posteriorly with many branches to the nerve cord.

4. The **subneural vessel** (single) is found under the nerve cord. This blood vessel is the main vein. It receives blood from the nerve cord and passes it backward toward the tail and upward through the paired **parietal vessels** in each segment (from somite 12 posteriorly). The parietal vessels also drain the blood from the nephridia and from the body wall and return it to the dorsal vessel.

In this scheme it will be seen that the circulation of the alimentary tract is the most involved, for its ventral half is supplied by the ventral intestinal vessels from the subintestinal vessel and its dorsal half by paired typhlosolar vessels (two per somite) from the dorsal vessel. Nearly all the blood from the alimentary canal returns

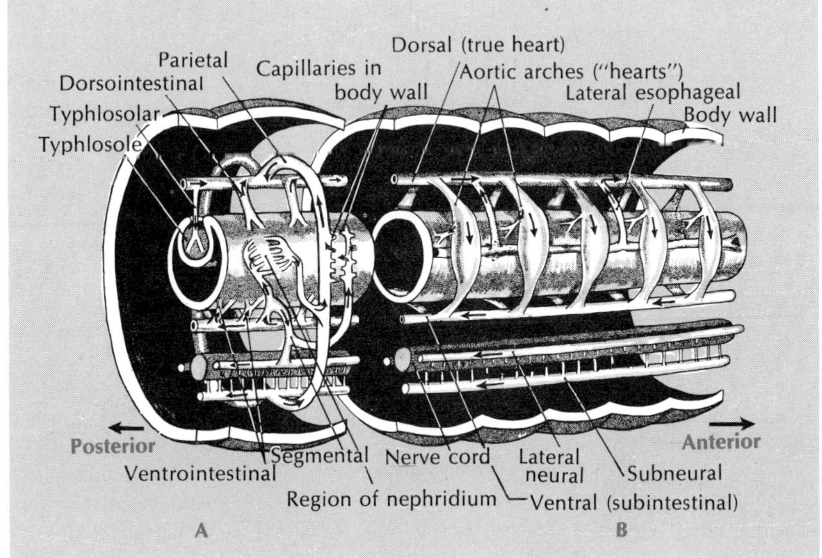

FIG. 17-6

Scheme of circulatory system in earthworm *Lumbricus terrestris* showing direction (by arrows) of blood flow in principal blood vessels (semilateral view). **A,** Circulation in any somite posterior to esophagus. **B,** Circulation in somites 7 to 11 showing aortic arches around esophagus. Septa not shown. Blood is distributed to dorsal vessel (true pumping organ) by parietals, dorsointestinals, and lateral esophageals; dorsal vessel sends blood to dorsal wall of gut by typhlosolars and to subintestinal by aortic arches; subintestinal gives off ventrointestinals to ventral part of intestine and segmentals to lateral neurals, body wall, and nephridia; parietals pick up from nephridial, subneural, and dermal vessels before entering dorsal vessel. (Modified from many sources.)

to the dorsal vessel by the dorsointestinal vessels (two pairs per somite). Since the parietal vessels do not extend anteriorly to somite 12, the anterior end is drained by the lateral esophageal vessels, which empty into the dorsal vessel at somite 10 and into the parietal vessels at somite 12.

The propulsion necessary to force the blood along is provided by the peristaltic or milking action of the muscular walls of the blood vessels, particularly the dorsal vessel. Valves in the vessels prevent backflow.

The blood of the earthworm is made up of a **liquid plasma** in which are colorless ameboid cells, **corpuscles.** Dissolved in the blood plasma is the pigment hemoglobin, of enormous molecular weight. This gives a red color to the blood and aids in the transportation of oxygen for respiration.

Excretory system. The organs of excretion are the **nephridia,** a pair of which is found in each somite except the first three and the last one. Each one is found in parts of two successive somites (Fig. 17-7). A ciliated funnel, known as the **nephrostome,** is found just anterior to an intersegmental septum and leads by a small ciliated tubule through the septum into the somite behind, where it connects with the main part of the nephridium. This part of the nephridium is made up of several complex loops of increasing size, which finally terminate in a bladderlike structure leading to an aperture, the **nephridiopore;** this opens to the outside near the ventral row of setae. By means of cilia, wastes from the coelom are drawn into the nephrostome and tubule, where they are joined by organic wastes from the blood capillaries in the glandular part of the nephridium. All the waste is discharged to the outside through the nephridiopore. Chlorogogue cells may store waste temporarily before releasing it into the coelomic fluid.

Respiratory system. The earthworm has no special respiratory organs, but the gaseous exchange is made in the moist skin, where oxygen is picked up and carbon

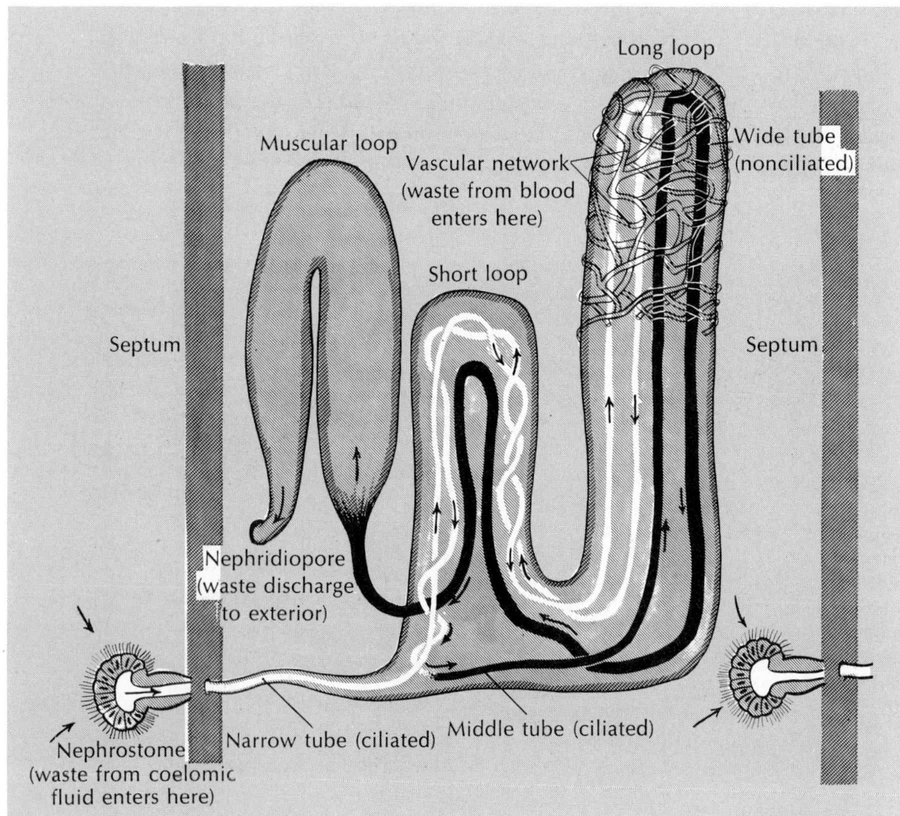

FIG. 17-7

Earthworm nephridium. Wastes are picked up by ciliated nephrostome in one somite, carried through tube enclosed in loops of connective tissue, and expelled through nephridiopore in next somite. Only part of extensive network of blood vessels is shown. Note that tube is differentiated into characteristic regions. (Redrawn with modifications from Moment: General zoology, Houghton Mifflin Co.)

dioxide given off. Blood capillaries are fairly numerous just below the cuticle, and the oxygen combines with the hemoglobin of the plasma and is carried to the various tissues.

Nervous system and sense organs. The nervous system in earthworms (Fig. 17-8) consists of a **central system** and **peripheral nerves.** The central system is made up of a pair of **suprapharyngeal ganglia** (brain) just above the anterior part of the pharynx; a pair of **circumpharyngeal connectives,** which run from the brain around the pharynx to the **subpharyngeal ganglia,** located in somite 4; a **ventral nerve cord** (really double), which runs along the floor of the coelom to the last somite; and a pair of fused **ganglia** on the ventral cord in each somite. Each pair of fused ganglia gives off six lateral nerves to the body structures, such as muscles, epidermis, nephridia, and setae, in each somite. Both sensory and motor fibers are found in these lateral nerves. The sensory fibers come from special cells in the epidermis and carry impulses originating there to the ventral nerve cord. Motor nerves run from cells in the ganglia to muscles or glands. The unit of nervous structure here, as in all higher forms, is the **neuron,** which is a nerve cell with its branches. Thus the sensory fibers belong to sensory neurons and motor fibers belong to motor neurons. The brain of an earthworm contains neurosecretory cells, and the segmental ganglia have chromaffin cells; each of these types of cells may have an endocrine function.

For rapid escape movements the nerve cord of earthworms is provided with three giant fibers (neurochords), which run the length of the cord (Fig. 17-9). Each neurochord is made up of fibers (axons) contributed by nerve cells in each segment. These axons are fused end to end at the intersegmental synapses, which allow rapid transmission of impulses because of the direct one-to-one relation. The giant fibers carry impulses at a rate of 100 feet per second; in other nerves the speed is only 20 feet per second. The median neurochord is concerned with sensory stimulation in the anterior part of the animal and transmits impulses to posterior effectors (muscles or glands). The lateral neurochords (which are connected) are stimulated behind that level and send messages to anterior effectors. This mechanism explains the speed with which worms can withdraw into their burrows.

Sense organs are distributed all over the body and are particularly abundant at the anterior and posterior ends. Each sense organ consists of sensory cells surrounded by supporting epidermal cells (Fig. 17-10). The sensory cells are provided with small, hairlike tips, which project through pores in the cuticle; the bases of these projections are attached to sensory nerve fibers, which run to the central system. There are also light-sensitive cells (**photoreceptors**) in the epidermis, which

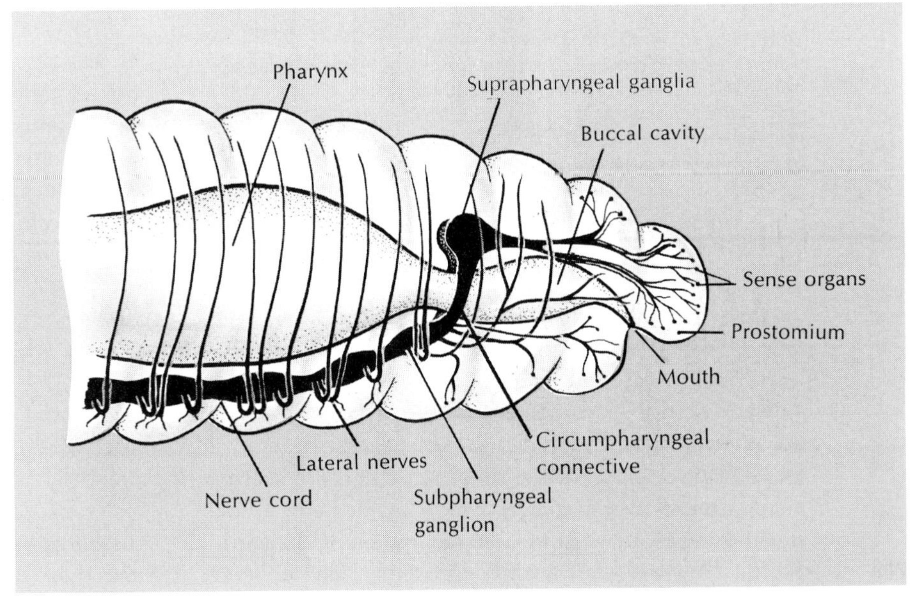

FIG. 17-8

Anterior portion of earthworm and nervous system. Note concentration of sense organs in this region. (Modified from Hess and others.)

FIG. 17-9

How an earthworm jerks back into its burrow. Nerve cord has three dorsal giant fibers adapted for fast movement. Ordinary crawling involves succession of reflex acts from anterior to posterior somites; stretching of one somite stimulates next one to stretch, producing waves of muscle contraction. When danger threatens, the three dorsal giant fibers allow transmission five times as fast as that in regular nerves so that every segment can contract simultaneously. Median fiber conducts toward tail, lateral fibers toward head. Arrangement of simple reflex arc is shown in right foreground.

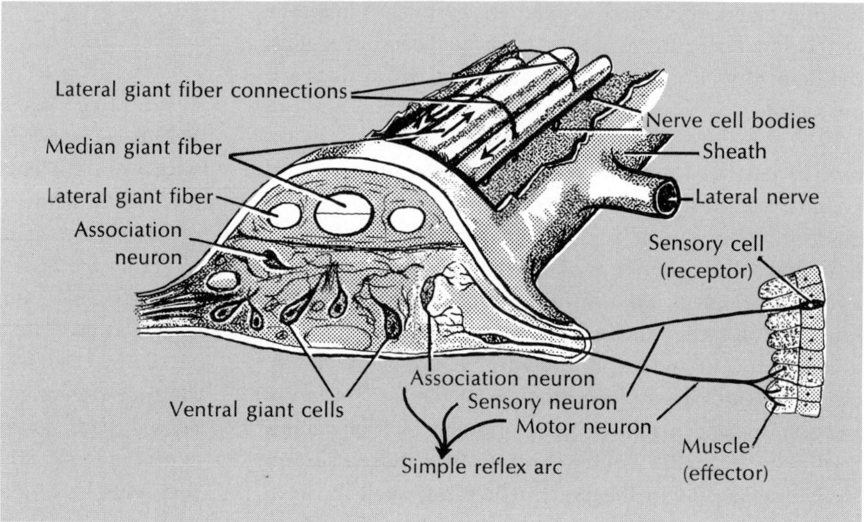

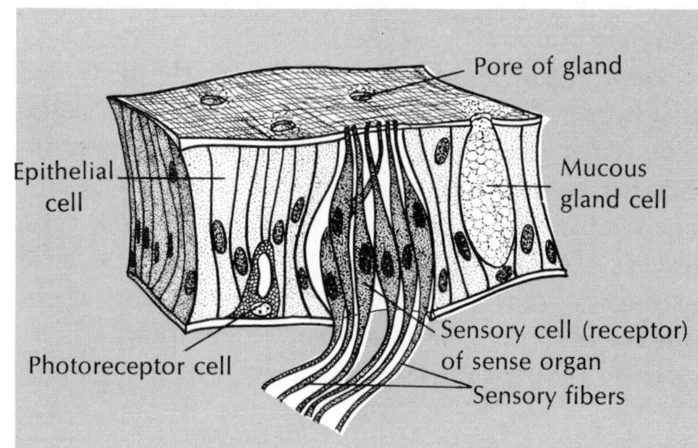

FIG. 17-10

Portion of epidermis of earthworm showing its various specializations. Evidence indicates that earthworms are sensitive to mechanical vibration, light, temperature, taste, and touch. Whether earthworms have differentiated sense organs for each of these senses is not known, but several different types have been demonstrated.

pick up different degrees of light intensity. In addition to these sensory organs, there are also free nerve endings between the cells of the epidermis, which are concerned with sense perception.

Earthworm behavior is largely, if not entirely, a matter of **reflex acts.** These may be considered the unit of physiologic activity. In the simplest reflex arc a sensory neuron makes direct contact with a motor neuron, and such arcs may occur in the nervous system of the earthworm. However, earthworms apparently have a more complicated kind of arc, which involves not only sensory and motor but also **association** neurons (Fig. 17-9). Stimuli are picked up by the **receptor,** or sensory neuron, and the impulse is carried into the central system; here, motor neurons may immediately receive it, or it first may be sent to the association neurons that relay it along to the motor. The motor neuron then carries the impulse to the **effector** (muscle or gland), and a reflex act is consummated. Reflex acts are usually more involved than this simple one, for many receptors are stimulated and many effectors act at the same time. The association neurons and fibers are mainly localized in the three **giant fibers** that are found in the dorsal side of the ventral nerve cord and connect the nerve cells in the ganglia with each other, thus facilitating widespread contractions of the worm's body.

Reproductive system. Earthworms are monoecious, or hermaphroditic; that is, both male and female organs are found in the same animal (Fig. 17-11). The male organs consist of (1) two pairs of small, hand-shaped **testes** in somites 10 and 11, (2) a **sperm funnel** behind each testis, (3) a small tube, the **vas efferens,** connected to each sperm funnel, (4) a pair of **vasa deferentia,** each of which is made up of two vasa efferentia on a side, (5) the openings of the two vasa deferentia on the ventral side of somite 15, and (6) three pairs of large white **seminal vesicles,** two pairs of which surround the testes. Undifferentiated sperm cells from the testes mature in the seminal vesicles before they are discharged during copulation through the sperm funnels and duct systems to the outside. The female system

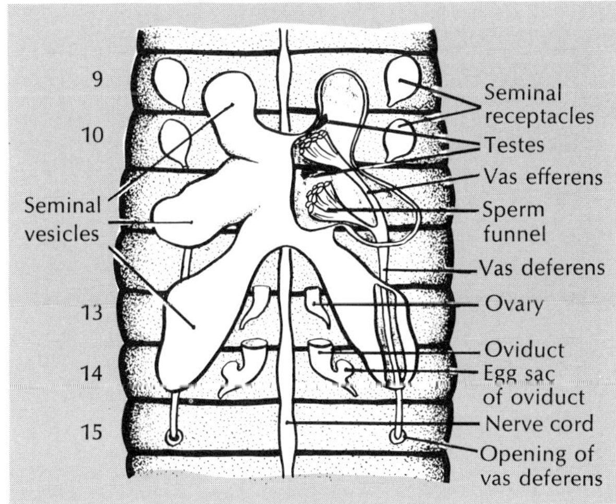

FIG. 17-11

Reproductive organs of earthworm. Dorsal view, with seminal vesicles partly removed on right side.

FIG. 17-12

Two earthworms in copulation. Anterior ends point in opposite directions as their ventral surfaces are held together by mucus bands secreted by clitellum. (Courtesy Guy Carter.)

contains (1) a pair of small **ovaries** in somite 13, (2) a pair of **oviducts,** which open internally by ciliated funnels into the coelom on somite 13 and lead to the exterior on somite 14, and (3) two pairs of **seminal receptacles** in somites 9 and 10, which store sperm received from another worm during copulation. The ovaries discharge mature eggs into the coelomic cavity, whence they are passed into the oviducts.

REPRODUCTIVE PROCESS. Reproduction in earthworms may occur at any season, but it is most common in warm moist weather such as the spring of the year. The earthworm does not self-fertilize its eggs but receives sperm from another worm during **copulation,** which usually occurs at night. When two worms mate, they extend their anterior ends from their burrows and bring their ventral surfaces together with their anterior ends pointed in opposite directions (Fig. 17-12). This arrangement of the bodies places the seminal receptacle openings of one worm in opposition to the clitellum of the other worm, somite 26 of each making contact with somite 15 of the other. They are held together by mucous bands and by special ventral setae, which penetrate each other's bodies in the regions of contact. Each worm secretes a slime tube about itself from somites 9 to 36. Sperm pass out of the vasa deferentia of each worm and travel by seminal canals or grooves on the ventral surface to the openings of the seminal receptacles of the other. Thus a reciprocal exchange of sperm is made, and the worms separate. This process of copulation requires about two hours. Later each worm secretes a barrel-shaped cocoon about its clitellum within the posterior end of the slime tube. Eggs from the oviducts on somite 14 and albumin from the skin glands are passed to the cocoon while it still encircles the clitellum. The worm then backs out, allowing the slime tube and cocoon to be slipped forward over the head. As the cocoon passes the openings of the seminal receptacles between somites 9 and 10 and 10 and 11, sperm stored from the opposite animal are poured into it. Fertilization of the eggs now takes place within the cocoon. When the cocoon leaves the worm, its ends close, producing a lemon-shaped body. (Figs. 17-13 and 17-14.) The size of the cocoon varies with different species of earthworms; those in *Lumbricus terrestris* are about 7 by 5 mm. In this form only one of several fertilized eggs develops into a worm, the others acting as nurse cells. Cocoons are commonly deposited in the earth, although they may be found at the surface near the entrance of burrows. Between copulations the earthworm continues to form cocoons so long as there are sperm in the seminal receptacles.

In their development the eggs are holoblastic, but the cleavage is unequal and spiral. The embryo passes through the blastula and gastrula stages and forms the three germ layers typical of the development of higher

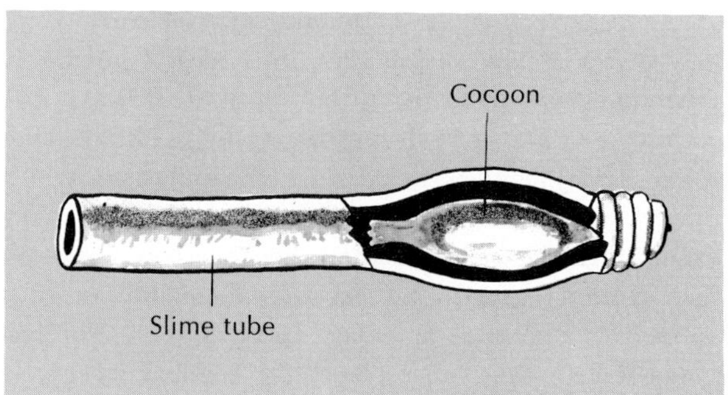

FIG. 17-13

Slime tube and cocoon of earthworm after being cast from body. Each copulating earthworm secretes a slime tube around its segments 9 to 36. Sperm are exchanged, and then cocoons are secreted over clitellum within slime tube, either at time of copulation or after worms have separated. Eggs and albumin are deposited in cocoon while still on clitellum. As worm backs out of slime tube and cocoon, sperm from seminal receptacles enter to fertilize eggs. When cocoon is freed from body, its ends close by constriction of slime tubes (Foote and Strobell). In some species, many eggs develop in each cocoon; in *Lumbricus*, only one.

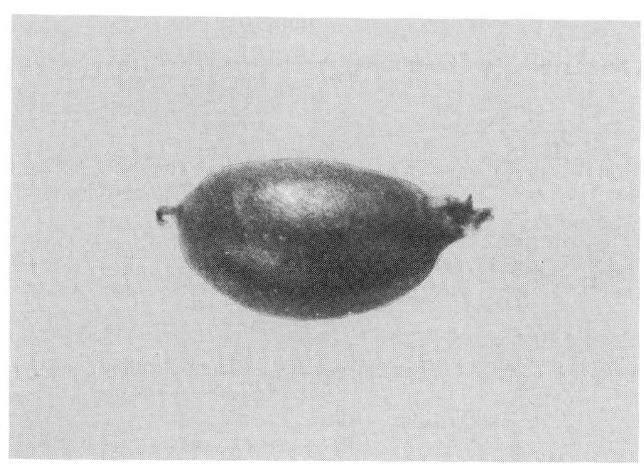

FIG. 17-14

Earthworm cocoon.

forms. The young worm is similar to the adult and escapes from the cocoon in two to three weeks. It does not develop a clitellum until it is sexually mature.

General behavior. Earthworms are among the most defenseless of all living creatures, yet their abundance and wide distribution indicate their ability to survive. Although they have no specialized sense organs, they are sensitive to many stimuli that play a part in their survival. Among the stimuli to which they are sensitive are **mechanical,** to which they are positive when it is moderate; **vibratory** (such as a footfall near them), which causes them to retire quickly into their burrows; and **light,** which they avoid unless it is very weak. They also have chemical responses that undoubtedly aid them in the choice of food. When irritated, they eject coelomic fluid through the dorsal pores.

Experiments show that earthworms have some learning ability. They can be taught to avoid an electric shock, and thus an association reflex can be built up in them. Darwin credited earthworms with a great deal of intelligence in pulling leaves into their burrows, for they apparently seized the leaves by the apex or narrow end, which is the easiest way for drawing such a shaped object into a small hole. Darwin assumed that the seizure of the leaves by the worms was not due to random handling or to chance but was purposeful in its mechanism. Careful investigations by others since Darwin's time have shown that the process is mainly one of trial and error and is accomplished as a chance effect, for earthworms would often seize a leaf several times before the right position was attained.

Annelid worms are perhaps the most highly organized animals that have the power of complete regeneration. Not all of them have this capacity, and in most of them there are certain limitations in the regeneration of lost parts. Leeches have little or no regenerative abilities. Earthworms vary; some species can form two complete worms when cut in two, but other species cannot. In the common earthworm (*Lumbicus*) a posterior piece may regenerate a new head of three to five segments, and an anterior piece (from segment 35 posteriorly) may form a new tail. In the latter case the level of the cut will determine the number of segments regenerated. A cut at segment 50 will regenerate ten fewer segments than one made at the level of segment 40. Earthworms can also be grafted, and pieces of several worms may be grafted end to end to form long worms. The axial gradient theory of the physiologic dominance of the anterior end seems to apply to earthworm regeneration the same as it does to planarians.

Earthworm farming. Aristotle called earthworms the "intestines of the soil." Gilbert White, in his well-known *Natural History of Selborne,* spoke of their value in promoting the growth of vegetation by perforating and loosening the soil. He pointed out that a monograph on the economic value of earthworms to agriculture should be written some day. About a century later, Charles Darwin fulfilled this need by writing his classic work *The Formation of Vegetable Mould Through the Action of Worms.* This work records the observations of the great naturalist on the habits of earthworms over a period of many years. He showed how worms brought the subsoil to the surface and mixed it with the topsoil. He estimated that from 10 to 18 tons of dry earth per acre pass through their bodies annually and are brought to the surface. All vegetable mold, he states, passes through the intestines of worms many times. They expose the mold to the air and sift it so that only small particles are left in it. They drag leaves, twigs, and organic substances into their burrows and bring them closer to the roots of plants. The earthworm is known to ingest its own weight in soil every 24 hours. Not the least of the worms' value in enriching the soil is the great amount of food elements such as potassium and phosphorus that they bring to the surface from the subsoil; the latter is often richer in these elements than the topsoil itself. Moreover, the soil that passes through the earthworms' digestive systems may have valuable nitrogenous products from the worms' metabolism. From these benefits and others Darwin came to the conclusion that it may be doubted whether there are many other animals that have played so important a part in the world's history as have the lowly earthworms.

Many individuals have stressed the importance of culturing earthworms to build up the soil. They think that the 25,000 to 50,000 earthworms per acre that Darwin estimated could be multiplied, with a consequent improvement of the soil. A great deal of work has been done by selective feeding and breeding to determine what kinds of earthworms are best suited for certain types of soil and food. It is found that certain kinds will thrive only within a range of certain soil acidity; whereas others live in much wider ranges of acidity and alkalinity. Worms are propagated under favorable conditions; then the worms and their egg capsules are planted on soils with the idea of improving them. So far the reports of such experiments have been conflicting, and many scientists are not convinced that such methods of soil improvement are as effective as has been claimed.

Other common oligochaetes

The more than 2,000 species of oligochaetes are found in a great variety of sizes and habitats. Most are terrestrial or freshwater forms, but some are parasitic. They also vary a great deal in bodily structures and organization. Some of the more common oligochaetes other than earthworms (chiefly small freshwater forms) are *Aeolosoma* (1 mm. long), which contains red or green pigments, has bundles of setae, and is often found in hay cultures; *Nais* (2 to 4 mm. long), which is brownish in color, with two or three bundles of setae on each segment; *Stylaria* (10 to 25 mm. long), which has two bunches of setae on each segment, the prostromium extended into a long process, and black eyespots; *Dero* (5 to 10 mm. long), which is reddish in color, lives in tubes, and has three tail gills; *Tubifex* (30 to 40 mm. long), which is reddish in color and lives with its head in mud at the bottom of ponds and its tail waving in the water; *Chaetogaster* (10 to 15 mm. long), which has only ventral bundles of setae; and the Enchytraeidae, small whitish worms, which live in both moist soil and water. Some oligochaetes such as *Aeolosoma* may form chains of zooids asexually by transverse fission (Fig. 17-15).

Giant earthworms (*Megascolides*), some as long as 11 feet, 1 inch in diameter, and weighing more than a pound, are found in Australia. Some in South America are more than 6 feet long. Cocoons of these giant earthworms may be more than 2 inches long and ½ inch in diameter. Naturally the burrows of these giants are large and extensive.

ORDER HIRUDINEA (CLASS CLITELLATA)

When one thinks of leeches, he invariably thinks of blood-sucking creatures, and that is precisely what they are. Leeches are well adapted for this mode of life, for they have anterior and posterior suckers for locomotion and attachment and chitinous jaws for making incisions in the skin to promote the flow of blood from their victims. They have definite annelid characteristics, such as a ventral nerve cord with segmental ganglia, serial nephridia, and gonads in the coelom. The body is divided into somites (usually 34). However, these animals lack setae, which most other annelids possess, and they have copulatory organs and genital openings on the midventral line, which other annelids do not have.

Hirudo medicinalis—medicinal leech

Structural characteristics. Leeches appear to have more metameres than they really have because their somites are marked by transverse grooves (annuli) (Fig. 17-16). In this species and many others the anterior sucker surrounds the mouth. The body is covered with

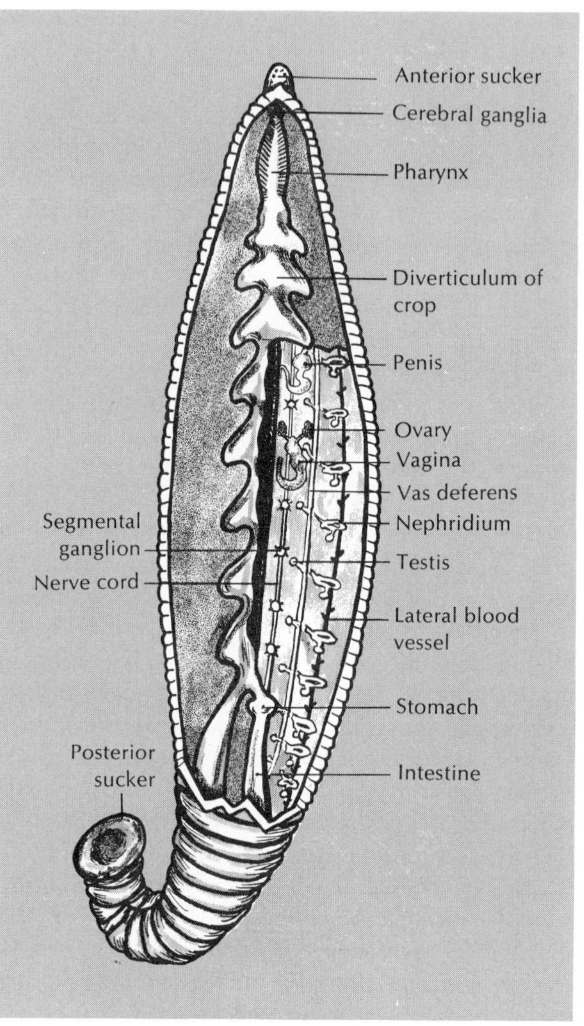

FIG. 17-16

Internal structure of leech *Hirudo medicinalis*. Dorsal view, with part of long crop cut away to show underlying structures.

FIG. 17-15

Some aquatic annelids (Oligochaeta). These are small forms found in mud and debris of stagnant pools and ponds. Their body walls are thin and their internal organs easily seen. Likely to be found in any pond culture, especially one containing blanket algae.

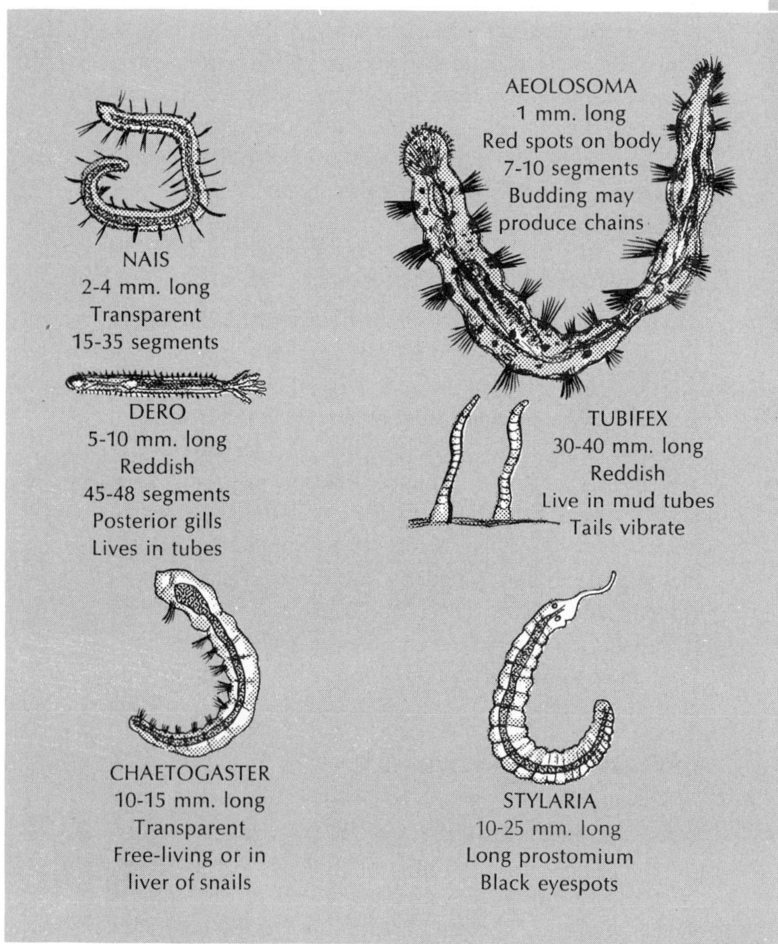

a cuticle, which is secreted by an epidermis beneath, and there are many mucous glands that open on the surface. A clitellum is found on segments 10 to 12 in the breeding season. Pigment and blood vessels are in the dermis. The muscular system is well developed, with circular, longitudinal, and oblique bands. Internally the coelom is reduced by mesenchyme and visceral organs to a system of sinuses. The alimentary canal is made up of a mouth with three jaws and chitinous teeth, a strong muscular pharynx with salivary glands, an esophagus, a crop with eleven pairs of lateral ceca, a slender intestine, a rectum, and an anus; the latter opens anterior to the posterior sucker. The circulatory system has the typical annelid plan of dorsal, ventral, and lateral longitudinal vessels with many cross connections. Respiration takes place through the skin, and the excretory system has about seventeen pairs of nephridia. The nervous system is not greatly different from that of the typical annelid plan, and there are sensory organs of taste, touch, and sight. Leeches are hermaphroditic, but they have cross-fertilization. The male organs are the paired testes beneath the crop, a pair of vasa deferentia with some glands, and a median penis, which opens into the male pore. Female organs include a pair of ovaries with oviducts, an albumin gland, and a vagina, which opens near the male pore. The sperm is transferred in little packets (spermatophores) by the filiform penis, which penetrates the vagina of the mate in mutual copulation. The fertilized eggs are deposited in cocoons formed by glandular secretions. These cocoons may be attached to stones or other objects or even to the leech itself.

Behavior. Leeches are found both on land and in water. They move in a manner similar to a measuring worm, that is, by looping movements of the body. When the medicinal leech fastens itself to another animal by means of its suckers, the sharp chitinous teeth make an incision in the skin, and at the same time an anticoagulant substance (hirudin) from the salivary glands is introduced into the wound to make the blood flow freely. Then the blood is sucked up by the muscular pharynx and stored in the large crop. A leech is said to suck up three times its own weight in blood, which may take several months to digest. This is a useful adaptation, for leeches may not often have the chance to eat.

There are many different species of leeches. Some of them are jawless but have an eversible proboscis with which they can pierce the body of another animal. Fish

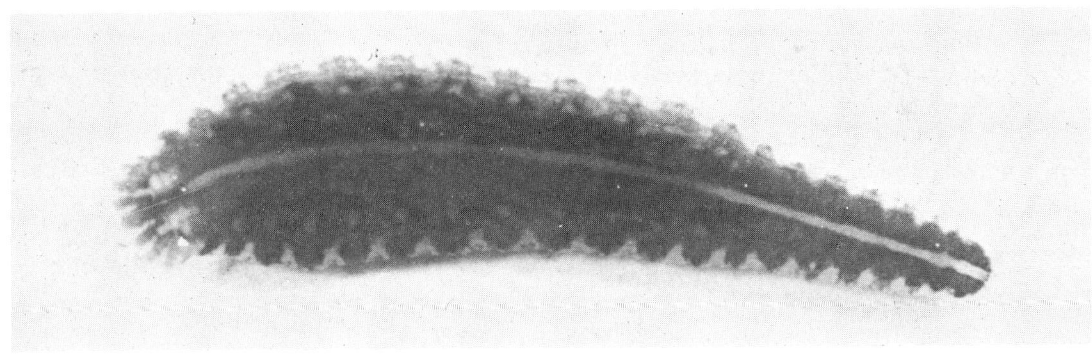

FIG. 17-17

Placobdella, common leech found on turtles. A living specimen, about 1 inch long.

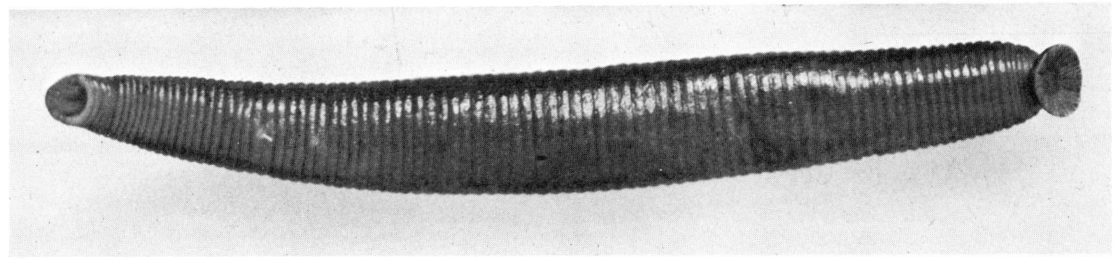

FIG. 17-18

Hirudo medicinalis, medicinal leech. This form was once widely used in bloodletting. This one is contracted, but it can stretch itself out to much greater length. About 4 inches long but is capable of great contraction and elongation.

and turtles are parasitized by them (Fig. 17-17). Others live mainly on dead animals, and some are predaceous. Tropical countries are plagued by more leeches than are temperate countries. Many of these attack human beings and are a nuisance. In Egypt and elsewhere in that region a small aquatic leech is often swallowed in drinking water and, by fastening on the pharynx and epiglottis, becomes a serious pest.

The leech in medical practice. For centuries the medicinal leech was employed in medical practice for bloodletting because of the mistaken idea that bodily disorders and fevers were caused by a plethora of blood. Since the leech is 4 or 5 inches long and can extend to a much greater length when distended with blood, the amount of blood it can suck out of a patient is considerable (Fig. 17-18). Leech collecting and leech culture in ponds were practiced in Europe on a commercial scale during the nineteenth century. Wordsworth's interesting poem "The Leech-Gatherer" was based on this use of the leech. In some of our museums containing the relics of old pharmacies, there still can be seen bottles labeled "Leeches" in which the animals were kept for the use of doctors of that period.

CLASS POLYCHAETA

Comparison of Polychaeta with Oligochaeta. The name Polychaeta comes from a Greek word meaning "many setae," and herein lies one of the main differences between this class and the oligochaetes, which have few setae. There are other differences; some concern advancements and some the structures that are less complex than those of the earthworm group. Polychaetes have a well-differentiated head with sensory appendages, lateral parapodia with many setae, and usually separate sexes. Their development is indirect, for they undergo a form of metamorphosis that involves a type of trochophore larva. In contrast to the oligochaetes, members of Polychaeta have no permanent sex organs, and they possess no permanent ducts for their sex cells. However, the polychaetes show a marked differentiation of some body somites and a marked specialization of sensory organs practically unknown among the oligochaetes.

Neanthes (Nereis) virens—clam worm

Habitat. The clam worm (sandworm) (Fig. 17-19) lives in or near the low-tide line of the seacoast. These animals often live in burrows that are lined with mucus from their bodies, and sometimes they are found in temporary hiding places such as under stones where they stay, bodies covered and heads protruding. They are most active at night, when they wiggle out of their hiding places and swim about or crawl over the sand in search of food.

Structural characteristics. The body is made up of about 200 somites and may be longer than 15 inches. The anterior somites are distinct from the others and form a definite **head**, which is divided into the **prostomium** and **peristomium** (Fig. 17-20). The prostomium has a pair of stubby **palps** (for touch and chemical sense), a pair of short **prostomial tentacles,** and two pairs of small dorsal **eyes.** The peristomium is made up of the ventral **mouth,** a pair of chitinous **jaws,** and four pairs of **peristomial tentacles** on the dorsal side. The tentacles and eyes represent specialized organs for sen-

FIG. 17-19

Clam worm *Neanthes virens*. Head with specialized structures at top. (Preserved specimen.)

sory perception; the tentacles are for touch, the palps are for taste and smell, and the eyes are for light perception.

Along the sides of the body are the fleshy **parapodia,** a pair to each somite except those forming the head. Each parapodium is formed of two lobes: a dorsal **notopodium** and a ventral **neuropodium.** Each lobe is supported by one or more chitinous rods (acicula). The parapodia bear numerous setae and are abundantly supplied with blood vessels. Covering the body of the animal is a cuticle and epidermis, underneath which are circular and longitudinal muscles (Fig. 17-21).

The **coelomic cavity** is lined with peritoneum and is divided by septa between the somites. Holding the digestive system in place and dividing the coelomic cavity of each somite into right and left halves are the dorsal and ventral mesenteries. The **digestive system** contains a mouth, a protrusible pharynx with chitinous jaws, a short esophagus, a stomach-intestine, and an anus on the terminal segment, or pygidium. Digestive glands open into the esophagus. The main blood vessels of the **circulatory system** are two longitudinal vessels, one ventral and the other dorsal, from which transverse vessels run to the body wall and various visceral organs. Like the earthworm, the clam worm has red

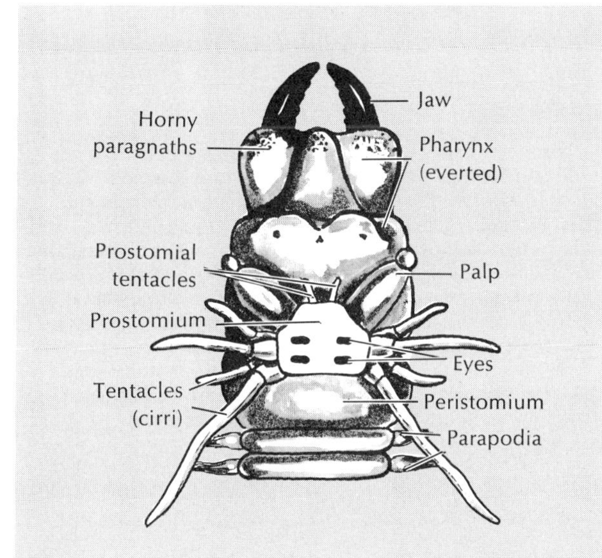

FIG. 17-20

Dorsal view of head region of *Neanthes,* clam worm, with pharynx protruded.

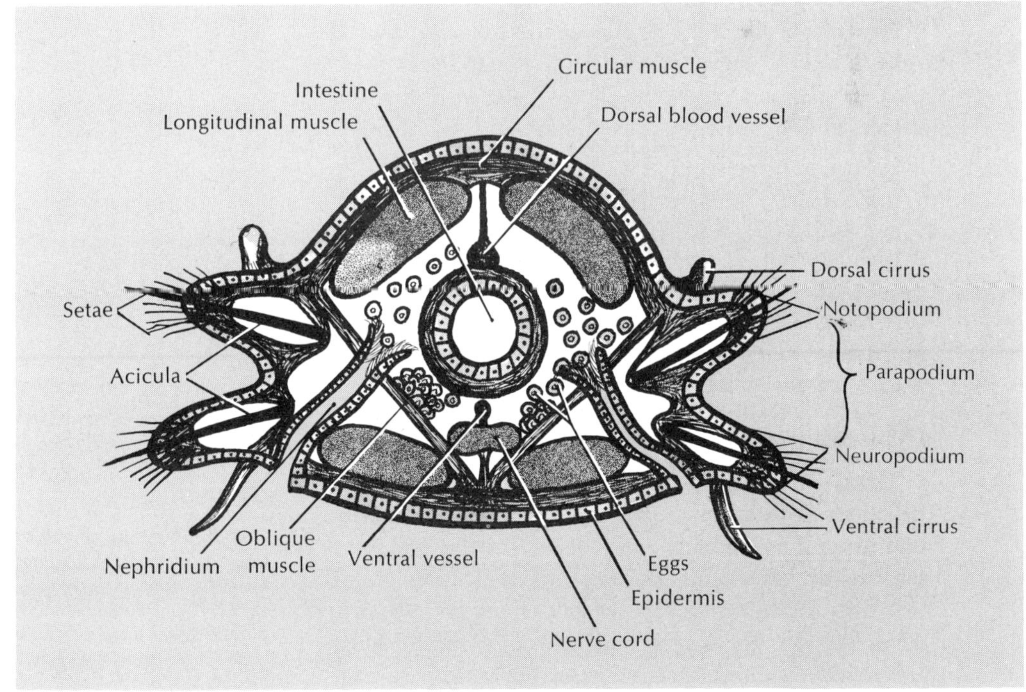

FIG. 17-21

Transverse section through polychaete *Neanthes.* Note sharp-pointed, chitinous acicula, one in each lobe of parapodium. Acicula, which are really enlarged setae, help support and move parapodium. Contrast this cross section with that of earthworm in Fig. 17-5.

blood. There are no special respiratory organs; this function is taken care of by the body wall and by the parapodia. Paired **nephridia** in most of the somites take care of **excretion.** Each nephridium opens into the coelomic cavity by a ciliated funnel, passes posteriorly in coils, and opens to the exterior near the base of a parapodium by the nephridiopore. The whole nephridium is enclosed in a mass of connective tissue.

The **nervous system** is made up of a pair of cerebral ganglia, circumpharyngeal connectives to the ventral nerve cord, and a pair of ganglia with lateral nerves in each somite. Sexes are separate, but the reproductive organs are not permanent, for the sex cells are budded off from the coelomic lining and are carried to the outside by the excretory ducts and by bursting through the body wall. Fertilization is external, and the zygote develops into a free-swimming trochophore larva, which later transforms into a worm.

Locomotion. The worm moves by means of its circular and longitudinal muscles and by its parapodia. The latter are manipulated by oblique muscles that run from the midventral line to the parapodia in each somite. Parapodia are used both for creeping over the sand and for swimming. The animal swims by a lateral wriggling of the body and can dart through the water with considerable speed.

Physiologic aspects. The clam worm lives upon small animals, other worms, larval forms, etc. It seizes them with its chitinous jaws, which are protruded through the mouth when the pharynx is everted. By withdrawing the pharynx, the food is swallowed. Movement of the food through the alimentary canal is by peristalsis.

The worm will usually seek some kind of burrow if it can find one. When a worm is placed near a glass tube, it will wiggle in without hesitation. In its burrow it is able to suck or pump water in by dorsoventral undulatory movements that pass in waves from the anterior to the posterior end of the body.

Other common polychaetes

There are many species of polychaetes, some with structures and habits similar to *Neanthes* and others that are quite different. Some belong to the errant or the free-moving group; others to the sedentary group that lives chiefly in tubes; and still others are intermediate between the errant and sedentary forms. Most are found in fairly shallow water, but some live in

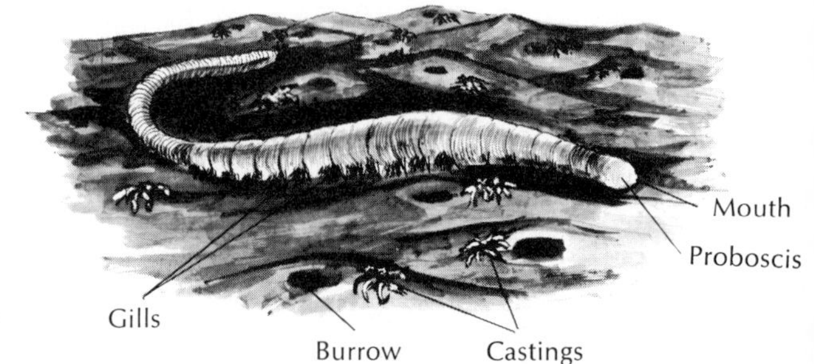

FIG. 17-22

Lugworm *Arenicola.* A burrowing polychaete that lives in intertidal mud flats. When worm is in burrow, mound of castings indicates position of hind end; the crater indicates head end. Worm may reach length of 8 to 10 inches and diameter of 3/4 inch in thickest part. Its narrow posterior end lacks parapodia and chaetae. Feeding habits are similar to those of earthworm, for it swallows great amounts of indigestible material that it discards in castings from its burrow. In burrowing it makes use of eversible proboscis and stiffening of anterior part of body by forcing coelomic fluid forward when it contracts its muscles. Its well-developed circulatory system contains red blood, and there is a row of tufted gills along each side of middle back region.

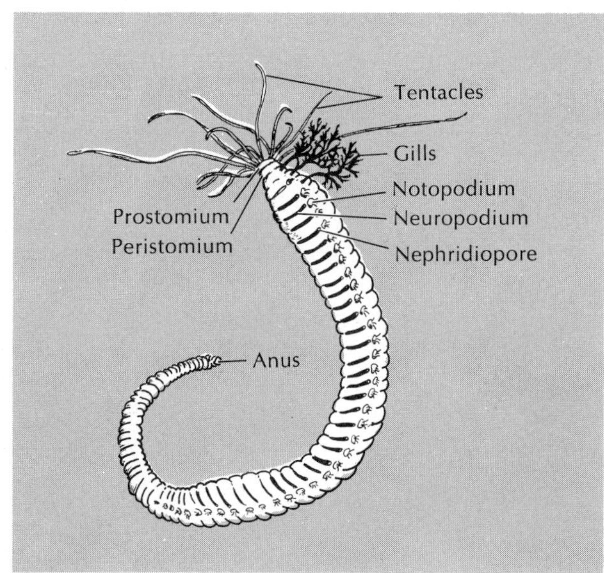

FIG. 17-23

Amphitrite ornata, a marine polychaete common to our eastern coast. It lives in mucus-lined tube buried in sand or mud near low-tide level. Its long extensible tentacles are feeding organs, each with ciliated groove that sweeps food particles toward mouth. Three pairs of gills are hollow, vascular outgrowths of body. Setae are located in the notopodia, and long, hooked seta, or uncinus, lies in each neuropodium.

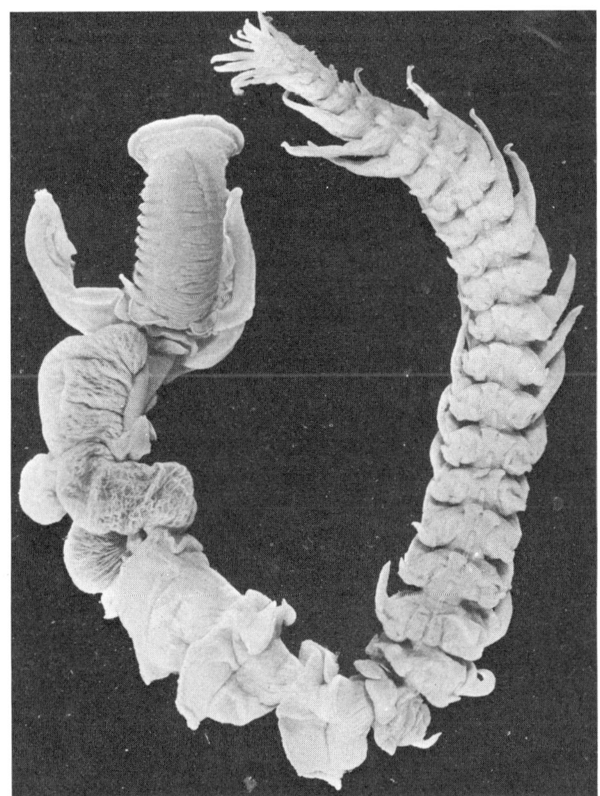

FIG. 17-24

Chaetopterus, highly specialized polychaete worm. Worm lives permanently in U-shaped tube near surface of mud flats. It uses its fan-shaped parapodia to propel currents of water past its body in the tube. (Preserved specimen.)

deep seas. *Arenicola,* the lugworm (Fig. 17-22), has the interesting habit of burrowing through the sand and forming castings. On certain of its somites are paired gills. *Aphrodite,* the sea mouse, has an oval body that bears large plates and very long setae. *Amphitrite* (Fig. 17-23) has long, extensible tentacles and three pairs of branched gills.

The palolo worm *Eunice viridis,* whose habitat is the South Pacific, lives in burrows among the coral reefs at the bottom of the sea. Just before swarming, their posterior somites become filled with enormous numbers of eggs or sperm. These somites are cast off as one unit at the time of swarming and float to the surface, where they burst, releasing the sex cells. This swarming always occurs on the first day of the last quarter of the October-November moon and lasts for a few days. Usually, just before sunrise on that day, the surface of the sea is covered with these posterior units of the worms, which burst just as the sun rises. Fertilization of the eggs occurs at this time. The anterior part of the worm regenerates a new posterior part. A related form (*Leodice*) found in the Atlantic waters swarms in the third quarter of the June-July moon.

Chaetopterus (Fig. 17-24) is a polychaete that lives in a U-shaped burrow along the seashore. This form has flaplike structures formed by the union and modification of certain segments and appendages. By means of these it can draw water into its tube like a suction pump. This worm also has powers of luminescence.

Some authorities place the peculiar order Myzostomata under Polychaeta. The Myzostomata, or sucker-mouthed worms, live mainly as parasites on echinoderms, especially crinoids. They are disk shaped or oblong, with cirri around the edge of the body, and the paired parapodia are provided with hooks. They also have suckers. In reproduction they function first as males, then as hermaphrodites, and finally as females. *Myzostomum* is the most common genus.

Derivation and meaning of basic terminology

Amphitrite (Greek mythology, sea nymph). A common genus of marine polychaete annelids.

Archiannelida (Gr. *arch,* first, + *annelus,* little ring, + *ida,* pl. suffix). A former class of simple, primitive worms now considered an order under Polychaeta.

Arenicola (L. *arena,* sand, + *colo,* inhabit). A genus of polychaete worms.

chlorogogue (Gr. *chloros,* green, + *gogue,* a leading). Special spongy tissue around interior of earthworms.

clitellum (L. *clitellae,* packsaddle). A thickened glandlike body on certain portions of midbody segments of earthworms and leeches.

Enchytraeidae (NL. *enchytrae,* to live in an earthen pot, + *idea,* suffix meaning family). These small, white or reddish worms were often encountered by florists in potting plants.

Lumbricus (L. intestinal worm). Genus of common earthworm.

metamere (Gr. *meta,* after, + *meros,* part). Other names are somite and segment.

Myzostomata (Gr. *myzo,* suck in, + *stoma,* mouth, + *ata,* characterized by). A highly modified parasitic polychaete.

Neanthes (Gr. new bud). Genus of common clam worm.

parapodium (Gr. *para,* beside, + *podos,* foot).

peristomium (Gr. *peri,* around, + *stoma,* mouth).
Polygordius (Gr. *polys,* many, + *gordius,* knot).
prostomium (Gr. *pro,* before, + *stoma,* mouth).
pygidium (Gr. *pyge,* rump). The terminal segment of annelids. New segments are formed in front of this segment.
seta (L. bristle). A needlelike chitinous structure of the integument of annelids and related forms.
typhlosole (Gr. *typhlos,* blind, + *solen,* channel). Longitudinal fold in digestive cavity in certain earthworms and other animals.

Annotated references

Barnes, R. D. 1968. Invertebrate zoology, ed. 2. Philadelphia, W. B. Saunders Co. *An excellent and comprehensive account of the Annelida.*

Barrett, T. J. 1947. Harnessing the earthworm. Boston, Bruce Humphries, Inc. *An explanation of earthworm farming and the possibilities it has. A popular account.*

Bell, A. W. 1947. The earthworm circulatory system. Turtox News **25**:89-94.

Buchsbaum, R. 1948. Animals without backbones, rev. ed. Chicago, University of Chicago Press. *Good illustrations of many annelid forms.*

Buchsbaum, R., and L. J. Milne. 1960. The lower animals. Garden City, N. Y., Doubleday & Co., Inc. *A superb work on invertebrates with unsurpassed photographs (many in color) by two famous field naturalists.*

Cambridge Natural History. 1896. Annelida. London, Macmillan Co., Ltd. *Good authoritative account.*

Darwin, C. R. 1911. The formation of vegetable mould through the action of worms. *A classic account of the way in which earthworms improve and transform the surface of the soil.*

Edmondson, W. T. (editor). 1959. Fresh-water biology, ed. 2. New York, John Wiley & Sons, Inc. *Good sections on aquatic Oligochaeta by C. J. Goodnight and on Polychaeta by O. Hartman. Keys and figures included.*

Hess, W. N. 1925. Nervous system of the earthworm, *Lumbricus terrestris* L. J. Morph. Physiol. **40**:235-259. *A widely known investigation of great value to all students of the annelids.*

Hickman, C. P. 1967. Biology of the invertebrates. St. Louis, The C. V. Mosby Co.

Krivanek, J. O. 1956. Habit formation in the earthworm *Lumbricus terrestris.* Physiol. Zool. **29**:241-250. *An interesting study in animal behavior.*

Moment, G. B. 1953. On the way a common earthworm, *Eisenia foetida,* grows in length. J. Morph. **93**:489-503.

Moore, J. P. 1956. Annelida. Encyclopaedia Britannica, Chicago, Encyclopaedia Britannica, Inc. *A comprehensive description of the group with many revealing illustrations.*

Parker, T. J., and W. A. Haswell. 1940. A textbook of zoology, 2 vols., ed. 6. New York, The Macmillan Co. *A comprehensive treatment of the phylum, with emphasis upon morphology.*

Russell-Hunter, W. D. 1969. A biology of the higher invertebrates. New York, The Macmillan Co. *A concise and up-to-date discussion of this great group.*

Zappler, G. 1958. Darwin's worms. Natural History **67**: 488-495. *An account of an experiment on the annelid intelligence by the great naturalist. Should be read by all beginning zoology students.*

CHAPTER 18

• PHYLUM MOLLUSCA*
(MAJOR EUCOELOMATE BILATERAL GROUP)

BIOLOGIC PRINCIPLES

Organ-system level of organization

1. All organ systems are present and well developed.
2. Adult body plan is different from that of any other invertebrate group but is sharply defined and easily recognized.
3. This is a highly successful phylum that is typically marine but has also invaded the land and fresh wtaer. This represents the second largest invertebrate group.
4. Bilateral symmetry is the rule, although this has been modified in the snails (Gastropoda) into an asymmetric plan.
5. They have evolved a body plan without any suggestion of metamerism except in the recently discovered Monoplacophora.
6. Great diversity of form is due to plasticity of mantle and related structures.
7. Within the phylum the members display a great range of organization from the lowest to the highest, as shown by a comparison of the relatively simple Amphineura with the highly modified and specialized Gastropoda and Cephalopoda.
8. Mollusks belong to the protostome branch, or schizocoelous coelomates, of the animal kingdom and have spiral and determinate cleavage.

Biologic contributions

1. They introduce for the first time a fleshy **mantle,** which in most cases secretes a shell.
2. Another unique organ in the invertebrate kingdom is the **radula.**
3. Shells in most types are well developed, but these are not peculiar to mollusks, although their use of the mantle in the shell formation may be considered a unique plan.
4. Another contribution to the animal blueprint is the ventral **muscular foot,** a distinct molluscan character.
5. The highly developed **eye** in the higher mollusks has arisen as a skin derivative, in contrast to the brain eye of vertebrates. This independent evolution must be considered as an example of convergent evolution.
6. Morphologically the invertebrate reaches its greatest size in mollusks.

*Mol-lus'ka (L. *molluscus,* soft).

Position in animal kingdom

1. Many mollusks have a trochophore larval form (veliger), which has a resemblance to the trochophore larva of marine annelids.
2. Since most mollusks are not segmented, they must have branched from the main evolutionary line before segmentation arose.
3. There is some evidence that mollusks and annelids have come from a common platyhelminth origin, probably a turbellarian form. The newly found monoplacophorans may indicate an annelid relationship.
4. Their evolutionary adaptive radiation has been guided by the modifications within the bilateral head-foot and the radial or biradial visceropallium (viscera and mantle).

GENERAL RELATIONS

Next to the arthropods the mollusks have the most named species in the animal kingdom. The name Mollusca (L. *molluscus,* soft) indicates one of their distinctive characteristics, a soft body. The group ranges in form from fairly simple organisms to some of the most complex invertebrates and in size from almost microscopic to a length of 50 feet—the largest of all invertebrates.

Two structural features of the mollusks that set them aside from all other animals are the ventral muscular **foot** and the fleshy **mantle.** The mantle is a sheath of skin that surrounds the soft parts and hangs down as a free fold around the body like a skirt, enclosing the mantle cavity space. It secretes the shell and forms the siphons. The gills and other respiratory devices, such as the lungs of pulmonate snails, develop from the mantle. The exposed edge of the mantle in certain gastropods and scaphopods is used for respiration. Almost all the blood of mollusks is oxygenated in some part of the mantle or its modification. In cephalopods the muscular mantle is used for locomotion and, mechanically, also for respiration.

The phylum is very old, with a continuous record

since Cambrian time, as shown by certain bivalve and gastropod fossils. Perhaps no group has left more or better fossils than mollusks because their shells facilitated fossil formation. Mollusca is a well-organized phylum, the adults being quite distinct from those of other phyla, making it somewhat difficult to establish their relationships to other groups. The trochophore-like larvae common in many marine mollusks as well as their type of egg cleavage, indicate an affinity with the annelids. This view is supported by the recent discovery of the group Monoplacophora, which is segmented, although their segmentation may be secondary and not primitive. Some mollusks also have a ladderlike nervous system similar to that of the turbellarian flatworms. Thus it is possible that both the annelids and the mollusks have diverged from a common platyhelminth form.

Relationship between the various mollusk classes is equally difficult, for each represents distinct evolutionary tendencies. Zoologists have tried to reconstruct a hypothetical primitive mollusk with features to fit the ancestor of all molluscan classes. Such a generalized ancestor (Fig. 18-1) might have a body dorsally arched, with a calcareous shell; a strong, creeping muscular foot on the ventral side; a mantle cavity formed from the soft integument of the dorsal side; a simple digestive tube from front to rear; a pair of feather-shaped gills near the anus; and a pair of ganglia in the head, with two nerve trunks at different levels. Such a primitive plan therefore would involve a bilaterally symmetric head-foot, with an anteroposterior axis, and a radially or biradially symmetric visceropallium (viscera and mantle), with a dorsoventral axis. Evolutionary diversity of molluscan form has resulted in modifications of this basic pattern. Amphineura (*Chiton*) is considered the most primitive molluscan class, although its fossil record dates from a more recent period than that of the other classes. Scaphopoda and Gastropoda both have a univalve shell and radula. Pelecypoda (bivalves) with their pointed foot and lack of head, eyes, or tentacles resemble the Scaphopoda. The recent discovery of a bivalve gastropod *Tamanovalva limax*, off the coast of Japan may provide a "missing link" between the classes Gastropoda and Pelecypoda, for this species has a slug-shaped head and a creeping foot, although its shell is made up of two equal valves characteristic of the pelecypods. Its early development is that of a typical gastropod, but it soon changes into a bivalve form. The highly advanced Cephalopoda (squids and octopuses) seem isolated from the other classes but share some characteristics with the gastropods.

FIG. 18-1

Hypothetical ancestral mollusk. This primitive mollusk type is supposed to fit structural ancestral pattern of all molluscan classes.

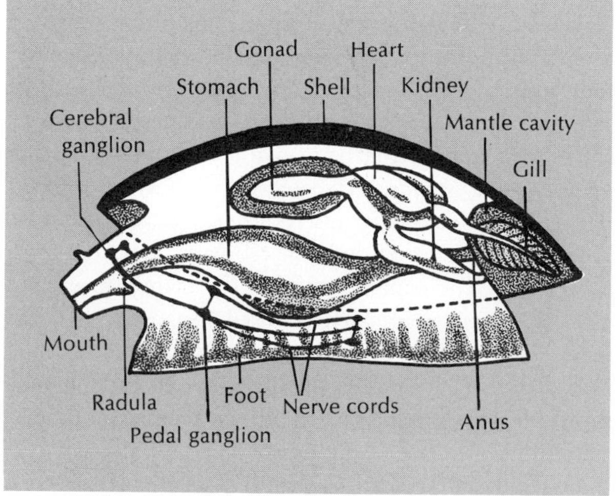

Mollusks are found in nearly all places that will support life, in all latitudes, and at altitudes up to 20,000 feet. Most are marine, living in shallow water, along the seashore, in the open sea, or at great depths. Some are found in fresh water, and some have been successful on land. The fossil evidence indicates that mollusks originated in the sea. Much of their evolution probably took place in littoral zones (along the shore) because such a region has an abundance of food, a variety of habitats, and a diversity of physical conditions. It is especially suitable for a group that stresses creeping and burrowing. The more mobile cephalopods are naturally pelagic (live in open water), but some live close to the bottom or near shore. Only gastropods have mastered land conditions.

Only the Gastropoda and the Pelecypoda left the sea and invaded the land and fresh water. These groups gradually became adapted to the conditions produced by tides and the reduced concentration of salt in estuaries. The mode of nutrition (filter feeding) of pelecypods restricted them to water. Many species are found in the estuaries of large rivers and are intermediate between the marine and freshwater forms. Such mollusks tolerate a salinity between that of the sea and fresh water. Burrowing animals such as mollusks had a better chance to invade and tolerate the conditions of estuaries. In time estuarian forms became tolerant of fresh water and invaded the latter. The transformation of a marine pelecypod to a freshwater type was not difficult, for both types breathe and feed in the same way. Among the gastropods a vascular lining of the mantle cavity made possible the development of a lung.

Only gastropods have actually invaded land because of their lung and other morphologic changes. Whereas there are only a few genera of Pelecypoda in fresh water, gastropods have undergone an amazing adaptive radiation, especially on land. Terrestrial snails are mostly restricted in their range by humidity, by shelter from heat and light, and by the presence of lime in the soil. Many pulmonates have evolved an operculum for closing the apertures of their shells during hibernation or aestivation and can remain inactive for a long time. According to fossil records, pulmonate snails first invaded terrestrial habitats in the Carboniferous period. Gastropods usually have slow methods of dispersal, and the evolution factor of isolation (physical barriers) has operated to a greater extent with this group than with most other animals. Mutational forms had a better chance to become stabilized because of fewer opportunities for hybridization.

Mollusks are most abundant and diverse of form in the tropics and subtropics. Here the most species are found, as well as the most strikingly beautiful color adaptations. Pelagic forms are usually colorless, whereas the nudibranchs may adopt the color of forms on which they feed (green algae, anemones, hydroids, etc.).

Life cycles are generally short, although some mollusks live for several years. Nudibranchs probably live only a year; oysters may live up to ten years; *Unio*, twelve years; freshwater snails, four to five years; squid (*Loligo*) up to two years; and giant squid, ten years (Spector).

In temperate and cold climates mollusks often hibernate in burrows, crevices, or mats of leaves. They withdraw into the shell and secrete a membrane (epiphragm) over the aperture, while body metabolism sinks to a low ebb.

CHARACTERISTICS

1. Body unsegmented (except in Monoplacophora) and typically bilaterally symmetric (bilateral asymmetry in some)
2. External body with three typical divisions: an anterior head (absent in some) with mouth, appendages, and sense organs; a **ventral muscular foot** variously modified but chiefly for locomotion and a dorsal **mantle** that usually secretes a shell (absent in some)
3. Body surface usually covered with ciliated epithelium bearing many mucous glands and sensory nerve endings
4. Coelom reduced and represented mainly by the pericardium, gonadal cavity, and kidney
5. Digestive system complete with digestive glands and liver; with a rasping organ (**radula**) usually present
6. Circulatory system of heart, pericardial space and blood vessels; blood mostly colorless, with erythrocruorin restricted and hemocyanin more common
7. Respiration by gills, by lungs, or direct
8. Excretion by one or two pairs of nephridia or a single nephridium opening internally into pericardium and externally onto body surface
9. Nervous system of paired **cerebral, pleural, pedal,** and **visceral ganglia,** with nerves, ganglia centralized in ring (Cephalopoda and Gastropoda)
10. Sense organs of touch, smell, taste, vision (in some), and statocysts for equilibrium
11. Reproduction dioecious or monoecious; one or two gonads with gonoducts, which may open into renal ducts or to exterior
12. Fertilization external or internal
13. Spiral and determinate cleavage; trochophore-like larval form (**veliger**) in some

ECONOMIC IMPORTANCE

A group as large as the mollusks would naturally affect man in some way. As food, oysters and clams are popular everywhere, and snails are widely used in some areas. Pearl buttons are obtained from shells of bivalves. More than 40 species of mollusks are suitable for this purpose. The Missouri and Mississippi river basins furnish material for most of this industry in the United States. In some regions supplies are becoming so depleted that attempts are being made to propagate them artificially. Pearls, both natural and cultured, are produced in the shells of clams and oysters, most of

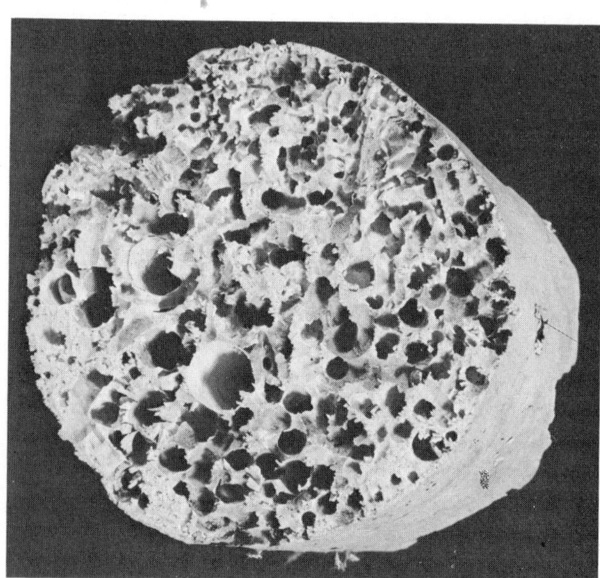

FIG. 18-2

Piece of wood showing destructive burrows of shipworm *Teredo.*

them in a marine oyster, *Meleagrina,* found around eastern Asia.

Brightly colored shells have been used as ornaments and also for utensils by primitive people in all ages. Purple snails (*Murex*) were used by the ancients as their chief source of dye. Cowries (brightly colored snails of the genus *Cypraea*) have been employed as money in the Far East and in the South Pacific.

Some mollusks are destructive. The burrowing shipworm *Teredo* does great damage to wooden ships and wharves (Fig. 18-2). *Teredo* has an elongated body, with a pair of slender siphons on its posterior end. The anterior end of the animal has two movable valves by which the mollusk burrows into wood, sometimes as far as 3 or 4 feet. The siphons extend from its body to the water to provide oxygen and small particles of food as well as to discharge waste. Some of its food is in the wood that it excavates. To prevent the ravages of the shipworm, wharves are either creosoted or built of cement.

Snails and slugs are known to damage garden and other vegetation. In addition, snails often serve as intermediate hosts for serious parasites, such as the blood flukes (*Schistosoma*), liver flukes of sheep, and many others. *Urosalpinx* is second only to the sea star in destroying oysters (Fig. 18-7).

CLASSES

The classes of mollusks are based on such features as type of shell, type of foot, and shape of shell. Five classes have been recognized for many years, but the discovery in 1952 of a few specimens of living mollusks 2 miles deep near the west coast of Mexico has caused a reappraisal of the classes. These new mollusks (*Neopilina galatheae*) (Fig. 18-3) are small, with a limpet-shaped (low and rounded) shell. They are bilaterally symmetric and have a complete digestive system, anterior mouth (with radula), stomach with crystalline style, two-branched liver, and posterior anus. Five pairs of gills are situated in rows on each side of the ventral foot. (A more recent species, *N. ewingi,* has six pairs of gills.) Internally there are five pairs of dorsoventral muscles, five pairs of nephridia, and five pairs of gill hearts. Sexes are separate, and sex cells from the gonad pass to the outside through nephridia. There is a well-developed coelom and clearly marked **internal segmentation.** The body is composed of five segments, with three in the head.

Class Monoplacophora (mon′o-pla-kof″o-ra) (Gr. *monos,* one, + *plax,* plate, + *pherein,* to bear)—**segmented mollusks.** Body bilaterally symmetric with a broad flat foot; mantle covered with a single limpetlike shell; mantle cavity with five or six pairs of gills; large coelomic cavities; radula present; intestine much coiled; single ventricle with two pairs of auricles; internal segmentation only; six pairs of nephridia, two of which are gonoducts; nervous system with longitudinal pallial and pedal cords; separate sexes. Example: *Neopilina* (Fig. 18-3).

Class Amphineura (am′fi-neu″ra) (Gr. *amphi,* both, + *neuron,* nerve)—**chitons.** Elongated body with reduced head; bilaterally symmetric; radula present; row of eight dorsal plates usually; large, flat ventral foot, which is absent in some; nervous system consisting of a ring around the mouth with two pairs of ventral longitudinal nerve cords; sexes usually separate, with a trochophore larva. Example: *Chiton* (Fig. 18-4).

Class Scaphopoda (ska-fop′o-da) (Gr. *skapha,* boat, + *podos,* foot)—**elephant tusk shells.** Body enclosed in a one-piece tubular shell open at both ends; conical foot; mouth with tentacles; head absent; mantle for respiration; sexes separate; trochophore larva. Example: *Dentalium* (Fig. 18-6).

Class Gastropoda (gas-trop′o-da) (Gr. *gaster,* belly, + *podos,* foot)—**snails and others.** Body usually asymmetric in a coiled shell (shell absent in some); head well developed, with radula; foot large and flat; mantle modified into a lung or gill; nervous system with cerebral, pleural, pedal, and visceral ganglia; dioecious or monoecious, with

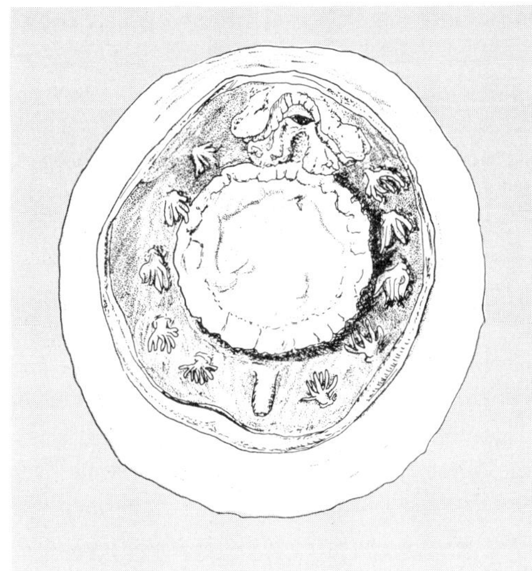

FIG. 18-3

Neopilina, a monoplacophoran, ventral view. Note mouth (upper end), anus, and five pairs of gills surounding foot. (From Hickman: Biology of the invertebrates, The C. V. Mosby Co.)

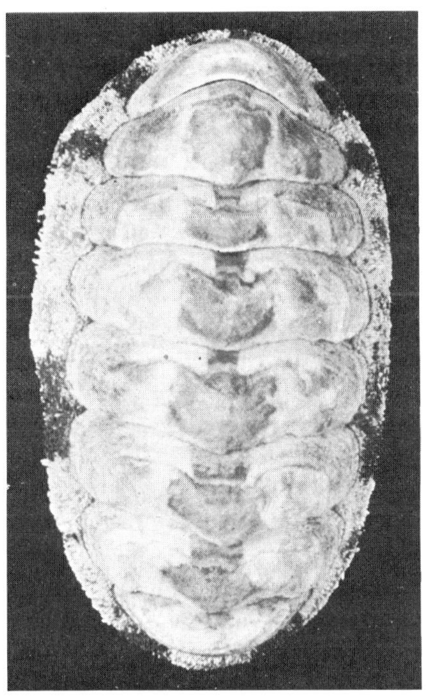

FIG. 18-4

Dorsal view of *Chiton*.

or without pelagic larva. Examples: *Littorina, Physa, Helix.*

Class Pelecypoda (pel-e-syp′o-da) (Gr. *pelekus,* hatchet, + *podos,* foot)—**bivalves.** Body enclosed in a two-lobed mantle; shell of two lateral valves of variable size and form, with dorsal hinge; no head, but mouth with labial palps; no eyes (except a few) or radula; foot usually wedge shaped; gills platelike; sexes usually separate, with trochophore or glochidial larva. Examples: *Anodonta, Teredo, Venus.*

Class Cephalopoda (cef′a-lop″o-da) (Gr. *kephale,* head, + *podos,* foot)—**squids and octopuses.** Body with a shell, often reduced or absent; head well developed with eyes and a radula; foot modified into arms or tentacles; siphon present; nervous system of well-developed ganglia, centralized to form a brain; sexes separate, with direct development. Examples: *Loligo, Octopus, Sepia.*

REPRESENTATIVE TYPES

CLASS AMPHINEURA

The class Amphineura is the most primitive of all mollusks, having a fossil record extending back to the Ordovican period of the Paleozoic era. The members of this strictly marine group have an elongated, bilaterally symmetric body, covered by a mantle bearing calcareous spicules embedded in a cuticle and often with transverse plates. A flattened foot may cover most of the ventral surface but is reduced in some. A mouth and anus at the ends and a reduced head without tentacles or eyes are characteristic of the class. Their name is derived from the two pairs of longitudinal nerve cords (pedal and pallial), which are connected anteriorly to a ring around the mouth region. There are two groups or orders—Polyplacophora (chitons) and Aplacophora (Solenogastres).

The chitons (Fig. 18-4) are the most numerous of the Amphineura. They are elongated, somewhat flattened animals with a convex dorsal surface that bears eight articulating limy plates or valves that overlap posteriorly. In early fossil forms the plates did not overlap. Most chitons are only 1 or 2 inches long, and the largest (*Cryptochiton*) rarely exceeds 8 to 10 inches. A marginal **girdle** formed from the mantle surrounds or covers the central mass of plates. It may contain calcareous spines and scales, which give it a shaggy appearance. The mantle, which secretes the plates, covers the dorsal and lateral surfaces, and a broad muscular foot very much like that of a snail covers most of the ventral surface. The **pallial groove** between the foot and mantle surrounds the animal. The head on the underside is separated from the foot by a narrow groove and bears the mouth, but it has no eyes or tentacles. Posteriorly the **anus** is found in the pallial groove.

The internal structure of *Chiton* (Fig. 18-5) is made up of an **alimentary canal,** with a radula in the floor of the mouth cavity, two pairs of salivary glands, a short pharynx, a thin-walled stomach, and coiled intestine; a **circulatory system** of a heart (one ventricle and two auricles) surrounded by a pericardium in the posterodorsal region of the body, an anterior aorta, and two large sinuses; an **excretory system** of two long, folded kidneys (nephridia), which carry waste away from the pericardial cavity to the exterior; a **respiratory system** of gills (4 to 80) or ctenidia, which lie in the bottom of the pallial groove; a **nervous system** of two pairs of longitudinal nerve cords (with few or no ganglia) and connected in the buccal region by a cerebral commissure; a **sensory system** of shell eyes (in some) on the surface of the shell, a pair of osphradia (sense organs for sampling water) near the anus, and scattered small sense organs; and a **reproductive system** of a single gonad (of either sex) between the aorta and intestine, with paired gonoducts that open to the outside.

In general, chitons resemble the hypothetical ancestral mollusk described earlier. There are some differences such as the gill arrangement, for the chiton usually has many, and the ancestral prototype has only a single pair.

Chitons are sluggish and creep slowly on their flat foot. They live upon seaweed or other plant life along the sea floor or shore. Their broad feet can adhere to rocky surfaces along protected shores. A favorite depression in a rock that is exposed at low tide may be used for countless generations by chitons. Some attach to the underside of rocks. Chitons are mostly intertidal invertebrates, although some have been taken at great depths. Molested, they may roll up like pill bugs, because the plate joints are flexible. Females lay their eggs in masses or strings of jelly; fertilization is external. In the West Indies the natives cook them ("sea beef"). *Nuttallina* and *Cryptochiton* are familiar along the west coast; the tiny *Chaetopleura* is one of the commonest east coast forms.

The Solenogastres (order Aplacophora) are wormlike forms with no foot or shell (except minute spicules in mantle). The body is completely enclosed in the mantle, the edges of which meet in a groove under the body. The digestive tract is straight and some have a radula. The vascular system is open (sinuses), and hemoglobin corpuscles may be present. Gills are restricted to a posterior cavity. The animals are hermaphroditic; sex cells are discharged into the pericardium and carried out by the nephridia. The nervous system resembles that of the chiton. The status of the Solenogastres has been doubtful, some authorities maintaining that they are closer to the worms than to mollusks.

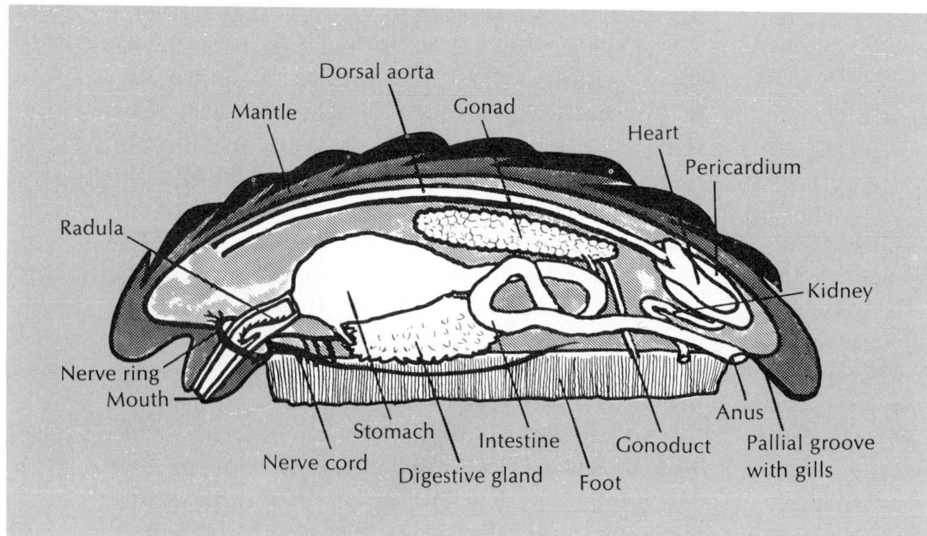

FIG. 18-5

Longitudinal section of *Chiton* showing internal anatomy.

Others think they represent Amphineura, whose development has been arrested, or neoteny. They are usually found in fairly deep water and live on hydroids and corals. *Neomenia* and *Chaetoderma* are common species along the Atlantic coast.

CLASS SCAPHOPODA

The mollusks of class Scaphopoda are commonly called the tooth shells, or elephant tusk shells, because of their resemblance to those structures. They have a slender, elongated body covered with the mantle, which secretes a tubelike shell open at both ends. A burrowing foot protrudes through the larger end of the shell. The mouth, which is near the foot, is provided with a radula and contractile tentacles, which are sensory and prehensile. Respiration takes place through the mantle, and the circulatory system consists merely of sinuses that are distributed among the different organs. They have two saclike kidneys that open to the outside near the anus. Their nervous system has the same basic plan as that of other mollusks. Members of this class are marine and live embedded in sand in shallow water, or sometimes at great depths, and they feed upon animals and plants of microscopic size. The sexes are separate, and the larva is a trochophore. After developing a mantle, the larva sinks to the bottom. *Dentalium* (Fig. 18-6) is a familiar example along our eastern seashore. Few living Scaphopoda are more than 3 inches long, but some fossil forms reached a length of 2 feet.

CLASS GASTROPODA

Among the mollusks the class Gastropoda is by far the largest and most successful. It is made up of members of such diversity that there is no single general term in our language that can apply to them as a group. Their scientific name is derived from the Greek *gaster*, belly, and *podos*, foot. They include snails, limpets, slugs, whelks, conchs, periwinkles, etc. The group includes animals that basically are bilaterally symmetric, but by torsion the visceral mass has become asymmetric. A shell, when present, is always of one piece (univalve) and is often coiled (some are cap shaped and uncoiled). The class has become adjusted to habitats on land and in fresh water as well as in salt water. Their original habitat, as revealed by fossils, was the ocean. Land gastropods are among the largest group of land invertebrates. Their range of habitat is large. In the sea they are common in the littoral zones, at great depths, and some are even pelagic (free swimming). Some are adapted to brackish water and some to fresh water. On land they are restricted by such factors as the mineral content of the soil and extremes of temperature, dryness, and acidity. Some have been found at great altitudes and even in polar regions. Snails have all kinds of habitats—woodlands, pastures, small pools or large bodies of water, under rocks, in

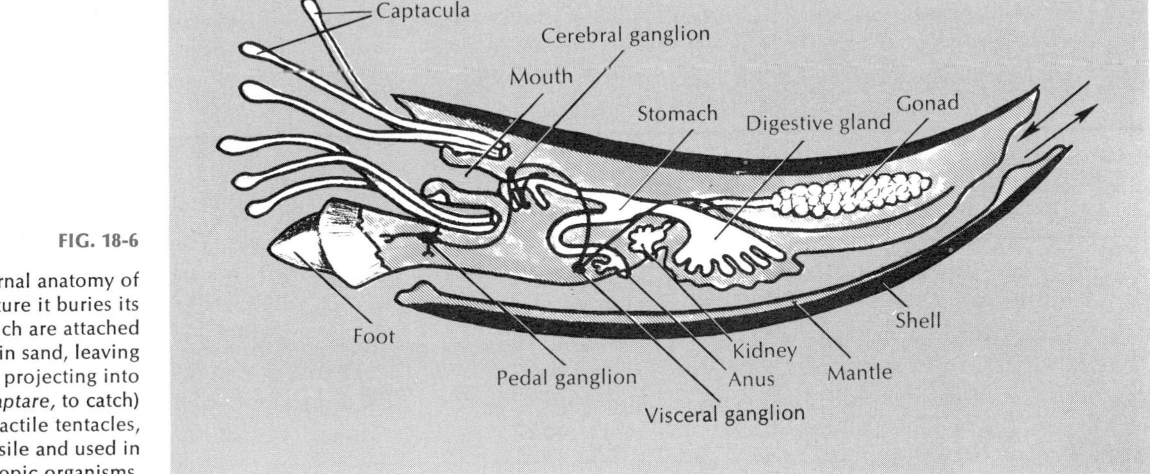

FIG. 18-6

Internal anatomy of *Dentalium*. In nature it buries its head end (to which are attached numerous tentacles) in sand, leaving posterior narrow end projecting into water. Captacula (L. *captare*, to catch) are ciliated, contractile tentacles, which are prehensile and used in capturing microscopic organisms.

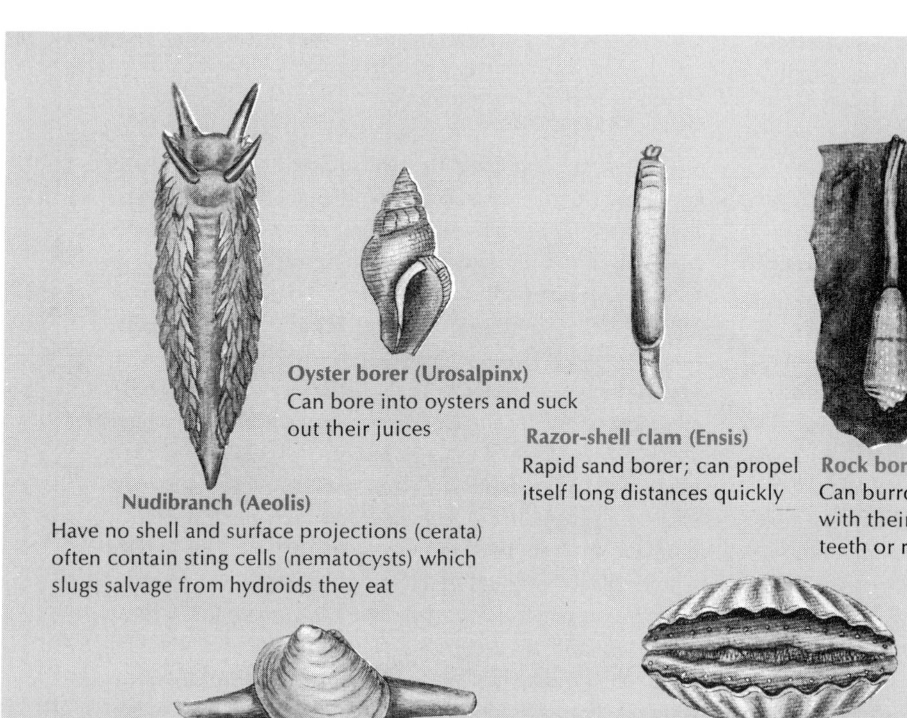

FIG. 18-7

Some mollusks with unusual habits or structures. Nudibranchs and the oyster borer belong to class Gastropoda; the others belong to class Pelecypoda.

mosses, on cliffs, underground, in trees, and in fairly warm springs.

Gastropods range from microscopic forms to giant whelklike, marine snails that exceed 2 feet. Most of them are ½ inch to 3 inches. Some fossil gastropods were 5 or 6 feet long. Their life-span is not well known, but some live from five to fifteen years.

Gastropods are usually sluggish, sedentary animals because most of them have heavy shells and slow locomotor organs. Some are specialized for climbing, swimming, or burrowing. Shells are their chief defense, although they are also protected by coloration and by secretive habits. Some are distasteful to other animals, and a few such as *Strombus* can deal an active blow with the foot, which bears a sharp operculum. However, they are eaten by birds, beetles, small mammals, fish, and other predators. Serving as intermediate hosts for many kinds of parasites, snails are often harmed by the larval stages of the parasites.

Most gastropods live on plants or plant debris. Many marine forms live on seaweed and algae that they scrape from the rocks. A few live on detritus strained from the water. Many are scavengers, living on dead and decayed flesh; others are carnivorous, preying upon clams, oysters, and worms. Some carnivores are provided with an extensible proboscis for drilling holes in other mollusks to eat the soft parts (Fig. 18-7, *Urosalpinx*). To obtain and rasp food, snails have a **radula,** which is a long ribbon bearing a series of transverse rows of tiny chitinous teeth. By means of muscles the radula moves rapidly back and forth like a hand saw over a cartilage in the upper part of the pharynx, thus tearing up the food. The arrangement, shape, and number of teeth are useful in taxonomic determinations.

The phenomenon of **torsion** (Fig. 18-8), which occurs in the early embryo, sets gastropods off from all other mollusks. The early gastropod embryo is symmetric, with anterior mouth and posterior anus—which is probably the primitive ancestral condition. Rather abruptly in the veliger stage there is a 180-degree counterclockwise rotation of the visceral mass upon the head and foot, which results in the typical gastropod asymmetry; that is, the anus, mantle, and gill (all of which formerly lay posteriorly) are now placed back of

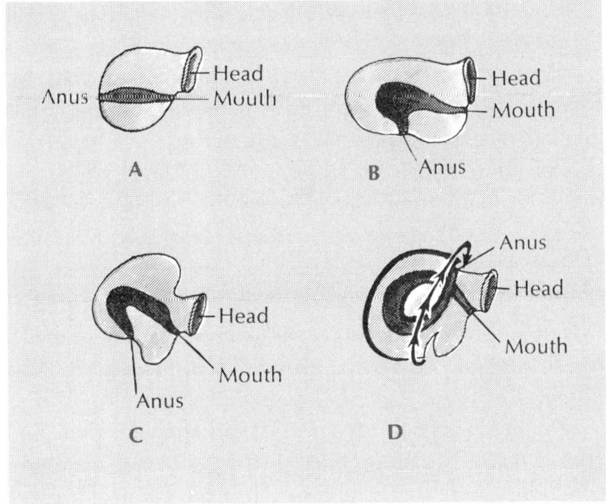

FIG. 18-8

Body torsion in snail. Early larva is symmetric, with mouth and anus at opposite ends of body, **A.** Most snails, however, undergo asymmetric growth in which anus shifts downward, **B,** then forward, and comes to lie near mouth, **C.** Later, anus and other parts rotate upward and lie above head, **D.** This rotation of visceral mass counterclockwise through angle of 180 degrees is due to more rapid growth of left side of visceral mass. Spiral winding of shell and visceral mass of snail is different process from body torsion described. Spiral coiling of visceral mass is due partly to atrophy of original left-handed organs, causing mass to coil around an axis at right angles to torsion axis, giving a more compact form and reduced diameter to shell and contents. In left-handed (sinistral) snails, organs of left side are preserved, whereas those on right atrophy. Coiling of shell may have arisen before body torsion.

the head. There are two phases to the movement, which result in torsion. First, the posterior anus shifts forward with the ventral flexure of the intestine to lie below the mouth. Second, the anus, its mantle cavity, and other visceral parts rotate upward and come to lie above and to the right of the head, and the organs, which are shifted from the left side to the right, tend to disappear. There are varying degrees of torsion among the different groups of gastropods.

Torsion must be distinguished from the coiling or spiral winding of the shell, as they are separate processes. The coiling of the shell and visceral mass may occur simultaneously with the torsion process, but fossil records indicate that coiling of the shell occurred before torsion. The coiling may be caused by differential growth and muscular contraction so that a corkscrew-shaped cone is produced at right angles to the axis of the torsion. Coiling is not found in some snails or else is suppressed in some way (limpets). In nudibranchs a coiled shell is found in the embryo but is absent in the adult. The reasons for torsion are obscure, but it has been suggested that having the gills forward made better respiration possible. The direction of coiling (right- or left-handed) of the shell is determined by the orientation of the early cleavage spindle, and its heredity is unique in that the character of the coiling is determined in the egg before fertilization, by the action of the mother's genes.

Major groups of gastropods

There are three major groups of gastropods, which some authorities call subclasses and others call orders. Each subclass or order is subdivided on the basis of distinctive characteristics.

Prosobranchia (subclass or order). In these gastropods the gills (ctenidia) are located anteriorly in front of the heart. Another name for this group is Streptoneura, which refers to the twisted nature of the nervous system (often in a figure eight). They have two tentacles, and the sexes are separate. An operculum is nearly always present. The Prosobranchia are divided into two groups or orders: Aspidobranchia, with a rather diffused nervous system and usually two auricles in the heart, and Pectinibranchia, with concentrated nervous system and one auricle. These two groups contain most of the marine snails and a few of the freshwater ones. They range in size from the periwinkles and small limpets (*Patella* and *Fissurella*) to the giant conch (*Strombus*), the largest univalve in America. Familiar examples of prosobranchs are the abalone (*Haliotis*), which has an ear-shaped shell; the giant whelk (*Busycon*) (Fig. 18-9), which lays its eggs in double-edged, disk-shaped capsules attached to a cord a yard long; the common periwinkle (*Littorina*), introduced from Europe, where it is widely used as food; the slipper or boot shell (*Crepidula*), which has an internal limy diaphragm; the oyster borer (*Urosalpinx,* Fig. 18-7), which bores into oysters and sucks out their juices; the rock shell (*Murex*), of which a European species was used for making the royal purple of the ancient Romans; and the freshwater forms (*Goniobasis* and *Paludina*).

Opisthobranchia (subclass or order). In these the gill is displaced to the right side or rear of the body. Two pairs of tentacles are usually found, and the shell is reduced or absent. All are monoecious. They are all marine, most of them shallow-water forms, hiding under stones and seaweed; a few are pelagic. There are two groups or orders: Tectibranchia, with gill and shell usually present, and the Nudibranchia, in which there is no shell or true gill, but adaptive gills are present around the anus. The opisthobranchs are an odd assemblage of mollusks, which includes sea slugs, sea hares, sea butterflies, canoe shells, etc. Among the Tectibranchia are the sea hare (*Tethys,* or *Aplysia*), which grows to be more than 1 foot long and has large earlike anterior tentacles and vestigial shell; and the pteropods, or sea butterflies (*Carderia* and *Clione*), with the foot modified into fins for swimming; thus they are pelagic and form a part of plankton fauna.

The Nudibranchia are represented by the sea slugs, which are often brightly colored and carnivorous in their eating habits. The plumed sea slug *Aeolis* (Fig. 18-7), which lives on sea anemones and hydroids, often draws the color of its prey into the elongated papillae (cerata), which cover its back. It also salvages the nematocysts of the hydroids for its own use.

FIG. 18-9

A, Shell of large marine snail, or whelk, *Busycon.* **B,** Dry string of egg cases of *Busycon.* Disk-shaped egg cases are strung close together along cord, and each case contains many eggs. They are secreted into water by special gland.

Pulmonata (subclass or order). This extensive group includes the land and freshwater snails and slugs (and a few brackish or saltwater forms). They have a lung instead of a gill, one or two pairs of tentacles, and a single, monoecious gonad. The aquatic species have one pair of nonretractile tentacles, at the base of which are the eyes; land forms have two pairs of tentacles, the posterior pair bearing the eyes. Among the thousands of land species the most familiar American forms are *Helix, Polygyra, Succinea, Anguispira, Zonitoides, Limax,* and *Agriolimax.* Aquatic forms are represented by *Helisoma, Viviparus, Campeloma, Lymnaea,* and *Physa.* The latter is a left-handed (sinistral) snail; that is, the snail coils to the left when viewed from the apex. Dextral shells (coiling to the right) are far more common among snails than are sinistral. Genetic investigation has shown that the direction of coiling is always determined before the egg is fertilized.

Common snail

Structure. Some of our most common terrestrial snails belong to genus *Polygyra,* but an imported European snail, *Helix aspersa,* is often studied in this country because of its size and the ease with which it can be collected. In some of our southern states it is known as the garden snail.

The snail has a well-developed **head,** which bears two pairs of retractile **tentacles,** a pair of **eyes** and the **olfactory organs** on the longer tentacles, and a **mouth** (Figs. 18-10 to 18-12). The tentacles are hollow and can be inverted, and the eyes are adapted for light perception. A muscular **foot** is attached to the head, and the visceral mass forms a dorsal hump, on top of which is the **shell.** The visceral mass is surrounded by the **mantle,** which also secretes the shell. The mantle cavity is just beneath the mantle. When the soft parts are exposed, they are protected by a mucous membrane. Other than the mouth, openings to the exterior include the **genital pore** on the right side near the mouth and the **anus** and **respiratory pore,** both located in the margin of the mantle at the edge of the shell. By means of the columella muscle, all soft parts can be withdrawn into the shell.

The **digestive system** is made up of the **mouth,** a **pharynx** bearing a **radula** (Fig. 18-11), an **esophagus,** a thin-walled **crop,** a **stomach,** a coiled **intestine,** and the **anus.** A pair of salivary glands opens into the pharynx, and a large digestive diverticulum (sometimes called liver) high in the spiral shell leads to the stomach.

The **circulatory system** has a **heart** (one auricle and one ventricle) and arteries, which deliver blood to the organs. In some snails (*Planorbis*) the blood contains erythrocruorin. For aeration of blood, land snails have a **lung** which is the modified mantle cavity provided with a network of blood vessels. Air is drawn in through the respiratory pore.

The **excretory system** is composed of a **nephridium** (kidney), which removes waste from the pericardial space and carries it to the mantle cavity.

FIG. 18-10

A, Common land snail *Anguispira* extended and traveling. **B**, Common garden snail, or slug, *Limax*.

The **nervous system** in snails is more condensed than it is in mussels, for the various ganglia (cerebral, buccal, pedal, visceral) are concentrated around the pharyngeal region. Nerves from these ganglia run to the body organs. The sensory organs include the eyes and olfactory organs on the tentacles, a pair of **statocysts** for equilibration near the pedal ganglia, and tactile and chemical sensory organs in the head and foot.

These land snails are monoecious, and the reproductive gland, **ovotestis,** is located high in the shell surrounded by a coil of the liver. The ovotestis produces both eggs and sperm. From the ovotestis the **hermaphroditic duct** connects to the **albumin gland,** which furnishes albumin to the eggs. The hermaphroditic duct carries both eggs and sperm. Where the albumin gland joins the duct, two tubes, often imperfectly separated, are given off—the **vas deferens,** which conducts sperm to the **penis** at the **genital opening,** and the **oviduct,** which leads to the **vagina** and also empties at the common genital opening. To the vagina is connected the duct of the **seminal receptacle** as well as the **oviducal glands,** the **dart sac,** and the **digitiform glands.** A slender flagellum by which sperm are formed into spermatophores is connected to the penis. Although this snail is hermaphroditic, cross-fertilization is the rule. In copulation each member inserts its penis into the vagina of the other and transfers a spermatophore. Many terrestrial pulmonates have interesting habits of courtship and mating, involving the ejection of a dart (which heightens sexual excitement) from the dart sac into the partner's body. After separating, each deposits its eggs in shallow burrows in the ground, usually in damp places. Development is direct, and the young emerge as small snails.

Behavior and natural history. Snails are usually most active at night, when they glide by wavelike contractions of the foot muscle. A slime gland is located at

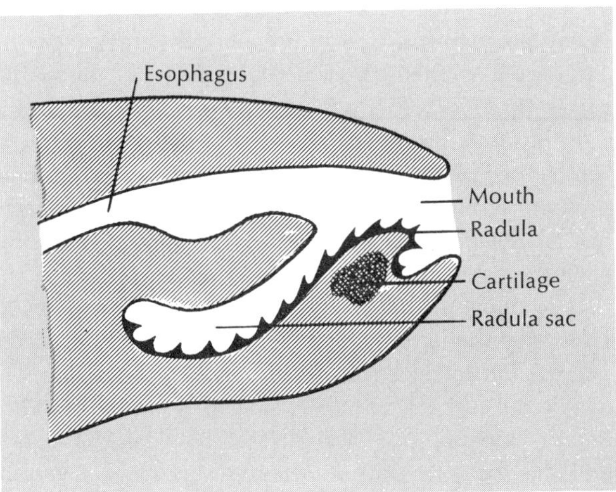

FIG. 18-11

Median section through head and mouth of pond snail showing radula (diagrammatic). With use of muscles, radula is worked backward and forward for rasping food. Radula is usually distinctive for each species and is useful for taxonomic studies. Radula undergoes replacement as transverse rows of teeth are added progressively at caudal end in radula sac and are shed from oral end.

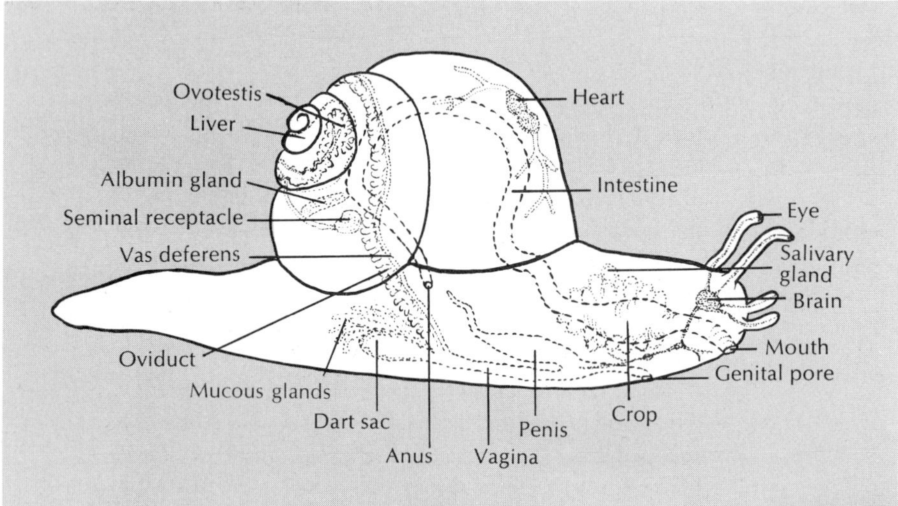

FIG. 18-12
Internal structure of land snail.

the anterior end of the foot and deposits a mucous film over which the snail moves. Locomotion is very slow, a "snail's pace," and may not exceed 10 to 12 feet per hour, although some snails are known to travel faster.

Their food consists of green vegetation, which they rasp off by means of their radulae. They are partial to damp situations and by day are often found under patches of leaves or in burrows. When threatened with very dry weather, they form a temporary covering, or epiphragm, of mucus and limy secretions that cover the shell aperture. Some snails have a permanent **operculum,** which covers the aperture when the body is in the shell.

CLASS PELECYPODA

Class Pelecypoda includes the mussels, oysters, scallops, shipworms, and clams found in both fresh water and salt water. Many of them burrow in the sand and mud; others crawl on or attach themselves to solid objects. The group includes more than 7,000 species widely distributed over the world. The size range is from 1 mm. to 1 meter (giant clam); most are 1 to 2 inches. Most of them are specialized for a sedentary life and are provided with a filtering mechanism for obtaining their food.

The freshwater mussel is often studied because of its typical structural pattern and the ease with which it can be procured. *Lampsilis, Anodonta, Elliptio,* and *Quadrula* are some of the common American genera often used. There are only minor differences among them.

Anodonta—freshwater mussel

External structure. The shell is somewhat oval when examined from the side, being rounded at the anterior end and more pointed posteriorly (Fig. 18-15). It is composed of symmetric **right** and **left valves** that are thicker on the dorsal side. They are held together along the inner dorsal surface by an elastic hinge **ligament,** which draws the valves together dorsally, causing them to gape ventrally. A rounded prominence, the **umbo,** is the oldest part of each valve. Surrounding the umbo are concentric lines of growth, indicating the intervals between successive growth stages. Several lines may be formed in one season, some more prominent than others. In some forms, but not in *Anodonta,* there may be dorsal hinge **teeth** to help hold the valves together.

The shell consists of three layers: (1) the external horny **periostracum** (of an organic substance, conchyolin), which is often absent on the umbo; (2) the middle **prismatic** layer of crystalline calcium carbonate; and (3) the inner (lamellar) layer of iridescent **nacre,** or mother-of-pearl, which is formed of many thin layers of calcium carbonate. The nacre is thickest at the umbo and thinnest at the margin. In the formation of the shell the nacre is produced by the whole surface of the mantle and the other two layers are produced by its edge. The shell grows in surface size by additions at the margin and in thickness by additions within.

When a foreign substance, such as a grain of sand or larva of a worm, becomes enclosed between the mantle and the shell, the mantle secretes successive layers of

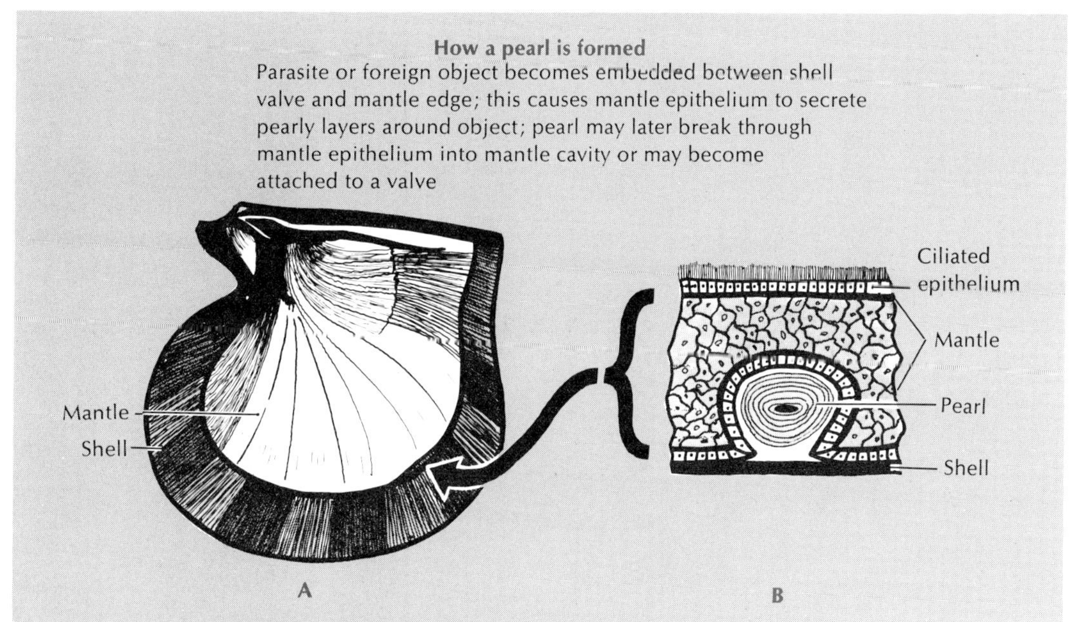

FIG. 18-13

Pearl oyster *Margaritifera*. **A,** Interior of valve, with arrow pointing to site of pearl formation. **B,** Enlarged section of mantle, with pearl in position.

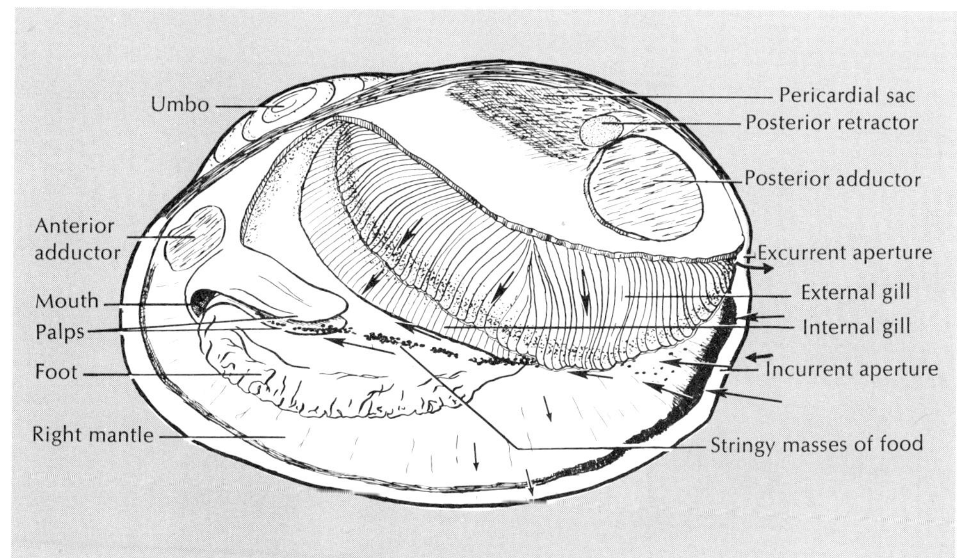

FIG. 18-14

Feeding mechanism of clam. Left shell and mantle are removed. Food particles are carried in water current by means of cilia on gills, mantle, and palps; become entangled in stringy masses of mucus secreted by gills; and are guided by ciliated palps to mouth. Sand and debris drop into mantle cavity and are removed by ciliary action.

nacre around it (Fig. 18-13). The pearl thus produced is made up of concentric layers of calcium carbonate surrounding the irritating substance. Pearls are cultured by opening the oyster, inserting small particles into the mantle, and placing the oyster in a wire cage, back in the ocean. A few years later the cage is lifted and the oyster and pearl removed.

Internal structure. Inside the valves and adhering to their inner surfaces is the **mantle** (Fig. 18-14). Between the mantle lobes and attached to the mantle dorsally is the soft body that is made up of the **visceral mass,** a muscular **foot,** and a pair of **gills (ctenidia)** on either side of the visceral mass. The space between the right and left lobes of the mantle and surrounding the body is called the **mantle cavity.**

The outer edge of the mantle attachment to the shell is the **pallial line.** The mantle secretes carbonate of lime, which is added to the edge and inner surface of the shell. Posteriorly the mantle is modified to form the dorsal **excurrent aperture** and the slightly fringed

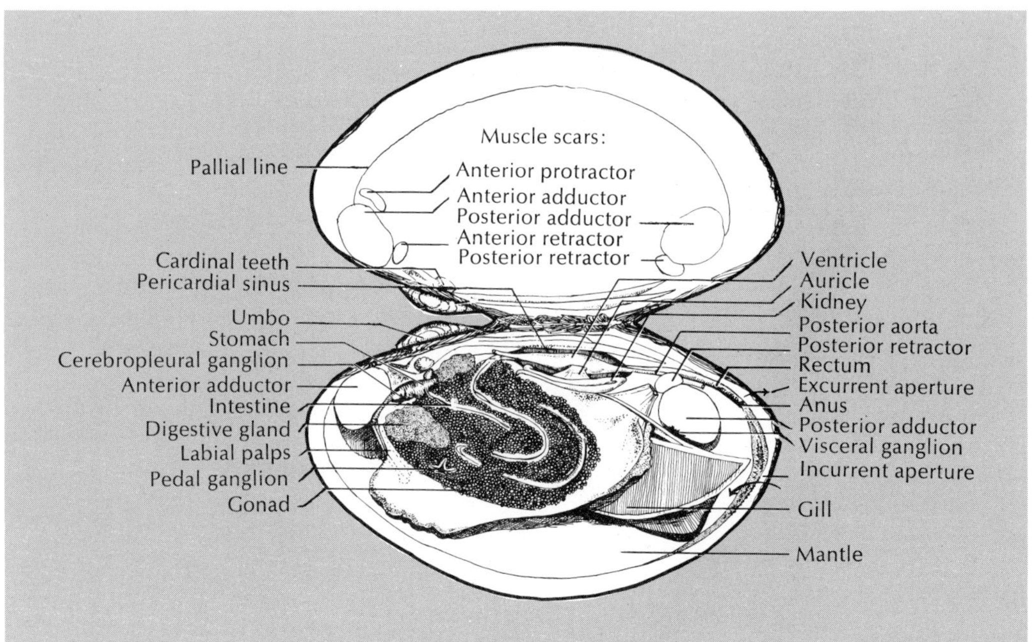

FIG. 18-15

Structure of clam. Visceral mass shown in sagittal section.

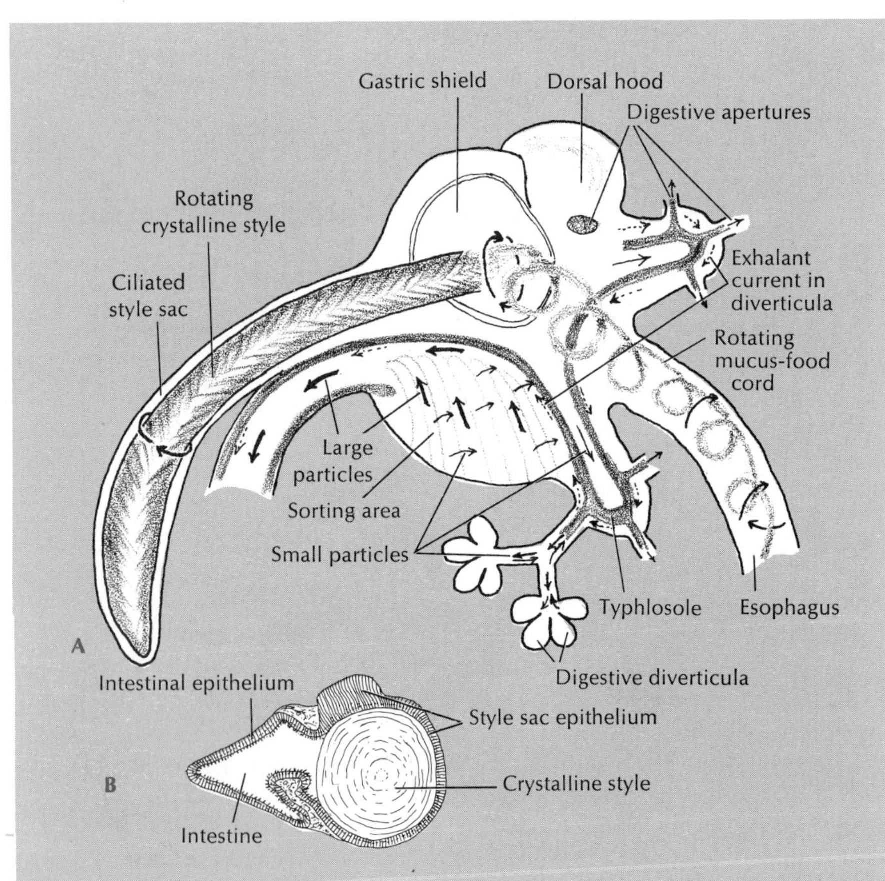

FIG. 18-16

A, Stomach and crystalline style of lamellibranch ciliary feeder. From volumes of water taken in, particles are engaged in cord of mucus, which is kept rotating by ciliary action on crystalline style. Ridged and ciliated sorting area directs large particles to intestine and small particles to digestive diverticula. **B,** Transverse section through straight portion of intestine of *Cardium* showing crystalline style. (From Hickman: Biology of the invertebrates, The C. V. Mosby Co.)

ventral **incurrent aperture,** which regulate the intake and outgo of water. Cilia on the inner surfaces of the gills and mantle direct the flow of water over the two pairs of gills.

On the inner surface of a clean valve are conspicuous scars made by the attachments of various muscles. The **anterior** and **posterior adductors** draw the valves together; the **anterior** and **posterior retractors** pull the foot into the shell; and the **anterior protractor** aids in the extension of the foot (Figs. 18-14 and 18-15).

The **digestive system** is made up of (1) the **mouth,** between the two pairs of fleshy **labial palps,** which are provided with cilia to carry food into the mouth; (2) a short **esophagus** leading to (3) a dilated **stomach,** which receives digestive enzymes from the large **digestive gland** (liver); (4) the coiled **intestine;** (5) the dorsal **rectum** surrounded by the heart and pericardium; and (6) the **anus,** which opens near the dorsal excurrent siphon. Within the rectum is a longitudinal fold, the **typhlosole,** which increases the surface area of that portion of the alimentary canal.

The mussel is a filter feeder, living on microscopic animal and plant matter carried in through the incurrent siphon, or aperture, by ciliated gills and mantle. As the water passes over and into the gills, food and debris are filtered out and are caught in stringy masses of mucus, which, by ciliary action are guided between the labial palps and into the mouth. The floor of the stomach is much folded and ciliated for sorting and disposing of the continuous stream of particles. A cylindric cecum, called the crystalline style sac, opening into the stomach may secrete a gelatinous rod, the **crystalline style,** which projects into the stomach and

FIG. 18-17

Anterolateral view of cross section through heart region of clam to show relations of circulatory and respiratory systems (diagrammatic). Arrows indicate direction of blood flow and water currents. Scheme of blood circulation: ventricle pumps blood forward through anterior aorta to sinuses of foot and most of viscera and backward through posterior aorta to sinuses of rectum and mantle; blood from mantle returns to auricles, and from other organs to kidneys (nephridia); blood from kidneys to gills; then to auricles; from auricles to ventricle. Scheme of water circulation to aerate gills: water drawn in through incurrent aperture by cilia; passes through gill pores into water tubes, which run into suprabranchial chambers; water in its passage gives up oxygen to blood of gills, picks up carbon dioxide, feces, and sex cells, and finally discharges through excurrent aperture to outside.

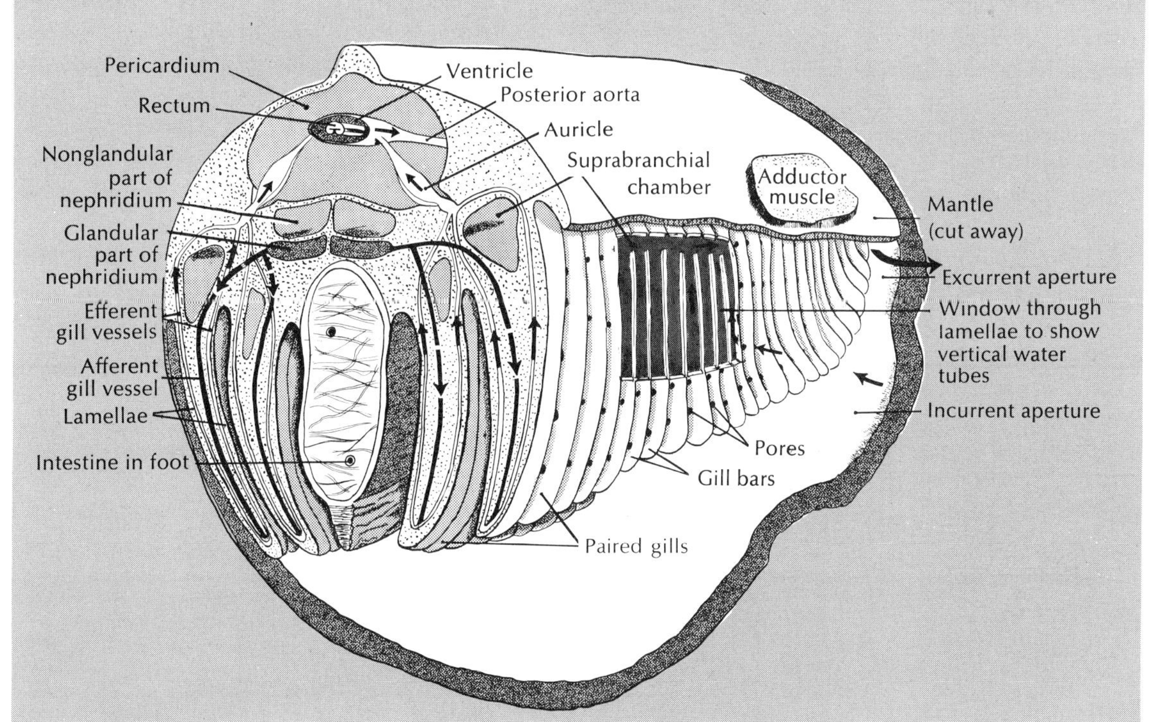

is kept rotating by strong cilia in the sac (Fig. 18-16). The style is composed of mucoprotein and some enzymes (for example, amylase). Surface layers of the style dissolve in stomach fluid, freeing enzymes for extracellular digestion. The end of the rotating style becomes attached to the stringy mucus mass of food, and as it rotates, the food particles are detached from the mass and are sorted on the stomach floor. Large or unsuitable particles are rejected and are sent directly to the intestine. Smaller or partly digested nutritive particles may be absorbed into cells of the digestive gland or picked up by amebocytes for intracellular digestion before reaching the intestine.

A recent review (P. B. Van Weel) indicates that mollusks as a group have a great variety of enzymes (carbohydrases, proteolytic enzymes, and esterases), although there are some differences in the distribution of the enzymes among the various classes.

The **circulatory system** (Fig. 18-17) is an open one and consists of a heart, arteries, sinuses, and veins. Water, however, cannot enter the system. The heart, which lies in the pericardial cavity, is made up of two auricles and a ventricle and beats at the rate of six times per minute. Blood is pumped through an **anterior aorta** to the foot and most of the viscera and through a **posterior aorta** to the rectum and mantle. Part of the blood is oxygenated in the mantle and is returned to the ventricle through the auricles; the other part circulates through sinuses, passes in a vein to the kidneys, thence to the gills for oxygenation, and back to the auricles. Carbon dioxide and other wastes are carried to the gills and kidneys for elimination. The blood is colorless and contains nucleated ameboid corpuscles.

Respiration is carried on by both the mantle and the gills. A pair of gills (**ctenidia**) hangs down on each side of the foot. Each ctenidium is formed of two walls (**lamellae**) (Fig. 18-18) joined together at their ventral margins. Each lamella contains many vertical **gill filaments** strengthened by chitinous rods. Water enters the gills through innumerable small **ostia** in the walls and is propelled by ciliary action. Partitions between the lamellae divide the gill internally into many vertical **water tubes,** which carry water upward (dorsally) into a common **suprabranchial chamber** and through it posteriorly to the excurrent aperture. Blood vessels or spaces in the interlamellar partitions are used for exchange of gases. The water tubes in the female double as brood pouches for the eggs and larvae during the breeding season. The different orders of Pelecypoda are based upon the types of gills they have.

Excretion is performed by two U-shaped **kidneys** just below the pericardium. Each kidney consists of an opening from the pericardial space into a ciliated tube, which in turn leads to a bladder. The bladder empties into the suprabranchial chamber. The kidneys remove waste from both the blood (which circulates through the kidney network) and the pericardial space.

Coordination is effected by a **nervous system** of several ganglia scattered throughout the body in pairs (Fig. 18-15). These include the **cerebropleural ganglia** near the mouth, the **pedal ganglia** in the foot, and the **visceral ganglia** just below the posterior adductor muscle. The members of each pair are linked by a

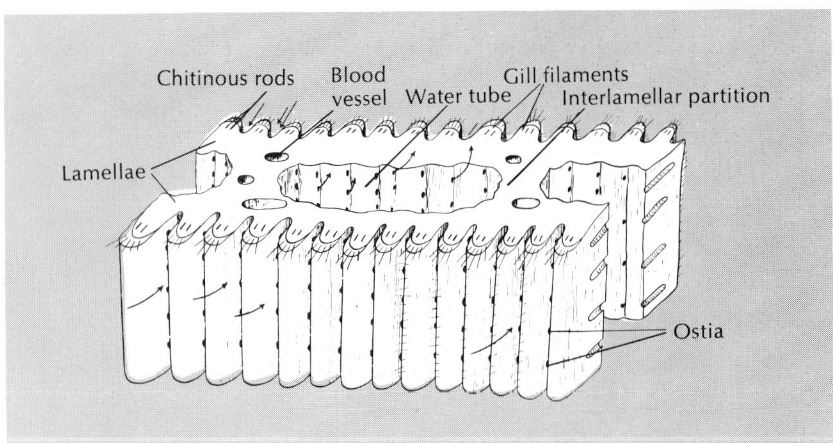

FIG. 18-18

Section through portion of clam gill showing relation of lamellae and water tubes. Cilia on gill surface draw water through small pores into tubes, which carry it up to suprabranchial chambers and out with exhalant current. Blood vessels in partitions bring blood close to oxygen supply in water. Females use water tubes of external gills as brood pouches for developing glochidia larvae during certain seasons.

commissure. Also, the three kinds of ganglia are joined to each other by connectives. Nerves lead from the ganglia to the organs. Neurosecretory cells are also found in certain mollusks. Neuron cell bodies in the cerebropleural and visceral ganglia produce neurohumors, such as acetylcholine, which are carried by axons to their terminals for storage and release. These substances may produce the same effects as comparable neurohumors in vertebrates and arthropods. **Sensory organs** are not well developed, although light-detecting organs occur in the aperture margins, tactile organs along the mantle margins, a pair of **statocysts** for equilibrium in the foot, and an **osphradium** of yellow epithelial cells over each visceral ganglion. The osphradia may be used to test the chemical nature of incoming water.

The sexes are separate. **Reproductive organs** are much-branched, lobate masses, located around the intestinal coils of the visceral mass just above the foot. The vasa deferentia in the male or the oviducts in the female open into the suprabranchial chamber near the openings to the kidneys. There are no copulatory organs or accessory glands.

Development. The sperm cells are discharged into the suprabranchial chamber by the vas deferens and escape through the dorsal aperture to be carried in the water to a female. Eggs are retained in the body. When they are discharged by the oviduct into the suprabranchial chamber, they pass into the water tubes of the gills, which enlarge to form brood chambers (**marsupia**). Here the eggs are fertilized by sperm carried in through the ventral aperture. The fertilized egg, or zygote, undergoes cleavage, passes through blastula and gastrula stages, and forms a larva called the **glochidium** (Fig. 18-19). In the brood chambers the larvae may live on the epithelial cells of the gills during incubation. The time of fertilization varies with different species; in *Anodonta* it usually occurs in August. The glochidium has two valves (only one in the embryo at first), which are closed by an adductor muscle. The glochidia of *Anodonta* bear ventral hooks on the valves and a larval thread between the valves (absent in some species). The glochidia are discharged into the water through the excurrent aperture and are swept along by the water currents, or they may sink to the bottom, for they cannot swim. When they come into contact with the gills of a passing fish, they attach themselves by snapping their valves closed. The larvae encyst and live as parasites on the fish for eight to twelve weeks. During this time they develop into miniature clams and the cysts break to release them. They then sink to the bottom, where they begin their existence as independent clams. This larval behavior of hitchhiking helps to distribute a form whose locomotion is very limited.

FIG. 18-19

Glochidium, or larval form of freshwater clam. When larva is released from brood pouch of mother, it may become attached to fish by clamping its valves closed. It remains as parasite on fish for several weeks. (Size, about 0.3 mm.)

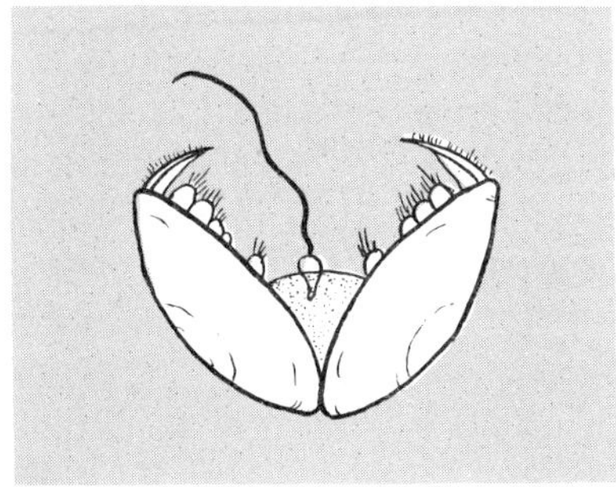

Behavior and natural history. Mussels move by extending the muscular foot anteriorly between the valves into the mud or sand. Blood flow swells the end of the foot and anchors it. Then longitudinal muscles in the foot contract and the clam is pulled forward. In lagoons and cutoffs from the main streams, the trails clams make through the mud can easily be seen. When the mussels are not moving, their behavior is restricted to the opening and closing of the apertures, which are sensitive to light, touch, and other stimuli. When disturbed in the vertical position, mussels often fall upon their sides. Some of the marine bivalves have the mantle apertures enclosed and extended into long, muscular siphons (Fig. 18-20). The clam can burrow into mud or sand and extend the siphons up to the water. When the ground is exposed at low tide or when the clam is disturbed, the siphons can be contracted and withdrawn from danger.

Because of the composition of their shells, mussels are found in very "hard" water, or water rich in limy salts. This factor of salt content often determines their abundance or scarcity.

For many years studies have been made of oysters—their habits, enemies, best habitats, food, and means of cultivation. Extensive oyster beds have been cultivated

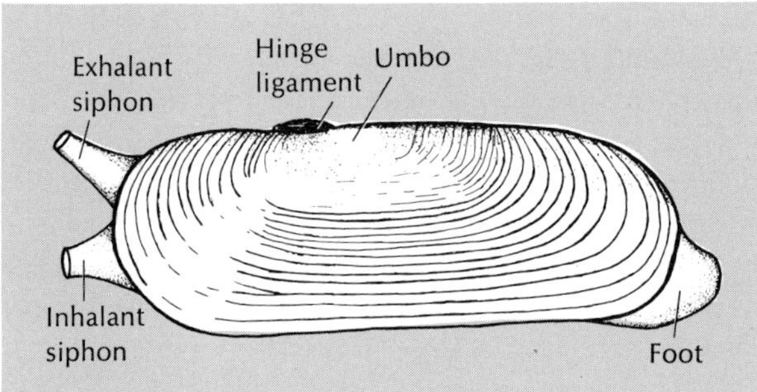

FIG. 18-20

Stubby razor clam *Tagelus gibbus* showing its two siphons (left) and muscular foot (right). It burrows into mud in shallow water and extends its siphons to surface.

FIG. 18-21

Internal structure of oyster *Crassostrea (Ostrea) virginica*, with left mantle and body wall removed (diagrammatic).

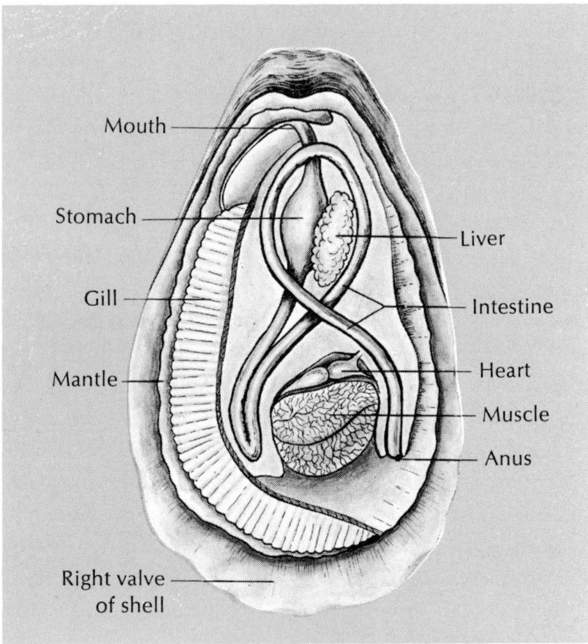

along our Atlantic coast and to some extent along the Pacific coast. Some of these beds are world famous for fine oysters. The larval forms (spats) swim about for two weeks before settling down to attach themselves to some hard surface. Before the larvae settle they are often netted and transported to desirable beds, where they are provided with stones or cement for attachment. It takes about four years for an oyster to grow to commercial size. More than 400,000 tons are taken in the waters of the United States each year.

The evolution of the Pelecypoda has centered mainly around their feeding mechanism and the development of the ctenidia, or gills (Fig. 18-21). They have evolved a form of filter feeding that more and more involves assistance of the ctenidia. Primitive forms such as *Nucula* had very small ctenidia but very elongated and ciliated palps that conveyed the food to the mouth, but more advanced pelecypods had larger ctenidia that directed ciliary currents containing food to the small palps, which in turn passed it to the mouth. Thus the ctenidia have come to serve the double function of respiration and food collecting. However, such a specialized feeding mechanism is accompanied by certain limitations in pelecypods, for example, loss of the radula, poor cephalization, and a restriction to a water habitat.

The class Pelecypoda shows interesting adaptive radiation, especially with reference to one of their most important morphologic units, the foot. Perhaps the most common method of locomotion is burrowing through sand and mud (*Venus* and *Anodonta*), but the creeping mode of locomotion is perhaps the primitive type and is represented by a few forms (*Solemya* and *Leptor*). Other pelecypods can swim (*Pecten* [Fig. 18-7] and *Lima*), leap over surfaces (*Yoldia*), climb up a surface (*Kellia*), bore or burrow into hard substances (*Pholas* [Fig. 18-7] and *Teredo* [Fig. 18-2]), and become attached by byssus threads (*Mytilus*) or by a secretion (*Ostrea*).

Other members of class Pelecypoda

There are many genera of clams found in our fresh-water streams and ponds, such as *Anodonta, Unio, Quadrula,* and *Lampsilis*. Some of them prefer a quiet pond or pool, but others are partial to moderately swift water. Those found in still water tend to have thinner shells. Clams found in our bigger lakes often have diurnal migratory habits, coming from the deeper water during the night and wandering about the shallow water near the shore. Early in the daytime they migrate back to the deeper waters.

Belonging to this same class are the shipworms (*Teredo*) already mentioned. Some of the marine clams such as *Pecten* have the interesting habit of swimming by clapping their shells together and ejecting a stream of water. One pelecypod of great interest is the rock-drilling *Pholas,* which manages to drill into fairly soft rock by means of its roughened shell (Fig. 18-7).

Other marine forms of this class are *Mytilus,* which attaches itself to solid objects by secreting numerous byssal threads and is found hanging in masses on wharfs and rocks; *Venus,* or quahog, which is large with an oval shell and is widely used for food; *Sima,* also a swimming clam with a fringe of long tentacles along the mantle edge; *Nucula,* one of the most primitive living members of the class, with small ctenidia and large labial palps; and *Mya,* or the long-necked clam, which is esteemed for chowders on our eastern coast and is provided with long siphons (Fig. 18-7).

Many members of this class have a trochophore-like larva, the **veliger.** In this form the larva swims about for a time and, after acquiring a shell gland, sinks to the bottom of the water to become a bivalve. Because of the many hazards in their life cycles, most of the mollusks produce an enormous number of eggs. It is said that the oyster, for example, may produce more than 50 million eggs in a single season.

CLASS CEPHALOPODA

Class Cephalopoda is far more advanced than any other class of Mollusca and in some respects is more advanced than any other invertebrates. All are marine, and they include the squids, octopuses, nautiluses, devilfish, and cuttlefish. They derive their name from the Greek *kephale,* head, and *podos,* foot. This derivation describes one of their most unusual features—the concentration of the foot in the head region. The edges of the foot are drawn out into arms and tentacles, which bear sucking disks for seizing prey. Part of the foot (epipodium) is modified to form the funnel for carrying water from the mantle cavity. The group goes back to the Cambrian period, with remarkable fossil records. The largest invertebrate known is the giant squid (*Architeuthis*), which may be up to 50 feet long. *Rossia,* a squid on the west coast, is only 1½ inches long.

Mollusks appear to have differentiated along three lines of life habits. Bottom-dwelling filter feeders with a slow locomotion gave rise to pelecypods; herbivorous or carnivorous feeders with slow creeping movements evolved into gastropods; whereas a third group of active swimming predators became the cephalopods. As predators the cephalopods are not only swift, but they also have prehensile arms and tentacles for seizing and suckers for holding their prey. They can put out protective "smoke screens" and possess marvelous patterns of color changes. Although the earliest cephalopods bore heavy external shells, the shells were buoyant with gas chambers separated by septa and connected to the body by a tube, the **siphuncle.** In later cephalopods

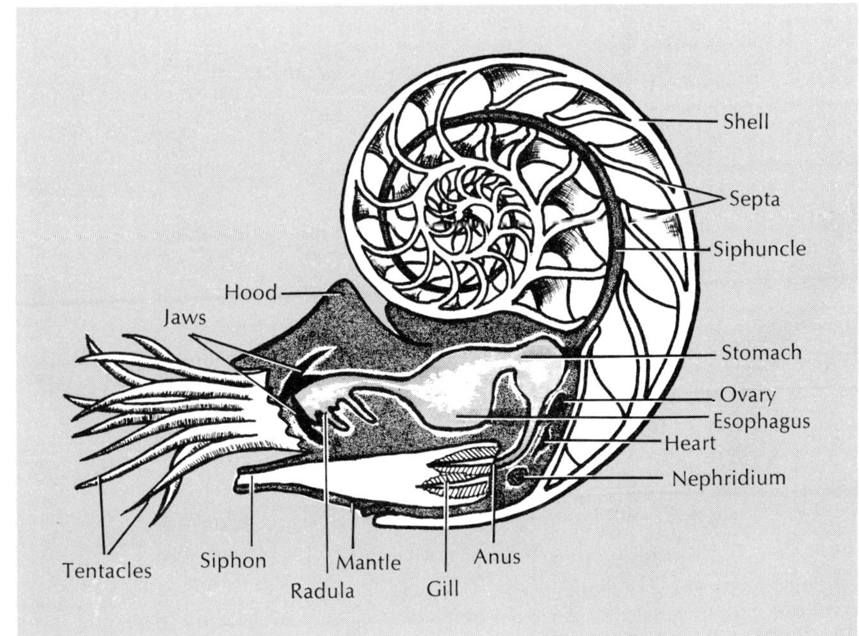

FIG. 18-22

Median section through shell and viscera of *Nautilus* showing internal anatomy (semidiagrammatic). This is only surviving genus of Tetrabranchia, which flourished millions of years ago in tropical seas. It inspired O. W. Holmes' famous poem "The Chambered Nautilus."

the shell was reduced until it was internal or absent, and the animals relied on their speed and an ink screen for protection.

Cephalopods probably originated from a form similar to the hypothetical mollusk ancestor. It is thought that the simple limpetlike shell became elongated as the visceral mass shifted away from the apex of the shell. Behind the visceral mass a septum was secreted at each growth period, so that the shell became a series of successive compartments. As the fossil record shows, the shell was first straight (*Orthoceras*, or *Michelinoceras*) but later became coiled, producing the *Nautilus* type of shell (Fig. 18-22). The evolution of the nonshelled or reduced-shell forms is obscure because of lack of fossils, but the evolutionary tendency for a degenerate shell or none at all is evident.

The natural history of the cephalopods is known only in part. They are saltwater animals and appear sensitive to the degree of salinity. Few are found in the Baltic Sea, where the water has a low salt content. The *Octopus* is often found in the intertidal zone, lurking among rocks and crevices; the active squids are rarely found in this zone. Cephalopods are found at various depths. *Nautilus* is usually taken from the ocean floor near islands (southwestern Pacific) where the water is several hundred meters deep. Some squids have been taken at 5,000 meters. Octopoda are usually in shallow water near shore but occasionally are found at great depths.

Color changes of cephalopods are produced in the skin by the contraction and expansion of special pigment cells called **chromatophores,** manipulated by tiny muscles attached to the edge of the cells. The pigment colors are black, brown, red, and yellow so that a squid or octopus can assume a variety of colors when emotionally disturbed or for protection. All cephalopods except *Nautilus* have ink sacs from which they expel ink when attacked. The ink contains melanin (black) pigment, which is formed by the oxidation of the amino acid tyrosine through the action of an enzyme. Some authorities think the discharged ink assumes the shape of a "dummy" to distract an enemy predator. Or the ink may paralyze the enemy's sense of smell.

All cephalopods are predaceous and carnivorous. Their chief food is small fish, mollusks, crustaceans, and worms. They are strong enough to pull clams apart; their horny beaks can quickly tear the flesh from a crustacean skeleton. They will even eat each other. Cephalopods are preyed upon by whales, seals, sea birds, and moray eels. The slender moray eel can go where the octopus hides and overcome it.

The sexes are separate in cephalopods. Females sometimes outnumber the males as much as 100 to 15. There is a certain amount of sexual dimorphism, too, so that it is possible to distinguish the sexes in some cases. One of the male arms is modified for transferring sperm to the female. The sperm are arranged in long tubes called **spermatophores,** which are formed in a special sac of the vas deferens. During mating, the male clasps the female and with his **hectocotylus** arm withdraws a bundle of spermatophores from his siphon and places them near her mouth or within her mantle cav-

FIG. 18-23

Hectocotylized arm of cephalopod. In most male cephalopods one of the arms is modified (hectocotylized) for transferring sperm capsules (spermatophores) to mantle cavity of female. In some members of Octopoda (for example, *Argonauta)* hectocotylus arm is autonomous, that is, becomes detached and lodged in female.

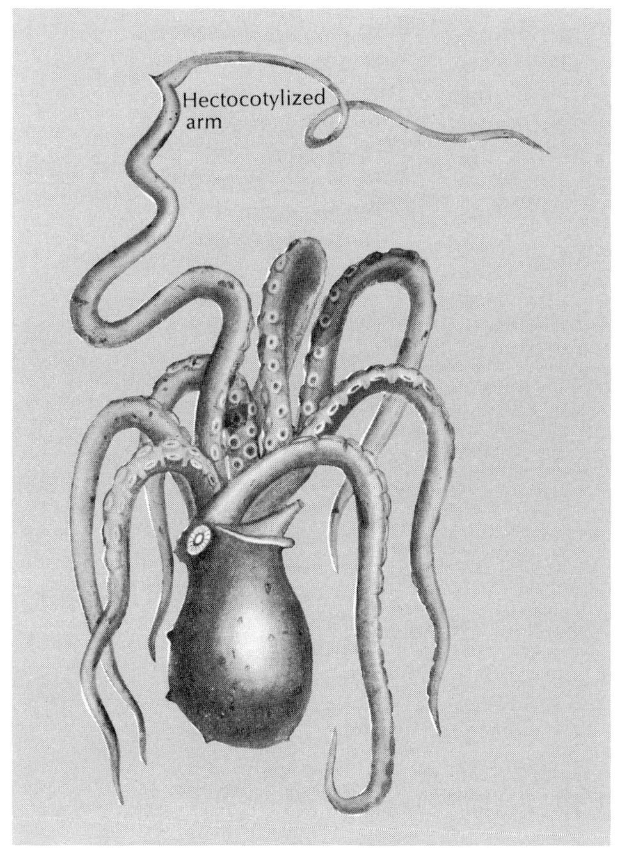

ity. In *Argonauta* (Fig. 18-23) and a few others, part of this arm is disengaged and left within the mantle chamber of the female; in others only the tip of the arm is detached. The hectocotylus arm is usually one of the fourth pair of arms in the squid; one of the third in the octopus. The squid lays her eggs in pencil-shaped masses of jelly and attaches them to some object. They are called "deadman's-fingers." The octopus lays eggs in long strings or bunches attached to a rock, where she remains to care for them.

Major groups of cephalopods

There are two orders of cephalopods: Tetrabranchia (four-gilled) and Dibranchia (two-gilled). Tetrabranchia is the more primitive. Its members populated the Paleozoic and Mesozoic seas but left only one genus, *Nautilus* (Fig. 18-22), of which there are three species. This order is characterized by having external calcareous shells, which may or may not be coiled (based on the only living form, *Nautilus*), and two pairs of gills and nephridia, many tentacles, no suckers, no ink sac, eyes without lenses (Fig. 18-24), and a passive mantle for holding the viscera and secreting the shell. Paleontologists divide the Tetrabranchia into two suborders: Nautiloidea, with simple septa between the chambers, and Ammonoidea, divided by fluted septa. The Nautiloidea are geologically older.

FIG. 18-24

Eye of *Nautilus*. Example of pinhole camera eye. Such an eye corresponds to stage of development in more complicated eyes of *Octopus* and *Loligo*. This type of eye focuses rays directly upon retina without focusing device such as a crystalline lens and is the only known pinhole camera eye among animals.

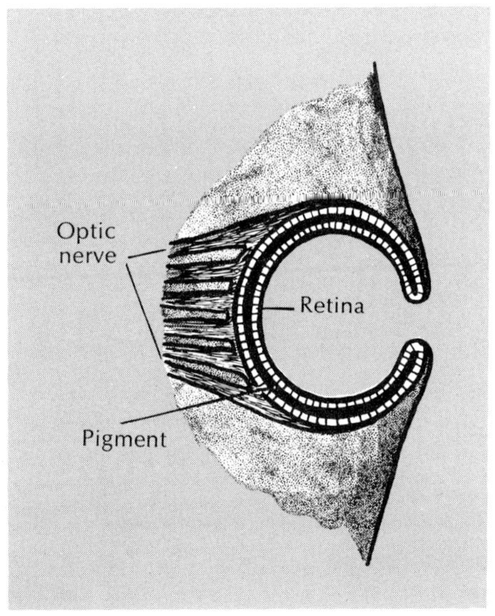

The order Dibranchia includes all living cephalopods except *Nautilus*. It has an internal shell or none at all, a cylindric-shaped body that may have a fin, a pair of gills, a pair of kidneys, eight to ten arms or tentacles with suckers, eyes with lenses, and a muscular mantle for locomotion. There are two suborders: Decapoda, with ten arms and large coelom, and Octopoda, with eight arms and reduced coelom. Squids belong to the Decapoda and the octopuses to the Octopoda.

Two of the decapod's arms are modified into tentacular arms for seizing prey. They can either be retracted into special pouches or doubled back upon themselves. They bear suckers only at the ends and are situated between the third and fourth arms on each side of the head. The suckers in squids are stalked (pedunculated), with horny rims bearing teeth; in octopuses the suckers are sessile and have no horny rims.

Loligo—squid

External structures. The squid (Figs. 18-25 and 18-26) has an elongated torpedo-shaped body with a large head, which bears two large eyes and a mouth surrounded by ten arms provided with suckers. One pair of arms, the retractile tentacles, are longer than the others. Along each side of the body is a fleshy triangular fin. The mantle encloses the mantle cavity in which are the internal organs. This mantle ends just behind the head in a free margin, the **collar.** Under the collar there projects a conical structure, the **siphon,** from which water can be forced by the contraction of the mantle. The shell, or **pen,** of *Loligo* is much reduced, consisting of a feather-shaped plate just beneath the skin of the back or anterior wall. It offers little protection but does stiffen the body. There is also cartilage support for the neck region, the siphon, and the fins.

Internal structures (Fig. 18-27). The **digestive system** is made up of the usual divisions: mouth, pharynx, esophagus, stomach, cecum, intestine, and anus, which opens into the mantle cavity. The pharynx has a pair of horny **jaws** and two pairs of salivary glands, and the stomach has the ducts of the **liver** and **pancreas** connected to it. A glandular **ink sac** opens into the mantle cavity near the anus. A **radula** is also present in the pharynx.

The circulatory system (Fig. 18-28) is closed, with

FIG. 18-25

School of young squids. As they course back and forth through aquarium, each individual carefully maintains his position and distance with reference to others. If this pattern is disturbed, squids quickly revert to their original position formation.

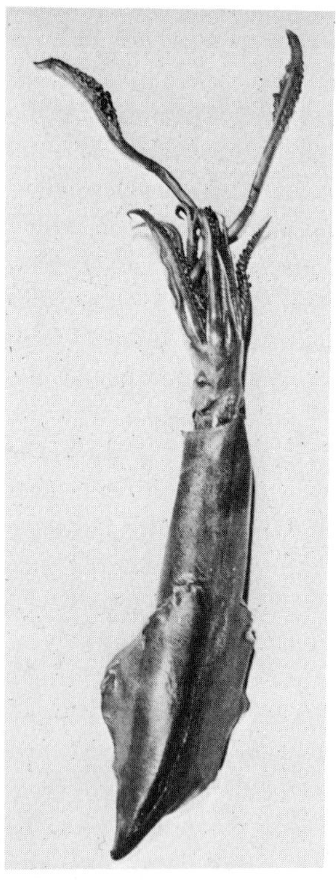

FIG. 18-26

Squid *Loligo*. (Preserved specimen.)

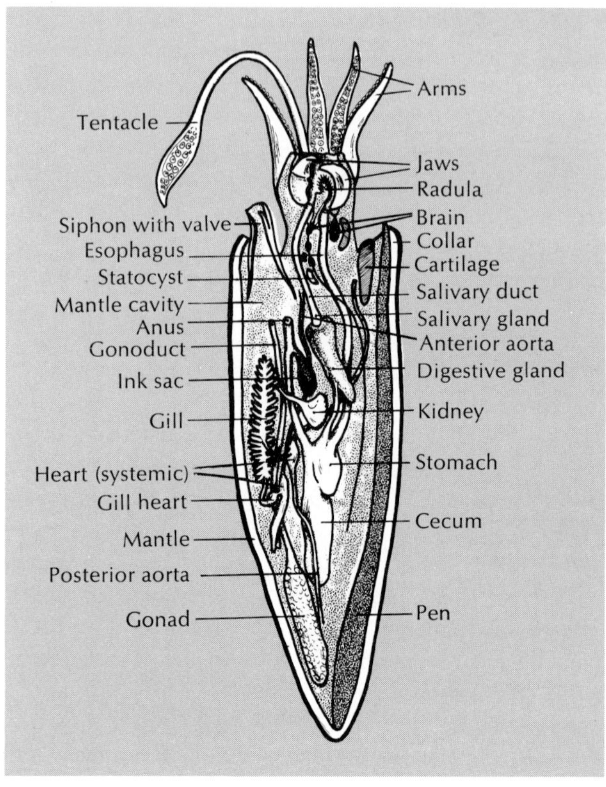

FIG. 18-27

Internal anatomy of squid *Loligo*. Side view, with left half of mantle removed (semidiagrammatic).

branchial, or gill, **hearts** for pumping blood through the gills and a **systemic heart,** which forces blood to the various other organs. A pair of **kidneys** connect the pericardial space with the mantle cavity. **Respiration** is carried on by a pair of **gills** in the lower part of the mantle chamber.

The **nervous system** contains many pairs of ganglia concentrated mainly in the head region. This region is protected by a cartilaginous case. The **sensory** organs are fairly well developed. There are two complex **eyes** (Fig. 18-29), which contain cornea, lens, chambers, and direct retina with rods. They can form real images, as do the eyes of vertebrates, but because they are derived in a different manner, they are not homologous. Other sense organs are a pair of **statocysts** below the brain for equilibration and a pair of **olfactory organs.**

The sexes are separate, and from the **gonad** in each sex a duct leads forward to empty into the mantle cavity near the anus. The male is provided with a

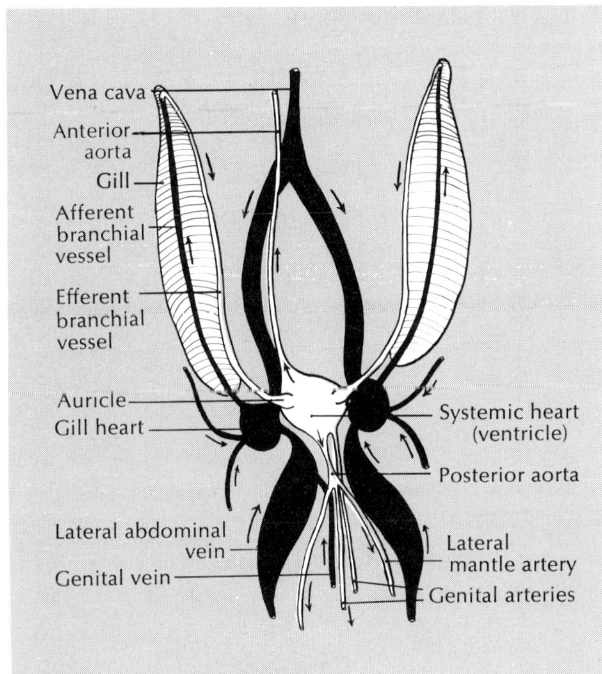

FIG. 18-28

Cephalopod gills with "booster hearts" and related circulatory system. Circulatory system of most cephalopods is mainly a closed system with endothelial-lined arteries, veins, and capillaries. Blood is pumped to gills by gill (branchial) hearts that are expanded portions of afferent branchial veins at base of gills. These hearts give a booster effect by ensuring efficient blood circulation through gills. As in most mollusks, kidneys are close to pericardium. Two thin-walled renal capsules enclose each division of afferent branchial vessel and terminal parts of lateral abdominal veins. Venous blood returning from body gives off waste to renal capsules before entering gills.

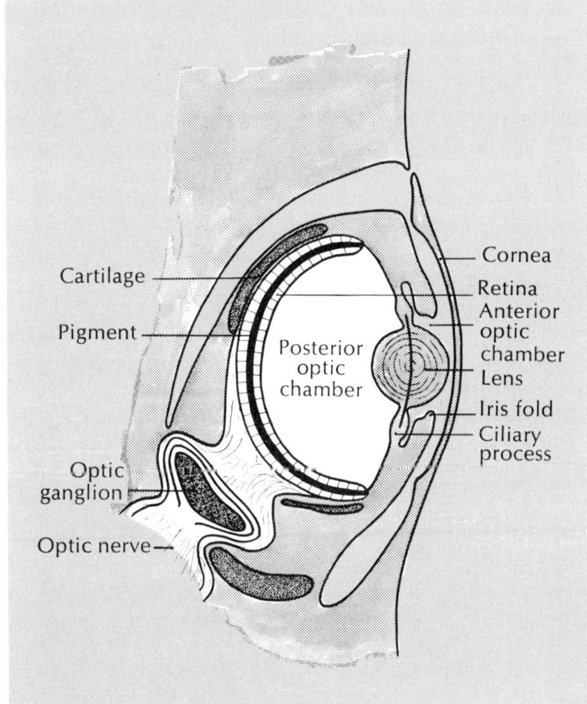

FIG. 18-29

Section through eye of cephalopod such as *Loligo*. Eye is similar to vertebrate eye, but sensitive rods of retina face toward light instead of away from it, as in vertebrate eye. Compare with simpler eye of *Nautilus*, Fig. 18-24.

hectocotylus arm (Fig. 18-23) for transferring sperm to the female.

Behavior. Squids have an interesting method of locomotion, which involves a type of "jet propulsion." When going backward, which they can do with great speed, they take water into the mantle cavity, the collar closes tightly around the neck, and the water is forcibly ejected in a jet from the siphon, which is directed toward the arms. In going forward, the siphon is directed backward. The two fins are used in steering and for swimming.

Squids also have two important devices for protecting themselves against their enemies. One of these is their remarkable power of changing color. Their skins contain many chromatophores with red, blue, purple, and yellow pigments. By contracting or expanding these, it is possible for the animals to assume rapidly many different shades of color, from the darker hues to those that are paler. The other method of protection involves the ink sac. The squid secretes the ink, which assumes the shape and size of a squid, as a decoy while the squid changes from a dark to a pale color and swims away in a different direction.

Squids live upon fish, mollusks, and crustaceans, which they capture with their arms and specialized tentacles. The prey is drawn by the arms to the mouth, where the horny jaws bite out pieces that are then swallowed. The jaws and radula are operated by the highly muscular pharynx.

Other members of class Cephalopoda

The squid *Loligo* is little more than 1 foot long, but the giant squid *Architeuthis* may be more than 50 feet long, the largest of all invertebrates. It is found off the

FIG. 18-30

Living octopus *Octopus*. Its eight arms bear powerful suckers for crawling over rocks and seizing prey (mostly crabs). (From film *Marine Life*, Encyclopaedia Britannica Films, Inc.)

coast of Newfoundland. Another squid, called the cuttlefish *(Sepia)*, produces sepia-colored ink, which is used by artists. The cuttlefish has a large pen or cuttlebone which is often given canaries as a source of calcium.

The octopus, or devilfish, has no shell but possesses a large body and eight sucker-bearing tentacles (Fig. 18-30). Some of these animals are only a few inches in diameter and are harmless, but the giant octopus of the Pacific may reach an overall diameter of 30 feet and is very dangerous to divers.

The chambered nautilus is found on the bottom of the South Pacific seas. Its spiral shell in one plane is up to 10 inches in diameter and is made up of a series of compartments, each of which has been occupied in succession as the animal has grown larger. Thus each new chamber is larger than the preceding one. The animal occupies the outermost compartment. The unoccupied compartments are filled with gas, probably secreted by the **siphuncle**, a body mass of blood vessels and tissues enclosed in a tube that runs through the center of the partitions. The heads of these forms bear sixty to ninety arms. The simple "pinhole camera" eye of the nautilus is shown in Fig. 18-24.

The paper nautilus *(Argonauta)* has a delicately coiled shell formed from glands in its tentacles. This shell is adapted for housing its eggs and for a nursery for the young after they hatch.

Derivation and meaning of basic terminology

Anodonta (Gr. *an*, without, + *odontos*, tooth). A common genus of freshwater clams.

Busycon (Gr. *bu*, huge, + *sykon*, fig). Giant whelk.

Chiton (Gr. coat of mail, tunic). Refers to plates that cover this primitive mollusk.

Dentalium (L. *dentalis*, tooth). Genus of Scaphopoda.

glochidium (Gr. *glochin*, point, + *idion*, dim.). Larva of a clam.

hectocotylus (Gr. *hekaton*, hundred, + *kotyle*, cup-shaped). Transformed, and sometimes autonomous, arm that serves as a male copulatory organ in cephalopods.

Helix (Gr. twisted). Genus of land snails introduced from Europe.

marsupium (L. pouch). A brood pouch.

nacre (F. mother-of-pearl). Innermost layer of mollusk shell.

Nautilus (Gr. *nautilos*, sailor). This sole survivor of the most ancient mollusks is an active swimmer.

Nudibranchia (L. *nudus*, naked, + Gr. *branchia*, gills). These gastropods have no shells.

Opisthobranchia (Gr. *opisthen*, behind, + *branchia*, gills). Gills are located posteriorly in these gastropods.

osphradium (Gr. *osphradion*, strong scent). A sense organ that tests incoming water.

periostracum (Gr. *peri*, around, + *ostrakon*, shell). Outer horny layer of mollusk shell.

Physa (Gr. bubble). Refers to bubble of air carried by snail when it submerges.

Polygyra (Gr. *poly*, many, + *gyros*, circle). Large genus of land snails.

Polyplacophora (Gr. *poly*, many, + *plakos*, flat, + *phorein*, to bear). An order of Amphineura with a shell of eight plates.

Prosobranchia (Gr. *proso*, front, + *branchia*, gills). Gastropods with gills located anteriorly.

Pulmonata (L. *pulmonis*, lung, + *ata*, group suffix).

radula (L. scraper). Rasping tongue of certain mollusks.

Solenogastres (Gr. *solen*, pipe, + *gaster*, belly). Synonym of Aplacophora.

Strombus (L. spiral snail). Giant conch.

umbo (L. boss of a shield). The part of a shell resembling a boss.

veliger (L. sail-bearing). Larval form of certain mollusks.

Annotated references

Baker, F. C. 1898-1902. The Mollusca of the Chicago area. Part I: The Pelecypoda. Part II: The Gastropoda. Chicago, The Chicago Academy of Science. *An authoritative work by a great specialist in this field. Excellent plates. Taxonomy somewhat outdated.*

Buchsbaum, R. M., and L. J. Milne. 1960. The lower animals: living invertebrates of the world. Garden City, N. Y., Doubleday & Co., Inc. *A work of superb photographs (many in color) and concise accounts of the many invertebrate phyla. This book will stimulate and inspire all students of zoology.*

Cambridge Natural History. 1895. Mollusca (A. H. Cooke). London, Macmillan & Co., Ltd. *A standard work on mollusks. Good general descriptions.*

Edmondson, W. T. (editor). 1959. Ward and Whipple's fresh-water biology, ed. 2. New York, John Wiley & Sons, Inc. *This is a revision of the well-known work of Ward and Whipple published many years ago. A taxonomic key to all the freshwater families of mollusks is found, together with illustrations of the principal members. The mollusks represent only one of the many fine features of this outstanding work of many specialists.*

Encyclopaedia Britannica. 1956. Art: Mollusca and the various classes. Chicago, Encyclopaedia Britannica, Inc. *Clear descriptions and some illustrations in color.*

Grave, B. H. 1928. Natural history of the shipworm, *Teredo navalis*, at Woods Hole, Mass. Biol. Bull. **55**: 260-282. *An excellent account of the habits of this destructive mollusk.*

Hyman, L. H. 1967. The invertebrates: Mollusca (vol. 6). New York, McGraw-Hill Book Co. *This volume covers four classes of the mollusks: Aplacophora, Polyplacophora, Monoplacophora, and Gastropoda. Hyman divides former class Amphineura into classes Aplacophora (solenogasters) and Polyplacophora (chitons). A second volume will describe the three remaining classes. The present treatise upholds the fine traditions of the other volumes in this outstanding series.*

Keen, A. M. 1963. Marine molluscan genera of Western North America. Stanford, Calif., Stanford University Press.

Lankester, E. R. (editor). 1906. A treatise on zoology. Part V.: Mollusca (P. Pelseneer). London, A. & C. Black. *This is the best monograph on the mollusks so far published. All students of the group make use of this fine work as a source of information.*

Lemche, H. 1957. A new living deep-sea mollusk of the Cambro-Devonian class Monoplacophora. Nature **179**: 413. *An interesting account of the recently discovered Neopilina. This small limpet-shaped mollusk is segmented and poses, therefore, the problem of annelid relationship. This segmentation, however, may be independently acquired, for there is no evidence that these new forms belong to the primitive ancestors of Mollusca.*

MacGinitie, G. E., and N. MacGinitie. 1967. Natural history of marine animals, ed. 2. New York, McGraw-Hill Book Co. *A section is devoted to a fine account of Mollusca with several excellent photographs of representative forms.*

Malek, E. A. 1962. Laboratory guide and notes for medical malacology. Minneapolis, Burgess Publishing Co. *A useful manual on those mollusks (mostly snails) that act as hosts for certain stages of parasites. Good illustrations of snail structure.*

Parker, T. J., and W. A. Haswell. 1940. A textbook of zoology, ed. 6, 2 vols. (revised by O. Lowenstein). London, Macmillan & Co., Ltd. *This standard text is very useful for a general survey of Mollusca.*

Pennak, R. W. 1953. Fresh-water invertebrates of the United States. New York, The Ronald Press Co. *A chapter each is devoted to the Gastropoda and the Pelecypoda. General descriptions of their structure, physiology, distribution, and ecology, as well as taxonomic keys given.*

Spector, W. S. (editor). 1956. Handbook of biological data, pp. 183-184. Philadelphia, W. B. Saunders Co.

Wells, M. J. 1962. Brain and behavior in cephalopods. Stanford, Calif., Stanford University Press. *A fascinating study of the behavior patterns in these highly developed invertebrates.*

Wilbur, K. M., and C. M. Yonge (editors). 1964, 1966. Physiology of Mollusca, vols. 1 and 2. New York, Academic Press Inc. *A pretentious monograph that summarizes much of the research work on this important group of invertebrates, including their classification, evolution, ecology, and physiology. Volume 2 deals with certain specific physiologic aspects with special emphasis on the cephalopods.*

CHAPTER 19

• PHYLUM ARTHROPODA* (MAJOR EUCOELOMATE BILATERAL GROUP)

Subphylum Chelicerata and minor groups

BIOLOGIC PRINCIPLES

Organ-system level of organization

1. Arthropods have some of the characteristic structure of higher forms—bilateral symmetry, triploblastic, coelomic cavity, and organ system.
2. They share with annelids the property of conspicuous segmentation, which is manifested especially in the body, muscles, and nervous elements.
3. The arthropod plan has emphasized a greater variety and grouping of somites for specialized purposes and has added on to the somites the jointed appendages, with pronounced division of labor, thus making for greater variety of action.
4. In arthropods, furthermore, the chitinous exoskeleton is an important feature, being modified into a great variety of specialized structures.
5. Arthropods by their locomotory mechanism and other adaptations were the first great group to make the transition from water to land, where they have undergone amazing adaptive radiation. The animal can now walk without dragging the body.
6. Arthropods belong to the protostome branch, or schizocoelous coelomates, of the animal kingdom and have spiral and determinate cleavage.

Biologic contributions

1. Although **chitin** is found in a few other forms below arthropods, its use is better developed in the arthropods.
2. **Cephalization** makes additional advancements, with centralization of fused ganglia and sensory organs in the head.
3. The presence of paired **jointed appendages** diversified for numerous uses makes for greater adaptability.
4. Locomotion is by extrinsic limb muscles, in contrast to the body musculature of annelids.
5. The **somites** have gone beyond the sameness of the annelid type and are now **specialized** for a variety of purposes, forming functional groups of somites (tagmosis).
6. The gills, and especially the **tracheae**, represent an efficient breathing mechanism.
7. **Striated muscles** are emphasized, thus ensuring rapidity of movement.
8. The alimentary canal shows greater specialization by chitinous teeth, compartments, and gastric ossicles.
9. Behavior patterns have advanced far beyond those of most invertebrates, with the development of primitive intelligence and **social instincts** in some of the groups.
10. **Metamorphosis** is common in development.

Position in animal kingdom

1. The evidence indicates that arthropods are more closely related to annelids than to any other group.
2. Although they cannot be said to come directly from annelids, they probably came from the same ancestors as did segmented worms such as polychaetes.
3. Phylum Onychophora, with both annelid and arthropod characters, represents a connecting link. This form can be considered as a descendant from a line close to the primitive ancestor of annelids and arthropods. *Aysheaia,* a fossil form of the middle Cambrian period, shares many common characteristics with *Peripatus.*
4. Arthropods have been guided mainly in their evolutionary diversity of adaptive radiation by the modifications and specializations of their exoskeleton and jointed appendages.

GENERAL RELATIONS

Phylum Arthropoda is the most extensive group of animals in the animal kingdom, containing more than three fourths of all known forms. The total number of species recorded to date is between 700,000 and 800,000, and probably as many more remain to be classified. Among the living forms the phylum includes crustaceans, spiders, ticks, millipedes, centipedes, and insects. In addition, many fossil forms belong to the arthropods, for this phylum goes back to Precambrian times in geologic history.

*Ar-throp′o-da (Gr. *arthron,* joint, + *podos,* foot).

Arthropoda (Gr. *arthros,* joint, + *podos,* foot) means joint footed. Arthropods are characterized by having a **chitinous exoskeleton** and a **linear series of somites,** each with a pair of **jointed appendages.** Body organs and systems are usually well developed, for they represent, on the whole, a very active and energetic type of life. They share with the nematodes an almost complete absence of **cilia.**

Arthropods live in a greater variety of habitats than do the members of any other phylum. They are adapted for life in and on land, in water, and in air. They are found on the highest mountains (spiders were found on Mount Everest at 22,000 feet) and at great depths in the sea. They are often found in places where no other forms could survive. The brine shrimp *(Artemia salina)* and the brine flies *(Ephydra)* of Great Salt Lake are about the only living animals in the highly concentrated salt water of that lake. Some arthropods are parasitic on plants and animals, although parasitism is not dominant in this group. In no other group of invertebrates has social organization been carried as far. The gregarious termites, ants, and bees have worked out marvelous systems of division of labor of great ingenuity and complexity.

Arthropods are man's greatest competitors, contending for food supplies and spreading serious diseases. No sooner do we suppress a destructive insect than another springs up to do mischief. However, not all arthropods are harmful; some, such as lobsters, shrimp, and crabs, serve as food, silkworms furnish clothing, insects are necessary for cross-pollination of plants, bees furnish honey and beeswax, and other insects yield useful drugs and dyes.

The arthropods have the pattern of organization characteristic of higher invertebrates. They have the organ-system level of organization, bilateral symmetry, coelomic cavity, centralized nervous system, separate sexes, and paired reproductive organs and ducts. In some respects they are more specialized than lower forms, for they have a chitinous exoskeleton, a variety of modified appendages, metamorphosis of development, and high metabolism. Distinct advancements over most invertebrates are greater cephalization, better sense organs, greater specialization and modifications of somites, more efficient breathing (gills and tracheae), higher development of social organization and instinct, and better development of protective coloration and protective resemblance.

Since there are so many common points between the organization of segmented worms and arthropods, zoologists nearly all agree that they must have evolved from the same ancestors. Both have striking metamerism, but arthropods show advancement in the reduced number of somites and in their differentiation and grouping. The striking similarity between the parapodia of the polychaete annelids and the limbs of the living Branchiopoda (Crustacea) and of the fossil Trilobita is often cited as evidence of close affinity between the two phyla. Phylum Onychophora, with characteristics of both arthropods and annelids, appears to be closest to the ancestral form. The generalized structure of Branchiopoda places it close to the bottom of the arthropod series. The relationship of the various arthropod classes seems to indicate that the groups Onychophora, Crustacea, Myriapoda, and Insecta have evolved along one line and the radically different Arachnida and related forms along another. The Insecta appear to have been derived from primitive Precambrian annelids and are more closely related to centipedes, millipedes, and especially the symphylids than to other arthropods.

WHY HAVE ARTHROPODA BEEN SO SUCCESSFUL?

Some of the criteria for the success of an animal group are number and variety of species, variety of habitats, widespread distribution, ability to defend themselves, variety of food habits, and power to adapt themselves to changing conditions. The fact that arthropods are so common and so diversified indicates that they have met most of these requirements. Some structural and physiologic patterns that have been helpful to them stand out in bold relief. We may briefly summarize some of these.

Chitin. Chitin is nonliving and noncellular and is secreted by the underlying epidermis. It is a protein-carbohydrate compound and is composed of several different substances. It is made up of an outer waxy layer, a middle horny layer, and an inner flexible layer. These layers are modified among the various arthropods and also among the different parts of the body. In some the chitin is soft and permeable; in others it forms a veritable coat of armor. Between joints and between segments it is flexible and thin to permit free movements. It is harder in crustaceans, in which it is infiltrated with calcium salts. In general its structure is admirably adapted for protection of delicate internal organs, attachment of muscles, serving as levers and centers of movement, preventing the entrance and loss of water, and (because of its arrangement) affording the maximum amount of protection without sacrificing mobility.

Although hard protective structures are common among other groups of animals, none have used them so effectively as have the arthropods. Chitin in arthropods is used for biting jaws, for grinders in the stomach, for lenses of the eye, for sound production, for sensory organs, for copulatory organs, for organs of defense, and for ornamental purposes; some arthropods even have a chitinous lining in the digestive tract.

A chitinous exoskeleton limits the size of the animal, which, in order to grow, must shed its outer shell at intervals and must grow a larger one—a process called **ecdysis**, or molting. While waiting for the new shell to harden, the animal is vulnerable to enemies. Arthropods must undergo from four to seven moltings before reaching adult size. This chitinous exoskeleton limits the size and weight of the members, for aside from a few crabs and lobsters with long slender legs, few arthropods exceed 2 feet in length and most are far below this limit. The largest is the Japanese crab *(Macrocheira)*, which has about an 11-foot span; the smallest is the parasitic mite *(Demodex)*, which is less than 0.1 mm. long.

The presence of chitin helps arthropods adapt themselves to a wide variety of land habitats, including deserts and dry places that would mean fatal desiccation to forms not provided with such a cuticle. Chitin in arthropods probably reaches a climax in quantitative importance, although its synthesis is a primitive property of the animal cell. It has been found in all Protostomia, with the exception of Platyhelminthes, Rhynchocoela, and Sipunculida. It is present in many different anatomic structures, such as eggshells, chaetae, membranes, and hooks, as well as in the integument. In some cases it may exist as free chitin, but mostly it is glycoprotein in nature. It appears to be entirely absent in the Deuterostomia.

Segmentation and appendages. Arthropods share with annelids and vertebrates the characteristic of having the body divided into similar segments. Each somite typically is provided with a pair of jointed appendages, but this arrangement is often modified, with both segments and the appendages specialized for adaptable functions. This has made for great efficiency and wider capacity for adjustment to different habitats.

Respiratory devices. Aquatic arthropods breathe mainly by some form of gill that is quite efficient; most land arthropods have the unique and highly efficient **tracheal system** of air tubes that delivers the oxygen directly to the tissue cells. This makes possible the high metabolism so characteristic of active insects.

Sensory organs. No other group of invertebrate animals has the diversity of specialized and delicate organs that arthropods have. These are found in great variety, from the mosaic eye to those simpler senses that have to do with touch, smell, hearing, balancing, chemical reception, etc. They are keenly alert to what goes on in their environment.

Locomotion. Their jointed appendages have been modified and adapted into swift and efficient locomotor organs, such as walking legs, swimming appendages, and wings.

Reproduction and metamorphosis. They lay large numbers of eggs, and many of them pass through metamorphic changes in reaching maturity—the larva, pupa, and adult stages. Some have a series of nymphal stages preceding the adult stage. This results in less competition within a species, for the larval form is often adapted for eating a kind of food different from that of the adult. The caterpillar, for instance, lives on vegetation, whereas the adult butterfly sucks the nectar of flowers.

Behavior patterns. Arthropods exceed most other invertebrates in the complexity and organization of their activities. Most of their behavior patterns fall under the so-called instinctive action, which is supposed to reach its peak in arthropods. Whether or not learning is involved to any great extent in their reactions to environmental stimuli is open to question (Chapter 43), but no one can deny the complex adaptability of the group. As an example of arthropod adaptability, the time-measuring mechanism of fiddler crabs has been investigated by Brown and associates in recent years. This work showed how these crustaceans, with great precision, regulated their rhythmic color patterns of dark by day and light by night by means of an internal time clock that may work independently of external influences, can be set for different cycles, and is definitely inherited.

CHARACTERISTICS

1. Symmetry bilateral; triploblastic; body metameric

2. **Appendages jointed,** with one or two pairs to a somite and often modified for specialized functions
3. **Exoskeleton of chitin** secreted by the underlying epidermis and shed at intervals
4. Body often divided into **three regions:** the **head,** usually of six somites, the **thorax,** and the **abdomen,** the latter two divisions having a variable number of somites; head and thorax often united into a cephalothorax
5. Muscles mostly **striated** and rapid in action; unstriated muscle in visceral organs
6. True coelom small in adult; most of body cavity a **hemocoel filled with blood**
7. Digestive system complete with mouth, enteron, and anus; **mouth parts modified from somites and adapted for different methods of feeding**
8. Circulatory system open, with dorsal heart, arteries, and mesenchymal blood cavities (sinuses)
9. **Cilia practically absent throughout group**
10. Respiration by body surface, gills, **air tubes (tracheae),** or **book lungs**
11. Excretory system by green glands or by a variable number of **malpighian tubules** opening into the digestive system
12. Nervous system of dorsal brain connected by a ring around the gullet to a double nerve chain of ventral ganglia
13. Sensory organs well developed and include eyes, antennae (tactile and chemical), balancing organs, auditory organs, and sensory bristles
14. Sexes nearly always separate, with paired reproductive organs and ducts; fertilization internal; oviparous or ovoviviparous; metamorphosis direct or indirect; parthenogenesis in a few forms

CLASSIFICATION

Arthropoda is such an extensive phylum, with so many different groups, that authorities have subdivided it in various ways. A strict phylogenetic grouping is impossible with the knowledge available at present. Some zoologists merely assign class rank to all the definite groups, but the arrangement given here recognizes higher taxonomic divisions on the basis of common morphologic characteristics and phylogenetic relationships.

Subphylum Trilobita (tri'lo-bi"ta) (Gr. *tria,* three, + *lobos,* lobe). All fossil forms; Cambrian to Carboniferous; body divided by two longitudinal furrows into three lobes; head, thorax, abdomen distinct; somites except last with biramous appendages. Example: *Triarthrus.*

Subphylum Chelicerata (ke-lis'e-ra"ta) (Gr. *chele,* claw, + *keros,* horn, + *ata,* group suffix). First pair of appendages modified to form chelicerae with claws; pair of pedipalps and four pairs of legs; no antennae; cephalothorax and abdomen usually unsegmented.

Class Merostomata (mer'o-sto"ma-ta) (Gr. *meros,* thigh, + *stoma,* mouth, + *ata,* group suffix). Cepalothorax; compound lateral eyes; appendages with gills; sharp telson.

Subclass Eurypterida (u'rip-ter"i-da) (Gr. *eurys,* broad, + *pterys,* wing or fin, + *ida,* pl. suffix). Extinct; largest of fossil arthropods, some to 6 feet; exoskeleton of chitin with cephalothorax (prosoma) completely covered by dorsal carapace; abdomen (opisthosoma) with twelve segments and postanal telson; six pairs of appendages, first pair of which are chelicerae; ventral mouth; pair of simple ocelli and pair of compound eyes; separate sexes. Example: *Eurypterus.*

Subclass Xiphosurida (zif'o-su"ri-da) (Gr. *xiphos,* sword, + *oura,* tail). Body composed of cephalothorax in form of convex, horseshoe-shaped carapace; abdomen unsegmented and terminated by long spine; three-jointed chelicerae and six-jointed walking legs; pair of simple eyes and pair of compound eyes; book gills; paired genital openings. Example: *Xiphosura (Limulus)* (king crab).

Class Pycnogonida (pik'no-gon"i-da) (Gr. *pyknos,* compact, + *gonos,* gonad) (**Pantopoda**). Size usually small (3 to 4 mm.), but some reach 500 mm.; body chiefly cephalothorax; abdomen tiny; usually eight pairs of long walking legs, but some with ten to twelve pairs; pair of subsidiary legs (ovigers) for egg bearing; mouth on long proboscis; four simple eyes; no respiratory or excretory system. Example: *Pycnogonum* (sea spider).

Class Arachnida (ar-ack'ni-da) (Gr. *arachne,* spider). Body with anterior somites fused into a cephalothorax with two chelicerae with claws, two pedipalpi, and four pairs of legs; no antennae or true jaws; abdomen segmented or unsegmented with or without appendages and generally distinct from cephalothorax; respiration by gills, tracheae, or book lungs; excretion by malpighian tubules or coxal glands; dorsal bilobed brain connected to ventral ganglionic mass with nerves; simple eyes; sexes separate; chiefly oviparous; no true metamorphosis. Examples: scorpions, spiders, mites, ticks, harvestmen.

Subphylum Mandibulata (man-dib'u-la"ta) (L. *mandibula,* mandible, + *ata,* group suffix). One or two pairs of antennae form first two pairs of appendages, and functional jaws (mandibles) form third pair of cephalic appendages.

Class Crustacea (crus-ta'she-a) (L. *crusta,* shell, + *ea,* characterized by). Aquatic with gills; body with dorsal carapace: telson at posterior end; hard exoskeleton of chitin reinforced with limy salts; appendages biramous and modified for capturing food, walking, swimming, respiration, and reproduction; coelom reduced and hemocoel present; head of five segments with two pairs of antennae, a pair of jaws, and two pairs of maxillae; sexes usually separate; development with nauplius stage; paired sex openings. Examples: *Homarus, Cambarus, Asellus, Eubranchipus, Cyclops, Daphnia.*

Class Diplopoda (di-plop'o-da) (Gr. *diploos,* double, + *podos,* foot). Body subcylindric; head with short antennae and simple eyes; body with variable number of somites; short legs, usually two pairs to a somite; maxillae and jaws; separate sexes; oviparous; malpighian tubules for excretion; dorsal brain with double ventral nerve cord. Examples: *Julus, Spirobolus* (millipedes).

Class Chilopoda (ki-lop'o-da) (Gr. *cheilos,* lip, + *podos,* foot). Form elongated and dorsoventrally flattened; pair of jointed maxillae and jaws with variable number of somites, each with a pair of legs; malpighian tubules for excretion; respiration with tracheae; separate sexes; oviparous; dorsal brain and double ventral nerve cord; pair of long antennae. Examples: *Cermatia, Lithobius, Geophilus* (centipedes).

Class Pauropoda (pau-rop'o-da) (Gr. *pauros,* small, + *podos,* foot). Minute (1 to 1.5 mm.); cylindric body of double segments and bearing nine or ten pairs of legs; no eyes; genital openings near head end. Example: *Pauropus.*

Class Symphyla (sym'fy-la) (Gr. *syn,* together, + *phylon,* tribe). Slender (1 to 8 mm.) with long, filiform antennae; body of fifteen to twenty-two segments with ten to twelve pairs of legs; no eyes; genital openings near head end. Example: *Scutigerella* (garden centipede).

Class Insecta (in-sec'ta) (L. *insectus,* cut into). Body with head, thorax, and abdomen distinct and usually marked constriction between thorax and abdomen; pair of antennae; mouth parts modified for different food habits; head with six somites; thorax with three somites, and abdomen with variable number, usually eleven somites; thorax with two pairs of wings (sometimes one pair or none) and three pairs of jointed legs; respiration by branched tracheae; brain of fused ganglia and double ventral nerve cord; eyes both simple and compound; separate sexes; usually oviparous; metamorphosis gradual or abrupt. Examples: various orders to be described in Chapter 21.

ECONOMIC IMPORTANCE

A group as common and widely distributed as the arthropods must necessarily have great economic importance. Their relations to other members in the animal kingdom are both harmful and beneficial. We may group the economic importance under three headings—arthropods as food, beneficial arthropods, and harmful arthropods.

Arthropods as food. Lobsters, crabs, shrimp, and in some localities crayfish are widely used as food all over the world. Honey from bees has been a delicacy since primitive times. Plankton, made up of small organisms found at the surface of waters, contains large numbers of crustaceans and is an important source of food for fish. Insects furnish many birds and animals with food.

Beneficial arthropods. Insect predators that live upon other insects aid in checking the ravages of the harmful ones. Cross-pollination, so essential to fruit growing, is effected by insects. Arthropod products include shellac produced by certain scale insects, cochineal (a histologic dye) obtained from another type of tropical scale insect, silk spun by the larvae of silkworm moths, beeswax from bees, and a drug from the Spanish fly.

Harmful arthropods. Harmful arthropods are numerous. Only a few of these will be pointed out here. Insects rank first, destroying millions of dollars worth of food each year. Insects as well as other arthropods carry devastating diseases. The most widespread is malaria, carried by the mosquito. Other arthropods important in restricted regions are the copepods, which carry larval stages of the guinea worm and fish tapeworm; mites and ticks, which carry diseases and cause irritation and debility by living as ectoparasites; and spiders and scorpions, which do harm by poison bites. Barnacles foul the bottom of ships, and crayfish, through their burrowing habits, do much harm to levees and also to crops in lowlands. Crustaceans such as sow bugs do much harm in greenhouses.

COMPARISON OF ARTHROPODA WITH ANNELIDA

Similarities between Arthropoda and Annelida are as follows:

1. External segmentation
2. Segmental arrangement of muscles
3. Metamerically arranged nervous system with dorsal cerebral ganglia

The most striking differences between the two phyla are that arthropods have the following:

1. Fixed number of segments
2. Usually a lack of intersegmental septa
3. Open (lacunar) circulatory system
4. Body segments usually grouped into three regions—head, thorax, and abdomen
5. Coelomic cavity reduced
6. Special mechanisms (gills, tracheae, book lungs) for respiration

7. Chitin for exoskeleton
8. Jointed appendages
9. Compound eye and other well-developed sense organs
10. Absence of cilia
11. Metamorphosis in many cases

REPRESENTATIVE TYPES

SUBPHYLUM TRILOBITA

Trilobites flourished during the Cambrian period and became extinct by the Permian period (200 million years ago). Their great variety and complexity (more than 10,000 species) indicate that their beginning was millions of years before the Cambrian period. They are more primitive than true crustaceans and probably descended from a Precambrian ancestor that also gave rise to all the arthropods. As marine forms their fossils were laid down when seas covered what is now land. Since they are so abundant, they are useful to geologists in the indexing of rock layers.

Their body was covered by a hard chitinous-calcareous shell, which was divided into three longitudinal lobes by two dorsal furrows (Fig. 19-1). They had three transverse lobes: head, thorax, and pygidium (a posterior platelike part). The head was one piece but showed signs of former segmentation; the thorax had a variable number of somites; and the pygidium also had a variable number of somites fused together in a plate. Most of them could roll up like a pill bug. They were from 2 to 27 inches long. The head contained a pair of jointed antennae, usually a pair of large compound eyes (sometimes on stalks), and four pairs of biramous (two-branched), jointed appendages on the ventral side. On the ventral side of the thorax and pygidium each somite (except the last, or telson) bore a pair of two-branched, jointed appendages with a fringe of filaments probably serving as gills. They lived on other invertebrates and some were scavengers. Fossilized trilobite eggs have been found.

FIG. 19-1

Trilobite (dorsal view) from plaster cast impression. All members of this class are now extinct. Some of the abundant fossils of this group may be the remains of molted exoskeletons.

SUBPHYLUM CHELICERATA

The chelicerate arthropods are characterized by a lack of mandibles and antennae and the presence of six pairs of appendages, which include one pair of pedipalps, one pair of chelicerae, and four pairs of legs. They suck up liquid food from their prey. The group is a very ancient one and includes the eurypterids (extinct), horseshoe crabs, spiders, ticks, and some others.

CLASS MEROSTOMATA

SUBCLASS EURYPTERIDA

The members of extinct subclass Eurypterida were the largest of all fossil arthropods, some of them reaching a length of 9 feet. They have been found in rocks from the Ordovician to the Carboniferous periods. Eurypterids resembled king crabs. The prosoma (head) had six fused segments and bore two simple and two compound eyes. Six pairs of appendages were found beneath the prosoma. The body of eurypterids was encased in a chitinous covering. The twelve segments of the abdomen (opisthosoma) were divided into the mesosoma (anterior six segments) and the metasoma (last six segments plus the spikelike telson). They also had many structural features in common with existing scorpions, which may be considered their land representatives, for both have the same number of segments in the three regions of the body and the same arrangement of appendages in the prosoma. However, the last pair of legs in eurypterids were much more developed than they are in scorpions. There are conflicting theories regarding their early habitats. Some maintain that eurypterids evolved mainly in fresh water along with ostracoderms; others hold that they arose in brackish lagoons.

SUBCLASS XIPHOSURIDA

Xiphosura polyphemus—king, or horseshoe, crab

Subclass Xiphosurida is often referred to as a "living fossil," for it represents a very ancient group of animals (Fig. 19-2). Although the genus *Xiphosura* goes back only to the Triassic period, other xiphosurans can be traced back to the Cambrian period. There are five living species divided among three genera as follows: *Xiphosura* along the Atlantic coast of North America, *Carcinoscorpius* along the southern shore of Japan, and *Tachypleus* in the East Indies and along the coast of southern Asia.

FIG. 19-2

Ventral view of horseshoe crab *Xiphosura* (class Merostomata). They grow up to 15 to 18 inches long.

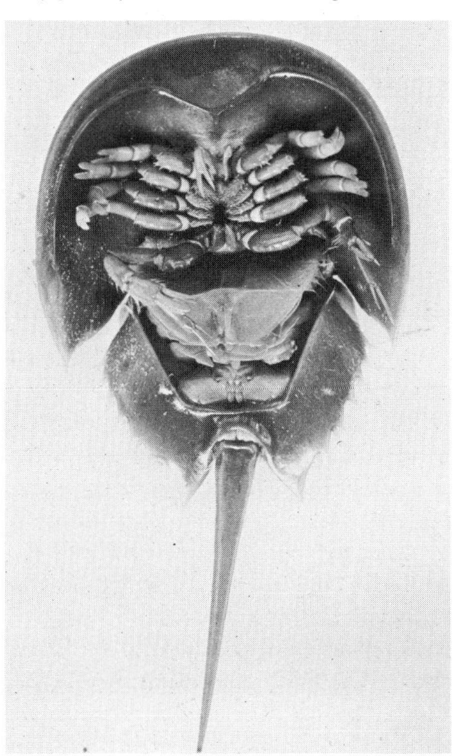

Xiphosurans live in shallow water and are often left stranded at low tide. They are characterized by an unsegmented, horseshoe-shaped carapace (hard dorsal shield) and a broad hexagonal abdomen, which has a long telson, or tailpiece. The cephalothorax bears on the ventral side five pairs of walking legs and a pair of chelicerae, whereas the abdomen has six pairs of broad thin appendages that are fused in the median line. On some of the abdominal appendages, book gills (leaflike gills) are exposed. There are two compound and two simple eyes on the carapace. The horseshoe crab swims by means of its abdominal plates and can walk with its walking legs. It feeds at night on worms and small mollusks, which it seizes with its chelicerae. Fertilization is external, and the larvae are segmented like the trilobites. The latter are often considered the ancestors of the king crabs.

Xiphosurans were formerly classified with the Arachnida, but the former differ in having a venous system, aquatic book gills, paired genital openings, a "trilobite larval stage," a pair of compound eyes, a heart that is blind behind, and other distinctions.

CLASS PYCNOGONIDA (PANTOPODA)

A common name for the odd animals of class Pycnogonida is **sea spiders.** Some are only a few millimeters long, but others are much larger. They have small bodies and usually four pairs of legs, but twelve-legged forms are known. Some species are provided with chelicerae and palps. One unique feature is the subsidiary pair of egg-bearing legs (ovigers) in the males (and a few females). Their body consists principally of a cephalothorax, for the abdomen is rudimentary. The mouth is located at the tip of a suctorial proboscis that may be longer than the body. Most of them have four simple eyes. They have a heart but no blood vessels. Excretory and respiratory systems are absent. The males carry the developing eggs on their ovigers. Because of the small size of the body, the digestive system sends branches into the legs, and most of the gonads are also found there. Sea spiders are exclusively marine and are found in all oceans from the littoral zone to depths of 2,000 fathoms, but they are most abundant in polar waters. They feed on coelenterates and soft-bodied animals, from which they suck out the juices by means of their long proboscis. The group is probably more closely related to the Crustacea than to any other arthropods, although they do not have a nauplius larva. *Pycnogonum* is a common intertidal genus found on both the Atlantic and Pacific coasts.

CLASS ARACHNIDA

Class Arachnida is considered an isolated group of Arthropoda. It is not as closely knit a group as the insects, for it has considerable variety of bodily organization. The name comes from the Greek word *arachne*, spider. Besides spiders, the group includes scorpions, ticks, mites, harvestmen, and others. There are many differences among these with respect to form and appendages. Their most distinguishing characteristics are the fusion of the head and thorax into a cephalothorax, the presence of four pairs of walking legs instead of three pairs as in insects, and the lack of antennae and mandibles. Most of them are free living and are far more common in warm, dry regions than elsewhere. They are provided, as a rule, with claws, poison glands, fangs, and stingers. Most are highly predaceous and suck the fluids and soft tissues from the bodies of their prey. Some have interesting adaptations, such as the spinning glands of the spiders.

Economic importance

Most arachnids are harmless and actually do much good by destroying injurious insects. A few, such as the black widow spider, can harm man by their bites. The sting of the scorpion may be quite painful. Some ticks and mites are vectors of diseases as well as causes of annoyance and painful irritations. Certain mites damage plants by sucking their juices or by damaging valuable fruits.

Phylogenetic relations

Arachnids represent a very old group of invertebrates. It is thought that arthropods split into two main branches probably as early as the Cambrian period. One of these branches became arachnids and the other developed into the other classes of arthropods. Some of the earliest arachnids were the large Paleozoic eurypterids. It is generally agreed that spiders are closely related to scorpions, but the stem ancestor of spiders is unknown. Some fossil spiders have a segmented cephalothorax—a primitive condition. There are authorities who think spiders have come from some scorpion stock and by pedogenesis have developed and stressed their web-weaving habits. Their web-making may have originated from their habit of making silky cocoons.

Although the earliest arachnids were aquatic, the great majority of the present-day ones are terrestrial.

Characteristics

1. Body of unsegmented cephalothorax and abdomen usually
2. Antennae and mandibles lacking
3. Six pairs of appendages usually, of which two pairs are the chelicerae and pedipalps and the others are walking legs
4. Sucking mouth parts mainly
5. Poison glands in some
6. Respiration by book gills or by book lungs or tracheae
7. Excretion by malpighian tubules and coxal glands
8. Circulatory system typically of heart, arteries, veins, sinuses
9. Nervous system of arthropod plan, or more concentrated anteriorly
10. Eyes simple usually
11. Separate sexes
12. Development direct

Miranda (Argiope) aurantia—garden spider (order Araneae)

The spiders are a very large group of more than 35,000 species distributed all over the world. They are found in most kinds of habitats, in forests, on mountains, in deserts, on plains, in swamps, etc. All are predaceous, but they have different ways of catching their prey. Some chase and others simply ambush their food, but most of them spin a net in which to trap the forms they live upon. Many of them have poison glands in connection with their fangs, but although this poison is effective in overcoming small invertebrates, very few have poison bites that are dangerous to man. They are mostly nocturnal in their habits. Outside of a relatively few species, they lie more or less concealed during the day. The large garden spider *Miranda aurantia* is often studied in the laboratory.

External structure. The body is compact and consists of a distinct **cephalothorax** and **abdomen**, both divisions without segmentation, joined by a slender **peduncle.**

Eight simple eyes are on the dorsal side of the cephalothorax, and six pairs of appendages are on its ventral side. The first pair of appendages is the **chelicerae,** which have basal segments and terminal fangs (claws). Each fang may be provided with a duct that leads to a poison gland. The **pedipalps** (second pair of appendages) have basal parts (maxillae) with which they chew and squeeze their food; they also have sensory functions and are used by the males to transfer their sperm. The four pairs of **walking legs** each have seven joints and terminate in two or three claws. In addition, some spiders have hairy pads between their claws for holding onto steep surfaces. In spiders, scorpions, and other arachnoids flexor muscles are used to flex the limbs at hinge joints, as in other arthropods, but they extend the limbs by the fluid pressure within the limb on the principle of a hydraulic system. There are no extensor muscles, which other arthropods have. This pressure of fluid may originate within the body of the spider.

The openings found in the spider are the **mouth** between the maxillae; the opening on either side to the **book lungs;** the **genital opening** on the ventral surface, covered by the epigynum plate; a single **spiracle** just anterior to the anus and connected to the tracheal system; two or three pairs of **spinnerets** posterior to the spiracle, used for spinning threads; and the **anus.**

Internal structure (Fig. 19-3). The **digestive system** is made up of the mouth, slender esophagus, stomach provided with strong muscles for sucking, digestive stomach with five pairs of ceca, long intestine with two enlargements (one where the ducts of the digestive gland join it and the other at the stercoral pocket), and anus. The digestive gland, or liver, is large and surrounds a great part of the intestine. It secretes a fluid that is emptied into the intestine. The stercoral pocket may store feces.

The **circulatory system** is made up of a dorsal heart, arteries, veins, and sinuses. The heart is located in a pericardial space and has three pairs of ostia. There are an anterior aorta, with branches that run to the stomach, legs, eyes, and other organs, and a caudal aorta that runs to the posterior region of the body. The blood is colorless, with ameboid corpuscles. In its course it is carried to the book lungs, where it is aerated.

Respiration is carried on by both book lungs and tracheae. The latter, however, play a minor part. The book lungs are peculiar to the arachnids, and they are usually paired. Each consists of many parallel invaginated air pockets from a posterior chamber into a blood-filled anterior chamber. Air enters the posterior chamber by a slit in the body wall. Because these air pockets are flattened and leaflike, the whole structure is called a **book lung.** The blood carries the oxygen, for such tracheae as are present do not go everywhere as they do in insects.

The **excretory system** consists of the malpighian tubules, which empty into the intestine, and a pair of **coxal glands** in the cephalothorax, which discharge through ducts between the legs.

The **nervous system** is that of the arthropod plan,

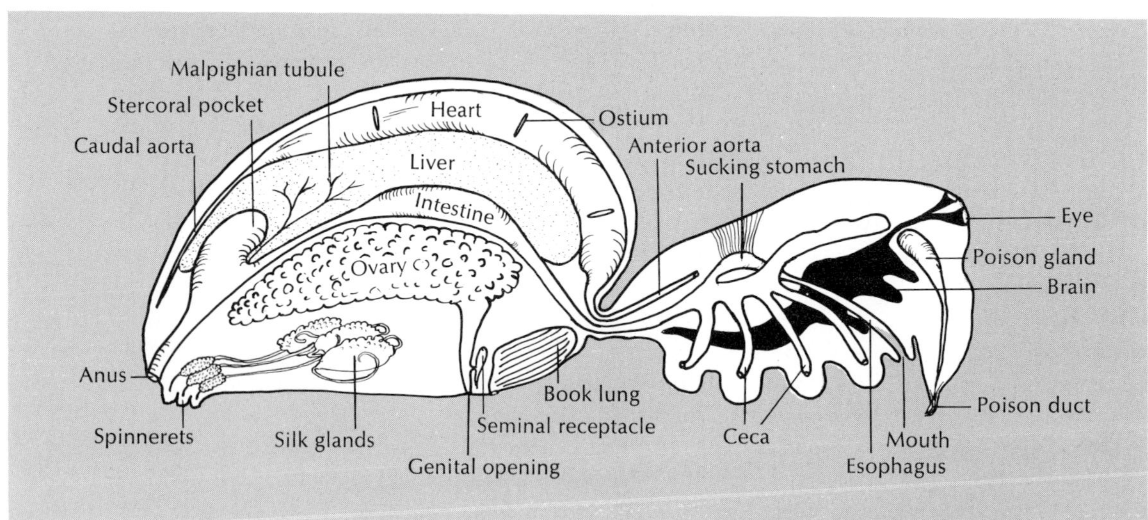

FIG. 19-3

Internal structures of female spider (diagrammatic).

although a little more concentrated than some. It comprises a dorsal brain, a subpharyngeal ganglionic mass of many fused ganglia from which nerves run to the various organs. This type of system will be described more fully in the crayfish later. The **sense organs** are centered mainly in the sensory hairs, and there are usually eight **simple eyes.** The eyes are chiefly for the perception of moving objects, but some may form distinct images. Each eye is provided with a lens, optic rods, and a retina. Just what senses spiders have is not known completely, but they are sensitive to touch and smell and probably to some other stimuli.

The **sexes** are separate, and the reproductive organs of each sex are located in the ventral part of the abdomen. The **male** organs are the paired testes below the intestine, the coiled vasa deferentia, and a single seminal vesicle, which leads to the genital opening. The paired ovaries of the **female** system are hollow, each being connected to an oviduct, which opens into the common vagina. Two seminal receptacles are joined to the vagina. In the transfer of sperm the male spins a small web, deposits his sperm on it, and stores the whole in the cavities of the pedipalps. When he mates, he inserts his pedipalps into the female genital opening, and the sperm are stored in her seminal receptacles. Sometimes the male then serves as a meal for the much larger female. Before the mating act, spiders (usually the male) perform various courtship rituals, such as waving the appendages, assuming peculiar attitudes, touching the tip of the female's legs, and even offering her insect prey.

When the eggs are laid, they are fertilized by the sperm as they pass through the vagina. The eggs are usually laid in a silk cocoon; this may be carried around by the female, or it may be attached to a web or plant. A single cocoon may contain hundreds of eggs. About two weeks are necessary for hatching, but the young remain in the sac for a few weeks longer and molt once before leaving the sac. Several molts are necessary before they become mature.

Web-spinning habits of spiders. No aspect of spider life is more interesting than the spinning of webs. Not all spiders spin webs, for some, such as the huntsman spider (*Lycosa*), simply chase and catch their prey, although they may spin an anchor thread so that they can return to a certain spot (Fig. 19-4). The majority of spiders, however, spin some kind of web in which to ensnare and wrap up their food. Here, entrapped forms are killed by the poison fangs. The spider punctures the body of its prey with its fangs, then alternately injects digestive fluid through the puncture and sucks up the dissolved tissues until the prey has been sucked dry. Tarantulas, wolf spiders, and others may crush the prey with very strong jaws to facilitate the digestive process. Usually only small invertebrate forms are caught in these webs, but instances are known where mice have actually been caught. *Dolomedes,* a species common east of the Rocky Mountains, is known to kill and eat small fish.

The spinning organs of spiders consist of two or three pairs of **spinnerets,** fingerlike appendages containing many hundreds of microscopic tubes that run to special abdominal glands. A protein secretion of these glands passes through these tubes to the outside, where it hardens into silk thread on contact with the air.

Spiders use these threads for many purposes, such as lining their nests, forming cocoons, for balloons, and for spinning their webs. Two kinds of silk threads are used by spiders in making their nets, elastic and inelastic. The inelastic threads are generally used to make the framework of the net, which consists of threads radiating out from a center to an extensive periphery. The elastic type forms the spirals that run in concentric

FIG. 19-4

Huntsman spider strikes defensive pose that shows his appendages, chelicerae, and eyes to good advantage.

rows from the center outward and are supported by the radiating fibers. These spiral threads have viscid masses of sticky material for holding the prey when it becomes entangled in the web.

Different species of spiders make different kinds of nets. Some are simple and primitive and consist merely of a few strands radiating out from a spider's burrow or place of retreat. On the other hand, the webs of the orb-weaving spiders are beautiful geometric patterns (Fig. 19-5). Cobwebs, which are usually irregular strands of silk, are formed by certain species of spiders. These untidy masses are often rendered more so by the dust that collects on them. The silk threads of spiders are stronger than steel threads of the same diameter.

FIG. 19-5

Web of orb-weaving spider. Most spiders bear three pairs of spinnerets on posterior ventral surface of abdomen. From silk glands inside abdomen, liquid is forced out of spigots of spinnerets under pressure and hardens on contact with air. Each of four or five different kinds of glands secrete different kind of silk. Orb weaver follows definite pattern in constructing web, but finished web may show many variations in given species. Starting with a "bridge thread," framework is made of boundary threads of dry silk glued in place and is usually an irregular four- or five-sided figure. Spokes, or radii, of dry silk are next spun and held in place at "hub" or center by platform of spiral dry silk thread. Functional spiral of sticky threads is next spun by spider, working inward from rim to hub, being careful to walk on nonsticky radii while doing so.

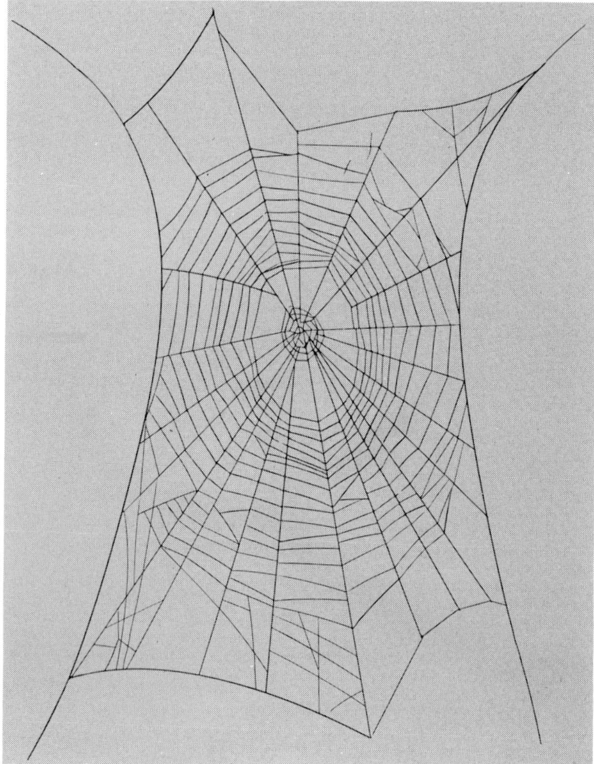

All spiders produce silk, but only some form webs. The first webs were formed of nonviscid silk, and the viscid type was a later innovation. Early ancestors of spiders may have had no silk apparatus for catching prey, and when silk first evolved, it was used for making egg sacs or covering eggs. The first web may have appeared when a spider hid in a crevice with an egg sac and formed for the shelter, from its drag line, a lining that became tubular in time. Some primitive spiders still build this type of net, whereas the orb web is a later development (B. J. Kaston).

Students who are interested in the many types of spider webs and the habits of spiders should consult that fascinating work on spiders by McCook. Although out of date with regard to classification and some other particulars, it is still one of the most interesting accounts of this group ever written.

Our most interesting spider—trap-door spider. Although spiders as a group have many interesting examples of habits and adaptations, perhaps none is more fascinating than the trap-door spider. There are several species of trap-door spiders, which are related to the well-known tarantulas. They are found in the southern and western parts of our country, although they have been most extensively studied in southern California. The common species found there is known as *Bothriocyrtum californica.* This spider exercises great ingenuity and architectural ability in the construction of her nest, which is a burrow in the ground that she excavates with her fangs, palps, and front legs. The burrow she makes is about 6 to 10 inches deep and a little more than 1 inch in diameter. Its walls are firm and smooth and are lined with a silken web. The walls are ash gray in color, and the burrow is waterproof. The trapdoor, which is semicircular in outline, is hinged at the straight edge by means of the web that lines the inner surfaces of both the door and the burrow (Fig. 19-6). When closed, the door fits snugly into the beveled entrance of the burrow flush with the surface of the surrounding ground. The door is carefully camouflaged with moss, lichen, and other vegetation so that it is difficult to detect. On the inside surface of the door are little "arm holds" of silken web by which the spider, with her fangs, can keep the door closed against intruders. When watching for food, she holds the lid partly ajar, seizes her prey, and drags it into her burrow. Her food consists mainly of insects and small crustaceans. She spends her entire life in the burrow, where she raises her young, and the length of time she has been in it can be estimated by the number of web layers on the underside of the door, one layer for each year of occupation. Some have been known to live more than seven years. The small males have rarely been found.

FIG. 19-6

Burrow of trap-door spider, with lid thrown open and its owner just retreating within.

Trap-door spiders have their enemies, as do most animals. The one that does them the most harm is a wasp, *Pedinaspis planatus,* which is able either to slip in while the door is ajar or to force it open with her jaws. Inside, she overcomes the spider and paralyzes her by stinging. On the abdomen of the spider the wasp lays an egg that hatches in a few days into a larva that lives on the paralyzed spider. Authorities state that more than a third of all burrows reveal dead spiders that have been destroyed in this way.

It is interesting to note that a spider in Africa has a similar habit of making a trap-door burrow, except that this particular species makes its home in the soft bark of trees. The burrow in this case is also lined with a silken web but is much smaller and more shallow than that found in America.

Our most dangerous spider—black widow. Spiders have a bad reputation the world over and some can give painful bites, but most of them are harmless. Nor are they as aggressive as one commonly supposes when he sees a spider running toward him, for they will fight and bite only when they are tormented or when they are defending their young or eggs cases. There is one, however, in the United States that deserves some of the bad reputation spiders have. This is the black widow (*Latrodectus mactans*) (Fig. 19-7), which can give severe, even fatal, bites. This spider is not a large one. It is coal black with a prominent orange or reddish colored "hourglass" beneath the abdomen, which usually serves to identify it. The name "widow" has been given to it because she was reputed to eat her mate immediately after mating. Those who have observed her habits closely conclude that the male is seldom sacrificed in this way, although such practices are known to occur among other spiders.

FIG. 19-7

This black widow spider *Latrodectus*, suspended on her web, has just eaten large cockroach. Note "hourglass" marking (orange colored) on ventral side of abdomen.

The distribution of the black widow seems to be a wide one; her presence has been reported from all of our states. However, she seems to be far more abundant in the warm regions such as our southern states and southern California. Her habitat may be almost anywhere around rubbish, in dark cellars, and under stones and objects in gardens. Dark outbuildings are favorite places, and it is said that 90% of the people bitten by them were in outdoor toilets at the time.

A considerable number of the bites occurred on or around the groins or genital organs. Many of the male victims were bitten on the penis. The symptoms have varied somewhat with individual cases. In general, there is acute pain, often sharp and stinging. There are often great burning sensations, which may be local or general. Severe muscle spasms also occur as well as vomiting, general restlessness, and cyanosis. Most of the symptoms are characteristic of a neurotoxic venom, that is, venom that acts upon the nervous system. Most of the patients are incapacitated for several days.

In the treatment of the black widow bite various procedures are followed by doctors, such as those commonly used with neurotoxic poisons. Partial success has been achieved with antivenom and serums.

Several hundred authentic cases of bites from the black widow have been reported. These cases cover 32 states, and deaths from the bites have been reported from 17 states. Of the more than 50 deaths reported, 32 of them have been in California. The mortality rate is about 5%.

Scorpions (order Scorpionida)

Although scorpions are more common in tropical and subtropical countries, they have been reported from at least 30 of our states. More than 600 species are known. Their habitat is in trash piles, under boards and other objects, around dwellings, and in burrows of desert regions. Most of them will burrow, but a few will not. They are most active at night when they seek their prey (insects, spiders, etc.). The elongated body is divided into two major regions: the cephalothorax (prosoma) and the abdomen (preabdomen and postabdomen). The postabdomen, or metasoma, is often called the tail. The cephalothorax is made up of six segments and is enclosed by a dorsal chitinous plate, the carapace, and by various ventral plates. The carapace bears from two to twelve eyes (depending on the species), which are grouped into median and sometimes lateral eyes. From the cephalothorax six pairs of appendages arise: (1) the small paired chelicerae, each of three joints, (2) the paired pedipalps, each of six joints and a pincer, and (3) the four pairs of walking legs, each of eight joints. The chelicerae and pedipalps, which are provided with jaws and teeth, are used for seizing and tearing their prey.

The abdomen consists of twelve segments (seven in

FIG. 19-8

Tropical blue scorpion *Centrurus,* which is common in Cuba. Order Scorpionida. Note terminal poison claw. (Preserved specimen.)

FIG. 19-9

Pseudoscorpion, or false scorpion. Order Chelonethida (Pseudoscorpionida). Most members of this group do not exceed 1/5 inch in length. They live under stones, bark of trees, and sometimes between pages of books. Their food is chiefly small insects and mites. In winter they construct cocoons from silk glands, which open on chelicerae. Note large pedipalps, which resemble those of true scorpions. (Courtesy Robert Weber and Bill Vesey, Fort Wayne, Ind.)

the preabdomen and five in the postabdomen, or "tail"). At the end of the postabdomen is the postanal telson, which bears the terminal poison claw or stinger (Fig. 19-8). Scorpions may or may not use the stinger in overcoming their prey. On the ventral side of the abdomen are the curious comblike pectines, which are tactile organs used for exploring the ground and for sex recognition. Of the more than 40 American species, only two are said to be dangerous to man. These two belong to the genus *Centruroides* found mainly in Arizona and nearby states. Their venom affects the nervous system, whereas the bite of most scorpions produces only a painful swelling. Scorpions bring forth living young, which are carried on the back of the mother, but they do not feed upon her tissues (a popular superstition).

In mating, scorpions have an interesting courtship ceremony in which the two mates seize each other's claws and perform a dance.

The pedipalps of the small pseudoscorpion are similar to those of the true scorpions, but the former carries its poison glands within the pedipalps.

Mites and ticks (order Acarina)

Mites and ticks have the cephalothorax and abdomen fused and there is no external sign of segmentation. They are found almost everywhere, but their small size causes them to be overlooked even when they are abundant. Some live in water, both fresh and marine, others live on vegetation and on the ground, and still others are parasitic on animals. The itch mite burrows into the skin, where the female lays her eggs. Another species is responsible for mange in dogs and other domestic animals.

Among the worst pests to contend with are the **chiggers,** or red bugs (*Eutrombicula*). These are the larval forms of red mites; they have only six legs, which is the number the larval forms of other mites and ticks have. When a chigger attaches itself to the skin, it forms, with the aid of a digestive secretion, a type of burrow at the site where it is eating. Many persons are irritated by this fluid, and a large reddish blotch and intense itching result. Chiggers do not suck blood. They are especially abundant in raspberry patches and often on lawns. The precaution of dusting sulfur on the hose around the ankles is fairly effective in discouraging their attacks. After feeding for a time, the chigger will drop off to the ground, although some are known to be carried in clothing of infested persons. Chiggers attack nearly all land vertebrates.

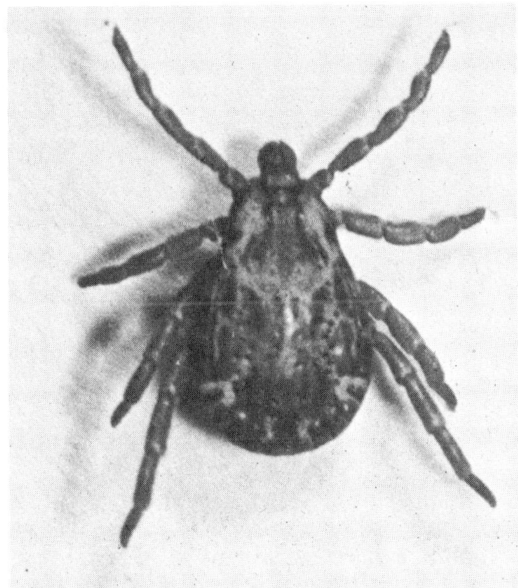

FIG. 19-10

The wood tick *Dermacentor,* one species of which transmits Rocky Mountain spotted fever and tularemia, as well as producing tick paralysis.

Ticks are usually larger than mites and feed upon the blood of various vertebrate animals. With their mouth parts they pierce the skin and draw up blood with their sucking pharynx until their bodies are enormously distended. They can survive long periods of time without feeding. The female lays her eggs on the ground; these eggs hatch into larvae, which climb on bushes and fasten themselves to the host that happens to pass that way. After filling themselves, the ticks will drop off, digest their meal, undergo molting, climb up another bush, and patiently wait for another meal.

Ticks are among the greatest arthropod vectors of disease. Among the diseases for which they are responsible are relapsing fever, Rocky Mountain spotted fever, and Texas cattle fever. The wood tick (*Dermacentor*) (Fig. 19-10) that infests various mammals, including man, is the vector for Rocky Mountain spotted fever, which is caused by a rickettsia organism carried in the salivary secretions of the tick.

• • •

For derivation and meaning of basic terminology see the end of Chapter 21.

Annotated references

Arachnida

Baerg, W. J. 1958. The tarantula. Lawrence, University of Kansas Press. *A monograph on the habits and natural history of a greatly misunderstood member of an animal group, which is one of the most fascinating in the animal kingdom.*

Baker, E. W., and G. W. Wharton. 1952. An introduction to acarology. New York, The Macmillan Co. *A work on the much-neglected group of ticks and mites. Emphasizes taxonomy.*

Barrington, E. J. W. 1967. Invertebrate structure and function. New York, Houghton Mifflin Co. *An excellent up-to-date account.*

Cloudsley-Thompson, J. E. 1958. Spiders, scorpions, centipedes, and mites. New York, Pergamon Press, Inc. *This monograph emphasizes the behavior and ecology of the group.*

Comstock, J. H., and W. J. Gertsch. 1940. The spider book, ed. 2. New York, Doubleday, Doran & Co., Inc. *A well-written account of spiders. Much emphasis is given to their habits and behavior.*

Fabre, J. H. 1919. The life of the spider. New York, Dodd, Mead & Co. *An interesting description of the adaptations of the spider. Especially good for the beginner in zoology.*

Herms, W. B. 1950. Medical entomology, ed. 4. New York, The Macmillan Co. *A section of this book is devoted to Arachnida. The role arachnoids play in disease transmission is emphasized.*

Hickman, C. P. 1967. Biology of the invertebrates. St. Louis, The C. V. Mosby Co.

Kaston, B. J. 1966. Evolution of the web. Natural History **75**:26-33 (April). *Traces the evolution of the spider's web and proposes a phylogenetic tree according to the kind of web woven. An exciting and interesting account for all students of spiders.*

Kaston, B. J., and E. Kaston. 1953. How to know the spiders. Dubuque, Iowa, William C. Brown Co. *This is an excellent taxonomic manual of the common spiders, fully illustrated. It contains much information about spiders in general. If you are interested in spiders, study this book.*

Lougee, L. B. 1964. The web of the spider. Bloomfield Hills, Mich., Cranbrook Institute of Science. *A delightful, although brief, work on spiders. Many photographs of the various webs made by spiders, but text is kept at a minimum.*

McCook, H. C. 1889-1893. American spiders and their spinningwork. Philadelphia, Academy of Natural Science. *A great classic work that in many ways has never been surpassed in this field.*

Meglitsch, P. A. 1967. Invertebrate zoology. New York, Oxford University Press.

Savory, T. H. 1952. The spider's web. New York, Frederick Warne & Co., Ltd. *An interesting account of the way spiders spin and make use of their webs.*

Savory, T. H. 1964. Arachnida. New York, Academic Press, Inc.

Savory, T. H. 1968. Hidden lives. Sci. Amer. **219**:108-114 (July). *Describes the numerous invertebrates (cryptozoa) that are found living concealed near the surface of the ground under rocks and debris and how these forms enjoy certain advantages in living where they do.*

Snodgrass, R. E. 1952. A textbook of arthropod anatomy. Ithaca, N. Y., Comstock Publishing Associates. *A fine comparative study of all groups in this vast field. The author also points out the inconsistencies of arthropod structure with theories of arthropod relationships.*

CHAPTER 20

• PHYLUM ARTHROPODA

Subphylum Mandibulata—except insects

CLASS CRUSTACEA

● The members of class Crustacea get their name from the hard shells they bear (L. *crusta,* shell). The class includes lobsters, crayfish, shrimp, crabs, water fleas, copepods, barnacles, and some others. There are about 30,000 species in the class. Many of them are marine, some live in fresh water, and others are found in moist soil. Most of them are free living, but a few are sessile, commensal, or parasitic. They differ from other arthropods chiefly by having gills for breathing, by having two pairs of antennae, one pair of mandibles, and two pairs of maxillae, by having the appendages modified for various functions, and by lacking malpighian tubules.

General nature of a crustacean

The crustacean body is made up of segments that vary in number among the different taxonomic groups. Most crustaceans have between sixteen and twenty, but some primitive forms have sixty or more segments. The more advanced crustaceans tend to have fewer segments as well as increased tagmatization. There are usually three major body divisions, or tagmata: head, thorax, and abdomen. These three regions are not always clear cut because of the fusion of metameres together from different divisions. Thus the cephalothorax of the crayfish consists of both cephalic and thoracic segments. The most natural and most advanced group of crustaceans are the Malacostraca, which represent the morphologic type of organization called the **caridoid facies.** This type is typically made up of a body form in which the head has five or six, the thorax eight, and the abdomen six or seven segments. At the anterior end is the nonsegmented acron and at the posterior end is the nonsegmented telson, which, with the last abdominal segment and its uropods, form the tail fin in many forms. Primitively, each segment typically bears one biramous pair of appendages, but there are many modifications.

Relationships and origin of crustaceans

The relations of the crustaceans to other arthropods has long been a puzzle. According to a widely held theory, the trilobites are considered the ancestors of the crustaceans, but some zoologists have proposed that both these groups evolved independently from different nonarthropod ancestors. Some light was shed on the problem when the primitive crustacean *Hutchinsoniella macracantha* was discovered in 1954 in Long Island Sound. This form was assigned to a new subclass of its own (Cephalocarida) because of its biramous trunk limbs. It also has some features found only in the nauplius (larval) stages of other crustaceans, such as its ventral median eye. It is considered the most primitive of all known crustaceans. It shares with the trilobites limbs that are alike and not specialized (except the first) for a specific function but are used for locomotion and food getting. This little form (about 4 mm. long) may represent the primitive arthropod limb pattern that became highly specialized in other crustaceans and may also indicate a definite trilobite relationship.

Crayfish

The crayfish is found in freshwater streams, ponds, and swamps over most of the world. There are a number of genera, and more than 130 species have been described in the United States. Common genera in North America are *Orconectes* and *Cambarus,* which are found east of the Rocky Mountains, and *Astacus,* which occurs mainly on the western slopes of the

Rockies; the latter is also common in Europe. The various species resemble each other very closely except for minor details, and any one of them can well serve as a representative type for study. Even the large lobster (*Homarus*) has about the same plan of structure.

Habitat. Most students are familiar with the natural history of this form, for it is one of the most common animals in fresh water. Some are found in slow-moving water, others prefer swift streams, and some blind ones dwell in caves. They are primarily bottom dwellers and spend the day under rocks and vegetation, coming out at night in search of food. Some are terrestrial in their habits and make characteristic chimneylike burrows in the soil if the water level is not too far under the surface. When hiding in its retreat, the crayfish keeps its head end at the entrance, with its antennae and pincers extended out. One way of catching

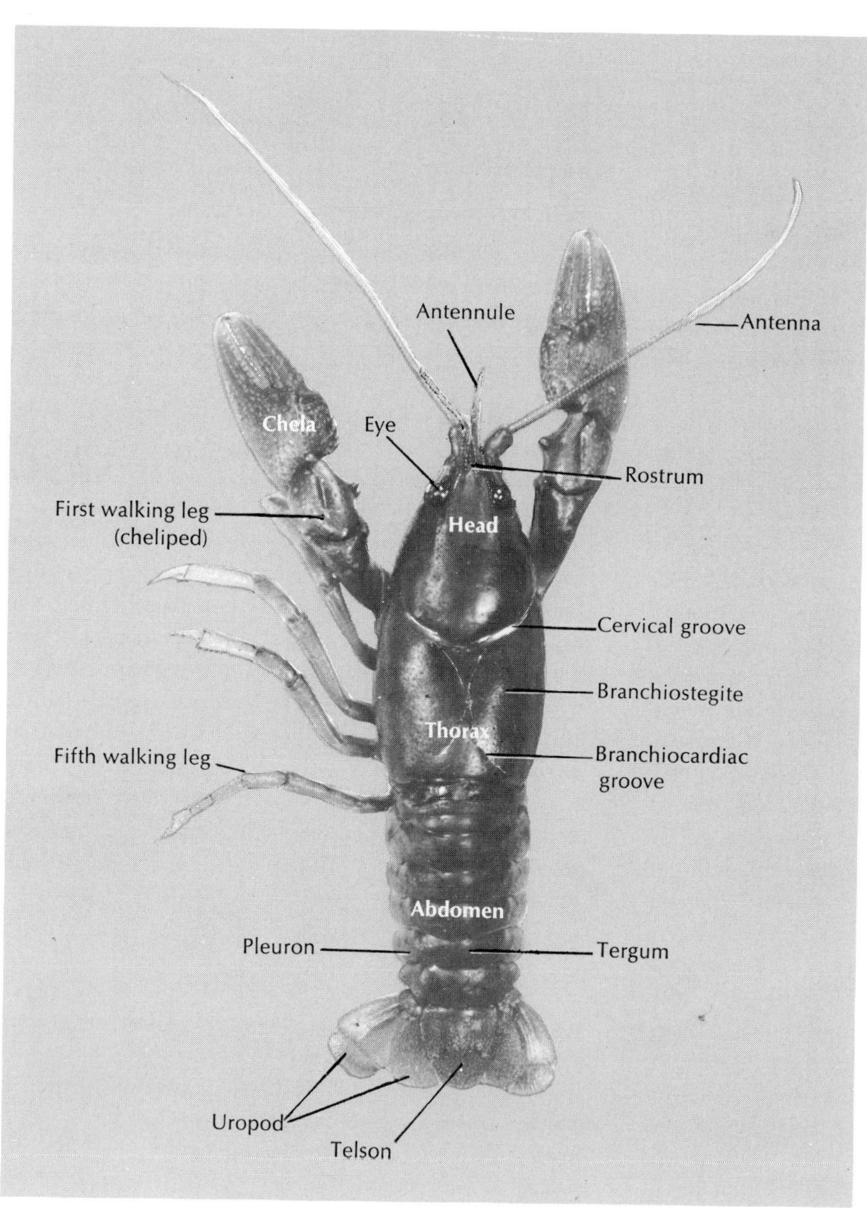

FIG. 20-1

Dorsal view of crayfish.

them is to drag a piece of meat on a hook over the bottom of a pool, for they will grasp any food they can reach.

Behavior. Endangered crayfish can dart off to a hiding place with considerable speed. In their burrows they face outward so that they can dart out for food. While stationary, they keep currents of water moving by waving the bailer and swimmerets back and forth. They can walk in any direction, with most of the weight supported chiefly by the fourth pair of legs. When escaping from danger they move rapidly backward by extending and flexing the abdomen, uropods, and telson, thus producing a series of backward darts.

With reference to orientation, crayfish are positively thigmotactic and try to get most of the body in contact with a surface. Many chemical substances, unless concentrated, will attract them. Most light sources will cause them to retreat, although they do have a liking for red. They are mainly nocturnal animals.

The behavior of the crayfish is mostly instinctive, but they can be taught simple habits through experience.

Regeneration and autotomy. Crayfish have the power to regenerate lost parts. In general, any of the appendages and the eyes will be renewed when removed, although regeneration is faster in young animals. A lost part is partially renewed at the next molting, and after several moltings it is completely restored. The new structure is not always the same as the one lost. If only part of the eye stalk is cut off, normal regeneration will occur, but if the entire eye stalk is removed, a

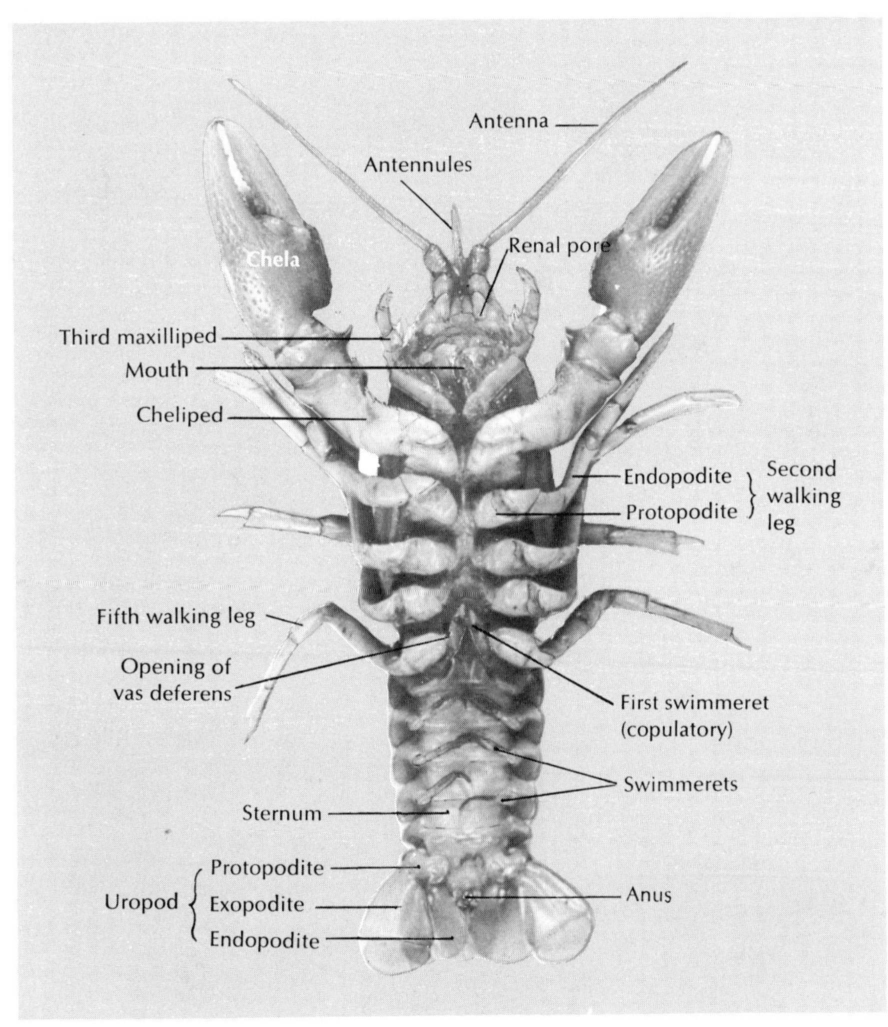

FIG. 20-2
Ventral view of male crayfish.

structure similar to antenna replaces it. Whenever the part regenerated is different from the lost part, such a regeneration is called **heteromorphosis.**

The power of self-amputation is called **autotomy.** It refers to the breaking off of the legs and chelae at a definite point whenever they are injured. The definite breaking point is near the base of the legs and is marked by an encircling line on the basal segment of the chelae and at the third joint on the walking legs. If one of these appendages is injured, all parts terminal to the breaking point are cast off. The process is effected by a special muscle. Autotomy has the advantage of preventing excess loss of blood, for the wound closes more quickly when the legs are broken off at the breaking point. After a part is cast off in this manner, a replacement regenerates in the regular way.

External features. The body, about 2 to 4 inches long, is covered with an exoskeleton composed of chitin and lime. This hard protective covering is soft and thin at the joints between the somites, allowing flexibility of movement. The somites are grouped into two main regions: the **cephalothorax** (head and thorax) and the **abdomen.** There are nineteen somites in the body: five in the head, eight in the thorax, and six in the abdomen. Each somite has a pair of jointed appendages.

The cephalothorax is enclosed dorsally and laterally

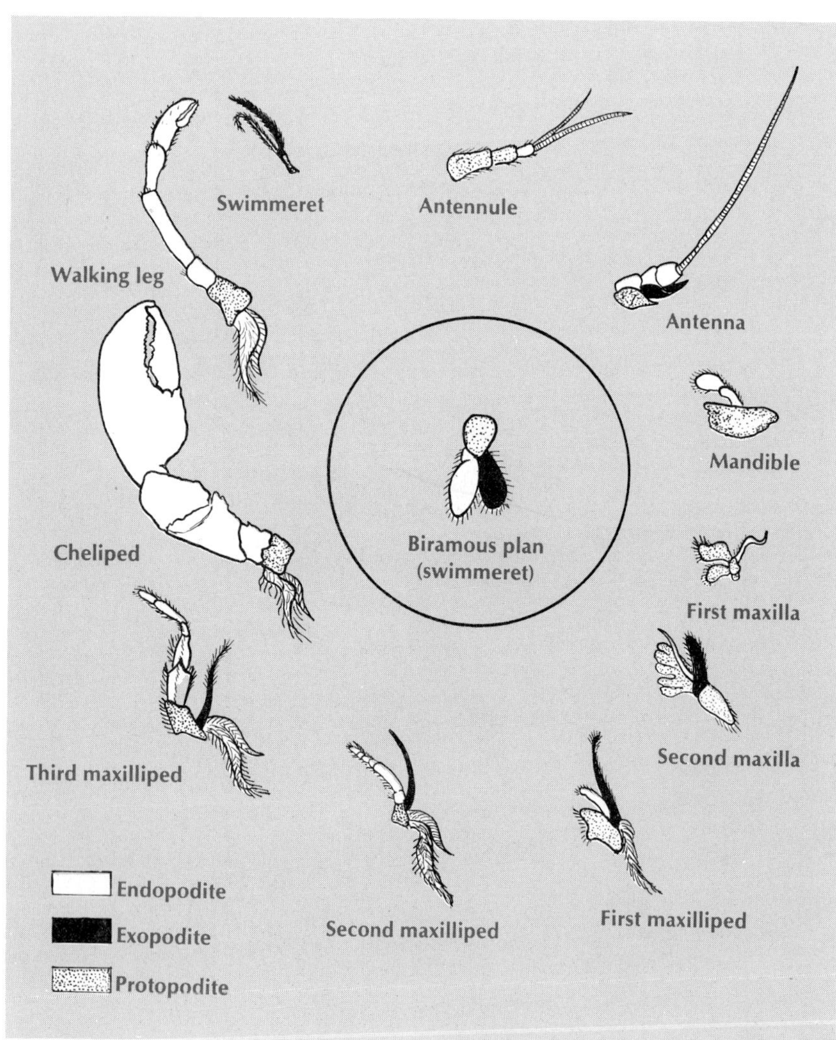

FIG. 20-3

Appendages of crayfish showing how they have become modified from basic biramous plan, as found in swimmeret.

by the continuous skeletal shell, the **carapace.** The joints between somites are obliterated except for the cervical groove, which marks the division between the head and thorax (Fig. 20-1). The anterior tip of the carapace is called the **rostrum.** The compound eyes, which are stalked and movable, lie beneath and on either side of the rostrum and have arisen from the acron, the anterior portion of the embryonic arthropod.

A typical somite in the abdomen consists of a dorsal plate, or **tergum,** and a ventral transverse bar, or **sternum,** joined together by a lateral **pleuron** on each side. The segmented abdomen terminates in the broad, flaplike **telson,** which is not considered a somite. On the ventral side of the telson is the **anus** (Fig. 20-2).

The openings of the paired **vasa deferentia** are on the median side at the base of the fifth pair of walking legs, and those of the paired **oviducts** are at the base of the third pair. In the female the opening to the seminal receptacle is located in the midventral line between the fourth and fifth pairs of walking legs.

Appendages. The crayfish typically has one pair of jointed appendages on each somite. These appendages differ from each other, depending on their functions. All, however, are variations of a common plan. This common plan, best illustrated by the swimmerets of the abdominal region, is a 2-branched or **biramous appendage** (Fig. 20-3). It consists of a basal **protopodite,** which bears a lateral **exopodite** and a median **endopodite.** The protopodite is made up of two joints, **coxopodite** and **basipodite,** whereas the exopodite and endopodite have from one to several segments each. From this common biramous type of appendage have come all the different kinds of appendages in the crayfish. Three kinds are recognized in the adult: (1) **foliaceous,** such as the second maxillae, (2) **biramous,** such as the swimmerets, and (3) **uniramous,** such as the walking legs. All these appendages have been derived from the biramous type, as shown in the embryonic crayfish, in which all the appendages arise as two-branched structures. Structures that have a similar basic plan and have descended from a common form are said to be **homologous,** whether they have the same function or not. Since the specialized walking legs, mouth parts, chelipeds, and swimmerets have all developed from a common type and have become modified to perform different functions, they are all homologous to each other (serially homologous). In this structural modification some branches have been reduced, some lost, some greatly altered, and some new parts added. The crayfish and its allies are among the best examples of **serial homology** in the animal kingdom.

Table 20-1 shows how the various appendages have become modified from the biramous plan to fit specific functions.

Internal features. The crayfish has all the organs and systems found in the higher forms (Fig. 20-4). A few of the systems, such as the muscular and nervous, show segmentation, but most of them are modified from this plan. Most of the changes involve concentration of parts in a particular region or else reduction or complete loss of parts, for example, the intersepta. In contrast to annelids, arthropods have a much reduced **coelomic cavity,** which is divided into a number of separate spaces. One of these cavities encloses the ex-

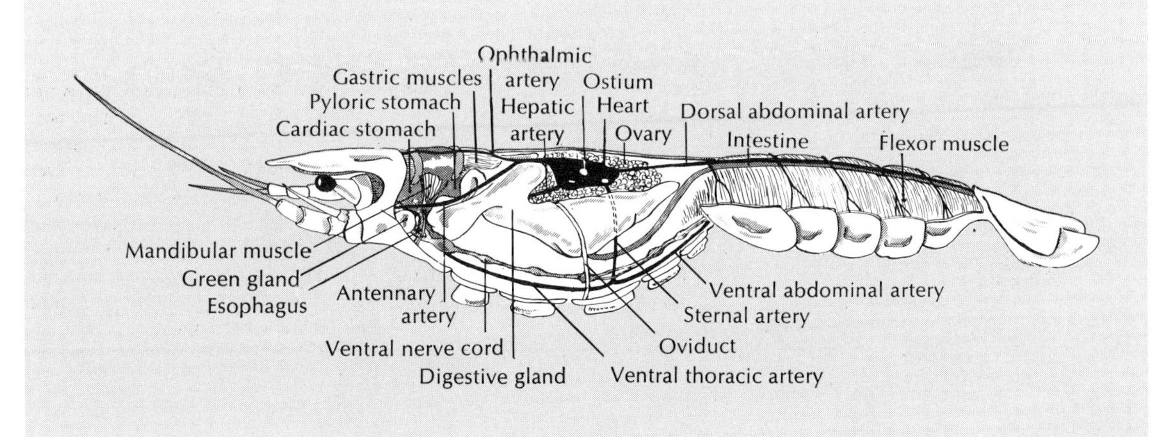

FIG. 20-4
Semidiagram of internal structure of large female crustacean such as crayfish.

TABLE 20-1

Crayfish appendages

Appendage	Protopodite	Endopodite	Exopodite	Function
Antennule	3 segments, statocyst in base	Many-jointed feeler	Many-jointed feeler	Touch, taste, equilibrium
Antenna	2 segments, excretory pore in base	Long, many-jointed feeler	Broad, thin, pointed squama	Touch, taste
Mandible	2 segments, heavy jaw and base of palp	2 distal segments of palp	Absent	Crushing food
First maxilla	2 thin medial lamellae	Small unjointed lamella	Absent	Food handling
Second maxilla	2 bilobed lamellae, extra plate, epipodite	1 small pointed segment	Dorsal plate, the scaphognathite (bailer)	Draws currents of water into gills
First maxilliped	2 medial plates and epipodite	2 small segments	1 basal segment plus many-jointed filament	Touch, taste, food handling
Second maxilliped	2 segments plus gill	5 short segments	2 slender segments	Touch, taste, food handling
Third maxilliped	2 segments plus gill	5 larger segments	2 slender segments	Touch, taste, food handling
First walking leg (cheliped)	2 segments plus gill	5 segments with heavy pincer	Absent	Offense and defense
Second walking leg	2 segments plus gill	5 segments plus small pincer	Absent	Walking and prehension
Third walking leg	2 segments plus gill; genital pore in female	5 segments plus small pincer	Absent	Walking and prehension
Fourth walking leg	2 segments plus gill	5 segments, no pincer	Absent	Walking
Fifth walking leg	2 segments; genital pore in male; no gill	5 segments, no pincer	Absent	Walking
First swimmeret	In female reduced or absent; in male fused with endopodite to form tube			Transfers sperm to female
Second swimmeret				
Male	Structure modified for transfer of sperm to female			
Female	2 segments	Jointed filament	Jointed filament	Creates water currents; carries eggs and young
Third, fourth, and fifth swimmerets	2 short segments	Jointed filament	Jointed filament	Create current of water; in female carry eggs and young
Uropod	1 short, broad segment	Flat, oval plate	Flat, oval plate; divided into 2 parts with hinge	Swimming; egg protection in female

cretory green glands and another the reproductive organs. The larger cavities around the alimentary canal are not true coelomic cavities; they contain blood and are known as **hemocoels.**

Muscular system. Striated muscles make up a considerable part of the body of a crayfish. It uses them for body movements and for manipulation of the appendages. The muscles are often arranged in opposite pairs. **Flexors** draw a part toward the body; **extensors** straighten it out. The abdomen has powerful flexors, which are used when the animal swims backward—its best means of escape. Strong muscles on either side of the stomach manipulate the mandibles.

Respiratory system (Fig. 20-5). Crayfish breathe by means of gills, which are delicate featherlike projections of the body wall and are located on either side of the thorax in the **gill chambers.** The gill chamber is covered by the **branchiostegite,** or lateral wall of the carapace, and opens ventrally and at both ends. The bailer of the second maxilla draws water over the gill filaments by moving back and forth. In *Cambarus* the gills are arranged in two rows (in some others there is a third row). Gills in the outermost row are called the **podobranchiae** and are attached to the coxopodites of appendages VII to XII; those in the inner double row are the **arthrobranchiae** and are attached to the membranes that join these appendages to the thorax. Altogether there are seventeen gills on each side.

Digestive system. The alimentary canal is made up of the following: (1) The **mouth** opens on the ventral surface between the mandibles (jaws). (2) A short tubular **esophagus.** (3) The **stomach** is a large, thin-walled cavity divided into an anterior **cardiac** chamber and a smaller **pyloric** chamber (Fig. 20-6). In the cardiac portion is the **gastric mill,** consisting of one median and two lateral chitinous ossicles manipulated by powerful muscles for grinding the food. Between the cardiac and pyloric chambers is a strainer of hair-like setae, which permits only fine particles to pass through. Small calcareous bodies, **gastroliths,** may also be present in the cardiac walls. These gastroliths enlarge during molting, for they serve as storage for calcium withdrawn from the exoskeleton. (4) A short midgut. (5) The long, slender **intestine** extends dorsally along the abdomen and opens through the **anus** on the ventral side of the telson. (6) Two large digestive glands lie beneath and posterior to the stomach and open by separate ducts into the midgut. Each digestive gland consists of three lobes composed of many tubules lined with glandular epithelium, which produce the digestive secretion. With the exception of the midgut and its digestive glands, the entire digestive system is lined with delicate chitin. At each molt this lining is shed, and when renewed it is hardened by the calcareous gastroliths.

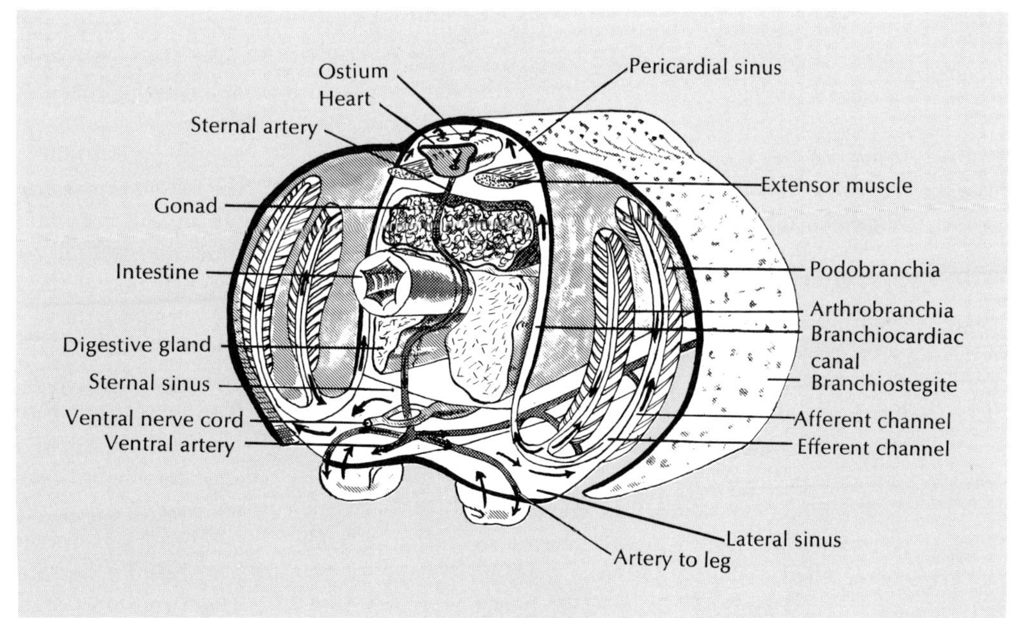

FIG. 20-5

Diagrammatic cross section through heart region of crayfish showing direction of blood flow in this "open" type blood system. Blood is pumped from heart to body tissues through arteries, which empty into tissue sinuses. Returning blood enters sternal sinus, is carried to gills for gas exchange, then back to pericardial sinus by branchiocardiac canals. Note absence of veins.

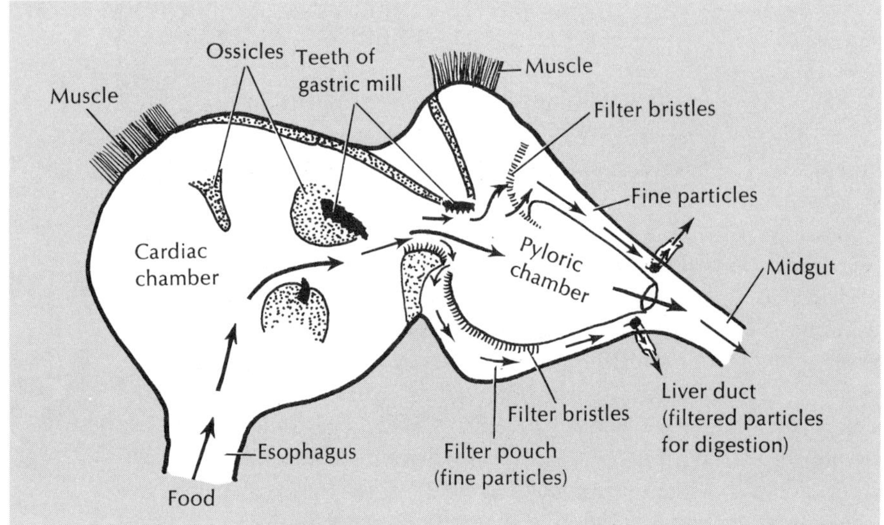

FIG. 20-6

Malacostracan stomach showing gastric "mill" and directions of food movements. Note that mill is provided with chitinous ridges, or teeth, and setae for churning and straining the food before it passes into the pyloric stomach. (From Hickman: Biology of the invertebrates, The C. V. Mosby Co.)

Metabolism. Crayfish will eat almost anything that is edible—insects, worms, snails, flesh of dead animals, and even plants. Before reaching the mouth, the food is broken into small pieces by the maxillipeds, maxillae, and mandibles. The latter are especially adapted for crushing the food. When the food reaches the cardiac stomach, it is further subjected to the grinding action of the gastric mill. Only the finer particles pass the strainer between the cardiac and pyloric stomachs; coarser particles are further acted upon by the grinding mechanism. When the food is fine enough, it passes in a fluid stream to the tubules of the digestive glands, where digestion is completed by enzymes and the food is absorbed. The indigestible part of the food is passed on into the intestine to be eliminated by the anus. Because of the thorough treatment the food gets before reaching the intestine, the latter is less important in digestion than is the case with many other animals.

After the digested food is absorbed into the blood, it is carried to the tissue cells to be utilized. The metabolic waste is removed by the antennal glands (excretory organs, sometimes called green glands) (Fig. 20-8). Oxygen that is picked up by the circulating blood of the gills is transported in the blood plasma by the pigment **hemocyanin;** carbon dioxide is given off from the gills in the exchange.

Circulatory system. The crayfish has an **open** or **lacunar** blood system in which veins are absent. It will be recalled that annelids have a closed system, as do the highest group of all, the vertebrates.

The circulatory system (Figs. 20-4 and 20-5) is made up of a muscular **heart;** seven **arteries,** which carry blood to the body; and certain **sinuses,** which return the blood to the large middorsal **pericardial sinus** surrounding the heart. The heart is held in place by six ligaments attached to the walls of the pericardial sinus. Blood from the pericardial sinus enters the heart through three pairs of valves, known as **ostia.** The arteries are (1) **ophthalmic artery,** which runs in a median dorsal direction over the stomach and supplies the cardiac stomach, the esophagus, and head; (2) two **antennary arteries,** which arise on each side of the ophthalmic to run forward and downward and supply branches to the cardiac stomach, to the antennae, to the green glands, and to the muscles of the head; (3) two **hepatic arteries,** which arise from the heart below the antennary arteries and supply the digestive glands; (4) **dorsal abdominal artery,** which passes backward from the ventral part of the heart and supplies the dorsal region of the abdomen and the appendages; and (5) **sternal artery,** which leaves the heart near the origin of the dorsal abdominal and extends straight down to the nerve cord. It passes through the cord, then divides into the **ventral thoracic artery,** which runs anteriorly to supply the thoracic appendages, mouth, and esophagus, and the **ventral abdominal artery,** which runs posteriorly to supply the abdominal appendages and muscles.

Valves in the arteries prevent a backflow of blood. The large arteries give rise to smaller arteries, which

FIG. 20-7

Female crayfish with eggs attached to swimmerets. Crayfish carrying eggs are said to be "in berry." The young, when hatched, also cling to swimmerets, protected by tail fan.

empty into the tissue sinuses, which in turn discharge into the large **sternal sinus.** From the sternal sinus afferent channels carry blood to the gills, where O_2 and CO_2 are exchanged. The blood now is returned to the pericardial sinus by the efferent **branchiocardiac canals.**

Blood in arthropods is largely colorless. It includes a number of ameboid cells and hemocyanin, a copper-containing respiratory pigment. This blood has the property of clotting, which prevents loss of blood in minor injuries.

Reproductive system. The crayfish is dioecious and there is some sexual dimorphism, for the female has a broader abdomen than the male and lacks the modified swimmerets, which serve as copulatory organs in the male. The **male organs** consist of two whitish, three-lobed **testes** lying just beneath the pericardial sinus and two long, coiled **vasa deferentia,** which pass from the testes out over the digestive glands and down to **genital pores** located at the base of the fifth walking legs. The **female organs** are paired **ovaries,** resembling the testes and located in a similar place, and short **oviducts,** which pass over the digestive glands and down to the genital pores at the base of the third walking legs.

Crayfish mate in the spring or early fall. If they copulate in the fall, the eggs are usually not laid till spring. In the process of copulation the male inverts the female, holds her with his body, chela, and telson, and transfers his sperm from the openings of his vasa deferentia to her seminal receptacle by means of the first two pairs of his swimmerets (Fig. 20-2). The seminal receptacle is a shallow cavity in the midline between the fourth and fifth pairs of walking legs. Here the sperm cells are retained until the mature eggs pass out of the oviducts. Two to three hundred eggs are discharged at one time, and as they pass by in slimy strings, they are fertilized by the sperm from the seminal receptacle. After fertilization, the masses of eggs are attached to the swimmerets like bunches of grapes and remain there during development (Fig. 20-7). It takes five to six weeks for hatching, and each embryo resembles the adult except for size. The young remain attached to the mother for several weeks, during which time they begin their molting. After leaving the mother they undergo several more molts during the first season, reaching a length of up to 2 inches by fall. Crayfish have a life span of three to five years.

Ecdysis, or molting, is absolutely necessary for the body to increase in size. Molting occurs less frequently as the animal grows older. In the adult, molting occurs in the spring and fall. The cuticle, secreted by the epidermis, is composed of a thin outer **epicuticle** (mostly wax) and a thicker **endocuticle.** Just before each molt inorganic salts are withdrawn from the exoskeleton and stored in the gastroliths and elsewhere. At the same time a new cuticle is secreted beneath the old cuticle, while part of the old endocuticle is being digested away by enzymes in the molting fluid. By absorbing air and water, the crayfish ruptures the old cuticle, usually along the middorsal line, and backs out of the old exoskeleton, shedding even the lining of the digestive system and the cornea of the eyes as well as the gross external structures. Then follows a rapid redeposition of the salvaged inorganic salts and other constituents to harden the new cuticle, together with tissue growth.

During the period of molting the animal is defenseless and remains hidden away.

Excretory system. The excretory organs are a pair of antennal, or green, glands found in the ventral part of the head anterior to the esophagus. The antennal gland consists of an internal end-sac or glandular portion bathed in blood, an excretory tubule or labyrinth, and a dorsal bladder, which opens to the exterior by a pore on the ventral surface of the basal antennal segment (Fig. 20-8). Wastes are probably removed from the blood by ultrafiltration (hydrostatic pressure) into the end-sac, and as the filtrate passes through the excretory tubule, it is modified by resorption of salts and water. Secretion of urinary components may also occur in the excretory tubule. Crayfish urine is mostly hypotonic (hyposmotic), and its concentration of certain ions may be much lower than that in the blood.

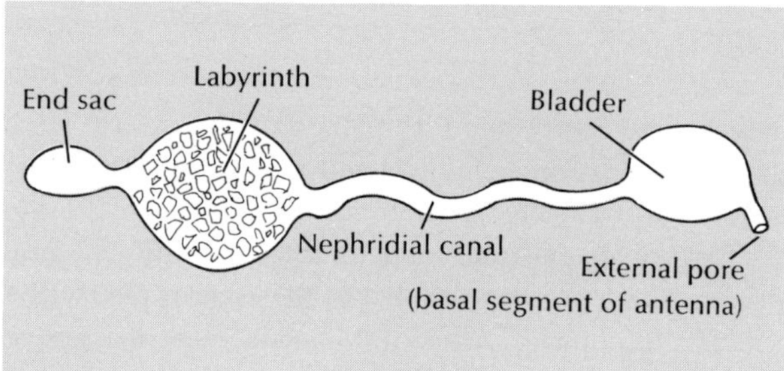

FIG. 20-8

Scheme of antennal gland (green gland) of crayfish. (In natural position organ is much folded.) Most selective resorption takes place in labyrinth, a complicated mass of tubules.
Some crustaceans lack labyrinth, and excretory tubule (nephridial canal) is a much-coiled tube.

Nervous system. The nervous systems of the crayfish and earthworm have much in common, although that of the crayfish is somewhat larger and has more fusion of ganglia (Fig. 20-9). The **central** nervous system consists of (1) a **brain,** or supraesophageal ganglia, which supplies nerves to the eyes, antennules, and antennae; this is connected by (2) a pair of **circumesophageal connectives** to the **subesophageal ganglion,** which lies at the anterior end of the ventral nerve cord and represents a fusion of at least five pairs of ganglia that supply nerves to the mouth, appendages, esophagus, and green glands; and (3) a double **ventral nerve cord** (Fig. 20-10, *B*). The cord typically has a fused

FIG. 20-9

Anterior part of nervous system of crayfish. Note similarity to annelid plan. In adult crayfish double ganglia and nerve cords of each somite are fused into one. Many ganglia are displaced and fused together, and some ganglia may be lost. Brain is a complex of many ganglia and gives off nerves to eyes, antennules, and antennae. Fused subesophageal ganglion, made up of five or six pairs of ganglia, sends nerves to mandibles, maxillae, maxillipeds, and excretory organs. Along ventral nerve cord fused ganglia give off paired nerves to appendages and body parts.

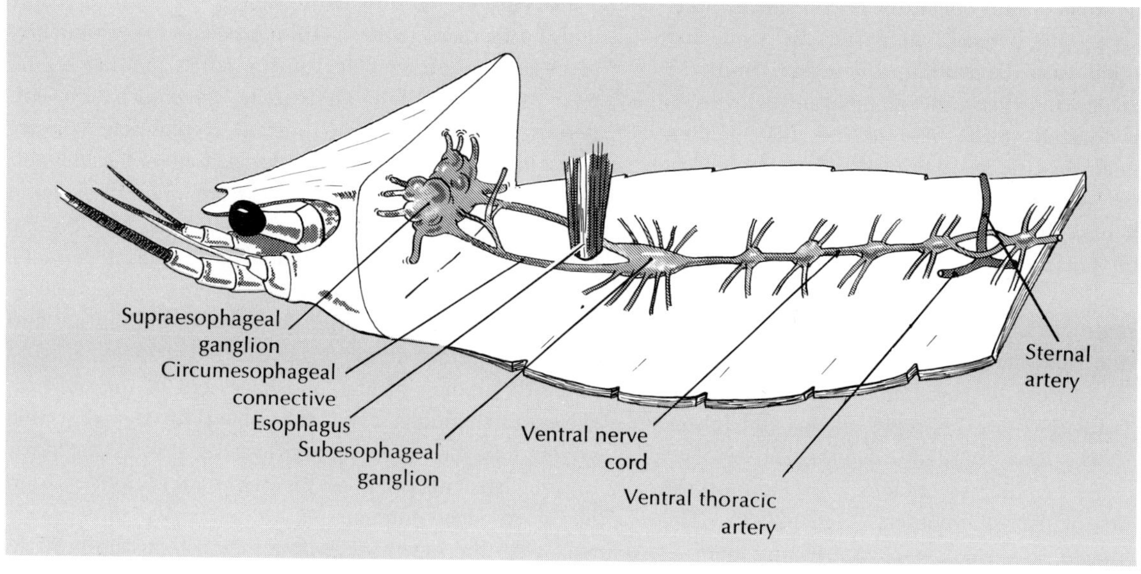

pair of ganglia for each somite from 8 to 19. These ganglia give off nerves to the appendages, muscles, etc. In addition to this central system, there is also a visceral system, which arises partly from the brain and partly from the circumesophageal connectives and passes to the pyloric stomach. In the primitive branchiopods the ventral nerve cord has the ladder arrangement characteristic of flatworms and some annelids, for the two parts are separated and are connected by transverse commissures.

Sensory system. The crayfish has better developed sense organs than do the annelids. The largest sense organs are the two **eyes** and the two **statocysts.** Tactile organs are widely distributed over the body in the form of **tactile hairs,** delicate projections of the cuticle, which are especially abundant on the chelae, mouth parts, and telson. The chemical senses of **taste** and **smell** are found in hairs on the antennules, antennae, mouth parts, and other places. A saclike **statocyst** is found on the basal segment of each antennule and opens to the surface by a dorsal pore. The statocyst contains a ridge that bears sensory hairs formed from the chitinous lining and grains of sand that serve as **statoliths.** Whenever the animal changes its position, corresponding changes in the position of the grains on the sensory hairs are relayed as stimuli to the brain, and the animal can adjust itself accordingly. The chitinous lining of the statocyst is shed at each molting (ecdysis), and with it the sand grains are also lost, but new grains are picked up through the dorsal pore when the animal renews its statocyst lining.

FIG. 20-10

Types of crustacean nervous systems. **A,** *Branchinecta* (a fairy shrimp). **B,** *Astacus* (a crayfish). **C,** *Argulus* (an ectoparasite). Note tendency toward concentration and fusion of ganglia. Ladderlike arrangement in **A** may be considered a primitive condition, whereas that in **B** is similar to nervous system of annelid type. (From Hickman: Biology of the invertebrates, The C. V. Mosby Co.)

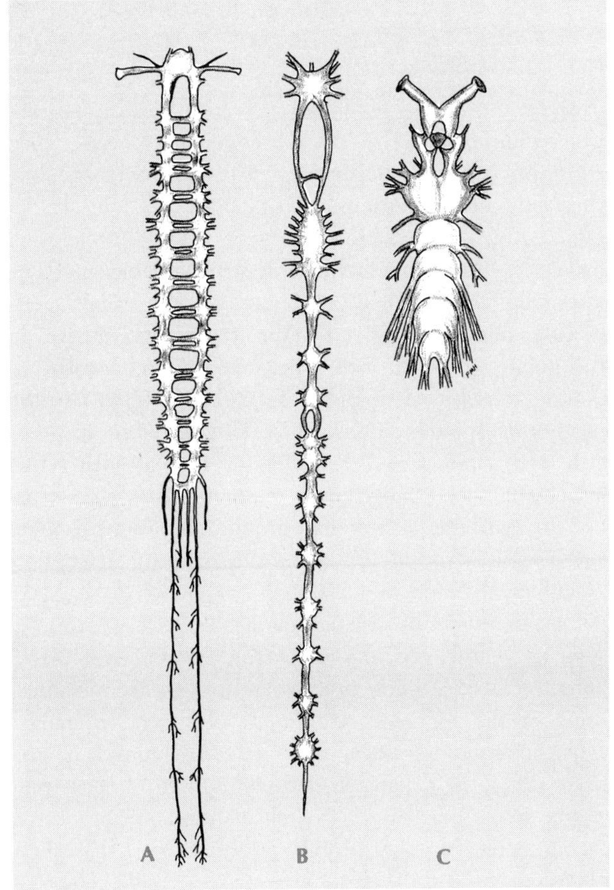

The eyes in crayfish are **compound** and are made up of many units called **ommatidia.** Covering the rounded surface of each eye is the transparent **cornea,** which is divided into some 2,500 small squares known as **facets,** representing the outer ends of the ommatidia. Each ommatidium, starting at the surface, consists of a **corneal facet;** two **corneagen cells,** which form the cornea; a **crystalline cone** of four **cone cells** (vitrellae); a pair of **retinular cells** around the crystalline cone; several retinular cells, which form a central **rhabdome;** and black **pigment cells,** which separate the retinulae of adjacent ommatidia. The inner ends of the retinular cells connect with sensory nerve fibers that pass through optic ganglia to form the optic nerve to the brain. The movement of the pigment in the arthropod compound eye makes possible two kinds of vision. In each ommatidium are three sets of pigment (distal retinal pigment cells, proximal retinal pigment cells, reflecting pigment cells), and these are so arranged that they can form a more or less complete collar or sleeve around each ommatidium. For strong light or day adaptation the distal retinal pigment moves inward and meets the outward moving proximal retinal pigment so that a complete pigment sleeve is formed around the ommatidium (Fig. 20-11). In this condition only those rays that strike the cornea directly will reach the retinular cells, for each ommatidium is shielded from the others. Thus each ommatidium will see only a limited area of the field of vision (a mosaic, or apposition, image). In

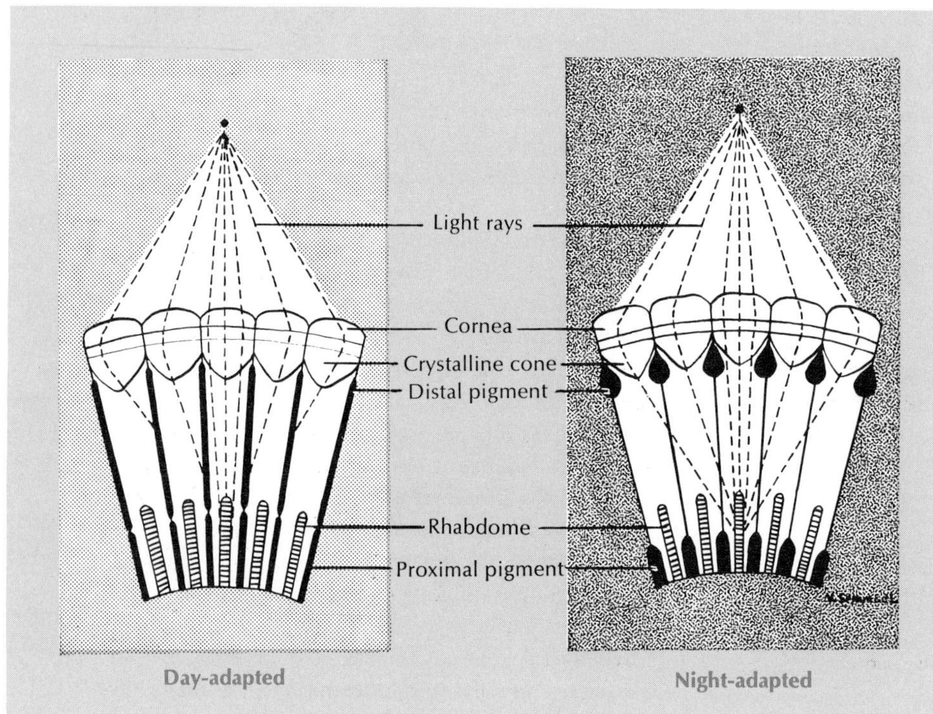

FIG. 20-11

Compound eye of arthropod showing migration of pigment in ommatidia for day and night vision. Five ommatidia represented in each diagram. In daytime each ommatidium is surrounded by a dark pigment collar so that each ommatidium is stimulated only by light rays that enter its own cornea (mosaic vision); in nighttime, pigment forms incomplete collars, and light rays can spread to adjacent ommatidia (continuous, or superposition, image). (Redrawn from Moment: General zoology, Houghton Mifflin Co.)

dim light the distal and proximal pigments separate so that the light rays, with the aid of the reflecting pigment cells, have a chance to spread to adjacent ommatidia and to form a continuous, or superposition, image. This second type of vision is less precise but takes advantage of the amount of light received. Compound eyes also have the power to analyze polarized light, as shown by the honeybee.

Endocrine functions. The **sinus gland** at the base of the eyestalk is known to have a number of hormones. They are supposed to control the spread of pigment in the chromatophores of the epidermis and in the compound eyes. They also seem to have some regulatory power over molting and affect the deposition of limy salts in the exoskeleton. The blood probably distributes the hormone, just as in higher forms.

The exact mechanism by which these physiologic processes are carried out is still obscure. Extensive research indicates that there is an x organ in the eyestalk along with the sinus gland. Neurosecretory cells in the x organ and in the brain produce a molt-preventing hormone, which is stored in the sinus gland. When eyestalks are removed experimentally from a nonmolting specimen, molting will occur in a few days because the inhibiting effect of the hormone is removed; when eyestalks from nonmolting crayfish are implanted into the body of an eyestalkless specimen, molting is delayed. A y organ, which produces a molt-accelerating hormone, has been described in some crustaceans. The interaction of the molt-preventing and the molt-accelerating hormones may be the regulatory device in the molting process. The y organ, located beneath adductor muscles of mandibles, is homologous to the prothoracic glands of insects and its hormone is probably ecdysone (p. 367). Evidence indicates that this important hormone induces metamorphosis by increasing the synthesis of proteins through alterations in gene activity patterns, in line with the modern concept of biochemical genetics.

The pigments of crustaceans are of a great variety, such as yellow, red, orange, green, brown, and black. Some of these are lipochromes and others are melanins. Most of the pigments are found in special branched cells (chromatophores), but some are found in the tissues. For the expansion and contraction of these pigments into and out of the chromatophore processes, certain chromatophorotropic hormones in the sinus gland appear to be responsible, as revealed by the removal of the eyestalk (darkening effect) or by the injection of eyestalk extracts (paling effect in some, darkening in others).

A specific hormone from the sinus gland is known to control the retinal pigment movements also.

In 1954 H. Charniaux-Cotton, a French investigator, discovered in an amphipod (*Orchestia*, the common beach flea) a pair of **androgenic** glands, which produce hormones that control the male sexual characteristics. These glands may be found in all male Malacostraca. When transplanted into an immature female, they produce masculinization of sex characters such as testes instead of ovaries. Their removal will cause spermatogenesis to cease in the testes. In isopods the glands are located in the testes; in all other malacostracans they are found between the muscles of the coxopodites of the last walking legs and are partly attached near the ends of the vasa deferentia.

Other crustaceans

The crustaceans are an extensive group with many subdivisions. There are many patterns of structure, habitat, and mode of living among them. Some are much larger than the crayfish; others are smaller. Some are highly developed and specialized; others have simpler organizations. The older classification divided the crustaceans into two subclasses—Entomostraca and

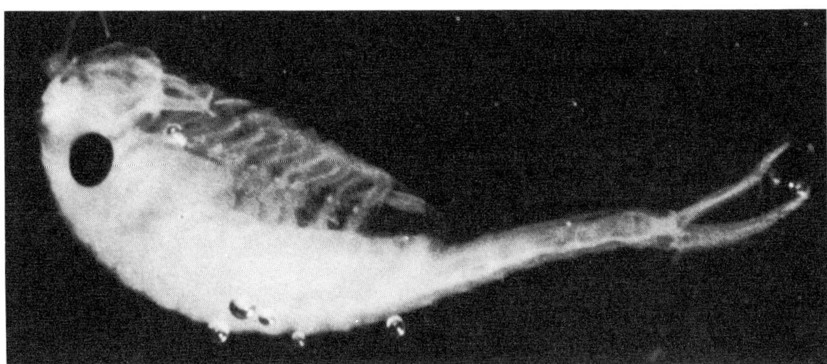

FIG. 20-12

Fairy shrimp *Eubranchipus*. Often swims with ventral side up.

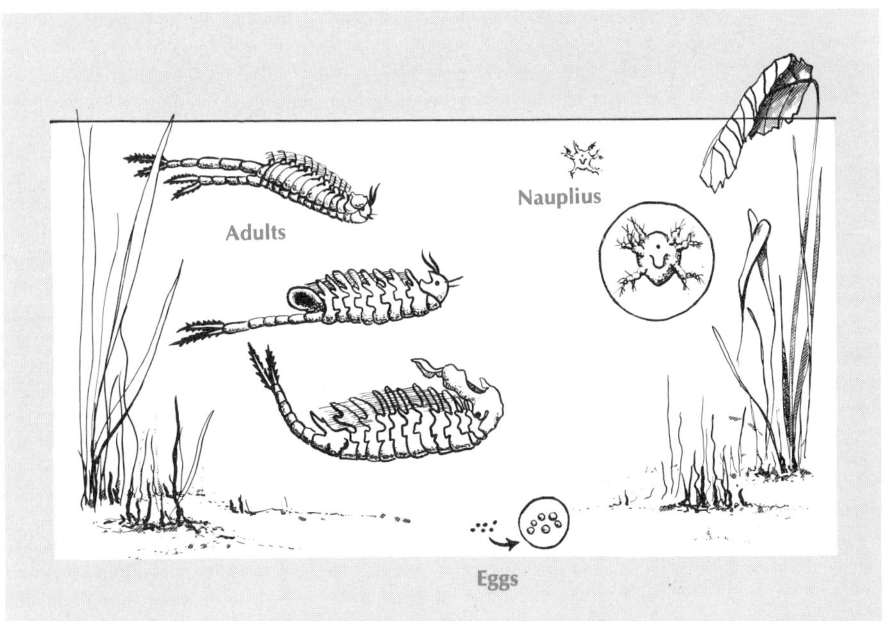

FIG. 20-13

Seasonal cycle of *Eubranchipus*, fairy shrimp. Order Anostraca. These beautiful crustaceans are found chiefly in vernal pools and ponds that dry up during summer. Their appearance is sporadic and their distribution irregular. Female eggs, in clutches of 10 to 250, can withstand drying during summer. Eggs in temperate climates usually hatch in winter and early spring, pass through a nauplius stage, and develop quickly into adults. In certain latitudes, adults may be found during the summer if ponds do not dry up. Drying promotes hatching of eggs but is not always necessary. Twenty-seven species have been recorded for North America. Most species are around 1 inch in length, but some are smaller or larger than this. (Redrawn from Moment: General zoology, Houghton Mifflin Co.)

Malacostraca. The entomostracans are simpler in structure and usually smaller than the malacostracans and do not have abdominal appendages. The Malacostraca form a natural division, for its members have an eight-segmented thorax, a six- or seven-segmented abdomen, a gastric mill, and abdominal appendages. The term "Entomostraca" is largely being discontinued, for its members lack morphologic unity.

Brief classification of class Crustacea

Subclass Branchiopoda (bran′chi-op″o-da) (NL. *branchio,* gill, + *podos,* foot). The members of this group are among the most primitive of all the crustaceans. One common example is the transparent fairy shrimp (*Eubranchipus*) (Figs. 20-12 and 20-13), which is found in temporary pools in pasture fields and elsewhere early in spring when melting snows have left little pools of water. They have eleven pairs of broad, leaflike trunk appendages, which are all basically alike. These appendages are used for locomotion, respiration, and egg bearing and bear chromatophores, which add to their beauty. Males are not common in some species and parthenogenesis frequently occurs in the brine shrimp. The males of fairy shrimp are provided with penes for the transfer of sperm to the female. The developing eggs are carried by the female in a ventral brood sac, where they are released in clutches at intervals of a few days. Released eggs are resistant to freezing and desiccation and remain viable after the ponds dry up. Both freezing and drying stimulate hatching but are not always necessary. The following spring, usually between January and May in our northern states, these eggs hatch into free-swimming nauplius larvae with three pairs of appendages and a single eye. Their distribution is very sporadic, both geographically and in annual occurrence. The eggs may be distributed by the wind and on the feet of birds.

The subclass Branchiopoda is divided into four orders: Anostraca (fairy shrimps and brine shrimps); Notostraca (tadpole shrimps such as *Triops*); Conchostraca (clam

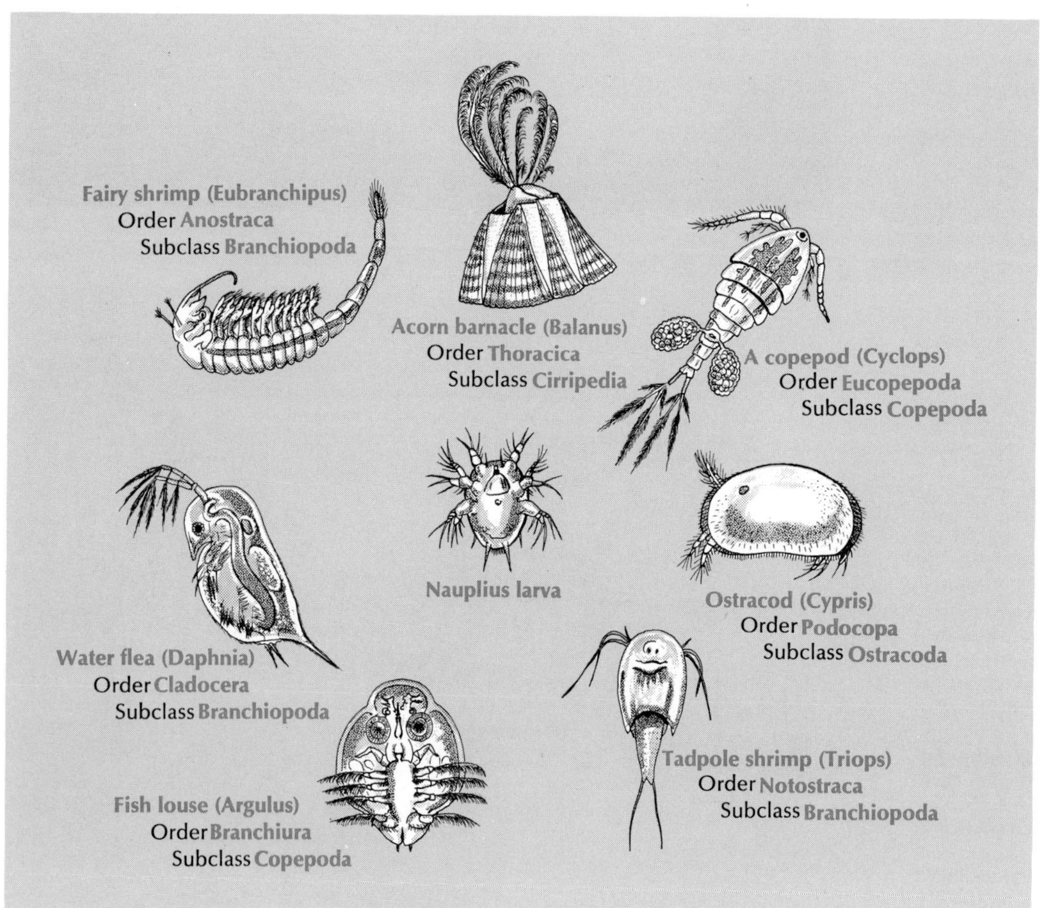

FIG. 20-14

Group of smaller crustaceans. Orders Anostraca and Notostraca live exclusively in fresh water; order Thoracica is exclusively marine; and orders Branchiura, Cladocera, Eucopepoda, and Podocopa are found in both fresh water and marine water. Nauplius larva is common to group.

shrimps such as *Lynceus*); and Cladocera (water fleas such as *Daphnia*) (Fig. 20-14).

Sublcass Cephalocarida (sef′a-lo-kar″i-da) (Gr. *kephale*, head, + *karis*, shrimp, + *ida*, pl. suffix). This is a small group of one or two species (genus *Hutchinsoniella*), which have been found along both the Atlantic and Pacific coasts. They are strictly marine (sometimes found in brackish water). They are provided with five pairs of biramous thoracic appendages but have no abdominal appendages.

Subclass Ostracoda (os-trak′o-da) (Gr. *ostrakodes*, testaceous). These are enclosed in bivalve shells and resemble small clams. When they move, they thrust out their two pairs of appendages through the open shell. Ostracods make up a part of the crustacean population of plankton. *Cypridina* and *Cypris* (Fig. 20-14) are common genera.

Subclass Copepoda (ko-pep′o-da) (Gr. *kope*, oar, + *podos*, foot). These are small crustaceans with elongated bodies and forked tails. One of the common forms is *Cyclops* (Fig. 20-14), which has a single median eye in the head region. Some copepods serve as intermediate hosts for certain parasites such as *Diphyllobothrium*, the broad tapeworm of fish. *Argulus* is a common parasite on freshwater fish (Fig. 20-14).

Subclass Cirripedia (sir′ri-pe″di-a) (L. *cirrus*, curl, + *pedis*, foot) (Figs. 20-15 and 20-16). These include the barnacles (*Balanus*), which are enclosed in a calcareous shell. At one time they were mistaken for mollusks, but they have jointed appendages, which they use for creating currents of water. In the larval stage they are free swimming but soon attach themselves to a firm surface, where they remain throughout their lives. Barnacles frequently foul ships' bottoms. So great may their number be that the speed of ships may be reduced 30% to 40%. This necessitates drydocking the ship and removing them. An important parasite belonging to this group is *Sacculina* (Fig. 20-17), which parasitizes crayfish and crabs.

Subclass Malacostraca (mal′a-kos″tra-ka) (Gr. *malakos*, soft, + *ostrakon*, shell). These include the larger crustaceans and also some not so large such as lobsters, crayfish, crabs, shrimp, sow bugs, and amphipods. Three common orders are Isopoda, Amphipoda, and Decapoda.

Order Isopoda (i-sop′o-da) (Gr. *iso*, equal, + *podos*, foot). These are found both in water and on land. They are flattened dorsoventrally, lack a carapace, and have similar legs except the anterior and posterior pair. The thorax and abdomen are usually fused. A common land form is the sow bug (*Porcellio*), which lives under stones and objects. Although a land form, it breathes by gills, which is possible only under moist conditions. *Asellus* is a common freshwater form (Fig. 20-18). The

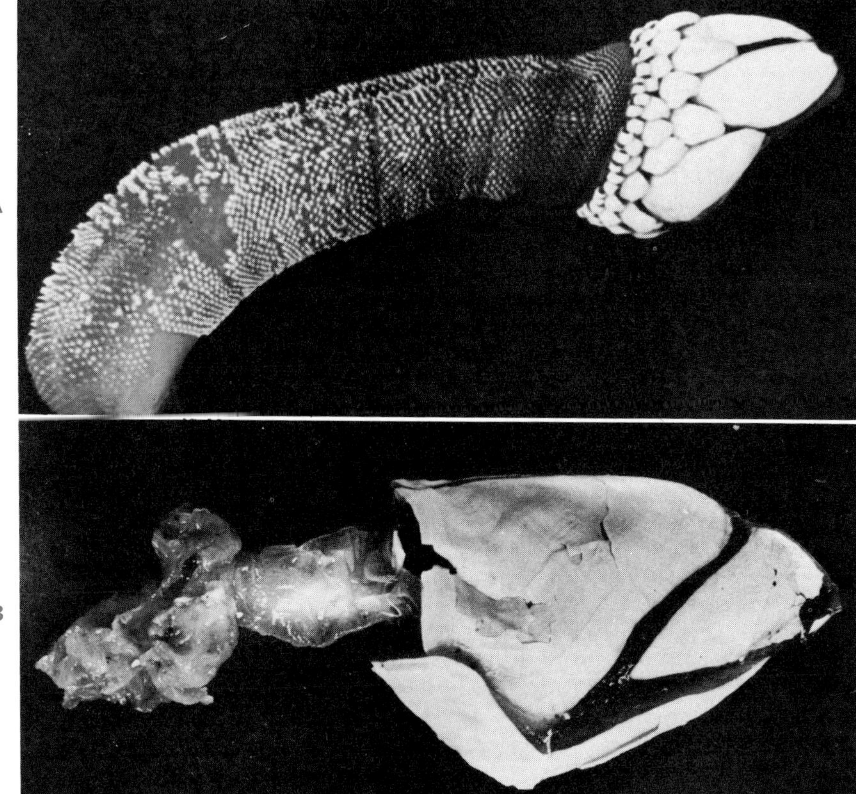

FIG. 20-15

Two stalked barnacles; these are highly modified crustaceans. Appendages retracted within crown of calcareous plates. **A,** *Mitella.* **B,** *Lepas.* Subclass Cirripedia.

A   B

FIG. 20-16

A, Group of acorn barnacles, *Balanus,* and sea mussels, *Mytilus* (Vancouver, Canada). **B,** Large cluster of goose barnacles, *Lepas,* which have hitchhiked ride on fishing net float off coast of British Columbia. *Balanus* and *Lepas* from subclass Cirripedia. (Courtesy C. P. Hickman, Jr.)

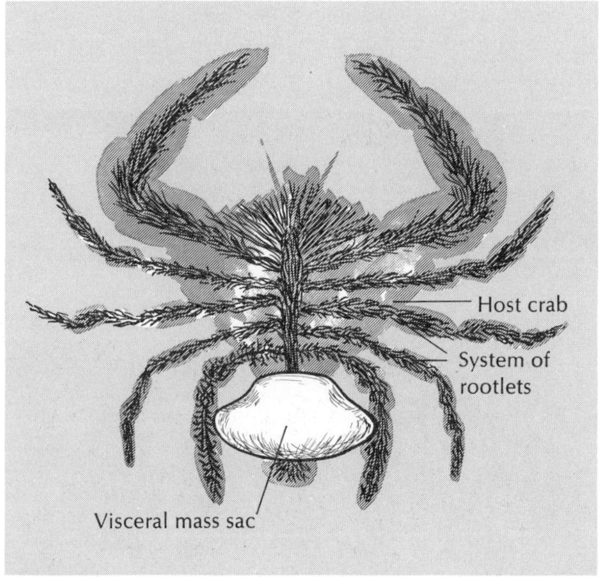

FIG. 20-17

Sacculina, unusual crustacean (subclass Cirripedia) that parasitizes crustaceans—the crab and crayfish. *Sacculina* larva enters host through thin cuticle of an articular membrane on crab's body and discharges cells into crab's blood. At junction of crab's stomach and intestine, these cells become attached and form mass, which sends system of branching rootlets to all parts of body of crab (or crayfish) to supply parasite with nourishment. Eventually *Sacculina* forms opening on ventral side of crustacean and extrudes a soft sac filled with eggs. Eggs develop parthenogenetically into nauplius larvae that infect other hosts. Parasite destroys crab's reproductive organs and so alters its sex hormones that host always assumes female form at next molt.

marine isopod (*Bathynomus*) grows to be 14 inches long. Some isopods are parasites on fish and crustaceans.

Order Amphipoda (am-phip′o-da) (Gr. *amphis,* double, + *podos,* foot). These forms are laterally compressed and have no carapace. Thorax and abdomen are not sharply marked off from each other. Of the eight pairs of thoracic appendages, the first five are used in feeding and the others in crawling. The six pairs of abdominal appendages are employed in swimming and jumping. These include beach fleas (*Orchestia*) and the aquatic forms *Hyalella* and *Gammarus* (Fig. 20-18).

Order Decapoda (de-cap′o-da) (Gr. *deka,* ten, + *podos,* foot). These all have five pairs of walking legs, of which the first pair is modified to form pincers (chelae). The larger crustaceans belong to this group and include lobsters, crayfish, and shrimp (Fig. 20-18). This is an extensive group of many thousand species. The crabs, especially, exist in a great variety of forms. Although resembling the pattern of crayfish, they differ from the latter in having a broader cephalothorax and a much-reduced abdomen. Familiar examples along the seashore are the hermit crabs, which live in snail shells (*Pagurus*) (Fig. 20-19), the fiddler crabs (*Uca*) (Fig. 20-20), and the spider crabs (*Libinia*).

Biogenetic laws as illustrated by Crustacea

Although the young of crayfish resemble the adult, this is not true of all members of this class. In some the larval stages are unlike the adult. Some of these larvae have a strong resemblance to types that are lower in the scale of life. One common larval form, called **nauplius** (Figs. 20-18 and 20-21), is found in the life cycle of the shrimp *Penaeus* and some other species. The nauplius larva has an unsegmented body, frontal eye, and three pairs of biramous appendages. With successive molts the nauplius is transformed into a **metanauplius,** with six pairs of appendages; a **protozoea,** with seven pairs of appendages and developing somites; a

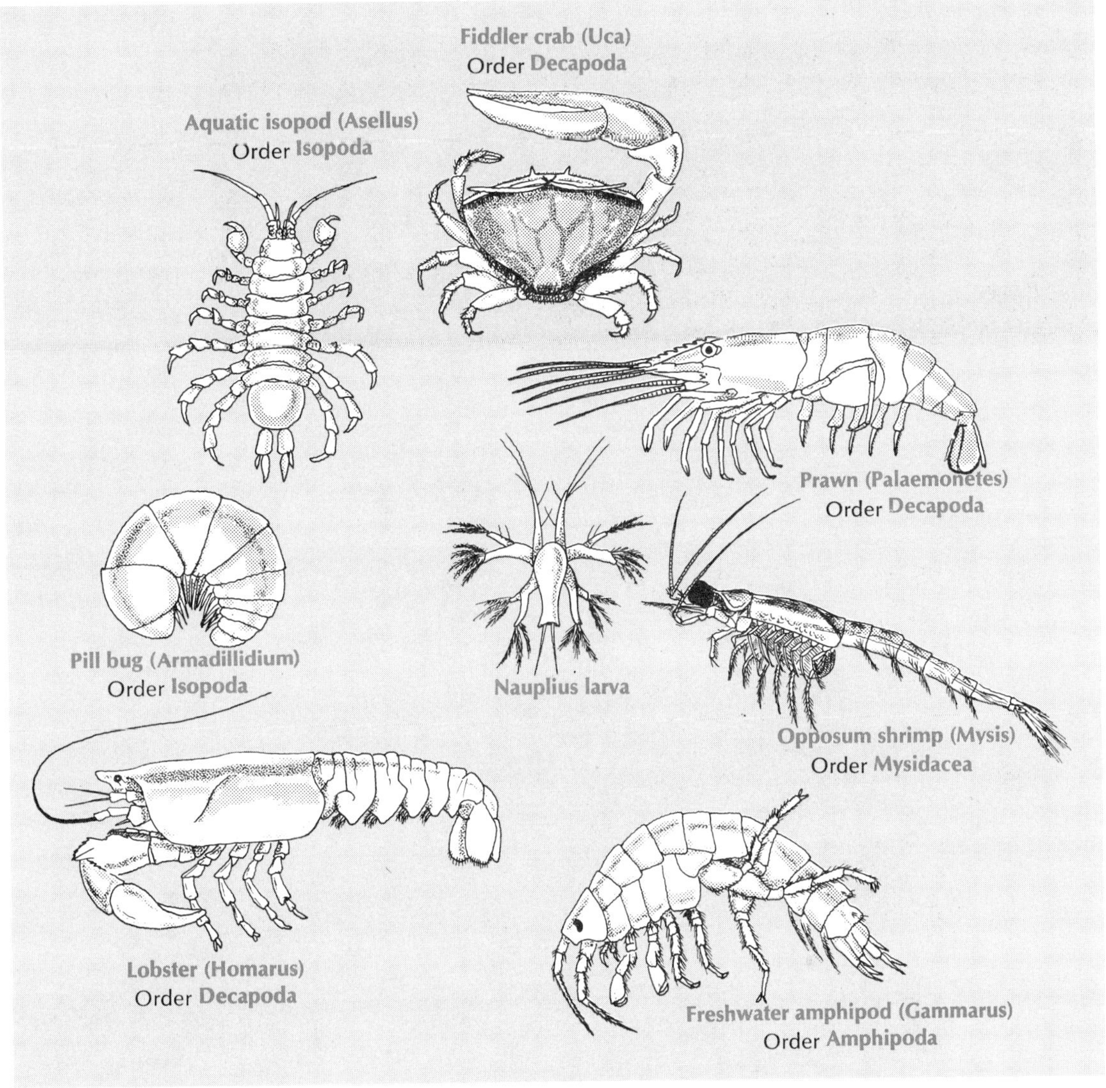

Fiddler crab (Uca)
Order Decapoda

Aquatic isopod (Asellus)
Order Isopoda

Prawn (Palaemonetes)
Order Decapoda

Pill bug (Armadillidium)
Order Isopoda

Nauplius larva

Opposum shrimp (Mysis)
Order Mysidacea

Lobster (Homarus)
Order Decapoda

Freshwater amphipod (Gammarus)
Order Amphipoda

FIG. 20-18

Larger crustaceans (subclass Malacostraca). All members of this subclass have abdominal appendages, gastric mill, eight-segmented thorax, and typical body of nineteen segments. (Not drawn according to size.)

FIG. 20-19

Hermit crab *Pagurus* lives in empty shells of marine gastropods. As it increases in size, it moves into larger shell, and wherever it goes it carries its shell with it.

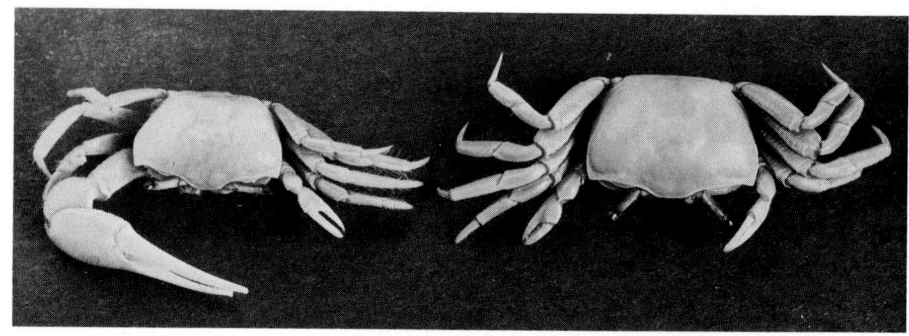

FIG. 20-20

Fiddler crab *Uca.* Male (left) waves its large claw back and forth in presence of female; hence the name "fiddler." Subclass Malacostraca.

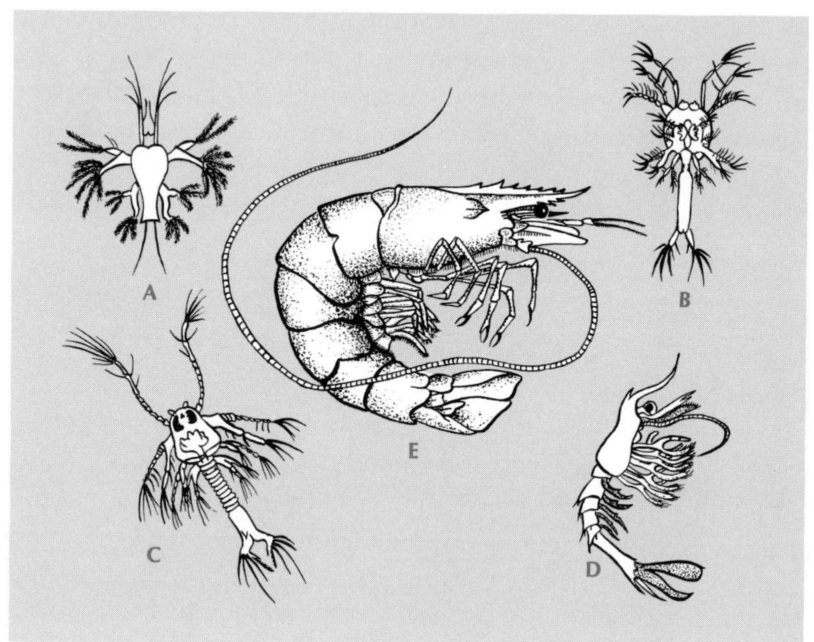

FIG. 20-21

Life history of shrimp. **A,** Nauplius; **B,** protozoea; **C,** zoea; **D,** mysis (note exopods on thoracic legs); **E,** adult. (Redrawn from Moment: General zoology, Houghton Mifflin Co.)

zoea, with eight pairs of appendages and six more in early stages of development, as well as a distinct cephalothorax and abdomen. From the zoea stage develops the **mysis** larva, bearing thirteen pairs of biramous appendages on the cephalothorax. Then the adult shrimp with nineteen pairs of appendages comes from the mysis larva. One or two of these larval stages resemble the adults of lower crustaceans, especially the mysis stage, which closely resembles the still living adult *Mysis.*

This correspondence between larval stages and the adults of types lower in the animal scale is called the **biogenetic law of recapitulation.** According to this principle, animals in their individual development pass through stages in the evolution of the race. Thus ontogeny repeats phylogeny. Although the biogenetic law in its original sense has been criticized, the description of the crustacean stages may at least give an insight into the course of evolutionary development of this group.

CLASS CHILOPODA

Classes Chilopoda (the centipedes) and Diplopoda (the millipedes) are often referred to together as Myriapoda, but the two groups are sufficiently different from each other to justify placing them in separate classes.

The members of class Chilopoda are land forms whose bodies are somewhat flattened dorsoventrally and may contain from a few up to 177 somites (Fig. 20-22).

FIG. 20-22

Centipede *Scolopendra*. Class Chilopoda. Most segments have one pair of appendages each. First segment bears pair of poison claws, which in some species can inflict serious wounds to man. Some tropical forms are nearly 1 foot long. Centipedes are carnivorous and prey upon earthworms, insect larvae, and even larger prey.

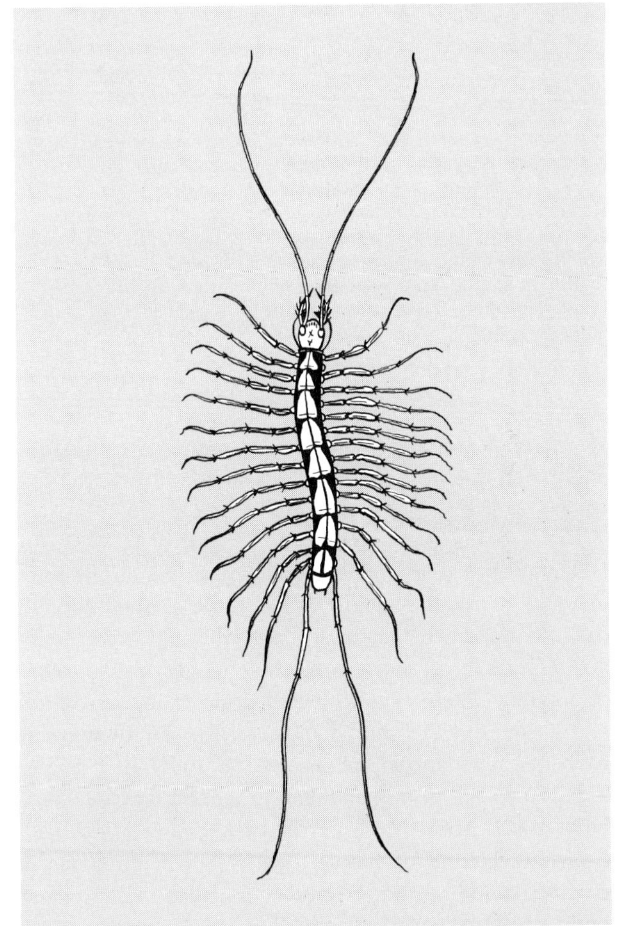

FIG. 20-23

Common house centipede *Cermatia (Scutigera) forceps*. Class Chilopoda. Often seen scurrying around the house, where it eats roaches, bedbugs, and other insects. Its bite was once believed to be poisonous but is now known to be harmless to man.

Each somite, with the exception of the one behind the distinct head and the last two posterior ones, bears a pair of jointed appendages. The appendages of the first body segment are modified to form poison claws.

The head is made up of six somites, the appendages of which are modified similarly to those of an insect. There is a single pair of antennae of few or many segments, a pair of mandibles with no palps, and one or two pairs of maxillae, of which the second pair are usually fused together. A pair of **eyes** are on the dorsal surface of the head and consist of groups of ocelli.

The digestive system is a straight tube into which salivary glands empty at the anterior end. Two pairs of malpighian tubules empty into the hind part of the intestine and take care of the excretory system. The circulatory system contains an elongated heart with a pair of arteries to each somite. Respiration is by means of a tracheal system of branched air tubes, which come from a pair of openings (spiracles) in each somite. The nervous system consists of a pair of cerebral ganglia (brain), a pair of esophageal connectives, and a double nerve cord with ganglia in each somite. There is also a visceral nervous system. Sexes are separate. The reproductive system in each sex contains an unpaired gonad with paired ducts, which open by a single aperture at the posterior end of the body. Some lay eggs and others are viviparous. The young are similar to the adults.

Centipedes have a preference for moist places, such as those under logs, bark, and stones. They are very agile and carnivorous in their eating habits, living upon earthworms, cockroaches, and other insects. They kill their prey with their poison claws and then chew it with their mandibles. The common house centipede *Cermatia forceps* (Fig. 20-23), with fifteen pairs of legs, is often seen scurrying around bathrooms and damp cellars, where they catch insects. Most species

FIG. 20-24

Millipede *Spirobolus*. Class Diplopoda. They have two pairs of jointed appendages on each of their segments except the short thorax of four somites, each of which has one pair of appendages. In some the last one or two segments also have only one pair. Long abdomen is really composed of double segments, which accounts for two pairs of appendages on each apparent somite. In contrast to centipedes, millipedes are usually vegetarian animals. (Courtesy Carolina Biological Supply Co., Burlington, N. C.)

are harmless to man. Some of the tropical centipedes may reach a length of 1 foot.

CLASS DIPLOPODA

These forms are called millipedes, which literally means "thousand legged" (Fig. 20-24). Even though they do not have that many legs, they do have many appendages in proportion to their length and number of somites. Their cylindric bodies are made up of 25 to 100 somites. The short thorax consists of four somites, each bearing one pair of legs; each abdominal somite has two pairs of appendages, a condition that may have arisen from the fusion of two somites. The head bears two clumps of simple eyes, a pair of antennae, a pair of mandibles, and a pair of maxillae. The general body structures are similar to those of centipedes, with a few variations here and there. There are two pairs of spiracles on each abdominal somite. Each spiracle is located in front of a leg and opens into an air chamber, which gives off the tracheal air tubes, branched or unbranched. There are two genital apertures, which are found toward the anterior end.

In most millipedes the appendages of the seventh somite are specialized for copulatory organs. After copulation the eggs are laid in a nest and carefully guarded by the mother. The larval forms have only one pair of legs to each somite. The adults have all the somites, except those of the thorax, fused in pairs.

Millipedes are not so active as centipedes and are herbivorous instead of carnivorous. They prefer dark moist places under logs or stones. They eat decayed matter, whether plant or animal, although sometimes they eat living plants. When disturbed, they often roll up into a ball. Common examples of this class are *Spirobolus* and *Julus*, both of which have wide distribution.

• • •

For derivation and meaning of basic terminology see the end of Chapter 21.

Annotated references

Crustacea

Barnard, J. L., R. J. Menzies, and M. C. Bacescu. 1962. Abyssal Crustacea. New York, Columbia University Press. *A series of three papers based on the findings of the Columbia University research vessel Vema. Emphasis is on systematics, including new species.*

Buchsbaum, R., and L. J. Milne. 1960. The lower animals. Garden City, Doubleday & Co., Inc. *Many fine descriptions of crustaceans and other invertebrates.*

Calman, W. T. 1909. Crustacea. In E. R. Lankester: A treatise on zoology, Part VII, third fascicle. London., A. & C. Black, Ltd. *This account meets the high standards of this outstanding series of zoologic treatises. Its taxonomy is outdated, but all serious students of the arthropods will find a wealth of information in it.*

Edmondson, W. T. (editor). 1959. Ward and Whipple's fresh-water biology, ed. 2. New York, John Wiley & Sons, Inc. *Eight sections are devoted to the various freshwater crustaceans in this imposing and comprehensive handbook of many specialists.*

Green, J. 1961. A biology of Crustacea. London, H. F. & G. Witherby, Ltd. *A concise account of the structure and physiology of this group. Excellent for the beginner.*

Hickman, C. P. 1967. Biology of the invertebrates. St. Louis, The C. V. Mosby Co.

Huxley, T. H. 1880. The crayfish: An introduction to the study of zoology. London, Trubner & Co. *A classic study that is often used as a model of clear and simple biologic presentation.*

Jackson, R. M., and F. Raw. 1966. Life in the soil. (Paperback.) New York, St. Martin's Press, Inc. *Shows how organisms form an integral part of soil, and their importance in soil formation and plant growth.*

Passano, L. M. 1961. The regulation of crustacean metamorphosis. Amer. Zool. 1:89-95.

Pennak, R. W. 1953. Fresh-water invertebrates of the United States. New York, The Ronald Press Co. *The many chapters on crustaceans in this fine work will arouse the interest of the student. Taxonomic keys with illustrative drawings are unusually clear. Extensive bibliographies add much to the usefulness of the work.*

Russell Hunter, W. D. 1969. A biology of the higher invertebrates. (Paperback.) New York, The Macmillan Co. *A concise and up-to-date discussion of this great group.*

Schmitt, W. L. 1965. Crustaceans. Ann Arbor, The University of Michigan Press. *A concise, readable account that will stimulate the interest of the student.*

Smith, G., and W. F. R. Weldon. 1909. Crustacea. Cambridge Natural History, vol. 4. London, Macmillan & Co., Ltd. *A good account of the general structure and organization of crustaceans.*

Waterman, T. H. (editor). 1960-1961. The physiology of Crustacea; metabolism and growth, vol. 1. Sense organs, integration, and behavior, vol. 2. New York, Academic Press, Inc. *This work represents the most recent and up-to-date monograph on this important group of arthropods.*

CHAPTER 21

• PHYLUM ARTHROPODA

Subphylum Mandibulata—insects

CLASS INSECTA

● The insects are the most successful biologically of all the groups of arthropods. Although they comprise only one class out of more than fifty classes of animals, there are more species of insects than of all the others combined. It is estimated that the recorded number of insect species is about 800,000, with thousands of other species yet to be discovered and classified. There is also striking evidence that evolution is continuing among insects at the present time, even though the group as a whole is considered to be stable, according to the fossil record. Studies on *Drosophila* by Patterson, Dobzhansky, and others and on termites by Emerson afford some clear-cut cases of present-day evolutionary change.

It is difficult to visualize the significance of this extensive group and its role in the biologic pattern of animal life. Their bearing upon man's welfare, the competition they offer at nearly every stage of man's existence, and the many useful aspects of this highly specialized group pose problems that are a true challenge to all of man's ingenuity. The science of insects (**entomology**) occupies the time and resources of skilled men all over the world. The struggle between man and his insect competitors seems to be an endless one, for no sooner are they suppressed at one point than they break out at another. Yet such is the paradox of the whole matter that insects have so interwoven themselves into the economy of things in so many useful roles that man would have a difficult time without them.

Distribution

Insects are among the most abundant and widespread of all land animals. They have spread into practically all habitats that will support life except that of the sea. They have shied away from salt water, and only an insignificant few are found there. The marine water striders *(Halobates)* are about the only insects that live on the open sea, but a considerable insect fauna is found in brackish water, in salt marshes, and on sandy beaches. They are found in fresh water, in soils, in forests, in plants, in deserts and wastelands, on mountain tops, and as parasites in and on the bodies of plants and animals.

Their wide distribution is made possible by their powers of flight and their highly adaptable nature. In most cases they can easily surmount barriers that are well nigh impassable to many other animals. Their small size allows them to be carried by currents of both wind and water to far regions. Their well-protected eggs can withstand rigorous conditions and can be carried long distances by birds and animals. The qualities of agility and aggressiveness enable them to fight for every possible niche in a location. Whenever they get a foothold, they do not give up until the last one is completely eradicated. No single pattern of biologic adaptation can be applied to them.

Size range

Insects range all the way from forms smaller than 1 mm. in length to those that are 7 or 8 inches long. Some of the tropical moths have a wingspread of 8 to 12 inches. The smallest forms are probably certain parasitic insects. As a general rule, the largest insects are found in tropical countries. Most insects, however, are rarely more than 1 inch long, and a considerable number fall below this dimension. Some beetles are only $\frac{1}{100}$ inch long.

Relationships and origin

It is difficult to work out the ancestry of insects. Fossils give little help in solving the problem, although the fossil record indicates that the first insects were wingless and date back to the Devonian period. All of the few thousand species of fossil insects that have been found in amber and volcanic ash were winged, but wingless forms (order Collembola) have been found in older rocks. Both chilopods and insects have sharply marked off heads, provided with antennae and jaws, but insects have a thorax, which is wanting in chilopods, and lack the large digestive glands of the crustaceans. Some zoologists think they have come from a crustacean larval form, such as the zoea; others believe they are derived from polychaete worms. One theory holds that insects probably arose from the ancestral stock of the class Symphyla.

Characteristics

1. Body of three clearly defined regions—**head, thorax,** and **abdomen**
2. Head of six segments, with two antennae and two mandibles and two pairs of maxillae; **mouth parts adapted for sucking, chewing,** and **lapping**
3. Thorax of three segments, each with a pair of jointed walking legs; thorax may have two pairs, one pair, or no pair of **wings**
4. Abdomen of not more than eleven segments and **modified posteriorly as genitalia**
5. Respiration by a many-branched **tracheal system,** which communicates with the outside by **spiracles** on the abdomen
6. Digestive system of fore-, mid-, and hindgut and provided with salivary glands
7. Circulatory system of heart, aorta, and hemocoel; no capillaries or veins
8. Excretion by **malpighian tubules** that empty into the hindgut
9. Coelom very much reduced
10. Nervous system of a dorsal brain, subesophageal ganglia, and a double ventral nerve cord provided typically with a pair of ganglia to each somite
11. Sense organs consisting of simple and compound eyes, receptors for taste about the mouth, receptors for touch on various parts of body, and receptors for sound
12. Reproduction by separate sexes; paired gonads with single duct in each sex; fertilization internal; few reproducing by parthenogenesis; most exhibiting **metamorphosis**

Adaptability

Insects have marvelous powers of distribution and the capacity to adjust themselves to new habitats. A survey of any particular community will reveal that insects have occupied more available biologic niches than any other group of animals. Most of their structural modifications center around the wings, legs, antennae, mouth parts, and alimentary canal. This wide diversity of habits enables this vigorous group to take advantage of all available resources of food and shelter. Some are parasitic, some suck the sap of plants, some are predaceous, some chew up the foliage of plants, and some live upon the blood of various animals. Within these different groups, specialization occurs, so that a particular kind of insect will eat, for instance, the leaves of one kind of plant and others will dine only upon another kind. This specificity of eating habits lessens competition among them and to a great extent accounts for their biologic success.

Insects have fitted themselves for a wide range of habitats, especially in dry and desert regions. The hard and protective chitinous exoskeleton prevents evaporation, but the insects also extract the utmost in fluid from food and fecal material, as well as moisture from the water by-product of bodily metabolism. The exoskeleton is made up of a complex system of plates known as sclerites connected to one another by concealed, flexible hinge joints. The muscles between the sclerites enable the insect to make precise movement. The rigidity of its exoskeleton is due to the unique scleroproteins and not to its chitin component, and its lightness makes possible flying. By contrast, crustaceans have stiffened their cuticle by mineral matter and the arachnid by organic materials.

Food habits

The food habits of insects are determined to some extent by their kind of mouth parts, which are usually biting or sucking in nature. The majority of insects feed on plant juices and plant tissues. Such a food habit is called **phytophagous.** Some insects will restrict their feeding to certain varieties of plants; others, such as the grasshoppers, will eat almost any plant that comes their way. It is well known that the caterpillars of many moths and butterflies will eat the foliage of only certain plants. Monarch butterflies are known to be poisonous to birds because their caterpillars assimilate from certain species of milkweed cardiac glycosides that are poisonous to the vertebrate heart.

Ants are known to have fungus gardens on which

they subsist. Many beetles and the larvae of other insects will live upon dead animals (**saprophagous**). Other insects are highly **predaceous,** catching and eating not only members of their own group but those of other groups as well. For these types of feeding, the mouth parts are adapted in a specialized way. The sucking or suctorial mouth parts are usually arranged in the form of a tube and can pierce the tissues of plants or animals. This arrangement is well shown in the water scorpion *(Ranatra fusca),* a member of the order Hemiptera. This elongated, sticklike insect with a slender caudal respiratory tube has a beak in which are four piercing, needlelike stylets made up of two mandibles and two maxillae. These parts are fitted together to form two tubes, a salivary tube for injecting saliva into the prey and a food tube for drawing out the body fluids of the prey. In butterflies and moths the well-known proboscis, which is usually coiled up when not in use, is fitted as a sucking tube for drawing nectar from flowers. Biting mouth parts are adapted for seizing and crushing food; those of most carnivorous insects are sharp and pointed in addition for piercing their prey.

The kind of mouth parts an insect has determines the type of spray used in destroying it. Those that bite and chew their food can be destroyed by applying poison directly to the food; those that suck must be smothered with gaseous mixtures that interfere with their respiration.

Many insects, adults, as well as larvae, are **parasitic.** Fleas, for instance, live on the blood of mammals, and the larvae of many varieties of wasps live upon spiders and caterpillars. In turn, many are parasitized by other insects. Some of the latter are highly beneficial by controlling the numbers of injurious insects. When parasitic insects are themselves parasitized by other insects, the condition is known as **hyperparasitism,** which often becomes quite involved.

Power of flight

Insects share with birds and flying mammals (bats) the power of flight. Most insects have two pairs of wings, one on the mesothorax, the other on the metathorax. However, the wings of insects are not homologous to those of birds and bats, for the latter are derived in an entirely different manner. Wings of insects are extensions of the integument and thus are different from the limb buds of birds and mammals. They vary a great deal and are used for making distinctions in classification. When only one pair of wings is present (Diptera), the missing pair (the metathoracic) is represented by a pair of clublike threads called **balancers,** or **halteres.** In flight these halteres vibrate rapidly in a fixed plane, producing an effect like that of a gyroscope. In many cases the wings are thin and membranous and are called **membranous wings.** Beetles and some others have the front pair of wings thickened and hardened into **horny wings (elytra),** which protect the more delicate flying wings behind. Grasshoppers and closely related forms have the front wings modified into flexible **leatherlike wings (tegmina).** Butterflies and moths have their wings covered with fine

FIG. 21-1

How an insect uses its wings. Chief muscles that move wings of insects have no direct connection with wings but produce flight by changing shape of body wall to which wings are attached. Two sets of muscles attached to inner body wall necessary for flight movements. Vertical muscles, **A,** between tergum and sternum contract to flatten tergum and cause wings to rise. Longitudinal muscles, **B,** contract, causing tergum to bulge upward and wings to be lowered. Alternate contraction of these two sets produces flight. Other muscles attached directly to wings rotate wings as they are lowered and also draw wings to resting position when not in use. Lever-fulcrum attachment of wing is such that slight change in body wall movements produces wide range in wing tips. In dragonflies wings are always in horizontal position and are controlled by direct muscles that produce slight but rapid up-and-down movements. (Modified from Snodgrass.)

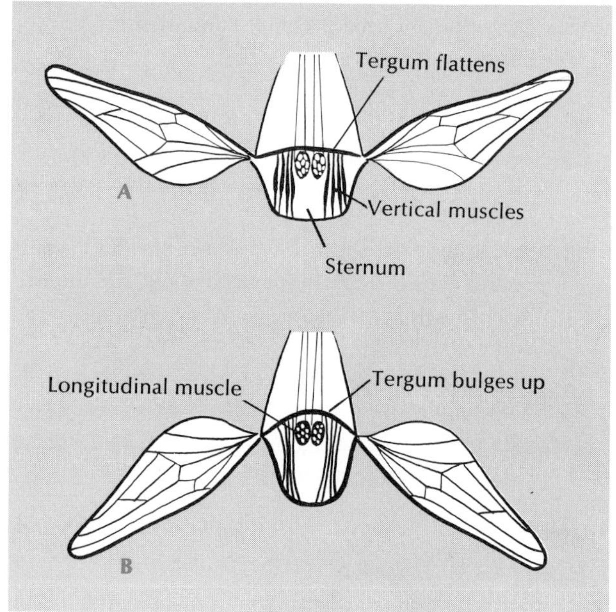

scales, which are easily shed when handled. The pattern of wing venation is more or less peculiar to families and orders and is useful in classification.

The wing beat, as well as the speed, of insects varies greatly with different insects. Many butterflies have very slow wing beats of only 5 or 6 per second; those of honeybees may be as many as 200 per second. Likewise, insects also vary greatly in their speed of flying. Some of the flies are reported by a number of observers to have great speeds, but when these flying records are carefully checked, they are usually found to be exaggerated. In a few orders of insects there are no wings at all, and others have generations without wings followed by generations with wings. For the mechanics of wing movement see Fig. 21-1.

FIG. 21-2

Striking case of protective resemblance in butterfly *Kallima,* which resembles leaf when perched on twig. This butterfly is native of East Indies and was first described by famous English naturalist Alfred Russell Wallace.

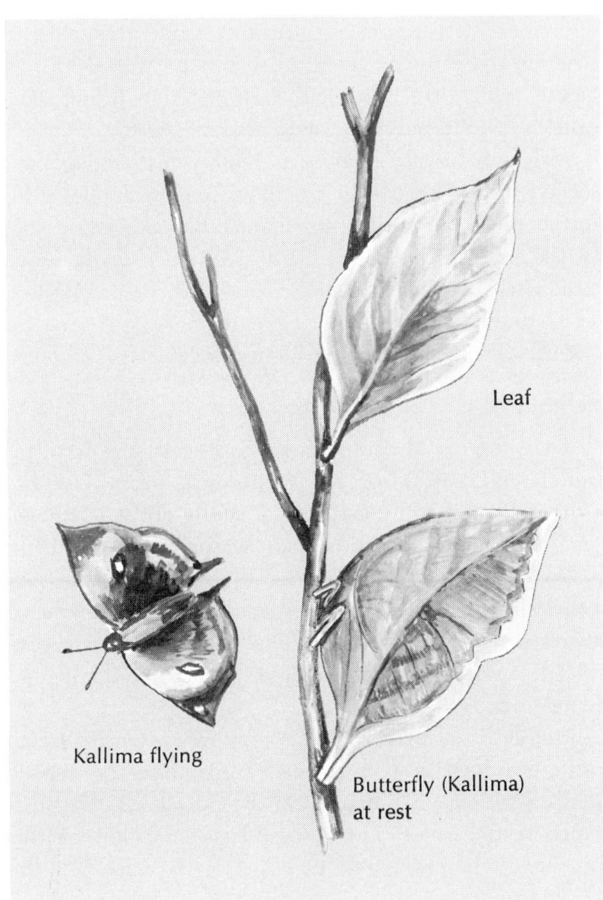

Protection and coloration

Insects as a group display many colors. This is especially true of butterflies, moths, and beetles. Even in the same species the color pattern may vary in a seasonal way, and there also may be color differences between males and females. Some of the color patterns in insects are probably highly adaptive, such as those for **protective coloration, warning coloration, mimicry,** and others (Fig. 21-2).

Besides color, insects have other methods of protecting themselves. The chitinous exoskeleton affords a good protection for many of them; others, such as stink bugs, have repulsive odors and taste; and others protect themselves by a good offense, for many are very aggressive and can put up a good fight (for example, bees and ants); and still others are swift in running for cover when danger threatens. Since bats can detect their prey by echolocation, certain moths have evolved

FIG. 21-3

Nervous systems of three insects showing variation in organization. Two ventral nerve cords lie close together or fused. Paired ganglia are usually fused and communicate by commissures. In primitive termites there is a pair of ganglia for each segment of body. Number is reduced in higher forms (beetles and flies). Supraesophageal ganglion (brain) is connected to subesophageal ganglion by connectives, one of which passes on each side of the esophagus. General trend in higher insects is toward greater degree of centralization and cephalization.

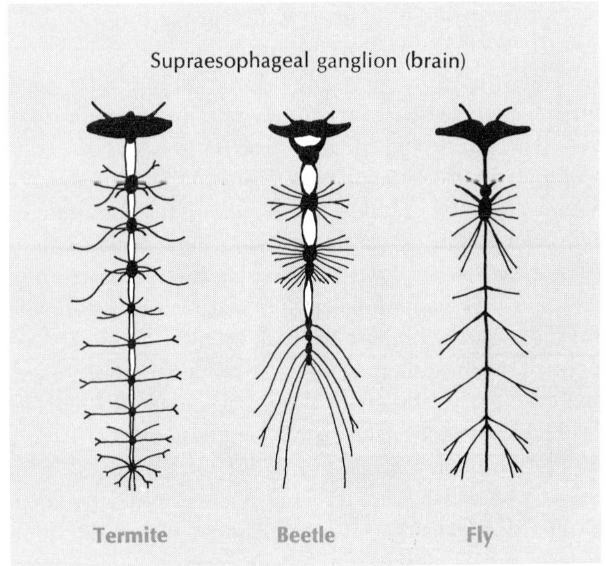

special ultrasonic ears (tympanic membranes) by which they can pick up the bat chirps and thus evade capture.

Neuromuscular coordination

Insects are active creatures and this implies good neuromuscular coordination. Their muscles are strong and numerous (more than 4,000 have been found in a caterpillar) and are mainly of the striated variety. Their strength is all out of proportion to their size, for a flea can hop a distance a hundred times its own length, and a honeybee is known to pull many times its own weight. The nervous system of insects is similar to that of the earthworm, with a ventral double nerve cord and paired ganglia in each somite. In some insects there is a tendency toward centralization and cephalization, the ganglia being concentrated toward the anterior end of the body (Fig. 21-3). The skill and dexterity with which many insects can avoid danger are well known, for everyone realizes how quickly flies can avoid swats and dragonflies can evade a butterfly net. Along with their neuromuscular coordinations the sensory perceptions of insects are unusually keen, especially those involving sight and smell. The compound eyes of insects are adapted for detecting slight movements.

Sound production and reception

A sense of hearing is not present in all insects but appears to be well developed in those that produce sound. Everyone is familiar with many of the sounds of insects, such as the buzzing of bees, the chirping of crickets, and the humming of mosquitoes and flies. Sounds are produced in a variety of ways. Some are the result of the rubbing together of rough surfaces, such as those of the integument. Grasshoppers produce a sound effect by rubbing the femur of the last pair of legs over rough ridges on the forewings. Male crickets scrape their wing covers to produce their characteristic chirping. The hum of mosquitoes and bees is due mainly to the rapid vibration of their wings. Some Hymenoptera produce their sound by a combination of means, such as the vibration of the wings and the special leaflike appendages in the tracheal system. The sound of the cicada is a long drawn-out one produced in a special chamber between the thorax and abdomen. Within this chamber is a membrane connected to a muscle whose rapid contractions cause the membrane to vibrate at different pitches. The cavity amplifies the sound by acting as a resonance chamber.

The humming of bees varies with the temperament of the hive. When excited, the more rapid vibration of the wings produces a difference in sound that is readily detected by those familiar with their ways. Sound may be a means of communication by which insects are able to warn of danger, to call their mates, etc.

Behavior

The keen sensory perceptions of insects enable them to respond to many stimuli. It has been proved experimentally that their chemical senses are far more sensitive than they are in man. Most, if not quite all, of their responses are **reflexes.** Their **taxes** are in many cases clear cut and definite, such as the attraction of the moth for light, the detection of rotting flesh by carrion flies, and the avoidance of light by cockroaches. To attract their mates, many insects emit a delicate odor that is detected by the opposite sex. The taxis of contact (**thigmotaxis**) is illustrated by crickets and beetles, which are often found in narrow crevices; **rheotaxis,** or reaction to water currents, is shown by the caddis fly larvae, which live in rapids. It is now known that mosquitoes are attracted by lactic acid in sweat.

Although insect behavior is mainly instinctive, their behavior patterns can be modified somewhat. Bees, for instance, can be taught to make simple associations between food and color, and ants will learn to make associations between certain odors and food supplies. Thus to some extent they have memory sufficient for the establishment of a conditioned reflex.

Reproduction

The sexes are always separate in insects, and fertilization is internal. Most are **oviparous,** but a few are **viviparous** and bring forth their young alive. **Parthenogenesis** occurs in aphids, gall wasps, and others. In a few (for example, *Miastor*) a process called **pedogenesis** is found. This involves parthenogenesis by larval stages rather than by the adults. Many larvae are produced, some of which pupate to become male and female adults.

Methods of attracting the opposite sex are often quite involved among insects. Some, like the female moth, give off a scent that can be detected a long distance by the males. Fireflies use flashes of light for this purpose, whereas many can find each other by the sounds they make.

Insects usually lay a great many eggs. Perhaps the greatest number of eggs is produced by the queen honeybee, which may lay more than a million eggs during her lifetime. At the other extreme, some viviparous flies bring forth a single young at a time. There seems to be a relation between the number of eggs produced and the care of the offspring. Forms that make no provision for their young bring forth many hundreds of eggs; those that have to provide for the larvae, such as the solitary wasps and bees, lay fewer eggs. Fewness of eggs in one generation may be offset by short life cycles. Houseflies and fruit flies require only about ten days to complete their cycles of development and growth. On the other hand, the number of offspring produced bears no relation to the number of eggs laid, for in some chalcid flies each egg gives rise to more than a hundred embryos (**polyembryony**).

Insects reveal marvelous instincts in laying their eggs. Butterflies will lay their eggs only on the particular kind of plant on which the caterpillar feeds, and the ichneumon fly, with unerring accuracy, seeks out a certain kind of larva on which her young are parasitic. Many, however, drop their eggs, which are often well protected, wherever they happen to be and make no further provision for them.

Metamorphosis and growth

When the young of animals undergo abrupt or pronounced changes in appearance during their development to the adult stage, the process of transition is called **metamorphosis.** Although this condition is not restricted to insects, they illustrate this biological principle better than does any other group. The transformation, for instance, of the hickory horned devil caterpillar (Fig. 21-4) into the beautiful royal walnut moth represents an astonishing change in development. In insects metamorphosis is an outcome of the evolution of wings, which are restricted to the reproductive stage where they can be of the most benefit. Not all insects undergo metamorphosis, but most of them do in some form or other.

FIG. 21-4

Great hickory horned devil. Largest caterpillar in North America; may exceed 5 inches in length. It develops into royal walnut moth *Citheronia regalis*.

Complete metamorphosis (which nine tenths of all insects have) is of great adaptive value, for it separates the great physiologic processes of growth (larva), differentiation (pupa), and reproduction (adult) from each other so that each stage of development can function most efficiently without hindrance from the others. Metamorphosis speeds up the energy-transforming mechanisms of the insect life and gives a broader ecologic niche relationship, for the larvae often live in an entirely different environment from that of the adults and have different food habits. This specialization of development stages promotes also the evolution rate because of greater possibilities of mutations.

Since the exoskeleton acts as a restrictive armor that prevents expansion of the body, an insect can change its form or size by the process of **molting,** or **ecdysis.** Thus, when its cuticula becomes too small for it, a second epidermis is formed by the hypodermis, the old epidermis splits open along the back of the head and thorax, and the insect works its way out of the old exoskeleton.

With regard to their growth and development, insects may be divided into four groups—those having no metamorphosis and those having incomplete, gradual, or complete metamorphosis.

No metamorphosis. A few insects called collectively the **ametabola** have no metamorphosis at all. In these the young hatch from the egg in the same form as the adult insect and development consists of merely growing larger. Good examples among the various orders of insects are the Thysanura and the Collembola. The stages of development in the life cycle of these are (1) egg, (2) young, or juvenile, and (3) adult.

Incomplete metamorphosis. In some insects (Ephemeroptera, Odonata, Plecoptera) the eggs are laid in water and develop into aquatic naiads or nymphs, which are quite different from the the adults (Fig. 21-5). The immature stages of these insects are thus spent in water, whereas the adults are aerial. The naiads have tracheal gills and other modifications for an aquatic life. They grow by successive molts, crawl out of water,

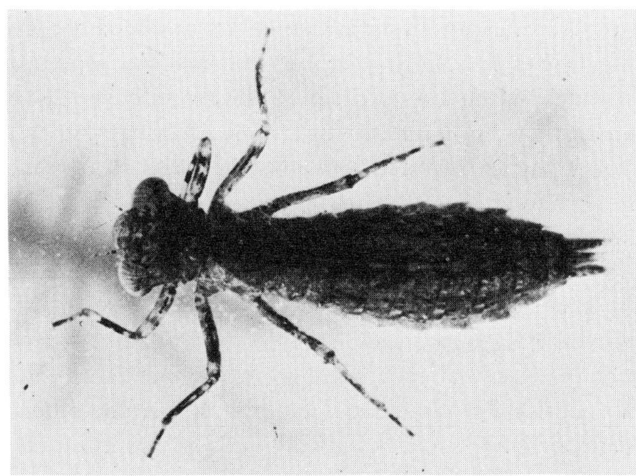

FIG. 21-5

Dragonfly naiad. Order Odonata. Found in bottom of pools and streams.

FIG. 21-6

A, Young praying mantes (nymphs) emerging from their egg capsule. Egg capsules (oothecae) are glued to shrubbery and other objects in late summer and fall. When eggs hatch in spring, enormous swarm of wingless nymphs emerge from single capsule. **B,** Praying mantis, about life size. It gets this name from the way it holds its forelimbs but is far more interested in preying on other insects than in pious devotions. Order Orthoptera. (Courtesy Joseph W. Bamberger.)

and after the last molt become winged adults. Since it includes a partial metamorphosis, it is called **hemimetabola,** and the stages of its life cycle are (1) egg, (2) naiad, and (3) adult. The three orders that have this type of metamorphosis are not closely related phylogenetically but have evolved this type of larval adaptation independently.

Gradual metamorphosis. In this type the newly hatched individual resembles the adult in general bodily features but has no wings or genital appendages (Fig. 21-6). The bodily proportions of the immature form (nymph) are also different from those of the adult. At each **instar** (growing stage) after each molt the nymph looks more and more like the adult. Wing buds appear in the later instars, and finally wings are developed. Both nymphs and adults have the same type of mouth parts and food habits. This type of metamorphosis is called **paurometabola** and is found among Orthoptera, Hemiptera, Homoptera, and many others. The stages of development in the life cycle of these are (1) egg, (2) nymph, and (3) adult.

Complete metamorphosis. A large number of insect orders in their larval development to adults undergo changes that are referred to as complete metamorphosis (Fig. 21-7) and the group as the **holometabola.** About 88% of all insects experience this type of metamorphosis. In this type the young emerge as wormlike segmented larvae, with little difference between the head, thorax, and abdomen. These wormlike forms are called by various names, such as caterpillars, maggots, bagworms, fuzzy worms, and grubs. The larva goes through several instar stages, increasing in size between molts, and then passes into a type of resting period, the **pupa (chrysalis).** It forms around its body a **case** from its outer body covering or a **cocoon** by spinning silk threads around itself. Within the cocoon or case the final metamorphosis occurs, and finally the adult, or **imago,** appears. When it emerges, the adult is as large as it ever will be, for it undergoes no further molting. In complete metamorphosis the stages of development are (1) egg, (2) larva, (3) pupa, and (4) adult.

Physiology of metamorphosis. Metamorphosis in insects is controlled and regulated by hormones—a process that has been much studied. There are three major endocrine organs involved in development through the larval stages to the pupa and eventually to the emergence of the adult. These organs are the **brain,** the **prothoracic glands,** and the **corpora allata** (Fig. 21-8). The intercerebral part of the brain and the ganglia of the nerve cord contain several groups of neurosecretory cells that produce an endocrine substance called the **brain,** or **activation, hormone.** These neurosecretory cells may send their axons to another organ behind the brain, the **corpora cardiaca,** which serves as a storage place for the activation hormone. The corpora cardiaca are of nervous origin, similar to the neurohypophysis of vertebrates. In the blood the activation hormone is carried to the prothoracic gland, a glandular organ in the prothorax, which is stimulated to produce the **molting hormone,** or **ecdysone.** This hormone sets in motion certain processes that lead to the casting off of the old skin (ecdysis) by proliferation of the epidermal cells. If the larval form is retained at the end of this process, it is called simple molting; if the insect undergoes changes into pupa and adult, it is called metamorphosis.

FIG. 21-7

A, Caterpillar of angulifera moth *Callosamia angulifera.* **B,** Pupa of angulifera moth. **C,** Angulifera moth.

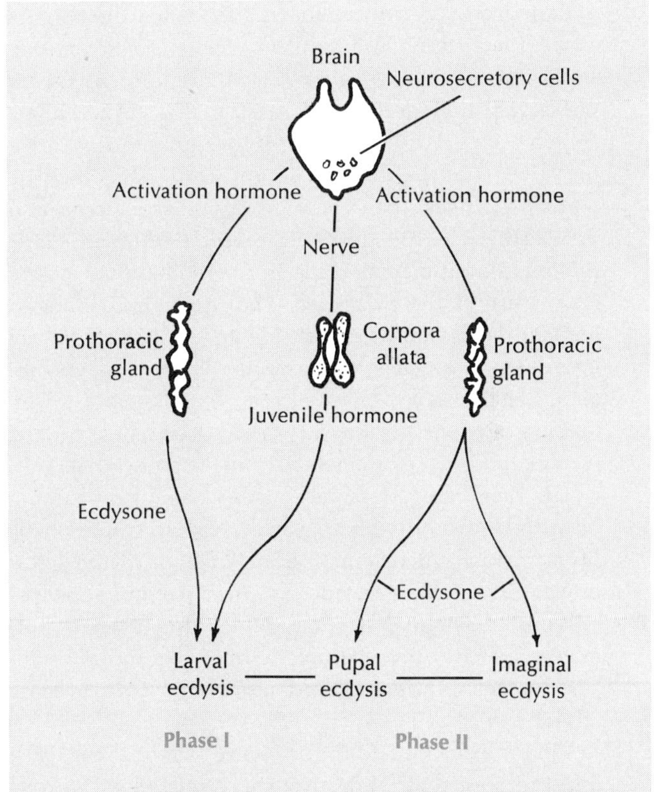

FIG. 21-8

Hormone control in complete metamorphosis of insect. Molting hormone (ecdysone) sets in motion the process of casting off skin (ecdysis) in larva. If juvenile hormone is present along with ecdysone (phase I), only simple molting of larva will occur, each ecdysis producing larger larva. When only ecdysone is secreted (phase II), larva will molt into pupa, and pupa will molt into mature form, or imago (metamorphosis).

Simple molting persists as long as a certain **juvenile hormone** (neotenine) is present in sufficient amounts, along with the molting hormone in the blood, and each molting simply produces a larger larva.

The juvenile hormone is produced by a pair of tiny glands (**corpora allata**) located near the corpora cardiaca. The kind of cuticle that is produced depends on the amount of juvenile hormone present. If only a small amount of this hormone is present, a pupal cuticle is the result. When the corpora allata cease to produce the juvenile hormone, the molting hormone alone is secreted into the blood and the adult emerges (metamorphosis). It is thus seen that the molting hormone is necessary for each molt but is modified by the juvenile hormone.

Experimental evidence shows that, when the corpora allata (and thus the juvenile hormone) are removed surgically, the following molt will result in metamorphosis into the adult. Conversely, if the corpora allata from a young larva are transplanted into an old larva, the latter can be converted into a giant larva, because no metamorphosis can occur. Many other experimental modifications on this theme have been performed. Some progress has also been made in determining the chemical nature of the hormones. The mechanism of molting and metamorphosis just described is that found in insects with complete metamorphosis (holometabola), but the same factors also apply in general to the molting nymphal stages of those that have gradual metamorphosis (paurometabola or hemimetabola) in which there are no pupal stages. The blood-sucking bug *Rhodnius,* on which so many classic studies have been made about metamorphosis, belongs to the latter group. A recent method of insect control involves the use of compounds that mimic the juvenile hormones which prevent insects from becoming sexually competent when treated just before they become adults.

What factors initiate the sequence role of these three different hormones? How are they correlated with cyclic events in the life histories of insects? Experimentally it has been shown that low temperature activates the neurosecretory cells of the intercerebral gland of the brain, which then sets in motion the sequence of events already related. The chilling of the brain seems to be all important in the initiation of metamorphosis. Adults cannot molt and grow because they have no prothoracic glands. Many aspects of the control mechanism of these interesting processes have not yet been worked out.

Diapause

Diapause refers to a condition or state of physiologic dormancy or arrested development. Although the concept may apply to variant similar conditions in other animals, its original meaning has direct reference to insects. It is well known that there are periods in the life cycle of many insects when eggs, pupae, or even adults remain for a long time in a state of dormancy because external conditions of climate, moisture, etc., are too harsh or unfavorable for survival under states of normal activity. Because of diapause the insect egg has a mechanism for preventing evaporation from dry surroundings, the pupa can withstand extreme cold, and the adult can synchronize its life cycle with an abundance of food. Altogether, it is an important adaptation in the embryonic larvae and pupal stages of most insects of the northern hemisphere. Diapause is that stage of the life cycle when the insect's morphogenesis is interrupted because of unfavorable environmental conditions and is resumed when climate, season, and food are favorable for development and survival. The evidence indicates that hormones are responsible for the control of diapause, for the latter occurs whenever the neurosecretory cells of the brain fail to secrete the molting hormone. Diapause always occurs at the end of an active growth stage of the molting cycle so that, when the diapause period is over, the insect is ready for another molt, or ecdysis.

Social instincts

Some insects such as bees and ants exhibit very complicated patterns of social instincts. It is true that most insects are more or less solitary and come together only for mating, and that some are at times found together in large gregarious swarms, but others have worked out complex societies involving **division of labor.** In these societies the adults of one or both sexes live together with the young in a cooperative manner. The size and complexity of these insect organizations vary with the kind of insects. Among the bumblebees the groups are small and the groupings last only a season. The honeybee, however, has worked out one of the most striking examples in the insect world. Instead of lasting one season, their organization continues for a more or less indefinite period. As many as 60,000 to 70,000 bees may be found in a single hive. Of these, there are a single **queen,** a few hundred **drones** (males), and the rest **workers** (infertile females). The workers carry on all the activities of the hive except the laying of eggs. They gather the nectar from flowers, manufacture honey, collect pollen, secrete wax, take care of young, and ventilate and guard the hive. Each worker appears to do a specific task in all this multiplicity of duties. Their life span is only a few weeks. One drone fertilizes the queen and stores sperm enough in her spermathecae to last her a lifetime. The life span of drones is usually for the duration of the summer, for they are driven out or killed by the workers. A queen may live as long as five seasons, during which time she may lay a million eggs. She is responsible for keeping the hive going during the winter, and only one queen will be tolerated in a hive at one time.

The efficiency of a honeybee community in summary, according to a recent appraisal by C. G. Butler, depends on the following:

1. A fine division of labor between the queen and workers and between the workers themselves
2. A queen substance of known chemical constitution that must be sufficiently present on the body of the queen to attract workers and to hold the colony together
3. A system of communication by which workers are informed about food substances and sources
4. A method of carefully distinguishing between members of their own colony and intruders
5. A system of control that prevents a new queen from being developed as long as a satisfactory queen is present, and to reproduce the colony by swarming when necessary

The social vespids, or paper wasps, such as the bald-faced hornets (Fig. 21-40) and the yellow jackets, also have a caste system of queens, workers, and drones. They construct a nest (Fig. 21-9) of papery material consisting of wood or foliage chewed up and elaborated by the wasp.

Ants and termites also have complicated social lives. An ant colony has a single fertile queen and, at times, fertile males (drones). Of the infertile females, some are soldiers, some are workers to gather food, some are nursemaids for the young, etc. Among termites, social life is still more complex (Fig. 21-10). Their colonies contain two castes. One of these consists of fertile males and females; the other, of infertile males and females. The reproductive individuals may or may not have wings. If they have wings, they leave the colony, mate, lose their wings, and start a new colony. Those reproductive individuals without wings may, under certain

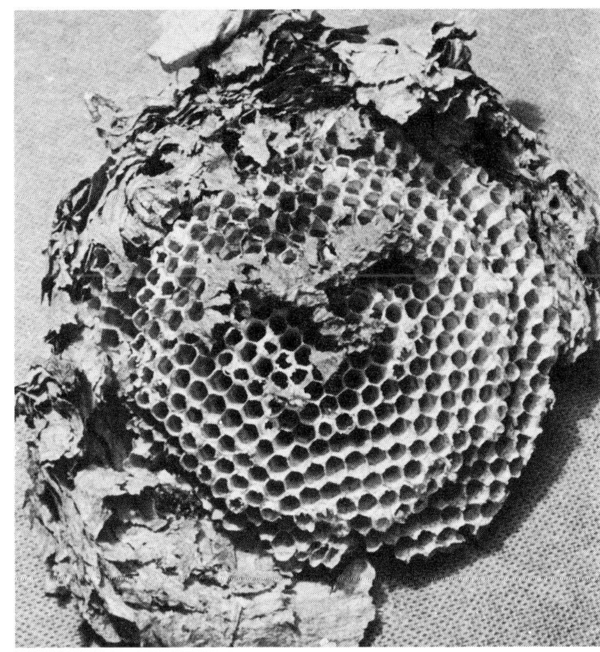

FIG. 21-9

Paper nest of bald-faced hornet *Vespula maculata,* cut open to show one of the horizontal combs. These nests are attached to bushes or trees and are composed of fibers of weatherworn wood. Larvae are reared in comb cells. See Fig. 21-40 for photograph of hornet.

conditions, substitute for the king and queen. The sterile members have no wings and make up the workers and soldiers. Within the castes, there are also different types. These caste differentiations are not due to genetic but to extrinsic factors. Reproductive individuals and soldiers secrete **ectohormones** containing inhibiting substances that are passed to the nymphs through a mutual feeding process called **trophallaxis.** These inhibitory ectohormones prevent the nymphs from differentiating into reproductive members and soldiers, and such undifferentiated nymphs become sterile workers instead. In large populations some nymphs do not become inhibited, and these differentiate into the other castes. In termites and certain ants the sterile workers are represented by both sexes, but among social bees and most ants the workers are infertile females. The phenomenon of trophallaxis appears to be common among all social insects because it serves to integrate the colony and permits its members to rec-

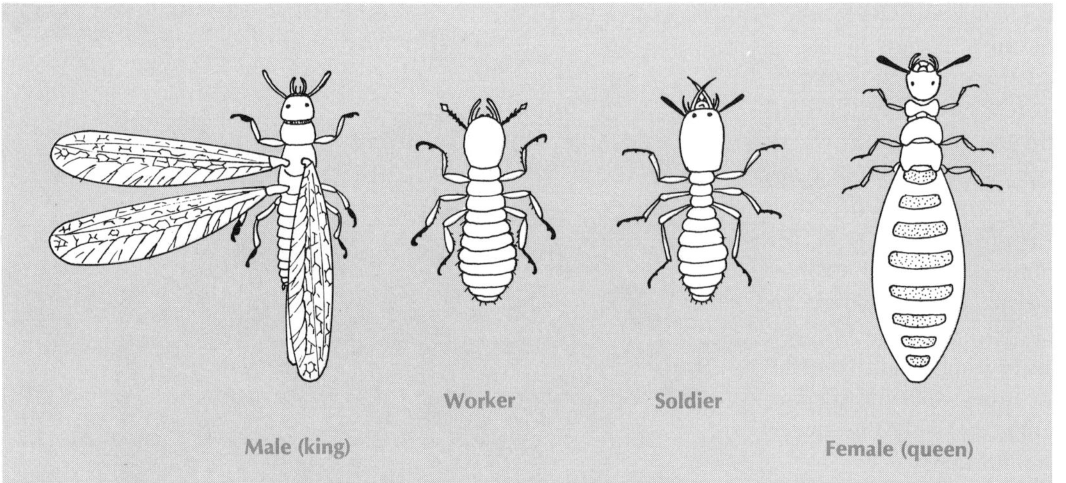

FIG. 21-10

Castes of termites. Parents of a colony are king and queen. Both are winged, but after swarming they shed their wings. If taken over by group of workers, they start colony and queen begins to lay eggs as her body, filled with eggs, grows to enormous size. Workers and soldiers may be of either sex, but are sterile. Many subcastes of major castes are also found.

ognize one another in large populations. The process involves the feeding of the young by the queen and workers, which in return lick the secretions given off by the young members.

Ants and termites have reached a peak of insect social evolution, for they have evolved striking patterns of economic behavior, such as making slaves, farming fungi, herding "ant cows" (aphids), sewing their nests together with silk, and using tools.

Relation to man's welfare

It would require a large amount of space to enumerate all the ways insects benefit and harm man's interests. More are probably injurious than helpful.

Beneficial insects. The beneficial insects (Fig. 21-11) may be listed as follows:

1. Those insects that produce useful products for man's use. Among these may be mentioned first the products of the honeybee, such as honey, which amounts to several thousand tons each year, and beeswax, which amounts to many hundred tons annually. Another valuable product is silk produced by the silkworm. Some 25,000 cocoons are necessary to make 1 pound of silk, and 50 million pounds of silk are produced each year. Shellac is made from a wax secreted by the lac insects, which belong to family Coccidae; and the dye cochineal, formerly much used in histology, is made from the dried bodies of another coccid, which lives on the cactus plant.

2. Insects that are necessary to cross-fertilize the blossoms of fruits and crops uscful to man. These include the bees that are indispensable in raising fruits, clover, and other crops. To raise the Smyrna fig in California it was necessary to make use of the small fig wasp (*Blastophaga*), which carries pollen from the nonedible caprifig.

Insects and higher plants (angiosperms) diversified at the same time in the Cretaceous and Tertiary periods. They also formed an intimate relationship of mutual adaptations that have been to each other's advantage. Insects exploit flowers for food, and flowers exploit insects for pollination. Insects are able to distinguish basic flower types, which explains the pollination relationship between the two groups. Each flower type or floral development of petal and sepal arrangement is correlated with the sensory adjustment of certain pollinating insects. The same kind of flower is visited by an insect highly adapted as a pollinator for that kind of flower. Throughout a long evolutionary period the mutual adaptations of insects and their flower hosts have resulted in amazing devices of allurements, traps, specialized structures, precise timing, etc., which pose evolutionary problems of the first order (H. F. Becker).

3. Predaceous insects that destroy other insects harmful to man. Among these are tiger beetles, aphid lions, ant lions, praying mantes, ladybird beetles, wasps, and many others. Many insects control injurious insects by parasitizing them. Such insects usually lay their eggs on the larvae of the harmful ones, and the larvae hatched from these eggs slowly devour their host.

4. Insects that are beneficial because of their scavenger habits. Many beetles and flies live on both animal and plant refuse and litter. Dead animals are quickly taken care of by the maggots of flies that lay

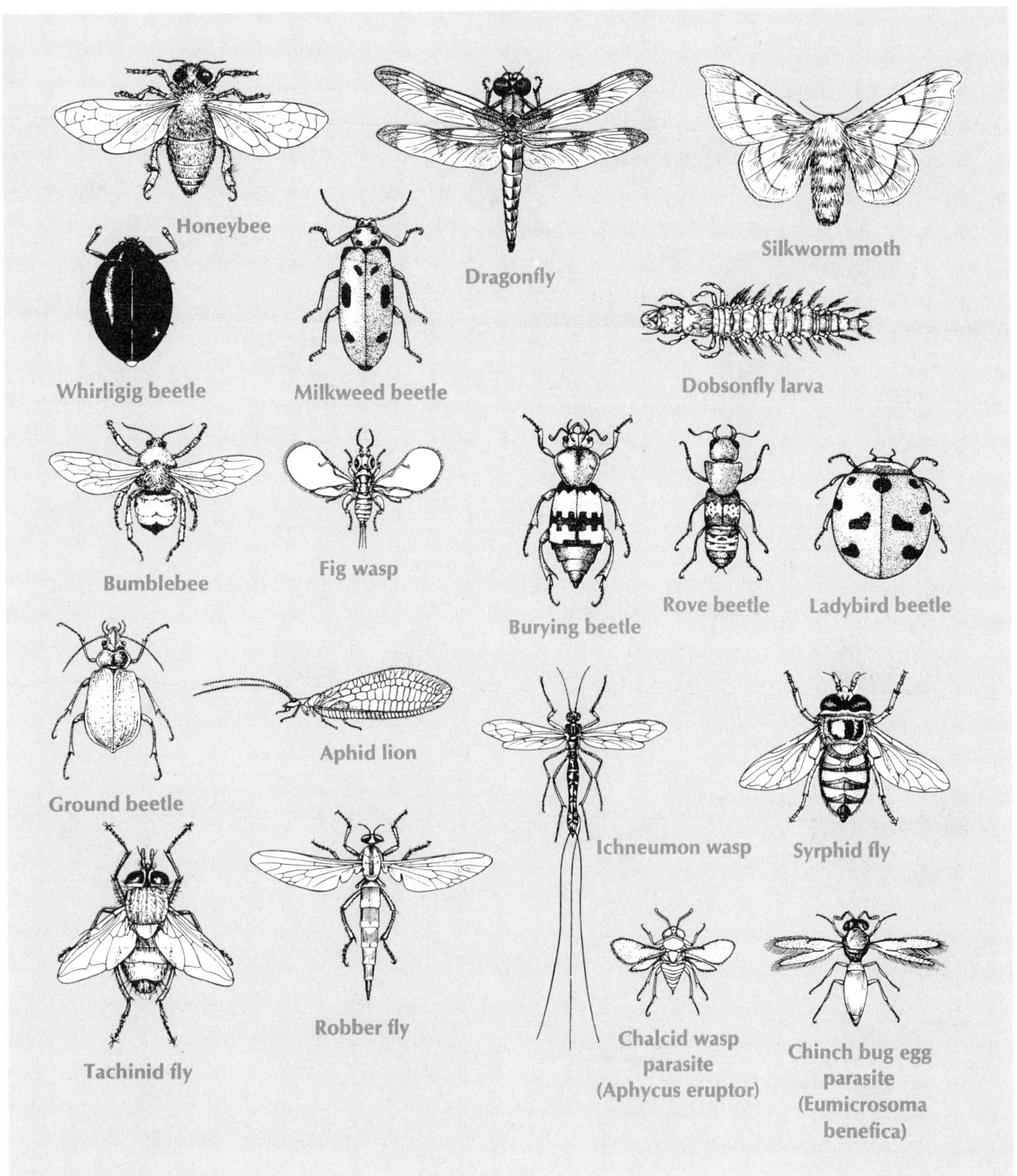

FIG. 21-11

Beneficial insects. (Courtesy General Biological Supply House, Inc., Chicago.)

their eggs in the carcasses. Tumblebugs roll up balls of dung in which they lay their eggs; the developing larvae eat up the dung.

5. Insects as food. Many birds and animals depend upon insects for their food supplies. Some fish also get a considerable part of their food supply from aquatic insects.

Harmful insects. The harmful insects (Fig. 21-12) may be grouped as follows:

1. Those insects that eat and destroy plants and fruits. These include grasshoppers, chinch bugs, Hessian flies, corn borers, cotton-boll weevils, San Jose scales, Mediterranean fruit flies, grain weevils. wireworms, and scores of others; the amount of damage done by these insects is more than a billion dollars each year. Every cultivated crop is bothered to some extent by insect pests.

2. Those insects that annoy and harm domestic animals. This is a large group and includes lice, blood-sucking flies, warble flies whose larvae burrow into the

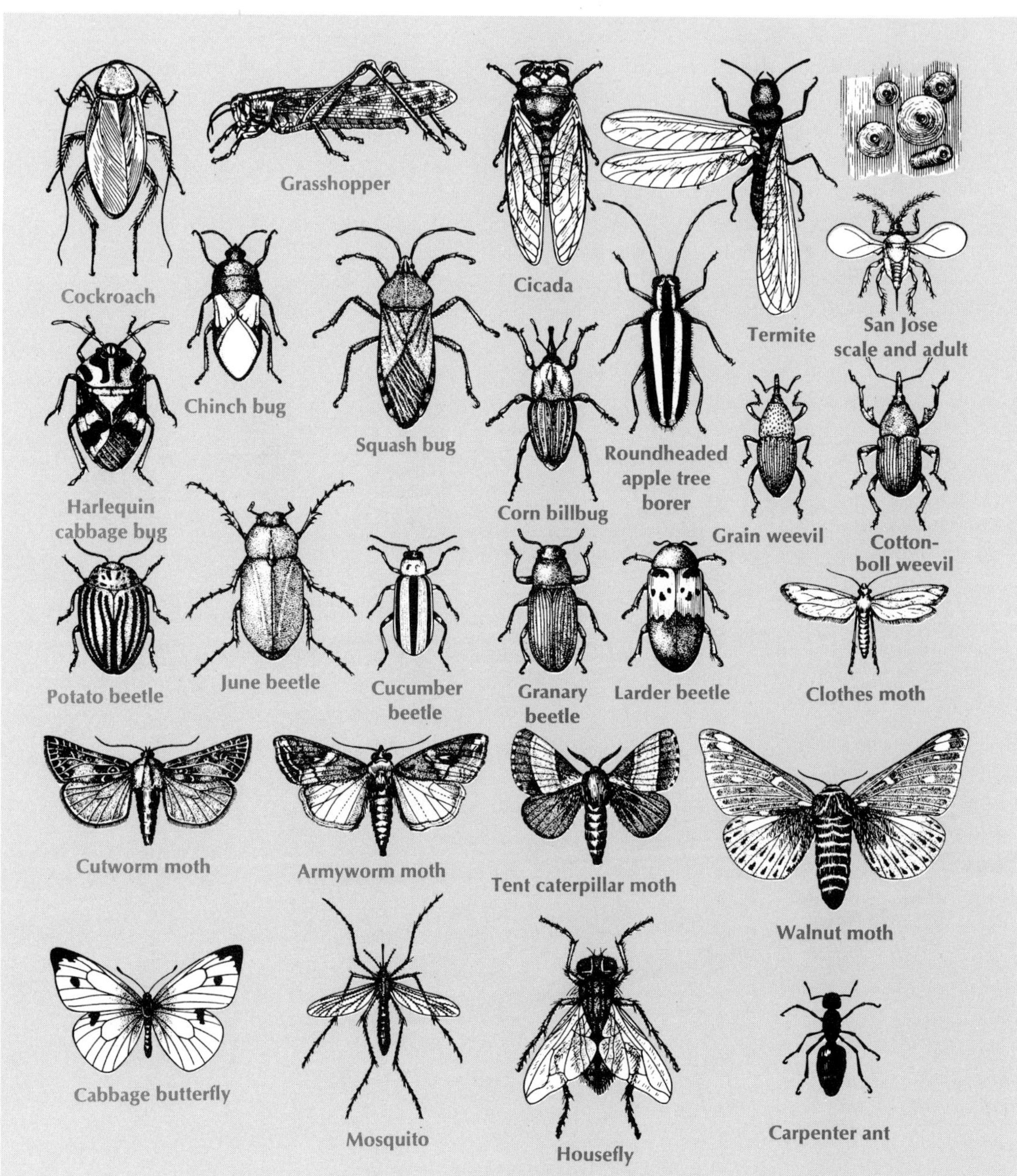

FIG. 21-12

Harmful insects. (Courtesy General Biological Supply House, Inc., Chicago.)

skin of cattle, larvae of botflies in the stomach of horses, etc.

3. Insects responsible for transmitting diseases. These have an enormous influence on man, for some of our most devastating diseases are carried by insects. Among the chief vectors of disease are the mosquitoes, which carry malaria, yellow fever, and filariasis; houseflies, which carry typhoid fever, dysentery, and other diseases; tsetse flies, which carry African sleeping sickness; fleas, which carry bubonic plague; and body lice, which carry typhus fever.

4. Those insects that are destructive in the household. These include insects that injure or damage food, such as weevils, cockroaches, and ants, and those that damage clothing and furnishings, such as clothes moths (Fig. 21-13) and carpet beetles. Among these

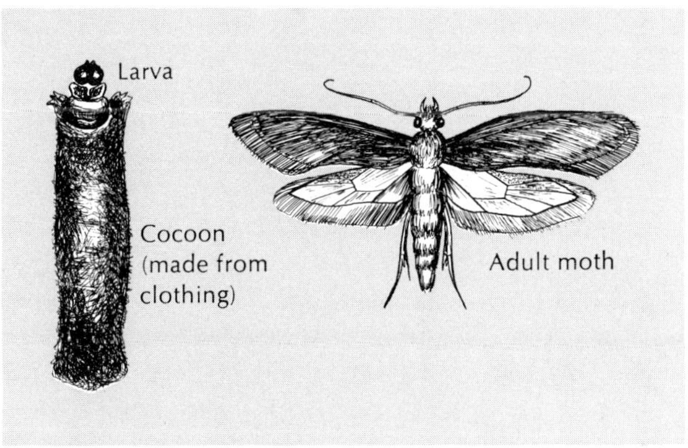

FIG. 21-13

Clothes moth *Tinea* and its larval case. Injury is restricted to larvae, which build their cocoons from fabrics, usually woolen, upon which they feed. Adults lay eggs upon clothing or fabric not in daily use and kept more or less in the dark.

are the termites which are highly destructive to buildings and wooden structures.

Romalea microptera—lubber grasshopper

The insects show a considerable variety of morphologic characters. Some have a more or less generalized plan of body structure, and others, because of some special habit of food getting or living conditions, are specialized in certain particulars. The grasshopper, or locust, is a good representative of the generalized type and is commonly studied in our laboratories for that reason. The big lubber grasshopper is a favorite for study, but the description that follows may apply to grasshoppers in general, for their structural patterns are similar.

Habitat. Grasshoppers have a worldwide distribution and are found where there are open grasslands and abundant leafy vegetation. The prairies of the west have immense hordes of them, because there they have abundant food and ideal places to breed. Most American grasshoppers do not migrate to any extent, but those in Europe and Asia do so frequently, often depleting the food in one region and then moving on to another. Some species have very short wings or no wings at all and thus are restricted in their range.

Grasshopper plagues. The early settlers of the great plains of our West often had to contend with great migratory swarms of grasshoppers, which were driven out of an arid region, where food was scarce, to the cultivated fields of wheat and corn. Many farms there had to be abandoned because of the ravages of these pests. Stories are handed down of these great plagues. In Salt Lake City there is a monument to the gulls that saved the early Mormons from a grasshopper plague. So great were some of their swarms that railroad trains were unable to make their way through the teeming masses. The insects still flair up in those regions, but better control measures have usually kept them in check. The worst grasshopper plagues have probably been in the Old World, such as in Russia, southern Europe, and northern Africa. One of the worst locust plagues ever reported occurred in Tunis and Algiers in 1908, when swarms of locusts darkened the sun for days as they flew in from the deserts and arid regions. They literally ate up every form of vegetation wherever they were, devastated hundreds of square miles, and caused all railroad transportation to come to a standstill.

Various devices are used to control grasshoppers, such as sprinkling poisoned mash over the fields, collecting them in traps and ditches covered with oil (which suffocates them), and early fall plowing, which destroys the eggs laid in the soil by the females during the summer.

External features. The body is composed of the typical insect plan of head, thorax, and abdomen (Fig. 21-14). The head is made up of six fused somites; the thorax, three somites, on which are the legs and wings; and the abdomen, eleven somites. Covering the body is the **exoskeleton,** or **cuticle,** of chitin secreted by the epidermis underneath. The exoskeleton is divided into hard plates, **sclerites,** which are separated from each other by soft cuticula (sutures). This permits the coat of armor to be moved freely. The head is made up of a dorsal portion, the **epicranium;** a region in front, the **frons;** and the sides, or **genae.** Below the frons is the plate, or **clypeus.** On each side of the head is a **compound eye,** and three **simple eyes (ocelli)** are located in the region between the compound eyes. A pair of slender **antennae** are also found on the head. On the ventral side of the head (Fig. 21-15) are the chewing mouth parts, consisting of (1) the upper lip, or **labrum,** attached to the clypeus; (2) a membranous tonguelike **hypopharynx** just back of the mouth; (3) two heavy jaws, or **mandibles,** toothed for chewing food; (4) two **maxillae,** each with several parts; and (5) the lower lip, or **labium,** which is made up of a number of parts, including a pair of **labial palps.**

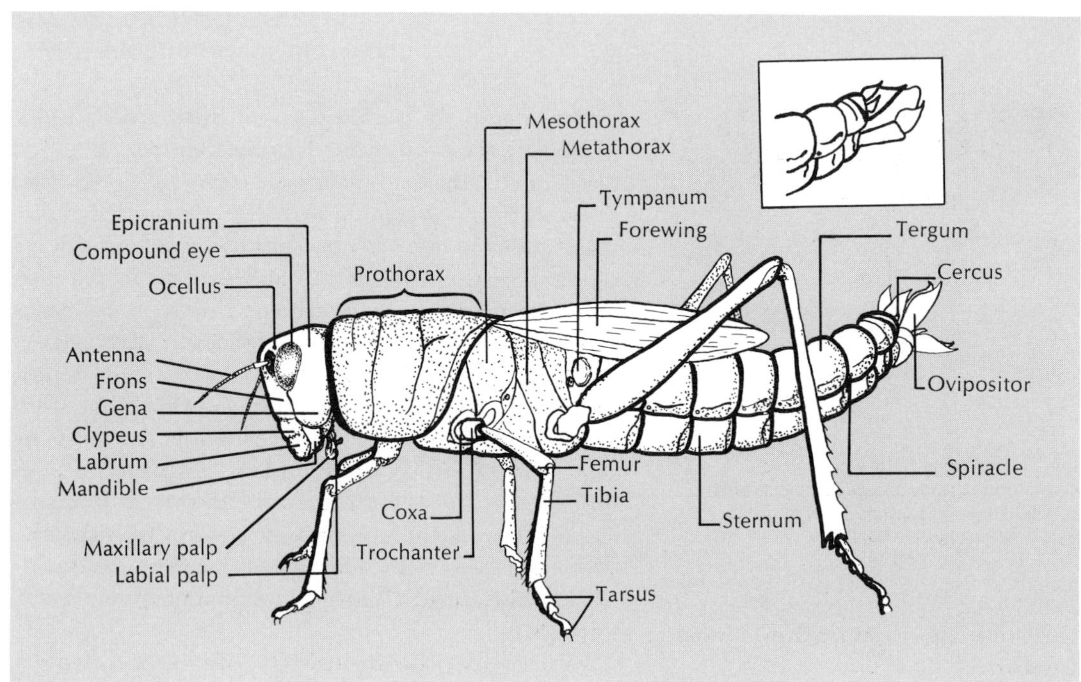

FIG. 21-14

External features of female grasshopper. Terminal segment of male shown in insert.

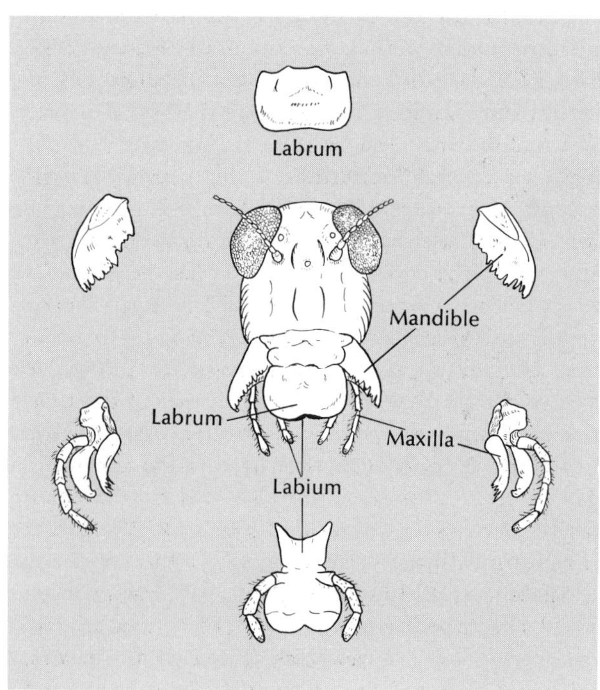

FIG. 21-15

Mouth parts of grasshopper.

The **thorax** contains the anterior **prothorax,** which bears the saddlelike pronotum, a middle **mesothorax,** and the posterior **metathorax.** Each of these segments bears a pair of legs, and the mesothorax and metathorax each bear a pair of wings also. There are eleven sclerites in each somite, divided among a dorsal **tergum** of four, a **pleuron** of three on each side, and a ventral **sternum** of one. Each leg has the following segments (Figs. 21-14 and 21-16): the **coxa** attached to the body; the **trochanter,** short and fused to the large **femur;** the slender **tibia;** and the **tarsus,** which contains three visible segments, the proximal one bearing four pairs of ventral pads and the terminal one a pair of **claws,** between which is the fleshy **pulvillus.** The claws and pulvilli are used by the insect in clinging. The metathoracic legs are adapted for leaping. The **hindwings** are membranous. Many are veined and fold up under the narrow leathery **forewings** like a fan. These wings are outgrowths of the epidermis and consist of a double membrane, which contains the tracheae. The **veins** represent the thickened cuticle around the tracheae and serve to strengthen the wing. Although these veins vary in their patterns among the different species, they are constant in individuals of certain species, where they serve for classification.

The **abdomen** is elongated and tapers toward the end, where the terminal somite is specialized for copulation or egg laying. Ten pairs of **spiracles,** small openings into the respiratory system, are found along the lower sides of the abdomen. The first segment of the abdomen has its sternum united to the thorax, and its tergum bears on either side the oval **tympanic membrane,** which covers the auditory sac of hearing. The terminal segments of the abdomen are modified in the two sexes for copulation and egg laying (Fig. 21-14). The end of the abdomen in the male is rounded; that of the female, pointed. The first seven abdominal segments are alike. In both sexes the terga of 9 and 10 are partly fused. In the male the tergum of 11 forms the **supra-anal** plate over the anus. A small process called the **cercus** projects on each side behind 10, and the sternum of 9 is long and bears the subgenital plate, which terminates dorsally in two short projections. The subgenital plate covers the male genital apparatus. In the female the sternum of 9 is elongated and the abdomen terminates in two pairs of lobes, or valves, with a smaller pair hidden between the larger valves. The **ovipositor,** or egg-depositing mechanism, is made up of these three pairs of valves.

Internal features (Fig. 21-17). The internal cavity of the grasshopper is a **hemocoel,** that is, contains blood, and is not a true coelomic cavity. Striated muscles are grouped for the movement of the mouth parts, wings, and legs. In the abdomen there are segmental muscles for respiratory and reproductive movements.

The most conspicuous organ system in the body is the **digestive system.** It consists of (1) a **mouth,** surrounded by the mouth parts, into which the **salivary glands** open; (2) a short tubular **esophagus;** (3) a thin-

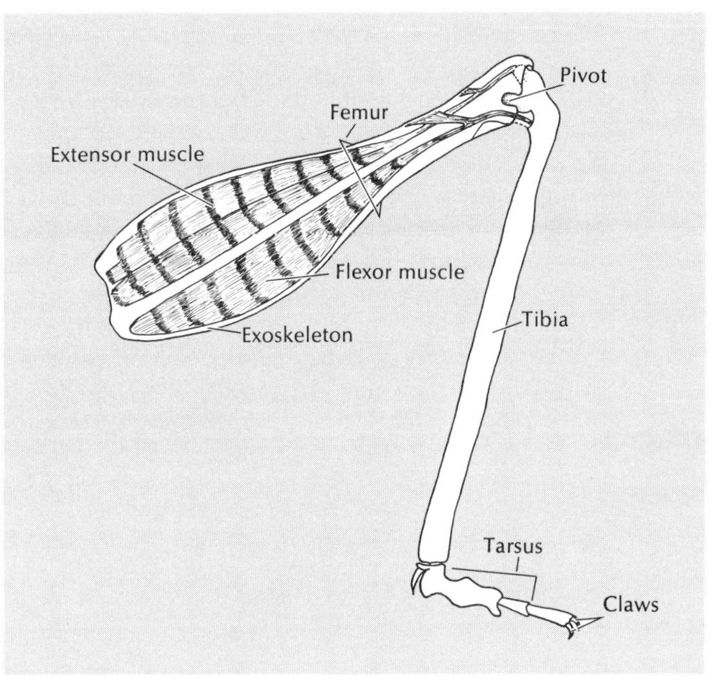

FIG. 21-16

Hind leg of grasshopper. Muscles that operate leg are found within hollow cylinder of exoskeleton. Here they are attached to internal wall, from which they manipulate segments of limb on principle of lever. Note pivot joint and attachment of tendons of extensor and flexor muscles, which act reciprocally to extend and flex limb.

FIG. 21-17

Internal structures of female grasshopper with right body wall removed (diagrammatic).

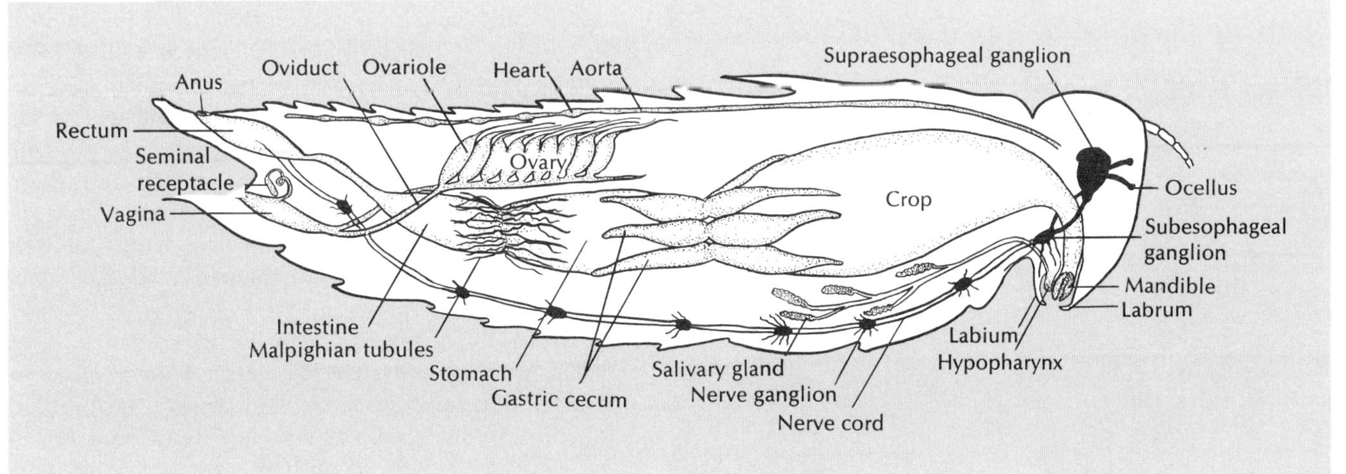

walled **crop;** (4) a **proventriculus,** or gizzard, for grinding food; (5) a **stomach,** or **ventriculus;** (6) a series of six double thin-walled **gastric ceca,** which open into the stomach; (7) an **intestine;** (8) an enlarged **rectum;** and (9) an **anus.** The first four divisions mentioned form the **foregut,** the next two make up the **midgut,** and the last three comprise the **hindgut.** Both the foregut and the hindgut are lined with chitin, and thus absorption of food is confined mainly to the stomach portion.

The **circulatory system** is much reduced compared with that of many other arthropods. There are (1) a tubular **heart** lying in the pericardial cavity close to the dorsal wall of the abdomen with small openings, the **ostia;** (2) a **dorsal aorta,** which extends from the heart into the head region; and (3) a **hemocoel** made up of spaces between the internal organs. The system is an open one (lacunar), for there are no capillaries or veins. Its sole function appears to be the transportation of food, for the grasshopper, in common with other insects, has a separate tracheal system for respiration.

FIG. 21-18

Portion of tracheae of insect. Fine transversely striated appearance is due to spiral thickenings in walls to prevent them from collapsing. (Photomicrograph.)

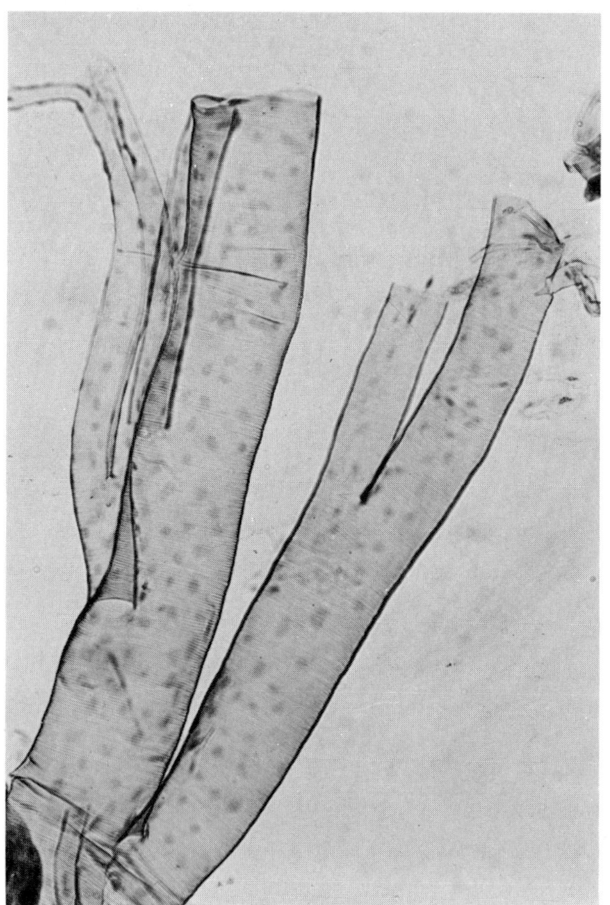

Respiration is taken care of by an extensive network of tubes, **tracheae** (Fig. 21-18), that go to every part of the body. The tracheal tubes consist of a single layer of cells and are lined with cuticle, which is shed at molting. The larger tubes are prevented from collapsing by spiral threads of chitin. The **spiracles** on each side of the body lead by branches into a longitudinal trunk. The finer air tubes, called **tracheoles,** are connected directly to the body tissues to deliver oxygen and carry away carbon dioxide. There are also several **air sacs** in the abdomen, which pump air in and out of the tracheal system by the alternate contraction and expansion of the abdomen. The action of the spiracles is so synchronized that the first four pairs of spiracles are open at inspiration and closed at expiration, while the other six pairs are closed at inspiration and open at expiration.

The **excretory system** consists of the **malpighian tubules,** which are joined to the anterior end of the hindgut. Their free ends are closed, and they remove waste from the blood in the hemocoel and pass it into the hindgut.

The **nervous system** consists of (1) a **brain** of three fused ganglia (**supraesophageal ganglion**), which supplies the head organs; (2) two **connectives,** which connect to the **subesophageal ganglion;** and (3) the ventral **nerve cord,** made up of paired ganglia and longitudinal connectives. A pair of ganglia is found in each thoracic somite, and five pairs are scattered through the abdomen. The smaller number in the abdomen is explained by the fusion of certain ganglia. Nerves run from the ganglia to the visceral organs, legs, and wings. There is also an **autonomic nervous system** in two divisions. Nerves from this system supply the muscles of the digestive system, the spiracles, and the reproductive system.

Grasshoppers have all the major senses—touch, taste, smell, hearing, and sight. The chief sensory receptors are the **olfactory** organs on the antennae; **tactile hairs** on the antennae, palps, cerci, and legs; **taste organs** on the mouth parts; **compound eyes** concerned with vision; **ocelli** for light perception; and **auditory organs,** which are located on the sides of the first abdominal somite and consist of a tympanic membrane within a circular chitinous ring. Grasshoppers produce sound by rubbing the hind tibia with its rough surface against the wings.

Sexes are separate in grasshoppers, and distinction between male and female can be determined by the posterior ends of the abdomen. In the male it is round; in the female it is pointed because of the **ovipositor.** In the male the **reproductive system** (Fig. 21-19) consists of the two **testes,** above the intestine; the two **vasa deferentia** that lead from the testes to the **seminal vesicles,** which unite to form the common **ejaculatory** duct; and the **copulatory** organ (penis). **Accessory glands** secreting a fluid open into the ejaculatory tube. In the female (Figs. 21-17 and 21-19) are two **ovaries** made up of egg tubules (**ovarioles**), two **oviducts** from the ovaries, a median **vagina** formed by the union of the two oviducts, and a small **seminal receptacle,** which stores sperm from copulation. The genital opening is between the plates of the ovipositor.

Fertilization and development. In copulation the male inserts his copulatory organ into the vagina of the female and transfers his sperm. The sperm are stored in the seminal receptacles until the eggs are laid. The mature eggs, 3 to 5 mm. long, pass down the oviduct and pick up the yolk and shell before fertilization. A small opening in the egg, the **micropyle,** enables the sperm to enter and fertilize the egg. The female makes a tunnel in the ground with her ovipositor and then deposits her eggs. The eggs are usually laid in lots of twenty, and a single female may lay several lots. A few days later the adults die. Development lasts about three weeks and ceases when cold weather comes. Growth begins in the spring when the temperature is warmer. The young **nymph** that hatches from the egg resembles the parent, but its head is disproportionally large and it lacks wings. As the young grasshopper grows and becomes too large for its chitinous exoskeleton, which is shed periodically, wings finally develop and it reaches the adult form.

FIG. 21-19

Reproductive organs of grasshopper. Male on left; female on right.

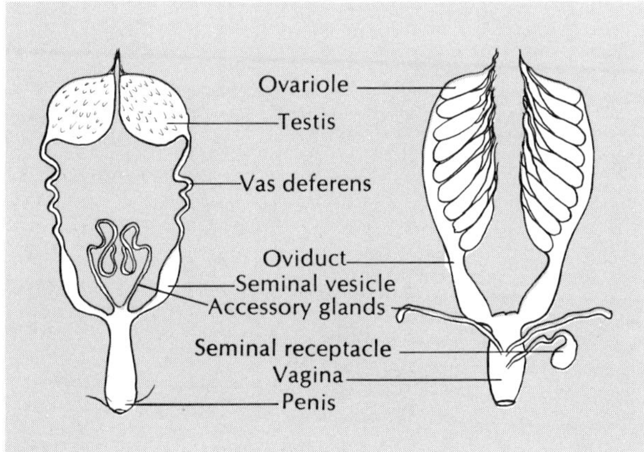

Some structural variations among insects

Since the grasshopper is about the only insect studied in our general zoology courses, it is well to point out a few of the modifications of its structural pattern shown by other insects. The grasshopper represents a generalized plan into which many other insects fit, but some are highly specialized in their habits and reactions, and this is often accompanied by a corresponding change in bodily structures. These differences are more pronounced in external characteristics than they are in internal features. Some of these variations are described here to get a view of their adaptive modifications. Others have already been mentioned in the first part of our discussion on insects.

Body form. There are many patterns of body shape. Some insects are of the thick plump variety, such as beetles (Figs. 21-32 to 21-35); others have long slender bodies, such as the damselfly, crane fly, and walking stick (Fig. 21-24). Many have bodies of a distinctly streamline form, which is represented by aquatic bugs and beetles (Fig. 21-32). Some insects are very much flattened (for instance, cockroaches, Fig. 21-12), which is an adaptation for living in crevices. The termination of the abdomen often has a lot to do with the impression one gets of the general shape of the body. The abdomen in insects has appendages only at the posterior end, and in the female of various species the ovipositor may be extremely long (ichneumon wasp, Fig. 21-39). Some also bear modifications of the cerci, such as the horny forceps of earwigs (Fig. 21-25) and those of stone flies and silverfish. Some insects such as moths have hairy coverings. Bees have many bristles for collecting pollen (Fig. 21-21).

Mouth parts. The mouth parts of insects are for chewing or sucking. The sucking type may be modified

FIG. 21-20

Various types of insect antennae. From left to right: mosquito (plumose); May beetle (laminate); click beetle (serrate); tenebrionid beetle (moniliform); and water scavenger beetle (clavate).

also for piercing, as in the mosquito. Insects that live on vegetation usually have mandibles for crushing, whereas those of carnivorous insects are specialized for piercing and sucking. Those of the honeybee are fitted for both chewing and sucking. The chewing mouth type may be considered the generalized type; the piercing one usually has the labrum and the epipharynx modified into a tubelike structure.

Antennae. Antennae may be long, as in cockroaches, some grasshoppers, and katydids, or short, as in dragonflies and most beetles. Some have plumed antennae, as in moths, and others have naked and club-shaped ones (Fig. 21-20). Butterflies have little knobs on the ends of their antennae.

Legs. Legs of insects show modifications for special purposes. Terrestrial forms have walking legs with terminal pads and claws as in beetles. These pads may be sticky for walking upside down, as in houseflies.

FIG. 21-21

Adaptive legs of honeybee (left side). In foreleg toothed indentation covered with velum is used to comb out antennae. Spur on middle leg removes wax from wax glands on abdomen. Inside of hind leg (metatarsus) bears pollen comb (not shown); long hairs of pecten remove pollen from comb of opposite leg, then auricle presses it into pollen basket when leg joint is flexed back. Bee carries load in both baskets to hive, pushes pollen into cell, to be cared for by other workers.

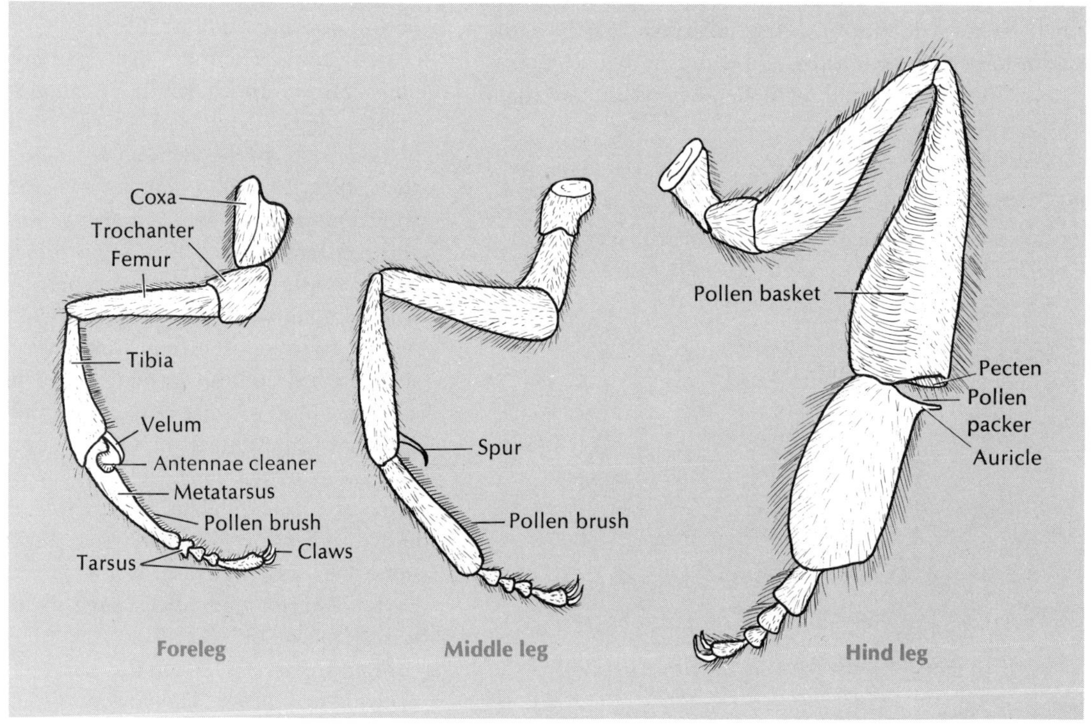

The mole cricket has the first pair of legs modified for burrowing in the ground. Water bugs and many beetles have paddle-shaped appendages for swimming. For grasping its prey, the forelegs of the praying mantis are large and strong.

The **honeybee** is a good example of how an insect's legs are developed for special purposes (Fig. 21-21). The first pair of legs in this insect is suited to collect pollen by having a feathery **pollen brush** on the tarsus and a fringe of hairs along the medial edge of the tibia for cleaning the compound eye. A semicircular indentation lined with teeth is found in the metatarsus, and this is covered over with a spine, the **velum** from the tibia. As the antenna is pulled through this notch, it is cleaned of pollen; hence this structure is called the **antennae cleaner.** The middle leg has a **pollen brush** on the first tarsal joint and a **spur** at the distal end of the tibia. This spur is for the removal of the wax from the wax glands located on the ventral side of the abdomen. The hind limb is the most specialized of all, for it bears the **pollen basket,** the **pollen packer,** and the **pollen combs.** The pollen basket is made up of a concavity on the outer surface of the tibia, with hairs along both edges. These hairs are kept moist with secretions from the mouth. The pollen packer consists of a row of stout bristles on the lower end of the tibia and the auricle, a smooth plate on the proximal end of the metatarsus. The pecten removes the pollen from the pollen comb of the opposite leg onto the auricle. When the leg is flexed, the auricle presses against the end of the tibia, compressing the pollen. Pollen combs are found on the inner surface of the metatarsus and consist of rows of stout spines.

Light production

Some four or five orders of insects are represented among forms that are self-luminous. Others may appear luminous, but this is probably due to luminous bacteria. The best-known insects that produce their own light are the glowworm and the firefly. The former may be the larvae of a fly (the New Zealand glowworm) or that of a beetle (Lampyridae, the common one of Europe and elsewhere). Some glowworms are wingless females. The firefly (which belongs to a family of the beetles) is famed all over the world for its display of light. In these the photogenic organs are located on the ventral surface of the last abdominal segment and consist of two kinds of cells—those that serve as a reflector (dorsal mass) and large cells with granules that are the photogenic cells (ventral mass). Running into the mass of photogenic cells is an extensive network of tracheae, which are connected to tracheal end cells. The organ is thus ensured of a good supply of oxygen. The actual source of the light is probably the granules in the cells. The organ appears to be under nervous control, for nerves run to it.

Brief review of insect orders

The following is a classification of insects with a brief description of each order (Fig. 21-22). Some entomologists restrict the definition of an insect to those arthropods that have six legs and fourteen postcephalic segments and do not add segments in postembryonic stages. By this definition the orders Protura and Collembola would be excluded as insects because their segmentation differs from that of the other orders.

Subclass Apterygota (ap-ter'y-go"ta) (Gr. *a,* not, + *pterygotos,* winged). Primitive wingless insects, that is, have not come from winged ancestors; with little or no metamorphosis; usually stylelike appendages on pregenital abdominal segments, in addition to cerci.

Order 1. Protura (pro-tu'ra) (Gr. *proto,* first, + *oura,* tail). These are considered the most primitive of insects, for they have no wings, no antennae, no compound eyes, and no metamorphosis. Appendages are present on abdomen as well as thorax. They are small, around 1 mm. in length, and are found in damp places, such as under leaves, bark, and moss. Example: *Acerentulus.*

Order 2. Collembola (col-lem'bo-la) (Gr. *kolla,* glue, + *bole,* dart)—**springtails** (Fig. 21-22). These have no wings, compound eyes, or tracheae (usually). They have a peculiar springing organ (furcula) on the ventral side of the fourth abdominal segment. They derive their name from the sticky secretion from a gland near the labium, by which they can adhere to objects. Most are under 5 mm. long. They are often found in damp places under leaves and bark. They are especially abundant sometimes in early spring on snowbanks. Example: *Achorutes.*

Order 3. Thysanura (thy'sa-nu"ra) (Gr. *thysanos,* tassel, + *oura,* tail)—**bristletails** (Fig. 21-22). These are also wingless, with long antennae. The abdomen is provided with two or three long, jointed cerci. Some are quite small and others may be more than 1 inch long. A familiar form is the silverfish (*Lepisma*), which is often found in homes, where they eat the starch of book covers and clothing. Another one is the firebrat (*Thermobia*), often found about fireplaces.

Subclass Pterygota (pter'y-go"ta) (Gr. *pterygotos,* winged). Usually winged, but if wingless, the condition is acquired; no abdominal appendages except cerci. This subclass includes 97% of all species of insects.

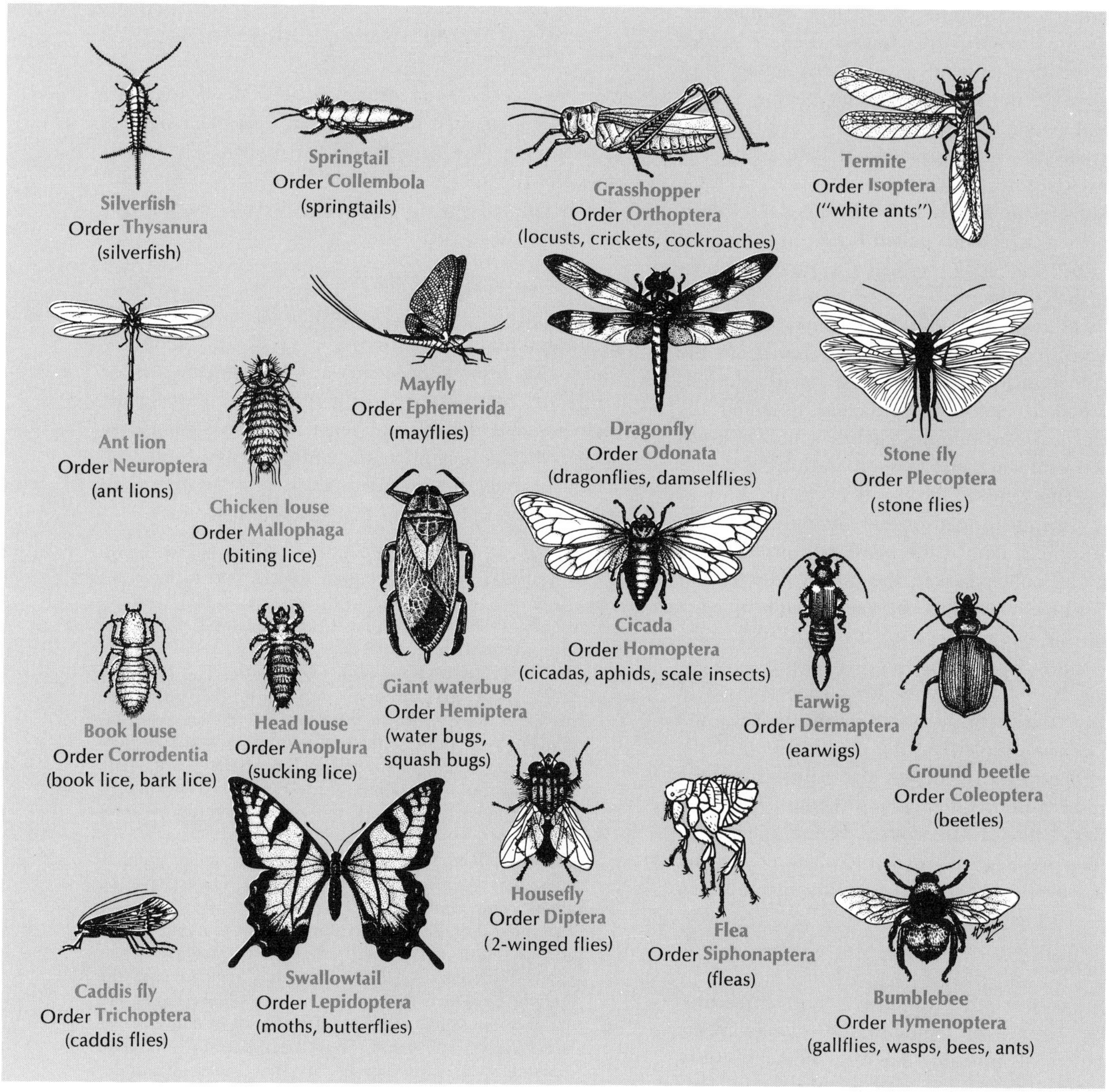

Silverfish
Order Thysanura
(silverfish)

Springtail
Order Collembola
(springtails)

Grasshopper
Order Orthoptera
(locusts, crickets, cockroaches)

Termite
Order Isoptera
("white ants")

Ant lion
Order Neuroptera
(ant lions)

Chicken louse
Order Mallophaga
(biting lice)

Mayfly
Order Ephemerida
(mayflies)

Dragonfly
Order Odonata
(dragonflies, damselflies)

Stone fly
Order Plecoptera
(stone flies)

Cicada
Order Homoptera
(cicadas, aphids, scale insects)

Book louse
Order Corrodentia
(book lice, bark lice)

Head louse
Order Anoplura
(sucking lice)

Giant waterbug
Order Hemiptera
(water bugs,
squash bugs)

Earwig
Order Dermaptera
(earwigs)

Ground beetle
Order Coleoptera
(beetles)

Caddis fly
Order Trichoptera
(caddis flies)

Swallowtail
Order Lepidoptera
(moths, butterflies)

Housefly
Order Diptera
(2-winged flies)

Flea
Order Siphonaptera
(fleas)

Bumblebee
Order Hymenoptera
(gallflies, wasps, bees, ants)

FIG. 21-22

Orders of insects. (Courtesy General Biological Supply House, Inc., Chicago.)

FIG. 21-23

Mole cricket *Gryllotalpa*. Note how forelegs are adapted for digging. Order Orthoptera.

Division 1. Exopterygota (ek'sop-ter'i-go"ta) (Gr. *exo*, outside, + *pterygotos*, winged). With gradual metamorphosis.

Order 4. Orthoptera (or-thop'ter-a) (Gr. *orthos*, straight, + *pteron*, wing)—**grasshoppers (locusts), crickets, cockroaches, etc.** (Fig. 21-22). Two pairs of wings are found in this order. The forewings (tegmina) are thickened, and the hindwing is folded like a fan under the forewing. These insects have chewing mouth parts and gradual metamorphosis. The group is a very extensive one and includes the grasshoppers, cockroaches, crickets, walking sticks, and praying mantes (Figs. 21-23 and 21-24). Most of them are harmful, but the praying mantis (Fig. 21-6, *B*) is useful in destroying other insects. Example: *Romalea.*

FIG. 21-24

Walking stick. Note resemblance to twigs. (Shown slightly less than life size.)

Order 5. Dermaptera (der-map'ter-a) (Gr. *derma*, skin, + *pteron*, wing)—**earwigs** (Figs. 21-22 and 21-25). The forewings of earwigs are very short, with large membranous hindwings. They have biting mouth parts and gradual metamorphosis. The tip of the abdomen bears a pair of curious, forcepslike cerci. *Forficula* is a common example.

Order 6. Plecoptera (ple-kop'ter-a) (Gr. *pleko*, fold, + *pteron*, wing)—**stone flies** (Fig. 21-22). The four wings are membranous and held pleated on the back when not in use. Mouth parts (not always present) are for chewing, and the metamorphosis is incomplete. The larval form (naiad) is aquatic and bears tufts of tracheal gills. Example: *Pteronarcys.*

Order 7. Isoptera (is-sop'ter-a) (Gr. *isos*, equal, + *pteron*, wing)—**termites** (Fig. 21-22). These are often wrongly called white ants. They have chewing mouth parts and gradual metamorphosis. They can be distinguished from true ants by the broad union of the thorax to the abdomen. Sexual forms have four similar wings, which they shed after mating; workers and soldiers are wingless and blind. There are many subcastes. Termites are one of the best examples of a social insect, for they live in large colonies. Their diet is exclusively wood, and in tropical countries they are among the most destructive of insects. They are also fairly common in the temperate zones. To aid in their digestion of wood, termites have in their intestines flagellate protozoans that secrete enzymes for the breakdown of cellulose. The mounds of the colonies in the tropics are often imposing affairs. Example: *Reticulotermes.*

Order 8. Ephemerida (efh'e-mer"i-da) (Gr. *ephemeros*, lasting but a day, + *ida*, pl. suffix)—**mayflies** (Fig. 21-22). The wings are membranous, with the forewings larger than the hindwings. Adult mouth parts are vestigial, and the metamorphosis is incomplete. The naiads are aquatic, with lateral tracheal gills. *Ephemera* is a common form.

FIG. 21-25

Earwig. Forcepslike cerci at posterior end are usually better developed in male and are used as organs for defense and offense. Order Dermaptera. (Stained preparation, greatly enlarged.)

Order 9. Odonata (o-do-na'ta) (Gr. *odontos,* tooth, + *ata,* characterized by)—**dragonflies, damselflies** (Fig. 21-22). This order gets its name from its toothlike biting mouth parts. These insects have two pairs of membranous wings, incomplete metamorphosis, and large compound eyes. They represent a beautiful group of insects that are often seen flying gracefully over ponds hawking for their food. The larval forms are aquatic (Fig. 21-5), those of the dragonfly being provided with a long, hinged labium with which they capture their prey. The naiad has gills in its rectum and breathes by alternately drawing in and expelling water. *Gomphus* is a common example. The members of this order have nonflexible wings that cannot be folded flat over their bodies. These and the mayflies are often called the Palaeoptera (ancient-winged) because of this characteristic, in contrast to the Neoptera (new-winged), which can fold their wings.

Order 10. Corrodentia (cor'ro-den"ti-a) (L. *corrodens,* gnawing, + *ia,* pl. suffix)—**book lice** (Fig. 21-22). These are small insects with chewing mouth parts and four membranous wings (sometimes absent). Metamorphosis is gradual. They are sometimes found in books, since they have a fondness for the starch of the bindings, and also in bird's nests and under bark. *Troctes* is an example.

Order 11. Mallophaga (mal-lof'a-ga) (Gr. *mallos,* wool, + *phago,* eat)—**biting lice** (Fig. 21-22). These insects are less than ¼ inch long and are wingless. Their legs are adapted for clinging to the host, and their mouth parts are for chewing. Their metamorphosis is gradual. They live exclusively on birds and mammals, eating feathers, hairs, and skin debris. The common chicken louse is *Menopon.*

Order 12. Embioptera (em'bi-op"ter-a) (Gr. *embios,* lively, + *pteron,* wing)—**embiids.** These are small insects with elongated bodies, with wingless females and usually winged males. Their mouth parts are for chewing, and their metamorphosis is gradual. They make silk-lined channels in the soil and are colonial. They are mostly tropical forms. *Embia* is an example.

Order 13. Thysanoptera (thy'sa-nop"ter-a) (Gr. *thysanos,* tassel, + *pteron,* wing)—**thrips.** These are only a few millimeters long or smaller. Some are wingless, but others have four similar wings. They have sucking mouth parts and gradual metamorphosis. Parthenogenesis is common among them. They live by sucking the juices of plants. *Thrips* is an example.

Order 14. Anoplura (an'o-plu"ra) (Gr. *anoplos,* unarmed, + *oura,* tail)—**sucking lice** (Fig. 21-22). The bodies of these insects are small and depressed, and they are wingless. Their mouth is adapted for piercing and sucking, and they have no metamorphosis. These are the true lice, and three kinds have become pests to man: (1) the head louse (*Pediculus capitis*), which lives on the head hair and lays its eggs (nits) there; (2) the body louse (*Pediculus corporis*), sometimes called the "cootie," which lives on the body and head, lays its eggs in the clothing and hair, and is responsible for carrying typhus fever, trench fever, and other diseases; and (3) the crab louse (*Phthirius pubis*), which often gets in the pubic hair. Many other kinds are found on various mammals.

Order 15. Hemiptera (he-mip'ter-a) (Gr. *hemi,* half, + *pteron,* wing)—**true bugs** (Fig. 21-22). This is an extensive group of great economic importance. The front

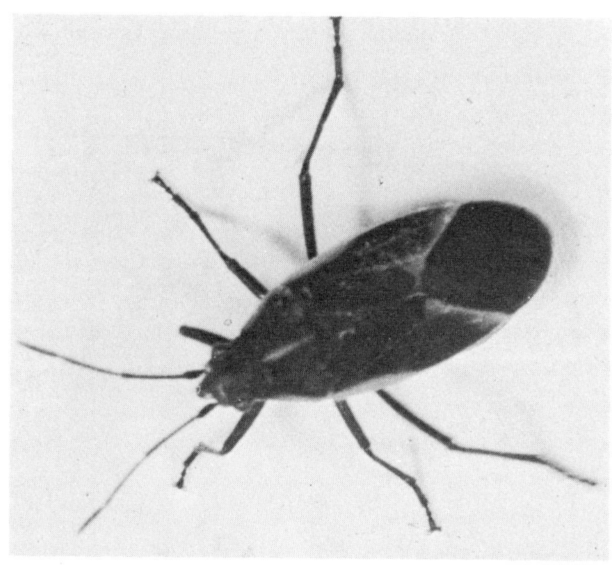

FIG. 21-26

Box elder bug *Leptocoris.* These often become a nuisance in the fall when they enter houses in swarms, seeking place to hibernate. However, they do no damage to house contents. Order Hemiptera.

FIG. 21-27

Harlequin cabbage bug *Murgantia.* Order Hemiptera.

wings of these insects are thickened and leatherlike at the anterior half but membranous at the posterior half, whereas the hindwings are membranous and fold under the front ones. They have piercing and sucking mouth parts, and the metamorphosis is gradual. This order includes such groups as the water bugs, bedbugs, stinkbugs, chinch bugs, assassin bugs, and water striders (Figs. 21-26 and 21-27). *Gerris* is the familiar water strider.

Order 16. Homoptera (ho-mop'ter-a) (Gr. *homos*, same, + *pteron*, wing)—**cicadas, aphids, scale insects, leaf hoppers** (Fig. 21-22). These insects have two pairs of wings (absent in some) of uniform thickness and texture. The mouth parts are for piercing and sucking, and there is gradual metamorphosis. One of the most noted members of this order is the cicada, or 17-year locust (*Magicicada septemdecem*). Eggs are laid in trees, where they hatch into nymphs, which then drop to the ground. Then for 17 years they make their home in the soil, living on plant juices from the roots of trees. At the end of this time they crawl up a tree trunk,

FIG. 21-29

Hellgrammite. Larval form of dobsonfly *Corydalis*, much prized by fishermen for bait. Order Neuroptera.

FIG. 21-28

Aphid *Aphis*. Aphids not only have an interesting reproductive cycle but certain kinds also excrete honeydew for ants, which in turn take care of the aphid's eggs and preserve adults from harm. Order Homoptera. (Photomicrograph.)

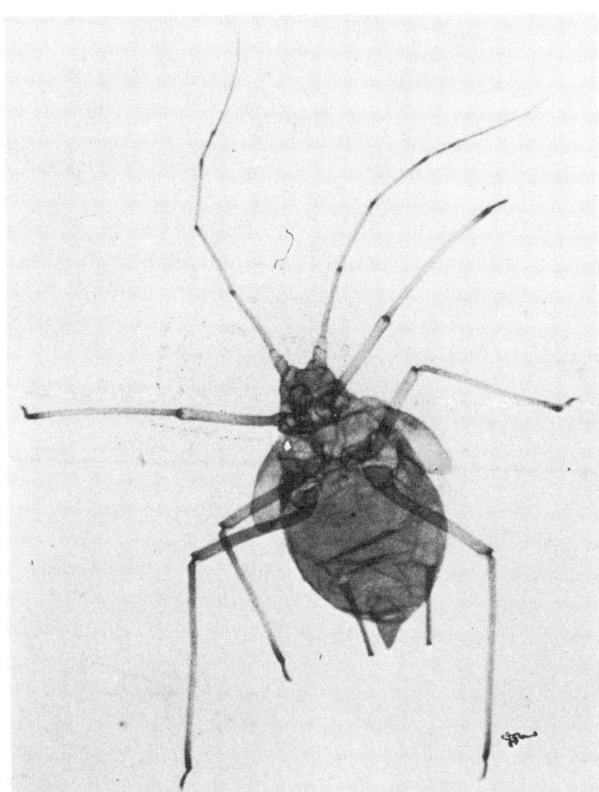

FIG. 21-30

Head of ant lion larva *Myrmeleon* showing large mandibles for seizing its prey as it lies concealed in its pit. Order Neuroptera. (Photomicrograph.)

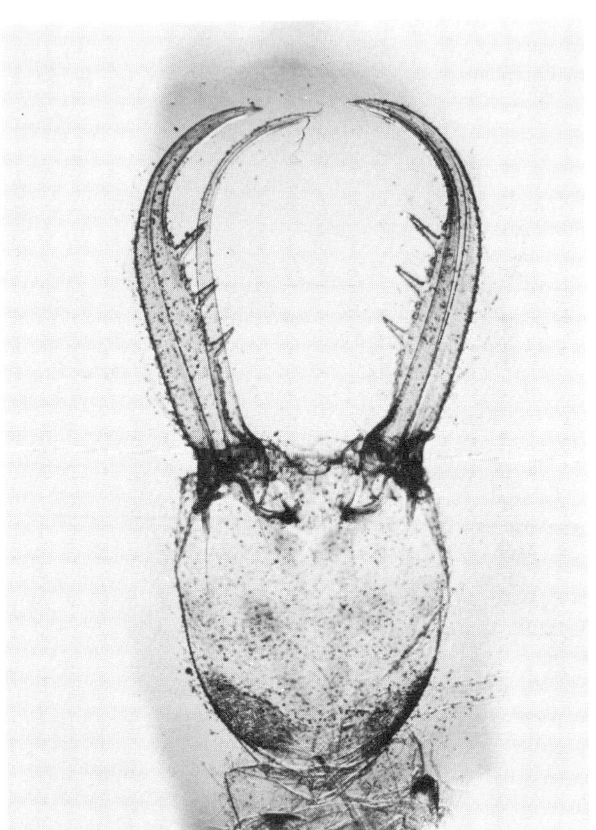

undergo their final molt, and emerge as adults. Some southern species require only 13 years for their cycle. Another interesting member of the order is the aphid (*Aphis mali*), or plant louse (Fig. 21-28). Aphids have both sexual and parthenogenetic generations, and they destructive to plants. Scale insects are likewise destructive by sucking plant sap. Some are protected by a soft cottony covering.

Order 17. Zoraptera (zo-rap'ter-a) (Gr. *zoros,* pure, + *apterygos,* wingless). These are small insects not exceeding 3 mm. in length. They have some resemblance to termites, for they occur in colonies and both winged and wingless forms are found in spite of their name. The winged forms have two pairs of wings, which they shed, as do termites. The wingless forms are blind. Of 16 species, only 2 occur in the United States. Unlike termites, they feed as predators or scavengers on small arthropods. They are commonly found under bark and in rotten logs. *Zorotypus* is a common genus.

Division 2. Endopterygota (en'dop-ter'y-go"ta) (Gr. *endon,* inside, + *pterygotos,* winged). With complete metamorphosis.

Order 18. Neuroptera (neu-rop'ter-a) (Gr. *neuron,* nerve, + *pteron,* wing)—**dobsonflies, ant lions** (Fig. 21-22), **lacewings.** This order takes its name from the many cross veins in the wings. The four wings are alike and are membranous. They have complete metamorphosis, with biting mouth parts. The larval form of *Corydalis,* the huge dobsonfly, looks formidable with its large mandibles but is harmless (Fig. 21-29). It is excellent bait for fish. The larva (doodlebug) (Fig. 21-30) of the ant lion has the interesting habit of making a conical crater in the sand and lying concealed in it until its prey accidentally falls into it (Fig. 21-31). With its very large jaws the larva quickly seizes and makes a meal of it.

Order 19. Coleoptera (ko'le-op"ter-a) (Gr. *koleos,* sheath, + *pteron,* wing)—**beetles, weevils** (Fig. 21-22). The beetles are the most extensive group of animals in the world. About one animal out of every three is a beetle. The forewings (elytra) are thick and leathery, whereas the hindwings are membranous and are folded under the forewings. Some beetles are wingless. They have chewing mouth parts and complete metamorphosis. This large group is divided into many families, each with thousands of species. Among the most familiar of these family groups are the ground beetles, tiger beetles, carrion beetles, whirligig beetles, click beetles, darkling beetles, stag beetles, fireflies, and diving beetles (Figs. 21-32 to 21-35). The other section of this important group is the weevil. Weevils have their jaws modified into snouts, and the most familiar one is the cotton-boll weevil (*Anthonomus grandis*).

Order 20. Strepsiptera (strep-sip'ter-a) (Gr. *strepsis,* a turning, + *pteron,* wing)—**stylops.** There is a marked sexual dimorphism in these small forms, for the males have tiny or vestigial forewings and fan-shaped hind-

FIG. 21-31

Conical crater pit of ant lion. When an ant starts to slide into sandy pit, ant lion helps out by undermining the sand beneath the ant and awaits it with open jaws.

FIG. 21-32

Giant diving beetle *Dytiscus.* This beetle is more than 1 inch long, is very active in water, and will eat any prey it can overcome. Order Coleoptera. The larval form of *Dytiscus* is shown in Fig. 41-12, *C.*

FIG. 21-33

Common stag beetle *Lucanus*, another coleopteran.

FIG. 21-34

Colorado potato beetle *Leptinotarsa*. Order Coleoptera.

FIG. 21-35

Rhinoceros beetle *Dynastes*, another coleopteran.

wings and the females no wings, eyes, or antennae. The mouth parts are for chewing, and the life cycle is complex (**hypermetamorphosis**). The females and larvae are wholly parasitic in bees, wasps, and other insects. There are relatively few species in the group. *Xenos* is a parasite in the wasp (*Polistes*).

Order 21. Mecoptera (me-kop'ter-a) (Gr. *mekos*, length, + *pteron*, wing)—**scorpion flies.** These have four narrow, membranous wings (some are wingless) and chewing mouth parts. Metamorphosis is complete. The male has a curious clasping organ at the tip of the abdomen, which resembles the sting of a scorpion; hence the name of the order. *Boreus*, which is often found on snow in the winter, is one of the more familiar forms.

Order 22. Lepidoptera (lep'i-dop"ter-a) (Gr. *lepido*, scale, + *pteron*, wing)—**butterflies, moths** (Fig. 21-22). These insects are famed for their great beauty and are known the world over. Two pairs of wings are membranous and are covered with overlapping scales. The mouth parts are for sucking and are kept coiled under the head when not in use. The metamorphosis is complete, and the larval form is called a caterpillar. Butterflies have a knob at the tip of the antennae; moths have plumed or feathered antennae as a usual feature. The larval forms are provided with glands for spinning their cocoons (Fig. 21-7).

The pupa is sometimes called a chrysalis. The major families are the tiger moths, regal moths, bagworm moths, swallow-tailed butterflies, sulfur butterflies, and gossamer butterflies (Figs. 21-7 and 21-36). Example: *Anosia plexippus*.

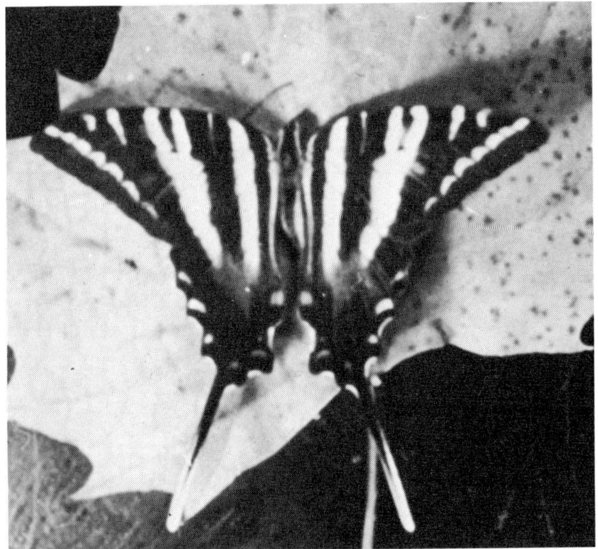

FIG. 21-36

Swallow-tailed butterfly *Papilio*. Order Lepidoptera.

Order 23. Diptera (dip'ter-a) (Gr. *dis,* two, + *pteron,* wing)—**flies** (Figs. 21-22 and 21-37). These are the true flies. They are unique among insects in having only two wings, although some are wingless. In place of hindwings, they have **halteres.** Their metamorphosis is complete, and they have piercing and sucking mouth parts. Their larval forms are often known as maggots and those developing in water, as wigglers. They are commonly separated into two great sections: the long-horned flies with antennae of more than five segments and the short-horned flies with antennae of five or less joints. Among the long-horned flies are the crane flies, mosquitoes, moth flies, midges, gnats, and blackflies. Representatives of the short-horned flies are the fruit flies, flesh flies, botflies, houseflies, and bee flies. *Musca domestica* is the common housefly.

Order 24. Trichoptera (tri-kop'ter-a) (Gr. *trichos,* hair, + *pteron,* wing)—**caddis flies** (Fig. 21-22). These insects have two pairs of membranous wings with silky hairs. Metamorphosis is complete, and the mouth parts are vestigial. The larval forms have the interesting habit of living in fairly rapid waters in cases composed of sand and sticks bound together by their secretions. *Hydropsyche* is a common genus.

Order 25. Siphonaptera (si'fo-nap"ter-a) (Gr. siphon + *a,* without, + *pteron,* wing)—**fleas** (Fig. 21-22). Fleas are wingless, with sucking mouth parts. Their bodies are laterally compressed, with legs adapted for leaping. Compound eyes are lacking, and simple eyes may be suppressed. They are ectoparasites on mammals and birds. There are different species of fleas, but they readily change hosts whenever the opportunity offers. Some of them are vectors for the bubonic plague and typhus fever. The one that is most annoying to man is *Pulex irritans.*

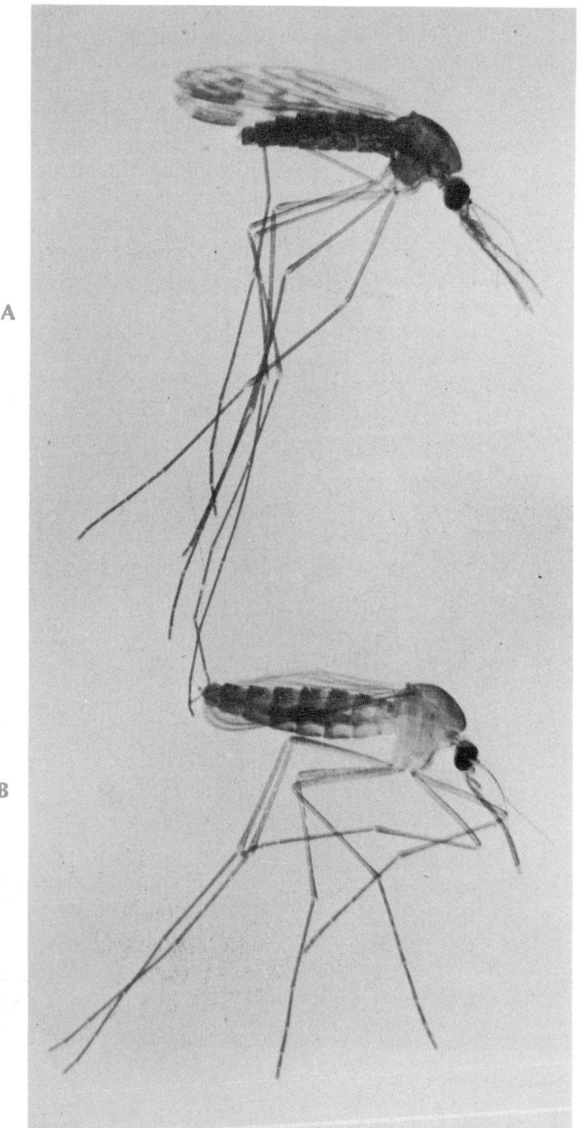

FIG. 21-37

Two common mosquitoes (females). **A,** *Anopheles,* the malaria carrier, bears dark blotches on its wings. **B,** *Culex.* In feeding, *Anopheles* holds its body at an angle to surface, whereas *Culex* holds its body horizontally. Order Diptera.

FIG. 21-38

Stinger of honeybee after dissection. (Photomicrograph.)

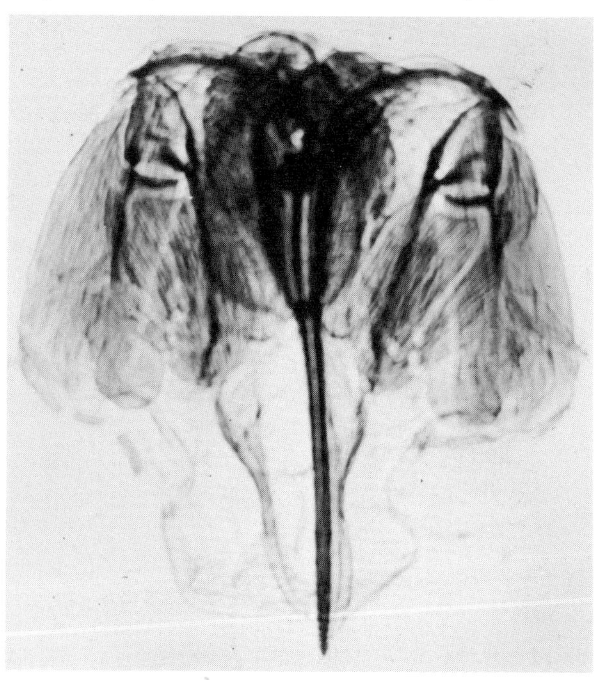

FIG. 21-39

Ichneumon wasp. By means of long ovipositor, female can bore deeply into tree and lay an egg near wood-boring beetle larva. There egg hatches into tiny larva, which parasitizes beetle larva. Ichneumon wasps are large insects; this specimen had an overall length of more than 6 inches. Insert shows typical compound insect eyes, antennae, and mouth parts of ichneumon head. Order Hymenoptera.

FIG. 21-40

Bald-faced hornet *(Vespula maculata)* that has just been rudely awakened from his winter sleep. Brought in from his hibernation in February. This is one of the paper wasps noted for their globular, papery nests (Fig. 21-9). Order Hymenoptera.

Order 26. Hymenoptera (hy′me-nop″ter-a) (Gr. *hymen,* membrane, + *pteron,* wing)—**ants, bees, wasps** (Fig. 21-22). This order gets its name from the four membranous wings, which may be absent in some. They have complete metamorphosis and chewing or sucking mouth parts. Their wings have the peculiarity of being held together with hooks (hamuli). The ovipositor in the female is modified into a stinger (Fig. 21-38), piercer, or saw. Both social and solitary species are found. This group is a very large one and includes some of the most specialized members of the insect world (Fig. 21-39). Some are useful and others are destructive to man's interests. Among the bees the most familiar are the bumblebees, carpenter bees, honeybees, and mason bees. Mud-dauber wasps and bee wasps are among the most common of the wasps. The great family of ants has carried the social organization as far as any group of insects, and their marvelous instincts and reactions are among the most interesting in the animal kingdom. *Apis mellifica* is the common honeybee. *Vespula* is a common genus of hornets (Fig. 21-40).

Derivation and meaning of basic terminology

Apterygota (gr. *a,* not, + *pterygotos,* winged). The subclass of wingless insects.

Asellus (L. little ass). A genus of freshwater isopods.

autotomy (Gr. *autos,* self, + *tome,* cutting). The animal voluntarily breaks off a part of itself.

Cambarus (Gr. *kammaros,* a sea crab). The most common genus of freshwater crayfishes.

Chelicerata (Gr. *chele,* claw, + *keros,* horn, + *ata,* characterized by). Instead of jaws these arthropods have a pair of jointed appendages that bear horny claws.

chitin (Gr. *chiton,* tunic). A constituent of arthropod cuticle.

chrysalis (Gr. *chrysallis,* gold). Refers to gold-colored pupa.

ecdysis (Gr. *ekdysis,* put off). Shedding of outer cuticular layer; molting.

Entomostraca (Gr. *entomon,* insect, + *ostrakon,* shell). A resemblance to insects enclosed in a shell.

Eurypterida (Gr. *eurys,* broad, + *pteryx,* wing or fin). Refers to the shape of some of the appendages.

haltere (Gr. *halter,* leaping weight). Club-shaped organs in place of second pair of wings in Diptera.

Homarus (OF. *homar,* lobster). The genus of the common lobster.

Latrodectus (L. *latro,* robber, + Gr. *dektes,* biter). The genus of the black widow spider.

Malacostraca (Gr. *malakos,* soft, + *ostrakon,* shell). This group of crustaceans has a soft shell, as compared with that of a clam.

Mandibulata (L. *mandibula,* mandible, + *ata,* characterized by). Subphylum of arthropods with jaws for crushing and chewing.

metamorphosis (Gr. *meta,* after, + *morphe,* form, + *osis,* state of). Marked change in form during postembryonic development.

Miranda (L. wonderful). Refers to its beautiful coloration. A common genus of spiders.

pedipalps (L. *pedis,* foot, + *palpo,* feel). Second pair of appendages of arachnids.

Pterygota (Gr. *pterygotos,* winged). The subclass of winged insects.

Trilobita (Gr. *tria,* three, + *lobos,* lobe). Dorsal shield is marked in three lobes.

Xiphosura (Gr. *xiphos,* sword, + *oura,* tail). Refers to the pointed tail.

Annotated references

Borror, D. J., and D. M. Delong. 1964. An introduction to the study of insects (rev. ed.). New York, Rinehart & Co. *This up-to-date text emphasizes both the study and the identification of insects. Its taxonomic keys are very complete and both line drawings and photographs are included in the illustrations. An excellent glossary, but lacking derivations, is included.*

Butler, C. G. 1955. The world of the honeybee. New York, The Macmillan Co. *Honeybees have been much in the limelight since von Frisch's work of a few years ago. The time, therefore, is ripe for a monograph such as the present one on the organization and behavior of the honeybee community in the light of recent knowledge (such is the force of new discoveries on old concepts!). The many photographs are clear and revealing.*

Comstock, J. H. 1940. An introduction to entomology, ed. 9. Ithaca, N. Y., Comstock Publishing Co. *One of the best general texts in the field of entomology. Somewhat technical but can be understood by the beginner.*

Dethier, V. G. 1963. The physiology of insect senses. New York, John Wiley & Sons, Inc. *This treatise shows how insects with few sense cells accomplish about the same functions as higher forms do with many sensory units.*

Frisch, K. von. 1950. Bees: their vision, chemical senses, and language. Ithaca, N. Y., Cornell University Press. *An outstanding work on the way bees communicate with each other and reveal the sources of food supplies. A marvelous revelation of animal behavior.*

Goetsch, W. 1957. The ants. Ann Arbor, University of Michigan Press. *A concise and authoritative account of ants and their ways. The author describes many of his own experiments on the reactions and behavior of these interesting forms.*

Herrick, G. W. 1926. Insects injurious to the household and annoying to man. New York, The Macmillan Co. *The common insect pests of man around his home are described and methods for their control suggested. A practical book for the beginning student.*

Jaques, H. E. 1951. How to know the beetles. Dubuque, Iowa, William C. Brown Co. *A useful and compact manual for the coleopterist.*

Johannsen, O. A., and F. H. Butt. 1941. Embryology of the insects and myriapods. New York, McGraw-Hill Book Co. *A technical work on the development of insects and some of their allies.*

Lanham, U. 1964. The insects. New York, Columbia University Press. *A concise monograph on insects, dealing with their origin, evolution, ecology, and place in the order of nature. Does not emphasize their systematics, but stresses the nature of this extensive group of animals. An excellent approach for beginning entomologists and students of zoology in general.*

Lees, A. D. 1955. The physiology of diapause in arthropods. Cambridge, Cambridge University Press. *The temporary lagging of growth or reproduction typical of many animals is called diapause and has received much attention and investigation in recent years. In insects, and perhaps other animals, the dormant and active periods are synchronized with available food supplies. Light reactions are thought to play a part here. This excellent monograph presents our present state of knowledge about this interesting physiologic adaptation.*

Little, V. A. 1957. General and applied entomology. New York, Harper & Brothers. *An excellent work for beginning students in entomology. It treats the subject from the viewpoints of anatomy, physiology, metamorphosis, and control. Little attention is given to classification other than general surveys of the various orders. The illustrations include a number of excellent photographs. A selected bibliography is also included.*

Miall, L. C. 1922. The natural history of aquatic insects. London, Macmillan & Co., Ltd. *Excellent descriptions of both adult and larval forms of aquatic insects. Interesting to beginner.*

Neider, C. (editor). 1954. The fabulous insects. New York, Harper & Brothers. *An anthology of selections dealing with interesting insects and written by eminent authorities. The beginner will greatly profit from the reading of this book.*

Pesson, P. 1959. The world of insects. Translated by R. B. Freeman, New York, McGraw-Hill Book Co. *All zoology students will have their interest in insects quickened by this fascinating volume of illustration (many of them in perfect kodachrome colors) and the excellent pithy descriptions of the natural history of this "most abundant and the most diverse of all animals."*

Pierce, G. W. 1949. The songs of insects. Cambridge, Mass., Harvard University Press. *The author, a physicist, has applied the apparatus and methods of physics to an investigation of the sounds made by insects and has made many revealing discoveries about the patterns of sound found in this group of animals. Many of his methods have been applied with great success to the problems of echolocation in bats.*

Pringle, J. W. S. 1957. Insect flight. New York, Cambridge University Press. *This little monograph summarizes the present state of knowledge of the complicated methods of flight of insects. The physiology, anatomy, and aerodynamics are discussed. There is an interesting chapter on the histology and physiology of the flight muscles.*

Scheer, B. T. (editor). 1957. Recent advances in invertebrate physiology. Eugene, University of Oregon Publications. *This work is based on a symposium held at the University of Oregon on the various aspects of invertebrate physiology by eminent specialists. Among the interesting topics discussed are neuromuscular action, hormonal control, and patterns of rhythms.*

Wenner, A. M. 1964. Sound communication in honeybees. Sci. Amer. **210**:116-124 (April).

Wheeler, W. M. 1910. Ants. New York, Columbia University Press. *The great classic work on these social insects.*

Wigglesworth, V. B. 1954. The physiology of insect metamorphosis. New York, Cambridge University Press. *The author believes that metamorphosis is merely another case of polymorphism, which is almost universal among animals. He adduces evidence that all levels of complexity are determined by the supply or deficiency of raw materials that may be produced within an endocrine gland and circulate as a hormone.*

Wilson, D. M. 1968. The flight-control system of the locust. Sci. Amer. **218**:83-90 (May). *Stresses a central control system in which the output pattern of motor nerve impulses are coded genetically without proprioceptive feedback.*

CHAPTER 22

• PHYLUM ECHINODERMATA* (MAJOR EUCOELOMATE RADIAL-BILATERAL PHYLUM)

BIOLOGIC PRINCIPLES

Organ-system level of organization

1. The echinoderms share with the annelids, mollusks, and arthropods the distinction of reaching the highest organization of the invertebrates.
2. Unlike the other three phyla, this group has radial symmetry, but this type of symmetry has been secondarily acquired, for their larval forms are bilaterally symmetric.
3. As a phylum, echinoderms show a great degree of specialization that is manifested by bizarre characters not found elsewhere.
4. They have no segmentation or well-defined head region.
5. They belong to the deuterostome branch, or enterocoelous coelomates, of the animal kingdom, which include the phyla Chaetognatha, Echinodermata, Hemichordata, Chordata, and a few minor phyla.
6. Echinoderms have radial and indeterminate cleavage.

Biologic contributions

1. Most of the echinoderm characters are so out of line that few of them are copied by other phyla.
2. Some of their unique features are the **water-vascular system, tube feet, pedicellariae, dermal branchiae,** and **calcareous endoskeleton.**
3. They have a **mesodermal endoskeleton** of plates, which may be considered the first indication of the endoskeleton so well developed among vertebrates.
4. They have a remarkable power of autotomy (self-mutilation), together with that of regeneration of lost parts.
5. They have contributed a pattern of embryonic development similar to that of the highest group, the chordates. This pattern includes (a) an anus derived from the embryonic blastopore, (b) a mouth formed from a stomodaeum, which connects to the endodermal esophagus, (c) a mesoderm from evaginations of the archenteron (enterocoelous), and (d) a nervous system in close contact with the ectoderm.

Position in animal kingdom

1. The echinoderms are a very ancient group of animals, which, according to fossil records, were differentiated back to Cambrian times. The fossil record gives no clues as to their origin.
2. The most primitive echinoderms were probably the stalked members, and from these the free forms arose. These early echinoderms were noncrinoid Pelmatozoa now wholly extinct.
3. From their larvae the evidence indicates that their ancestors were bilaterally symmetric and that their radial symmetry was secondarily acquired. Even in the adult condition certain aspects of bilateral symmetry can be discerned under the disguise of radial symmetry.
4. Of all invertebrates, echinoderms are placed nearest to the chordates because of the features referred to under biologic contributions *(5)*.
5. Another strong evidence of their chordate affinities is the similarity between the larval type of echinoderms and that of the prechordate acorn worm *(Balanoglossus)*.
6. From the evidence at hand it appears that echinoderms and chordates may have originated from a common ancestor or at least from the same side of the phylogenetic tree.
7. Within the group the holothuroids are supposed to have come from a common stem with the crinoids, whereas the asteroids, echinoids, and ophiuroids have risen from a common pelmatozoan but noncrinoid ancestry.
8. The evolution of the group has been guided and restricted by the hydraulic water-vascular system of tube feet, which had primarily a food-catching function at first but which has been variously modified for other functions (locomotion, respiration, mucus production, burrowing, and sensory perception).

GENERAL RELATIONS

The echinoderms are marine forms and include the sea stars, brittle stars, sea urchins, sea cucumbers, and sea lilies. They represent a bizarre group sharply distinguished from all other members of the animal kingdom. Their name is derived from the spiny characteristic of their integument (Gr. *echinos,* sea urchin, hedgehog, + *derma,* skin). A calcareous endoskeleton is found in all members of the phylum, either in the forms of plates or represented by scattered tiny ossicles.

*E-ki'no-der"ma-ta (Gr. *echinos,* sea urchin, hedgehog, + *derma,* skin, + *ata,* characterized by).

Echinoderms are abundant along the seashore and extend to depths of many thousand feet. None can move rapidly and some are sessile. None of them are parasitic. There is a great variety of colors among the 6,000 species, including oranges, reds, purples, blues, and browns.

The most marked characteristics of the echinoderms are (1) the spiny endoskeleton of plates, (2) the water-vascular system, (3) the pedicellariae, (4) the dermal branchiae, (5) the amebocytes, and (6) radial symmetry. Radial symmetry is not limited to echinoderms, but no other group with such complex organ systems has radial symmetry.

They are an ancient group of animals extending back to the Cambrian period. An excellent fossil record gives no indication, however, of echinoderm ancestors. For a long time Echinodermata were placed with Coelenterata and the two groups were called Radiata. There is every reason to believe that the echinoderms have descended from bilateral ancestors in spite of their present type of symmetry. This fact is the more evident when one considers the secondary character of the radial symmetry, for it appears late in development; the larvae are bilaterally symmetric. Even in the adult, radial symmetry merely disguises an underlying bilateral symmetry. Of all invertebrates, the echinoderms are considered to be nearest in relation to the chordates. The type of larvae of echinoderms and of *Balanoglossus* (prechordate) are much alike. Although these two forms of larvae could have arisen independently by convergent evolution, evidence indicates that their similarity has real evolutionary meaning and that both echinoderms and chordates have come from a common ancestor. Chordate segmentation could have arisen after the two groups diverged.

The phylogeny of the echinoderms is obscure. The extinct class Heterostelea, one of the stem-bearing forms, has some of the qualifications of an ancestral type. It was bilaterally symmetric. The free-moving forms (subphylum Eleutherozoa) have probably arisen from the more ancient and primitive stem-bearing varieties (subphylum Pelmatozoa), which include the living crinoids and several extinct classes. Among the free-moving classes, the sea stars (Asteroidea) and brittle stars (Ophiuroidea) seem to be closely related, whereas the sea cucumber (Holothuroidea) no doubt arose from some crinoidlike ancestor. Asteroids also show the primitive, open ambulacral groove characteristic of the pelmatozoans, whereas the grooves are closed in the other Eleutherozoa.

CHARACTERISTICS

1. Body unsegmented with **radial symmetry;** often in **divisions of five** (pentanumerous); body rounded, cylindric, or star shaped
2. Three germ layers; mesoderm of endomesodermal origin
3. **No head;** body surface of five (or more) radiating areas (ambulacra) with alternating spaces, or interambulacra (interradii)
4. **Endoskeleton of dermal calcareous ossicles with spines;** covered by an epidermis (ciliated in most); pedicellariae (in some)
5. A unique **water-vascular system** of coelomic origin, which pushes out the body surface as a series of tentacle-like projections, podia; or tube feet, which are protruded or retracted by alterations of fluid (sea water or coelomic) pressure within them; an external opening (madreporite or hydropore) usually present
6. Locomotion usually by **tube feet** (podia), which project from the ambulacral spaces
7. **Coelom extensive,** forming the perivisceral cavity and the cavity of the water-vascular system; coelom of enterocoelous type; coelomic fluid with amebocytes
8. Digestive system usually complete; axial or coiled; anus absent in ophiuroids
9. Vascular system reduced; hemal or lacunar system enclosed in coelomic channels
10. Respiration by **dermal branchiae,** by **tube feet,** by **respiratory tree** (in some), and by **bursae** (ophiuroids)
11. Nervous system with circumoral ring and radial nerves; usually two or three systems of networks located at different levels
12. Sensory system (poorly developed) of tactile organs, chemoreceptors, podia, terminal tentacles, photoreceptors, and statocysts
13. Excretory organs absent
14. Sexes separate (a few hermaphroditic) with large gonads, single (holothuroids) but multiple in most, with simple ducts
15. Fertilization usually external
16. **Development through specialized free-swimming larval stages** of many kinds, with metamorphosis
17. Regeneration of lost parts conspicuous

ECONOMIC IMPORTANCE

Because of the spiny nature of their structure, echinoderms have a limited use as food for other animals. The eggs of these forms may serve as food, and the sea cucumber (trepang) is used by the Chinese for soup. Where echinoderms are common along a seashore, they have been used for fertilizer.

Sea stars feed mainly on mollusks, crustaceans, and other invertebrates, but their chief damage is to clams and oysters, for which they have a great fondness. A single star may eat as many as a dozen oysters or clams in a day. To rid shellfish beds of these pests, rope nets in which the sea stars become entangled are sometimes dragged over oyster beds, and the collected sea stars destroyed. A more effective method is to distribute lime over areas where they abound. Lime causes the delicate epidermal membrane to disintegrate; lesions are then formed, which destroy the dermal branchiae and ultimately the animal itself.

The eggs of echinoderms are widely used in biologic investigations, for the eggs are usually abundant and easy to collect and can be handled conveniently. The investigator can follow their developmental stages with great accuracy. Artificial parthenogenesis was first discovered in sea urchin eggs when it was found that,

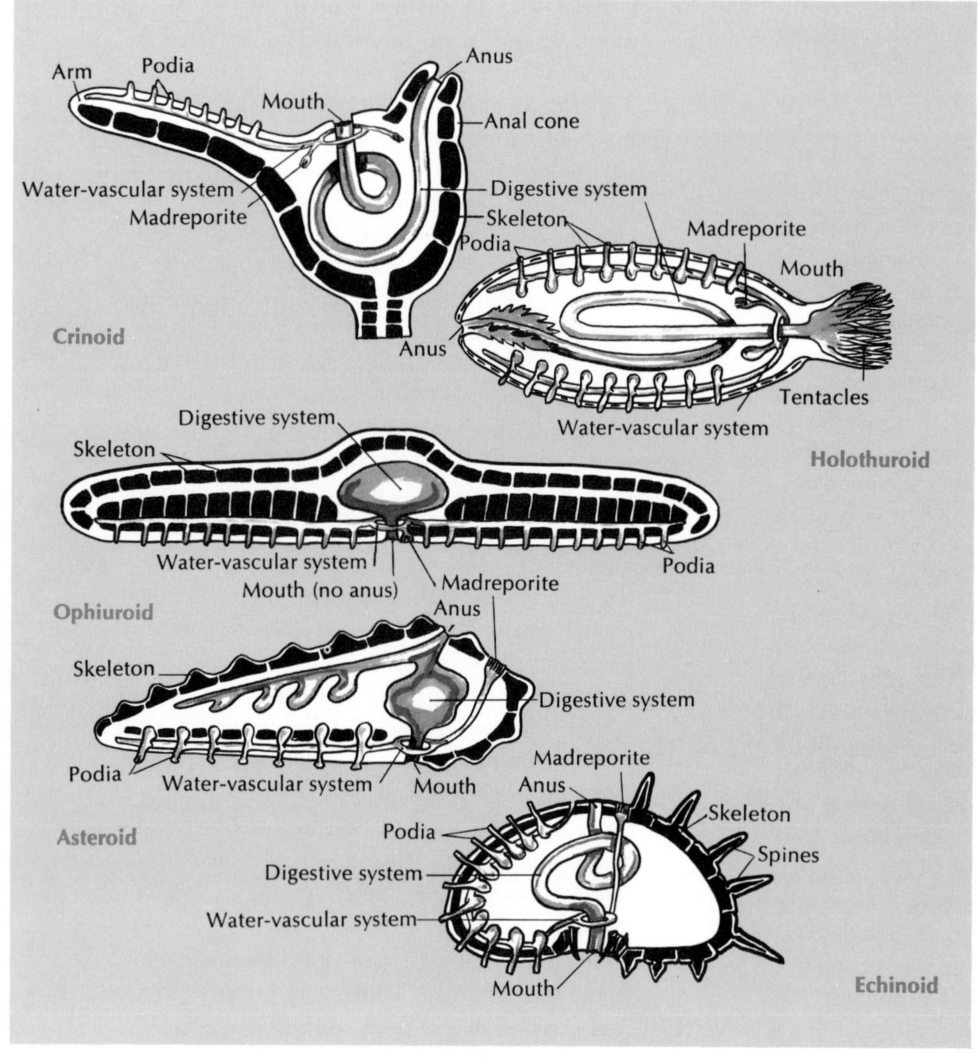

FIG. 22-1

Schematic cross sections of representatives of five classes of echinoderms showing comparatively the skeletal, water-vascular, and digestive systems. Skeleton is shown in black.

by changing the chemical nature of sea water, development would take place without the presence of sperm.

Echinoderms have no parasitic members as far as is known.

CLASSIFICATION

Echinoderms are divided into two subphyla: Pelmatozoa (chiefly stem-bearing forms) and Eleutherozoa (free-moving animals). There are about 4,000 to 6,000 living and 20,000 extinct or fossil species. Five classes of existing echinoderms are recognized and about that many extinct classes are known to invertebrate paleontologists (Fig. 22-1). Most of the extinct classes belong to the subphylum Pelmatozoa, which now has only one living class (Crinoidea). Fossil classes differed mainly from existing classes (1) in having a heavy body wall of closely fitting plates (theca), (2) in having both mouth and anus on the oral side, and (3) in being sessile, attached by the aboral side. Some of these features are retained by living species.

Diagnostic features

Echinoderms belong to the Deuterostomia branch of the animal kingdom and are enterocoelous coelomates. The other phyla of this group are Chaetognatha, Hemichordata, Chordata, and Pogonophora. It will be recalled that the deuterostomes have the following features in common: an anus from the blastopore, a coelom budded off from the archenteron (enterocoelous), radial and indeterminate cleavage, a nervous system in close contact with the ectoderm, and a larva (when present) of the **dipleurula** type. The primitive pattern of the echinoderms seems to have included radial symmetry, radiating grooves (ambulacra), and a tendency for the body openings (oral side) to face upward, as seen in sessile forms. Radial symmetry with arm extensions would be an advantage to a sessile animal; it could get its food from all directions. Living crinoids follow this primitive pattern. Modifications of the plan are found in free-moving forms that have been favored by evolution, for attached forms, once plentiful, are now limited to the one class Crinoidea.

Zoologists have constructed a hypothetical ancestral larval form (**dipleurula**), of which existing larval forms may be modifications. Dipleurula is pictured as an elongated, bilaterally symmetric, two-sided animal without a skeleton and with a complete digestive system and a coelom of three paired sacs (axocoel, hydrocoel, somatocoel). Through attachment on one side and some degeneration or shifting of structures, this bilateral larva was transformed into the radial adult form. Although an attractive theory and widely accepted, many zoologists are doubtful about its usefulness. Perhaps a more satisfactory theory is the pentactula concept of five radial tentacles around the mouth, but this larval concept could be regarded as a later evolutionary development of the dipleurula.

Embryologic evidence indicates that the unique water-vascular system arose as hollow protrusions (tentacles) of the body wall carrying coelomic branches. Side branches of these protrusions become podia, or tube feet, which served originally as sensory or food-collecting structures. In sea stars, urchins, and cucumbers the podia have acquired suckers and are used in locomotion; food is no longer conveyed by ciliated grooves but is taken by mouth. The tube feet have also been modified for other functions. Some are pointed and without suckers for burrowing, many are mucus-producing for food catching and plastering burrow walls, and others with thin walls or leaflike structures serve for respiration.

The calcareous endoskeleton of most echinoderms is an important aspect of their evolution. Primitive echinoderms were heavily armored with complicated plates, but in existing forms the skeleton tends to be reduced for flexibility. In most groups it consists of closely fitting plates provided with spines and tubercles and held together by muscles and mesenchyme. Holothurians have almost no endoskeleton.

Subphylum Eleutherozoa (e-lu'ther-o-zo"a) (Gr. *eleutheros*, free, + *zoon*, animal).

- **Class Asteroidea** (as'ter-oi"de-a) (Gr. *aster*, star, + *eidos*, form, + *ea*, characterized by)—**sea stars.** Star-shaped echinoderms, with the arms not sharply marked off from the central disk; ambulacral grooves with tube feet on oral side; tube feet with suckers; anus and madreporite aboral; pedicellariae present. Example: *Asterias* (Fig. 22-3).
- **Class Ophiuroidea** (o'fi-u-roi"de-a) (Gr. *ophis*, snake, + *oura*, tail, + *eidos*, form)—**brittle stars.** Star shaped, with the arms sharply marked off from the central disk; ambulacral grooves absent or covered by ossicles; tube feet without suckers and not used for locomotion; pedicellariae absent; anus present. Example: *Ophiothrix* (Fig. 22-10).
- **Class Echinoidea** (ek'i-noi"de-a) (Gr. *echinos*, sea urchin, hedgehog, + *eidos*, form) (Fig. 22-1)—**sea urchins.** More or less globular echinoderms with no arms; compact skeleton or test; movable spines; ambulacral

grooves covered by ossicles; tube feet with suckers; pedicellariae present. Examples: *Arbacia* (Fig. 22-12), *Strongylocentrotus* (Fig. 22-11), *Mellita* (Fig. 22-13, *B*).

Class Holothuroidea (hol'o-thu-roi"de-a) (Gr. *holothurion,* sea cucumber, + *eidos,* form)—**sea cucumbers.** Cucumber-shaped echinoderms with no arms; spines absent; ossicles confined to thick muscular wall; anus present; ambulacral grooves concealed; tube feet with suckers; circumoral tentacles (modified tube feet); pedicellariae absent; madreporite plate internal. Examples: *Thyone, Stichopus* (Fig. 22-11).

Subphylum Pelmatozoa (pel'ma-to-zo"a) (Gr. *pelmatos,* stalk or sole, + *zoon,* animal).

Class Crinoidea (kri-noi"de-a) (Gr. *crinon,* lily, + *eidos,* form, + *ea,* characterized by)—**sea lilies.** Body attached during part or all of life by an aboral stalk of dermal ossicles; mouth and anus on oral surface; five arms branching at base and bearing pinnules; ciliated ambulacral groove on oral surface with tentacle-like tube feet for food collecting; spines, madreporite, and pedicellariae absent (Figs. 22-17 and 22-18). Example: *Antedon.*

Larval forms of echinoderm classes

The early development of the larval form is similar in all echinoderms (Fig. 22-2). The egg is usually fer-

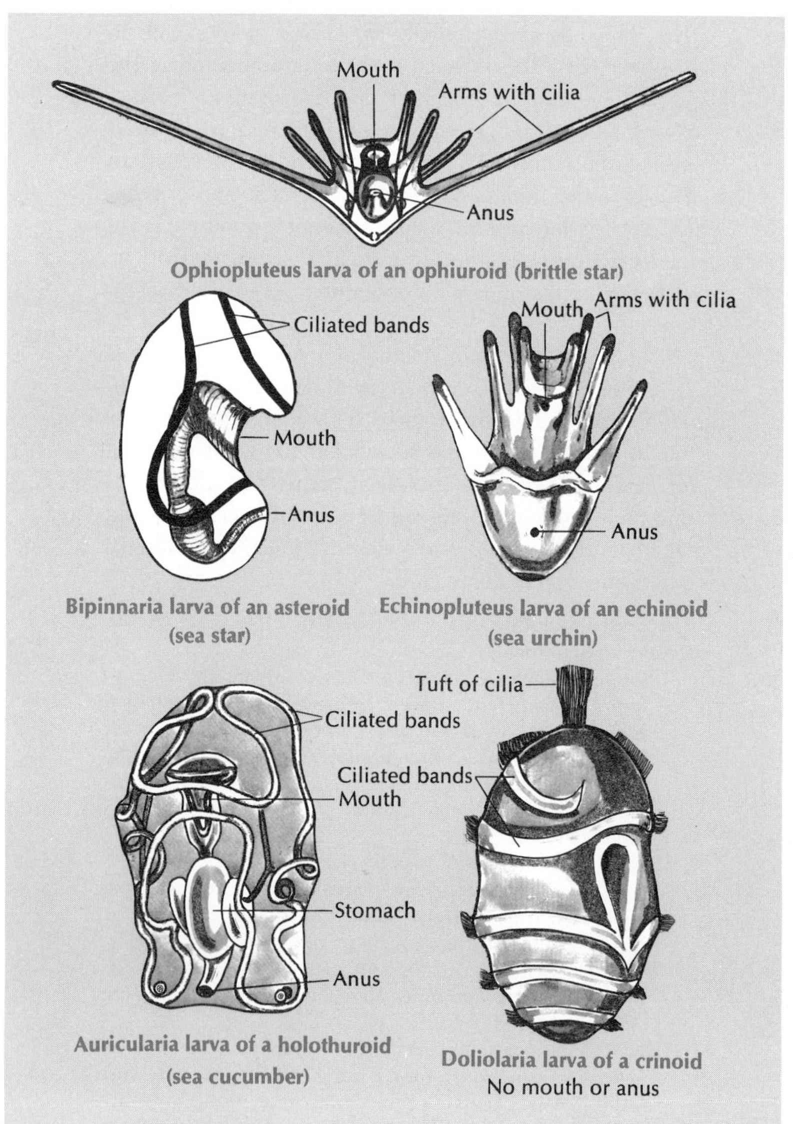

FIG. 22-2

Representative larva of each class of echinoderms. Early development stages of various classes are similar, and hypothetical common ancestor, dipleurula larva, has been proposed for all echinoderms. (Modified from Lang and others.)

tilized in sea water or in brood pouches. It divides by total cleavage that is indeterminate. It passes through successive stages: a hollow single-layered blastula; a double-layered gastrula with an archenteron and a wide blastocoel; paired outpocketings of the archenteron, which form the coelom and water-vascular system; mesenchyme formed in the blastocoel from ectodermal and endodermal cells; a mouth by the breaking through of a stomodaeum; and eventually a free, pelagic larva (in most), which shows similarities as well as differences among the various classes.

In most cases this early larva is bilateral and free swimming, and it lacks a calcareous skeleton but has calcareous spines, probably for support. The coelom consists of three pairs of pouches, and the future ventral side becomes concave. Some call this stage the dipleurula. Cilia that first covered most of the body are now restricted to a band around the concavity. This band, used in locomotion, is folded into loops, which vary in the different larval forms.

FIG. 22-3

Aboral surface of common sea star *Asterias*. Class Asteroidea.

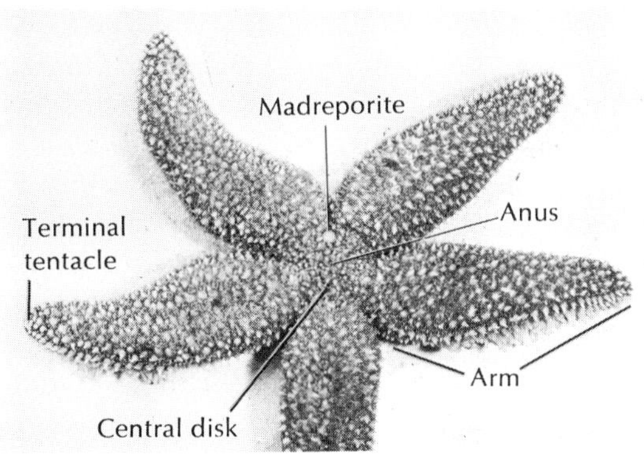

One of the most primitive of the echinoderm larvae is the **auricularia** (Holothuroidea). Its body is elongated, with a ciliated band partly around the preoral lobe and partly on body folds. In the **bipinnaria** (Asteroidea) larva, which is similar to the auricularia, the preoral ring of cilia is separated from the rest. In the other types of larvae the body lobes become elongated with supporting rods, and the ciliated bands become more elaborate. The transformation of the larvae into adults by metamorphosis is a complicated process and differs in several groups. This change involves shifting of the mouth position, development of the endoskeleton, torsion whereby the left side becomes the oral and the right side the aboral surface, development of a coelomic pouch into the water-vascular system, and assumption of radial symmetry.

REPRESENTATIVE TYPES

CLASS ASTEROIDEA

Sea stars are found in all oceans, usually on rocky seashores but also at great depths in the ocean far from the shoreline. More than a thousand species are known. Although five rays is the usual number, there are species that have as many as forty or fifty; the number,

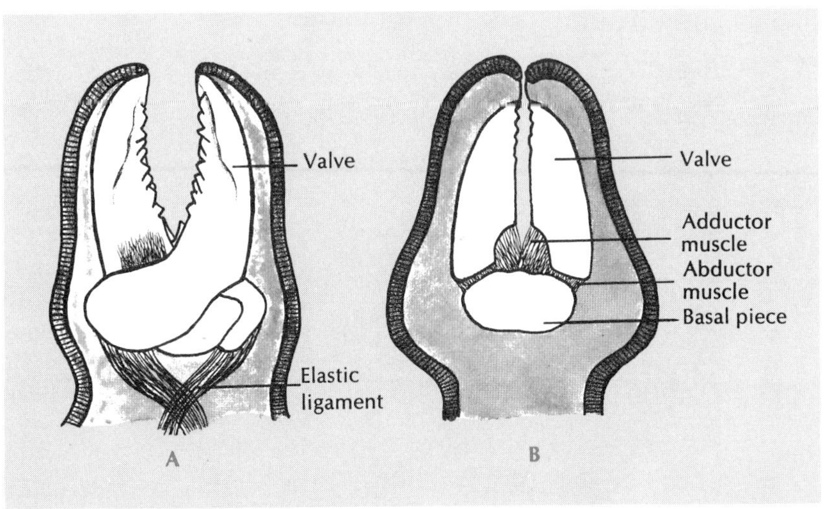

FIG. 22-4

Two types of pedicellariae found in sea stars. **A,** Crossed-jawed type. **B,** Straight-jawed type, opened by abductor muscles, closed by adductor muscles.

however, is not constant if in excess of five or six. At low tide the rocks along the shore may have large numbers of sea stars upon them. They often cling so tenaciously that it is difficult to dislodge them without tearing loose many of the tube feet.

Asterias—sea star

External structure. *Asterias* is one of those genera that has five arms (Fig. 22-3). The body consists of a central **disk** and five tapering arms, or **rays.** On the upper or **aboral** surface are many spines, around the bases of which are grouped in rosettes the minute pincerlike **pedicellariae** (modified spines) (Fig. 22-4). Between the spines are the soft, delicate **dermal branchiae** (papulae), or skin gills, which function in respiration. The pedicellariae, which have jaws manipulated by muscles, help keep the body free from debris, aid in capturing food, and protect the skin gills. On the aboral surface are the small **anus** and the conspicuous circular **madreporite,** which acts as a sieve leading to the water-vascular system. The axes, or imaginary lines that run from the center of the disk to the tips of the arms, are known as **radii** and the spaces on the disk between them, as **interradii.** On the **oral** or lower surface the **mouth** in the center of the disk is surrounded by the soft **peristomial membrane.** Along the oral surface of each ray a median **ambulacral groove** is bordered by large spines (Fig. 22-5). From the groove project two or four rows of **tube feet** (podia). At the tip of each ray is a small **tentacle** and a red **eyespot,** which marks the position of many pigment-cup **ocelli,** each lined with retinal cells.

FIG. 22-5

Portion of oral surface of sea star showing arrangement of tube feet along ambulacral grooves.

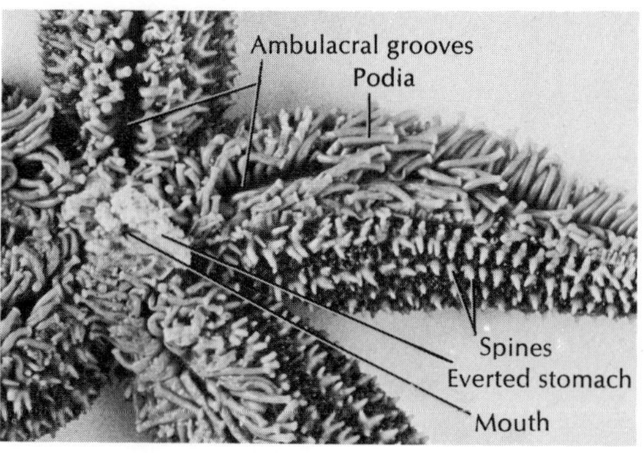

Ciliated **epidermis** covers the entire body. Beneath it, and secreted by the dermis, is the mesodermal **endoskeleton** of small calcareous **ossicles,** with projecting **spines** and tubercules. They are bound together in a definite pattern by muscle and connective tissue. On the spines the epidermis and its cuticle may be worn off. In the ambulacral groove the ossicles form a trough for the tube feet. Skin color is due to pigment granules in the epidermis.

Sea stars move their rays by muscles in the body wall. Transverse and longitudinal muscle fibers in the ambulacral grooves bend the rays aborally and partially close the grooves by drawing in their margins.

Internal structure (Figs. 22-6 and 22-7). The large, branched **coelom** is lined with ciliated epithelium (**peritoneum**). Circulating in a lymphlike **coelomic fluid,** are **amebocytes** (coelomocytes), which function in respiration, circulation, and excretion. The coelom extends into the dermal branchiae so that the fluid is brought close to the sea water for gas exchange. In excretion, waste is gathered by amebocytes, which then escape through the walls of the dermal branchiae to the outside. The **digestive system** has a **mouth** on the oral side, with sphincter and radial muscles and a short **esophagus** leading to a large saclike **stomach** composed of two parts. The lower **cardiac** part has thin folded walls and is attached to the body wall by **gastric ligaments,** which prevent the stomach from being everted too far; the smaller **pyloric** stomach connects with ducts from five pairs of pyloric **ceca.** A short **intestine** with a pair of **rectal ceca** ends at the **anus** on the top (aboral) side. The pyloric ceca (digestive glands) fill a large part of each ray. The layers of the digestive tube, like those of the body wall and peristomial membrane, consist of epithelium, connective tissue, and muscle.

The **circulatory** or **hemal system** is made up of vessels enclosed in coelomic sinuses, or hyponeural canals. In each arm under the radial canal of the water-vascular system is a radial hemal vessel, which is divided into halves by a longitudinal septum. These vessels communicate with an oral ring vessel that encircles the mouth. The hemal system is not well developed in sea stars and is difficult to see.

The **nervous system** consists of three units placed at different levels in the disk and arm. These are (1) the **oral** (**ectoneural**) nervous system, composed of a circumoral ring around the mouth and five radial nerve cords, one in each arm, just beneath the radial canals;

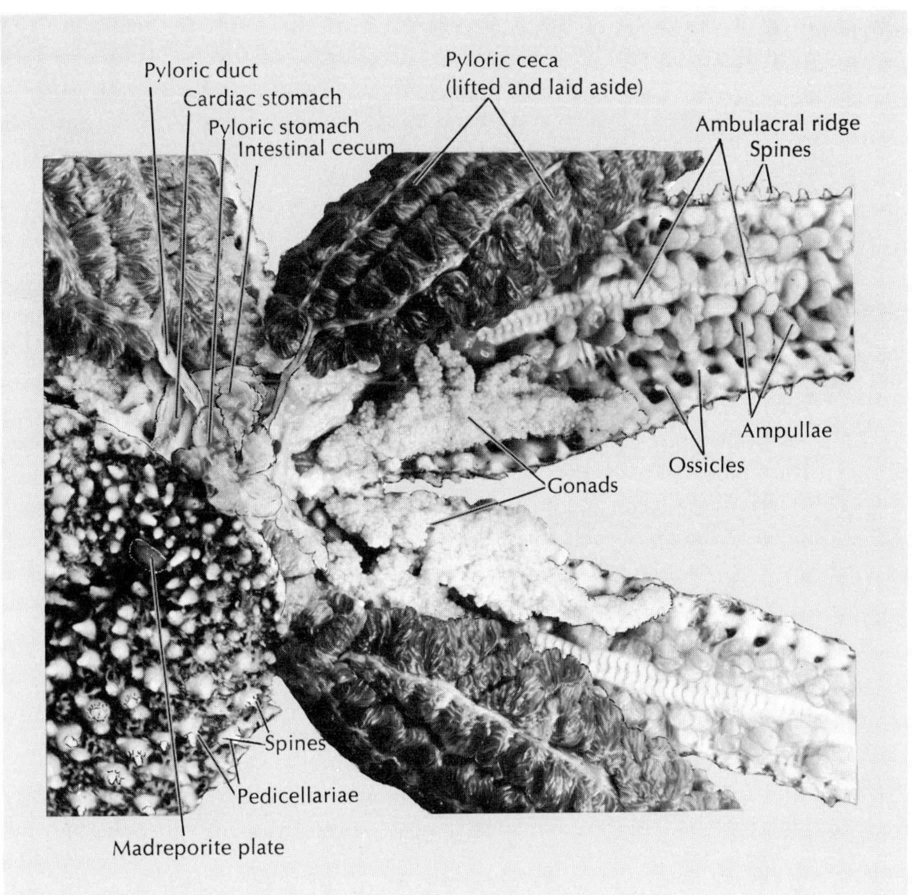

FIG. 22-6

Sea star dissection, aboral view, showing at right portions of two arms with digestive glands lifted aside to expose gonads in interradial spaces and ampullae on either side of ambulacral ridge. At lower left two arms remain undissected to show madreporite and spines.

FIG. 22-7

Longitudinal section through disk and arm of sea star showing principal structures. In most sea stars gonads are dorsally located and open on aboral surface.

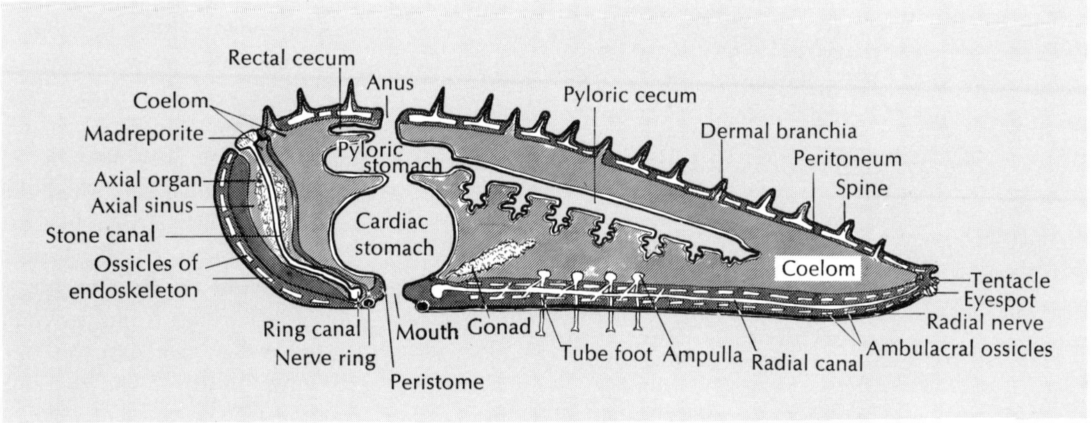

(2) the **deep (hyponeural)** nervous system, consisting of a double circumoral ring above the ectoneural ring and giving off paired branches, which run on each side of the radial nerve; and (3) the **coelomic (aboral)** nervous system, containing an anal nerve ring and nerves along the roof of the ray. Subepidermal plexuses or nerve nets freely connect these systems with the body wall and related structures. The ectoneural elements appear to coordinate the tube feet, and the deep elements regulate the muscular action of the rays. In sea stars the ectoneural and aboral systems are poorly developed. The **sense organs** are not well developed; tactile organs are found over the surface and an eyespot at the tip of each arm.

The sea star has separate sexes. The **gonads,** either **testes** or **ovaries,** look alike but can be distinguished by microscopic examination. They are made up of saclike masses that resemble tiny bunches of grapes, and there is a pair of them in each interradial space. The gonads are greatly enlarged at the breeding season. The ducts by which the eggs or sperm are discharged to the outside are minute pores on the aboral surface near the base of the arms, although in some species the gonads are ventrally located and their gonopores open on the oral surface. **Fertilization** is external and occurs in early summer when the eggs and sperm are shed into the water. It has recently been shown that the maturation and shedding of sea star eggs are stimulated by a secretion from neurosecretory cells located on the radial nerves (H. Kanstani). This active extract (a polypeptide) has been isolated. Calcium ions (in sea water) may increase the rate of maturation or meiosis, but may not be absolutely necessary.

FIG. 22-8

Water-vascular system of sea star. Upper left, detail of spines and skin gills (dermal branchiae).

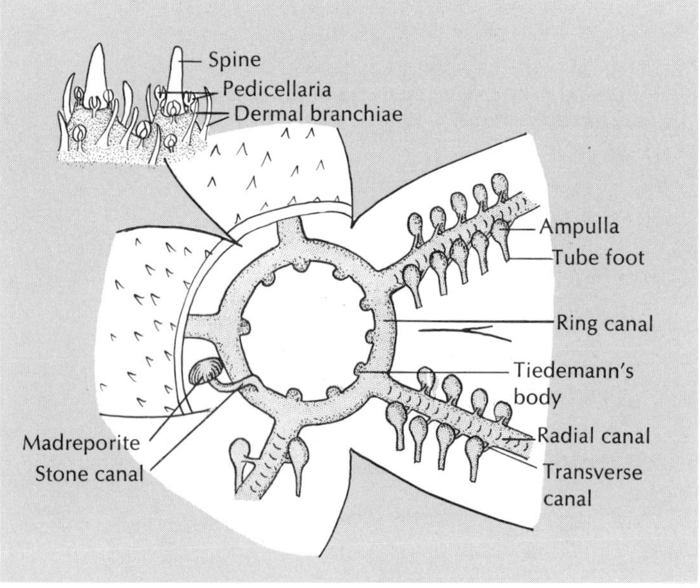

The **water-vascular system,** which is unique among the echinoderms, is made up of a system of canals and specialized tube feet and in sea stars serves as a method of locomotion (Fig. 22-8). It is made up of (1) the **madreporite** on the aboral surface, a finely grooved sieve through which water enters; (2) the **stone canal,** which runs from the madreporite to (3) the **ring canal** around the mouth; (4) five **radial canals,** one in each ray above the ambulacral groove and concealed under the ambulacral bridge; (5) the **lateral canals,** which connect the tube feet with the radial canals and which are each provided with a valve; and (6) the **tube feet.** Each tube foot is a thin-walled cylinder with a rounded muscular sac, the **ampulla,** at its inner end and a **sucker** at its outer end. The ampullae lie within the ray; the tube feet proper are outside in the ambulacral groove. The tubes that connect the ampullae with the suckers pass through small pores between the ambulacral ossicles. The ampullae contain circular muscles in their walls, whereas the tube feet have longitudinal muscles. On the inner wall of the ring canal are nine tiny spherical swellings, **Tiedemann's bodies.** There is no evidence that they produce amebocytes, as formerly supposed.

The stone canal and the brownish, spongy **axial gland** close by are surrounded by a tubular coelomic cavity called the **axial sinus.** The axial gland is a part of the hemal system and some authorities think it is the remnant of a heart.

Behavior. The sea star uses the water-vascular system for locomotion. When an ampulla contracts, the fluid within it is prevented by a valve from flowing back into the radial canal and thus is forced into the tube foot. The elastic tube foot extends and can twist about by its muscular wall. When the tube foot touches a substratum, it becomes attached by its sucker. Then the longitudinal muscles contract, shorten it, and force the water back into the ampulla. Thus the animal is drawn forward. The coordinated effort of all or many tube feet is sufficient to draw the animal slowly up a vertical surface. The muscles of the arms and tube feet are controlled by the motor nerves of the subepidermal plexus.

If the sea star happens to be on a soft surface, such as muck or sand, the suckers are ineffective, and so the tube feet are employed as legs. Locomotion now becomes mainly a stepping process involving a backward swinging of the middle portion of the podia, followed by a contraction, shoving the animal forward. Sea stars can move about 6 inches a minute. They can also move by twisting and bending their rays; when inverted, the sea star twists its rays until some of its tube feet attach to the substratum as an anchor, and then it slowly rolls over.

The food of the sea star is mainly mussels, clams, oysters, snails, tube worms, and other slow-moving forms that the animal can overtake and overpower. Oysters and clams are the main diet. The sea star arches its body in a humped-up position over the clam and grips the opposite valves with the tube feet. Then it begins a steady pull at right angles to the surface of the shell, using its feet in relays. A force of some 1,300 grams can be exerted in this way. In half an hour or so the adductor muscles of the bivalve fatigue and relax. When the valves gape, the star everts the lower part of its stomach, inserts it between the two valves, and wraps it around the soft parts of the shellfish. Secretions from the stomach and digestive glands digest the food in the shell. Enzymes are known to be involved in the process. The partly digested food is pulled into the stomach and pyloric ceca, where digestion is finished. Digestion is entirely extracellular. At the completion of the process, the sea star draws its stomach back into its mouth. This is not done by retractor muscles, as usually stated, but by contraction of muscles in the stomach and gastric filaments and by relaxation of muscles in the body wall along with the return of coelomic fluid into the arms. Very little indigestible material is taken in, so that only a tiny amount of fecal matter is ejected through the anal pore.

Sea stars are rarely active during the day, remaining

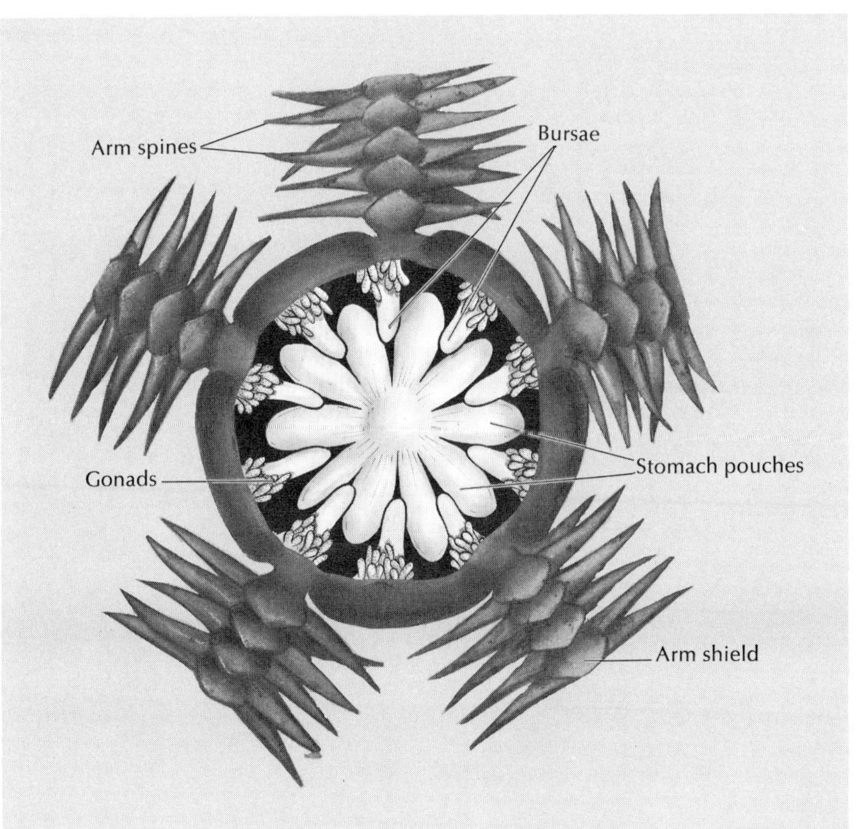

FIG. 22-9

Ophiuroid with aboral disk wall cut away to show principal internal structures. Only bases of arms shown.

quietly attached to some object. At night they are active, in search of food. Their reactions are mainly to touch, light, temperature, and chemicals. Apparently they can be taught a simple habit, such as righting themselves with certain arms, as Professor Jennings demonstrated many years ago.

Regeneration and autotomy. The sea star can regenerate lost parts. The arms regenerate readily; if all are removed from the disk, all will grow back. A single ray with a small portion of the disk will regenerate an entire animal. Sea stars also have the power of **autotomy,** or voluntarily discarding a part. An injured arm is cast off by the animal near the base, although months may be required for its replacement.

CLASS OPHIUROIDEA

In class Ophiuroidea, as in Asteroidea, the members have a central disk with five (sometimes more) distinct arms (Fig. 22-9). The arms, however, are long and slender and are sharply marked off from the disk. They represent the largest class of echinoderms in number of species. They are abundant wherever found. Basket stars have their rays branched in a complex fashion. Members of this class are found in shallow and deep water, and they have a wide distribution.

Some common ophiuroids along our Atlantic coast are *Amphipholis* (viviparous and hermaphroditic), *Ophioderma,* and *Ophiothrix.* Along the Pacific coast are *Orthasterias* (very long arms); in British Columbia, *Amphiodia;* and in California, *Ophioplocus* (viviparous). The basket star *(Gorgonocephalus)* is usually found at considerable depths. Some ophiuroids have variegated color patterns.

Ophiothrix—brittle star

Brittle stars, unlike sea stars, have no pedicellariae, ambulacral grooves, or dermal branchiae. They have tube feet, called **tentacles,** largely sensory in function and without suckers; they can pass food along the rays to the mouth and have a limited function in locomotion. Each of the jointed arms consists of a column of calcareous vertebrae connected by muscles and covered by plates. On the oral surface of the central disk are the **madreporite** and the **mouth,** with five movable plates that serve as jaws (Fig. 22-10). There is no anus. The

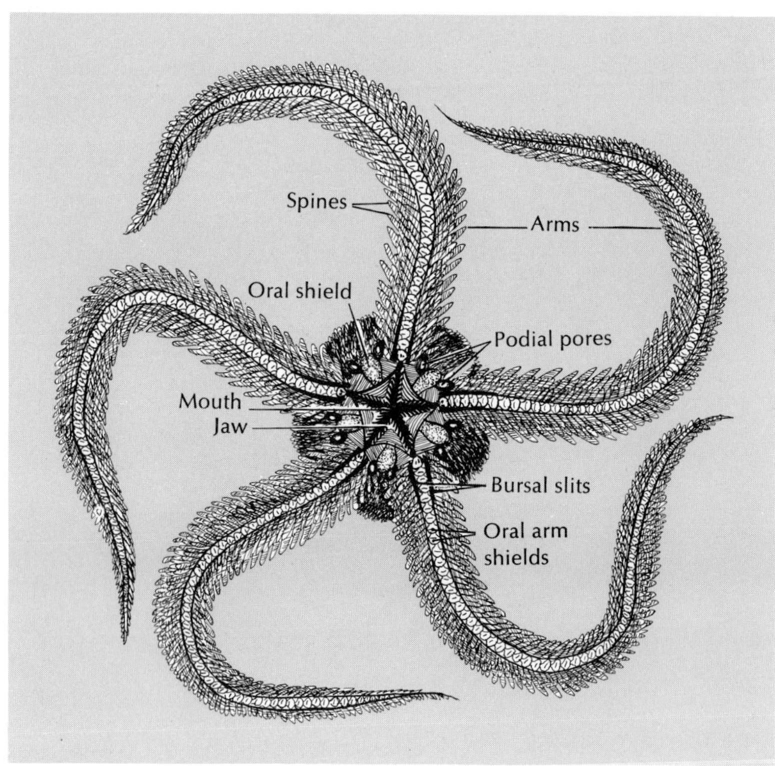

FIG. 22-10

Spiny brittle star *(Ophiothrix)* oral view.

skin is leathery, with dermal plates (ossicles) and spines arranged in characteristic patterns. Cilia are mostly lacking.

The visceral organs are confined to the central disk; the rays are too slender to contain them. The **stomach** is saclike and there is no intestine. Indigestible material is cast out of the mouth. Five pairs of **bursae** (peculiar to ophiuroids) open toward the oral surface by **genital slits** at the bases of the arms. Water circulates in and out of these sacs for respiration. On the coelomic wall of each bursa are small **gonads** that discharge into the bursa their ripe sex cells, which pass through the genital slits into the water for fertilization. Sexes are usually separate; a few are hermaphroditic. Some brood their young in the bursae; the young escape through the genital slits or by rupturing the aboral disk. The larva, called the **ophiopluteus** (Fig. 22-2), metamorphoses into the adult. Water-vascular, nervous, and hemal systems are similar to those of the sea stars. In each arm there is a small **coelom,** a **nerve cord,** and a **radial canal** of the water-vascular system.

Behavior. Brittle stars are often found under stones and seaweed at low tide because they are negatively phototactic and positively thigmotactic. At high tide they are active, wandering about in search of small animals, which they capture with their rays. They move with a writhing, serpentlike motion of the arms. They can swim with their rays, but they often hold to objects with one or more rays while pushing with the others. Regeneration and autotomy are even more pronounced in brittle stars than in sea stars. Many individuals are regenerating parts most of the time, for they are very fragile.

FIG. 22-11

Group of common west coast echinoderms. **A,** Pacific purple stars *(Pisaster);* **B,** sun star *(Solaster);* **C,** common sea cucumber *(Stichopus);* **D,** sea urchin *(Strongylocentrotus);* **E,** 21-rayed star *(Pycnopodia);* **F,** 5-rayed star *(Dermasterias).* (Photographed at the Vancouver Public Aquarium, British Columbia.)

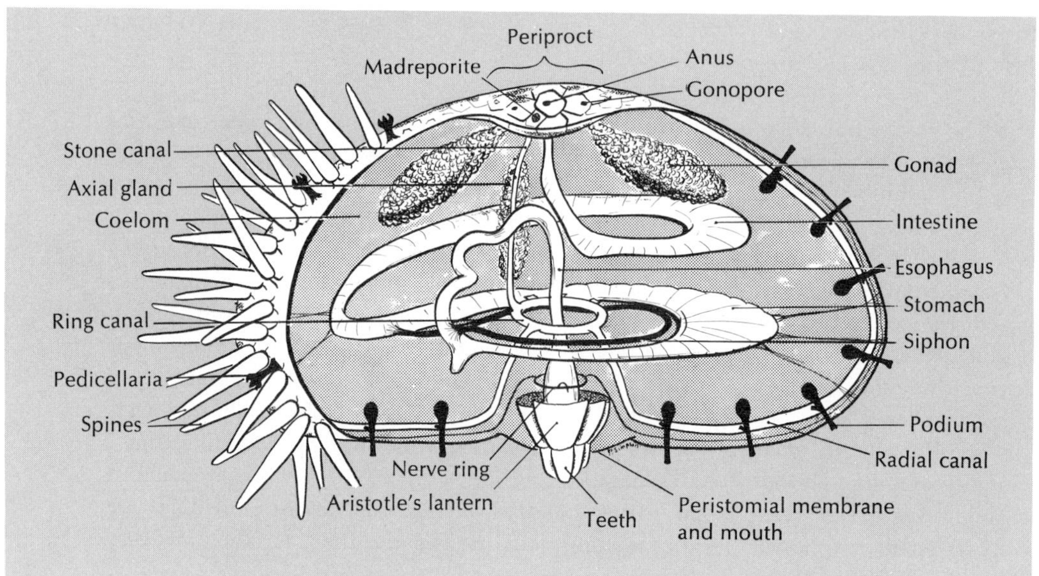

FIG. 22-12

Semidiagrammatic view of some internal and external structures of sea urchin *Arbacia*.

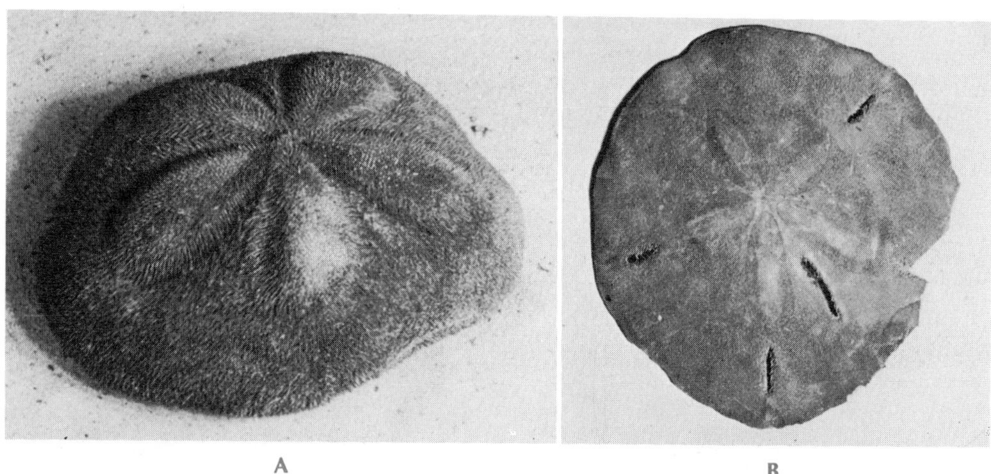

FIG. 22-13

Tests of two types of sand dollars. **A,** Sea biscuit *(Clypeaster)*. **B,** Keyhole sand dollar *Mellita*. In latter, slitlike openings called lunules may be useful in burrowing to allow flow-through of sand and water. Class Echinoidea.

CLASS ECHINOIDEA
Sea urchins and sand dollars

Sea urchins and sand dollars of the class Echinoidea lack rays and have rounded bodies made up of continuous endoskeletons of closely fitting plates (Figs. 22-11 to 22-13). Sea urchins are hemispherical, sand dollars are disk shaped, and heart urchins are ovoid. Sea urchins, with their long sharp spines, resemble chestnut burrs. One of the most common sea urchins of the eastern coast is *Arbacia punctulata*, found in both shallow and deep waters and often in tide pools concealed under seaweeds. Along the Pacific coast, *Strongylocentrotus* is the common form.

Structure. The **test,** or shell, is a compact skeleton of ten double rows of plates that bear movable, stiff spines. The plates are firmly sutured. Five pairs of these ambulacral rows are homologous to the five arms of the sea star and have pores for the long tube feet. Alternating with the ambulacral rows are the interambulacral spaces. The plates bear small tubercles, or sockets, in which the round ends of the spines articulate. These spines move by small muscles around the bases. The four or five kinds of **pedicellariae** are three jawed and are mounted on long stalks; they help keep the body clean and capture small organisms. The **mouth** is surrounded by five converging **teeth,** with an enclosing

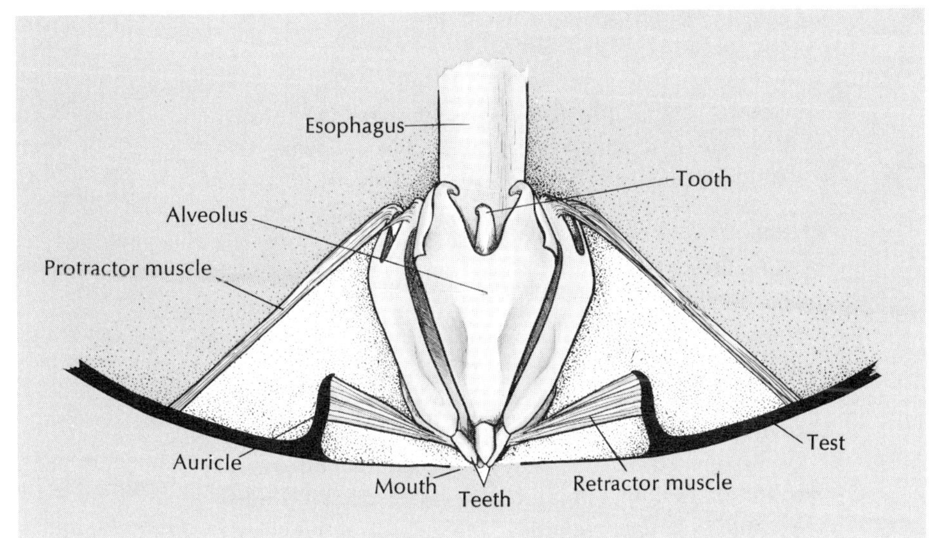

FIG. 22-14

Aristotle's lantern, complex mechanism used by sea urchin for masticating its food. Five pairs of retractor muscles draw lantern and teeth up into test; five pairs of protractors push lantern down and expose teeth. Other muscles produce variety of movements. Only major skeletal parts and muscles are shown in diagram.

collar-shaped lip. Ten branched gills (modified podia) encircle the peristome. The rounded aboral end bears the centered **anus,** a number of **genital** openings, and the **madreporite.** This area contains a number of endoskeletal plates and is called the **periproct.**

Inside the test (Fig. 22-12) is the coiled **digestive system**—the complicated **Aristotle's lantern** (Fig. 22-14) to which the teeth are attached, a slender esophagus, a dilated stomach with ceca, an intestine, and a rectum, which terminates at the anus. A peculiar tubelike ciliated siphon connects the esophagus to the intestine and enables the water to bypass the stomach to concentrate the food for digestion in the intestine. The **hemal system** consists of an esophageal ring and radial vessels to the inner surface of the test. Around the esophagus is the ring canal, with five radial canals that extend along the interior of the test and connect to the tube feet. The ring canal is connected to the madreporite by the stone canal, which is accompanied by a spongy axial gland. The chief **nervous system** consists of a nerve ring around the mouth; five radial nerves, which run along the radial canals; and a subepidermal plexus, which innervates the podia, spines, and pedicellariae. There are few special sense organs, but the podia, spines, and pedicellariae are also sensory. A number of **gonads** are attached to the inner aboral surface, and from each a duct leads to one of the genital openings. The sexes are separate and the larval form is a **pluteus.**

The sand dollar (Fig. 22-13) (*Echinarachnius*) differs from *Arbacia* in having a flattened disk-shaped body and also in certain minor details, such as small calcareous spines and a marginal anus. The tests of some sand dollars *(Mellita)* are perforated with holes, called **lunules,** which may serve for the passage of sand and water in burrowing.

Behavior. The echinoids live on seaweed and dead animal matter. They move about by means of their spines and tube feet. Their spines and hard test afford them considerable protection. When prodded they will turn the spines toward the source of irritation. One sea urchin found along the coast of Florida and the Gulf of Mexico has poisonous spines. However, echinoids are preyed upon by some fish and marine carnivores.

CLASS HOLOTHUROIDEA

In a phylum characterized by odd annimals, class Holothuroidea contains members that both structurally and physiologically are among the strangest of all. These soft-bodied animals have a remarkable resemblance to the vegetable after which they are named (Fig. 22-11, *C*). In their evolution they appear to be more closely related to Echinoidea than to any other echinoderms. They are bottom-dwelling forms, living mostly in sand and mud. Low-tide pools with mucky bottoms are favorite places. Here they lie buried, with their tentacles sticking up into the clearer water.

Common species along the eastern seacoast are *Cucumaria frondosa, Thyone briareus,* and the translucent *Teptosynapta.* Along the Pacific coast there are several species of *Cucumaria* and the striking reddish brown *Stichopus*, with very large papillae. The following description applies to either *Thyone* or *Cucumaria.*

Sea cucumbers

Structure. The bodies of sea cucumbers are elongated. The **mouth** and retractile tentacles are found at the oral end and the **anus** at the aboral end. They have leathery skins in which are embedded microscopic calcareous plates. The ten to thirty retractile **tentacles** around the mouth correspond to the oral tube feet of other echinoderms. The **body wall** contains both circular and longitudinal muscles and is covered by a cuticle and nonciliated epidermis. The dorsal side bears two longitudinal zones of tube feet; the ventral side has three. However, podia are absent in some species. The ventral side often becomes flattened and is called the **sole.**

The **coelomic cavity** is large and is not divided into compartments. It is filled with a fluid similar to sea water and contains many coelomocytes. The **digestive**

FIG. 22-15

Longitudinal section of sea cucumber (similar to *Stichopus)* showing internal anatomy (semidiagrammatic).

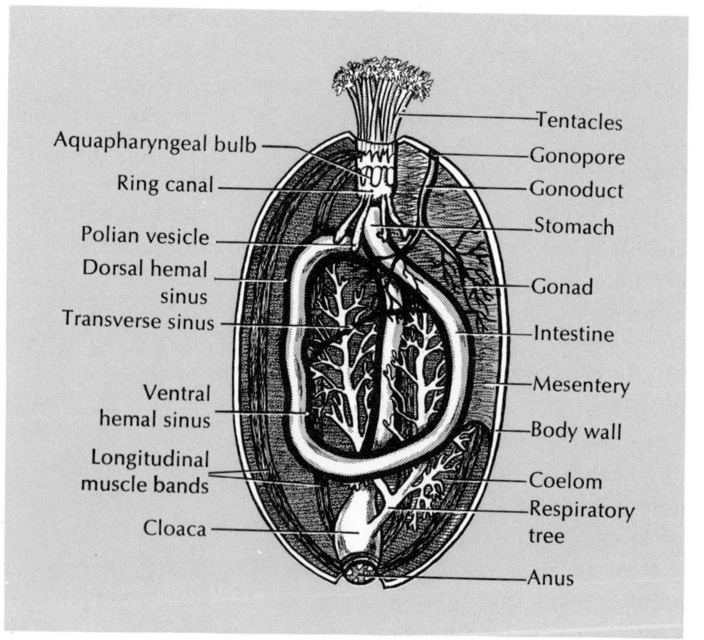

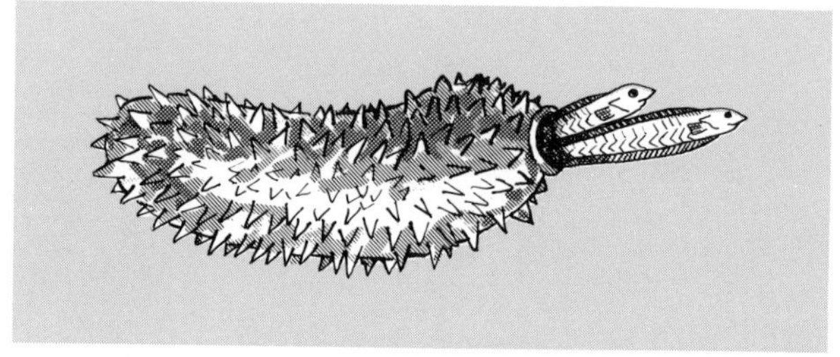

FIG. 22-16

Holothurian and its commensal fish *Carapus*, or *Fierasfer*. The fish (4 to 5 inches long) use cloaca and respiratory tree for shelter. Only a small percentage of holothurians harbor the fish.

FIG. 22-17

Crinoid with part of stalk. Some crinoids have stalks 2 feet long.

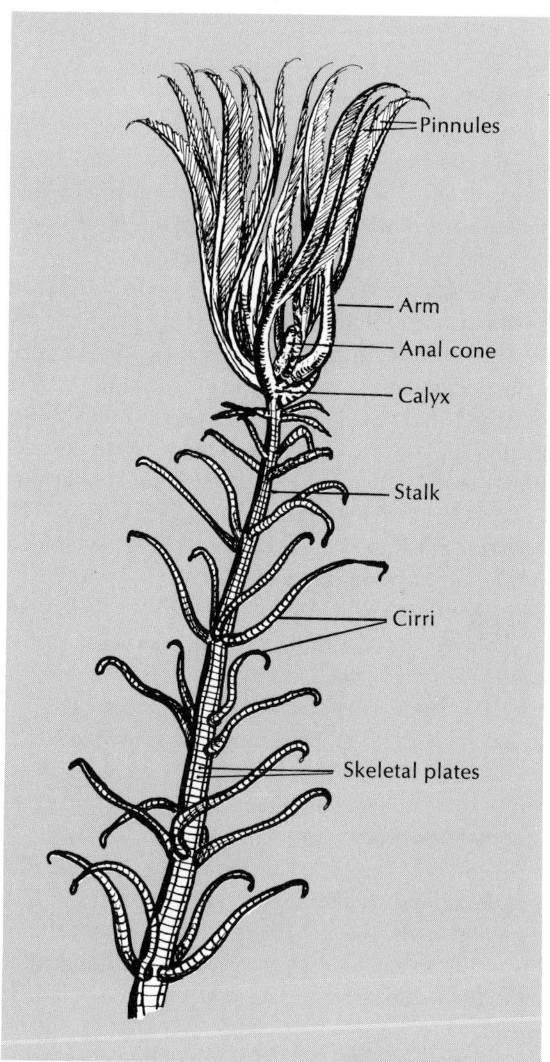

system contains a mouth, an esophagus, an oval stomach, a long, looped intestine (supported by mesenteries) enlarged at the posterior end into the cloaca, and the anus (Fig. 22-15). A respiratory tree (two long, branched tubes through which the muscular cloaca pumps water) is formed by evaginations of the digestive tract and serves for both respiration and excretion. Water also passes through the walls of the respiratory tree into the coelom. The hemal system is well developed. It consists of a ring around the esophagus, with radial vessels along the water canals and two main sinuses along the digestive system. The **hemal system** is especially large in *Stichopus.*

The **water-vascular system** consists of an internal madreporite, a ring canal around the esophagus, and five radial canals that connect to the tube feet. Opening into the ring canal are a number of **polian vesicles,** elongated sacs hanging in the coelom and serving as expansion chambers for the water-vascular system.

The **nervous system** is made up of an oral nerve ring with five radial nerves. There appear to be sense organs for touch and light, and some species have statocysts.

The sexes are separate, but some holothuroids are hermaphroditic. There is one gonad in *Thyone* and *Cucumaria,* two in *Stichopus.* Each gonad is composed of numerous tubules united at their base to form a tuft, which may be large at sexual maturity. A common gonoduct empties the sex cells through a **gonopore** to the outside, where fertilization occurs. The larval stage is called an **auricularia** (Fig. 22-2). Some species brood the young either inside the body or somewhere on the body surface.

Behavior. Sea cucumbers are sluggish, moving partly by means of their ventral tube feet and partly by waves of contraction in the muscular wall, which contains five powerful longitudinal muscle bands as well as circular muscle fibers. The dorsal tube feet are respiratory and

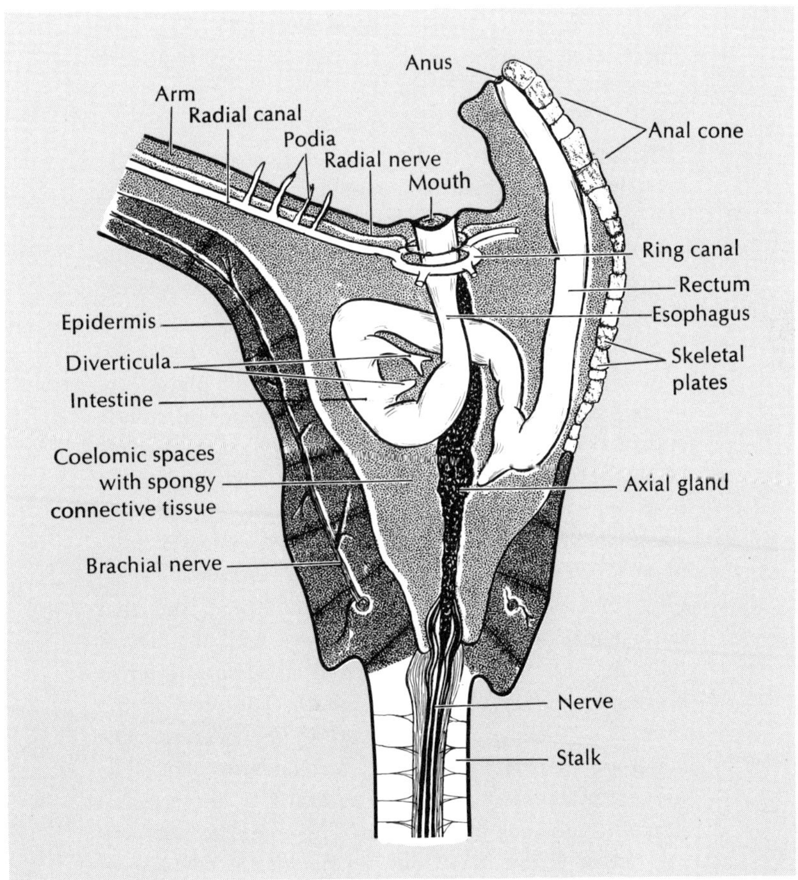

FIG. 22-18

Semidiagram of section through calyx of typical crinoid showing principal internal structures. (Modified from Lang and others.)

tactile. The food consists of small organisms, which they entangle in the sticky mucus of their tentacles and suck into the mouth. Sea cucumbers have a peculiar power of self-mutilation. Some, when irritated, may cast out a part of their viscera by a strong muscular contraction, which may either rupture the body wall or evert its contents through the anus. The lost parts are soon regenerated. An interesting commensal relationship between a sea cucumber and certain fish is shown schematically in Fig. 22-16.

CLASS CRINOIDEA

The crinoids are the most primitive of the echinoderms. As fossil records reveal, they were once far more numerous than now. They are essentially a deep-water form, although a few species live near shore. They differ from other echinoderms by being attached during part or all of their lives. The feather stars (suborder Comatulida) have long, many-branched arms, and the adults are free swimming. At one stage of their life cycle they are attached to stalks, which they later absorb (Fig. 22-17).

Sea lilies or feather stars

Structure. The body disk, or **calyx,** is covered with a leathery skin (tegmen) containing calcareous plates. Cuticle and epidermis are poorly developed. Five flexible arms branch to form many more arms, each with many lateral **pinnules** arranged like barbs on a feather. Calyx and arms together are called the **crown.** Sessile forms have a long, jointed **stalk** attached to the aboral side of the body. This stalk is made up of plates, appears jointed, and may bear **cirri.** Madreporite, spines, and pedicellariae are absent. The upper (oral) surface bears the mouth, which opens into a short esophagus, from which the long **intestine** with diverticula proceeds aborally for a distance and then makes a complete turn to the **anus,** which may be on a raised cone (Fig. 22-18). Crinoids feed upon small organisms that are caught in the ambulacral grooves with the aid of tube feet and mucous nets. Ciliated **ambulacral grooves** on the arms carry food to the mouth. Tube feet in the form of tentacles are also found in the grooves. The **water-vascular system** has the echinoderm plan. The **nervous system** is made up of an **oral ring** and a **radial nerve,** which runs to each arm. The aboral or entoneural system is the main one in crinoids, in contrast to most other echinoderms. Sense organs are scanty and primitive. The sexes are separate. The gonads are simply masses of cells in the genital cavity of the arms and pinnules. The gametes escape without ducts through a rupture in the pinnule wall. The larvae (doliolaria) are free swimming for a time before they become attached and metamorphose. Most crinoids are from 6 to 12 inches long.

Derivation and meaning of basic terminology

ambulacra (L. *ambulare,* to walk). Radiating grooves where podia of water-vascular system project to outside.

Arbacia (Gr. *Arbakes,* ancient king). Refers to chief sea urchin.

bipinnaria (L. *bi,* double, + *pinna,* wing, + *aria,* like or connected with). Refers to shape of this asteroid larva.

brachiolaria (L. *brachiolatus,* with arms). This asteroid larva has three preoral processes.

coelomocyte (Gr. *koiloma,* hollow, + *kytos,* cell). Another name for amebocyte, primitive or undifferentiated cell of the coelom and the water-vascular system.

dipleurula (Gr. *dis,* two, + *pleura,* side, + *ula,* dim.). This hypothetical echinoderm larva has bilateral symmetry.

Echinarachnius (Gr. *echinos,* sea urchin, hedgehog, + *rhachis,* spine). A common genus of sand dollars.

lunules (L. *luna,* moon, + *ulse,* dim.). These slitlike openings in the sand dollar test may be crescent shaped.

madreporite (F. *madre,* mother, + Gr. *poros,* pore, + *ite,* suffix). Sievelike structure that is the intake for the water-vascular system.

ossicle (L. *ossiculum,* small bone). Small separate pieces of endoskeleton.

pedicellaria (NL. *pedicel,* little foot, + *aria,* like or connected with). Minute pincerlike organ on surface of certain echinoderms.

periproct (Gr. *peri,* around, + *proktos,* anus). Region of aboral plates around the anus of echinoids.

pluteus (L. painter's easel). These echinoid larvae have elongated processes like the supports of an easel.

rosette (L. *rosa,* rose, + *ette,* dim.). Arrangement or cluster resembling a rose.

Annotated references

Boolootian, R. A., and A. C. Giese. 1959. Clotting of echinoderm coelomic fluid. J. Exp. Zool. **140**:207-229.

Buchsbaum, R. 1948. Animals without backbones, rev. ed. Chicago, University of Chicago Press. *Excellent illustrations of echinoderms.*

Burnett, A. L. 1960. The mechanism employed by the starfish *Asterias forbesi* to gain access to the anterior of the bivalve *Venus mercenaria.* Ecology **41**:583-584. *This investigator and others have shown that the starfish uses no narcotic agent to produce a small* *gape between the clam's valves through which the starfish can squeeze its stomach.*

Cambridge Natural History. 1906. Echinodermata (E. W. MacBride). London, Macmillan & Co., Ltd. *Authoritative and detailed treatment of general structures.*

Carter, G. S. 1951. A general zoology of the invertebrates, London, Sidgwick & Jackson, Ltd. *An excellent work with emphasis on physiologic aspects of the group.*

Chuang, S. H. 1963. Digestive enzymes of the echiuroid, *Ochetostoma erythrogrammon.* Biol. Bull. **125**:464-469.

Encyclopaedia Britannica. 1956. Echinoderma. Chicago, Encyclopaedia Britannica, Inc. *A fine, concise account of echinoderms with clear illustrations.*

Grasse, P. P. (editor). 1948. Traité de zoologie. XI. Echinodermes-Stomocordes-Protocordes (L. Cuénot). Paris, Masson & Cie.

Harvey, E. B. 1956. The American *Arbacia* and other sea urchins. Princeton, N. J., Princeton University Press. *A comprehensive monograph on this interesting group, which have furnished so many basic concepts in the field of cytology and development.*

Hyman, L. H. 1955. The invertebrates: Echinodermata, vol. 4. New York, McGraw-Hill Book Co. *The latest and most comprehensive work yet published on the echinoderms.*

Jennings, H. S. 1907. Behavior of the starfish *Asterias forreri* De Loriol. Berkeley, Univ. Calif. Pub. in Zool. **4**:339-411. *An account of the reactions of the starfish, including the righting movement.*

Lankester, E. R. (editor). 1900. A treatise on zoology. Part III. The Echinoderma (F. A. Bather). London, A. & C. Black. *The technical descriptions of echinoderms in this work will always be of great value.*

MacGinitie, G. E., and N. MacGinitie. 1968. Natural history of marine animals. ed. 2, New York, McGraw-Hill Book Co. *The section on echinoderms includes some good descriptions and photographs of representative forms, especially those of the Pacific coast.*

Millott, N. (editor). 1967. Echinoderm biology. New York, Academic Press, Inc. *An interesting symposium on various aspects of a "noble group especially designed to puzzle the zoologist" (Hyman).*

Nichols, D. 1962. Echinoderms. London, Hutchinson & Co., Ltd.

Parker, T. J., and W. A. Haswell, 1940. A textbook of zoology, ed. 6, 2 vols. (revised by O. Lowenstein). London, Macmillan & Co., Ltd. *Good general descriptions with considerable detail.*

Ricketts, E. F., and J. Calvin, 1952. Between Pacific tides, ed. 3 (revised by J. W. Hedgpeth). Stanford, Calif., Stanford University Press. *In many ways this is a unique book of seashore life. It stresses the habits and habitats of the Pacific coast invertebrates (including echinoderms), and the illustrations are revealing. It includes an excellent systematic index and annotated bibliography.*

Smith, R. I., and others (editors). 1957. Intertidal invertebrates of the central California Coast. Berkeley, University of California Press. *This is a revision of S. F. Light's Laboratory and Field Text in Invertebrate Zoology. Consists mainly of taxonomic keys to the forms found in the intertidal zone.*

CHAPTER 23

PHYLA CHAETOGNATHA, HEMICHORDATA, AND POGONOPHORA (MINOR EUCOELOMATE BILATERAL GROUP)

These three phyla are all enterocoelous coelomates, or deuterostomes. Two of them, Hemichordata and Pogonophora, are closely related, but the Chaetognatha appear not to be closely related to any other group and may represent an early offshoot from the main line leading to other deuterostomes. They are placed here with the other two phyla mainly because the chaetognaths and the others are minor deuterostomes. The embryologic pattern of the chaetognaths is different from that of other deuterostomes. They form their coelom by a backward extension from the archenteron and not by pinching off coelomic sacs, as other deuterostomes do. In most ways their structure resembles that of the pseudocoelomates, especially that of the aschelminths. Their body wall with only longitudinal muscle, their ring type of nervous system, the lack of a true peritoneum, and the pharynx with its muscular end bulb are all aschelminth characteristics, but the chaetognaths have other characteristics that divorce them from basic affinities with that pseudocoelomate phylum.

Phylum Chaetognatha*

Another name for these organisms is arrowworms. They are marine animals and are considered by some to be related to the nematodes and by others to be related to the annelids. However, they actually show no distinct relations to other groups and are aberrant. The name Chaetognatha is derived from the Greek words *chaeton,* bristle, and *gnathos,* jaw. These forms bear sickle-shaped bristles on each side of the mouth—hence their name. This is not a large group, for there are fewer than fifty known species. Their small, straight bodies, which resemble miniature torpedoes, are from 1 to 3 inches long and are transparent and difficult to see. They are the only invertebrates with more than one layer of cells in the epidermis.

Characteristics. Bilateral symmetry; unsegmented; body divided into head, trunk, and tail; body with lateral fins and caudal fins; coelom present; digestive sys-

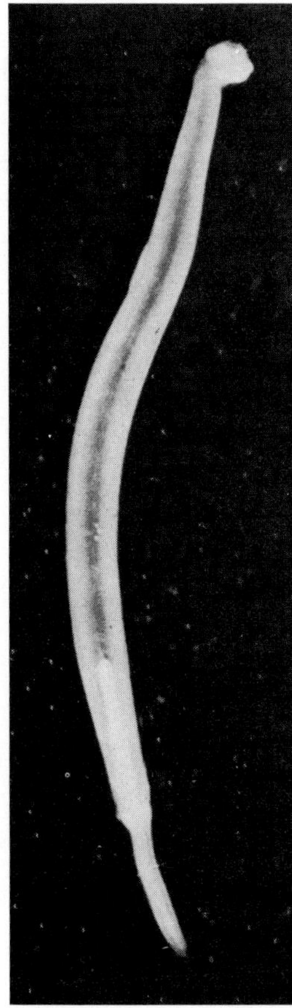

FIG. 23-1

Arrowworm *Sagitta.* Head (top) is largely covered with hood formed from epidermis. When worm is engaged in catching its prey, hood is retracted to neck region. (Preserved specimen.)

*Ke-tog'na-tha (Gr. *chaeten,* bristle, hair, + *gnathos,* jaw).

tem complete; vascular, excretory, and respiratory organs absent; dorsal and ventral ganglia; head with eyes; hermaphroditic, with self- or cross-fertilization; no metamorphosis; belong to the Deuterostomia.

Structure and behavior. Arrowworms are fairly advanced worms, as attested by their complete digestive system, their well-developed coelomic cavity, their distinct regions of the body, and their prominent nervous system. However, their lack of vascular, respiratory, and excretory systems indicates a rather primitive structure. Their postanal tail is found in no other group except the chordates. A unique hood (fold of body wall) can be drawn over the head.

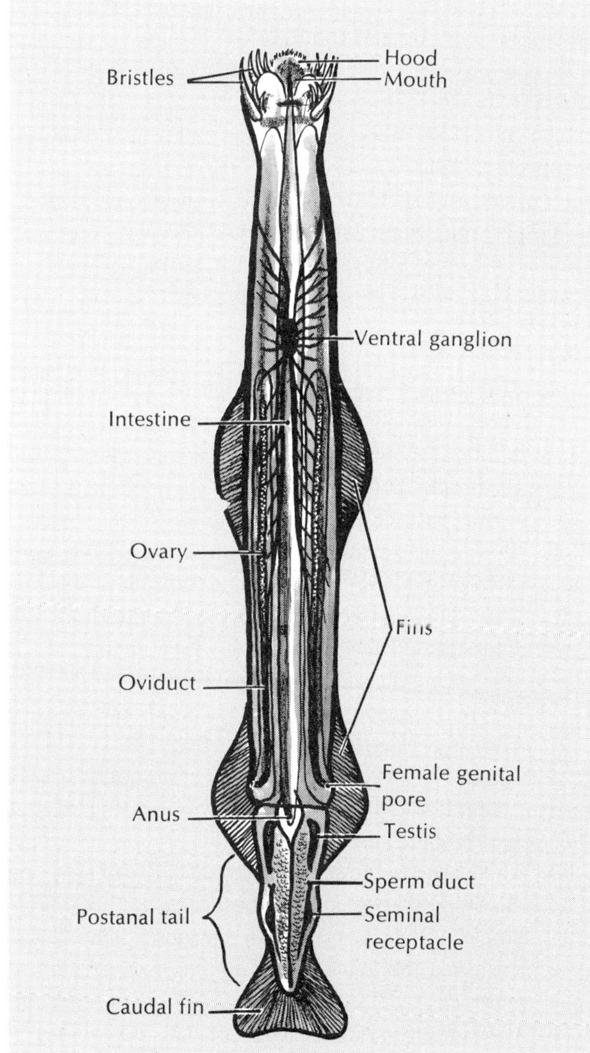

Most of these forms swim near the surface, although sometimes they may be found at a depth of several hundred feet. They have the habit of coming to the surface at night and descending to lower depths during the day. They are rapid swimmers. Arrowworms are predaceous and feed on small plants and animals.

Each specimen has two ovaries and two testes; these are provided with oviducts and vasa deferentia. The sperm of one animal enter the oviducts of another, fertilizing the eggs internally, although self-fertilization may also occur. When the eggs are laid, they develop directly into worms without metamorphosis.

The most common representative is *Sagitta,* the common arrowworm (Figs. 23-1 and 23-2).

Phylum Hemichordata*

BIOLOGIC PRINCIPLES

Organ-system level of organization

1. Hemichordates are a group that have a combination of both invertebrate (echinoderm) and chordate characteristics.
2. A chordate plan of structure is vaguely suggested by gill slits and a restricted tubular dorsal nerve cord.
3. Both classes (Enteropneusta and Pterobranchia) have a tripartite body composed of a proboscis, collar, and trunk, but one class is adapted for a sluggish burrowing habit and filter feeding, the other for a sessile, colonial existence and a ciliated method of feeding.
4. Each of the three body regions (segments) has its own body cavity, or coelom, which is unpaired in the proboscis but paired in the other two. The coelomic pouches of the proboscis and collar have pores (coelomostomes) to the exterior, which are comparable to the water pores of echinoderms.
5. They belong to the deuterostome branch of the animal kingdom and are enterocoelous, with radial cleavage.
6. Because of their close relationship to the chordates, this phylum and Pogonophora are called prechordates.

*Hem'i-kor-da"ta (Gr. *hemi,* half, + L. *chorda,* cord).

FIG. 23-2

Arrowworm *Sagitta,* ventral view. These worms, rarely more than 2 or 3 inches long, form important part of marine plankton in both littoral and open sea waters. They have many resemblances to certain pseudocoelomates, and some authorities hesitate to call them coelomate animals, although they are enterocoelous and are placed in Deuterostomia. Among their features are postanal tail, hood, fins, and stratified epidermis.

Biologic contributions

1. The class Enteropneusta has developed the **filter-feeding** mode of life and the class Pterobranchia, the sessile condition typical of the ancestral prevertebrates.
2. A **tubular dorsal nerve cord** (in collar zone) foreshadows the future condition in chordates, and a diffused net of nerve cells is similar to the uncentralized, subepithelial plexus of echinoderms.
3. The **gill slits** so characteristic of chordates are used primarily for filter feeding and only secondarily for breathing and are thus comparable to some of the protochordates.
4. The **stomochord** (**notochord** by tradition), an outpocketing forward from the roof of the mouth cavity, with its chitinous plate, is of debatable phylogenic status. It is sometimes called a buccal diverticulum.

Position in animal kingdom

1. The best evidence of relationship to the chordates are the gill slits and U-shaped tongue bars (which are absent in the Pterobranchia).
2. The affinity of the hemichordates with the echinoderms is more clear cut, for example, the embryologic (larval) resemblance between the two groups, general similarity of their nervous systems, and the functional similarity of the hydraulic mechanism of the proboscis-collar coelom with the water-vascular system of echinoderms.
3. The presence of both phosphocreatine (a vertebrate energy compound) and phosphoarginine (an invertebrate energy compound) in *Balanoglossus* may indicate that the latter is a connecting link between vertebrates and invertebrates, but this theory is not stressed.

GENERAL RELATIONS

The taxonomic status and phylogenetic relationship of the hemichordates has been somewhat of a puzzle among zoologists for years. Many authorities still consider them a subphylum under the chordates and lump them among the subphyla Tunicata (Urochordata) and Cephalochordata to form the Protochordata. This classification was based mainly upon certain characteristics of the hemichordates, such as gill slits and a supposed rudimentary notochord, which members of the phylum Chordata possess. Some hemichordates have the beginning of a dorsal hollow nerve cord, which distinguishes the chordate nerve cord from that of the invertebrates. The group also is somewhat unique in having many invertebrate as well as chordate characteristics. Their affinity with the echinoderms is marked, for the **tornaria larva** of *Balanoglossus* is remarkably like certain echinoderm larvae. There are also other resemblances to echinoderms, such as the coelomic pouches that act like a water-vascular system and the general plan of the subepithelial plexus nervous system, characteristic of both groups. Both the hemichordates and the echinoderms also share many habits in common, such as feeding methods and ecologic niches. Many zoologists are highly skeptical about the presence of a true notochord in Hemichordata, but instead they consider such an organ as a **stomochord,** which may not be homologous to the notochord of chordates.

Because of these and other reasons, the hemichordates are placed in a phylum of their own, phylum Hemichordata, which is made up of two classes—Enteropneusta and Pterobranchia. These two classes have many similar as well as dissimilar features. Enteropneusta are highly specialized for burrowing and filter feeding; Pterobranchia are sessile and colonial, with lophophore feeding.

All three groups—echinoderms, hemichordates, and chordates—are deuterostomous and have enterocoelous coeloms (as do the Chaetognatha and a few others).

The class Pterobranchia shows affinities with the Ectoprocta, Brachiopoda, and others because of the lophophore and sessile habits. There is strong evidence to suggest that the early vertebrate ancestor may have been sessile, but filter feeding with gill slits developed due to loss of the lophophore system.

CHARACTERISTICS

1. Soft-bodied animals of elongated (wormlike) or short compact body with **stalk** for attachment; bilateral symmetry; body typically divided into **proboscis, collar,** and **trunk; stomochord** in posterior part of proboscis; segmentation absent
2. Body wall of unicellular epidermis with mucus-secreting cells, basement membrane, musculature of smooth muscle mostly longitudinal
3. One group (Enteropneusta) free living and of burrowing habits; another (Pterobranchia) sessile with free-living and colonial members in chitinous tubes
4. Digestive tract straight and complete or U shaped, with two or many arms bearing ciliated bands (pterobranchs)
5. Coelomic cavities correspond to each of the three body regions; proboscis coelomic pouche single, other two paired; proboscis and collar coelomic pouches open to exterior by dorsal pores
6. Circulatory system of a median dorsal and a median ventral longitudinal vessel intercon-

nected by small lateral vessels and joined to a heart dorsal to the stomochord

7. Respiratory system of gill slits (few or none in Pterobranchia) forming a dorsolateral row in the pharynx behind the collar
8. Excretory system of a single glomerulus (proboscis gland) connected to blood vessels
9. Nervous system of a subepidermal plexus of cells and fibers, which is thickened to form two longitudinal nerve cords, one mediodorsal and the other medioventral, with a ring connective between the two cords in the collar; dorsal nerve cord of collar hollow in some
10. Sexes separate in Enteropneusta, with saclike gonads projecting into body cavity and arranged in a row on each side in the genital region of the trunk; in Pterobranchia reproduction may be sexual, with paired ovaries and pigmented oviducts or paired testes near the anus (a few monoecious), or asexual (in some) by budding; external fertilization; tornaria larva in some Enteropneusta but without larval stages in others; in *Rhabdopleura* (Pterobranchia) individuals bud from a stolon to form a colony of zooids

CLASSES OF HEMICHORDATA

Class Enteropneusta (en'ter-op-neus"ta) (Gr. *enteron,* gut, + *pneustos,* breathed)—**acorn, or tongue, worms.** Body vermiform with no stalk; proboscis cylindric and tapering to a blunt point; active, free living, and burrowing; many gill slits in a row on each side of anterior region (pharynx) of trunk; alimentary canal straight with anus at terminal end; separate sexes with many saclike gonads arranged serially; tornaria larva in some. Examples: *Balanoglossus, Saccoglossus.*

Class Pterobranchia (ter'o-bran"ke-a) (Gr. *pteron,* feather or wing, + *branchion,* gill)—**pterobranchs.** Compact body with stalk; proboscis shield shaped; sessile in chitinous tubes with lophophore bearing ciliated arms; a single pair of gill slits in pharynx or none; alimentary canal U shaped with anus near mouth; separate sexes or monoecious, budding in some. Examples: *Cephalodicus, Rhabdopleura.*

(**Class Planctosphaeroidea,** represented by a few pelagic larvae, is recognized by some.)

REPRESENTATIVE TYPES

CLASS ENTEROPNEUSTA

Enteropneusta are vermiform hemichords that are common in sand or mud flats in rather shallow water, although specimens have been collected at great depths. They vary in length from an inch or two to several feet. The name *Balanoglossus* has been applied to many genera but should be restricted to one genus. This genus has a worldwide distribution. Several species of *Saccoglossus* (Fig. 23-3) are found along both the east and west coasts. *S. kowalevskii* is common along the east coast, *S. pusillus* along the California coast. Some of them have bright orange and red colors.

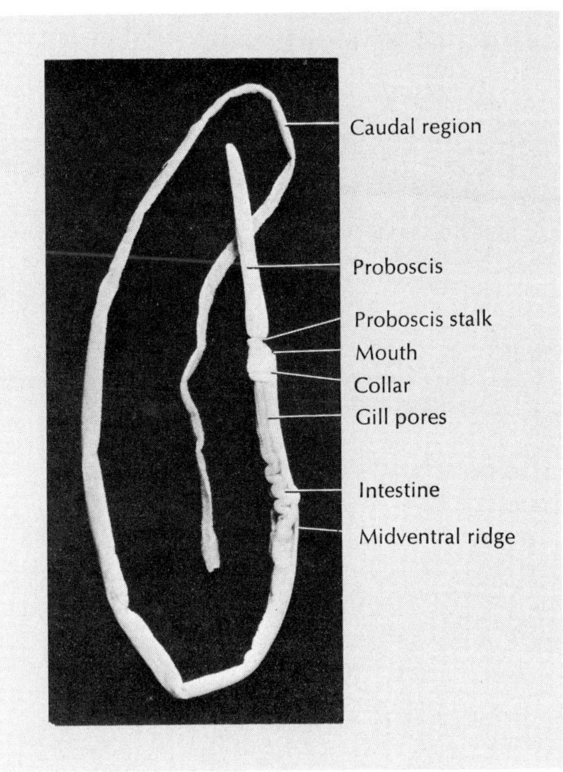

FIG. 23-3

Tongue, or acorn, worm *Saccoglossus.* Proboscis appears dense and rigid, with collar folded just behind it. Note coils of intestinal tract. Class Enteropneusta.

The body is made up of a **proboscis, collar,** and an elongated **trunk.** In the hind part of the proboscis lies the **stomochord** (called the notochord until recently), which is an outpocketing of the dorsal wall of the buccal cavity. On the ventral surface of the stomochord is a chitinous skeletal plate, which helps support the proboscis. The many **gill slits** form a dorsolateral row on each side just behind the collar. These slits serve as passages from the pharynx to the exterior. The external opening of each slit is a simple pore, but the inner opening into the pharynx is U shaped, produced by the

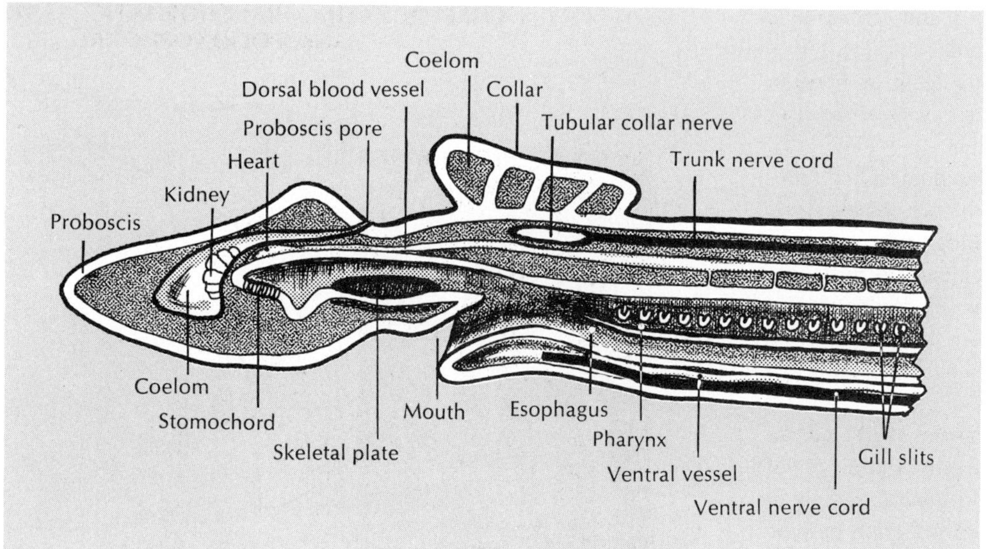

FIG. 23-4

Longitudinal section through anterior end of *Saccoglossus*. Class Enteropneusta.

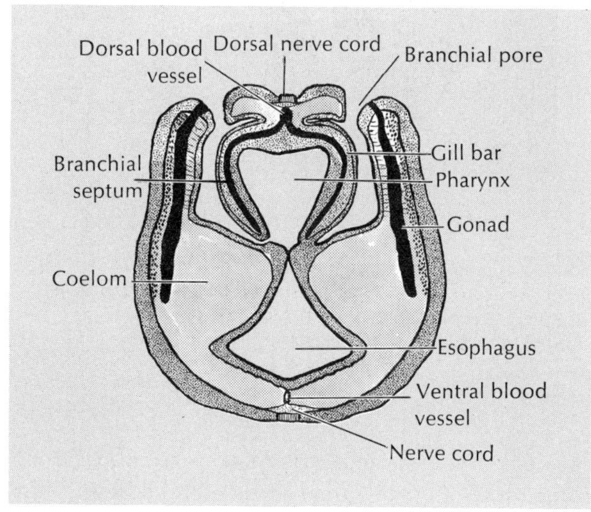

FIG. 23-5

Cross section through pharyngeal region of tongue worm. Class Enteropneusta. (Modified from Lang.)

downgrowth of branchial gill bars. These gill bars are provided with capillaries and function in respiration. The gill slits and pouches serve to pass outward the water that enters the pharynx and thus serve as food strainers. There is a single coelomic space in the proboscis, paired ones in the collar and trunk. The spaces in the proboscis and collar can fill with water through dorsal pores (usually paired), and thus the anterior end of the animal can become turgid as an aid in burrowing. The **digestive system** is made up of a wide mouth at the anteroventral margin of the collar, a buccal cavity within the collar, the pharynx with its gill slits, a straight intestine bearing dorsal hepatic ceca, and the anus at the terminal end (Fig. 23-4). The alimentary canal is supported by the double walls of the longitudinal partition which divides the trunk coelom into two cavities. The anterior end of the digestive system is also divided into the dorsal pharynx and the ventral esophagus. The **vascular system** consists of a median dorsal and a median ventral longitudinal blood vessel which are interconnected by small branches, especially in the pharyngeal region (Fig. 23-5). A **heart vesicle** lies dorsal to the stomochord, but propulsion is probably done by peristaltic contractions of the large blood vessels. The blood is colorless (and may have cells) and flows anteriorly in the dorsal blood vessel. In the proboscis the vascular system gives rise to a network of blood sinuses (the proboscidal glomerulus), which may have excretory functions.

The body is covered by a thick, ciliated, unicellular epithelium, which contains many mucous cells. This epithelium rests upon a basement membrane underneath which is the musculature that makes up most of the **body wall.** Nearly all the muscles are longitudinal, but a few may be circular or pseudocircular. Most enteropneusts give off an unpleasant smell like that of iodoform, emitted in the slime. The **nervous system** consists mostly of a subepithelial network or plexus of fibers and cells, to which processes of epithelial cells are attached. Thickenings or concentrations of this net form nerve cords along the middorsal and midventral lines of the trunk. These cords are united posterior to the collar by a ring connective, and the dorsal cord, which is here thickened and invaginated into a tubular form in some, continues on into the collar and furnishes many fibers to the plexus of the proboscis.

The sexes are separate in class Enteropneusta. The gonads, which are simple or branched sacs projecting into the body cavity, are arranged in a dorsolateral row on each side of the anterior region of the trunk from behind the collar to near the hepatic ceca. When mature, each gonad discharges its contents to the exterior through a separate genital pore. The gonads do not open into the coelom and new ones are constantly being formed at the posterior end of each row. Fertilization of the small eggs occurs externally in the sea water, and in some species a pelagic, ciliated larva, the **tornaria,** is found during development. This larva has such a marked resemblance to the auricularia larva of certain echinoderms that it was at one time described as belonging to the echinoderm group. The tornaria larva differs, however, in having a perianal band of cilia and a pair of eyespots near the apical tuft of cilia. The familiar *Saccoglossus* of American waters does not have a tornaria stage.

Enteropneusts are delicate, sluggish animals that use their proboscis and collar for burrowing through sandy or muddy sea bottoms. By taking in water through the pores into the coelomic sacs, the proboscis and collar stiffened for burrowing. Then, by contracting the body-wall musculature, the excess water is driven through the gill slits while the silt and mud, containing usable organic food, is passed along the ventral esophagus into the intestine, where digestion occurs. Like earthworms, hemichordates pass a great deal of indigestible material through the alimentary canal. Some, however, do not make burrows but feed by mucous-ciliary action on the skin, which directs the food into the mouth.

CLASS PTEROBRANCHIA

The basic plan of this class is similar to that of the Enteropneusta, but certain structural differences are correlated with the sedentary mode of life of pterobranchs. The first pterobranch ever reported was obtained by the famed "Challenger" expedition of 1872-1876. Although first placed among the Polyzoa (Entoprocta and Ectoprocta), its affinities to the hemi-

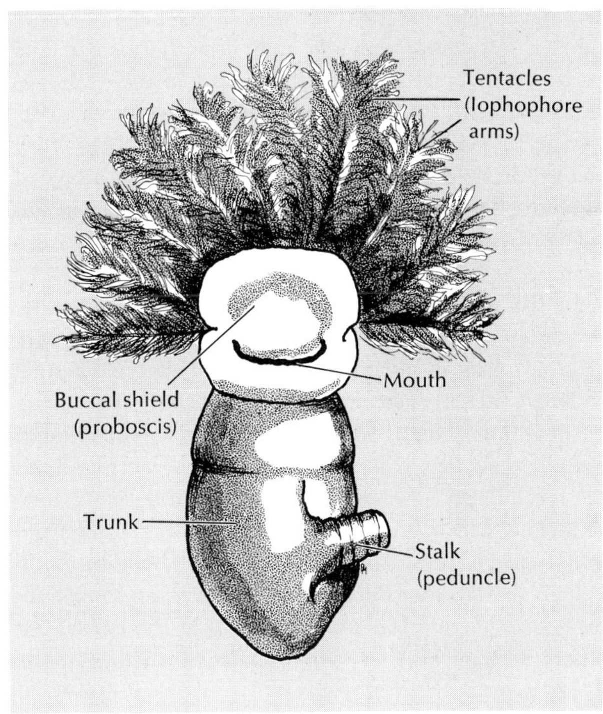

FIG. 23-6

Cephalodiscus, a pterobranch. These tiny sessile forms do not exceed 2 mm. in length and live in coenecium tubes in which they can move about. Ciliated bands on arms carry currents of food toward mouth. Patches of stiff epithelial cells in pharyngeal region are called a notochord (?) by some. Pair of so-called gill slits serve merely as outlet for water. It is thought that these deep-sea organisms are close to ancestral stock of both echinoderms and chordates. (Modified from Lang and others.)

chordates were later recognized. Only two genera (*Cephalodiscus* and *Rhabdopleura*) are known in any detail. They are small animals, usually within the range of 1 to 7 mm. in length, although the stalk may be longer. The members of *Cephalodiscus* are free living, but many individuals live together in gelatinous tubes, which often form an anastomosing system. Through apertures in these tubes, they extend their crown of tentacles. They are attached to the walls of the tubes by body stalks, which are very extensible and can jerk the owners back when necessary. The body of *Cephalodiscus* is divided into the three regions—proboscis, collar, and trunk—characteristic of the hemichordates.

There is only one pair of gills, and the alimentary canal is U shaped, with the anus near the mouth. The proboscis is shield shaped. At the base of the proboscis many pairs of branching arms with ciliated bands arise, similar to lophophores. By means of these cilia they collect their food. The two gonads open in front of the anus. Some species are dioecious and others monoecious. Asexual reproduction by budding may also occur.

In the other genus, *Rhabdopleura,* which is smaller than *Cephalodiscus,* the members remain together to form a colony of zooids, each with its contractile stalk enclosed in a coenecium tube (Fig. 23-6). The collar in these forms bears two branching arms or lophophores. No gill clefts or glomeruli are present. New individuals are reproduced by budding from a creeping basal tube or stolon, which branches on a substratum. There are two types of individuals in a colony—**budding** individuals and **feeding** individuals. In none of the pterobranchs is there a tubular nerve cord in the collar, but otherwise their nervous system is similar to that of the Enteropneusta.

The fossil graptolites of the middle Paleozoic era are often placed as an extinct class under Hemichordata. Their tubular chitinous skeleton and colonial habits indicate an affinity with *Rhabdopleura.* They are considered important index fossils of the Ordovician and Silurian geologic strata.

Phylum Pogonophora*

BIOLOGIC PRINCIPLES

Organ-system level of organization

1. This is a new phylum in the process of analysis. It is sometimes called Brachiata.
2. It is the only free-living metazoan phylum without a digestive system.
3. Other organ systems are present.
4. They belong to the Deuterostomia branch, with enterocoelous formation of the coelom and unequal determinative cleavage.

Biologic contributions

1. Body is typically divided into three regions—**protosome, mesosome,** and **metasome** (trunk)—similar to hemichordate pattern.
2. There is some indication of segmentation in trunk.
3. A tentacular mass originates on the protosome.
4. The type of cleavage does not fit into either the spiral or radial but is of a unique pattern.
5. Negative characteristics are the complete **lack of a digestive system** and the **absence of a blastopore** in gastrula formation.
6. The tentacles with pinnules form a device for collecting food and probably also for absorbing the extracellularly digested food.

Position in animal kingdom

Belonging to the deuterostomes, pogonophores (beard worms) are in the same group with the hemichordates, the echinoderms, and the chordates. Their tripartite body regions and coelom indicate a relationship to the hemichordates.

GENERAL RELATIONS

Specimens of this phylum, the most recently described in the animal kingdom, were collected from deep sea dredgings (1900) in the waters off the coast of Indonesia. They have since been discovered in several seas, and sufficient material for the phylum's appraisal has only recently been available. So far about 80 species have been described. These elongated tubicolous forms have left no known fossil record and show closest affinities to the hemichordates. Many details of structure are vague and uncertain.

CHARACTERISTICS

1. **Body elongated** and **tripartite** (protosome, mesosome, and metasome); body enclosed in a **secreted tube;** faint evidences of segmentation in trunk; constrictions between the protosome and mesosome may or may not be present; mesosome and metasome separated by muscular diaphragm; dorsal and ventral sides not evident
2. Protosome small, with 1 to more than 200 **tentacles,** each provided with **pinnules** or lateral projections; basal part of tentacles may be fused into a spiral; protosome terminating in rounded **cephalic lobe**
3. Body covered with **columnar epidermis** with cuticle; epidermis may be provided with glands and cilia; trunk with pair of raised girdles (**belts**) bearing chitinous adhesive organs
4. Coelom subdivided into a single protocoel (protosome) and a pair of coelomic sacs in each of the mesosome and metasome divisions
5. **No digestive system**
6. **Closed circulatory system** of two median longitudinal vessels, one of which may be enlarged to form a heart

*Po'go-nof"e-ra (Gr. *pogon,* beard, + *phoros,* bearing).

7. No gills or special respiratory system
8. Excretory system of a **pair of nephridial coelomoducts,** which connect the unpaired protosomal coelom to the surface
9. Nervous system of a ring-shaped or elongated brain in the cephalic lobe, with one or more median longitudinal cords; epidermal in position
10. Musculature of both circular and longitudinal fibers; special muscles in protosome and the septum or diaphragm
11. Sexes separate; gonads paired elongated bodies in the metacoel, with gonopores to the exterior; spermatophores present
12. Fertilization occurring in tube; cleavage holoblastic and unequal; bilateral embryos develop in tube; gastrulation without blastopore

CLASSIFICATION OF POGONOPHORA

Order Athecanephria (a-thek'a-nef″re-a) (Gr. *a,* without, + *theca,* case, + *nephros,* kidney, + *ia,* pl. suffix). Protosome-mesosome divided by constriction; coelomoducts with lateral nephridiopores; tentacles usually few and separate; postannular trunk with scattered adhesive papillae; fusiform spermatophores. Examples: *Oligobrachia, Siboglinum.*

Order Thecanephria (Thec'a-nef″re-a) (Gr. *theca,* case, + *nephron,* kidney). Protosome-mesosome usually without external constriction; coelomoducts with median nephridiopores; tentacles numerous and may be basically fused; postannular trunk with transverse rows of adhesive papillae; flat spermatophores. Examples: *Heptabrachia, Galathealinum.*

GENERAL FEATURES

External structure. Beard worms are cylindric worms with elongated, slender bodies, which are enclosed in secreted tubes. The different species vary from 80 to 350 mm. in length, and from 0.5 to about 2 mm. in diameter. The body is divided into a short anterior part, which in some is subdivided by a constriction into a protosome and a mesosome, and a very long, slender trunk (metasome). The latter is separated from the mesosome by a septum or diaphragm. The protosome bears the cephalic lobe, at the base of which originate the fringed tentacles (1 to 200 in number). In some the tentacles may be fused together at their bases (Fig. 23-7). All tentacles are hollow extensions of the coelom. A pair of ridges on the mesosome is known as the **bridle,** and a pair of elevated girdles with platelets on the trunk are called the **belts.** That region of the trunk anterior to the belts is the **preannular region** with a median ciliated band; posterior to the belts is the postannular region. Adhesive papillae to anchor the worm in its tube are found on the trunk. Although classed among the coelomate Bilateria, dorsal and ventral surfaces are not evident.

Internal structure. The columnar epidermis may bear many glands. Beneath the epidermis are circular and longitudinal muscles, and the protosome is provided with additional muscles. The coelom is divided into a single sac (protocoel) in the protosome and paired sacs in each of the mesosome and metasome divisions (Fig. 23-8). Peritoneum is scanty. There is no digestive system or special respiratory system. The closed circulatory system usually consists of two median vessels, one of which may serve as a muscular heart. Tentacles and their pinnules are well supplied with blood. In the protosome the unpaired coelom opens to the surface by a pair of ciliated nephridial coelomoducts. The ner-

FIG. 23-7

Cross section of tentacular crown of pogonophore *Lamellisabella.* Tentacles arise from ventral side of protosome at base of cephalic lobe. Tentacles (which vary in number in different species) enclose a cylindric space with the pinnules forming a kind of food-catching network. Food may be digested in this pinnular meshwork and absorbed into the blood supply of tentacles and pinnules. (From Hickman: Biology of the invertebrates, The C. V. Mosby Co.)

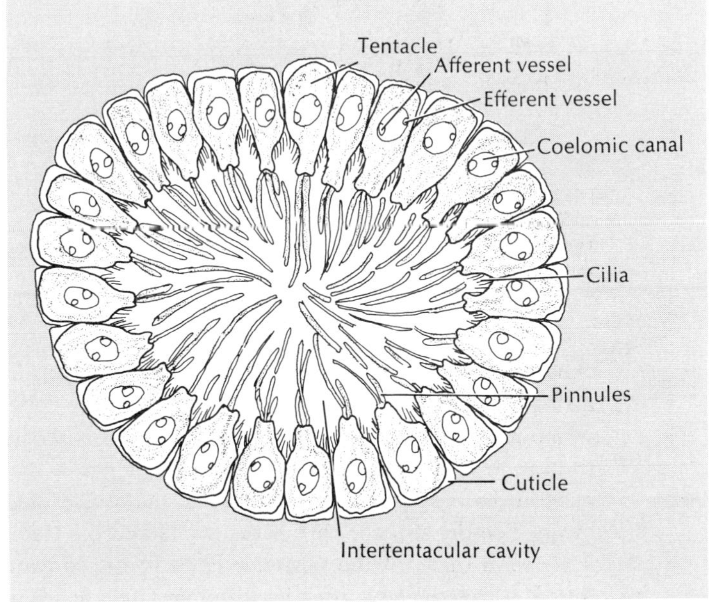

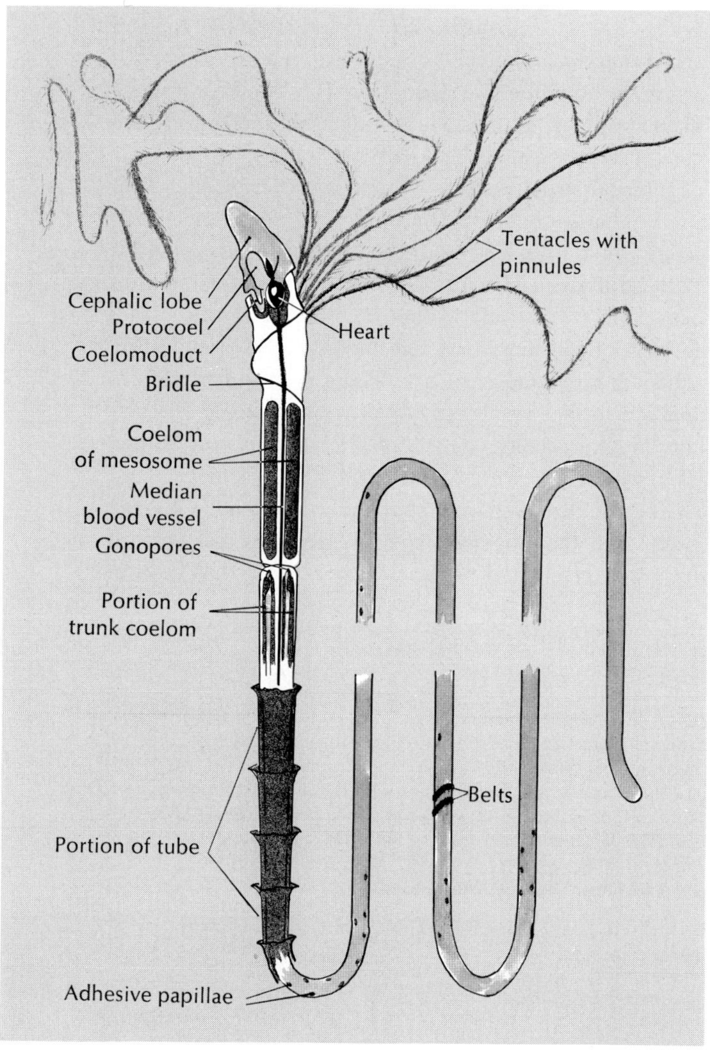

FIG. 23-8

Diagrammatic view of pogonophore showing principal external and internal structures. Portions of trunk have been omitted. Tentacles are often fused into cylinder. (Modified from Ivanov and others.)

vous system is epidermal in position and is made up of a ring-shaped or elongated brain in the cephalic lobe, which gives rise to one or two longitudinal cords to the trunk region. The sexes are separate, with paired gonads in the metacoel of the metasome, the ovaries and oviducts in the anterior part of the trunk, and the testes and sperm ducts in the posterior half. The sperm are found in spermatophores. Fertilization and development occur in the tube. The unequal but holoblastic cleavage produces a bilateral larva.

Behavior and natural history. Most pogonophores live in the ooze on the bottom of the ocean floor, but some have been found in littoral waters. They are obtained only by dredging. The tubes they secrete around themselves are usually longer than the animals and consist of cellulose (tunicin). They are not fastened in these tubes but are partially protruded for food getting. Since they lack a digestive system, it has been suggested that they use their tentacles and pinnules as food-catching nets, where digestion also occurs. The digested products are then absorbed through the thin walls of the pinnules, which are abundantly supplied with blood. Recent evidence also indicates the pogonophores get their principal nutrition by taking up amino acids and micromolecules directly from solution in sea water. It is known that the cuticle over the forepart of the body and the tentacles secretes a number of enzymes. Considerable quantities of amino acids have been found in sea water near the sediment where they live.

Derivation and meaning of basic terminology

Athecanephria (Gr. *a,* without, + *theca,* case, + *nephros,* kidney, + *ia,* pl. suffix). Coelomoducts are far apart.

Balanoglossus (Gr. *balanos,* acorn, + *glossa,* tongue). Refers to the shape of the proboscis in this genus.

fin (O.E. *fin,* fin or feather). Thin, transparent epidermal extension in chaetognaths.

hood (O.E. *hod,* hat). A fold of the body wall that can be drawn over the head in chaetognaths.

mesosome (Gr. *mesos,* middle, + *soma,* body). Collar or middle part of pogonophores and hemichordates.

metasome (Gr. *meta,* next, + *soma,* body). Posterior part of the body of hemichordates and pogonophores.

protosome (Gr. *protos,* first, + *soma,* body). First body division or proboscis of pogonophores and hemichordates.

Saccoglossus (Gr. *sakkos,* sac, + *glossa,* tongue). The most familiar genus of enteropneusts.

Sagitta (L. arrow). Refers to the shape of the body in this common genus of chaetognaths.

stomochord (Gr. *stoma,* mouth, + L. *chorda,* cord). The thick-walled forward evagination of the dorsal wall of the buccal cavity into the proboscis; the buccal diverticulum; may be a homologue of the notochord or a primitive notochord.

Thecanephria (Gr. *theca,* case, + *nephros,* kidney, + *ia,* pl. suffix). Coelomoducts are close together.

tornaria (L. *tornare,* to turn). This larva rotates in circles.

Annotated references

Hemichordata

Hyman, L. H. 1959. The invertebrates: smaller coelomate groups (phylum Hemichordata), vol. 5. New

York, McGraw-Hill Book Co. *The best up-to-date account.*

Kowalevsky, A. 1866. Anatomie des *Balanoglossus.* Mémoires de l'Académie impériale des sciences de St. Petersburg, ser. 7, vol. 10, no. 3. *A classic paper and the first accurate description of this group.*

Newell, G. E. 1951. The stomochord of Enteropneusta, Proceedings of the Zoological Society **121**:741. *An appraisal of the status of the stomochord in comparison with a true notochord.*

Van der Horst, C. J. 1932. Enteropneusta. In W. Kunkenthal and T. Krumbach: Handbuch der Zoologie, vol. 3, part 2. *A detailed study of the phylum.*

Van der Horst, C. J. 1935. Hemichordata. In H. G. Bronn (editor), Klassen und Ordnungen der Tierreichs, vol. 4, part 4, book 2.

Pogonophora

De Beer, G. 1955. The Pogonophora. Nature **176**:888. *A brief survey and appraisal.*

Hartman, O. 1954. Pogonophora Johansson. Systematic Zoology **3**:183-185.

Hyman, L. H. 1959. The invertebrates: smaller coelomate groups, vol. 5, New York, McGraw-Hill Book Co. *The best appraisal in English of this strange group.*

Ivanov, A. V. 1956. The main features of the organization of the Pogonophora. In C. S. (Doklady), Academy of Science, U.S.S.R., 100 (translated by A. Petrunkevitch in System. Zool. 4).

Ivanov, A. V. 1963. Pogonophora (translated from Russian by D. B. Carlisle). New York, Consultants Bureau Enterprises, Inc. *The most recent appraisal of this relatively new group by the investigator who first studied the phylum in detail. Recently discovered species are also described.*

Kuhl, W. 1938. Chaetognatha. In H. G. Bronn (editor). Klassen und Ordnungen der Tierreichs, vol. 4, sect. 4, part 1, book 2. *The best technical account.*

CHAPTER 24

• PHYLUM CHORDATA* (MAJOR EUCOELOMATE BILATERAL GROUP)

Ancestry and evolution; general characteristics; protochordates

BIOLOGIC PRINCIPLES

Organ-system level organization

1. Chordates have most of the features of the higher invertebrate phyla, such as bilateral symmetry, three germ layers, coelomic cavity, and, in common with arthropods and annelids, metamerism. Metamerism, however, has arisen independently of the other groups.
2. Organ-systems are well represented and have reached a stage of development (vertebrates) greater than have those in the highest invertebrates.
3. In general there is a marked regional differentiation of the body into a head, trunk, and tail.
4. A neck is found also in the lung-breathing forms (many vertebrates).
5. Chordates belong to the Deuterostomia of the animal kingdom.

Biologic contributions

1. A **living endoskeleton** is characteristic of the entire phylum. Two endoskeletons are present in the group as a whole. One of these is the rodlike **notochord,** which is present in all members of the phylum at some time; the other is the **vertebral column,** which largely replaces the notochord in higher chordates.
2. The endoskeleton does not interfere with **continuous growth,** for it can increase in size with the rest of the body. There is, therefore, no necessity for shedding it, as is the case with the nonliving exoskeleton of the invertebrate phyla. Moreover, the endoskeleton allows for almost indefinite growth so that many chordates are the largest of all animals.
3. The nature of the endoskeleton is such that it affords much surface for muscular attachment, and since the muscular and skeletal systems make up most of the bulk of animals, other bodily systems must also become specialized in both size and function to meet the metabolic requirements of these two great systems.
4. The endoskeleton in higher chordates consists of the **axial** and **appendicular** divisions. The axial is made up of the cranium, vertebral column, ribs, and sternum; the appendicular is composed of the pectoral and pelvic girdles and the skeleton of the appendages.
5. A **postanal** tail is a new addition to the animal kingdom and is present at some stage in most chordates.
6. A **ventral heart** is a new characteristic, and a closed blood system is better developed than it is in other phyla. Chordates have also developed a **hepatic portal system,** which is specialized for conveying food-laden blood from the digestive system to the liver.
7. **Pharyngeal gills** are introduced for the first time. Gill slits or traces are present in the embryos of all chordates. Terrestrial chordates have developed lungs by modification of this same pharyngeal region.
8. A dorsal hollow nerve cord is universally present at some stage.

Position in animal kingdom

1. All available evidence indicates that chordates have evolved from the invertebrates, but it is impossible to establish the exact relationship.
2. Two possible lines of ancestry have been proposed in the phylogenetic background of the chordates. One of these is the annelid-arthropod-mollusk group; the other is the echinoderm-protochordate group.
3. The echinoderms as a group have certain characteristics that are shared with the chordates, such as **indeterminate cleavage, same type of mesoderm and coelom formation, anus derivation from blastopore with mouth of secondary origin,** and the same biochemical substance (phosphocreatine). Thus the echinoderms appear to have a close kinship to the chordate phylum.
4. Taking the phylum as a whole, there is more fundamental unity of plan throughout all the organs and systems of this group than there is in any of the invertebrate phyla.
5. From gill filter-feeding ancestors to the highest vertebrates, the evolution of chordates has been guided by the specialized basic adaptation of the living endoskeleton, paired limbs, and nervous system.

BACKGROUND

The great phylum chordata derives its name from one of the few common characteristics of this group—the **notochord** (Gr. *noton,* back, + L. *chorda,* cord). This structure is possessed by all members of the phy-

*Kor-da'ta (L. *chorda,* cord).

lum, either in the larval or embryonic stages or throughout life. The notochord is a rodlike, semirigid body of vacuolated cells, which extends, in most cases, the length of the body between the enteric canal and the central nervous system. Its primary purpose is to support and to stiffen the body, that is, to act as a skeletal axis.

The structural plan of chordates retains many of the features of invertebrate animals, such as bilateral symmetry, anterior-posterior axis, coelom, tube-within-a-tube arrangement, metamerism, and cephalization.

One distinguishing characteristic of the chordates is the **endoskeleton,** which, as we have seen, is first found in the echinoderms. An endoskeleton is an internal structure that provides support and serves as a framework for the body. Most chordates possess two types of endoskeletons in their life cycle. The first is the **notochord** (Fig. 24-1), possessed at some stage by all chordates. The second is the **vertebral column** and accessory structures such as the appendages. This second type of endoskeleton, which is more specialized and more adaptable for evolutionary growth, is possessed by only part, although the greater part, of the chordate phylum.

Even though the chordates have emphasized an endoskeleton, they have by no means cast aside the exoskeleton of the invertebrates. Many of the higher chordates (that is, the vertebrates) have keratinoid exoskeletons, although here the exoskeleton is mainly for protection and not for attachment of muscles. Another marked distinction is that the endoskeleton is a living tissue, whereas the exoskeleton is composed of dead noncellular material. The endoskeleton has the advantage of allowing continuous growth, without the necessity of shedding. For this reason vertebrate animals can attain great size; some of them are the most massive in the animal kingdom. Endoskeletons provide much surface for muscle attachment, and size differences between animals result mainly from the amount of muscle tissue they possess. More muscle tissue necessitates greater development of body systems, such as circulatory, digestive, respiratory, and excretory. Thus it is seen that the endoskeleton is the chief basic factor in the development and specialization of the higher animals.

FIG. 24-1

Structure of notochord and its surrounding sheaths. Cells of notochord proper are thick walled, pressed together closely, and filled with semifluid. Stiffness due mainly to turgidity of fluid-filled cells and surrounding connective tissue sheaths. This primitive type of endoskeleton is characteristic of all chordates at some stage of life cycle. Notochord provides longitudinal stiffening of main body axis, base for myomeric muscles, and axis around which vertebral column develops. In most vertebrates it is crowded out of existence. In man slight remnants are found in nuclei pulposi of intervertebral disks. Its method of formation is different in the various groups of animals. In *Amphioxus* it originates from the endoderm; in birds and mammals it arises as an anterior outgrowth of the primitive streak. (Modified from Eaton.)

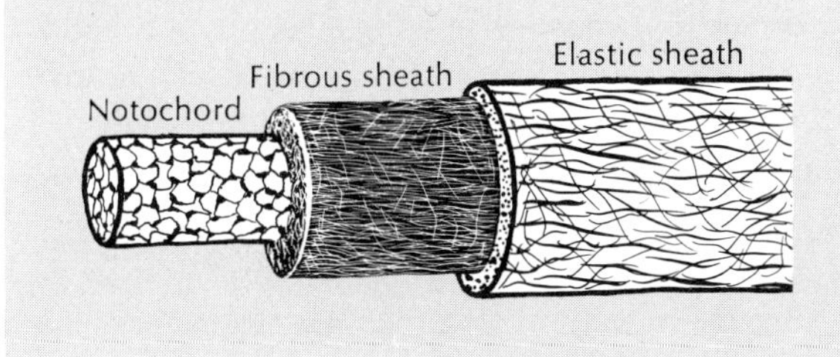

From an evolutionary viewpoint the function of the skeleton, as represented by the exoskeleton and the endoskeleton, has shifted more from a protective to a supportive one. The limy shells of clams and other mollusks and the chitinous armor of arthropods are excellent defensive armors, even though they also serve for attachment of muscles and support of bodily structures. However, endoskeletons have their protective functions as well as supporting ones, as revealed by such excellent protective boxes as the cranium for the brain and the thorax for important visceral organs.

The animals most familiar to the student belong to the chordates. Man himself is a member and shares the common characteristics of this group. Ecologically the phylum has been very successful in the animal kingdom. They are among the most adaptable of organic forms and are able to occupy most kinds of habitat. From a purely biologic viewpoint, chordates are of primary interest because they illustrate so well the broad biologic principles of evolution, development, and relationship. They represent as a group the background of man himself.

ANCESTRY AND EVOLUTION

That vertebrates have come from invertebrates is not doubted by most biologists. The best evidence available is that which involves the protochordates and the echinoderms. The great chasm, however, between the invertebrates and the chordates has never been bridged in spite of many attempts of biologists to do so. Whatever this ancestor may have been, there are no fossil records to show. There is reason to believe that it was soft bodied, which would account for its failure to be preserved as a fossil. The primitive chordates that we refer to as the **protochordates** are so different from the invertebrates as a group that they throw little light on the problem. Apparently only the vertebrates were sufficiently hard and durable to be laid down as fossil forms. It has been possible to trace with considerable success the evolutionary patterns of most vertebrates, for the sequence of their fossil records is convincing in many cases.

The ancestor of the chordates can be reconstructed to some extent from our present knowledge of existing protochordates. This ancestor probably was sessile and quite simple, having a filter device for collecting food, an alimentary canal, and a reproductive system, all enclosed in a soft body.

Echinoderm theory. Of the many theories to account for the probable invertebrate ancestor of chordates, only the echinoderm theory deserves serious consideration. Several lines of evidence of an embryologic and biochemical nature strongly suggest a close relationship between the two groups. In the first place, there is a marked resemblance between the bipinnaria larva of certain echinoderms and the tornaria larva of the hemichordates (a phylum with some chordate characteristics), for both of them have similar ciliated bands in loops, sensory cilia at the anterior end, and a complete digestive system of ventral mouth and posterior anus. Both echinoderms and chordates have indeterminate cleavage; that is, each of the early blastomeres has equivalent potentialities with each of the other blastomeres. Echinoderms and chordates belong to the deuterostome branch of the animal kingdom; that is, the mouth is formed as a secondary opening, and the blastopore of the gastrula becomes the anus. The coelom in these two phyla is enterocoelous and thus is budded off from the archenteron of the embryo.

Biochemically, with few exceptions, deuterostomes use phosphocreatine in the energy cycle of their muscular contraction; most of the protosomes (other phyla) use phosphoarginine for the same purpose. In this connection it is interesting to note that certain hemichordates use both phosphocreatine and phosphoarginine in their muscle cycle, which may indicate that these forms are connecting links between vertebrates and invertebrates.* Serologic tests also show a closer relationship of vertebrates to echinoderms than to other phyla.

Earliest chordates (prevertebrates). If the phylum Chordata has an evolutionary relationship with the echinoderms and probably sprang from the same ancestors, what was the nature of this primitive chordate, and what chordate today is most like it? The fossil record cannot tell us, for it is unlikely that such a primitive form could be fossilized. The gap between the invertebrates and the vertebrates may always remain unbridged. What we can find out about these matters must be acquired from a comparative study of living forms, especially from their larval and embryologic stages. The simplest chordates that exist today are a few lowly forms that possess a notochord but no vertebral column (backbone). These backboneless animals and those with a backbone, or the vertebrates, make up the phylum Chordata as we know it. The vertebrates comprise by far the greatest number of the chordates so that the terms "vertebrate" and "chordate" are sometimes used as synonyms. The backboneless members are often referred to as the protochordates, or prevertebrates, and include two types or subphyla: (1) Cephalochordata, represented by the lancelet (*Amphioxus,* or *Branchiostoma*); and (2) Urochordata (Tunicata), represented by *Ciona.* Closely linked to the protochordates and often included with them is the phylum Hemichordata, which is made up of the acorn worms and the pterobranchs.

The American geologist Chamberlain, who gave us the theory of the freshwater origin of vertebrates in 1900, also constructed a hypothetical protovertebrate that might be considered the ancestor of vertebrates. According to his scheme, the chief features of such an ancestor would include a spindle-shaped or fusiform body, bilateral symmetry, a stiff axial rod and segmentally arranged muscles, a jawless mouth fitted for filter feeding, internal gills, a nervous system and brain, and a solid tail of muscle. Such an active swimming form is supposed to have been evolved under the influence of flowing continental streams or rivers, where its ancestors were driven by enemies, by the necessity of finding algae or the rich detritus (organic material) of river mouths, by seeking unoccupied ecologic niches, etc. It is generally agreed among evolutionists that whatever

*This line of evidence is questioned by G. A. Kerkut, who points out the presence of both phosphocreatine and phosphoarginine in each of many invertebrate phyla.

the nature of this protovertebrate, it arose in fresh water and was adapted for filter feeding. The feeding mechanism of early vertebrates appears to have passed through three stages. The earliest ancestral forms fed on small organisms brought in by cilia-induced water currents and mucous entanglement, similar to that of mollusks and other filter feeders. A slightly more advanced stage is found in ostracoderms and cyclostomes, in which bottom feeding, mud swallowing, and parasitism are stressed. The gnathostome stage, with certain gill arches modified as jaws, permitted a much wider range of feeding and is characteristic of nearly all vertebrates.

What existing or fossil animal best fits the form and organization of this hypothetical prevertebrate? There is no agreement about the answer to this question. Authorities such as Colbert insist that the classical *Amphioxus* (Fig. 24-20) is still the logical structural ancestor of the vertebrates in spite of objections advanced by others regarding the specialization and aberrant nature of this well-known form. He regards the lancelet as a very primitive chordate that meets most of the requirements of the hypothetical ancestor.

Homer Smith's reconstruction of the hypothetical protovertebrate, as sketched in his well-known book *From Fish to Philosopher,* has a remarkable resemblance to *Amphioxus.* Yet that authority denies that *Amphioxus* could be the prototype of chordates because it is impossible to derive the vertebrate nephron from the nephridial complex of the lancelet. Romer regards *Amphioxus* as degenerate and as a divergent side branch between the lower chordates and the vertebrates.

Another theory of chordate origin is the ascidian theory advocated by Garstang in 1928. This theory stresses the idea that the early chordate ancestors were filter feeding, marine, and sessile. For collecting food, gill slits were evolved, and these later became respiratory in function. The ascidians themselves may have come from the sessile pterobranchs, one of the divisions of the phylum Hemichordata. The ascidian tadpole larva, with its basic vertebrate organization, was evolved according to this theory from the sessile form and became pelagic to exploit the plankton of oceanic surface waters. After swimming around for a time, this larva usually attaches to a substratum and, after a degenerative metamorphosis, assumes the sessile adult form. Certain of these tadpole larvae, it is believed, became neotenous (for example, sexually mature in the larval stage), did not metamorphose into the adult sessile form, and entered the estuaries and river mouths, where they could live upon the rich detritus brought down from the continents. Zoologists have long considered the class Larvacea of the tunicates as an example of neoteny in which later stages are omitted in its evolution. To invade the inland regions of the continents by way of streams, a correlated evolutionary change had to take place in these neotenous larvae. Invasion meant facing and overcoming the water currents flowing toward the sea, and morphologic and physiologic changes, such as strong locomotor equipment, increase in size of body, more alert senses, and a kidney adapted for a freshwater existence, had to be evolved. Segmentation of the body, especially of the muscles, promoted the efficiency of the animal in swimming against currents. (This segmentation is thus independently acquired and does not indicate kinship with the annelids and arthropods.) Only a few groups of early Paleozoic animals managed to exploit the ecologic niches of fresh water, and among these were the protovertebrates and the arthropods. According to this theory, *Amphioxus* may have been one of these early protovertebrates that evolved under the impact of fresh water but, returning to the sea to breed, became readapted to a filter-feeding marine existence. This theory of the ascidian origin of vertebrates has been revived and vigorously supported in recent years by Berrill of McGill University and Romer of Harvard University.

Romer also emphasizes the dual nature of the basic pattern of chordate organization. One of the two components of such an animal is the **visceral,** which is made up of the structures of the ancestral sessile adult, such as the food-collecting apparatus, the alimentary canal, the reproductive organs, and the regulative factors (hormone and nervous) associated with the viscera. The second component is called the **somatic** and is represented by the new additions of the larval tunicate or active free-swimming form, such as the well-defined sensory and nervous systems and a locomotor apparatus of striated muscles built around a supporting notochord. Romer also points out that this anatomic duality is correlated with a duality of behavior, for the visceral, or internal, responses are regulated chiefly by sympathetic nerves and hormones; the somatic, or external, responses are regulated by means of somatic sensory, nervous, and muscular structures. Higher vertebrates have tended to fuse the visceral and somatic components into a more integrated and more functional whole,

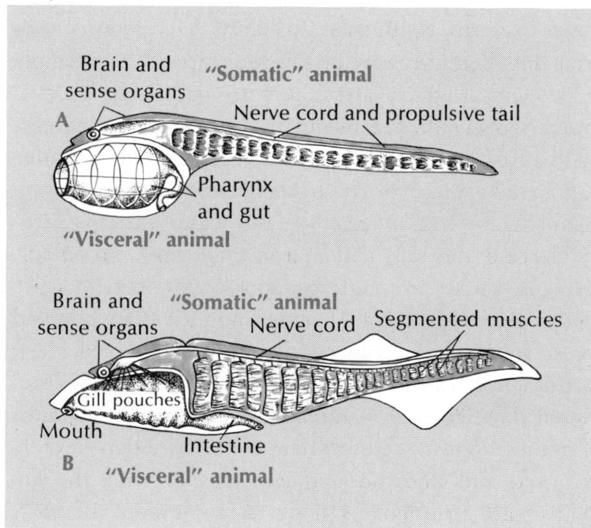

FIG. 24-2

Double origin of chordate organization. **A,** Visceral component (lighter compact area) is assumed to represent adult tunicate, fitted for sessile existence and stressing digestive and reproductive systems. Somatic component (in darker shading) is larval tunicate, stressing locomotion by means of muscular, nervous, and sensory systems. **B,** Visceral and somatic components are integrated, as seen in ostracoderm, making new patterns of vertebrate morphology possible. Theory of anatomic duality has significant psychologic implications (for example, Freudism?). (Redrawn from Roe and Simpson: Behavior and evolution, Yale University Press.)

FIG. 24-3

Jamoytius, small jawless, fishlike fossil found in Silurian deposits in England. It has many requirements of chordate archetype, such as lateral fin folds, notochord, primitive myotomes, and lack of general internal skeleton and gills. As such it could well serve as ancestor of prevertebrates and ostracoderms. It is at present an enigma to paleontologists, who await further discoveries and appraisals.

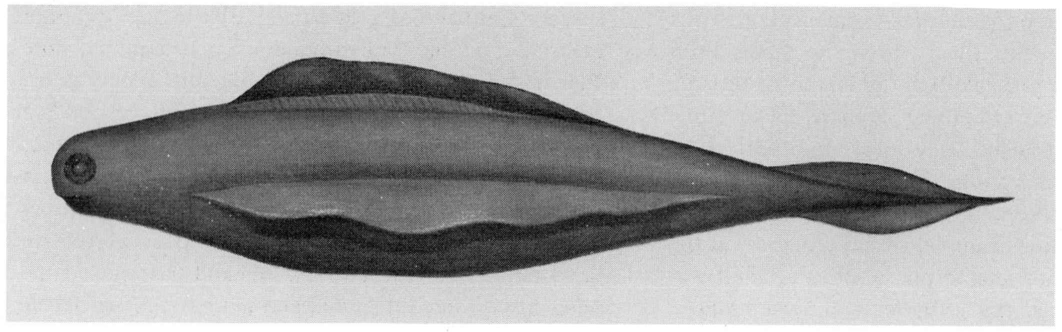

but the behavior patterns of all vertebrates can be interpreted on the basis of this dual nature (Fig. 24-2).

Sequence of vertebrate origins. The foregoing account of the possible prevertebrate origin must always remain speculative to some extent in the absence of a fossil record. Among existing vertebrates the most primitive members belong to the class Cyclostomata, which includes the lampreys and hagfish. This group is often referred to as Agnatha (without jaws) and also includes some notable fossil members (ostracoderms). The adult cyclostomes cannot altogether be considered as primitive, for they have certain specialized structural features, such as the lack of a bony skeleton and the presence of a rasping tongue for a parasitic habit. However, the ammocoete larva of the lamprey has many resemblances to the chordate prototype as we have pictured it, and its archetypal characteristics are much stressed by evolutionists at the present time. Although this larva gives one an understanding of the basic structural plan of chordates, it cannot altogether be pinpointed as the exact ancestor of vertebrates. The fossil record must, therefore, be our main reliance for primitive vertebrates.

The first indication of fossil vertebrates were some scales or bony plates found in Ordovician freshwater deposits in Colorado. These first evidences of vertebrates from the geologic record are so fragmentary and incomplete that it is impossible to identify them with any particular animal, although some paleontologists consider them as belonging to the ostracoderms. During the Ordovician geologic period the invertebrates were the dominant animals. In the next geologic periods, upper Silurian and Devonian, the first true vertebrate fossils were found in considerable numbers. These were the well-preserved ostracoderms (shell or bony skin), which have aroused an enormous amount of interest since their discovery in Colorado, Canada, Europe, and especially

Spitsbergen (the large island north of Norway). The epoch-making investigation of Stensio (1927) has focused much attention on these ancient fish, which are believed to have flourished 400 million years ago. From the Devonian period onward the fossil record of the vertebrates begins to unfold with great clearness in the successive layers of the earth's crust. This sequence of vertebrate origin can best be considered in the following brief summary of the various vertebrate groups—when they flourished, how some became extinct, and how they are related to existing groups.

Jamoytius. In 1946 White, an English paleontologist, described a primitive, unarmored jawless chordate (*Jamoytius,* Fig. 24-3) from the Silurian rocks of England, which may supplant the ostracoderms as the earliest fossil vertebrates to be discovered. Whether or not this form is as old as the oldest ostracoderm may be questioned, but its morphology is, without doubt, more primitive. The fossil, which was mainly an impression in the deposits, is difficult to analyze satisfactorily. It may be a primitive ostracoderm. It was about 7 inches long, with a more or less fusiform body, on either side of which were lateral fin folds. A median dorsal fin fold was also present, and there were indications of muscle myotomes similar to the arrangement in *Amphioxus.* The only internal skeleton was a notochord, which gave support to the body. Its head was somewhat blunt and a little flattened. There were no gill slits. Its primitive nature could well qualify it as an ancestor of the amphioxus and ostracoderms. Paleontologists are not agreed on the exact status of this interesting form, and a few of them accept White's contention that it is near the archetypal chordate. Perhaps more fossils will have to be discovered before it can be correctly appraised.

Ostracoderms. Paleontologists are agreed that the ancestors or forerunners of higher fish were the ostracoderms (Fig. 24-4), which belong to the jawless group known as Agnatha. They were abundant during the upper Silurian and Devonian periods and are the oldest known vertebrates. They were freshwater forms, and many of them were preserved as fossils in the bottom sediments of streams in many parts of the world, as mentioned before. They were represented by a great variety of types, and some were no doubt highly specialized. Much of our knowledge about them has been due to the studies of Stensio on *Cephalaspis,* which belongs to the group of Cephalaspida. They were small animals, rarely exceeding 1 foot in length, and were covered by a well-developed armor, the head by a solid shield (rounded anteriorly) and the body by bony plates. They had no axial skeleton or vertebrae. The mouth was ventral and anterior, and they were jawless and toothless. Their paired eyes were located close to the middorsal line. A pineal eye was also present, in

FIG. 24-4

Dorsolateral view of ostracoderm. This group represents oldest fossil vertebrate group yet discovered. They rarely exceeded 1 foot in length and were related to living cyclostomes (lampreys and hagfish). Like larval forms of cyclostomes, ostracoderms were filter feeders. Many fine specimens have been found in Spitzbergen and elsewhere. Outstanding work of Stensio has revealed amazing amount of detail about these primitive jawless vertebrates, most typical being genus *Cephalaspis.* They were all covered by bony armor, and some may have been provided with internal bony skeleton. They flourished from Ordovician to Devonian times, becoming extinct about 300 million years ago. Oral flaps are not considered to be homologous to pectoral fins of higher fish. (Modified from Stensio and Romer.)

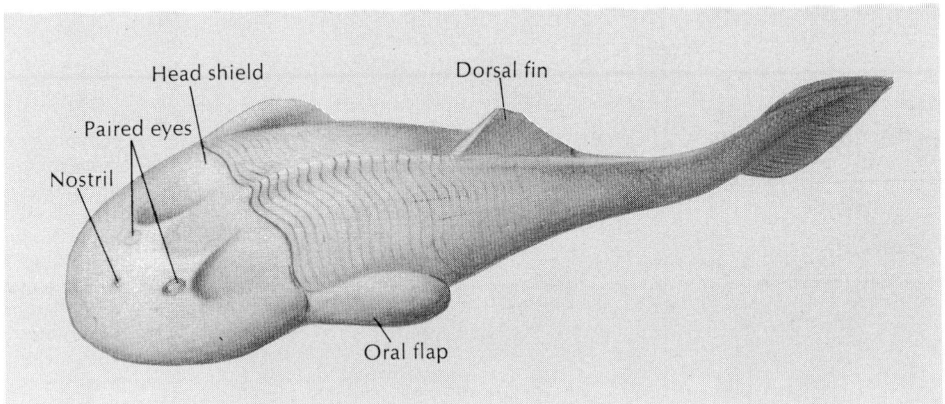

front of which was a single nasal opening. At the latero-posterior corners of the head shield were a pair of flap-like appendages, but it is doubtful that they represent pectoral fins (the common sensory system of lower vertebrates). The trunk and tail appeared to be adapted for active swimming. Between the margin of the head shield and the ventral plates there were ten gill openings on each side. They also had a lateral line system. They were adapted for filter feeding, which may explain the large expanded size of the head, made up as it is of a large pharyngeal gill-slit filtering apparatus. Much of their structure is similar to that of lampreys, and the two groups are closely related and placed together in the Agnatha. Since ostracoderms had a bony external skeleton, bone rather than cartilage is considered a primitive characteristic.

Fossil ostracoderms, as we find them, were specialized and the products of a long evolutionary past. They probably came from unarmored ancestors, such as *Jamoytius.* Although successful for a time, during which they became adapted to many ecologic niches, they could not in the end compete with the jawed fish that evolved in such diversity during the Devonian period.

Placoderms. The ostracoderms were probably the ancestors of the placoderms, the first fish to have **jaws.** The fossil record indicates that placoderms lived in fresh water also, such as streams and estuaries of rivers. Yet the fossil record fails to show any connecting link between the jawless and the jawed fish. The appearance of jaws represented a great revolution in vertebrate feeding, for now fish could evolve and spread into a great variety of habitats and make use of a greater variety of food. Many of them became predaceous, which led to the evolution of an efficient muscular system for locomotion. Predation also put a premium on the sensory and nervous system. Jaws were derived from gill arches. Some ostracoderms had as many as ten gill openings. Gill arches are skeletal structures or rods that afford support for the muscles opening and closing the slits. Jaws originated from the first pair of gill bars in front of the first gill slit.

Another great contribution of placoderms was **paired appendages.** Appendages may have had their beginning in lateral folds, such as those in *Jamoytius.* This fold may have broken up into a series of fins, such as is found in certain primitive placoderms (acanthodians). In these, however, the anterior and posterior pairs were larger than the others and eventually became the pectoral and pelvic fins; the intermediate ones disappeared. Some paleontologists think, however, that these numerous paired fins may have arisen independently as separate structures. Their internal skeleton so far as is known was composed of bone.

Placoderms (Fig. 24-5) evolved into a great variety of types. Many of them were aberrant and grotesque in appearance and some were quite large. They were armored fish and were covered either with diamond-shaped scales or with large plates of bone. All of them became extinct by the end of the Paleozoic era. **The placoderms represent the only class of vertebrates to become wholly extinct;** the other classes are all represented by certain living members.

Higher fish (sharks and bony fish). It is not known definitely that placoderms gave rise to the higher fish,

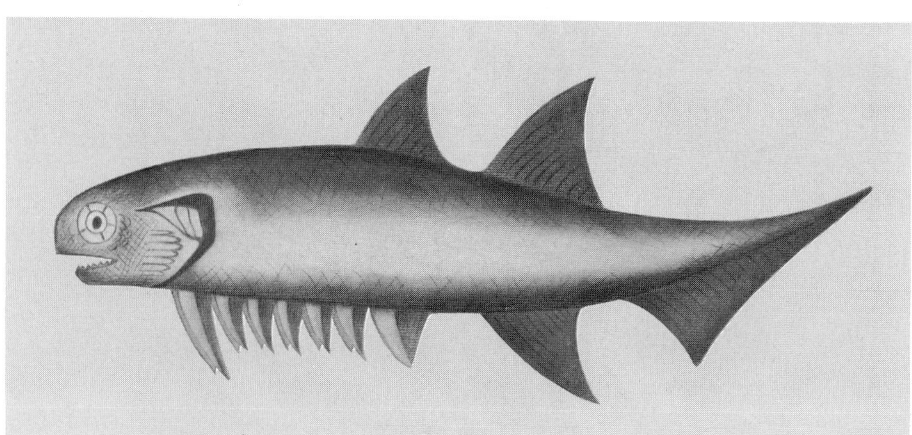

FIG. 24-5

Placoderm—first fish with jaws. Some of these early fish belonged to group called acanthodians, which was represented by common fossil genus *Climatius.* One of their interesting characteristics was smaller paired fins between larger pectoral and pelvic fins. These smaller fins may have evolved from lateral fin folds, or they may have arisen independently. Placoderms arose in early Devonian period and must have played important part in early evolution of vertebrates before they became extinct. They are only vertebrate class of which there are no existing members. (Modified from Romer.)

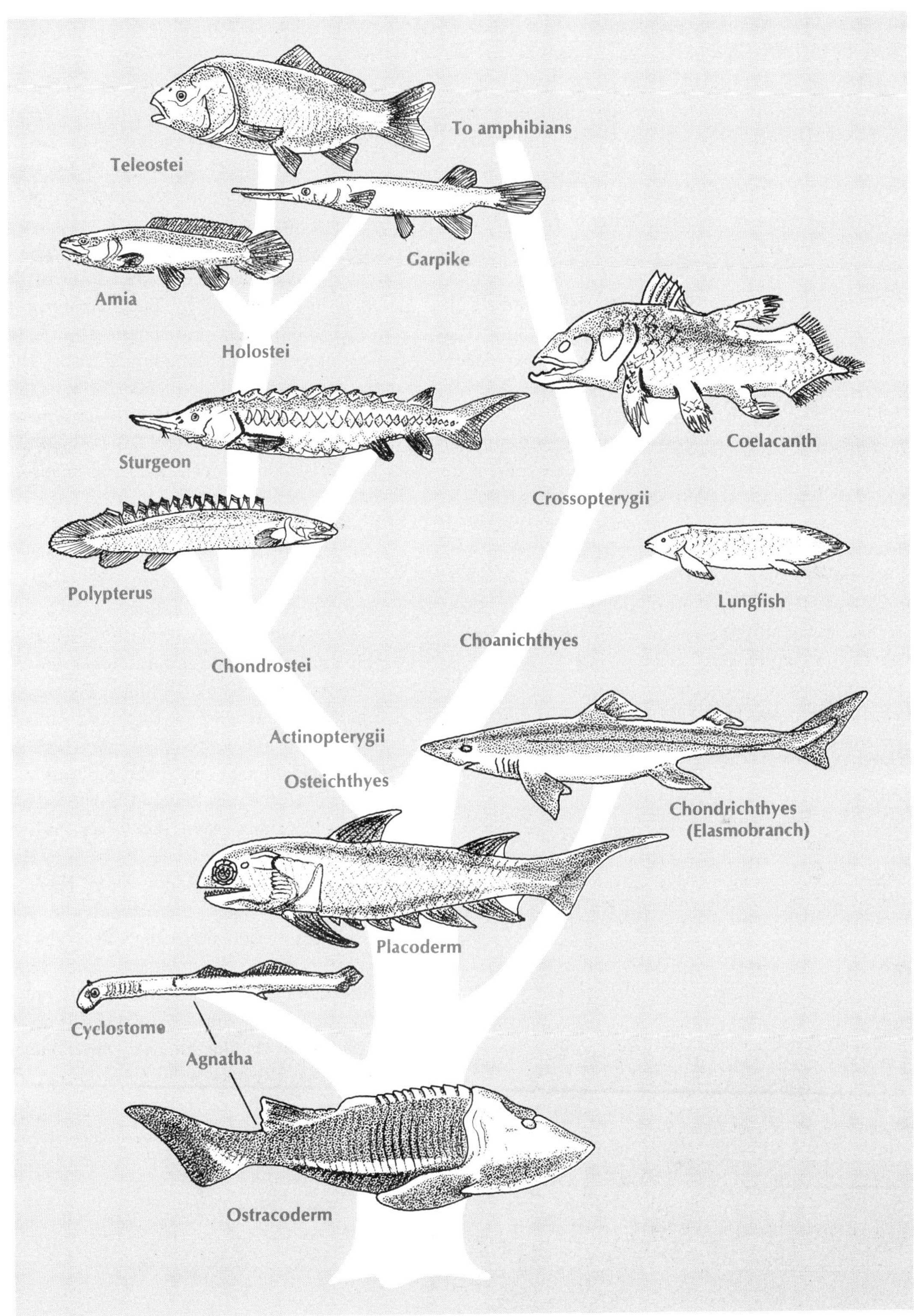

FIG. 24-6

Evolutionary tree of major groups of fish (Pisces). (Modified from Colbert and others.)

but some placoderms were so primitive that they could well serve as the ancestors of the sharks and possibly the bony fish (Fig. 24-6). The sharks (cartilaginous Chondrichthyes) did not appear in the fossil record until the mid-Devonian period; the bony fish (Osteichthyes) date from the early Devonian period. Sharks are thus not as old as bony fish, contrary to popular opinion. Moreover, bone is a primitive characteristic, and its absence in the cartilaginous Chondrichthyes is an indication of degeneration. Chondrichthyes are also degenerate rather than primitive in other features as well. The higher fish were definitely superior to the ostracoderms and placoderms because they were better swimmers and because they evolved along many lines for efficient feeding and for protection. Their success is attested by the fact that there are more species of fish than of all other vertebrates combined, and in population numbers they far exceed those of other vertebrate classes. The chief morphologic changes these higher fish have introduced are (1) a better streamlined body, (2) an efficient array of fins (both median and paired), (3) a specialization of jaws (such as the hyomandibular support), (4) a more highly developed ossified internal and external skeleton (Osteichthyes), (5) a functional lung or swim bladder in many, and (6) better sensory and nervous regulation.

Both sharks and bony fish evolved in fresh water, the same as did ostracoderms and placoderms, but many of them took up a marine existence later.

Bony fish differentiated into two great groups or subclasses—Actinopterygii and Choanichthyes. The first of these are the ray-finned fish, which make up most of the existing fish (teleosts) today. The Choanichthyes include those fish with internal nostrils, or nostrils that open into the mouth. They comprise two small but important groups—the Dipnoi, or lungfish, and the Crossopterygii, or lobe-finned fish. The Crossopterygii are ancestral to land forms (tetrapods) (Fig. 24-7). Although supposed to have been extinct since Cretaceous times, several lobe-finned fish (*Latimeria*) (Fig. 24-8) have been collected in recent years off the coast of Africa and Madagascar. Their paired fins show a basic plan of a jointed series of bones that could evolve into the limbs of tetrapods. They also were lung breathers. Limbs and lungs were necessary qualifications for tetrapod evolution.

Amphibians. Paleontologists agree that the first amphibians arose from certain crossopterygians. The fossil *Ichthyostega,* from the late Devonian period, was found in Greenland in 1932 and possessed both crossopterygian and amphibian characteristics. The earliest amphibians known were the labyrinthodonts, so called because of the infolding of their teeth. Why did the crossopterygians leave the water and go on land? It is known that they lived in fresh water, and if they happened to be in places where there was a seasonal drying up of pools, there would be a great incentive to move to more favorable ones. The search for food may also have been a factor. Since they had the prerequisites for a tetrapod limb, it is not difficult to see how such limbs could be evolved. Labyrinthodonts did not look much like modern amphibians, for their flat head was covered with bony armor, their body was

FIG. 24-7

Osteolepis, primitive crossopterygian fish of middle Devonian times. This fish must be considered in direct line of descent between fish and amphibians because its type of skull was similar to that of primitive land vertebrates, and its lobe fin was of a pattern that could serve as beginning of tetrapod limb. This type of fin (archipterygium) consisted of median axial bones, with small bones radiating out from median ones. Some of its bones can be homologized with limb bones of tetrapods, such as humerus or femur and the ulna-radius or tibia-fibula elements. *Osteolepis* was covered by primitive cosmoid scales, not found in existing fish. These scales were of rhombic shape and consisted of basal bony layers, with a spongy layer of blood vessels covered with cosmine (dentin) and enamel. (Modified from Romer.)

rounded in sections with bony scales, at least on the belly, and their legs were short and placed at right angles to the body. Some were more than 2 feet long. The Permian labyrinthodont *Eryops* (Fig. 24-9) was more than 6 feet long and was able to compete with the reptiles of its time.

Changes are also found in the auditory organ, for the first embryonic gill slit became the eustachian tube, an ear ossicle (stapes) was formed from the hyomandibular arch to conduct sound waves, and a tympanic membrane for detecting sound was also found. The labyrinthodont amphibians became extinct at the end of the Triassic period, after giving rise to two great groups—the anuran amphibians (frogs and toads) and the reptiles. The other amphibians (salamanders and caecilians), which are in existence today, came from another group of primitive amphibians, the lepospon-

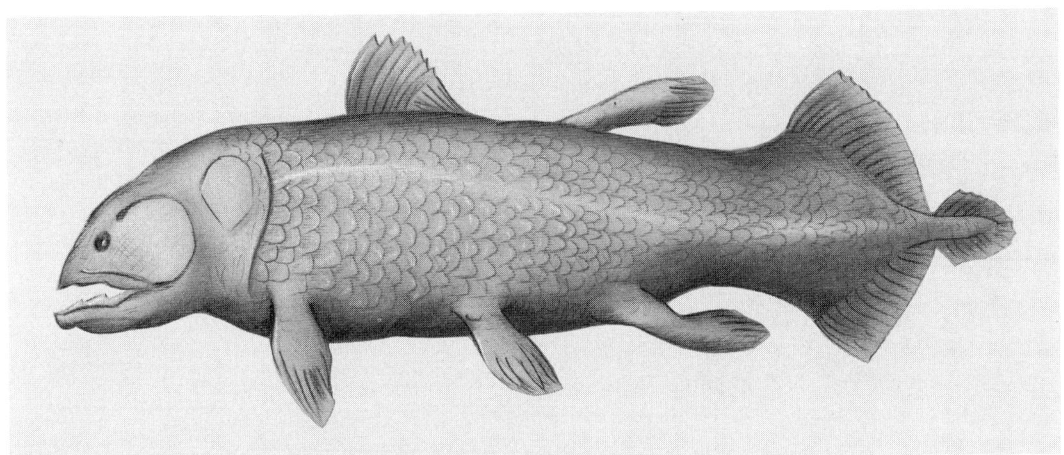

FIG. 24-8

Latimeria, living representative of crossopterygian, or lobe-finned fish. Lobe-finned fish were assumed to have become extinct at end of Cretaceous period nearly 70 million years ago. In 1938 a specimen was found near Madagascar; since then many related specimens have been collected. Although the crossopterygian fish are direct ancestors of land forms (tetrapods) through amphibians, *Latimeria* belongs to specialized side branch of crossopterygians known as coelacanths. Another branch, rhipidistians, represented by such forms as *Osteolepis,* were actual ancestors of four-legged vertebrates. Rhipidistians were freshwater fish and are now extinct; coelacanths are marine, but their ancestors probably came from fresh water. Striking similarity between living *Latimeria* and fossil coelacanths of 300 million years ago indicate that these fish have been able to adapt to changing environment without structural changes. In this sense, *Latimeria* may be called a "living fossil," but it is not a "missing link," for it does not connect two known types of animals

FIG. 24-9

Labyrinthodont amphibian *Eryops.* Most primitive tetrapods were icthyostegids, which have been found in Devonian deposits of Greenland and have been definitely classified as amphibians. These and other members of superorder Labyrinthodontia such as *Eryops* represent important group in early evolution of amphibians. Their head armor of bony plates and other features indicate that they have come from crossopterygian ancestors. For land adaptation pectoral and pelvic fins of crossopterygians were transformed into arms and legs in labyrinthodonts.

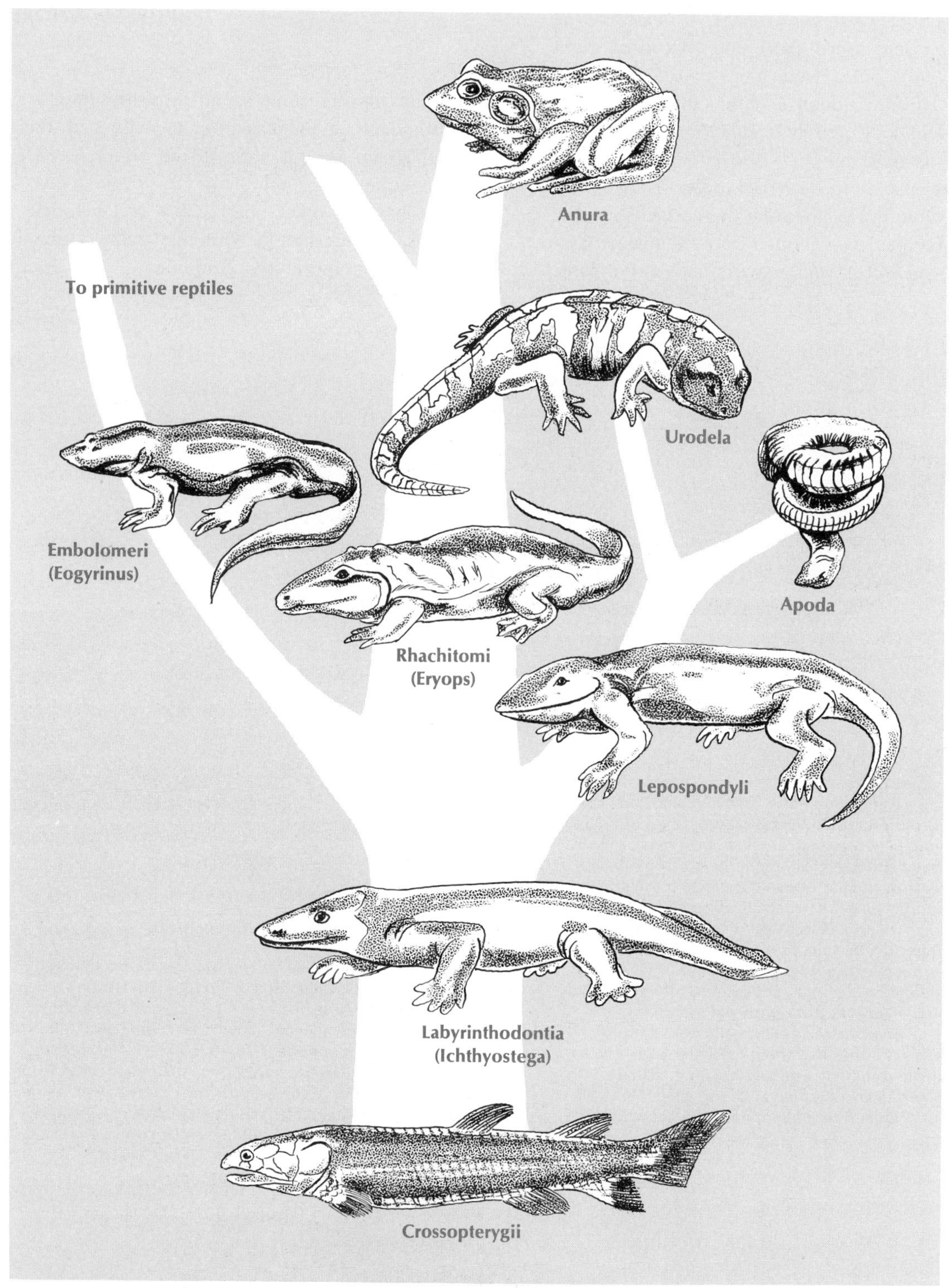

FIG. 24-10

Evolutionary development of amphibians. Some fossil type genera are shown in parentheses. Reptiles probably arose from stock close to Embolomeri. (Modified from Colbert and others.)

dyls, which were contemporary with the labyrinthodonts (Fig. 24-10). The lepospondyls were small snakelike forms that were adapted to ecologic niches in undergrowth and swamps where labyrinthodonts were not commonly found.

Reptiles. Reptiles first appeared during the Carboniferous period and became the dominant terrestrial vertebrates of the Mesozoic era. The transition between the primitive amphibians and the reptiles is well shown in the famous form *Seymouria* (Fig. 24-11), which has a combination of both amphibian and reptile characteristics. This interesting fossil was found near the town of Seymour, Texas, in 1917, and few fossils have attracted more attention among paleontologists. The first reptiles were cotylosaurs, to which *Seymouria* belonged. They were not greatly different from labyrinthodont amphibians, which are supposed to be the ancestors of the cotylosaurs. The establishment of a land existence was made possible by the development of the **amniotic egg.** Most amphibians have to return to water to lay their eggs, but the reptiles, even before they took to land, developed an egg that had a tough outer shell and shell membrane and amniotic membrane enclosing the amniotic fluid. In this fluid the embryo floats, protected from injury and drying out and provided with an adequate supply of yolk. Such an egg required internal fertilization and the development of mating habits. Reptiles were thus freed from an aquatic life and could become true terrestrial tetrapods. Most reptiles had become terrestrial tetrapods by the end of the Paleozoic era.

Perhaps no group of vertebrate animals has ever displayed more evolutionary diversity and adaptive radiation than has the reptiles. They gave rise to adaptations that enabled them to invade the land, the water, and the air. From the basic cotylosaur stem, there developed reptiles from those of small and insignificant size to those like the dinosaurs, which were the largest terrestrial animals that have ever existed. Some reptiles were grotesque and bizarre, with spines and other structures. Others were adapted for aquatic life (ichthyosaurs, Fig. 24-12). The glory of the reptiles passed with the Mesozoic era; the present-day reptiles are mere vestiges of their former conditions.

Morphologically the greatest advance shown by reptiles as a group over the amphibians was the development of a locomotor pattern in which limbs furnished the propulsive power instead of the body undulation and belly-dragging of the amphibians.

Among the many diverse groups of reptiles, two of them resulted in the great classes of birds and mammals (Fig. 24-13).

Birds (Aves). Structurally, birds are so close to reptiles that they have often been referred to as "glorified reptiles" (Huxley). Birds arose from a group of reptiles called the archosaurians, which also gave rise to the order Pterosauria (flying reptiles), or pterodactyls, in the Jurassic period. These reptiles flew by means of membrane wings, which were supported mainly by

FIG. 24-11

Seymouria, fossil tetrapod that serves as connecting link between amphibians and reptiles. Although too specialized to be direct ancestor of reptiles, its transitional characteristics indicate that it must have come from ancestors close to basal stock of stem reptiles. Many of its characteristics are similar to those found in labyrinthodont amphibians.

FIG. 24-12

Icthyosaurus, extinct marine reptile that flourished during Jurassic and Cretaceous periods. This fishlike reptile was more than 10 feet long, and its legs were modified into paddles, which were used for balance and steering. It breathed by means of lungs, and many of this group brought forth their young alive. This return to water of a reptile is illustrated by many others, as shown by fossil record. (Modified from Romer.)

elongated last fingers. Some pterosaurs had a wingspread of 25 feet, but most were smaller. Their bodies were relatively small and their bones light and hollow. Whatever resemblance they had to birds was due to convergent evolution, for birds had a separate evolution. They became extinct before the end of the Cretaceous period.

The first known birds appeared during Jurassic times. Our knowledge about these earliest birds is obtained from two fossil specimens found in limestone in Bavaria, Germany. They are called *Archaeopteryx* (Fig. 24-14). These fossils show plainly the presence of feathers, which the pterosaurs did not have, but they had many reptilian characteristics, such as teeth and elongated tails. It has been suggested that bird flight may have originated from rapid running on the ground (some reptiles were specialized that way) and the flapping of their forelimbs, or it could have originated from the habit of gliding to the ground from trees. Many physiologic changes also occurred before birds could become efficient flyers, such as a constant body temperature, highly specialized sensory reactions, and efficient neuromuscular coordination for balancing. It was not until Cretaceous times that birds became modernized in such respects as the fusion of the skull bones, development of pneumatic bones, coalescence of the pelvis and sacrum, suppression of the tail, etc.

Mammals. Mammals arose from mammal-like reptiles—the Therapsida in the Jurassic period—although some may have appeared earlier. One of these mammal-like reptiles was *Cynognathus* (Fig. 24-15), which was an early Triassic carnivore about the size of a large dog. Related forms were much smaller. This type showed many mammalian as well as reptilian characteristics. These animals at first were small and insignificant and were no match for the ruling reptiles of that time. Mammals probably had a polyphyletic origin, and each subclass was derived separately from a distinct therapsid line. Selection based on physiologic factors in all lines of therapsids would have tended toward the mammalian conditions. When the large dominant reptiles (dinosaurs, ichthyosaurs, etc.) disappeared, a lot of ecologic niches were now opened to the mammals, and by great adaptive radiation they were able to fill many of these niches during the Cenozoic era. The early fossil record of mammals is very scanty and incomplete, but the Mesozoic mammals were establishing the types that later developed into the successful group as we now know it. By the close of the Cretaceous period mammals had developed into two main groups, the marsupials and the placentals, which had probably arisen independently from the Pantotheria. Mammals underwent many changes morphologically and physiologically from their reptilian ancestors. The most striking of these changes involved a

FIG. 24-13

Adaptive radiation of reptiles. First vertebrates to possess land were reptiles, amazing in their variety. Transition from certain labyrinthodont amphibians to reptiles occurred in Carboniferous period to Mesozoic times. This transition was effected by development of amniote egg, which made land existence possible, although egg may well have developed before oldest reptiles had ventured far on land. Explosive adaptation by reptiles may have been due partly to variety of ecologic niches into which they could move. Fossil record shows that five lines that arose from stem reptiles led to turtles, mammal-like reptiles ichthyosaurs, plesiosaurs, and stem-ruling reptiles. Some of these returned to the sea. Later radiations led to flying reptiles, birds, dinosaurs, etc. Of this great assemblage, the only reptiles now in existence belong to four orders shown above (Chelonia, Crocodilia, Squamata, and Rhynchocephalia). How are the mighty fallen! (From several sources.)

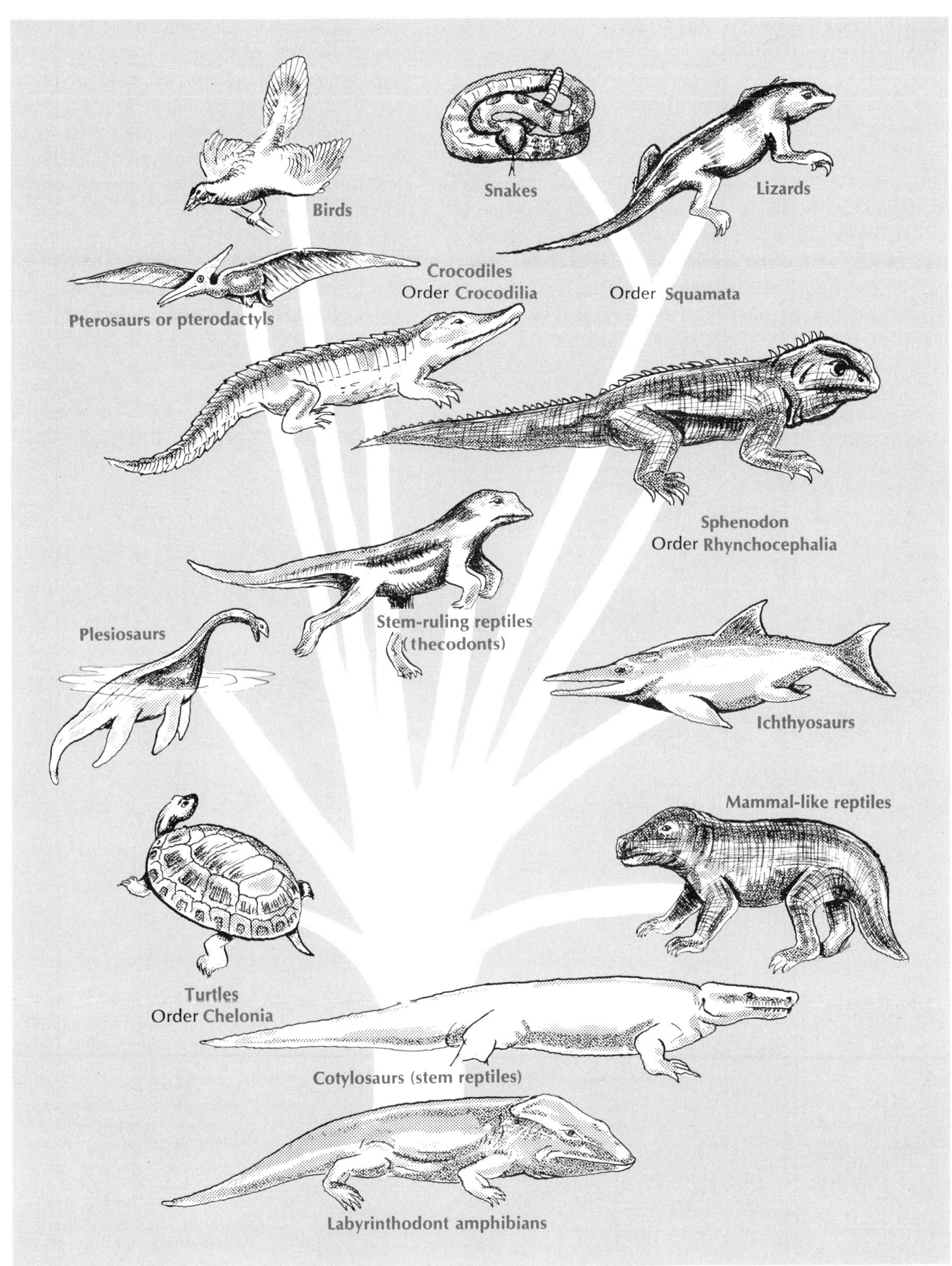

FIG. 24-13

For legend see opposite page.

greater brain with a higher degree of intelligence; reproduction and care of young, with the development of characteristic behavior patterns; development of a constant body temperature; transformation of the articulating elements between jaw and skull into the ear ossicles; and a differentiated dentition of canine, incisor, and molar teeth. Many skeletal changes involved the fusion of the pelvic bones to form a single element; the appearance of two occipital condyles instead of one (reptiles); and alterations in the ribs and digits.

The early placental mammals of the Cretaceous period are known only from a few fossils. They were small and were the direct ancestors of the most primitive group of living mammals, the Insectivora (moles and shrews), which may be the ancestors of all other placental mammals. By adaptive radiation from this stem all the great variety of mammals arose (Fig. 24-16).

CHARACTERISTICS OF CHORDATES

1. Bilateral symmetry; segmented body; three germ layers; coelom well developed
2. **Notochord** (a skeletal rod) present at some stage in life cycle

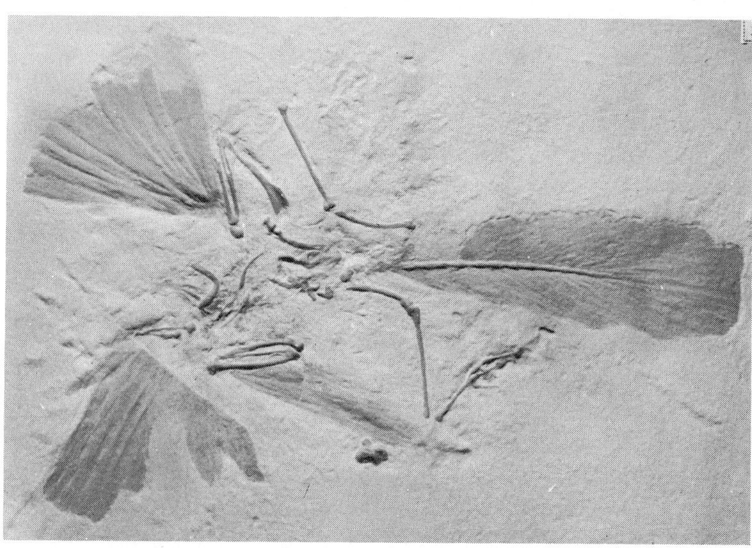

FIG. 24-14

Cast of *Archaeopteryx*, lizard bird. (Courtesy Ward's Natural Science Establishment, Inc., Rochester, N. Y.)

FIG. 24-15

Cynognathus, mammal-like reptile of Triassic age. Mammal-like reptiles evolved early in evolutionary history of reptiles, and some attained size of large dog. These reptiles, called therapsids, flourished until ruling reptiles (dinosaurs) emerged. First true mammals, which arose from mammal-like reptiles about Jurassic times, were small and unimportant during reign of dinosaurs. When latter became extinct at end of Mesozoic era, great adaptive radiation of mammals occurred so that Cenozoic era is called Age of Mammals.

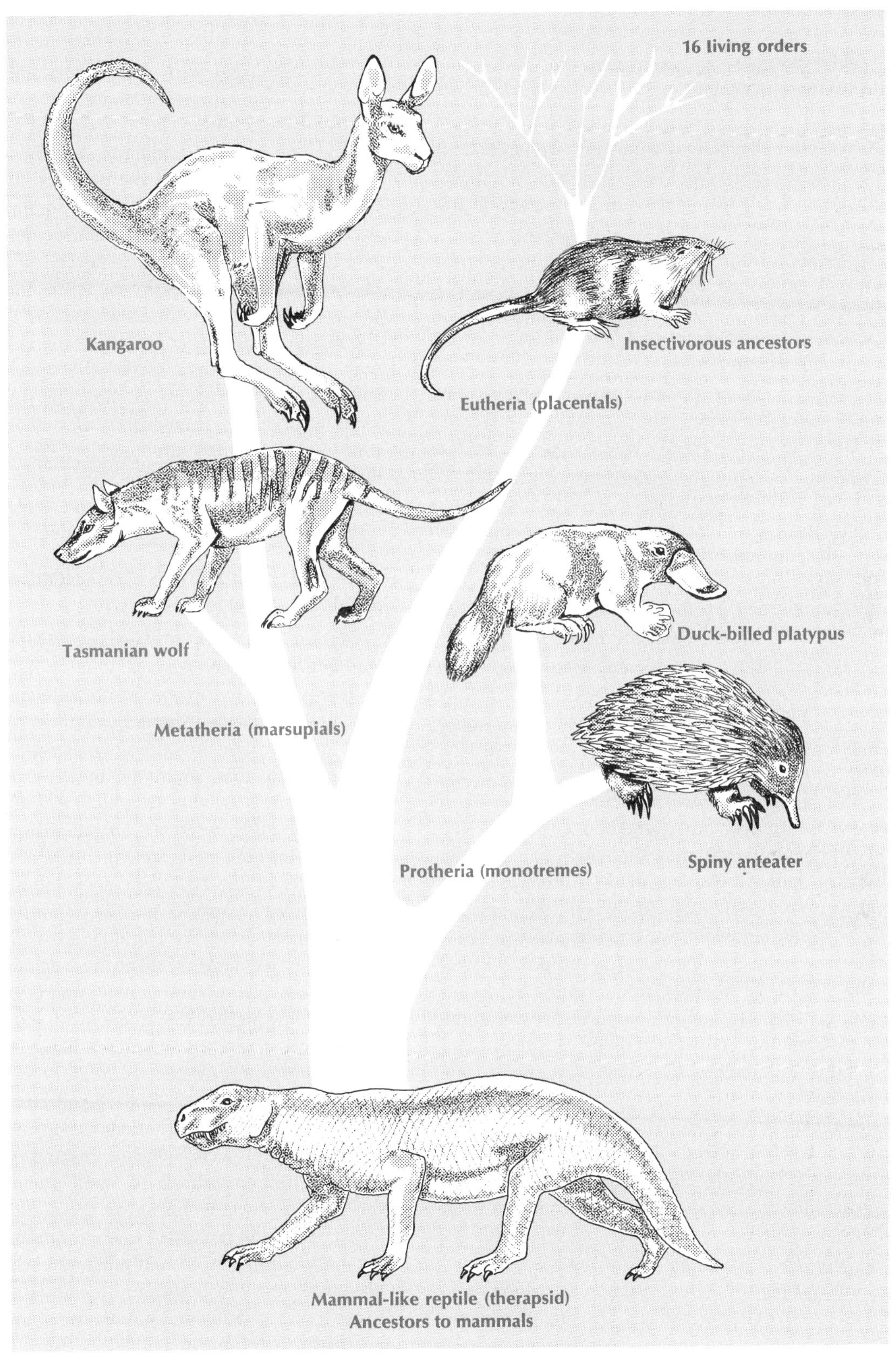

FIG. 24-16

Evolution of major groups of mammals. (Modified from several sources.)

3. **Nerve cord dorsal and tubular;** anterior end of cord usually enlarged to form brain
4. **Pharyngeal gill slits present at some stage in life cycle** and may or may not be functional
5. A **postanal tail** usually projecting beyond the anus at some stage and may or may not persist
6. **Heart ventral,** with dorsal and ventral blood vessels; closed blood system
7. Complete digestive system
8. Exoskeleton often present; well developed in some vertebrates
9. A cartilage or bony **endoskeleton** present in the majority of members (vertebrates)

The three distinctive characteristics that set chordates apart from all other phyla are the **notochord, dorsal tubular nerve cord,** and **pharyngeal gill slits.** These characteristics are always found in the early embryo, although they may be altered or may disappear altogether in later stages of the life cycle.

These three features are so important that each merits a short description of its own.

Notochord. This rodlike body develops in the embryo as a longitudinal outfolding of the dorsal side of the alimentary canal. It is endodermal in origin, although in some forms there is a possibility that the other germ layers have contributed to its formation. In most it is a rigid, yet flexible, rod extending the length of the body. It is the first part of the endoskeleton to appear in the embryo. As a rigid axis on which the muscles can act, it permits undulatory movements of the body. In most of the protochordates and in primitive vertebrates the notochord persists throughout life. In all vertebrates a series of cartilaginous or bony vertebrae are formed from the connective tissue sheath around the notochord and replace it as the chief mechanical axis of the body.

Dorsal tubular nerve cord. In the invertebrate phyla the nerve cord (often paired) is ventral to the alimentary canal and is solid, but in the chordates the cord is dorsal to the alimentary canal and is formed as a tube. The anterior end of this tube in vertebrates becomes enlarged to form the brain. The hollow cord is produced by the infolding of ectodermal cells on the dorsal side of the body above the notochord. Among the vertebrates the nerve cord lies in the neural arches of the vertebrae, and the anterior brain is surrounded by a bony or cartilaginous cranium.

Pharyngeal gill slits. Pharyngeal gill slits are perforated slitlike openings that lead from the pharyngeal cavity to the outside. They are formed by the invagination of the outside ectoderm and the evagination of the endodermal lining of the pharynx. The two pockets break through when they meet, to form the slit. In higher vertebrates these pockets may not break through and only grooves are formed instead of slits; all traces of them usually disappear. In forms that use the slits for breathing, gills with blood vessels are attached to the margins of the slits and make the gaseous exchange with the water that enters the mouth and passes through the pharyngeal gill slits. The slits have in their walls supporting frameworks of gill bars. Primitive forms such as *Amphioxus* have a large number of slits, but only six or seven are the rule in the fish. The transitory appearance of the slits in land vertebrates is often used as evidence for evolution.

WHAT ADVANCEMENTS DO CHORDATA SHOW OVER OTHER PHYLA?

Certain structures in chordates give them some advantages over other animals. One of these is the **endoskeleton.** With the exception of the echinoderms and a few others that have vague beginnings of an endoskeleton, the chordates are the only phylum that has gone all out with this important mechanical device. The endoskeleton is a living tissue, composed of living cells, and grows and undergoes changes the same as other tissues. Thus the endoskeleton grows along with the other parts of the body and does not have to be shed periodically to allow for growth, as is the case with the invertebrates that have chitinous exoskeletons. The endoskeleton may lack a little of the mechanical advantage of the exoskeleton, but it more than compensates for this by allowing greater freedom of movement.

Another advantage chordates have is their method of **breathing.** An efficient respiratory system has gone hand in hand with a well-developed circulatory system. Certain arthropods, with their direct tracheal system, have evolved a very efficient respiration, but such a plan is fitted to animals of small size only. In either the gills of aquatic forms or the lungs of terrestrial forms, the blood circulates freely through the respiratory organs, ensuring rapid and efficient exchange of gases. Moreover, the blood system of chordates is admirably fitted to carry on so many functions that it has become a general factotum for bodily functions.

No single system in the body is more correlated with functional and structural advancement than is the **ner-**

vous system. Throughout the invertebrate kingdom we have seen that there has been a more or less centralization of nervous systems. This tendency has reached its climax in the higher chordates in which we find the highly efficient tubular nervous system. Such a system allows the greatest possible utilization of space for the nervous units so necessary for well-integrated nervous patterns. Along with the advanced nervous system goes a better sensory system, which partly explains the power of this group to adapt itself to a varied environment.

COMPARISON OF CHORDATA WITH INVERTEBRATA

Some of the most striking differences between chordates and higher invertebrates may be seen by the following summary of comparisons.

Nervous system. The nerve cord is dorsal in chordates, ventral in higher invertebrates. Both have dorsal brains.

Circulatory system. The heart is ventral in chordates, dorsal in invertebrates. In the dorsal blood vessel the blood flows posteriorly in chordates, anteriorly in invertebrates.

Endoskeleton. Chordates have an endoskeleton in the form of a notochord or a more highly developed vertebral system; invertebrates lack this.

Digestive system. In all larval and in some adult chordates the anus terminates anterior to the posterior part of the body, producing a postanal tail; higher invertebrates have the anus terminating at the posterior part of the body. Pharyngeal gill slits are found in the pharynx of chordates (at some stage) but are lacking among the invertebrates.

SUBPHYLA

There are three subphyla under phylum Chordata. Two of these subphyla are small, lack a vertebral column, and are of interest primarily as borderline or first chordates (protochordates). Since these subphyla lack a cranium, they are also referred to as Acrania. The third subphylum is provided with a vertebral column and is called Vertebrata. Since this phylum has a cranium, it is also called Craniata.

Protochordata (Acrania)

Subphylum Urochordata (u'ro-kor-da"ta) (Gr. *oura,* tail, + L. *chorda,* cord, + *ata,* characterized by) (**Tunicata**). Notochord and nerve cord only in free-swimming larva; adults sessile and encased in tunic. Example: *Molgula.*

Subphylum Cephalochordata (sef'a-lo-kor-da"ta) (Gr. *kephale,* head, + L. *chorda,* cord). Notochord and nerve cord found along entire length of body and persist throughout life; fishlike in form. Example: *Branchiostoma (Amphioxus).*

Craniata

Subphylum Vertebrata (ver'te-bra"ta) (L. *vertebratus,* backbone). Bony or cartilaginous vertebrae surround spinal cord; notochord in all embryonic stages and persists in some of the fish. This subphylum may also be divided into two groups (superclasses) according to whether or not they have jaws.

Superclass Agnatha (ag'na-tha) (Gr. *a,* not, + *gnathos,* jaw). Without true jaws or appendages. Example: *Petromyzon.*

Superclass Gnathostoma (na-thos'to-ma) (Gr. *gnathos,* jaw, + *stoma,* mouth). With jaws and (usually) paired appendages. Example: *Homo.*

PROTOCHORDATA: FORERUNNERS OF VERTEBRATA

Two of the three subphyla of the chordates are often referred to collectively as the **protochordates,** that is, the first or early chordates. These primitive bor-

FIG. 24-17

Structure of sea squirt. This is zooid of colonial ascidian *Perophera viridis.* Although zooids are very small and translucent and are attached to long vinelike stolons, their general structure is typical of many of larger solitary simple ascidians such as *Molgula* or *Styela.*

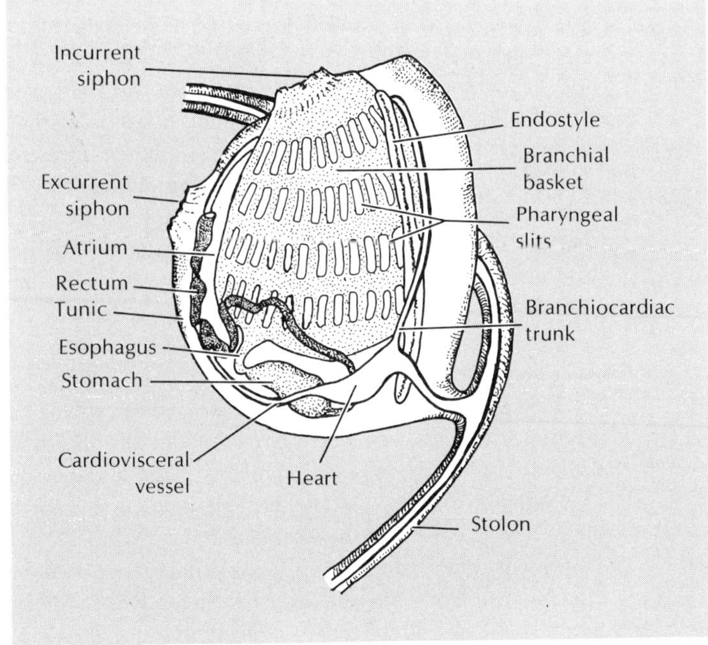

derline forms have little economic importance but are of great interest to biologists because they exhibit the characteristics of chordates in simple form.

SUBPHYLUM UROCHORDATA (TUNICATA)

The tunicates (Fig. 24-17) have a wide distribution, being found in all seas from near the shoreline to great depths. Most of them are sessile, at least as adults, although some are free living. The name tunicate is suggested by the nonliving tunic that surrounds them and contains cellulose. A common name for them is sea squirt because some of them discharge water through the excurrent siphon when irritated. They vary in size from microscopic forms to several inches in length.

As a group they may be considered as degenerative or specialized members of the chordates, for they lack many of the common characteristics of chordates. For a long time they were classified among the mollusks. In 1866 Kowalevsky, the Russian embryologist, worked out their true position.

Urochordata is divided into three classes—**Ascidiacea, Larvacea,** and **Thaliacea.** Of these, the members of **Ascidiacea,** commonly known as the ascidians, are by far the most common and are the best known. One of this group is described below as the type of tunicates. The ascidians are often considered as a group that has regressed in its evolution, for most of them are attached as adults but have evolved from free-moving ancestors. Ascidians may be solitary, colonial, or compound. Each of the solitary and colonial forms has its own test, but among the compound forms many individuals may share the same test. In some of these compound ascidians each member has its own **incurrent siphon,** but the **excurrent opening** is common to the group. Most ascidians are monoecious, but some are dioecious, and they can also reproduce asexually by budding or gemmation. The larvae may develop outside or in the atrium of the parent. Ascidians vary in color, such as black, pink, and scarlet.

The **Larvacea** and **Thaliacea** are pelagic forms of the open sea and are not often found in the intertidal zones where ascidians are common. The members of Larvacea are small, tadpolelike forms under 5 mm. in length and appear to be ascidian tadpoles. They may represent persistent larval forms that have become neotenous. They secrete around themselves cellulose tunics and are filter feeders. *Oikopleura* is a larvacean form often collected in townet samplings of ocean plankton. The class Thaliacea is made up of members that may reach a length of 3 or 4 inches. Their transparent body is spindle shaped or cylindric and is surrounded by bands of circular muscles, with their incurrent and excurrent siphons at opposite ends. They are mostly carried along by currents, although by contracting their circular muscle bands they can force water out of their excurrent siphons and can move by jet propulsion. Many are provided with luminous organs and give a brilliant light at night. Most of their body is hollow, with the viscera forming a compact mass on the ventral side. They appear to have come from attached ancestors like the ascidians. Some of them have complex life histories. In forms like *Doliolum* there is alternation of generations between sexual and asexual forms. After hatching from the egg the larval tadpole changes into a barrel-shaped nurse or asexual stage, which produces small buds on a ventral stolon. These buds break free, become attached to another part of the parent, and develop into three kinds of individuals, one kind of which breaks free to become the sexual stage. *Salpa* also has alternation of generations and is a common form along the Atlantic coast.

Adult ascidian—Molgula

Molgula is globose in form and is attached by its base to piles and stones. Lining the test or tunic is a membrane or **mantle.** On the outside are two projections: the **incurrent** and **excurrent siphons** (Fig. 24-17). Water enters the incurrent siphon and passes into the pharynx through the mouth. On the midventral side of the pharynx is a groove, the **endostyle,** which is ciliated and secretes mucus. Food material in the water is entangled by the mucus in this endostyle and carried into the esophagus and stomach. The intestine leads to the anus near the excurrent siphon. The water passes through the pharyngeal slits in the walls of the pharynx into the atrial cavity. As the water passes through the slits, respiration occurs.

The circulatory system contains a ventral **heart** near the stomach and two large vessels, one connected to each end of the heart. The action of the heart is peculiar in that it drives the blood first in one direction and then in the other. This reversal of blood flow is found in no other animal. The excretory system is a type of nephridium near the intestine. The nervous system is restricted to a nerve ganglion and a few nerves that lie on the dorsal side of the pharynx. A notochord is lacking. The animals are hermaphroditic, for both ovaries and testes are found in the same animal. Ducts lead from the gonads close to the intestines and empty near the anus. The germ cells are carried out the excurrent siphon into the surrounding water, where cross-fertilization occurs.

It will be seen that, of the three chief characteristics of chordates, adult tunicates have only one, the pharyngeal gill slits. However, the larval form gives away the secret of their true relationship.

Ascidian tadpole. The tadpole larvae (Fig. 24-18) among the different ascidians vary in certain details, but the basic plan is much the same in all. The development of the egg through the blastula and gastrula stages is somewhat similar to that of amphioxus. However, cleavage is determinate, and the mesoderm arises not from pouches but from clumps of cells of the archenteron. After a development of about two days the embryo hatches out into an elongated transparent larva about 1 to 5 mm. long. Its tail is four or five times as long as its trunk. The tail is provided with a slender cuticular fin and contains the following structures: a **notochord** of vacuolated cells arranged in a single row; a hollow dorsal **nerve chord** extending from the tip of the tail to the sensory vesicle and made up of small cells; and a striated muscle band on each side of the notochord. Some mesenchymal cells are also found in the tail. In the larger head and trunk regions are found the three adhesive papillae; a digestive system of dorsal mouth, short esophagus, large pharynx with endostyle and **gill slits,** which open into the atrium, stomach, intestine, and anus opening into the atrium; the brain, which is a continuation of the nerve cord of the tail; a sensory vesicle containing an otolith for balance; and a dorsal median eye with lens and pigmented cup. A coelom and a circulatory system are present, but the heart is not formed until after metamorphosis. The larva does not feed but swims around for some hours, during which time it is at first positively phototactic and negatively geotactic but later becomes negatively phototatic and positively geotactic. By its adhesive papillae it now fastens itself vertically to some solid object and then undergoes retrograde metamorphosis to become an adult. In this process the tail is absorbed by phagocytes; the notochord, muscles, and nervous system (except a trunk ganglion) degenerate; the branchial sac enlarges with many gill slits; and the alimentary canal and circulatory system (with a heart) enlarge and develop. The body also undergoes a rotation so that the mouth and atrial openings (siphons) are shifted to the upper unattached end. Gonads and ducts arise in the mesoderm, and the whole animal becomes enclosed in a test or tunic.

The evolutionary significance of the ascidian tadpole has already been discussed.

SUBPHYLUM CEPHALOCHORDATA

Amphioxus

Subphylum Cephalochordata is the most interesting of all the protochordates, for one of its members is *Branchiostoma (Amphioxus)* (Fig. 24-19), one of the classic animals in zoology. This group is found mainly on the sandy beaches of southern waters, where they burrow in the sand, with the anterior end projecting out. One American species, *B. virginiae,* is found from Florida to the Chesapeake Bay. Altogether there are 28

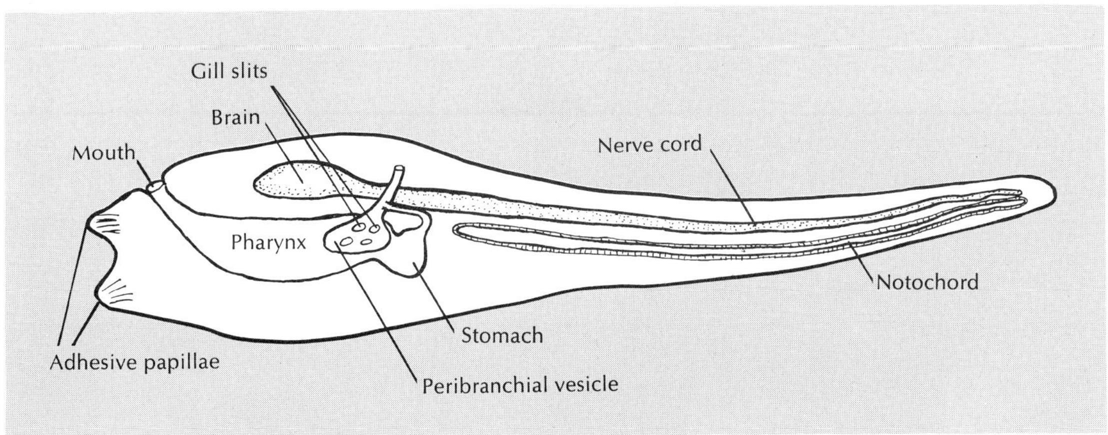

FIG. 24-18

Structure of tunicate larva (ascidian tadpole) showing all three chordate characteristics: notochord, dorsal nerve cord, and gill slits.

species, of which 4 are American, scattered over the world. They can swim in open water by swift lateral movements of the body.

Amphioxus is especially interesting, for it has the three distinctive characteristics of chordates in simple form, and in other ways it may be considered a blueprint of the phylum. It has a long, slender, laterally compressed body 2 to 3 inches long (Figs. 24-19 and 24-20), with both ends pointed. There is a long **dorsal fin,** which passes around the tail end to form the **caudal fin.** A short **ventral fin** is also found. These fins are reinforced by **fin rays** of connective tissue. The ventral side of the body is flattened and bears along each side a **metapleural fold.** There are three openings to the outside; the ventral anterior **mouth,** the **anus** near the base of the caudal fin, and the **atriopore** just anterior to the ventral fin.

The body is covered with a soft **epithelium** one layer thick resting upon some connective tissue. The **notochord,** which extends almost the entire length of the body, is made up of cells and gelatinous substance enclosed in a sheath of connective tissue. Above the notochord is the tubular dorsal **nerve cord,** with a slight dilation at the anterior end known as the **cerebral vesicle.** Along each side of the body and tail are the numerous <-shaped **myotomes,** or muscles, which have a metameric arrangement. The myotomes are separated from each other by **myosepta** of connective tissue. The myotomes of the two sides alternate with each other. The anterior end of the body is called the **rostrum.** Just back of this and slightly below is a median opening surrounded by a membrane, the **oral hood,** which bears some twenty **oral tentacles (buccal cirri).** The oral hood encloses the chamber known as the **vestibule,** at the bottom of which lies the true **mouth** with a membrane, the **velum,** around it. Around the mouth are twelve **velar tentacles.** The cirri and tentacles serve to

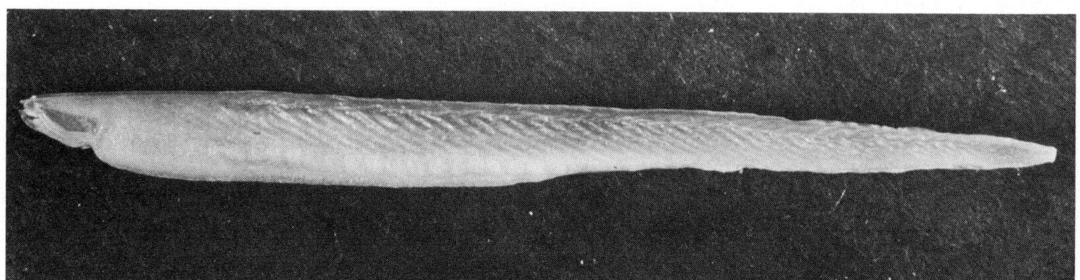

FIG. 24-19

Branchiostoma (Amphioxus), best known of protochordates. This is mature specimen (about ×2). Note myotomes and block-shaped gonads.

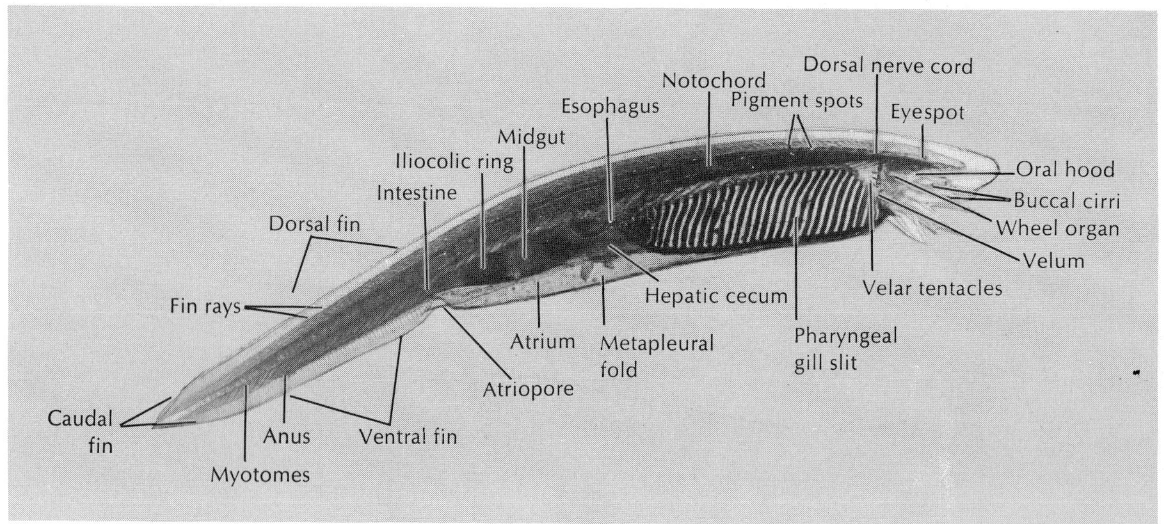

FIG. 24-20

Structure of *Amphioxus.* Photomicrograph of juvenile; gonads not present.

strain out large particles and have sensory functions. Ciliated patches on the walls of the buccal cavity in front of the velum produce a rotating effect and are called the **wheel organ,** which propels water currents. On the dorsal side of the oral hood is Hatschek's groove and pit, an embryonic relic from the first coelomic sac on the left. It may be homologous with the pituitary of vertebrates. Just behind the mouth is the large compressed pharynx with more than a hundred pairs of **gill slits,** which act as strainers in filter feeding as well as in respiration. From the pharynx the narrow tubular **intestine** extends backward to the anus. On the ventral side of the intestine is a large diverticulum, the **hepatic cecum.** The **coelom** is reduced and is confined to the region above the pharynx and around the intestine. Connecting the coelom to the atrium are about a hundred pairs of ciliated **nephridia** of the solenocyte type, a modified kind of flame cell (Fig. 13-7, *B*). The big cavity around the pharynx is the **atrium**; it is lined with ectoderm and is therefore not a coelom. The pharynx has a middorsal groove, the **hyperbranchial** (epi-

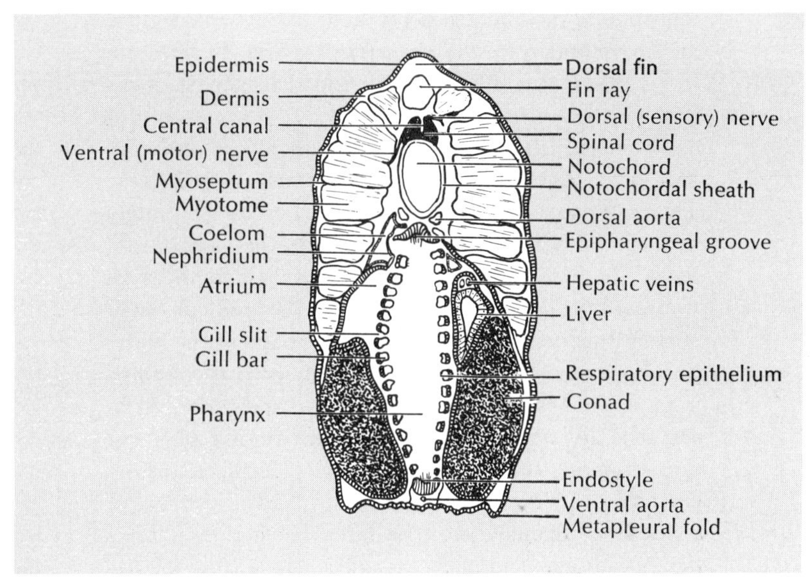

FIG. 24-21

Cross section of amphioxus through pharynx and gonads. (See text for general description.) (From Hickman and Hickman: Laboratory studies in integrated zoology, ed. 2, The C. V. Mosby Co.)

FIG. 24-22

Scheme of circulation in amphioxus. (From Hickman and Hickman: Laboratory studies in integrated zoology, ed. 3, The C. V. Mosby Co.)

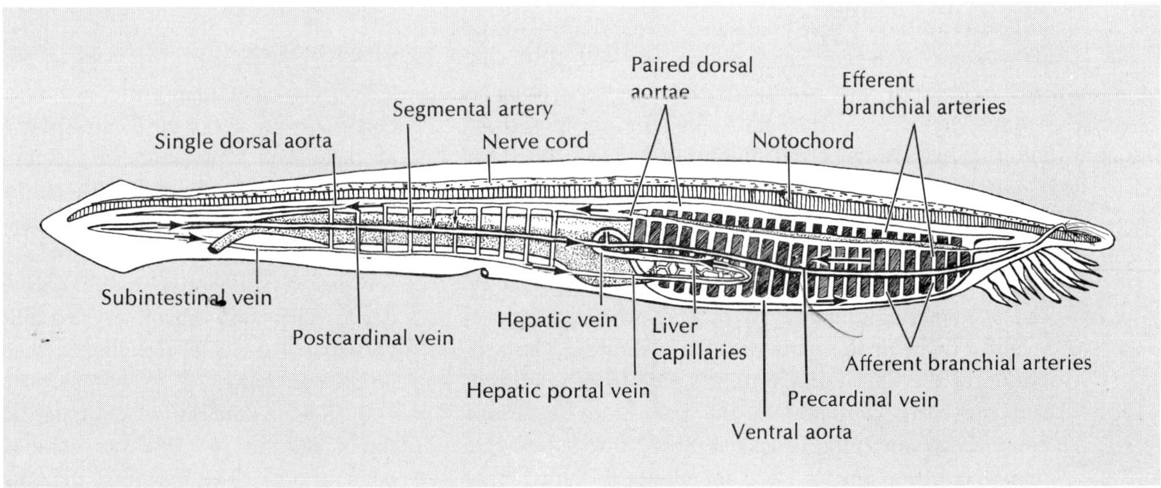

pharyngeal) **groove,** and a midventral one, known as the **endostyle.** Both of these grooves are lined with cilia and gland cells (Fig. 24-21). Food is entangled by the mucus of the endostyle and is carried to the intestine; the water passes through the gill slits into the atrium and gives up oxygen to the blood vessels in the **gill bars.**

Although there is no heart, the **blood system** is similar to that of higher chordates (Fig. 24-22). The blood moves posteriorly in the **dorsal aorta** and anteriorly in the **ventral aorta;** a **hepatic portal** vein leads from the intestines to the liver. Blood is propelled by contractions of the ventral aorta and is carried to the dorsal aorta by vessels in the gill bars. The blood is almost colorless, with a few red corpuscles.

The **nervous system** is above the notochord and consists of a single dorsal **nerve cord,** which is hollow. This nerve cord gives off a pair of nerves alternately to each body segment, or myotome, the dorsal root having both sensory and motor functions and the ventral root having motor functions only. Ciliated cells with **sensory** functions are found in various parts of the body. Sexes are separate, and each sex has about twenty-five pairs of gonads located on the wall of the atrium. The sex cells are set free in the atrial cavity and pass out the atriopore to the outside, where fertilization occurs. Cleavage is total (holoblastic) and a gastrula is formed by invagination. The larva hatches soon after deposition and gradually assumes the shape of the adult.

No other chordate shows so well the basic diagnostic chordate characteristics as does the amphioxus. Not only are the three chief characters of chordates—**dorsal nerve cord, notochord,** and **pharyngeal gill slits**—well represented but also secondary characteristics, such as postanal tail, liver diverticulum, hepatic portal system, and the beginning of a ventral heart. Indicative also of the condition in vertebrates is the much thicker dorsal portion of the muscular layer. This is in contrast to the invertebrate phyla in which the muscular layer is about the same thickness around the body cavity. The metameric arrangement of the muscles suggests a similar plan in the embryos of vertebrates. The separation of the dorsal and ventral spinal roots may indicate the early condition in the vertebrate ancestors. From these and other considerations, this interesting animal is often placed close in affinity to the higher chordates, the vertebrates. Just where it is placed in the evolutionary blueprint of the chordates and the vertebrates is a controversial point. It is placed by many authorities near the primitive fish, ostracoderms, but whether it comes before or after these fish in the evolutionary line is not settled. Many regard the amphioxus as a highly specialized or degenerate member of the early chordates and believe that the overdeveloped notochord was developed in them as a correlation to their burrowing habits. The forward extension of the notochord into the tip of the snout may be one of the reasons for the small development of the brain of the amphioxus.

Among other serious objections that have been advanced against amphioxus as a generalized ancestral type of chordates are its solenocyte type of protonephridia, such as is found in certain polychaetes and which has no resemblance to the glomerular-tubular nephron of vertebrates; its unique atrium, which has no counterpart in vertebrates; and its vast number of gill slits. Many authorities therefore assign amphioxus to a divergent side branch of some stage intermediate between the early filter-feeding prevertebrates and the vertebrates.

CRANIATA
SUBPHYLUM VERTEBRATA

The third subphylum of the chordates, Vertebrata, has the same characteristics that distinguish the other two subphyla, but in addition it has a number of features that the others do not share. The characteristics that give the members of this group the name Vertebrata or Craniata are the presence of a braincase, or **cranium,** and a spinal column of vertebrae which forms the chief skeletal axis of the body.

Characteristics

1. The chief diagnostic features of chordates—**notochord, dorsal nerve cord,** and **pharyngeal gill slits**—are all present at some stage of the life cycle.
2. They are covered with an **integument** basically of two divisions, an outer **epidermis** of stratified epithelium from the ectoderm and an inner **dermis,** or corium, of connective tissue derived from the mesoderm. This skin has many modifications among the various classes, such as glands, scales, feathers, claws, horns, and hair.
3. The notochord is more or less replaced by the spinal column of vertebrae composed of cartilage or bone or both. The vertebral column with the cranium,

visceral arches, limb girdles, and two pairs of jointed appendages forms the distinctive **endoskeleton.**

4. Many **muscles** are attached to the skeleton to provide for movement.

5. The complete **digestive system** is ventral to the spinal column and is provided with large digestive glands, liver, and pancreas.

6. The circulatory system is made up of the **ventral heart** of two to four chambers; a closed blood vessel system of arteries, veins, and capillaries; and a blood fluid containing red blood corpuscles and white corpuscles. Paired aortic arches connect the ventral and dorsal aortae and give off branches to the gills among the aquatic vertebrates; in the terrestrial types the aortic arch plan is modified into pulmonary and systemic systems.

7. A **coelom** is well developed and is largely filled with the visceral systems.

8. The **excretory system** is made up of paired kidneys (opisthonephric or metanephric types) provided with ducts to drain the waste to the cloaca or anal region.

9. The brain is typically divided into five vesicles.

10. Ten or twelve pairs of cranial nerves with both motor and sensory functions is the rule; a pair of spinal nerves supplies each primitive myotome; and an autonomic nervous system controls involuntary functions of internal organs.

11. An **endocrine system** of ductless glands scattered through the body is present.

12. The sexes are nearly always separate, and each sex contains paired gonads with ducts that discharge their products either into the cloaca or into special openings near the anus.

13. The **body plan** consists typically of **head, trunk,** and postanal **tail.** A **neck** may be present in some, especially terrestrial forms. Two pairs of appendages are the rule, although they are entirely absent in some. The coelom is divided into a pericardial space and a general body cavity; in addition, mammals have a thoracic cavity.

AMMOCOETE LARVA AS CHORDATE ARCHETYPE

As pointed out in a previous section, the oldest known group of vertebrates was the Agnatha, which included the extinct ostracoderms and the existing cyclostomes (lampreys and hagfish). It is logical, therefore, to look for a vertebrate ancestor among these primitive forms. Is there a living form that can serve as a generalized vertebrate ancestor? What features must such a prototype possess? Adult cyclostomes are too specialized and too degenerative in many respects for meeting the requirements of such a generalized type. The ammocoete larva of lampreys, however, possesses many of the basic structures one would expect to find in a chordate archetype. Many of its structures are simple in form and similar to those in higher vertebrates. It has a heart, ear, eye, thyroid gland, and pituitary gland, which are characteristic of vertebrates but are lacking in amphioxus. This larva is so different from the adult lamprey that it was for a long time considered to be a separate species; not until it was shown to metamorphose into the adult lamprey was the exact relationship explained. This eel-like larva spends several years buried in the sand and mud of shallow streams, until it finally emerges as an adult that may continue to live in fresh water (freshwater lampreys) or else may migrate to the sea (marine lampreys).

Since Stensio's important work on ostracoderms in 1927, the similarity of this ammocoete larva to the cephalaspids of that ancient group of fish has become more and more apparent, and many zoologists are substituting it for amphioxus as a basic ancestral type. It is true that the ammocoete has some degenerative specializations of its own, for it lacks the bony exoskeleton, an important feature in ostracoderms. Stensio, Romer, and other paleontologists have emphasized that a hard or bony exoskeleton is characteristic of ancestral vertebrates and that cartilaginous structures in the adult represent a specialized embryonic condition which has been retained. Homer Smith has suggested that the heavy armor of the ostracoderms was a protection not against predators but against the osmotic effect of passing from salt to fresh water, where a rapid and fatal absorption of water into the organism would occur unless checked by the bony exoskeleton. Romer has shown that cartilage serves a real purpose in the embryo. Cartilage is not present in dermal bones such as certain skull bones that are laid down directly in membrane and have simple growth, but only in internal bones where it is necessary to maintain complicated relationships with blood vessels, muscles, and other bones throughout the entire growth period. Bone grows only by accretion and does not have the power to expand, which cartilage can do, and thus the latter represents an ideal embryonic material before the adult elements are fully formed.

Some of the generalized characteristics of the ammocoete larva will be pointed out in the following summary of its basic structures.

General chordate features. The ammocoetes has a long, slender body, with the front end broader and blunter (Fig. 24-23). A median membranous fin fold extends along most of the posterior dorsal border, passes around the caudal end, where the fin is broader, and then continues forward on the ventral side. The **notochord** is large and extends from the very tip of the tail to a region near the posterior end of the brain. The **dorsal nerve cord,** unlike that of the amphioxus, is enlarged anteriorly to form a complete brain. Instead of the many gill slits of the amphioxus, there are only seven pairs of gill pouches and slits in the ammocoetes (there are six pairs in shark embryos). Muscular segmentation is also found in the form of myotomes along the dorsal part of the body. The skeleton is meager and in a degenerate condition. Such parts as are found are entirely cartilaginous, for example, the gill bars of the branchial basket, the scattered plates of the braincase, and the small vertebrae near the notochord. The well-developed notochord is the chief supporting skeleton. There are no paired fins or jaws.

Digestive and respiratory systems. At the ventral anterior end of the larva is a cup-shaped **oral hood,** which encloses the **buccal cavity.** Numerous **oral papillae,** or branched projections, are attached to the sides and roof of the oral hood and surround the mouth cavity. They have a sensory function. Between the buccal cavity and the **pharynx** is the **velum,** consisting of a pair of flaps that help create currents of water entering the mouth. The expanded pharynx makes up a large part of the alimentary canal and bears in its lateral walls the seven pairs of **gill pouches.** Each of these pouches opens to the exterior by a **gill slit.** Each gill slit has a fold or **gill** on both its anterior surface and posterior surface, and the wall of the pharynx between adjacent gill slits contains supporting rods of cartilage (**gill bars**). The gills are richly supplied with blood capillaries and are bathed by currents of water that enter the mouth and pass to the exterior through the gill slits. Oxygen from the water enters the blood in the gills and carbon dioxide is given off by the blood in exchange. The **endostyle** (**subpharyngeal gland**), a closed furrow or tube extending for the length of four gill pouches, is found in the floor of the pharynx. It secretes mucus, which is discharged into the pharynx by a small duct. This sticky mucus entangles the food particles brought in by water currents produced by muscular contractions of the pharynx. Cords of food thus formed are carried into the intestine by the ciliated groove in the floor of the pharynx. During metamorphosis a portion of the endostyle is converted into the **thyroid gland,** which secretes the thyroid hormone containing iodine.

The pharynx narrows at its posterior end to form a short **esophagus,** which opens into the straight **intestine.** Opening into the intestine by the **bile duct** is the **liver** with which is associated a large and conspicuous

FIG. 24-23

Structure of ammocoete larva. Photograph of stained slide.

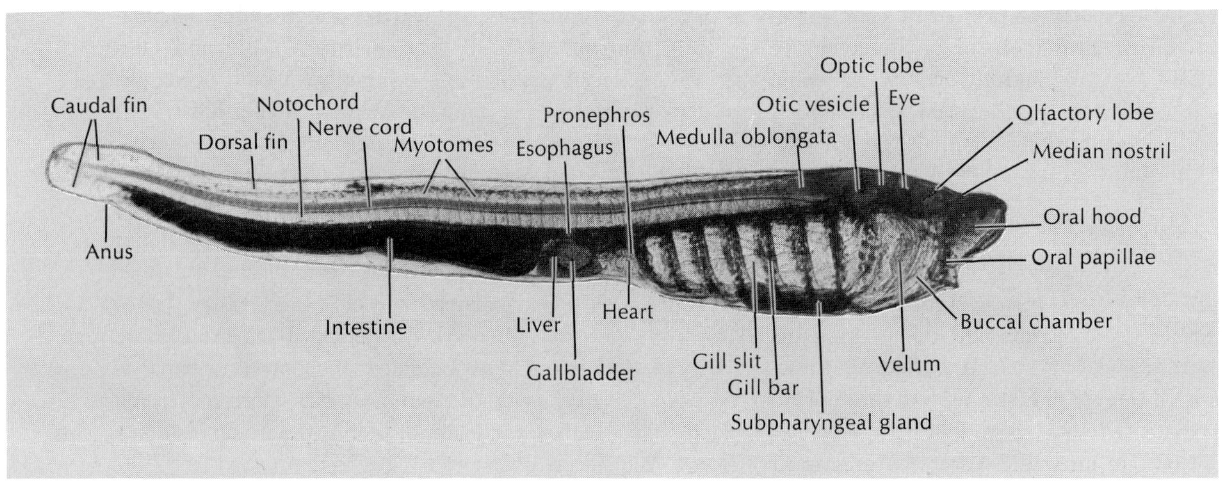

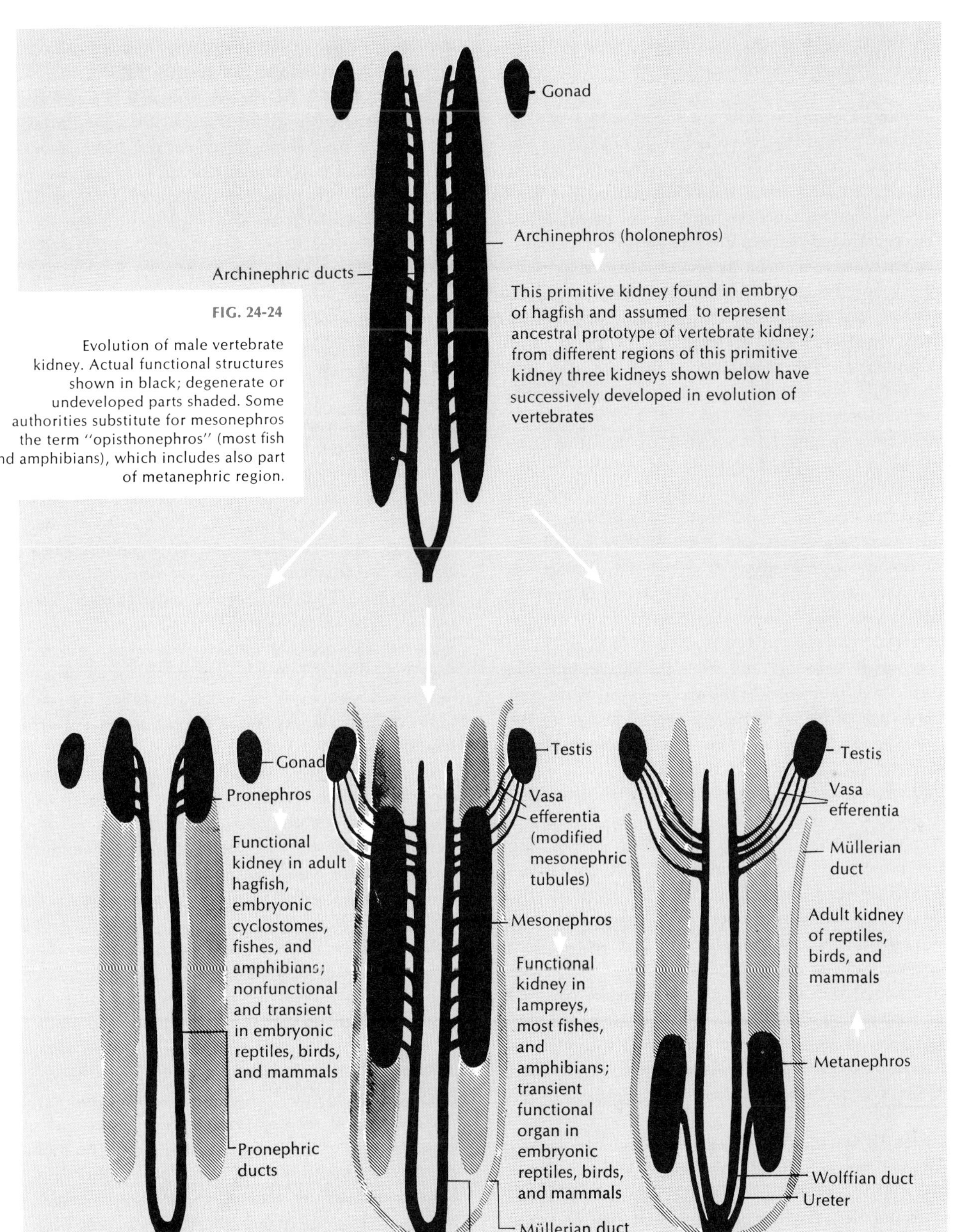

FIG. 24-24

Evolution of male vertebrate kidney. Actual functional structures shown in black; degenerate or undeveloped parts shaded. Some authorities substitute for mesonephros the term "opisthonephros" (most fish and amphibians), which includes also part of metanephric region.

gallbladder. Pancreatic cells are found in the wall of the anterior part of the intestine but do not form a distinct gland. The intestine opens posteriorly into the cloaca, which also receives the kidney ducts. The anus is found a short distance in front of the postanal tail.

The generalized vertebrate features of the ammocoetes are thus seen to be its jawless filter feeding, its relatively undifferentiated alimentary canal, its gill arrangement, and its endostyle characteristic of primitive feeding organisms. The development of the thyroid gland from part of the endostyle, as well as the muscular branchial movement, also represents a plan that higher vertebrates have followed.

Circulatory system. The hypothetical, primitive chordate plan of four major longitudinal blood vessels—**dorsal aorta, subintestinal, right cardinal vein,** and **left cardinal vein**—and two major connections between these blood vessels—**right** and **left ducts of Cuvier** and the **aortic arches**—is generally followed in the ammocoetes with certain modifications. The posterior end of the subintestinal vein has become modified to form the **hepatic portal vein,** the anterior portion to form the **heart** of one **auricle** (atrium) and one **ventricle** arranged in tandem. From the ventricle the short **ventral aorta** runs forward to give off eight pairs of **aortic arches** to the gill pouches. Each arch is composed of an **afferent branchial artery** carrying blood to the capillaries of the gills and an **efferent branchial artery** carrying aerated blood from the gill capillaries to the **dorsal aorta.** The dorsal aorta gives off many branches to the body tissues, and a large posterior branch, the **intestinal,** to the intestine. The **cardinal veins** return blood from the tissues to the right and left **ducts of Cuvier,** which empty into the **sinus venosus,** a thin-walled chamber that empties into the atrium, and thence to the ventricle of the heart. Each cardinal vein is made up of an **anterior cardinal** and a **posterior cardinal branch.** The hepatic portal vein picks up blood laden with nutrients from the intestine and carries it to the liver. The **hepatic vein** carries blood from the liver to the **sinus venosus,** and so back to the heart.

Excretory system. The ancestral vertebrate kidney is supposed to have extended the length of the coelomic cavity and was made up of segmentally arranged uriniferous tubules. Each tubule opens at one end into the coelom by a nephrostome and at the other end into the common archinephric duct. Such a kidney has been called an **archinephros,** or **holonephros,** and is found in the embryos of hagfish (Fig. 24-24). The kidneys of higher vertebrates presumably develop from this primitive plan. Embryologic evidence indicates that vertebrates pass through successive developments of three different regions (pronephros, mesonephros, metanephros) of this primitive archinephros. Evolutionary differences in the internal environment of the different vertebrate groups have produced a differential complex of tubules in specific regions of the ancient kidney.

In the amniotes (reptiles, birds, mammals) each individual, therefore, in its development passes through stages that correspond to a region of anterior tubules (pronephros), a region of middle tubules (mesonephros), and a region of posterior tubules (metanephros). The pronephros and mesonephros disappear in amniotes, leaving only the metanephros as the functional kidney, although the mesonephros may function during embryonic life. However, in forms lower than the amniotes the pronephros and mesonephros grades of tubules are functional in varying combinations of the two regions. Thus cyclostomes have stressed the pronephric type of tubules, whereas fish and amphibians have emphasized the mesonephric type. Among fish and amphibians, however, the adult mesonephros has developed posteriorly into the region of the metanephros of higher forms and is given the name of **opisthonephros.**

In summary, we may state that the evolutionary sequence of adult vertebrate kidneys has been archinephros, opisthonephros, and metanephros.

It is seen that the excretory system of the ammocoetes conforms to the basic chordate plan, whereas the solenocyte type of flame cell found in *Amphioxus* is altogether different.

Reproductive system. The **gonads** are paired ridgelike structures on the dorsal side of the coelom. Each gonad appears to have been formed by the fusion of a number of units. Since they lack genital ducts, the adult lampreys shed their gametes into the coelom, where an opening into the **mesonephric duct** allows the gametes to escape to the outside through the **urogenital papillae.**

Nervous and sensory system. Both brain and spinal cord conform to the basic chordate plan. The **brain** has the typical three divisions of **forebrain, midbrain,** and **hindbrain.** Each of these divisions is associated with an important sense organ—olfactory, vision or eyes, and auditory, respectively. From the dorsal side of the forebrain are two outgrowths or stalks, each of which bears a vestigial **median eye,** the only instance among vertebrates of two median eyes. Other vertebrates may have two outgrowths, but the anterior one is the parietal body, which appears to have been a median eye, and the posterior one (epiphysis) is the pineal gland. In no living vertebrate does a median eye function as such. In some vertebrates only the pineal gland or body is present. A **pituitary gland,** formed from an evagination (infundibulum) of the forebrain and the **hypophysis** from the **nasohypophyseal canal** of the pharynx, is found on the ventral side of the brain. The functional **eyes** of the ammocoetes are small and develop from the forebrain. The spinal cord gives off a pair of **dorsal roots** (mainly sensory) and a pair of **ventral roots** (motor) in every muscle segment. The dorsal and ventral roots do not join as they do in higher vertebrates, nor do the nerves have myelin sheaths.

Derivation and meaning of basic terminology

Amphioxus (am'fi-ox"us) (Gr. *amphi,* double, + *oxys,* sharp). Often used as a synonym for *Branchiostoma,* the correct generic name; the lancelet.

Archaeopteryx (ar'ke-op"ter-iks) (Gr. *archaio,* ancient, + *pteryx,* wing or fin). A fossil reptilelike bird.

Ichthyostega (ik'thy-os"te-ga) (Gr. *ichthyo,* fish, + L. *os,* bone, + Gr. *stegos,* covering). A fossil with both fish and amphibian characters of the late Devonian period.

Ostracodermi (os'tra-ko-der"mi) (Gr. *ostrakon,* shell, + *derma,* skin). A fossil class of fishlike animals of Silurian and Devonian rocks; the oldest recorded vertebrates.

Placodermi (plak'o-der"mi) (Gr. *plakos,* plate, + *derma,* skin). The extinct class of armored fish of the late Silurian and Devonian rocks.

Seymouria (sey'mo-re"a) (after Seymour, Texas). A fossil cotylosaur with both amphibian and reptilian characters.

Annotated references

Barrington, E. J. W. 1965. The biology of Hemichordata and Protochordata. (Paperback.) San Francisco, W. H. Freeman & Co. *A synthesis of recent work on these deuterostomes most closely related to vertebrates. Discusses the possible homologies between the endostyle and the vertebrate thyroid gland.*

Beer, de, G. R. 1951. Vertebrate zoology, rev. ed. London, Sidgwick & Jackson, Ltd. *The student will glean a knowledge of representative types of vertebrates and how they fit into the evolutionary scheme from this excellent work, which should be read by all serious students of the zoologic sciences.*

Berrill, N. J. 1955. The origin of vertebrates. New York, Oxford University Press. *The author stresses the tunicates as the basic stock from which other protochordates and vertebrates arose. He believes that such a sessile filter feeder was really the most primitive animal and was not a mere degenerate side branch of chordate evolution.*

Colbert, E. H. 1955. Evolution of the vertebrates. New York, John Wiley & Sons, Inc. *A clear and well-written presentation of the history of the backboned animals through time. One of the best treatises in the field.*

Roe, A., and G. G. Simpson (editors). 1958. Behavior and evolution. New Haven, Conn., Yale University Press. *A masterpiece that integrates two great disciplines—evolution and behavior.*

Romer, A. S. 1945. Vertebrate paleontology. Chicago, University of Chicago Press. *An authoritative work of the first rank by a master paleontologist.*

Romer, A. S. 1959. The vertebrate story. Chicago, University of Chicago Press. *A comprehensive background of the evolutionary trends and relationships of the various vertebrate groups leading up to that of man himself.*

Smith, H. M. 1960. Evolution of chordate structure. New York, Holt, Rinehart & Winston, Inc. *This excellent introduction to comparative anatomy gives a fine appraisal of the basic structures of primitive chordates.*

Smith, H. W. 1953. From fish to philosopher. Boston, Little, Brown & Co. *The evolutionary history of the kidney. A most revealing treatise on the relations of kidney functions to the evolution of vertebrates.*

CHAPTER 25

• PHYLUM CHORDATA (THE VERTEBRATES: FISH)

Classes Cyclostomata, Chondrichthyes, and Osteichthyes

● It is customary to group vertebrates into two major groups: (1) Pisces* (fish), which includes the classes Cyclostomata, Chondrichthyes, and Osteichthyes; and (2) Tetrapoda (four footed), which includes the classes Amphibia, Reptilia, Aves, and Mammalia. The former is made up of strictly aquatic forms and the latter, of land-dwelling animals. A second method of grouping is (1) Anamnia, or those without fetal membranes (Cyclostomata, Chondrichthyes, Osteichthyes, Amphibia), and (2) Amniota, or those with fetal membranes (Reptilia, Aves, Mammalia).

There is no question of the advancement of the sharks over the cyclostomes, for the former have jaws, paired appendages, true teeth, scales, and reproductive ducts, which are entirely lacking in the latter. Both are cartilaginous, but this probably has little significance. As emphasized previously, it is logical to assume that living cyclostomes and the fossil ostracoderms came from the same common stock of primitive ancestral vertebrates so that the two groups are placed in the same taxonomic group—Agnatha, or jawless vertebrates. With Chondrichthyes and Osteichthyes, however, it is impossible to pick out any ancestral type from such a varied assemblage as the placoderms. It was formerly thought that the Chondrichthyes, because of their complete absence of bone and other characteristics, were very primitive and that they appeared on the evolutionary scene before the bony fish. This view is no longer held; cartilage is considered a degenerate retention of an embryonic condition rather than primitive. The fossil record indicates that the Chondrichthyes appeared after the bony fish. It appears that this class had its origin in fresh water, the same as did other vertebrates, but quite early took to the sea and mostly disappeared from fresh water. A few species are known to inhabit fresh water permanently or temporarily. In the sea they have undergone many evolutionary specializations and have been a very successful and highly compact group of fish. Altogether, there are about 3,000 species of Chondrichthyes, as compared with the 30, 000 species of bony fish.

*Pis'ez (L. *pisces*, fishes).

CLASS CYCLOSTOMATA*—lampreys and hagfish

The primitive cyclostomes derive their name from their circular mouth. They are the lowest vertebrates and the only existing ones without jaws (superclass Agnatha) and are thus distinguished from the remaining vertebrates, which have jaws (superclass Gnathostomata). Cyclostomata are represented by about 50 species, almost equally divided between two orders. Because of their close relationship to the extinct ostracoderms, some authorities consider Agnatha as a class made up of two subclasses (Ostracodermi and Cyclostomata). There are also other taxonomic arrangements of these two groups.

Characteristics

1. Body slender, **eel-like**, rounded, with **soft skin** containing **mucous glands** but **no scales**
2. Median fins with cartilaginous fin rays, but **no paired appendages**
3. **Fibrous** and **cartilaginous** skeleton; notochord persistent
4. **Ventral suctorial mouth; single nasal sac**
5. Heart with one auricle and one ventricle; aortic arches in gill region; blood with erythrocytes and leukocytes
6. Six to fourteen pairs of gills

*Si'klo-sto"mata (Gr. *kyklos*, circular, + *stoma*, mouth.)

7. Two **pronephric** kidneys (mesonephros or opisthonephros in adult) with ducts to urogenital papillae
8. Dorsal nerve cord with differentiated brain; eight to ten pairs of cranial nerves
9. Digestive system lacking a stomach, and the intestine provided with a fold, or **typhlosole**
10. Sensory organs of taste, smell, hearing, and sight present; each auditory organ with one to two semicircular canals
11. Sexes separate in lampreys; hermaphroditic in hagfish; gonad single and no duct; fertilization external; long larval period in lampreys

Classification

Body is cylindric with well-developed dorsal fin; skin smooth without scales; jaws absent; mouth suctorial with horny teeth; nasal aperture; appendages absent; gill pouches, six to fourteen pairs.

Order 1. Petromyzontia (pet'ro-my-zon"te-a) (Gr. *petros,* stone, + *myzon,* suck, + *ia,* pl. suffix)—**lampreys.** Mouth suctorial with horny teeth; nasal sac not connected to mouth; gill pouches, seven pairs. Examples: *Entosphenus, Petromyzon.*

Order 2. Myxinoidea (mik'si-noi"de-a) (Gr. *myxa,* slime, + *oid,* like)—**hagfish and slime eels.** Mouth terminal with four pairs of tentacles; buccal funnel absent; nasal sac with duct to pharynx; gill pouches, ten to fourteen pairs; partially hermaphroditic. Example: *Myxine, Bdellostoma.*

ORDER PETROMYZONTIA (HYPEROARTII)—lampreys

All the lampreys of the northern hemisphere belong to the family Petromyzontidae. The destructive marine lamprey *Petromyzon marinus* is found on both sides of the Atlantic Ocean (America and Europe) and may attain a length of 3 feet. Other genera, such as *Entosphenus* and *Lampetra,* also have a wide distribution in North America and Eurasia and are usually from 6 to 24 inches long. There are 19 species of lampreys in North America. About half of these belong to the nonparasitic brook type; the others are parasitic. According to Hubbs, a noted authority on lampreys, the nonparasitic species have arisen from the parasitic forms by degeneration of the teeth, alimentary canal, etc. They may have done so by evolving from the parasitic species through pedomorphosis (reproduction by young, especially by parthenogenesis). The genus *Ichthyomyzon,* which contains three parasitic and three nonparasitic species, is restricted to eastern North America. On the west coast of North America the chief marine form is represented by *E. tridentatus.* The southern hemisphere is represented by two families—Geotriidae and Mordaciidae.

All lampreys, the marine as well as the freshwater forms, spawn in the spring on shallow gravel beds in streams of fresh water. With their buccal funnels the males clear away the pebbles from a sandy bottom and form a type of pit (Fig. 25-1). When a female anchors herself to a pebble over one of these pits, a male seizes her, winds his tail around her, and discharges his sperm over the eggs as they are extruded from her body into the depression. More than one pair may spawn in the same nest. The adults soon die after their spawning act.

The eggs hatch in about two weeks into small larvae

FIG. 25-1

A, Lamprey nest with four individuals hard at work removing pebbles. **B,** Eggs of brook lamprey *Lampetra lamattei.* (**A,** About ⅓ natural size; **B,** about twice natural size.) (Courtesy J. W. Jordan, Jr.)

A

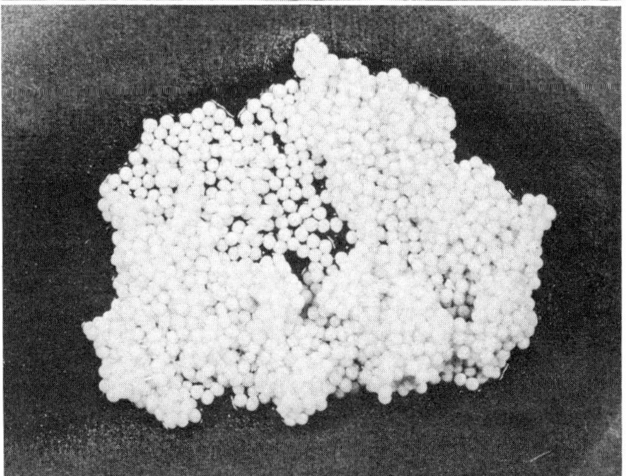
B

(ammocoetes), which stay in the nest until they are about ½ inch long (Fig. 25-2); they then burrow into the mud and sand in quiet water and emerge at night to feed on the organic ooze that is caught in mucus strings on the floor of the pharynx. The ammocoete periods last from 3 to 7 years, according to the species. During this time the ammocoetes grows and then in the fall rapidly metamorphoses into an adult. This change involves the development of larger eyes, the replacement of the hood by the oral disk with teeth, a shifting of the nostril to the top of the head, and the development of a rounder but shorter body.

Parasitic lampreys either migrate to the sea, if marine, or else remain in fresh water, where they attach themselves by their suckerlike mouth to fish and, with their sharp horny teeth, rasp away the flesh and suck out the blood (Fig. 25-3). To promote the flow of blood, the lamprey injects an anticoagulant into the wound. When gorged, the lamprey releases its hold but leaves the fish with a large gaping wound that may prove fatal. The parasitic freshwater adults live a year or more before spawning and then die; the marine forms may live longer.

The nonparasitic lampreys do not feed after emerging as adults, for their alimentary canal degenerates to a nonfunctional strand of tissue. Within a few months they also spawn and die.

The invasion in recent years of the upper Great Lakes by the sea lamprey has posed a great economic problem to the fisheries of that region. It has been estimated that about nine tenths of the lake trout and whitefish have been destroyed by the depredations of this parasite. Control methods of trapping and preventing the lampreys from spawning have been only partially successful.

Distinctive characteristics of adult lamprey

The anatomy of different species of lampreys varies somewhat, especially between parasitic and nonpara-

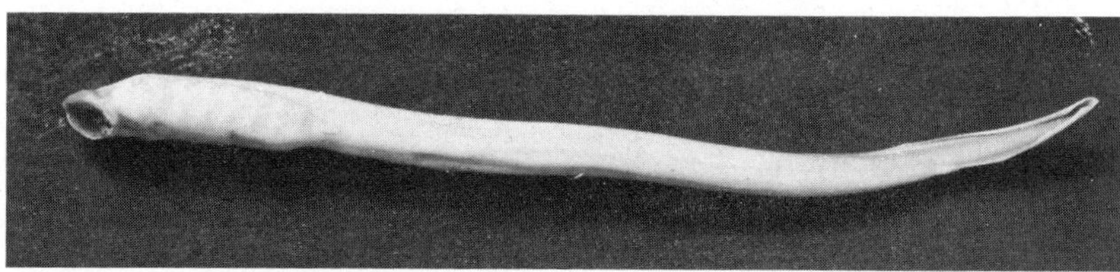

FIG. 25-2

Ammocoetes, larval form of lamprey. This one is about 2 inches long and has undergone its metamorphosis in bottom sand of stream. Compare with earlier stage in Fig. 24-23.

FIG. 25-3

Whitefish with sea lamprey *Petromyzon marinus* attached. When lamprey attaches itself with its sucking mouth, it proceeds to rasp off small bits of flesh with its chitinous teeth. Lamprey then injects an anticoagulant and sucks blood of host fish. Such wounds often prove fatal to fish, especially if point of attachment is in abdominal region of body. In many Great Lakes regions commercial fishing has been reduced annually from many millions of pounds to just a few thousand pounds. Many devices have been used to control lampreys, such as poison and electrical barriers, but none have been wholly effective. (U. S. Fish and Wildlife Service.)

sitic members, but in general they all have the same basic plan. Their skin is smooth and slimy, with many unicellular glands. There are no scales. They have no jaws or paired fins but do have median fins, with fin rays on the posterior dorsal region and tail. The mouth or buccal disk is suckerlike and, together with the muscular protrusible tongue, is provided with horny, epidermal teeth (degenerate in nonparasitic forms). The tongue creates suction by acting like a plunger. The primitive skeleton is cartilaginous, with a persistent notochord. No vertebral centra are formed.

The seven pairs of gills are not connected directly with the pharynx but are found in spherical pouches, which open into a respiratory chamber and to the outside through tubes (Fig. 25-4). The opening into the respiratory chamber is controlled by a flap, or velum. When the animal is attached, water for respiration passes into as well as out of the gill slits. The single nasal opening is on top of the head and opens internally into the olfactory sac, which connects with the cavity of the pituitary.

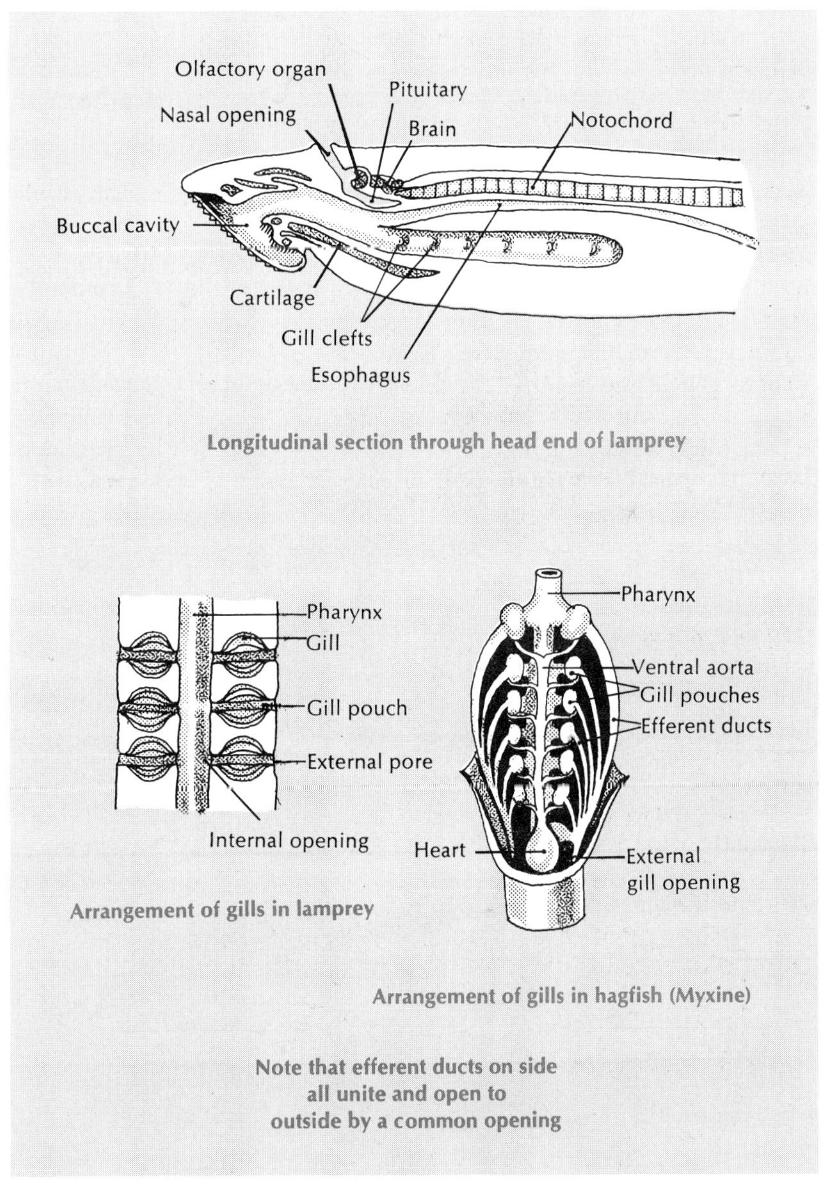

FIG. 25-4

Some structural features of cyclostomes. (Partly redrawn from Atwood: A concise comparative anatomy, The C. V. Mosby Co.)

The simple digestive system (degenerate in nonparasitic lampreys) consists of an esophagus and an intestine, which has a spiral longitudinal fold (typhlosole) or spiral valve. A liver and a gallbladder (in some) are present. No spleen or pancreas (as a definite gland) is found. The compact paired kidneys (mesonephroic divisions of the archinephroi) open by ureters into a urogenital papilla. The circulatory system is similar to that of the ammocoete larva. No renal portal system is present. Among its sense organs is a lateral line system. The sexes are separate, and the single gonad with no duct discharges its gametes through the urogenital sinus.

ORDER MYXINOIDEA (HYPEROTRETI)—hagfish and slime eels

The members of this order are often called "borers" because of their habit of burrowing into fish for flesh consumption. They are really internal parasites. They are all marine and spawn on the ocean floor. Some may reach a length of 36 inches. The hagfish *(Myxine)* on the Atlantic coast and the hagfish *(Polistotrema)* on the Pacific coast are the most common species in North America. Other species are found off the coasts of Japan, Africa, and South America.

They differ from lampreys in several ways (Fig. 25-5). The dorsal fin is not divided and may be absent. Their nostril near the front of the head opens into a canal, which runs into the roof of the pharynx. Their eyes are vestigial. They have no buccal funnel but have a suctorial mouth, with one large epidermal tooth. Around the mouth and nostril are six tentacles. Their gills (six to fourteen pairs) are located far behind the head region and their efferent ducts join into a common external opening on each side. Their brain is poorly developed, and the dorsal and ventral roots of spinal nerves are united. A single semicircular canal is found in the ear.

The yolk-filled egg may be nearly 1 inch in diameter and is enclosed in a horny shell. There is no larval stage and growth is direct. They are hermaphroditic but can produce only one kind of gamete at a time; a single individual may produce sperm at one season and eggs the next, or vice versa.

• • •

The evolutionary studies of the cyclostomes have been discussed under ammocoete larva as a chordate archetype, p. 441.

Lampreys and hagfish are probably not closely related according to protein differences in their blood (C. Manwell). Because of the similarities between the hemoglobin of lampreys and that of higher vertebrates, the lamprey is considered to be nearer the vertebrate ancestral line, whereas the hagfish evolved into a side branch, with no close affinities to other groups.

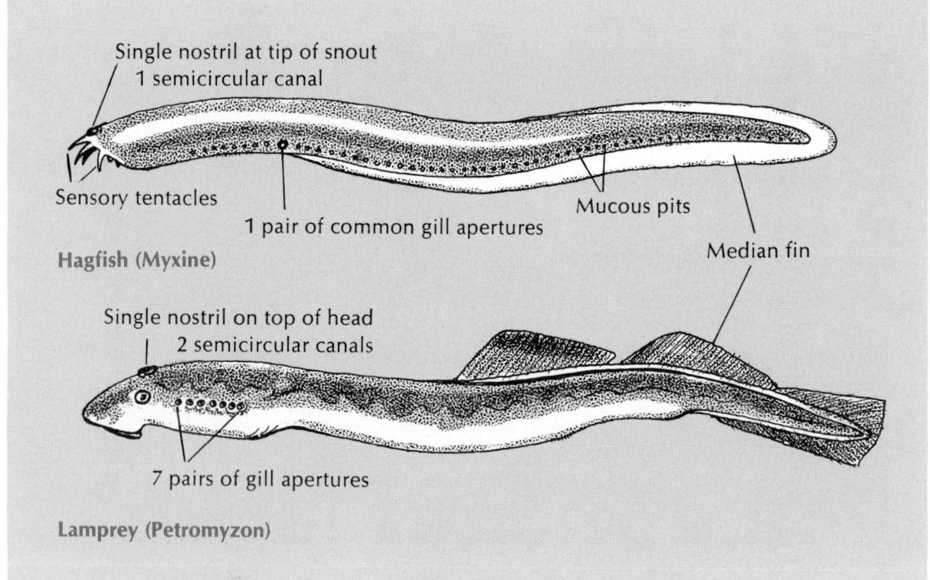

FIG. 25-5

Comparison of hagfish and lamprey (class Cyclostomata). Mucous pits indicate enormous amount of mucin produced by hagfish.

Class Chondrichthyes includes the sharks, rays, and chimaeras. They have many resemblances to the true fish, but they also have many differences. The group is a very ancient one and has left many fossil forms. One of their distinctive features is their cartilaginous skeleton, which must be considered degenerate instead of primitive. Although there is some calcification here and there, bone is entirely absent throughout the class. Sharks are extensively studied in nearly all vertebrate anatomy classes, for their basic structural plan is also the pattern found in the embryos of higher forms. This early blueprint of vertebrate structure is modified in forms above sharks into plans characteristic of each particular group.

Characteristics

1. **Body fusiform** or **spindle shaped,** with a **heterocercal** caudal fin (Fig. 25-18); paired pectoral and pelvic fins, two dorsal median fins; pelvic fins in male modified for "**claspers**"; fin rays present
2. **Mouth ventral; two olfactory sacs which do not break into the mouth cavity;** jaws present
3. Skin with **placoid** scales (Fig. 30-5) and **mucous glands;** teeth modified placoid scales
4. **Endoskeleton entirely cartilaginous;** notochord persistent; vertebrae complete and separate; appendicular, girdle, and visceral skeleton's present
5. Digestive system with a J-shaped stomach and intestine with a spiral valve; liver, gallbladder, and pancreas present
6. Circulatory system of several pairs of aortic arches; dorsal and ventral aorta, capillary and venous systems, hepatic portal and renal portal systems; two-chambered heart
7. Respiration by means of five to seven pairs of gills with separate and exposed gill slits; **no operculum**
8. No **swim bladder**
9. Brain of two olfactory lobes, two cerebral hemispheres, two optic lobes, a cerebellum, and a medulla oblongata; ten pairs of cranial nerves
10. Sexes separate; gonads paired; reproductive ducts open into cloaca; oviparous or ovoviviparous; direct development; fertilization internal
11. Kidneys of opisthonephros type

*Kon-drik'thy-es (Gr. *chondros,* cartilage, + *ichthys,* fish).

Classification

Streamlined form with heterocercal tail; cartilaginous skeleton; leathery skin with placoid scales (dermal denticles); restricted notochord; mouth and two nostrils ventral; jaws and paired appendages; males with claspers; eggs with large yolks.

Subclass Elasmobranchii (e-las'mo-bran"che-i) (Gr. *elasmos,* plate, + *branchia,* gills). Gills in separate clefts along pharynx; a spiracle behind and above each jaw; cloaca present.

Order Selachii (se-la'ke-i) (Gr. *selachos,* fish having cartilage instead of bones)—**modern sharks.** Body spindle shaped; five to seven pairs of lateral gills not covered by operculum; pectoral fins not enlarged. Example: *Squalus (Acanthias).*

Order Batoidei (ba-toi'de-i) (Gr. *batos,* a kind of ray, + *oid,* like)—**skates and rays.** Body spread out; pectoral fins enlarged and attached to head and body; five pairs of gill slits on ventral side; spiracles large. Examples: *Raja* (common skate), *Dasyatis* (stingray).

Subclass Holocephali (hol'o-cef"a-li) (Gr. *holos,* entire, + *kephale,* head)—**chimaeras or ghostfish.** Gill slits covered with operculum; aberrant shape; jaws with tooth plates; single nasal opening; without scales; accessory clasping organs in male; lateral line an open groove. Example: *Chimaera.*

With the exception of the whale, sharks are the largest living vertebrates. The larger sharks may reach 40 to 50 feet in length. The dogfish sharks so widely used in zoological laboratories rarely exceed 3 feet. Sharks are noted for being voracious, and some of them have attained great notoriety in this respect. The man-eater *Carcharodon,* which often reaches a length of 30 feet, will not hesitate to attack a human being when the opportunity offers. Another shark, *Sphyrna,* known as the hammerhead, has a head in the form of a transverse projection with an eye at each end.

Distinctive characteristics

The body of a shark such as a dogfish shark (Fig. 25-6) is fusiform or spindle shaped. In front of the ventral mouth is a pointed **rostrum;** at the posterior end the vertebral column turns up to form the **heterocercal** tail. The fins consist of the paired **pectoral** and **pelvic** fins supported by appendicular skeletons, two median **dorsal** fins (each with a spine in *Squalus*), and a median **caudal** fin. A median **anal** fin is present in the smooth dogfish *(Mustelus).* In the male the medial part of the pelvic fin is modified to form a **clasper,** which is used in copulation. The paired **nostrils** (blind pouches) are ventral and anterior to the mouth. The lateral eyes are lidless, and behind each eye is a spiracle (remnant of the first gill slit). Five gill slits are found anterior to each pectoral fin. The leathery skin is covered with placoid scales (dermal denticles), each of which consist of a wide basal plate of dermal dentin and a spine covered with vitrodentin, or a shiny enamel-like dentin. These scales are modified to form teeth in the mouth and are the remnants of the dermal plates of placoderms. A lateral line sensory system is made up of canals that extend along the side of the trunk and tail and over the head region.

Internally the cartilaginous skeleton is made up of a **chondrocranium,** which houses the brain and auditory organs and partially surrounds the eyes and olfactory organs; a vertebral column; a visceral skeleton; and an appendicular skeleton (Fig. 25-7). The jaws are suspended from the chondrocranium by ligaments and cartilages. Both the upper and the lower jaws are provided with many sharp, triangular teeth which, when lost, are replaced by other rows of teeth. Teeth serve to grasp the prey, which is usually swallowed whole. The muscles are segmentally arranged and are especially useful in the undulations of swimming.

The mouth cavity opens into the large **pharynx,** which contains openings to the separate gill slits and spiracles. A short, wide esophagus runs to the J-shaped stomach. A **liver** and **pancreas** open into the short, straight **intestine,** which contains the unique **spiral**

FIG. 25-6

Dogfish shark.

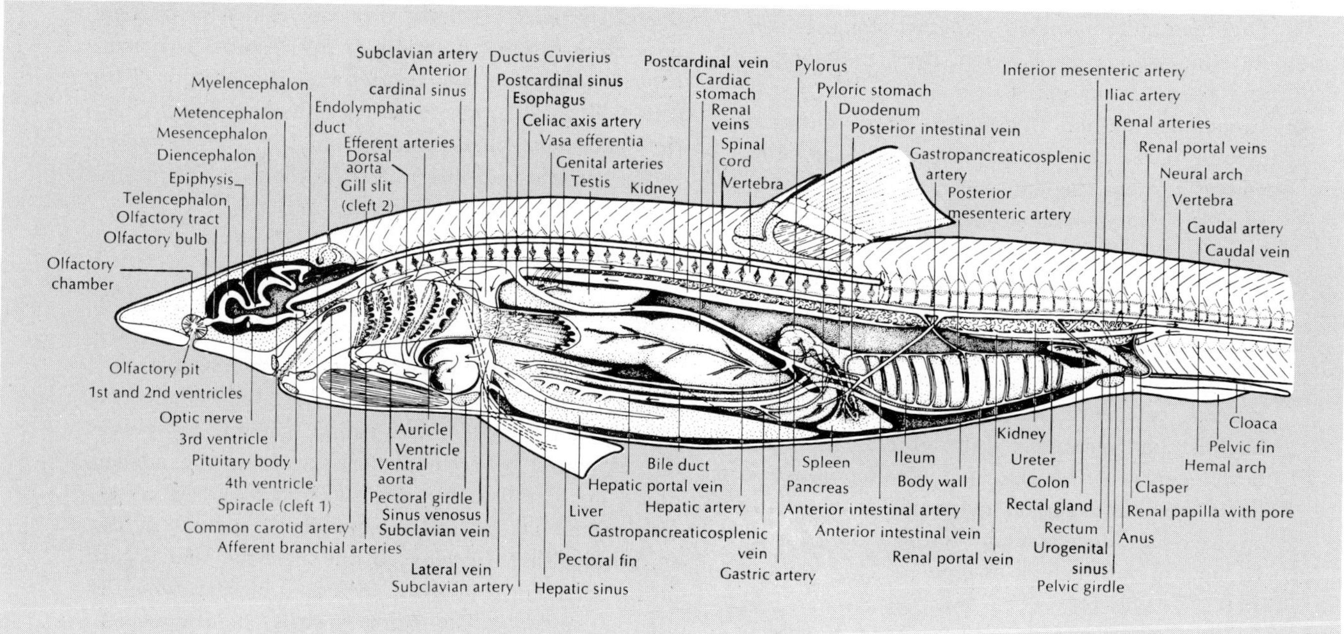

FIG. 25-7

Dogfish shark *Squalus acanthias*. Longitudinal section. (From Wodsedalek: General zoology laboratory guide, Wm. C. Brown Co.)

valve that delays the passage of food and increases the absorptive surface. Attached to the short rectum is the **rectal gland,** which is now known to secrete salt and regulate the ion balance of the shark's body (J. W. Burger and W. N. Hess). The chambers of the **heart** are arranged in tandem formation, and the circulatory system is basically the same as that of the embryonic vertebrate and of the ammocoetes.

The opisthonephroi, or **kidneys,** are two long, slender organs above the coelom and are drained by the **wolffian ducts,** which open into a single urogenital sinus at the **cloaca.** The wolffian ducts also carry the sperm from the testes of the male, which uses a clasper to deposit the sperm in the female oviduct. The müllerian duct, or oviduct (paired), carries the eggs from the **ovary** and coelom and is modified into a **uterus** in which a primitive placenta may attach the embryo shark until it is born. Such a relationship is actually **viviparous reproduction;** others simply retain the developing egg in the uterus without attachment to the mother's wall (**ovoviviparous reproduction**). Some sharks and rays deposit their fertilized eggs in a horny capsule called the "mermaid's purse" (Fig. 25-8), which is attached by tendrils to seaweed. Later the young shark emerges from this "cradle."

The nervous system is more advanced than that of ammocoete larva and is developed directly from the dorsal nerve cord of the embryo. The brain is typically made up of the three basic parts of the vertebrate brain—forebrain, midbrain, and hindbrain. These three parts form five subdivisions or regions—telencephalon, diencephalon, mesencephalon, metencephalon, and myelencephalon—each with certain functions. There are ten pairs of cranial nerves that are distributed largely to the head regions. Surrounding the spinal cord are the neural arches of the vertebrae. Along the spinal cord a pair of spinal nerves, with united dorsal and ventral roots, is distributed to each body segment.

FIG. 25-8
"Mermaid's purse."

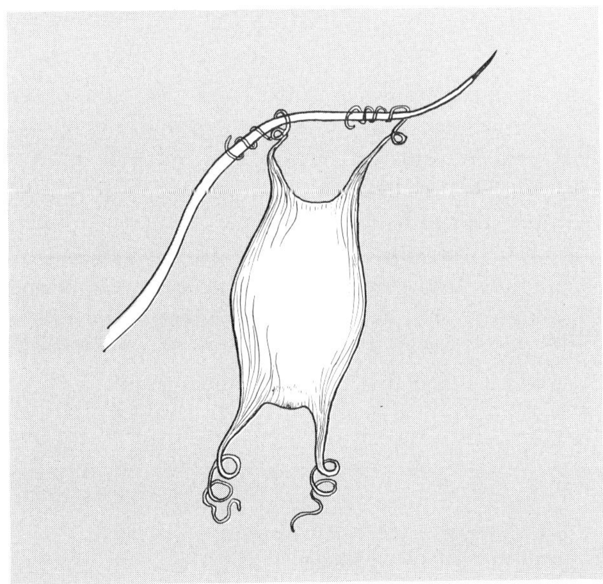

Members of the order Batoidei (skates and rays) (Figs. 25-9 and 25-10) are specialized for bottom dwelling. In these the pectoral fins are greatly enlarged and are used like wings in swimming. The gill openings are on the underside of the head, and the spiracles are unusually large. Water for breathing is taken in through these spiracles to prevent clogging the gills, for their mouth is often buried in sand. Their teeth are adapted for crushing their prey, which consists mainly of mollusks, crustaceans, and an occasional small fish. Two members of this group are of especial interest—the stingrays (Fig. 25-10) and the electric rays. In the stingrays the caudal and dorsal fins have disappeared and the tail is slender and whiplike. The tail is armed with one or more saw-edged spines, which can inflict very dangerous wounds. Such wounds may heal slowly and leave complications. Electric rays have smooth, naked skins and have certain dorsal muscles modified into powerful electric organs, which can give severe shocks and stun their prey. Stingrays also have electric organs in the tail.

Sharks have considerable economic importance. Most are highly destructive to fish, lobsters, and crabs. In some localities sharks are used as food by man. Commercially shark-liver oil is extracted and used in medicine as a source of vitamins A and D, and sharkskin leather is made into many useful articles.

CLASS OSTEICHTHYES*—bony fish

The bony fish include many species and are most familiar of all the fishlike animals. Their skeletons are, at least in part, bony, and most are covered by dermal scales. The skull and pectoral girdles are covered by investing bony plates in the dermal skin. The bony fish

*Os'te-ik"thy-es (Gr. *osteon*, bone, + *ichthys*, a fish).

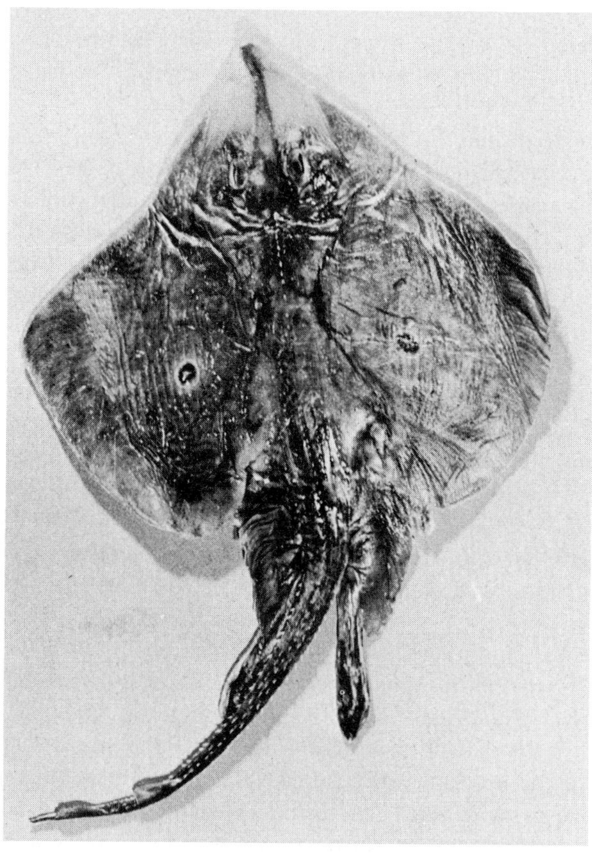

FIG. 25-9

Common skate *Raja*. Order Batoidei. Note in this male large leglike claspers of pelvic fins for internal fertilization of eggs in female.

FIG. 25-10

Stingray swimming by flapping pectoral fins. Tail is slender, whiplike, and provided with one or more dangerous spines, which may inflict blood-poisoning wound. (Courtesy C. P. Hickman, Jr.)

are also characterized by having the gills covered by opercular folds, which are provided with bony supports. This extensive group is found in a great variety of aquatic habitats. One fifth are strictly freshwater dwellers, whereas others divide their time between the two kinds of aquatic habitats, but most species are marine.

Bony fish have been the most successful of all aquatic forms. Their 30,000 species indicate that they are the most numerous of all vertebrates, at least in number of species and probably also in number of individuals. Although some groups of fish have flourished and declined in the past, the class as a whole (especially the Teleostei) has reached at the present time a degree of success never attained in the past.

From whence came the bony fish? There are two great subclasses of existing fish—the Actinopterygii and the Choanichthyes. When first detected in the fossil record of the middle Devonian freshwater deposits, they were both well-defined groups. Their common ancestor is unknown. Two of their most characteristic features were their bony skeletons and their air or lung sacs. In most of the bony fish the lung is modified into the hydrostatic organ: the air or swim bladder. Some aspects of their organization pattern show a resemblance to that found in certain placoderms (acanthoderms), and some authorities think that the early bony fish ancestor had a close affinity to the ancestor of the placoderms.

Characteristics

1. **Skeleton more or less bony,** which represents the primitive skeleton; vertebrae numerous; notocord may persist in part; **tail usually homocercal**
2. Skin with mucous glands and with embedded dermal scales of three types: **ganoid, cycloid,** or **ctenoid;** some without scales; no placoid scales
3. Fins both median and paired, with **fin rays of cartilage or bone**
4. **Mouth terminal** with many teeth (some toothless); jaws present; olfactory sacs paired and may or may not open into mouth
5. Respiration by gills supported by bony gill arches and covered by a **common operculum**

6. **Swim bladder** often present with or without duct connected to pharynx
7. Circulation consisting of a two-chambered heart, arterial and venous systems, and four pairs of aortic arches; blood of nucleated red cells
8. Nervous system of a brain with small olfactory lobes and cerebrum and large optic lobes and cerebellum; ten pairs of cranial nerves
9. Sexes separate; gonads paired; fertilization usually external; larval forms may differ greatly from adults

Fish vary greatly in size. Some of the minnows are less than 1 inch long; other forms may exceed 10 feet in length. The swordfish is one of the largest and may attain a length of 12 to 14 feet. Most fish, however, are around 1 to 3 feet.

Classification

Body primitively fusiform, but variously modified in many; body divided into three regions—head, trunk, and tail; skeleton mostly bony; mouth usually terminal; skin usually with embedded dermal scales; paired and lateral fins supported by dermal fin rays usually present; gills on bony gill arches in a common chamber on each side of pharynx and covered by an operculum.

Subclass Actinopterygii (ak'ti-nop'te-ryj'e-i) (Gr. *aktino,* ray, + *pterygion,* fin or small wing)—**ray-finned fish.** Paired fins supported by dermal rays and without basal lobed portions; one dorsal fin (may be divided); nasal sacs open only to outside.

Superorder Chondrostei (kon-dros'te-i) (Gr. *chondros,* cartilage, + *osteon,* bone)—**primitive ray-finned fish.**

Order Acipenseroidei (as'i-pen'ser-oi"de-i) (L. *acipenser,* sturgeon, + Gr. *oid,* like). Ossified dermal skull and unossified chondral skull; endoskeleton mostly of cartilage; body mostly scaleless except for rows of bony (ganoid) scutes; snout and barbels; mouth on underside of head; no teeth in adult; dorsal swim bladder may be present; tail heterocercal; notochord slightly constricted by vertebrae; spiral valve. Examples: *Acipenser* (common sturgeon, Fig. 25-11), *Polyodon* (paddlefish).

Order Polypterini (pol'ip-ter"i-ni) (Gr. *poly,* many, + *pteros,* winged, + *inus,* like). Ossified skeleton; dorsal fin divided into eight or more finlets; body slender with thick ganoid scales; lobed pectoral fins; caudal fin diphycercal; ventral air bladder of two lobes and opens into pharynx by a common duct. Example: *Polypterus* (bichir).

Superorder Holostei (ho-los'te-i) (Gr. *holos,* entire, + *osteon,* bone)—**intermediate ray-finned fish.**

Order Protospondyli (pro'to-spon"dy-li) (Gr. *protos,* first, + *spondylos,* vertebra). Body covered with overlapping cycloid scales; dorsal fin long and low; modified heterocercal tail; chondrocranium partly ossified and not closely integrated with the bony dermal skull; bilobed swim bladder may serve for respiration. Example: *Amia* (bowfin).

FIG. 25-11

White sturgeon *Acipenser.* These grow to large size and ascend rivers to spawn. Superorder Chondrostei.

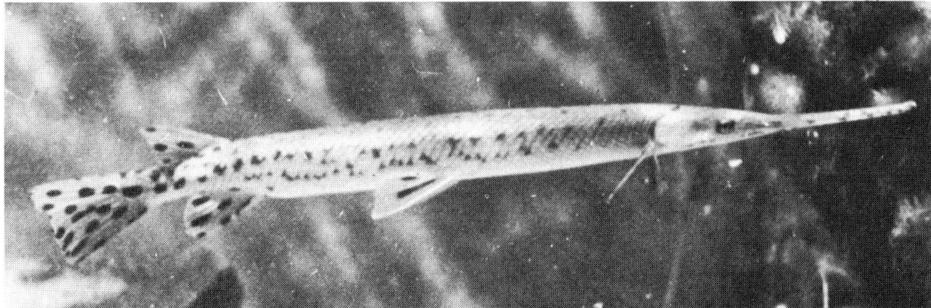

FIG. 25-12

Long-nosed garpike *Lepidosteus.* Extremely voracious, feeds on fish, and is commercially unimportant. Superorder Holostei.

Order Ginglymodi (jing'li-mo"di) (Gr. *ginglymos,* hinge joint). Body slender and cylindric and covered with thick, ganoid scales; long jaws armed with teeth; swim bladder may serve for respiration; small dorsal and anal fins. Example: *Lepidosteus* (garpike, Fig. 25-12).

Superorder Teleostei (tel'e-os"te-i) (Gr. *teleos,* complete, + *osteon,* bone)—**climax bony fish.** Body covered with thin scales without bony layer (cycloid or ctenoid) or scaleless; dermal and chondral parts of skull closely united; caudal fin mostly homocercal; mouth terminal; notochord a mere vestige; swim bladder mainly a hydrostatic organ and usually not opened to the esophagus; endoskeleton mostly bony; more than 30 different orders and some 350 families recognized. These orders may be placed in two basic groups: Isospondyli, or soft-rayed fish, and Acanthopterygii, or spiny-rayed fish. Five clear-cut and distinctive major groups (orders) are recognized in this scheme (Figs. 25-13 to 25-16).

Order Isospondyli (i'so-spon"dy-li) (Gr. *isos,* equal, + *spondylos,* vertebra). Fins with soft dermal rays; pelvic fins in posterior abdominal position; open duct to air bladder; most primitive teleosts. Examples: *Clupea* (herring), *Oncorhynchus* (Pacific salmon), *Salmo* (Atlantic salmon), *Sarinops* (Pacific sardine).

FIG. 25-13

C-O sole *Pleuronichthys.* Common name derived from markings on tail. It is a bottom-dwelling flatfish; protruding eyes can see while rest of body is buried in sand. Superorder Teleostei. (Courtesy C. P. Hickman, Jr.)

FIG. 25-14

Yellow perch *Perca flavescens.* This fish is of commercial importance and may attain length of more than 14 inches. It has been introduced into many states where it is not native. Superorder Teleostei. (Courtesy C. P. Hickman, Jr.)

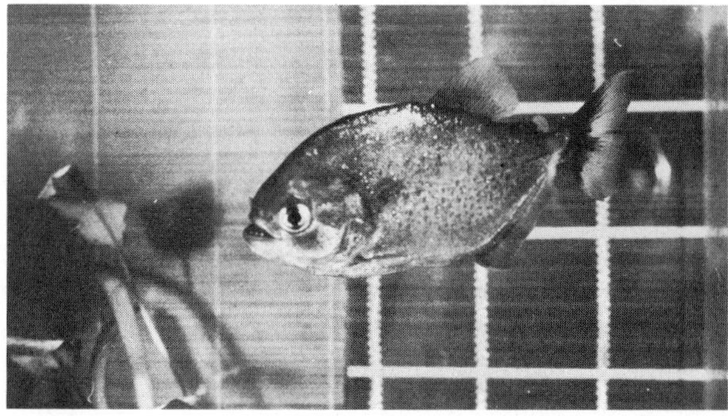

FIG. 25-15

Piranha, or piraña, fish *Serrasalmo* is noted for attacking living animals, but accounts of its ferocity are probably exaggerated. It operates in packs and is native of South American rivers. Superorder Teleostei. (Courtesy C. P. Hickman, Jr.)

FIG. 25-16

Starry flounder *Platichthys.* In common with other flatfish, this one has both eyes on same side of head. Note twisted, distorted mouth. Flounders have remarkable powers to change colors in imitation of their background. Superorder Teleostei. (Courtesy C. P. Hickman, Jr.)

Order Apodes (ap'o-des) (Gr. *apodos,* footless). Body long and slender; fins with soft rays; scales vestigial or absent; pelvic fins usually absent; air bladder with duct. Example: *Anguilla* (freshwater eel).

Order Mesichthyes (me-sik'thy-es) (Gr. *mesos,* middle, + *ichthys,* fish). Intermediate teleosts; fins with soft rays; pelvic fins abdominal; jaws with many teeth; air bladder with open duct. Example: *Esox* (common pike).

Order Ostariophysi (os-ta'ri-o-fy"si) (Gr. *ostarion,* dim. of *osteon,* bone, + *physa,* bladder). Fins with some rays spiny; chain of little bones (ossicles) connecting air bladder with internal ear (weberian organ); body covered with cycloid scales or bony plates or naked; barbels (in some). Examples: *Catostomus* (sucker), *Cyprinus* (common carp), *Ictalurus* (channel catfish), *Electrophorus* (electric eel).

Order Acanthopterygii (ak'an-thop'te-ryj"e-i) (NL., fr. *acantho,* spine or thorn, + Gr. *pterygion,* fin or small wing). Teleosts with spiny rays on dorsal, anal, and paired fins; maxilla short; air bladder without duct; pelvic fins forward beneath thoracic region or head; scales mostly ctenoid. Examples: *Perca* (perch), *Gadus* (codfish), *Hippocampus* (sea horse, Fig. 25-17), *Pomoxis* (crappie), *Symphurus* (sole), majority of teleosts.

FIG. 25-17

Sea horse *Hippocampus.* Male is provided with brood pouch for sheltering eggs. Superorder Teleostei.

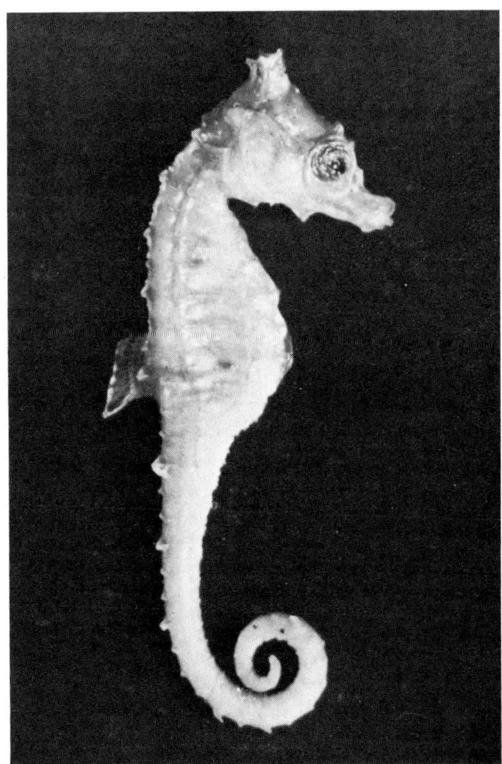

Subclass Choanichthyes (ko'a-nik"thy es) (Gr. *choane,* funnel or nostril, + *ichthys,* fish)—**lobe-finned or air-breathing fish.** Body primitively fusiform, but slender to thick in existing forms; diphycercal tail; nostrils connected to mouth cavity; paired fins lobed or axial; two dorsal fins; primitive cosmoid scale modified to thin cycloid type.

Order Crossopterygii (cros-sop'te-ryg"i-i) (Gr. *krossoi,* fringe or tassels, + *pterygion,* fin or small wing)—**lobed-finned fish.** Heavy bodied; paired fins lobed with internal skeleton of basic tetrapod type; premaxillae, maxillae present; scales large with tubercles and heavily overlapped; three-lobed diphycercal tail; skeleton with much cartilage; bony spines hollow; air bladder vestigial; gills hard with teeth; intestine with spiral valve; spiracle present.

Suborder Coelacanthini (se'la-kan"thi-ni) (NL., fr. Gr. *koilos,* hollow, + *akantha,* thorn or spine, + *inus,* like) (**Actinista**). Examples: *Latimeria, Malania.*

Order Dipnoi (dip'noi) (Gr. *di,* two, + *pnoe,* breath)—**lungfish.** All median fins fused to form diphycercal tail; fins lobed or of filaments; scales of cycloid bony type; teeth of grinding plates; no premaxillae or maxillae; air bladder of single or paired lobes and specialized for breathing; intestine with spiral valve; spiracle absent. Examples: *Epiceratodus, Protopterus, Lepidosiren.*

Evolutionary patterns of bony fish

No group of vertebrate animals has surpassed the bony fish in evolutionary diversity. Nowhere else do we see better examples of adaptive radiation where, from certain generalized types, species have evolved whose adaptations fit them for nearly every kind of aquatic ecologic niche. Their many varieties of body form and size may be correlated with particular aquatic habitats. Some have fusiform or streamlined bodies for reducing friction and other adaptations for rapid swimming. Predaceous fish not only have trim, elongated bodies but also powerful tail fins and other mechanical advantages for swift pursuit. Sluggish bottom-feeding forms have flattened bodies for movement and concealment on the ocean floor. Many have striking protective coloration. Some are fitted for deep-sea existence. Scores of other types, even more striking, could be mentioned. Any particular type of teleost fish will reveal an amazing array of specialized structures for food getting, for offense and defense, for reproduction, and for other purposes.

The fossil record reveals that the actinopterygian bony fish, which were found in the freshwater deposits of the middle Devonian period, were small with large eyes and extended mouths. Their tails were **heterocercal** (Fig. 25-18). They had a single dorsal fin and a single anal fin; paired fins were represented by the anterior pectoral fins and the posterior pelvic fins. Their skeletons were largely bone. Their trunks and tails were encased in an armor of heavy, rhombic scales (**ganoid**) (Fig. 25-27). Most of these early fish had functional lungs, but these were used chiefly as swim bladders (hydrostatic organs). All had gills (five pairs or less) and spiracles. These early actinopterygians belong to the order Palaeoniscoidea (now extinct). One common genus of this order was *Cheirolopis,* a generalized type that had some resemblance to certain acanthodians (placoderms). From such an ancestor the actinopterygians have evolved. In their evolution they passed successively through the stages represented by the superorders Chondrostei, Holostei, and Teleostei. Certain evolutionary trends are evident in this succession. The first two superorders, represented today by only a few forms, flourished in the early development of the bony fish (Permian, Triassic, Cretaceous periods). Although the teleosts are thought to have originated in fresh water and many of the existing lower forms are freshwater forms, the major evolution of the group occurred in the sea, where the majority of species now live. The first true teleost recognized by paleontologists is *Leptolepis,* a small Triassic fish that had definite primitive and generalized characteristics, such as soft dermal fin rays, pelvic fins in the abdominal position, and air bladders with ducts. There is no satisfactory explanation for this constant replacement of one type by another. Aquatic media are fairly stable in comparison with land habitats. Bony fish do vary, but there is no reason to suspect a higher mutation rate among this group than among others. It is known that convergent or independent evolution occurs among fish. No definite statements can be made with certainty about any criteria of success as they apply to modern teleosts. But the diversity within the group is attested by the many thousands of different species.

In what ways are modern fish different from their ancient ancestors? In the first place, there has been an almost inconceivable variety of different body forms in present teleosts, as compared with the normal fusiform or spindle-shaped body of primitive fish (Fig. 25-19). This is shown in such fish as flounders, eels, flying fish, swordfish, batfish, sea horses, sargassum fish, catfish, lizard fish, headfish, moonfish, toadfish, remora, and many other specialized types. The skeleton of primitive

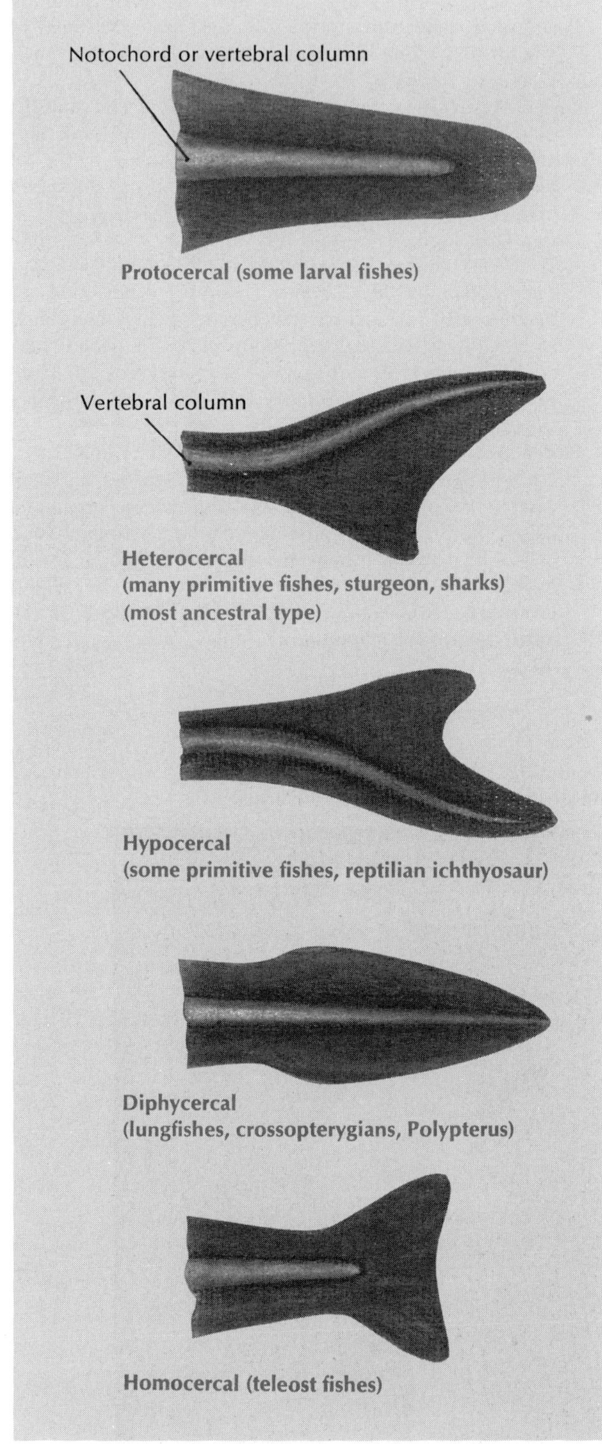

FIG. 25-18

Types of caudal fins among fish. Some functional correlations may be seen among these different types. Heterocercal tail, for example, is found in fish without swim bladder, for it tends to counteract gravity while swimming.

fish was largely ossified, but this condition regressed to a partly cartilaginous state among many of the Chondrostei and Holostei. Teleosts, however, have an internal skeleton almost completely ossified like the primitive members. The dermal investing bones of the skull (dermatocranium) and the chondrocranium (endocranium) around the brain and sense organs form a closer union among the teleosts than they did in the primitive bony fish. Other evolutionary changes among the teleosts were the movement of the pelvic fins forward to the head and thoracic region, the transformation of the lungs of primitive forms into air bladders with hydrostatic functions and without ducts, the changing of the heterocercal tail of primitive fish and of the intermediate superorders into a homocercal form, and the development of the thin cycloid and ctenoid scales from the thick ganoid type of early fish. Among other changes were the loss of the spiracles and the

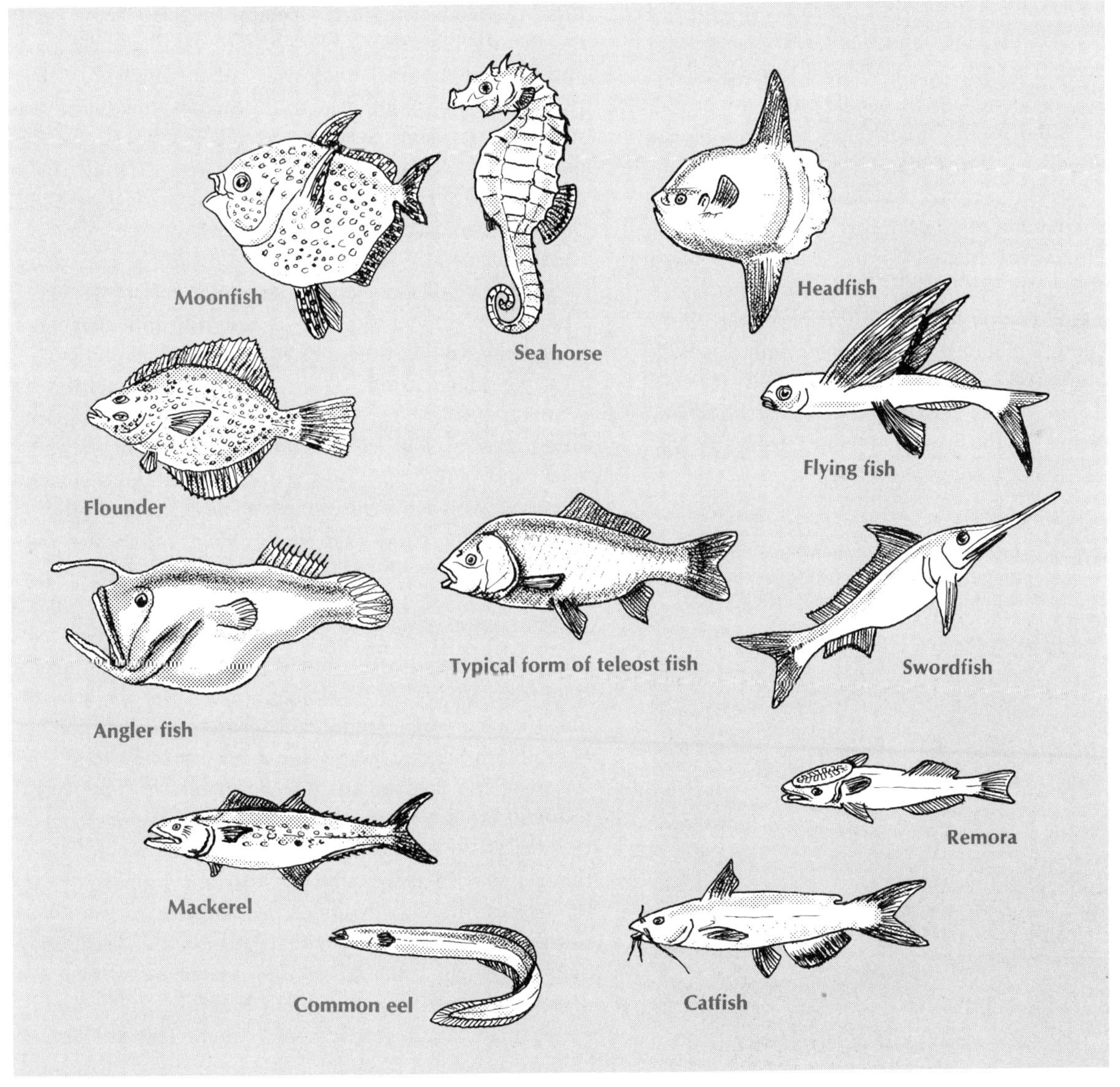

FIG. 25-19

Adaptive radiation of bony fish (teleosts). Variety of body forms have fitted them for many diverse habitats and conditions of existence. It is not always possible, however, to explain all their adaptive shapes and structures.

development of stout spines in the fins, especially in the pectoral, dorsal, and anal fins.

The other great subclass (Choanichthyes) of bony fish has had a less spectacular evolutionary development than the actinopterygians, but it is of far greater interest and importance in an evolutionary sense, for its members are close to the ancestral stock of the higher vertebrates. This subclass has nostrils that open into the mouth, swim bladders that can act as lungs, and paired **lobed fins.** The ray-finned fish are an important part of vertebrate evolution and adaptive radiation, but they are a side issue in the evolutionary line of higher vertebrates. The lobe-finned fish apparently originated and evolved in fresh water and flourished during late Paleozoic times. The subclass is divided into the Crossopterygii (fringe finned) and the Dipnoi (lungfish). They first appeared in Devonian times, and one of the common generalized forms was *Osteolepis,* a crossopterygian that has been found in Old Red Sandstone of Great Britain. Among the primitive characteristics of this ancient form were the fusiform shape, the position of the paired fins, the presence of two dorsal fins, and a heterocercal tail. The paired fins in this or similar types also bore some resemblance to a tetrapod limb, for they consisted of a basal arrangement of median or axial bones, with other bones radiating out from these median ones. Some of the proximal bones seem to correspond with the three chief bones of the tetrapod limb. The scales of these primitive fish were of the **cosmoid** types, a thick complex scale of dentinlike cosmine, enamel, and vascular pulp cavities. This type of scale is not found in modern fish but has been replaced by the bony **cycloid** type. From these and related forms the early amphibians arose.

FIG. 25-20

Lungfish *Protopterus* just removed from its mud "cocoon" in which it has lived during dry season. This fish is native to Africa. Subclass Choanichthyes, order Dipnoi. (Courtesy General Biological Supply House, Inc., Chicago.)

Osteolepis belonged to a crossopterygian group that were mainly freshwater fish. The coelacanths were marine forms that appeared in the late Devonian times and flourished during the Mesozoic era. They were derived apparently from the osteolepids but had certain characteristics of their own. Although the tail was of the **diphycercal** type, they also possessed a small lobe between the upper and lower caudal lobes, producing a three-pronged structure. Coelacanths also show some degenerate features, such as more cartilaginous parts and a swim bladder that was either calcified or else persisted as a mere vestige. Although this form was supposed to have become extinct in the Cretaceous period, several specimens of *Latimeria,* a living coelacanth, have been collected near Madagascar since 1938.

The other order (Dipnoi) (Fig. 25-20) of the subclass Choanichthyes is considered to be a specialized and aberrant offshoot of the primitive crossopterygians. They are commonly known as **lungfish** and were once considered to be the ancestors of the amphibians—a view no longer held. They have many structures in common with the crossopterygians, such as internal nares, the cycloid scale modified from the cosmoid type, and paired fins that are somewhat lobe shaped. Fossil primitive lungfish show a closer relationship to the crossopterygians than do existing forms, for they had a heterocercal tail, two dorsal fins, and a well-ossified skull—structures that have undergone considerable modification in modern lungfish. The major evolutionary trends of this ancient group, which probably originated in middle Devonian times, were specializations, such as bone reduction, change in dentition toward tooth-bearing plates for crushing hard food, the fusion of the median fins into a symmetric diphycercal tail, and the development of functional lungs not unlike those of tetrapods (Fig. 25-21). The fossil record shows the genus *Dipterus* to be the earliest lungfish. From this genus, dipnoan evolution led directly to the genus *Ceratodus,* a Triassic form that had a wide distribution over the earth. From *Ceratodus,* lungfish evolution led directly to the living Australian lungfish, *Epiceratodus,* which may attain a length of 5 feet. This lungfish is able to survive in stagnant pools by coming to the sur-

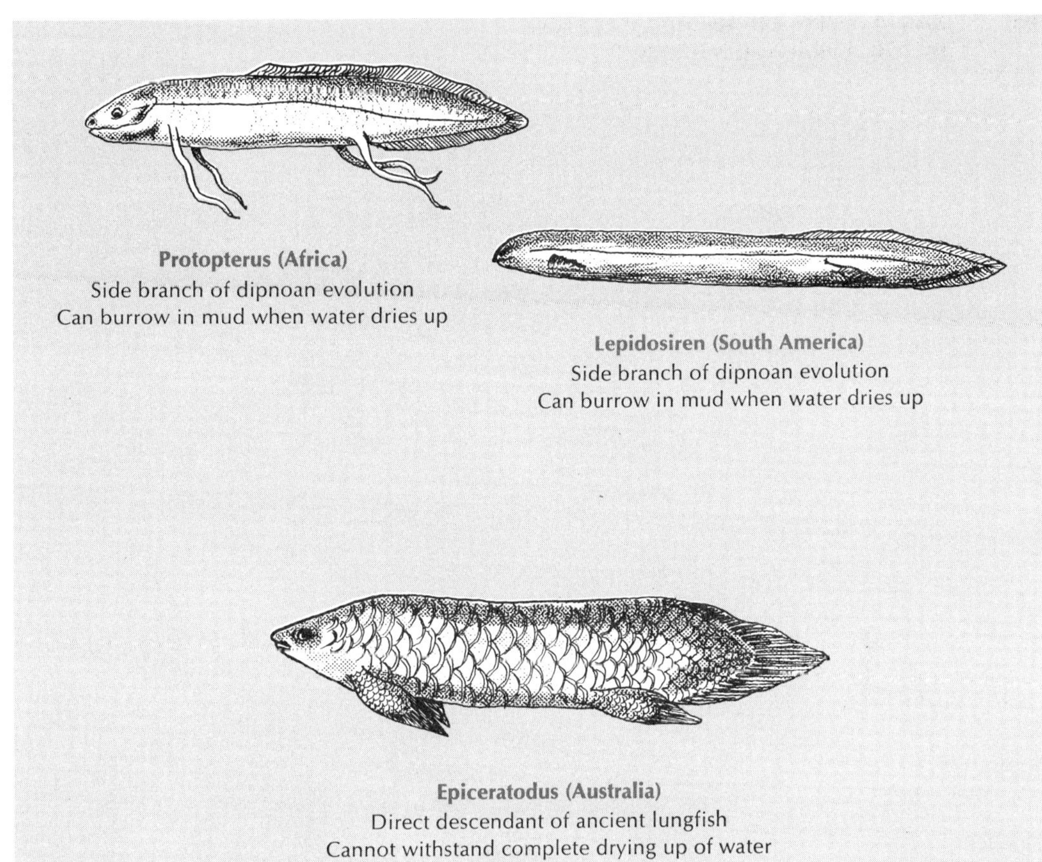

FIG. 25-21

Lungfish, order Dipnoi. In all three fish, air bladder is lunglike structure by which they can breathe air when necessity arises.

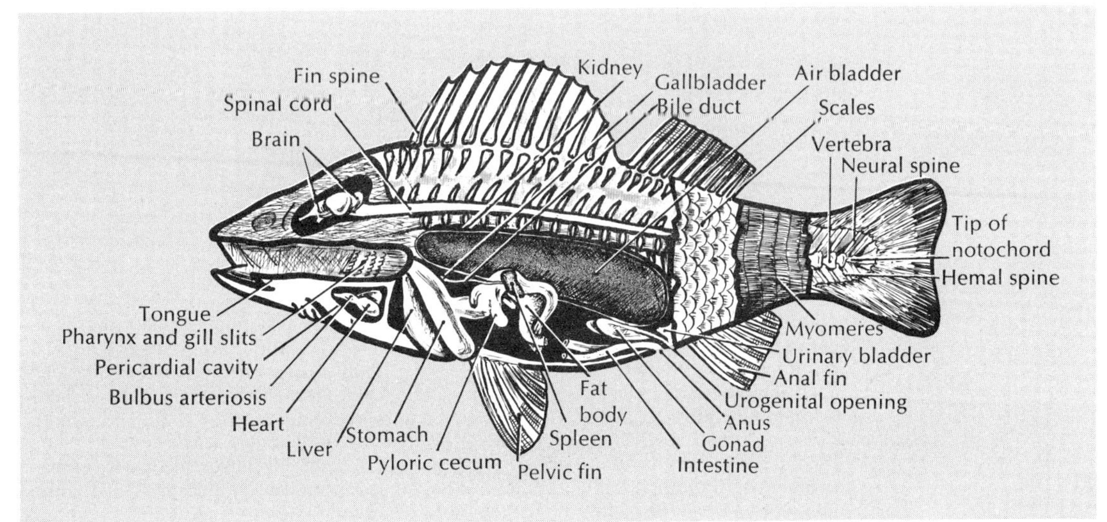

FIG. 25-22

Visceral organs of teleost fish such as yellow perch *Perca flavescens*. Part of intestine has been cut away.

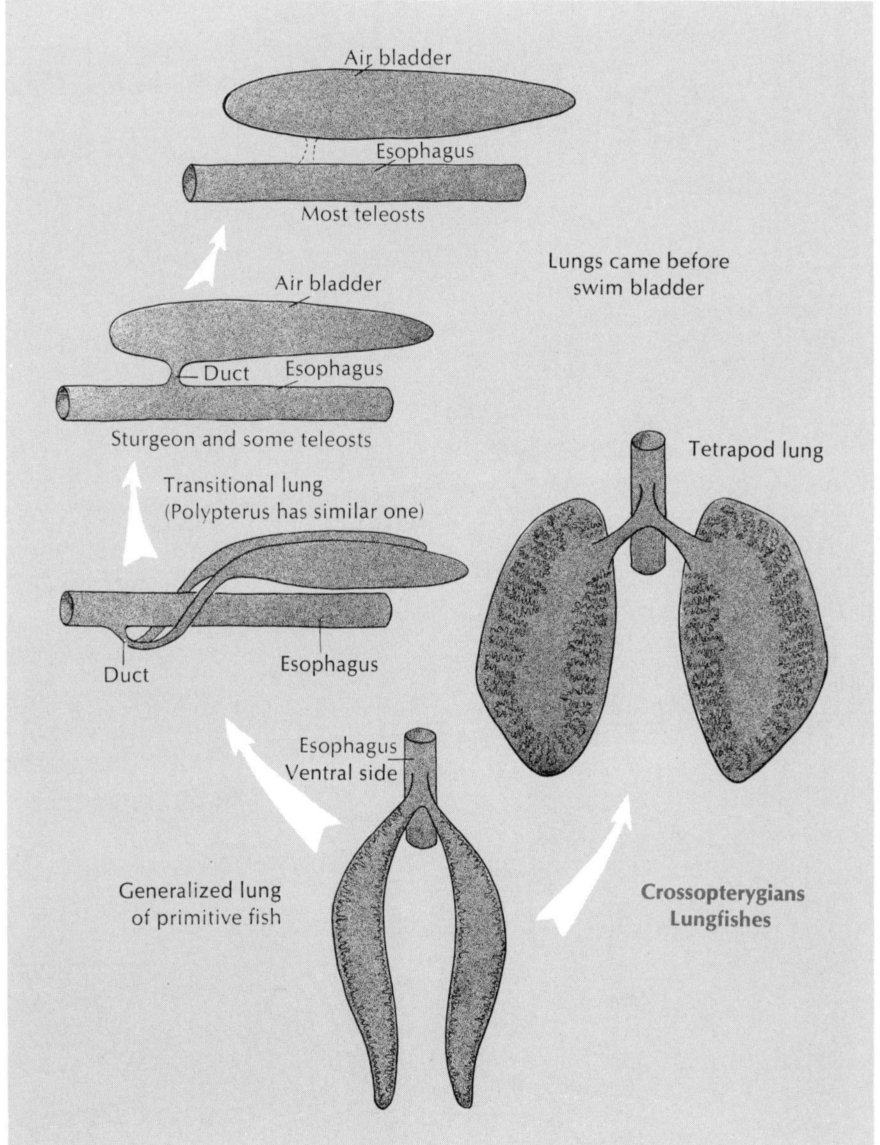

FIG. 25-23

Evolution of lungs and air bladders. Fossil records of primitive fish indicate that most of them were provided with lungs that were adapted to climatic conditions existing during early evolution of fish. Lung originated on ventral side as double sac connected to throat by single duct. Embryologically, it may have started as gill pouches. From this generalized lung condition two lines of evolution occurred. (1) One line led to swim, or air, bladder of modern teleost fish. Various transitional stages show that air bladder and its duct (which is eventually lost) have shifted to dorsal position above esophagus to become structurally a hydrostatic organ for flotation instead of for breathing. (2) Second line of evolution has led by extensive internal foldings, but no radical change in position, to tetrapod lung found in land forms.

face and gulping air into its single lung, but it cannot live out of water. The South American lungfish *Lepidosiren* and the African lungfish *Protopterus* are evolutionary side branches of the Dipnoi, and they can live out of water for long periods of time by breathing through openings connecting their mud burrows with the surface. All three types of lungfish live in habitats that alternate between wet and dry seasons.

Structural adaptations of fish

Swim bladder. The swim bladder, found in all bony fish (Fig. 25-22) except a few bottom forms (*Lophius,* etc.), is a development from the paired lungs of primitive Osteichthyes, or their ancestors the placoderms, that lived in alternate wet and dry regions where lungs were necessary for survival. The generalized condition of the lungs in these primitive forms may have been similar to the lungs found in the existing *Polypterus,* a chondrostean fish of the fresh waters of tropical Africa. The crossopterygians that gave rise to the amphibians no doubt had similar structures, although there are only vestigial lungs in *Latimeria* (Fig. 25-23). Functional lungs are also present in existing lungfish. In all other bony fish the lungs have mostly lost their original function and have become swim bladders or air bladders.

In *Amia* and *Lepidosteus* (Holostei) the bilobed swim bladder functions in breathing, but in other actinopterygians the swim bladder may serve as a hydrostatic organ, as a sense organ, or as an organ of sound production. The swim bladder, which in teleosts functions chiefly as a hydrostatic organ, can alter the specific gravity of the fish by filling itself with gas (lessening the hydrostatic pressure) or by emptying itself (increasing the hydrostatic pressure). The fish can thus float higher or sink lower in the water accordingly. In those fish in which the swim bladder is not connected to the pharynx by a duct (Physoclisti), gases (oxygen, carbon dioxide, nitrogen) are mostly secreted into the bladder by a special anterior gland, the **red gland,** with its remarkable network of blood vessels, the **rete mirabile.** A posterior **oval gland** of the swim bladder has the power to absorb these gases to lessen its size. In those fish with a swim bladder connected to the pharynx (Physostomi), the bladder may be filled by gulping air. Gas secretion and resorption are under the control of the autonomic nervous system.

The lung or swim bladder originates as a diverticulum from the ventral side of the pharynx, the position occupied by the lungs of *Polypterus, Lepidosiren, Protopterus,* and tetrapods. This position tended to make aquatic forms top heavy, and so the swim bladder shifted to the dorsal side of the pharynx in most bony fish. *Epiceratodus,* the Australian lungfish, still retains, however, the ventral duct connection to the pharynx.

Sound production in fish, which mainly involves the swim bladder, is discussed in Chapter 43.

Fins. Fins in fish are always of two kinds: (1) **paired,** which include the **pectoral** and **pelvic** fins (Fig. 25-24); and (2) **unpaired,** which consist of the **dorsal, caudal,** and **anal** fins. Paired fins have arisen several times independently or from the primordial fin fold (J. R. Nursall). Among the various species the fins vary as to location and number. Fish swim mainly by lateral movements of the tail and tail fin, while the paired fins are held closely against the side and the other unpaired fins are spread out to keep the animal in a vertical position. In their undulations they make use of alternate contractions of their segmentally arranged muscles. The body as a whole is thrown into a sinuous curve and not merely the tail (E. J. Marey). When swimming quietly they may use their paired lateral fins. The shape or form of a fish has an important bearing on its rate of locomotion. Some bodies have a more efficient "streamline" resistance than others. The mackerel family is especially well adapted for fast swimming. The only vertebrate parasite of man, the candiru of the South American catfish, has a slender body adapted for entering the sex organ orifices of man. One species (*Vandellia cirrhosa*) is especially feared for this reason because it may

FIG. 25-24

Tomcod *Microgadus* has pelvic fins anterior to pectoral fins. Many other fish have pelvic fins well forward, an adaptation that fish morphologists think prevents fish from rising in water when it stops.

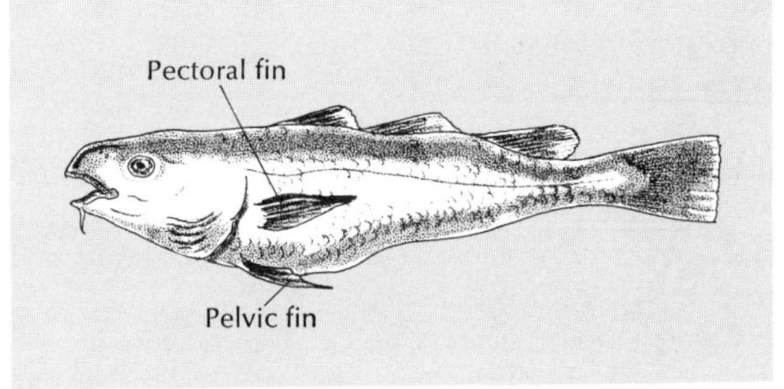

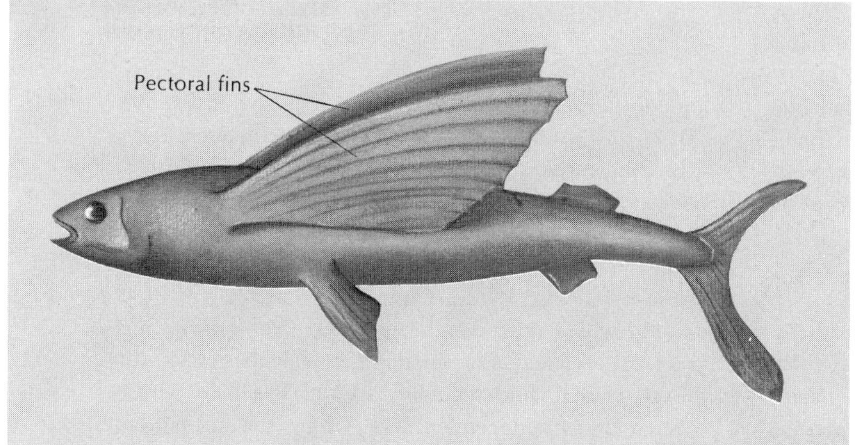

FIG. 25-25

Flying fish *Cypselurus*, example of highly structural and functional adaptation among fish. Flying fish do not fly but glide, with their modified pectoral fins held in rigid position. By vigorous side-to-side swimming movements of their tails, they taxi for several feet on surface and gain sufficient momentum for their takeoff. Their flight usually lasts only a few seconds and distance of their glide varies from a few feet to several hundred feet.

FIG. 25-26

Climbing perch *Anabas* can move along ground and climb low trees by means of paired fins, spines on gill covers, and anal fin. It has special air-breathing chamber, or labyrinthic organ, above gills. Superorder Teleostei.
(Courtesy C. P. Hickman, Jr.)

mistake the flow of urine during micturition for the respiratory current of water from fish gill cavities in which it normally lives.

The flying fish use their large and extended pectoral fins for gliding (Fig. 25-25), and the climbing perch of India (Fig. 25-26) use their gill cover and anal spines for ascending the branches of shrubs and trees found in their habitats.

Kidneys and osmoregulation. The kidney in fish is called an **opisthonephros** because it is the spatial equivalent of both the mesonephros and metanephros, although it is at the **mesonephros** (which is its classic term) level. The primitive kidney was adapted for a freshwater existence because it originated in primitive freshwater fish. These early kidneys were designed mainly to get rid of excess water, just like the contractile vacuole of freshwater amebas. In freshwater fish the blood and tissues have a salt (NaCl) concentration of about 0.6%, and there is a tendency for water from the outside to enter the body through the gills and mouth membrane because of this difference in osmotic pressure (the outside fresh water having only a negligible amount of salt). The protovertebrates that entered fresh water from the sea had kidneys segmentally arranged, with each coelomic segment provided with a pair of tubules, each of which had one end (nephrostome) opened into the coelom and the other to the outside. This method served to drain the coelomic fluid with its waste to the exterior. But such a method was inadequate to cope with a freshwater existence, and so a tuft of blood capillaries (glomerulus) enclosed in a capsule was developed in the tubules for filtering, under high blood pressure, the excess water from the blood. In time the nephrostome disappeared from the kidney tubules of higher vertebrates and the glomerulus alone did all the work of the kidneys. A few primitive fish such as *Amia* still retain the nephrostome, which serves to return coelomic fluid to the circulation by emptying into a venous sinus. In freshwater fish the **nephron** then consists of the renal corpuscle (glomerulus plus Bowman's capsule) and the uriniferous tubule. The latter tube is typically divided into two segments, a proximal and a distal part, and receives blood from the efferent glomerular artery and the renal portal vein. As the blood filtrate passes down this uriniferous tubule, food and salt molecules are resorbed by its walls. Much of the nitrogenous waste in freshwater fish is excreted through the gills in the form of ammonia and urea; a little, such as uric acid, is excreted through the nephron.

In marine fish the problem is to keep the body from losing water because of the high osmotic pressure of sea water (3.5% NaCl) against the lower osmotic pressure (1.5% NaCl) of the fish's blood. Marine fish therefore tend to get rid of the glomerulus and depend more upon tubular excretion, which does not require the filtration of water. Some marine fish such as the toadfish *(Opsarus)* have no glomeruli (aglomerular). Such fish swallow a great deal of water and get rid of excess salt by means of special chloride-secreting cells in the gills. That marine fish have not entirely rid themselves of glomeruli indicates perhaps that they have left fresh water too recently to have acquired completely this adaptation.

Osmoregulation determines the ability of some to live in either fresh water or salt water. Many have little or no powers of regulating their osmotic pressure or adjusting themselves to a water concentration different from their normal habitat. Those that can tolerate only very narrow ranges of salt concentration in water are called **stenohaline;** those with wide toleration are **euryhaline.** Some fish such as *Anguilla* may be both stenohaline and euryhaline during the life cycle. Those fish that migrate from the sea to spawn in fresh water are **anadromous,** such as salmon, shad, and marine lampreys; on the other hand, freshwater forms that resort to the sea to breed are **catadromous,** such as the freshwater eel (*Anguilla*). In such cases, adjustments to either fresh water or sea water involve osmotic regulation of salt and water balance, which may be under the control of hormonal activity, especially that of the adrenal cortex and posterior pituitary lobe, with the possibility that the thyroid gland may be involved.

"Bloodless fish." Although fish have the characteristic vascular pattern of vertebrates, such as red blood, nucleated corpuscles, and specialized hemoglobin for transporting oxygen, in recent years certain fish collected from the Antarctic regions are exceptions to this rule. The icefish (*Chaenocephalus*) has transparent blood with little iron and no red blood corpuscles; white corpuscles, however, are present. Oxygen transportation appears to take place only by physical solution in the plasma with low oxygen capacity. Such fish apparently are able to survive only in very cold water, but they do show that vertebrates may exist without hemoglobin.

Color. Many fish have striking colors, although the common game fish are rather modestly attired. The males of some species such as the horned dace and darters, have beautiful colors during the breeding season, but the most striking colors are found in tropical fish, especially those that live in and around coral reefs. Color is chiefly due to the presence of pigment cells (**chromatophores**) found in the dermal layer of the skin. The pigments are red, orange, black, and yellow. Various combinations of these can produce other shades of color. **Guanine** present in certain cells gives the silvery appearance often noticed in fish. An absence of pigment produces a whitish appearance.

Many fish can change their color patterns to harmonize with their surroundings by contracting or expanding the pigment in the chromatophores. The flounder is one of these. Placed on artificial mosaic backgrounds, these fish assume the same kind of pattern by the manipulation of their chromatophores. Other fish can alter their color to a lesser extent.

The mechanisms for explaining color changes are not clear in all cases, but the neurohumoral theory, which states that the neurons to the chromatophores produce acetylcholine and adrenaline (sympathin) for dispersing or aggregating the pigment, respectively, has received wide acceptance.

Scales. Both fish and reptiles bear scales in their skin, but the scales are not homologous in the two groups. In reptiles, scales are epidermal (ectodermal) in origin; in fish they are dermal (mesodermal) structures. Some fish such as catfish have no scales at all, but most do possess at least one of the three types found in the group—**ganoid, cycloid,** or **ctenoid** (Fig. 25-27). Scales usually overlap like the shingles on a roof, but they may be separated, as in eels.

Ganoid scales are platelike bony forms covered externally with enamel. They vary greatly in variety and form among the various species. In some they are rhombic plates fitted side by side. **Cycloid** scales are thicker in the center, like the boss on a shield. They are marked by concentric lines and are arranged to overlap. **Ctenoid** scales are rounded, but the exposed parts that are not overlapped bear teeth. Intermediate types are also found between the cycloid and ctenoid varieties. Also, the same fish may bear both cycloid and ctenoid scales. Flounders, for instance, have ctenoid scales dorsally and cycloid scales ventrally.

Scales grow throughout the life of the fish. The age of certain fish such as salmon and trout can be determined on the scales by the interruptions (winter marks, or annuli) between regular groups of circuli. During winter there is slower growth that results in fewer lines of growth spaced close together; in summer there is more growth, with the growth lines farther apart.

Reproduction. The teleosts show many types of sexual reproduction patterns. Although the hermaphroditic condition may occasionally occur abnormally in many species, only one or two families (for example, Serranidae) are truly hermaphroditic. In hermaphroditic forms the gonads are each divided into testicular and ovarian zones.

The fish *(Poecilia formosa)* discovered in Texas illustrates well the odd type of parthenogenesis called **pseudogamy**, or gynogenesis. This process involves the entrance and activation of an egg by a spermatozoon whose nucleus does not make genetic fusion with the nucleus of the egg. Sperm are furnished by males of related species, but the descendants are all like that of the female because they are genetically alike.

The **testes** are usually elongated, whitish organs divided into lobules that contain cysts of maturing germ cells. Within each cyst the maturing cells are always of the same stage of development. The lobules open into the spermatic duct (with secretory lining), which runs into the urogenital sinus. Males often become sexually mature before the females, and their testes may be active throughout the year; in others the testes have seasonal rhythms in reproductive activity. The **ovaries** may run the length of the abdominal cavity and are made up of many ovarian follicles supported by connective tissue. The ovary, with its membranous covering, may be continuous with the oviduct, or the ovaries may be naked and discharge their eggs into the peritoneal cavity, whence they are picked up by the oviducts (müllerian ducts). The paired oviducts may open through a common urogenital pore behind the anus, or they may open through genital pores. Some fish such as trout and salmon have no oviducts; others such as the freshwater eel have neither sperm ducts nor oviducts. Usually eggs are produced during a seasonal rhythm and the ovaries are quiescent at other times. A few (for example, hake) are known to have active ovaries at all times. Some fish such as the cod produce enormous numbers of eggs (9 million have been found in the ovaries of a single female).

Most teleost fish are oviparous, laying eggs that are fertilized in the water by the sperm discharged by the male, usually in close contact with the female. Gametes in water have limited viability unless they are united. Certain fish, however, are ovoviviparous (young

FIG. 25-27

Types of fish scales. **A,** Ganoid. **B,** Cycloid. **C,** Ctenoid.

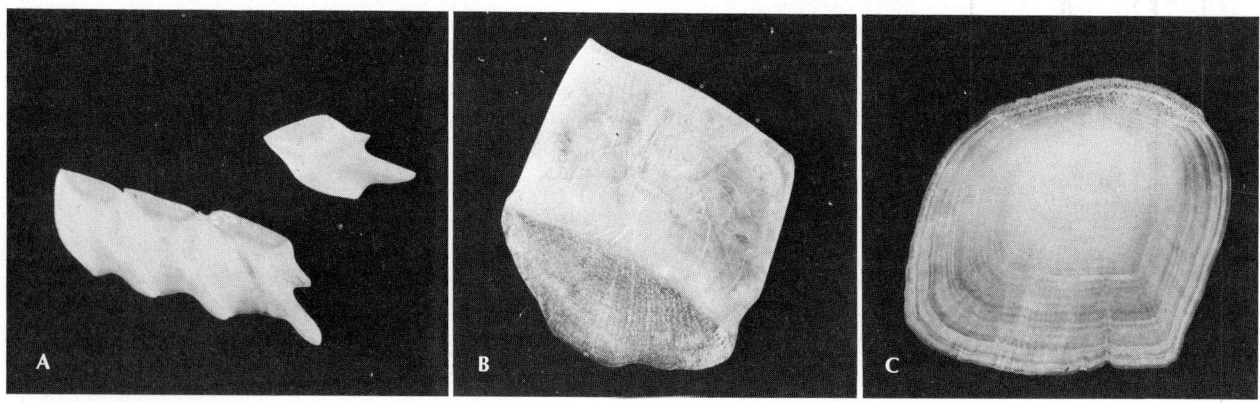

born alive but nourished by egg yolk in mother) or viviparous (young with type of placental attachment to wall of uterus). Ovoviviparity or viviparity is found in the mosquito fish (*Gambusia*) and certain sea perch (Embiotocidae) as well as a few others.

Male fish have evolved many devices for transferring sperm into the female. Copulatory organs include the urogenital papillae, anal fins, and other specialized structures. Fertilization usually takes place while the egg is still in the ovarian follicle. In *Rhodeus* the female lays her eggs in the gill spaces of a freshwater mussel by means of a very long urogenital papilla. In fish that are ovoviviparous, the young develop within a cavity of the oviduct.

Soon after eggs are laid in water, they take up water and harden. Cleavage (meroblastic) occurs in the blastodisk of the zygote, and a blastoderm is formed. As cleavage continues, the blastoderm spreads over and encloses the yolk mass. The space between the blastoderm and yolk is the segmentation cavity, or blastocoel. Development proceeds, and eventually a larval form of fishlike appearance with a large yolk sac is hatched (Figs. 25-28 and 25-29). Temperature has a great effect on regulating the speed of hatching and subsequent development.

FIG. 25-28

Chinook salmon eggs—"eyed" stage. Eyes of young fish visible as two black spots. (Courtesy W. F. Kubichek, U. S. Fish and Wildlife Service.)

Derivation and meaning of basic terminology

anadromous (Gr. *ana,* up, + *dromos,* running). Refers to those fish that migrate up streams to spawn.

catadromous (Gr. *kata,* down, + *dromos,* running). Refers to those fish that migrate from fresh water to the ocean to spawn.

Choanichthyes (Gr. *choane,* funnel or nostril, + *ichthys,* fish). Nostrils of these fish are connected to the mouth cavity.

Chondrostei (Gr. *chondros,* cartilage, + *osteon,* bone). Their skeleton is a mixture of cartilage and bone.

Crossopterygii (Gr. *krossoi,* fringe or tassels, + *pterygion,* fin or small wing). These fish have lobed fins.

Dipnoi (Gr. *di,* two, + *pnoe,* breath). So called because they can breathe both by gills and by swim bladders.

euryhaline (Gr. *eurys,* broad, + *hals,* salt). Such fish can tolerate wide ranges of saltwater concentrations.

Holostei (Gr. *holos,* entire, + *osteon,* bone). These were the first fishes to have the chondrocranium ossified.

FIG. 25-29

Development of salmon from egg to fingerling. (Courtesy H. Kelly, U. S. Fish and Wildlife Service.)

Physoclisti (Gr. *physa*, bladder, + *kleistos*, closed). Swim bladder not connected to pharynx by duct.

Physostomi (Gr. *physa*, bladder, + *stoma*, opening). Swim bladder connected to pharynx by duct.

rete mirabile (L. *rete*, network, + *mirabilia*, wonder). A network of small blood vessels so arranged that the incoming blood runs parallel to the outgoing blood and thus makes possible a counterexchange between the two bloodstreams. Such a mechanism ensures a constancy of gases in the swim bladder.

stenohaline (Gr. *stenos*, narrow, + *hals*, salt). Such fish have restricted ranges of saltwater concentrations.

Annotated references

Applegate, V. C., and J. W. Moffett. 1955. The sea lamprey. Sci. Amer. **192**:36 (April). *An account of the life history of this lamprey and the destruction it has wrought on the game fish of the Great Lakes.*

Berg, L. S. 1940. Classification of fishes, both recent and fossil. Ann Arbor, Mich., Edwards Brothers, Inc. *A comprehensive treatise of great value.*

Curtis, B. 1949. The life story of the fish. New York, Harcourt, Brace & Co., Inc.

Daniel, J. F. 1934. The elasmobranch fishes, ed. 3. Berkeley, University of California Press. *A very useful study of this group for the advanced student.*

Gilbert, P. W. 1962. The behavior of sharks. Sci. Amer. **207**:60-68 (July).

Goodrich, E. S. 1909. Cyclostomes and fishes. In Lankester: Treatise on zoology, London, A. & C. Black, Ltd. *A good appraisal of these groups for the specialist.*

Goodrich, E. S. 1930. Studies on the structure and development of vertebrates. London, Macmillan Co., Ltd. *A classic work.*

Hoar, W. S., and D. J. Randall (editors). 1969. Fish physiology, 3 vols. New York, Academic Press, Inc. *A treatise on all aspects of fish physiology by many eminent specialists.*

Hubbs, C. L. 1956. Cyclostomata (Encyclopaedia Britannica). Chicago, Encyclopaedia Britannica, Inc. *Gives the distinctive characteristics, life history, and evolution of this oldest existing group of vertebrates.*

Johansen, K. 1968. Air-breathing fishes. Sci. Amer. **219**: 102-111 (Oct.). *Traces the evolution of those fishes that can obtain oxygen from the air. Present-day fishes that have these adaptations include certain genera in the Chondrostei, two American genera of the Holostei, and the three genera of lungfishes. Considers that lungs evolved in response to changes in the aquatic environment.*

Lagler, K. F. 1956. Freshwater fishery biology, ed. 2. Dubuque, Iowa, William C. Brown Co. *This is an excellent treatise on the principles and methods of freshwater fishery and research. Nearly every aspect of the subject is treated and the work is well documented throughout.*

Lanham, U. 1962. The fishes. New York, Columbia University Press. *An excellent, concise account of the evolution, structure, and function of fishes.*

Limbaugh, C. 1961. Cleaning symbiosis. Sci. Amer. **205**: 42-49 (Aug.). *An account of the fascinating natural history of marine organisms that clean other organisms of parasites and other materials.*

Millot, J. 1955. The coelacanth. Sci. Amer. **193**:34-39 (Dec.). *The description and significance of this "living fossil" discovered in 1938.*

Norman, J. R. 1963. A history of fishes, ed. 2 (revised by P. H. Greenwood). New York, Hill & Wang, Inc. *An up-to-date revision of a famous treatise that covers nearly all aspects of fish study.*

Romer, A. S. 1959. The vertebrate story. Chicago, University of Chicago Press.

Schultz, L. P., and E. M. Stern. 1948. The ways of fishes. New York, D. Van Nostrand Co., Inc. *A somewhat popular discussion of the behavior of fish. Especially good for the beginning student in zoology.*

Young, J. Z. 1963. The life of vertebrates, ed. 2. New York, Oxford University Press. *Many chapters in this excellent treatise are devoted to the structure, evolution, and adaptive radiation of fish.*

CHAPTER 26

• PHYLUM CHORDATA (THE VERTEBRATES: AMPHIBIANS)

Class Amphibia

HOW ANIMALS HAVE CHANGED TO LAND EXISTENCE

• The vertebrates already considered are adapted to a strict aquatic life. The dipnoans, it is true, showed a modification of the aquatic breathing system to meet the conditions of a terrestrial life, but this case is a mere incident in the transition to land. The other classes of vertebrates we are to consider are modified more or less for the great change of terrestrial existence. Amphibians are on the border line between the aquatic and the land modes of life. Aquatic and terrestrial modes of living entail differences in nearly every system of the body. Actually, only three phyla include strictly terrestrial groups—mollusca, arthropods, and chordates.

PHYSICAL CONTRAST BETWEEN AQUATIC AND LAND HABITATS

There are many drastic differences between water and land habitats. In general, animals that live in water have more restrictions than do terrestrial forms.

Oxygen content of water and air. Air contains much more oxygen per unit volume than does water. Air has about 210 ml. of oxygen per liter; water usually has about 3 to 9 ml. per liter. This variation is sometimes striking, for example, in lakes at high altitude. Equilibrium is reached between the oxygen of the air and the small amount of oxygen in the water, which, as in the lakes of the high Andes, may be too small to support life at all.

Dissolved substances in water. Most water contains dissolved salts and other substances leached out of the soil. In sea water the salt content may vary from 3% or 4% in our large seas to 27% in some of our salt lakes. Pollution by refuse is also an important factor.

Temperature contrasts on land and in water. Temperature changes are more radical in terrestrial habitats than in water. Water tends to have more constant temperature. Climatic conditions vary more on land so that one region may undergo freezing, thawing, drying, flooding, and other changes.

Cover and shelter. Land habitats as a rule afford a greater variety of cover and shelter than do aquatic habitats. Aquatic animals in open water depend on speed to avoid enemies. Forms near shore find crevices and cover spots for shelter. Land forms, on the other hand, have numerous types of refuge, such as grasslands, forests, rocks, soil, and holes in trees and the ground.

Medium for locomotion. Water affords support for the body that is largely lacking in air. Land also provides a variety of habitats that demand different forms of locomotion.

Breeding places. Land affords a greater variety of breeding places than does water. Shelters as well as nests and burrows are used for this purpose. Many aquatic forms use the shore and shallow water for breeding, but many discharge their eggs directly into the water before or after fertilization.

HOW ANIMALS HAVE MET TERRESTRIAL MODE OF LIFE

The transition from water to land was gradual, and certain of the modifications were more striking than others. Some of the structural modifications may be summarized.

Skin. Terrestrial forms are protected from drying out by having hard dry skins. Instead of the soft epidermis of aquatic forms, the outer layers of land forms are cornified and are composed of dead cells.

Amniotic egg. Existence on land required an egg that could be laid on land. Such an egg must be protected against drying out and mechanical injury and thus is provided with a tough but porous shell, large yolk, and special sacs and membranes (amnion, chorion, allantois). Since it requires internal fertilization, many modifications of mating habits occurred. This type of egg is first found in reptiles and may well have first developed in animals not yet adapted for land existence. The lack of it has kept amphibians close to water.

Breathing. Terrestrial forms have developed lungs instead of gills. This adaptation was not difficult, for lungs are primitive and the ancestral crossopterygians had them. The breathing organs of land forms must be situated deeper in the body to protect their delicate structure from the drying action of air. Along with this change in position has come the development of special air passageways, such as trachea and bronchi, which have no counterparts in aquatic animals.

Circulation. With the development of the lungs there are corresponding changes in the circulatory system. In fish the gill circulation (aortic arches) is placed directly in the path of the blood from the ventral aorta. Terrestrial forms have modified this aortic arch plan into a double circulation—a **systemic** circulation over the body and a **pulmonary** circulation to the lungs. The heart must take on additional chambers so that part of the double heart receives blood from the body and the other part receives blood from the lungs.

Locomotion. The paddlelike fins of aquatic animals are replaced on land by jointed appendages, which became specialized for walking, running, climbing, flying, etc.

Sensory organs. Changes also occurred in sensory organs in the transition from water to land. Perhaps olfactory organs undergo some degeneration in land forms, for in water these organs carry a greater burden of sensory impression because of the poor development of other sense organs. Accordingly, the olfactory lobes in many fish are exceptionally large. In most terrestrial animals the eye is protected with a lid to prevent drying out. The lens is accommodated for distant vision, whereas fish are mostly nearsighted. It is doubtful whether fish can hear in the ordinary sense of the word, although they are sensitive to vibrations through their lateral line organs. Sound waves are carried through the water more easily than through the air, which probably accounts for the better ear in land animals.

Waste metabolism. Freshwater forms excrete their nitrogenous waste chiefly in the form of ammonia, which is toxic in quantities. Such aquatic animals have plenty of water to dilute the ammonia to innocuous levels in excretion. On the other hand, terrestrial animals must conserve their water, which they do by converting ammonia into urea, or (birds and some reptiles) into uric acid, as the final product of nitrogenous waste excretion.

SUBPHYLUM VERTEBRATA

CLASS AMPHIBIA*—frogs, toads, and salamanders

Amphibians were the first animals to attempt the transition from water to land. Strictly speaking, their crossopterygian ancestors were the animals that made the first attempt with any success—a feat that would have a poor chance now because present well-established competitors make it impossible for a poorly adapted transitional form to gain a foothold. Amphibians are not completely land adapted and hover between aquatic and land environments. This double life is expressed in their name. Structurally they are between the fish on the one hand and the reptiles on the other. Although more or less adapted for a terrestrial existence, few of them can stray far from moist conditions, but many have developed devices for keeping their eggs out of water, where the larvae would be exposed to enemies. They have also tried all kinds of ways of breaking away from a strictly aquatic existence, but have not wholly succeeded.

In their transition from water to land, amphibians have developed limbs in place of fins, lungs in place of gills, and some skin changes. Their circulatory system provides for lung circulation. All of them as larval forms retain a link with the aquatic life by having gills, and some retain gills throughout life. There are also other structural differences from fish that are mainly correlated with their mode of life, such as skeletal and muscular differences. There are about 2,000 species of amphibians.

Characteristics

1. Skeleton mostly bony, with varying number of vertebrae; ribs present in some, absent in

*Am-fib′e-a (Gr. *amphi*, both or double, + *bios*, life).

others; notochord does not persist; **exoskeleton absent**

2. Body forms vary greatly from an elongated trunk with distinct head, neck, and tail to a compact, depressed body with fused head and trunk and no intervening neck
3. **Limbs usually four (tetrapod)**, although some are legless; forelimbs of some much smaller than hind limbs, in others all limbs small and inadequate; **webbed feet often present**
4. **Skin smooth and moist with many glands,** some of which may be poisonous; **pigment cells (chromatophores)** common, of considerable variety, and in a few capable of undergoing various patterns in accordance with different backgrounds; **no scales,** except concealed dermal ones in some
5. Mouth usually large with small teeth in upper or both jaws; **two nostrils open into anterior part of mouth cavity**
6. Respiration by gills, lungs, skin, and pharyngeal region either separately or in combination; external gills in the larval form and may persist throughout life in some
7. **Circulation with three-chambered heart,** two auricles and one ventricle, and a double circulation through the heart; skin abundantly supplied with blood vessels
8. Excretory system of paired opisthonephroi
9. Ten pairs of cranial nerves
10. Separate sexes; fertilization external or internal; metamorphosis usually present; **eggs with jelly-like membrane coverings**

Brief classification

Body with moist skin, which contains many glands; no scales; usually two pairs of limbs; two nostrils, connected to mouth; skull with two occipital condyles; more than 2,000 species of all orders.

Order 1. Gymnophiona (jim'no-fi"o-na) (Gk. *gymnos,* naked, + *ophioneos,* of a snake) (**Apoda**)—**caecilians.** Body worm-like; limbs and limb girdle absent; mesodermal scales may be present in skin; tail short or absent.

Family Caeciliidae (se'se-li"i-de) (L. *caecilia,* lizard, from *caecus,* blind, + *idae,* family suffix). Example: *Ichthyophis.*

Order 2. Urodela (u'ro-de"la) (Gk. *oura,* tail, + *delos,* visible) (**Caudata**)—**salamanders, newts.** Body with head, trunk, and tail; no scales; usually two pairs of equal limbs.

Family Proteidae (pro-te"i-de) (from *Proteus,* from Greek mythology, sea god who could change shape, + *idae,* family suffix). Body depressed; tail with fin; gills and lungs; no eyelids; aquatic. Example: *Necturus.*

Family Cryptobranchidae (cryp'to-bran'ki-de) (Gr. *kryptos,* hidden, + *branchia,* gills). Body large and depressed with fleshy folds; gills absent; no eyelids; teeth larval. Example: *Cryptobranchus.*

Family Ambystomidae (am'bi-stom"i-de) (Gr. *amby,* blunt, + *stoma,* mouth). Body small to large; lungs; neotenic forms with gills; eyelids present; vomerine teeth; nasolabial groove absent. Example: *Ambystoma.*

Family Salamandridae (sal'a-man"dri-de) (Gr. *salamandra,* salamander). Body small to large; lungs; nasolabial groove absent; adults usually without gills; eyelids present; vomeropalatine teeth diverge posteriorly. Example: *Notophthalmus.*

Family Amphiumidae (am'fi-u"mi-de) (Gr. *amphi,* both or double, + *pneuma,* breath). Body large and eel-like; lungs; no eyelids; limbs diminutive; no nasolabial groove; larval teeth. Example: *Amphiuma.*

Family Plethodontidae (pleth-o-don"ti-de') (Gk. *plethos,* mass, + *odon,* having teeth of a specified kind). Body small to medium; nasolabial groove present; no lungs or gills; some neotenic species; vomeropalatine teeth usually present; eyelids present. Example: *Plethodon.*

Family Sirenidae (si-ren"i-de') (Gr. *seiren,* sea nymph). Body elongated and eel-like; anterior limbs present, hind limbs absent; three pairs of gills; eyelids absent; larval teeth. Example: *Siren.*

Order 3. Salientia (sa'li-ench"e-a) (L. *saliens,* leaping, + *ia,* pl. suffix) (**Anura**)—**frogs, toads.** Head and trunk fused; no tail; no scales; two pairs of limbs; mouth large; lungs; 10 vertebrae, including urostyle.

Family Pelobatidae (pel'o-bat"i-de) (Gr. *pelos,* mud or clay, + *bates,* walker, + *idae,* family suffix) (**Scaphiopodidae**). Hind foot with horny spade on inner margin; pupil of eye elliptical and vertical; snout blunt. Example: *Scaphiopus.*

Family Bufonidae (bu-fon"i-de') (L. *bufo,* toad). Skin with many warts; large parotid gland behind each eye; pupil not vertical; maxillary teeth absent. Example: *Bufo.*

Family Hylidae (hy"li-de') (Gk. *hyle,* wood). Body small; teeth in both jaws usually; hind leg long; toes with adhesive disks; terminal bone of each digit usually claw shaped. Example: *Hyla.*

Family Ranidae (ran"i-de') (L. *rana,* frog). Body with large tympanum; teeth in upper jaw; toe disks absent; warts absent; no parotid glands. Example: *Rana.*

Family Ascaphidae (a-skaf"i-de') (Gr. *a,* not, + *skaphos,* a digging). Male with tail-like copulatory organ; female with short anal tube; pupil vertical; tympanum not visible; ribs present. Example: *Ascaphus.*

Origin and relationships

The osteolepids, members of Crossopterygii, had some of the characteristics of the early amphibians, such as internal and external nares and a form of lung; and the pentadactyl limb of amphibians is believed to have arisen from such fins as the osteolepids possessed. It may be surmised that the early ancestor developed girdles and fins that were useful not merely for swimming but also for supporting the body while crawling from one desiccated basin of water to another. The primitive fossil form *Ichthyostega,* found in Greenland, has both crossopterygian and amphibian characteristics. Early amphibians such as the Gymnophiona still possess small scales in the skin; and the lateral line system, so well developed in fish, is retained in the larvae of present-day Amphibia. In the geologic time scale, however, the osteolepids flourished during the Devonian period; the earliest amphibians are from the Lower Carboniferous period, often referred to as the Age of Amphibians.

An extinct superorder of amphibians, the Labyrinthodontia (Fig. 24-10), were forms that resembled salamanders and had the head enclosed with dermal bones or plates. Many of them also had large teeth, and some may have been 15 feet long. One group of these, the Embolomeri, may have given rise to the reptiles. However, there are no convincing links between these early labyrinthodonts and modern amphibians, for intermediate fossils have not been discovered. Although some modern amphibians have resemblances to living dipnoans, it is thought that there is no direct genetic affinity between the two and that the likenesses are due to convergence or parallel evolution.

FIG. 26-1

Head and anterior region of caecilian. Order Gymnophiona (Apoda). These legless and wormlike amphibians may reach length of 18 inches and diameter of ¾ inch. Their body folds give them appearance of segmented worm. They have many sharply pointed teeth, a pair of tiny eyes mostly hidden beneath skin, a small tentacle between eye and nostril, and some forms have embedded mesodermal scales. (Courtesy General Biological Supply House, Inc., Chicago.)

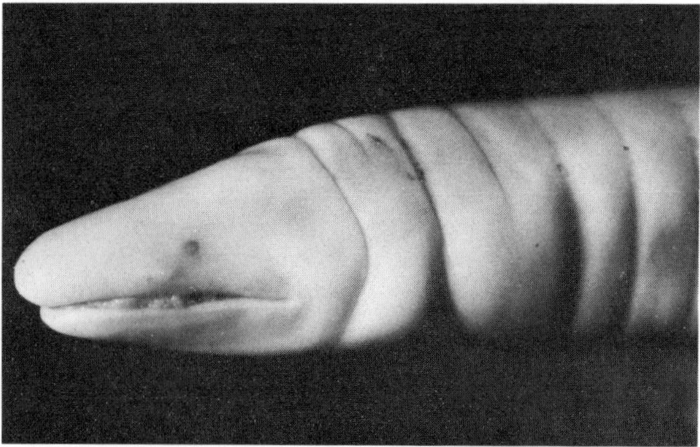

Structure and natural history of orders

Gymnophiona (Apoda). There are about 50 species of this little-known order (Fig. 26-1). They are mostly found in Africa, Asia, and South America and are commonly called caecilians. In North America no species is found north of Mexico. Aside from the long, slender, wormlike body, they are characterized by having small scales in the skin, many vertebrae, long ribs, small concealed eyes, no limbs, and terminal anus. They are strictly burrowing forms and are rarely seen above the surface. Their food is mostly worms and small invertebrates, which they find underground. Fertilization is internal, and the male is provided with a protrusible cloaca by which he copulates with the female. The eggs are usually deposited in moist ground near the water; the larvae may be aquatic or the complete larval development may occur in the egg. In some species the eggs are carefully guarded in folds of the body during their development. None of this group has ever been found in a fossil form. *Ichthyophis* is a common form in southeast Asia; *Typhlonectes* is a South American aquatic caecilian that is ovoviviparous.

Urodela (Caudata)—salamanders and newts. Order Urodela has about 150 species. Although found to a limited extent in other parts of the world, the temperate part of North America is the chief home of the tailed amphibians. The largest caudate known is the Japanese salamander, more than 5 feet long. Most of those in North America are from 3 to 6 inches long, although a few are longer (*Necturus*).

These forms have primitive limbs set at right angles to the body with the forelimbs and hind limbs about the same size. In some the limbs are rudimentary (*Amphiuma*) (Fig. 26-2), and in others (*Siren*) there are no hind limbs. Many of these amphibians never leave the water in their entire life cycle, although others assume a terrestrial life, living in moist places under stones and rotten logs, usually not far from the water. All have gills at some stage of their lives; some lose their gills when they become adults.

Although some species have lungs in place of gills, others have neither and breathe through the skin and pharyngeal region. This is true with the family Plethodontidae, a common group in North America assumed

FIG. 26-2

Congo eel *Amphiuma*.

to have originated in swift mountain streams of the Appalachian mountains. Mountain brook water, which is cool and well oxygenated, is excellent for cutaneous breathing. The cold temperature of the water slows down metabolism and thus less oxygen is required. This family also has an interesting structural adaptation, the nasolabial groove (Fig. 26-3), which helps clear the nostrils of water. The groove is flushed out by the secretions of a gland that empties into it and by cilia that carry the excess water away. Some plethodontids, such as *Aneides,* have large blood sinuses in the tips of the toes for digital respiration. It is thought that lungs are absent in some because they may act as hydrostatic organs and would prevent their possessors from hiding quickly under aquatic covers.

In color, salamanders and newts are usually modest and unassuming but are occasionally strikingly brilliant. Color changes are not nearly so pronounced among them as among their relatives, the frogs.

Neither do the caudates show as much diversity of breeding habits as do Salientia. Both external and

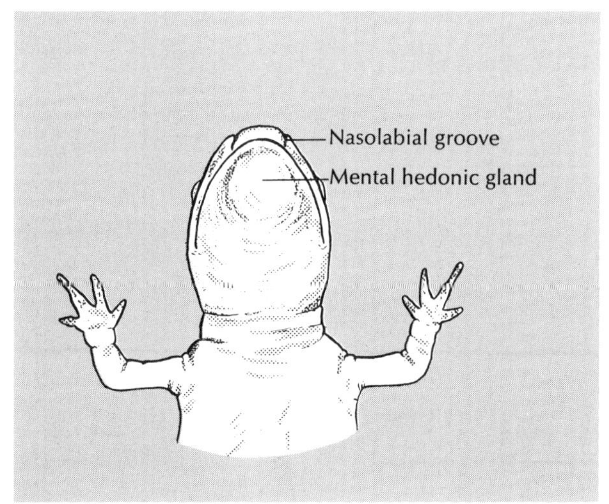

FIG. 26-3

Ventral side of head of male plethodontid salamander showing mental hedonic gland and nasolabial grooves. Hedonic gland, most prominent during breeding season, is assumed to stimulate female during courtship. Nasolabial grooves may function in clearing nostrils of water.

internal fertilization are found in the group, but some males deposit their sperm in capsules called **spermatophores** (Fig. 26-4). These are placed on leaves, sticks, and other objects, and the female picks them up with her cloacal lips and thus fertilizes her eggs. Aquatic species lay their eggs in clusters (Fig. 26-5) or stringy masses in the water; terrestrial forms may also lay their eggs in the water or in moist places. In *Salamandra,* a European form (Fig. 26-6), the eggs are retained within the body of the female until the larvae have completed part of their development.

Some salamanders show distinctive courtship behavior patterns. Plethodontid males often have a secondary sex character in the form of a hedonic or mental gland under the chin (Fig. 26-3). This gland is a slight elevation or swelling and is probably a modified mucous gland. Hedonic glands may be found on other parts of the body, such as the tail or groin. Such glands are assumed to produce a secretion that excites the female during courtship.

Blind salamanders are found in limestone caves in certain parts of the United States and Austria. One of these species is *Typhlotriton spelaeus,* which has functional eyes in the larval form and lives near the mouth of caves. As an adult, it withdraws deeper into the caves and the eyes degenerate. If the larval forms are kept in the light, they retain functional eyes when they mature; if they metamorphose in the dark, they lose the sight of their eyes. This blind effect is not hereditary, for the larvae always have eyes.

Some urodeles exhibit **neoteny,** that is, sexual reproduction during larval periods. This is strikingly shown by the tiger salamander, *Ambystoma tigrinum.* This

FIG. 26-5

Cluster of developing salamander eggs showing little embryos. (Courtesy C. Alender.)

FIG. 26-4

Spermatophore of *Plethodon glutinosus,* consisting of jelly stalk and sperm cap. Males deposit these on leaves or sticks. During courtship display, male presses his mental hedonic gland against female skin, inducing her to detach sperm cap with cloacal lips and fertilize her eggs internally. (Courtesy J. A. Organ, Museum of Zoology, University of Michigan.)

FIG. 26-6

Spotted salamander of Europe, *Salamandra salamandra.* This common salamander with black and yellow markings gives birth to larvae that complete their development in water. (Courtesy C. P. Hickman, Jr.)

species is widely distributed over the United States into Central Mexico. The larvae, known as **axolotls** (Fig. 26-7), breed in Mexico and in the southwestern part of the United States, where they apparently never acquire the adult form. When transferred to the eastern states, they lose their gills, assume lungs, and become native tiger salamanders. At one time axolotls were considered a separate species, for the eastern *A. tigrinum* after a short larval period becomes mature.

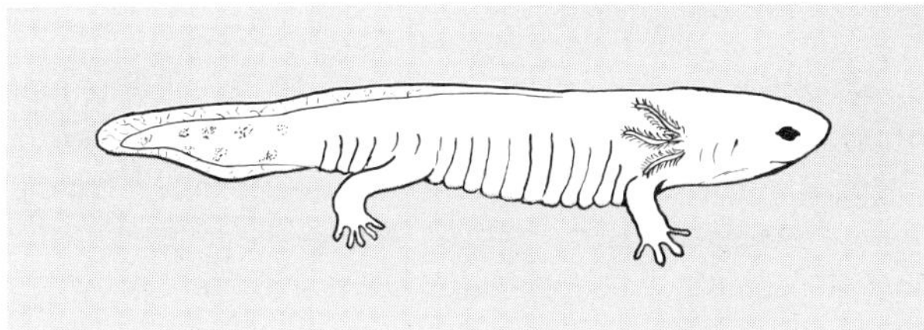

FIG. 26-7

An axolotl, larval form of tiger salamander *Ambystoma tigrinum*. In Mexico and southwestern states, larva does not metamorphose but breeds in this form.

Salamanders and newts live on worms, small arthropods, and small mollusks. Most of them will eat only things that are moving. Their food naturally is rich in proteins, and they do not usually store in their bodies great quantities of fat or glycogen. They are cold-blooded animals and have a low metabolism.

FIG. 26-8

Red-backed salamander *Plethodon cinerus* has dorsal reddish stripe with gray to black sides.

FIG. 26-9

Two-lined salamander *Eurycea bislineata* is yellow to brown with two dorsolateral black stripes.

FIG. 26-10

Long-tailed salamander *Eurycea longicauda* is yellow to orange with black spots that form vertical stripes on sides of tail.

FIG. 26-11

Slimy salamander *Plethodon glutinosus* is black with white spots.

FIG. 26-8 FIG. 26-9

FIG. 26-10 FIG. 26-11

Some common American salamanders. Most North American salamanders belong to the family Plethodontidae, which contains more species than all the other families combined. All the species illustrated in Figs. 26-8 to 26-13 belong to family Plethodontidae. The most common genus of this family in the eastern United States is *Desmognathus* (the dusky salamander), of which there are several species. On the west coast the more familiar genera of plethodontids are *Aneides* and *Batrachoseps.* The primitive family Salamandridae is represented in North America by the American newt (*Notophthalmus viridescens*), which is found all over the eastern United States. This salamander usually passes through a land phase (eft) in its development before becoming an aquatic adult. The California newt (*Taricha torosa*) is common in the coast ranges of California. Another common family is Ambystomidae, which includes such familiar salamanders as the tiger salamander, spotted salamander (*Ambystoma maculatum*), and Jefferson salamander (*A. jeffersonianum*). Certain species of this family are also found on the Pacific coast. Family Cryptobranchidae is represented by the giant salamander *Cryptobranchus,* which may reach a length of more than 2 feet. There are two species that are restricted to certain river systems in Pennsylvania and the Midwest. This salamander and those of Sirenidae are the only American salamanders that have external fertilization.

Salientia (Anura)—frogs and toads. In certain lines of behavior, anurans are not surpassed anywhere in their diversified adaptations. This is especially true of their breeding habits, which are discussed more fully in Chapter 43. The present section will be devoted to other aspects of their behavior and adaptations.

The skin of both frogs and toads has many varia-

FIG. 26-12

Zigzag salamander *Plethodon dorsalis* has zigzag pattern on back.

FIG. 26-13

Cave salamander *Eurycea lucifuga,* one of the most beautiful and also one of the rarest of Middle West. They are reddish orange with black spots.

tions. Toads usually have warty skins, and frogs tend to have smooth, slimy skins. Whenever they live in or near the water, their skins are more or less smooth and slimy; in deserts or dry regions, however, their skins are rough and warty. The skin is usually well supplied with glands. One type secretes mucus used mainly as a lubricant; the other type (Fig. 26-15) secretes a granular poison that may be highly irritating. The poison of *Dendrobates,* a South American frog, is used by Indian tribes to poison the points of their arrows.

A skin modification occurs in the so-called "hairy frog," *Astylosternus,* found in the Cameroons of Africa (Fig. 26-18, *B*). The males have fine cutaneous filaments on the thighs, groins, and sides, which have a remarkable resemblance to hair. These curious structures may have a respiratory function. The female surinam toad *Pipa* has a modified skin on her back for carrying eggs and young (Fig. 26-14).

Anurans are usually defenseless, but in the tropics and subtropics many frogs and toads are aggressive, jumping and biting at their potential enemies. Some defend themselves by feigning death ("playing possum"). Most anurans can blow up their lungs so that they are difficult to swallow. When disturbed along the margin of a pond or brook, a frog will often remain quite still; when it thinks it is detected, it will jump, not always into the water where enemies may be awaiting it but into grassy cover on the bank. When held in the hand a frog may cease its struggles for an instant and then leap violently, at the same time voiding its urine. Their best protection is their ability to leap and their use of poison glands. Bullfrogs in captivity will not hesitate to snap at tormenters and are capable of inflicting painful bites.

Migration of frogs and toads is correlated with their breeding habits. Males usually return to a pond or stream in advance of the females, whom they then attract by their calls. Some salamanders are also known to have a strong homing instinct, returning year after year to the same pool for reproduction. D. G. O. Anderson and V. Twitty found that the homing ability in the newt *Taricha rivularis* was greatly reduced by cutting the olfactory nerves. The initial stimulus for migration in many cases is due to a seasonal cycle in the gonads plus hormonal control that increases their sensitivity to temperature and humidity changes. Frogs may be induced to discharge their sex cells when in-

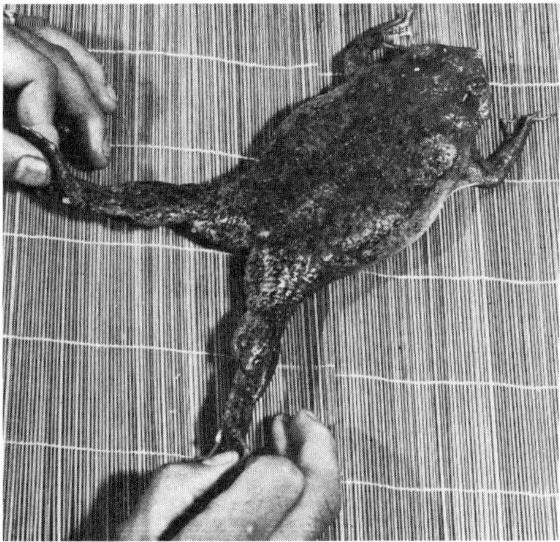

FIG. 26-14

Surinam toad *Pipa.* This odd toad is quite flat and has a triangular head but no tongue. This one is male; female carries eggs in little pockets on her back. Fully metamorphosed young emerge in about three months. (Courtesy C. P. Hickman, Jr.)

FIG. 26-15

Giant South American toad *Bufo marinus.* Some of these are more than 6 inches long. Their large parotid glands produce most poisonous secretions to be found among amphibians. (Courtesy C. P. Hickman, Jr.)

jected with hormones from the anterior pituitary. Amphibians are sensitive to moisture gradients or to the odors of aquatic vegetation. Migration also may be an instinctive return to the ancestral breeding grounds.

Unlike the salamanders, which mostly have internal fertilization, nearly all frogs and toads fertilize their eggs externally. When the female lays her eggs, the male embraces her and discharges his sperm over the eggs as they extrude from her body (Figs. 26-16 and 26-17). A notable exception is the famed bell toad *(Ascaphus truei)* of the Pacific coast region (Fig. 26-18, *C*). This small toad (family Ascaphidae), which is only about 2 inches long, is found in swift mountain streams of low temperature from British Columbia to northern California and has a conspicuous extension of cloaca, which serves as an intromittent or copulatory organ for fertilizing internally the eggs of the female. *Ascaphus* is the only American frog that has ribs in the adult condition. A related genus, *Liopelma,* is found in New Zealand. The only frog to bring forth its young alive is the ovoviviparous *Nectophrynoides* of Africa. This frog also has internal fertilization but has no external copulatory organ.

FIG. 26-16

Pair of toads in amplexus. As eggs are extruded from cloaca of female, male fertilizes them with his sperm. (Courtesy C. Alender.)

The largest anuran is known as *Rana goliath,* which is more than 1 foot long from tip of nose to anus; it is found in west Africa. This giant will eat animals as big as rats and ducks. The smallest frog recorded is *Phyllobates limbatus,* which is only about ½ inch long. This tiny frog, which is more than covered by a dime, is found in Cuba. Our largest American frog is the bull frog *(Rana catesbeiana),* which reaches a length of 8 or 9 inches. Most of our common species are only a few inches long, and the tree frogs are smaller than this.

THE FROG AS A VERTEBRATE TYPE

Habitats and distribution

The frogs as a group are usually found close to water, although some such as the wood frog *(R. sylvatica)* spend most of their time on damp forest floors, often a

FIG. 26-17

Toad eggs. Toads lay eggs in strings; frogs lay eggs in clusters. (Courtesy C. Alender.)

distance from the nearest water. The wood frog probably returns to pools only for breeding in early spring. The larger frogs *R. catesbeiana* and *R. clamitans* (Figs. 26-19 and 26-20) are nearly always found in or near permanent water or swampy regions. The leopard frog *(R. pipiens)* (Fig. 26-21) has a wider variety of habitats and, with all its subspecies and phases, is perhaps the most widespread of all the North American frogs in its distribution. It has been found in some form in nearly every state but is sparingly represented along the extreme western part of the Pacific coast. It also extends far into northern Canada and as far south as Panama. The bullfrog *(R. catesbeiana)* is native east of the Rocky Mountains but has been introduced into most of the western states. *Rana clamitans* is confined mainly to the eastern half of the United States, although it has been introduced elsewhere. Within the range of any species of frogs, they are often restricted to certain habitats (for instance, to certain streams or pools) and may be absent or scarce in similar habitats of the range. The pickerel frog *(R. palustris)* is especially noteworthy this way, for it is known to be abundant only in certain localized regions. Figs. 26-22 to 26-24 show some of the common American tree frogs.

General behavior and activities

Frogs of different species show considerable differences in behavior. Most of our larger frogs are solitary in their habits except during the breeding season. During the breeding period most of them, especially the males, are very noisy. Each male usually takes possession of a particular perch, where he may remain for a long time, trying to attract a female to that spot. At times frogs are mainly silent, and their presence is not detected until they are disturbed. Many of them such as the leopard frog are very agile and may leap a distance of 5 to 6 feet in a single jump. When they enter the water, they dart about swiftly and reach the bottom of the pool, where they kick up a cloud of muddy water.

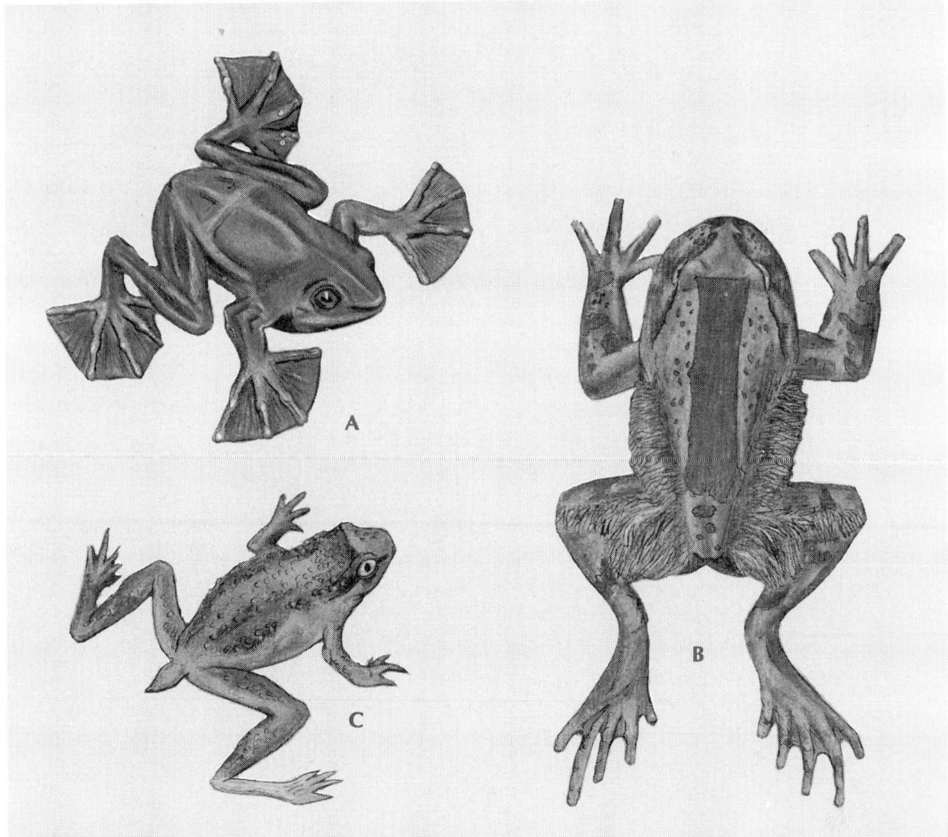

FIG. 26-18

Three frogs with unusual features. **A,** "Flying" frog of Borneo, *Polypedates nigropalmatus*. Large webs between digits of feet aid it in gliding from higher elevation to lower one. **B,** "Hairy frog" of Africa, *Astylosternus*. Hairlike filaments on groins and sides of male are actually cutaneous papillae, probably used for respiration. These filaments are unusually well developed during breeding season. **C,** Bell toad of northwestern Pacific coast, *Ascaphus truei*. Male's cloacal appendage serves as copulatory organ for fertilizing female's eggs. This frog and certain ovoviviparous frogs of Africa are only known salientians that have internal fertilization. (From various sources.)

FIG. 26-19
Bullfrog *Rana catesbeiana* is largest of all American frogs.

FIG. 26-20
Green frog *Rana clamitans* is next to bullfrog in size. Body is usually green, especially around jaws; has dark bars on sides of legs.

FIG. 26-21
Leopard frog *Rana pipiens* has light-colored dorsolateral ridges and irregular spots.

FIG. 26-22
Spring peepers *Hyla crucifer,* the darlings of warm spring nights, when their characteristic peeping is so often heard. It is small (1 to 1½ inches) and light brown, with an "X" marked on back.

FIG. 26-23
Swamp cricket frog *Pseudacris nigrita triseriata,* common tree frog of early spring, is about the size of spring peeper. A small frog (1 to 1½ inches) with smooth skin and three dark longitudinal bands on back.

FIG. 26-24
Gray tree frog *Hyla versicolor.* Note large adhesive disks on ends of digits. Its sound is one of most familiar on summer night.
(Figs. 26-19 to 26-24 courtesy C. Alender.)

In swimming, they hold the forelimbs near the body and kick backward with the webbed hind limbs, which propels them forward. When they come to the surface to breathe, only the head and foreparts are exposed, and as they usually take advantage of any protective vegetation, they are difficult to see.

Frogs can croak under water as well as on land, and they make their characteristic noises by forcing the air back and forth over the vocal cords into the lungs. The chief function of the voice appears to be the attraction of their mates. Many males have resonating organs or sacs that balloon out under the chin or on the side of the throat when they are calling (Fig. 26-25). Most species utter characteristic croaks that identify them. One of the loudest is the familiar "jug-o-rum" bullfrog. The bass notes of the green frog are banjolike, and those of the leopard frog are long and guttural. Many frog sounds are now available on phonograph records.

Frogs are mainly carnivorous and feed on worms, insects, and even tadpoles and smaller frogs if the chance affords. They will snap with their protrusible tongue, which is attached at the front end and free behind, at any moving object within their range. The free end of the tongue is highly glandular and produces a stick secretion with which it adheres to the prey.

During the winter months most frogs **hibernate** in the soft mud of the bottom of pools and streams. The wood frog hibernates under stones, logs, and stumps in the forest area. Naturally their life processes are at a very low ebb during their hibernation period, and such energy as they need is derived from the glycogen and fat stored in their bodies during the spring and summer months.

Adult frogs have numerous enemies, such as snakes, aquatic birds, turtles, racoons, man, and many others; only a few tadpoles survive to maturity.

FIG. 26-25

Spring peeper *Hyla crucifer* with its resonating vocal sac enlarged just before it gives its high note, which can be heard a long distance. It will be seen that the whole body as well as vocal sac is inflated. (Courtesy R. Fuson.)

Parasites

In common with most animals, frogs serve as hosts for many different kinds of parasites. In certain surveys made, protozoan parasites seem to be more common in tadpoles and young frogs than they are in adults, although in *R. pipiens* and the toad some protozoans such as *Opalina* are found in all stages. Frogs in captivity tend to shed their parasites rapidly and in a week or so may show few specimens, especially if the frogs are not fed. According to some authorities, the degree of parasitism depends upon the abundance of food and the abundance of rainfall. Land forms have fewer parasites than aquatic ones.

Among the protozoans the large flagellate *Opalina* and ciliate *Nyctotherus* are most frequently found in the intestine and rectum. *Entamoeba raravurn* and flagellates, such as *Hexamita* and *Trichomonas*, are often found in the same region. In the blood, *Trypanosoma* and *Haemogregarina* are frequently present. Many ectozoic protozoans may be found on the skin and gills of tadpoles, such as *Epistylis, Vorticella, Opercularia,* and *Trichodina.*

Tapeworms (Cestoda) are not common in frogs though some have been recorded.

The most striking parasites of the frog belong to the trematodes (Fig. 26-26), usually found in the lungs and the urinary bladder. Most of the lung flukes belong to the genus *Haematoloechus* (old name, *Pneumonoeces*). In the bladder *Gorgodera* and *Gorgoderina* are common. Another common trematode is *Clinostomum attenuatum,* which is often found encysted in the mesenteries and under the peritoneum of *R. pipiens* and *R. catesbeiana. Megalodiscus* is sometimes present in the rectum, whereas *Loxogenes* is known to occur in cysts on the liver or in the bile duct of 3 of 4 different species of frogs. The intestine may harbor many parasites such as *Cephalogonimus* and *Glypthelmins.* In the mouth or

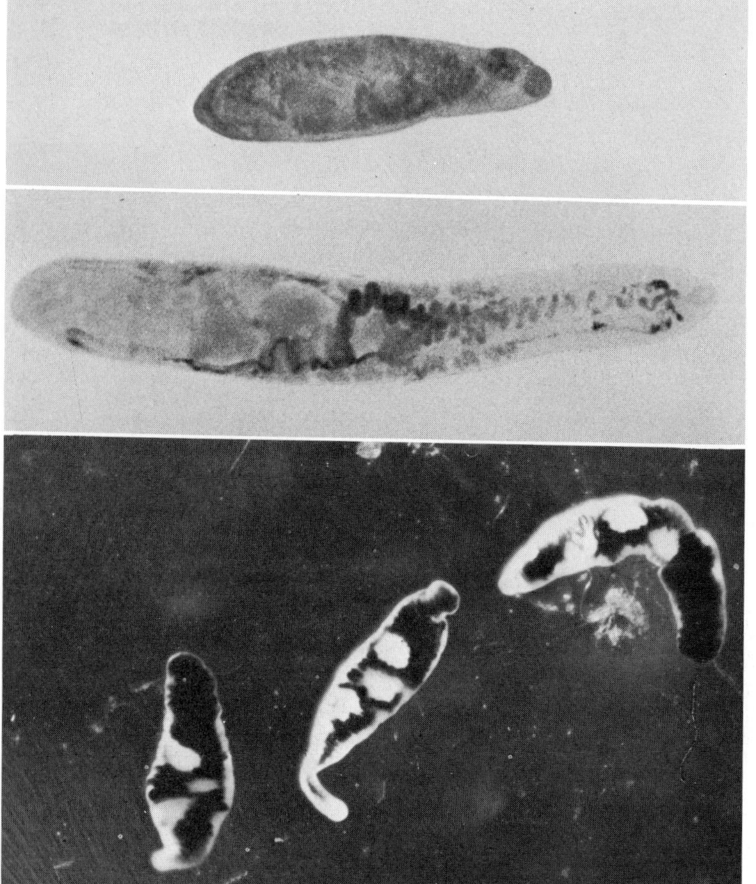

FIG. 26-26

A, Common lung fluke *Pneumobites,* parasite of frog. These flukes have complicated life history. Eggs are shed from frog and ingested by snails. In snails, cercariae are produced that later find their way into rectum of dragonfly larva, or naiad, where they encyst as metacercariae and remain throughout metamorphosis of nymph into dragonfly. Cycle is completed when frog snaps up dragonfly. **B,** Stained preparation of lung fluke *Haematoloechus.* **C,** *Haematoloechus.* Living specimens photographed just after removal from lung of freshly killed frog.

pharynx, *Halipegus* occurs in certain frogs, including *R. pipiens.*

Nematodes are found chiefly in the lungs, intestine, and heart, although they may be found elsewhere. Some of the more common ones found are *Rhabdias, Isociella, Oswaldocruzia, Falcustra,* and *Aplectana.* The common hairworms (Gordiacea) are also known to be parasitic in the frog during part of their larval history.

The frog as a morphologic type

The frog, although specialized, is a fairly typical vertebrate, with an arrangement of organ systems in line with those of land vertebrates, in which increased skeletal and muscular tissue demand more nutrition, more oxygen, and a more efficient elimination of waste. A form that is adapted for land locomotion requires an entirely different pattern of skeletal and muscular elements. The simple sheetlike (myotome) muscles of fish, for instance, must be highly modified to meet the requirements of a skeleton fitted for locomotion on land.

The following description applies mainly to *R. pipiens,* which is commonly used for laboratory study.

External features

Body plan. The body of the frog is divided into **head** and **trunk,** without an intervening neck region. There are two pairs of **legs** but no tail. The head bears a pair of nostrils, or **external nares,** a large transverse **mouth,** two protruding **eyes** (which can be depressed into their orbits when the frog closes its eyes), and behind each eye a flat **tympanic membrane,** or eardrum. A posterior terminal **cloacal opening** represents the external orifice of the **cloaca.** Sometimes visible on top of the head is a light-colored **frontal organ,** which represents the vestigial pineal eye. Recent investigations show that the frontal organ is photosensitive to the longer wavelengths, producing color changes in the skin.

The forelimbs are short and turned in, and each has

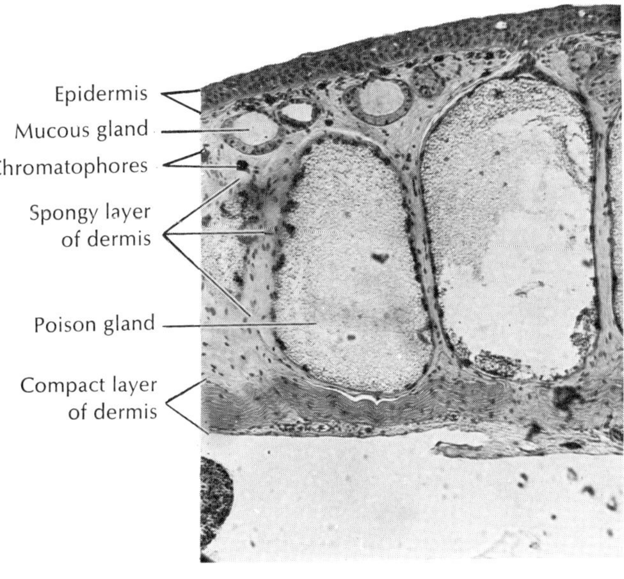

FIG. 26-27

Histologic section of frog skin. Stratified epidermis is seen as dark layer at surface with thicker dermis below. Note small mucous glands and large poison glands in dermal layer.

four digits. On male frogs the inner digit is thickened into the **nuptial pad** for clasping the female during mating. The long **hind limbs** are adapted for jumping and swimming and are folded when the frog is not active. The five slender toes of the hind limbs are connected by broad webs, which are swimming adaptations.

Integument. The skin of the frog is thin and moist and is attached loosely to the body only at certain points. Behind each eye a dorsolateral fold, or **dermal plica,** is formed by a thickening of the skin. Histologically the skin is made up of two layers—an outer stratified **epidermis** and an inner spongy **dermis** (Fig. 26-27). The epidermis consists of a somewhat horny outer layer of epithelium, which is periodically shed, and an inner layer of columnar cells, from which new cells are formed to replace those that are lost. The frog molts a number of times during its active months. In the process the outer layer of skin is split down the back and is worked off as one piece. The dermis is made up mostly of glands, pigment cells, and connective tissue. On its outer portion are the glands—small **mucous glands,** which secrete mucus for keeping the skin moist, and the larger **poison glands,** which secrete a whitish fluid that is highly irritating to enemies.

Skin color in the frog is produced by pigment granules scattered through the epidermis and by special pigment cells, **chromatophores,** located in the dermis (Figs. 26-27 and 26-28). Types of chromatophores include **guanophores,** which contain white crystals, **melanophores** with black and brown pigment, and **lipophores** (xanthopores) with red and yellow pigment. Frogs have some power to change color to suit their background by the manipulation of their various chromatophores or pigment. All the chromatophores have branched cytoplasmic processes. Darkened effects result whenever the pigment granules become scattered through the branched processes; light effects occur whenever the pigment becomes concentrated toward the center of the pigment cell. There is evidence to show that pigment changes are due, in part at least, to influences through the eye, although the specific regulation is hormonal and nervous in nature.

Dermal scales are lacking in all modern amphibians except caecilians.

Internal structures

Coelomic cavity and its structures. The body cavity, or **coelom,** is lined with a thin transparent membrane (**parietal peritoneum**) and the viscera are covered with a thin **visceral peritoneum.** The double-layered peritoneum that holds the various organs to the dorsal body wall is called the **mesentery.**

The organ systems that are revealed when the body cavity is opened are the digestive, circulatory, respiratory, excretory, and reproductive systems.

Four systems of the frog's body lie more or less outside of the coelomic cavity. They are the skeletal, muscular, nervous, and sensory systems. These systems have the important roles of support, protection, movement, regulation and coordination, and reception of stimuli.

Skeletal system

The exoskeleton is practically nonexistent in modern amphibians, for their glandular skin has no hard, ectodermal structures. The well-developed **endoskeleton** of bone and cartilage provides support and a framework for the muscles in movement, as well as protection for the viscera and nervous system. In the early development of the frog the endoskeleton is entirely of cartilage, but in the adult most of its parts are of bone, with cartilage on the ends of long bones

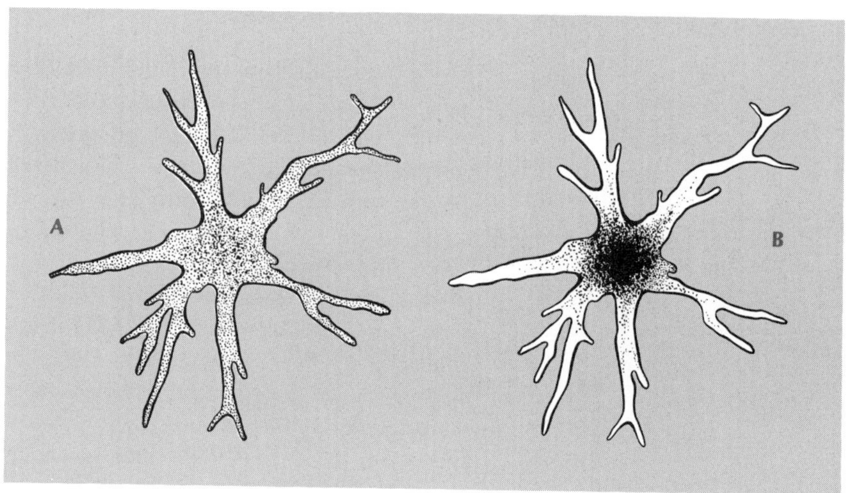

FIG. 26-28

Pigment cells (chromatophores). **A,** Pigment dispersed; **B,** pigment concentrated. Pigment cell does not contract or expand; color effects are produced by streaming of cytoplasm, carrying pigment granules into cell branches for maximum color effect or to center of cell for minimum effect. Chromatophore of cephalopod, however, does change shape by muscular contraction. Control over dispersal or concentration of pigment is mostly through light stimuli of eye, which may cause direct nervous stimulation of chromatophores or may cause nerve fiber endings to secrete neurohumors that diffuse to the pigment cells. Some hormones (intermedin) are known to influence activity of chromatophore. Types of chromatophores depend upon pigments they bear, for example, melanophores (brownish black), xanthophores (yellow or red), and guanophores (white).

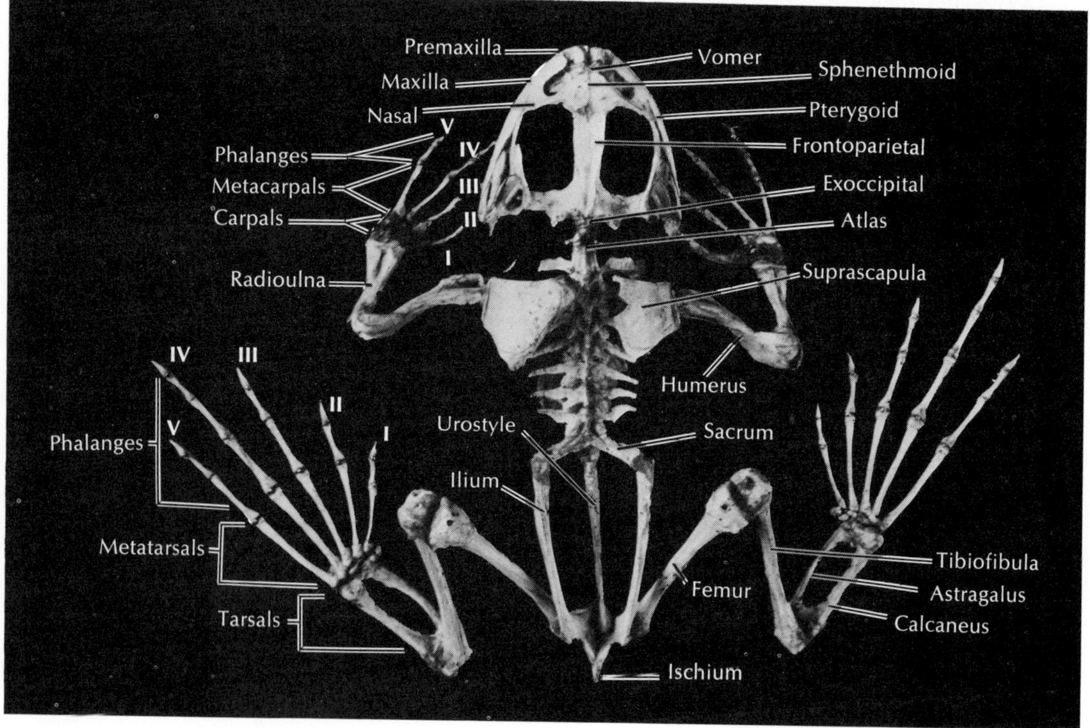

FIG. 26-29

Dorsal view of frog skeleton.

and in other scattered places (Fig. 26-29). The frog's skeleton is correlated with its specialized body. This is marked in the hind limbs fitted for jumping, in the absence of the tail and ribs, and in the reduction of the vertebrae.

Like other vertebrates, the frog skeleton may be divided into the **axial skeleton,** made up of the skull, vertebral column, and sternum, and the **appendicular skeleton,** consisting of the pectoral and pelvic girdles and the limbs.

The **skull** of the frog is flat and broad and is made up of **cranial** and **visceral** parts. The cranial division consists of the cranium, which encloses the brain, the olfactory and auditory capsules, and the optic orbits. The visceral portion contains the two jaws, the hyoid cartilage, and the laryngeal cartilages (Figs. 26-30 and 26-31).

The **vertebral column,** which supports the body and houses the spinal cord, consists of nine vertebrae and the long **urostyle,** in which the end of the spinal cord terminates.

The **pectoral girdle** serves as a support for the fore-limbs and as a protection for structures within that region of the body. On each side the girdle is made up of a dorsal flat cartilaginous **suprascapula,** a lateral **scapula,** and, on the ventral side, a slender **clavicle** and a broad **coracoid.** Both clavicles and coracoids join the breastbone, or **sternum** (a part of the axial skeleton). The **glenoid fossa,** a concavity in which the head of the humerus of the forelimb fits, is located at the junction of the scapula and coracoid on each side.

Each **forelimb** is made up of a **humerus, radioulna, carpus** of six small bones in the wrist, five **metacarpals** in the palm, and ten **phalanges** in the four functional **digits.** The rudimentary thumb, or first digit, is represented by the first metacarpal.

The **pelvic girdle** consists of two **innominate** bones, each of which is made up by fusion of the long anterior **ilium,** the posterior **ischium,** and the ventral **pubis.** The three bones meet at the **acetabulum,** the concavity into which the **femur** bone of the hind limb fits. The pelvic girdle is attached to the vertebral column by means of the ilia, which articulate with the transverse processes of the ninth or **sacral vertebra.**

The bones of the **hind limb** include the **femur,** the **tibiofibula,** the ankle, or **tarsus,** consisting of the astragalus, calcaneus and two smaller bones, the five **metatarsals,** and the five digits, with fourteen **phalanges** among them. A rudimentary digit (prehallux) is found near the upper part of the first digit and corresponds to the great toe of the human being.

A **joint** is the meeting place of two bones. Some joints are immovable (**synarthroses**) (Fig. 26-32), such as those between skull bones; others are freely movable (**diarthroses**) (Fig. 26-33), including **hinge** joints, such as those of the knee and elbow, and **ball-and-**

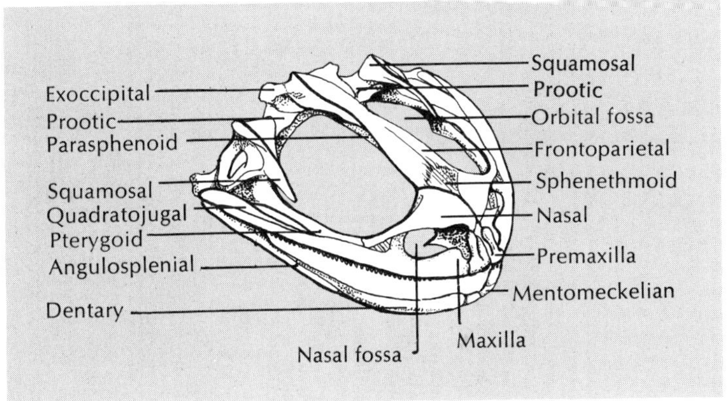

FIG. 26-30

Dorsolateral view of frog skull.

FIG. 26-31

Skull of frog, ventral view. (From Hickman and Hickman: Laboratory studies in integrated zoology, ed. 3, The C. V. Mosby Co.)

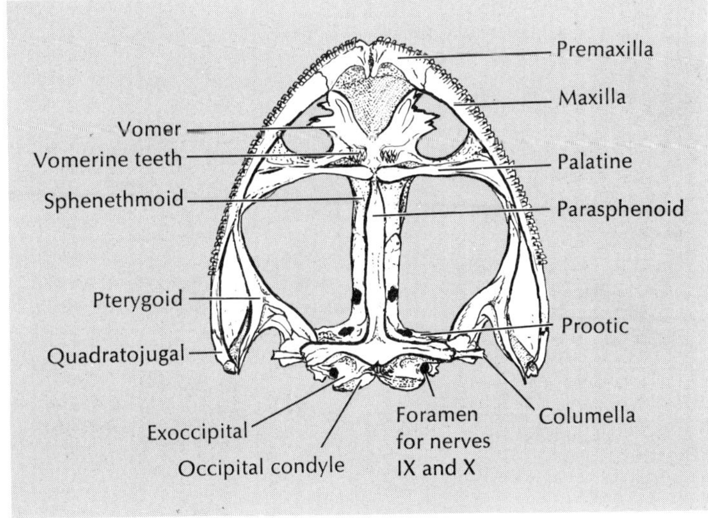

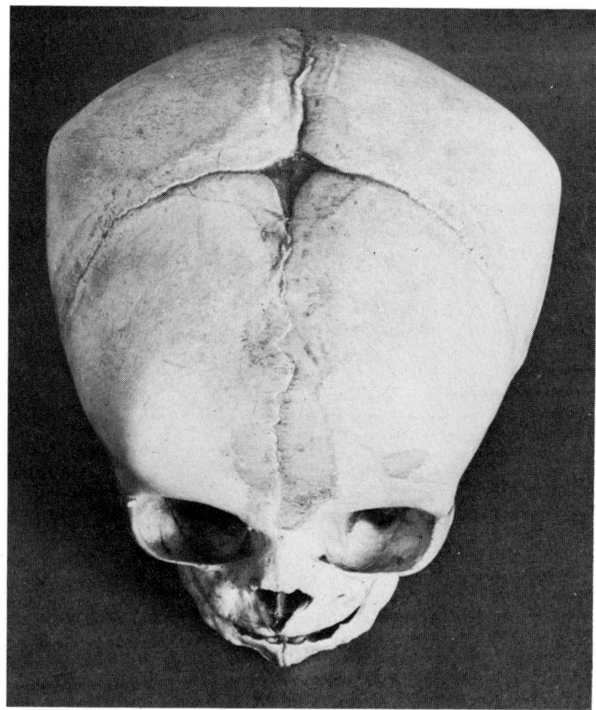

FIG. 26-32

Skull of infant showing sutures between skull bones. Example of synarthrosis joint.

FIG. 26-33

Structures of diarthrosis joint (longitudinal section).

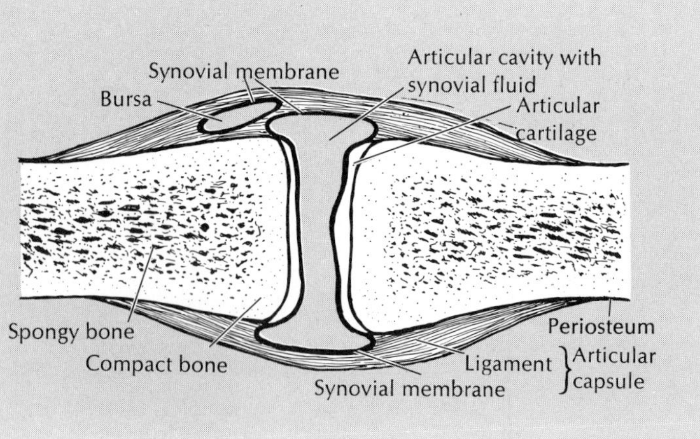

socket joints found at the hips and shoulders. There are a number of specialized structures at a joint. Where the bones meet each other, cartilage pads are between them to reduce friction. Little closed sacs (**bursae**) are formed by these cartilage surfaces for supplying the **synovial fluid** used in lubrication. The joint cavity is surrounded by a fibrous, liquidtight capsule, which aids in holding the bones together by atmospheric pressure. Running over and around the joint capsule are the various muscles and tendons needed to manipulate the movements of the joint.

Muscular system

Types of muscles. Three types of muscle fibers are found in vertebrates: skeletal (striated), smooth, and cardiac.

Skeletal, or striated, muscles. Striated muscle fibers, or cells (Fig. 7-15, *A*), are elongated and are bound together to make up the gross muscles that form most of the musculature of the body. They are under the control of the will and are thus vitally concerned with voluntary movement. Each fiber consists of many longitudinal **myofibrils** that bear alternate light and dark segments, or striations; these account for the striped effect of these muscles (Fig. 30-16). Skeletal muscles act faster, tire more easily, and are less capable of stretching than other types of muscle fibers.

Smooth muscles. Smooth muscles are usually found in sheetlike arrangements encircling hollow organs, such as the digestive tract, blood vessels, and bladder. The cells are spindle shaped (Fig. 7-14) and not striated. They are supplied with nerves from the autonomic nervous system; thus, they are involuntary and slow in action.

Cardiac muscle. Cardiac muscle (Fig. 7-15, *B*) is found only in the hearts of vertebrates. It has some resemblance to both the other types of muscles. It is striated but involuntary. It consists of fibers, but these fibers branch and anastomose with each other to form a network. In action, cardiac muscle is neither as fast as skeletal muscle nor as sluggish as smooth muscle.

Structure of gross muscle. A gross muscle is made up of striated fibers bound together with connective tissue. The opposite ends of the muscles are usually connected to bones by means of **tendons.** Gross muscles vary in shape and form according to their functions. Some are long and tapering, some are broad and sheetlike, others are short and thick, and still others form sphincters with circular arrangement of the fibers. The less movable end of a muscle is called the **origin**;

the more movable end, the **insertion.** The middle mass of muscle is the **belly**, and the shining connective tissue that encloses the muscle is the **fascia. A muscle's only action is to contract,** which causes it to become shorter and thicker in the belly. Muscles are usually arranged in antagonistic groups so that movement is effected by the contraction of one group and the relaxation of the opposite group. Muscles may be classified according to their action (Fig. 26-34).

abductor Moves the party away from the median axis of the body (**deltoid**)
adductor Moves the part toward the median axis of the body (**adductor magnus**)
flexor Bends one part on another part (**biceps brachii**)
extensor Straightens out a part (**triceps brachii**)
depressor Lowers a part (**sternohyoid**)
levator Elevates a part (**masseter**)
rotator Produces a rotary movement (**gluteus**)

Many of the muscles of the frog have the same names and action as those of man. (See Fig. 26-34 and Table 26-1.)

Nervous system

The nervous system coordinates and integrates the various physiologic processes of the body as it adjusts to its environment. The system is specialized to interpret the stimuli and sensations it receives and to originate the proper responses. The basic structure of all nervous systems is the **neuron** (Fig. 7-16).

The nervous system is commonly divided into (1) the **central nervous system,** made up of the brain and spinal cord; (2) the **peripheral nervous system,** consisting of the cranial and spinal nerves; and (3) the **autonomic nervous system,** composed of a chain of special ganglia on either side of the spinal column. This division is mainly one of convenience, for the entire system is unified to work as a unit.

The brain and spinal cord are protected by the cranium of the skull and by the vertebrae. Both brain and cord are surrounded by two connective tissue membranes called **meninges.** The outer one (**dura mater**), adhering to the bone, is thicker and tougher; the inner one, adhering to the nervous tissue, is the delicate, vascular **pia mater.**

Central nervous system. The **brain** (Fig. 26-35) consists of five basic parts which are described beginning anteriorly. (1) The **cerebral hemispheres** (telencephalon) are the seat of memory; they bear anteriorly the **olfactory lobes,** concerned with the sense of smell. (2) The **diencephalon,** or 'tween-brain, is concerned with balance and vision. It bears dorsally a small **epiphysis** (**pineal body**) extending to the brow spot, and it bears ventrally the bilobed **infundibulum,** to which is attached the **hypophysis,** or **pituitary gland.** On the ventral side, anterior to the infundibulum, the **optic chiasma** is formed by fibers of the optic nerves, which cross there before entering the diencephalon. (3) The **midbrain** (mesencephalon) is the main visual center. It bears dorsally the prominent, rounded **optic lobes,** which inhibit spinal cord reflexes. (4) The **cerebellum** (metencephalon), a small transverse ridge, controls equilibrium. (5) The **medulla oblongata** (myelencephalon) narrows posteriorly to join the spinal cord. It controls most of the body functions in amphibians, which are less dependent upon higher centers of the brain than are most other vertebrates.

FIG. 26-34

Chief superficial muscles of frog (diagrammatic).

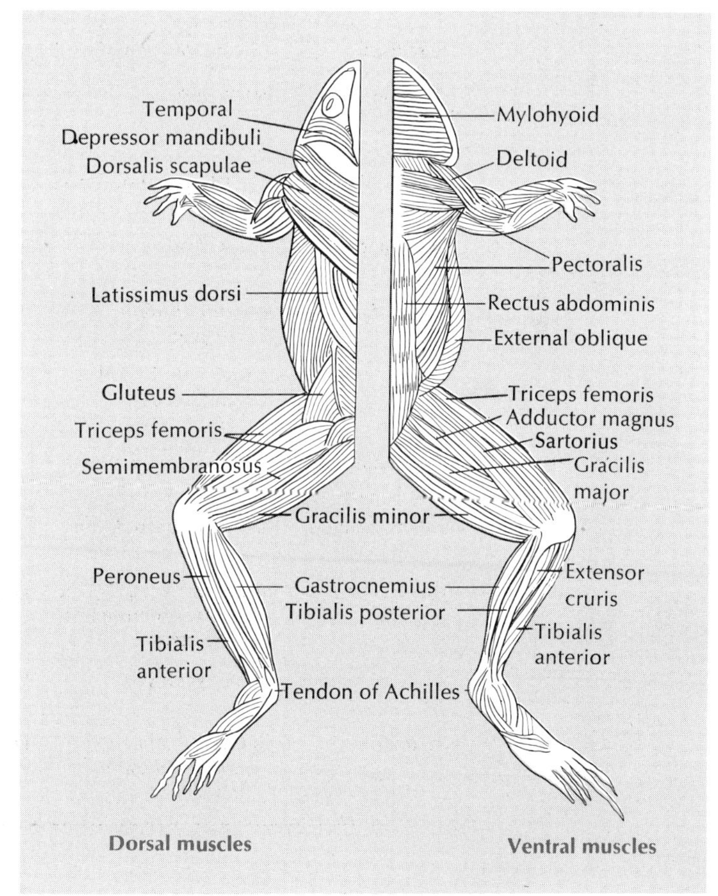

TABLE 26-1

Principal superficial muscles of frog—origin, insertion, and action

Name	Origin	Insertion	Action
		Muscles of jaws and tongue	
Temporal	Side of skull	Posterior end of lower jaw	Elevates lower jaw and closes mouth
Masseter	Zygomatic process of tympanic bone and quadratojugal	Lower jaw	Elevates lower jaw and stretches tympanic
Depressor mandibuli	Behind tympanic ring and dorsal fascia	Tip of mouth and jaw	Depresses lower jaw and opens mouth
Mylohyoid (submaxillary)	Medial surface of mandible	Median line of lower jaw	Raises floor of mouth in breathing and swallowing
Geniohyoid	Tip and border of lower jaw	Processes and body of hyoid	Lowers mandible and elevates hyoid
Sternohyoid	Sternum and coracoid	Ventral surface of hyoid	Lowers floor of mouth in breathing
Hyoglossus	Thyroid process of hyoid	Tongue	Retracts tongue
Genioglossus	Lower jaw	Tongue	Protracts tongue
		Muscles of trunk	
Dorsalis scapulae	Dorsal surface of suprascapula	Lateral side of humerus	Extends arm
Latissimus dorsi	Dorsal fascia	Lateral border of humerus	Raises forelimb upward and backward
Longissimus dorsi	Anterior third of urostyle	Skull	Extends back and elevates head
Coccygeosacralis	Lateral anterior half of urostyle	Arch and transverse process of ninth vertebra	Draws back nearer urostyle or turns back to one side
Coccygeoiliacus	Lateral side of urostyle	Ilium	Fixes urostyle with respect to pelvic girdle
External oblique	Dorsal fascia and ilium	Linea alba	Supports and reduces abdominal cavity
Transversus	Ilium, dorsal fascia, and transverse processes of vertebrae	Linea alba, sternum, and coracoid	Constriction of abdomen
Rectus abdominis	Pubic symphysis	Sternum	Supports abdomen and fixes sternum in place
Pectoralis	Sternum and fascia of rectus abdominis muscle	Deltoid ridge of humerus	Adducts, flexes, and rotates arm

TABLE 26-1

Principal superficial muscles of frog—origin, insertion, and action—cont'd

Name	Origin	Insertion	Action
		Muscles of thigh	
Sartorius	Pubic symphysis	Just below head of tibia	Flexes shank and adducts thigh; draws limb forward
Adductor magnus	Ischial and pubic symphysis	Distal end of femur	Adducts thigh and leg; draws thigh ventrally
Adductor longus	Ventral part of ilium	Femur; joins adductor magnus	Adducts thigh
Triceps femoris	One head from acetabulum and two heads from ilium	Below head of tibia; upper end of tibiofibula	Adducts thigh; extends shank
Gracilis major and gracilis minor	Posterior margin of ischium	Proximal end of tibiofibula	Adducts and extends thigh; flexes or extends shank, depending on its position
Semitendinosus	Ischium	Proximal end of tibiofibula	Adducts thigh and flexes shank
Biceps femoris (ileofibularis)	Dorsal side of ilium	Tibiofibula	Flexes shank and extends thigh
Semimembranosus	Dorsal half of ischium	Back of head of tibiofibula	Adducts or extends thigh and flexes or extends shank, depending on its position
Gluteus	Outer dorsal side of ilium	Head of femur	Rotates femur forward
Iliacus	Ilium and pubis	Middle third of femur	Flexes and rotates thigh
		Muscles of shank	
Gastrocnemius	Distal end of femur and triceps femoris	Tendon of Achilles	Extends angle and foot; flexes shank
Tibialis posterior	Posterior surface of tibiofibula	Proximal end of tibiale (astragalus)	Extends foot when flexed; flexes foot when fully extended
Tibialis anterior	Distal end of femur	Fibulare (calcaneum) and tibiale	Flexes foot and extends shank
Extensor cruris	Distal end of femur	Tibiofibula	Extends shank
Peroneus	Distal end of femur	Lower end of tibiofibula; head of calcaneum	Extends shank; when foot extended; extends it farther; if flexed, flexes it farther

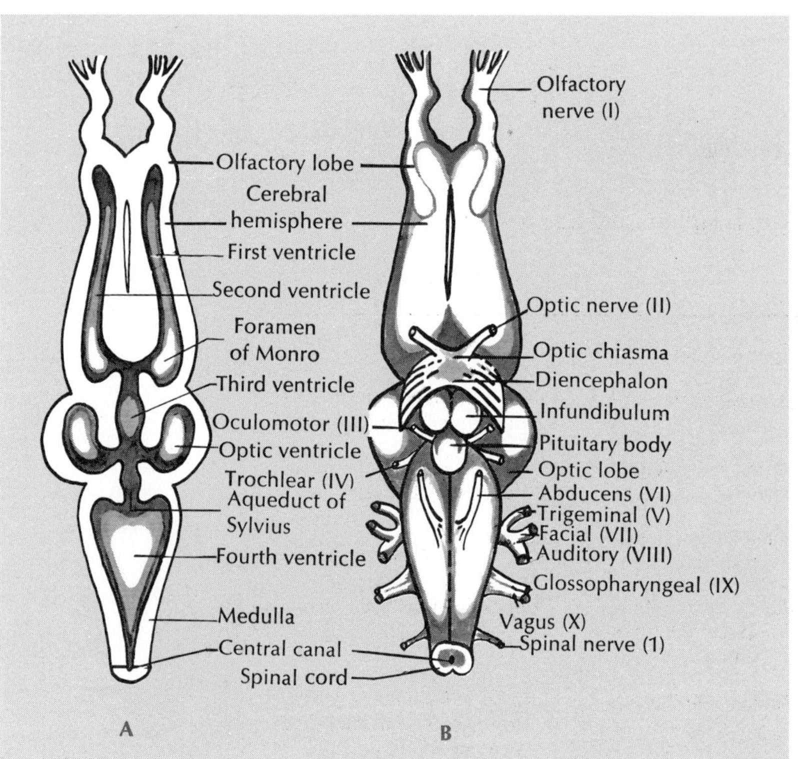

FIG. 26-35

Brain of frog. **A,** Longitudinal section showing dorsal view of ventricles. **B,** Ventral view of brain and cranial nerves.

TABLE 26-2

Cranial nerves of frog—origin, distribution, and function

No.	Name	Origin	Distribution	Function
0	Terminal	Forebrain	Lining of nose	Sensory (probably)
I	Olfactory	Olfactory lobe	Lining of nose	Sensory for smelling
II	Optic	Diencephalon	Retina of eye	Sensory for vision
III	Oculomotor	Ventral side of midbrain	Four muscles of eyes	Motor
IV	Trochlear	Dorsal side of midbrain	Superior oblique muscle of eye	Motor
V	Trigeminal	Side of medulla	Muscles of jaw; skin of face and mouth; tongue	Sensory and motor
VI	Abducens	Ventral region of medulla	External rectus muscle of eye	Motor
VII	Facial	Side of medulla	Chiefly muscles of face	Motor and sensory, mostly motor
VIII	Auditory (acoustic)	Side of medulla	Inner ear	Sensory for hearing and equilibrium
IX	Glossopharyngeal	Side of medulla	Tongue, hyoid, pharynx	Sensory and motor
X	Vagus, or pneumogastric	Side of medulla	Larynx, lungs, heart, esophagus, stomach, intestine	Sensory and motor

Within the brain are cavities known as **ventricles.**

Dorsal to the brain are two plexuses of blood vessels that excrete a **cerebrospinal fluid,** which fills the ventricles and the central canal of the spinal cord and circulates between the meninges and the brain and cord. The fluid forms a liquid protective cushion and provides a source of nourishment and a means of other metabolic exchanges for the nervous tissue.

The **spinal cord** continues from the medulla, lies in the neural canal of the vertebral column, and ends as a fine filament in the urostyle. Its **brachial enlargement** and **sciatic (lumbar) enlargement** are associated with a greater nerve supply to the limbs and are absent in fishes and snakes. The spinal cord has **dorsal** and **ventral fissures** and a **central canal** which is a continuation of the ventricles of the brain.

Peripheral nervous system. There are ten pairs of **cranial nerves** (Fig. 26-36 and Table 26-2) extending from the lateral and ventral surfaces of the brain, through openings in the skull, to the head, throat, and trunk. Fish also have ten pairs of cranial nerves, whereas reptiles, birds, and mammals have twelve pairs. An additional pair, the **nervus terminalis,** has been found in some vertebrates at the anterior end of the brain.

Ten pairs of **spinal nerves** come from the spinal cord and emerge between the vertebrate to be distributed on the dorsal wall of the abdomen just under the peritoneum. Each spinal nerve joins the cord by two

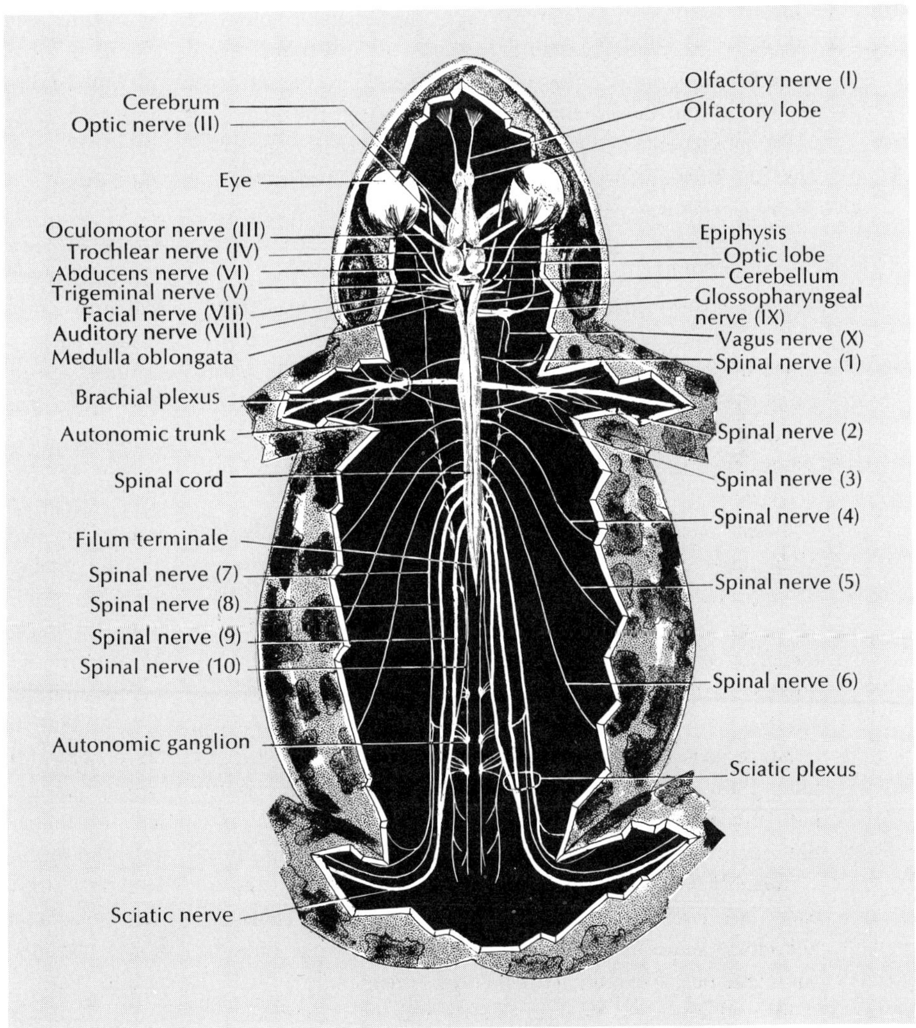

FIG. 26-36

Dorsal view of nervous system of frog.

roots. A **dorsal sensory root** carries sensory impulses into the cord, and a **ventral motor root** carries motor impulses from the cord to glands and muscles of the body. On each side of the body, the first, second, and third nerves form the **branchial plexus,** which provides nerves to the forelimb and shoulder region. The fourth, fifth, and sixth nerves supply the abdominal wall; the seventh, eighth, and ninth nerves on each side form a **sciatic (lumbosacral) plexus** to the hind limb, and the tenth pair goes to the bladder and cloaca.

Sympathetic nervous system (autonomic). The sympathetic nervous system in the frog consists of a pair of slender nerve trunks, which start at the cranium and run along the dorsal wall of the coelomic cavity. Each trunk has **ten ganglia,** which are connected by nerves (**rami communicantes**) with the adjacent spinal nerves. From these ganglia branches are given off to the visceral organs. The sympathetic system regulates many internal involuntary functions, such as the heartbeat, movements of the alimentary canal, secretions of the digestive juices, tone of blood vessels, and action of the urogenital, respiratory, and reproductive systems.

Sensory system

The sensory system of the frog is made up of sense organs, or receptors, which receive information (stimuli) concerning changes in the external or internal environment. Sensory nerves carry the nervous impulses aroused by the stimuli to the central nervous system, where they are interpreted by the frog as characteristic sensations.

Sense organs of skin. The skin is richly supplied with nerve endings and is sensitive to many kinds of stimuli, such as touch, chemicals, temperature, humidity, and light. The tadpole has a **lateral line system,** which is similar to that of fish and is concerned with vibrations in the water, but this system is absent in the adult.

Sense organs of mouth. The mouth epithelium contains many general nerve endings whose functions are not fully well known, but there are many **taste buds** on the tongue and on the floor and roof of the mouth.

Specialized sense receptors. Smell in the frog is located in the **olfactory epithelium** lining the nasal cavity. **Olfactory cells** have tufts of fine cilia on their outer ends and nerve connections on their inner ends.

Frogs have only two portions of the vertebrate ear, the middle and the internal. The external ear is absent in frogs. The middle ear is closed externally by the **tympanic membrane,** or eardrum, a conspicuous structure on frogs. Just underneath the eardrum is the cavity of the middle ear, which communicates with the mouth through the eustachian tube. Connecting the eardrum to the internal ear is a rod-shaped **stapes** (columella), which extends across the cavity of the middle ear and transmits vibrations of the tympanic membrane to the oval window of the internal ear. The latter is a membranous labyrinth surrounded by cartilage and bone. It is filled with a fluid, **endolymph,** and bears the sensory nerve endings of the auditory (eighth) cranial nerve. Sound waves transmitted to the inner ear cause the endolymph to vibrate, and sound impressions are registered by the sensory end organs of the auditory nerve. The sense of equilibrium is taken care of in the inner ear by the **semicircular canals,** which are filled with fluid. The pressure of this fluid stimulates certain nerve endings that carry the impulses over a branch of the auditory nerve to the brain, where they are interpreted as sensations of equilibrium. The endolymphatic ducts (blind, tubular outgrowths of the sacculus part of the membranous labyrinth) are very large in the frog. They run dorsally and ventrally around the brain and down the trunk inside the vertebrae. Where the spinal nerves emerge, the ducts are covered with calcium carbonate, producing the little white spots easily seen in dissection. The frog ear also has a unique sensory structure, the **amphibian papilla,** near the upper part of the sacculus. It may have a role in hearing.

The **eye** is specialized for responding to light. The frog's eyes are built on the same plan as are those of man. The eyeballs are globular in form and are placed in the orbits, where each eye is manipulated by six muscles attached to its posterior wall. Two of these muscles are called the **external oblique** and the **internal oblique** muscles, and the other four are called the **rectus** muscles. The outer covering of the eyeball is the tough white **sclerotic coat** of connective tissue that is modified anteriorly to form the transparent **cornea.** Underneath this coat is the **choroid coat,** pigmented and vascular, which has an opening in its pigmented **iris,** the **pupil.** The innermost coat is the **retina,** containing the sensory **rods** and **cones.** Light impulses are carried from the rods and cones by means of the optic nerve (second cranial) to the brain. Behind the pupil, which contracts or dilates to regulate the amount of light entering, is the spherical crystalline **lens.** Unlike the lens of the human eye, the frog's lens does not change its shape or position, and so the frog's eye can form images of objects only beyond a certain distance. The lens is held in place by the **ciliary processes,** which extend from the lens to the choroid wall. The region over the cornea and beneath the lids is lined with the transparent **conjunctiva.** A third eyelid, a thin membranous **nictitating membrane,** can be drawn up over the eye for protection. A more detailed description of the ear and eye structure will be found in Chapter 32.

Digestive system

The plan of the digestive system of the frog is similar in most respects to that of other vertebrate animals. The large **mouth** or **buccal cavity** secretes mucus for lubricating the food, for there are no salivary glands in the frog (Fig. 26-37). The frog is carnivorous, living on insects, worms, crustaceans, or anything small enough to catch and swallow whole. A large extensible **tongue** is attached to the anterior end of the floor of the mouth. It is covered with a sticky secretion, and the back of the tongue can flip out rapidly (in about 1/20 of a second) to capture the prey. The **maxillary** and **vomerine teeth** in the upper mouth help keep the prey from escaping. Swallowing is achieved by a combination of muscular movements, mucous secretion, ciliated lining of the mouth cavity, and lowering of the eyes into their sockets, which depresses the roof of the mouth. The back part of the mouth cavity is the **pharynx,** which opens into a very short but muscular **esophagus** leading to the **cardiac end** of the **stomach.** Food is stored temporarily in the stomach, and digestion of proteins is begun there (Fig. 26-38). The stomach has relatively thick muscular walls compared with the rest of the alimentary canal. The **pyloric sphincter** is the constriction between the stomach and the small intestine.

The small intestine is made up of the short **duodenum** and the longer **coiled ileum.** Into the duodenum the common bile duct from the **gallbladder** and the pancreatic duct from the **pancreas** empty by a common opening. Bile, which emulsifies fat, is secreted by the **liver** and is stored in the gallbladder before being poured into the intestine. Pancreatic juice contains enzymes that act upon proteins, fats, and carbohydrates. Intestinal juice may also contain digestive enzymes. Most digestion and absorption take place in the small intestine. The undigested residue passes into the large intestine. Rhythmic waves of muscular contraction, called **peristalsis,** in the walls of the stomach and in-

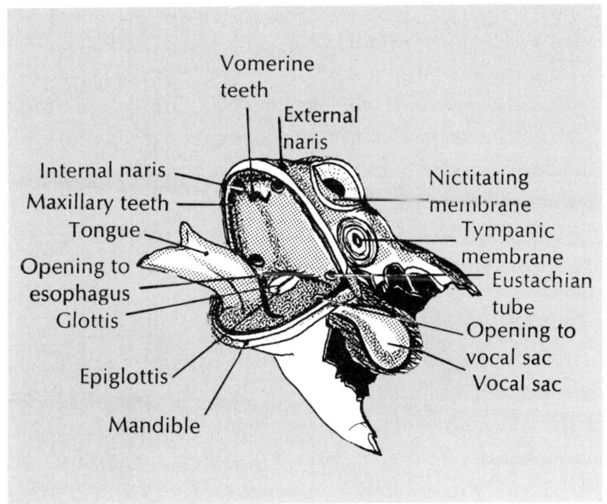

FIG. 26-37

Head and mouth region of frog with vocal sac exposed.

FIG. 26-38

Ventral view of frog's digestive system. Liver lobes pushed aside to show gallbladder.

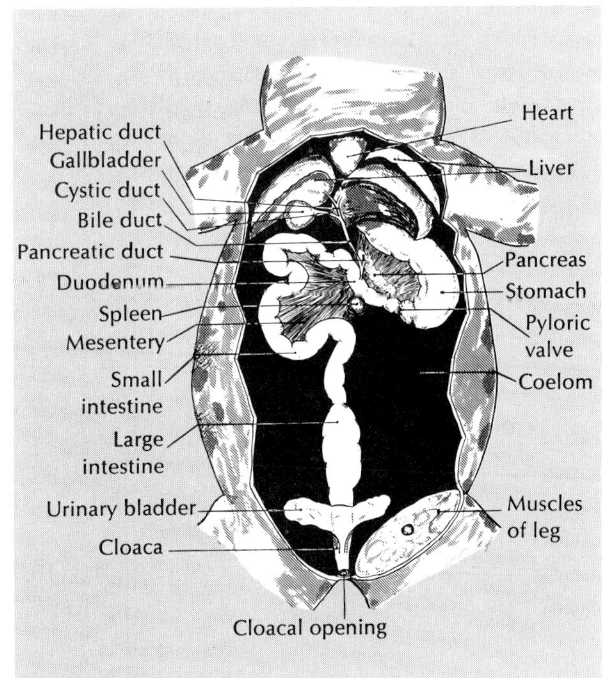

testine keep the food moving along. Emptying of the cloaca is called **egestion.**

The wider large intestine is the storage place for **feces,** the rejected and undigested part of the food. The posterior part of the large intestine opens into the **cloaca,** which also receives the ducts of the urogenital system. The cloaca opens to the outside by the **cloacal opening.** The entire digestive tract is supported dorsally by mesenteries.

Respiratory system

Respiration is effected in the frog both through the moist surface of the outer skin and through the lungs, with some gaseous exchange taking place through the lining of the buccal cavity. The lungs, of course, are the most important, but when the frog is hibernating, the skin does most of the breathing. The skin can function both in and out of water. Whether through the skin or lungs, the basic plan is the same, for before oxygen can diffuse into the blood it must first dissolve in a moist surface. That is why frogs stay where their skin remains moist and does not dry out. Air passes into the mouth through **external nares** or nostrils that connect with **internal nares,** just lateral to the vomerine teeth (Fig. 26-37). The **glottis** is a slitlike opening in the floor of the mouth leading into the **larynx,** or voice box. The larynx is reinforced with cartilages and provided with elastic **vocal cords.** In male frogs **vocal sacs** are located near the corner of the mouth and are inflated to amplify the sound, especially during the mating season. Also opening into the mouth cavity, although not a part of the respiratory system, are the

FIG. 26-39

Respiratory organs of frog.

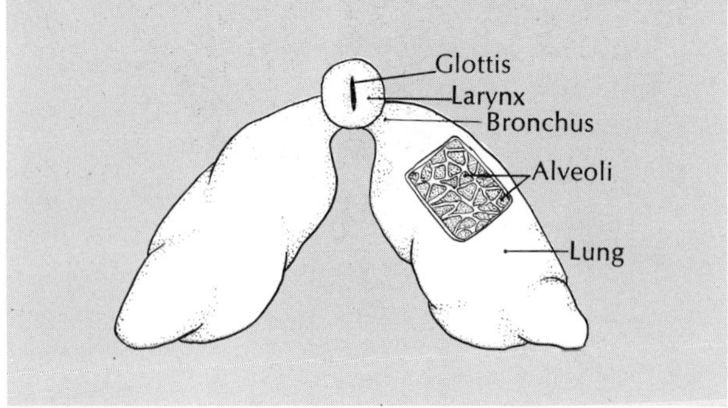

eustachian tubes, which connect with the middle ear and equalize the air pressure on the tympanic membranes. From the larynx a very short **bronchus** leads to each lung (Fig. 26-39). The **lungs** are ovoid, saclike, and elastic. Their inner surfaces are divided by a network of folds into small chambers called **alveoli,** the walls of which are richly supplied with blood vessels for gaseous exchange.

To draw air into the lungs (**inspiration**), the frog closes its glottis and depresses the floor of its mouth, thus drawing air through the nares into the mouth. Closing the external nares and compressing the buccal cavity forces the air through the glottis into the lungs. At **expiration,** the muscles of the body wall contract, compressing the lungs to force out the air. In addition, the frog performs certain oscillatory throat movements by which air is passed in and out of the mouth through the nares. During this process the glottis remains closed, and no air enters or leaves the lungs, but gaseous exchange takes place through the mucous membrane lining of the buccal cavity. When a frog is at rest, these throat movements may continue for some time before the flank movements indicate that the lungs are being emptied.

Circulatory system

The circulatory system of the frog is a closed system carrying red blood in its circuit. Its principal functions are to carry digested food products to the tissues, to carry oxygen from the lungs and skin to the various organs, to carry carbon dioxide and other waste products away from the tissues, and to carry hormones and blood sugar to wherever they are needed. The system is made up of a heart, arteries, capillaries, veins, lymphatic vessels, and the fluid media—blood and lymph.

Blood contains a colorless liquid, the **plasma,** in which are suspended various types of cells, the formed elements of the blood. Blood plasma is composed of water, blood proteins, salts, sugars, various waste products, and other soluble substances. Plasma has the power to coagulate whenever a blood vessel is injured and the blood comes in contact with a foreign substance. The formed elements of the blood include (1) the **erythrocytes,** or red corpuscles, which are elliptical in shape, nucleated, bear the respiratory pigment **hemoglobin,** and are about 22 μ long; (2) the **leukocytes,** or white corpuscles, which are colorless and nucleated and are of different types; and (3) the spindle cells, or **thrombocytes,** which are elongated and nucleated. The red corpuscles, which number from 250,000 to 450,000 per cubic millimeter of blood, are mainly responsible for carrying oxygen; the white corpuscles (about 5,000 to 7,000 per cubic millimeter) are phagocytic against bacteria; and the spindle cells may be involved in blood clotting or the formation of red corpuscles. The various blood cells are formed in **bone marrow** and in the **spleen**; the latter also destroys the worn-out cells.

The **heart** is the pump responsible for driving the blood through the blood circuit (Fig. 26-40). It is enclosed in a two-layered sac, the **pericardium.** The heart consists posteriorly of a single conical **ventricle** with thick muscular walls, two anterior atria (auricles) with thin walls, a triangular **sinus venosus** on the dorsal surface of the heart, and the large, tubular **conus arteriosus** on the ventral surface. The chambers are separated by valves to keep the blood flowing in one direction. Blood is brought by the venous system to the sinus venosus, which forces it into the right atrium. The left atrium receives freshly oxygenated blood from the lungs. Contraction of the two atria then drives the blood into the ventricle. Experimental evidence shows that the two kinds of blood mix here and that some of the unoxygenated blood is pumped to the tissues along with the oxygenated blood. Contraction of the heart is called **systole;** its relaxation is termed **diastole.**

The **arterial system** (Fig. 26-41) of the frog may be said to begin where the conus arteriosus divides into a left and a right **truncus arteriosus,** each of which subdivides into three arches: the **pulmocutaneous,** the **systemic,** and the **common carotid.** Each pulmocutaneous branch gives rise to a **pulmonary artery** to the lungs and a **cutaneous artery** to the skin for oxygenation of the blood. Each common carotid arch gives off the small **external carotid** to the tongue and the larger **internal carotid** to the mouth, brain, and eye.

The two systemic arches pass dorsally around the alimentary canal and unite to form the **dorsal aorta,** which runs toward the posterior part of the body. In its course each systemic arch gives off small arteries to the throat, jaw, skull, and vertebral column and a large **subclavian artery** to the shoulder and arm. The **dorsal aorta** runs just underneath the vertebral column and gives off the **coeliacomesenteric** to the digestive tract, a number of **urogenital arteries** to the kidneys and reproductive organs, **lumbar arteries** to the dorsal body wall, and a single **posterior mesenteric** to the large intestine. Just behind this artery the dorsal aorta bifurcates into the two large arteries, the **common iliacs,** which give rise to the femoral and sciatic arteries to the legs.

The **venous system** (Fig. 26-42) includes those blood vessels in which the blood flows toward the heart. Veins are usually thinner but are larger in diameter than corresponding arteries. The left atrium of the heart receives blood from the lungs through the **pulmonary veins;** the **sinus venosus** receives blood from three large trunks: the paired **anterior venae cavae** and the single **posterior vena cava.** Each anterior vena cava

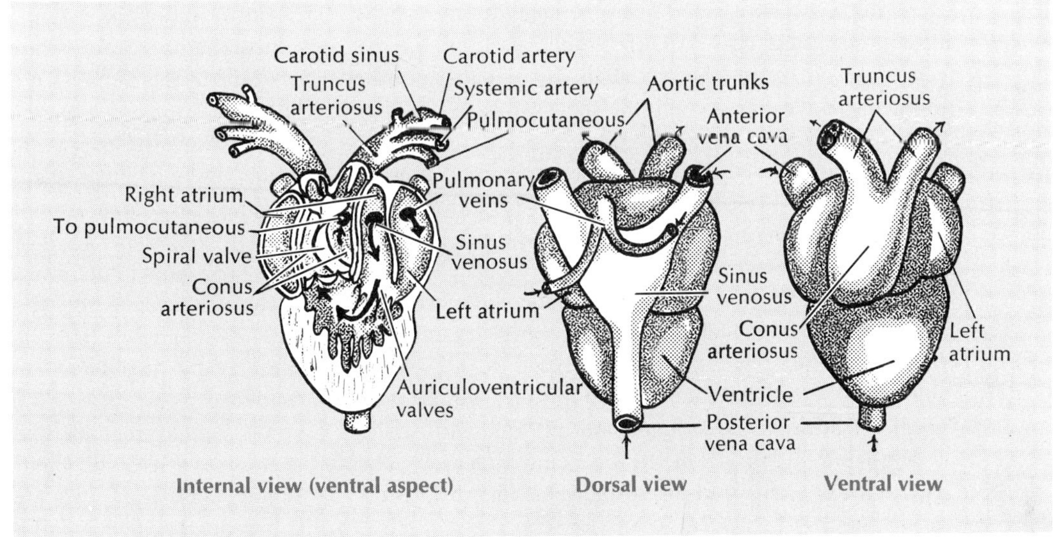

FIG. 26-40

Structure of frog's heart.

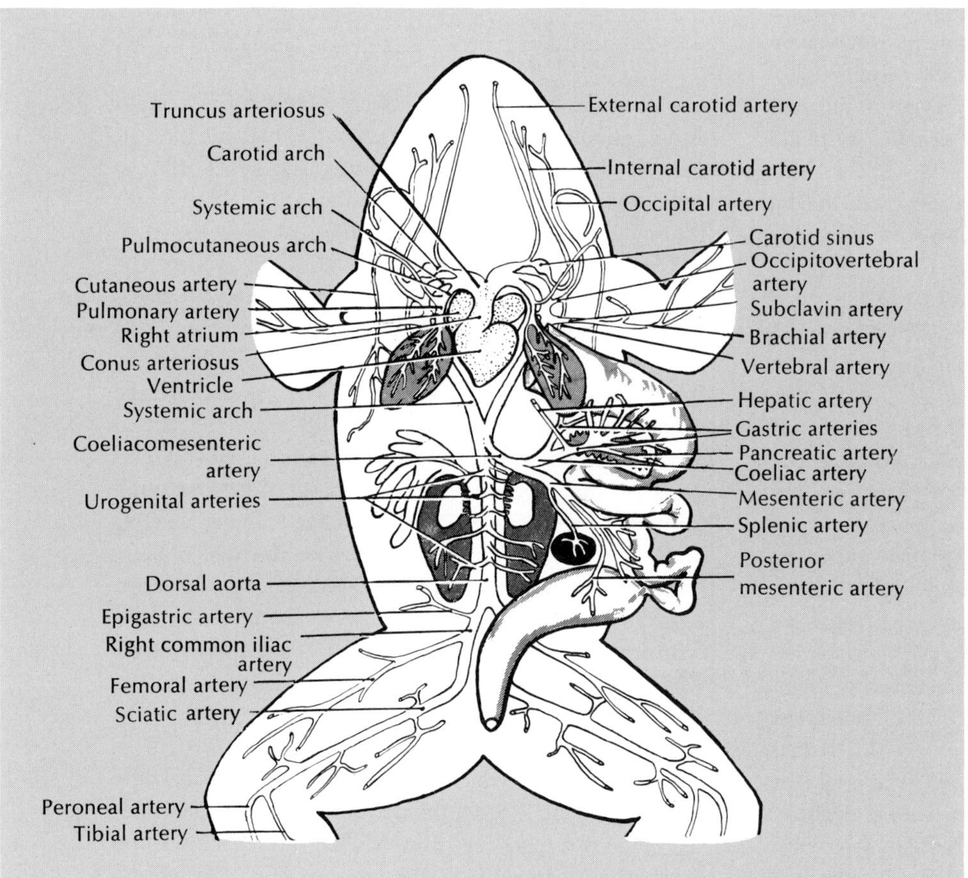

FIG. 26-41

Arterial system of frog. Ventral view.

collects blood from (1) the **external jugular,** which drains the tongue and floor of the mouth; (2) the **innominate,** which receives blood from the head by way of the **internal jugular** and from the shoulder by way of the **subscapular;** and (3) the **subclavian,** which receives blood from the forelimb by means of the **branchial** and from the side of the head and body by the **musculocutaneous.**

The **posterior vena cava** receives two large **hepatic veins** from the liver, **renal veins** from the kidney, and **spermatic** or **ovarian** veins from the reproductive organs. Two **portal systems** are found in the frog. Such a system does not return the venous blood directly to the heart but to a capillary system in some organ, from whence another vein returns the blood to the heart. One of these is the **hepatic portal system,** which picks up the blood from the stomach and intestine and carries it to a sinusoid system in the liver and thence by the hepatic veins to the posterior vena cava. The purpose of the hepatic portal system is to carry the digested food products to the liver, which either stores them or acts upon them in some way before releasing them to the circulation. The hepatic portal vein also receives the **ventral abdominal vein,** carrying blood from the hind limbs, bladder, and ventral body wall. The **renal portal system** carries blood to a capillary system in the kidneys. It is made up of two **renal portal veins,** which receive blood from the legs and back. By this plan the blood from the hind limbs may return to the heart, either by way of the ventral abdominal vein to the liver (hepatic portal system) or by way of the kidneys (renal portal system). There is no renal portal system in man.

Capillaries are the small blood vessels that connect the arteries with the veins. Whenever an artery approaches a capillary bed, it branches into **arterioles,** which, by contraction and dilation of their muscular walls, largely regulate the supply of blood to an organ. Arterioles subdivide into capillaries, which are provided with thin walls for the exchange of materials between the blood and tissues. For the defense of the

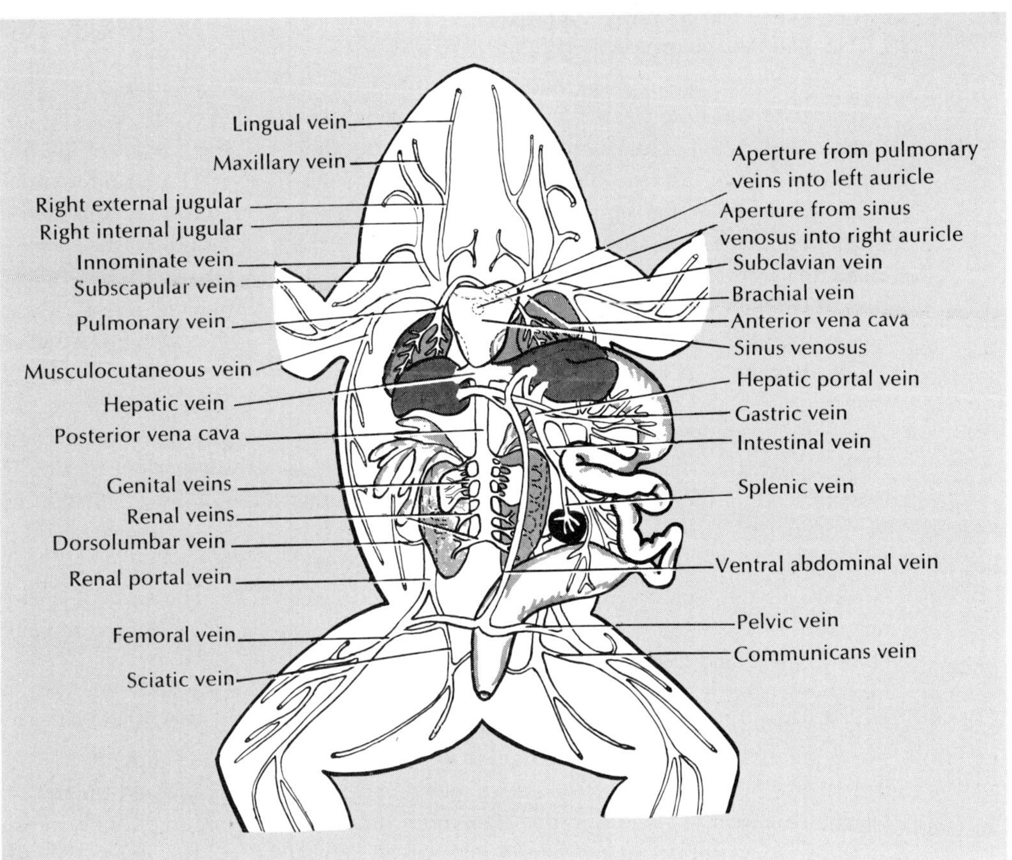

FIG. 26-42

Venous system of frog. Ventral view.

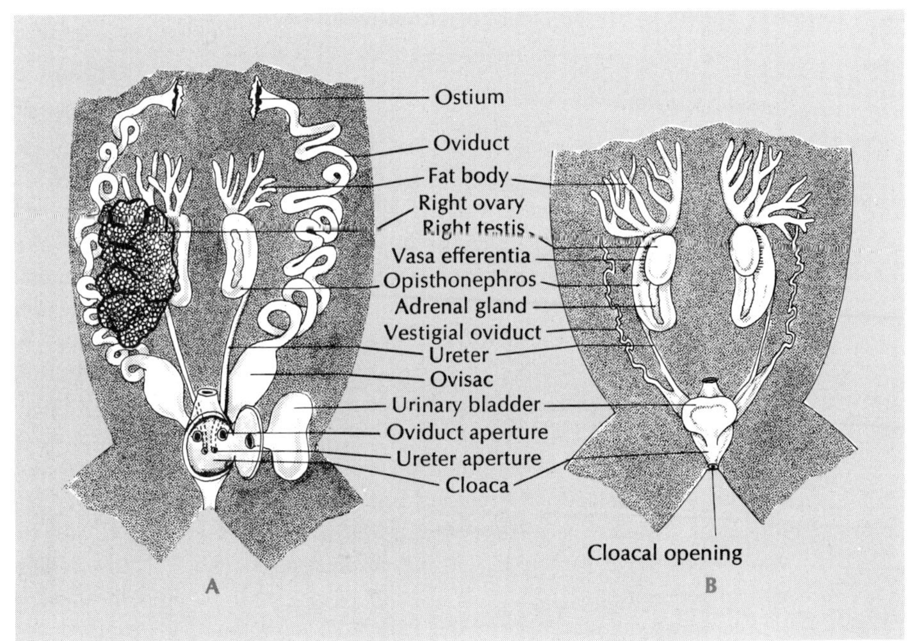

FIG. 26-43

Urogenital system of frog *Rana pipiens*, ventral view. **A,** Female; **B,** male. Male leopard frog is the only common frog that has vestigial oviduct, which indicates that in early embryo there are beginnings of organs of both sexes (bisexuality).

body, white blood corpuscles can migrate through the walls (**diapedesis**) into the tissues, from whence they are carried back into the blood by the lymphatic system. To complete the circuit through the capillaries, small **venules** join to form the veins that carry the blood toward the heart. To see capillary action at its best advantage the networks in the web of the frog's foot is a classic demonstration.

The **lymphatic system** of the frog is more primitive than that of higher vertebrates. There is an abundance of subcutaneous lymph sinuses all over the body, especially under the skin, which partly accounts for the looseness of the skin. The lymph spaces are separated by connective tissue septa, and the larger ones are lined with thin endothelial cells. One of the most important is the **subvertebral lymph sinus (cisterna magna)**, which extends above the kidneys along most of the dorsal body wall. The colorless **lymph** contains leukocytes and various constituents of blood plasma. It is formed by the filtering of blood plasma through the capillaries. Lymph flow is sluggish and inconstant but is aided by the pulsating of two pairs of **lymph hearts.** One pair, found near the transverse processes of the third vertebra, pumps lymph into the vertebral vein of the internal jugular; the other pair, on either side of the tip of the urostyle, pumps the lymph into a branch of the renal portal veins. The lymphatic system functions as an accessory transportation system between the blood and the tissues.

Excretory system

Excretion is the removal of the end products of metabolism. Frogs, in common with other vertebrates, have a number of organs for the disposal of waste, such as the skin, lungs, bile of the liver, and, more especially, the regular excretory system. The latter is made up of two kidneys, certain ducts (ureters), and a urinary bladder. Because of the intimate association of the excretory and reproductive systems in the frog, they are often considered together as the **urogenital system** (Fig. 26-43).

The **kidneys** (opisthonephroi) are two flat, reddish organs lying dorsal to the coelom and peritoneum in the large lymph space—the **cisterna magna.** On the ventral surface of each kidney is the **adrenal** gland (an endocrine gland).

The histologic structure of the kidney reveals about 2,000 units or **nephrons,** each consisting of a **renal corpuscle** and a **uriniferous tubule** surrounded by capillaries. The role of these nephrons is the separation of waste and certain other products from the blood by the process of filtering, etc.

The uriniferous tubules of a kidney join to form **collecting tubules** that empty into the **ureter.** The liquid waste, **urine,** passes down the ureters to the **cloaca,** where it may pass to the outside through the **anus** or else be stored temporarily in the **urinary bladder,** which is attached to the ventral side of the cloaca. Interesting histologic structures, known as **nephrostomes,** are found on the ventral surface of the kidney. They are ciliated funnels that open by one end into the coelom and by the other into the renal veins or, in tadpoles, into the uriniferous tubules. They pass waste from the coelom to the blood and represent an interesting stage in the evolution of the nephron.

The histology and physiology of the kidneys is discussed more fully in Chapter 31.

Endocrine system

Endocrine glands produce hormones, which are diffused directly into the blood or lymph instead of being discharged upon a surface by ducts. **Hormones** have an important role in stimulating or inhibiting other parts of the body. The frog probably has most of the endocrine glands characteristic of higher vertebrates. The action of these glands, however, is better known in higher animals. Vertebrate endocrine glands and their hormones will be discussed in Chapter 33.

Reproductive system

Morphologically the sexes in frogs show few external differences. The male possesses vocal sacs, which are noticeable only when in use, and nuptial pads on the inner digits of the forelegs. These are lacking in the female. Internally, however, there are marked sexual differences.

The **male reproductive system** (Fig. 26-43, *B*) consists of two testes and a series of tubules for carrying the sperm from the testes. Each **testis** is a whitish, oval body attached by a mesentery (mesorchium) near the anteroventral surface of the kidney. It is made up of a coiled mass of **seminiferous tubules** in which the sperm are produced. From each testis a number of delicate tubules, the **vasa efferentia,** pass through the mesorchium, penetrate the inner margin of the kidney, and connect to the anterior uriniferous tubules. The ureter, or wolffian duct, serves to convey the sperm down to the cloaca. The posterior end of the ureter is enlarged as a **seminal vesicle** in which the sperm may be stored temporarily. The ureter in the male thus serves a double function, for it carries urine from the kidneys and sperm from the testes. Near the anterior end of the testes are the yellowish, much-branched, large **fat bodies,** which provide food reserves for hibernation and for the functioning of the sex glands. A pair of vestigial structures, the müllerian ducts, which are homologous to the oviducts in the female, are found as small wavy tubes near the kidneys. They enter the cloaca near the ureters. The embryonic testis of the frog has an anterior Bidder's organ, which usually disappears in the adult frog but persists in adult toads, in which it develops into a functional ovary if the testis is removed.

The **female reproductive system** (Fig. 26-43, *A*) of the frog is made up of two ovaries and two oviducts for carrying the eggs to the cloaca. Each ovary is fastened to the dorsal body wall of the coelom by a mesentery (**mesovarium**). In the summer and fall each ovary is a small grayish mass; in the early spring it is a large swollen gland filled with large numbers of dark round eggs. In structure an ovary is a lobed hollow sac made up of a double wall. Between the layers of this wall the eggs lie enclosed in follicles of cells. The ciliated funnel-like openings (**ostia**) of the two **oviducts** do not connect directly to the ovaries but are placed anteriorly in the body cavity near the lungs. The oviducts are whitish in color, much convoluted, and provided with glands, which secrete gelatinous coats around the eggs. Just before entering the cloaca, the oviducts are dilated into enlargements, the **ovisacs,** where the eggs are collected before being discharged to the outside through the cloaca. When the ripe eggs ovulate, they break through the thin ovarian walls into the body cavity. By the action of the cilia that cover the peritoneum and by muscular movements of the abdominal cavity, the eggs are moved anteriorly to the ostia. Within the oviducts the eggs are moved down by ciliary action and pick up their gelatinous coats in their passage.

Reproduction and life cycle

Frogs are cold-blooded (poikilothermous) animals; their distribution and activities are therefore controlled by seasonal changes and climatic conditions. Their activities are restricted to the warmer seasons of the year, when they breed, feed, and grow. During the winter months in colder climates they spend their time in hibernation. During hibernation they are lethargic, do not feed, and live upon their food reserves—fat bodies, glycogen of liver, etc. Naturally their metabolic states are at a very low ebb at this time. Their breathing is slow, their heartbeat is decreased, and their body temperature is only slightly above that of their surroundings.

The time of spring emergency varies with different species. One of their first interests after leaving their dormant period is breeding. At this time the males are vociferous with their croaking. The males of many species have vocal sacs to amplify their sounds. Although the females are mostly silent during this time, they have the power to croak, which they do when they are seized by predators or when in pain. The breeding season usually extends for several weeks. When their eggs are ripe, the females enter the water and are mounted and clasped by the males in the process called **amplexus.** The male holds the female by pressing the nuptial pads of his thumbs against her breast just back of her forelegs. As the female lays her eggs, the male discharges his seminal fluid containing the sperm over the eggs. The sperm, by movements of their tails, work their way through the jelly layers of the eggs and come in contact with the egg. Only one spermatozoan is necessary to fertilize an egg, and when one penetrates the egg, other sperm in the immediate vicinity are kept out by changes in the egg substance. After fertilization the jelly layers absorb water and swell. Eggs are laid in great masses, which may include several thousands in the leopard frog. The egg masses are usually anchored to vegetation or debris by the sticky jelly layers around the egg. Not all the eggs have a chance to develop, for some may not be fertilized and others are eaten by turtles, insects, and other enemies.

Development of the fertilized egg (zygote) begins about 2 to 3 hours after fertilization (Fig. 26-44). The process involves cleavage, or segmentation of the egg. Cleavage occurs more rapidly at the black, or animal, pole, where there is more protoplasm. The yolk or white (vegetal) pole delays the process of cleavage. Because of this inequality of cell division, there gradually result many small cells at the animal pole side of the egg and fewer larger cells at the vegetal pole. By collecting masses of frog eggs early in the morning, it is possible to find eggs in various stages of develop-

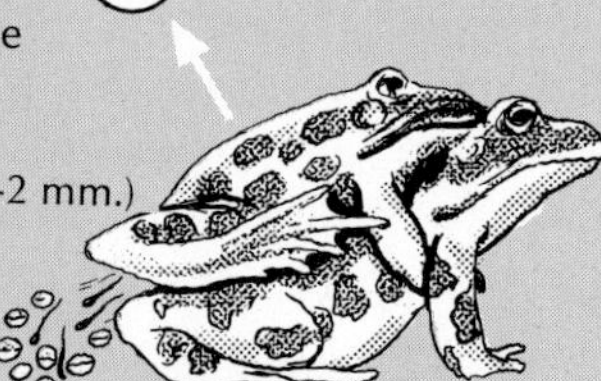

Clasping of male arouses egg-laying reflexes in female; lays 500 to 5000 eggs in one or many masses, which are attached to vegetation and float in water; male fertilizes eggs as they are shed; egg laying may last 10 minutes and occurs at night or early dawn, usually in March or April

3 jelly coats of each egg swell with water and enclose egg with its dark animal pole up and its light vegetal pole down (1-2 mm.)

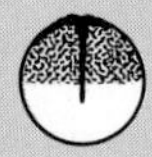

First cleavage occurs in 3-12 hours (depending upon temperature); successive cleavages at about 1-hour intervals

Development produces ciliated embryo, which can move about in egg membrane (5 mm.)

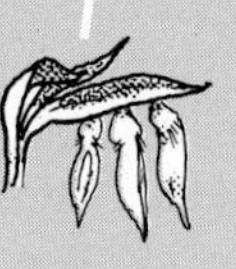

Hatches in 6-9 days into tadpole with rudiments of external gills and lives on yolk packed in its gut; clings to submerged vegetation with its sucker (6 mm.)

3 pairs of external gills and mouth develop and tadpole feeds on algae (6-9 days) (8 mm.)

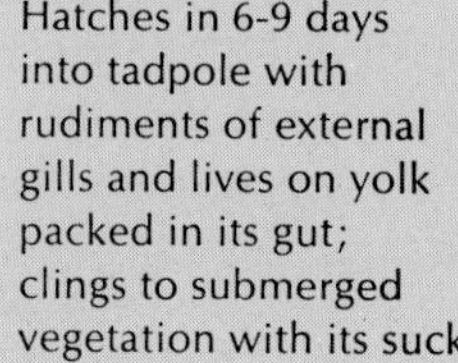

Operculum or skin fold grows over external gills, which degenerate and are replaced by internal gills; pore or spiracle on left side is exit for water (12 days)

(11 mm.)

Hindlegs appear; forelimbs developing under operculum (60+ days)

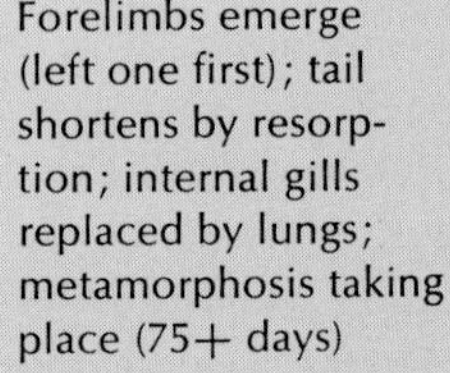

Forelimbs emerge (left one first); tail shortens by resorption; internal gills replaced by lungs; metamorphosis taking place (75+ days)

Metamorphosis completed; tail completely resorbed; functional lungs; emerges as air-breathing, juvenile form (90+ days)

Juvenile frog—1 year (18-31 mm.)

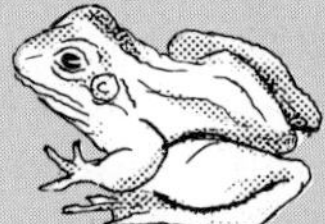

Juvenile frog—2 years (28-41 mm.)

Sexually mature frog —3 years (60-110 mm.)

FIG. 26-44

Life cycle of frog.

ment, such as 2-, 4-, and 8-cell stages. Generally one finds them still further along in development. Factors such as temperature influence the rate of development. (See Chapter 7, pp. 98-99 for early frog development.)

Eggs usually hatch into tadpoles within a period of 6 to 9 days (Fig. 26-44). At the time of hatching, the tadpole has a distinct head and body with a compressed tail. The mouth is located on the ventral side of the head and is provided with horny jaws for scraping off vegetation from objects for food. Behind the mouth is a ventral adhesive disk for clinging to objects. In front of the mouth are two deep pits, which later develop into the nostrils. Swellings are found on either side of the head, and these later become external gills. There are finally three pairs of external gills, which are later replaced by three pairs of internal gills within the gill slits. On the left side of the neck region is an opening, the **spiracle**, through which water flows after entering the mouth and passing the internal gills. Regarding the limbs, the hind legs appear first, while the forelimbs are hidden by the folds of the operculum. In time the forelimbs break through the skin, the left leg usually coming out first through the spiracle. The process of metamorphosis varies in length for different species of frogs. During this process the tail is resorbed (by digestive enzymes released from lysosomes), the intestine becomes much shorter, the mouth undergoes a transformation into the adult condition, the lungs are developed, and the gills are resorbed. The leopard or meadow frog usually completes its metamorphosis within a year or less; the bullfrog takes two or three years to complete the process.

Metamorphosis in the frog is triggered and controlled by the chain reaction of a series of hormones. The hypothalamus of the brain first sends signals or factors to the pituitary gland, which releases a thyroid-stimulating hormone (TSH). In turn the thyroid gland is stimulated by TSH to secrete the hormone thyroxine. This hormone together with some other factors as yet unknown initiates and controls the process of metamorphosis.

• • •

For derivation and meaning of basic terminology see the end of Chapter 27.

Annotated references

Barbour, T. 1934. Reptiles and amphibians, ed. 2. New York, Houghton Mifflin Co. *An interesting account of the habits of amphibians and reptiles.*

Bishop, S. C. 1943. Handbook of salamanders. Ithaca, N. Y., Comstock Publishing Co. *The best handbook on the habits and taxonomy of the salamanders of the United States and Canada.*

Conant, R. 1958. A field guide to reptiles and amphibians of eastern North America. Boston, Houghton Mifflin Co. *A handy pocket-sized guide that is indispensable to the field worker.*

Dunn, E. R. 1926. The salamanders of the family Plethodontidae. Northampton, Mass., Smith College. *An excellent and comprehensive monograph of this interesting family of salamanders. A model for all such treatises.*

Holmes, S. J. 1928. The biology of the frog, ed. 4. New York, The Macmillan Co. *A standard reference book on frogs for the elementary student. Stresses their structure and behavior.*

Marshall, A. M. 1928. The frog, ed. 12. New York, The Macmillan Co. *The well-known English work on the morphology of the frog. Practical and descriptive directions.*

Moore, J. A. (editor). 1964. Physiology of the Amphibia. New York, Academic Press, Inc.

Noble, G. K. 1931. The biology of the Amphibia. New York, McGraw-Hill Book Co. *Morphology, behavior, and classification of frogs and other amphibians.*

Orton, G. L. 1952. Key to the genera of tadpoles in the United States and Canada. The American Midland Naturalist 47:382-395.

Parker, G. H. 1948. Animal colour changes and their neurohumours. New York, Cambridge University Press. *Parts of this work on the color changes of animals are devoted to the amphibians.*

Schmidt, K. P. 1953. A checklist of North American amphibians and reptiles. American Society of Ichthyologists and Herpetologists. Chicago, University of Chicago Press. *This work give scientific names and the distribution of the various species.*

Stebbins, R. C. 1951. Amphibians of western North America. Berkeley, University of California Press. *An up-to-date account of our western amphibian fauna, including both life histories and classification.*

Wright, A. H., and A. A. Wright. 1949. Handbook of frogs and toads of the United States and Canada. Ithaca, N. Y., Comstock Publishing Co. *The best work of its kind in existence.*

Young, J. Z. 1962. The life of vertebrates, ed. 2. New York, Oxford University Press. *A pretentious work that attempts the integration of all aspects—embryology, anatomy, physiology, etc.—of vertebrate life. It is a book for the serious student, for it gives a unified view of vertebrate life and its evolution.*

CHAPTER 27

• PHYLUM CHORDATA (THE VERTEBRATES: REPTILES)

Class Reptilia

CLASS REPTILIA*—lizards, snakes, turtles, and crocodiles

● Reptiles represent the first class of vertebrates that have gone all out for a terrestrial life. They include snakes, lizards, turtles, tortoises, alligators, and crocodiles. So closely affiliated in structures are they with birds that the two classes are sometimes referred to as the Sauropsida. There are more than 6,000 species of reptiles in the world, and of these more than 300 species are found in the United States. They were far more common and dominant in the dim geologic past; the Mesozoic period is called the Age of Reptiles. Reptiles were the first vertebrate class to break away from breeding in the water. Although many of them, such as alligators, snakes, and turtles, live in or near the water, they always return to the land to lay the eggs. The name of the class refers to the method of locomotion common among many of them.

Origin and adaptive radiation of reptiles

It is generally agreed that reptiles arose from labyrinthodont amphibians sometime before the Permian period. The stem reptiles belonged to the order Cotylosaura, which is represented by two basic members—*Seymouria* and *Limnoscelis*. *Seymouria,* a small, partly aquatic tetrapod fossil found in Texas, is a connecting link between the amphibians and reptiles, for it has characteristics of both groups. Paleontologists are not certain about its exact status. The other basic member, *Limnoscelis,* was found in New Mexico and dates from the early Permian period. This form had many characteristics that fit it as a prototype of the reptilian class. It had more reptilian characteristics than the other, but its skull and other skeletal features were definitely amphibian. However, both *Seymouria* and *Limnoscelis* appeared too late in the geologic record to be considered true ancestral reptiles, for the latter were already established by Permian times.

The adaptive radiation of reptiles, especially pronounced in the Triassic period, was correlated with the new ecologic niches provided by the climatic and geologic changes that were taking place at that time, such as a variable climate from hot to cold, mountain building and terrain transformations, and a varied assortment of plant life.

The Mesozoic was the age of reptiles. Why did reptiles decline from their former greatness? Most of the great reptilian orders died out completely by late Cretaceous times. No one factor can be blamed, for groups in wholly different environments became extinct. A combination of climatic and ecological factors, excessive specialization, low reproduction rate, etc., may have been responsible, but all these are speculative. Why did some survive against the fierce competition of the mammals? Turtles had their protective shells, snakes and lizards evolved in habitats of dense forests and rocks where they could meet the competition of any tetrapod, and crocodiles, because of their size and natural defense and offense, had few enemies in their aquatic habitats.

Characteristics

1. Body variable in shape, compact in some, elongated in others; **body covered with an exoskeleton of horny epidermal scales** with the addition sometimes of bony dermal plates; **integument with few glands**
2. **Limbs paired, usually with five toes,** and adapted for climbing, running, and paddling; absent in snakes
3. Skeleton well ossified; ribs with sternum forming a complete thoracic basket; **skull with one occipital condyle**

*Rep-til'e-a (L. *repere,* to creep).

4. Respiration by lungs; **no gills**; cloaca used for respiration by some; branchial arches in embryonic life
5. **Three-chambered heart; crocodiles with four-chambered heart**; usually one pair of aortic arches
6. Kidney a metanephros (paired)
7. Nervous system with the optic lobes on the dorsal side of brain; **twelve pairs of cranial nerves** in addition to nervus terminalis
8. Sexes separate; fertilization internal; meroblastic (amniote) **eggs, which are covered with leathery shells**
9. Embryonic membranes including the **amnion, chorion, yolk sac,** and **allantois** present during embryonic life

Orders

Order 1. Squamata (squa-ma'ta) (L. *squamatus,* scaly, + *ata,* characterized by). Skin of horny epidermal scales or plates, which is shed; teeth attached to jaws; quadrate freely movable; vertebrae usually concave in front; anus a transverse slit. Examples: snakes (3,000 species), lizards (3,800 species), chameleons.

Order 2. Testudinata (tes-tu'di-na"ta) (L. *testudo,* tortoise) (**Chelonia**). Body in a bony case of dermal plates with dorsal carapace and ventral plastron; jaws without teeth but with horny sheaths; quadrate immovable; vertebrae and ribs fused to shell; anus a longitudinal slit. Example: turtles and tortoises. 400 species.

Order 3. Crocodilia (croc'o-dil"e-a) (L. *crocodilus,* crocodile, + *ia,* pl. suffix) (**Loricata**). Four-chambered heart; vertebrae usually concave in front; forelimbs usually with five digits, hind limbs with four digits; quadrate immovable; anus a longitudinal slit. Examples: crocodiles and alligators. 25 species.

Order 4. Rhynchocephalia (rhyn'ko-ce-fa"le-a) (L. *rhyncho,* snout, + Gr. *kephale,* head). Vertebrae biconcave; quadrate immovable; parietal eye fairly well developed and easily seen; anus a transverse slit. Example: *Sphenodon* only species existing.

How Reptilia show advancement over Amphibia

Reptiles have certain adaptations not found in amphibians. Some of these advancements shown by reptiles are as follows:

1. Reptiles have developed some form of copulatory organ so necessary for internal fertilization.

2. The amniote eggs of reptiles are leathery and limy, which resist desiccation and air exposure. Amphibian eggs have gelatinous covering.

3. Reptiles have dry, scaly skin, which is adapted to land life.

4. Reptiles have protective embryonic membranes, which are lacking in amphibians.

5. Reptiles also have a partial or complete separation of the ventricle, thus ensuring a higher type of oxygenation, but there is some mixing of venous and arterial blood through right and left arches.

6. Most reptiles have developed limbs well adapted for efficient locomotion on land.

Distinctive structures of reptilian body

In contrast to the soft, naked body of amphibians reptiles have developed an **exoskeleton** that is largely waterproof. This exoskeleton consists of dead horny scales formed of keratin, a protein substance found in the epidermal layers of the skin. Reptilian scales are not homologous to fish scales, which are derived from the dermis and represent a kind of bone. Reptilian scales may be flat and fitted together like a mosaic, or they may be widely separated; in some cases they overlap like roof shingles. Underneath each scale is a dermal vascular papilla, which supplies nutriment to the actual scale. In some the outer layer of the scales is continually being shed, either in small bits or sloughed off periodically in one piece. Turtles, however, add new layers of keratin under the old layers in the scales. Modified forms of scales are found in the reptile group. The scutes of a turtle shell are large, platelike scales. Also, in some reptiles the epidermal scales are reinforced by dermal plates (osteoderms). Scales are of diagnostic value in the identification of some reptiles, such as snakes.

The **skeleton** of the early reptiles (cotylosaurs) was similar to that of the labyrinthodont amphibians. Most changes in later reptiles involved a loss of skull elements (by fusion or otherwise) and adaptable transformations for better locomotion and other functions. The nostrils of an alligator or crocodile are on the dorsal side of the head and the internal nares are at the back of the throat, which can be closed off by a fold. Thus the reptile can breathe while holding its prey submerged. The reptilian skull has developed a more flexible joint with the vertebral column, and more efficient girdles were evolved for supporting the body. The toes are provided with claws. Their peglike teeth vary somewhat but do not show the differentiation of the mammal; they may be set in sockets (thecodont) or fused to the surface of the bone (acrodont). In many the teeth are found in two rows along the edges of the premaxillae and maxillae, in the upper jaw, and along the dentaries of the lower jaw. Teeth may also be present on some of the palate bones. They are absent in turtles, in which only a horny beak is present.

Muscular development has kept pace with the greater limb movements of reptiles as compared with amphibians. Trunk muscles show less importance, although their segmented nature is conspicuous in some. Much of the muscular arrangement of reptiles is similar to that found in mammals.

The **body cavity** of reptiles is mostly divided into sacs by mesenteries, ligaments, and peritoneal folds. The heart is always enclosed in a pericardial sac. Among the turtles the lungs lie outside the peritoneal cavity. Lizards have a posthepatic septum that divides the peritoneal cavity into two divisions, and crocodiles have a similar one that contains muscle and may function in respiration. This partition, however, is not homologous to the mammalian diaphragm.

Most reptiles are carnivorous and their **digestive system** is adapted for such a diet. All are provided with a tongue. This is large, fleshy, and broad in crocodiles and turtles. In crocodiles a tongue fold with a similar fold of the palate can separate the air passage from the food passage. In some reptiles (chameleon) the tongue is highly protrusible and is used in catching their prey. When not in use, the anterior part of such a tongue is telescoped into the posterior portion. Buccal glands vary a great deal. In snakes the upper labial glands may be modified into poison glands. The stomach is usually spindle shaped and contains gastric glands. Pebbles or gastroliths are found in some reptiles (crocodiles) for grinding the food. A short duodenum receives the ducts from the liver and pancreas. The walls of the midgut are thrown into folds, but there are few glands. The **cloaca,** which receives the rectum, ureters, and reproductive ducts, may be complicated. A urinary bladder is found in *Sphenodon,* turtles, and most lizards and opens into the ventral wall of the cloaca.

The **excretory system** is made up of the paired elongated or compact kidneys (metanephroi), which contain no nephrostomes. Ureters carry the urine (fluid in turtles and crocodiles; semisolid with insoluble urates in the others) to the cloaca.

All reptiles have **lungs** for breathing. The glottis behind the tongue is closed by special muscles. The larynx contains arytenoid and cricoid cartilages but no thyroid cartilages. The trachea is provided with semicircular cartilage rings to keep it open. Lungs are mainly simple sacs in *Sphenodon* and snakes (in which one is reduced), but in turtles and crocodiles they are divided into irregular chambers, with the alveoli con-

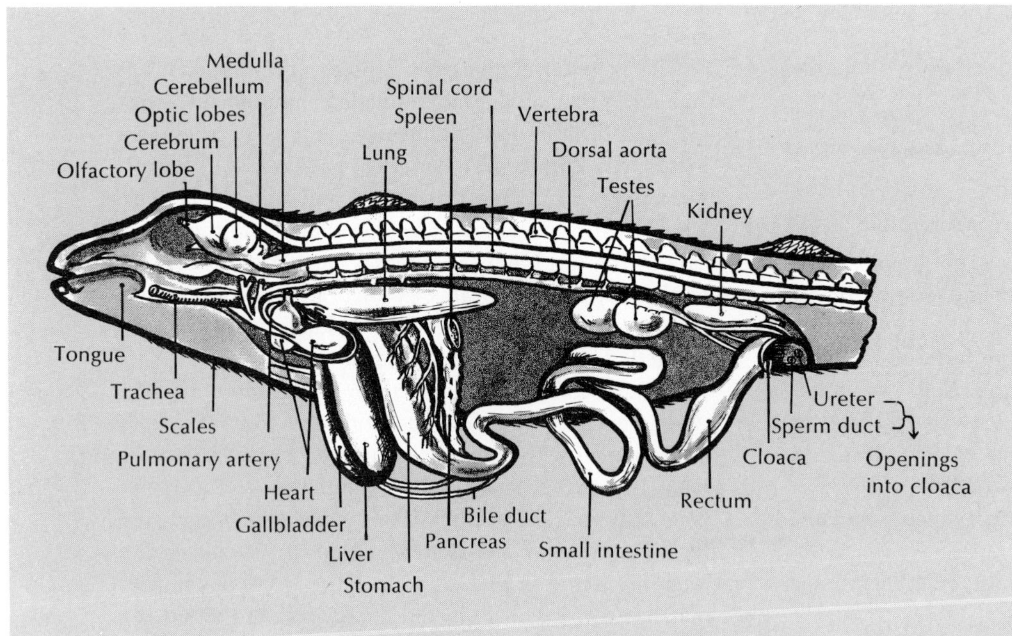

FIG. 27-1

Internal structures of male lizard. Reptilian body shows advancement over amphibians in having (1) scaly skin for dry land, (2) amniotic egg for land existence, (3) better ossified skeleton and more efficient limbs, (4) heart partly or completely separated into four chambers, and (5) beginning regulation of body temperature by behavior patterns.

nected to branched series of bronchial tubes. In chameleons long, hollow processes of the lungs pass posteriorly among the viscera and represent forerunners of the air sacs of birds. Air is drawn into the lungs by the movements of the ribs and, in crocodiles, by the muscular diaphragm.

Since there is no branchial **circulation** in reptiles, on each side the fifth aortic arch is lost, the third becomes the carotid arch, the fourth the systemic arch, and the sixth the pulmonary arteries. The systemic arches are paired in contrast to the single one of birds and mammals. In crocodiles there are two completely separated ventricles; in the other groups the ventricle is incompletely separated (Fig. 27-1). **Crocodiles are thus the first animals with a four-chambered heart.** The conus and truncus arteriosus are absent. Venous blood is returned to the sinus venosus of the heart through the paired precaval and the single postcaval veins. Renal and hepatic portal systems are present. The blood contains oval, nucleated corpuscles that are smaller than those of amphibians.

The male **reproductive system** consists of paired elongated testes that are connected to the vasa deferentia (the wolffian or mesonephric ducts). The latter carry sperm to the copulatory organ, which is an evagination of the cloacal wall and is used for internal fertilization. These copulatory organs are single in crocodiles and turtles but paired in lizards and snakes, in which they are called **hemipenes** (Fig. 27-2). The female system is made up of large paired ovaries, and the eggs are carried to the cloaca by oviducts, which are provided with funnel-shaped ostia. The glandular walls of the oviducts secrete albumin and shells for the large amniote eggs. The two embryonic membranes, amnion and allantois, first appear in reptiles and are used for the protection and respiration of the embryo.

FIG. 27-2

Paired hemipenes of male snake. These copulatory devices of snakes and lizards are fingerlike sacs in lateral wall of cloaca. In copulation one hemipenis is everted (like fingers of glove) with spines outward, inserted into female cloaca, and held there by the spines until completion. Sperm are conducted in grooves to female oviducts. When not in use, hemipenes are drawn back into tail pockets by retractor muscles.

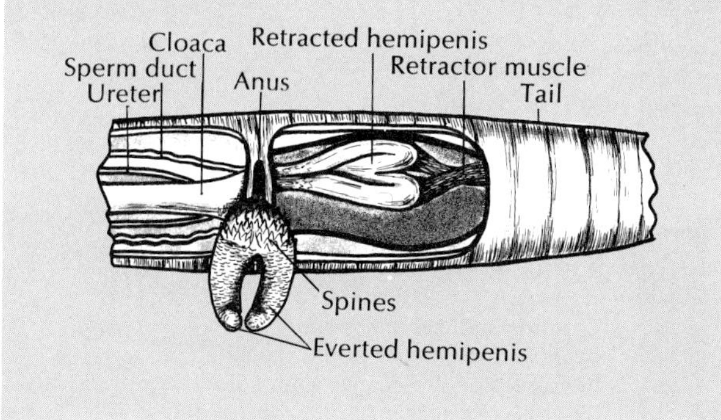

The reptilian **nervous system** shows many advancements over that of the amphibians. The parts of the brain are enlarged and fiber connections are increased; relatively, however, the brain is small, never exceeding 1% of the body weight. There are twelve pairs of cranial nerves in addition to the nervus terminalis. A better developed peripheral nervous system is associated with the better limbs of reptiles. Sense organs vary among the different reptilian groups, but in general they are well developed. The lateral line system, however, is entirely lost. The sense of hearing is poorly developed in most. All reptiles have a middle and inner ear, and crocodiles have an outer one as well. The middle ear contains the ear ossicle (stapes) and communicates with the pharynx by the eustachian tube. A unique sense organ, Jacobson's organ, is a separate part of the nasal sac and communicates with the mouth; it is especially well developed in snakes and lizards. It is innervated by a branch of the olfactory nerve and is used in smelling the food in the mouth cavity. This organ in some form is found in other groups, including the amphibians.

Structure and natural history of orders

Squamata. This order is made up of snakes, lizards, and chameleons. All of them shed the outer dead layers of the skin periodically, for their scales are bound together in a continuous armor. The group is usually divided into suborders Saura, or Lacertilia, which includes the lizards, and Serpentes, or Ophidia, which includes the snakes. Lizards have movable eyelids, external ear openings, and legs (usually); snakes lack these.

Lizards are extremely diversified (Figs. 27-3 and 27-4), ranging in length from 1 or 2 inches to several feet. They are found from the hottest desert to forested regions and the water. *Draco,* a lizard found in India, is able to volplane from tree to tree because of skin extensions on the side. Its limbs are well developed for running and climbing. A few lizards such as the glass lizard are limbless. The skin of lizards is flexible, with the scales arranged in rows. On the ventral surface they have small overlapping scales instead of transverse scutes, which snakes have. Some lizards have thin dermal scales (osteoderms) in the skin in contrast to the thick, bony (dermal) scales of crocodiles and alligators.

Some lizards have evolved methods for regulating their body temperature within narrow limits. Bogert and others have shown that lizards are able to do this even when the surrounding temperatures may vary widely. Although they lack the internal temperature controls of warm-blooded animals, lizards can obtain a differential effect of the sun's rays by orienting their bodies, either at right angles to the sun for maximum effect or parallel to the rays for minimum effect. Thus basking becomes a fine art with these animals. They can also regulate the absorption of heat by expanding their skin chromatophores when they are cold or by contracting them when the body becomes too warm. Their optimum temperature zone for activity seems to center around 93° F. In cooler temperatures lizards are slow to react; to avoid capture by predators some species hide in safe places. Other species remain active at fairly low temperatures but compensate for the slowing effects of such temperatures by becoming shier and taking flight sooner when an enemy approaches (A. S. Rand).

FIG. 27-3

Five-lined skink *Eumeces,* widely distributed lizard of North America.

FIG. 27-4

Carolina anole *Anolis.* Family Iguanidae. These lizards are popularly called chameleons because they can change their color, like true chameleons of the Old World.

The tongues of some lizards, chameleons in particular, have the power of being extended quickly to catch insect prey. Lizards often lose their tails, which they easily regenerate. Lizards also have a bladder connected to the cloaca, and the male is provided with two hemipenes in the side of the cloaca. In copulation these hemipenes are everted and projected into the female cloaca.

The only poisonous lizard in the United States is the Gila monster found in the southwestern states, Arizona in particular. Although somewhat sluggish, it can move its head quickly in biting. With poison fangs in the lower jaw, it works its poison into its prey by chewing movements. It adapts readily to captivity and requires little care. In the same region with the Gila monster is *Phrynosoma,* the so-called "horned toad," which is really a lizard. Although its grotesque spines give it a formidable appearance, it is harmless and makes an interesting pet.

Snakes (Ophidia) with their limbless, elongated form represent one of the most specialized groups of animals in the world. This loss of limbs is not restricted to the appendages but also applies to the pectoral and pelvic girdles (the latter being found as vestiges in pythons). Snakes also differ from lizards in having no sternum, eyelids, external ear openings, or bladder. Snakes conserve water through the reabsorption of water from their fecal content by the walls of their cloaca and large intestine. The jaws of snakes are loosely connected to the skull so that the mouth may be greatly expanded. Because their ribs are not attached ventrally and because of the great expansion of their mouths, snakes can swallow food much greater in diameter than their own bodies. While swallowing their prey, they hold it firmly with their teeth, which are pointed backward; by moving the jaws first on one side and then on the other, the snake gradually swallows the prey. To breathe while swallowing a large object, snakes have their glottis located far anterior in the floor of the mouth, just behind the teeth.

Like lizards, snakes bear rows of scales that overlap as do shingles on a roof. In some snakes the scales are keeled and in others, smooth. Nearly all snakes have on their ventral surface from chin to anus a single row of transverse scales or scutes and one or two rows on the ventral surface of the tail. In moving, the snakes make use of these scutes by projecting their margins and using them for clinging against a surface while the body is driven forward by lateral undulations. On very

FIG. 27-5

Rat snake *Elaphe obsoleta*—a harmless snake and one of the four largest snakes in the United States. This living specimen is more than 6 feet long, but some are known to grow longer. Kills its prey by constriction.

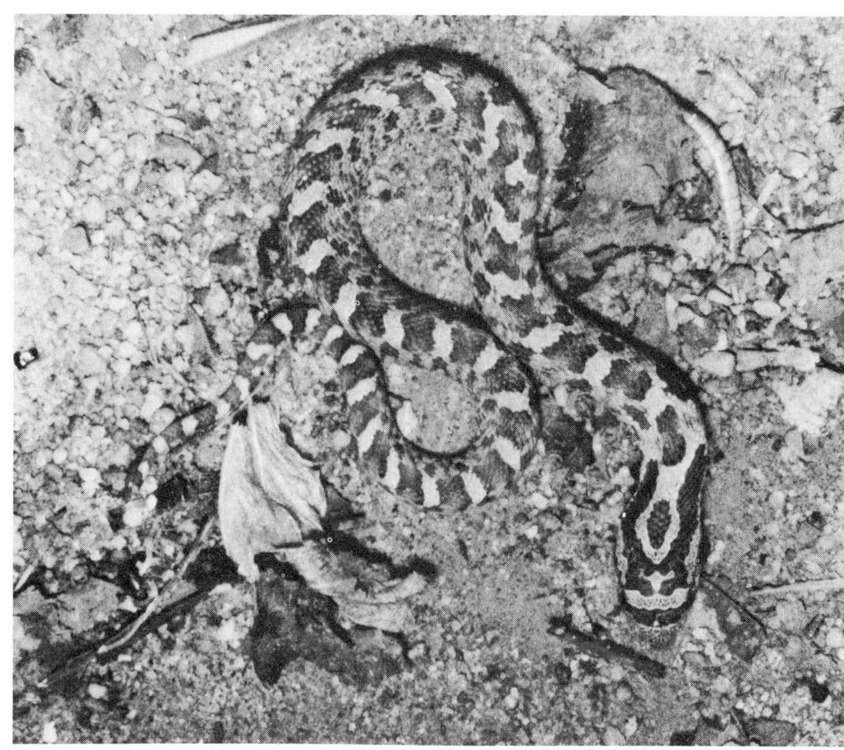

FIG. 27-6

Young hog-nosed snake *Heterodon platyrhinos*. This small snake is harmless but puts up great bluff by flattening its head and hissing. It also feigns death by turning over upon its back.

FIG. 27-7

Ring-necked snake *Diadophis punctatus*. This harmless species rarely exceeds 1 foot in length and is seldom seen because of its habits of concealment.

smooth surfaces snakes cannot move forward easily. Snakes also move by alternately throwing the body into coils and then straightening it out. Most species are good swimmers; they swim by lateral convolutions of the body.

The forked tongue of the serpent is neither poisonous nor harmful; it is merely a sensory organ for detecting chemical stimuli. The tongue can be withdrawn into a sheath in the floor of the mouth. When the mouth is closed the tongue can also be thrust out of a groove between the two jaws. The teeth are sharp and curved backward and are used for holding the prey in swallowing process. In poisonous snakes a pair of teeth on the maxillary bones are modified as fangs. These are grooved or tubular for conducting the poison from the poison sac (a modified salivary gland) into the prey that is bitten. This mechanism is therefore on the order of a hypodermic needle.

The internal organs of snakes are correlated with the elongated body. Usually only the left lung is present, and the alimentary canal is mostly a straight tube. Organs such as the kidneys are at different levels in the body cavity to conserve space.

Most snakes lay eggs (oviparous), but some bring forth the young alive. There is no evidence to show that snakes swallow their young to protect them.

Young copperheads have yellowish tails that they wiggle above the ground to attract the attention of possible prey.

There are more than 100 species of snakes in the United States (Figs. 27-5 to 27-7), of which fewer than 20 species are venomous. The latter include rattlesnakes, copperheads, water moccasins, and coral snakes (Fig. 27-8). All these are pit vipers (except the coral snakes) and derive their name from a small cavity just anterior to the eye. This pit is a specialized sense organ which reacts to temperature and enables the snake to detect a warm-blooded animal. Nearly all pit vipers have long, curved fangs that lie against the upper wall of the mouth when not in use. When striking, however, these fangs (Fig. 27-9) are erected to a position at right angles to the mouth surface and are driven straight into their prey, and the venom is injected at the same time. Just how many people are bitten each year by venomous snakes in the United States is not accurately known but probably not more than a few hundred. Of those bitten, only a small percentage die. More people are bitten by the copperhead *Agkistrodon mokasen* than by any other species, although more deaths are caused by the Texas diamondback rattlesnake *Crotalus atrox* (Fig. 27-10). Rattlesnakes are characterized by the **rattle,** which consists of horny, ringlike segments held loosely together on the end of their tails. When aroused, the snake vibrates these rapidly, producing a buzzing sound. Whenever the skin is shed, the posterior part remains behind to form another ring of the rattle. The number of rattles is not

FIG. 27-8

Coral snake *Micrurus fulvius,* a very poisonous snake that inhabits southern United States and tropical countries. Only representative of cobra family in North America. Body bands black, red, and yellow. (Courtesy F. M. Uhler, U. S. Fish and Wildlife Service.)

FIG. 27-9

Head of diamondback rattlesnake *(Crotalus adamanteus)* showing long fangs in roof of mouth, glottis, and forked tongue in sheath in floor of mouth. Anterior position of glottis enables snake to breathe while slowly swallowing prey.

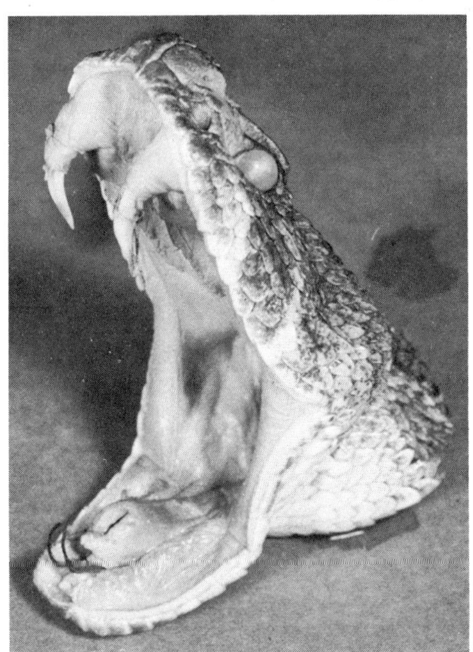

an accurate indication of age, for the snake often sheds more than once a year, and rings of the rattle are frequently lost. The practice of vibrating the tail when excited is common in many species of snakes, venomous or nonvenomous. The famed bushmaster (*Lachesis muta*) of Central America is often referred to by the natives as the "silent rattler" because it has this habit of vigorous vibration of its tail. Our largest poisonous snake in the United States is the eastern diamondback rattlesnake *(Crotalus adamanteus)*, which may reach a length of 8 feet.

FIG. 27-10

Texas diamondback rattlesnake *Crotalus atrox*. More deaths are caused by this snake than by any other species of poisonous snakes in United States. (Courtesy E. P. Haddon, U. S. Fish and Wildlife Service.)

The tropical and subtropical countries are the homes of most species of snakes, both of the venomous and nonvenomous varieties. However, even here most of the members are nonpoisonous. Among warm countries only a few regions such as New Zealand are free from native snakes. Madagascar has no poisonous snakes. In India the death toll from snake bites averages about 25,000 annually. Many persons used to die from poisonous snakes in South America until antivenom serums were developed effectively. The tropics also furnish the enormous constrictor snakes (Fig. 27-11), some of which, like the regal python of the Malay Peninsula, attain a length of 30 feet; the anaconda of South America is another large snake. Their prey rarely exceeds the size of a large pig. The largest of the venomous snakes are the king cobra (hamadryad), which may reach 15 to 18 feet in length, and the bushmaster (*Lachesis*) of Central and South America, which, although never exceeding 10 feet in length, is thick and muscular. Our own Florida diamondback rattlesnake also ranks among the large poisonous snakes of the world.

Poisonous snakes are usually divided into two groups based on type of fangs: the vipers, with long movable fangs, and the Elapidae, with anterior short immovable fangs that chew their venom into the blood of their prey. Examples of Elapidae are the Australian blacksnakes, the cobras, the mambas, and the coral snakes. Most of the back-fanged snakes (Opisthoglypha) are mildly poisonous. Closely related to the cobras are the very venomous sea snakes (Hydrophiidae). Pit vipers,

FIG. 27-11

Boa constrictor *(Boa constrictor)*. This specimen was kept at DePauw University for 23 years, until its death (1961) at nearly 30 years of age. During its vigorous years it ate from 15 to 30 rats or pigeons each summer (by first constricting them to death) but refused to eat in winter. During its last years it ate only 4 or 5 rats a year. It grew 2 to 3 feet in captivity; was nearly 9 feet long.

mostly found in the New World, are represented by the bushmasters, fer-de-lance, rattlesnakes, water moccasins *(Agkistrodon piscivorus)*, and copperheads *(A. mokeson)*. Among the pitless vipers are the great Gaboon viper, the river jack of Africa, and Russell's viper of India.

Snake venom is produced by modified parotid salivary glands.

The mouth secretions (saliva) of all harmless snakes possess some toxic properties, and it is logical that this toxic tendency could be stressed by certain species. Venom is frequently collected from snakes by "milking" the glands. This is done by holding the snake by the neck, placing a small beaker in the jaws, and manipulating the gland with the fingers. Certain venoms have a medicinal value, such as alleviating the pain of cancer; they are also used in making antivenom serums. Snake poison varies with the type of snake. It is usually a thick, yellowish, slightly cloudy liquid that, on exposure to the air, will crystallize into yellow crystals. In a container these crystals may remain toxic for a long time. They are soluble in weak salt solutions. The toxic power of the venom may be destroyed by agencies such as heat and radium.

There are two types of snake venom. One type acts mainly on the nervous systems (neurotoxic), affecting the optic nerves (causing blindness) or the phrenic nerve of the diaphragm (causing paralysis of respiration). The other type is hemolytic; that is, it breaks down the red blood corpuscles and blood vessels and produces extensive extravasation of blood into the tissue spaces. Many venoms have both neurotoxic and hemolytic properties.

Several factors determine the degree of harm the bite of a venomous snake may do. Usually the larger the specimen, the more venom it may inject. Or, if the snake has recently bitten another animal, its poison glands may not have produced their full amount of poison. Venoms do differ in degree of toxicity. This is determined by the minimal lethal dose on laboratory animals. By this standard the venom of *Bothrops insularis*, a member of the fer-de-lance family in South America, appears to be the most deadly of poisons drop for drop.

Even the most deadly snakes have enemies. In the United States the king snakes (*Lampropeltis*) will eat other snakes, especially poisonous ones. The slender king snake will encircle even the big diamondback rattlesnake in its coils and squeeze it to death. The king snake is immune to the poison of the rattler.

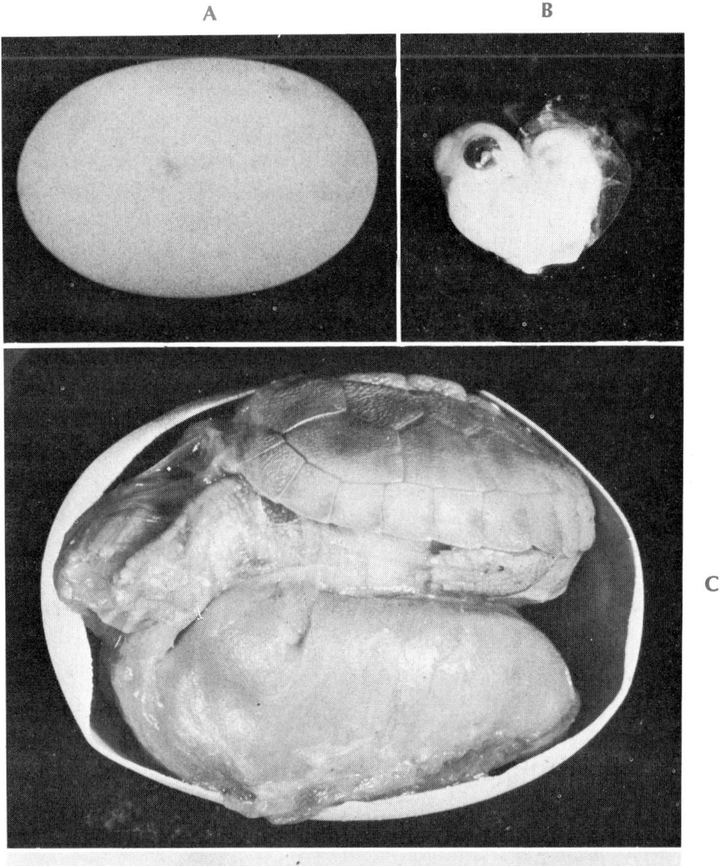

FIG. 27-12

Life history of turtle. **A,** Egg. **B,** Early embryo. **C,** Embryo and large yolk sac enclosed in amniotic membrane, just before hatching. **D,** Baby turtle.

Where venomous snakes abound, natural enemies in some form are sure to act as a curb on their numbers. In India the mongoose (*Herpestes*), a little mammal, attacks and eats the hooded cobra and other poisonous snakes. Many snakes feed upon other snakes, which is the case with the king cobra of southeastern Asia, but the snakes it kills are mostly harmless. In South America the fer-de-lance has two deadly enemies, the skunk (*Conepatus*) and musurana (*Clelia*), a mild-appearing snake of the Brazilian forests. Snakes have many bird enemies, especially some of our large hawks.

Testudinata (Chelonia). Tortoises and turtles are enclosed in shells consisting of a dorsal carapace and a ventral plastron. The shell is so much a part of the animal that it is built in with the thoracic vertebrae and ribs. Into this shell the head and appendages can be retracted for protection. No sternum is found in these forms, and their jaws lack teeth but are covered by a horny sheath. The nasal opening is single. They have lungs, although aquatic forms have vascular sacs in the cloaca that serve for breathing when the animals are submerged. On their toes are horny claws for digging in the sand, where they lay their eggs. Some of the marine forms have paddle-shaped limbs for swimming. Fertilization is internal by means of a cloacal penis on the ventral wall of the male cloaca. All turtles are oviparous, and the eggs have firm, calcareous shells (Fig. 27-12).

Turtles range from a few inches in diameter to the great marine ones that may weigh a thousand pounds. Sea turtles usually grow larger than land forms (Fig. 27-13), although some of the latter in the Galápagos Islands may weigh several hundred pounds. Most turtles are rather sluggish in their movements, which may ac-

FIG. 27-13

Green sea turtle *Chelonia*. Note that limbs are modified into flippers. Such turtles are strictly aquatic except when they lay their eggs on sandy shore. Some of these turtles may weigh as much as 400 to 500 pounds and are greatly prized for turtle soup. (Courtesy C. P. Hickman, Jr.)

FIG. 27-14

Common box turtle *Terrapene*.

FIG. 27-15

Western painted turtle *Chrysemys*, common turtle of ponds and lakes.

count for their longevity; some are believed to live more than a 100 years.

Turtles eat both vegetable and animal products. Many marine forms capture fish and other vertebrates. Land tortoises live on insects, plants, and berries. The common box turtle (*Terrapene*) (Fig. 27-14) grows fat during the wild strawberry season.

The term "tortoise" is usually given to the land forms, whereas the term "turtle" is reserved for the aquatic forms (Fig. 27-15). Among the former, the box turtle (*Terrapene*) is one of the most familiar. It is about 6 inches long. It has a high arched carapace, with the front and rear margins curled up. The lower shell is hinged, with two movable parts so that it can be pulled up against the upper shell. The color markings vary, but usually the shell is a dark brown color with irregular yellow spots. Box turtles are found in woods and fields and sometimes in marshes. In spite of their slow movements, marked individuals have often been found a considerable distance away from the point of release. They lay their eggs in cavities dug out of loose soil and cover them over.

The diamondback terrapin (*Malaclemys*) is widely used as food. This turtle dwells in salt marshes and derives its common name from the markings on its shell. In some eastern regions terrapin farms are maintained on a commercial basis. Diamondbacks grow to be about 10 inches long.

Snapping turtles (*Chelydra*) are found in nearly every pond or lake in the eastern half of this country. They grow to be 12 to 14 inches in diameter and 20 to 40 pounds in weight. They are ferocious and are often referred to as the "tigers of the pond." They are entirely carnivorous, living on fish, frogs, waterfowl, or almost anything that comes within reach of their powerful jaws. They are wholly aquatic and come ashore only to lay their eggs.

Crocodilia. Crocodiles are the largest members of Reptilia; some have been captured that were more than 25 feet long. This order is divided into crocodiles and alligators. Crocodiles have relatively long slender snouts; alligators have short and broader snouts. With their powerful jaws and sharp teeth, they are formidable antagonists. Although all are carnivorous, many will not attack man. The "man-eating" members of the group are found mainly in Africa and Asia. The estuarine crocodile *(Crocodylus porosus)* found in southern Asia grows to a great size and is very much feared. Alligators are usually less aggressive than crocodiles. Alligators are almost unique among reptiles in being able to make definite sounds. The male alligator can give loud bellows in the mating season. Vocal sacs are found on each side of the throat and are inflated when he calls. In the United States, *Alligator mississipiensis* is the only species of alligator; *Crocodylus americanus* is the only species of crocodiles. The latter is confined to Florida and is almost extinct. The American alligator is found from North Carolina to Florida and west to Texas. Few specimens now caught are more than 12 feet long. Although alligators can put up a severe fight when cornered, they are timid toward man and will avoid him. There is no authentic case of an American alligator attacking man, and bathers in southern waters need have no fear of them. The crocodile found in Florida is likewise a harmless animal to man. Fig. 27-16 is an alligator *(Caiman sclerops)* from Central America or South America often sold in U. S.

Alligators and crocodiles are oviparous. Usually from 20 to 50 eggs are laid in a mass of dead vegetation. The eggs are about 3 inches long. The penis of the male is an outgrowth of the ventral cloaca.

Rhynchocephalia. This order, which has many fossil forms, is represented by only one living species, the tuatara (*Sphenodon punctatum*) of New Zealand (Fig. 27-17). This "living fossil" is found on one or two islands in Cook straits and is protected by the New Zealand government. It is a lizardlike form about 2

FIG. 27-16

Small alligator *(Caiman sclerops)* from Central America or South America. Often sold as North American alligator.

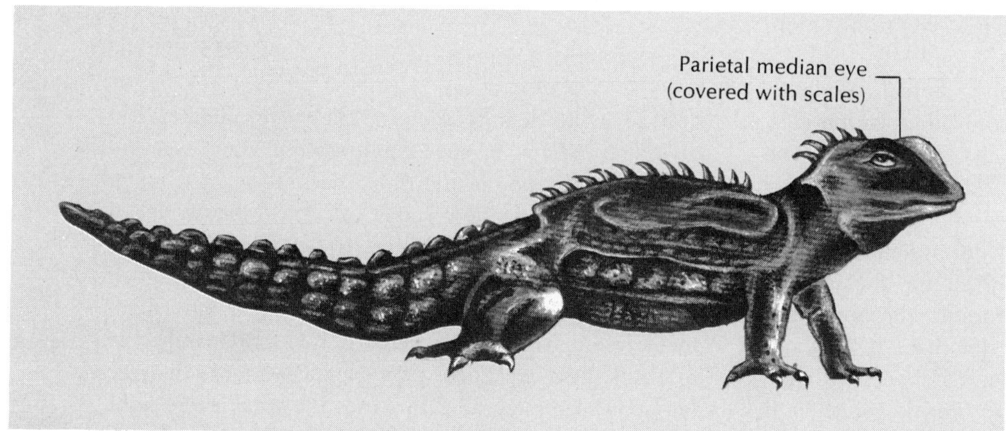

FIG. 27-17

Sphenodon punctatum, the only living representative of order Rhynchocephalia. This "living fossil" reptile has well-developed parietal "eye" with retina and lens on top of head. Eye is covered with scales and is considered nonfunctional but may have been important sense organ in early reptiles.

feet or less in length and has a number of primitive characteristics, such as unique skull peculiarities, abdominal ribs, amphicoelus vertebrae, and a well-marked **parietal eye** that is less degenerate than those in other animals and is one of its most distinguishing structures. This eye even has evidences of a retina. The upper surface of the animal is covered with small scales, and the ventral region is covered with transverse rows of squarelike plates. *Sphenodon* lives in burrows among the rocks, is nocturnal in habits, and eats small animals. This form may not be an ancestor from which modern lizards have descended but may represent an independent specialized type. The members of this order appeared in the Triassic period and all became extinct during the Mesozoic, save only *Sphenodon.* The latter, in spite of a long evolution of 170 million years, has retained many primitive characteristics and represents one of the slowest rates of evolution known among vertebrates.

Brief classification

Body covered with horny (ectodermal) scales or plates; usually four limbs, each with five claws; skeleton ossified; one occipital condyle; lungs throughout life.

Order 1. Testudinata (Chelonia). Body enclosed in a shell of dorsal carapace and ventral plastron; jaws with horny sheaths; no teeth; quadrate bone immovable; vertebrae and ribs fused to shell usually.

Family Chelydridae (ke-lid″ri-de′) (NL. *chelydra,* modif. of Gr. *chelydros,* amphibious serpent, tortoise, + *idae,* family suffix)—**snapping turtles.** Head, neck, and limbs cannot be withdrawn into shell; plastron small with ten plates; upper jaw hooked; carapace and tail tuberculated. Example: *Chelydra.*

Family Kinosternidae (kin-o-ster″ni-de′) (NL. *kin,* from Gr. *kinein,* to move, + *sternon,* breast)—**musk and mud turtles.** Plastron hinged at both ends; edge of carapace not flaring; plastron with nine to eleven plates; odor musky. Example: *Sternotherus.*

Family Testudinidae (tes-tü-din″i-de′) (L. *testudo,* tortoise, akin to L. *testa,* shell)—**tortoises and terrapins.** Carapace with flaring edges; plastron with twelve plates. Example: *Chrysemys.*

Family Cheloniidae (kel′o-ni″i-dae) (Gr. *chelone,* tortoise, + *idae,* family suffix)—**sea turtles.** Body large; limbs like flippers; marine; shell with smooth horny shields. Example: *Chelonia.*

Family Trionychidae (tri′o-nik″i-de′) (Gr. *tria,* three, + *onyx,* nail of finger or toe, claw)—**soft-shelled turtles.** Carapace leathery without horny plates or scales; snout long and flexible. Example: *Amyda.*

Family Dermochelyidae (der″mo-che-ly′i-de) (Gr. *derma,* skin, + *chelys,* tortoise)—**leatherback turtles.** Marine; limbs flipperlike; carapace leathery; large. Example: *Dermochelys.*

Order 2. Rhynchocephalia. Parietal organ (third "eye") present; scales granular; middorsal row of spines; quadrate bone immovable; vertebrae biconcave. Example: *Sphenodon.*

Order 3. Squamata. Skin with horny epidermal scales; quadrate bone movable; vertebrae procoelus usually; copulatory organ (hemipenes) present.

Suborder 1. Sauria (so′re-a) (Gr. *sauros,* lizard) **(Lacertilia)—lizards.** Body slender, usually with four limbs; rami of lower jaw fused; eyelids movable; copulatory organs paired.

Family Gekkonidae (ge-kon″i-de′) (Malayan, *ge′kok,* so called from its cry, + *idae,* family suffix)—**geckos.** Body small; toes with adhesive pads usually; eyes without movable lids usually; vertebrae biconcave; tongue protrusible. Example: *Phyllodactylus.*

Family Iguanidae (i-gwa″ni-de′) (Sp., from Arawakan, *iwana*)—**New World lizards.** Head and body scales small; teeth homodont; tongue not protrusible; eyelids present. Example: *Anolis.*

Family Agamidae (a-gam′i-de) (NL.)—**Old World liz-**

ards. Teeth heterodont; tongue short and thick; throat sacs present in some. Example: *Draco.*

Family Chamaeleontidae (ke-me'le-on"i-de) (NL. *chamaeleon*)—**chameleons.** Body somewhat bilaterally compressed; tail prehensile; toes suited for grasping; tongue prehensile; large eyes independently movable; lungs with air sacs; color changes. Example: *Chamaeleo.*

Family Lacertidae (la-ser"ti-de') (L. *lacerta,* lizard)—**Old World lizards.** Body covered with small granular or wedge-shaped scales; pleurodont teeth; head covered with large shields; scales of trunk in transverse rows. Example: *Lacerta.*

Family Scincidae (sking"ki-de' or sin"si-de') (NL. *scincus,* skink)—**skinks.** Body with large and smooth scales; skin folds lacking on side; tongue with indented tip and papillae; legs small. Example: *Eumeces.*

Family Amphisbaenidae (am'fis-be'ni-de) (Gr. *amphis,* on both sides, + *bainein,* to walk)—**worm lizards.** Body elongated, wormlike; limbs absent or rudimentary; scales not overlapping; ears not visible. Example: *Rhineura.*

Family Helodermatidae (he-lo-der-mat"i-de') (Gr. *helos,* nail, + *derma,* skin)—**poisonous lizards.** Body with beadlike scales; tail short and thick; tongue protrusible; lower jaw with grooved poison fangs. Example: *Heloderma.*

Family Anguidae (an"gwi-de') (L. *anguis,* snake)—**plated lizards.** Body elongated; scales large and squarish; fold of skin along each side; limbs small or absent; tongue long and forked; tail long and fragile. Example: *Ophisaurus.*

Suborder 2. Serpentes (ser-pen'tes) (L. *serpens,* serpent)—**snakes (Ophidia).** Body elongated; limbs and ear openings absent; mandibles jointed anteriorly by ligaments; eyes lidless and immovable; tongue bifid and protrusible; teeth conical, and on jaws and roof of mouth.

Family Leptotyphlopidae (lep'to-tif-lop"i-de) (Gr. *leptos,* peeled, + *typhlos,* blind, + *ops,* eye or organism with a specified kind of eye, + *idae,* family suffix)—**blind snakes.** Body small, wormlike; blind; teeth on lower jaw only; vestiges of femur and pelvic bones. Example: *Leptotyphlops.*

Family Boidae (bo"i-de') (L. *boa,* water snake)—**boas and pythons.** Body with smooth scales; pupils vertical; vestiges of pelvic girdle and hind limbs; tails short and obtuse. Example: *Python.*

Family Colubridae (ko-lu"bri-de) (L. *coluber,* snake)—**common snakes.** Body with smooth or keeled scales; facial bones movable; squamosals loosely attached to skull; teeth in both jaws. Example: *Drymarchon.*

Family Elapidae (e-lap"i-de') (MGr. *elaps,* from Gr. *elopa,* fish; perhaps akin to *lepis,* scale)—**immovable-fang snakes.** Body with rounded tail; pupil round; front pair of upper teeth forming short poisonous fangs; very venomous. Example: *Naja.*

Family Crotalidae (kro-tal"i-de') (I. *crotalum,* rattle)—**pit vipers.** Pupil vertical; deep pit between eye and nostril; pair of poison fangs in front part of roof of mouth, folded back when not in use. Example: *Crotalus.*

Order 4. Crocodilia (Loricata). Body long; head large with long jaws; teeth many and conical; short limbs with clawed toes; tail long and heavy and bilaterally compressed; thick leathery skin with horny scutes; tongue nonprotrusible.

Family Gavialidae (ga've-al"i-de) (F., modif. of Hindi, *ghariyal,* + *idae,* family suffix)—**gavials.** Snout very long; first and fourth lower teeth bite into a groove in upper jaw; nasal bones not part of nasal aperture; teeth about equal; scutes on neck and back the same. Example: *Gavialis.*

Family Alligatoridae (al'i-ga-tor"i-de') (Sp. *el legarto,* the lizard, from L. *lacerta,* lizard)—**alligators and caimans.** Head short and broad; first and fourth lower teeth bite into pits in upper jaw; nasal bones form part of nasal aperture; teeth unequal; scutes on neck may be distinct from those on back. Example: *Alligator.*

Family Crocodylidae (krok'o-dil"i-de') (L. *crocodilus,* crocodile)—**crocodiles.** Head is long and narrow; first tooth bites into a pit; the fourth into a groove in upper jaw; nasal bones form part of nasal aperture; teeth unequal; scutes on neck may be distinct from those on back. Example: *Crocodylus.*

Derivation and meaning of basic terminology (amphibians and reptiles)

Ambystoma (Gr. *amby,* blunt, + *stoma,* mouth). Often erroneously called Amblystoma, although Ambystoma is the original term.

Anura (Gr. *an,* without, + *oura,* tail). Order of amphibians to which frogs belong.

Archosauria (Gr. *archos,* chief ruler, + *sauros,* lizard). Great subclass of fossil reptiles that dominated the Age of Reptiles and from which some of our existing reptiles have come.

axolotl (Sp. *axolotl,* servant of the water). Larval stage of *Ambystoma tigrinum,* exhibiting neotenic reproduction.

Cotylosauria (Gr. *kotyle,* cup, + *sauros,* lizard). Fossil stem reptiles that gave rise to the various groups of later reptiles.

Crocodilia (L. *crocodilus,* crocodile, + *ia,* pl. suffix). Order of reptiles; synonym of Order Loricata.

Ichthyostega (Gr. *ichthys,* fish, + *stegos,* covering). This genus of fossil forms is considered to be the oldest amphibians. They had some crossopterygian characteristics and are considered close to the amphibian ancestral stock.

Labyrinthodontia (Gr. *labyrinthos,* tortuous passage, + *odontos,* tooth). An important group (superorder) of fossil primitive amphibians from which most amphibians evolved. Their teeth had complex patterns of enamel infolding.

Lacertilia (L. *lacerta,* lizard). Common genus of lizards.

Ophidia (Gr. *ophis,* snake). Suborder of Squamata, which includes the snakes.

Salientia (L. *saliens,* leaping). Order of Amphibians; same as Anura.

Sphenodon (Gr. *sphen,* wedge, + *odon,* having teeth of a specified kind). Only genus of the order Rhynchocephalia.

Annotated references

Barbour, T. 1934. Reptiles and amphibians, ed. 2. Boston, Houghton Mifflin Co. *Many interesting reptiles are described in this work.*

Buckley, E. E., and N. Porges, 1956. Venoms. Washington, D. C., American Association for the Advancement of Science. *This is an excellent appraisal of the many problems connected with animal poisons. Nearly every phylum from Protozoa to Chordata is represented, but little is known about the nature of the various toxins, which animals employ.*

Carr, A. F., Jr. 1952. Handbook of turtles. Ithaca, N. Y., Cornell University Press. *One of the best handbooks on the subject.*

Conant, R. 1951. The reptiles of Ohio, ed. 2. Notre Dame, Ind., University of Notre Dame. *This work is one of the better state surveys of reptiles and is useful for studying the reptiles also in adjacent states.*

Ditmars, R. L. 1944. Snakes of the world. New York, The Macmillan Co. *A general and popular account of the group by one of the world's greatest authorities.*

Gadow, H. 1901. Amphibia and reptiles (Cambridge Natural History). London, Macmillan & Co., Ltd. *A classic but somewhat outdated survey. Good morphologic descriptions.*

Goin, C. J., and O. B. Goin. 1962. Introduction to herpetology. San Francisco, W. H. Freeman & Co., Publishers. *An elementary text of the basic biologic principles of amphibians and reptiles. A good orientation text for this interesting group.*

Klauber, L. M. 1956. Rattlesnakes, 2 vols. Berkeley, University of California Press. *Everything about the habits and life histories of rattlesnakes, together with a full description of all species, is included in this amazing handbook.*

Moore, J. (editor). 1964. Physiology of the Amphibia. New York, Academic Press, Inc. *A useful and up-to-date treatise by many contributors. A work for the advanced student.*

Pope, C. H. 1937. Snakes alive and how they live. New York, The Viking Press. *An accurate, well-written, semipopular account.*

Pope, C. H. 1955. The reptile world. New York, Alfred A. Knopf, Inc. *All the four major groups of reptiles are represented in this interesting and revealing work. Each of these groups is introduced by such general topics as food, size, enemies, intelligence, reproduction, hibernation, and locomotion. The numerous photographs cannot be surpassed.*

Schmidt, K. P., and D. D. Davis. 1941. Field book of snakes of the United States and Canada. New York, G. P. Putnam's Sons. *One of the most useful field manuals on snakes. Interesting to the beginner.*

Smith, H. M. 1946. Handbook of lizards of the United States and Canada. *An excellent and authoritative manual. The illustrations are mostly photographs which add to the value of the work.*

Wright, A. H., and A. A. Wright. 1957. Handbook of snakes of the United States and Canada, 2 vols. Ithaca, N. Y., Comstock Publishing Co. *This fine, definitive work on snakes is constructed along the same lines as that of the author's great work on frogs and toads. The authors are really field naturalists and their emphasis is on snakes as they are found in the wild. Photographs are clear and numerous. Distribution maps spot the location of the different species.*

CHAPTER 28

• PHYLUM CHORDATA (THE VERTEBRATES: BIRDS)

Class Aves

SUBPHYLUM VERTEBRATA

CLASS AVES*—birds

● Birds are one of the most interesting and most widely known groups of animals. There are more than 8,600 species of birds distributed all over the world. Their taxonomy has been thoroughly worked out, and most authorities do not expect to find many new species in the future. Birds have wide appeal for amateurs. Bird clubs are found in nearly every community, and enthusiasts never tire of learning about the ecologic relations, songs, and identifying characteristics of birds.

Although birds are gifted more than most animals in ease of moving from one habitat to another, some of them are restricted to special regions. One island or mountain valley may have species found nowhere else. These cases, however, are usually exceptional; birds ordinarily range far and take in varied habitats. Many birds have adapted themselves to certain climatic zones and do not stray from them. Thus the arctic and tropic regions have extensive bird life that is unique for those areas.

Birds share with mammals the highest development in the animal kingdom. The nervous system of mammals shows greater advancement, but in most body parts, birds have greater specialization, much of which is correlated with their powers of flight. They are very active forms; this accounts for their higher rate of metabolism and higher body temperature.

Origin and relationships

Since the bones of birds are light and disintegrate quickly, it is only under the most favorable conditions that their remains are preserved as fossils. This explains the difficulty of working out their early relationships. The earliest known bird is *Archaeopteryx,* two specimens of which were found embedded in Jurassic slate in Bavaria in 1861 and 1877. One of these forms is slightly different from the other and is called *Archaeornis.* This land form was about the size of a crow, with a skull not unlike the skulls of modern birds. There were bony teeth in the jaw sockets, and the jaws were elongated into a beak. The tail was long and bore two rows of feathers set obliquely, and each wing had three fingers, each bearing a claw. The foot consisted of a tarsometatarsus with four digits. With the exception of feathers, these birds had a general resemblance to dinosaurs. Other toothed birds of later geologic periods have also been found, especially in the United States. The evidence therefore is strikingly in favor of a reptilian ancestor of birds. The ancestors of birds no doubt came from a branch of the archosaurians (the ruling reptiles), which in turn were derived from the thecodonts. Their exact ancestors are not known. Over the years more and more fossil birds have come to light. By 1950 over 700 different fossil species had been recorded. The modernization of birds took place chiefly during the Cretaceous period, and they were thoroughly modern by early Cenozoic times. Two well-known fossil birds, *Ichthyornis* and *Hesperornis,* were obtained from Cretaceous chalk beds of Kansas. Teeth were present in both these forms, and *Hesperornis,* an aquatic form, had almost completely lost its wings. The famous Rancho La Brea asphalt pits of Los Angeles have yielded many fossil birds of great importance.

Adaptive radiation among birds has produced many types for different adaptations. Just when this adaptive radiation occurred is not clear from the fossil record. Paleontologists think that the basic plan of bird structure was determined early in their evolution because of the restrictions of flight. They believe that few

*A'vez (L. *avis,* bird).

structural changes have occurred in them during the past 50 or 60 million years. But there are evidences that some birds have evolved during the Cenozoic period. Many types have become extinct and have been replaced by others.

Available evidence seems to indicate that birds have evolved from a single ancestor and thus have a **monophyletic** origin. Some authorities have contended that flying birds have had a different origin from flightless forms (**diphyletic** origin).

Existing birds are divided into two groups: (1) **ratite** (Ratitae—ra-ti′te, L. *ratis,* raft), or those that have a flat sternum with poorly developed pectoral muscles and are flightless, and (2) **carinate** (Carinatae—car′i-na″te, L. *carina,* keel), or those that have a keeled sternum with large pectoral muscles and can fly. Most paleontologists think that the carinate group are the more primitive and that the flightless forms were derived from those that could fly. Most flightless forms are found where there are few carnivorous enemies, or else where they can outrun predators so that wings are not necessary for ground-feeding birds.

On the basis of the differences between ancient and modern birds, they are commonly divided into the following groups:

Subclass Archaeornithes (ar′ke-or″ni-thes) (Gr. *archaios,* ancient, + *ornithos,* bird). This included *Archaeopteryx* and possibly one or two other genera.

Subclass Neornithes (ne-or′ni-thes) (Gr. *neos,* new, + *ornithos,* bird). Modern birds are placed in this group. Some extinct species with teeth (Fig. 28-1) are also included here because of their likeness to modern forms.

Birds as a group present a marvelous uniformity of structure. Many authorities maintain that there is less diversity in the entire class than there is in an order of other animals. Perhaps the uniformity of the class is tied up with the closely knit specialized character of the group.

Characteristics

1. Body usually spindle shaped, with four divisions: head, neck, trunk, and tail; **neck disproportionately** long for balancing and food gathering
2. Limbs paired, with the **forelimbs usually adapted for flying;** posterior pair variously adapted for perching, walking, and swimming; foot with four toes (chiefly)

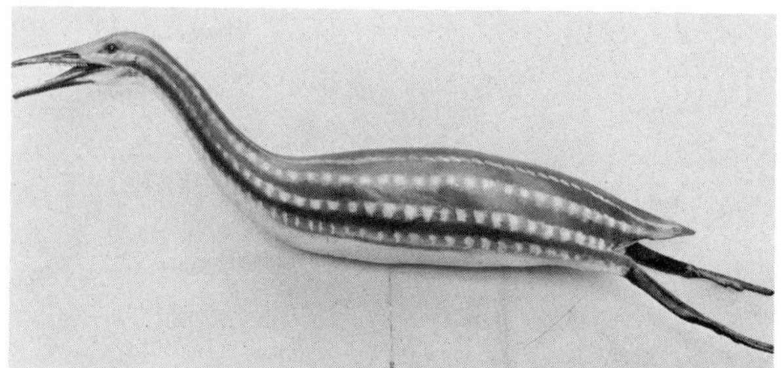

FIG. 28-1

Restoration of *Hesperornis*, a toothed bird that lived during Cretaceous period. This bird was an aquatic flightless form, and fossils of it have been found in the United States. (Courtesy Chicago Natural History Museum.)

3. Epidermal **exoskeleton of feathers** and **leg scales;** thin integument of epidermis and dermis; no sweat glands; oil or preen gland at root of tail; **pinna of ear rudimentary**
4. **Skeleton fully ossified with air cavities or sacs;** skull bones fused with **one occipital condyle;** jaws covered with **horny beaks;** small ribs; vertebrae tend to fuse, especially the terminal ones; sternum well developed with keel or reduced with no keel; **no teeth**
5. Nervous system well developed, with brain and twelve pairs of cranial nerves
6. Circulatory system of **four-chambered heart,** with the **right aortic arch persisting;** reduced renal portal system; nucleated red blood cells
7. Respiration by slightly expansible lungs, with thin air sacs among the visceral organs and skeleton; **syrinx (voice box) near junction of trachea and bronchi**
8. Excretory system by metanephric kidney; ureters open into cloaca; **no bladder; urine of urates, semisolid**
9. Sexes separate; testes paired, with the vas deferens opening into the cloaca; **females with left ovary** and **oviduct;** copulatory organ in ducks, geese, ratites, and a few others
10. Fertilization internal; **eggs with much yolk** and **hard calcareous shells;** embryonic membranes in egg during development; **incubation external;** young active at hatching (**precocial**) or helpless and naked (**altricial**)

What is a feather?

Birds are the only animals that have feathers. Feathers are modified from the epidermis, just as hair is in mammals, and serve for insulation, support of the body in flight, protection of the skin, and regulation of body heat. A typical feather consists of a hollow **quill,** or calamus, thrust into the skin and a **shaft,** or rhachis, which is a continuation of the quill and bears the **barbs** (Fig. 28-2). An aftershaft is also present in some birds (grouse and quail) at the junction of the principal shaft and quill. On the sides of each barb are the smaller **barbules,** whose opposing rows are held together by small **barbicels** with hooks (hamuli). Some flightless birds (ostrich) lack this interlocking mechanism and have a fluffy plumage. If the barbs and barbicels form a flat expansive surface, the structure is called a **vane;** when the barbs form only a fluffy mass, it is called **down.** By means of muscles in its skin, a bird can ruffle its feathers.

A feather originates in much the same way as an epidermal scale. Both are formed from a dermal papilla that pushes up against the overlying epidermis (Fig. 28-3). However, instead of flattening like a scale, the

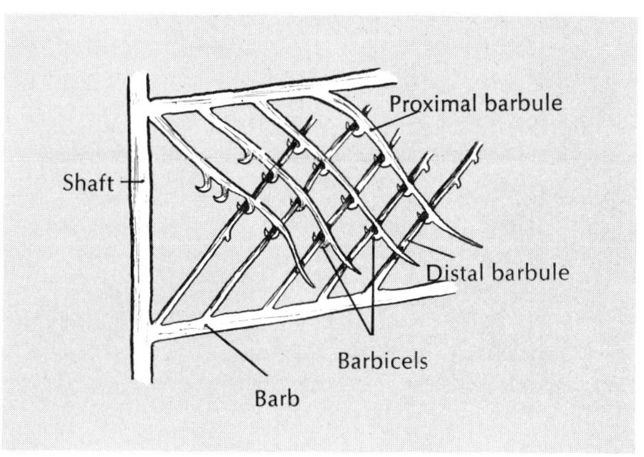

FIG. 28-2

Interlocking mechanism between adjacent barbs in feather vane of bird. Minute barbicels (hooklets) hold opposing rows of barbules loosely together to form continuous surface (vanes).

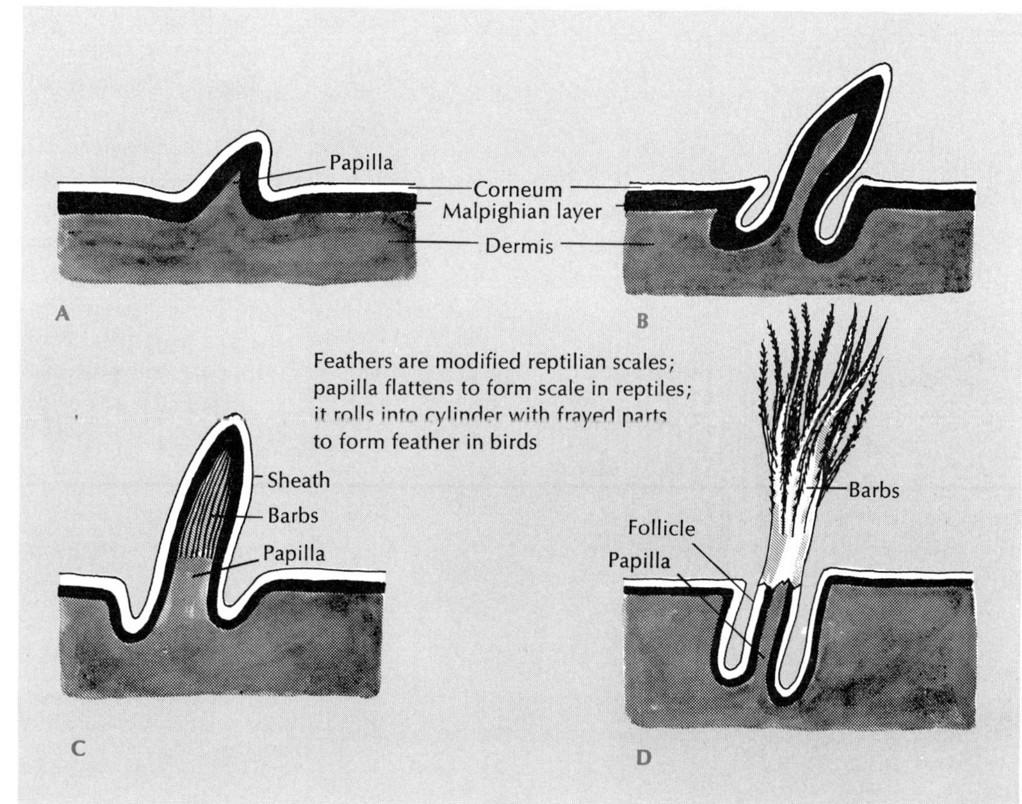

FIG. 28-3

Development of a down feather. **A** to **D,** Successive stages. In contour feather one ridge, or rib (as in **C**), forms a shaft, and when sheath splits, barbs around median shaft spread out to form vane. Pulp cavity of quill, or original dermal papilla with blood vessels, dries out and forms hollow tube with opening at each end (umbilici).

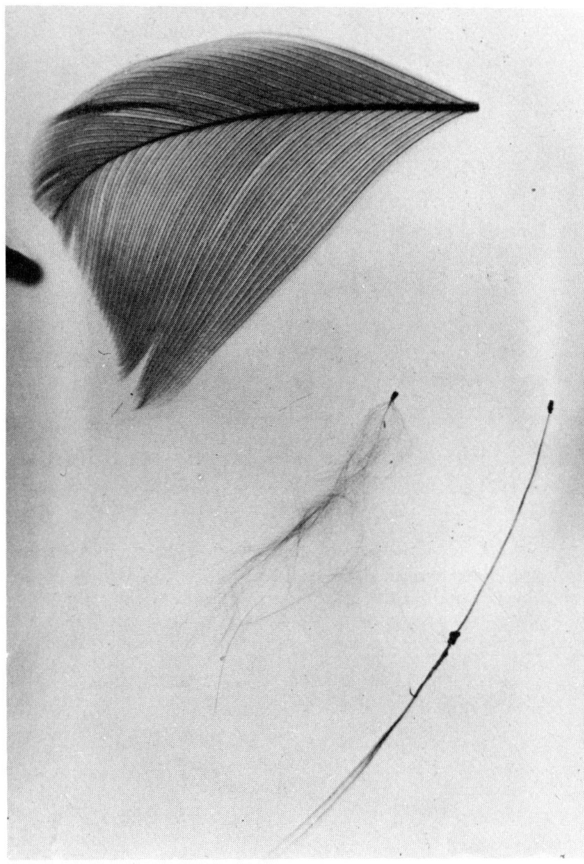

FIG. 28-4

Types of bird feathers. Contour feather above, down feather in middle, and filoplume feather below.

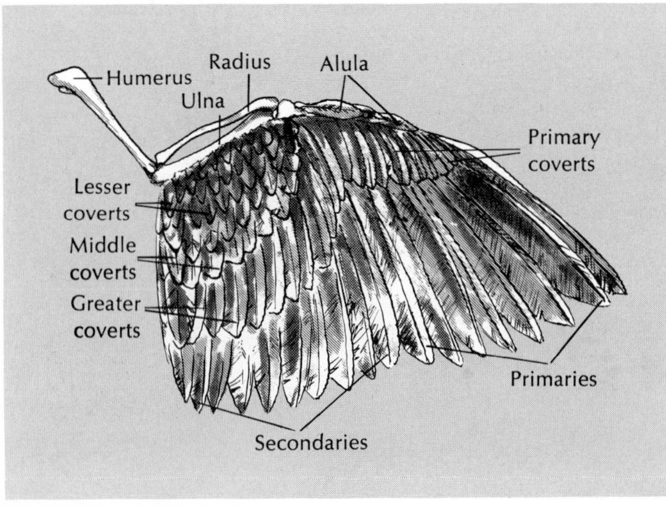

feather rolls into a cylinder or feather bud and is covered with epidermis. This feather bud sinks in slightly at its base and comes to lie in a feather follicle from which the feather will protrude. A layer of keratin is produced around the cylinder or bud and encloses the pulp cavity of blood vessels. This surface layer of keratin splits away from the deeper layer to form a sheath. The deeper layer now becomes frayed distally to form parallel ridges, the median one of which grows large to form the shaft (contour feathers) and the others the barbs. Then the sheath bursts and the barbs spread flat to form the vane. The pulp cavity of the quill dries up when growth is finished so that the quill is hollow, with openings (umbilici) at its two ends. If the feather is to be a down feather, the sheath bursts and releases the barbs without the formation of a shaft or vane. Pigments (lipochromes and melanins) are added to the epidermal cells during growth in the follicle.

The feathers are divided into three types (Fig. 28-4):

1. The **contour feather** is one of the most typical and consists of a central shaft and parallel barbs, arranged to form a vane. The shaft may be either straight or curved, depending upon the position of the feather in the body. These feathers give shape to the bird's body by the overlapping of the vanes and also afford a good heat-conserving surface. There are several types of contour feathers, such as the wing feathers (**remiges**), which include primaries on the hand, secondaries on the forearm, tertiaries on the upper arm (humerus), and tail feathers (**rectrices**). Each feather is usually covered above and below by rows of other feathers known as **coverts** (Fig. 28-5).

2. **Down feathers** are entirely of down and are found interspersed among the contour feathers. They are useful for increasing insulation. They have short quills and short barbules. They are especially abundant on the breasts and abdomens of certain birds such as water birds and birds of prey.

FIG. 28-5

Spread right wing of typical bird. Forelimb of bird modified for flight by changes in carpus and hand. Humerus, ulna, and radius are little changed, but there are only two free carpals (ulnare and radiale); other carpal bones fuse with metacarpals to form carpometacarpus. Of the three digits (II, III, and IV), second has short metacarpal and one phalanx and bears alula; third has long metacarpal and two phalanges; fourth has one long metacarpal and one phalanx. (Compare with Fig. 28-7.) Primary flight feathers are supported by "hand" (digits III and IV and metacarpus), secondary flight feathers by ulna and radius, and tertiary feathers (if present) by humerus.

3. **Filoplume feathers** are a kind of hair feathers in which the shaft is greatly reduced with few or no barbs. They are the pinfeathers that remain on a plucked bird. Modified filoplumes form rictal bristles about the mouth of flycatchers and whippoorwills.

Feathers are distributed over certain areas, known as feather tracts, or **pterylae** (Fig. 28-6). The bare spaces between are the **apteria.** These tracts vary with different species. In penguins and kiwis, feathers occur all over the skin. The term **plumage** refers to all the feathers collectively. **Molting** is the shedding and replacement of feathers, which is an orderly process that takes place gradually so that bare spots are avoided. At certain seasons, usually spring and fall, the molting continues until it is complete. There are many variations of molting. Usually a bird has four moltings during its first year of life, such as postnatal, postjuvenal, first prenuptial, and first postnuptial. Birds in poor health may omit a molt entirely. A molt usually requires about six weeks.

FIG. 28-6

Distribution of feather tracts (pterylosis) of pigeon (dorsal view). Feathers are restricted to certain areas (pterylae); bare areas are called apteria. There are usually eight major feather tracts in birds. In kiwis and penguins, feather tracts are lacking and feathers are uniformly distributed.

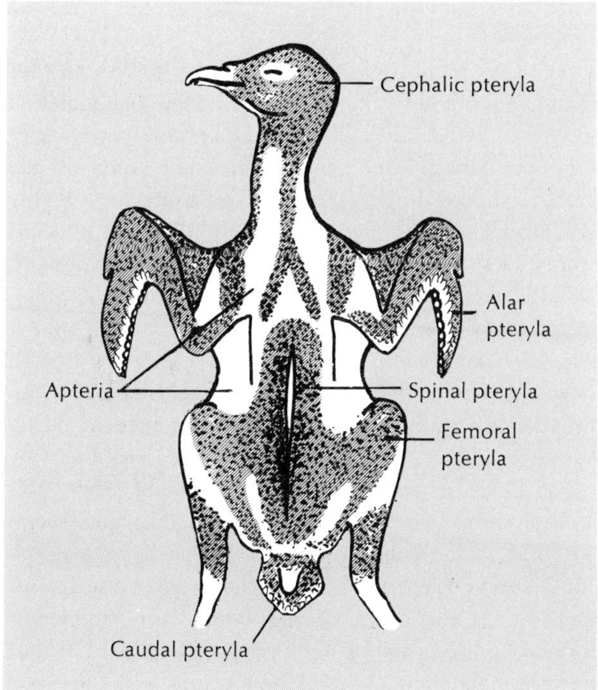

Feather counts vary greatly with the different species. A hummingbird may have less than 1,000 feathers, whereas a whistling swan may have more than 25,000. The same species may show a seasonal variation in number, the greatest being in the winter. The remiges and rectrices are remarkably constant in number.

Advancements made

Although birds are grouped quite often with the reptiles (Sauropsida) and share with the latter many common features, birds have made certain advances of their own. Some of these bird characteristics may not belong strictly to the category of advances and advantages but are developments of structures correlated with the specialized lives of birds. However, some definite advancements have been made by this great class of vertebrates.

1. Their high body temperature is carefully regulated and correlated with the animals' great energy.

2. Their method of locomotion is perhaps the most efficient in the animal kingdom.

3. The four-chambered heart initiated in some reptiles (crocodiles) is firmly established in birds, thus ensuring a complete separation of arterial and venous blood in the heart.

4. Birds have developed the voice, with all the varied features of songs and calls—in striking contrast to the silent reptiles.

5. Finally, birds have developed patterns of behavior, such as parental care of young, nest building, courtship, attachment of mates, and migration, which are practically unknown in their near relatives the reptiles.

Some peculiarities of structure

A highly specialized group of animals such as birds must have numerous unique features. Many of these peculiarities center around their power of flight. Just as in airplane design certain things must be stressed to promote efficient flight, so in birds should we expect the same basic plan to be followed. Although birds have the same fundamental blueprint of body structures as do other higher forms, they have modified these parts to meet their own unique adaptations.

Skeleton (Fig. 28-7). The bones are light and delicate, although strong, and many contain air cavities. The bird's skeleton affords an interesting study in adap-

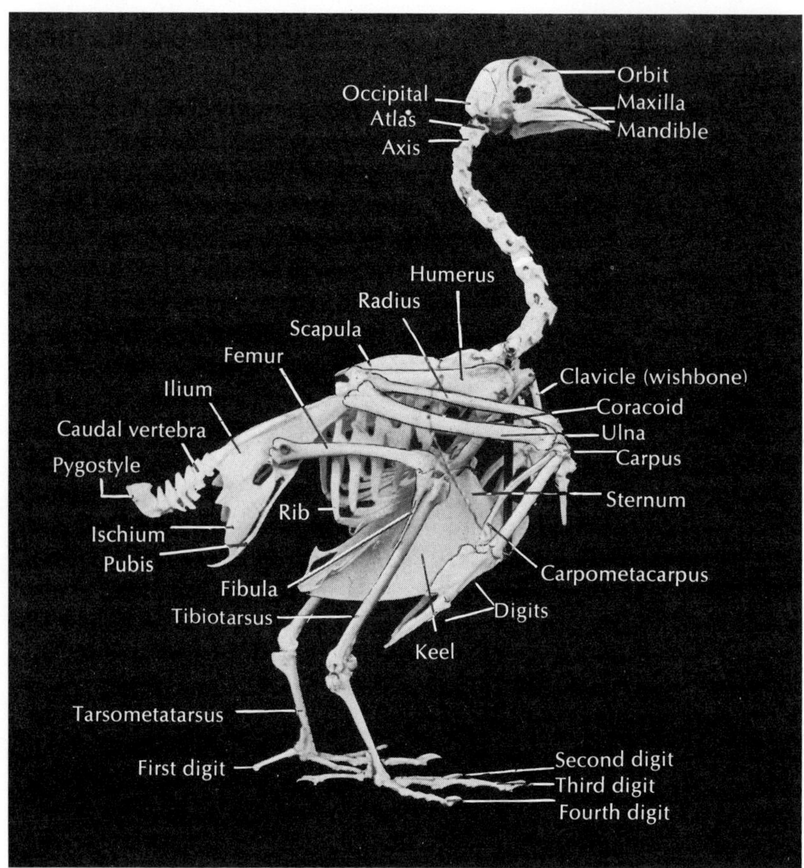

FIG. 28-7

Skeleton of bird.

tation. Because of the specialized nature of the forelimb for flying, birds' skulls and jaws are modified for the performance of many of the duties commonly carried on by the forelimbs of mammals. The skull is mostly fused into one piece in the adult. The rounded braincase and orbits are large, and the anterior bones of the skull are elongated to form the beak. The beak is made up of a horny sheath (bill) and the jaws. The upper jaw consists of the enlarged premaxillae, the maxillae, and a few other bones; the lower jaw, or mandible, is a complex of many bones. The lower jaw has a loose articulation with the movable quadrate, which connects to the squamosal, making possible a larger mouth opening. Another unique feature of the jaws is the ability of some birds to move the upper jaw. In parrots, for instance, there is actually a movable hinge between the premaxillae and the anterior part of the skull. This is made possible by the arrangement of certain bones (pterygoid, palatine, etc.) between the quadrate and the upper jaw. When the quadrate moves forward, the upper jaw is pushed upward. This device ensures greater adaptability of the beak in food manipulation and other performances. The beak of birds varies with the food habits—from generalized types, such as the strong, pointed beaks of crows, to grotesque, highly specialized ones of flamingos, hornbills, and toucans (Fig. 28-8). The palatal structure of the jaws also affords a basis for classifying birds into two groups—**neognathous** (new jaw), with long palatines and movable pterygoids, and **palaeognathous** (old jaw), with short palatines and immovable pterygoids. Most flying birds are neognathous and most flightless ones are palaeognathous.

The bones of the pelvis (ilium, ischium, and pubis on each side) are fused with the lumbar and sacral vertebrae to form the **synsacrum,** which bears on each side a socket (acetabulum) for the head of the femur. Each leg is made up of the **femur,** the **tibiotarsus** (formed by the fusion of the tibia and proximal tarsals), the **tarsometatarsus** (formed by the fusion of the distal

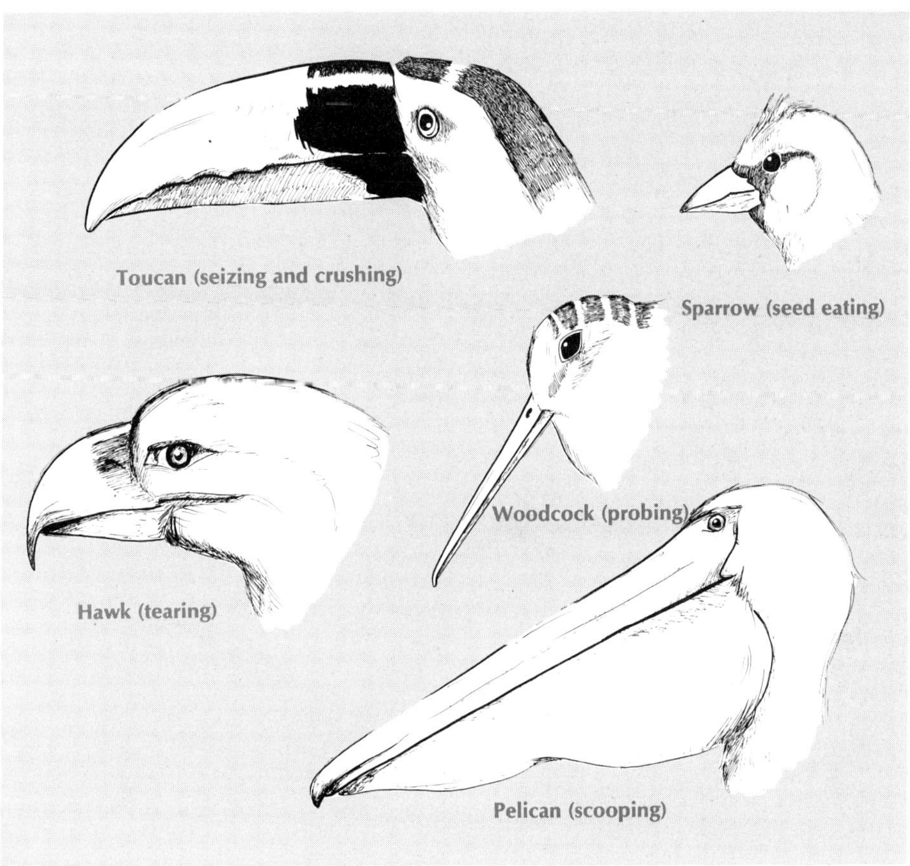

FIG. 28-8

Some bills of birds showing variety of adaptations.

tarsals and metatarsals), and the four **toes** (three in front and one behind). A sesamoid bone (the patella) is found at the knee joint. There are two to five phalanges in each toe. Woodpeckers and others have two front and two hind toes. A few birds have only three toes, and the ostrich has two toes, unequal in size. Bird feet show a wide range of adaptations—walking, climbing, seizing, swimming, wading, etc. (Fig. 28-9).

The trunk is rigid, mainly because of the fusion of the vertebrae and fusion of the ribs with the vertebrae and sternum. Special processes called **uncinate processes** form an additional brace by passing posteriorly from one rib over the one behind. This rigidity affords a firm point of attachment for the wings. To assist in this support and rigidity, the pectoral girdle of scapulae, clavicles, and coracoids is more or less firmly united and joined to the sternum. Only the flexible neck of eight to twenty-four cervical vertebrae and the caudal vertebrae (four free and pygostyle) are free for movement in the axial skeleton. In all flying birds the sternum is provided with a marked keel for the insertion of the two major flight muscles. The forelimbs, or wing appendages, are the most highly modified of the paired appendages. Each consists of a **humerus,** a **radius** and **ulna,** two **carpals,** and three **digits** (II, III, and IV). The other carpals are fused to the three metacarpals to form the **carpometacarpus,** which consists of two long bones. Of the digits, the middle one is longest, consisting of two phalanges; the second and fourth usually have only one. The second digit is called the **alula.** (See Fig. 28-5.)

Muscular system. In birds the muscles are specialized for bipedal locomotion and for flight. Most of their muscles are concerned with the head, neck, and limbs. Segmental arrangements of muscles are scarce. The largest muscle is the **pectoralis major,** which depresses the wing in power flight. It originates on the sternal crest and clavicle and is inserted on the ventrolateral side of the humerus. In flying birds its fibers are red, but in flightless birds it forms most of the "white meat"

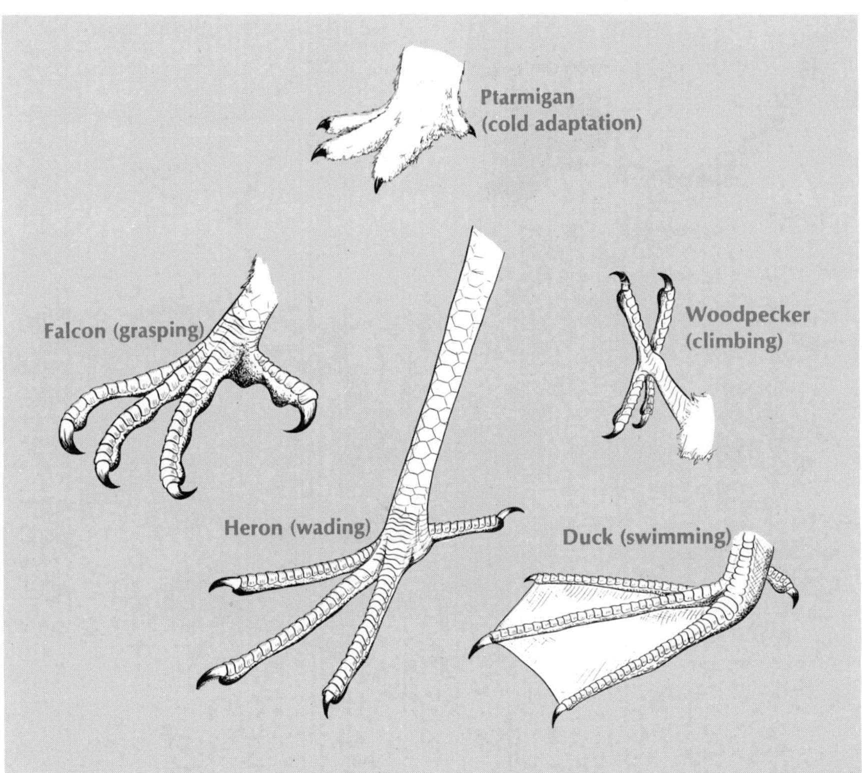

FIG. 28-9

Specialized adaptations of feet of birds.

of the barnyard fowl. For elevating the wing, the **pectoralis minor,** or deep pectoral, lies under the pectoralis major. This muscle originates on the sternum and is inserted on the dorsomedial part of the humerus by a tendon that passes through the foramen triosseum, an opening formed by the clavicle, scapula, and coracoid bones. When the pectoralis minor contracts, its tendon works through this foramen like a rope in a pulley to raise the wing.

Other muscles besides the pectoralis group are involved in flight. Many of these help the pectoralis minor, some assist the pectoralis major, and others have various roles in movements around the shoulder region. The muscles of the back are greatly reduced, whereas those of the leg are enlarged and strong. There are few muscles on the shank and feet; this accounts for their slender and delicate appearance in most species. Long tendons attached to muscles in the upper part of the legs are used to move the toes. To prevent the bird from falling while asleep on a perch, there is a **perching mechanism** (Fig. 28-10), consisting of several leg muscles (ambiens, gastrocnemius, peroneus longus, flexors of the digits, etc.) whose tendons pass behind the heel and shank to be inserted separately on the toes. When the foot touches a perch and squats, a grip reflex flexes the toes and locks the bird to its perch. Other muscles (extensors) open the toes.

Digestive system. The digestive system of birds is adapted for rapid and efficient digestion, for birds are selective in their diet and eat food that can be largely utilized. The **rectum** is short because the fecal matter is relatively small. There are no teeth in the mouth, and the poorly developed salivary glands rarely secrete diastatic enzymes but mainly secrete mucus for lubricating the slender, horny covered **tongue.** There are few taste buds. Hummingbirds and some others have sticky tongues, and woodpeckers have tongues that are barbed at the end. From the short **pharynx** a relatively long elastic **esophagus** extends to the **stomach.** In many birds there is an enlargement (**crop**) at the lower end of the esophagus (Fig. 28-11).

In pigeons and some parrots, milk is produced by the breakdown of the epithelial cells lining the crop; this "bird milk" is regurgitated by both male and female into the mouth of the young squabs. It has a much higher content of fat than cow's milk.

Perching tendons

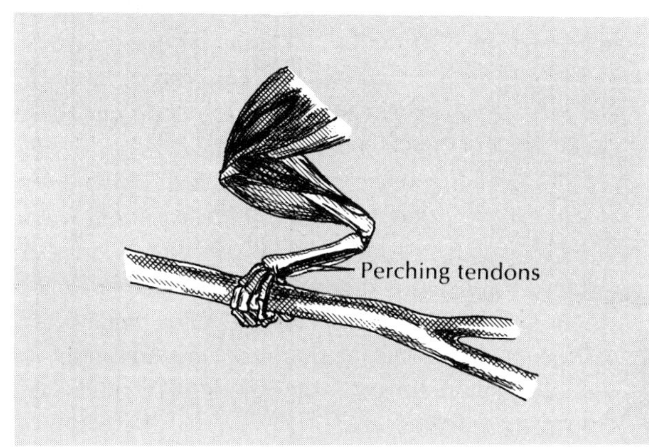

FIG. 28-10

Perching mechanism of bird. When bird alights on perch, grip reflex is initiated by sensory receptor on plantar part of foot so that, by means of several tendons from flexor muscles, toes flex and lock as bird settles into resting or sleeping position.

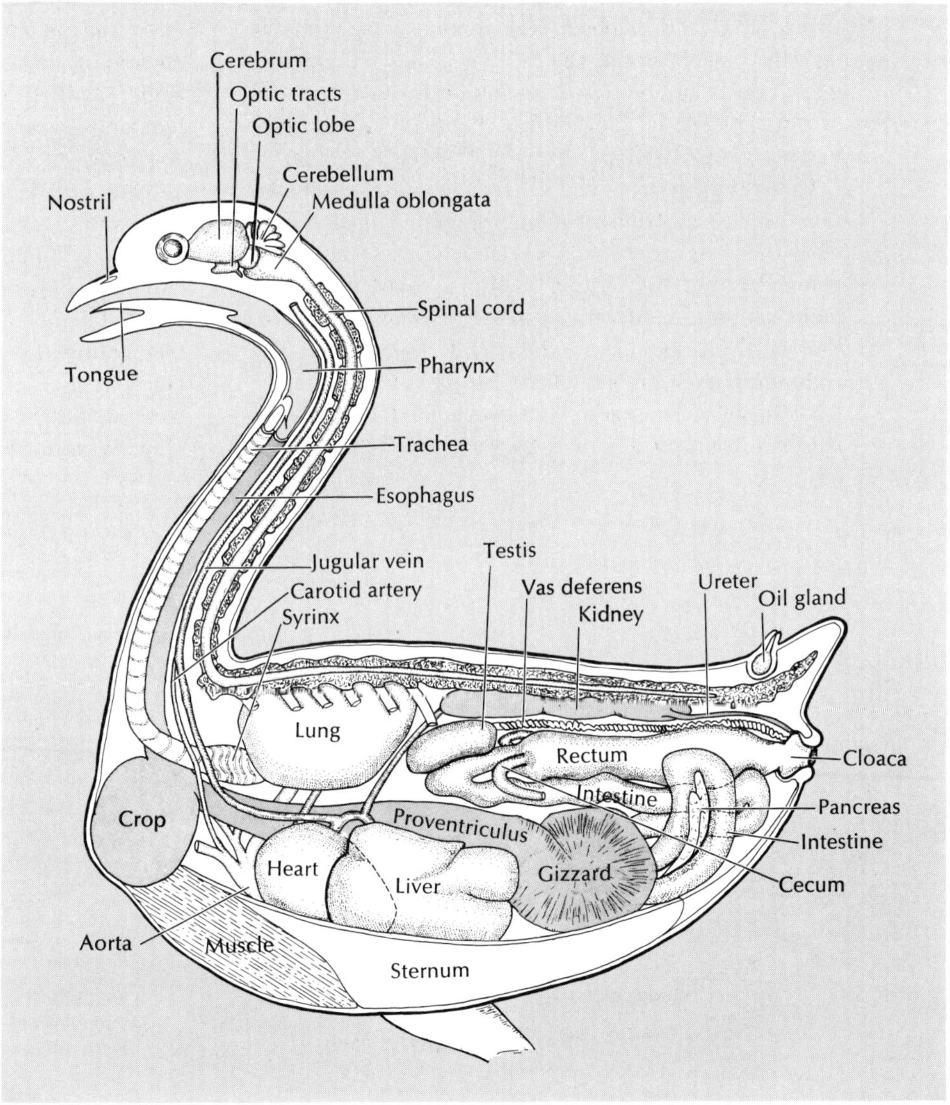

Cerebrum
Optic tracts
Optic lobe
Cerebellum
Medulla oblongata
Nostril
Spinal cord
Tongue
Pharynx
Trachea
Esophagus
Jugular vein
Carotid artery
Syrinx
Testis
Vas deferens
Kidney
Ureter
Oil gland
Lung
Rectum
Cloaca
Intestine
Pancreas
Crop
Proventriculus
Intestine
Heart
Liver
Gizzard
Cecum
Aorta
Muscle
Sternum

FIG. 28-11

Internal structure of male bird. (Modified from Storer and Usinger: General zoology, McGraw-Hill Book Co.)

The stomach proper consists of a **proventriculus,** which secretes gastric juice, and the muscular **gizzard,** which grinds the food. To assist in the grinding process, birds swallow coarse, gritty objects or pebbles, which lodge in the gizzard. Certain birds of prey such as owls form pellets of indigestible materials, for example, bones and fur, in the proventriculus and eject them through the mouth. At the junction of the **intestine** with the rectum there are paired **ceca,** which may be well developed in some birds. Two **bile ducts** from the **gallbladder** (lacking in some) or the lobes of the liver and two or three **pancreatic ducts** empty into the duodenum, or first part of the intestine. The **liver** is relatively large and bilobed. The terminal part of the digestive system is the **cloaca,** which also receives the genital ducts and ureters; in young birds the dorsal wall of the cloaca bears the bursa of Fabricius of unknown function (Fig. 28-12).

Circulatory system. The general plan of bird circulation is not greatly different from that of mammals. However, there are a few unique characteristics. The **four-chambered heart** is large, with strong ventricular walls, and thus they share with mammals a complete separation of the respiratory and systemic circulation. The **right aortic arch,** instead of the left as in the mammals, leads to the dorsal **aorta.** The two **jugular veins** in the neck are connected by a cross vein, an adaptation for shunting the blood from one jugular to the other as the head is turned around. The **brachial** and **pectoral** arteries to the wings and breast are unusually large. There is a well-developed **hepatic portal system,** but the renal portal system is much reduced compared with that in reptiles. The heartbeat is extremely fast, varying usually from 300 to 1,000 per minute. It is slower in large birds than it is in small ones. Bird's **blood** contains nucleated, biconcave red corpuscles, which are somewhat larger than those of mammals. The phagocytes, or mobile ameboid cells, of the blood are unusually active and efficient in birds in the repair of wounds and in destroying microbes.

The high body temperature (104° to 112° F.) is correlated with the high basal metabolic rate but can be quite variable. Its fluctuation rhythm of 10° F. or more can be influenced by the time of day, activity, amount of food in the stomach, etc. Experimentally, Fuller and Hiestand found that the lethal maximum temperature for the domestic fowl *(Gallus domesticus)* was between 45° and 46° C. (113° F.) These investigators concluded that birds live closer to their maximum temperature ceiling than do mammals. Bartholomew and Howell found that certain sea birds (albatrosses and pelicans), which are subjected to periods of high external temperature, are able to regulate their body temperature by losing heat through their highly vascular webbed feet or through the gular pouch at the base of the beak, the gular flutter. Birds also have other ways to control their temperature. They do not

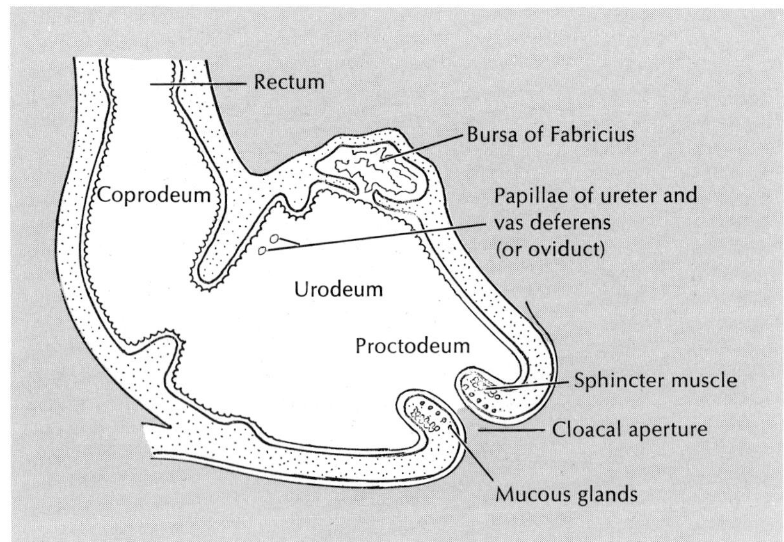

FIG. 28-12

Longitudinal section through cloaca of pigeon *(Columba livia).* Bursa of Fabricius (in young birds), a dorsal diverticulum of the cloaca, has no known function in digestion and eventually becomes lymphoid. (Modified from Streseman, 1943.)

sweat, and insensible water loss is very slight because of their insulating feathers. They pant to dissipate their heat but panting requires energy and tends to increase the heat to be lost. In very high environmental temperatures they may have hyperthermia, and to offset it they may acquire a higher level of body temperature and thus reestablish the temperature difference between their body and their environment. In this way they are able to lose some heat passively, but their temperature is now set at a higher level.

Respiratory system. The high metabolism of birds makes necessary many unique features in their respiratory system. The oval-shaped nostrils or **external nares** open near the base of the bill and connect to the **internal nares,** which open into the pharynx. From the floor of the pharynx a **glottis** leads into a **trachea** (windpipe), which is stiffened by a series of bony and cartilaginous rings. This trachea may be extremely long in some aquatic birds such as the whooping crane. At the upper end of the trachea is the **larynx,** which consists of three cartilages and is rudimentary in birds. The trachea branches at its lower end into two **bronchi.** At this junction the **syrinx,** or voice box, of birds is located. The syrinx is made up of modified tracheal and bronchial rings that form a chamber containing a pair of semilunar membranes with muscles. The latter, which are complicated in singing birds, alter the pitch of the sound.

FIG. 28-13

Respiratory system of pigeon *Columba livia* showing principal air sacs. (From many sources.)

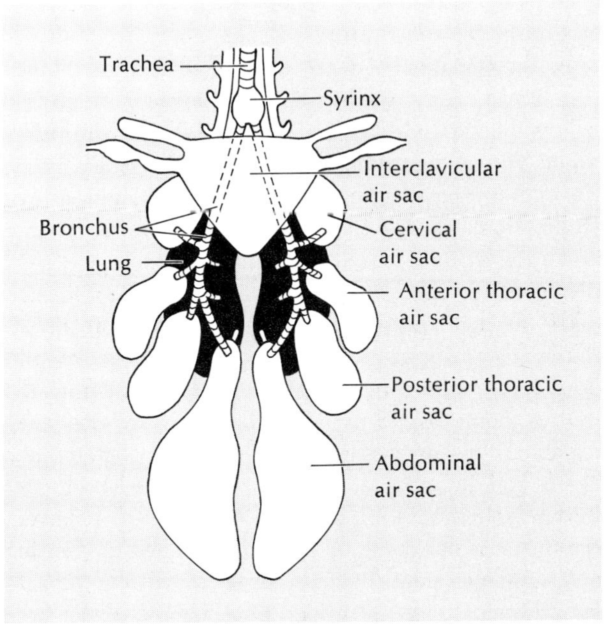

The **lungs** of birds have a different method of gaseous exchange from that of mammals and is not fully understood. The two compact lungs are small, with little elasticity. After branching from the trachea, each bronchus passes through the lungs, giving off a number of smaller **bronchioles.** From the bronchioles a complicated series of ramifying and anastomosing air passages (parabronchi, ventrobronchi, dorsobronchi) are formed. There are no blind pouches or alveoli; instead there are **air capillaries** connected to the air passages that serve as respiratory membranes for exchange of the gases O_2 and CO_2. From the lungs, branches of the bronchi or bronchioles pass through them to the unique system of thin-walled and nonvascular **air sacs,** which are distributed among the viscera and even into some of the larger bones (Fig. 28-13). There are nine of these sacs in the pigeon, and they fill up much of the body cavity. Their function is not to lighten the body, as was once supposed, but to cool the body by internal evaporation or dissipation of heat and also to take care of the residual (dead) air, thus ensuring a complete renewal of air in the lungs in the breathing process. In **inspiration** the lungs (attached to the ribs) dilate by contraction of rib muscles and other muscles and air flows through the passageways of the lungs and into the air sacs. In **expiration,** which is the active part of respiration, thoracic and abdominal muscles compress the air sacs, which force the air out by almost the same route it entered. The act of flying also aids breathing by the muscular contraction of the thorax. Unlike other vertebrates, the air in birds passes completely through the lungs at each breath. In flying, even the residual air of the air sacs is completely renewed.

The great demand for oxygen requires a high breathing rate in birds, but they can adjust themselves quickly to external conditions. House wrens, for example, have been shown to have a breathing rate of 28 at 74° F. but 340 at their normal body temperature (104°+ F.).

Excretory system. The paired metanephric kidneys are three-lobed and are attached to the dorsal wall of the synsacrum. From these the ureters run to the **cloaca.** A urinary bladder is absent (except in the ostrich), and the urine is semisolid, consisting mostly of urates. The whitish material in bird feces is due to these urates. Much of the water is absorbed in the cloaca, and as in reptiles, the excretion of nitrogen waste as uric acid instead of urea involves the use of little water, for uric acid is mainly insoluble in water and precipitates out easily. The fecal matter of sea birds may accumulate in large deposits, such as the famed guano beds off the coast of South America. Such guano forms a rich fertilizer that is in demand all over the world.

Nervous and sensory systems. The nervous system in birds is characterized by unusually large **optic lobes** and **cerebellum.** Their cerebrum is relatively small, but neurologists think that their well-developed hyperstriatum, instead of the cerebrum, is the seat of their intelligent behavior, which ranks very high in the animal kingdom. The well-developed optic lobes, together with very large eyes, indicate **keen sight,** a sense that is probably unsurpassed in the animal kingdom. Hearing is also well developed in birds; taste and smell, however, are poor. The large and much-convoluted cerebellum is correlated with delicate equilibrium and great muscular coordination. In the vitreous humor of the eye is the highly vascular and fan-shaped body, the **pecten,** which may aid in nutrition, accommodation, and directional orientation. Birds also possess a **nictitating membrane,** vestigial in the mammalian eye, which can be drawn across the eyeball from the inner angle of the eye.

Tactile sense organs are not well developed except in a few places where they would be of adaptive value, such as the bill in ducks or other aquatic birds, which is used for probing around in the mud and debris of stream bottoms. Rictal bristles of nighthawks have sensory nerve endings at their base and can be used for sensory detection. But the bird depends mainly upon **vision** for its sensory impression. Vultures or turkey buzzards detect their carrion by sight, not smell. The side position of the eyes indicates monocular vision, that is, each eye having its own field of vision. The forward position of the owl's eyes may enable it to have binocular vision. The fovea, or region of keenest vision on the retina, is placed (in birds of prey and some others) in a deep pit, which makes it necessary for the bird to focus exactly on the source. Many birds, moreover, have two sensitive spots (foveas) on the retina—the central one for sharp monocular views and the posterior one for binocular vision. The ease with which birds can turn their heads makes possible a wide field of vision. Woodcocks can probably see binocularly both forward and backward. Bitterns, in their freezing stance of bill pointing up, can also see binocularly. The visual acuity of a hawk is thought to be eight times that of a man, and an owl's ability to see in dim light is ten times that of the human eye. Birds have some color vision, especially toward the red end of the spectrum.

Reproductive system. In the male the paired **testes** and accessory ducts are similar to those in many other forms, but the female has only the left ovary and left oviduct, the right ones being vestigial. Some birds, including ducks and geese, have a large, well-developed **copulatory organ** (penis). It is a modified and thickened portion of the ventral wall of the cloaca; it is provided with a groove on its dorsal side for the transfer of sperm. The inactive penis has its distal end invaginated by an elastic ligament. The ostrich has a solid penis, which can be drawn back into a sheath of the cloaca. With most birds, however, copulation is a mere matter of bringing the cloacal surfaces of the two sexes into contact—the so-called "cloacal kiss." From the **testes** of the male the **vasa deferentia** run to the cloaca. Before being discharged, the sperm are stored in the **seminal vesicle,** the enlarged distal end of the vas deferens. This seminal vesicle may become so large with stored sperm during the breeding season that it causes a cloacal protuberance. The high body temperature that tends to inhibit spermatogenesis in the testes is probably counteracted by the cooling effect of the abdominal air sacs. The testes of birds undergo a great enlargement at the breeding season, shrinking to tiny bodies afterwards.

In the female the **ovary** is close to the left kidney (Fig. 28-14). Eggs discharged from the ovary are picked up by the expanded end of the oviduct, the **infundibulum.** The oviduct runs posteriorly to the cloaca. While the eggs are passing down the oviduct, **albumin,** or egg white, from special glands is added to them; farther down the oviduct, the shell membrane, shell, and shell pigments are also secreted about the egg. Fertilization takes place in the upper oviduct several hours before the laying of the eggs. Hens have been known to produce fertile eggs three weeks after separation from the rooster. Some hawks and owls have two ovaries, each capable of producing eggs. Birds may be determinate layers and lay only a fixed number (clutch) of eggs in a season. If any of the eggs of a set are removed, the deficit is not made up by additional laying (herring gull). Indeterminate layers, however, will continue to lay additional eggs for a long time if some of the first-

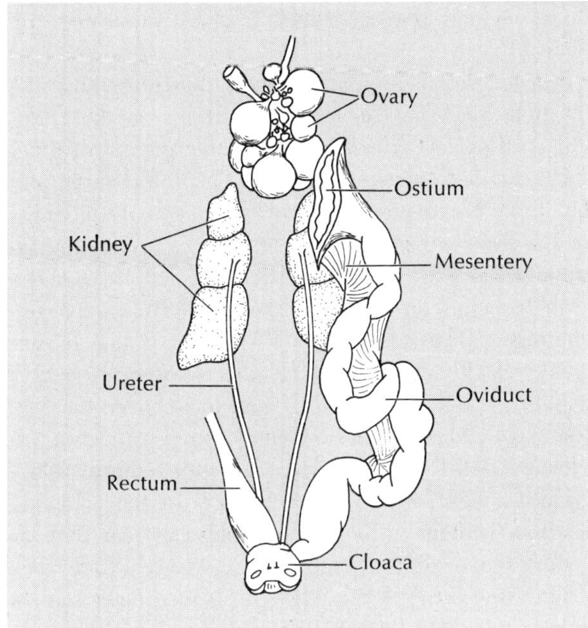

FIG. 28-14

Urogenital system of female pigeon *Columba livia* (partly diagrammatic). Right ovary and right oviduct (except a vestige not shown) disappear. It is assumed that presence of two oviducts and two ovaries would cause difficulties in pelvic girdle if two eggs were to be laid simultaneously. Single oviduct and ureters open into urodeum division of cloaca.

laid eggs are continually removed (flickers, ducks, domestic poultry). Most birds are probably determinate layers. Many birds such as songbirds lay an egg a day until the clutch is completed; others stagger their egg laying and lay every other day or so. Domestic geese usually lay every other day, which is probably the pattern for the large birds of prey. The European cuckoo (a parasitic bird that lays its eggs in the nest of others) tends to lay eggs similar in size and pattern to those of the host birds.

Endocrine system. Birds have well-developed regulatory systems of endocrine glands, such as are characteristic of mammals and other animal forms. Much investigation has been conducted on this system in birds. Glands such as the **thyroid** in the neck, the **pituitary** at the base of the brain, the **islets of Langerhans** in the pancreas, the **adrenals** on the ventral surface of the kidneys, and the endocrinal tissue of the **gonads** are well represented. The functions of these various glands are, on the whole, typical of such glands in other forms. Song and coloration, for instance, are controlled by hormones from the gonads.

Adaptive structures and natural history

Flight. Before birds acquired the power of flight, they may have passed through a sequence pattern of swift running, flying leaps, tree climbing, parachute gliding from tree to tree, and a general arboreal existence. Many of their adaptations, for example, the perching mechanism and active climbing habits, indicate such an apprenticeship. As far as birds are concerned, feathers were an absolute requirement for true flight, for there is no reason to suppose that they passed through a stage of wings composed of skin membranes, such as the pterodactyls had. Other flight adaptations (streamlined body, skeleton, internal organs, bodily functions, etc.) have already been mentioned. In ordinary flying, birds have to make use of the same principles and solve the same problems that confront human heavier-than-air aircraft. When such objects move through air, there is a lift force acting upward that must be sufficient to sustain the weight of the object and a contrary force or drag force that tends to stop the motion. Both of these forces are proportional to the square of the speed, and no object can stay aloft in still air unless its speed produces a lift force equal to its weight.

Wings are required to function both as propellers and planes. In flying, birds elevate the wings, and then pull them forward, downward, and backward. This is accomplished by the large pectoralis major muscles. The wings are lifted back into position by a quick flip of the pectoralis minor muscles. When the wing is moved downward, the air is displaced and the bird is kept up or raised; the backward movement gives horizontal velocity to the body; and the air resistance, which retards the forward movements, also has a lifting force because the bird's wing is convex above and offers less resistance than the lower concave surface. The alula, by being open, tends to prevent stalling. Between strokes the loss of altitude may be slight in swift flying, but it is quite evident in the up-and-down flight of woodpeckers and goldfinches. Rapidity of flight within limits lessens the energy required in flight. It is estimated that the energy expended by a pigeon in taking off is five times as great as that needed to attain its regular speed.

There are different shapes of wings for different types of flying. The factors that determine the kind and shape of wing are as follows:

1. The relationship of wing area to the load it carries. Small wings are necessary for swift flapping flight, whereas a large wing area allows slow flight and good soaring. Large birds have relatively larger wings in comparison to their bodies than do small birds if they are to have the same wing area per gram of weight, for the weight increases as the cube and the wing area as the square. This wing surface per body weight ratio is not the same, however, for small and large birds. In the crow the ratio is 3 kilograms of body weight to 1 square meter of wing area; in warblers it may be 1 to 1. Smaller birds, therefore, have a greater margin of safety.

2. Aspect ratio, that is, the ratio between the wing length and breadth. A high aspect ratio allows a slow rate of descent while gliding and requires a small expenditure of energy. This is found mainly in birds that fly fast by flapping flight, for they tend to stall at slow soaring rates. In the albatross the ratio is 25 to 1; in the sparrow, 5 to 1.

3. The shape of the wings as related to the type of flying. A pointed wing is found only in fast flyers and is provided with large hand (primary) feathers; short broad wings are more suitable for slower but more maneuverable flyers and stresses the arm feathers.

4. The curvature, or camber, of the wing. The upper convex surface of the wing allows air to flow off the feathers when the wing is raised and produces a positive pressure on the underside of the wing. To minimize air turbulence and to promote a smooth flow of air over the surfaces, slots are formed at the tips of the wings, especially on the upbeat.

There are three types of bird flight: gliding, flapping, and soaring.

Gliding flight. In this type a bird attains a certain velocity and then planes without moving the wings, or having reached a certain altitude, it descends without wing stroke. Birds use this method in landing. A gliding bird nearly always loses altitude when gliding, but wind direction and speed of takeoff determine how far it can go without sinking. This is probably the most primitive method of flying.

Flapping flight. This type (already described) refers to the up-and-down movement of the wings and represents the most complicated mechanism of flight. It is ordinary bird flight and is often described as a screw-like wing motion, with the primary feathers acting as propellers and the secondary feathers furnishing the plane lift.

Soaring flight. In soaring flight, birds usually take advantage of updrafts and air currents so that flapping is dispensed with for considerable periods of time. The long, narrow wings of gulls and albatrosses and the short, broad wings of hawks are equally effective for this type of flight. Hawks often make use of the ascending warm air that arises from warmed areas of the earth to mount in circles to great heights. In soaring, albatrosses take advantage of currents of air of unequal velocity at different heights (faster at greater heights), which are found at low levels over the sea. The bird glides down the wind with great speed to a lower level, then turns, and rises with reduced velocity into a faster-moving layer of air. In this way the albatross without visible wing stroke can soar with or against the wind for some time.

The wing beats of the larger birds may make sounds audible to nearby human ears, but small birds usually produce ultrasonic tones (beyond the frequency of man's hearing) in their flight. Most owls, however, are ultrasonically quiet, which is highly adaptive to these birds in catching their prey (small mammals) that could detect ultrasonic tones. Owls have feather fringes and downy upper surfaces that are mainly responsible for their silent flight (Griffin and Thorpe).

How fast can birds fly? A lot of our small songbirds are feeble flyers compared with swifts, swallows, and many birds of prey. How fast they fly depends to a great extent upon the conditions of the air. Against a strong headwind their speed is naturally cut down. Under favorable conditions most small songbirds fly from 20 to 40 miles per hour. Larger birds such as ducks usually fly from 40 to 80 miles per hour. Some swifts are known to fly more than 100 miles per hour, and some birds of prey probably exceed this in diving after their prey. Many estimates of speed, however, are purely guesswork and lack accurate measurement.

Coloration. Perhaps no group of animals has more beautiful and more striking colors than do the birds. This beauty reaches its peak in tropical birds, but many that dwell in the temperate zones are also renowned for their colors. Numerous birds are undoubtedly protectively colored by their plumage, and the brighter colors assumed by the male during the breeding season gave rise to Darwin's conception of sexual selection, a theory that has not found favor with most zoologists.

The color is partly due to pigments and partly to interference colors produced by light reflection and refraction. Some of the pigments (melanins) are granules of yellow, black, red, and a few others. Other pigments are the lipochromes, such as zooxanthin (yellow) and zooerythrin (red). Colors produced this way always appear the same, but those due to reflection and refraction may appear different, depending upon the conditions under which they are seen. White is produced by reflection. The surface markings as well as the internal structure play a part in this interference coloration. Whenever there is an absence of pigment, an albino may result.

Nearly all birds undergo **molting,** a seasonal shedding and replacement of feathers. Molting may be accompanied by a change in the color of the plumage. The ptarmigan is white in winter and mottled brown at other seasons. The juvenile plumage in young birds may resemble that of the adult female. When the colors of males and females of the same species differ, the condition is called **sexual dimorphism.** In such cases the male is usually the brighter. Examples are the cardinal and scarlet tanager.

Songs. The vocal organ in the bird is the **syrinx** already mentioned. When air passes through this organ, the semilunar membrane vibrates to produce sounds. In some species the range and variety of songs is most striking; in others it is definitely restricted. In the song sparrow more than 800 different song variations have been recorded. Nearly all songbirds studied have different songs for different purposes, many of which convey precise information. The more birdsongs are studied, the more amazing seems to be their scope and meaning. Much remains to be done before the language of birds can be unraveled, but better techniques and electronic devices for analyzing birdsongs have yielded much significant information.

In addition to songs, which are far more common in the males during the breeding season, birds have distinctive call notes, which are uttered when they are alarmed or are used for attracting mates or young, as well as for territory rights. The pelican and some others are voiceless. Many birds have great powers of mimicry; among these are the brown thrasher, catbird, mocking bird, myna, and, of course, the parrot.

Food. Because birds are very active their food requirement is large. Their body metabolism and body temperature are the highest known among animals. The food habits of the various species vary enormously. Many birds are strictly vegetarian, consuming great quantities of foliage, seeds, fruits, etc. because of the less concentrated nature of the food. Many game birds belong to this group. Others such as birds of prey are entirely carnivorous. Many small songbirds such as flycatchers and woodpeckers live exclusively upon insects. Still other birds are omnivorous, eating both vegetable and animal foods. The young of some birds may live on different foods from that of the adults. During the nesting period many songbirds feed their nestlings insects, although the adults themselves are vegetarians. Some birds, such as the hummingbird that lives upon the nectar of flowers and the kingfisher that lives upon fish, have rather restricted food habits. The hummingbird requires so much food that it would starve to death at night except that it goes into a hibernation state, with low breathing rate, low heart rate, and low body temperature. Perhaps no bird has a wider range of diet than does the common American crow, which may account for its wide distribution and large numbers. Carrion-eating birds such as the condor and buzzard may eat so much at times that they are unable to fly.

A striking example of a bird's changing its eating habits is found in the case of the New Zealand parrot (*Nestor notabilis*), which formerly lived on fruits, seeds, and nuts. When sheep were introduced into that country, the parrot acquired the habit of digging out the kidneys and fat of sick or weakened animals.

How marine birds drink salt water. All marine birds drink salt water instead of fresh water. Since marine water is more than 3% salt and the blood of birds less than 1% salt, the excess salt must be eliminated. Because using kidneys for this purpose would involve loss of water, seabirds have evolved special salt glands on the head, either over each eye or between the eyes and the nasal cavity, for eliminating this salt. These glands consist of many parallel lobes, each with many branching tubules. Blood capillaries carry the blood containing the salt to the tubules, where the sodium and chloride ions against an osmotic gradient pass from the lower salt concentration of the blood to the higher salt concentration of the tubules. From the glands, ducts carry to the nasal cavities the salt secretions (sometimes more than 5% salt), which then drips from the nostrils and beak.

Sea reptiles such as marine turtles have glands behind the eyeball that function in a similar way and for a similar reason.

Care of young. To produce offspring, all birds lay eggs that must be incubated by one or both parents.

Cowbird eggs require only 9 to 10 days for hatching; most songbirds, about 14 days; the hen, 21 days; and ducks and geese, at least 28 days. Most of the duties of incubation fall upon the female, although in many instances both parents share in the task, and occasionally only the male performs this work.

Most birds build some form of nest in which to rear their young. These nests vary from depressions on the ground to huge and elaborate affairs (Fig. 28-15). Some birds simply lay their eggs on the bare ground or rocks and make no pretense of nest building. Some of the most striking nests are the pendant nests constructed by orioles, the neat lichen-covered nests of hummingbirds (Fig. 28-16) and flycatchers, the chimney-shaped mud nests of cliff swallows, and the huge brush pile nests of the Australian brush turkey. Most birds take considerable pains to conceal their nests from enemies. Woodpeckers, chickadees, bluebirds, and many others place their nests in tree hollows or other cavities; kingfishers excavate tunnels in the banks of streams for their nests; and birds of prey build high in lofty trees or on inaccessible cliffs. A few birds such as the American cowbird and the European cuckoo build no nests at all but simply lay their eggs in the nests of birds smaller than themselves. When the eggs hatch, the young are taken care of by their foster parents. Most of our songbirds lay from three to six eggs, but the number of eggs laid in a clutch varies from one or two (some hawks and pigeons) to eighteen or twenty (quail).

Nesting success is very low with many birds, espe-

FIG. 28-15

A, Pendant nest of Baltimore oriole. **B,** Nest of red-eyed vireo. **C,** Nest of phoebe—always placed in sheltered position, such as under bridges, shelving rocks, and buildings. **D,** Nest of cardinal—usually placed in thickets and brambles and not easily detected. **E,** Mud-lined nest of robin.

cially in altricial species. Surveys vary among investigators, but one investigation (V. Noland, Jr.) of 170 altricial bird nests reports only 21% as producing at least one young. Of the many causes of nest failures, predation by snakes, skunks. chipmunks, blue jays, crows, etc. is by far the chief factor. Birds of prey probably have a much higher percentage of reproductive success.

When birds hatch, they are of two types; **precocial** or **altricial.** The precocial young, such as quail, fowl, ducks, and most water birds, are covered with down when hatched and can run or swim as soon as their plumage is dry. The altricial ones, on the other hand, are naked and helpless at birth and remain in the nest for a week or more. The young of both types require care from the parents for some time after hatching. They must be fed, guarded, and protected against rain and the sun. The parents of altricial species must carry food to their children almost constantly, for most young birds will eat more than their weight each day. This enormous food consumption explains the rapid growth of the young and their quick exit from the nest. The food of the young, depending upon the species, includes worms, insects, seeds, fruit, etc. Pigeons are peculiar in feeding their young with "pigeon milk," the sloughed-off epithelial lining of the crop.

FIG. 28-16

Nest of hummingbird with two eggs. Collected in Arizona. (Courtesy F. M. Hickman.)

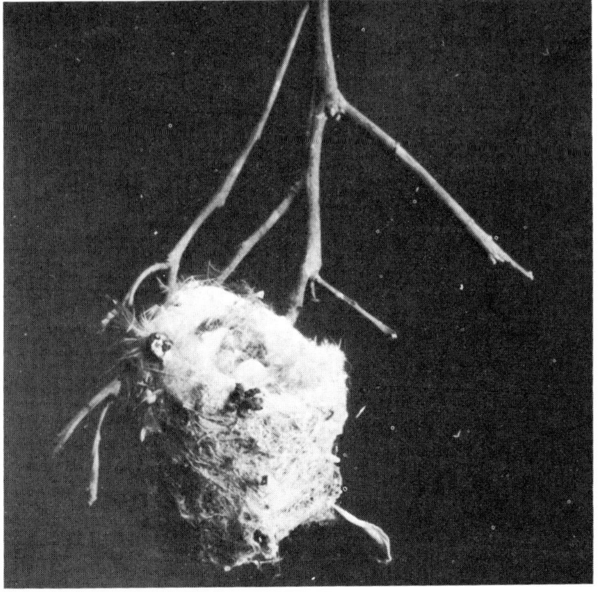

Many birds, such as the eagle and some of the songbirds, are known to mate for life. Others mate only for the rearing of a single brood. There are also cases in which one female mates with several males (**polyandry**), as illustrated by the European cuckoo; in other cases one male mates with several females (**polygyny**); for example, the ostrich. In most bird populations there are usually many sexually mature individuals that have no mates at all. Elaborate courtship rituals are found in many birds, such as the prairie chicken, sage grouse, bower birds, great crested grebes, and others. Simpler ritual forms are found among most songbirds and consist mainly of male displays and songs.

Do birds hibernate? For many centuries, bird observers believed that birds hibernate in the mud of ponds, in stony crevices, and in other places. Aristotle had views of this kind, and Gilbert White, in his delightful book *The Natural History of Selborne,* tries to account for the sudden appearance of swallows in the spring in this way. This belief has largely been discredited by trained observers, and yet in recent years some bird students have revived the idea. Among these is Professor E. C. Jaeger of California, who found poorwills in dormant conditions in rock crevices in his native state. His observations seem to verify what certain English observers had previously discovered in Persia, where they found swallows apparently hibernating in burrows. Whether such practices are common is to be doubted, but such observations are of considerable interest.

Bird populations. Many censuses have been taken to ascertain bird populations within a particular area. The National Audubon Society and the Federal Fish and Wildlife Service have sponsored many such counts. Some are concerned with game birds and species on the verge of extinction. Emphasis is often placed upon breeding birds, making use of the territorial singing of the males. Some birds lend themselves to more accurate counts than do others, such as those that nest in colonies or have particular nesting habitats. Students of birds use various techniques for identifying birds, such as sight, song, type of flying, and call notes. In 1914 a bird census made in the northeastern United States revealed about 125 pairs of birds per 100 acres (open farms) and 199 pairs per 100 acres of woodland. In 1949 a survey made in a spruce-fir forest in Maine gave a count of 370 pairs of breeding birds per 100 acres. Another count in the same region in 1950 showed 385 pairs of breeding birds per 100 acres.

Many censuses are incomplete and unreliable. With individual differences among observers, not all reports are of the same accuracy. There are many other sources of error in samplings. Birds tend to congregate where food is abundant, for instance, in an orchard. At certain seasons quail may be found in large numbers in a wheat field but may be scarcely noticed elsewhere. As for numbers of species, in the eastern half of the United States, robins and house sparrows are most common near dwellings, whereas in the woodlands other species are more common. Many species tend to be localized in distribution.

Selection of territories. A pair of birds will usually select a territory on which to raise a brood. This territory is selected in the spring by the male, who jealously guards it against all other males of the same species. The male sings a great deal to help him establish priority on his domain. Eventually he attracts a female, and the pair start mating and nest building. The female apparently wanders from one territory to another until she settles down with a male. How large a territory a pair takes over depends upon location, abundance of food, natural barriers, etc. In the case of some birds such as robins a house may serve as the dividing line between two adjacent domains, and each pair will usually stay close to the lawn on its particular side of the house. When members of another species trespass, the pair usually pay little attention. Competition is greatest among the members of the same species. Song sparrows, however, try to keep off members of other species as well as their own. A recent study indicates that birds may also defend their territories against other species because of environmental limitations and changes, where competition for food or other factors between different species (usually closely related) may occur (G. H. Orians and M. F. Willson).

This concept of territory claims by birds was greatly developed by H. E. Howard, an English ornithologist, in 1920. Since that time other competent students have verified and extended the concept. One of these was Mrs. M. M. Nice, whose work on the song sparrow is now classic; another was Lack, an English ornithologist, who worked with the English robin.

Many modified aspects of territory are found. Some birds restrict their territories to nesting regions and share feeding grounds with others. Among hummingbirds the female has a separate nesting site, which she defends herself. Territories are usually deserted at the close of the nesting season and new ones are staked out the following spring. Song sparrows, however, keep their territories the year around. Territories are not absolutely fixed areas, but vary as the economic pressures vary.

Behavior and intelligence. Birds have some of the most marvelous instincts in the animal kingdom. This would indicate a complex and well-organized nervous system. Among their amazing behavior reactions are the elaborate and skillfully built nests characteristic of many species, the migratory instinct that enables birds to travel thousands of miles (see discussion on migration) without deviating from their courses, the dexterity they show in food capture, the courtship and mating rituals of some, and, not least, their power of producing sweet and beautiful music.

Their sense of sight is perhaps the keenest in the animal kingdom. A hawk gliding several hundred yards in the air can spot the movements of a mouse hidden in the grass below. Most birds, too, can hear well. Owls at night can hear slight rustling sounds not detectable to the ears of most animals. Smell and taste, however, are not highly developed in birds, for they depend mainly upon sight and hearing for their information.

In studying the behavior of birds, it is not always possible to distinguish between strictly inborn reflexes and acquired associations. Many of the former are found in newly hatched birds, for they are able to perform them without previous experience, but the parents are undoubtedly responsible for furnishing the stimuli in the development of the instinctive behavior of the young. The power birds have of radically changing their food and nesting habits, examples of which are well known, indicates that they can establish simple associations. Birds thus may be credited with a limited power of adjusting their behavior in accordance with simple trial-and-error experimentation. Many behavior patterns of birds have never been satisfactorily explained—for instance, "anting," the habit some birds (usually passerines) have of rubbing crushed ants (sometimes other objects) over and under their primary feathers. Some think that its primary purpose is to get rid of ectoparasites.

Birdbanding. Birdbanding is a method of marking live specimens with a special aluminum band that bears a serial number and other data. When these specimens are recovered, returns are made usually to some official organization such as the United States Fish and Wildlife Service. Much useful information about birds has been acquired by this method, such as migration routes, distribution, and population dynamics. Birdbanding, to be effective, requires the cooperation of many banders and responsible organizations. Birdbanders now number several thousand in the United States and Canada. Special federal and state permits are required of birdbanders. Various forms of traps are employed for catching specimens. A funnel trap, in which birds can find their way in but not out, is a popular type.

Economic importance

Birds are both useful and harmful to man's interests. Many birds, such as fowls, geese, ducks, turkeys, pigeons, and others, have been domesticated, and their total value in flesh and eggs is great. Game birds, such as pheasants, quail, and grouse, are hunted both for food and for the zest of hunting.

The value of birds in consuming insect and weed seed pests should not be underrated. Hawks and owls help control vermin that might otherwise overrun agricultural crops. They undoubtedly do some dam-

FIG. 28-17

Group of ratite birds.

age to poultry and game birds, but even here they may do a service by getting rid of the sick and weakly.

Birds also serve another useful purpose, and that is the esthetic interest that is manifested in them in nearly all civilized countries. To study birds, thousands of people take to the fields and woods. This has proved fruitful in several ways, for such interests have also led to better bird protection and conservation.

Résumé of orders

Class Aves (birds) is made up of about 27 orders of living birds and a few fossil orders. More than 8,600 species and many subspecies have been described. Probably only a relatively few species remain to be discovered and named, but many subspecies are added yearly. With their powers of flight and wide distribution, most species of birds are more easily detected than are many animals. Only those that are solitary, shy, and restricted to remote regions have a chance of remaining undiscovered for any length of time. Altogether, the species are grouped into 170 families. Of the 27 recognized orders, 20 are represented by North American species.

The first 4 orders in the following list make up

FIG. 28-18

Rookery of king penguins showing enormous number that may be found in one locality. These birds, which during summer months hatch eggs in folds of flesh between their legs, do not build nest at all. They breed in large rookeries, usually on hard level beaches close to water. Order Sphenisciformes. (Courtesy Nature Magazine, Washington, D. C.)

FIG. 28-19

Group of emperor penguins. Order Sphenisciformes. The largest of all penguins and restricted to Antarctic regions. Some are nearly 4 feet tall. (Courtesy Chicago Natural History Museum.)

FIG. 28-20

Great northern diver, or common loon. Weird, lonesome cry of loon heard on our northern lakes is unforgettable sound. Usually only a pair of these birds are found on a single lake. Order Gaviiformes. (Courtesy Chicago Natural History Museum.)

FIG. 28-21

The pied-billed grebe *(Podilymbus podiceps)*. They have complex courtship rituals and build their nests on a floating raft of aquatic vegetation. Order Podicipediformes. (Courtesy Natural Science Museum, Cleveland.)

FIG. 28-22

The red-footed booby *(Sula sula)* with nest and young. Their common name is derived from their unwary, stupid behavior when hunted by man. Order Pelecaniformes. (Courtesy Natural Science Museum, Cleveland.)

the group of **ratite,** or flightless, birds (Fig. 28-17); the remainder are the **carinate** or flying birds.

Order Struthioniformes (stru'thi-on'i-for"mes) (LL. *struthio,* ostrich, + L. *forma,* form)—**ostriches**

The ostrich (*Struthio camelus*) (Fig. 28-17) is the largest of living birds, some specimens being 8 feet tall and weighing 300 pounds. These birds cannot fly. The feet are provided with only two toes of unequal size covered with pads, which enable the birds to travel rapidly through sandy country. The ostrich is found in the desert country of Africa and Arabia. Ostrich feathers are highly prized, and ostrich farming is extensive in South Africa, California, and elsewhere. There are 4 species, of which *Struthio camelus* is the largest.

Order Rheiformes (re'i-for"mes) (Greek mythology, *Rhea,* mother of Zeus, + form)—**rheas**

These flightless birds are restricted to South America and are often called the American ostrich (Fig. 28-17).

Order Casuariiformes (cas'u ar'e i for"mes) (NL. *Casuarius,* type genus, + form)—**cassowaires, emus**

This is a flightless group of birds found in Australia, New Guinea, and a few other islands (Fig. 28-17). Some specimens may reach a height of 5 feet.

Order Apterygiformes (ap'ter-yg'i-for"mes) (Gr. *a,* not, + *pterygion,* small wing or fin, + form)—**kiwis**

Kiwis (Fig. 28-17) are flightless birds about the size of the domestic fowl, found only in New Zealand. They all belong to the genus *Apteryx,* of which there are 3 species. Only the merest vestige of a wing is present. The egg is extremely large for the size of the bird.

Order Tinamiformes (tin-am'i-for"mes) (NL. *Tinamus,* type genus, + form)—**tinamous**

These are flying birds found in South America and Mexico.

They resemble the ruffed grouse and are classed as game birds. There are more than 60 species in this order.

Order Sphenisciformes (sfe-nis'i-for"mes) (Gr. *spheniskos,* dim. of *sphen,* wedge, from the shortness of the wings, + form)—**penguins**

Penguins (Figs. 28-18 and 28-19) are found in the southern seas, especially in Antarctica. Although carinate birds, they use their wings as paddles rather than for flight. The largest penguin is the emperor penguin (*Aptenodytes forsteri*) of the Antarctic, which breeds in enormous rookeries on the shores of that region.

Order Gaviiformes (ga'vi-i-for"mes) (L. *gavia,* bird, probably sea mew, + form)—**loons**

Remarkable swimmers and divers, they live exclusively on fish and small aquatic forms. The familiar great northern diver (*Gavia immer*) (Fig. 28-20) is found mainly in northern waters.

Order Podicipediformes (pod'i-ci-ped'i-for"mes) (L. *podex,* rump, + *pedis,* foot)—**grebes**

The pied-billed grebe (Fig. 28-21), or dabchick (*Podilymbus podiceps*), is a familiar example of this order. These birds are found on ponds and lakes all over the eastern half of the United States. They are shy, secretive birds and dive quickly when disturbed. Grebes are most common in old ponds where there are extensive growths of cattails, rushes, and water flags, of which they build their raftlike nests that float on the surface of the water.

Order Procellariiformes (pro'sel-lar'e-i-for"mes) (L. *procella,* tempest, + form)—**albatrosses, petrels, fulmars, shearwaters**

As far as wingspan is concerned (more than 12 feet in some), albatrosses are the largest of flying birds. *Diomedea* is a common genus of albatrosses.

Order Pelecaniformes (pel'e-can'i-for"mes) (LL. *pelecanus,* pelican, + form)—**pelicans, cormorants, gannets, boobies** (Fig. 28-22), **etc.**

All the members of this group have all their four toes included within the web.

Order Ciconiiformes (si-ko'ne-i-for"mes) (L. *ciconia,* stork, + form)—**herons, bitterns, storks, ibises, spoonbills, flamingos** (Fig. 28-23)

A familiar wading bird of eastern North America is the great blue heron (*Ardea herodias*), which frequents marshes and ponds.

The American bittern (*Botaurus lentiginosus*) is one of the shyest birds of the swamps and marshes. Its favorite haunts are cedar swamps, cattail beds, and stagnant marshy regions where its concealment coloration makes it extremely difficult to see. Its peculiar notes, uttered in the mating season, resemble the sounds of pumping and stake driving.

Order Anseriformes (an'ser-i-for"mes) (L. *anser,* goose, + form)—**swans, geese, ducks** (Fig. 28-24)

The members of this order have the web restricted to the front toes and have a long breastbone with a low keel. The common domestic mallard duck is *Anas platyrhynchos.*

Order Falconiformes (fal'ko-ni-for"mes) (LL. *falco,* falcon, + form)—**eagles, hawks, vultures, falcons, condors, buzzards** (Figs. 28-25 to 28-27)

These are the great birds of prey (except owls) and are represented by many species. There are two American species

FIG. 28-23

European white stork *(Ciconia ciconia).* This bird is woven into folklore of many European countries such as Holland and Denmark, where it often nests on tops of chimneys. Order Ciconiiformes. (Courtesy Chicago Natural History Museum.)

FIG. 28-24

Pair of trumpeter swans *(Cygnus buccinator).* These rare birds are almost extinct and are rigidly protected in their few nesting sites. Order Anseriformes. (Courtesy W. E. Banko, U. S. Fish and Wildlife Service.)

FIG. 28-25

Bald eagle *(Haliaeetus leucocephalus)*. This eagle is national emblem of our country but is found in only a few restricted areas. Order Falconiformes. (Courtesy Chicago Natural History Museum.)

FIG. 28-26

FIG. 28-27

FIG. 28-26

South American or Andean condor *Vultur,* largest flying bird (by weight) in the world. It may have a wingspread of more than 12 feet, lives chiefly on carrion. Order Falconiformes. (Courtesy Smithsonian Institution, Washington, D. C.)

FIG. 28-27

Harpy eagle *Harpia,* fierce bird of prey that ranges forests of tropical America and lives mainly on monkeys and sloths. Order Falconiformes. (Courtesy Smithsonian Institution, Washington, D. C.)

of eagles, the American golden eagle *(Aquila chrysaëtos)* and the bald eagle (*Haliaeetus leucocephalus*).

Order Galliformes (gal'li-for"mes) (L. *gallus,* cock, + form)—**quail, grouse, pheasants, ptarmigan, turkeys, domestic fowl** (*Gallus domesticus*) (Figs. 28-28 and 28-29)

Some of the most desirable game birds are in this order. The bobwhite quail *(Colinus virginianus)* is found all over the eastern half of the United States. The ruffed grouse (*Bonasa umbellus*), or partridge, is found in about the same region, but in the woods instead of the open pastures and grain fields, which bobwhite frequents.

The American wild turkey (*Meleagris gallopavo*) is now confined to the wilder parts of the South and a few of the northern states.

Order Gruiformes (gru'i-for"mes) (L. *grus,* crane, + form) —**cranes, rails** (Fig. 28-30), **coots, gallinules**

Order Charadriiformes (ka-rad're-i-for"mes) (NL. *Charadrius,* genus of plovers, + form)—**shore birds, such as gulls, oyster catchers, plovers, sandpipers, terns, woodcocks** (Fig. 28-31)

Order Columbiformes (co-lum'bi-for"mes) (L. *columba,* dove, + form)—**pigeons, doves**

Order Psittaciformes (sit'ta-ci-for"mes) (L. *psittacus,* parrot, + form)—**parrots, parakeets**

Order Cuculiformes (cu-cu'li-for"mes) (L. *cuculus,* cuckoo, + form)—**cuckoos, roadrunners**

The common cuckoo (*Cuculus canorus*) of Europe lays its eggs in the nests of smaller birds, who rear the young cuckoos. The incubation period of the cuckoo's egg is about 12 days, often less than that of the eggs of the foster parents. When hatched, the young cuckoo works its way under its companions and backs them out of the nest one by one.

The American cuckoos, black billed and yellow billed, rear their own young.

Order Strigiformes (stri'ji-for"mes) (L. *strix,* screech owl, + form)—**owls** (Figs. 28-32 and 28-33)

Owls are chiefly nocturnal birds and have probably the keenest eyes and ears in the animal kingdom.

Order Caprimulgiformes (kap'ri-mul'ji-for"mes) (L. *caprimulgus,* goatsucker, + form)—**goatsuckers, nighthawks, poorwills**

The birds of this group are most active at night and in

FIG. 28-28

Willow ptarmigan *(Lagopus lagopus)* showing marked difference between winter and summer plumage. Order Galliformes. (Courtesy Chicago Natural History Museum.)

FIG. 28-29

Ruffed grouse *(Bonasa umbellus)* one of the most prized of American game birds. Order Galliformes. (Courtesy Chicago Natural History Museum.)

twilight. They have small, weak legs, wide mouths, and short, delicate bills. The mouth is fringed with bristles in most species. The whippoorwills (*Antrostomus vociferus*) are common in the woods of the eastern states, and the nighthawk (*Chordeiles minor*) is often seen and heard in the evening flying around city buildings.

Order Apodiformes (a-pod'i-for"mes) (Gr. *apodos,* footless, + form)—**swifts, hummingbirds**

The swifts get their name from their speed on the wing. The familiar chimney swift (*Chaetura pelagica*) fastens its nest in chimneys by means of saliva.

A swift found in China (*Collocalia*) builds a nest of saliva that is used by the Chinese for soup making.

Most species of hummingbirds (Fig. 28-34) are found in the tropics, but there are 14 species in the United States, of which only one, the ruby-throated hummingbird, is found in the eastern part of the country.

Most hummingbirds live upon nectar, which they suck up with their highly adaptable tongue, although some catch insects also.

The nest (Fig. 28-16) of the ruby-throated hummingbird is exquisite. About the size of a thimble, it is usually saddled on a small limb or twig and made of downy fibers and spider's web. It blends into the surroundings as though it were a small knot on the limb. The outside of the nest is covered with tree lichens.

Order Coliiformes (ko'le-i-for"mes) (Gr. *kolios,* green woodpecker, + form)—**mousebirds**

Africa.

Order Trogoniformes (tro-gon'i-for"mes) (Gr. *trogon,* gnawing, + form)—**trogons**

Tropical.

Order Coraciiformes (ko-ra'se-i-for"mes or koar'-se'i-for" mes) (NL. coracii [Gr. *korax,* raven or crow], + form)—**kingfishers, hornbills, etc.**

In the eastern half of the United States the belted kingfisher (*Megaceryle alcyon*) is common among most waterways of any size. It makes a nest in a burrow in a high bank or cliff along a water course.

Order Piciformes (pis'i-for"mes) (L. *picus,* woodpecker, + form)—**woodpeckers, toucans, puffbirds, etc.**

Woodpeckers are adapted for climbing, with stiff tail

FIG. 28-31

Woodcock *(Philohela minor)* on nest. Vesper flight song of male is interesting courtship ritual. Order Charadriiformes. (Courtesy R. G. Schmidt, U. S. Fish and Wildlife Service.)

FIG. 28-30

Yellow rail *(Coturnicops noveboracensis).* Their slender bodies have given rise to expression "thin as a rail." They are weak fliers and usually escape danger by darting around or by concealment in marshy vegetation. Order Gruiformes. (Courtesy Natural Science Museum, Cleveland.)

FIG. 28-32

Screech owl *(Otus asio).* Order Strigiformes.

FIG. 28-33

Barn owl *(Strix flammea)* often called monkey-faced owl is one of the most useful of owls, for it destroys rats and other vermin around barns. Order Strigiformes. (Courtesy Nature Magazine, Washington, D. C.)

FIG. 28-34

Ruby-throated hummingbird *(Archilochus colubris)*. Of 14 species of hummingbirds in United States, ruby-throated bird is the only one found east of the Mississippi. Order Apodiformes. (Courtesy F. M. Hickman.)

FIG. 28-35

Mockingbird *(Mimus polyglottos)*. One of the most famous songsters of North America. It sings at any season at any time of day and is great imitator of other birds' songs. Order Passeriformes. (Courtesy Natural Science Museum, Cleveland.)

feathers and toes with sharp claws. Two of the toes extend forward and two backward. There are many species of woodpeckers in North America, the more common of which are the flickers, downy, hairy, red bellied, red headed, and yellow bellied. The largest is the pileated woodpecker, which is rare and is found only in deep and remote woods.

Order Passeriformes (pas′er-i-for″mes) (L. *passer*, sparrow, + form)—**perching birds**

This is the largest order of birds and is made up of 69 families. To this order belong the songbirds found in all parts of the world. Among these are the skylark, nightingale, hermit thrush, mockingbird (Fig. 28-35), meadow lark, robin, and hosts of others. Others of this order, such as the swallow, magpie, starling, crow, raven, jay, nuthatch, and creeper, have no songs worthy of the name.

Derivation and meaning of basic terminology

pecten (L. comb). A pigmented, vascular, and comblike process that projects into the vitreous humor from the retina at point of entrance of optic nerve (reptiles and birds). Its functions are obscure, but its peculiar shadow on the retina may make the bird more sensitive to movement in the visual field. It may also enable the bird to determine the position of the sun.

syrinx (Gr. pipe). The voice box of birds. It is not homologous to the larynx (also found in birds) but is a modification of the trachea and bronchi and is situated where the two main bronchi begin. Voice is produced by the vibrations of a bony ridge (pessulus) and certain membranes.

Annotated references

Allen, A. A. 1936. Ornithology laboratory notebook. Ithaca, N. Y., Comstock Publishing Co. *A workbook for exercises on the birds, with descriptions and photographs of nests, together with distribution maps.*

Allen, R. P. 1947. The flame birds. New York, Dodd, Mead & Co., Inc. *A popular account of the roseate spoonbill and its sanctuaries in the southern states.*

Audubon, J. J. 1937. The birds of America. New York, The Macmillan Co. *This is a reissue of the famous work first published in 1828 to 1838. This masterly treatise, with superb pictures, is without equal in the field of ornithology.*

Bent, A. C. 1919. Life histories of North American birds. U. S. National Museum Bulletins. *More than a score of monographs have already been published in this outstanding series and more to come.*

Broun, M. 1949. Hawks aloft. New York, Dodd, Mead & Co., Inc. *An account of the migration of hawks as observed from Hawk Mountain, Pennsylvania, with observations on the problem of protecting desirable birds of prey.*

Cobb, S. 1960. Observations on the comparative anatomy of the avian brain. Perspect. Biol. Med. **3**:383-408.

Collias, N. E. 1965. Evolution of nest building. Natural History **74**:44-47. *A fine account of the nest-building behavior patterns of birds.*

Forbush, E. H. 1939. Natural history of the birds of eastern and central North America. Boston, Houghton Mifflin Co. *A somewhat abbreviated edition of the author's great work, Birds of Massachusetts. The plates are excellent and the descriptions are full.*

Gilliard, E. T. 1958. Living birds of the world. New York, Doubleday & Co., Inc. *A superb book of birds with illustrations (many in color). Note, among others, the fine Kodachrome of the European robin, famed in tradition and folklore, opposite p. 272. Without a doubt the finest book of its kind.*

Gordon, M. S. (editor). 1968. Animal function: principles and adaptations. New York, The Macmillan Co. *An outstanding work on the current status of the functional features of animals. Although intended for the undergraduate student, it brings into perspective some of the latest investigation on the ecologic physiology of animal function and adaptations.*

Grant, K. A., and V. Grant. 1968. Hummingbirds and their flowers. New York, Columbia University Press. *An excellent monograph on the interaction of birds and the flowers they visit for pollination. There are numerous color plates of birds and their flowers.*

Headstrom, R. 1949. Birds' nests. New York, Ives Washburn, Inc. *Good photographs of nests with descriptions. Nests are grouped according to a scheme of nest construction.*

Kendeigh, S. C. 1952. Parental care and its evolution in birds. Urbana, University of Illinois Press. *The author believes that parental care has evolved independently in the different phyla, and that the complex patterns for the care of the young are definitely correlated with the development of the nervous and sensory systems.*

Peters, J. L. 1931. Checklist of birds of the world. Cambridge, Mass., Harvard University Press.

Peterson, R. T. 1947. Field guide to the birds, ed. 2. Boston, Houghton Mifflin Co. *One of the best field manuals for ready identification.*

Pettingill, O. S., Jr. 1947. Silent wings. Madison, Wisconsin Society for Ornithology, Inc. *A pathetic account of the extinction of the passenger pigeon.*

Rand, A. L. 1956. American water and game birds. New York, E. P. Dutton & Co. *A finely illustrated book, with clear text descriptions of the various forms considered. Silhouettes add a great deal of interest and value to the work.*

Stettner, L. J., and K. A. Matyniak. 1968. The brain of birds. Sci. Amer. **218**:64-76 (June). *Shows that the intelligence of birds depends little upon the cerebrum, but on another part of the brain, the hyperstriatum.*

Sturkie, P. D. 1954. Avian physiology. Ithaca, N. Y., Cornell University Press. *Dealing with the specialized physiology of birds and intended primarily for research workers, it includes data on nearly all aspects of birds' organ systems and their physiology. The book is well documented.*

Van Tyne, J., and A. J. Berger. 1959. Fundamentals of ornithology. New York, John Wiley & Sons, Inc. *An up-to-date account of the structure, physiology, distribution, and taxonomy of one of the most interesting groups of animals. The chapter on migration is only one of many fine accounts about behavior patterns of birds.*

Wallace, G. J. 1955. An introduction to ornithology. New York, The Macmillan Co. *An up-to-date book on nearly every aspect of bird life. For the beginner there is no better introductory work on birds. It is clearly written and well illustrated.*

Wolfson, A. (editor). 1955. Recent studies in avian biology. Urbana, University of Illinois Press. *This summary by various specialists is important to all serious students of birds, for it includes an evaluation of the concepts and problems of evolution, systematics, anatomy, migration, breeding behavior, diseases, etc. Excellent bibliographies are included.*

Wood, N. A. 1951. The birds of Michigan. Ann Arbor, University of Michigan Press. *Description of habits and life histories.*

CHAPTER 29

• PHYLUM CHORDATA (THE VERTEBRATES: MAMMALS)

Class Mammalia

SUBPHYLUM VERTEBRATA

CLASS MAMMALIA*—mammals

● The term "Mammalia" was given by Linnaeus (1758) to that group of animals which are nourished by milk from the breasts of the mother. This group as a whole is considered the highest in the animal kingdom. Their advancement over other groups is quite pronounced from whatever viewpoint they are considered. Many other groups show a greater evolutionary diversity, for there are only between 4,000 and 5,000 named species of mammals, together with many thousand subspecies. Mammals have stressed the nervous system as their contribution to animal evolution. They have been a successful group, for they adapt themselves readily to new situations and to new food habits. As a climax to the evolutionary development of the nervous system, man himself has been the outcome.

Origin and relationships

The ancestor of all mammals appears to have been a therapsid reptile that lived when the dinosaurs flourished during the Jurassic period. These small mammal-like reptiles probably survived because of their speed. Some of them may have been no larger than mice and dwelt in trees. One of these early reptiles was *Varanope,* whose fossils have been discovered in Texas. This and other similar forms left no direct descendants, but later mammal-like reptiles were larger and their descendants have been better traced.

By the Triassic period the mammal-like reptiles had become a relatively important part of the fauna of the world. One of the most advanced of these mammal ancestors was *Cynognathus,* discovered in South Africa. It was 4 or 5 feet long and oddly resembled a cross between a lizard and a dog. Its sharp teeth indicated carnivorous habits. The fossil record is not clear enough to draw the line between the therapsid reptiles and mammals. When the huge dinosaurs disappeared, the small mammal-like animals came into their own. Probably at least five different groups of the mammal-like reptiles developed mammal-like characteristics and were mammalian in at least 50% of their osteologic features. Modern taxonomists recognize these as three different subclasses: Prototheria, Metatheria, and Theria. The oldest known fossil mammals are the Pantotheria, an extinct group of the subclass Theria. From this primitive group the marsupials and the insectivores appear to have arisen independently, probably in the late Jurassic period. From these insectivores the other placental mammals (most of the living orders of mammals) arose. As a result of convergent evolution the marsupials and placentals have evolved similar ways of life (Fig. 29-1). Throughout the Cenozoic era the mammals became dominant. Mammals have had a checkered career, for so many orders of mammals are extinct.

Although mammals have evolved from reptiles, the two groups show many important structural differences. Some important comparisons follow:

1. Most mammals have a body covering of hair instead of scales, although some scales persist, as on the tails of certain mammals.
2. Mammals have two occipital condyles instead of one, as in reptiles, and they have a larger cranium.
3. The muscular diaphragm of the mammal is found nowhere else. (Birds have a nonmuscular septum.)
4. The lower jaw in mammals is composed of one bone; the reptiles have more.
5. In mammals the lower jaw articulates directly with the skull and not through a quadrate bone, which is found in reptiles.

*Mam-ma'le-a (L. *mamma,* breast).

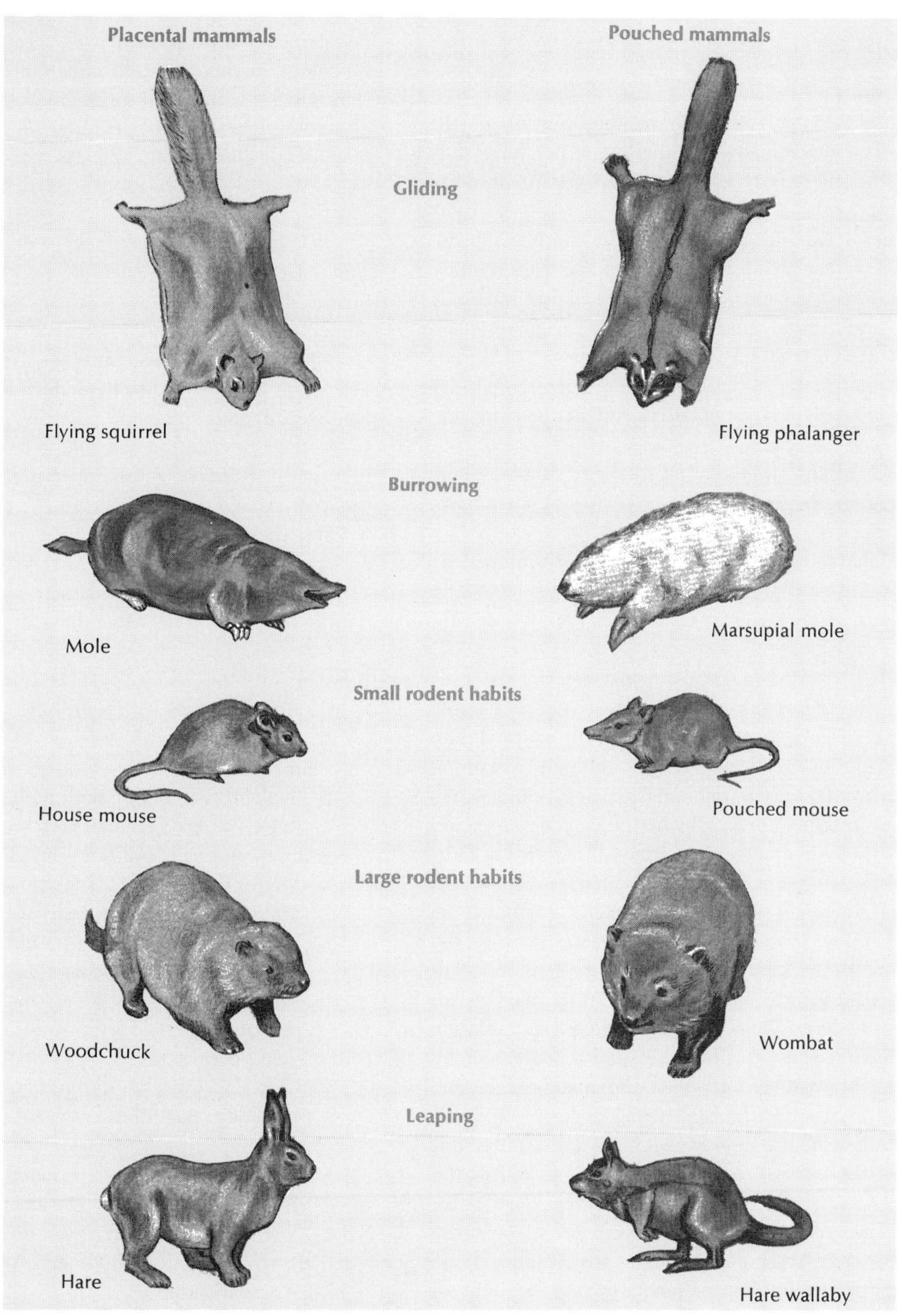

FIG. 29-1

Convergent evolution among mammals. Two groups of mammals not closely related (placentals and marsupials) have independently evolved similar ways of life and occupy similar ecologic niches. It will be noted that for every member of the ecologic niche in one group there is a counterpart in other group. This correspondence is not restricted to similarity of habit but also includes morphologic features. (From many sources.)

6. Mammals have a chain of three bones in the middle ear (incus, malleus, stapes); reptiles have only one columella (stapes) in the ear and retain the other two at the angle of the jaw.

7. The deciduous and permanent teeth of mammals have replaced the polyphyodont teeth of reptiles.

8. Mammals have a four-chambered heart and only the left aortic arch; most reptiles have a three-chambered heart and both aortic arches.

9. Mammals have developed the voice apparatus (larynx and epiglottis), which is rudimentary in reptiles.

10. One of the most unique methods of nourishing the young is the milk-secreting glands of mammals; none in reptiles.

Some characteristics that are highly developed in mammals are only primitive in reptiles; others have no counterpart at all.

Adaptive radiation

When the dinosaurs vanished near the beginning of the Cenozoic era, mammals suddenly erupted into varied evolutionary patterns. This sudden expansion was due partly to the numerous ecologic niches vacated by reptiles, into which the mammals could move as their divergent adaptations fitted them. During the Eocene and Oligocene periods most of the orders of mammals as we know them originated so that, including those that later became extinct, the number of orders at that time far exceeded those of the present day. Only a few of our existing mammalian orders arose later. This pattern of adaptive radiation among mammals is a widespread phenomenon among all animal populations in which the members branch out to form types suited for particular niches.

The limb structure among mammals best shows this concept (Fig. 29-2). According to this scheme, the early ancestral (stem) mammal had rather short limbs, with no specialized adaptations except for a terrestrial existence, such as shrews have at the present time. From this stem type of mammal, by modification of limbs and other structures, there diverged the various types of locomotion, such as running (horses and deer), burrowing (moles and gophers), flying (bats), and swimming (seals and whales). There are also modifications of these five basic patterns of locomotion, such as gliding (flying squirrels) and leaping (kangaroos). The student will recall the principle of homology in this adaptive radiation plan. He will note that the limb involved in each case of adaptation is a modification of the pentadactyl limb of the stem mammal, a fact that indicates common relationship.

Advancements made

What has enabled mammals to flourish and to adapt themselves to such a variety of environments? The one factor above all others is their nervous system; in other respects nonmammals are probably as well equipped as mammals. Another factor is that they are warm blooded, which enables them to be independent of environmental changes. They can survive frigid polar regions or can adapt to temperate or torrid zones. Reptiles must hibernate during much of the year except in torrid zones.

Other helpful factors are their methods of nursing and caring for their young and their behavior patterns. Their active curiosity has led them to explore, and they tend to hold onto places they have occupied.

Characteristics

1. **Body covered with hair,** but reduced in some
2. **Integument with sweat, sebacous,** and **mammary glands**
3. Skeletal features of skull with two occipital condyles, **seven cervical vertebrae** (usually), and often an elongated tail
4. Mouth with teeth on both jaws
5. **Movable eyelids** and **fleshy external ears**
6. Four limbs (reduced or absent in some) adapted for many forms of locomotion
7. Circulatory system of a four-chambered heart, **persistent left aorta,** and **nonnucleated red blood corpuscles**
8. Respiratory system of lungs and a voice box
9. **Muscular partition between thorax** and **abdomen**
10. Excretory system of metanephros kidneys and ureters that usually open into the bladder
11. Nervous systems of a well-developed brain and twelve pairs of cranial nerves
12. **Warm blooded**
13. Cloaca present only in monotremes
14. Separate sexes; reproductive organs of a penis, **testes (usually in a scrotum),** ovaries, oviducts, and vagina
15. Internal fertilization; **eggs develop in a uterus** with **placental attachment** (except mono-

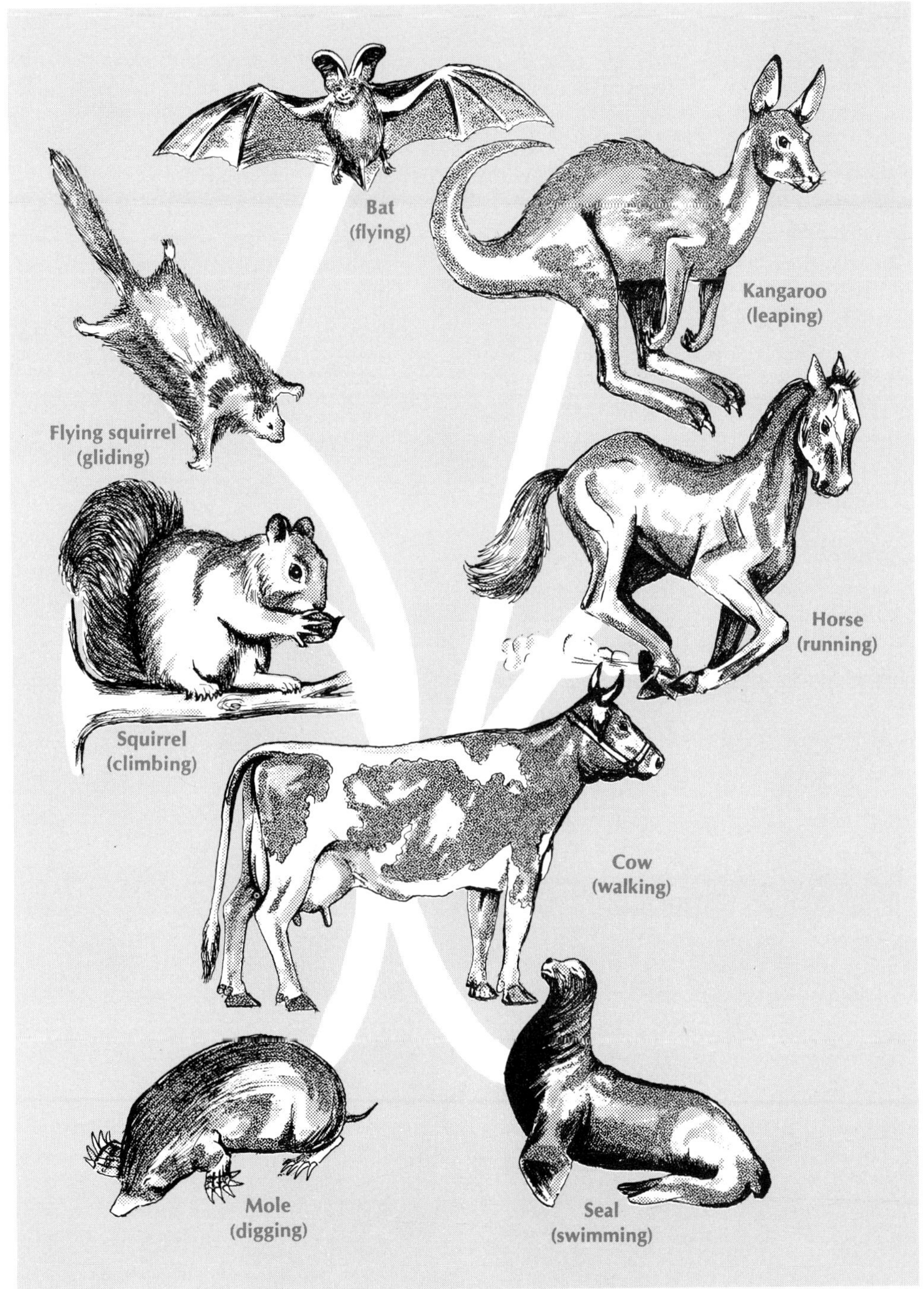

FIG. 29-2

Adaptive locomotion among mammals. Primitive mammal may have been terrestrial or arboreal, but ambulatory or walking method may well have been one from which many others have arisen. (From several sources.)

tremes); **fetal membranes** (**amnion, chorion, allantois**)

16. Young nourished by **milk from mammary glands**

Size ranges

The smallest mammal known is the pigmy shrew (*Sorex*), which has a body length of less than 1½ inches and weighs only a fraction of an ounce. The largest, of course, is the whale, certain species of which may reach a length of 103 feet and may weigh more than 100 tons. The whale is the largest animal that has ever lived and is larger than the extinct dinosaurs. The African elephant, which may reach a height of 11 feet at the shoulders and may weigh 7 to 8 tons, is the largest living terrestrial mammal. In no other group of animals do we find such a great size range, which indicates the wide adaptability of mammals.

General structures

External appearance. The bodies of mammals are divided into head, neck, trunk, tail, and appendages. Aquatic mammals are streamlined for swimming. The **head** in most mammals is large in proportion to the rest of the body because of the well-developed brain. The face typically projects forward to form a snout. The location of the **eyes** depends upon the habits of the animal. Animals such as the rabbit, which is a vegetarian, have eyes on the side for watching their enemies; carnivorous forms have the eyes placed more in front of the head for seeing their prey. External **ears,** characteristic of mammals, are large and movable in many such as the rabbit and horse, are small in animals that burrow, and may be absent in aquatic mammals. The **neck** in burrowing forms is short and may be absent altogether in the whale, whereas the giraffe has a neck length out of proportion to the rest of the body. The body **trunk** ranges all the way from heavy and ponderous in the rhinoceros and elephant to slender in the weasel. **Tails** are used for a variety of purposes. Some are long and bushy (squirrels), flat and rubberlike (beavers), ropelike (elephants), and long and prehensile (monkeys).

Limbs are modified in mammals for walking or running, climbing, swimming, digging (Figs. 29-2 and 29-3), jumping, and flying. The typical mammal plan has four limbs with **five toes** on each foot, but this is found only in generalized forms such as man and the primates. Many mammals have a reduced number of toes modified for various adaptations.

Integument and its modifications. In general the skin is thicker in mammals than in other classes of vertebrates, although it is made up of the two typical divisions—epidermis and corium (dermis). Among the

FIG. 29-3

Mole *(Scalopus aquaticus)* showing adaptations for life underground. Note enlarged forelimbs (for digging), reduced eyes and ears, and naked snout and tail, both of which have tactile hairs for orientation in its tunnel system. Order Insectivora.

mammals the corium becomes much thicker than the epidermis. The epidermis varies in thickness. It is relatively thin where it is well protected by hair, but in places subject to much contact and use, such as the palms or soles, its outer layers become thick and cornified with keratin. Some mammals have unusually thick skins, such as the pachyderms (elephants).

Many structures are modified from the integument. Most of these come from the epidermis, such as nails, claws, hoofs, horns of various animals, glands, and hair. The antlers of deer are exceptional in being bony outgrowths of the skull with a covering of skin, or "velvet." When this velvet is worn off, the antlers are bare bones and may be said in this condition to have no relation to the integument. Also of epidermal origin is the keratin-fiber horn of the rhinoceros, which arises from the cornified layer of the epidermis and is made up of a compact mass of keratin fibers cemented together. Armadillos have a fused armor of both epidermal scales and bony plates. However, in most mammals the scales are replaced with hair, although they persist to some extent in odd forms such as the scaly anteater and on the scaly tails of the beaver, rat, opossum, lemur, and shrew.

Some mammals have extensive masses of subcutaneous fat for insulation. Whale blubber is an example.

Hair. Hair is characteristic of mammals, although in the whale and some other aquatic mammals it is reduced to only a few bristles on the upper lip. Hairs are epidermal and are formed by a column of cells (hair shaft) from this layer pushing down into the corium and enclosing there a tiny cup of blood vessels, known as the dermal papilla (Fig. 30-3). Epidermal cells grow in around the hair root to constitute the **root sheaths.** The **hair follicle** is made up of these sheaths and the hair root. Opening into the follicle from the side is the sebaceous gland whose oily secretion keeps the hair moist. The hair usually has three layers: the medulla or pith in the center of the hair, the cortex with pigment granules next to the medulla, and the outer cuticle composed of imbricated scales.

Hair follicles are provided with smooth muscles (**arrectores pilorum**), which cause the hair to assume an erect position. This is the cause of the tingling scalp sensation in a badly frightened man and the erect hairs on the neck of an angry dog.

Hairs are said to be homologous with the scales and feathers of reptiles and birds. However, hair probably originated from the tactile sensory pits (prototriches) of fish and amphibians, probably from apical bristles that at first were of sensory function. The distribution was the same as that of scales, since reptilian sensory pits were located on the apices of epidermal scales. This primitive pattern of distribution has been lost in advanced mammals.

The hair in cross section may be elliptical or circular. The circular ones are usually straight, whereas the flattened ones are curly. Mammals usually have two kinds of hair: (1) the thick and soft underhair next to the skin for insulation and (2) the coarser and longer guard hair for protection against wear. Around the nose and eyes of many are the long tactile **vibrissae.** The hair covering, or **pelage,** varies greatly with different mammals. Animals in northern climates usually have much denser fur than do those in warmer regions. Hair is usu-

FIG. 29-4

Porcupine *(Erethizon dorsatum)*. Hair has been modified to form spines. Order Rodentia. (Courtesy L. K. Couch, U. S. Fish and Wildlife Service.)

ally shed once or twice a year. Many northern animals such as hares have a white coat in winter and a brown one in summer. Some hairs, such as those in the mane of a horse, may persist throughout life. The hair making up the furs of most animals ceases to grow after reaching a certain length, but those on the scalp of man may continue to grow unless they are shed.

Among interesting varieties of hair are the **spines** of the porcupine (Fig. 29-4) and hedgehog, the stiff **bristles** of hogs, and the **wool** of sheep.

Coloration. Most mammals have somber colors mainly for protective purposes. Rarely do mammals have solid colors, such as the polar bear, but most of them have different shades of color on various parts of the body, with stripes and bars common. The color is due principally to pigmentation in the hair, although in a few, bare surfaces of skin may be found with bright hues, such as in the cheeks and sternal callosities of the mandrill (a species of baboon), which may be due to pigment or to blood capillaries in the skin. At least two types of chromatophores are found in mammals—melanophores (black and brown pigment) and xanthophores (red and yellow pigment). Pigment granules may also lie outside the regular pigment cells. Although the color of hair may fade to some extent, any marked change in the color of a mammal's fur coat must be brought about by molting.

The color patterns of most mammals fit into the color of the environment. This may be due to natural selection, for there is no reason to believe that the environment itself could affect the colors of the animals which live in it. Some think that climatic factors such as humidity may play a part in determining the color patterns of animals.

An interesting aspect of color is the pair of rump patches of the pronghorn antelope, which are composed of long white hairs erected by special muscles. When alarmed, the animal can flash these patches in a manner visible for a long distance. They may be used as a warning signal to other members of the herd.

Dichromatism, or two-color phases in the same species, is found in foxes and some other mammals. The silver fox, prized for its pelt, may occur in a litter of red foxes.

Albinism, or a lack of pigment, may happen in most kinds of mammals, as also may **melanism,** or an excess of black pigment.

Glands. Mammals have a great variety of integument glands. Whatever the type of gland, they all appear to fall into one of three classes: eccrine, apocrine, and holocrine (Fig. 29-5).

The **eccrine glands** (sweat glands) are found only in hairless regions (foot pads, etc.) in most mammals, although in some apes and in man they are scattered all over the body and are important devices for heat regulation. These glands have developed by the time of birth and are true secretory, or merocrine, glands; that is, the cell remains intact or is not destroyed in the process of secretion. Their secretory coils are restricted to the dermal region.

Sweat glands are used mainly to regulate the body temperature. They are common on such animals as the horse and man but are greatly reduced on the carnivores (cats) and are entirely lacking in shrews, whales, and others. Dogs are now known to have sweat glands all over the body. In human beings, racial differences are pronounced. Negroes, who have more than whites, can withstand warmer weather. **Lacrimal,** or tear, glands keep the surface of the eye moist and clean.

FIG. 29-5

Sweat glands (eccrine and apocrine). Phylogenetically apocrine glands are older. Eccrine glands, best developed in primates, develop from epidermis and play important role in temperature regulation. Most glands in dog, pig, cow, horse, etc. are apocrine, but these have declined in man, along with hair, for they develop from follicular epithelium. Apocrine glands are not involved in temperature regulation, but their odorous secretions play a part in sexual attraction.

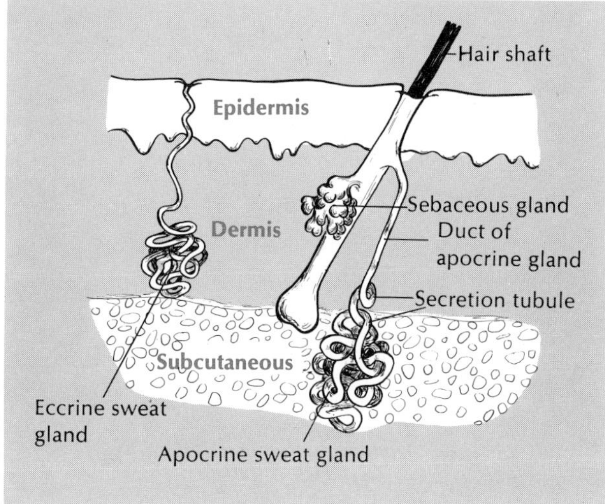

Apocrine glands are larger than eccrine glands and have longer and more winding ducts. Their secretory coil is in the subdermis. They always open into the follicle of a hair or where a hair has been. Phylogenetically they are much older than the eccrine gland and are found in all mammals, some of which have only this kind of gland. Negroes have more apocrine glands than whites, and women have twice as many as men. They develop about the time of sexual puberty and are restricted (in man) to the axilla, mons pubis, breasts, external auditory canal, prepuce, scrotum, and a few other places. Their secretion is not watery like ordinary sweat (eccrine gland) but is a milky, whitish or yellow secretion that dries on the skin to form a plastic film. Only the tip of the secretory cell is destroyed in the process of secretion. Their secretion is not involved in heat regulation, but their activity is known to be correlated with certain aspects of the sex cycle, among other possible functions.

The most common apocrine glands include the **scent** glands, found in all terrestrial species. Their location and function vary greatly. Some are defensive in nature, others convey information to members of the same species, and still others are involved in the mating process. These glands are often located in the preorbital, metatarsal, and interdigital regions (deer); preputial region near the penis (muskrats, beavers, canine family, etc.); base of tail (wolves and foxes); and anal region (skunks, minks, weasels). These last, the most odoriferous of all glands, open by ducts into the anus and can discharge their secretions forcefully for several feet. During the mating season many male mammals give off strong scent for attracting the females.

It is not always possible to state from which of the three major types of glands a particular mammalian gland has evolved. Mammary glands, anal glands, inguinal glands of rabbits, and the glands of the auditory canal are believed to be modified apocrine glands.

Mammary glands, which give the name to the group, are modified apocrine glands that occur on all female mammals and on most, if not all, male mammals; on the latter they are often covered by hair. They develop by the thickening of the epidermis to form a milk line along each side of the abdomen in the embryo. On certain parts of these lines the mammae appear, while the intervening parts of the ridge disappear. They secrete milk for the nourishment of the young. When distended with milk, the glands produce marked integumentary swellings: the breasts, or mammae. The outlets of the gland are by elevated nipples (absent in monotremes) (Fig. 29-6). The glands are located on the thorax of primates, bats, and a few others but on the abdomen or inguinal region in other mammals. Nipples vary in number from two in the human being, horse, bat, etc., to twenty-five in the opossum. The number is not always constant in the same species. Mammary glands are periodic in their functioning, growing during pregnancy and secreting during the nursing period of the young.

The third type of gland (**holocrine**) is one in which the entire cell is discharged in the secretory process and must be renewed for further secretion. Most of them open into hair follicles, but some are free and open directly onto the surface. The **sebaceous gland** is the most common example. In most mammals sebaceous glands are found all over the body; in man they are most numerous in the scalp, forehead, and face. Sebaceous glands that open into the hair follicles keep the skin and hair soft and glossy. A modified sebaceous

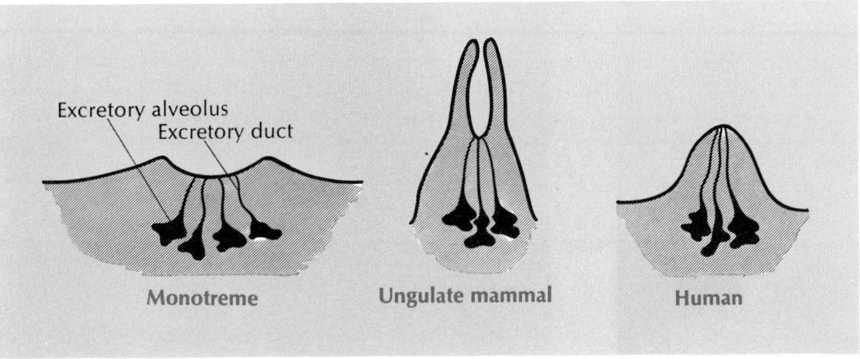

FIG. 29-6

Types of mammalian nipples. Monotremes have no nipples and young lick up milk from ridged depression as milk exudes from mother's skin. Mammary glands are assumed to have originated from apocrine sweat glands. Primitive arrangement of nipples (which vary in number) consists of two series, or milk lines, along abdomen. Composition of milk varies among different species of mammals. Whale milk, for instance, contains four times more protein and ten times more fat than that of cow, but it lacks sugar.

gland, known as the meibomian gland, is found at the edge of each eyelid and provides an oily film between the eyelids and eyeball.

Teeth. All mammals, with the exception of certain species of whales, monotremes, and anteaters, have teeth. The character of the dentition is correlated with the food habits of the mammal. Typically, mammals have two sets of teeth: deciduous and permanent. They are set in sockets in the jaw, and the various types are molars, premolars, incisors, and canines. The rounded or pointed eminence on the masticating surface is called a **cusp.** Each type of tooth is specialized for some aspect of food getting or mastication. Incisors with simple crowns and slightly sharp edges are mainly for snipping or biting; canines with long conical crowns are specialized for piercing; premolars with compressed crowns and one or two cusps are suited for shearing and slicing; and the molars with large bodies and variable cusp arrangement are for crushing and mastication. Molars always belong to the permanent set.

Each tooth is made up of **dentin** from the corium and the covering **enamel** from epithelium. **Cementum** from the corium lies around the **root** of the tooth, within which is the **pulp cavity** of nerves and blood vessels. Certain insectivores cut only milk teeth. This condition is called **monophyodont;** in contrast is the **diphyodont** dentition of both deciduous and permanent teeth. Teeth that are alike are called **homodont,** which is characteristic of lower vertebrates; when they are differentiated to serve a variety of purposes, they are called **heterodont.** Teeth were already differentiated into these four types in the higher mammal-like reptiles. Carnivorous animals have teeth with sharp edges for tearing and piercing. They have well-developed canines, but some of the molars are poorly developed. In the herbivores the canines are suppressed, whereas the molars are broad, with enamel ridges for grinding. Such teeth are also usually high crowned, in contrast to the low crowns of carnivores. The incisors of rodents have enamel only on the anterior surface so that the softer dentin behind wears away faster, resulting in chisel-shaped teeth that are always sharp. Moreover, rodents' incisors grow throughout life and must be worn away to keep pace with the growth. If two opposing incisors fail to meet, the growth of the incisors continues and results in serious consequences to the animal.

The **tusks** of the elephant and the wild boar are modifications of teeth (Fig. 29-7). The elephant tusk is a modified upper incisor and may be present in both males and females; in the wild boar the tusk is a modified canine present only in the male. Both are formidable weapons.

The number and arrangement of permanent teeth are expressed by a **dental formula.** The figures above the horizontal line represent the number of incisors,

FIG. 29-7

Wart hog *(Phachochoerus aethiopicus)*, native of Africa, is example of animal in which canine teeth have become modified into tusks. Order Artiodactyla. (Courtesy Smithsonian Institution, Washington, D. C.)

canines, premolars, and molars on one half of the upper jaw; the figures below the line indicate the corresponding teeth in one half of the lower jaw.

Man	Dog
2-1-2-3	3-1-4-2
2-1-2-3	3-1-4-3

Internal structures. Internally the structure of mammals is basically the same as that of other vertebrates. The coelomic cavity, however, is divided into thoracic and abdominal cavities, separated by a unique muscular diaphragm. The thoracic region is divided into three coelomic cavities: two lateral pleural cavities and a median pericardial cavity.

Digestive system. A **hard palate** of bone and tissue separates the nasal chambers from the mouth and is supplemented behind by the fleshy **soft palate.** The passageway from the mouth to the pharynx is known as the **fauces,** which has the tonsils on each side of it. The **glottis,** which is the opening into the trachea, has the flaplike **epiglottis** over it to prevent the entrance of food. Both mucous and salivary glands pour their secretions into the mouth. The **tongue** is unusually well equipped with numerous **papillae** and **taste buds.** It has many uses, such as drawing grass into the mouth in herbivores, licking up ants in the anteater, and smoothing out the fur in fur-bearing forms.

Among the interesting features of the digestive tract is the four-chambered stomach of ruminants (cattle, camels, deer, etc.), which "chew the cud." The stomach compartments are (1) **rumen,** a large cavity; (2) **reticulum,** a space lined with shallow pits; (3) **omasum,** much folded; and (4) **abomasum,** which is the only compartment that contains glands (Fig. 29-8). These animals collect food rapidly, mix it with saliva, and pass it to the rumen. After feeding, the animal lies down and regurgitates the food into the mouth, thoroughly chews it and then swallows it. The food then passes through the other three compartments. Although the mucosa of the camel's rumen contains small chambers and glands (absent in other ruminants), these saclike compartments are not used for storing water, as commonly supposed (Schmidt-Nielsen).

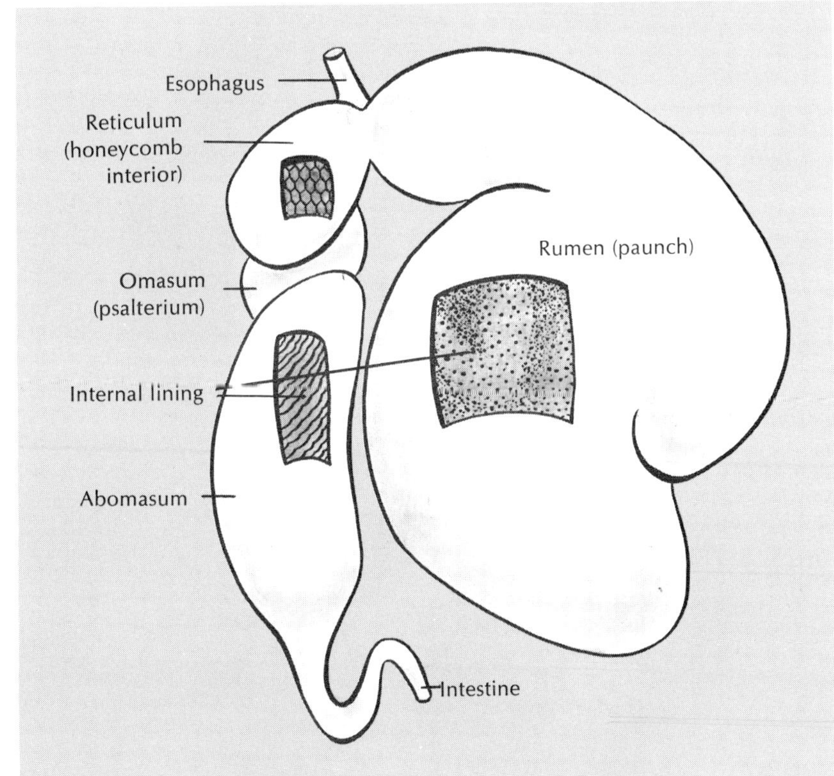

FIG. 29-8

Stomach of ruminant. By rapid eating, ruminants fill paunch with partially masticated food, which is reduced to pulp by bacteria and ciliates. When animal "chews the cud," masses of food enter reticulum, in which they are rolled into cud, regurgitated, and thoroughly masticated in mouth. When swallowed the second time, cud goes first to omasum and then on to abomasum to be mixed with gastric juice for digestion before it enters intestine. Concentrated food such as grain bypasses the rumen and passes directly into reticulum. The cuds chewed usually have been in the stomach at least 4 days.

The vampire bat has the fundus of its stomach drawn out into a long diverticulum, or pouch, in which it stores blood drawn from its victims.

The **cecum** between the small and large intestine has many modifications. Herbivorous mammals usually have large ceca, but carnivores have small ones or none at all. In monotremes a **cloaca** is present, but in other mammals the anus is separated from the openings of the urinary and reproductive systems.

Circulatory system. Mammals and birds have the most efficient blood systems in the animal kingdom. The heart is four-chambered (Fig. 29-9) and the systemic and pulmonary systems are separated. The left aorta persists instead of the right, as in birds. A hepatic portal system is found in mammals, but the renal portal system has disappeared.

Respiratory system. Mammals in their breathing make use of the complete separation of the thorax from the abdomen. The partition between these two cavities is the muscular **diaphragm,** which is in the form of a dome, with the convex side anteriorly. The **lungs** are

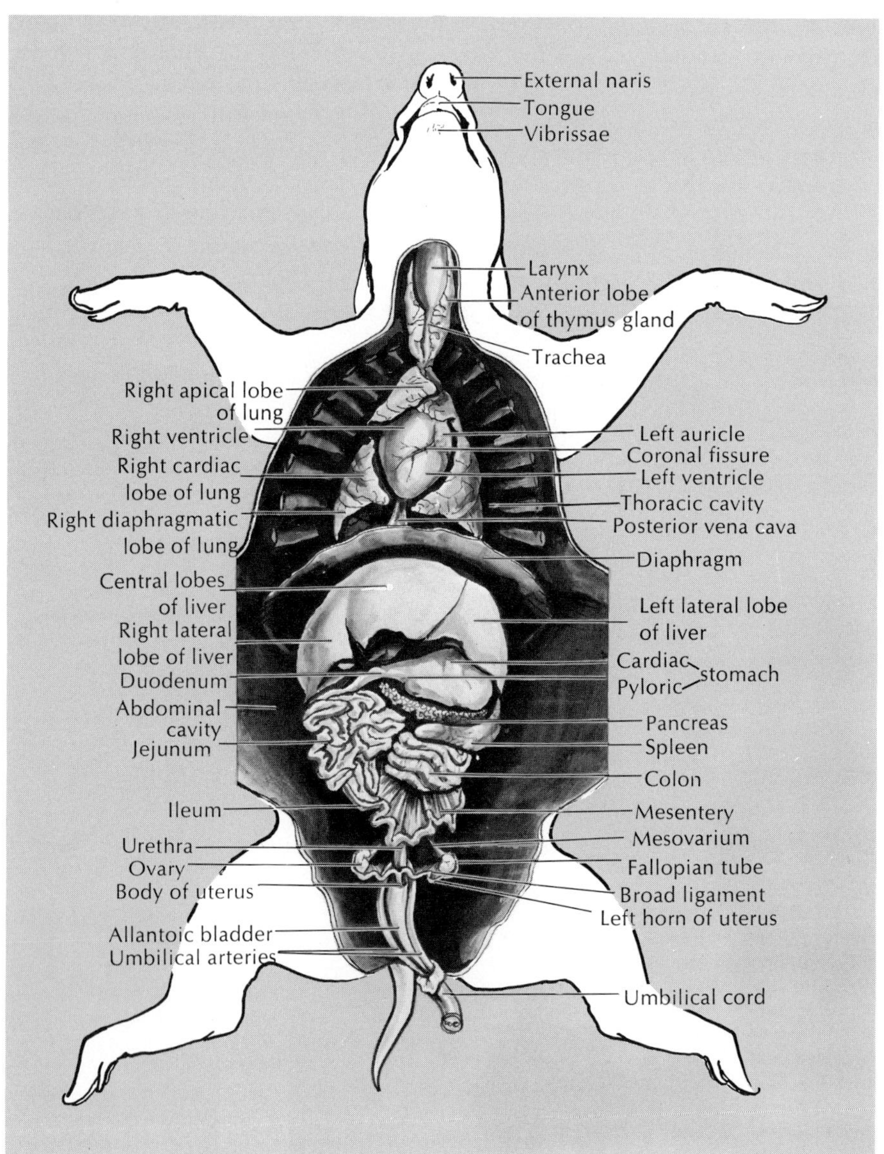

FIG. 29-9

Visceral organs of female fetal pig *(Sus scrofa)*, ventral view.

located in the thorax in spaces called the pleural cavities. When the thoracic cavity is expanded by the elevation of the ribs and the depression of the diaphragm, air is drawn into the lungs. Relaxation of the muscles of the ribs and diaphragm forces the air out. The voice box (larynx) is well developed in most mammals.

Excretory system. All mammals have the third or metanephros kidney (or that part which develops from the caudal region of the archinephros), although during embryonic life they have a mesonephros. Connecting the kidney with the urinary bladder are the two ureters. The bladder opens to the outside by the **urethra,** except in monotremes, in which it empties into the cloaca.

Nervous system. The cerebrum and cerebellum especially show marked advancements over other vertebrates. Only the monotremes have a reptilian type of brain. Higher mammals have the cerebral surface thrown into many convolutions, and all have the cerebellum convoluted, as in birds. The two optic lobes of other classes are divided, becoming the four **corpora quadrigemina** in mammals. The general trend in the mammalian brain is for the upper part and sides of the forebrain to expand and become the cerebral cortex. Here cortical centers differentiate for localization of functions, which in other vertebrates are controlled at lower levels. The spinal cord in mammals does not reach the end of the bony vertebral canal, which is filled with roots of spinal nerves below the end of the cord, forming the so-called **cauda equina.** In common with birds and reptiles, mammals have twelve pairs of cranial nerves.

Sensory system. In correlation with the highly developed nervous system, mammals are well endowed with the sense organs. Cutaneous sense organs, which reach their highest development in mammals, are repre-

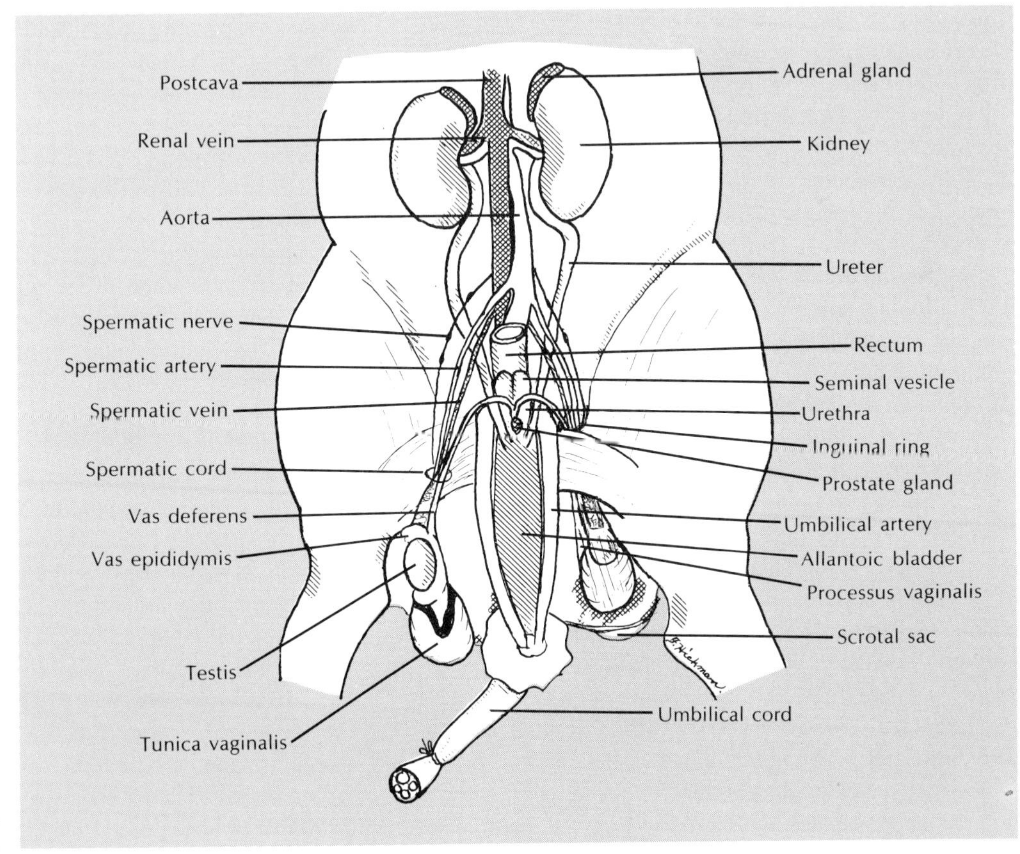

FIG. 29-10

Male urogenital organs of fetal pig.

sented by many forms of corpuscles and free nerve endings. The middle ear is now provided with three ossicles (malleus, incus, stapes), and the sense of hearing is acute. The external ear (pinna) is found in most mammals. The nictitating membrane so well developed in the eye of birds tends to be reduced in mammals. The chemical senses of smell and taste reach a high stage of development in mammals, although some such as whales have little or no chemical sense.

Endocrine system. The endocrine glands of mammals are better known than those of any other group. They include the pituitary, thyroid, parathyroid, islets of Langerhans, adrenals, and gonads.

Reproductive system. The sexes are always separate in mammals, as they are in practically all vertebrates. The paired **testes** of the male are usually enclosed in a scrotal sac, which hangs down from the body in a more or less pendulous condition (Fig. 29-10). In some (rodents, bats, camels) the testes descend into the scrotum only during the breeding season, and at other times they are withdrawn into the body cavity. In monotremes, elephants, whales, etc., they always remain in the body cavity. The penis of mammals is a closed tube, except in monotremes, in which the urethra is a groove. The glans penis is double in opossums, and in some carnivores, seals, cetaceans, moles, bats, and some monkeys the penis is stiffened by a penis bone—**os priapi.**

The female organs (Fig. 29-9) are the paired **ovaries,** the **fallopian tubes** (oviducts), the **uterus,** and the **vagina.** Basically, the uterus is doubled but is found in different degree of fusion among the various mammals. In rodents the horns of the uterus enter the vagina separately (**duplex**); in carnivores they fuse at the base (**bipartite**); in ungulates the fusion is more complete, forming a common chamber for the embryos (**bicornuate**); and in apes and man the fusion is complete and the uterus is a single chamber (**simplex**).

Muscular system. The better-developed appendages of mammals have well-developed muscles to meet their varied adaptations. On the other hand, the trunk muscles have been reduced and changed. Some muscles have divided or migrated. Only the intercostal, invertebral, and rectus abdominis muscles show segmentation. Some new developments in muscles also appear. Integumental or cutaneous muscles, such as the **panniculus carnosus,** appear in marsupials and reach a high degree of development in the horse and other forms but become greatly reduced in primates. Another addition is the diaphragm muscle, probably a derivative of the neck myotomes. Many of the muscles in mammals are similar to those in lower vertebrates except that mammals have greatly stressed those on the head, neck, and limbs. Division and migration have often made it difficult to homologize mammalian muscles with those of birds and reptiles.

Skeletal system. The general plan of the mammalian endoskeleton is similar to the skeleton of birds and reptiles. Some marked differences, however, are found in the axial skeleton. The bones of the cranium are firmly knit together, and the lower jaw is more firmly articulated. Birds, reptiles, and fish have loose connections between the skull and lower jaw. Usually these vertebrates have a series of bones that serve for the connection between the skull and the lower jaw so that the latter is suspended from, rather than directly articulated with, the skull. There is also a considerable fusion of bones in mammals. The mammalian shoulder girdle shows several advances beyond the reptilian ancestors of mammals. The **coracoid,** except in monotremes, is no longer a separate bone but is a process on the scapula. The scapula has acquired shelves and projections for the attachment of muscles for the varied forms of locomotion. The vertebral column of mammals, with few exceptions, contains seven cervical vertebrae (Fig. 29-11). With regard to the thoracic and lumbar vertebrae, mammals vary to some extent. **Amphiplatyan** vertebrae (that is, those flat on both ends) are the chief type in mammals, but some other types are found here and there. The vertebrae of mammals also represent a fusion of the centrum with bony disks, a process unlike that of other vertebrates.

Natural history and behavior

No group of animals has more interesting behavior patterns than the mammals. With their highly developed nervous system, alertness, and adaptations, mammals display a remarkable range of activity. Mammals demonstrate the highest range of intelligence patterns in the animal kingdom and have worked out ingenious devices for survival.

Body temperature. Part of the great activity of mammals may be attributed to the fact that they are warm blooded (homoiothermic or endothermal). Many of the larger members have temperatures from 100° to 103° F. Man's temperature is 98.6° F. Yet many mammals

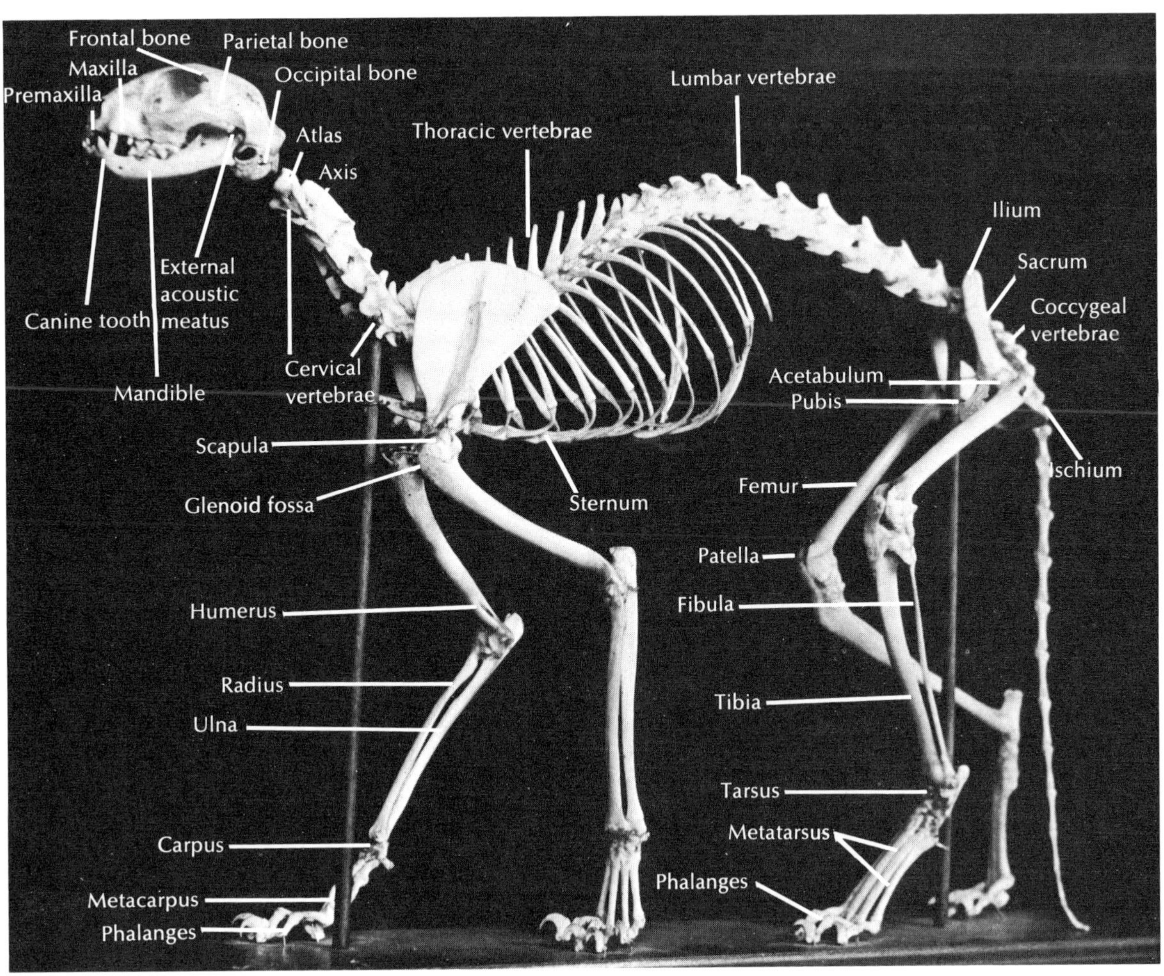

FIG. 29-11
Skeleton of dog.

have an unstable temperature that fluctuates or is seasonal in character. Daily rhythms are found in practically all, including man. Rectal temperature is 1° to 2° F. higher than mouth temperature, and skin temperature is 7° to 9° F. lower than the internal temperature (man). Primitive mammals (monotremes) have a variation of about 10° F. in their temperatures. Such mammals are called **heterothermal** and their temperature is regulated chiefly by variations of heat production (increased by activity) and by the surrounding temperature. To this group belong also newly born mammals, spiny anteaters (*Echidna*), armadillos, bats, and all true hibernating mammals. Sloths placed in cold surroundings will have a drop in temperature of 15° to 20° F. Mammals in hibernation may have a temperature that fluctuates like that of a cold-blooded form. The upper limits of high temperatures (lethal) for mammals is between 104° and 112° F.; lower limits may extend down to a few degrees from freezing for some species.

Mammals that live in deserts face special problems of heat regulation because of the high temperature of the physical environment during the day. Smaller desert mammals are mostly fossorial (fitted for digging burrows) and nocturnal; larger ones make physiologic adjustments of their homeostatic mechanisms of thermoregulation or osmoregulation to avoid undue loss of water by evaporation. Hair and fur (pelage) are not damaged by fairly high external temperatures and act as a shield to the body. A steep temperature gradient exists between the surface of the pelage and the skin surface when mammals are exposed to high solar radiation. Heat from the pelage is returned to the environment by reradiation and convection. Light colored and glossy fur also may reflect many wavelengths of sunlight. Sweating reduces the gradient between the skin and the internal temperature of the body. The camel can store heat during the day, raising its body temperature several degrees; during the night its temperature drops several degrees. It can also endure a much greater loss of body water (dehydration tolerance) than other mammals (Schmidt-Nielsen).

On the other hand, the physiologic mechanisms involved in adaption to a cold environment are different. Such arctic animals as foxes, Eskimo dogs, and arctic sea gulls make use not only of thick fur and feathers for better insulation but also of special vasomotor controls, such as a rete arrangement of blood vessels. In such a vasomotor pattern the arteries and veins run close together and intertwine, and when the warm arterial blood enters a limb, it is cooled by the returning cold venous blood by a countercurrent exchange. This mechanism tends to prevent undue heat loss by convection and radiation from the surface of the skin. Such cold-adapted animals can tolerate very low skin temperatures (even zero or less) of the feet and other extremities. The critical temperature (the range of external temperatures in which there is no increase in basal heat production) is very great in large arctic animals—from 30° to –30° C., or a total range of 60° C. The range for smaller arctic animals and for tropical animals may not exceed 10° C. (Irving).

Distribution. Mammals are found in most habitats that support life, but few are adaptable to living in all the conditions found in most of our continents. Some, however, are able to range far wider than others. One of these is the shrew (*Sorex cinereus*), which is found from Alaska and northern Canada to our southern and southwestern states. Within such a wide area, this tiny animal is able to adapt itself to a great variety of ecologic habitats. On the other hand, some gophers and bats are restricted to small regions. This is particularly the case with forms that may be more or less isolated by the nature of the terrain. Factors that are mainly responsible for the distribution of mammals are natural barriers of water and land, temperature, climate, food, shelter, and enemies.

Aquatic mammals live in varied environments, as shown by strictly aquatic forms, such as whales and porpoises; by seashore forms that spend part of the time in the water, such as seals and walruses; and by freshwater forms, such as beavers, muskrats, and minks.

Mammals, however, are mainly terrestrial and are found in nearly every kind of habitat on land. Woodlands attract them for the shelter, nesting sites, and protection they afford. Squirrels, monkeys, and various carnivores that are strictly arboreal are rarely found on the ground. Others, such as moles, shrews, rabbits, and hares, are found on the surface of soil or within burrows. Mammals are found at nearly all altitudes on our high mountain ranges, some of them far above timber line, such as mountain sheep and conies. Treeless and grassy regions often support large populations of gophers, prairie dogs, and other rodents as well as many hoofed animals. Many mammals are active only at night and spend the daytime in their shelters and places of retreat.

Home range. Many of the larger mammals literally "stake out" claims where they will not tolerate other members of the same species. This seems to be the case with the larger carnivores that are solitary in their habits, such as the grizzly bear and the mountain lion. The grizzly bear, for instance, has a range of many square miles that it guards zealously against all other grizzlies. Just how these animals establish priority or mark the boundaries of their ranges is not exactly known. It is known that some of them leave claw marks on trees that may serve as a warning to intruders, and some mark their rights with urine. Whenever a new territory is being colonized, the first individuals to enter are usually the males, as Darling found in his famous study on the red deer. The practice of territory claims may be far more common than we yet know.

The home range refers to the area an animal covers in its normal activities of living. This is often determined by the nature of the territory, the supply of food, and the shelter. Small herbivorous animals, such as rabbits, ground squirrels, and squirrels, have relatively small ranges; carnivorous forms must range farther in seeking their prey. A woodchuck, for instance, may stay within its own half acre of a luxurious clover field, but a mink is known to travel several miles in a single night. Both the home range and territory of the same animal often vary during its life cycle.

Population surveys. Many surveys have been made to determine the number and kind of mammals found within a given area. These surveys, for which a certain amount of error must be allowed, are made by trapping, observation, tracks, signs, and other devices. Surveys are of great practical importance in conservation programs and ecologic studies. Several different techniques are employed. Actual counts of all the individuals of a species population may be made on a given area, such as Darling did with various herds of red deer, provided conditions are favorable. Also used are indirect methods of marking captured specimens, releasing them, and from the ratio of recaptures to the marked numbers, estimating the number in the whole population of the species in the area being studied. Another common method is the sampling method; individuals are counted on a specific part of a large area and then an estimate of the total on the large area is made from the number on the sample area. Results of these surveys show that the population of any species of mammal tends to vary from year to year. The population of most mammals is greatest just after the breeding season because of the additional young members.

Fluctuations of animal populations are often known as cycles. A cycle may take several years, during which time a species may build up to a peak and then decline. Meadow mice, for instance, usually have a cycle of about three to four years; the snowshoe hare, ten years; and squirrels, five years. Usually smaller mammals have a shorter cycle than larger species. Responsible for these cyclic variations may be such factors as the abundance of food, the pressure of enemies, epidemic diseases, reproductive rate, and weather conditions. The abundance of one species may be correlated with that of another. The cycle of the Canadian lynx is closely correlated with the cycle of the rabbit or hare, for the lynx preys on these animals. Whenever a species declines rapidly, an epidemic disease is suspected. Many such outbreaks have been observed. The denser the population, the more rapidly such diseases spread.

Population densities of the various species of mammals depend on shelters, food, enemies, and kind of species. Small mammals are usually far more common per unit area than are larger ones. Mice and shrews under favorable conditions may number 100 to 200 or even more per acre; jack rabbits, about 10 to 20 per square mile; and deer, about 12 to 15 per square mile.

Ecologic density, which refers to the habitable parts of any total area being studied, is also an important concept in population studies. Rarely do we find an area as big as a township that has a uniformity of ecologic conditions all over it. Such an area may include grassland, forest, marsh, and streams, and any particular species population will be far more concentrated in those habitats for which it is best adapted.

Homes and shelters. Nearly all mammals have places where they rear their young or shelter themselves when they are not actively engaged in feeding or other pursuits. Many have permanent quarters from which they seldom stray far and to which they return to rest. Others such as deer, which range far and wide to forage, are usually not restricted to a permanent home but take advantage of whatever is at hand. In winter even deer have tramped-out yards in remote forests near which they are always found. But the smaller mammals usually establish their residency in some protected home for long periods or even for life. Arboreal species, squirrels, raccoons, opossums, and mice, make use of holes in trees. Rabbits, woodchucks, prairie dogs, coyotes, and skunks excavate burrows in the ground. Some squirrels and mice build elaborate nests in the

FIG. 29-12

Nest of fox squirrel *(Sciurus niger)*, used for both winter and summer home. Nest is 30 feet from ground.

branches of trees (Fig. 29-12). Many mammals make snug nests in their shelters, notably the muskrat, beaver, and chipmunk.

Food and storage. On the basis of food habits, animals may be divided into herbivorous, carnivorous, omnivorous, and insectivorous. Within each of these dietary classes the food of a species may show considerable variation, as mammals are highly adaptable. **Herbivorous** animals feed upon grasses and vegetation. This group is large and includes most domestic animals, deer, elephants, rabbits, squirrels, and hosts of others. The **carnivorous** forms feed mainly upon the herbivorous animals and include foxes, weasels, cats, dogs, fishers, wolverines, lions, tigers, and others. **Omnivorous** mammals live on both plants and animals. Examples of these are man, raccoon, rats, and bears. Many carnivorous forms eat fruits, berries, and grasses when hard pressed. The fox, which usually feeds upon mice, small rodents, and birds, will eat frozen apples, beechnuts, and corn when the normal sources are scarce. Those that subsist chiefly on insects are called **insectivorous,** and mammals having these food habits are the bats, moles, shrews, etc. Many other mammals, such as bears, raccoons, mice, and ground squirrels, will catch and eat insects.

Mammals will often consume amounts of food out of all proportion to their size. Many will eat an amount of food in 24 hours equal to their own body weight. Shrews and moles will starve if deprived of food for a few hours. A large carnivorous mammal, such as the mountain lion, is known to kill an average of at least one deer each week and, when game is abundant, even more.

Mammals have many problems in obtaining food. Seasonal changes in food supplies are marked in temperate zones when inclement weather may cut off most normal supplies. Mammals have many ways to meet these emergencies. Some migrate to regions where food is more abundant. Others hibernate and sleep through the winter months. Many carnivores that do not migrate have to range far and wide to eke out an existence. Even so, they undergo periods of fasting between feeding periods. But some provident mammals build up stores during periods of plenty. This habit is most pronounced in many of our rodents, such as squirrels, chipmunks, gophers, and certain mice. All the tree squirrels, red, fox, and gray, collect nuts, conifer seeds, and fungi and bury these caches for winter use. Later they locate these caches by their marvelous sense of smell. The chipmunk is one of the greatest providers, for it spends the autumn months in collecting nuts and seeds. Some of its caches may exceed a bushel in amount. Even carnivorous animals do a certain amount of storing, usually temporarily buried in the ground or under rubbish from which they do not stray far until it is all consumed.

Migration and emigration. Migration refers to the periodic passing from and the return to a region. Birds are renowned for their migratory habits, but many mammals also have the practice, though their ranges of migration are less striking. Ecologists recognize several types of migration. Some of the factors causing migration among mammals are the seasonal scarcity of food (alimental migration), severe climatic conditions (climatic migration), and the desire to have suitable places for rearing their young (gametic migration). One of the most remarkable migratory mammals is the fur seal (Fig. 29-13). The breeding grounds of these animals are on the Pribilof Islands off the coast of Alaska. During the winter the females and young winter far to the south of the islands. The old bulls do not go so far south. Toward spring all of them migrate back to the islands for breeding and for rearing their young. For the females this means a journey of 2,000 to 3,000 miles. On their return the young are born and cared for during the summer months. Late in the fall the

FIG. 29-13

Fur seal *(Callorhinus ursinus)* rookery. Fur seals have many interesting behavior patterns, not the least of which is their remarkable migration. (Courtesy V. B. Scheffer, U. S. Fish and Wildlife Service.)

various seals return to their winter quarters. This is an example of seasonal migration. The caribou of Alaska and Canada perform great mass migrations. Availability of food seems to be the primary reason. Some species of deer and mountain sheep undergo altitudinal migrations, spending the summer on the high mountains and returning to lower altitudes for the winter. Some of the bats spend the winter in caves in the northern regions; others migrate as far as the West Indies for the winter (seasonal and latitudinal migration).

Emigration means the movement away from a territory with no intention of returning. It may be induced by lack of food or overpopulation or by a combination of factors. **Immigration** is the coming into a new region. The lemming (*Lemmus*) of Norway and Sweden is one of the best known cases of emigration. These small rodents are found on the high plateaus where they live on the moss and vegetation of that rough terrain. Usually they produce one or two litters of four or five young each season. But every four or five years their reproductive power is greatly increased, probably caused by a hormone or vitamin that they get from their food, and they will have three or four litters of eight to eleven young. This leads to overpopulation and mass emigration is the result. They overflow into the lower land masses, into the rivers and fiords, and even into the sea, where they perish. Mass movements of gray squirrels were frequent during pioneer days, and there are many authentic accounts of these within recent years. Emigration of the Norway rat accounts for the large number of these rodents in places where they were uncommon before. The introduction of the gray squirrel (*Sciurus carolinensis*) into the British Islands in the latter part of the last century shows how explosive immigration into a new country by a mammal may be. At first introduced here and there in small numbers, the squirrels have spread in the past few decades over more than 40% of the total land surface of England, Scotland, and Wales and have also invaded several counties in Ireland. This wide distribution is all the more remarkable because these countries have far fewer woods (a necessary habitat for squirrels) than America, their native home.

Hibernation. Many mammals solve the problems of winter scarcity of food and low climatic temperatures by undergoing (1) a state of drowsy inactivity and intermittent sleep or (2) true hibernation. In the first of these processes the mammal becomes dormant for several weeks, during which time it has intermittent periods of sleep and wakefulness. When asleep it responds quickly to stimulation and its metabolic processes are only a little lower than those of an active animal. There is little to no lowering of temperature. Such animals may remain in a dormant condition for considerable lengths of time, but the light sleepers frequently interrupt their winter sleep by stirring around. Good examples of this type of winter sleep are skunks, bears (Fig. 29-14), opossums, badgers, and raccoons. True hibernation, on the other hand, involves a whole syndrome of physiologic states different from normal activity. It involves an inactive state in which bodily processes are lowered, with a marked fall in temperature, which may be only slightly higher than that of the surroundings, and an inability to control the body temperature. For instance, in a ground squirrel the respiratory rate may be nearly 200 during activity but only 4 or 5 while hibernating; comparable values for the heart rate are 150 and 5. However, the hibernating animal maintains a fixed internal environment (homeostasis) such as an acid-base balance with little changes in electrolytes and blood sugar. Very little cell growth occurs during hibernation, and development of sex

FIG. 29-14

Black bear *(Ursus americanus)*. (Courtesy E. P. Haddon, U. S. Fish and Wildlife Service.)

organs mainly occurs after the hibernating period. Thus, most hibernators have time for only one litter a year.

Although drowsy, torpid, and difficult to awaken while in their sleep, hibernating animals will awaken when their surroundings approach freezing, to keep from freezing to death. All true hibernating animals usually store up great amounts of fat before going into hibernation, although this is also done by some that are not true hibernators (bears). All hibernating animals are heterothermal animals and their temperature during active states is somewhat lower than that of nonhibernators. American mammals that hibernate include ground squirrels, woodchucks, bats, and jumping mice. The primary stimulus for starting hibernation may be a lack of food supplies, low temperature, and other factors not well understood.

Summer torpor, or **aestivation,** is practiced by some mammals, especially by ground squirrels in the western parts of our country. During the hot months of July and August, they seek out deep burrows and remain sleeping there during these hot and dry months. Aestivation in warm and tropical countries is common among a great variety of animals.

Enemies. Practically all mammals have enemies. Most herbivorous animals are preyed upon by flesh-eating animals, and some of the carnivorous forms are eaten by larger carnivores. Many birds of prey, hawks, owls, and eagles, live on the smaller mammals, such as squirrels, rabbits, and mice. Snakes eat many mammals. Man kills predator mammals that prey on his livestock and catches fur-bearing mammals for their fur. All mammals are parasitized, and many diseases are peculiar to them. Epidemic diseases are known to decimate mammal populations whenever they become too crowded.

Behavior patterns. Mammals have learning powers so great that it is often difficult to distinguish between actions that are instinctive and those that are acquired. The range in this respect varies, of course, from the lower to the higher levels of mammals. A mouse or shrew, for instance, will not demonstrate the same learning capacity as a chimpanzee. In nearly all varieties of learning, however, mammals will score much higher than other groups, whether it is conditioned responses, selective learning, insight solutions of problems, or elementary reasoning. The subject of mammalian intelligence is discussed more fully in Chapter 43 but two or three aspects of their behavior may be mentioned here. In the first place, the psychologic superiority of man over other mammals is due chiefly to his capacity for language communication involving a systematic code of symbol expression whereby he is able to convey meaning to others. There is no evidence that nonhuman mammals have such language activities. But they do have limited powers of communication by which they can influence each other. They can do this by mimetic signs, by voice, and in other ways.

Most mammals can make use of their voices for warning each other, for scaring their enemies, for calling their young to them, for mating, and for calling each other together. Some apparently make sounds just to get rid of their emotions and pent-up energies. Some mammals, such as cattle, moose, and many monkeys, have powerful voices that can be heard for long distances. Many female mammals make characteristic sounds to their young. Just what meanings primates such as apes can convey with their utterances are not known. Bats use their ultrasonic notes to guide them in their flight, for these notes echo from nearby objects and so the bats can avoid such obstacles.

Recently a most striking behavior pattern has been observed among shrews (*Crocidura*) on the continent of Europe. Known as the caravan formation, it was photographed for the first time in 1957. It is a method employed by a mother shrew for removing all her litter of offspring at one time from a place of danger (Fig. 29-15). In tandem formation the first youngster seizes the mother's fur near the root of her tail, is in turn seized the same way by the next youngster in the procession, and so on. The behavior may be partly innate but learning is involved, for considerable practice seems to be necessary before an efficient caravan is attained. The behavior has not been observed in other shrews, but variant forms of it have been found in field mice and other mammals.

Reproduction and secondary sex characteristics. Fertilization is always internal, and they are all viviparous except the monotremes, which lay eggs (Fig. 29-16). Most mammals have definite mating seasons, usually in the winter or spring. Many males are capable of fertile copulation at any time, but the female mating function is restricted to a periodic cycle, known as the **estrus cycle,** or "heat." At times other than during this period, they will not allow the male to approach them. The estrus cycle is marked by certain characteristic changes in the vagina and uterus. The cycle is divided into the

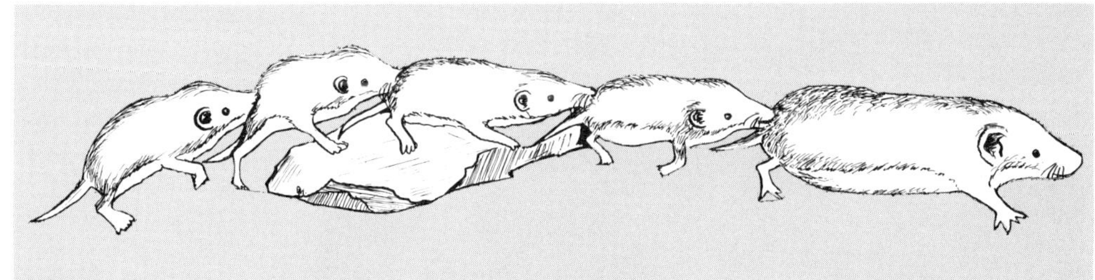

FIG. 29-15

Caravan formation of European shrew *Crocidura,* by which mother transports her litter to place of safety when danger threatens. Evidence indicates that young must be taught and that method is not instinctive. Modifications of this method have been observed among other small mammals such as mice.

FIG. 29-16

Mammal that lays eggs—duck-billed platypus *Ornithorhynchus anatinus.* Order Monotremata. These monotremes are found only in restricted regions of Australia, Tasmania, and New Guinea, where they are found in rivers and ponds; they feed on insects and shellfish. They make complicated burrows in banks of their water habitats. Eggs are about 3/4 inch in size and are incubated by mother for about 2 weeks before hatching. From her fur, young suck milk that seeps from her milk glands. (Courtesy New York Zoological Society.)

anestrum, or resting period; **proestrum,** or preparation for mating; **estrum,** or period of accepting the male; and **metestrum,** or period of regressive changes in the uterine and vaginal walls. Animals vary regarding the time of ova discharge from the ovary, but usually it occurs during the estrus period or shortly thereafter. How often females are in heat also varies greatly among the different mammals. Unless she has fruitfully mated, the female rat comes in estrus about every 4 days; the female dog, about every 6 months; the female house mouse, every 4 to 6 days; and the cow, every 21 days. Female rabbits are believed to breed at any time. Those animals that have only a single estrus during the breeding season are called **monoestrus;** those that have a recurrence of estrus during the breeding season are called **polyestrus.** Dogs, foxes, and bats belong to the first group; field mice and squirrels are all polyestrus. In the anthropoid primates the female may be receptive and the male potent throughout the reproductive cycle, although the estrus period may have some influence on the time of mating.

Gestation, or period of pregnancy, varies greatly among the mammals. Mice and rats have about 21 days; rabbits and hares, 30 to 36 days; cats and dogs, 60 days; cows, 280 days; and elephants, 22 months. The marsupials (opossum) have a very short gestation period of 13 days; at the end of that time the tiny young leave the vaginal orifice and make their way to the marsupial pouch where they attach themselves to nipples. Here they remain for more than 2 months (Fig. 29-17).

The number of young produced by mammals in a

FIG. 29-17

Mother opossum *(Didelphis virginiana)* with four young. Young are first carried in her abdominal pouch and later on her back. Order Marsupialia. (Courtesy F. M. Blake, U. S. Fish and Wildlife Service.)

season depends on many factors. Usually the larger the animal, the smaller the number of young in a litter. Perhaps one of the greatest factors involved is the number of enemies a species has. Small rodents that serve as prey for so many carnivores produce, as a rule, more than one litter of several young each season. Field mice are known to produce seventeen litters of four to nine each in a year. Most carnivores have but one litter of three to five young a year. Large mammals, elephants and horses, have only one young, and the same is true for many others.

The condition of the young at birth also varies. Those young born with hair and open eyes and ability to move around are called **precocial** (ungulates and jack rabbits); those that are naked, blind, and helpless (carnivores and rodents) are known as **altricial.** Mammals exhibit a great deal of parental care and will fiercely fight in defense of their young. When disturbed they will often carry their young to more secure places.

Differences between the sexes of the same species of mammals are not so marked as they are in birds. The male is often larger and more powerful, especially in the larger mammals. The male fur seal may be four or five times as large as that of the female, although such disparity in sex sizes is uncommon. Scent glands may be more common in the male. Sexual variation in color is not common. The male of some monkeys may have a different shade from the female. Male deer are provided with antlers, which are lacking in the female. Most of the smaller mammals have few or no secondary sex characteristics.

Economic importance

Man's welfare has been closely related to that of other mammals. He has domesticated the horse, cow, sheep, pig, goat, dog, and many others. He uses these for beasts of burden, for food, and for clothing and many other products.

The fur-bearing animals have proved useful to man in all stages of his culture. For early man they were indispensable. Still basically a hunter, man hunts mammals for pleasure as well as for profit. This is one reason why we have conservation programs. Of fur-bearing mammals, the muskrat at present seems to be the most valuable. Many mink and fox farms have proved profitable. Although a number of wild fur-bearing animals have been almost exterminated, the annual value of furs in this country amounts to many millions of dollars.

Many mammals, including the small ones, destroy insects and seeds and are thus helpful. Skunks feed on grubs and cutworms. Moles and shrews consume enormous numbers of insect larvae.

Some mammals, however, are inimical to man's interests. Many rodents, rabbits, field mice, and woodchucks damage crops and fruit trees. Gophers and prairie dogs (Fig. 29-24) do damage with their burrows and by destroying valuable crops. A dozen jackrabbits will eat as much as a sheep. Predatory mammals, wolves, coyotes (Fig. 29-19), and panthers destroy much livestock.

Mammals also carry disease. Bubonic plague and typhus are carried by house rats. Tularemia or rabbit fever, is transmitted to man by the wood tick carried by rabbits, woodchucks, muskrats, and other rodents. Rocky Mountain spotted fever is carried by ticks on ground squirrels. Trichina worms and tapeworms are acquired by man through hogs, cattle, and other mammals.

Probably the most destructive mammal is the house rat. The amount of damage done by this crafty rodent can scarcely be estimated. Many effective controls have been used against rats, but so adaptable is this animal that it will probably be a menace for a long time.

Many authorities think that when all mammals are classified there will be some 20,000 species and subspecies. Fifteen thousand or more species and subspecies have been named, divided among 16 or 17 living **orders.** Mammals are classified according to blood relationships as far as possible. A physiologic approach is receiving more consideration in modern taxonomy. Taxonomists studying mammals are forced to do a great deal of lumping, splitting, and shifting of genera from one group to another. This accounts for the variation in classified lists as new studies are published.

The classification of mammalian orders is based upon major differences, such as the character of the teeth, modifications of the limbs or digits, the presence or absence of claws and hoofs, and the complexity of the nervous system. The following summary of living orders will acquaint the student with some of the representative forms.

Classification of mammals varies somewhat with different authorities. According to Simpson's classification of mammals, there are 18 living and 14 extinct orders of mammals. Of the living orders, many of their families and genera are also extinct. Class Mammalia is divided into two subclasses as follows: Subclass **Prototheria** includes the monotremes, or egg-laying mammals. Subclass **Theria** includes two infraclasses, the **Metatheria** with one order, the marsupials, and the **Eutheria** with the rest of the orders, all of which are placental mammals.

Subclass Prototheria (pro'to-thi"re-a) (Gr. *protos,* first, + *ther,* wild animal). The egg-laying mammals.
Order Monotremata (mo'no-tre"mah-tah) (Gr. *monos,* single, + *tremos,* hole)—**egg-laying mammals, e.g., duck-billed platypus, spiny anteater** (Fig. 29-16)
This order is represented by the duckbills and spiny anteaters of Australia, Tasmania, and New Guinea. The most noted member of the order is the duck-billed platypus (*Ornithorhynchus anatinus*). The adults are about 18 inches long and are adapted for an aquatic life, with webbed toes, a bill similar to that of a duck, and a thick coat of fur. Only the young have teeth. The males have on the hind feet horny spurs that are connected to poison glands.
The spiny anteater (*Tachyglossus*), about 17 inches long, is covered with coarse hair and spines. It has a long, narrow snout adapted for feeding on ants, which are its chief food. The female carries the one egg in her marsupium on the abdomen. This species is found in Australia, but a larger one (*Zaglossus*) is in New Guinea.
Monotremes represent the only order that is oviparous, and there is no known group of extinct mammals from which they can be derived. Their fossils date from the Pleistocene age.

Subclass Theria (thi're-a) (Gr. *ther,* wild animal)
Infraclass Metatheria (met'a-the"re-a) (Gr. *meta,* after, + *ther,* wild animal). The marsupial mammals.
Order Marsupialia (mar-su'pe-a"le-a) (Gr. *marsypion,* pouch)—**pouched mammals, e.g., opossums, kangaroos, kaola** (Fig. 29-17)
These are the primitive mammals. They are characterized by an abdominal pouch, the **marsupium,** where they rear their young, which are born in an immature condition. Although the young are nourished in the uterus for a short time, there is rarely a placenta present. The period of gestation is only 13 days. When born, the immature young (seven to fourteen in number) find their way from the urogenital orifice to the pouch, where each is attached to a nipple. After several weeks the young leave the pouch but stay close to the mother and reenter the pouch to feed or for shelter. This order is represented by the opossum, the kangaroo, the kaola, the Tasmanian wolf, the wombat, and many others. Only the opossum is found in the Americas, but the order is the dominant group of mammals in Australia.
It is thought that the American opossum (*Didelphis virginiana*) is but little modified from an ancestral stock of North American origin and of the Cretaceous period, which, on the one hand, gave rise to the American opossums and, on the other, to the marsupials of Australia. There are at least two other subspecies of *Didelphis* in North America—the Florida and the Texas opossums. There are a number

FIG. 29-18

Large brown bat *(Eptesicus fuscus)* often found in old barns and church steeples. They frequently hang head down as this one is doing. Single young is usually born in June. Order Chiroptera. (Courtesy F. M. Hickman.)

of genera and species of the opossum family in South America.

Infraclass Eutheria (yu-thi-re-a) (Gr. *eu,* true, + *ther,* wild animal). The placental mammals.

Order Insectivora (in'sec-tiv"o-ra) (L. *insectum,* an insect, + *vorare,* to eat)—**insect-eating mammals, e.g., shrews, hedgehogs, moles** (Figs. 29-3 and 29-15)

The principal food of animals in this order is insects. The most primitive of placental mammals, they are widely distributed over the world except Australia. Placental mammals and marsupials are thought to have arisen independently from common ancestors during the Cretaceous period, but in time the placentals became dominant in most parts of the world because of their superior intelligence. Insectivora are small, sharp-snouted animals that spend a great part of their lives underground. The shrews are the smallest of the group; some of them are the smallest mammals known. They have soft fur and sharply pointed muzzles, and their teeth show little differentiation. The North American forms are the long-tailed (*Sorex*) and the short-tailed shrews (*Blarina*), and also *Notiosorex, Microsorex, Cryptotis,* and others. *Sorex,* with its many species and subspecies, is distributed over most of North America; *Blarina,* with fewer species, is restricted to the eastern half of North America.

Order Chiroptera (ki-rop'ter-a) (Gr. *cheir,* hand, + *pteron,* wing)—**flying mammals** (Fig. 29-18)

The bats are in some respects the oddest of all mammals, for they are provided with wings. The wings are modified forelimbs in which the second to fifth digits are elongated to support a thin integumental membrane for flying. The first digit (thumb) is short with a claw.

There are many families and species of bats the world over. The common North American forms are the little brown bat (*Myotis*), the free-tailed bat (*Tadarida*), which lives in the Carlsbad Caverns, and the large brown bat (*Eptesicus*). In the Old World tropics the "flying foxes" (*Pteropus*) are the largest of bats, with a wingspread of 4 to 5 feet, and live chiefly on fruits.

The tropics have many kinds of bats, including the famed vampire bat (*Desmodus*). This bat is provided with highly specialized and sharp incisor teeth with which it can shave or rasp away the epidermis of the skin and expose the underlying capillaries. The bat then laps up the blood and pumps it into its specially modified stomach as the blood oozes from the wound.

Order Dermoptera (der-mop'ter-a) (Gr. *derma,* skin, + *pteron,* wing)—**flying lemurs**

These are related to the true bats and consist of the single genus *Galeopithecus.* They are found in the Malay peninsula and the East Indies. They cannot fly in the strict sense of the word but glide with their parachutes like flying squirrels.

Order Carnivora (car-niv'o-ra) (L. *caro,* flesh, + *vorare,* to

FIG. 29-19

Coyote *(Canis latrans).* His cunning in avoiding capture and his destruction of livestock has made him a serious pest in certain localities. Order Carnivora, family Canidae. (Courtesy E. P. Haddon, U. S. Fish and Wildlife Service.)

FIG. 29-20

Giant panda *(Ailuropoda melanoleuca).* This interesting animal belongs to racoon family. Order Carnivora, family Procyonidae. (Courtesy Chicago Natural History Museum.)

eat)—**flesh-eating mammals, e.g., dogs, wolves, cats, bears, weasels** (Figs. 29-19 to 29-23)

This order is one of the most extensive groups of mammals, and its members are among the swiftest, keenest, and strongest of animals. They all have predatory habits, and their teeth are especially adapted for tearing flesh since the incisors and canines are well developed and the molars are specialized for cutting. In most of them the canines are used for killing their prey. They are divided among two suborders: Fissipedia, whose feet contain toes, and Pinnipedia, with limbs modified for aquatic life.

Suborder **Fissipedia** consists of the well-known carnivores —wolves, tigers, dogs, cats, foxes, weasels, skunks, and many others. They vary in size from certain tiny weasels to the mammoth Alaskan bear and Bengal tiger. They are distributed all over the world except in the Australian and Antarctica regions, where there are no native forms. This suborder is divided into certain familiar families, among which are **Canidae** (the dog family), consisting of dogs, wolves, foxes, and coyotes; **Felidae** (the cat family), whose members include the domestic cats, tigers, lions, cougars, and lynxes; **Ursidae** (the bear family), made up of bears; and **Mustelidae** (the fur-bearing family), containing the martens, skunks, weasels, otters, badgers, minks, and wolverines.

Suborder **Pinnipedia** includes the aquatic carnivores, sea lions, seals, sea elephants, and walruses. Their limbs have been modified as flippers for swimming. They are all salt-water forms and their food is mostly fish. The well-known fur seal (*Callorhinus*) is found on the Pribilof Islands off the coast of Alaska, where it spends the summer, but for 9 months it wanders far away in the sea.

The evolution of the different groups of carnivores has varied greatly. Some have changed little from primitive ancestors (civets), others have undergone moderate rates of evolution (dogs), and some (bears) are quite recent.

FIG. 29-21

Spotted hyena *(Crocuta crocuta)*. Hyena's food is chiefly carrion, and it often robs graves in regions where it is found. Note low hindquarters. Order Carnivora, family Hyaenidae. (Courtesy Chicago Natural History Museum.)

FIG. 29-22

Pair of cheetahs *Acinonyx*. These are swiftest of all mammals (60 to 75 m.p.h.) and are native to Africa and some parts of Asia. Although placed in family Felidae, their claws are not retractile and their foot pads are doglike. Easily tamed, they make docile pets. They have been useful in running down coyotes in the southwest. Order Carnivora, family Felidae. (Courtesy Smithsonian Institution, Washington, D. C.)

FIG. 29-23

Young raccoon *(Procyon lotor)*. Often dips its food in water before eating it. Intelligent animal and interesting pet. Order Carnivora, family Procyonidae. (Courtesy F. M. Hickman.)

FIG. 29-24

Prairie dog *(Cynomys ludovicianus)* feeding. Where they are numerous, these rodents do a great deal of damage by burrowing and by destroying crops. Order Rodentia, family Sciuridae. (Courtesy D. A. Spencer, U. S. Fish and Wildlife Service.)

Order Tubulidentata (tu'bu-li-den-ta"ta) (L. *tubulus,* tube, + *dens,* tooth)—**aardvarks**

The aardvark is the Dutch name for earth pig, a peculiar animal with a piglike body found in Africa. The order is represented by only one genus (*Orycteropus*) with 3 or 4 species.

Order Rodentia (ro-den'te-a) (L. *rodare,* to gnaw)—**gnawing mammals, e.g., squirrels, rats, woodchucks** (Figs. 29-24 to 29-26)

FIG. 29-25

Muskrat *(Ondatra zibethica)*, most common fur-bearing animal in America. Order Rodentia, family Muridae. (Courtesy F. M. Hickman.)

FIG. 29-26

Beaver *(Castor canadensis)*. Trapped almost to point of extinction, this desirable animal is now rapidly increasing in numbers under rigid protection. Order Rodentia, family Castoridae. (Courtesy Nature Magazine, Washington, D. C.)

The rodents are the most numerous of all mammals. Most of them are small. They are found on all continents and many of the large islands. They have no canine teeth, but their chisel-like incisors (never more than four) grow continually. Their basic adaptive feature, therefore, is gnawing, which is necessary to prevent the teeth from becoming oversized. This adaptation has been largely responsible for the evolution of a very active and diversified group. Some rodents are useful for their fur. The beaver (*Castor*), the largest rodent in the United States, has a valuable pelt. Many rodents are utilized as food by carnivores and by man. The common families of this order are Sciuridae (squirrels and woodchucks), Muridae (rats and mice), Castoridae (beavers), Erethizontidae (porcupines), and Geomyidae (pocket gophers).

The rodents are the most successful order of mammals because of their diverse adaptive radiation, which has enabled them to occupy so many ecological niches. The most primitive living rodent is the tailless sewellel (*Aplodontia*), or mountain beaver, found in a restricted region of the Pacific coast.

Order Pholidota (phol'i-do"ta) (Gr. *pholis,* horny scale)—**pangolins**

In this order there is one genus (*Manis*) with 7 species. They are an odd group of animals whose body is covered with overlapping horny scales that have arisen from fused bundles of hair. Their home is in tropical Asia and Africa.

Order Lagomorpha (lag'o-mor"pha) (Gr. *lagor,* hare, + *morphe,* form)—**rabbits, hares, pikas**

The chief difference between this order and Rodentia is the presence of four upper incisors, one pair of which is small, and the other large, with enamel on the posterior as well as anterior surface of the tooth. The little pika (*Ochotona*) lives at high altitudes in the Rocky Mountains and Eurasia and has the interesting habit of collecting grass, curing it in the sun, and storing it for winter food.

Order Edentata (e'den-ta"ta) (L. *edentatus,* toothless)—**toothless mammals, e.g., sloths, anteaters, armadillos** (Figs. 29-27 and 29-28)

These forms are either toothless or else have degenerate teeth without enamel. The group includes the anteaters, sloths, and armadillos. Most of them live in South America, although the nine-banded armadillo (*Dasypus novemcinctus*) may extend up into Texas. The sloths are very sluggish animals that have the queer habit of hanging upside down on branches. The hairs of sloths have tiny pits in which green algae grow and render them invisible against a background of mosses and lichens.

One of the extinct groups was the ground sloths, which were represented by some members as large as small elephants, such as *Megatherium.*

Order Cetacea (se-ta'she-a) (L. *cetus,* whale)—**fishlike mammals, e.g., whales, dolphins, porpoises**

This order is well adapted for aquatic life. Their anterior limbs are modified into broad flippers; the posterior limbs

FIG. 29-27

Group of giant anteaters *Myrmecophaga.* These animals with their long heads and sticky, extensible tongues for collecting ants are among the most specialized of mammals. Order Edentata. (Courtesy Chicago Natural History Museum.)

FIG. 29-28

Armadillo *(Dasypus novemcinctus).* Although timid and inoffensive, armadillo has survived mainly because of its protective coat of armor. Order Edentata. (Courtesy Smithsonian Institution, Washington, D. C.)

are absent. Some have a fleshy dorsal fin and the tail is divided into transverse fleshy flukes. The nostrils are represented by a single or double blowhole on top of the head. Teeth may be absent, but when present they are all alike and lack enamel. They have no hair except a few on the muzzle, no skin glands except the mammary and those of the eye, and no external ear, and their eyes are small. The order is divided into two suborders: Odontoceti and Mysticeti.

Suborder **Odontoceti** is made up of toothed members and is represented by the sperm whales, porpoises, and dolphins. The killer whale (*Orcinus*), the most savage member, is the tiger of the sea, for, although rarely longer than 20 feet, it does not hesitate to attack the larger whales and to tear huge mouthfuls from their bodies. The killer is also destructive to seal rookeries. The sperm whale (*Physeter*) is the source of sperm oil, which is obtained from the head. A peculiar substance, ambergris, is formed in its stomach and is much used in perfumes. This substance may be derived from squids, which form the principle food of sperm whales. Porpoises and dolphins, which also belong to this suborder, are only 6 or 7 feet long and feed mainly on gregarious fish. Another member of this group is the narwhal (*Monodon*), which has one of its two teeth modified into a twisted tusk 8 to 10 feet long and projecting forward like a pike.

The other suborder, **Mysticeti,** or whalebone whales, includes many species, some of which are gigantic. Instead of teeth, they have a peculiar straining device of whalebone (baleen) attached to the palate. They live on the microscopic animals at the surface (plankton), which they strain out of the water with the whalebone. The largest of the whales is the blue whale (*Balaenoptera*), which has a dorsal fin and may grow 100 feet long and weigh 125 tons. Whales can submerge for several minutes, and then emerge to blow air through the blowhole. The warm air from the lungs is condensed by the cool sea air to form the familiar spout.

Order Proboscidea (pro′bo-sid″e-a) (Gr. *pro,* before, + *boscein,* to feed)—**proboscis mammals, e.g., elephants**

This order includes only the elephants, the largest of living land animals. They have large heads, massive ears, and thick skins (pachyderm). Hair is confined mainly to the tip of the tail. The two upper incisors are elongated as tusks, and the molar teeth are well developed.

There are two genera of elephants: the Indian (*Elephas maximus*), with relatively small ears, and the African (*Loxodonta africana*), with large ears. There is also a small African form, the pigmy elephant (*Elephas cyclotis*), which is found in West Africa. The larger elephants may attain a height of 10 to 11 feet and a weight of 6 to 7 tons. The Asiatic or Indian elephant has long been domesticated and is trained to do heavy work. The taming of the African elephant is more difficult but was extensively done by the ancient Carthaginians and Romans, who employed them in their armies. Barnum's famous "Jumbo" was an African elephant. Strictly herbivorous, elephants consume several hundred pounds of food each day.

Order Hyracoidea (hy′ra-coi″de-a) (Gr. *hyrax,* shrew)—**hyraxes, e.g., conies**

Conies are restricted to Africa and Syria. They have some resemblance to short-eared rabbits but have teeth like rhinoceroses, with hoofs on their toes and pads on their feet. They have four toes on the front and three toes on the back feet. They are herbivorous in their food habits and live among rocks or in trees.

Order Sirenia (si-re′ne-a) (Gr. *seiren,* sea nymph)—**sea cows, e.g., manatees** (Fig. 29-29)

Sea cows, or manatees, are large, clumsy aquatic animals. They have a blunt muzzle covered with coarse bristles, the only hairs these queer animals possess. They have no hind limbs, and their forelimbs are modified into swimming flippers. The tail is broad with flukes but is not divided. They live in the bays and rivers along the coasts of tropical and subtropical seas. There are only two genera living at present:

FIG. 29-29

Manatees *(Trichechus mamatus)*, or sea cows, are aquatic mammals that sometimes reach length of 10 feet and live in estuaries of tropical and subtropical America. Order Sirenia. (Courtesy Chicago Natural History Museum.)

FIG. 29-30

Malay tapir *(Tapirus indicus)*. Order Perissodactyla. (Courtesy Smithsonian Institution, Washington, D. C.)

Trichechus, found in the rivers of Florida, West Indies, Brazil, and Africa, and *Halicore*, the dugong of India and Australia.

Order Perissodactyla (pe-ris'so-dac"ty-la) (Gr. *perissos*, odd, + *dactylos*, toe)—**odd-toed hoofed mammals** (Fig. 29-30)

The odd-toed hoofed mammals have an odd number (one or three) of toes, each with a cornified hoof. They are often referred to as **ungulates**, or hoofed mammals, with teeth adapted for chewing. They include the horses, the zebras, the tapirs, and the rhinoceroses. The horse family (Equidae), which also includes asses and zebras, has only one functional toe. There are 2 species of tapirs: *Tapirella*, in Central and South America, and *Tapirus*, in the Malay peninsula and Sumatra. They have four toes on the front feet and three on the hind feet. They have a short proboscis formed from the upper lip and nose. The rhinoceros *(Rhinoceros)* includes several species found in Africa and southeastern Asia. Their most striking character is the horn (one or two) on top of the snout. The horn is modified from hair, Rhinoceroses have three toes on the hind limb and three or four on the front. All are herbivorous.

Order Artiodactyla (ar'te-o-dac"ty-la) (Gr. *artios*, even, + *dactylos*, toe)—**even-toed hoofed mammals** (Figs. 29-31 to 29-34)

The even-toed ungulates include swine, camels, deer, hippopotamuses, antelopes, cattle, sheep, and goats. Most of them have two toes, although the hippopotamus and some others have four. Each toe is sheathed in a cornified hoof. Many, such as the cow, deer, and sheep, have horns. Many of them are ruminants, that is, animals that chew the cud. Like Perissodactyla, they are strictly herbivorous. They are found all over the world. The group is divided into nine living families and many extinct ones and includes some of the most valuable domestic animals. This extensive order is commonly divided into three suborders: the Suina (pigs, peccaries, hippopotamuses), the Tylopoda (camels), and the Ruminantia (deer, giraffes, sheep, cattle, etc.).

FIG. 29-31

Group of Alaskan caribou *(Rangifer arcticus)*. Order Artiodactyla. (Courtesy Chicago Natural History Museum.)

A

B

FIG. 29-32

A, Bactrian camel *(Camelus)*. **B,** Llama *(Lama)*, with young. Common ancestors of camels and llamas developed and flourished in North America during late Eocene, but during Pleistocene one branch migrated to Asia to become Old World camels and the other to South America to become llamas. North American forms later died out. Hump of Old World camels is later adaptation for storage of fat. Order Artiodactyla. (Courtesy Smithsonian Institution, Washington, D. C.)

FIG. 29-33

Hippopotamus *(Hippopotamus amphibius)* and young. Order Artiodactyla. (Courtesy Smithsonian Institution, Washington, D. C.)

FIG. 29-34

Pair of mule deer *(Odocoileus hemionus)*. Name of these large deer derived from size of ears, which are disproportionately large in fawns. Order Artiodactyla. (Courtesy E. P. Haddon, U. S. Fish and Wildlife Service.)

In the odd-toed ungulates the middle, or third, digit is stressed (second and fourth also in some), and the main axis of weight passes through this. In the even-toed ungulates the third and fourth toes (sometimes also the second and fifth) are stressed, and the main axis of the leg passes between the third and fourth toes so that they bear equally the weight of the animal.

Order Primates (pri-ma'tez) (L. *prima,* first)—**highest mammals, e.g., lemurs, monkeys, apes, man**

This order stands first in the animal kingdom in brain development, although other structural features may be equaled or excelled by lower mammals. Most of the species are arboreal, apparently derived from tree-dwelling insectivores. The primates represent the end product of a line that branched off early from other mammals and have retained many primitive characteristics. It is thought that their tree-dwelling habits of agility in capturing food or avoiding enemies were largely responsible for their advances in brain structure. The brain of primates is so well developed that the cerebral hemispheres cover the rest of the brain, especially in the higher primates. As a group, they are generalized, with five digits (usually provided with flat nails) on both forelimbs and hind limbs. All have their bodies covered with hair except man, in whom it is confined to certain regions. Forelimbs are often adapted for grasping, as are the hind limbs sometimes. The group is singularly lacking in claws, scales, horns, and hoofs. There are three suborders:

FIG. 29-35

Ring-tailed lemur *(Lemur catta).* Order Primates, suborder Lemuroidea. (Courtesy Chicago Natural History Museum.)

1. **Suborder Lemuroidea** (lem'u-roi"de-a) (L. *lemures,* ghost) (Fig. 29-35)

These are primitive arboreal primates, with their second toe provided with a claw and a long nonprehensile tail. They look like a cross between squirrels and monkeys. They are found in the forests of Madagascar, Africa, and the Malay peninsula. Their food is mostly plants and small animals.

2. **Suborder Tarsioidea** (tar'se-oi"de-a) (Gr. *tarsos,* ankle)

There is only one genus *(Tarsius)* in this group. Tarsiers are small, solitary primates that live in the Philippines and adjacent islands. The snout is shortened and the eyes have been shifted into a position for binocular vision. The tarsal region of the foot is long, and two of the toes on each foot are provided with claws. The tips of all digits bear pads.

3. **Suborder Anthropoidea** (an'thro-poi"de-a) (Gr. *anthropos,* man)

This suborder consists of monkeys, apes, and man. They have well-developed, convoluted cerebral hemispheres, and their eyes have greater clarity of vision. This suborder represents the most advanced type of animal as far as the ner-

FIG. 29-36

Chimpanzee *(Pan satyrus).* Order Primates, superfamily Hominoidea. (Courtesy Smithsonian Institution, Washington, D. C.)

vous system is concerned. There are three superfamilies:

a. **Superfamily Ceboidea** (se-boi'de-a) (Gr. *kebos*, long-tailed monkey) (**Platyrhinii**)

These are New World monkeys, characterized by the broad flat nasal septum and by the absence of ischial callosities and cheek pouches. Their thumbs are nonopposable and their tails are prehensile. Familiar members of this superfamily are the capuchin monkey (*Cebus*) of the organ grinder, the spider monkey (*Ateles*), and the howler monkey (*Alouatta*).

b. **Superfamily Cercopithecoidea** (sur'ko-pi'the-koi"de-a) (Gr. *kerkops*, long-tailed monkey, + *theca*, pouch) (**Catarrhinii**)

These Old World monkeys have the external nares close together, and many have internal cheek pouches. They never have prehensile tails, there are calloused ischial tuberosities on their buttocks, and their thumbs are opposable. Examples are the savage mandrill *(Cynocephalus)*, the rhesus monkey *(Macacus)* widely used in biologic investigation, and the proboscis monkey *(Nasalis)*.

c. **Superfamily Hominoidea** (ho'mi-noi"de-a) (L. *homo, hominis*, man)

The higher (anthropoid) apes and man make up this superfamily. Their chief characteristics are lack of a tail and lack of cheek pouches. There are two families: Pongidae and Hominidae. The Pongidae family includes the higher apes, gibbon *(Hylobates)*, orangutan *(Simia)*, chimpanzee *(Pan)* (Fig. 29-36), and the gorilla *(Gorilla)*. Varying powers of intelligence are found among the members of the family. Chimpanzees seem to learn faster than others. The gorilla is the most powerful ape and may attain a weight of 500 pounds. The other family, Hominidae, is represented by a single genus and species *(Homo sapiens)*, modern man. Man differs from the members of family Pongidae in being more erect, in having shorter arms and larger thumbs, and in having lighter jaws with smaller front teeth. Most of the apes also have much more prominent supraorbital ridges over the eyes. Man's brain is larger, especially the cerebrum. Many of man's differences from the anthropoid apes are associated with his higher intelligence, his speech centers in the brain, and the fact that he is no longer an arboreal animal.

Derivation and meaning of basic terminology

cynodont (Gr. *kyon*, dog, + *odontos*, tooth). Referring to teeth like those of a dog.

Fissipedia (L. *fissi*, split, + *pedis*, foot). Carnivora with toes.

Lemuroidea (L. *lemures*, ghost). Name probably refers to their flitting nocturnal habits and large eyes.

Ornithorhynchus (Gr. *ornithos*, bird, + *rhynchos*, beak). Genus of the duck-billed platypus.

Pantotheria (Gr. *pantos*, all, + *therion*, wild animal). Extinct order of Jurassic mammals from which placentals and marsupials may have arisen.

Pinnipedia (L. *pinna*, fin, + *pedis*, foot). Carnivora with fins.

placenta (Gr. *plakous*, flat cake). Vascular structure through which the embryo and fetus are nourished in the uterus.

Polyphyodont (Gr. *poly*, many, + *phy*, grow, + *odontos*, tooth). A dentition that is made up of more than two successive sets of teeth at intervals.

Protothrix (pl. ***prototriches***) (Gr. *protos*, first, + *thrix*, hair). A tactile sensory pit of fish and primitive amphibians. In reptiles these pits counteracted the hard, sensory-impervious skin. The hair of mammals may have arisen from certain sensory bristles that are known to occur in these pits of small lizards. Later these tactile hairs acquired temperature control and other functions. Hairs are not homologous to scales.

Simia (L. *simia*, ape). Genus of orangutan.

ungulate (L. *ungula*, hoof). Hoofed mammals.

Annotated references

Anthony, H. E. 1928. Field book of North American mammals. New York, G. P. Putnam's Sons. *An excellent manual on the classification, distribution, and characteristics of mammals.*

Blair, W. F., A. P. Blair, P. Brodkorr, F. R. Cagle, and G. A. Moore. 1968. Vertebrates of the United States, ed. 2. New York, McGraw-Hill Book Co. *This work is of great importance to all students of vertebrates, especially to those who are interested in taxonomy. The taxonomic keys are illustrated and identify all vertebrates down to species.*

Burns, E. 1953. The sex life of wild animals. New York, Rinehart & Co. *An interesting account of the mating reactions of many mammals.*

Burt, W. H. 1957. Mammals of the Great Lakes region. Ann Arbor, University of Michigan Press. *Simple keys to the mammals of this region. There is a good introduction for the beginning student on many ecologic and evolutionary aspects.*

Burton, M. 1962. University dictionary of mammals of the world. (Paperback.) New York, Thomas Y. Crowell Co. *A handy volume, giving essential information on nearly every family and species of mammals.*

Cockrum, E. L. 1955. Manual of mammalogy. Minneapolis, Burgess Publishing Co. *A practical and comprehensive manual that considers the morphology, classification, ecology, and life histories of mammals.*

Collins, H. H. 1959. Complete field guide to American wildlife. New York, Harper & Brothers. *A section of this excellent field manual is devoted to mammals. Some color plates and distribution maps.*

Davis, E. E., and F. B. Golley. 1964. Principles of mammalogy. New York, Reinhold Publishing Corporation. *An excellent introductory text of the mammals, including their classification, adaptations, evolution, distribution, populations, and behavior.*

Flyger, V., and M. R. Townsend. 1968. The migration of polar bears. Sci. Amer. **218**:108-116 (Feb.). *Much* *information about their great migratory behavior was obtained by satellite and dye-marking immobilized animals. Bears equipped with transmitters communicate signals to the satellite and information computed.*

Gordon, M. S. (editor). 1968. Animal function: principles and adaptations. New York, The Macmillan Co. *Incorporates the latest results in a vast field of investigation.*

Grassé, P-P. (editor). 1955. Mammiféres. In Traité de zoologie, vol. 17, 2 parts. Paris, Masson & Cie. *A technical treatise in this extensive series.*

Hall, E. R., and K. R. Kelson. 1959. The mammals of North America, 2 vols. New York, The Ronald Press Co. *This is a magnificent and definitive work on North American mammals, giving full descriptions of all species and subspecies with distribution maps. Taxonomic keys, records, and revealing line drawings of skull characteristics are included in a work that will be the final authority on mammals for a long time. An extensive index and bibliography add much to the usefulness of this fine work.*

Hamilton, W. J., Jr. 1939. American mammals. New York, McGraw-Hill Book Co. *A well-written account of their habits and life histories.*

Hartman, C. G. 1952. Possums. Austin, University of Texas Press. *An excellent account of the life history and behavior by one who has extensively studied this odd animal.*

Mrosovsky, N. 1968. The adjustable brain of hibernators. Sci. Amer. **218**:110-118 (March). *Although many factors are involved in hibernators, it appears that they are able to achieve by smaller changes in the same systems (such as those of the hypothalamic regions of the brain) that nonhibernators have.*

Sanderson, I. T. 1955. Living mammals of the world. New York, Garden City Books (Hanover House). *A beautiful and informative work of many photographs and concise text material. It is a delight to any zoologist regardless of his specialized interest.*

Scheffer, V. B. 1958. Seals, sea lions, and walruses. A review of the Pinnipedia. Stanford, Calif., Stanford University Press. *This is the first comprehensive review of these aquatic mammals since Allen's monograph of more than 60 years ago. It treats the group from the standpoint of their evolution, characteristics, and classification. Many fine photographs and a good bibliography are included.*

Schmidt-Nielsen, K. 1964. Desert animals. New York, Oxford University Press. *This excellent treatise deals with the problems desert-dwelling forms (including man) must meet and solve to survive.*

Seton, E. T. 1925-1928. Lives of game animals, 4 vols. New York, Doubleday, Doran & Co.

Simpson, G. G. 1945. The principles of classification and a classification of mammals. Bulletin of the American Museum of Natural History **85**:1-350.

Wolstenholme, G. E. W., and M. O'Connor (editors). 1959. The lifespan of animals. The Ciba Foundation Colloquia on Ageing, vol. 5. Boston, Little, Brown & Co. *This interesting colloquium of many specialists deals with longevity and related problems in man and other animals.*

Young, J. Z. 1957. The life of mammals. New York, Oxford University Press. *This is an imposing work on nearly every aspect of mammalian life. It affords an excellent background for the student who wishes to know about mammals, especially their anatomy, histology, physiology, and embryology. Classification, however, is not treated.*

PART FIVE

PHYSIOLOGY AND STRUCTURE OF THE BODY SYSTEMS

● The animal is made up of many functional systems so integrated that by working together they produce a unified whole. Although all animals have about the same metabolic requirements, they have evolved different kinds of structures and processes for performing the same functions of nutrition, transport, growth, reproduction, support, and integration. All animals must have both energy and building materials from outside the body, but they have many methods for ingesting food, for transporting its digestive products to the various parts of the body, for eliminating waste products, for motility, for breathing, and for many other functions. From the simplest to the highest form of life there has been a gradual progression in specialization and complexity in the methods for meeting the basic requirements of life. This trend toward specialization is correlated with the increase in size of the animal. In a protozoan, for instance, the problems of maintenance are comparatively simple because a single cell is involved; in a mammal, on the other hand, numerous cells are far removed from direct contact with the environment, although all cellular processes are similar. In a coelenterate a multiple-functioning morphologic unit, the gastrovascular system, is sufficient to meet their needs. In higher forms this unit has been separated into the digestive and vascular systems for more efficient performance in a more complex animal. Exchange of gases can take place by direct diffusion into and out of cells that are in contact with the environment, but lungs, gills, or other devices plus transport facilities are necessary for gaseous exchange in complex animals. Thus only in higher forms do we find definite organ systems of specialized morphologic units for performing specific tasks that are done in lower forms by combining functions in the same unit.

In this part emphasis has been laid on the physiology and structure of the organ systems in higher forms (vertebrates), including man himself. In vertebrates the organ systems have reached their highest development and complexity, and an understanding of their functioning and integration should give the student a more penetrating view of the maintenance of the life process. Such a study should also give him an appreciation of man as an animal who shares with other animals the basic requirements of life.

In a broader sense the student should appreciate the gradual evolution of the intricacy of structural adaptations as they have evolved, the complementary nature of their structure and function, and the control mechanisms that regulate and integrate them into a unified whole.

CHAPTER 30

SUPPORT, PROTECTION, AND MOVEMENT

The following four chapters will treat in some detail the morphologic and functional aspects of the organ systems,* which in Part IV were shown to have gradually emerged in the evolutionary blueprint. In Part V, therefore, the various organization levels can be tied together and a summary given as well.

INTEGUMENT AMONG VARIOUS GROUPS OF ANIMALS

The skin is not merely a protective wrapping; it has many varied functions. In most forms it is tough and pliable, is impervious to water (land forms), and is resistant to most germs. It protects underlying cells from the rays of the sun and prevents excessive water loss. In warm-blooded animals it is vitally concerned with the regulation of body heat. The skin contains the receptors of many senses. It has excretory and, in some forms, respiratory functions as well. It can also form derivatives of many types and functions.

Invertebrate integument (Fig. 30-1). Many protozoans have only the delicate cell membranes or plasma membranes for external coverings; others such as paramecium have developed a protective pellicle. Most invertebrates have a tissue covering—the **epidermis,** which consists of a single layer of cells, except in chaetognaths. Others have added a noncellular **cuticle** or secreted covering of another sort. Sessile coelenterates such as *Obelia* have a protective chitinoid covering over the epidermis. The hydra has only an epidermis.

The nature of the epidermis and noncellular cuticle varies with different invertebrates. An epidermis is entirely lacking in trematodes and cestodes. The epidermis is ciliated in some flatworms, bryozoans, and mollusks. The integument of the annelids consists of a single layer (epidermis) of columnar cells resting on a basement membrane. Among the epidermal cells are goblet cells for mucus secretions and sensory cells. Over this epidermis is the thin, delicate striated cuticle. Setae are modified from the integument. In tapeworms and roundworms the cuticle is very thick and resistant, but is now known to be a living tissue.

*Refer to Chapter 2, Principle 14.

The molluscan epidermis is delicate and soft and contains mucous glands, some of which secrete the calcium carbonate of the shell. The cephalopod has developed a more complex integument, consisting of a cuticle, a simple epidermis, a layer of connective tissue, a layer of reflecting cells (iridocytes), and, finally, a thicker layer of connective tissue. In arthropods the epidermis (hypodermis) is a single layer of cells, from which is secreted the chitinous exoskeleton.

Vertebrate integument (Fig. 30-2). The basic plan of the vertebrate integument is a thin, outer stratified epithelial layer, the **epidermis,** derived from ectoderm and an inner, thicker layer, the **corium** (dermis), which is of mesodermal origin and is made up of nerves, blood vessels, connective tissue, pigment, etc. (Fig. 30-3). Only in cyclostomes is a noncellular dead cuticle found. The epidermis consists usually of several layers of cells. The basal part is made up of columnar cells that undergo frequent mitosis to renew the layers that lie above. Thus the outer layers, mostly cornified and dead, are sloughed off constantly. As the squamous cells degenerate, their cytoplasm is transformed into granules of keratin. In many vertebrates (fish and amphibians) the epidermis is provided with mucous glands that lubricate the exterior surface of the body. In fish the keratin is not abundant in the outer cells that are moulted before much keratin can be formed. Epidermal cells are slowly replaced, since they are sloughed off separately when the layer of mucus is worn away. Granular poison glands are also found in some amphibians.

Land forms such as reptiles, birds, and mammals have a thicker epidermis, the outer layer of which is much cornified with keratin. This is for added protection to prevent drying out. Mammals are well provided

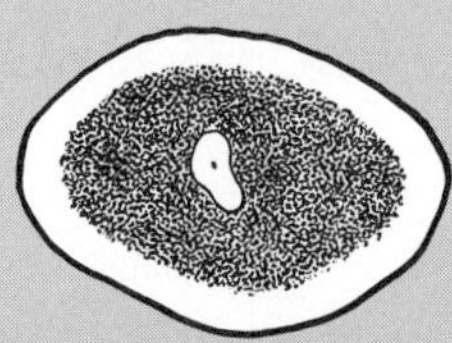

Differentiation of clear surface ectoplasm with its plasma membrane from inner granular endoplasm in certain protozoans is beginning of an integument

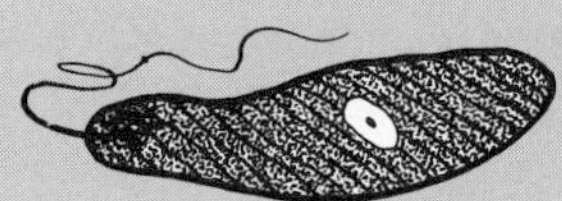

Surface of ectoplasm may differentiate to form pellicle that may be homogeneous or patterned in ridges, depressions, or spiral striations

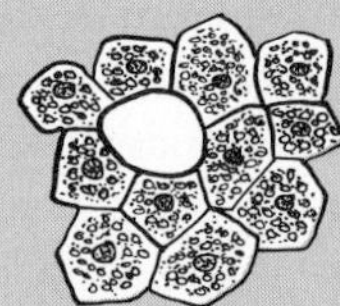

Flat, polygonal epithelial cells (pinacocytes) with bulging nuclei or a syncytium with scattered nuclei form surface layer (epidermis) of some sponges

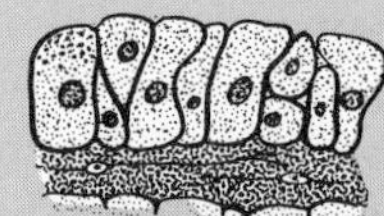

Coelenterate epidermis consists of epithelial cells of varying types, often interspersed with glands, sensory cells, and cnidoblasts; cuticle or perisarc may be secreted by epidermis

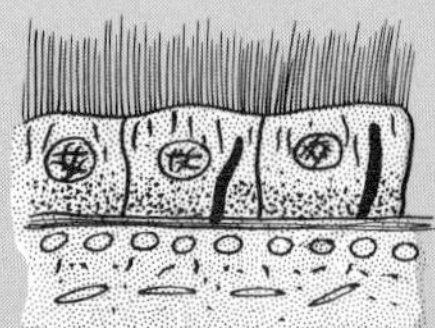

Free-living flatworms have 1-layer epidermis of flat or columnar cells, generally ciliated and sometimes syncytial

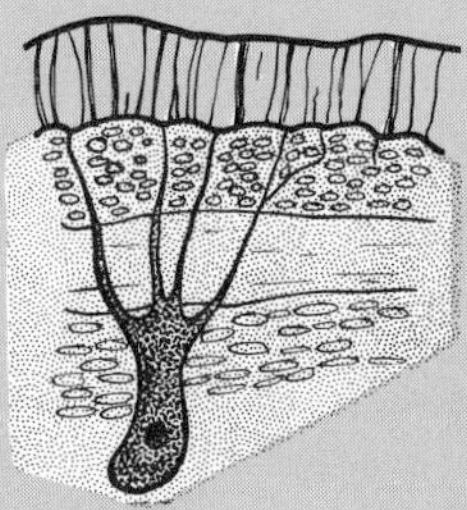

Epidermis is lacking in parasitic flatworms (trematodes and cestodes); a resistant cuticle (living) rests on subcuticular musculature and is secreted by special mesenchymal cells

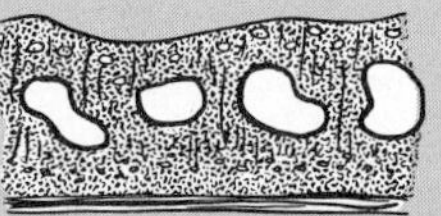

Acanthocephs are unique in having syncytial epidermis with lacunar system of fluid-filled spaces that distribute food

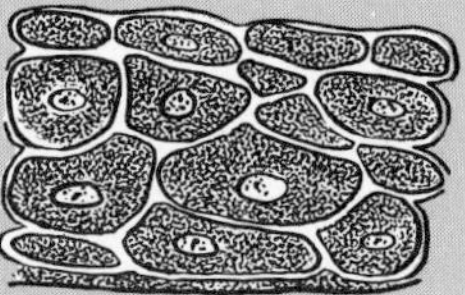

Chaetognaths are only invertebrates with stratified epidermis

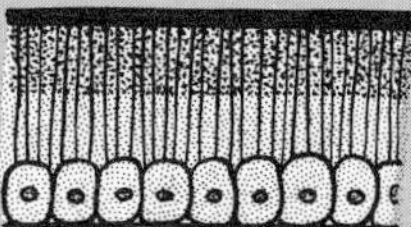

Integument of higher invertebrates (annelids, mollusks, arthropods) consists typically of single epithelial layer (epidermis or hypodermis) resting usually on a basement membrane of connective tissue and muscle and covered with a noncellular cuticle; cuticle of arthropods is made up of two layers—outer layer of waxes and proteins and inner layer of proteins and chitin

FIG. 30-1

Comparative structure of invertebrate integument.

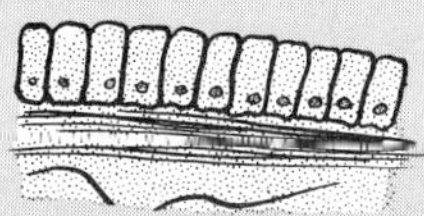

Simple chordates (*Amphioxus,* tunicates) and closely related phyla (hemichordates, echinoderms) have single-layered epidermis and connective tissue dermis; may have cilia, glands, and pigment; tunicates enclosed by overlying tunic of tunicin (cellulose) secreted by mesenchymal cells

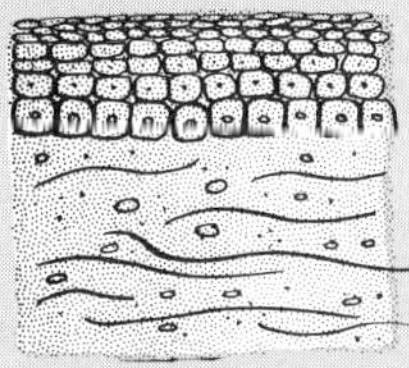

Vertebrate skin made up of stratified epidermis (ectodermal) and dermis of connective tissue, muscle, blood vessels, etc. (mesodermal), with many derivatives and modifications

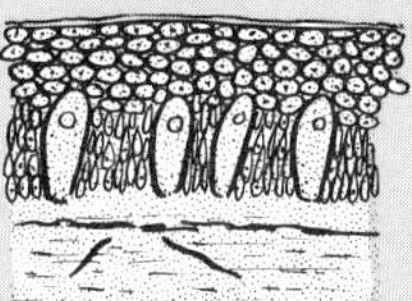

Cyclostome integument is smooth without scales but contains many unicellular mucous glands, some of which are club shaped and others thread cells; thin noncellular cuticle covers body

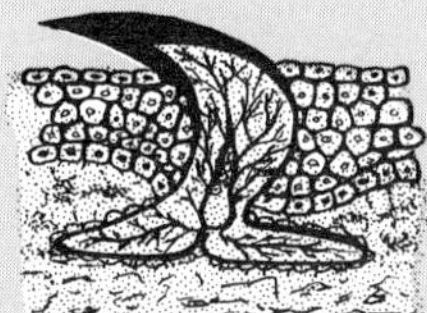

Tough epidermis of sharks contains much keratin and many mucous glands; scattered placoid scales are of dentin from mesodermal odontoblasts and enamel-like vitrodentin from mesoderm with enamel organs

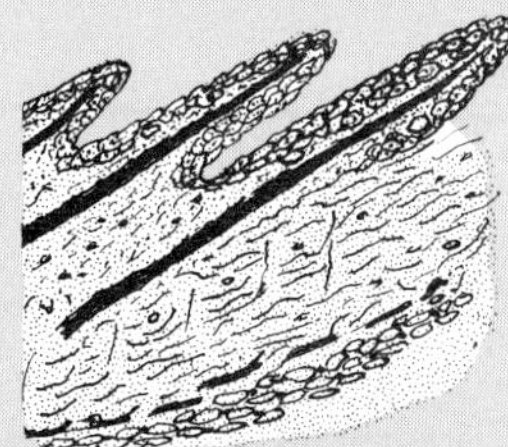

In most bony fish, entire epidermis alive but keratinized except for superficial cells that die and are replaced; many mucous glands; scales of many types formed by dermis and restricted to that region; chromatophores in epidermis and dermis; in scaleless forms, skin is thick, tough, and leathery

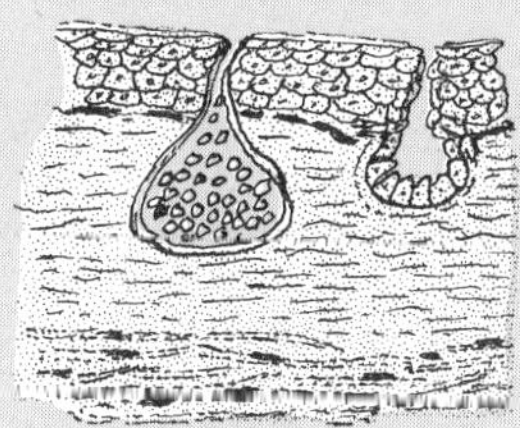

Superficial layer of amphibian integument cornified and shed at intervals; glands multicellular and specialized (mucous and poison); local thickenings of epidermis common, such as toad warts; scales absent (except Apoda); chromatophores in both epidermis and dermis

Integument of reptiles dry, lacking in glands, and provided with horny epidermal scales covered with cornified epidermis; entire horny layer, including scales, shed at intervals; bony plates may be found in dermis; pigment cells both epidermal and dermal

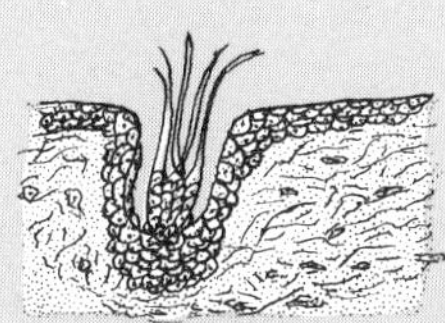

Birds have loose, dry skin with only cutaneous gland (uropygial); cornification mainly restricted to feathers; epidermal scales on legs

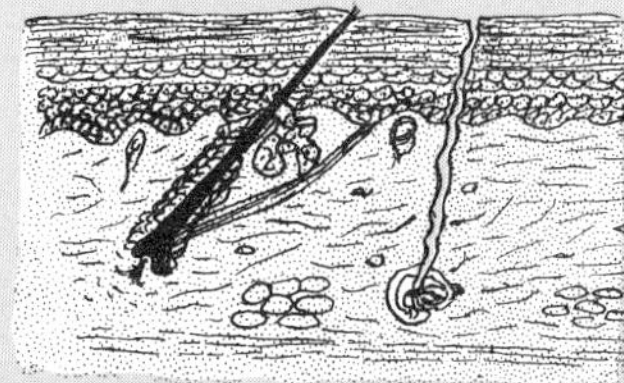

In mammals, epidermis varies from thin to thick (pachyderms), usually in 4 or 5 layers; epidermal scales restricted; many derivatives, mostly epidermal; hair and cutaneous glands of many types

FIG. 30-2

Comparative structure of vertebrate integument.

with glands (Fig. 30-4). Indeed, the entire epidermal cutaneous system of the amniotes may be considered a glandular system and, with the exception of the sweat glands, is mostly holocrine in nature. The keratinized outer layers, secreted by the basal epidermal cells, are constantly being shed in small fragments (mammals) or in a single piece (some reptiles). Hair, feathers, keratin, and sebum (all dead cells when shed) may be considered as a secretion of the epidermis.

The **color** of the skin is often due to special pigment that may be in the form of granules scattered through the layers of the epidermis (mammals) and to special pigment cells, **chromatophores** (Fig. 26-28), that are found chiefly in the dermis (fish and amphibians).

Five kinds of chromatophores occur in vertebrates skin: melanophores (black), erythrophores (red), xanthophores (yellow), leucophores (white), and guanophores, or iridophores (iridescent and reflecting). Control varies with different vertebrates. Most chromatophores are innervated by sympathetic fibers (contraction) and parasympathetic fibers (dispersion), but hormones (epinephrine, norepinephrine, intermedin, etc.) also exert a control in some fishes. Epinephrine and norepinephrine cause melanin concentration. Amphibian chromatophores are controlled mostly by the hormones epinephrine and norepinephrine for concentration and melanocyte-stimulating hormone (MSH) or adrenocorticotropic hormone (ACTH) for expansion. Reptiles use either hormone or nervous stimulation or both. Birds and mammals do not have chromatophores

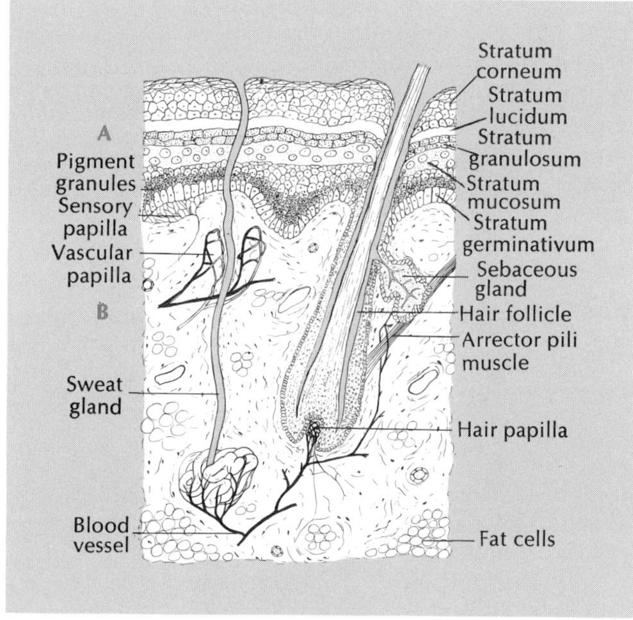

FIG. 30-3

Histologic section of mammalian skin. **A,** Epidermis. **B,** Dermis.

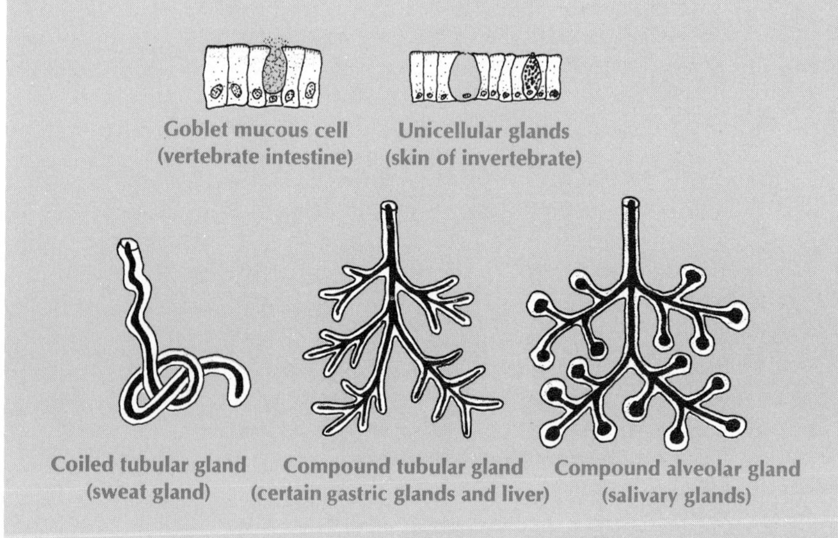

FIG. 30-4

Types of exocrine glands. Exocrine glandular products are either secretions (formation of useful products from raw materials of blood) or excretions (waste products from blood). They are carried outside cells that form them, either to interior of certain organs or to surface. Secretory function is usually displayed by epithelial tissue but sometimes also by nervous and connective tissue. Invertebrates often have glands that resemble those of vertebrates but invertebrates usually have greater variety of unicellular glands. Most glands form secretions in three ways: (1) merocrine, in which secretion is formed by cell; (2) apocrine, in which part of cell forms secretion; and (3) holocrine, in which entire cell is discharged in secretion.

proper, but they do have melanocytes in epidermal cells. An injection of MSH will cause darkening of the skin.

The skin is variously modified in different vertebrates to form the so-called skin derivatives. These include the bony and horny structures, such as scales, claws, nails, horns, and antlers, in addition to glands, hair, and feathers. True bony structures develop in the dermis, and bony plates were very common in such primitive forms as ostracoderms and placoderms. Certain bony plates of the head were modified to form the dermatocranium of the skull. Fish scales (Fig. 30-5) are bony dermal plates that are covered with live epidermis bearing a superficial layer of dead cells that are constantly being replaced. Amphibians have moist naked skins without scales (except the tiny dermal scales of the order Apoda). The superficial layer of their epidermis contains keratin, which is replaced when lost. In strictly land tetrapods, keratinized epithelial structures have largely replaced the bony plates. Reptiles have horny scales (of epidermal origin) that prevent loss of water. These scales are also found on the legs and feet of birds and on the tails of certain mammals. In the pangolin the entire body is covered with large horny scales. In crocodiles and some turtles the scales form horny plates that overlie the bony dermal plates of the back and belly. Some lizards also have bony plates as well as horny scales. Horny scales are formed by the folding of the epidermis over mesodermal papillae, the upper surface of which becomes the cornified scale.

Three kinds of horns or hornlike structures are found in mammals. **True horns** found in ruminants consist of

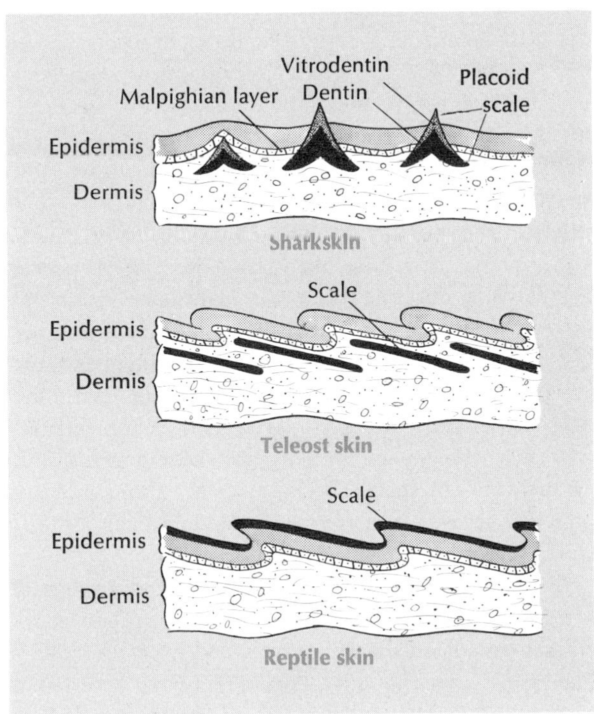

FIG. 30-5

Integument in classes Chondrichthyes, Osteichthyes, and Reptilia showing different types of scales. Placoid scales of sharks are derived from dermis and have given rise to teeth in all higher vertebrates. Teleost fish have bony scales from dermis, and reptiles have horny scales from epidermis. Only dermal scales are retained throughout life; epidermal scales are shed.

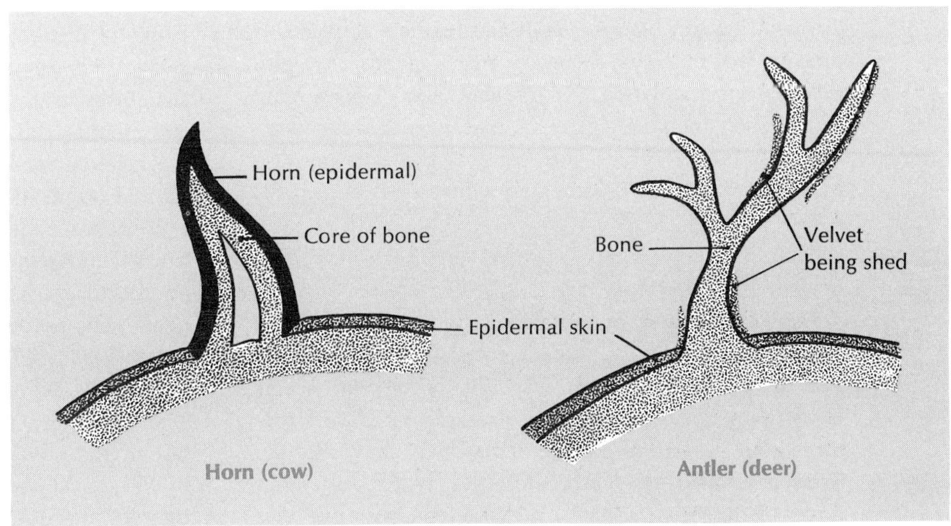

FIG. 30-6

Chief differences between horns and antlers. Bone, a dermal (mesoderm) derivative, forms basic part of each type, and when epidermal velvet with its hair is shed, bone forms all of antlers. Antlers are shed annually (in winter) when zone of constriction below burr appears near skull. Horns do not branch and are not shed. Injection of testosterone and estrogen will prevent shedding of antlers.

hollow sheaths of hardened epidermis that fit over a core of bone arising from the skull. Such horns are not shed, are not branched (although they may be greatly curved), and are found in both sexes. The American antelope is an exception, because its epidermal sheath may be branched and is shed periodically, and a new one is formed over the small core of dermal bone. The **antlers** of the deer family (Fig. 30-6) are entirely bone in the mature condition but during the growth period they have a covering of a vascular hairy epidermis (velvet), which is gradually worn away. Antlers are shed annually and each replacement usually has more prongs or branches than the previous one. With the exception of the caribou and reindeer, antlers are restricted to the males. Giraffes also have bony horns, but they are not shed. The horns of the rhinoceros are formed from hairlike horny fibers that arise from dermal papillae and are cemented together.

All claws, nails, and hoofs are keratinized epidermal structures. Mammals have inherited the reptilian claws and have modified them into nails and hoofs. A claw is shaped to cover the sides, top, and tip of a terminal joint; a nail is flattened and covers the dorsal surface of the distal phalange; and a hoof extends across the end of the digit and covers the plantar surface also. In the horse the hoof, which is developed from the claw of one toe, is the only part of the foot touching the ground. Other hoofed animals may have spongy pads or other parts of the foot on which to walk.

The skin in birds and mammals plays an important part in regulating the heat of the body, for both these classes are warm blooded. Hair and feathers help in this process, but in many there are **sweat glands** that also aid in heat regulation. To prevent heat loss in cold water, such mammals as seals and whales have deep layers of fat (blubber) just beneath the skin because hair is an efficient insulator only when air is entrapped within it.

SKELETAL SYSTEMS

Exoskeleton and endoskeleton. Some animals have only an exoskeleton, others have mainly endoskeletons, and still others have both or neither. Protection seems to be the major function of the exoskeleton. Hard structures built up on the outside of the body may take the form of shells, spicules, calcareous plates, or other forms of defensive armor. An exoskeleton also provides inner surfaces for the attachment of muscles. It may be rigid, as in shells, but in higher invertebrates such as arthropods it is jointed and movable, both on the appendages and the trunk. An endoskeleton is formed inside the body, is surrounded by soft tissues, and is composed of bones and cartilages. It is formed from the mesoderm, whereas the exoskeleton comes chiefly from ectoderm. The cells that secrete most exoskeletons deposit the hard substance in layers outside the cells; in the endoskeleton the cells secrete the limy salts between the cells. This enables the endoskeleton to grow for a long period of time, for it is a living tissue.

How invertebrates meet problems of support and protection (Fig. 30-7). One of the earliest forms of exoskeleton is found in some of the protozoans that are enclosed in a shell made up of grains of sand held together by a secretion. Other protozoans have exoskeletons formed of calcium carbonate or silica. Sponges rely upon spicules or networks of spongin for support. Some of the hydroid coelenterates (*Obelia*) have a chitinous perisarc. Mollusks, corals, and brachiopods have exoskeletons of calcium carbonate, noncellular and nonliving, that are not shed during their lives but merely increase at their margins and thicken with age. Exoskeletons in the arthropods are formed chiefly of **chitin** secreted by the epidermis (hypodermis) and are flexible at the joints of the appendages and between the body somites. Some arthropods have a chitinous covering reinforced with limy salts (crayfish). These nonliving exoskeletons cannot increase in size; therefore the animal must shed (molt) them periodically. After a molt the body increases in size before the new exoskeleton is formed and hardened.

Many vertebrates also have exoskeletons because traces of this external skeleton are found in the form of scales, fingernails, hair, feathers, and other cornified structures. The first appearance of the endoskeleton is the mesodermal plates of echinoderms; thus this form of skeleton, so well developed among the vertebrates, had its origin in the invertebrate group.

Vertebrate plan of skeleton (Fig. 30-8). The vertebrate endoskeleton is an internal framework of bone and cartilage. The earliest form of endoskeleton to appear is the **notochord**, a semirigid rod in the protochordates. This axial rod gives partial support to the body and serves as an axis for the working of the muscles. The notochord persists in amphioxi and cyclostomes, but in the other classes it is surrounded and replaced by the backbone of separate vertebrae. However, vestiges of the notochord often remain. Cyclostomes and

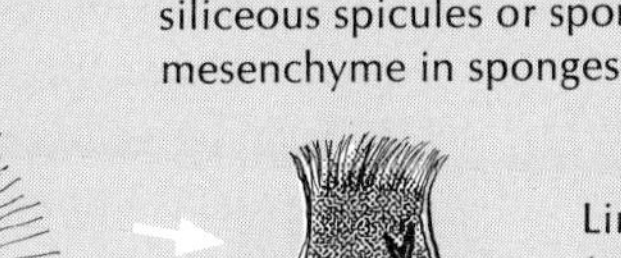
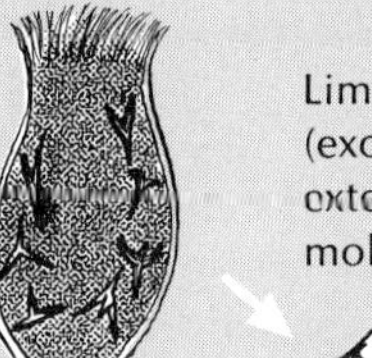

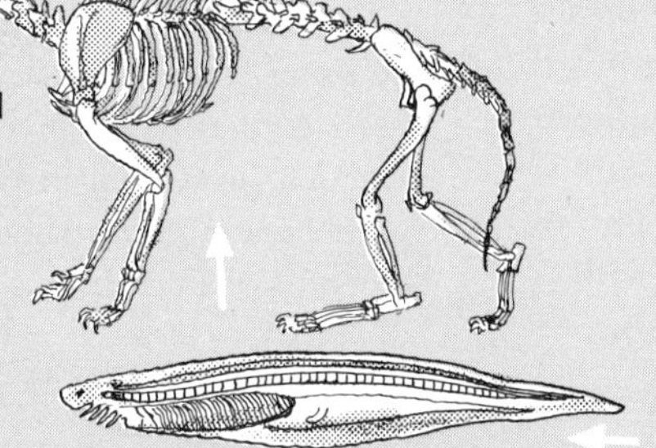

FIG. 30-7

Comparative skeletons in animal kingdom.

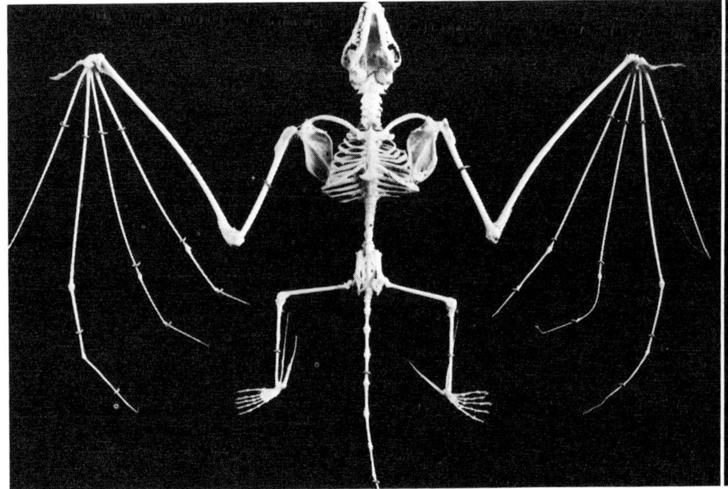
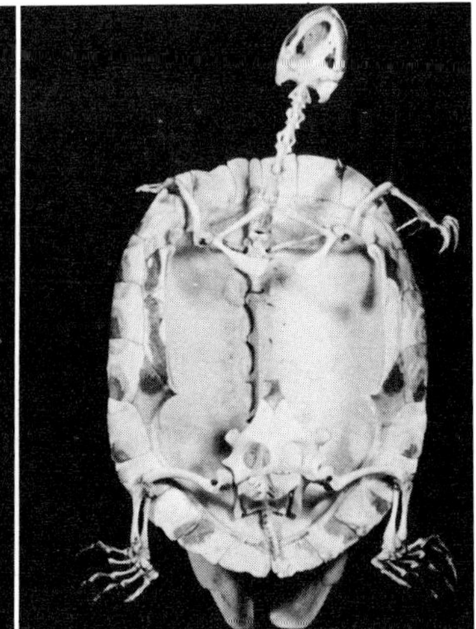

FIG. 30-8

Two highly modified vertebrate skeletons. In bat, forelimbs are adapted for flying. In turtle, various divisions of endoskeleton are more or less consolidated into compact structure.

elasmobranchs have cartilaginous skeletons; the other vertebrates have bony ones with some cartilage interspersed. Fossils and other lines of evidence indicate phylogenetically that bone is more primitive than cartilage, which may be considered an embryologic material. An adult condition of cartilage instead of bone in later vertebrates (sharks and sturgeons) may indicate a degenerate or specialized skeleton, or else such forms have retained their embryonic cartilage.

The intercellular substance that forms the vertebrate skeleton may be a chondromucoid material and collagenous fibrils (cartilage), or calcium, collagenous fibrils, and phosphorus salts (bone). Most bone develops from cartilage (cartilage replacement bone), but a few bones, such as certain ones in the face and cranium, are formed directly from sheets of mesenchyme tissue (membrane bones). The two types are alike histologically.

In elasmobranchs the skull is cartilaginous, but in higher forms most of it is replaced by bones, with a closer union of the capsules and upper jaw. In land vertebrates the visceral skeleton has undergone a great transformation because of the development of an entirely different method of breathing, and parts of it are converted to other structures, such as the bones of the middle ear and lower jaw and the cartilages of the larynx and epiglottis. The skull, moreover, has undergone great changes among the various vertebrates, especially in number of bones. Primitive forms tend to have a larger number of skull bones than recent forms. Some fish may have 180 skull bones; amphibia and reptiles, 50 to 95; and mammals, 35 or fewer. Man has 29.

The evolutionary history of the skull shows that it is derived from three sources; (1) the **endocranium,** or neurocranium, which is the original skull that surrounds the brain and is best seen in its primitive basic plan in the sharks; (2) the **dermocranium,** which represents the outer membranous bony cap that originated from fused dermal scales of the head and overlies the endocranium (best seen in the bowfin, *Amia*); and (3) the **splanchnocranium,** which is the endoskeletal part of the visceral skeleton that supports the gills and is also rep-

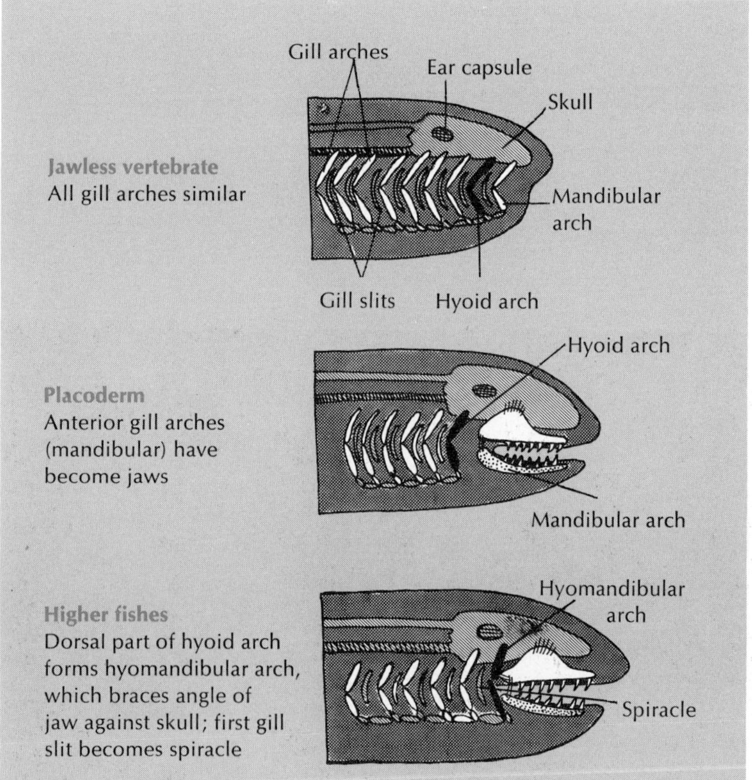

FIG. 30-9

How vertebrate got its jaws. First two arches in order are mandibular and hyoid; mandibular forms jaws, and hyoid forms supporting accessory structure. Jaws at first are separate from cranium, but later the two are consolidated. (From several sources.)

resented in a fairly primitive plan in sharks. The jaws are formed by certain visceral or gill arches that are a part of the splanchnocranium, as shown in Fig. 30-9. In the lower vertebrates these three skull components are more or less separated from each other; in higher forms they are all fused together or incorporated into a single unit—the vertebrate skull. There is a basic plan of homology in the skull elements of vertebrates from fish to man; evolution has meant reduction in numbers of bones through loss and fusion in accordance with size and functional changes. The best known diagnostic character of the mammalian skeleton is the lower jar that consists on each side of only one bone, the dentary.

The vertebral column supplants the notochord quite early in the phylogeny of the vertebrates. Vertebrae vary greatly with different animals and with different regions of the vertebral column in the same animal. In the caudal region of many vertebrates each vertebra has a ventral **hemal arch** around the blood vessels of that region; this arch is modified into riblike processes in the trunk region. The vertebral column in fish is differentiated only into **trunk** and **caudal** vertebrae; in many of the other vertebrates the column is differentiated into **cervical** (neck), **thoracic** (chest, Fig. 30-10), **lumbar** (back), **sacral** (pelvic), and **caudal** (tail) vertebrae. In birds and also in man the caudal vertebrae are reduced in number and size, and the sacral vertebrae are fused. The number of vertebrae varies among the different animals. The python seems to have the largest number, 435. In man, there are 33 in the child, but in the adult 5 are fused to form the **sacrum** and 4 to form the **coccyx.** Besides the sacrum and coccyx, man has 7 cervical, 12 thoracic, and 5 lumbar vertebrae. The first cervical vertebra is modified for articulation with the skull and is called the **atlas.** The number of cervical vertebrae (7) is constant in nearly all mammals. Manatees and the two-toed sloth, however, have 6, whereas the three-toed sloth has 9. The giant anteater has 8.

FIG. 30-10

Side view of thoracic vertebra.

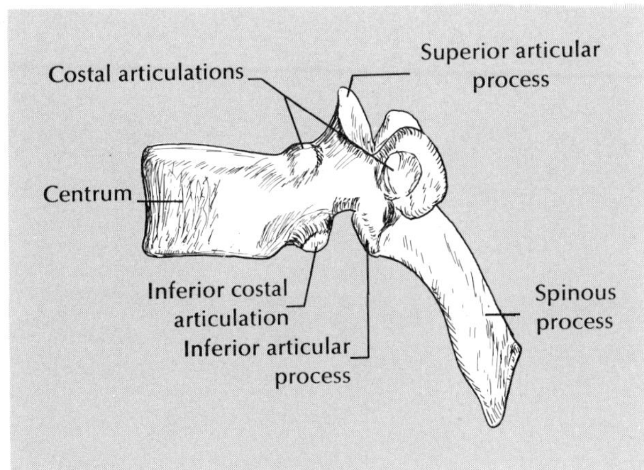

Ribs show many variations among the vertebrates. The basic plan seems to have been a pair of ribs for each vertebrae from head to tail, but the tendency has been to reduce the number from lower to higher forms. Certain fish have two ventral ribs for each vertebra, and in some fish there are sometimes dorsal and ventral (pleural) ribs on the same vertebra (*Polypterus* and many teleosts). In tetrapods the single type of rib is supposed to correspond to the dorsal one of fish. The ribs of many land vertebrates are joined to the sternum. The sternum is lacking in snakes. The ribs of vertebrate animals are not all homologous because they do not all arise in the same way. Ribs, however, are not universal among vertebrates; many, including the leopard frog, do not have them at all. Others such as the elasmobranchs and some amphibians have very short ribs. Man has twelve pairs of ribs (Fig. 30-11), although evidence indicates that his ancestors had more. The ribs together form the thoracic basket that supports the chest wall and keeps it from collapsing.

Most vertebrate animals have paired appendages. None are found in cyclostomes, but both the cartilaginous and bony fish have pectoral and pelvic fins that are supported by the pectoral and pelvic girdles, respectively. Forms above the fish (except snakes) usually have two pairs of appendages, also supported by girdles. The basic plan of the land vertebrate limb (tetrapod) is called the **pentadactyl,** because it terminates in five digits. Among the various vertebrates there are many modifications in the girdles, limbs, and digits that enable the animals to meet special modes of life. For instance, some amphibians have only three or four toes on each foot, and the horse has only one. Also, the bones of the limbs may be separate or they may be fused in various ways. Whatever the modification, the girdles and appendages in forms above fish are all built on the same plan and their component bones can be homologized. In man the pectoral girdle is made up of 2 scapulae and 2 clavicles; the best known diagnostic character of the mammalian skeleton is the lower jaw that consists on each side of only one bone, the dentary. The arm is made up of humerus, ulna, radius, 8 carpals, 5 metacarpals, and 14 phalanges. The pelvic girdle (Fig. 30-12) consists of 2 innominate bones, each of which is composed of 3 fused bones—ilium, ischium, and pubis; the leg is made up of femur, patella, tibia,

FIG. 30-11

Human skeleton. **A,** Ventral view. **B,** Dorsal view. Numbers in parentheses indicate number of bones in that unit. In comparison with other mammals, man's skeleton is a type of patchwork of primitive and specialized parts. Erect posture brought about by specialized changes in legs and pelvis enabled primitive arrangement of arms and hands (arboreal adaptation of man's ancestors) to be used for manipulation of tools. Development of skull and brain followed as consequence of premium natural selection put upon dexterity, better senses, and ability to appraise environment.

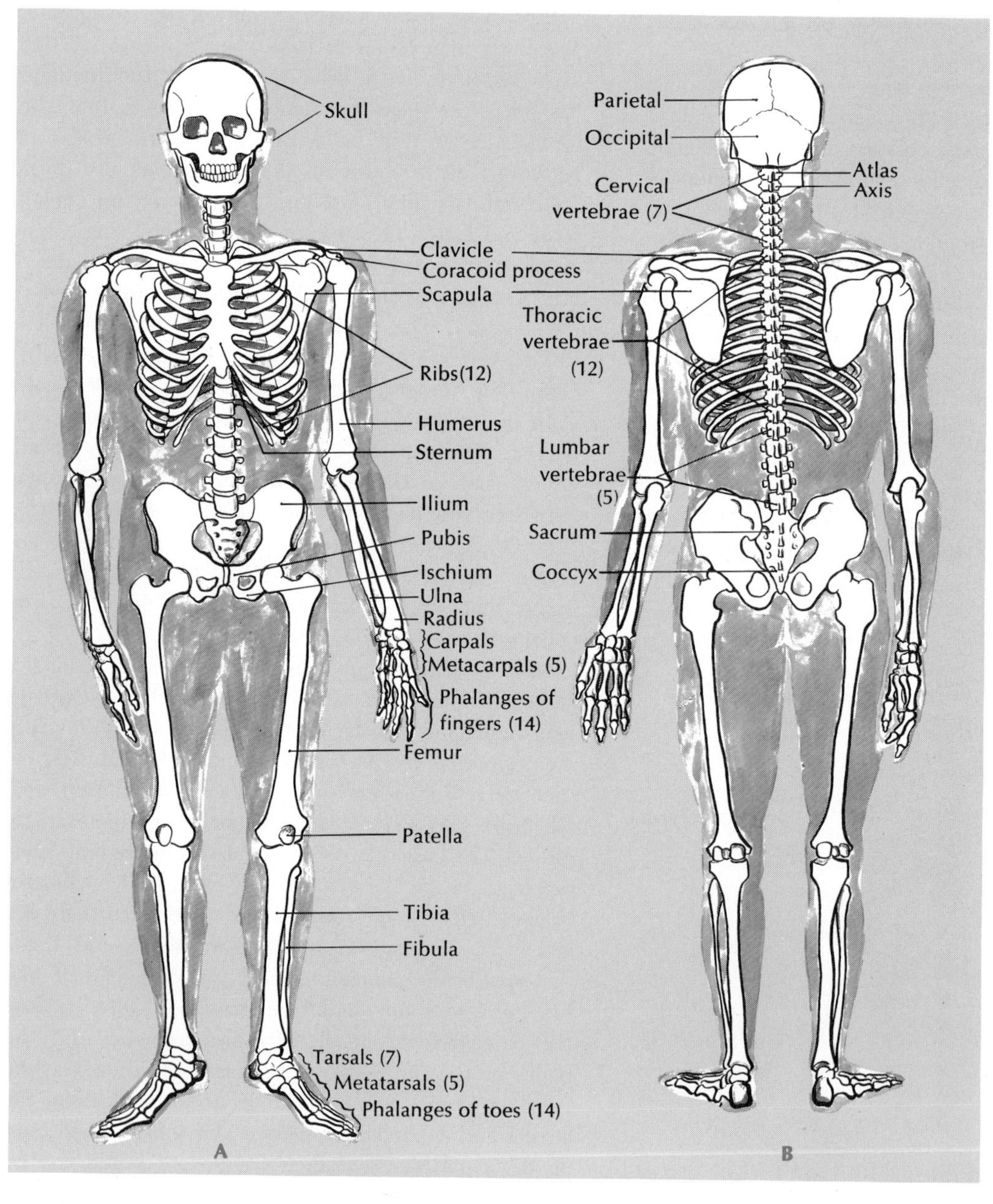

fibula, 7 tarsals, 5 metatarsals, and 14 phalanges. It will be noted that each bone of the leg has its counterpart in the arm, with the exception of the patella. This kind of correspondence between anterior and posterior parts is called **serial homology.**

Some bones (heterotopic) are not associated with the skeleton. These include the **os cordis** in the interventricular septum of the heart (ox, sheep, and goat), the **baculum** (os priapi or os penis) in the spongy bodies of the penis (rodents, carnivores, lower primates, and others), **sclerotic plates** of the eye (birds), and many others. Wherever stress occurs, the mesoderm has the potential to form bone.

FIG. 30-12

Chief difference between male and female skeletons is structure of pelvis. Female pelvis has less depth with broader, less sloping ilia, more circular bony ring (pelvic canal), wider and more rounded pubic arch, and shorter and wider sacrum. Most structures of female pelvis are correlated with child-bearing functions. In evolution of human skeleton, pelvis has changed more than any other part because it has to support weight of erect body. (Anterior view.)

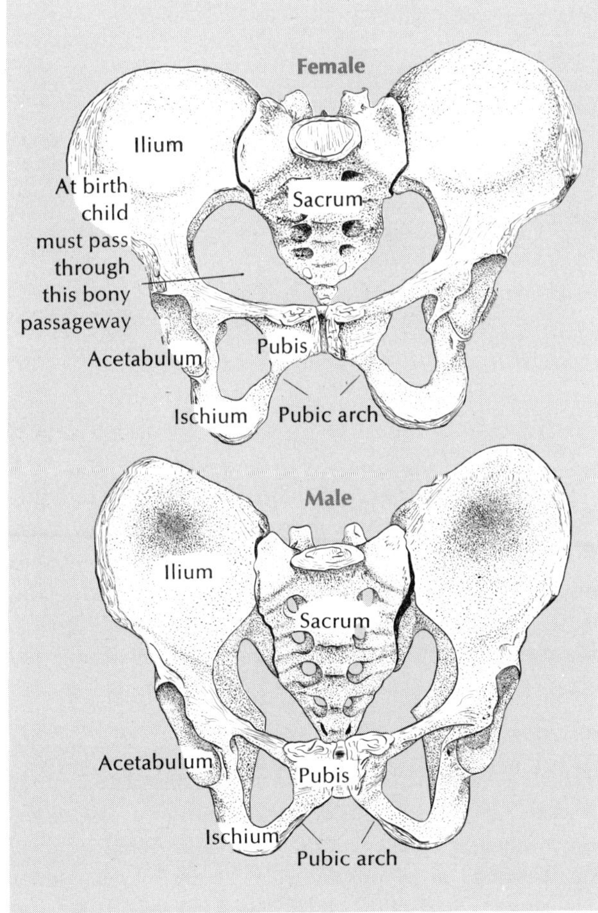

MUSCULAR SYSTEM

Muscles are specialized for shortening when stimulated and thus can pull the parts to which they are attached. When the stimulation has ceased, the muscle simply relaxes and returns to its original form. Most movements in both vertebrate and invertebrate animals are produced by the contraction of muscles.

Devices for movement in invertebrates

Invertebrates have various ways of producing movement (Fig. 30-13). Some of their movements are definitely not muscular. *Amoeba* makes use of the protoplasmic streaming in contracting or extending its body. Protozoans such as *Paramecium* and *Euglena* use cilia and flagella for locomotion. Some protozoans such as *Vorticella* have special contractile **myonemes.** The epitheliomuscular cells of coelenterates are suggestive of the circular and longitudinal muscles found in the body walls of higher invertebrates. Mollusks, echinoderms, and arthropods also have muscles joining body parts with the inner surface of the exoskeleton. The motor-unit plan of vertebrates is not usually found in invertebrates. Invertebrates also have multiple nerve endings per fiber and their nerve end plates are not well defined. The all-or-none pattern of contraction among invertebrates is usually lacking.

Classes of muscles

Four types of muscles are recognized among animals on the basis of structural fibers.

1. **Striated muscle,** has alternate light (isotropic) and dark (anisotropic) bands. This type is found in all animal groups from coelenterates through vertebrates and makes up 80% or more of all muscular tissue.

2. **Regular smooth muscle** lacks the light and dark bands, but has myofibrils. It is present in all types of animals that have muscles.

3. **Helical smooth muscle** has myofibrils that are twisted or helically arranged in a diamond-lattice structure. This type is usually restricted to certain invertebrates but is not present in vertebrates.

4. **Paramyosin smooth muscle** has large longitudinal myofibrils of large size and is ribbon shaped. It is restricted to mollusks.

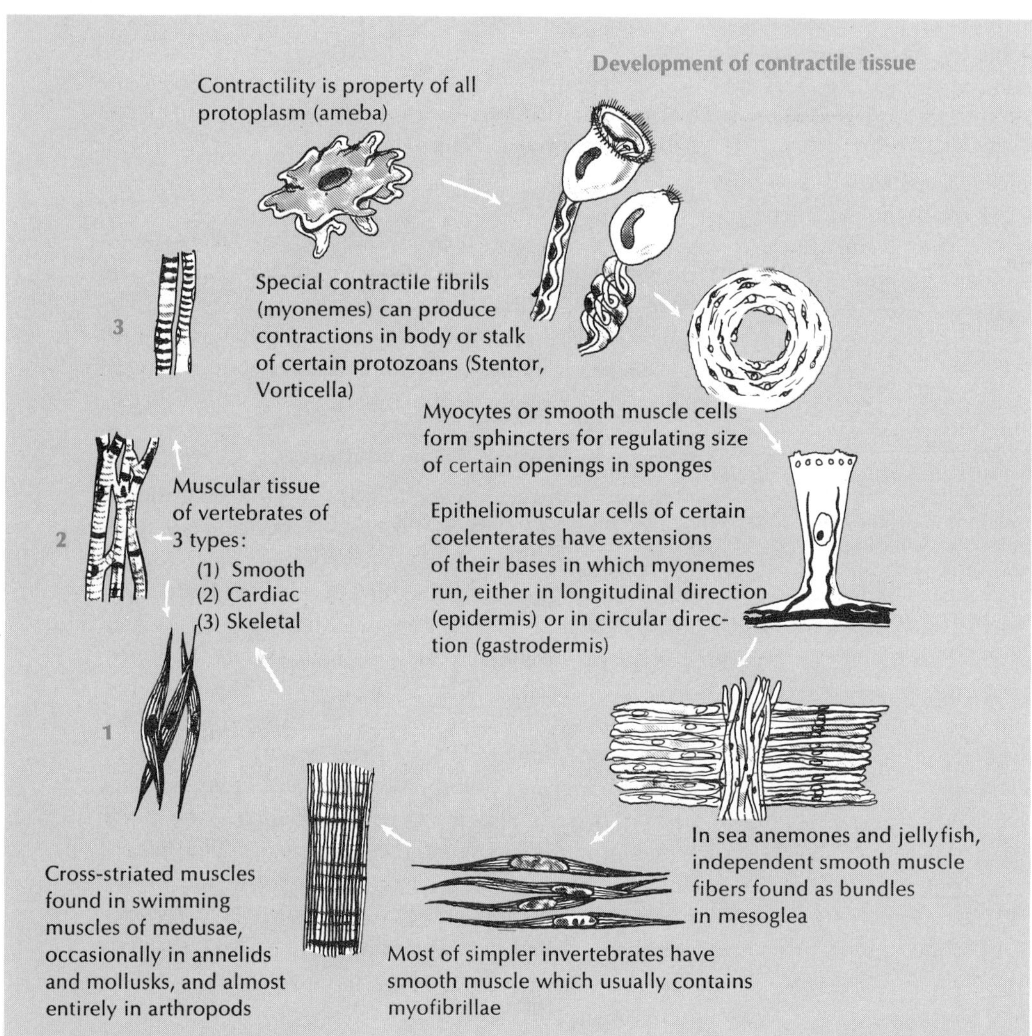

FIG. 30-13

Development of contractile tissue (muscle) in animal kingdom.

Muscular system of vertebrates

The great activity of most vertebrates is correlated with well-developed muscles. In the lower forms the muscles are predominantly segmented (Fig. 30-14). In protochordates, such as amphioxi, there are 60 or more pairs of muscle somites arranged alternately along the sides of the body. In most fish, amphibians, and, to some extent, reptiles, there is a segmental organization of muscles alternating with the vertebrae. This pattern is greatly altered in birds and mammals that no longer travel by the undulatory movements characteristic of the lower vertebrates. Segmental muscles in the higher vertebrates are found between the vertebrae and the ribs and in the abdomen. In the higher vertebrates, muscles have become specialized for certain activities. From the sheet form of musculature in the low vertebrates there arose, by splitting, by fusion, and by shifting, the varied muscles of birds and mammals. Thus each specialized body part developed the type of muscles best suited for its manipulation. The shapes and sizes of muscles are correlated with their tasks.

Physiology of muscle

Striated muscle. Each gross muscle of striated muscle is made up of thousands of muscle cells or muscle fibers. Each fiber is about 100 μ thick and contains many smaller units or myofibrils, each about 1 to 2 μ thick. The myofibrils contain alternating light and dark bands

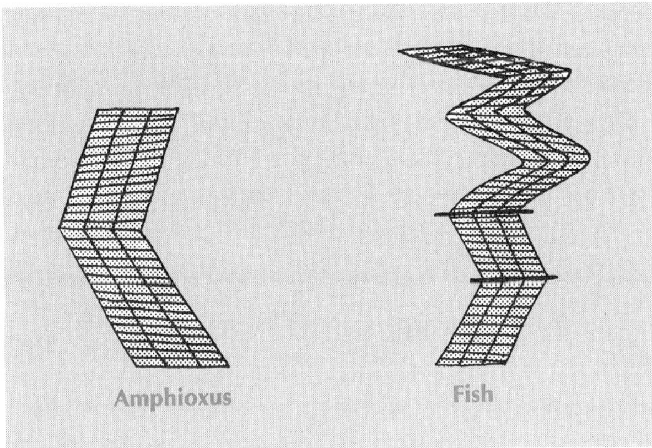

FIG. 30-14

Pattern of segmented muscle arrangement in lower chordates. Primitive plan *(Amphioxus)* is <—shaped chevron with point toward head; in many fish, zigzag form and sharp angles of myomeres are related to swift movements of trunk and tail. (Redrawn from Atwood: A concise comparative anatomy, The C. V. Mosby Co.)

with different optical properties. These bands are designated according to detailed histologic schemes. Skeletal muscle fibers in a gross muscle are arranged in groups of about 100; each group is under the control of a single motor nerve fiber (Fig. 30-15) and is called a **motor unit.** For this arrangement the single nerve fiber gives off many terminal branches, each of which innervates a muscle fiber. The attachment of a nerve to the muscle is called a **motor end plate** (Fig. 30-15), consisting of many terminal, beaded axons that form a characteristic pattern in the underlying muscle sarcoplasm. Acetylcholine is released by these motor end plates in nervous mediation of the muscles.

The number of motor units in a muscle depends mainly on the size of the muscle. Thus the gastrocnemius muscle of a cat has about 43,000 muscle fibers that would be divided among about 430 motor units. Motor units are supposed to obey the all-or-none law; that is, if they contract at all, they do so to their fullest extent. However, the gross muscle does not obey this law, because its extent of contraction depends on the number of its motor units that are active at any particular time. A few motor units in operation will produce a feeble contraction; many units in action will result in a stronger contraction. In this way many gradations of contraction may be found in a gross muscle.

In living animals, muscles contract when stimulated by nerve impulses; in the laboratory, artificial stimuli such as induced electric currents will cause them to contract. A single stimulus applied to a striated muscle results in a **simple twitch.** The gastrocnemius muscle of a frog may be removed with its motor nerve, the sciatic, and set up so that its contractions are recorded on a kymograph. In a simple twitch the graph will show a **latent period** between the application of the stimulus and the beginning of contraction; a **contraction period** during the actual shortening of the muscle; and a **relaxation period,** when the muscle returns to its resting condition. Repeated stimuli with sufficient time intervals for relaxation will result in **incomplete tetanus;** if the stimuli are too rapid to permit relaxation, the muscle will be thrown into a sustained contraction, pro-

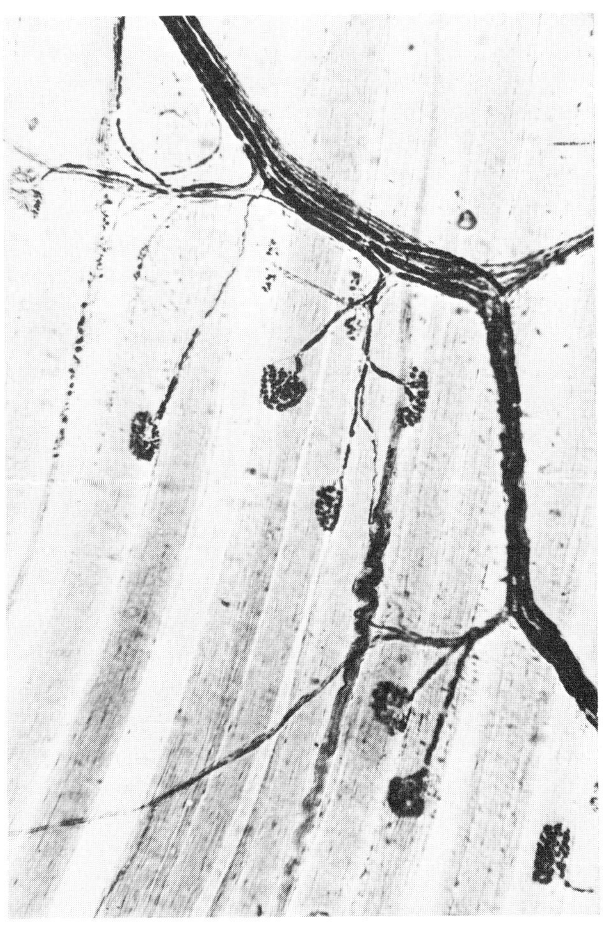

FIG. 30-15

Motor end plates of motor nerves on muscle fibers. (Courtesy J. W. Bamberger.)

ducing a smooth curve on the kymograph until the cessation of stimuli or fatigue ensues, when the lever will rapidly descend to the base line. This is called **complete tetanus.**

The duration of the simple muscle twitch of the frog is commonly given as 0.01 second for the latent period, 0.04 second for contraction, and 0.05 second for relaxation. The whole time duration for the twitch is thus 0.1 second. In warm-blooded forms, muscles contract more rapidly. Remember that the simple muscle twitch is a laboratory phenomenon and is convenient for analysis, but the normal contractions of muscle in the living body are always those of the tetanic type, in which many stimuli are sent to muscles in varying degrees of rapidity.

The extent or force of muscle contractions in the illustrations mentioned depends on the strength of the stimulus. If the stimuli are gradually increased, the muscle response will be greater, recording higher and higher contraction points until a maximum strength of stimulus is reached, after which no further increase in contraction will result. When the muscle is excited to a maximal contraction several times in rapid succession, as in incomplete tetanus, each twitch will be higher than its predecessor, a condition called **staircase,** or **treppe.** The explanation is that the chemical changes produced by one contraction promote a better one next time.

Muscle tonus. Muscle **tone** refers to that state of partial contraction present in all living skeletal muscles, even when they appear to be completely relaxed. It is thought that about 5% of the motor units are contracted at any one time to produce tone and that they act in relays so that none are overworked. Whenever a nerve to a particular muscle is cut, tone in that muscle ceases. Curare, injected, abolishes tone by blocking the motor end plate between nerve and muscle.

Chemistry of muscle contraction. When a muscle fiber contracts, its myofibrils do the contracting. The changes that take place in the muscle after stimulation are not all known, although the problem has been studied by many investigators. Many physicochemical changes occur in the contraction process. Work is performed; therefore energy is required. Muscles apparently use 20% to 40% of the energy value of food molecules in contraction; the rest is converted into heat. About four fifths of all the body heat comes from this source. In some way the energy released from certain biochemical reactions produces the physical changes necessary for the shortening of the muscle fiber. Much of this energy appears to be used during the relaxation phase rather than during contraction. In a contracting muscle, oxygen is used, carbon dioxide is produced, glycogen disappears, lactic acid forms, and heat production increases.

In addition, there are changes in two organic phosphates—**phosphocreatine** and **adenosine triphosphate**—which are found in muscle. According to the present state of knowledge, whenever a stimulus reaches a muscle cell, adenosine triphosphate (ATP) is broken down and releases energy under the influence of an enzyme myosin, which with another muscle protein (actin) forms actomyosin. The latter is the chief contractile structure of the myofibrils. This chemical energy so released causes the protein molecules of the myofibrils to shorten either by coiling or folding or by the myosin and actin filaments sliding past each other. In the breakdown of ATP, adenosine diphosphate (ADP) is formed by the release of a molecule of phosphoric acid. To restore ATP for additional contraction, ADP combines with phosphagen (phosphocreatine), which contains a high-energy reservoir of phosphate. But phosphagen is being used up and must also be restored. To furnish energy for this process, glycogen is metabolized by lactic acid. Part of this lactic acid is oxidized to carbon dioxide and water; the other part is converted into glycogen. Only this latter step requires O_2 (aerobic); the preceding ones do not (anaerobic).

To summarize the process of muscle contraction, the sequence of chemical phases in abridged form may be expressed thus:

(1) ATP $\rightleftarrows$ ADP + H_3PO_4 + Energy for contraction
(2) Phosphagen $\rightleftarrows$ Creatine + H_3PO_4 + Energy for resynthesis of ATP
(3) Glycogen $\rightleftarrows$ Lactic acid + Energy for resynthesis of phosphagen
(4) 1/5 Lactic acid + $O_2 \rightarrow CO_2 + H_2O$ + Energy for resynthesis of remaining 4/5 of lactic acid to glycogen

ATP furnishes the energy of contraction, the energy for the conversion of phosphagen (phosphocreatine), and the energy for the resynthesis of glycogen. The lactic acid formed in reaction 3 is carried in the blood to the liver, where it is converted to glycogen. The glycogen releases glucose into the blood, which is then converted back into glycogen in the muscle. This lactic acid-glycogen-glucose-glycogen cycle is called the Cori cycle and indicates the role of the liver in the metabolism of muscular contraction.

Experimental evidence for this theory of muscular contraction was afforded by Szent-Györgyi, Hungarian biochemist of the United States, who showed that artificial fibers of actomyosin will contract when they are placed in a solution of ATP.

Rigor mortis, or the rigor after death, is also explained by the theory, for under such conditions the ATP molecules are used up in the contraction of the actomyosin fibers and enzyme systems are destroyed so that no recovery or relaxation can take place.

The study of muscle structure and the nature of the contractile process has been the object of intensive research for many years. In the last decade H. E. Huxley, J. Hanson, and others have emphasized the sliding-filament theory (Fig. 30-16). By means of the electron microscope and x-ray diffraction methods, these investigators have shown that actin and myosin are located in separate filaments that overlap at a certain point and produce the striation pattern of voluntary or striped muscle. As the muscle contracts and relaxes, the slender filaments of actin slide past the thicker myosin filaments, which are provided with projections that alternately attach and detach to the actin filament very much like a ratchet. Just what the mechanism is that causes the filaments to move relative to one another is still in the speculative stage.

A muscle is able to contract in the complete absence of oxygen, but it fatigues faster. The reason is that lactic acid accumulates rapidly when the muscle is deprived of oxygen. Fatigue is thus caused primarily by an excess of lactic acid. In complete fatigue the exhausted muscle refuses to respond to nervous stimuli but it may still respond to certain direct mechanical stimuli. There is evidence that the site of this fatigue is the junction between nerve and muscle, or the motor end plate.

Oxygen debt. Ordinarily the oxygen supply to muscles is adequate for taking care of the lactic acid as it is formed in muscular contraction. However, in vigorous exercise an excess of lactic acid accumulates, because one cannot breathe fast enough to furnish the oxygen necessary to oxidize the lactic acid. The muscles incur what is called an **oxygen debt** because the excess lactic acid must be oxidized by extra oxygen. The limit of oxygen debt is about 100 grams of lactic acid for the trained athlete; it is less for the untrained. When this limit is reached, the individual is exhausted until he recovers by rapid breathing.

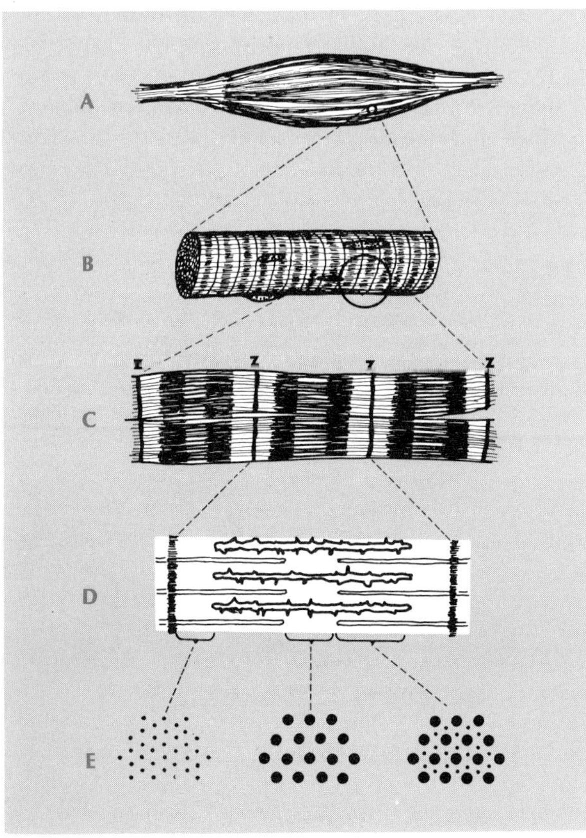

FIG. 30-16

Structure of striated muscle shown at successively higher magnifications from gross muscle to sarcomere, or contractile unit. **A,** Gross muscle made up of many fibers or cells. **B,** One muscle fiber with four nuclei. **C,** Portions of two myofibrils, of which there are many in each fiber, shown with alternate light and dark bands greatly magnified. Portion of one myofibril between two Z lines is called sarcomere. Three sarcomeres shown in each myofibril. **D,** Arrangement of myosin and actin filaments (myofilaments), as revealed by electron microscope. Note actin filaments attached to Z line and extending toward middle of sarcomere; myosin filaments arranged in middle, but not reaching Z line. Two sets may interdigitate and combine into actomyosin as they slide between one another in muscle contraction. According to Huxley-Hanson theory, myosin filaments are pulled toward Z lines as a result of interactions with actin filaments at certain sites. Exact mechanism of contraction is still unknown. **E,** Cross sections of three regions of sarcomere enclosed by brackets showing cross sections of actin, myosin, and actomyosin filaments.
(From several sources.)

Action of gross muscles

The human body contains approximately 696 skeletal muscles, most of which are arranged in antagonistic pairs for the manipulation of the skeleton (Fig. 30-17). This antagonistic action is seen also in most lower animals. Worms use their circular muscles to elongate and their longitudinal ones to contract. In the enterons of animals the circular and longitudinal muscles alternate in their action to propel the contents along (peristaltic movement).

Not all striated muscles are attached to bones. Some are of the sphincter type in which a set of circular muscles closes an opening and another set pulls radially away from the opening. Sphincters are found around the mouth and anal regions (striated muscles), at the pyloric and cardiac ends of the stomach, and in the iris of the eye (smooth muscle).

FIG. 30-17

Lateral view of human muscles.

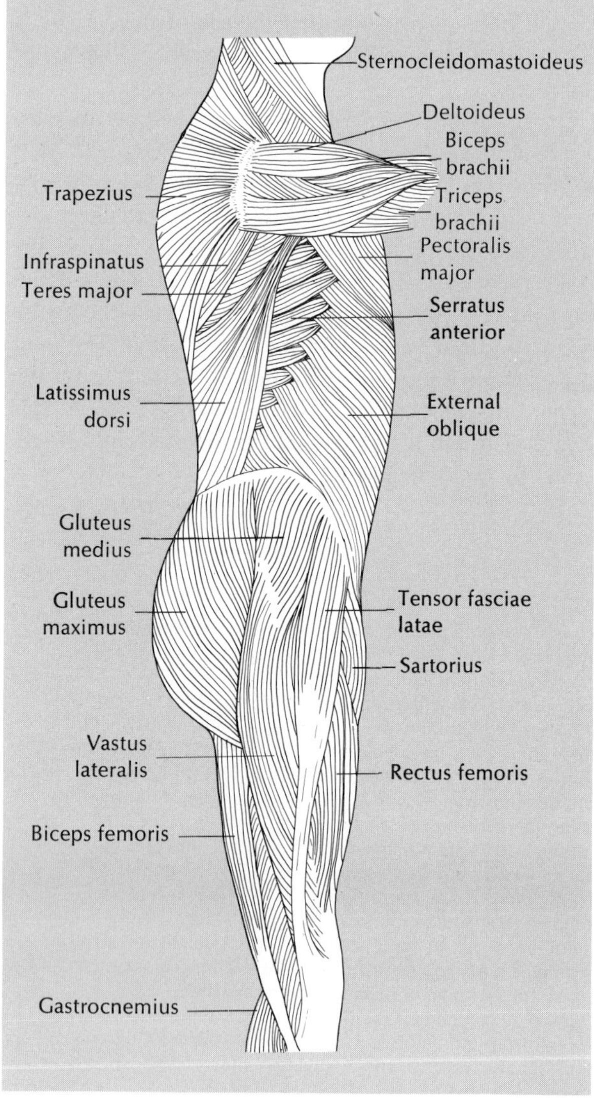

Contraction of involuntary muscle

Smooth muscle contraction is much slower than that of skeletal muscle and requires a stronger stimulus. Much smooth action is slow and rhythmical.

In cardiac muscle the phases of contraction are slower than in striped muscle, and its contraction is mostly rhythmical. Each beat of the heart is a single twitch. This muscle has a long **refractory period,** which is that period following one stimulus when it will not respond to another one. One cannot tetanize heart muscle.

Electrical activity during muscle contraction

In all cells there is an unequal distribution of ions between the inside and outside of the cell membrane. Because of this imbalance of ions, there exists a potential difference called the membrane potential between the inside and outside of cells (Fig. 30-18). In a resting muscle cell or fiber the outside is positive because

FIG. 30-18

Electrical activity in muscle. When muscle is at rest, **A,** outside of muscle is positive and membrane is polarized; when activated, membrane is depolarized by migration of sodium ions to inside. **B,** Restoration of membrane potential follows, so that fiber can react again when sodium ions migrate back to outside.

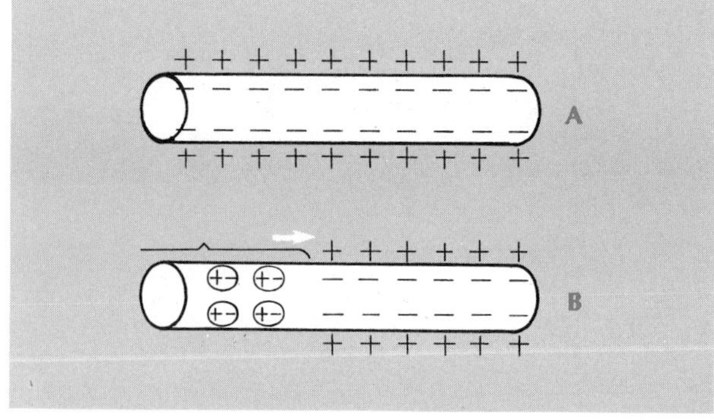

of the excess of positive ions on the surface. Although sodium readily enters the membrane (which is not impermeable to sodium ions as was once thought), the excess sodium ions on the surface may be due to an active transport system called the "sodium pump," which pumps out the sodium ions as fast as they enter. Whenever a muscle becomes active or contracts, an electrical activity is indicated by a potential difference between the active and nonactive regions of the fiber termed the "action potential." For an instant the active part of the fiber membrane becomes depolarized by allowing sodium ions to freely enter. When this happens, the muscle contracts. By quickly restoring the membrane potential, the fiber is ready to act again.

Other forms of movement

Protoplasmic streaming, which we have seen in protozoans, is of course common to all metazoan cells (cyclosis). Ameboid movement is found in the white blood cells of vertebrates. Ciliary movement is found somewhere in most metazoan forms. In amphibians, cilia are found in the lining of the pharynx. In most vertebrates, as well as invertebrates, ciliated epithelium lines the ducts of gonads, such as the uterine tubes and efferent ducts of testes, as well as the respiratory passages. Even flagella, which we found in some of the protozoans, sponges, and coelenterates, are found in vertebrates in the motile tails of the spermatozoa.

Annotated references

Arey, L. B. 1968. Human histology textbook in outline form, ed. 3. Philadelphia, W. B. Saunders Co. *This unique text should be on the desk of all zoology students.*

Carlson, A. J., and V. Johnson. 1948. The machinery of the body, ed. 3. Chicago, University of Chicago Press. *Good discussion of the physiology of the muscles.*

Eaton, T. H., Jr. 1960. Comparative anatomy of the vertebrates, ed. 2. New York, Harper & Brothers. *Good discussions of the skeleton and muscles.*

Kahn, F. 1953. Man in structure and function. New York, Alfred A. Knopf, Inc. *Unique illustrations of the mechanics of muscle and bone. A well-written treatise.*

Katchalsky, A., and S. Lifson. 1954. Muscle as a machine. Sci. Amer. **190**:72-76 (March).

Montagna, W. 1956. The structure and function of the skin. New York, Academic Press, Inc. *An account of this important organ. There is an interesting description of the relatively new concept of the apocrine sweat gland.*

Montagna, W. 1959. Comparative anatomy. New York, John Wiley & Sons, Inc. *A clearly written presentation of the comparative anatomy of the skin, skeleton, and muscles.*

Morton, D. J. 1952. Human locomotion and body form. Baltimore, The Williams & Wilkins Co. *An excellent account of the mechanics of movement with relation to body form.*

Rothman, S. 1954. Physiology and biochemistry of the skin. Chicago, University of Chicago Press. *A highly technical account of the skin, its physical properties, its physiologic functions, and its chemical constituents. Especially for the advanced student.*

Smith, H. M. 1960. Evolution of chordate structure. An introduction to comparative anatomy. New York, Holt, Rinehart & Winston, Inc. *A text that gives a fine appraisal of the evolutionary background of vertebrate morphology. The serious student who wishes to know the why and wherefore of structural patterns will be amply repaid by studying this superb treatise.*

Waring, H. 1963. Color change mechanisms of cold-blooded vertebrates. New York, Academic Press, Inc. *An integrated study of color change mechanisms at the specialist's level.*

CHAPTER 31

• DIGESTIVE, CIRCULATORY, RESPIRATORY, AND EXCRETORY SYSTEMS

● The animal requires energy for its living processes and materials for growth and repair. The source of materials for both energy and building is **food.** Most food cannot be utilized directly. First, the larger molecules must be broken down into smaller molecules for absorption. Then, they must be carried to wherever they are needed, to be built into body tissues or burned to provide energy. Finally, the waste products generated by these processes must be eliminated. The sum total of all these chemical and physical processes is called **metabolism.** Metabolism has two phases, or aspects: **anabolism** and **catabolism.** Anabolism is concerned with the building up of substances into new tissue or into storage materials; catabolism involves the breaking down of complex materials to simpler ones for the release of energy.

DIGESTIVE SYSTEM*

Historic background of study of digestion

The most classic investigation in the field of digestion was made by the American William Beaumont during the years 1822 to 1833. His observations were made on a Canadian wood ranger named Alexis St. Martin who accidentally shot himself with a shotgun. When the wound healed, a permanent opening, or fistula, was formed that enabled Dr. Beaumont to see directly into the stomach and so to observe how the lining of the stomach changed under different conditions, how foods varied in time of digestion, the effects of emotional states on the motility of the stomach and its rate of digestion, and many other facts about the whole cycle of digestion.

To study the nature of gastric juice, Ivan Pavlov, a Russian physiologist in 1887 constructed a pouch by sewing off a part of the stomach of a living animal (dog) in such a way that this artificial pouch opened to the outside through a hole in the abdominal wall. This pouch was lined with mucous membrane and retained its nerve supply. Whenever the main stomach functioned in response to food, emotion, and other factors, this artificial pouch also secreted gastric juice, which could be collected in a pure form. By this method, Pavlov was able to learn about the factors that stimulated or inhibited gastric digestion, the amount and consistency of gastric juice, and the phases in the cycle of digestion.

W. B. Cannon in 1898 found that by having animals (including man) swallow test meals mixed with bismuth salts, which are opaque to x-rays, the contours of the various divisions of the alimentary canal could be photographed with the rays. By taking photographs of the successive phases of digestion, it was possible to get an accurate picture of gastrointestinal movements as the food contents passed through the tract. Another American worker, A. J. Carlson (1915), added further knowledge to the movements of the stomach during normal and fasting periods by the balloon technique, in which balloons fastened to rubber tubes were swallowed and blown up in the stomach. The various movements of the stomach produced pressure changes in the balloons that could be transmitted through the rubber tubes to the tambour of a kymograph, on which records were made.

Feeding types

Every animal must adapt itself to the nutritional opportunities of its environment. This adaptation depends on such factors as the physical environment, the mode of progress within it, the nature of the food source, and the mode of its detection and prehension. The process of swallowing (deglutition) is also related to the anatomic and physiologic arrangements of breathing and prehension. Nearly every type of organic matter can be used by some member of the animal kingdom.

*Refer to Chapter 2, Principle 18.

Many years ago the British zoologist C. M. Yonge listed the variety of feeding types among animals. In his classification according to the nature of the food eating, he grouped the animals into those that fed on small particles (microphages) and those that fed on large particles (macrophages), including some animals that fed only on fluids. Each of these groups is subdivided. Microphages feed on such small particles that food must be taken in by bulk. Filter feeding, by passing the water with food through a device that strains out the suspended matter, is a common method of microphages. Deposit feeders obtain their food by scraping a substratum and also belong to this type. Macrophages are able to seize their food elements individually, and fluid feeders suck in fluids from prey. Many parasitic animals are able to absorb food through the body wall. Many examples of these various types are familiar to the student. Symbiotic organisms also aid in food breakdown and thus assist enzymatic action in some animals.

Sequence of metabolic stages

Food is **ingested** by most animals through the mouth and then **digested,** or simplified by physicochemical means, into smaller molecules in solution. These are

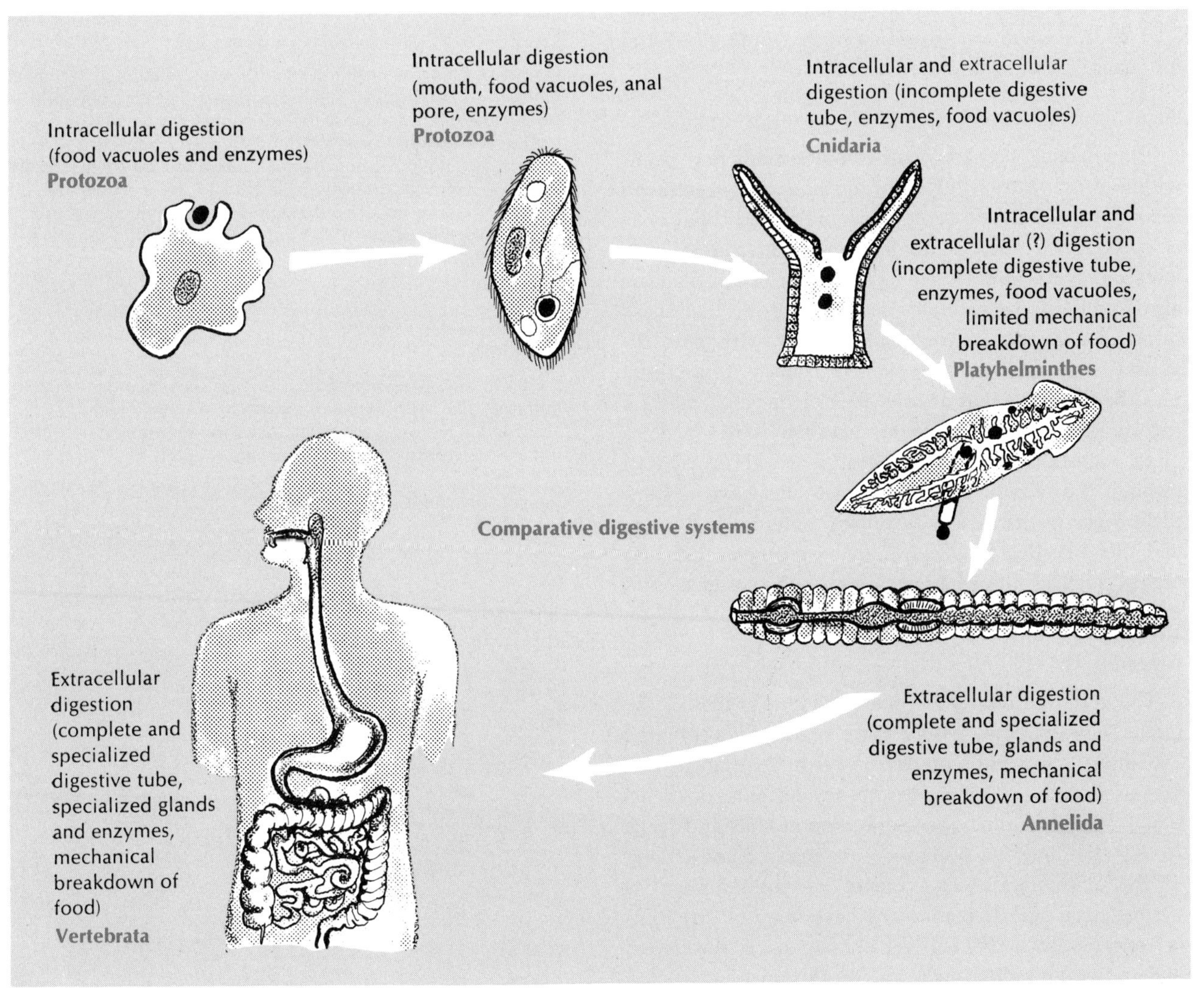

FIG. 31-1

Comparative types of digestive systems in animal kingdom.

absorbed into the circulatory system and **transported** to all tissues of the body, where they are **assimilated** into the protoplasm of the cells. Oxygen is also carried by the blood to the tissues, where the food products can be **oxidized,** or burned. By this means, energy and heat are produced, secretions synthesized, and waste substances formed as by-products. These wastes are **excreted** by the lungs, skin, and excretory system. Food products unsuitable for digestion are rejected by the digestive system and are **egested** in the form of feces. Much food is not immediately oxidized but is **stored** for future use. Simple sugars can be stored in the liver and muscles as glycogen and easily reconverted as needed. Excess sugars are stored as adipose (fat) tissue. Proteins are not stored as such, but their amino acids are split up and some eliminated as waste, some converted into energy, and some stored as fat.

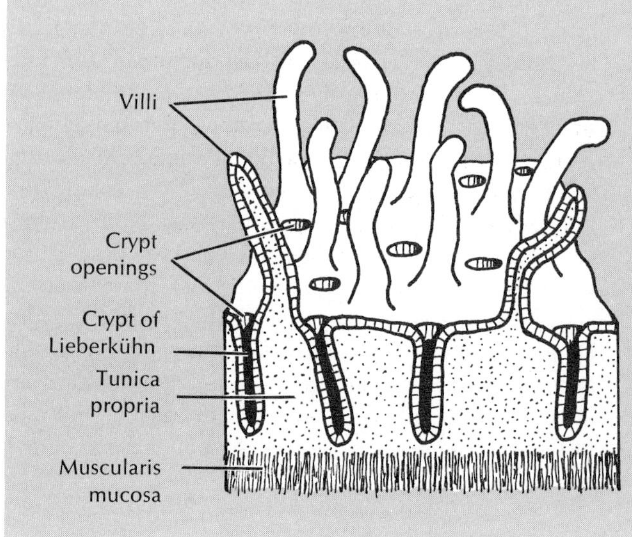

FIG. 31-2

Portion of lining of small intestine showing relation of epithelial lining to villi and crypts. Tunica (lamina) propria is a network of reticular fibers and loose areolar connective tissue with scattered lymphoid tissue. It extends between crypts of Lieberkühn and into cores of villi. In cross section a villus would appear as a circular or oval profile with a core of connective tissue and a covering of epithelium; a crypt would appear as a central lumen lined by epithelium and embedded in connective tissue. (Modified from Ham.)

Digestion in invertebrates

The chemical breakdown of complex foods may occur within cells (**intracellular**) or outside cells (**extracellular**) (Fig. 31-1). In protozoans and in the collar cells of sponges the food is retained in food vacuoles into which enzymes are secreted. This type of digestion is also found in coelenterates and flatworms, but these forms also have a **gastrovascular cavity** with both digestive and circulatory functions. Enzymes are secreted into the cavity so that at least part of the food may be digested extracellularly. Such a system is not a complete digestive system, for fecal material is egested through the mouth. Higher invertebrates have a complete digestive system, with mouth, enteron, and anus; and the digestive tube may also be differentiated into organs such as the pharynx, esophagus, stomach, and intestine.

FIG. 31-3

Border of intestinal epithelium of mouse showing microvilli and mitochondria. Microvilli (lower left) are seen only with electron microscope. (×32,000.) (Courtesy W. Andrew, Indiana University Medical Center, Indianapolis.)

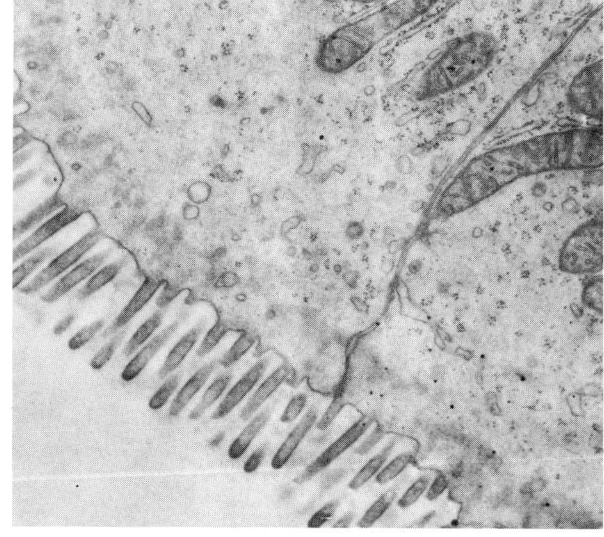

Digestion in vertebrates

The vertebrate digestive plan is similar to that of the higher invertebrates, with a more highly differentiated alimentary canal and with devices for increasing the surface area, such as greater length, inside folds, or diverticula. Elongation may be in the form of coils and loops so that the digestive system may be many times as long as the abdominal cavity. Lower vertebrates such as cyclostomes and elasmobranchs have longitudinal folds or spiral valves. Higher vertebrates have developed elaborate folds called **rugae** and small projections called

villi (Fig. 31-2). The electron microscope also reveals short, delicate processes known as **microvilli** (Fig. 31-3) along the border of the intestinal epithelium. These processes may be concerned with absorption or secretion. So effective is this method that in some animals the mucosa lining is ten times as great in area as the external surface of the tract. Diverticula are the side pouches, or **ceca,** that arise from the main canal. Some fish have pyloric ceca at the junction of the stomach and intestine. Higher vertebrates have colic ceca at the junction of the small and large intestines. In man this cecum is prolonged by the vestigial vermiform appendix.

Herbivorous animals such as sheep, cattle, and rabbits have long alimentary canals, for their food is so little concentrated that they must eat large quantities. Carnivorous animals that live on highly concentrated food do not require so long a tube. The postmortem length of the digestive tract is more than twice its length in the living state.

Histology of digestive tube

A section through the wall of any vertebrate alimentary canal reveals about the same histologic plan with four typical layers (Figs. 31-4 and 31-5). The inner **mucosa** is chiefly epithelial—simple in the stomach and intestine and stratified elsewhere. It is concerned with secretion and absorption and may be considered the chief functional component. The **submucosa,** mostly connective tissue, carries the capillaries and lymphatics. The **muscularis** layer is made up of inner circular and outer longitudinal muscles, by which peristalsis is effected. The outer thin **serosa** layer is a continuation of the peritoneum.

FIG. 31-4

Cross section of alimentary canal.

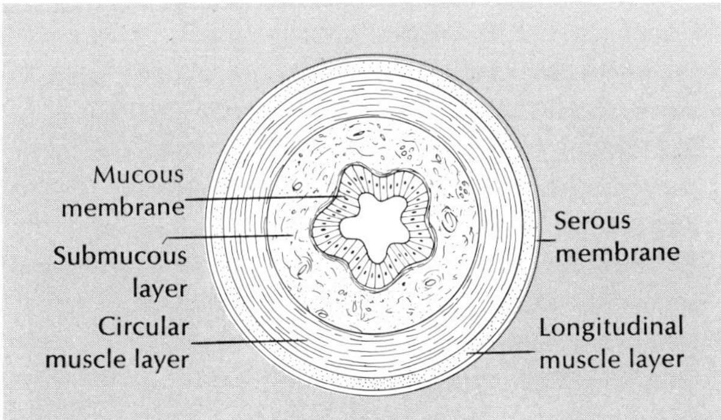

Regions of digestive system

The structural plan of the alimentary canal among the various vertebrates is quite similar (Fig. 31-6) and includes the mouth, pharynx, esophagus, stomach, small and large intestines, and mesenteries.

Mouth and mouth (buccal) cavity. The buccal cavity is surrounded by the cheeks, hard palate, soft palate, tongue, and pharynx. The mouth is provided with **teeth** for grasping and masticating food and with the **tongue** for manipulating, sampling, and swallowing the food. The **salivary glands,** which empty into the mouth cavity, lubricate the food and, in man at least, perform a limited amount of digestion. In man two sets of teeth are formed during life—the temporary or "milk teeth" of 4 incisors, 2 canines, and 4 molars in each jaw (20 teeth) and the permanent set of 4 incisors, 2 canines, 4 bicuspids (premolars), and 6 molars in each jaw (32 teeth). Teeth are attached to the jaw by different methods (Fig. 31-7).

FIG. 31-5

Histologic section of mammalian small intestine showing villi.

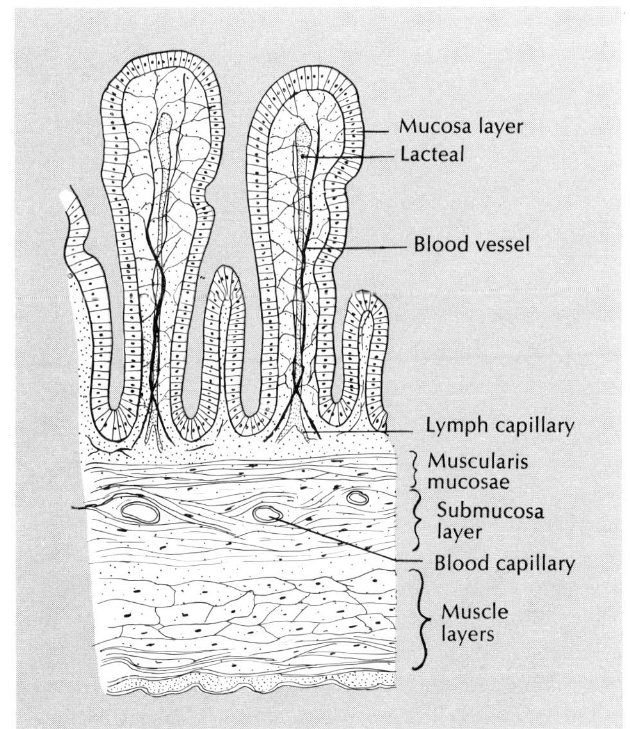

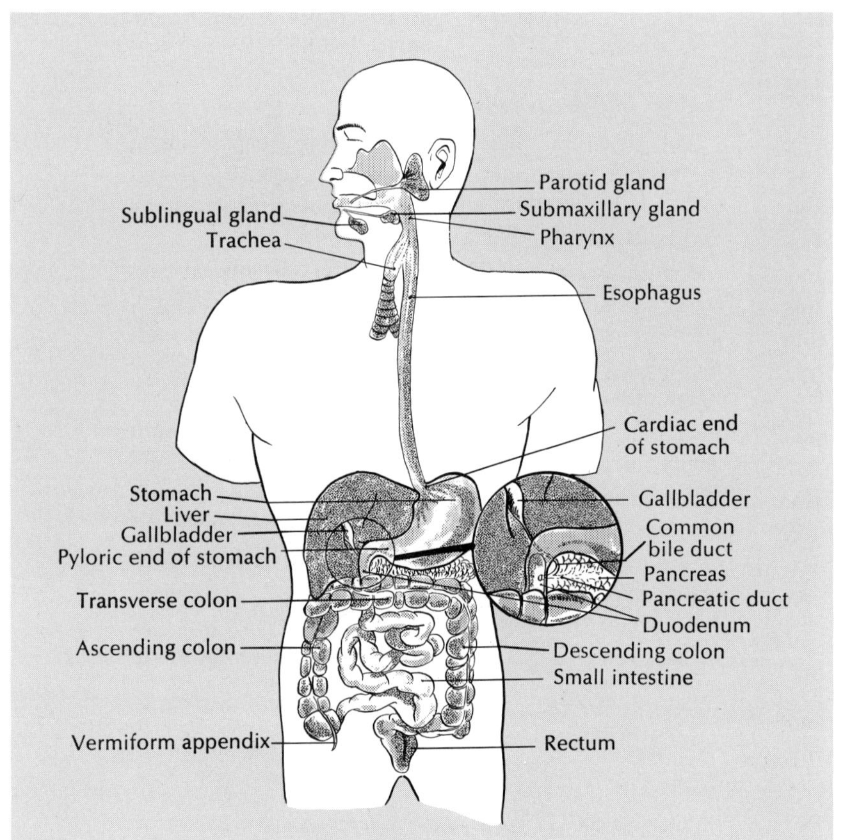

FIG. 31-6

Digestive system of man. Window insert shows relation of gallbladder, common bile duct, and pancreatic duct to small intestine (duodenum).

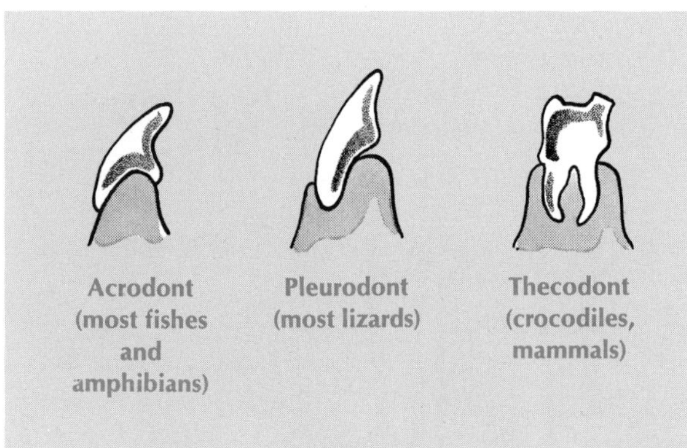

FIG. 31-7

Types of tooth attachment. Acrodont teeth are fastened to surface of jaw, pleurodont teeth are attached in inner margin of jaw, and thecodont teeth are set in sockets.

Pharynx. The pharynx, or throat cavity, serves for the passage of food and is the place where air crosses the path of food. In fish and some others it is the region of the gills and serves as the point of origin for the swim bladder; in land animals the lungs and certain other structures originate in this area. In man and many other animals it has seven openings: (1) two internal nares from the nasal cavity, (2) the opening from the mouth, (3) two eustachian tubes to the middle ear, (4) the opening into the esophagus, and (5) the glottis into the trachea.

Esophagus. The esophagus connects the pharynx with the stomach, and its length depends mainly on the presence or absence of a neck. In the frog it is very short, in man, about 13 inches long. The crop in birds is a differentiation of this tube and so is part of the complex stomach of ruminants. The few glands in the esophagus are mostly of a lubricating nature, and the well-developed muscles in its wall aid in swallowing. The muscles at the beginning of the tube are striped; those lower down are smooth.

Stomach. The stomach may be simply an enlargement of the food tract or it may be saclike, spindle shaped, J shaped, or bag shaped. The stomach of man is divided into regions called the **fundus, cardiac region,** and **pyloric region.** A pyloric sphincter valve regulates passage of food into the small intestine. The factors that cause the pyloric sphincter valve to open are complex but involve fluidity and acidity of the gastric contents, degree of filling of the stomach, parasympathetic nerve activity, and effect of enterogastrone. In most vertebrates gastric glands secrete enzymes for digestion, although these glands may be absent.

Small intestine. Most of the digestion occurs in the small intestine and the food is absorbed into the bloodstream for distribution to all parts of the body. Two large digestive glands, the **liver** and **pancreas,** empty into the duodenum. **Intestinal glands** furnish a digestive fluid, the intestinal juice (succus entericus). All digestive juices, with the exception of liver bile, contribute enzymes for digestion.

Large intestine (colon). The glands of the large intestine are mainly for lubrication and not for digestion. Villi are absent. Usually the diameter of the colon is greater than that of the small intestine. In man the large intestine is divided into **ascending, transverse,** and **descending** portions, with the posterior end terminating in the **rectum** and **anus.** At the junction of the large and small intestines is the **colic cecum** with its **vermiform appendix.** The **anus** is regulated by a sphincter muscle.

Mesenteries. The stomach, small intestine, and large intestine are all suspended in the body cavity by **mesenteries** that are modified from the peritoneum. Organs such as liver, spleen, and pancreas are also held in place by mesenteries, which carry blood and lymph vessels as well as nerves to the various visceral organs. Fat is often stored in mesenteries.

Physiology of digestion

Digestion involves both mechanical and chemical alterations of food. Mechanical factors that aid in the process are teeth, grinding organs such as gizzards, and muscular action of the stomach and intestinal walls. Chemical reactions in the breakdown are regulated by **enzymes.**

Action of enzymes. Most digestive enzymes produce their action by the process of **hydrolysis,** in which a molecule of water is added to the food molecule, which then separates into two other molecules. In hydrolysis, cleavage may involve several stages before the final molecules are obtained. In proteins, for example, the first stage in hydrolysis will yield molecules of several amino acids, and additional hydrolytic reactions will be necessary before amino acids will be split off. Before they can be absorbed, proteins must be split into amino acids, carbohydrates into simple sugars, and fats into glycerol and fatty acids. Specific enzymes for each of these processes are found in various regions of the alimentary canal. One enzyme may finish what another has started. Glands that secrete the various enzymes are controlled during digestion by nervous reflexes or by special hormones from the endocrine system.

Digestion in mouth. Chemical reactions in the mouth are usually restricted because of the short time food is retained in the mouth. Food is masticated and mixed with **saliva** that is secreted by three pairs of salivary glands—**parotid, submaxillary,** and **sublingual.** Saliva contains two enzymes, **salivary amylase** and **maltase,** which act upon carbohydrates. **Salivary amylase** splits starch and other complex carbohydrates into the double sugar **maltose.** Maltase breaks down maltose to glucose. Salivary digestion continues in the stomach after the food enters there, but as soon as the gastric contents become acid, the process ceases.

Swallowing. The act of swallowing is begun voluntarily by the tongue and cheeks pushing the food backward into the pharynx. Then by involuntary reflex action the soft palate and uvula are elevated to close off the nasal cavity, and the larynx rises to meet the lowering of the epiglottis, thus closing off the windpipe. Food slides over the epiglottis, and contraction of esophageal muscles (peristalsis) forces the food into the stomach. It takes about 10 seconds for food to pass to the stomach. The cardiac sphincter opens reflexly, the bolus glides into the stomach, and then the sphincter closes again to avoid regurgitation. The nerve center for swallowing is located in the medulla.

Digestion in stomach. Muscular movements thoroughly mix the food with gastric juice secreted by gastric glands. Waves of contractions start about the central portion and move the food toward the pyloric end of the stomach. The enzymes **pepsin** and **rennin** act mainly upon protein foods. Pepsin in the inactive form, **pepsinogen,** is converted into active pepsin by hydrochloric acid and also by other pepsin already present. Pepsin is active only in an acid medium (pH 2) and splits large molecules of protein into smaller molecules of proteoses and peptones. Acids and enzymes are produced by different cells in mammals, but by the same cells in elasmobranchs and amphibians. The protein-splitting enzyme papain of the papaya fruit is a common meat tenderizer. The enzyme rennin coagulates milk by changing **casein** (a milk protein) from a soluble to an insoluble form. Rennet, used in making junket pudding, is made of rennin, and rennin extracted from the stomachs of calves is used in cheese making. The fat-splitting **gastric lipase** is thought by some authorities to be present in the gastric juice.

The mechanism responsible for avoiding self-digestion includes a thick lining of mucus secreted by special cells; this prevents direct contact of enzymes on the wall. There is also the possibility of antienzymes. Sometimes the mechanism does break down as in gastric ulcers.

Digestion in small intestine. The major part of digestion occurs in the small intestine where three secretions, **pancreatic juice** (Fig. 31-8), **intestinal juice,** and **bile,** are secreted. The pancreatic juice has many enzymes and recent work has revealed new ones. The protease formerly considered a trypsin is now known to consist of several enzymes. One of these is **trypsin,** whose inactive zymogen is trypsinogen. The activation of the latter into trypsin by enterokinase from the intestinal wall has been disputed, but trypsinogen freed from its inhibitor can be activated by small amounts of trypsin. This latter activity is called an **autocatalytic reaction** and may be a general phenomenon of enzymatic activities. Trypsin can act upon natural proteins and reduce them to proteoses and peptides; if the proteins have been partly hydrolyzed by pepsin, trypsin can break them down to amino acids. Another protease is **chymotrypsin,** which is found in an inactive form as chymotrypsinogen. The latter is activated into chymotrypsin by trypsin. Chymotrypsin also acts on proteins and clots milk. One of the peptidase group of enzymes in pancreatic or intestinal juice is called **carboxypeptidase.** It acts upon polypeptides and splits off amino acids.

FIG. 31-8

Portion of pancreatic cell of mouse showing secretion granules (large oval bodies) and endoplasmic reticulum. These secretion granules give rise to pancreatic juice. (×59,000.) (Courtesy W. Andrew, Indiana University Medical Center, Indianapolis.)

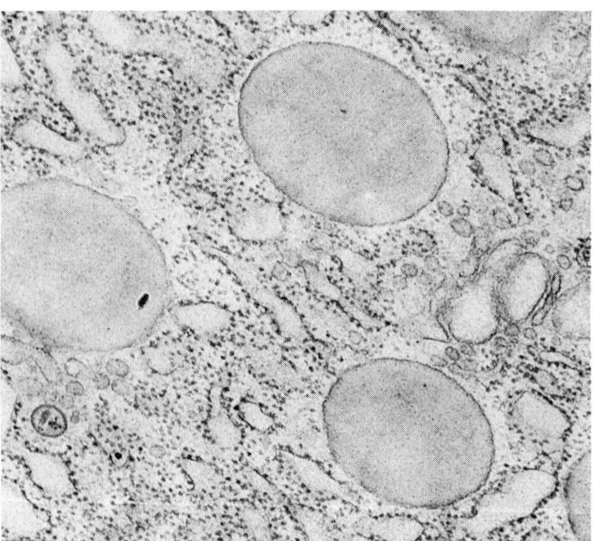

Of the other pancreatic juice enzymes, **amylopsin** (diastase) reduces whole or partly digested starches to maltose, and **pancreatic lipase** converts fats to fatty acids and glycerol. All of these enzymes work best in alkaline medium (pH 8) that is brought about by the carbonates of the pancreatic and intestinal juices. Other pancreatic enzymes are ribonuclease, which splits phosphate esters of RNA into nucleotides, and desoxyribonuclease, which does the same for the phosphate esters of DNA.

Intestinal juice from the glands of the mucosal lining furnishes a number of enzymes. One of these, aminopeptidase, completes the gastric digestion of peptides and proteoses and splits them into amino acids. Three other enzymes are concerned with carbohydrate splitting—**maltase** converts maltose to glucose, **sucrase** splits sucrose to glucose and fructose, and **lactase** breaks down lactose (milk sugar) into glucose and galactose. The acid contents from the stomach also cause the intestinal mucosa to release the hormone **secretin** that, carried in the blood to the pancreas, stimulates the flow of pancreatic juice.

Bile contains no enzymes. It is made up of water, bile salts, and certain pigments. Bile is usually stored in the gallbladder and is stimulated to flow down the common bile duct when food enters the small intestine. A hormone, **cholecystokinin,** secreted by the intestinal lining, plays a part in regulating the flow of bile. Bile salts (sodium taurocholate and sodium glycocholate) emulsify fat into small particles so that the fat-splitting enzymes may have a chance to reduce them. The bile pigments (**bilirubin** and **biliverdin**) are produced from the breakdown of hemoglobin in the destruction of red blood cells. They give bile its color, which varies with different animals. Human bile is a golden yellow color. Bile pigments also color the feces. Excess cholesterol is excreted by the liver and may be the source of gall-stones.

Bile is produced by **liver**, which includes among its many functions a storage of glycogen, production of fibrinogen in blood clotting, production of plasma proteins, protein synthesis, detoxification of nitrogenous waste by changing ammonia into urea, destruction of worn-out erythrocytes, formation and storage of the antianemia factor of the blood, deamination of amino acids, storage of vitamins A and D, and as a center for fat and carbohydrate metabolism.

Digestion in large intestine. The colon bacteria secrete enzymes that work on proteins and cellulose of plants. These enzymes are not very important in man, but in herbivorous animals they digest cellulose. Material that reaches the large intestine has most of its nutrients taken from it, although it is still in a liquid state. The colon stores the indigestible products and waste as feces and eliminates them from the digestive tract. Peristaltic movements force the contents slowly along until they reach the rectum. Peristaltic movements are greatly speeded up by the **gastrocolic reflex,** which occurs when food enters the stomach and produces the desire for defecation. The process of defecation involves the coordinated action of muscles of the large intestine, abdominal muscles, diaphragm, and sphincter muscles of the anus. The act is partly voluntary and partly involuntary. The desire to defecate is induced by the distention of the rectum and the resulting stimulation of the nerves in its walls. Whenever the signal is ignored, the rectum adapts itself to the new size and the desire passes off temporarily. The fecal content is made up of the indigestible residue of food, bile pigments, secreted heavy metals, and bacteria.

Factors that regulate secretions and movements of digestive tract

The physiology of the digestive system centers around two important functions—**secretions** and **movements.** All glands in the alimentary canal must be stimulated to secrete their products. The action of the glands is controlled by the nervous system and by hormones. Salivary glands are controlled entirely by the nervous system. Sensory receptors such as taste buds and olfactory receptors carry impulses to the salivation center in the medulla that mediates impulses to the salivary glands. The salivary glands may also be influenced by the higher centers of the brain, such as thinking about or seeing food. The flow of gastric juice is regulated partly by a nervous mechanism and partly by the action of the hormone **gastrin** that is produced in the mucosa cells of the stomach. To prevent the concentration of acid gastric juice from becoming too high, a gastrin-inhibitory hormone is produced by the pyloric mucosa. The hormone **secretin** stimulates the pancreas, but nervous impulses may also play a minor role. Intestinal juice is influenced by secretin and **enterocrinin** (a hormone), together with the action of the intrinsic nerves of the intestinal wall.

The most characteristic movements of the alimentary canal are those of **peristalsis** (several varieties) and **segmentation.** Peristaltic movements propel the food along the tract, but the segmental movements of the small intestine serve to divide and mix the food. Hormones and nerves influence the movements of the alimentary canal. **Enterogastrone,** produced in the duodenal mucosa, will slow gastric motility and decrease the secretion of gastric juice.

Absorption

Most foodstuffs are absorbed from the small intestine. In forms such as *Hydra* the food particles that are partly digested in the gastrovascular cavity are absorbed by the endodermal cells and are passed on to the other cells. Digestion in these animals is partially extracellular and partially intracellular. In Protozoa, food digested in the food vacuoles is absorbed directly into the protoplasm.

In man there is little absorption in the stomach. Some drugs and alcohol (in part) are absorbed there, which explains their quick action.

Villi are mainly responsible for absorption, since they contain a network of blood and lymph capillaries that pick up the digested materials. Villi can twist and shorten, thus facilitating the process of absorption by propelling the flow of lymph and blood. Amino acids and simple sugars are absorbed directly into the blood, which delivers them to the liver before they are sent into the general circulation. Glycerol and fatty acids enter the lymph vessels. Since these lymph vessels eventually enter the thoracic duct, fat also gets into the blood.

In the large intestine most of the water is absorbed; this accounts for the solid nature of the feces. Bacterial decomposition products may also be absorbed. Some of these are toxic and odorous, but the liver usually detoxifies them.

Absorption is not simply a diffusion process, for some of the absorption can be explained on the basis of an active secretory process similar to the forces that operate in glandular secretion.

Fate of absorbed materials. Absorbed amino acids and glucose are carried by the hepatic portal system to the liver, where they are stored, changed into other forms, and released to the blood. Many of the amino acids are deaminized in the liver by the removal of the amino group (NH_2), which then combines with carbon dioxide to form urea, $CO(NH_2)_2$, a waste product of urine. The other part of the amino acid is converted into fat or sugar for energy purposes. Other amino acids are released by the liver to the cells of the body to repair or replace living protoplasm.

Glucose is converted to glycogen (animal starch) in the liver, where it is stored to be released (as glucose) to the blood for the maintenance of the glucose level (0.1%). Some glucose combines with other substances to form a basic part of protoplasm, and some is also stored in the muscles as glycogen. Glucose is one of the most available sources of energy for muscular work and heat production.

Fat that enters the bloodstream from the thoracic duct is changed into fat characteristic of the animal's body by rearrangement of the fatty acids. Some fats help form the nuclear and plasma membranes. Excess fat is stored in adipose tissues that are located in the connective tissues between muscles and skin, in mesenteries, and around various organs.

Nutritional aspects of animal

A **food** may be defined as any substance that, when taken into the body, will furnish energy and materials for the structure and repair of tissues or has regulative action on body processes. The common classification of food includes **carbohydrates, proteins, fats, water, mineral salts,** and **vitamins.** The first three are required for energy and building materials, the latter three for building and regulative action. Although the needs of all animals for these substances are in general similar, they may have different ways of getting them. Some animals are exclusively **herbivorous** (rabbit), others are exclusively **carnivorous** (tiger), and still others are **omnivorous** (man). There are also differences in the amount and kind of food required. Rats do not need ascorbic acid because they make this vitamin in their own bodies, but man must include it in his diet. Water is acquired by animals in different ways. Aquatic animals take in copious amounts with their food, frogs absorb it through their skin, and some forms make use of the water formed in the oxidation of their food. Some animals have an intense liking for salt (many herbivorous forms), but carnivores usually spurn it in their diets.

Energy requirements. The energy unit is the **kilocalorie;** this is the amount of heat necessary to raise 1 kilogram of water from 15° to 16° C. The caloric values of foods utilized in metabolism are as follows:

1 gram carbohydrate	4.1 kg.-cal.
1 gram fat	9.3 kg.-cal.
1 gram protein	4.3 kg.-cal.

The daily expenditure of energy varies according to age, sex, weight, activity, and body proportions. To determine how much energy is required for various forms of activity, it is necessary to standardize the metabolic rate. This is done by first determining the **basal metabolic rate.** This rate for an adult male of average weight, relaxed and fasting, is about 1,600 kilocalories every 24 hours. As a result of many determinations, tables have been prepared that give the normal basal metabolic rate for a given size, height, sex, and body area. The energy expended in a basal metabolic condition is for the working of the vital organs and for maintaining the body temperature.

Basal metabolism can be determined directly by measuring the heat given off while the subject is in a specially constructed insulated chamber, but the more common method is by **indirect calorimetry,** in which the oxygen consumption is measured over a period of time. Since the heat and energy released depend on the oxidation of food, their amounts can be calculated from the oxygen consumed. On the basis of oxygen consumed, it is found that every liter of O_2 will yield about 4.8 kilocalories of heat energy for the average diet. Any activity beyond that of basal metabolism will require additional kilocalories of energy. The requirements for energy will depend on the kind of work in which one is engaged. Persons living a sedentary life use about 2,500 kilocalories daily; those engaged in heavy manual work, as many as 5,000 to 6,000 kilocalories daily.

Balanced diet. It is not enough to supply fuel foods—it is also necessary to furnish food components that will meet all the needs of the body. The **balanced diet** takes into consideration all the metabolic requirements of the body—energy, growth, replacement, and physiologic regulation. This must include energy or fuel food, mineral, green and yellow vegetables, roughage, vitamins, and water.

In the average American diet about two thirds of the energy comes from carbohydrates and the other one third from proteins and fats. Carbohydrates are widely used by most people because they are cheaper than other foods. Perhaps 50 grams of protein daily would meet the demands of the body, but the average American diet includes far more than this. The amino acids of proteins can be divided into two groups—essential amino acids, which the body cannot synthesize but which must be supplied ready-made in the diet, and nonessential amino acids, which the body can make from any amino group of the diet. Whenever the body is making a particular protein, all the amino acids necessary for that protein must be present at the same time. This means that each meal must be balanced so far as proteins are concerned; the requirements of other food elements of the diet can be reckoned on a daily basis. A complete protein is one that contains all the essential amino acids such as eggs, meat, and cheese. Some plant proteins are not complete.

The minerals required are **sodium chloride** for the blood and osmotic balance of the body, **iron** for the hemoglobin of the blood, **potassium** and **magnesium** for muscle contraction, **calcium** and **phosphorus** for the teeth and bones, and **iodine** for the hormone of the thyroid gland. As there is a steady loss of these salts from the body, they must be replaced in the food we eat. The chief source of sodium chloride is table salt; iron, meats and eggs; potassium and magnesium, meats and vegetables; calcium and phosphorus, milk and meat; and iodine, drinking water or iodized table salt. Water is necessary to the amount of at least 2,000 ml. daily.

Vitamins. Vitamins are somewhat simple compounds and are usually found in scanty amounts in foods, but they are absolutely essential to life. They are not sources of energy, but their lack from the diet causes pathologic disturbances. Their chief functions are to regulate various bodily functions, at least in the higher animals. Just what role they perform in lower animals is largely unknown. Each vitamin must be present in a minimal amount to prevent deficiency diseases. Vitamins are widely scattered through a variety of foods, and the chemical structures of most vitamins have been worked out. Many are made synthetically and sold in the form of pills. If the diet is sufficiently varied and balanced, it will include the proper amounts of vitamins, but in restricted (reduction) diets and in the average diets of alcoholics, there may be a serious lack of them.

Methods of preparing foods may cause serious loss of vitamins. Refined flour and canned foods may be lacking in vitamins unless they are fortified. Cooking may destroy important vitamins, and some are discarded in pot liquor. Chemically, each vitamin is unrelated and more or less isolated from other vitamins. Perhaps the greatest advancement in knowledge about them is the part many of them play in enzyme systems of bodily metabolism.

Most plants and animals need vitamins, although the requirements are not the same for all animals. Some animals have the power to synthesize certain vitamins in their own bodies; others cannot. Many animals make vitamin C in their bodies. Insects seem to require only the B complex vitamins. This variation among animals may be due to evolutionary changes or mutations.

Vitamins are usually classified as fat-soluble or water-soluble. On the basis of nutritional requirements, metabolic processes, and general distribution, they also may be divided into two groups. One of these includes the great family of B vitamins that play important roles in cellular metabolism and are of universal occurrence. The other group is made up of the fat-soluble vitamins and vitamin C that have specialized functions for certain tissues and are more restricted in distribution. Vitamin A, for instance, is universal in vertebrates but is found only in certain invertebrates, where it appears to be a requirement for vision; but vitamin A is not an absolute dietary requirement for any invertebrate so far as is known. Its presence may be accidental in some invertebrates in which it can serve as a source of vitamin A for vertebrate predators.

Instead of the letter designation so long used for vitamins, many are now called by their chemical names, if their chemical structures are known.

Vitamin A (fat-soluble, epithelium-protecting vitamin, B carotene)

Source: Butter, eggs, milk, carotene of plants, cod-liver oil

Function: Maintenance of epithelial cells of skin, eye, and mucous membranes; regenerates visual purple of eye; stable

Lack causes: Xerophthalmia, night blindness, retardation in growth

Prevalence of disorders: Among poorer classes, usually night blindness

Vitamin B complex (water-soluble)

1. Thiamine (B_1) (antineuritic)
   Source: Yeast, germ of cereals, egg yolk, liver, nuts, lean pork
   Function: Necessary for carbohydrate metabolism; acts as a coenzyme to carboxylase in conversion of pyruvic acid to acetaldehyde; stable in acid
   Lack causes: Beriberi, loss of appetite, cessation of growth, polyneuritis in birds
   Prevalence of disorders: Common among people of rice-eating countries; uncommon in United States but may be found in alcoholics
2. Riboflavin (B_2 or G)
   Source: Green leaves, eggs, meat, cheese, milk, liver
   Function: Concerned with oxidation processes and intermediate metabolism of food; hydrogen acceptor and donator for cellular synthesis; stable
   Lack causes: Stunted growth, inflammation at corners of mouth (cheilosis), dermatitis
   Prevalence of disorders: Fairly common in southern communities
3. Niacin (nicotinic acid) (antipellagric)
   Source: Green leaves, egg yolk, wheat germ, liver, yeast
   Function: Constituent of certain coenzymes; essential to cellular functions; stable
   Lack causes: Pellagra in man and pigs, blacktongue of dogs, degeneration of nerve cells
   Prevalence of disorders: Fairly common in the South
4. Pyridoxine (B_6)
   Source: Yeast, meat, eggs, nuts, cereals
   Function: Necessary in certain metabolic processes; as pyridoxal phosphate, functions as coenzyme of some of transmitting enzymes
   Lack causes: Failure to grow, together with anemia and dermatitis, in experimental animals; may be necessary for man
   Prevalence of disorders: None known among man
5. Folic acid
   Source: Green leaves, soybeans, yeast, egg yolk
   Function: Essential for growth and formation of blood cells; necessary for certain metabolic processes; labile
   Lack causes: Anemia and sprue in man, hemorrhage of kidneys, bone deformity in chickens
   Prevalence of disorders: Unknown
6. Pantothenic acid
   Source: Eggs, meat, sweet potatoes, cane molasses, milk
   Function: Forms coenzyme A of Krebs cycle metabolism; necessary for normal nerves and skin
   Lack causes: Dermatitis in chicks, graying of fur in black rats
   Prevalence of disorders: None known in man
7. Biotin (H)
   Source: Egg yolk, meat, molasses, fresh fruits, fresh vegetables, yeasts, cereal grains
   Function: Forms coenzyme necessary for carbon dioxide utilization
   Lack causes: Dermatitis in rats and chicks; egg-white injury
   Prevalence of disorders: Few cases reported in man
8. Cyanocobalamin (B_{12})
   Source: Milk, egg yolk, liver, oysters
   Function: Extrinsic factor of antianemic factor for red blood cell formation (erythrocyte maturation factor)
   Lack causes: Pernicious anemia, poor growth and wasting disease in some animals
   Prevalence of disorders: Fairly common

Vitamin C (ascorbic acid) (water-soluble, antiscorbutic vitamin)
   Source: Citrus fruits, tomatoes, cabbage, spinach
   Function: Formation of intercellular material and cement material between epithelial cells of capillary walls; labile
   Lack causes: Scurvy in man and guinea pig
   Prevalence of disorders: Among some on restricted diets

Vitamin D (fat-soluble, antirachitic vitamin, calciferol)
   Source: Eggs, fish oils, beef fat, skin exposure to ultraviolet radiation; precursor in skin, ergosterol
   Function: Regulates calcium and phosphorus metabolism; stable
   Lack causes: Rickets in young
   Prevalence of disorders: Common in congested regions

Vitamin E (alpha-tocopherol) (fat-soluble)
   Source: Green leaves, vegetable fats, wheat germ, meats, eggs
   Function: Nuclear growth and activity, necessary for differentiation in vertebrates
   Lack causes: Sterility in some animals, death of embryos
   Prevalence of disorders: Unknown, doubtful in man

Vitamin K (fat-soluble, antihemorrhagic vitamin)
   Source: Green leaves, spinach, soybean oil, egg yolk, kale, liver
   Function: Synthesis of prothrombin in liver, essential for blood clotting; stable
   Lack causes: Failure of blood to clot
   Prevalence of disorders: Sometimes in newborn infants

CIRCULATORY SYSTEM

The primary purpose of the circulatory system is the transportation of materials throughout the animal body. It serves to regulate the body temperature of warm-blooded animals. It helps regulate the water balance of the body because the blood supplies water to the various tissues and, in turn, receives the excess water formed from metabolic processes. Its white corpuscles and antibody content have developed an effective mechanism for combating disease germs.

Blood is constantly on the move and is constantly changing as it gives up various products and picks up others. Blood is remarkably stable, however, in its component parts, for it has the adaptive power to adjust itself whenever any factor upsets its balance.

Historic background of the study of blood and lymph circulation

Before the time of William Harvey, the English physician, ideas about the circulation of blood were largely erroneous. Centuries before, Galen had taught that air enters the heart from the windpipe and that blood was able to pass from one ventricle to the other through pores in the septum that separated the two. He also believed that the blood flowed first in one direction and then in the other. In 1616 Harvey was able to demonstrate the main facts about blood circulation. He made use of a variety of animals for his experiments, including the little snake found in English meadows. By tying ligatures on arteries, he noticed that the region between the heart and ligature swelled up. When veins were tied off, the swelling occurred beyond the ligature. When blood vessels were cut, blood flowed in arteries from the cut end nearest the heart; the reverse happened in veins. By means of such experiments, Harvey worked out a correct scheme of blood circulation, with the exception of the capillaries that he could not see because he lacked a microscope. It was not until 1628 that Harvey first published his account because of the opposition his results received from his contemporaries.

The Italian Marcello Malpighi was able to complete Harvey's work in 1661 by describing the capillaries in the tissues of the frog's lungs and pointing out their relations to the arteries and veins. He was able to do this by means of the simple lens of that day. Shortly afterward Leeuwenhoek was able to confirm Malpighi's work by observing capillaries in the tails of tadpoles. One of the best and simplest places to see capillaries is in the web of the frog's foot.

Gasparo Aselli, an Italian anatomist, first discovered the nature of lacteals in 1627. In a dog that had recently been fed and cut open, he noticed white cordlike bodies in the mesenteries of the intestine that he first mistook for nerves. When he pricked these cords with a scalpel, a milky fluid gushed out. It is now known that this fluid is largely fat that is carried after digestion to the thoracic duct. The thoracic duct and its relations to the lacteals were discovered by the Frenchman Jean Pecquet in 1647. These vessels are part of the lymphatic system that Thomas Bartholin, a Danish physician, first demonstrated in its general relations in 1653, when he made his investigations on dogs and executed criminals.

The first recorded demonstration of blood pressure was made in 1733 by Stephen Hales, an English clergyman. He tied a horse on its back, exposed the femoral artery in the thigh, and between two ligatures on the artery inserted a cannula in the form of a small brass pipe. To this pipe he fastened a glass tube 9 feet long, which was held in an upright position. When he untied the ligatures on the artery, the blood rose in the glass tube to a distance of more than 8 feet and fluctuated up and down in accordance with the systolic and diastolic heartbeats. The weight of the column of blood indicated the actual blood pressure. Blood pressure is commonly expressed in mercury, which is 13.6 times as heavy as water and is measured in millimeters. Hale's figures, expressed in millimeters of mercury, indicate that the pressure he measured in the horse was between 180 and 200 mm.

Plan of circulatory system

The circulatory system is made up of a system of channels, the **blood vessels,** for carrying the fluid medium; a propulsive organ, the **heart,** which pumps the blood through the body; and a circulating medium, the **blood,** which is kept constantly on the move by the driving action of the heart. In addition, there is a similar cooperating system, the **lymphatic system,** the function of which is to return lymph to the blood. Tissue fluid is formed from blood plasma that has filtered from the blood vessels but is unable to get back directly into the blood capillaries because of blood pressure. Tissue fluid bathes the cells of the tissues directly and carries the digested foods and oxygen that the cells take as needed. In return, the cells lose to the tissue fluid their waste substances—urea and carbon dioxide, which are then collected by the lymph in the lymphatic capillaries.

Body fluids

The fluid blood bears an intimate relation to the fluid balance of the body in its physiologic action. Body fluids, which are mostly water, with some electrolytes (ions) and nonelectrolytes, are distributed throughout the body both within and outside tissue cells. For convenience, these fluids may be thought of as compartmentalized into two large physiologic units, although each compartmental unit represents an aggregate of many smaller ones. According to this concept, the body fluids are found in two major compartments—the **intracellular,** or within the cell, and the **extracellular,** or outside the cell. The extracellular compartment may also be subdivided into **plasma** and **intercellular** (interstitial) compartments. The plasma is found in the blood vessels, and the intercellular fluids are found everywhere else outside the blood vessels and outside the tissue cells. The body weight is made up of more than 60% fluids, of which about 40% is intracellular and 20% extracellular. Of the extracellular fluids, plasma accounts for about 5% and the intercellular or interstitial (also called tissue fluid) accounts for about 15%. In terms of quarts the intracellular fluid makes up about 28 and the extracellular about 17, of which 3 is plasma (body weight of about 154 pounds).

Because there is constant interchange between the plasma and the interstitial fluid, the composition of these two fluids is about the same, except that the plasma has more proteins that are too large to pass through the capillary pores into the interstitial fluid. The intracellular fluid has a different composition than the extracellular fluid, especially in electrolytes. The fluids in the different compartments remain very stable in normal conditions, although there is a constant shift from one compartment to the other. In this shift, electrolytes and proteins play important roles.

Open and closed circulatory systems

In higher forms the circulatory system is a **closed** one in which the blood is confined to tubes throughout its course from the heart back to the heart. Among most invertebrates, part of the system is made up of well-developed blood vessels that pass from the heart to the body tissues; but there they open into spaces

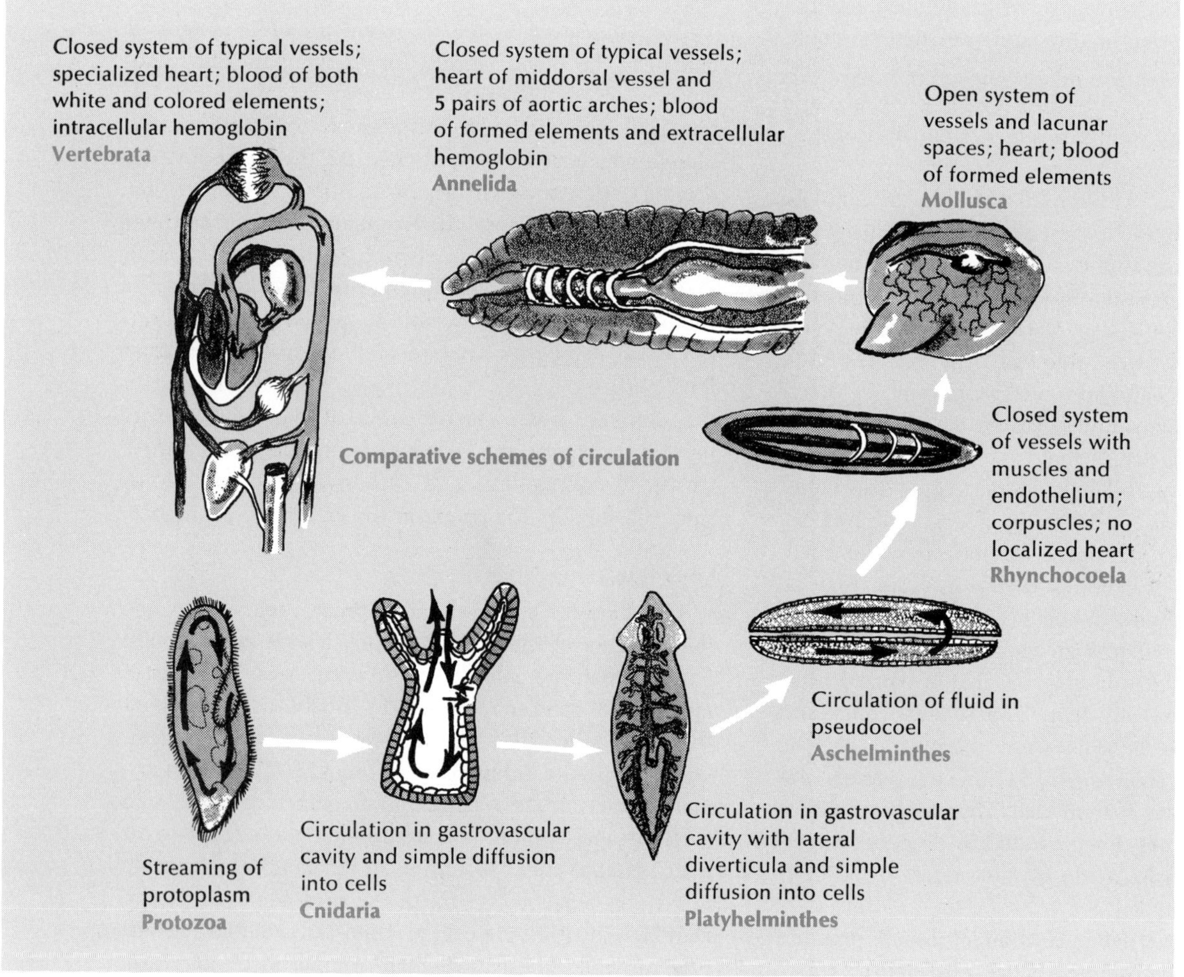

FIG. 31-9

Comparative schemes of circulation among different animals.

(**lacunae**) where the blood comes directly into contact with the cells. From these intercellular spaces blood returns to the heart. This latter arrangement is called an **open** system. A closed system keeps the blood moving rapidly through its various channels but requires an auxiliary lymphatic system where the fluid flow is slow and the tissue cells are bathed directly with the nutritive tissue fluid. The closed system is a far more efficient system for animals of large size and active habits, for a complete circulation of blood occurs in a matter of minutes or less.

The circulatory system has penetrated to nearly every part of the body, but there are a few places where blood vessels do not go. These regions are the epidermis of the skin, cornea of the eye, cartilage tissue, enamel of the teeth, feathers, hair, and a few others. Nutritive fluids from blood vessels reach many of these through interstitial spaces by a process called **seepage.**

Circulation in invertebrates

In a protozoan, food products and oxygen are taken into the cell and distributed, and the waste is eliminated by diffusion. In more complicated animals some cells are too far away to be in direct contact with food and oxygen, and some means had to be provided to carry these substances to them and to remove their metabolic wastes. In the sponges (Porifera) the extensive system of canals is sufficient to carry the food-laden water near enough to all the cells. Among coelenterates and flatworms the gastrovascular cavity serves a similar function because all cells are bathed with fluid or else are close enough to profit from direct diffusion. The development of a separate vascular system arose after a complete digestive system (tube-within-a-tube) evolved. Nemertean worms have a few blood vessels in

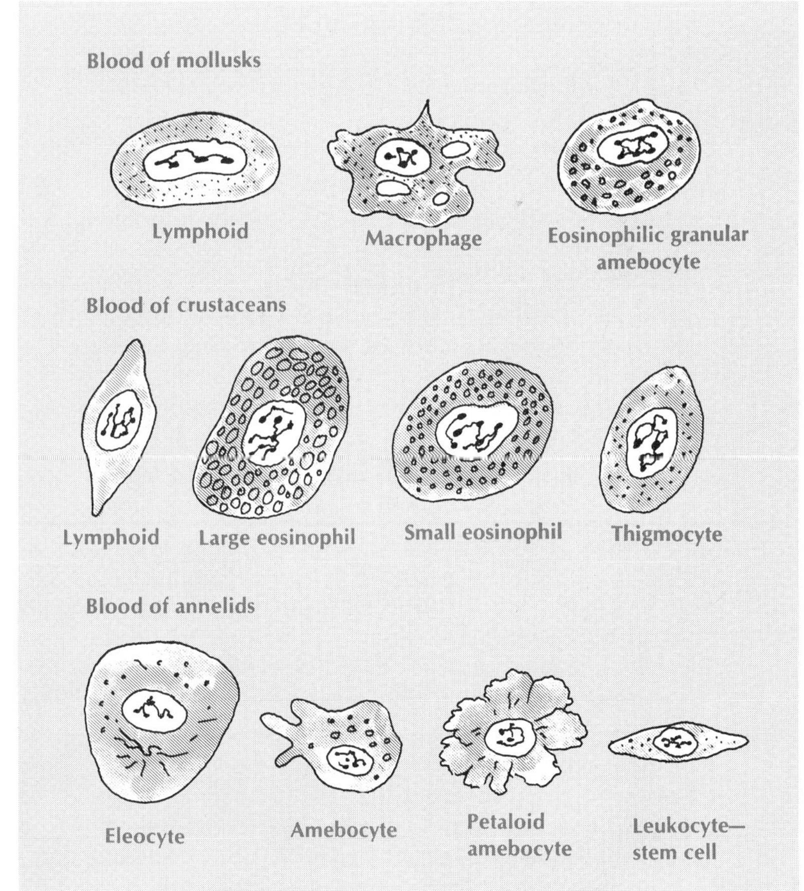

FIG. 31-10

Types of blood cells in blood of three invertebrate groups. Basic blood cell is leukocyte (white cell), but in some invertebrates, prototypes of all vertebrate blood cells may be found, although they are not homologous to vertebrate blood cells. Most invertebrate respiratory pigments (hemoglobin or erythrocruorin, hemocyanin, etc.) are extracellular, not intracellular as in vertebrates. Some sea cucumbers have blood cells that carry respiratory pigments. Insect blood usually has no respiratory pigments.

which the blood is propelled by the "milking" action of the muscular walls of the vessels.

The heart as a definite propulsive organ appears in the mollusk, annelid, and arthropod (Fig. 31-9). These are provided with well-developed vascular systems, although the arthropods and mollusks have the open or lacunar system. In the earthworm, in which a closed system is approached, the true heart is the dorsal blood vessel that forces the blood into the paired aortic arches (so-called "hearts"). The invertebrate heart is always located dorsal to the digestive tract.

The fluid media of invertebrates varies greatly (Fig. 31-10). In some it is mostly water, with some nutrients, dissolved gases, and waste; in others it is more like the lymph of vertebrate animals, with a greater protein content and less water. Respiratory pigments for carrying oxygen, especially in the higher invertebrates, may also be found.

The white blood cells (**hemocytes**) of insects have been found to vary greatly with the species, stages of development, and physiologic states. In holometabolous insects, for instance, the hemocyte count is much higher in the larval and pupal stages than in the adult. There are also variations in their number, types, and behavior during ecdysis and during pathologic conditions of disease, wounds, toxins, coagulation of blood, etc.

Circulation in vertebrates

Among vertebrates the circulatory systems are all provided with hearts, arteries, capillaries, and veins, with about the same plan of arrangement. The hearts of vertebrates have two, three, or four chambers. In the evolution of the higher vertebrates from lower ones, the principal changes in circulation have involved the heart in the transformation from gill to lung breathing. These changes have thus been brought about as an adaptation from an aquatic to a terrestrial life. Embryologically the heart develops from a tube that becomes modified into a series of chambers. The fish heart consists of two main chambers, auricle and ventricle, and two subsidiary chambers, sinus venosus and conus arteriosus. These four chambers are arranged in a row (tandem): sinus venosus, auricle, ventricle, and conus arteriosus. Fish have a **single-circuit** heart; that is, the blood passes through it only once in each complete circuit. Blood from veins passes through the **sinus venosus** (the receiving chamber of the heart) to the **auricle,** then to the **ventricle** (the muscular pumping chamber), and finally to the **conus arteriosus.** From here the blood is passed through the ventral aorta to the gills, to be oxygenated, and then through the dorsal aorta to all parts of the body. After passing through the capillary system of the various organs, the blood is returned by veins to the heart. In this circuit the blood has passed through two **capillary systems,** one in the gills and the other in the organ tissues.

In land forms a number of changes occurred correlated with the introduction of a new secondary circuit that returns oxygenated blood from the lungs to the heart before making a second circuit throughout the body. The first change in the evolution of the heart to meet this new plan was in lungfish and the Crossopterygii, in which the auricle is partially divided into a larger right and smaller left auricular chamber that receives blood from the swim bladder. The ventricle also shows the beginning of a division. The conus in these forms is also divided by a spiral septum in such a way that the arterial blood goes to the body and the venous blood goes to the swim bladder or lungs.

Amphibians and most reptiles have a three-chambered heart. A partition divides the auricle into left and right portions. The sinus venosus opens into the right auricle, and a vein from the lungs empties into the left auricle. Pulmonary arteries carry blood to the lungs. There is some mixing of aerated and nonaerated blood in the ventricle so that this arrangement cannot be called a complete double circuit.

In alligators and crocodiles the ventricle is also divided into left and right halves, and the four-chambered heart appears for the first time.

Birds and mammals have the four-chambered heart, and there are now two circuits, one through the lungs (**pulmonary**) and one through the body (**systemic**). The course of the blood in this double-circuit arrangement may be summarized as follows. The systemic circulation starts with the left ventricle. Blood passes through the aorta and its branches to all parts of the body and then into the capillary bed within the tissues; veins collect the blood from the capillaries and carry it back to the right auricle. Pulmonary circulation starts in the right auricle. Blood passes into the right ventricle and through the pulmonary artery to the lungs, where the gaseous exchange is made; it returns by veins to the left auricle and then to the left ventricle. In this complete circulation the blood has passed through the heart twice. The right side of the heart handles oxygen-poor blood, the left side, freshly oxygenated blood.

In the four-chambered heart plan there is a capillary bed in each circuit—the lungs in the pulmonary and the organ tissues in the systemic circuit. There is at least one marked exception to this principle in the systemic circuit—the **hepatic portal system,** which collects blood from capillary beds of the stomach, pancreas, intestine, and spleen and conducts it by way of the portal vein to the liver, where the vein breaks up into sinusoids. The latter unite to form the hepatic veins that empty into the inferior vena cava to the heart. All vertebrate classes, except mammals, have a **renal portal system** by which venous blood from the caudal regions of the body passes through a capillary network in the kidneys.

The advantages of the two-circuit over the one-circuit plan are many. There is no mixing of the oxygen-rich blood and the oxygen-poor blood in the two-circuit scheme; the blood in the aorta contains relatively more oxygen; a higher metabolic rate is thus possible; and a resulting higher temperature can be maintained in the animal body.

FIG. 31-11

Fate of aortic arches among different classes of vertebrates (see text for description). Although prototypic condition in embryonic fish and tetrapods is considered to be six pairs of aortic arches, greater number was probably found in primitive vertebrates. Some existing cyclostomes have as many as fifteen pairs. Since lungs, or their homologous forerunners (air bladders), are primitive, pulmonary artery is thought to have arisen as a branch from sixth aortic arch even among placoderm fish, but such an artery is mostly absent among modern fish.

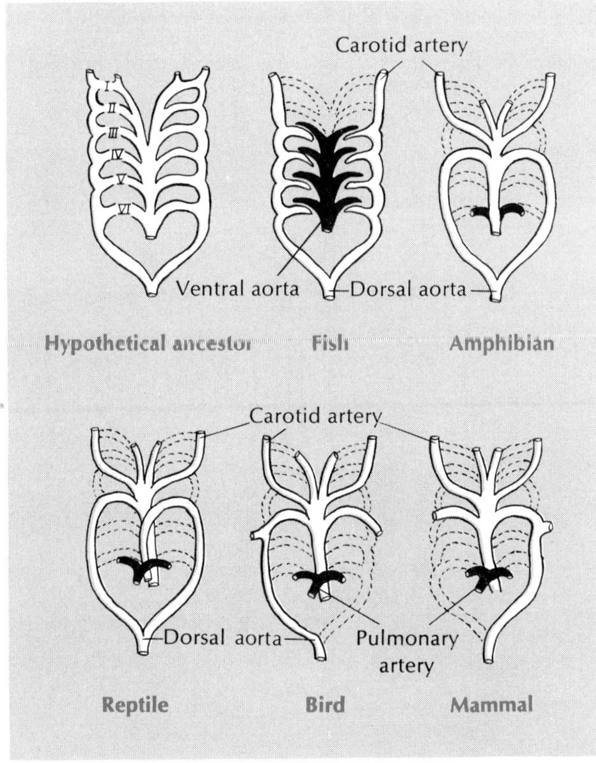

Aortic arches (Fig. 31-11). In the transition from water to land, there are also correlative changes in the aortic arches. In the embryos of all vertebrates there are six pairs of aortic arches that pass from the ventral aorta at the anterior end of the heart, run between the gill slits of the pharynx, and connect with the dorsal aorta. In this plan there is a pair of arches (blood vessels) for each pair of gills. When animals evolved lungs, only a single pair of blood vessels was necessary to supply them. In the course of evolutionary development some of these arches were lost and others underwent transformations. To understand the modifications that have taken place in these arches, they are numbered 1 to 6, beginning at the anterior end. The first two pairs are lost early, and arches 3 to 6 represent the ones found in adult fish. In consequence of the development of lungs, arch 3 on each side loses its connection with the dorsal aorta and becomes the carotid artery. Arch 5 disappears and arch 6 forms the pulmonary arteries to the lungs. Arch 4 remains as the only connection with the dorsal aorta. In higher amphibians and reptiles, this arch is paired; in birds, only the right arch persists; and in mammals, only the left.

The heart and its physiology

The first mechanism for propelling the fluid blood is the contraction of the muscular walls of the blood vessels themselves. This "milking" action is the only kind of propulsion among animals such as the nemertean worms, annelids, and some others. Mollusks and arthropods have more specialized hearts that are divided into chambers and possess valves to prevent backflow of blood. In the embryonic development of the heart the wall of the endocardial tube becomes the **endocardium** (lining membrane); the muscular wall that forms around the tube, the **myocardium** (cardiac muscle); and a thin layer that develops around the outside of the heart, the **pericardium.**

The vertebrate heart is ventral to the alimentary canal—just the opposite of the invertebrate heart that is dorsal. Birds have proportionately larger hearts than other vertebrates. Small animals usually have larger hearts in proportion to their size than do the larger forms. The heart is also larger in wild animals than it is in domestic animals of the same size. The adult human heart weighs 9 to 11 ounces and is a little larger in males than in females.

The heart is really a complex network of cardiac muscle fibers that branch and fuse in most directions and planes. The dark lines (intercalated disks) represent the end-to-end attachments of the cardiac muscles. Because of this arrangement, the heart beats as a unit and obeys the **"all-or-none" laws**; that is, if heart muscle beats at all, it does so to its maximum effect. The **refractory period,** or period of nonirritability and noncontractility, is very long in heart muscle. This prevents the heart from overworking. The heartbeat is rhythmic and automatic, but it can be influenced by nervous control, by temperature, and by certain salts in the blood plasma, as well as by certain hormones. In the four-chambered heart (Fig. 31-12) the valve between the right auricle and right ventricle is the **tricuspid**; that between the left auricle and left ventricle, the **bicuspid** or **mitral.** Where the big arteries, the **pulmonary** from the right ventricle and the **aorta** from the left ventricle, leave the heart, **semilunar valves** prevent backflow. These valves are the only remnants of the conus arteriosus found in other classes of vertebrates. In the hearts of birds and mammals the sinus venosus has been incorporated into the right auricle.

In the heart of man and some other mammals there is a special conducting tissue concerned with the instigation and regulation of the heartbeat (Fig. 31-13). This specialized tissue, called **nodal tissue,** is necessary because of the functional separation of the auricles from the ventricles, since there is no muscular connection between these chambers. To produce a functional stimulation of the auricles and ventricular beats, this nodal tissue conducts impulses so rapidly to the ventricles that all parts of them contract almost simultaneously. This special conducting tissue is made up of the **sinoatrial**

FIG. 31-12

Internal structure of mammalian heart.

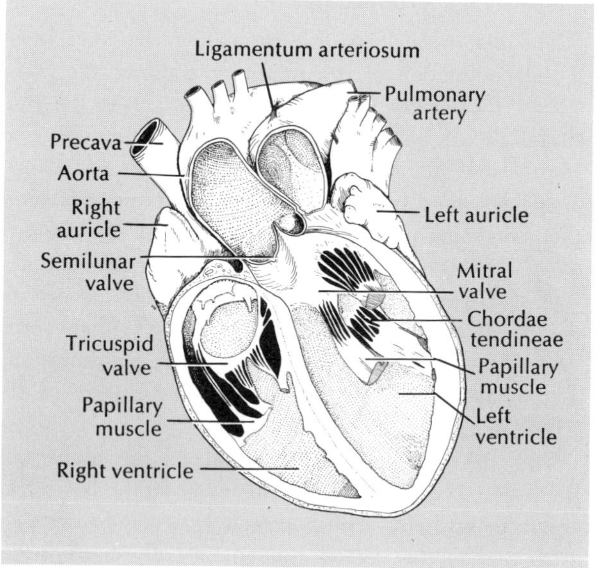

FIG. 31-13

Scheme of neuromuscular mechanism of conduction in mammalian heart. Arrows indicate spread of waves of excitation. Sinus venosus of frog heart is present in mammalian heart as vestigial nodule in right auricle near entrance of large veins. This nodule is called sinoauricular node (S-A) and is pacemaker of heart. From this node, wave of contraction spreads over auricles at rate of about 1 meter per second and then down to auriculoventricular (A-V) node and over the ventricles at 5 meters per second. The more rapid ventricular rate is made possible by His-Tawara (A-V) bundle and Purkinje fiber system, which are specialized myocardium for conducting impulses through heart septum. This produces simultaneous contraction of ventricles to ensure efficient pumping of blood through semilunar valves at their location.

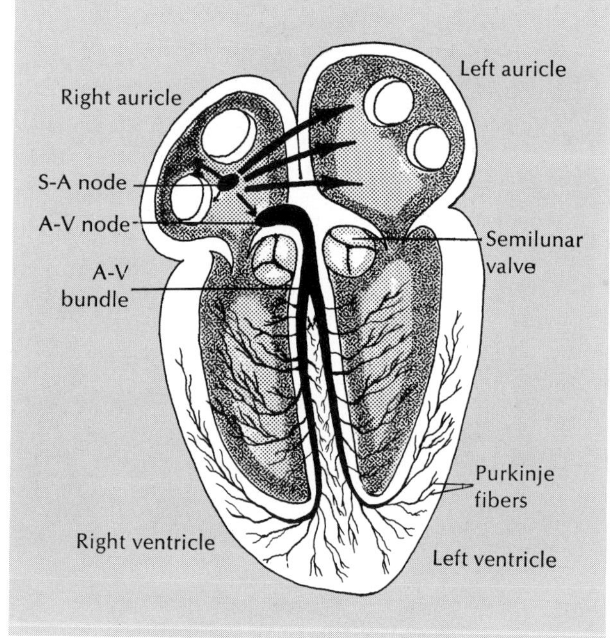

node (S-A node), commonly called the pacemaker, in the right auricle, the **atrioventricular node (A-V node)** between the auricles, and the Purkinje network of modified muscle fibers that pass to all parts of the ventricular walls (Fig. 31-13).

The rate of heart beat is under the nervous control of a heart-rate center located in the floor of the fourth ventricle of the medulla (Fig. 31-14). This control center consists of a cardioaccelerator center and a cardioinhibitor center that are functionally independent, but are located close together. Two sets of motor nerves pass from the control center to the heart. One set passes by way of the sympathetic nerve trunk and accelerates the heart rate, and the other set by the vagus nerve decreases the heart rate. Both sets terminate in the sinoatrial node where they increase or decrease the frequency of impulses. When certain afferent (sensory) nerves in the wall of the vena cava are stimulated by distension of the vessel, they carry impulses to the heart-rate center, resulting in a decrease of inhibition and an increase in acceleration. Sensory nerves in the walls of the aortic arch and carotid sinus, when stimulated by increased blood pressure in the aorta and carotid sinus, slow the heart by conducting impulses to the heart center via the vagus nerve. The action of these two feedback mechanisms provides a nice adjustment to the metabolic demands of the body. Correlated with these reflexes is another system of reflexes that alters the blood pressure in the arterioles through the vasomotor center of vasoconstrictors and dilators.

In vertebrates and mollusks the hearts are myogenic (the pacemaker activity originates in the muscle or modified muscle); in the majority of crustaceans and insects the hearts are neurogenic (the pacemaker activity originates in ganglion cells).

Heart muscle has a unique blood supply. Capillaries actually penetrate into the fibers of heart muscle. This

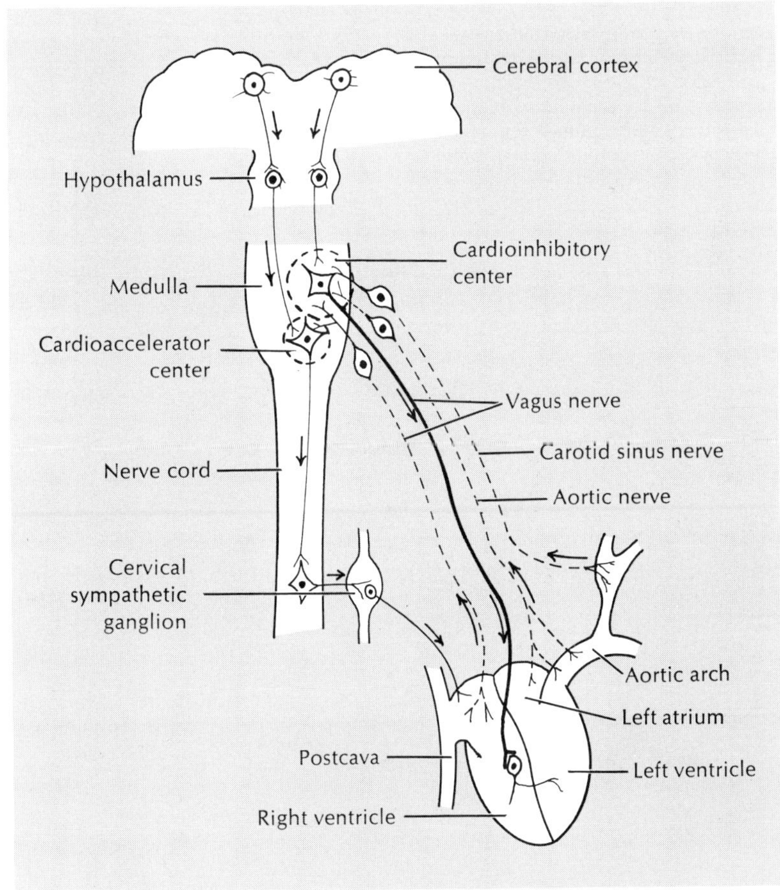

FIG. 31-14

Nervous control of heart. (See text for description.)

arrangement ensures a quick and efficient blood supply to an organ that must keep going. Heart muscle is also well supplied with **sarcosomes,** granules that may contain enzymes.

The cycle of heartbeat consists of a contraction, or **systole,** of the heart muscle followed by its relaxation, or **diastole.** The rate of heartbeat depends on many factors such as age, sex, fevers, metabolic rates, etc. Its normal rate is about 70 to 80 beats per minute. The auricles contract first, followed by the contraction of the ventricles. During a part of the cycle all the chambers are in a relaxed condition. When the heart beats, characteristic sounds can be picked up by a stethoscope ("lubb-dup"). They are supposed to be produced by the closure of the heart valves, the contraction of the ventricular muscles, and the closure of the semilunar valves. The heart muscle, when in action, produces **action currents** that can be picked up and recorded by a sensitive **electrocardiograph.** Each beat produces a characteristic graph that reveals a great deal about the normal or abnormal functioning of the heart (Fig. 31-15).

FIG. 31-15

Normal and abnormal electrocardiograms. Electrocardiogram (ECG) gives a record of action potential associated with contraction of heart muscle. The ECG normally has a definite pattern, and irregularities in heartbeat deflections indicate that heart is not beating normally. In normal pattern, **A,** P wave is associated with atrial contraction, QRS complex with ventricular activity, and T wave with repolarization of ventricles. In **B** a myocardial infarction (a region of blood flow interference in heart muscle) is indicated by prominent Q wave, elevation of the S-T segment, and inversion of T wave.

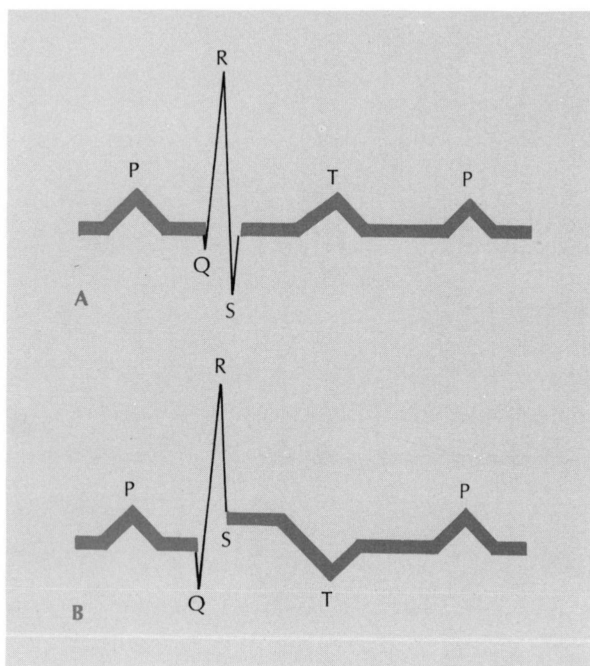

When an individual is resting, the normal heart pumps about 75 ml. of blood each beat; but at maximum output, it can increase this to 200 ml. each beat. During severe exercise, the rate may increase from 70 to more than 150 beats per minute. This increase is effected by several factors: (1) stretching the heart muscle by the distension of the chambers with blood (**law of the heart**); (2) increasing the carbon dioxide of the blood; (3) increasing the temperature that affects the pacemaker of the heart; (4) the **Bainbridge reflex,** or the stimulating effect of a large amount of blood in the right auricle; (5) hormones, such as adrenaline and thyroxine; and (6) the two sets of nerves—sympathetic and parasympathetic.

Physiologic anatomy of blood vessels

In the vertebrate such as man, blood passes through three types of blood vessels, **arteries, capillaries,** and **veins** in a complete circulation. Arteries carry blood from the heart to the tissues; veins return blood from the tissues to the heart. Ordinarily, arteries carry aerated blood, but the pulmonary artery carries nonaerated blood; veins usually carry nonaerated blood, but the pulmonary veins carry aerated blood.

The structures among the different arteries and veins

FIG. 31-16

Cross section of vein and corresponding artery.

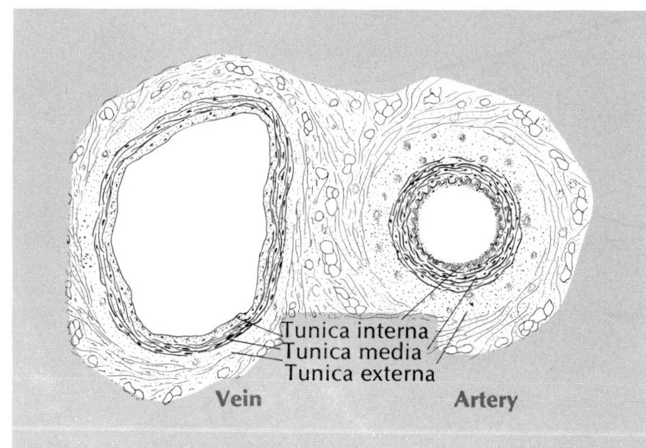

are correlated with their functions. All arteries and veins are typically made up of three coats, or layers (Fig. 31-16): (1) an outer (**tunica externa**), composed mostly of connective tissue; (2) a middle (**tunica media**), composed of connective tissue and muscle; and (3) an inner (**tunica interna**), composed of connective tissue and endothelial lining. The connective tissue components enable the vessels to withstand pressure; the muscle regulates the amount of blood delivered to an organ; and the endothelium affords a smooth surface for the lumen in which the blood flows. Even the smallest arteries (arterioles) have all these coats, but they are thinner and have fewer components. The arteries, as they pass from the heart to the capillary bed, tend to shed parts of their coats until the **capillaries** have walls composed of little more than the endothelium. Capillaries effect the exchange of food and gases between the tissues and blood because the walls of other blood vessels are too thick for diffusion. Capillaries are found in enormous numbers, forming extensive networks in nearly all tissues. In muscle there are said to be more than 2,000 per square millimeter, or 1,250,000 per square inch. Their diameter rarely exceeds 10 μ and in some the blood corpuscles literally have to squeeze through their lumens.

There are also other tiny channels that resemble capillaries. One type is the **sinusoids,** which are found in the spleen, suprarenal gland, liver, and bone marrow. Sinusoids have a large, irregular caliber and an incomplete lining of scattered cells that may be phagocytic (reticuloendothelial system). Sinusoids connect arterioles with venules or venules with venules. Another type is the **rete mirabile,** which is a plexus of capillaries found in the course of an arteriole or venule. A good example is the renal glomerulus, where a network of capillaries connect an afferent arteriole with an efferent arteriole. The swim bladder of some fish also has a rete mirabile.

Veins have three coats also, but they differ in having thinner walls and no elastic connective tissue. A vein is about twice the cross section of its corresponding artery. Veins, especially in the lower parts of the body are provided with **valves** to prevent the backflow of blood.

The difference in blood flow in the various blood vessels depends on the cross-sectional area of the blood vessels, the flow being inversely proportional to the cross-sectional area. All the blood has to pass through the aorta, which divides into smaller and still smaller arteries, until the smallest arteries discharge into the capillary network. Although these branches of the aorta are smaller than the aorta, their total cross-sectional area is much greater. The ratio between the cross-sectional area of the aorta and all the body capillaries is about 1 to 800. Most arteries have a rate of flow of 300 to 500 mm. per second; in the capillaries, the flow is from 0.5 to 1 mm. per second. The blood flow in the veins is about one half that of corresponding arteries.

The flow from the heart into the aorta is intermittent, that is, pulsatile. This is due to the intermittent heartbeat with its systolic and diastolic rhythm. By the time the blood reaches the capillaries, it has become a steady flow (nonpulsative). This steady flow in the capillaries is due to the stretch and elastic recoil of the arterial walls that keeps the blood moving. The alternating stretching and contracting of the arterial walls produced by the intermittent discharge of the blood from the heart into the aorta gives rise to the pressure **pulse,** which passes along the arterial wall at the rate of 5 to 8 meters per second. The frequency of the pulse is identical with the ventricular beat of the heart. The time for a complete circuit of blood through the body naturally varies with the size, kind of animal, etc. It is obtained by injecting a dye or tagged atoms into a vein and timing their appearance in an artery of the corresponding region. Some rates are man, 23 to 25 seconds; dog, 16 to 17 seconds; rabbit, 7 to 8 seconds; crabs, 38 to 65 seconds; cockroaches, 5 to 6 minutes.

Blood pressure is the pressure against the walls of the blood vessels produced by the discharge of blood from the heart. It shows a marked gradient of pressure, being greatest in the arteries near the heart and dropping gradually in the more distant arteries, to decline markedly in the small arterioles and capillaries. In the veins the pressure drops still more, until it reaches the veins near the heart, where there may be a negative pressure (below atmospheric pressure). It is blood pressure that keeps the blood moving and keeps supplying the capillaries with a steady stream of blood. Several factors influence blood pressure, such as the blood output of the heart, the peripheral resistance offered by the arterioles and capillaries, the viscosity of the blood, the volume of blood, and the elasticity of the arteries. If the heart speeds up or there is an increase of the resistance of the blood vessels to blood flow, blood pressure will be elevated (Fig. 31-17).

There are two phases of arterial blood pressure—

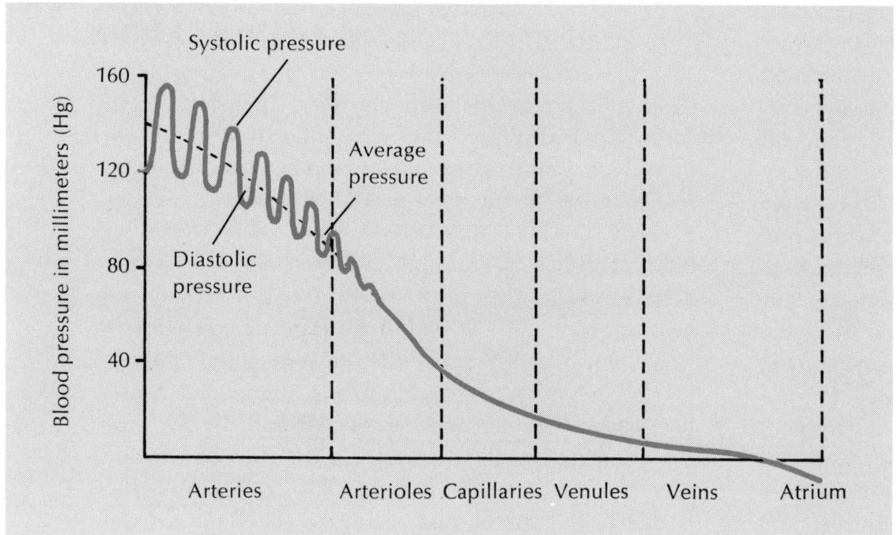

FIG. 31-17

Blood pressure in different parts of cardiovascular system. Blood pressure is highest when blood is leaving heart and lowest in large veins, where pressure may be less than atmospheric pressure (below zero) near heart because of the negative pressure in chest cavity.

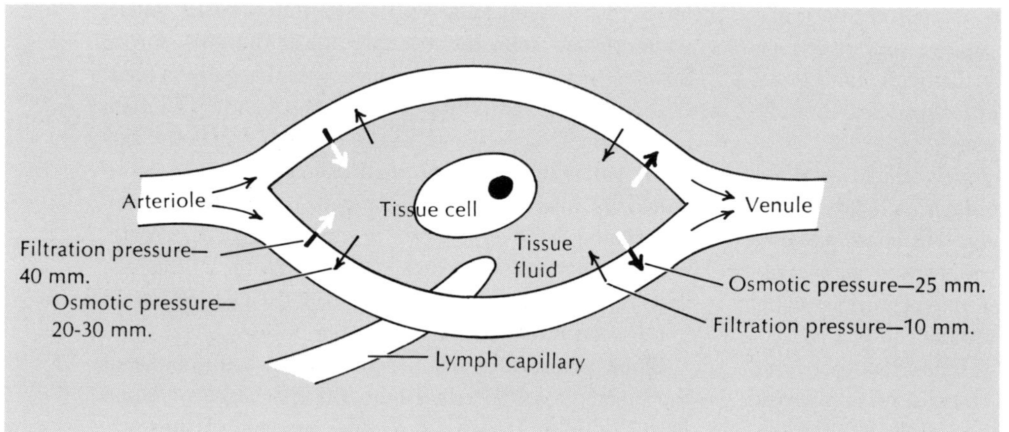

FIG. 31-18

Exchange of materials in a capillary bed. Two direction forces are involved. Blood pressure in capillary produces a filtration, tending to drive fluid and its dissolved substances out of capillary; blood proteins tend to draw fluid into capillary. Large arrows indicate the greater of these forces. At arteriole end of capillary bed, filtration pressure is greater than osmotic pressure; at venule end the reverse occurs. Normally, blood volume remains constant because these forces tend to balance each other. The small difference is returned by lymphatic system.

systolic and **diastolic.** The difference between these two pressures is the **pulse pressure.** In man the systolic pressure is around 120 mm. of mercury; the diastolic, about 80 mm. of mercury. Blood pressure is taken by means of a device called the **sphygmomanometer,** and its measurement is a routine practice in medical diagnosis. Blood pressure plays an important role in the exchange of materials in the capillaries. Within the capillaries blood pressure is about 20 to 40 mm. This is the **filtration pressure.** As a contrary force, there is the osmotic pressure of the blood proteins that tends to move water into the capillaries (Fig. 31-18). This osmotic pressure is around 20 to 30 mm. The difference between the filtration pressure and the osmotic pressure determines the direction the water and its dissolved substances will go. If the filtration pressure is greater, the water will be forced out into the tissue spaces; if the osmotic pressure is the greater, water will enter the capillaries. There are conditions when one or the other of these two forces is dominant. Normally the water that passes out of the blood equals that which comes in.

Blood vessels are under the control of the **vasomotor system,** which has both constrictor (sympathetic) and dilator (parasympathetic) fibers. Whenever the vasoconstrictor center located in the medulla is stimulated the arterioles and capillaries constrict and blanching occurs. On the other hand, stimulation of the dilator

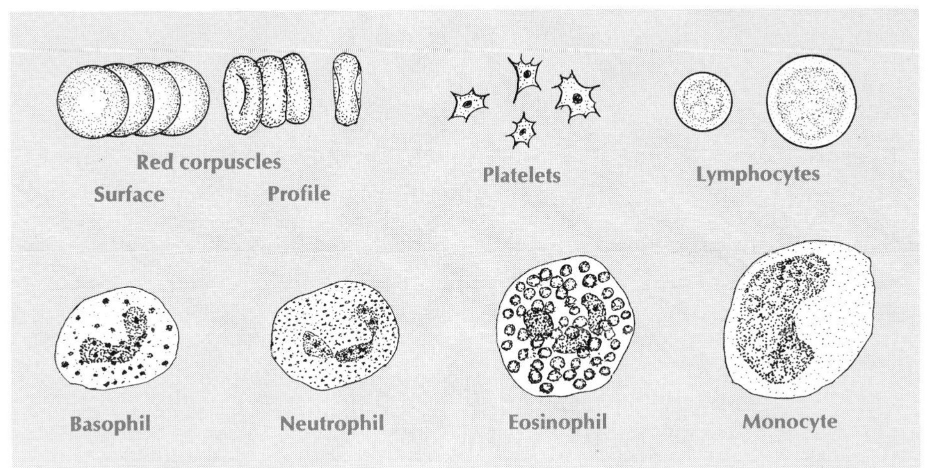

FIG. 31-19
Formed elements of human blood.

nerves causes the blood vessels to increase in diameter and flushing takes place.

Blood and its functions

The fluid medium, **blood,** is a liquid tissue composed of several kinds of cells (formed elements) and an intercellular fluid (plasma). The amount in man is 5 to 6 liters, about 7% or 8% of body weight. It transports oxygen and food products to the tissues and removes carbon dioxide and other wastes, provides for the proper distribution of water throughout the body, equalizes and controls the body temperature, carries hormones from glands to their place of action, maintains the acid or basic reaction of the body fluids, and defends the body against disease germs by its white cells and antibodies.

By volume, blood is 55% plasma and 45% formed elements (corpuscles). **Plasma** is more than 90% water and 8% to 10% solids. Plasma is a variable solution containing glucose, proteins, amino acids, fats, salts, enzymes, hormones, antibodies, and gases. It has some fairly stable constituents: plasma proteins (serum albumin, serum globulin, fibrinogen), about 7%; the inorganic salts (chlorides, sulfates, carbonates, etc.), 0.9%; and glucose, about 0.1%.

The formed elements of the blood are the **red blood corpuscles** (erythrocytes), **white blood corpuscles** (leukocytes), **platelets,** and cell fragments (Fig. 31-19). Erythrocytes are nonnucleated biconcave disks 7 to 8 μ in diameter. They are made up of a stroma framework of protein, lecithin, and other substances and a red iron-bearing pigment, **hemoglobin.** They number about 5,500,000 per cubic millimeter in the male and about 5,000,000 per cubic millimeter in the female. Babies have more and the aged have fewer than these figures. Hemoglobin of the erythrocyte is specialized for carrying oxygen. A human hemoglobin molecule consists of four polypeptide subunits arranged in two identical pairs called alpha and beta chains. The molecule also contains four iron-bearing heme groups. During the early part of gestation, fetal hemoglobin has a different beta chain than in the adult condition and has a greater oxygen affinity. Each 100 ml. of blood contains about 16 grams of hemoglobin, which is able to transport about 20 ml. of oxygen.

Hemopoiesis refers to the formation and development of blood corpuscles. This occurs in several tissues (liver, spleen, etc.) during embryonic existence but is restricted mainly to the red bone marrow in the adult. The red blood corpuscles in their early development have nuclei and undergo mitosis. After the cells acquire hemoglobin their nuclei degenerate, and they become typical erythrocytes. Recent work indicates that a hormone, **erythropoietin,** is produced in the glomeruli of the kidney and regulates in some way the formation of erythrocytes. Investigations show that this hormone in excess will cause an excess of reticulocytes (immature red blood corpuscles) and an excess of red blood corpuscles in the blood. The kidney is stimulated to produce erythropoietin by hemorrhage, high altitudes, cobalt, and other agents. The life-span of red blood corpuscles, according to tracer experiments, appears to be about four months; they are destroyed by certain cells in the liver and spleen. Most of the iron is salvaged to be used over again, and other parts of the hemoglobin

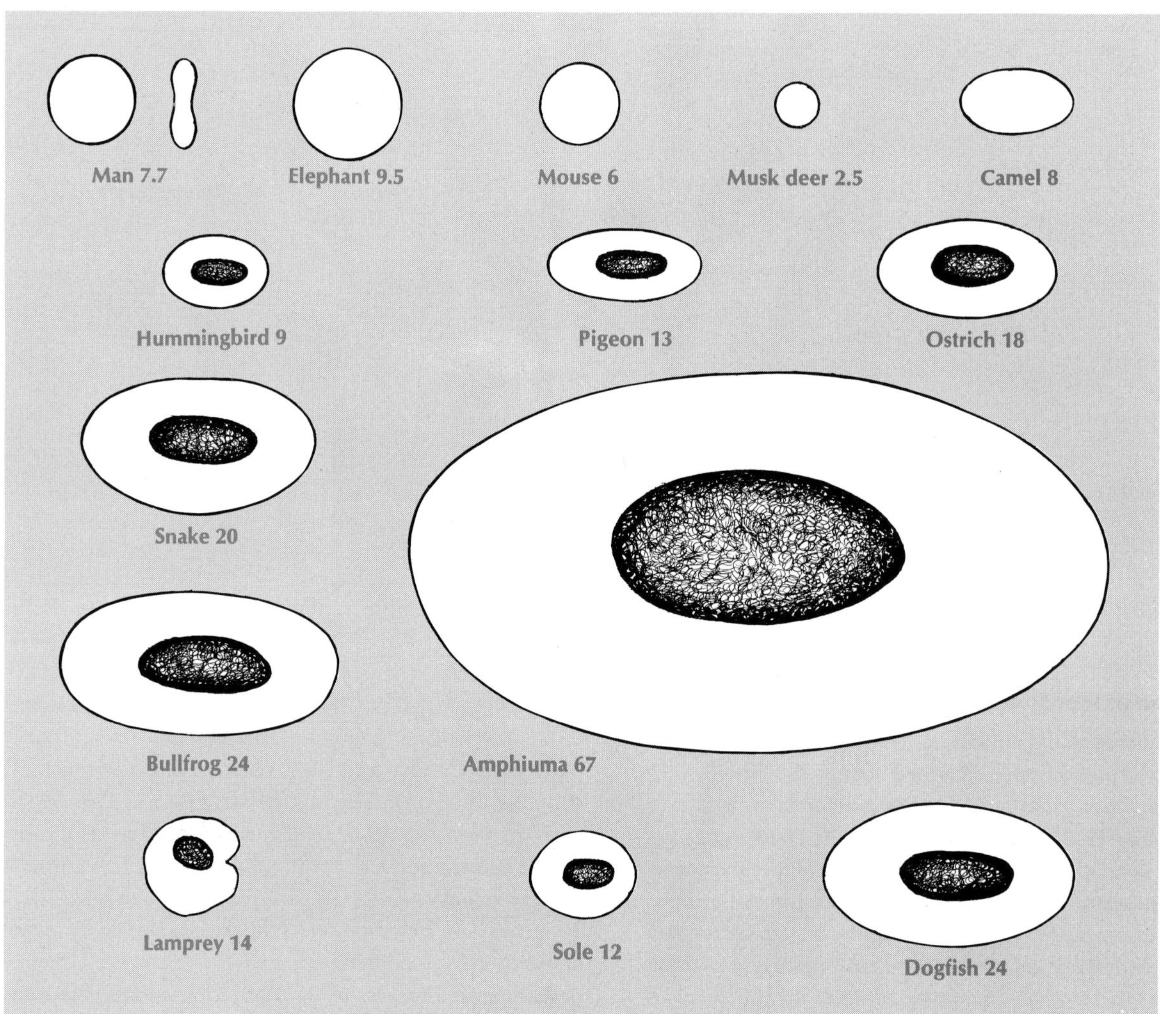

FIG. 31-20

Comparative sizes and shapes of red blood corpuscles of various vertebrate animals. Number following name of each animal indicates the mean of greatest diameter in microns. It will be seen that mammalian erythrocytes are all nonnucleated and are all flattened or biconcave disks except those of camels, which have ellipsoidal cells. All other vertebrate red blood corpuscles are nucleated. Only lamprey among vertebrates has irregularly shaped corpuscle. (Modified from Orton and others.)

are converted into bile pigments. During every second of our existence, many millions of red cells are destroyed in our bodies. The red blood corpuscles vary in size and number among the different vertebrates (Fig. 31-20).

The **white blood corpuscles**, or leukocytes, are much fewer in number than the red (5,000 to 10,000 per cubic millimeter) and are each provided with a nucleus but with no hemoglobin. The ratio of white cells to red cells is about 1 to 700. Many of them are larger than erythrocytes and have active ameboid movement. They can pass through the walls of the capillaries, which the red cells cannot do. Their different types and percentages are given as follows:

Nongranular	
Lymphocytes	20%-25% of total white cells
Monocytes	2%-6% of total white cells
Granulocytes	
Neutrophils	60%-70% of total white cells
Eosinophils	3%-4% of total white cells
Basophils	0.5% of total white cells

The chief function of white blood cells is to defend the body against disease germs. Some of them (monocytes) have great power to engulf bacteria; in others this power is limited. The proportion of white cells of each type is obtained by a **differential white cell count.** The variations in this count have some significance in the diagnosis of certain diseases. The origin of the leukocytes varies. Lymphocytes are produced in the lymphoid tissues (lymph nodes, tonsils, spleen, etc.); monocytes, in the spleen and connective tissue; and the others, in red bone marrow. Their life-span is unknown, but it is thought to be much shorter than that of the red corpuscles.

Lymphocytes as well as certain connective tissue cells form the basis of **immunity** by producing antibodies that can destroy or neutralize toxic molecules (antigens). Many disease microorganisms are antigens. Antigen-antibody reactions are usually specific; and agglutinins, or antibodies, may be built up in serum against almost any foreign agent. **Histamine** is sometimes produced or released during the neutralization of antigens and causes extensive vasodilatation, or fall in blood pressure. Mast cells (connective tissue) or basophilic leukocytes have been found recently to be the chief source of histamine.

The other formed element of blood is the **platelet,** or thrombocyte. Platelets are tiny bodies about one fourth the diameter of red corpuscles; they are colorless and nonnucleated. They originate in the bone marrow from giant cells (megakaryocytes). Their number shows considerable variation, being recorded as anywhere from 250,000 to 600,000 per cubic millimeter. They are supposed to be the source of thromboplastin, which initiates blood clotting. Lower vertebrates lack platelets but have spindle cells instead.

Coagulation of blood

Blood clotting is to prevent excessive loss of blood from the body. In some invertebrates, such as the crayfish and insects, loss of blood and body fluid is prevented by a **spasmic** contraction of the muscles in the walls of the blood vessels. Their blood pressure is very low and actually may be negative. Coagulation of blood is a function of the plasma. One of the constituents of blood proteins is the soluble **fibrinogen.** When tissue cells are damaged in a wound, a substance, **thromboplastin,** is liberated from disintegrated platelets and from the damaged tissue as well. Thromboplastin in the presence of calcium salts changes the inactive **prothrombin** in blood plasma to the active enzyme **thrombin** (thrombase). Thrombin then converts fibrinogen into fibrin. The mass of fibrin threads entangles the red blood corpuscles and the **clot** is formed. The clot later shrinks and squeezes out the **blood serum.** The clotting time in man is 4 to 5 minutes; in horses, it is longer.

The detailed mechanism of blood coagulation is still somewhat obscure. An antihemophilic factor (AHF) is supposed to promote the rupture of platelets and tissue at the site of an injury, and a factor V (a protein from the liver) seems to be necessary in the transformation of prothrombin into thrombin. Vitamin K is required for the formation of prothrombin in the liver but does not enter directly into the clotting reaction. Agitation, heat, and alum will hasten coagulation; cooling, leech extracts, heparin, and precipitation of the calcium salts will retard it. Persons who have the disease hemophilia have a very slow coagulation rate because of the stability of their platelets in an abnormal type of plasma.

The blocking of blood flow by an intravascular clot is called thrombosis, which is quite serious when it involves the blood vessels of the heart, brain, and other vital places. When the clot (thrombus) breaks away and is carried in the bloodstream, it is an **embolus.** An internal clot can be initiated whenever thromboplastin is released by injuries to blood vessels and the breakdown of platelets through contact with rough, injured tissue.

Blood types

In blood transfusions the donor's blood is checked against the blood of the recipient. Blood differs chemically from person to person, and when two different (incompatible) bloods are mixed, **agglutination** is the result. The basis of these chemical differences is the presence in the red blood corpuscles of **agglutinogens (antigens)** A and B and, in the serum or plasma, **agglutinins (antibodies)** a and b. According to the way these antigens and antibodies are distributed, there are four main blood groups: O, A, B, and AB (Table 31-1). Group O contains antibodies a and b but no antigens; group A, antibody b and antigen A; group B, antibody a and antigen B; group AB, antigens A and B but no antibodies. In these groups normally no blood agglutinates itself because corresponding antigen and antibody, as, for example, A and a or B and b, are not present together, for a is anti-A and b is anti-B. On the other hand, A is compatible with b and B is compatible with a. Each major group is also divided into subtypes, but transfusion reactions between blood of these subtypes are rare.

Although persons with type O blood are called universal donors and those with type AB are called universal recipients, doctors in actual practice insist on giving blood of the same type as the patient's blood to prevent any possibility of incompatibility.

The red blood corpuscles also contain other agglutinogens, but there are no corresponding agglutinins in the plasma. These agglutinogens are called M and N, and all individuals have one or both of these. There are also other factors.

Blood groups are present in many other animals such as dogs, cats, rabbits, chickens, and monkeys.

In blood transfusion practices, whole blood and blood plasma are commonly used. In blood banks, blood from several individuals of the same type is pooled and a preservative added. It is then put into storage in a refrigerator at about 4° to 6° C. Dried plasma is about as effective as whole blood for shock, although it is prepared without the red cells. For severe hemorrhage whole blood is best. For dried plasma, blood from many individuals of various types is used; thus the various agglutinins are diluted and pooled, the red cells removed by centrifuging, and the plasma made into a powder by freezing and drying. By adding an equal amount of distilled water, the plasma is made ready for use. Dried plasma is much easier to use than whole blood because it keeps longer, requires no typing, and is easily transported.

Rh factor

In 1940 there was discovered in the red blood corpuscles a new factor called the Rh factor, named after the Rhesus monkeys in which it was first found. In the white race about 85% of individuals have the factor (positive) and the other 15% do not (negative). It was found also that Rh-positive and Rh-negative bloods are incompatible and that shock and even death may follow their mixing when Rh-positive blood is introduced into an Rh-negative person who has had a previous transfusion of Rh-positive blood. The Rh factor is inherited as a dominant; this accounts for a peculiar and often fatal form of anemia of newborn infants called **erythroblastosis fetalis.** If the father is Rh positive, the mother Rh negative, and the fetus Rh positive (by inheriting the factor from the father), blood from the fetus may pass through defects in the placenta into the mother's blood. The fetal blood will stimulate the formation of Rh-positive antibodies in the blood of the mother. These antibodies then may diffuse back into the fetal circulation and produce agglutination and destruction of the fetal red blood cells. With a first pregnancy this effect may be slight, but a subsequent pregnancy may cause a buildup of these antibodies. The life of the first child may be threatened if the mother has had at some time previously a transfusion of Rh-positive blood. Testing for the Rh factor is as important as testing for the major blood types. If this testing is done in advance on the parents, the danger to

TABLE 31-1

Standard blood groups (white persons, United States)

Blood group	Antigens in red corpuscles	Antibodies in serum	Can give blood to	Can receive blood from	Frequency (%)
O	None	a, b	All	O	45
A	A	b	A, AB	O, A	42
B	B	a	B, AB	O, B	10
AB	AB	None	AB	All	3

the child's life can be prevented in most cases by methods known to medical science.

Lymphatic system (Fig. 31-21)

The lymphatic system is an accessory blood system, and its main function is to correct certain omissions of the major circulatory system. When the filtration pressure of the blood capillaries filters out the liquid part of plasma into the spaces among the tissues' cells, there is formed **tissue fluid,** a clear, colorless fluid. Lymph is about the same as plasma, minus a great deal of its proteins whose molecules are too large to diffuse through the capillary walls. All the cells of the body are bathed in tissue fluid, which returns to the circulation in two ways: (1) by entering into the venous ends of the capillaries where the osmotic pressure of the blood proteins exceeds the filtration pressure and (2) by means of the lymph capillaries and lymph vessels. Tissue fluid varies in different regions of the body because of the differential permeability of the blood vessels, the volume of blood, and the varied requirements of cells. Some cells also give off more waste than others and tissue fluids are relatively stagnant. **Lymph** is the fluid within the lymphatic system and has been collected from tissue spaces by diffusion through the blind-end capillaries, and thus lymph varies in different body regions. It contains lymphocytes, but no red cells, and has less calcium and phosphorus than blood. Lymph is a supplementary method for the drainage of tissue fluid.

Lymph vessels carry lymph only toward the heart. They are made up of the **peripheral lymph capillaries,** which are tiny vessels closed at one end; **larger lymph vessels,** provided with numerous valves, and the large left **thoracic duct,** which enters the left subclavian vein in the neck region. Along the course of the lymph vessels are the **lymph nodes,** which filter out bacteria and other substances and produce lymphocytes. Lymph is kept flowing in the vessels by the squeezing action of adjacent muscles and inspiratory movements of the chest cavity. The valves prevent its backflow. Its movements are very sluggish, and despite the wide extent of this system, only about 2,000 ml. per day are discharged into the subclavian vein.

In some lower animals such as the frog, there are special lymph hearts that propel the lymph forward; these are absent in man.

Reticuloendothelial system

This is a widespread or diffused system of highly phagocytic cells. The cells do not form a true endothelium, and epithelial cells do not belong to this system. All highly phagocytic cells, with the exception of blood cells, belong to this system. The system is made up specifically of free monocytes and macrophages and fixed special endothelial cells of lymph nodes, spleen, liver, bone marrow adrenals, and part of the anterior lobe of the pituitary. The fixed cells constitute the walls of lymph sinuses in lymph nodes where the flow of lymph is slow. In other organs they line vascular capillaries such as the sinusoids in liver and venous sinuses in the spleen. At times, these cells and those of the reticular connective tissue may break loose and act as free endothelial-reticular cells. Special cells as the Kupffer's cells

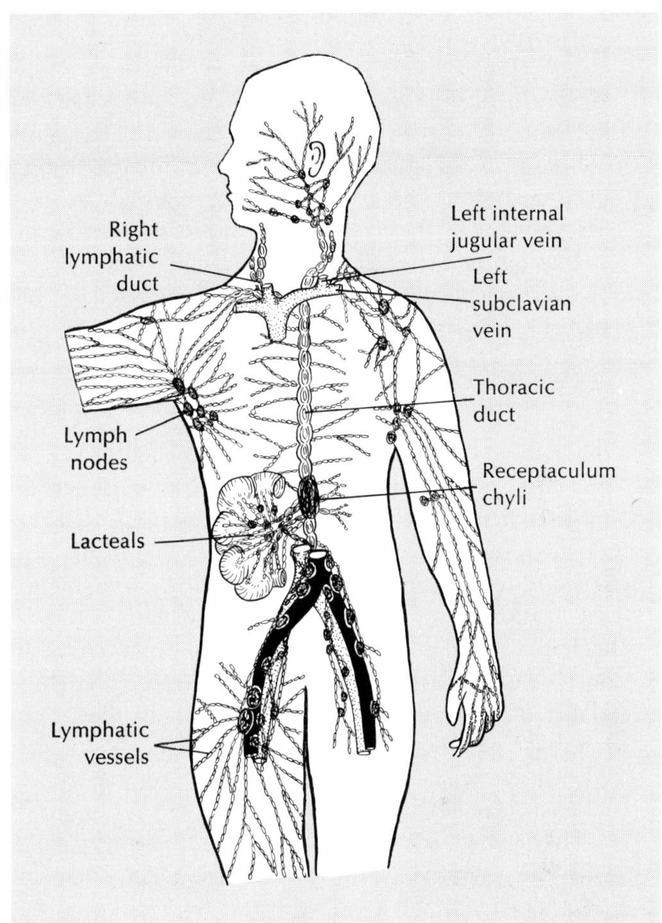

FIG. 31-21

Lymphatic system.

(liver sinusoids) and the microglia of the central nervous system may be mentioned as typical examples.

The system has a wide range of functions. It is known to play an essential part in the destruction of red blood corpuscles and in bile formation. They may also be involved in antibody formation. Foreign particulate matter in the bloodstream is removed by the macrophages of the liver, spleen, and bone marrow as well as by the macrophages of the lymph nodes. Some of their functions are not well understood, such as the part they play in lipid metabolism.

RESPIRATORY SYSTEM

The most common source of energy is oxidation, the union of oxygen with other elements. Energy is bound up in food and must be released to be available for use. It must be changed from a potential form to kinetic form. A few animals are able to live in the absence of free oxygen (anaerobic), but they are able to get the necessary oxygen from the metabolism of carbohydrates and fats in their own bodies. Some of these anaerobic animals are worms and arthropods that live in the muck at the bottom of deep lakes; others are intestinal parasites. Anaerobic metabolism also occurs when lactic acid is formed in muscular contraction of all animals or in glycolysis.

The ultimate source of all energy is the sun; plants, with the aid of solar energy and the green pigment **chlorophyll,** are able to make sugars from carbon dioxide and water. These sugars are converted into starches, fats, and proteins, which animals use as food. When these foods have been changed back into glucose by the animal that eats them, they are ready to be acted on by oxygen. Oxygen combines with the carbon of the glucose molecule to form carbon dioxide and water; during this process, energy that held the molecules together is released. This reaction, in an abbreviated form, may be expressed thus:

$$\underset{\text{Glucose}}{C_6H_{12}O_6} + \underset{\text{Oxygen}}{6O_2} \rightarrow \underset{\text{Carbon dioxide}}{6CO_2} + \underset{\text{Water}}{6H_2O} + \text{Energy}$$

Many separate reactions, each controlled by enzymes, are required for the whole process (see the discussion on cellular metabolism, p. 77). The ratio of the volume of CO_2 given off to the O_2 consumed is called the **respiratory quotient** (RQ). In the previous reaction the respiratory quotient is 1 $\left(RQ = \frac{6O_2}{6O_2} = 1\right)$. It varies with different foods. With fats the respiratory quotient is about 0.7; with proteins, about 0.8; and with the average mixed diet, about 0.85. The respiratory quotient is an index of the kind of metabolism that is taking place in the body because the nearer it is to 1, the more carbohydrates are being metabolized in the body at that particular time.

Land animals get oxygen from the air, which is about one-fifth oxygen; most aquatic animals use the dissolved oxygen of the water in which they live. The process of taking in oxygen and giving off carbon dioxide is called **respiration.** There are two kinds of respiration—**direct** and **indirect.** Direct respiration is the exchange of oxygen and carbon dioxide between the cells of the organism and the surrounding environment. **Indirect respiration** makes use of a specialized structure in which gaseous exchange is made and involves two phases—external and internal respiration. **External respiration** includes the exchange of gases between the external environment and the blood; **internal respiration** is the exchange between the bloodstream and the body cell. In animals that have direct respiration, both external and internal respiration are merged (Protozoa and Coelenterata).

FIG. 31-22

Chemical structure of heme. Hemoglobin molecule is made up of pigment, heme, and a carrier protein, globin (not shown). Heme is a tetrapyrrol (four pyrrol rings) with a single iron atom. Hemoglobin can carry 1 molecule of oxygen per atom of iron.

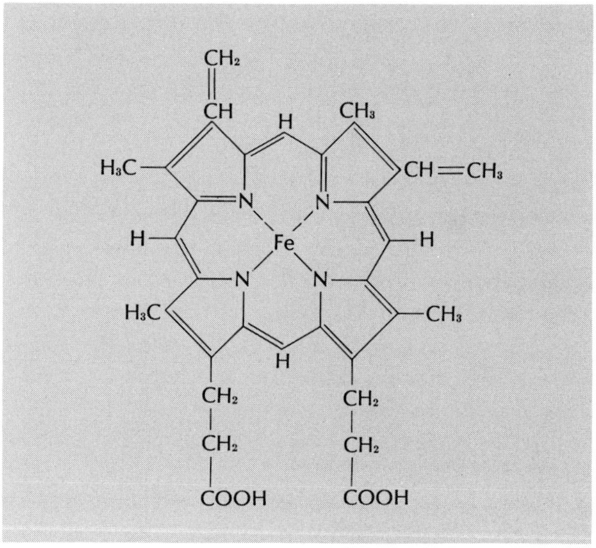

Respiratory or oxygen-carrying pigments

Besides external and internal respiration a third process is required in most animals—gas transport. In some animals the respiratory gases are simply dissolved in the body fluids, but in those with blood, respiratory pigments are efficient means of transporting oxygen to the cells. As will be seen later, carbon dioxide depends mainly on the body fluids for its transportation. Respiratory pigments do not follow any evolutionary pattern, for different pigments are found in the same group or phylum. Proteins are linked to all respiratory pigments and are responsible for the reversibility of the reactions of pigments with oxygen.

There are four types of oxygen-carrying pigments:

1. **Hemoglobin.** This is by far the most common blood pigment and has been found in most phyla, except sponges and coelenterates. Certain antarctic fish are the only vertebrates that do not have it. Hemoglobin occurs in blood cells, plasma, coelomic fluid, coelomocytes, muscle cells (myoglobin), and nerve cells. With oxygen, it is orange red; without oxygen, it is purple red. Its molecular weight in vertebrates is 68,000 but may be much greater in invertebrates. It is made up of the protein globin and the pigment heme that is a tetrapyrrol with a single iron atom (Fig. 31-22). Hemoglobin carries one molecule of oxygen per atom of iron. Myoglobin is the red protein in muscle that takes over the oxygen from the hemoglobin and stores it there until oxygen is required for oxidation.

2. **Chlorocruorin.** This pigment is green in dilute solutions and reddish in concentrated solutions. Its structure is very similar to the hemoglobin molecule and contains iron in its porphyrin prosthetic group. The iron to oxygen ratio is also one. It is dissolved in the plasma of the polychaetes, *Sabella* and *Serpula.*

3. **Hemerythrin.** A pigment that turns reddish or brownish when combined with oxygen. It has no heme

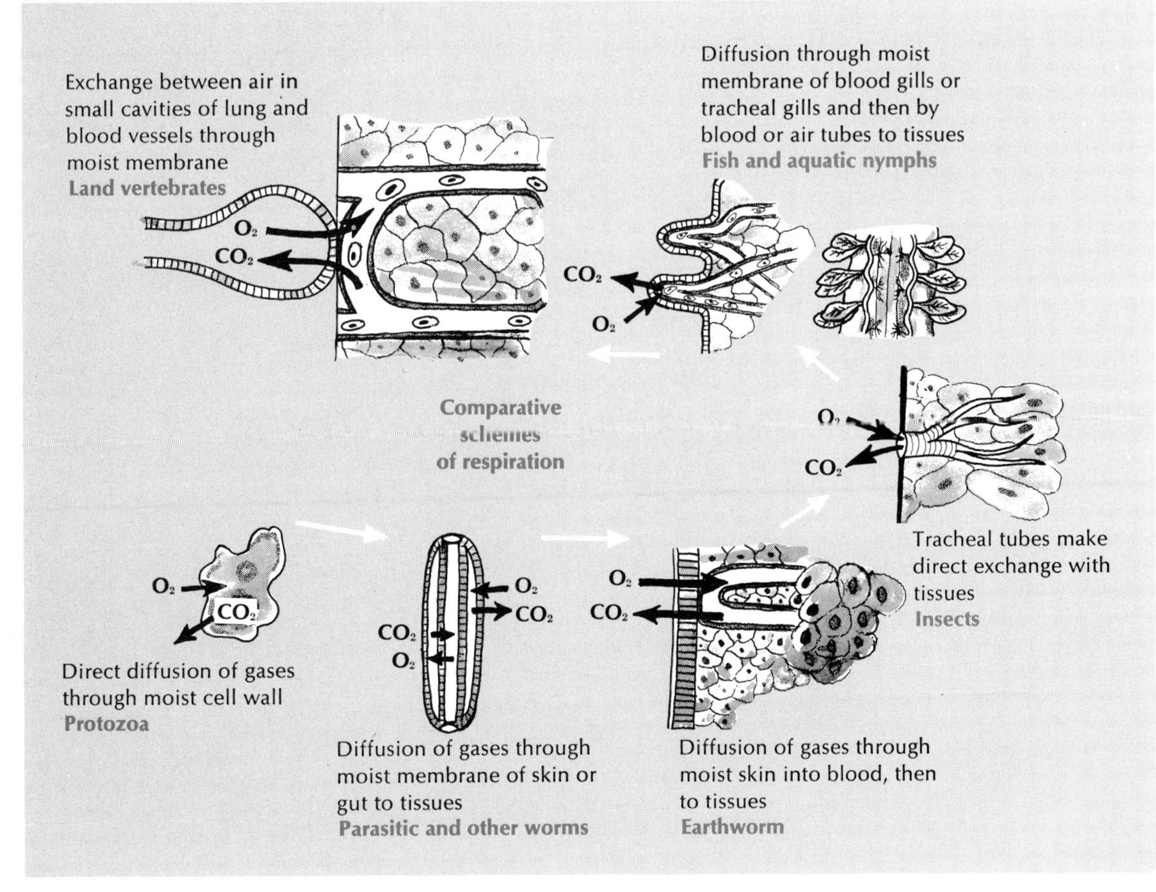

FIG. 31-23 Comparative schemes of respiration among animals.

group and its iron is bound to the protein sulfhydryl groups of cysteine. Its iron-oxygen ratio is 2:1. The pigment has been found in the Sipunculida, the Priapulida, and Brachiopoda, where it is found in the coelomocytes.

4. **Hemocyanin.** There is no heme group in this pigment and it uses copper instead of iron for carry-

FIG. 31-24

Internal structures of lungs among vertebrate groups. In general, evolutionary trend has been from simple sacs with little exchange surface between blood and air spaces to complex, lobulated structures of complex divisions and extensive exchange surfaces.

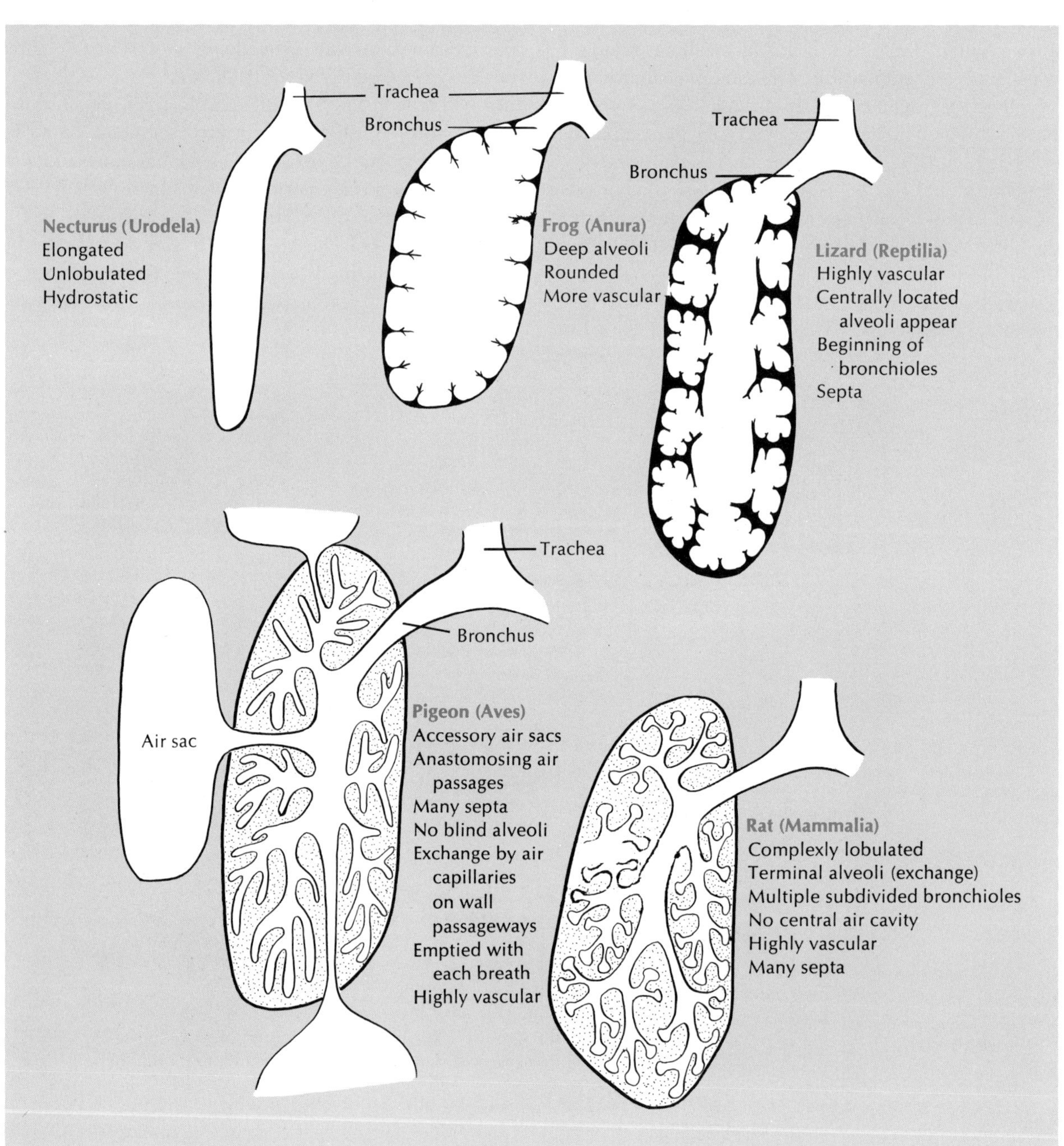

ing oxygen. The copper is bound to one or more amino acid side chains and requires two atoms of copper for each oxygen molecule. The pigment is colorless but turns blue with oxygen. It is found in gastropods, cephalopods, crustaceans, and arachnids, where it occurs in the plasma.

Respiration in invertebrates

Protozoa, sponges, coelenterates, and many worms have a direct diffusion of gases between the organism and the environment. Gaseous exchange in most annelid worms is made through a moist skin well provided with blood vessels. Some echinoderms make use of the finger-like **dermal branchiae** (papulae), evaginations from the coelomic cavity, as well as the tube feet. **Gills** are common in aquatic invertebrates. They are thin filaments covered with an epidermal membrane and are provided with blood vessels. Some are simple in structure (marine annelids) and others are more complicated (arthropods and mollusks). The most efficient respiratory apparatus in any animal is the **tracheal system** (Fig. 31-23) found in insects—oxygen is delivered to the tissue cells directly by a ramifying system of small tubes (tracheae). Sea cucumbers have the **respiratory tree,** which fills with water drawn in and out of the cloaca.

Respiration in vertebrates

Three types of devices are employed by vertebrates for respiration: (1) direct surfaces such as skin and pharyngeal regions, (2) gills, and (3) lungs.

Amphibians make use of the first type because their skin allows gases to diffuse easily through it into blood vessels. Most amphibians also possess either gills or lungs, but some salamanders (Plethodontidae) have neither and rely entirely on their skin and pharyngeal region that is highly vascularized. Some fish (mudhoppers and eels) also absorb O_2 through the skin.

Most aquatic vertebrates have gills, either external or internal. In the cyclostomes, water passes in and out of the gill openings and bathes the gill filaments in the gill pouches. The gaseous exchange is made between the water and the gill filaments. In the elasmobranchs, water enters through the mouth or spiracle and passes out the various gill slits. In bony fish, water enters through the mouth and passes over the gills and out through the opening of the protective operculum. Some larval forms have gills that are replaced by lungs in the adult.

Land vertebrates have developed **lungs,** which are internal cavities (Fig. 31-24). The exchange of oxygen and carbon dioxide is made between the air in the cavities and the blood capillaries that line them. Dipnoi, or lungfish, use their swim bladders for lungs during the dry season of their habitats and thus may be considered transition forms. In lower amphibians lungs are simple, baglike affairs lined with capillaries; in higher forms their inner surfaces have many folds and corrugations with minute pockets (air sacs) where the gaseous exchange with the blood is made. Many lungs are also subdivided into lobes and lobules for increasing the respiratory surface.

One of the main problems of lung-breathing forms is getting air into and out of the lungs. Frogs take air in (inspiration) by closing the jaws and lowering the floor of the mouth; this sucks the air into the mouth through the external nares. Then by closing the nares and raising the floor of the mouth, the air is driven into the lungs. Air is forced out (expiration) by opening the nares and contracting the body wall. Most reptiles, birds, and mammals breathe by movements of the ribs; such movements increase in inspiration or decrease in expiration the size of the thoracic cavity. Air is thus sucked in or forced out. Birds also employ an additional method in flying. Since their ribs are rigidly fixed to secure anchorage for their pectoral muscles, their lungs are filled and emptied by the action of the pectoral muscles during the process of flying and by the alternate expansion and contraction of their air sacs.

Respiratory system in man and other mammals

In mammals the respiratory system is made up of certain air channels and the lungs. The passageway consists of the nostrils (external nares); the **nasal chamber,** lined with mucus-secreting epithelium; the **posterior nares,** which connect to the **pharynx,** where the pathways of digestion and respiration cross; the **epiglottis,** a flap that folds over the **glottis** (the opening to the larynx) to prevent food from going the wrong way in swallowing; the **larynx,** or voice box; the **trachea,** or windpipe; and the two **bronchi,** one to each lung (Fig. 31-25). Within the lungs each bronchus divides and subdivides into smaller tubes (**bronchioles**) that lead to the air sacs and **alveoli.** The walls of the latter are thin and moist to facilitate the exchange of gases between the air sacs and the adjacent blood capillaries. Air passageways are lined with mucus-secreting ciliated epithelium and play an important role in conditioning

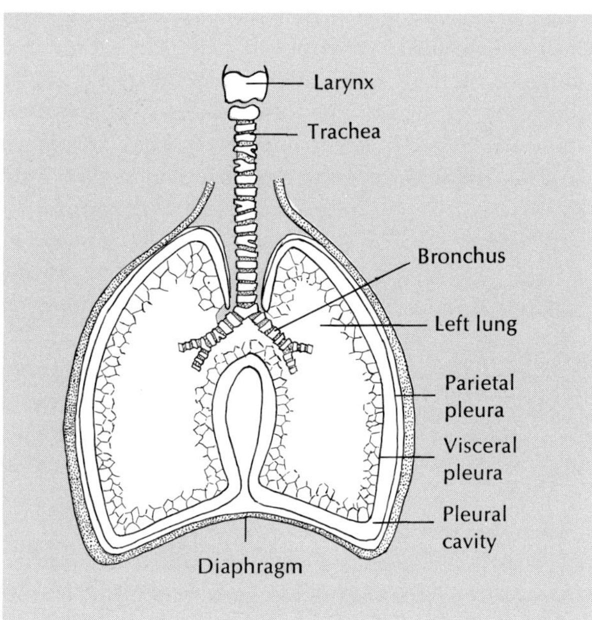

FIG. 31-25

Thorax and its relation to respiratory system in man.

the air before it reaches the alveoli. There are partial cartilage rings in the walls of the trachea, bronchi, and even some of the bronchioles to prevent those structures from collapsing. The human lungs are made up of some 750,000,000 alveoli, the total surface of which is about 100 square meters, or fifty times that of the skin surface.

In its passage to the air sacs, the air undergoes three important changes; (1) it is filtered free from most dust and other foreign substances, (2) it is warmed to body temperature, and (3) it is saturated with moisture, so that its relative humidity is 100%.

The lungs consist of a great deal of elastic connective tissue and some muscle. They are covered by a thin layer of smooth epithelium known as the **visceral pleura.** A similar layer, the **parietal pleura,** lines the inner surface of the walls of the chest. The two layers of the pleura are in contact and slide over one another as the lungs expand and contract. A small amount of pleural fluid for lubrication is found in the **pleural cavity,** a partial vacuum between the pleura. The chest cavity is bounded behind by the spine and back muscles, on the sides by the ribs, and in front by ribs and the breastbone. The diaphragm, a dome-shaped partition, forms the floor of the chest cavity and separates it from the abdomen.

Mechanism of breathing. The chest cavity is an airtight chamber, and as a result of the potential vacuum in the pleural space and the air pressure in the alveoli, the elastic lungs are held tightly against the chest wall. The volume of the lungs is thus increased or decreased in accordance with the size and shape of the chest cavity. In **inspiration,** when the ribs are elevated and the diaphragm contracted and flattened, the chest cavity is enlarged. This increase in the volume of the chest cavity (and lungs) causes the air pressure in the lungs to fall below atmospheric pressure, and air passes through the air passageways to the air sacs to equalize the pressure. **Expiration** is a less active process than inspiration. When their muscles relax, the ribs and diaphragm return to their original position and the chest cavity size is decreased. The distended, elastic lungs then contract and force the air out (Fig. 31-26).

In quiet breathing (eupnea) an individual breathes in with each breath about 500 ml. of air. Of this amount, only 350 ml. reach the lung alveoli; the other 150 ml. are left in the air passages, the so-called "dead space," where no gaseous exchange can take place. This dead space air is the first to be pushed out with the next expiration. Likewise, the last 150 ml. of air to be expelled from the air sacs remain in the passageway and will be the first to enter the alveoli at the next inspiration.

The 500 ml. of air breathed in and out at each breath are called the **tidal air.** After a normal inspiration, it is possible by deep and forcible inspiration to take in about 1,500 ml. more (**complemental air**); after expelling the tidal air, it is possible with forcible expiration to expel about 1,500 ml. more (**supplemental air**). After the deepest possible expiration, about 1,000 ml. of air remain in the lung (**residual air**). The **vital capacity** is the amount of air one can breathe in and expel with the greatest possible effort. It is somewhere around 3,500 ml. for the average person, although physically trained persons have a greater vital capacity than this. The vital capacity is equal to the sum of the tidal, complemental, and supplemental airs. The rate of quiet respiration in men is about 15 or 16 times per minute; for women and children it is about 20 times per minute. The rate at birth is much higher. Exercise and other factors increase the rate.

Composition of inspired, expired, and alveolar airs. The composition of expired and alveolar airs is not

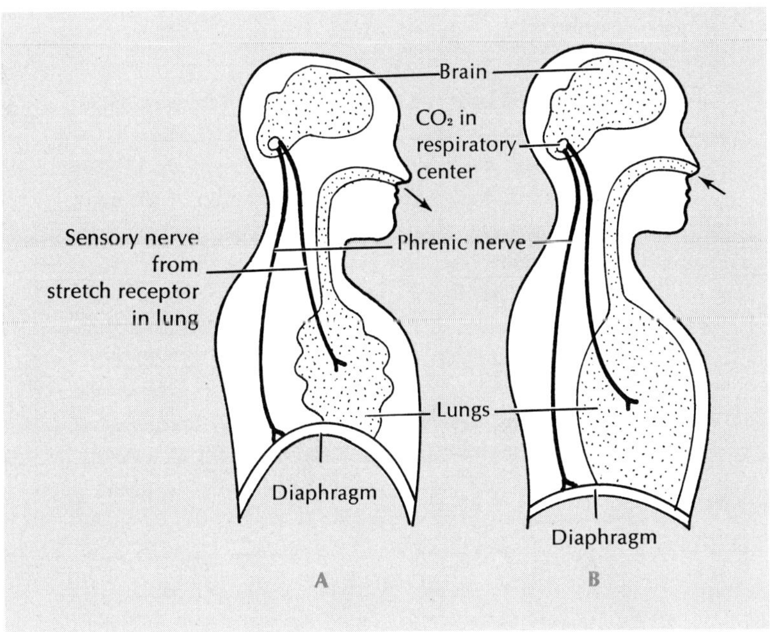

FIG. 31-26

Mechanism of breathing. In inspiration, **B,** CO_2 in blood stimulates respiratory center to send impulses by way of phrenic nerves to diaphragm, which, with elevation of ribs, produces inhalation of air. In **A,** impulses from stretch receptors in lungs inhibit respiratory center and exhalation occurs. (See text for explanation.)

TABLE 31-2

Variation in three kinds of air

	Inspired air (vol. %)	Expired air (vol. %)	Alveolar air (vol. %)
Oxygen	20.96	16.3	14.2
Carbon dioxide	0.04	4.0	5.5
Nitrogen	79.00	79.7	80.3

identical. Alveolar air contains less oxygen and more carbon dioxide than the air that leaves the lungs. Inspired air has the composition of atmospheric air. The variations in the three kinds of air are shown in Table 31-2.

Expired air is really a mixture of alveolar and inspired airs. The carbon dioxide in expired air is a little less than the oxygen taken into the blood, because some of the oxygen is given off in the form of water. The water given off in expired air depends on the relative humidity of the external air and the activity of the person. At ordinary room temperature and in performing light work with a relative humidity of about 50%, an individual will lose about 350 ml. of water from the lungs each day.

Gaseous exchange in lungs. The diffusion of gases, both in internal as well as external respiration, takes place in accordance with the laws of physical diffusion; that is, the gases pass from regions of high pressure to those of low pressure. The pressure of gas refers to the partial pressure that gas exerts in a mixture of gases. If the atmospheric pressure at sea level is 760 mm. of mercury, the partial pressure of O_2 will be 21% (percentage of O_2 in air) of 760, or 159 mm. The alveolar membrane (epithelium) is thin and offers little resistance to the passage of gases. However, this membrane must be kept moist, for oxygen is dissolved in this film and then passes through the membrane. The concentration of oxygen in the lung alveoli is greater (101 mm. mercury pressure) than it is in the venous blood of the lung capillaries (40 mm. mercury pressure). Oxygen then naturally diffuses into the capillaries. In a similar manner, the carbon dioxide in the blood of the lung capillaries has a higher concentration (46 mm. mercury) than has this same gas in the lung alveoli (40 mm. mercury), so that carbon dioxide diffuses from the blood into the alveoli. Thus in the diffusion of both these gases there is a marked diffusion gradient that determines the direction of their flow (Fig. 31-27).

These gases behave in a similar manner when the exchange occurs between the blood and tissues (internal respiration). Here the concentration of oxygen in the blood (100 mm. mercury pressure) is greater than the concentration of oxygen in the tissues (0 to 30 mm. mercury pressure), and the carbon dioxide concentration in the tissues (45 to 68 mm. mercury pressure) is greater than that in blood (40 mm. mercury pressure). The gases in each case will go from a high to a low concentration.

Transport of gases in blood. Oxygen is carried in the plasma and the red blood corpuscles. A small amount is carried in solution in the plasma. The red pigment hemoglobin is well adapted for carrying the major part of the oxygen. The respiratory pigment hemoglobin is a complex protein made up of **hematin** (5%), containing iron and giving the red color to blood, and **globin** (95%), a colorless protein. Each gram of hemoglobin can combine with about 1.3 ml. of oxygen. Each 100 ml. of blood in the normal man contains about 16 grams of hemoglobin; in the normal woman, about 14 grams. The amount of oxygen that will combine with hemoglobin depends on the tension of the gas in the alveoli; at 101 mm. mercury pressure the arterial blood is about 97% saturated; at lesser tensions smaller amounts of O_2 will combine with the blood. Oxygen saturation is the ratio of the actual oxygen content to the oxygen capacity expressed in percent. This relationship is usually expressed by the oxygen dissociation curve (Fig. 31-28). The degree of hemoglobin saturation with oxygen depends on the partial pressure of oxygen, the partial pressure of carbon dioxide, and the acidity (pH) of the blood. An increase in the metabolic rate in the tissues increases the carbon dioxide and acid metabolites. The oxygen partial pressure is thus lowered. When oxygen passes from the lung alveoli into the lung capillaries, it diffuses into the red cells and unites with hemoglobin to form oxyhemoglobin in accordance with this reaction:

$$\text{Hemoglobin} + \text{Oxygen} \rightleftarrows \text{Oxyhemoglobin}$$

The reaction is reversible, depending on the pressure concentrations of the gas at a particular region. In the lungs the reaction goes to the right because of the differences in pressure already described; in the tissues the reaction goes to the left, releasing oxygen. The color of blood depends on oxyhemoglobin and hemoglobin. Arterial blood is bright scarlet because of oxyhemoglobin; venous blood is purplish red because of hemoglobin.

Although carbon dioxide is converted into carbonic acid when it diffuses into the blood, it is transported in the blood in three ways: (1) about 5% of it is carried in solution in the plasma as carbonic acid (H_2CO_3);

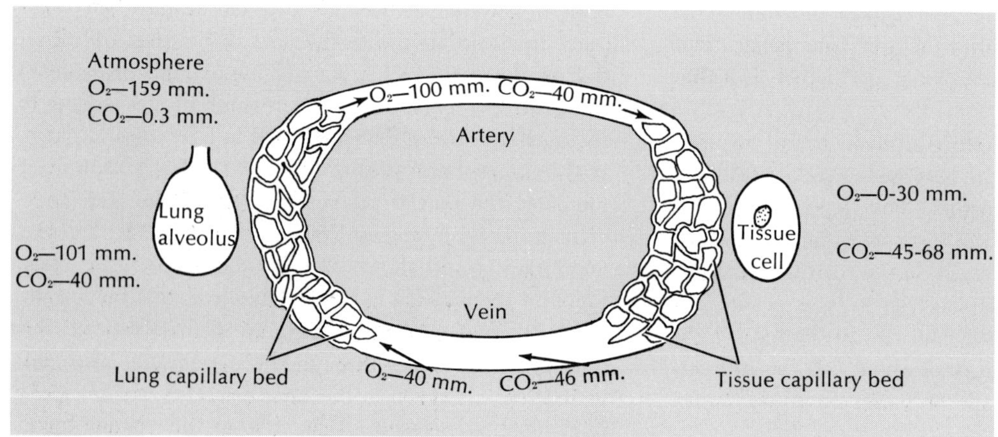

FIG. 31-27
Diffusion gradients responsible for movement of oxygen from lungs to tissues and of carbon dioxide from tissues to lungs. Numbers refer to tensions expressed in millimeters (mm.) of mercury. (See text for explanation.)

(2) 10% is carried in combination with the amino groups ($-NH_2$) of the hemoglobin; and (3) the other 85% is carried in the form of sodium or potassium bicarbonates in both the plasma and red blood cells. Thus carbon dioxide relies on the blood salts for most of its transportation. An important enzyme, **carbonic anhydrase,** present in the blood plays an important role in the conversion of carbon dioxide into carbonic acid in the tissue capillaries and in the conversion of carbonic acid back to carbon dioxide in the lung capillaries. This process in tissues involves the **chloride shift,** or the passage of chloride ions from the plasma into the red blood corpuscles, to balance the bicarbonate ions that have passed in the reverse direction, thus maintaining an acid-base equilibrium of pH 7.4 for the blood and the electrical neutrality of the red corpuscle. In the lungs the chloride shift is reversed.

The oxygen capacity of each 100 ml. of human blood is about 20 ml., which is the amount found in arterial blood—a percentage saturation of about 97%. Each 100 ml. of venous blood contains about 12 ml. of oxygen, or 60% saturation. The **utilization coefficient** is the fractional amount of oxygen that the hemoglobin gives up as it passes through the tissue capillaries. Under normal conditions the value of the utilization coefficient is about 27%. During strenuous exercise its value may reach 77%. The amount of carbon dioxide carried by the blood has a wider fluctuation, since each 100 ml. of blood carries from 30 to 60 ml. of carbon dioxide.

FIG. 31-28

Oxygen dissociation curves. Oxygen saturation of blood is a function of partial pressure of blood, but degree of hemoglobin saturation with O_2 depends also upon partial pressure of CO_2 and acidity of acid metabolites. Dotted lines show blood is about 80% saturated when partial pressure of O_2 in tissues at rest is about 45 mm. of mercury. At higher O_2 pressure more O_2 is bound by hemoglobin, as in lung alveoli. Higher CO_2 concentration, however, causes more O_2 to be released at any given O_2 pressure.

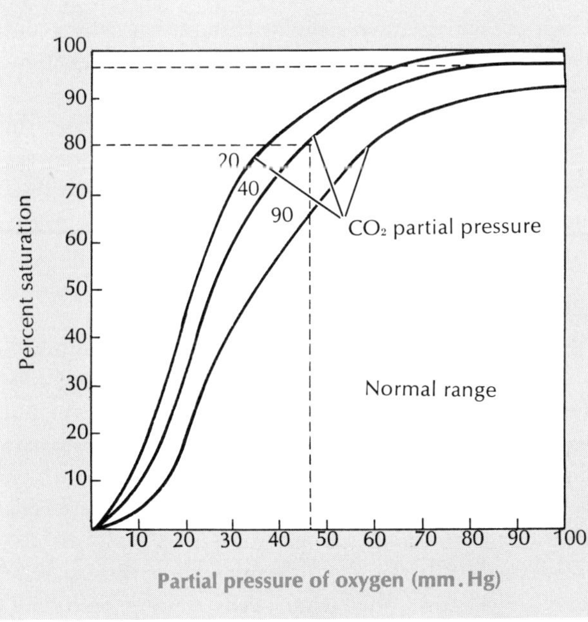

Cellular respiration and oxidation. The ultimate aim of all respiratory activities is the cellular oxidations that involve the combination of oxygen with food or metabolic products and the release of energy thereby. (See discussion on cellular metabolism, p. 77.)

Factors that control respiration. Respiration must adjust itself to the varying needs of the body for oxygen. The body in active states needs more oxygen and must give off more carbon dioxide than it does when it is resting. Respiration is essentially involuntary and automatic, but it is influenced and controlled voluntarily within limits. Normally, inspiration and expiration follow each other in rhythmic fashion and both are basically muscular in action. For the perfect coordination of the muscles and other structures involved in respiration, a nervous regulating mechanism is necessary. The center of this nervous mechanism is the **respiratory center** located in the medulla oblongata and connected with both afferent and efferent nerves. This nerve center may be a complex of separate inspiratory and expiratory centers lying close together. Although largely automatic, the center is influenced by (1) voluntary nervous control, (2) nervous reflex factors, and (3) chemical factors within itself and within the blood.

The chemical regulation of breathing centers around carbon dioxide. A slight rise of carbon dioxide (0.2%) in the alveoli will double the rate of respiration; a fall of 0.2% will decrease the rate of breathing. These changes in the alveolar carbon dioxide are reflected in the blood by diffusion. The respiratory center is very sensitive to changes in the carbon dioxide of the blood. Ventilating the lungs by rapid breathing will reduce the alveolar carbon dioxide. The individual has no desire to breathe until the carbon dioxide of the blood builds up and, by diffusion, raises the level of the gas in the alveoli. One breathes just often enough to keep the carbon dioxide of the alveoli at a constant level. In ordinary quiet

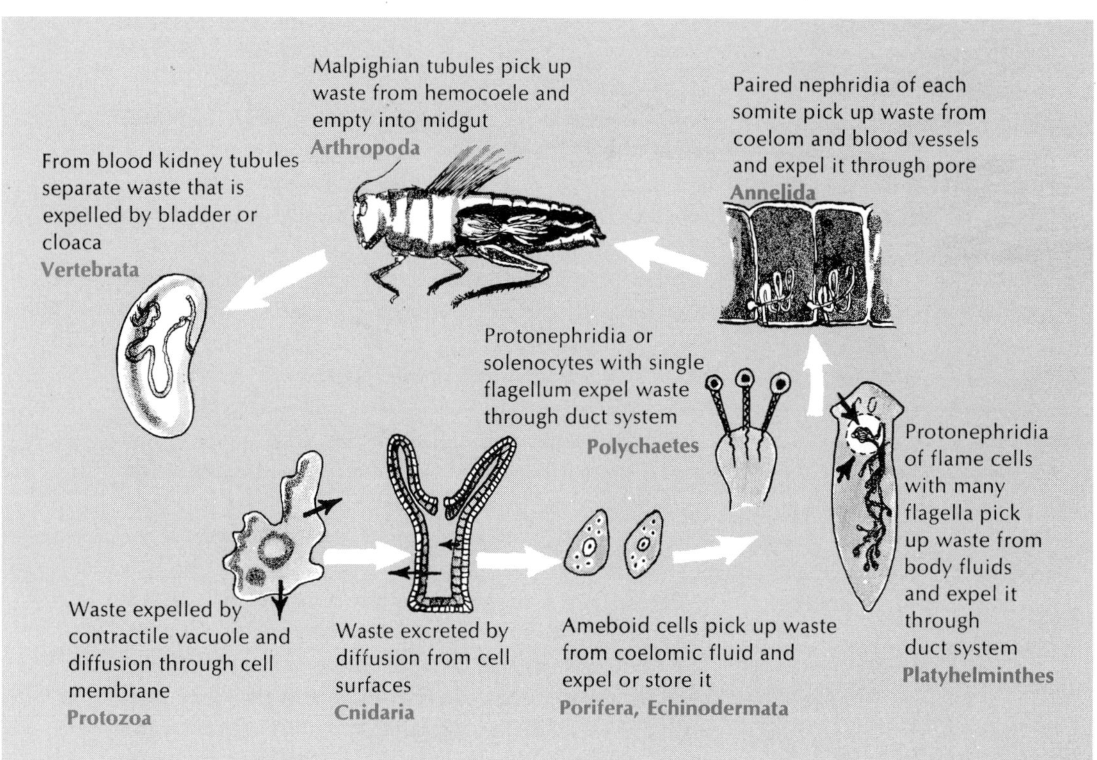

FIG. 31-29

Comparative mechanisms of excretion among different animals.

breathing, about 250 to 300 ml. of carbon dioxide are produced each minute by the body tissues. By way of the blood, this carbon dioxide reaches the alveoli and will diffuse into the alveoli until its concentration will be equal in both blood and alveoli. Exercise will step up the production of carbon dioxide, which leads to faster breathing. Carbon dioxide, however, plays little or no role in regulating breathing in most aquatic forms, because this gas is very soluble in water.

The respiratory center is stimulated from the chemoreceptors in the aortic arch and the carotid sinus bodies by high carbon dioxide or low oxygen concentrations in the blood. The nervous impulses so aroused will pass to the respiratory center and increase its activity.

EXCRETORY SYSTEM*

Waste products of the metabolic processes must be removed from the organism. Some, such as **carbon dioxide** and **water,** are formed by the various oxidative processes; others, such as **nitrogenous waste** (urea, purine bodies, etc.), arise from the breakdown of protein. Although toxic in excess quantities, some waste substances (for example, carbon dioxide) are useful in regulating certain physiologic processes such as those of respiration. Water is a waste when present in excess. One of the main functions of the excretory system is to maintain a constant internal environment for the cells, eliminating substances in harmful quantities and conserving those that are helpful for normal functioning.

Students often confuse the true wastes of metabolism with the refuse discharged in the feces. The feces are mainly indigestible material rejected by the intestinal tract as unsuitable for food and are voided through the anus.

Excretion in invertebrates

Excretion in Protozoa is simply a matter of diffusion through the cell membrane into the surrounding medium (Fig. 31-29), the contractile vacuole may also help excrete. Essentially the same plan of excretion is employed by the sponges and coelenterates, in which the waste is either diffused through the epidermal cells or else into the canals and gastrovascular cavity by the endodermal cells. In the flatworms there are definite excretory organs, the **flame cells** (protonephridia),

*Refer to Chapter 2, Principle 17.

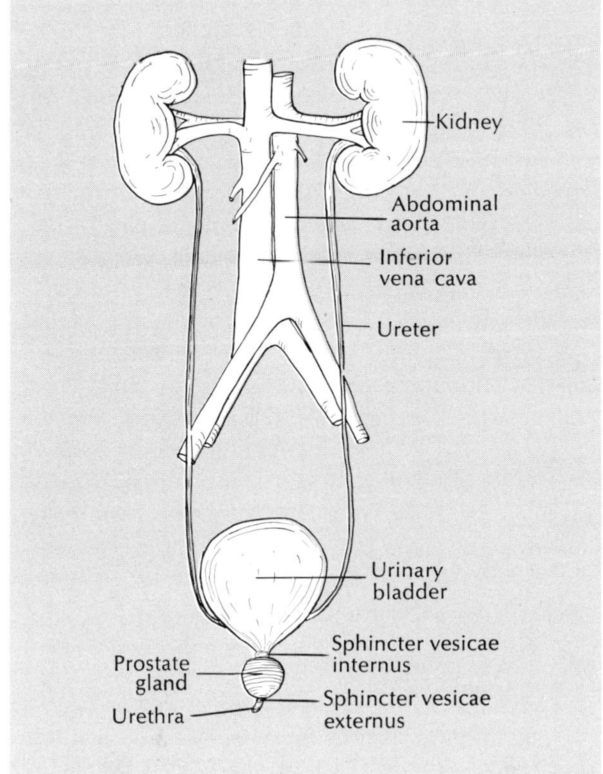

FIG. 31-30

Excretory system in man.

which are connected to a branched system of tubes that discharge the waste to the outside. Some invertebrates (echinoderms and others) make use of phagocytic cells, amebocytes, which engulf waste and carry it to the body surface for disposal or for storage. In the earthworm there is a pair of nephridia (metanephridia) for each segment. Insects have many blind **malpighian tubules** that pick up, by diffusion, waste substances from the body cavity and pass them into the digestive tract. In other arthropods, especially the crustaceans, excretory glands similar to the nephridia of earthworms are found. Mollusks have one or two pairs of nephridia that drain waste from the coelom and the blood.

Excretion in vertebrates

In vertebrates the following organs are concerned with ridding the body of wastes: (1) skin (water, salts, carbon dioxide), (2) lungs (carbon dioxide and water), (3) liver (constituents of bile, bile pigments), (4) alimentary canal (certain salts, calcium, iron, magnesium, fats), and (5) kidneys (urine and its constituents). The urinary system, made up of the kidneys and accessory organs, performs the main burden of taking care of the body waste. With the exception of the lungs, the other organs mentioned handle a relatively small amount of waste.

The urinary system is similar in all vertebrate animals (Fig. 31-30). It is composed of two **kidneys** located posterodorsally. From each kidney a **ureter,** or excretory duct, carries the urine posteriorly. In elasmobranchs, amphibians, reptiles, and birds these ureters open directly into the cloaca, which is provided with a **urinary bladder** in some but not all forms. In most mammals the ureters empty into the bladder, which discharges to the outside by a single duct, the **urethra.** Although the various kidneys in vertebrates are essentially specialized for removing waste from the body, they are not all homologous organs. The evolution of the urinary system in many forms has been closely interrelated with the reproductive system, so that the two systems share some common structures. Together they are often referred to as the **urogenital system.**

Renal-portal circulation

All vertebrate animals as embryos or adults have a renal-portal system. The system is absent in adult mammals. The renal-portal system is made up of veins that carry blood from the hind limbs and posterior trunk region to the kidneys in fishes, amphibians, reptiles, and birds. In these forms the renal-portal veins enter the kidneys and ramify around the renal tubules as capillaries in a low-pressure system. Most of these animals also have a separate blood system to the glomeruli in the form of the high-pressure arterial supply from the renal arteries. In addition, the renal tubules of the opisthonephros (mesonephros) receives a supply of capillaries from the efferent glomerular circulation as well as from the renal-portal system. Shunts connect the renal portal to the renal vein in amphibians, reptiles, and birds so that the blood may bypass the kidney. In this way the kidney unit (nephron) in some animals has blood from two sources—the glomerulus from arterial blood and the tubule mostly from the renal-portal blood. In those fishes without a glomerulus (aglomerular), the renal-portal blood to the tubules is the only source of eliminating waste from the blood.

In the mammalian metanephros, there is no renal-portal system and all the blood to the kidney is supplied through branches of the renal artery. When the renal-portal blood disappeared, the glomerular filtration became dominant and tubular excretion was less important. By having an elaborate reabsorptive system, mammals were able to form **hypertonic** urine. (See following sections.)

Histologic structure of man's kidney

The paired **kidneys** in man are bean shaped, and each weighs about 4 ounces. They are located just below the stomach, one on each side of the middorsal line, and rest upon the back muscles.

Inside, each kidney is made up of an outer zone, the **cortex,** and an inner zone, the **medulla.** In addition, there is a great deal of connective tissue and a rich vascular supply. The uriniferous tubules are called **nephrons** (Fig. 31-31). Each nephron, or excretory unit, is made up of a malpighian body, or **renal corpuscle,** and a much-convoluted **tubule.** A renal corpuscle is composed of a tuft of blood capillaries (glomerulus) surrounded by a double walled sac (Bowman's capsule). The tubule also has a rich supply of blood capillaries and joins onto a collecting tubule that also receives from many other nephrons, so that a relatively few collecting tubules take care of the many nephrons of the kidney. Each renal corpuscle is about 0.2 mm. in diameter; its tubule is about 40 to 50 mm. long. There are about a million nephrons in each kidney, and the total surface area of the glomeruli is upward of 2 square meters. The blood flow to the kidneys is very great, being about twice the weight of the kidneys per minute, or about 1700 quarts per day. There are no excretory nerves to the kidneys, but the sympathetic and parasympathetic fibers control the blood supply.

FIG. 31-31

Diagram of nephron (man).

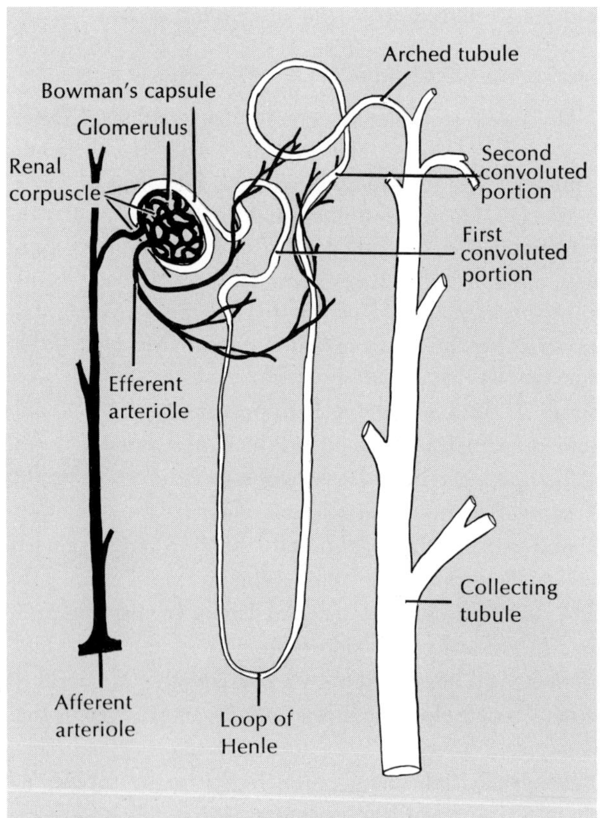

Mechanism of urine formation

The problem of the mechanism involved has been a challenge to physiologists for more than a hundred years. The theory that is now generally accepted by physiologists is the one proposed by Cushny, or a modification of it. All waste is brought to the nephrons by the blood, for in higher forms nephrons have no connection with the coelomic cavity, as they do in lower vertebrates. The function of the nephrons is to remove or separate the waste from the blood and discharge it into an independent series of channels for its final removal from the body.

The actual formation of urine involves three processes: **filtration, reabsorption,** and **tubular secretion.** All these steps take place before **urine** reaches the form in which it is eliminated from the body. Briefly, this means that a certain fluid with waste is separated from the blood into the kidney tubules, that certain substances in this fluid are then returned to the blood by selective absorption, and that finally other substances are added to the fluid before it is actually urine.

Filtration. In the renal corpuscles blood fluids (excluding proteins and formed elements) are filtered out of the capillaries and into the neck of Bowman's capsule and tubule. This filtered substance is called the **capsular filtrate.** It consists of water, salts, sugar, urea, uric acid, and some other substances. This process of filtration is produced by the force of excess blood pressure in the glomerular capillaries over the osmotic pressure of the blood colloids. This effective filtration pressure is equivalent to about 40 mm. mercury pressure and is sufficient to filter out about 20% of the blood plasma that passes through the glomerulus. There are so many glomeruli involved in a single kidney that the amount filtered averages about 120 ml. per minute, or 170 liters daily. The interesting experiments of Professor A. N. Richards have done much to clear up the nature of the capsular filtrate. By ingenious methods, he was able to obtain samples of the capsular filtrate and analyze it. He found that it was a protein-free plasma filtrate, that it contained the other constituents of plasma in the same concentration as plasma, and that it was alkaline in reaction. He also found that the 2,000 glomeruli of a frog's kidney produced about 4 to 16 ml. of capsular filtrate per hour; this is several times the amount of urine formed in the same time.

Reabsorption. The second step in the process of urine formation takes place in the tubular part of the nephron. This tubule is made up of straight and convoluted portions, provided with blood capillary networks that are furnished with blood from the blood vessel that leaves the glomerulus. As the capsular filtrate passes down the tubule, many substances in it are differentially reabsorbed into the blood of the capillary network that surrounds the tubule. About 99% of this capsular filtrate is so absorbed and taken back into the blood. In this way, many waste substances are greatly concentrated compared with their condition in the capsular fluid. Some substances are completely removed from the filtrate and taken back into the blood. This selective reabsorption depends on the nature of the substances and the needs of the body. Some (water and glucose) are reabsorbed in large amounts and are called **high-threshold** substances; others (urea, uric acid, certain salts) are partly absorbed and partly excreted, the **low-threshold** substances; and still others (sulfates and creatinine) are normally not reabsorbed at all, the **nonthreshold** substances. Explanations of this selective absorption are hazy, for the simple laws of diffusion cannot be made to apply to much of it. In part, at least, it may be an active secretory process that involves the expenditure of energy.

Tubular secretion. A few substances may be added to the formation of urine by tubular secretion. Artificially injected dyes such as phenol red are apparently secreted by the tubules as well as by the glomeruli. In forms such as the toadfish there are no glomeruli at all, and the entire nephrons consist of only the tubular part, yet they have no difficulty in secreting the normal constituents of urine. Birds and reptiles also have tubular secretion of uric acid. In man and other mammals, tubular secretion appears to be of little importance. After reaching the collecting tubules, urine may lose some water and acquire epithelial cells and mucus.

Countercurrent theory of urine concentration. In recent years a new concept of urine formation has emerged. It has long been known that in lower vertebrates the kidney is unable to form a urine with a higher osmotic concentration than the blood plasma flowing through the filters (glomeruli). In birds and to a greater extent in mammals the urine has a salt concentration much higher than the plasma.

The new concept is called the countercurrent theory because the scheme of the nephron arrangement of the loop of Henle and the collecting tubule forms a hairpin bend in which the direction of current flow is in opposite or counter directions (Fig. 31-32). Between these opposing currents there appears to be an exchange of water and some solutes. Newer sampling methods (for example, freezing the kidney and chemically analyzing the sections at different levels of the hairpin bend) have made possible exact determinations of the fluid content from the different parts of the nephron tubule. These determinations show that in comparison with the blood plasma the glomerular or capsular filtrate is isotonic; the tubular fluid is hypertonic at the tip of Henle's loop, isotonic or even hypotonic at the distal convoluted tubule, and hypertonic in the collecting duct (Fig. 31-32). To account for these differences in urine concentrations a countercurrent multiplier mechanism has been proposed. According to this scheme there is an active transfer of sodium from the ascending limb of Henle (which is impermeable to water) to the interstitial tissue. Some of the sodium will now diffuse from its higher tissue concentration to the descending limb, so that there is a gradual increase in salt concentration, until the fluid enters the ascending limb where the same amount of salt is transported back to the tissue again. By this mechanism, sodium is constantly being removed from the ascending limb and returned to the descending limb of Henle. As the fluid leaves the loop of Henle, or the distal convoluted tubule, and enters the collecting duct, the high concentration of salt in the interstitial tissue will draw water out of the filtrate in the collecting ducts and concentrate the urine to its final form.

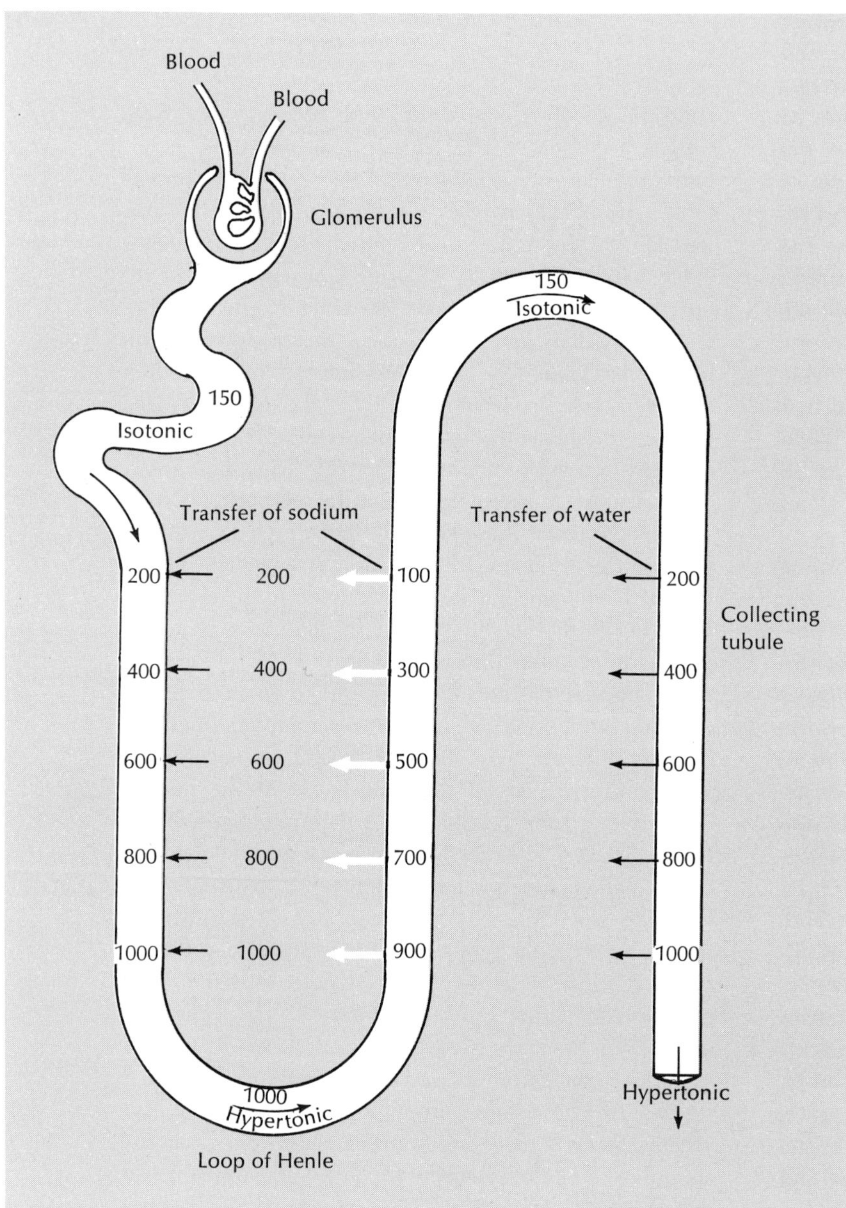

FIG. 31-32

Countercurrent multiplier mechanism. Ability of terrestrial vertebrates (especially birds and mammals) to form urine with higher osmotic concentration than their blood plasma is due to peculiar countercurrent flow mechanism associated with loop structure of their nephrons. Initial urine is isotonic with blood plasma; during its flow it then becomes more concentrated, then diluted, and then concentrated to its final form. Both simple diffusion (black arrows facing left) and active transport (white arrows) are involved. Solutes such as sodium shown here are actively transferred from ascending limb to surrounding interstitial tissue and are drawn passively into descending loop by diffusion. Water diffuses out of collecting duct because of higher sodium concentration in surrounding tissue, resulting in concentrated urine. Numbers represent relative sodium concentrations.

The advantages of this countercurrent multiplier system is that, starting with a small active transport system (for example, when sodium leaves the ascending limb), it is possible to build up a very concentrated urine by gradual concentration gradients and simple diffusion. In this way, after the system of countercurrent exchange is established, little energy is required. A steep concentration gradient, which would be required for a highly concentrated urine directly from the blood, would require a great deal of energy for active transport systems. The new concept indicates also that the degree of urine concentrations depends on the length of the loop of Henle and the collecting tubule.

Evolution of kidney nephron. The extensive work of Professor Homer W. Smith on the kidney has revealed that the early chordate kidney started out as a segmented structure that ran the length of the coelomic cavity. Each body segment was provided with a pair of kidney tubules, each of which opened at one end into the coelom by a nephrostome and at the other end, either to the outside, separately, or into a common longitudinal tube or groove. These primitive tubules also served to carry off the gametes that were shed into the coelom by the gonads. Such a kidney functions to wash out the waste of the coelomic fluid. Because of their freshwater origin and the high concentration of salts within their bodies, fish were faced with the problem of getting rid of excess water that continually entered their bodies because of this diffusion gradient.

A filtering device, such as a glomerulus (a tuft of capillaries), was an excellent device for ridding the blood of water. At first the glomerulus simply protruded into the coelom and there discharged its glomerular filtrate, but later it was inserted into the kidney tubule. The nephrostome disappeared in time, so that the whole burden of excretion was thrown upon the glomeruli, as it is in higher vertebrates. When many freshwater fish took up their existence in the sea, their problem then was to prevent undue loss of water, because the higher concentration of salts in the sea tended to draw water out of their bodies. Thus marine bony fish have tended to lose their glomeruli and depend entirely upon the tubule to remove their waste. Some have succeeded (the aglomerular fish); others have not been in salt water long enough to do this.

Composition and amount of urine excreted

The average amount of urine excreted daily is around 1,500 ml., but many factors influence its output. If large quantities of fluid are ingested, the amount of urine will reflect this increase. Also, if the individual perspires freely, the total quantity of urine will be markedly cut down. The kind of food also influences the amount of urine. Salty foods will cause an increase, for the excess salt must be eliminated. Diseases such as diabetes will cause a copious flow of urine to take care of the dissolved solids (sugar) in the blood. Certain forms of nephritis (inflammation of the kidneys) may cause a scanty flow if the glomeruli are involved; if the tubules are involved, the volume may be greater.

In the composition of urine, water naturally makes up the greater proportion of it (about 1,200 ml. daily). Of the other constituents, urea composes about 30 grams daily; uric acid, 0.5 gram; creatinine, 1 gram; various salts, 27 grams; and some others in small amounts. The color is due to a pigment—**urochrome.** The reaction of urine is usually on the acid side (pH 6) but varies with the diet. Proteins will produce an acid urine; vegetables and most fruits, an alkaline urine.

Substances that increase the flow of urine above normal are called **diuretics.** The common diuretics are water, salt water, tea, and coffee. These produce their action by increasing the glomerular filtrate, by decreasing tubular reabsorption, and by activating quiescent capillaries.

Regulative action of kidneys

In addition to getting rid of the waste, the urinary system performs other important functions. One of these is the elimination of foreign substances, such as drugs, toxins, and other things for which the body has no use, from the blood. By excreting excessively acid or alkaline substances, the pH of the blood can be maintained in a constant condition. The osmotic pressure of the blood, as well as its volume, is taken care of by the urinary system. Whenever the blood pressure drops, as from loss of blood, the filtration pressure in the glomeruli is lessened; thus less fluid is filtered and the body fluids are conserved thereby.

Mechanism of voiding urine

Urine is excreted continuously by the kidneys into the pelvis of the kidneys but is carried down the ureters in peristaltic waves (one to five per minute) to the urinary bladder. As the bladder fills, its muscular walls distend to accommodate the excess urine. Ordinarily the bladder holds about a pint; but persistent filling may increase its capacity. As the walls of the bladder are distended, certain sensory nerve endings there are stimulated and reflexes are set up which lead to the desire for urination, or micturition. These reflex centers are located in the sacral region of the spinal cord and in the brain. The urethra is provided with two sphincter valves: the **internal vesical sphincter** and the **external vesical sphincter.** The former is composed of smooth muscle and is involuntary in its action; the latter is of striped muscle and voluntary. When certain reflexes occur, the involuntary sphincter opens automatically, but the voluntary one remains closed until conscious volition opens it.

Annotated references

Adolph, E. F. (editor). 1960. The development of homeostasis. New York, Academic Press, Inc. *The equilibrium between organisms and environment is one of the most important concepts in the life process. This work tries to interpret the different mecha-*

nisms involved at different levels of biologic organization.

Andresen, P. H. 1952. The human blood groups. Springfield, Ill., Charles C Thomas, Publisher. *An authoritative account of this much-studied subject.*

Brooks, S. M. 1960. Basic facts of body water and ions. New York, Springer Publishing Co., Inc. *An excellent elementary account of the fluid and electrolyte balance in the body. Especially good for beginners in zoology.*

Burnet, F. M. 1962. The integrity of the body. Cambridge, Mass., Harvard University Press. *An up-to-date appraisal of modern immunology.*

Cannon, W. B. 1939. The wisdom of the body, rev. ed. New York, W. W. Norton & Co., Inc. *In this work a great American physiologist shows how the human body retains a constant condition despite disturbing influences, a principle he calls homeostasis.*

Carter, G. S. 1961. A general zoology of the invertebrates, ed. 4. London, Sidgwick & Jackson. *Although this work is not a textbook on all aspects of the invertebrates, it stresses the physiology and general biologic principles of the group.*

Cott, H. B. 1957. Adaptive coloration in animals. London, Methuen & Co., Ltd. *This important monograph demonstrates in convincing fashion the role of color adaptation in the animal kingdom. The author points out three important classes of adaptive coloration—concealment, advertisement, and disguise.*

Diggs, L. W., D. Sturm, and A. Bell. 1956. The morphology of human blood cells. Philadelphia, W. B. Saunders Co. *This is an atlas of the morphology of normal and pathologic human blood cells. Many of the illustrations are in color.*

Edney, E. B. 1957. The water relations of terrestrial arthropods. New York, Cambridge University Press. *Discusses the ways by which arthropods meet the problems of water economy in their environment. For conserving water, arthropods have devised adaptations that involve the three main potential sources of water loss—excretion, transpiration through the integument, and loss from respiratory surfaces.*

Guyton, A. C. 1964. Function of the human body. Philadelphia, W. B. Saunders Co. *An up-to-date text with revealing schematic illustrations and charts.*

Hoar, W. S. 1966. General and comparative physiology. Englewood Cliffs, N. J., Prentice-Hall, Inc. *An excellent treatise on the latest concepts of physiology.*

Potts, W. T. W., and G. Parry. 1964. Osmotic and ionic regulation in animals. New York, The Macmillan Co. *An excellent, up-to-date treatise on the present concepts of homeostatic mechanisms, with special emphasis on osmoregulation and fluid balance in the animal body.*

Prosser, C. L., and F. A. Brown, Jr. 1961. Comparative animal physiology. Philadelphia, W. B. Saunders Co. *This is a later edition of the well-known 1950 edition. Indispensable to all serious students of biology.*

Ramsay, J. A. 1952. A physiological approach to the lower animals. New York, Cambridge University Press.

Schmidt-Nielsen, K. 1964. Animal physiology, ed. 2. Englewood Cliffs, N. J., Prentice-Hall, Inc. *One of the best backgrounds for beginning the study of physiology before taking up the deeper physicochemical aspects of the subject.*

Smith, H. W. 1951. The kidney. New York, Oxford University Press. *One of the best technical treatises on the structure and function of the vertebrate kidney. Suitable only for the advanced student.*

Snively, W. D., Jr. 1960. Sea within: the story of our body fluid. Philadelphia, J. B. Lippincott Co. *A popular, interesting treatise on the "interior sea" and its importance in our bodies in health and disease.*

CHAPTER 32

• NERVOUS AND SENSORY SYSTEMS

NERVOUS SYSTEM*

● The origin of the nervous system is based on one of the fundamental principles of protoplasm—irritability. Each cell responds to stimulation in a manner characteristic of that type of cell. But certain cells have become highly specialized for receiving stimuli and for conducting impulses to various parts of the body. Through evolutionary changes, these cells have become the most complex of all body systems—the nervous system. In some animals the endocrine system is also used for coordination. However, the nervous system has wider and more direct control of body functions than the endocrine system.

The evolution of the nervous system has been correlated with the development of bilateral symmetry and cephalization. Along with this development, animals acquired exteroceptors and associated ganglia. The basic plan of the nervous system is to code the sensory information, internally or externally, and transmit it to regions of the central nervous system where it is processed into appropriate action. This action may be of several types, such as simple reflexes, automatic behavior patterns, conscious perception, or learning processes.

Nervous mechanisms among invertebrates

Nervous structures are largely absent in protozoans, although conduction of stimuli certainly occurs (Fig. 32-1). In some protozoans, however, some regions may be more sensitive to stimuli. The **neuromotor apparatus** of ciliates represents a structure for coordinating the beating of the cilia in response to stimuli. Few metazoan groups are without a nervous system of some form. The lowest metazoans, sponges, have a very restricted nervous system, although they may have a primitive type. In the **nerve net** of coelenterates the bipolar or multipolar nerve cells (**protoneurons**) may be separated from each other by synaptic junctions, but they form an extensive network that is found in and under the ectoderm over all the body. An impulse starting in one part of this net will be conducted in all directions, since the synapse is not restricted to one-way transmission. There are no differentiated sensory, motor, or connector components in the strict meaning of those terms. Branches of the nerve net connect to receptors in the epidermis and to the epitheliomuscular cells. Most responses tend to be generalized. Such a type of nervous system is retained among higher animals in the form of nerve plexuses in which such generalized movements as peristalsis are involved.

Flatworms are provided with two anterior **ganglia** of nerve cells from which two main nerve trunks run posteriorly, with lateral branches extending to the various parts of the body, thus beginning a central and peripheral differentiation. This is the first appearance of the **linear** type of nervous system, which is more developed in higher invertebrates. Higher invertebrates have a more centralized nervous system, with the two longitudinal nerve cords fused (although still recognizable) and many ganglia present. The annelids have a well-developed nervous system consisting of sensory and motor neurons, nerve cords, and fibers. At the anterior end, the ventral nerve cord divides and passes upward around the digestive tract to join the bilobed brain. In each segment the double nerve cord bears a double ganglion, each with two pairs of nerves.

Arthropods have a system similar to that of earthworms, except that the ganglia are larger and the sense organs better developed. Arthropods, especially crustaceans, have a unique arrangement of nerve and muscle fibers. One axon may serve two or more muscles, and each muscle fiber may receive two or more motor nerves. The single muscle fiber in such cases is connected to an excitatory and an inhibitory nerve fiber. When an inhibitory fiber is stimulated, impulses in

*Refer to Chapter 2, Principles 7 and 29.

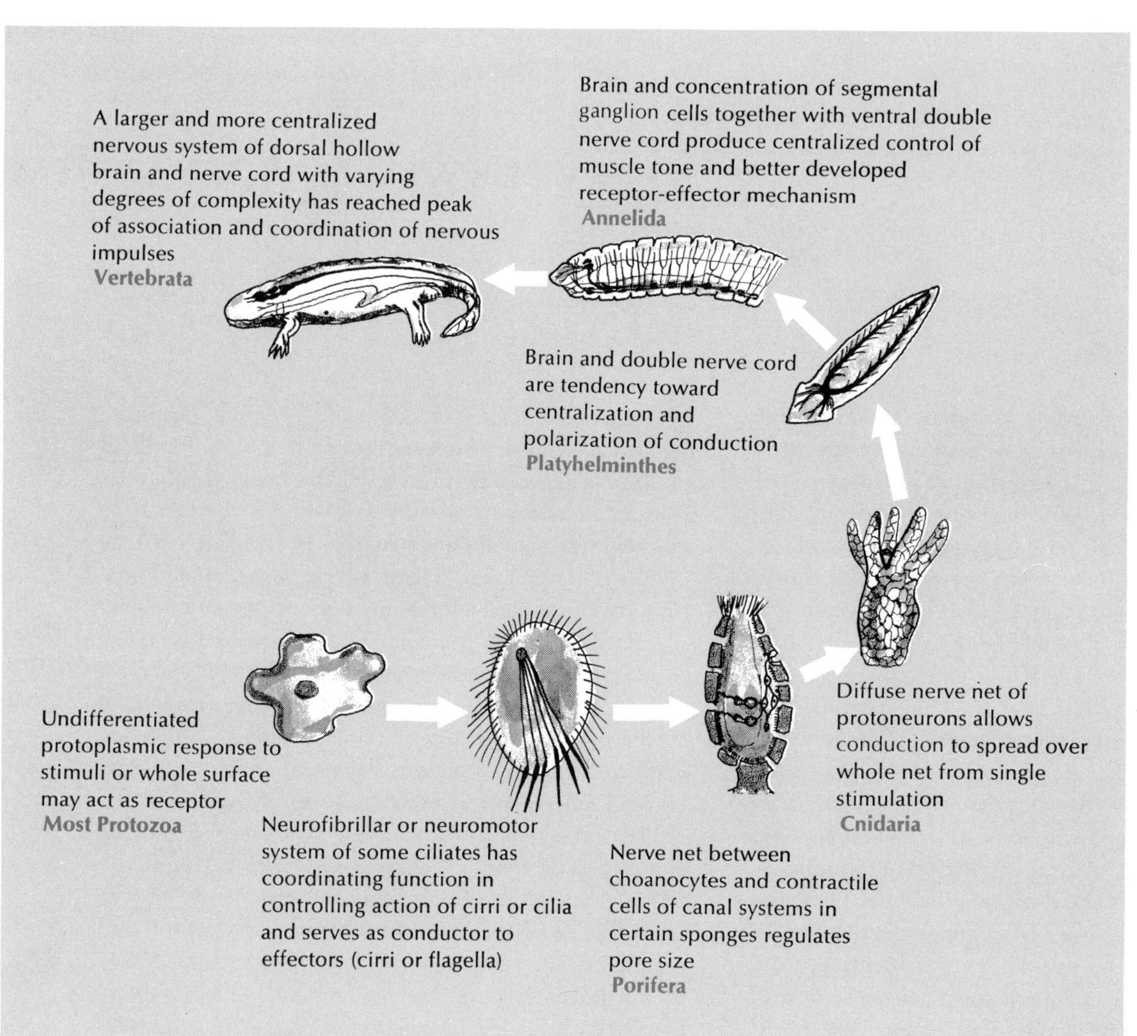

FIG. 32-1

How nervous system has evolved.

the excitatory fiber will have no effect. Claw muscles may have one set of inhibitory and two sets of stimulating fibers. When activated, one set of stimulating fibers will produce a quick contraction of muscle, and the other stimulating set will produce a slower and more forceful contraction. The inhibitory set can inhibit the action of the other two. Thus a graded muscular contraction can be produced by varying the frequency of stimulation among the multiple axons. This graded difference seems to be a function of the nerve axons involved, since the same muscle fiber responds differently to the varied conditions. How this mechanism works is not known. Many arthropods have both compound and simple eyes, as well as statocysts, or organs of equilibrium.

Mollusks have a system of three pairs of ganglia; one pair is near the mouth, another pair at the base of the foot, and one pair in the viscera. The ganglia are joined by connectives. The mollusks also have a number of sense organs, which are especially well developed in the cephalopods. Among the echinoderms the nervous system is radially arranged.

The nerve cord in all invertebrates is ventral to the alimentary canal and is solid. This arrangement is in marked contrast to the nerve cord of vertebrates, which is dorsal to the digestive system, single, and hollow.

Nervous system of vertebrates

Vertebrates have, as a rule, a brain much larger than the other part of the cord. In lower vertebrates this difference is not marked, but higher in the vertebrate kingdom the brain increases in size, reaching its maxi-

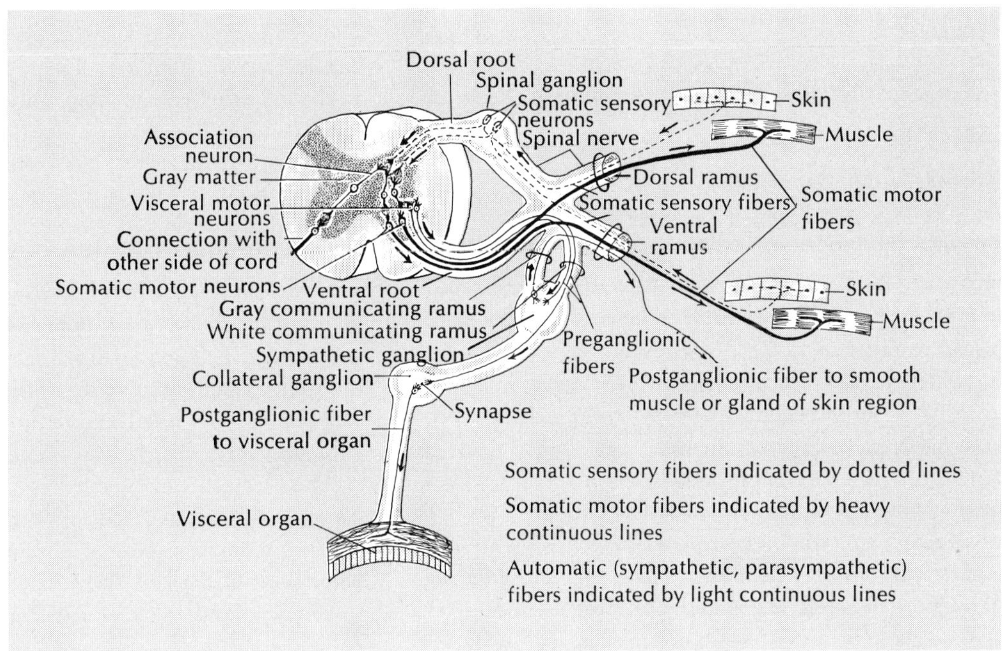

FIG. 32-2

Cross section of nerve cord and ganglia in higher vertebrates showing functional components of spinal and autonomic nerves. Ventral ramus nerves are chief spinal nerves; dorsal ramus supplies only skin and muscles of back. Each spinal nerve joins spinal cord by two roots—dorsal root with afferent sensory fibers and ventral root with efferent motor fibers. Sensory neurons have cell bodies in spinal ganglion; motor neurons have cell bodies in spinal cord. Thus each spinal nerve has both somatic afferent fibers from sense organs of skin and striped muscle and somatic efferent fibers to striped muscle and glands of skin. Autonomic (visceral) system arises from rami of spinal nerves and supplies nerves to smooth and cardiac muscle and to glands. Visceral motor components differ from somatic motor components by having two-neuron chains. First neuron of chain is preganglionic, has cell body in cord, and is myelinated; second neuron is postganglionic, has cell body in ganglion, and is nonmedullated. Autonomic conduction is carried by two types of preganglionic fibers: one synapses in sympathetic ganglion with postganglionic fiber to muscles and glands of skin; the other passes through sympathetic ganglion and synapses in collateral ganglion with postganglionic fiber to visceral organs.

mum in mammals, especially man, in which it may be larger than all the rest of the nervous system. Along with this enlargement has come an increase in complexity, bringing better patterns of coordination, integration, and intelligence. The nervous system is commonly divided into central and peripheral parts; the central division is chiefly concerned with integrative activity and the peripheral part with the reception of stimuli from the internal and external environment. The peripheral division also transmits impulses to and from the central nervous system.

Neuron as structural unit

A **neuron** is a nerve cell body and all its processes (Fig. 7-16). The nerve cell body contains a nucleus and certain typical cytoplasmic structures such as Nissl bodies and neurofibrils. The Nissl (tigroid) bodies are made up of parallel flat sacs of endoplasmic reticulum (as seen with the electron microscope) with many attached ribosomes. They stain deeply with methylene blue and toluidine blue, which may be due to the RNA in the bodies. The function of Nissl substance is the formation of proteins and enzymes, with RNA playing a central role. The processes include several **dendrites,** which carry impulses toward the cell body, and a single **axon,** which carries impulses away. The axons are usually covered with a soft, white myelin sheath, which in turn is enclosed by the neurilemma. Neurons are commonly divided into three types—**motor, sensory,** and **association** or **connector.** The dendrites of sensory neurons are connected to a **receptor,** and their axons are connected to other neurons; associators are connected only to other neurons; and motor neurons are connected by their axons to an **effector.** Nerves are actually made up of many nerve processes—axons or dendrites or both—bound together with connective tissue. The cell bodies of these bundles of nerves are located either in ganglia or somewhere in the central nervous system (brain or spinal cord).

Reflex arc as functional unit

Neurons work in groups called **reflex arcs** (Fig. 32-2). There must be at least two neurons in a reflex arc, but usually there are more. The parts of a typical reflex arc consist of (1) a **receptor,** a sense organ in the skin, muscle, or other organ; (2) an **afferent** or sensory neuron, which carries the impulse toward the central system; (3) a **nerve center,** where synaptic junctions are made between the sensory neurons and the association neurons; (4) the **efferent** or motor neuron, which makes synaptic junction with the association neuron; and (5) the **effector,** by which the animal responds to its environmental changes. Effectors may be grouped as follows: (a) muscles and glands, in most animals; (b) cilia and flagella, also of wide occurrence; (c) nematocysts, mainly restricted to the coelenterates; (d) electric organs, in certain fish; (e) luminous organs, in many groups; and (f) chromatophores, represented in both invertebrates and vertebrates. If only two neurons are involved, the afferent neuron makes a direct synapsis with the efferent neuron and the association component is omitted.

Association neurons may connect afferent and efferent neurons on the same side of the spinal cord, connect them on opposite sides of the cord, or connect them on different levels of the spinal cord, either on the same or opposite sides. In almost any reflex act a number of reflex arcs are involved. For instance, a single afferent neuron may make synaptic junctions with many efferent neurons. In a similar way an efferent neuron may receive impulses from many afferent neurons. In this latter case the efferent neuron is referred to as the **final common path.**

A **reflex act** is the response to a stimulus carried over a reflex arc. It is **involuntary** and may involve the cerebrospinal or the autonomic nervous divisions of the nervous system. Many of the vital processes of the body, such as breathing, heartbeat, diameter of blood vessels, sweat glands, and others, are reflex actions. Some reflex acts are inherited and innate; others are acquired through learning processes (conditioned).

The point at which two neurons are in contact is called a **synapse,** or synaptic junction. In any form of synaptic junction the neurons are not in anatomic connection, although they are in functional connection with each other. Two thin surface membranes form the barrier at the junction. There is a gap between the branched ends of the axon and the branched ends of the dendrite. The synapse has the power to allow some impulses to pass and to block others. Conduction of the impulse is slowed in its passage over the synaptic junction and is always unidirectional, that is, from afferent to efferent neurons, never in the reverse direction. It is very susceptible to fatigue, drugs, and other abnormal states. One theory accounts for the passage of the impulse over the synapse by the formation of a chemical substance, **neurohumor,** that forms a bridge over which the impulse can pass. The nature of this neurohumor is probably acetylcholine and norepinephrine.

The electron microscope reveals enlargements (boutons) at the ends of the fine terminal axonal branches. These boutons lie closely applied to the dendrites, or sometimes to the cell body. The boutons are rich in mitochondria and contain small membranous structures called synaptic vesicles, which may be associated with the chemical transmitter substances acetylcholine and norepinephrine.

Embryonic development of nervous system

The early formation of the nervous system will be briefly discussed in Chapter 34. The basic vertebrate plan is a dorsal longitudinal hollow nerve cord that runs from head to tail. At the anterior end, this cord expands to form a series of vesicles, at first three and later five in number. The three-part brain is made up of prosencephalon, mesencephalon, and rhombencephalon, associated in order, with the nose, eye, and ear with a lateral line system (in some). Each division in time develops into a major differentiation of the brain, cerebral hemispheres, midbrain (roof), and cerebellum, respectively. The prosencephalon and rhombencephalon each divide again to form the five-part brain characteristic of the adults of all vertebrates. The five-part brain includes the telencephalon, diencephalon, mesencephalon, metencephalon, and myelencephalon. From these divisions the different functional brain structures arise.

Organization of nervous system

Central nervous system. The central nervous system is composed of the brain and spinal cord.

Spinal cord. The spinal cord varies in size with different vertebrates. In the average man it is about 18 inches long, extending only to the level of the first lumbar vertebra. The cord is protected by three layers of

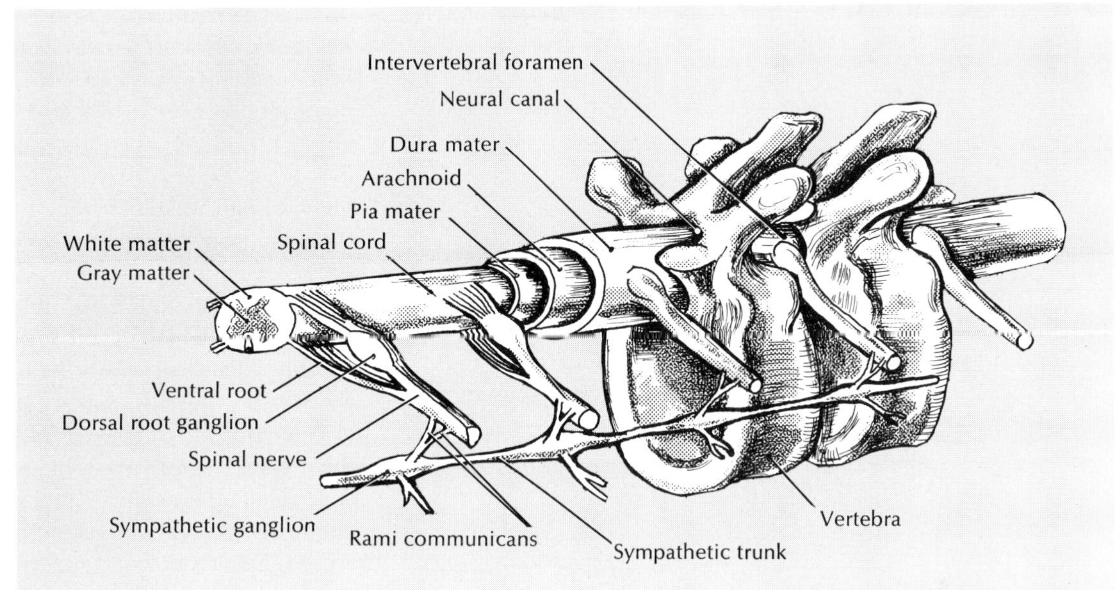

FIG. 32-3

Spinal cord and meninges with relation to spinal nerves, sympathetic system, and vertebrae. Three coats of meninges have been partly cut away to expose spinal cord. Only two vertebrae are shown in position. (Modified from several sources.)

meninges (Fig. 32-3)—the **dura mater, arachnoid,** and **pia mater.** Spaces between these protective layers contain cerebrospinal fluid that forms a protective cushion.

In cross section the cord shows two zones—an inner H-shaped zone of gray matter, made up of nerve cell bodies, and an outer zone of white matter, made up of nerve bundles of axons and dendrites. The gray matter contains association neurons and the cell bodies of motor neurons (Fig. 32-4). Just outside the cord on each side of the dorsal region are the **dorsal root ganglia,** which contain the cell bodies of the sensory neurons. The gray matter of the cord is divided into two posterior and two anterior horns.

The white matter of the cord is made up of bundles of nerves of similar functions—the **ascending tracts,** carrying impulses to the brain, and the **descending tracts,** carrying impulses away from the brain. The sensory (ascending) tracts are located mainly in the dorsal part of the cord; the motor (descending) tracts are found ventrally and laterally in the cord. In whatever tract they are located, the fibers somewhere in their course cross over from one side of the cord to the other, the sensory fibers crossing at a higher level than the motor fibers.

Brain. The brain in vertebrates shows an evolution from the linear arrangement in lower forms (fish and amphibians) to the much-folded and enlarged brain found in higher vertebrates (birds and mammals) (Fig.

FIG. 32-4

A, Gray matter of spinal cord showing distribution of nerve cell bodies. Nerve cells are darkish irregular bodies. **B,** Neuron from gray matter of spinal cord, as seen under higher magnification. (Courtesy J. W. Bamberger.)

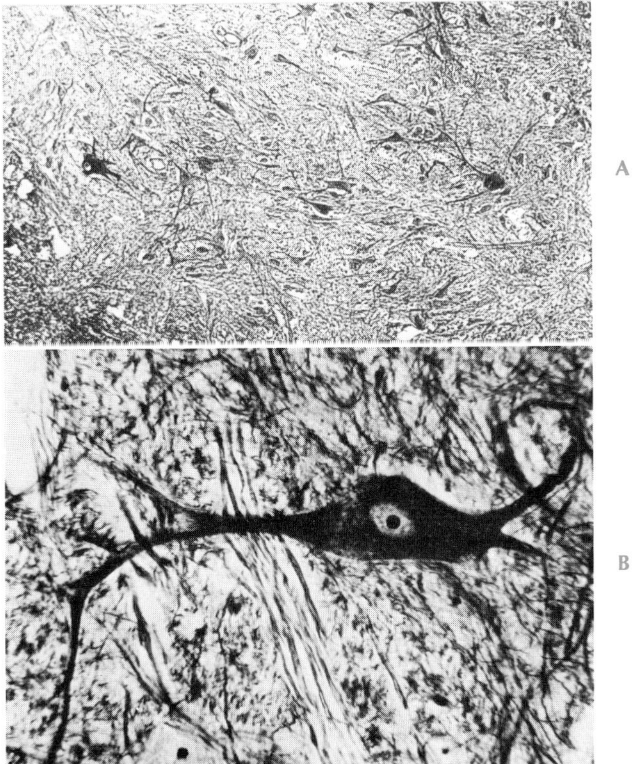

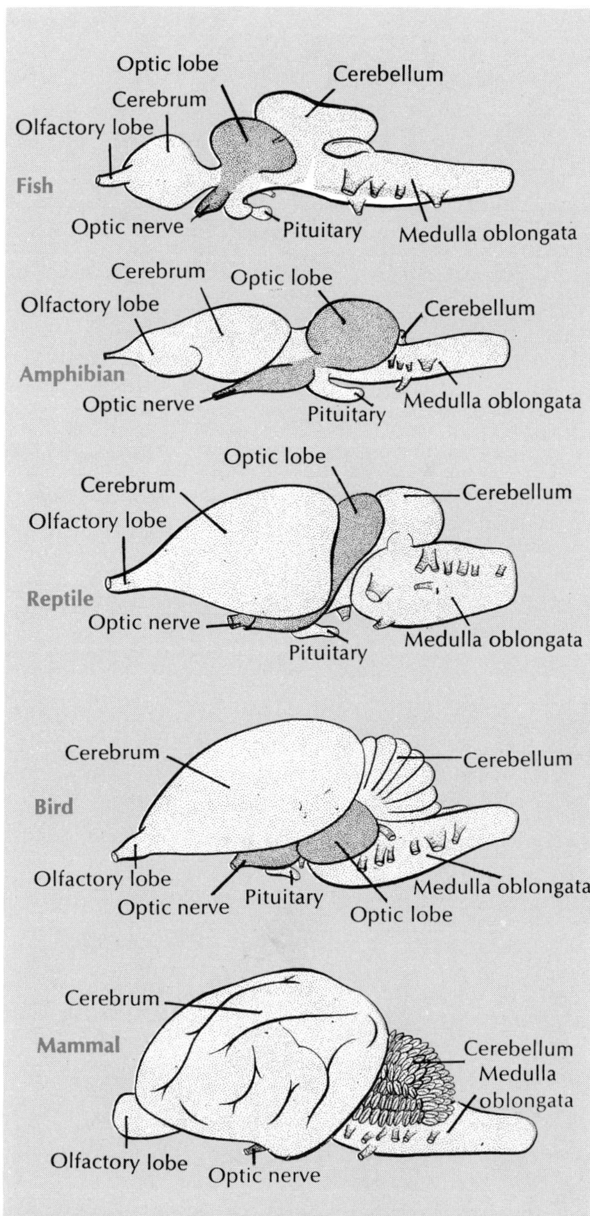

FIG. 32-5

Comparative structure of principal brain divisions in different vertebrate groups—fish, amphibian, reptile, bird, and mammal. Note progressive enlargement of cerebrum in higher groups. Stubs of certain cranial nerves are shown.

32-5). The brain is really the enlarged anterior end of the spinal cord. The ratio between the weight of the brain and spinal cord affords a fair criterion of an animal's intelligence. In fish and amphibians this ratio is about 1:1, in man the ratio is 55:1, or the brain is fifty-five times as heavy as the spinal cord. The average human brain weight is from 1,200 to 1,400 grams, but there are many variations.

The evolutionary trend toward a dominant brain has been correlated with better integration and better mastery over the environment. The brain of vertebrates has steadily advanced, with a better sensory reception and a better nervous adjustment for meeting a complex environment. The pallium, or cerebral cortex, has shown the greatest evolutionary advancement. In fish and most amphibians the pallium (roof of the telencephalon) is almost nonexistent, consisting only of a thin layer (the archipallium) chiefly concerned with smell. This region represented mainly by olfactory lobes in higher vertebrates was instrumental in food finding. A rudimentary pallium is found in reptiles, but in mammals an additional formation (neopallium) is added on to the archipallium and exceeds in size and importance the remainder of the central nervous system.

The brain is made up of both white and gray matter, with the gray matter on the outside, mostly in the convoluted **cortex.** (In fish and amphibians the brain mainly retains the spinal cord arrangement.) In the deeper parts of the brain the white matter of nerve fibers connects the cortex with lower centers of the brain and spinal cord or connects one part of the cortex with another. Also in deeper portions of the brain are collections of nerve cell bodies (gray matter) that provide synaptic junctions between the neurons of the higher centers and those of lower centers.

There are also nonnervous elements in the nervous system such as connective, supporting, and capsule cells and the **neuroglia** (Fig. 32-7). These neuroglia cells are supposed to play various vital roles in the functioning of the neurons. One of their functions is to bind together the nervous tissue proper. Another is their activity in pathologic processes of regeneration. They are also the chief source of tumors of the central nervous system. Actually, they greatly outnumber the neurons. There are three main types: **microglia** with small nuclei and twisted processes; **astrocytes,** or "spider cells," with large nuclei and numerous thick processes; and **oligodendrocytes** with small nuclei and few slender processes. Microglia develops from mesoderm and are phagocytic. The other two types come from ectoderm.

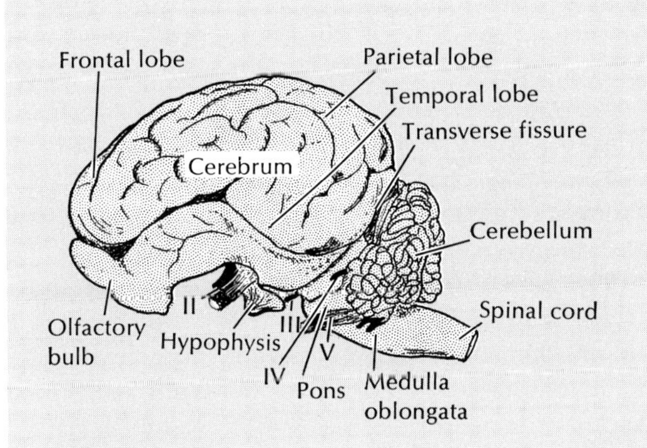

FIG. 32-6

Brain of pig, view of left side.

FIG. 32-7

Differentiation of neuroectodermal cells of neural tube. Germinal cells lining lumen of tube increase in number, elongate, and are pushed to periphery as neuroepithelial cells, which differentiate into two lines. One line develops into neuroblasts and finally into functional neurons. Second line becomes free spongioblasts that give rise to the neuroglia cells (astrocytes with many processes and oligodendrocytes, not shown, with few processes). Germinal cells that remain in place around lumen assume appearance of columnar cells with long processes (ependymal spongioblasts). They may at first have cilia on their inner border and eventually develop into ordinary ependymal cells lining central canal and ventricle of brain. (Modified from Ham, 1953.)

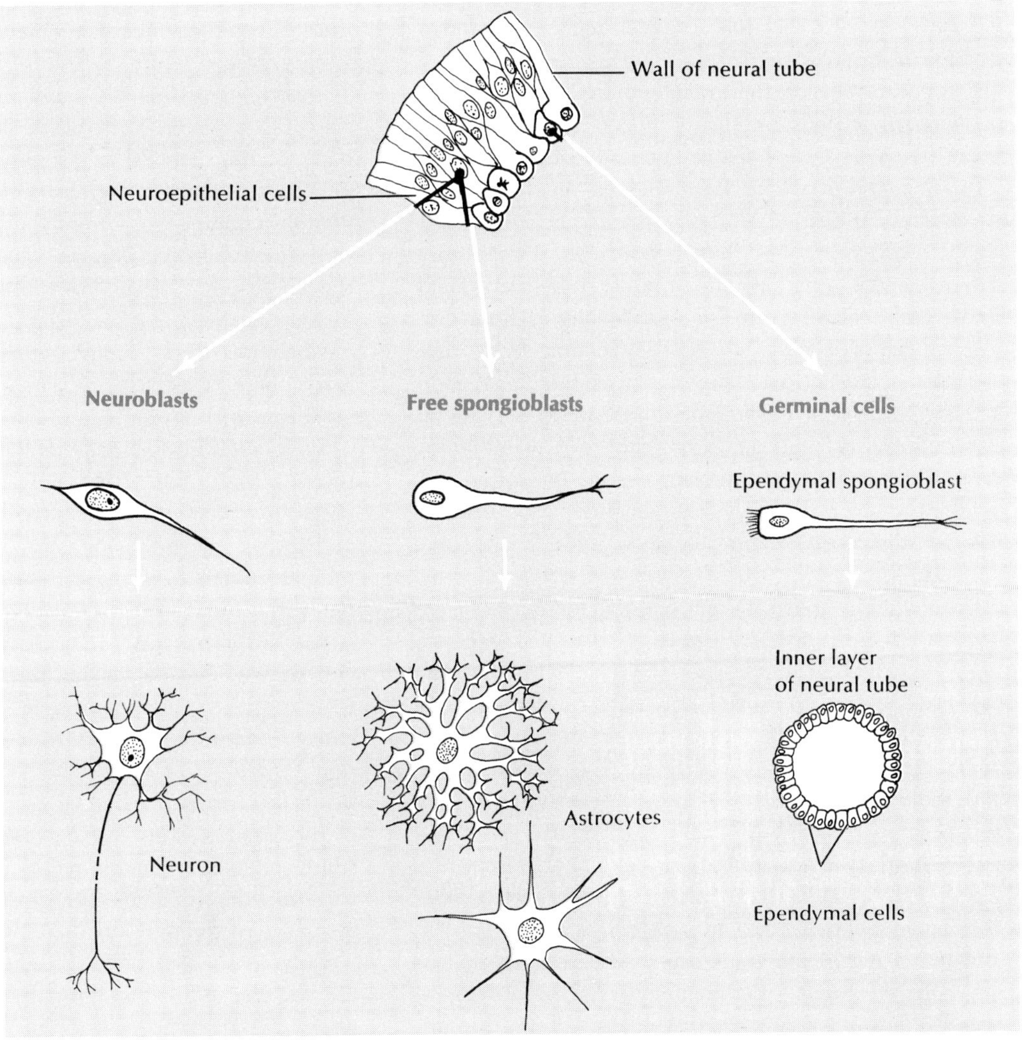

Neuroglia cells require special techniques for their demonstration.

The six main regions of the brain are the medulla oblongata, pons, midbrain, thalamus, cerebrum, and cerebellum (Fig. 32-6). The **medulla,** the most posterior, is really a conical continuation of the spinal cord. The central canal in the medulla is enlarged to form the fourth ventricle, and directly above it is the cerebellum. Cerebrospinal fluid passes from the ventricle through the pores to the spaces in the meninges. The gray matter of the medulla includes nerve centers, which control many vital processes such as heartbeat, respiration, vasomotor control, deglutition (swallowing), and others. The medulla serves as the origin of many cranial nerves. The white matter of the medulla consists mainly of nerve tracts that connect higher centers of the brain with the spinal cord.

The **pons,** between the medulla and the midbrain, is made up of a thick bundle of fibers that carries impulses from one side of the cerebellum to the other.

Between the pons and the thalamus and in front of the cerebellum lies the **midbrain.** Its **cerebral aqueduct** connects the third and fourth ventricles. In its gray matter are the nuclei of the third and fourth cranial nerves and reflex centers for muscle tone. The white matter consists of ascending and descending tracts that go to the thalamus and cerebrum. On the upper side of the midbrain are the rounded **optic lobes,** serving as centers for visual and auditory reflexes. The midbrain has undergone little evolutionary change in size among vertebrates but has changed in function. It is responsible for the most complex behavior of fish and amphibians.

The **thalamus** above the midbrain contains masses of gray matter surrounded by the cerebral hemispheres on each side. The thalamus is the relay center for the sensory tracts from the spinal cord. Here synapses are made with neurons that pass to the various sensory areas of the cerebrum. Centers for the sensations of pain, temperature, and touch are supposedly located in the thalamus. Near the thalamus in the floor (hypothalamus) of the third ventricle are centers that regulate body temperature, water balance, sleep, and a few other body functions. The hypothalamus also is known to be the center of emotional aspects of life (rage, pleasure, pain, etc.) and experimentally it has been demonstrated to be a center for controlling appetite in the rat. It also has the neurosecretory cells that produce neurohormones that pass down fiber tracts to the posterior pituitary where the hormones are released into the circulation. On the lateral side of each thalamus there is a triangular mass of gray matter, the **corpus striatum,** connected by fibers to the thalamus and to the cerebrum, cerebellum, and spinal cord. It may control muscle tone.

The largest division of the brain is the **cerebrum,** which is concerned with learned behavior, in contrast to the automatic behavior in the other divisions. It forms the most anterior part of the brain and, in man and most mammals, overlies most of the other parts of the brain. It is incompletely divided into two hemispheres by a longitudinal fissure. The outer **cerebral cortex** is much folded and is made up of gray matter. The uplifted folds are called **gyri,** the depressions, **sulci.** Deeper fissures divide the brain into regions. Within the hemispheres are the first and second ventricles. Both gray and white matter are found in the cerebrum. The cortex contains many billions of neurons and their synaptic junctions with other neurons. In the deeper parts of the cerebral hemispheres are other masses of gray matter that function as centers or relay stations for neurons running to or from the cortex. The white matter, which consists of nerve fiber tracts, lies deeper in the cerebrum. These fibers connect one region of a hemisphere with another region of the same hemisphere (**association fibers**), one hemisphere with the other hemisphere (**transverse** or **commissural fibers**), and the cerebrum with lower centers (**projection fibers**).

To a certain extent there is localization of function in the cerebrum (Fig. 32-8). This knowledge has been obtained by direct experimentation such as by the removal of parts of the brain, by checking of the locations of brain lesions, and by the sensations experienced by patients during operations, etc. It has been possible to locate the visual center (back of cerebrum [Figs. 32-8 and 32-9]), the center for hearing (side of brain or temporal lobe), the motor area that controls the skeletal muscle (anterior to central sulcus), and the area for skin sensations of heat, cold, and touch (posterior to the central sulcus). Large regions of the frontal lobe of the brain are the "silent areas," or **association areas.** These regions are not directly connected to sense organs or muscles and are for the higher faculties of memory, reasoning, and learning.

Only forms that have well-developed cerebral cortices are able to learn and modify their behavior by experience. Vital reflex centers and life can be sustained without a cortex, but there can be no learning and no analyses of sensations or stimuli. In such cases the organism is only an automaton.

The **cerebellum,** lying beneath the posterior part of the cerebrum, consists of two hemispheres and a central portion called the vermis. In man it is deeply folded and is composed of nerve cell bodies. Among its cells are the large, much-branched **Purkinje cells.** The white fiber tracts lie deeper in the cerebellum. The chief function of the cerebellum is regulation of muscular coordination.

ELECTRICAL CHANGES IN BRAIN. In the living state the brain is accompanied by electrical changes. The recordings of these changes are commonly referred to as **brain waves.** The instrument used for these recordings is called an **electroencephalograph.** When electrodes are attached to different parts of the scalp, this delicate instrument records the activity of the underlying cerebral cortex. These brain waves vary with the activity of the nerve cells. The brain is active awake or asleep. A very active brain will produce a large number of waves in a given time; a sluggish brain has fewer waves. Patterns of brain waves vary with mental disturbances; those for certain pathologic lesions such as epilepsy and brain tumor are rather characteristic and useful in diagnosis.

Peripheral nervous system. This system is made up of the paired cranial nerves that run to and from the brain and the paired spinal nerves that run to and from the spinal cord. They consist of bundles of axons and dendrites and connect with the receptors and effectors in the body (Fig. 32-10).

Cranial nerves. In the higher vertebrates, including man, there are 12 pairs of cranial nerves. They are primarily concerned with the sense organs, glands, and muscles of the head and are more specialized than spinal nerves. Some are purely sensory (olfactory, optic, auditory); some are mainly, if not entirely, motor (oculomotor, trochlear, abducens, spinal accessory, hypoglossal); and the others are mixed with both sensory and motor neurons (trigeminal, facial, glossopharyngeal, vagus). The majority arise from or near the medulla. Some of the cranial nerves bear autonomic nerve fibers, especially in the facial and vagus. For convenience the various cranial nerves are also designated by the Roman

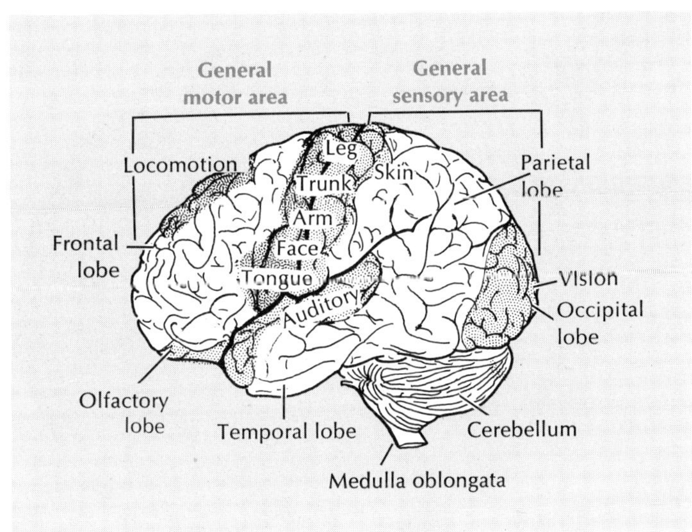

FIG. 32-8

Localization of brain function in left cerebrum.

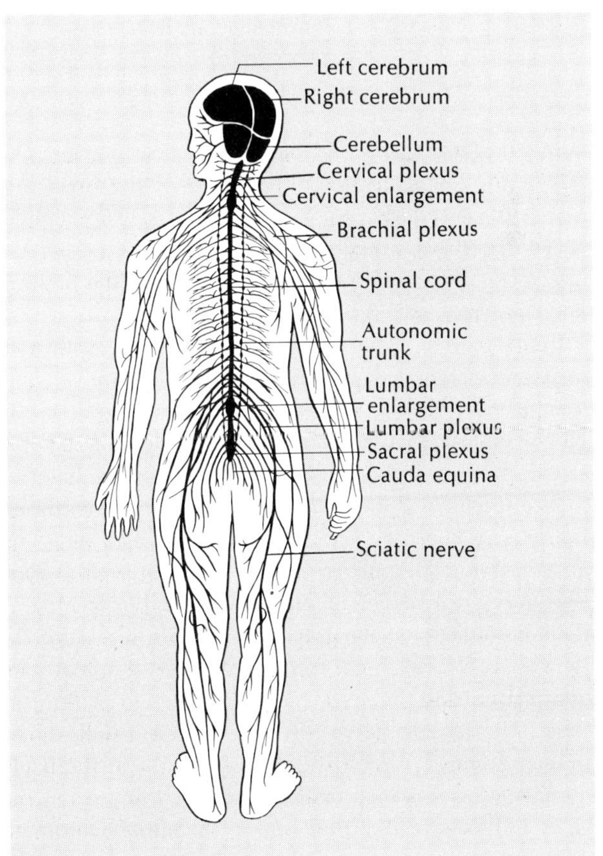

FIG. 32-9

Posterior aspect of nervous system in man.

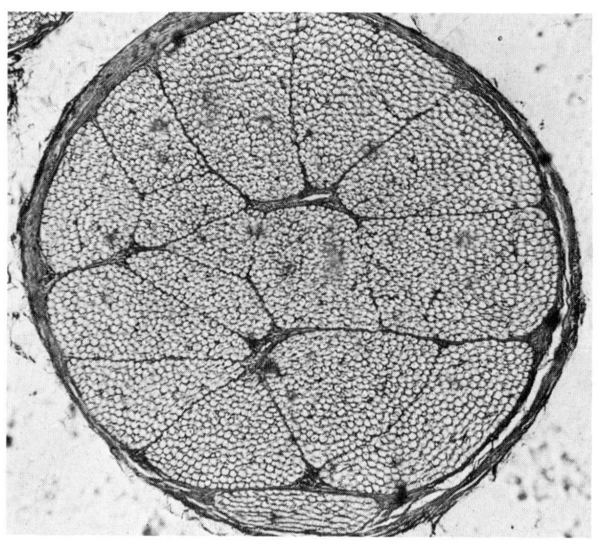

FIG. 32-10

Cross section of nerve trunk showing cut ends of nerve fibers (small white circles). Such a trunk may be made up of thousands of fibers. Both afferent and efferent fibers are represented.

numerals I to XII, as well as by specific names. The numbering begins at the anterior end of the brain and proceeds posteriorly. In 1895 another sensory cranial nerve (nervus terminalis) was found running from the olfactory membrane to the olfactory lobe of the brain in all vertebrates except birds.

Spinal nerves. The spinal nerves contain both sensory and motor components in approximately equal numbers. In higher vertebrates and man there are 31 pairs: cervical, 8 pairs; thoracic, 12 pairs; lumbar, 5 pairs; sacral, 5 pairs; and caudal, 1 pair. Each nerve has two roots by which it is connected to the spinal cord. All the sensory fibers enter the cord by the dorsal root, and all the motor fibers leave the cord by the ventral root. The nerve cell bodies of motor neurons are located in the ventral horns of the gray zone of the spinal cord; the sensory nerve cell bodies are in the dorsal spinal ganglia just outside the cord. Near the junction of the two roots, the spinal nerve divides into a small dorsal branch (ramus), which supplies structures in the back; a larger ventral branch, which supplies structures in the sides and front of the trunk and in the appendages; and an autonomic branch, which supplies structures in the viscera. To supply a large area of the body, the ventral rami of several spinal nerves may join to form a network (plexus). These are the **cervical, brachial,** and **lumbosacral plexuses.**

Autonomic nervous system. The autonomic nerves govern the involuntary functions of the body that do not ordinarily affect consciousness. The cerebrum has no direct control over these nerves; thus one cannot by volition stimulate or inhibit their action. Autonomic nerves control the movements of the alimentary canal and heart, the contraction of the smooth muscle of the blood vessels, urinary bladder, iris of eye, etc., and the secretions of various glands. Although these nerves have both sensory and motor components, the former are considered of minor importance and are ignored by many authorities. The efferent or motor nerves of this system arise from small nerve cells located at different levels from the midbrain to the sacral region of the spinal cord. After issuing from the central nervous system, these fibers make synaptic junctions in ganglia, which may lie close to the spinal cord or in the organs innervated.

There are thus at least two neurons in an autonomic efferent connection—a **preganglionic** fiber, which has its nerve cell body in the central system, and a **postganglionic** fiber, whose nerve cell body is located in the ganglion (Fig. 32-2). Subdivisions of the autonomic system are (1) the **parasympathetic,** which is centered partly in the brain and partly in the lower end of the spinal cord (craniosacral outflow), and (2) the **sympathetic,** which is centered in the middle part of the spinal cord (thoracolumbar outflow). Most organs in the body are innervated by both sympathetic and parasympathetic fibers, and their actions are antagonistic (Fig. 32-11). If one speeds up an activity, the other will slow it down. However, neither kind of nerve is exclusively excitatory or inhibitory. Parasympathetic fibers inhibit heartbeat but will excite peristaltic movements of the intestine; sympathetic fibers will increase heartbeat but slow down peristaltic movement.

The **parasympathetic** system consists of nerves, some of which emerge from the brain by certain cranial nerves and others from the pelvic region of the spinal cord by certain spinal nerves. In this division the preganglionic fiber is very long, because the ganglion in which it makes synaptic junction is located near or in the organ innervated. On this account the postganglionic fiber is very short. Parasympathetic fibers **excite** the stomach and intestine, urinary bladder, bronchi, constrictor of iris, salivary glands, and coronary arteries.

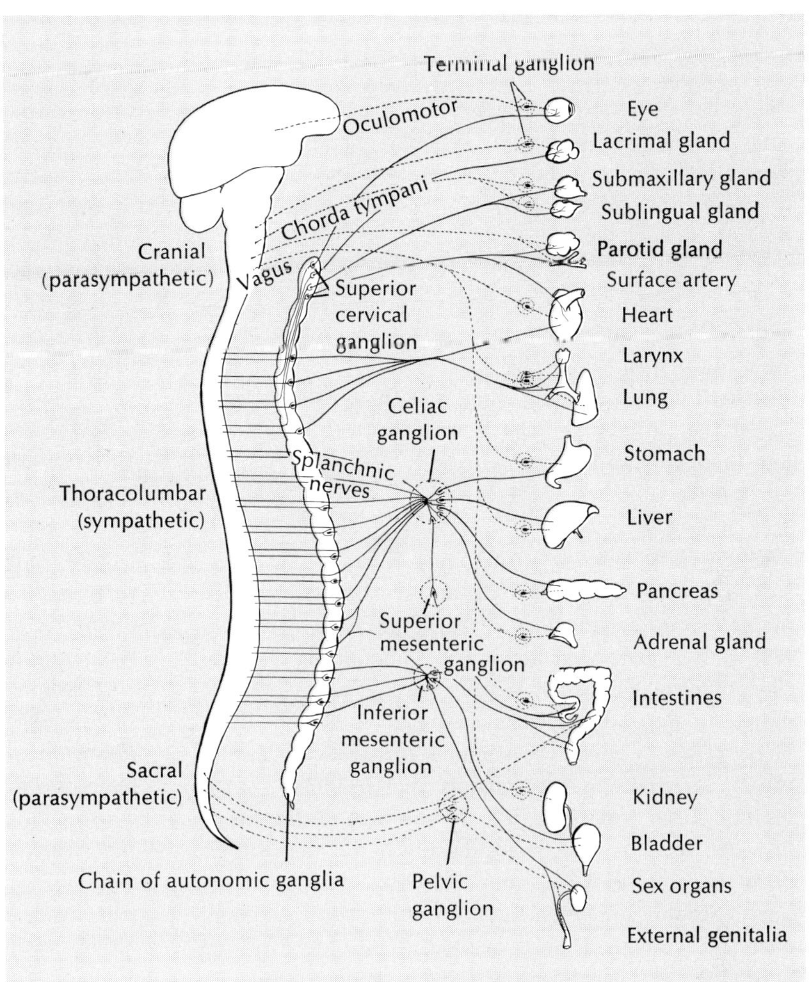

FIG. 32-11

Autonomic nervous system in mammals. Parasympathetic fibers are indicated by dotted lines; sympathetic fibers, by continuous lines. Note that most organs are innervated by both parasympathetic and sympathetic fibers.

They **inhibit** the heart, intestinal sphincters, and sphincter of the urinary bladder.

In the **sympathetic** division the nerve cell bodies are located in the thoracic and upper lumbar areas of the spinal cord. Their preganglionic fibers pass out through the ventral roots of the spinal nerves, separate from these, and go to the sympathetic ganglia, which are paired and form a chain on each side of the spinal column. In these ganglia the axons of the preganglionic fibers synapse with the postganglionic fibers that connect the ganglia with one another. Some of the postganglionic fibers run through spinal nerves to the limbs and body wall, where they innervate the blood vessels of the skin, the smooth muscles of the hair, the sweat glands, etc.; and some run to the abdominal organs as the splanchnic nerves. The cell bodies of the latter fibers are located in **prevertebral ganglia** along the aorta. Some of the sympathetic fibers lack a myelin sheath and are known as gray fibers. Sympathetic fibers **excite** the heart, blood vessels, sphincters of the intestines, urinary bladder, dilator muscles of the iris, and others. They **inhibit** the stomach, intestine, bronchial muscles, and coronary arterioles.

An enzyme of the blood, cholinesterase, checks undue spreading of the stimulation by acetylcholine. All preganglionic fibers, whether sympathetic or parasympathetic, release acetylcholine at the synapse for stimulating the ganglion cells. At the terminations of the postganglionic fibers on the organs, however, the parasympathetic fibers secrete acetylcholine, and the sympathetic fibers give off two neurohumors (epinephrine and norepinephrine). These chemical substances produce characteristic physiologic reactions. Since there is some physiologic overlapping of sympathetic and parasympathetic fibers, it is now customary to describe nerve fibers as either adrenergic (epinephrine effect) or cholinergic (acetylcholine effect).

The plexuses of Auerbach and Meissner, which are found in the walls of the digestive tract, are often included in the autonomic nervous system. They correspond in a way to the nerve net of invertebrates. It is thought by some that the ganglia of these plexuses represent the outlying ganglionic cells for the vagus nerve and that they are involved in certain reflexes of the alimentary canal.

Nature of nerve impulse

The **nerve impulse** is that physicochemical change in the nerve fiber membrane that is aroused by a stimulus and is carried along the nerve fiber to its termination. It may or may not produce excitation in a tissue or organ, depending on its strength or the condition of the tissue to which the stimulus is delivered. A **stimulus** is an environmental change that produces an alteration in an irritable tissue. In the case of the nerve impulse the alteration is produced in the nerve fiber or in a receptor, which transmits the change to the nerve. Stimuli may be in the form of electrical, thermal, chemical, and mechanical changes. The nature of the nerve impulse has been extensively studied since its rate was first determined by Helmholtz a hundred years ago, but much is still to be discovered about its nature. Superficially, the impulse resembles an electric current, but it travels much more slowly than electricity (speed of light) and it cannot be conducted by a dead neuron as an electric current can. It is commonly referred to as an electrochemical disturbance in the nerve fiber. It is a self-propagated disturbance and gets the energy for its transmission locally along the nerve fiber. A strong stimulus will not cause the impulse to travel faster than one induced by a feeble impulse, if the latter is of minimum intensity. All impulses are alike, whether they are conducted in motor, sensory, or association fibers. The impulse can be influenced by the condition of the neuron and by such agencies as drugs. In such cases the impulse may be retarded or blocked entirely.

The **rate** of the nerve impulse is faster in some animals than in others. Nerve fibers with large diameters have faster rates than those with small diameters. The rate is slower in nerve fibers that lack a myelin sheath. Depolarization (to be described) of myelinated nerve fibers occurs only in the regions of the nodes of Ranvier where the myelin sheath, acting as an insulator, is absent. The current is supposed to flow only in the nodal regions so that the impulse jumps from node to node (saltatory conduction), thus producing a faster rate. In some nerves in man it travels about 121 meters per second; in corresponding nerves of the frog its rate is only 30 meters per second. In the autonomic nerve fibers of man it travels about 10 meters per second.

Nerve fibers can transmit impulses in either direction. How far the impulse will travel will depend on the nearest synaptic junction, which permits transmission in only one direction—from afferent to efferent neurons.

The transmission of the nerve impulse is a metabolic process, involving the consumption of oxygen and the giving off of carbon dioxide. Heat is also produced, but the amounts of each of these three factors—heat, oxygen, and carbon dioxide—are very small.

The nerve impulse is considered to be a surface phenomenon of the membrane surrounding each nerve fiber—the **membrane theory** of nervous conduction. According to this theory, an impulse is made possible by the creation and storage of potential energy at the cell membrane produced by the unequal distribution of ions inside and outside the membrane. In the resting nerve, sodium and chloride ions predominate on the outside, whereas potassium ions are more common on the inside. Actually the concentration of sodium and chloride ions are ten and fourteen times higher, respectively, on the outside than within the membrane; potassium concentration is about twenty-seven times higher on the inside than on the outside. This ionic imbalance results in more positively charged ions on the outside of the membrane and more negatively charged ones on the inside so that the outside is positively charged with respect to the interior. When such a resting potential exists, the membrane is said to be **polarized.** This resting potential difference across the membrane amounts to about 0.06 to 0.09 volt. Although the concentration of ions in the resting condition remains very constant, there is a flux of ions in both directions through the membrane. The constancy of electrical potential and ionic concentration is maintained, at least in part, by the so-called **sodium pump** that pumps out the sodium as quickly as it enters. This pumping requires energy because it is an active transport process.

It is thus seen that the membrane in the resting condition is not entirely impermeable to ions but has a low permeability. It is more permeable to potassium ions than to sodium ions (although both have the same charge), but for every sodium ion extruded to the outside, a potassium ion is supposed to pass to the inside. It is not yet clear just how the low concentration of sodium ions and high concentration of potassium ions on the inside of cells are brought about.

When a neuron is excited and an impulse is produced by a stimulus, there is an increase in the permeability of the nerve membrane (Fig. 32-12). Sodium ions are now free to enter the inside and **depolarization** of the membrane occurs. As polarization is decreased, the sodium ion conductance is increased. This decreases the membrane potential, and the membrane becomes positively charged on the inside and negatively charged on the outside. Wherever the nerve impulse is passing, that point on the surface is electrically negative to the inactive nerve fiber and results in the upward spike of the action potential wave, as recorded by delicate galvanometers or oscilloscopes. The magnitude of the action potential is restricted or checked, however, by a delayed period of increased permeability to potassium ions so that there is an outward diffusion of those ions. Sodium ions cease to pass into the inside when the interior of the fiber becomes positively charged with respect to the exterior. The currents produced by the movement of the ions depolarizes the contiguous regions of the membrane ahead of the action current. New currents stimulate more distal regions, and the next part of the membrane is depolarized so that the impulse is propagated as a wave of depolarization at a velocity dependent on the conditions already mentioned. After its initiation, the impulse mechanism is self-regenerative. The action potential is merely a recording of the electrical changes that take place while the impulse is passing. As the impulse passes forward, the depolarized region immediately behind it becomes polarized again and restored to its active state because of the outward flow of potassium ions. This recovery requires a short amount of time, during which the fiber is inexcitable and will not respond to another stimulus. This very brief period (0.001 to 0.005 second) is the absolute refractory period.

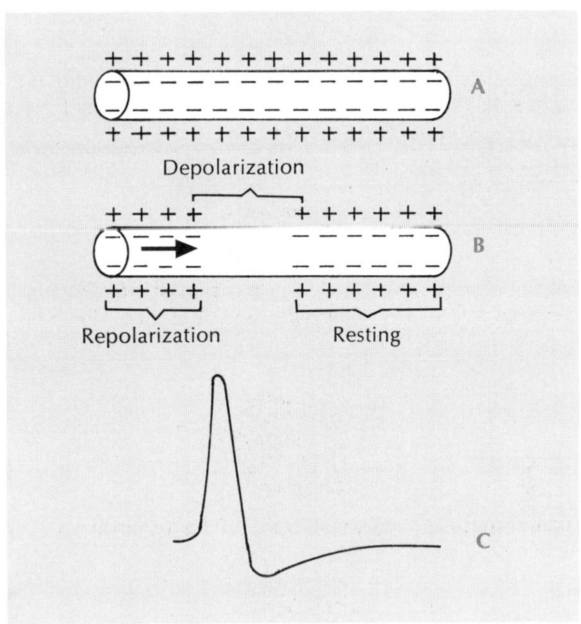

FIG. 32-12

Membrane theory of nerve impulse. In resting condition, **A,** neuron membrane is polarized by having positively charged inorganic ions on outside of membrane and negatively charged inorganic ions on inside. When nerve impulse is initiated, **B,** differential permeability and its polarization are lost at point where impulse is traveling. As current flows across membrane, adjacent part of membrane is depolarized (self-perpetuating) and wave of depolarization passes along neuron in direction of current (arrow). As impulse passes, recovery to former resting state occurs and depolarized region becomes polarized again. If nerve is stimulated in middle, impulse will pass in both directions. **C,** Action potential record, which accompanies wave of depolarization, is shown. This action potential indicates sharp upward spike potential (negative) and downward (negative afterpotential), followed by somewhat straight horizontal line (positive afterpotential).

SENSE ORGANS

Specialized receptors, or **sense organs,** have been developed for detection of delicate environmental changes. These are made up of cells that are unusually sensitive to certain types of stimuli (Fig. 32-13). A sense organ is stimulated by stimuli of low threshold intensity that are not strong enough to affect protoplasm or a nerve fiber directly.

Receptors are specific for stimuli of a certain type and will not respond to other types. Thus the eye is specialized for picking up light rays but is not affected by sound waves. Receptors are in direct contact with the environment and receive and transmit impressions of what is going on in the environment.

Sense organs are specialized parts of the sensory

Invertebrate sense organs

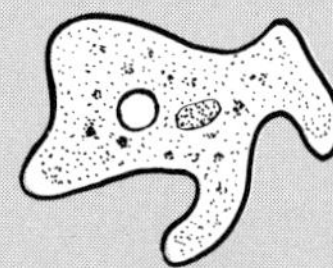

Unspecialized sensitivity of general protoplasm and no localized regions of sensitivity, or else whole external surface may act as receptor (ameba)

Eyespot representing light-sensitive region shielded by pigment, which makes light effective from one direction (euglena)

Light-absorbing pigment in front of light-sensitive cells (planaria)

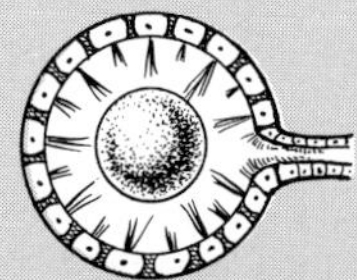

Statocyst is a common organ for perception of gravity; differentiation of perception depending on sensory hairs that are stimulated by statolith (pecten)

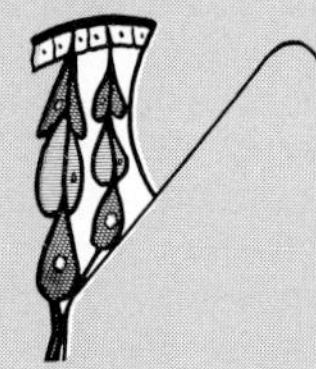

Tympanic membrane vibrates and transmits sound waves to scolophores, which make up sensory part of auditory organ (insects)

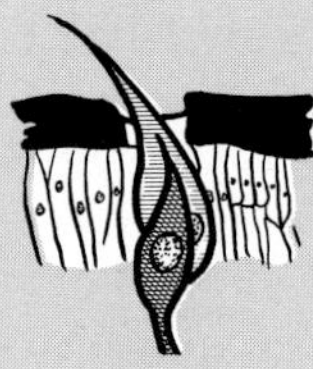

Tactile sense organs often modified hairs (crustaceans)

FIG. 32-13

Comparison of some of general sense organs of invertebrates (left) and vertebrates (right).

Vertebrate sense organs

Vertebrates with a variety of sensory receptors, such as those of general sensibility (touch, pressure, pain, temperature), and those of special sensibility (smell, taste, sight, hearing, balancing). Some organs of general sense are listed below:

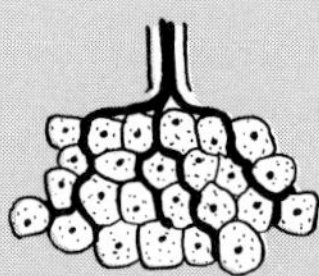

Free sensory nerve endings in epithelium for pain reception

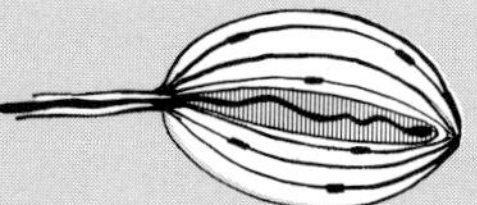

Pacinian corpuscle in superficial and deep parts of body for pressure reception

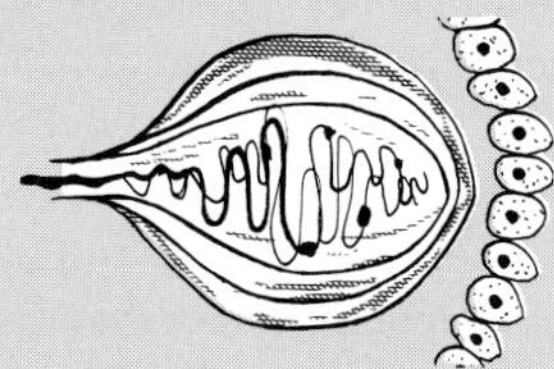

Meissner's corpuscle in dermal papillae of skin for light touch perception

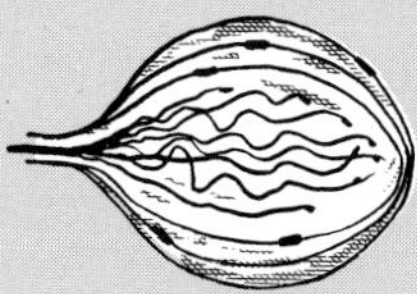

Krause's corpuscle in skin and mucous membrane for cold reception

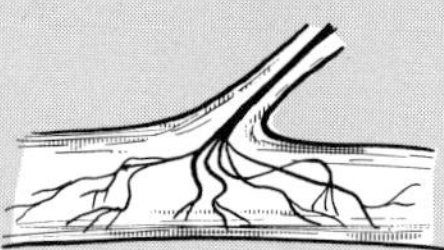

Neurotendinous spindles of tendon-muscle junctions for proprioception of position and tension of muscles

nerve fibers. Since all nerve impulses are qualitatively the same, the real perception of sensation is done in the brain. Sense organs have a hookup with localized regions of the brain, and any impulse that comes to this part of the brain is interpreted in a definite way. For instance, whatever comes over the optic nerve is interpreted in terms of light sensation. The picture one gets of his environment must necessarily be imperfect because many forms of stimuli cannot be picked up by the sense organs, or the sense organs may fail to register sensations because of the lack of attention or the presence of fatigue.

Classification of receptors

Receptors are classified on the basis of their location. Those near the external surface are called **exteroceptors** and are stimulated by changes in the external environment. Internal parts of the body are provided with **interoceptors,** which pick up stimuli from the internal organs. Muscles, tendons, and joints have **proprioceptors,** which are sensitive to changes in the tension of muscles and enable the organism to be aware of position and movement. These last are responsible for the so-called kinesthetic sense.

Receptors are divided into several types. Some have no specialized capsules around them and are merely **free nerve endings.** They often have small enlargements, or terminal varicosities, on their branches. Some form little knots of fiber networks. Many of them are concerned with the senses of **pain** and **heat** (end organs of Ruffini). Most receptors have some form of capsule around them and are thus called encapsulated. Because of their shape, they are also referred to as sense corpuscles. They lie in the connective tissues and include the Meissner touch corpuscles, the end bulbs of Krause (cold), and the pacinian corpuscles (pressure) (Fig. 32-14). Many of these receptors are confined to regions close to the body surface and belong to the **cutaneous receptors.**

Receptors may also be classified on the basis of the energy form used in stimulating them, such as **chemical, mechanical,** or **electromagnetic.** Some animals have made use of one type more than others, especially those animals that live in restricted environments. Also as important as sense receptors are animals that have arrived at higher levels of integration more by central nervous development which acquires sensory information than in the degree of precise receptor capabilities.

Chemoreception is one of the most primitive of senses and is universal in the animal kingdom. Most animals from protozoans to the highest evolved forms make use of these receptors for the location of food and avoidance of harmful substances. In a broader sense, chemical transmission within the body is involved in the general integration and control of activities—neurohumors of neural endings, synaptic junction transmission, and the chemical correlation and control of the endocrine system. Chemical receptors are those of taste and smell in which chemosensory cells may be selectively sensitive to many different substances. **Mechanoreceptors** are sensitive to quantitative forces such as touch, pressure, stretching, sound, gravity, etc. Such receptors are numerous as indicated by free nerve endings, various corpuscles, kinesthetic muscle spindles, lateral line receptors, and the highly specialized ear. **Electroreceptors** are sensitive to electromagnetic energy in some form, such as those for detecting changes in an electric field produced by electric fishes, temperature receptors, and those of vision.

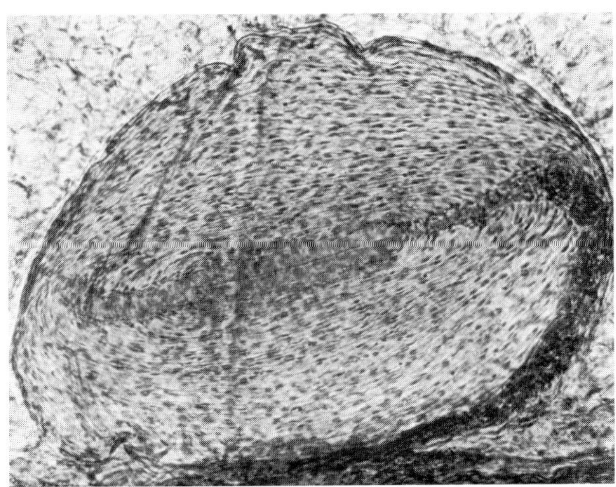

FIG. 32-14

Pacinian corpuscle for pressure reception; from mesentery of cat. (Photomicrograph.) (Courtesy J. W. Bamberger.)

Sense organs among invertebrates

In protozoans there are no special receptors unless the eyespot (stigma) of some forms be so considered. In the one-celled forms the stimuli strike the protoplasmic mass directly. There are no special sensory cells in sponges, but the cells react directly to stimuli. Coelenterates have many sensory cells scattered through the epidermis, especially on the tentacles and around the mouth. These cells are connected to the nerve network, which is connected to the epitheliomuscular cells of the epidermis. They are really tactile receptors. There are also found in this group eyespots sensitive to light, statocysts for equilibration, and sense pits as chemoreceptors. Flatworms have eyespots for light detection and chemoreceptors for taste and smell. Roundworms are provided with tactile receptors but with little else. Among the annelid worms, sense organs are much better developed and are found in the epidermis for touch, taste, and light perception. In some annelids (polychaetes), sense organs assume definite forms. Sense organs in mollusks and arthropods have attained their greatest development in the invertebrates. Statocysts for equilibration, tactile receptors, and chemoreceptors are common. Arthropods have both simple and compound eyes; among the cephalopods the eye is not unlike that of vertebrates, except that it has a different origin.

Chemical receptors

The chemical senses are taste and smell, which are stimulated by specific chemical substances in liquid or gaseous form. These primitive receptors have a wide distribution among the lower vertebrates, in which they may be found all over the body. In higher vertebrates they are localized. **Taste buds** (Fig. 32-15) in higher forms are found on the tongue and in the mucous membrane of the mouth cavity, pharynx, and larynx. A taste bud consists of a few sensitive cells surrounded by supporting cells and is provided with a small external pore through which the slender tips of the sensory cells project. The basal ends of the sensory cells contact nerve endings from cranial nerves. Taste bud cells in vertebrates have a short life of about ten days and are continually being lost and replaced.

FIG. 32-15

Taste buds in rabbit tongue. Buds are little oval bodies lined up on each side of slitlike recesses. (Courtesy J. W. Bamberger.)

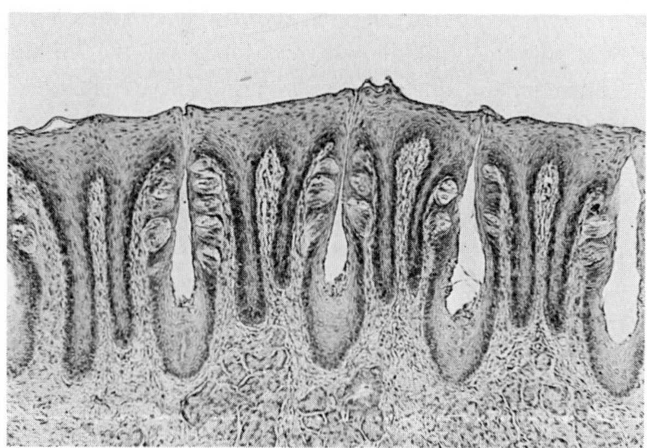

The four basic taste sensations—sour, salt, bitter, and sweet—are each due to a different kind of taste bud. The tastes for salt and sweet are found mainly at the tip of the tongue, bitter at the base of the tongue, and sour along the sides of the tongue. Taste buds are more numerous in ruminants (mammals that chew the cud) than in man. They tend to degenerate with age, for the child has more buds widely distributed over the mouth. The ability to distinguish certain tastes varies among people. This is especially the case with phenylthiocarbamide; the ability to taste this chemical is definitely inherited.

Sense organs of **smell** are found in a specialized mucous membrane located high in the nasal cavity and called the olfactory epithelium. Gases must be dissolved in a fluid to be smelled; therefore the nasal cavity must be moist. The sensory cells with projecting hairs are scattered singly through the olfactory epithelium. Their basal ends are connected to fibers of the olfactory cranial nerve that runs to one of the olfactory lobes. In lower vertebrates the olfactory centers are very well developed. The sensitivity to certain odors is delicate. The human nose can detect 1/25,000,000 of 1 mg. of the odoriferous principal of the skunk. Since taste and smell are stimulated by chemicals in solution, their sensations may be confused so that the taste of food is dependent to a great extent on odors that reach the olfactory membrane through the throat. Many substances are tasted when they are being swallowed. All the various forms of taste, other than the four basic ones (sweet, sour, bitter, salt), are really due to the flavors' reaching the sense of smell in this manner. The sense of smell may depend on a number of different receptors, each specific for molecules of a particular shape.

The ear

The ear is a specialized receptor for detecting sound waves in the surrounding air (Fig. 32-16). Another sense, equilibration, is also associated with the ears of all vertebrate animals. Among the invertebrates, only

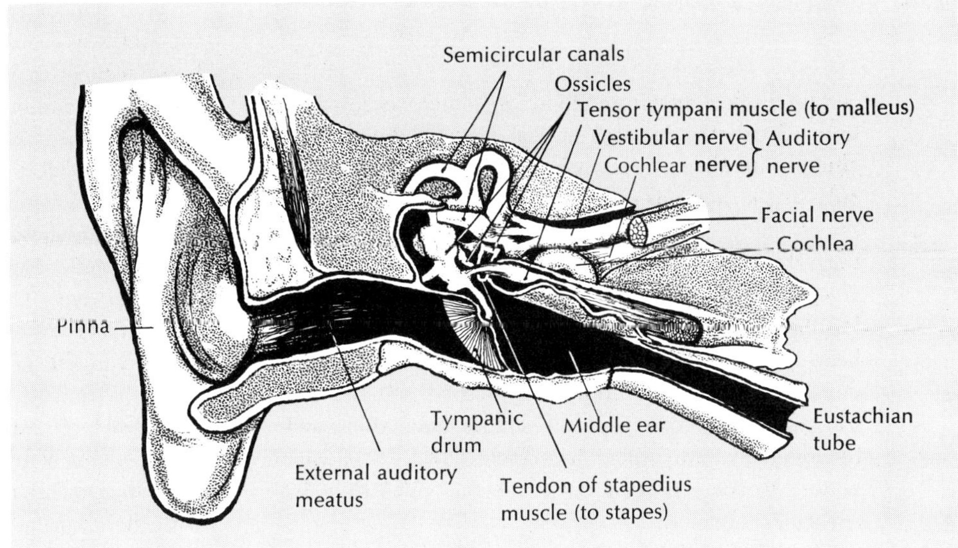

FIG. 32-16

Longitudinal section of ear of man. Note two muscles: tensor tympani and stapedius. Very loud noises cause these muscles to contract by reflex, thus stretching tympanic membrane and oval window and preventing damaging effect of loud, low-pitched sounds.

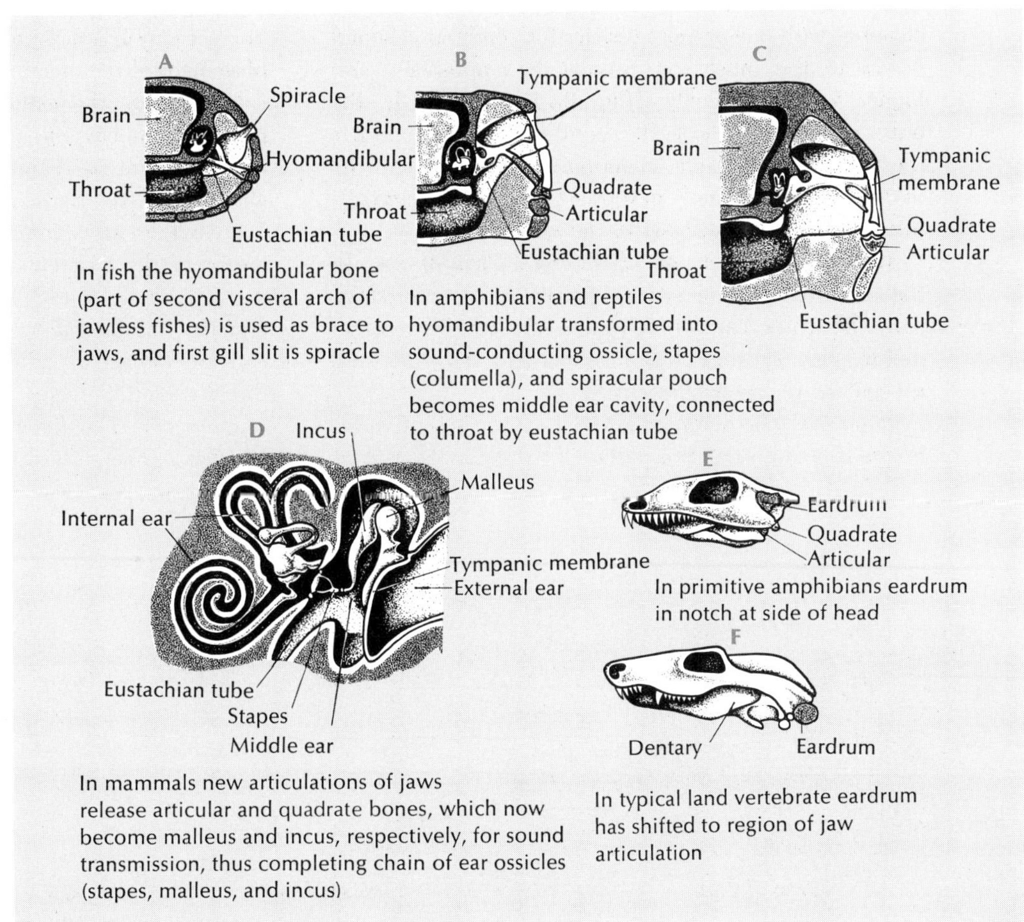

FIG. 32-17

Evolution of middle ear and auditory ossicles. Diagrammatic sections are made through otic region at level of ear and hind end of jaw of, **A,** fish; **B,** primitive amphibian; **C,** reptile; **D,** mammal. **E** and **F,** Side views of skull of ancient amphibian and land vertebrate. (Redrawn from Romer: The vertebrate story, University of Chicago Press.)

certain insects have any kind of sound receptors. In its evolution the ear was at first associated more with equilibrium than with hearing. Hearing sense is found only in the internal ear, which is the only part of the ear in many of the lower vertebrates; the middle and the external ears were added in later evolutionary developments. In fish the lateral line organs, specialized for the detection of water currents, take the place of hearing organs. The internal ear is considered to be a development of part of the lateral line system. Some fish apparently can transmit sound from their swim bladders by the weberian ossicles (series of small bones) to some part of the inner ear, since they lack a cochlea.

The ear found in higher vertebrates is made up of three parts: (1) the **inner ear,** which contains the essential organs of hearing and equilibrium and is present in all vertebrates; (2) the **middle ear,** an air-filled chamber with one or more ossicles for conducting sound waves to the inner ear, present in amphibians and higher vertebrates only (Fig. 32-17); and (3) the **outer ear,** which collects the sound waves and conducts them to the tympanic membrane lying next to the middle ear, present only in reptiles, birds, and mammals but most highly developed in the latter.

Structure and function of different parts of ear. In higher vertebrates the ear is typically made up of three parts—an outer ear for collection of sound waves, a middle ear for their transmission, and an inner ear specialized for sensory reception.

Outer ear. The outer, or external ear, of higher vertebrates is made up of two parts: (1) the **pinna,** or skin-covered flap of elastic cartilage and muscles, and (2) the **auditory canal.** In man the pinna serves some function in collecting sound waves; in many other mammals, such as the rabbit and cat, the pinna is freely movable and so is more effective. The auditory canal extends inward in an oblique direction so as to prevent hard objects from striking the tympanic membrane directly. Its walls are lined with hair and wax-secreting glands as a protection against the entrance of foreign objects.

Middle ear. The middle ear is separated from the external ear by the eardrum, or tympanic membrane, which consists of a stretched connective tissue membrane. Within the air-filled middle ear a chain of three tiny ossicles, **malleus, incus,** and **stapes,** conduct the sound waves across the middle ear. This chain of bones is so arranged that the malleus (hammer) is in contact with the eardrum and the stapes (stirrup) is in contact with the oval window membrane of the inner ear. When sound waves strike the tympanic membrane, its vibrations are transmitted by the chain of ossicles to the inner ear. To increase the tension of the tympanic membrane for delicate sounds or to counteract undue displacement of the membrane, a muscle (tensor tympani) is inserted on the malleus. Contraction of this muscle pulls the malleus and the tympanic membrane inward. A similar muscle (stapedius) is fastened to the stapes and controls the tension of the fluid in the internal ear. The middle ear communicates with the pharynx by means of the eustachian tube, which regulates the air pressure in the middle ear. Both the eustachian tube and the middle ear are lined with mucous membrane and are subject to invasion by disease germs from the throat region.

Inner ear. The inner ear consists essentially of two labyrinths, one within the other. The inner one is called

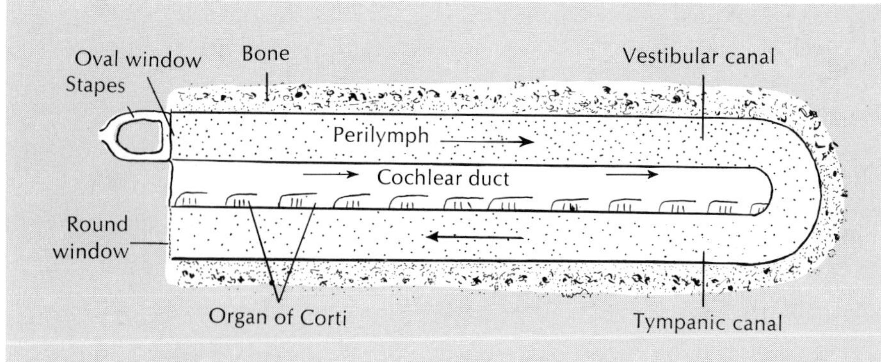

FIG. 32-18

Cochlea straightened out to show pathway of vibrations through scala vestibuli (vestibular canal) and scala tympani (tympanic canal).

the **membranous labyrinth** and is a closed ectodermal sac filled with the fluid, **endolymph.** The part involved with hearing (**cochlea**) is coiled like a snail's shell, making two and a half turns. Surrounding the membranous labyrinth is the **bony labyrinth,** which is a hollowed-out part of the temporal bone and conforms to the shape and contours of the membranous labyrinth. In the space between the two labyrinths, perilymph, a fluid similar to endolymph, is found.

The cochlea is divided into three longitudinal canals that are separated from each other by thin membranes (Figs. 32-16 and 32-18). These canals become progressively smaller from the base of the cochlea to the apex. One of these canals is called the **vestibular canal;** its base is closed by the oval window. The **tympanic canal,** which is in communication with the vestibular canal at the tip of the cochlea, has its base closed by the round window. Between these two canals is the **cochlear canal,** which contains the organ of hearing, the **organ of Corti** (Fig. 32-19). The latter organ is made up of fine rows of hair cells that run lengthwise from the base to the tip of the cochlea. There are at least 24,000 of these hair cells in the human ear, each cell with many hairs projecting into the endolymph of the cochlear canal and each connected with neurons of the auditory nerve. The hair cells rest on the **basilar membrane,** which separates the tympanic and cochlear canals, and are covered over by the tectorial membrane found directly above them. The basilar membrane is composed of transverse connective tissue fibers that vary in length at different levels of the cochlea.

In hearing a sound, sound waves are picked up by the external ear and transmitted through the auditory canal to the tympanic membrane, which is caused to vibrate. These vibrations are conducted by the chain of ear ossicles to the oval window, which transmits the vibrations to the fluid in the vestibular and tympanic canals. The vibrations of the endolymph cause the basilar membrane, with its hair cells, to vibrate so that the latter rub against the tectorial membrane. This stimulation of the hair cells causes them to initiate nerve impulses in the fibers of the auditory nerve, with which they are connected. In the **place theory** of pitch discrimination it is stated that when sound waves strike the inner ear the entire basilar membrane is set in vibration by a wave of displacement, which increases in amplitude from the oval window toward the apex of the cochlea. This displacement wave reaches a maximum at the region of the basilar membrane that resonates with the frequency of the incoming sound

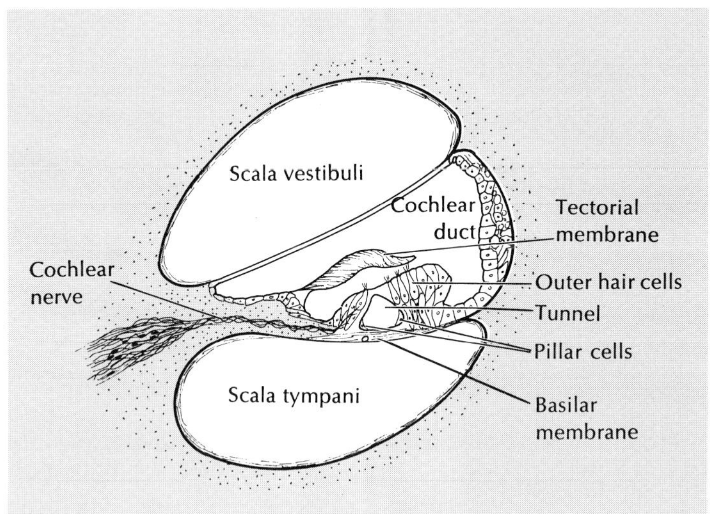

FIG. 32-19

Section through axis of cochlear spiral showing cellular types in organ of Corti.

FIG. 32-20

Chief gross structures of human middle and inner ear. Middle ear contains three ear ossicles and is air filled; inner ear consists of membranous tubes and sacs filled with endolymph fluid. Middle ear muscles (not shown) are attached to ear ossicles, and by contracting, reduce energy transmission at low frequencies.

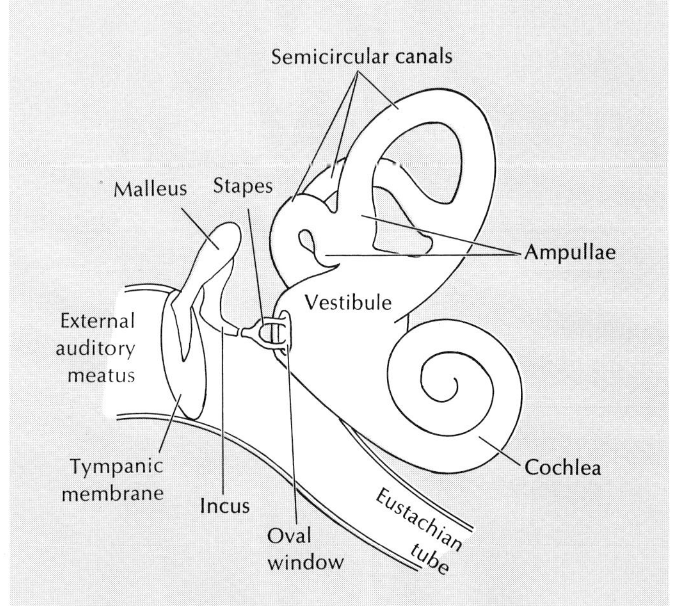

waves (von Bekesy). The particular hair cells in that region will be stimulated and the impulses conveyed to the fibers of the auditory nerve. Those impulses that are carried by certain fibers of the auditory nerve are interpreted by the hearing center as particular tones. The **loudness** of a tone depends on the number of hair cells stimulated, whereas the **timbre,** or quality, of a tone is produced by the pattern of the hair cells stimulated by sympathetic vibration. This latter characteristic of tone enables one to distinguish between different human voices and different musical instruments, even though the notes in each case be of the same pitch and loudness.

Sense of equilibrium. Closely connected to the inner ear and forming a part of it are two small sacs, the **saccule** and **utricle,** and three **semicircular canals.** Like the cochlea, they are filled with endolymph. They are concerned with the sense of balance and rotation. They are well developed in all vertebrates, and in some lower forms they represent about all there is of the internal ear, for the cochlea is absent in fish. They are innervated by the nonacoustic branch of the auditory nerve.

FIG. 32-21

Section through eye of vertebrate.

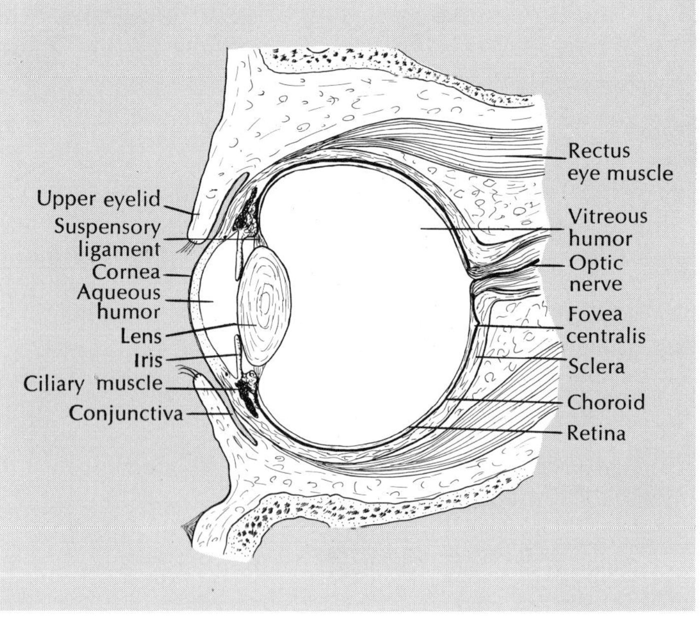

The utricle and saccule are hollow sacs lined with sensitive hairs and contain small stones, **otoliths,** of calcium carbonate. Whatever way the head is tipped, certain hair cells are stimulated; these are interpreted in a certain way with reference to position.

The three semicircular canals are at right angles to each other, one in each plane of space (Fig. 32-20). They are filled with fluid, and at the opening of each canal into the utricle there is a bulblike enlargement, the **ampulla,** which contains hair cells but no otoliths. Whenever the fluid moves, these hair cells are stimulated. Rotating the head will cause a lag, due to inertia, in certain of these ampullae. This lag produces consciousness of movement. Since the three canals of each internal ear are in different planes, any kind of movement will stimulate at least one of the ampullae.

The eye

The earliest eyes in the animal kingdom are the eyespots of invertebrates. These spots may be only a small differentiated mass in a cell, or they may consist of several light-sensitive cells clustered together, with some pigment to direct the light to the sensitive cells. Such eye spots record different intensities of light so that the organism can distinguish between light and dark and can determine the source of light. In the blind earthworms there are photoreceptors that are sensitive to light and enable the worm to avoid strong light. Arthropods have compound or mosaic eyes composed of many visual units (ommatidia), each being provided with a kind of lens and light-sensitive cells. Such eyes do not form a simple image but a mosaic one made up of separate images contributed by the numerous visual units. This eye is well suited for picking up motion, because the images registered by some of the ommatidia are quickly shifted to other ommatidia by the slightest movement of the object, thereby producing an exaggerated effect. Some of the cephalopods (squid and octopus) have well-developed skin eyes with cornea, lens, anterior and posterior chambers, and rod-bearing retina.

The eye of vertebrates (Fig. 32-21) is of the camera type, with a light-tight chamber containing the lens system at the front end that focuses the picture of objects on the sensitive retina at the back. In forming an image, the lens and accessory structures make use of the same laws of optics as a camera. That is why the wearing of glasses is able to correct defects in our lens system.

The eyeball is more or less spherical and is composed

of three layers: (1) the outer white **sclerotic** coat, which is composed of tough connective tissue for support and protection; (2) the middle **choroid** coat, which contains blood vessels for nourishment; and (3) the inner **retinal** coat, which contains the light-sensitive units. The anterior part of the sclerotic coat is transparent, forming the **cornea,** for the admission of light. A circular curtain, the **iris,** a modification of the choroid coat, regulates the size of the light opening, the **pupil.** Just behind the iris is the **lens,** a modification of the ectoderm of the skin. The lens is a transparent, elastic ball that bends the rays and focuses them on the retina. In land vertebrates the cornea also bends the rays and the lens can adjust the focus for near and far objects. Between the cornea and the lens is the outer chamber filled with the watery **aqueous humor;** between the lens and the retina is the much larger inner chamber, filled with the viscous **vitreous humor.** Surrounding the margin of the lens and holding it in place is the **suspensory ligament,** which in turn is attached to the **ciliary body.** In front of the ciliary body is the **ciliary muscle,** a ring of radiating muscle fibers attached to the suspensory ligament. This muscle, with the ligament, makes possible the stretching and relaxing of the lens for close or distant vision (accommodation).

The **retina** (Fig. 32-22), the sensory part of the eye, is only a partial coat, for it does not extend over the front region of the eye. It is made up of the photoreceptors, **rods** and **cones,** which in the human eye number about 125,000,000 rods and 7,000,000 cones. Cones are primarily concerned with light vision; rods, with dim or colorless vision. Back of the retina is the pigmented layer of cells that absorbs extra light rays and produces a dark interior. The retina is actually made up of three sets of neurons in series with each other: (1) photoreceptors, or the rods and cones, (2) intermediate neurons, and (3) ganglionic neurons whose axons form the optic nerve. At the point where the fibers leave the eyeball to form the optic nerve there are no rods or cones (the blind spot). The light rays must pass through these layers of neurons to reach the rods and cones.

The **fovea centralis,** the region of keenest vision, is located in the center of the retina, in direct line with the center of the lens and cornea and contains only cones. In other regions of the retina the cones and rods have an unequal distribution because at the peripheral parts of the retina only rods are found. This is why one can see better at night by looking out of the corners of

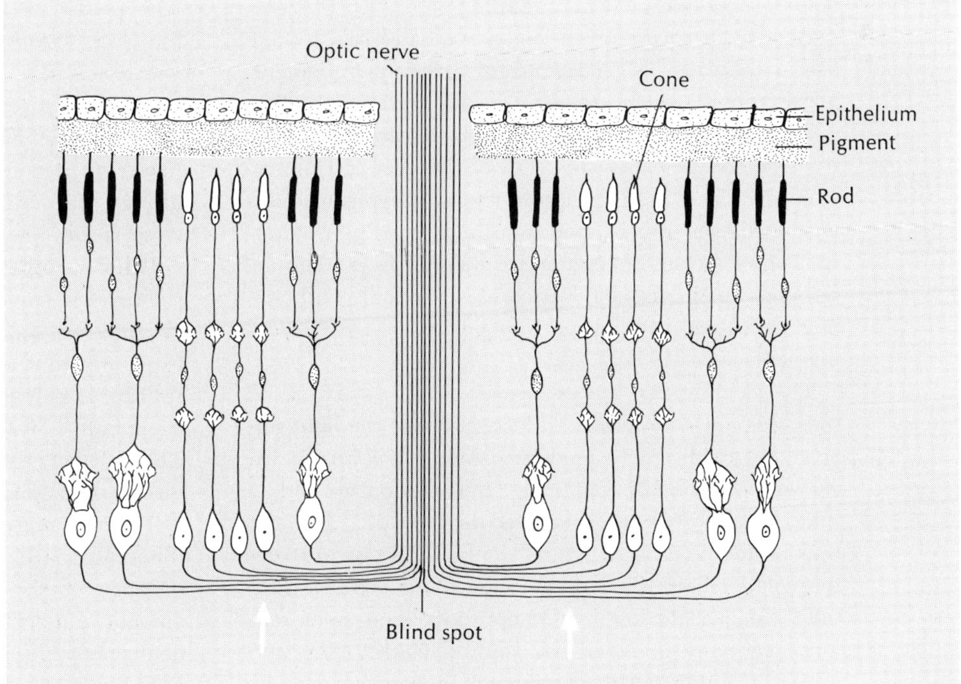

FIG. 32-22

Section through retina. Arrows indicate direction of light rays. Note that light rays, to reach sensitive cells at back of retina, must pass through many layers of neurons.

his eyes because the rods, adapted for dim vision, are brought into use.

Biochemistry of vision

Each rod contains a sensitive substance known as visual purple, or **rhodopsin.** This is a compound composed of a colorless protein, **opsin,** and a yellowish carotenoid, retinaldehyde, a vitamin A derivative. Retinaldehyde may also combine with a different isomeric opsin in the cones to form another visual pigment, visual violet, or **iodopsin.** Rhodopsin seems best to absorb light of around 500 $m\mu$ wavelength, but the curve of visual sensitivity in dim light of different wavelengths is the same as the absorption curve for rhodopsin. When quanta of light strike the rods or cones, they perform no photochemical work, but trigger the discharge of nerve impulses by the receptor cells. In the case of the rods, whose chemistry is better known than that of the cones, the molecules of rhodopsin are split into opsin and retinaldehyde after many changes of molecular structure. The energy of this reaction produces a nervous impulse and a bleaching of visual purple into visual yellow. Rhodopsin is always involved in a cyclic process of bleaching and resynthesis with the aid of ATP. If bleaching occurs at a more rapid rate than it can be regenerated, snow blindness may result.

Rhodopsin occurs in all land vertebrates and marine fish. Freshwater fish make use of a different pigment, **porphyropsin,** which absorbs a longer wavelength. This pigment reacts very much like rhodopsin. *Fundulus,* the common brackish-water fish of the Woods Hole region, may have both rhodopsin and porphyropsin. Tadpoles and some other larval forms may have porphyropsin before metamorphosis and rhodopsin later. The arthropods, mollusks, and vertebrates (animals with the best developed eyes) have retinaldehyde as the visual pigment.

The electron microscope reveals many details about rods and cones not disclosed heretofore by the light microscope. Each rod (a modified neuron) has a cylindrical outer segment containing the rhodopsin and a thicker inner segment connected to the outer segment by a narrow fibrillar structure, similar to the basal structure of a cilium. The outer segment is composed of tightly packed hollow membrane disks. The inner segment contains mitochondria and glycogen. The rod proper of outer and inner segments is connected to its cell body by a fiber. The cone is also a modified neuron, but its outer segment contains solid disks. Its shape resembles a flask, but otherwise it resembles a rod, except that it has no visual purple.

The primary function of cones is to perceive colors, but they do contain **iodopsin,** a light-sensitive pigment. The cones are far less sensitive to light than are rods and are useless in dim light. According to the modified **Young-Helmholtz** theory of light, there are three different types of cones that react respectively to blue, green, and red light. Each type of cone can respond to light with a wide range of wavelengths but more strongly to one of the three colors. Intermediate colors (other than blue, green, and red) are perceived by the stimulation of two or more types of cones. For instance, when green and red cones are stimulated equally by certain wavelengths, a yellow color is perceived. Color blindness occurs when one or more of the three types is absent. Except primates and a few others, most mammals are color blind. However, birds, lizards, frogs, and teleost fishes have color vision.

Accommodation and eye defects. The power to accommodate for close vision decreases with age. At rest, the lens is kept stretched and flattened by the tension of the suspensory ligament and the eye is focused for distant vision. When the ciliary muscles are contracted, their pull relieves the tension of the ligament by decreasing the distance between the ciliary body and the lens so that the lens is free to assume a spherical shape for close vision. Thus focusing on a distant object is not a muscular act, but focusing on a near one is. The lens becomes less elastic with age, and the power to accommodate for near vision is lessened. This loss of power to accommodate is called **presbyopia.** Bifocal glasses, with one part for distant vision and another for close vision, are often worn to overcome this handicap.

Other common defects of the human eye are nearsightedness (myopia), farsightedness (hyperopia), and astigmatism. In myopia the rays of light come to a focus in front of the retina; in hyperopia the light rays focus behind the retina. Astigmatism is due to the irregularity in the curvature of the cornea or lens. These defects can in most cases be corrected by wearing glasses with appropriate lens for each kind of defect.

The eye must also accommodate or adapt itself to differences in light intensity, as well as to differences in distance of the objects to be seen. To regulate the amount of light that enters the eye, the iris can increase or decrease the size of the pupil. The iris is composed of two sets of muscles, circular muscles, which can contract or decrease the size of the pupil and radial muscles, whose contraction dilates the pupil. These muscles are under the control of the autonomic nervous system, and changes in the size of the pupil are not instantaneous, for when one steps from a darkened room (where the pupils are dilated) into bright sunlight, the eyes are dazzled and painful until the pupils decrease. The iris is also responsible for the color of the eyes. If little pigment is present, the color is blue; other colors—green, hazel, and brown—are due to larger amounts of pigment.

Some variations among eyes of vertebrates. Among vertebrates there are two kinds of vision—day vision and night vision. With day vision, forms stand out sharply, and details of structure, as well as delicate shades of color, are distinguished. With night vision, things are perceived in outline with only vague details, and color is absent. This difference between the two types of vision forms the basis for the nocturnal and diurnal habits of animals. Man may be said to have both day vision and night vision because he possesses both rods and cones in considerable numbers. However, many animals have only one type of vision. Chickens have only day vision; this explains why they go to roost so early. Owls and flying squirrels are active only at night. Usually those animals that are active at night have large numbers of rods and few cones; diurnal forms, on the other hand, have mostly cones. However, there are a number of variations in this respect. Diurnal lizards have no rods, but crocodiles have many rods in their retinas. Some nocturnal snakes have few or no cones, but many rods. The retinas of most birds consist mainly of cones.

Many mammals and fish reflect light at night. Birds' eyes rarely do so and man's eyes not at all. The pigment back of the retina absorbs all light. Those animals that reflect light (well seen in the cat) have a special area of choroid layers called the **tapetum lucidum,** which acts as a mirror. In the dog or cat the tapetum lucidum is a triangular area in the upper half of the eye that has a blue-green appearance in the excised eye. No pigment is found in the epithelial cells of this region, but only several large flat layers of the choroid full of crystals, composed of zinc and the amino acid cysteine. It is thought that the tapetum lucidum increases sensitivity to dim light.

Annotated references

Brodie, B. B., and A. D. Bass (editors). 1959. Evolution of nervous control from primitive organisms to man. Washington, American Association for the Advancement of Science. A symposium. *This comparative study takes the logical approach that the roots of human nervous integration are found in the behavior of lower forms.*

Bullock, T. H., and G. A. Horridge. 1965. Structure and function in the nervous system of invertebrates. San Francisco, W. H. Freeman & Co., Publishers. *An excellent summary of nervous integration in invertebrates.*

Case, J. 1966. Sensory mechanisms. (Paperback.) New York, The Macmillan Co. *Gives a good evaluation of sensory mechanisms at an introductory level.*

Cold Spring Harbor Symposia in Quantitative Biology. Vol. XVII. 1952. The neuron. Cold Spring Harbor, The Biological Laboratory. *This symposium by many specialists represents the last word on the concept of the neuron. For the advanced student.*

Eccles, J. C. 1957. The physiology of nerve cells. Baltimore, The Johns Hopkins Press. *A summary of the present status of certain concepts of nervous integration, including the architecture of the neuron and the transmitter substances of the central nervous system.*

Gardner, E. 1947. Fundamentals of neurology. Philadelphia, W. B. Saunders Co. *A concise and accurate discussion of the subject. One of the best works on neurology for the beginning student.*

Geldard, F. A. 1953. The human senses. New York, John Wiley & Sons, Inc. *A summary of the latest theories on sense perception.*

Gordon, M. S. (editor). 1968. Animal function: principles and adaptations. New York, The Macmillan Co. *The sections on the sensory and nervous systems by A. D. Grinnell are especially revealing.*

Mountcastle, V. B. 1968. Medical physiology, vol. 2, ed. 12. St. Louis, The C. V. Mosby Co. *The section on the nervous system is especially well written in this outstanding medical physiology.*

Roeder, K. D. 1963. Nerve cells and insect behavior. Cambridge, Mass., Harvard University Press. *A study of neurophysiology and correlated behavior patterns at the cellular and subcellular level.*

Sherrington, C. S. 1947. The integrative action of the nervous system, rev. ed. New Haven, Conn., Yale University Press. *A classical work on the structural and functional plan of the nervous system. The basic concepts of neurophysiology laid down in this work have been little altered since its publication.*

Thruelsen, R., and J. Kobler (editors). 1959. Adventures of the mind. New York, Alfred A. Knopf, Inc. *An appraisal of the significant ideas and advances in knowledge of the present era by competent authorities from many disciplines. A stimulating book for the zoology student.*

CHAPTER 33

• REPRODUCTIVE AND ENDOCRINE SYSTEMS

● There is a logical reason for considering the reproductive and endocrine systems together. Nearly all the principal endocrine glands influence sex and reproduction in some way and in turn they are influenced by the reproductive organs. Various endocrine glands are concerned with every step of the reproductive cycle, including the development and implantation of the fertilized egg, the maintenance of pregnancy, and the development of the mammary glands.

HISTORIC BACKGROUND OF SPONTANEOUS GENERATION*

Spontaneous generation, or **abiogenesis,** is the belief that life can originate without preexisting life or from inorganic matter. This is in contrast to **biogenesis,** the theory that life always originates from previous life. A belief in spontaneous generation was natural before man had developed the basic concepts of cause and effect or before he had mastered the valuable scientific procedure of controlled experiment. The belief in abiogenesis often assumed grotesque forms, such as frogs arising from mud, mice from putrefied matter, and insects from dew. Before the advent of the microscope, belief that small organisms came out of nonliving matter was the only viewpoint one could take. If a beaker of blood were left standing open for a few days, it would teem with maggots, even though no flies were visible. It was quite natural that no association was made between the maggots and the flies.

In 1668 Francesco Redi, an Italian physician, exposed meat in jars, some of which were uncovered and others covered with parchment and wire gauze. The meat in all three kinds of vessels spoiled, but only the open vessels had maggots, and he noticed that flies were constantly entering and leaving these vessels. He concluded that if flies had no access to the meat, no worms would be found there. On the other hand, John T. Needham, an English Catholic priest, boiled mutton broth and put it in containers corked and closely sealed and found after a few days the medium was swarming with microscopic organisms (1748). He concluded that spontaneous generation was real, because he thought that he had killed all living organisms by boiling the broth and that he had excluded the access of others by the precautions he took in sealing the tubes. However, an Italian investigator, Lazaro Spallanzani (1767), was critical of Needham's experiments and conducted experiments that led to a telling blow against the theory of abiogenesis. He thoroughly boiled extracts of vegetables and meat, placed these extracts in clean vessels, and sealed the necks of the flasks hermetically in flame. He then immersed the sealed flasks in boiling water for several minutes to make sure that all germs were destroyed. As controls, he left some tubes open to the air. At the end of two days he found the open flasks swarming with organisms; the others contained none. However, this experiment did not settle the issue, for the advocates of spontaneous generation maintained that air, which Spallanzani had excluded, was necessary for the production of new organisms or that the method he used had destroyed the vegetative power of the medium. When oxygen was discovered (1774), the opponents of Spallanzani seized upon this as the vital principal that he had destroyed in his experiments.

Pasteur (1861) answered the objection of a lack of air by introducing fermentable material into a flask with a long S-shaped neck that was opened to the air. The flask and its contents were then boiled for a long time. Afterward the flask was cooled and left undisturbed. No fermentation occurred, for all organisms that entered the open end were deposited on the floor of the neck and did not reach the flask contents. When the neck of the flask was cut off, the organisms in the air could fall directly on the fermentable mass and fermentation occurred within it in a short time. The conclusion that

*Refer to Chapter 2, Principles 10, 11, and 35.

Pasteur drew from this experiment was that if suitable precautions were taken to keep out the germs and their reproductive elements (eggs, spores, etc.), no fermentation or putrefaction could take place.

REPRODUCTIVE SYSTEM*

Reproduction makes possible the continuity of the race. Although the earliest forms of life undoubtedly came from nonliving substance, there is no convincing evidence that such is occurring today.

The importance of reproduction is shown in the physical and physiologic activities necessary to ensure the fertilization of the eggs, the many methods of breeding, and the different devices for taking care of the offspring during its development. Morphologically, the secondary sex characters such as the mane of the lion, the gorgeous colors of male birds, and the size and strength of the bull and the male fur seal are due to certain aspects of reproduction. Physiologically, patterns of behavior have evolved because of the basic urge for reproduction. Many of the altruistic instincts of man and other animals have developed from the care that is bestowed on the helpless young and the provisions that are made to ensure their survival.

There are two main types of reproduction, **asexual** and **sexual** (Fig. 33-1). The asexual involves only one parent and no special organs or cells. Sexual reproduction involves, as a rule, two parents, each of which contributes one gamete or special cell to a union known as the zygote. Variant forms of sexual reproduction are the union of nuclei in the paramecium and the development of the egg without fertilization in parthenogenesis. There are usually two kinds of gametes, the **ovum** (egg) and the **spermatozoan.** Eggs are produced by the female, are nonmotile, and contain a great amount of yolk. Sperm are formed by the male, are motile, and are relatively small. The union of egg and spermatozoan is called **fertilization,** and the fused cell so formed is known as the **zygote,** which develops into a new individual.

Sexual reproduction is of universal occurrence among all higher forms and has certain biologic advantages and disadvantages over the asexual method. One of its advantages is that the characteristics of two organisms can combine and variations can be multiplied. This affords evolution a greater variety of forms to pick from in natural selection. Recombination of characters makes possible wider and more diversified evolution. The chief disadvantages of the sexual method are the hazards involved in the meeting of eggs and sperm and the possibilities of unfavorable growing conditions. Elaborate devices must be produced to ensure fertilization and to take care of the offspring.

*Refer to Chapter 7, Principle 10.

Asexual reproduction

Asexual reproduction is found only among the simpler forms of life such as protozoans, coelenterates, bryozoans, and a few others. It is absent among the higher invertebrates (mollusks and arthropods) and all vertebrates. Even in phyla in which it occurs, most of the members employ the sexual method. Asexual reproduction ensures rapid increase in numbers when the differentiation of the organism has not advanced to the point of forming highly specialized gametes.

The forms of asexual reproduction are fission, budding (both internal and external), fragmentation, and sporulation. **Fission** is common among protozoans and to a limited extent among metazoans. In this method the body of the parent is divided into two approximately equal parts, each of which grows into an individual similar to the parent. Fission may be either transverse or longitudinal. **Budding** is an unequal division of the organism. The new individual arises as an outgrowth (bud) from the parent. This bud develops organs like that of the parent and then usually detaches itself. If the bud is formed on the surface of the parent, it is an external bud, but in some cases internal buds, or **gemmules,** are produced. Gemmules are collections of many cells surrounded by a dense covering in the body wall. When the body of the parent disintegrates, each gemmule gives rise to a new individual. External budding is common in the hydra and internal budding in the freshwater sponges. Bryozoans also have a form of internal bud called statoblast. **Fragmentation** is a method in which an organism breaks into two or more parts, each capable of becoming a complete animal. This method is found among the Platyhelminthes, Nemertinea, and Echinodermata. **Sporulation** is a method of multiple fission in which many cells are formed and enclosed together in a cystlike structure. Sporulation occurs in a number of protozoan forms.

Sexual reproduction

Sexual reproduction is the general rule in the animal kingdom. It is a process involving a gamete or gametes

Reproduction is formation of living units by similar units already in existence; always involves division of parent or parents, which may or may not be destroyed in process; two types of reproduction: asexual and sexual

Asexual reproduction involves 1 parent and no special gametes (ova or sperm); represented by binary fission, external and internal budding, fragmentation, and multiple fission

Sexual reproduction involves a gamete or gametes (ova and sperm) that arise from parent or parents; represented by parental reproduction, parthenogenesis, pedogenesis, metagenesis, and conjugation

In binary fission individual divides into 2 or more approximately equal parts, each of which becomes like parent, which loses its individuality
Paramecium

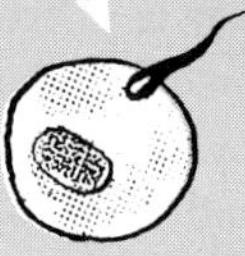

In biparental reproduction gametes from 2 individuals (usually male and female) fuse to form 1 cell (zygote), which develops into individual
Homo

In multiple fission nucleus divides into many nuclei, each of which becomes surrounded by mass of cytoplasm to form new individual (schizogony, sporulation)
Plasmodium

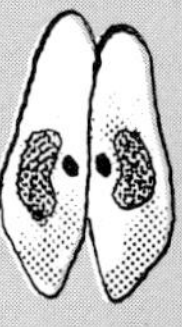

Conjugation, in which 2 individuals exchange nuclear substance during temporary union, may be considered variant form of biparental reproduction
Paramecium

In external budding outgrowth of parent becomes individual and individuality of parent retained
Hydra

Parthenogenesis occurs when 1 gamete (ovum) develops without being fertilized
Philodina

In internal budding masses of mesenchymal cells surrounded by protective capsules to form gemmules, which are released by disintegration of parent; each gemmule then forms new individual
Spongilla

When larval forms undergo parthenogenesis, it is pedogenesis; when larval characters are retained after maturity of gonad, it is neoteny
Miastor, Ambystoma

Fragmentation involves breaking up of parent body into 2 or more parts, each of which can give rise to new individual
Microstomum

Metagenesis involves alternation of sexual (diploid) generations and asexual (haploid) generations

FIG. 33-1

Types of reproduction.

Sperm

Function of testis to produce sperm in its seminiferous tubules and sex hormones in its interstitial tissue; in lower species (fish and salamanders) seminiferous tubules short, lobulated structures and all developing sperm cells in 1 part of tubule tend to be approximately at same stage of development

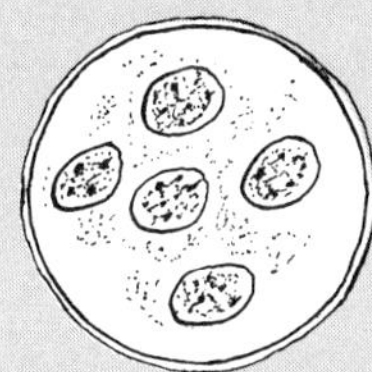

In higher species (including frog and man) seminiferous tubules are long and their walls contain sperm cells in various stages of development

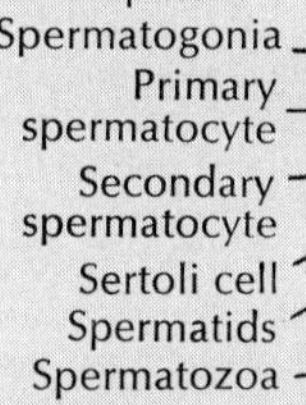

In final maturing of sperm, testes of vertebrates may be divided into 2 types. In 1 type (certain fish, salamanders, and frogs) anterior part of sperm duct does not form convoluted epididymis, and sperm mature and are stored in testis; this type of testis best suited for seasonal activity when sperm discharged at one time. In other type (higher vertebrates) sperm become physiologically functional only in convoluted epididymis where they are also stored; this type best adapted for more or less continuous reproduction

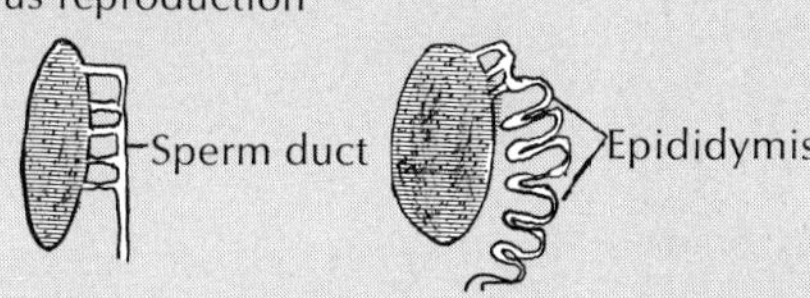

Ova

Ova formed in ovaries that vary among different vertebrate classes; 2 ovaries of frog saccular because interiors represented by large lymph spaces; each ovarian sac consists of 2 membranes, theca externa and theca interna; between these, young ova in various stages of development; each ovum surrounded by follicle cells (for nourishment), which are left behind when mature egg discharged into body cavity through rupture in theca membranes

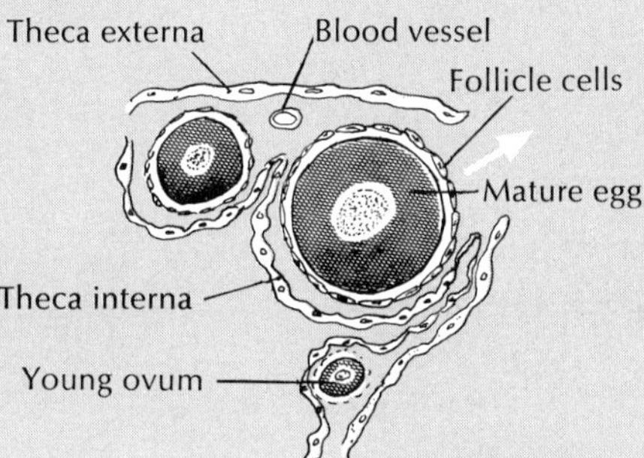

In mammalian ovary developing egg with its surrounding cells called graafian follicle. As egg or ovum enlarges, split appears between outer and inner layers of cells and follicular cavity formed; this cavity filled with liquor folliculi, which contains hormone estrogen; when mature follicle ruptures, freed egg surrounded with fuzzy coat of follicle cells

FIG. 33-2

Comparison of male and female gamete formation in vertebrates.

(Fig. 33-2). **Conjugation** among protozoans comes under this method because two individuals fuse together temporarily and exchange micronuclear material. Other forms of sexual reproduction occur in protozoans, in which there is a union between two special cells. These cells may be alike (**isogametes**) or they may be different (**anisogametes**). Usually the difference is one of size between the gametes, but in certain cases one kind of gamete may be motile and the other nonmotile. In some cases it is difficult to distinguish sex, for although two parents are involved, they cannot be designated as male and female. Work by Sonneborn and others on certain distinctive strains of paramecia would indicate the beginnings of sex distinctions because the members of some strains will not conjugate among themselves but only with those of another strain.

Among metazoans, some individuals can be called **male** and others **female.** Organs that produce the germ cells are known as **gonads.** The gonad that produces the

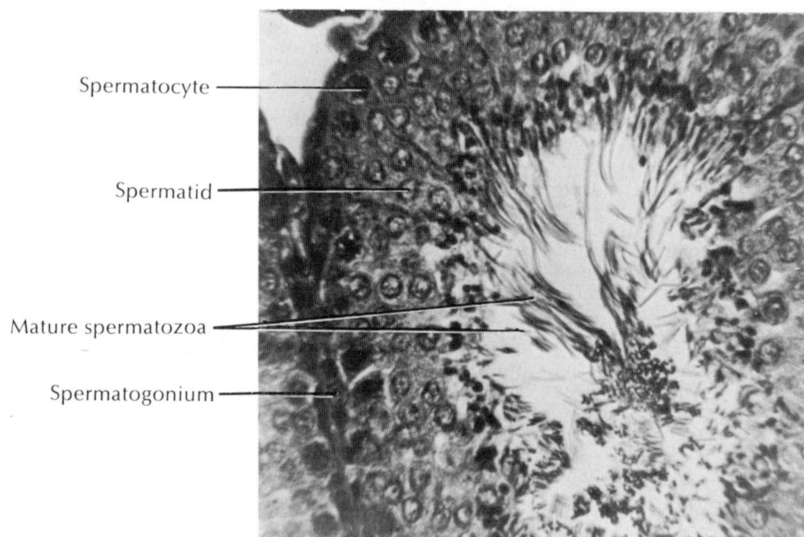

FIG. 33-3

Section through testis of rat showing seminiferous tubule with different stages of sperm formation. Mature sperm are nearest fluid-filled center of tubule; between them and outermost part of tubular wall are various stages of sperm formation. In rat each spermatogonium has 42 chromosomes, but by meiosis this number is reduced to 21 in each sperm. Corresponding figures for human being would be 46 and 23. (Courtesy J. W. Bamberger.)

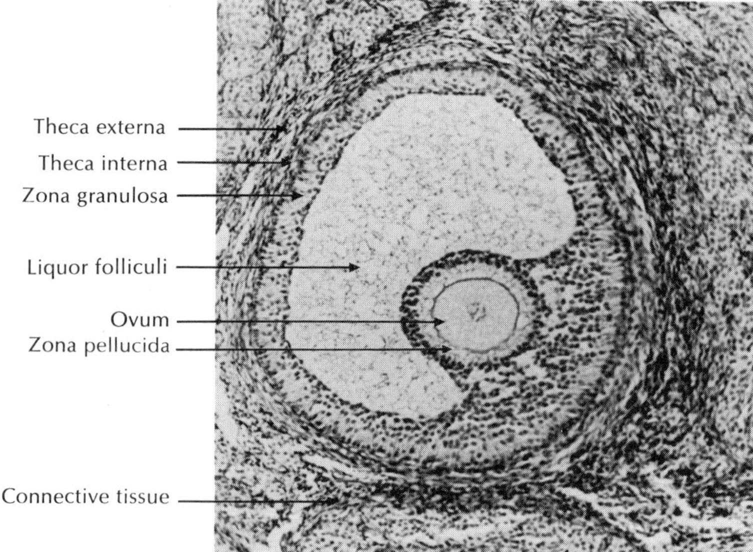

FIG. 33-4

Enlarged view of graafian follicle showing ovum, or egg, in position. Follicle is nearing maturity and is about ready to rupture and to discharge egg. In human ovary usually only one ovum ruptures each four weeks during active life of ovary. (Courtesy J. W. Bamberger.)

sperm is called the **testis** (Fig. 33-3) and that which forms the egg, the **ovary** (Fig. 33-4). The gonads represent the **primary sex organs**, the only sex organs found in certain groups of animals. Most metazoans, however, have various **accessory sex organs.** In the primary sex organs the sex cells undergo many complicated changes during their development, the details of which are described in a later section. In our present discussion we shall point out the various types of sexual reproduction —biparental reproduction, parthenogenesis, pedogenesis, and hermaphroditism.

Biparental reproduction. The common method of sexual reproduction involves two separate and distinct individuals—male and female. Each of these has its own reproductive system and produces only one kind of sex cell, spermatozoan or ovum, but never both. Nearly all vertebrates and many invertebrates have separate sexes, and such a condition is called **dioecious.**

Parthenogenesis. This is a modification of sexual reproduction in which an unfertilized egg develops into a complete individual. It is found in rotifers, plant lice, certain ants, bees, and crustaceans. Usually parthenogenesis occurs for several generations and is followed by a biparental generation in which the egg is fertilized. In some cases parthenogenesis appears to be the only form of reproduction. The queen bee is fertilized only once by a male (drone) or sometimes by more than one drone. She stores the sperm in her seminal receptacles, and as she lays her eggs, she can either fertilize the eggs or allow them to pass unfertilized. The fertilized eggs become females (queens or workers) the unfertilized eggs become males (drones).

Artificial parthenogenesis was discovered in 1900. Eggs that normally are fertilized can be artificially induced to develop without fertilization or the presence of sperm. The agents employed are dilute organic acids, hypertonic salt solutions, and mechanical pricking with a needle. Eggs of certain invertebrates, such as those of the sea urchin, were first used, but later vertebrate eggs were successfully induced to develop without fertilization. Many frogs of both sexes were developed beyond metamorphosis. Rarely do such forms complete development and they are usually smaller than normal ones. In recent years even a mammal (rabbit) has resulted from a stimulated unfertilized egg.

Pedogenesis. Parthenogenesis among larval forms is called **pedogenesis.** It is known to occur in *Miastor* (a gallfly), in which eggs produced by immature forms develop parthenogenetically into other larvae. **Neoteny,** or the retardation of bodily development, has about the same meaning as pedogenesis. The most striking example of this is the tiger salamander *(Ambystoma tigrinum)* that in certain parts of its range is found to mate in a larval (axolotl) form. Such larvae can be transformed into adults under certain conditions.

Hermaphroditism. Animals that have both male and female organs in the same individual are called hermaphrodites and the condition is called **hermaphroditism.** In contrast to the dioecious state of separate sexes, hermaphroditism is called **monoecious.** Many lower animals (flatworms and hydra) are hermaphroditic. Most of them do not reproduce by self-fertilization, but the individuals exchange germ cells with each other in cross-fertilization. The earthworm ensures that its eggs are fertilized by the copulating mate as well as vice versa. Another way of preventing self-fertilization is by developing the sex products at different times. In some monoecious forms the sperm are formed first and the eggs later (**protandry**), but this condition may be reversed (**protogyny**). However, some hermaphrodites have regular self-fertilization, such as tapeworms and certain snails. A recent type of protogyny was discovered in certain tropical sea basses known as Bahama groupers *(Petrometopon cruentatum).* These fish begin life as females and later change into males. The age of transformation from female to male has not been determined, since the counting of annual rings on scales is unreliable in tropical fish. The gonad is considered in these forms as a compound organ with female, male, and a combination of male and female tissue but with a delayed timing in the appearance of the sperm after the ova degenerate or disappear.

Reproductive systems in invertebrates and vertebrates

The basic plan of the reproductive systems is similar in all animals. Many structural differences are found among the accessory sex organs, depending on the habits of the animals, their methods of fertilizing their eggs, their care of the young, etc. Many invertebrates have reproductive systems as complex as those of vertebrates, as shown by flatworms, snails, earthworms, and others. There are often complicated accessory sex organs such as reproductive ducts, penis, seminal vesicles, yolk glands, uterus, seminal receptacles, and genital chambers. In vertebrate animals the reproductive and excretory systems are often referred to as the **urogenital system** because of their close connection. This association is very striking in their embryonic development and their use of common ducts. The male urogenital system usually has a more intimate connection than has the female. This is the case with those forms (some fish and amphibians) that have an opisthonephros kidney. In these the **wolffian duct** that drains the opisthonephros also serves as the sperm duct. In male reptiles, birds, and mammals in which there is a metanephric kidney with its own independent duct (**ureter**) to carry away waste, the wolffian duct is exclusively a sperm duct (**vas deferens**). In all of these forms, with the exception of mammals higher than monotremes, the ducts open into a **cloaca.** In higher mammals there is no cloaca, but the urogenital system has an opening separate from the anal opening. The **oviduct** of the female is an independent duct that, however, does open into the cloaca in forms that have a cloaca.

The plan of the reproductive system in vertebrates includes (1) **gonads** that produce the sperm and eggs; (2) **ducts** to transport the gametes; (3) **special organs** for transferring and receiving gametes; (4) **accessory glands** (exocrine and endocrine) to provide secretions necessary for the reproductive process; and (5) **organs** for storage before and after fertilization. This plan is modified among the various vertebrates, and some of the items may be lacking altogether.

Male reproductive system. The male reproductive system in man (Fig. 33-5) includes testes, vasa efferentia, vas deferens, penis, and glands.

Testes (testicles). The testes are paired and are responsible for the production and development of the sperm. Each testis is made up of about 500 **seminiferous tubules,** which produce the sperm, and the **interstitial** tissue, lying among the tubules, which produces the male sex hormone (testosterone). The two testes are housed in the scrotal sac, which hangs down as an appendage of the body. The scrotum acts as a thermoregulator for protecting the sperm against high temperature. Sperm apparently will not form at body temperatures, although they are able to do so in elephants and birds (with very high temperatures). In some mammals (many rodents) the testes are retained within the body cavity except during the breeding season, when they descend through the inguinal canals into the scrotal sacs.

Vasa efferentia. Vasa efferentia are small tubes connecting the seminiferous tubules to a coiled **vas epididymis** (one for each testis) that serves for the storage of the sperm.

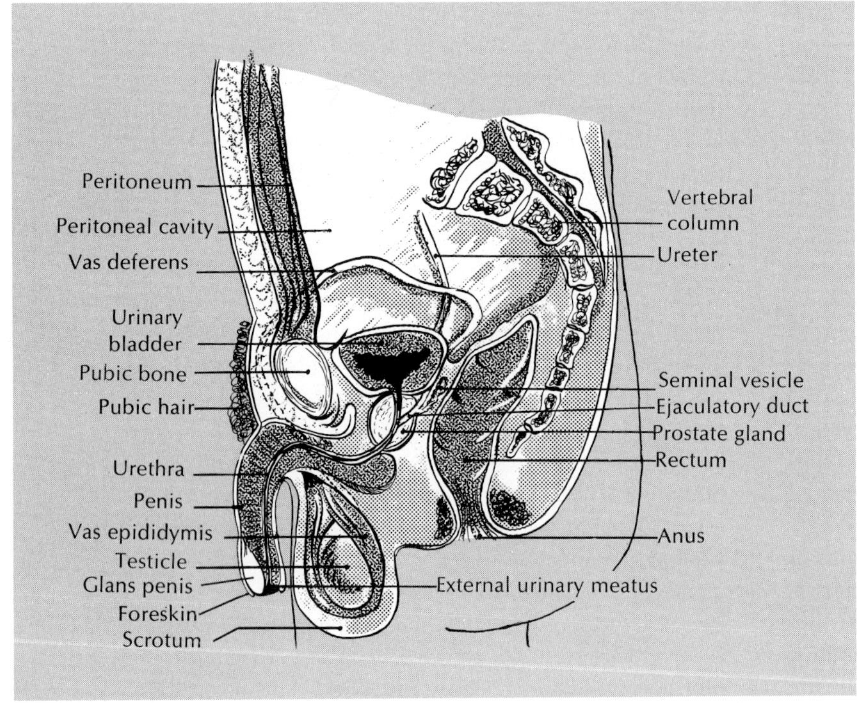

FIG. 33-5

Median section of male reproductive system in man showing relations to adjacent structures.

Vas deferens. This tube is a continuation of the epididymis and runs to the urethra, which it joins opposite its mate from the other testis. From this point the urethra serves to carry both sperm and urinary products.

Penis. The penis is the external intromittent organ through which the urethra runs. The penis contains erectile tissue for distention during the copulatory act.

Glands. There are at least three pairs of exocrine glands (those with ducts) that open into the reproductive channels. Fluid secreted by these glands furnishes food to the sperm, lubricates the passageways of the sperm, and counteracts the acidity of the urine so that the sperm will not be harmed. The first of these glands is the **seminal vesicle,** which opens into each vas deferens before it meets the urethra. Next are the **prostate glands,** which are really a single fused gland in man; it secretes into the urethra. Near the base of the penis lies the third pair of glands, **Cowper's glands,** which also discharge into the urethra. The secretions of these glands form a part of the seminal discharge.

Female reproductive system. The female reproductive system (Fig. 33-6) contains ovaries, oviduct, uterus, vagina, and vulva.

Ovaries. The ovaries are paired and are contained within the abdominal cavity, where they are held in position by ligaments. Each ovary is about as large as an almond and contains many thousands of developing eggs (ova). Each egg develops within a graafian follicle that enlarges and finally ruptures to release the mature egg (Fig. 33-4). During the fertile period of the woman about thirteen eggs mature each year, and usually the ovaries may alternate in releasing an egg. Since the female is fertile for only some thirty years, only about 400 eggs have a chance to reach maturity; the others degenerate and are absorbed.

Oviduct (fallopian tube). These egg-carrying tubes are not closely attached to the ovaries but have funnel-shaped ostia for receiving the eggs when they emerge from the ovary. The oviduct is lined with cilia for pro-

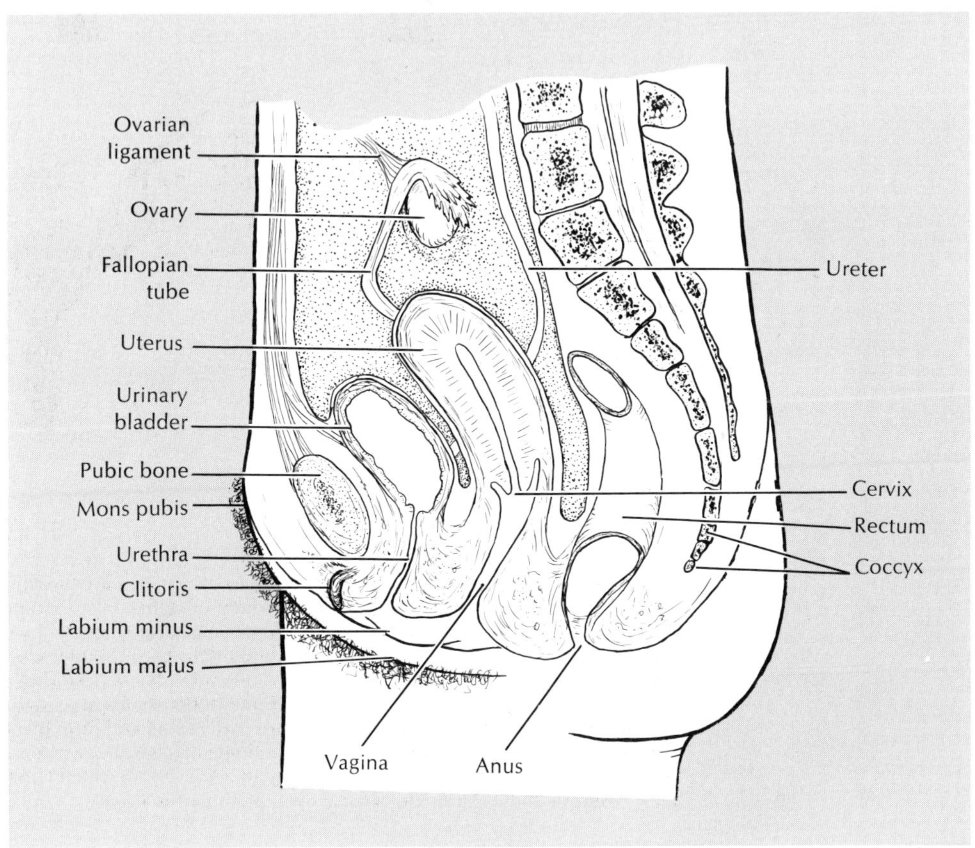

FIG. 33-6

Median section of human female reproductive system showing its relation to adjacent structures.

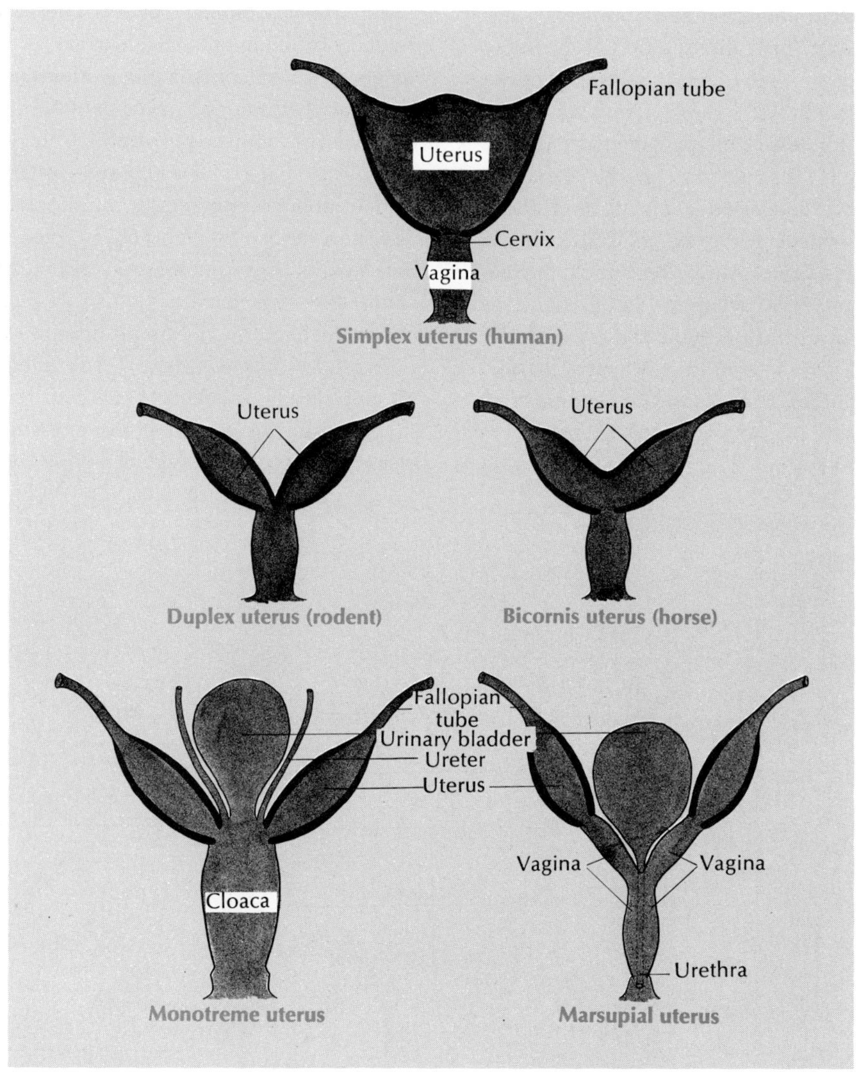

FIG. 33-7

Uteri and related structures of mammals. Oviducts of mammal are modified to form uterus for development of young and vagina for reception of male penis. Most primitive condition is found in monotremes, which lack vagina but have cloaca. They are the only mammals that lay eggs. Marsupials have double vagina and uterus because their oviducts are only partially fused at bases. Placental mammals, on the other hand, have single fused vagina with uteri in progressive stages of fusion. In some (rodents), uterus is two horned or duplex; in others (perissodactyls), bases of oviducts are partly fused and form bicornis (bicornate) type; in a few (primates), uterus is single median cavity (simplex). In carnivores and some others there is an intermediate type (not shown), in which two uteri are united at their posterior ends with single cervical opening (bipartite uterus).

pelling the egg in its course. The two ducts open into the upper corners of the uterus, or womb.

Uterus. The uterus is specialized for housing the embryo during the nine months of its intrauterine existence. It is provided with thick muscular walls, many blood vessels, and a specialized lining—the **endometrium.** The uterus varies with different mammals. It was originally paired but tends to fuse in higher forms. The different types are illustrated in Fig. 33-7.

Vagina. This large muscular tube runs from the uterus to the outside of the body. It is adapted for receiving the male's penis and for serving as the birth canal during expulsion of the fetus from the uterus. Where the vagina and the uterus meet, the uterus projects down into the vagina to form the **cervix.**

Vulva. The vulva refers to the external genitalia and includes two folds of skin covered with hair, the **labia majora**; a smaller pair of folds within the labia majora, the **labia minora**; a small erectile organ, the **clitoris,** at the anterior junction of the labia minora; and a fleshy elevation above the labia majora, the **mons veneris.** The opening into the vagina is the vestibule that is normally closed in the virgin state by a membrane, the **hymen.**

Homology of sex organs

For every structure in the male system, there is a homologous one in the female. This does not mean they have the same functions in the two sexes, for the various organs of the two sexes perform functions peculiar to each sex. Although homologous structures may be well developed in both sexes, many of them are functional in one sex and their homologues in the other may be vestigial and nonfunctional. To understand this sex organ homology, it is necessary to observe the way in which the reproductive systems have arisen in embryonic development. Although sex is probably determined at the time of fertilization, it is not until many weeks later that the distinct sex characters associated with one or the other sex are recognized. Before this time the external genitalia of the two sexes cannot be distinguished. The hormonal interpretation of sex shows how slight the differences are between the two sexes. The animal is a chemical hermaphrodite and bears the possibilities of becoming either sex, depending on the balance of the sex hormones.

Some of the chief homologies of the male and female reproductive systems are shown in Table 33-1.

Origin of reproductive cells

Protoplasm is commonly divided into two types—**somatoplasm** and **germ plasm.** The body cells are made up of somatoplasm and are called **somatic cells;** reproductive cells are formed of germ plasm and are called **germ cells.** All the somatic cells die within the individual. The germ plasm is continuous from generation to

TABLE 33-1

Organ homologies of male and female reproductive systems

Male	Indifferent stage of embryo	Female
Testis	Genital ridge	Ovary
Vas deferens	Wolffian duct	Vestigial
Epididymis	Wolffian body	Vestigial
Appendix of testis	Müllerian duct	Uterus, vagina, fallopian tube
Penis	Genital tubercle	Clitoris
Glans penis		Glans clitoridis
Anal surface of penis	Genital folds	Labia minora
Scrotum	Genital swellings	Labia majora

generation, whereas the somatoplasm is formed anew at each generation. At the present time this continuity is recognized as residing in the chromosomes and so the chromatin material of the nucleus is considered to be the germ plasm and the cell cytoplasm the somatoplasm. The distinction, however, between somatic and germ cells, as mentioned in another section, is not absolutely rigid. Many invertebrates are known to regenerate whole bodies from small parts of themselves.

The actual tissue from which the gonads arise appears in early development as a pair of ridges, or pouches, growing into the coelom from the dorsal coelomic lining on each side of the gut near the anterior end of the mesonephros. The primordial ancestors of the cells that are going to form gametes do not arise in the developing gonad but in the yolk-sac endoderm and migrate by ameboid movements (mammals) or through the circulatory system (chick) to the genital ridges or embryonic gonad. The genital ridge is a mesenchymal thickening covered over by mesothelium that becomes the germinal epithelium. The gonad at first is sexually indifferent, but if the gonad is to become a testis, the cells in the germinal epithelium grow into the underlying mesenchymal tissue (medulla) and form the seminiferous tubules. The inner walls of the tubules are formed of cells that have descended from those of the germinal epithelium; these cells then develop eventually into mature sperm. If the indifferent gonad is to become an ovary, the primordial germ cells grow into the mesenchyme and differentiate into ovarian follicles with eggs (ova). There are still many disagreements about the origin of the germ cells.

Meiosis. In ordinary cell division, or mitosis, each of the two daughter cells receives exactly the same number and kind of chromosomes. All the body or somatic cells of the organism are derived and contain two chromosome sets, or diploid complement. One set of chromosomes, called a **genome** or haploid complement, is of paternal and the other of maternal origin. The chief function of mitosis is to multiply the number of cells (or individuals in Protozoa). In most cases for every paternal chromosome in the diploid complement, there is also a corresponding maternal chromosome of similar form and function. The members of such a pair are called **homologous chromosomes.**

In sexual reproduction, however, the formation of the **gametes,** or **germ cells,** requires a different process than that of somatic cells. The fusion of two gametes (egg and sperm) produces the zygote or fertilized egg from which the new organism arises. If each sperm and egg had the same number of chromosomes as somatic cells, there would be a doubling of chromosomes in each successive generation. To prevent this from happening, germ cells are formed by a type of cell division called **meiosis.** Meiosis is a process whereby the chromosome number is reduced by one half so that mature gametes have only one member of each homologous pair, or a haploid (n) number of chromosomes. In man the zygotes and all body cells normally have the diploid number (2n) of 46; the gametes have the haploid number (n) of 23.

Meiosis is similar to mitosis in its morphologic changes and movements of chromosomes, but it has only one chromosomal division (Fig. 33-8). Meiosis consists of two successive nuclear divisions, each of which has the same four stages—prophase, metaphase, anaphase, and telophase—found in mitosis. The first meiotic di-

FIG. 33-8

Comparison of mitosis and meiosis. Two processes are similar in many respects. Each has conventional phases of prophase, metaphase, anaphase, and telophase; morphologic changes and movements of chromosomes are essentially similar. However, there are some basic differences. Prophase in meiosis is longer and is divided into several distinct stages. In mitosis there is doubling of chromosomes, followed by cell division in which number of chromosomes is halved so that **diploid** number of chromosomes remains same. In meiosis there is chromosome duplication, followed by two cell divisions, resulting in cells with only half the diploid number of cells, or **haploid** number. Unique pairing (synapsis) of homologous chromosomes in meiosis enables homologous chromosomes to exchange parts (crossing-over). Meiosis leads to genetic variation because of new combinations of genetic material in crossing-over and in distribution of homologous chromosomes into different daughter nuclei. It will be noted that each diploid complement of chromosomes is made up of two sets, one of paternal and the other of maternal origin. For every paternal chromosome in diploid nucleus, there is usually corresponding maternal one with same form, size, and genetic function. Pair of such corresponding paternal and maternal chromosomes are known as homologous chromosomes.

FIG. 33-8

For legend see opposite page.

Somatic cell (interphase) or
Primordial germ cell
(diploid number of 8 chromosomes)

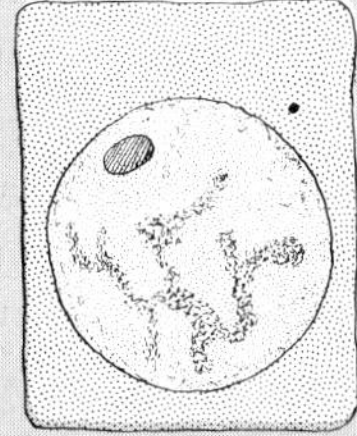

Mitosis

Meiosis

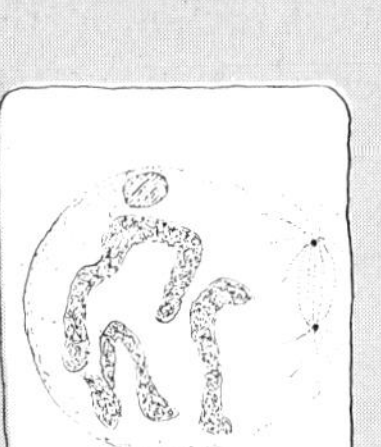

Chromosomes begin to appear

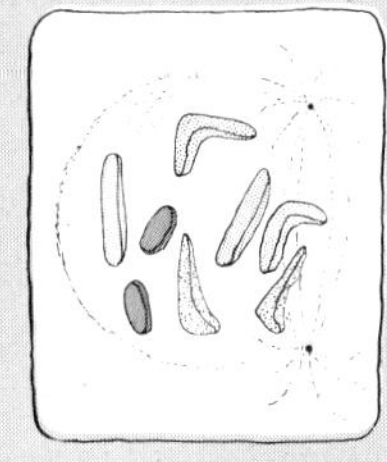

Each chromosome consists of 2 sister chromatids

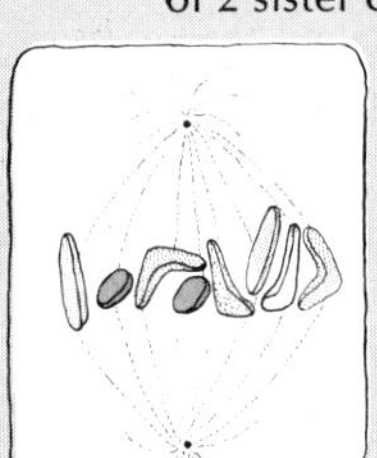

Chromosomes arranged on spindle

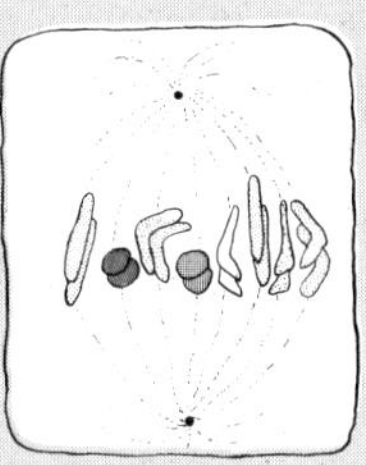

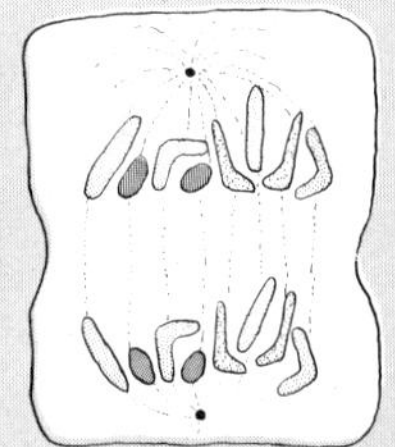

In cell division, one sister chromatid passes to one daughter cell and its mate to the other

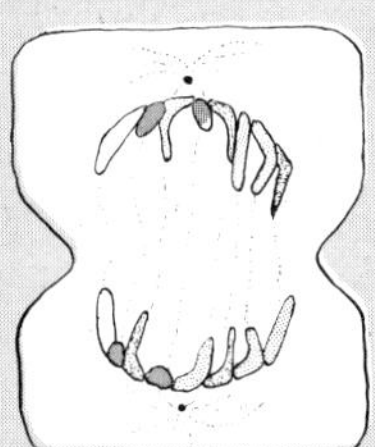

Each cell retains diploid number (8) of chromosomes

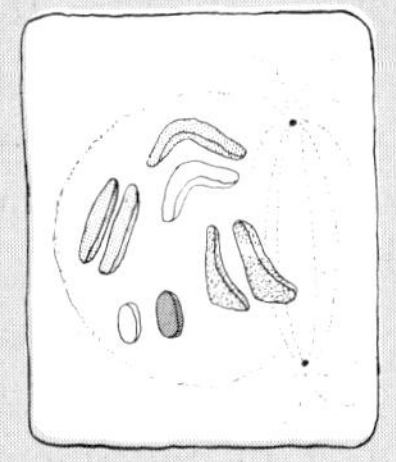

Homologous chromosomes, each of 2 chromatids, pair

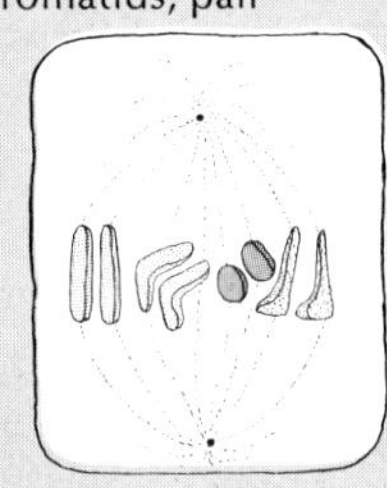

Paired chromosomes arranged on spindle

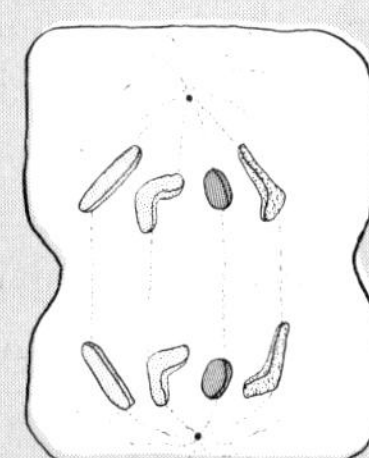

In first meiotic division, homologous chromosomes separate to opposite poles so that each daughter cell has only haploid number of chromosomes

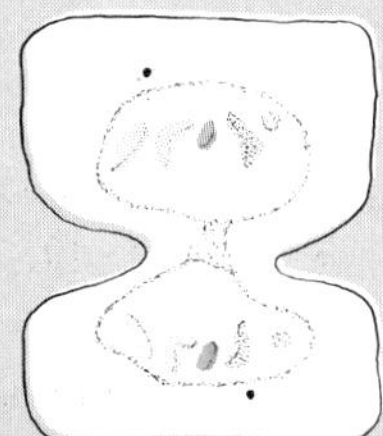

Second meiotic division (not shown) involves separation of sister chromatids of each chromosome to their respective daughter cells; each cell has only haploid number of chromosomes

vision involves the pairing of homologous chromosomes to form bivalent units, the resolution of each homologous chromosome into two half or sister chromatids, and the separation of homologous chromosomes to opposite poles of the cell. Each resulting daughter cell thus contains half the number of chromosomes characteristic of the diploid chromosomes of the organism. The second meiotic division results in a separation and distribution of the sister chromatids of each chromosome to opposite poles and thus involves no reduction in number of chromosomes. In contrast to mitosis, meiosis is concerned with genetic reassortment. It does this in two ways: (1) by random segregation of homologous chromosomes and (2) by crossing-over, or exchanging segments between each homologous pair. Another source of variation is, of course, the mutation of the gene. This source of inherited variability enables natural selection to bring about evolutionary changes.

Prophase I. The most striking difference between mitosis and meiosis occurs at the beginning of the first meiotic division. The prophase, or the first stage of meiosis, has five substages: leptotene, zygotene, pachytene, diplotene, and diakinesis.

1. **Leptotene.** In this stage the chromosomes (diploid in number) appear as long, thin threadlike structures and resemble strings of beads because of granules (chromomeres). Each pair of homologous chromosomes is identical as to size, position of centromere, etc. Each of these early prophase chromosomes is already divided into a pair of indistinguishable sister chromatids.

2. **Zygotene.** This stage involves the pairing (synapsis) of homologous chromosomes to form bivalent chromosome units. This process does not occur in mitosis. This results in paired units corresponding to the haploid number.

3. **Pachytene.** The pairing of the chromosomes is completed and the chromosomes undergo longitudinal contraction so that each bivalent is shorter and thicker, and the two chromosomes of each bivalent become twisted about one another.

4. **Diplotene.** In this stage the homologous chromosomes of each bivalent are now visibly double. Since each homologous chromosome consists of two sister chromatids, each chromosome pair, or bivalent, will show four chromatids, or a **tetrad.** The centromeres remain unsplit at this time. Since longitudinal separation is incomplete, the homologues of the bivalent remain in contact at various points, producing a characteristic X configuration called **chiasma** (pl. chiasmata). Each chiasma represents a region at which two nonsister chromatids are undergoing an exchange of parts (crossover). Thus two chromatids of the tetrads are structurally reorganized so that each is made up of an original and an exchanged component. The other two chromatids of the tetrad remain in their original form. Chiasmata are not found in meiosis in which there is no crossing-over, as in the male *Drosophila.*

5. **Diakinesis.** This stage is characterized by a maximum contraction of the chromosomes and a further separation of the homologous chromosomes, although the chromatids remain connected by the chiasmata. At the same time the nucleolus begins to disappear, and the nuclear membrane breaks down.

At the end of the first prophase of meiosis homologous chromosomes have paired, exchanged chromatid segments, and started their longitudinal separation.

Metaphase I. This phase begins when the nuclear membrane disappears and the spindle is formed. Each homologous chromosome (homologue) has its centromere (kinetochore) and the bivalent chromosomes (tetrads) line up on the equatorial plate, with the centromeres of the two homologues directed toward opposite poles.

Anaphase I. In this stage each homologue of a pair, with its daughter chromosomes united by their centromere, moves to its respective pole, each centromere taking half of the bivalent with it. Thus whole chromosomes are separated in anaphase, and each of the two resulting cells of the first meiotic division has a haploid number of chromosomes.

Telophase I and interphase. A nuclear membrane may be re-formed around the chromosomes, which often persist in a condensed form; they may become uncoiled; or no membrane may be formed at all and the chromosomes may enter directly into the second meiotic division. The interphase may not exist at all.

Prophase II and metaphase II. A short prophase in which a new spindle starts forming marks the beginning of the second meiotic division. The chromosomes become arranged on the equatorial plate. This is followed by the division of the centromeres for the first time and the longitudinal separation of the sister chromatids so that this division separates the two chromatids of each chromosome. Although these two chromatids are identical in their formation, they differ in those segments that have been exchanged by crossing-over.

Anaphase II and telophase II. The sister chromatids, now called chromosomes, move to their respective poles, and each of the two daughter nuclei has a complete set (genome) that corresponds to the haploid number. In the telophase the cytoplasm divides, and the chromosomes become longer and less visible. A nuclear membrane is then formed around each nucleus.

The result of the two meiotic divisions is the formation of four cells, each of which has the haploid number of chromosomes or one of each kind of chromosome of the homologous pairs that started meiosis. The first meiotic division is often called a reduction division, and the second meiotic division is called an equational division. However, the exchange of chromatid segments (crossing-over) and the fact that there is no reduction in total number of chromosomes have caused many cytologists to consider the terms "reduction" and "equational" obsolete.

Gametogenesis. The series of transformations that results in the formation of mature gametes (germ cells) is called gametogenesis. This process occurs in glands called **gonads**—the **testis** of the male and the **ovary** of the female. In certain animals, such as the invertebrates *Miastor* and *Sagitta,* it is possible to distinguish a certain region of the zygote that is going to give rise to the

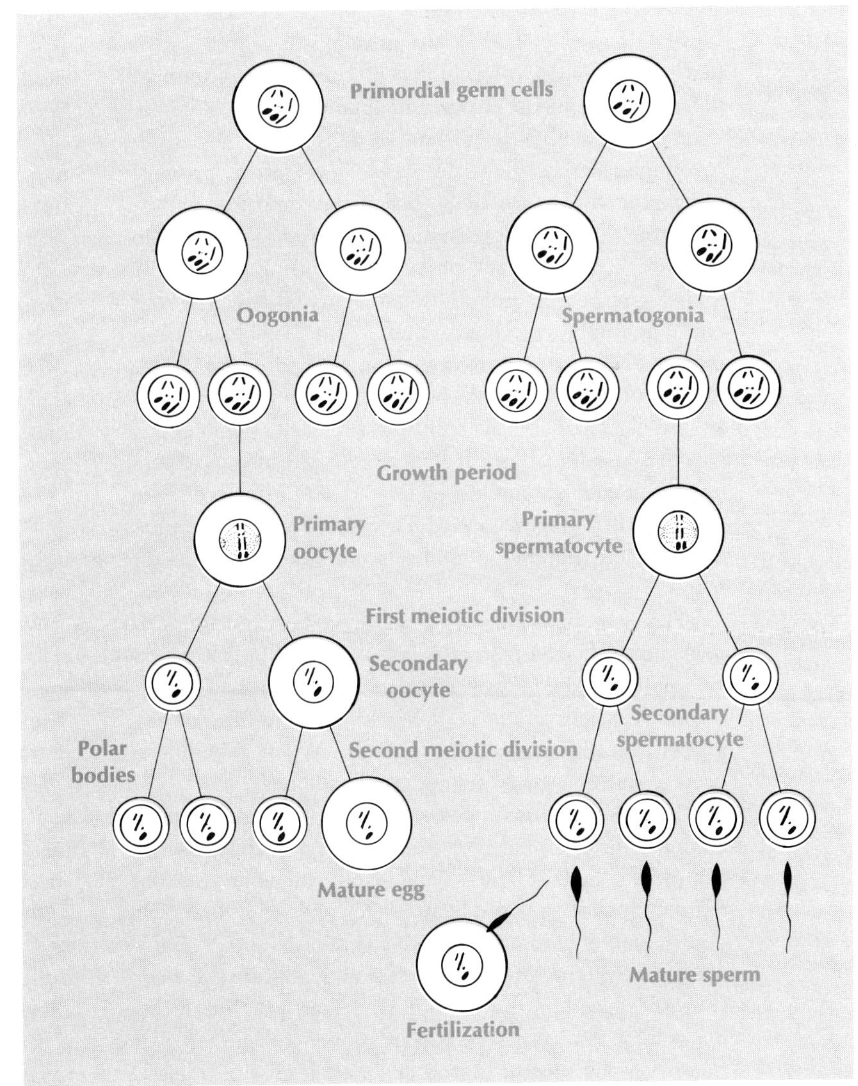

FIG. 33-9

Process of gametogenesis, or formation of germ cells. Oogenesis shown on left, spermatogenesis on right.

germ cells eventually. In higher forms the germ cells are not recognized until later. In this way both germ cells and somatic cells have come from the same one-celled zygote but have differentiated in different ways. The earliest germ cells recognized are the **primordial germ cells.**

Although the same essential processes are involved in the maturation of both sperm and eggs, there are some minor differences. Gametogenesis in the testis is called **spermatogenesis** and in the ovary it is called **oogenesis.**

Spermatogenesis (Fig. 33-9). Spermatogenesis occurs in the walls of the many seminiferous tubules of the testis (Fig. 33-3). These tubules contain the differentiating sex cells that are arranged to form a stratified layer about five to eight cells deep. The outermost layers are made up of spermatogonia, which have increased in number by ordinary mitosis. Each spermatogonium increases in size and becomes a **primary spermatocyte.** Before the primary spermatocyte undergoes the first meiotic division, its chromosomes come together in homologous pairs (**synapsis**). Each pair of homologous chromosomes is made up of one paternal and one maternal chromosome. After synapsis, each member of the chromosome pair appears doubled, either by the formation of a new chromosome from the nucleus or by a splitting of each homologous chromosome into two **chromatids.** As a result each pair of homologous chromosomes appears as a bundle of four components called a **tetrad.** There are as many tetrads as there are haploid number of chromosomes (23 in man).

These chromosomes, at first elongated and threadlike, now shorten and thicken. In the meantime a spindle is formed between the centrioles, and when the nuclear membrane is dissolved, the tetrads line up around the equator of the spindle. When metaphase occurs, the maternal and paternal members of a pair, or the homologous mates, separate, but the double chromosomes do not. At anaphase this separation is completed so that each homologous member and its double (called a **dyad**) move to one pole and the other double chromosome (dyad) to the other pole. How the different tetrads divide depends on the way they are placed on the spindle. On some spindles all the maternal pairs may face toward one pole and all the paternal pairs toward the other, or they may be mixed. One of the resulting daughter cells (**secondary spermatocytes**) of this division might have all maternal dyads and the other all paternal dyads, or each daughter could have part paternal and part maternal dyads. This division is called **reduction division** because the two homologous chromosomes, which came together to form a pair in synapsis, have separated from each other.

The second meiotic division (equational division) occurs usually just after the first, without the intervention of a resting period. It differs from ordinary mitosis in that the chromosomes are haploid in number and the chromatids may differ genetically (in case of crossing-over, etc.) from their original condition. A new spindle is formed in each cell at right angles to the spindle of the first division and the haploid number of dyads are arranged on its equator. The ensuing division results in a separation of the members of the dyads so that one member (chromatid) goes to one pole and the other to the other pole. The resulting cells are called **spermatids,** and each contains the haploid number (23) of chromosomes. A spermatid may have all maternal, all paternal, or both maternal and paternal chromosomes in varying proportions. Without further divisions the spermatids are transformed into mature sperm by losing a great deal of cytoplasm, by condensing the nucleus into a head, and by forming a whiplike tail.

It will be seen from following the divisions of meiosis that each primary spermatocyte gives rise to four functional sperm, each with the haploid number of chromosomes.

Production of mature sperm

The testes of higher forms such as mammals consist of seminiferous tubules and interstitial tissue lying between them. As already described the seminiferous tubules include the germ cell stages, and the interstitial tissue contains the special Leydig cells that, as mentioned later, secrete the male hormone testosterone. The seminiferous tubules contain, in addition to the germ cells, the nongerminal Sertoli cells, often called "sperm mother cells" because it is thought that the sperm heads become embedded in them during the development of the sperm. During the maturation of the final stages of sperm formation, parts of the cytoplasm of the spermatozoon are sloughed off as **residual bodies** (Fig. 33-10). These bodies are eventually engulfed by the Sertoli cells. In a recent theory (D. Lacy) these residual bodies cause the Sertoli cells to form the steroid Sertoli cell hormone (SCH) that enables the primary spermatocytes to complete their maturation di-

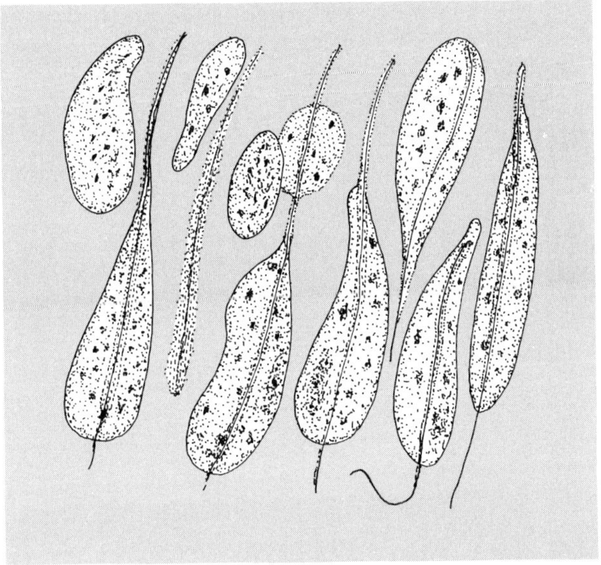

FIG. 33-10

Cluster of cytoplasmic remnants, or residual bodies, many of which are still attached to sperm tails. Sloughed off residual bodies are engulfed by Sertoli's cells of seminiferous tubules and are believed to contain the hormone (SCH) that stimulates primary spermatocytes to complete their maturation.

vision so that there may be a continued replenishment of the spermatid population. SCH is considered the controlling agent through which FSH (follicle-stimulating hormone) act indirectly on spermatogenesis.

Oogenesis (Fig. 33-9). The early germ cells in the ovary are called oogonia, which increase in number by ordinary mitosis. Each oogonium contains the diploid number of chromosomes. In the human being, after puberty, typically one of these oogonia develops each menstrual month into a functional egg. After the oogonia cease to increase in number, they grow in size and become **primary oocytes.** Before the first meiotic division, the chromosomes in each primary oocyte meet in pairs, paternal and maternal homologues, just as in spermatogenesis. They also form tetrads and dyads that behave as in spermatogenesis. When the first maturation (reduction) division occurs, the cytoplasm, however, is divided very unequally. One of the two daughter cells, the **secondary oocyte,** is large and receives most of the cytoplasm; the other is very small and is called the **first polar body** (polocyte). Each of these daughter cells, however, has received half the nuclear material or chromosomes.

In the second (equational) meiotic division, the secondary oocyte divides into a large **ootid** and a small polar body. If the first polar body also divides in this division, which sometimes happens, there will be three polar bodies and one ootid. The ootid grows into a functional ovum; the polar bodies disintegrate because they are nonfunctional. The formation of the nonfunctional polar bodies is necessary to enable the egg to get rid of excess chromosomes, and the unequal cytoplasmic division makes possible a large cell with sufficient yolk for the development of the young. Thus the mature ovum has the haploid number of chromosomes the same as the sperm. However, each primary oocyte gives rise to only **one** functional gamete instead of four as in spermatogenesis.

Gametes of various animals. Sperm among animals show a greater diversity of form than do ova. A typical spermatozoan is made up of a head, a middle piece, and an elongated tail for locomotion (Fig. 33-11). The head consists of the nucleus containing the chromosomes for heredity and an acrosome for puncturing the egg in fertilization. The total length of the human sperm is 50 to 70 μ. Some toads have sperm that exceed 2 mm. (2,000 μ) in length. Most sperm, however, are microscopic in size. Some invertebrates have sperm that vary from the typical form. *Ascaris* has a short conical-shaped sperm without a tail, and the crayfish has one with radially arranged prongs. All sperm are able to swim in a fluid medium.

Ova are oval or spherical in shape and are nonmotile. Usually, they contain a great deal of yolk (deuteroplasm) for the nourishment of the young. Mammals' eggs are very small (not more than 0.25 mm.) because the young receive nourishment from the mother. On the other hand, the eggs of some birds and sharks are very large, to supply nutritive material for the developing young before hatching. Some eggs (reptiles and birds) also contain a great deal of albumin, which also serves for nourishment. Most eggs are provided with some form of protective coating. This may be in the form of a calcified shell (birds), leathery parchment (reptiles), or albuminous coats (amphibians).

The number of sperm in all animals is greatly in excess of the eggs of corresponding females. The number of eggs produced is related to the chances of the young to hatch and reach maturity. This explains the enormous number of eggs produced by certain fish, as compared with the small number produced by mammals.

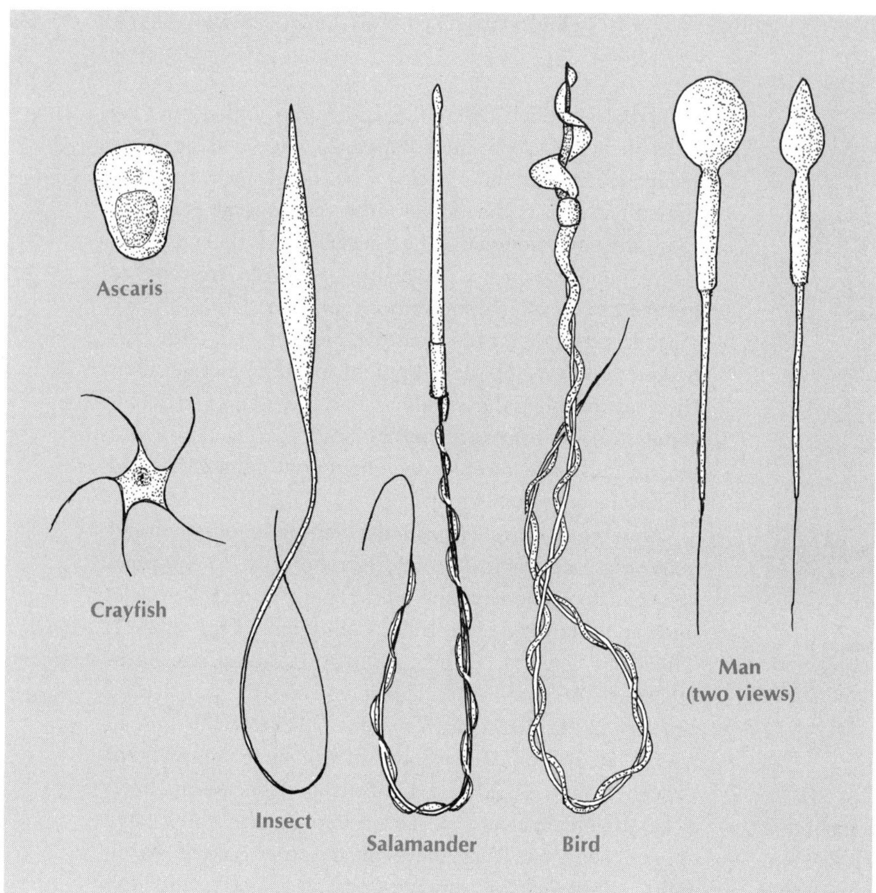

FIG. 33-11

Types of animal sperm, represented by both vertebrates and invertebrates. All belong to flagellate variety except those of *Ascaris* and crayfish that are nonflagellate sperm.

Fertilization (syngamy)

The formation of a **zygote** by the union of a spermatozoan and an ovum is called **fertilization.** This process restores the original diploid number of chromosomes characteristic of the species, stimulates the zygote to cleavage and development, and combines the hereditary characteristics of both male and female parents. The haploid egg or sperm nucleus is called a **pronucleus.** The union of the sperm and egg pronuclei occurs after the egg is mature. In *Ascaris* the spermatozoan enters the egg before the first meiotic division is finished; in the frog and some others, between the formation of the first and second polar body; and in some, after maturation is completed. Sometimes the entire spermatozoan enters the egg, but often the tail is left outside and only the head and a few other structures enter. The male head (pronucleus) absorbs materials from the cytoplasm of the egg and increases to a size similar to that of the egg pronucleus. The two pronuclei meet and the first cleavage division takes place soon after.

If the egg has a shell at the time of fertilization, there is a special pore through which the spermatozoan enters; in other eggs it may enter anywhere. Usually only one sperm enters an egg because a **fertilization membrane** formed at this time may prevent others from coming in, although the physiologic state of the egg cytoplasm may be the real barrier. In the fertilization of some eggs (for example, sea urchin) when the spermatozoan approaches the egg, its tip gives rise to an acrosomal filament by which the spermatozoan is attached to the egg. Cortical changes (cortical reaction) in the outer layer of the egg then occur, such as the formation of a funnel-shaped cone around the acrosomal filament, the disappearance of cortical granules, and the formation of the fertilization membrane. This cortical reaction appears to be necessary for the initiation of development. There is evidence that the egg has in its gelatinous coat a substance called **fertilizin,** which combining with a substance (antifertilizin) on the sperm, causes the latter to clump together and stick to the surface of the egg. Mammalian sperm are also known to produce an enzyme, **hyaluronidase,** which dissolves away the glue (hyaluronic acid) holding the follicle cells together so that the spermatozoan can enter and fertilize the egg.

Polyspermy (entrance of more than one sperm) occurs in birds and some others, but only one spermatozoan fuses with the egg pronucleus in such cases. The development of the egg may be induced by certain physicochemical agents (artificial parthenogenesis), as pointed out in a previous section.

When the egg and spermatozoan come together to form the zygote, the diploid number of chromosomes is restored and there is no doubling of the chromosome number, which would be the case if the gametes had the somatic (diploid) number of chromosomes. The reduction division of gametogenesis ensures a continuity of chromosome number from one generation to another.

Types of fertilization. Fertilization is accomplished in one of two ways: (1) by discharging the gametes directly into the water and allowing the germ cells to come together by chance (**external fertilization**) or (2) by discharging the sperm into special cavities of the female so that fertilization occurs there (**internal fertilization**). External fertilization is common among aquatic forms because the water affords an excellent medium for the locomotion of the motile sperm to the eggs. In this type there are devices employed to ensure fertilization. Some aquatic animals (lamprey and horned dace) make a nest in the form of a depression in the sand and shed their gametes there where they are close together. Others (frogs and toads) extrude their eggs and sperm when the male is clasping the female so that the gametes have an excellent chance of meeting.

In **internal fertilization** the eggs and sperm are thrown so close together that fertilization is inevitable. This is the type practiced by land forms (and also by some aquatic animals) because external fertilization would expose the delicate germ cells to the air and there would be lacking the fluid medium that is required for all fertilization. Animals vary with respect to the methods they employ in the transfer of the sperm to the female cavities. Some of the male salamanders deposit on leaves or other objects packets of sperm (spermatophores) that the female picks up with the cloaca. Usually those forms that have internal fertilization have special copulatory organs (penis, claspers, etc.) for transferring the sperm into the female vagina or cloaca.

Breeding habits of animals

The breeding habits of animals vary with different forms. These differences are correlated with methods for fertilization, with kinds of habitats, with the structure of the reproductive systems, with the prenatal care of the young, and with seasonal and physiologic changes in animals. Bats mate in the fall and the sperm is stored in the female till the following spring before fertilization occurs. The queen honeybee stores up enough sperm from the drone on one nuptial flight to fertilize all the eggs she lays during her lifetime. Salmon spend most of their lives in the sea but spawn far up inland rivers in fresh water. Eels grow to maturity in freshwater streams but migrate to the sea to spawn. Many animals provide nests of various sorts to take care of the young (birds and some fish). Others have cases for the eggs (insects and spiders). Some female animals carry the eggs attached to the body or to the appendages (crayfish and certain amphibians). Brood pouches for the eggs are provided by such forms as the mussel, the sea horse (a fish), and many others. Social insects (bees and ants) have huge colonial nests organized on a complex scale. Mammals are retained in the uterus of the female during early development and later are nourished by the milk from the mammary glands.

Animals may be divided into three classes on the basis of the methods they employ to nourish their young. Those animals that lay their eggs outside the body for development are called **oviparous.** In such cases the eggs may be fertilized inside or outside the body. Some animals retain their eggs in the body (in the oviduct) while they develop, but the embryo derives its sole nourishment from the egg and not from the mother. These are called **ovoviviparous.** In the third type the egg develops in the uterus, but the embryo early in its development forms an intimate relationship with the walls of the uterus and derives its nourishment directly from food furnished by the mother. Such a type is called **viviparous.** In both of the last two types the young are born alive. Examples of oviparity are found among many invertebrates and vertebrates. All birds are of this type. Ovoviviparity is common among certain fish, lizards, and a few of the snakes. Viviparity is confined mostly to the mammals.

ENDOCRINE SYSTEM (Fig. 33-12)

The physiologic mechanism of the body is under the control of two systems—nervous and hormonal. Nervous coordination is rapid, but in contrast the hormones produced by the endocrine glands are carried in the blood at a slower pace and their effects are usually longer lasting. A **hormone** is the specific product of an endocrine gland or specialized tissue secreted into the blood and carried to some part of the body where it produces a definite physiologic effect. This effect may be either excitatory or inhibitory in its action. Some hormones, also, have a widespread action on many tissues and organs. This control involves chiefly a catalytic influence on the tissue metabolism of the target organ. There are also chemical coordinators other than hormones, such as carbon dioxide and other metabolites. Such substances are often called **parahormones.** Although all hormones are organic substances, some are more complex than others.

FIG. 33-12

Human body showing location of principal endocrine glands. Both male and female represented.

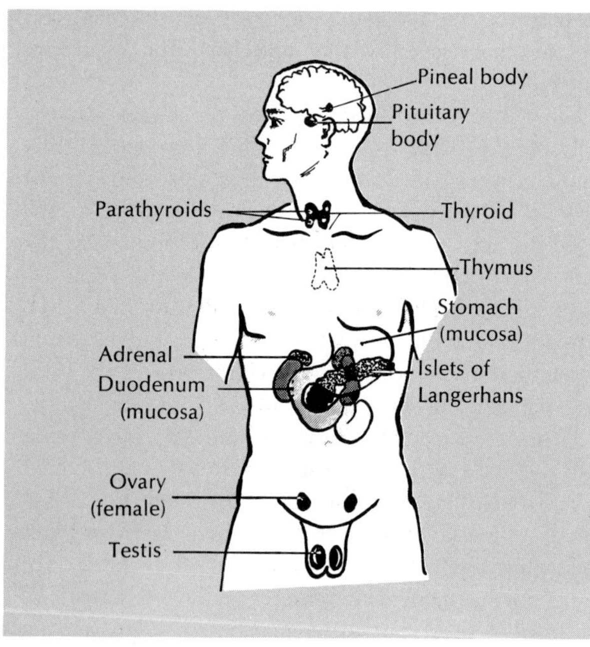

The chemical structure of many is well known and many are made synthetically. Knowledge about this system is fairly recent, mostly within the last sixty years. The science of its study is called **endocrinology,** which has been put on an experimental basis. The importance of its study was recognized early because of its application to various medical problems. Upsets in the balance of endocrine activities, hormonal imbalance, are responsible for various functional diseases.

Much of our knowledge about endocrinology has been acquired in the following ways:

1. Removing the glands in young and adults and observing many functional or structural disturbances that may arise.
2. Grafting the glands or parts of them into animals of different ages.
3. Observing the effects of clinical diseases associated with defect in particular glands.
4. Injecting extracts of glands or hormones into animals and noting what happens.
5. Replacing an excised or diseased gland with glandular extracts and hormones to compensate for the normal loss of hormonal influence.

Neurosecretion

It is well known that the two systems of communications, nervous and endocrine, are closely interrelated in function. Neurosecretory substances are produced by certain cells (neurosecretory cells) that have the structural and physiologic characteristics of neurons. These cells apparently have been found in the nervous tissues of all invertebrate and vertebrate phyla. They have been found recently in the *Hydra* (A. L. Burnett). Two types of these substances are (1) **neurohumors,** short-acting neurohormones (acetylcholine, norepinephrine, and serotonin) that are released by nerve terminals and act on muscles or on glands locally; (2) **neurosecretions,** long-acting neurohormones (oxytocin and vasopressin) that are more stable than neurohumors and may act at distant points after being released by nerve terminals. They may make up a large part of the central nervous system of the lower invertebrates, but in the higher organisms they are restricted to certain regions of the nervous system.

In vertebrates two groups of neurosecretory cells are found in the hypothalamus; one releases factors into a portal circulation to the anterior pituitary (adenohypophysis) for influencing there the production of various hormones, and the other group sends axons into the posterior pituitary (neurohypophysis) and there discharges hormones (Fig. 33-13). Like hormones, the secretions of the neurosecretory cells are released into the circulation and produce brief or prolonged effects on the organism. They release their neurosecretory substances through the club-shaped endings of their axons, which are found close to the wall of a capillary, or they may discharge into other structures such as the connective tissue bordering the nervous system. Some may even release their secretions to the outside. Their axons apparently do not synapse with other neurons, muscles, or exocrine glands. Some neurosecretory cells are apparently without processes and release their materials to capillaries lying close against them.

Although they are the subject of intense investigation, most is known about the neurosecretory complexes of the hypothalamoneurohypophyseal system of vertebrates and the molting and coloration regulating complexes of insects and crustaceans. The chemical nature of the neurosecretory substances (hormones) released by neurosecretory cells is largely unknown, but such hormones as oxytocin and vasopressin have been discovered in the neurosecretory endings of the neurohypophysis of the lower vertebrates. It is not always easy to distinguish neurosecretory cells from other neurons, but investigators rely on certain specific strains for their granular characteristics and on certain morphologic structures, such as swollen axonal endings and capillary relations, to determine their identity.

Neurosecretory cells are under the control of the nervous system, and their effects may be apparent soon after stimulation of certain nerve fibers. These cells serve as mediators between the regular endocrine and nervous systems and as sources of hormones for direct control of effector organs.

The earliest demonstration of neurosecretion was C. C. Speidel's investigations (1919) on the urohypophysis, a neurohemal organ in the posterior region of the spinal cord of elasmobranchs and teleosts. U. Dahlgren (1914) had earlier described the large cells that are formed from neuroblasts (elasmobranchs) or the ependyma of the central canal (teleosts). The function of the secretion is obscure, but it may be involved in osmoregulatory coordination.

Historic background of hormones

Although the action of chemical substances in certain physiologic processes of the body had long been suspected, it was not until 1902 that two English phys-

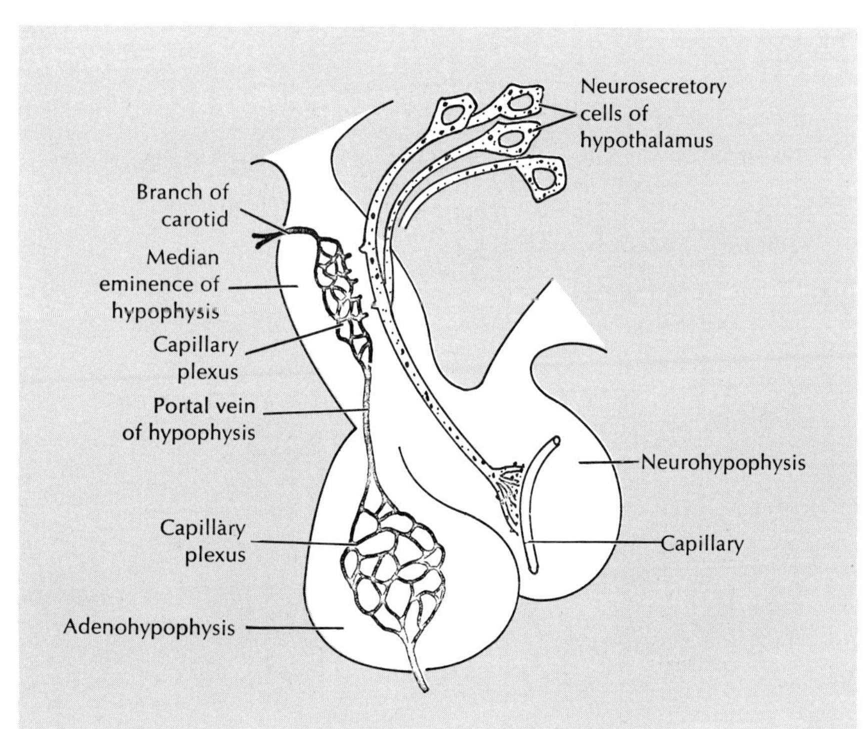

FIG. 33-13

Hypothalamic neurosecretory mechanism. Most neurosecretions of vertebrates originate in hypothalamus of diencephalon. Two systems are involved in transporting these secretions. (1) Hypophyseal portal system (in black) receives neurosecretions from nerve fibers in median eminence and carries them to anterior lobe. These secretions release certain tropic hormones in adenohypophysis. (2) Nerve fibers carry secretions (hormones) down infundibular stalk and release them into neurohypophysis, where they enter the bloodstream. Hypothalamic secretions thus either regulate endocrine-producing cells (adenohypophysis) or else are hormones to be stored temporarily in neurohypophysis, which does not produce the hormones (oxytocic and vasopressor principles), as formerly believed. (From many sources.)

iologists, William M. Bayliss and Ernest H. Starling, demonstrated the presence and action of an internal secretion. They were interested in determining how the pancreas secreted its digestive juice into the small intestine at the proper time of the digestive process. In an anesthetized dog they tied off a section of the small intestine beyond the duodenum (the part of the intestine next to the stomach) and removed all nerves leading to this tied-off loop, which retained its blood vessels intact. The injection of hydrochloric acid into the blood had no effect upon the secretion of pancreatic juice, but when these two investigators introduced 0.4% hydrochloric acid into the intestinal loop, a well-marked flow of pancreatic juice into the duodenum occurred through the pancreatic duct. When they scraped off some of the mucous membrane lining of the intestine and mixed it with acid, they found that the injection of this extract into the blood caused an abundant flow of pancreatic juice. They concluded that when the partly digested and slightly acid food from the stomach arrives in the small intestine, the hydrochloric acid reacts with something in the mucous lining to produce **secretin,** a small protein, which, carried in the bloodstream, stimulates the pancreas to secrete.

In 1889 Von Mering and Minkowski discovered that surgical removal of the pancreas of dogs caused severe symptoms of diabetes and resulted in the animals' death within a few weeks. Many attempts were made to isolate the diabetes-preventive factor in the pancreas, but all were unsuccessful because powerful protein-splitting digestive enzymes produced in the pancreas destroyed

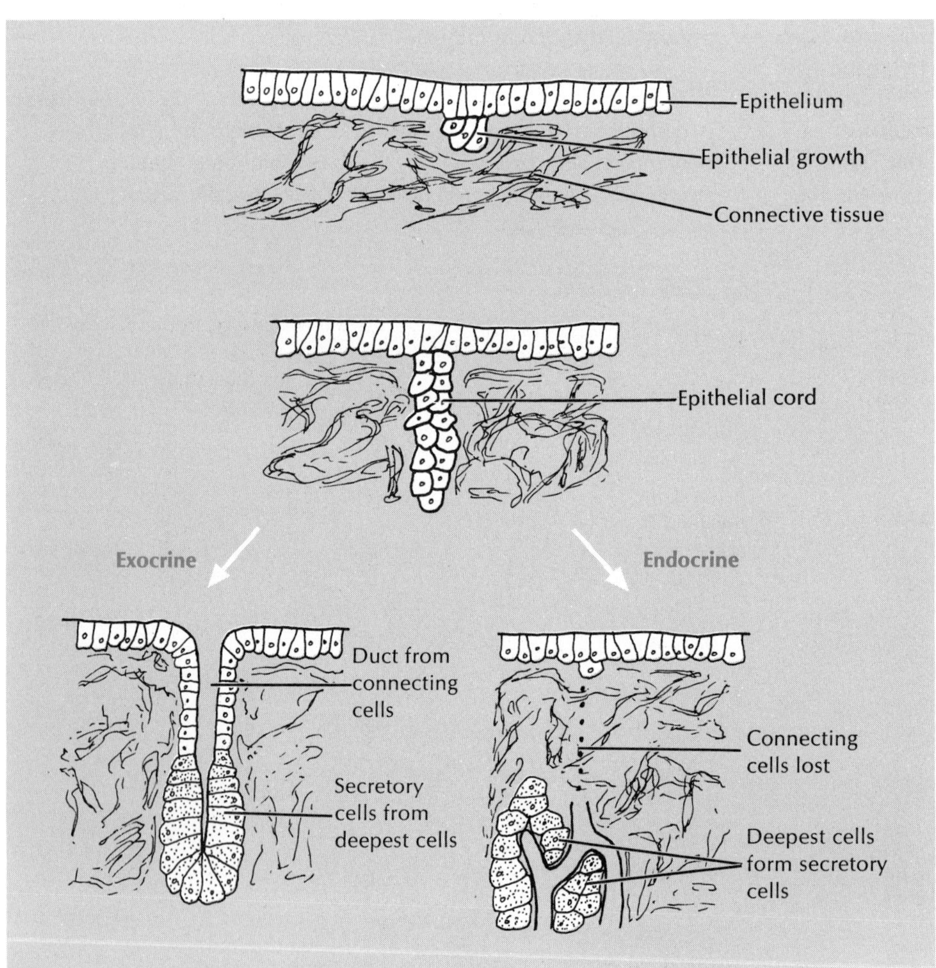

FIG. 33-14

Comparison of development of exocrine and endocrine glands. For both types, development begins with growth of an epithelial cord from an epithelium into underlying connective tissue. If an exocrine gland develops, cells near terminal end of epithelial cord differentiate into secretory cells; those between surface and secretory cells become ducts. On the other hand, if an endocrine gland develops, epithelial cells connecting secretory cells to surface disappear, leaving secretory mass as an isolated island. (Modified from Ham, 1953.)

the hormone during the extraction procedures. Then in 1920 Dr. Frederick Banting, a young Canadian physician, discovered in the literature that, when the pancreatic duct was ligated, the pancreatic cells that secrete the digestive enzymes degenerated but the islets of Langerhans, where insulin is formed were undisturbed. In collaboration with his former teacher, Professor J. J. R. Macleod, and with Dr. C. H. Best, and with the use of improved surgical techniques, Banting was able to isolate insulin from duct-ligated glands of dogs. The accomplishment meant that millions of persons with diabetes, who prior to the discovery could expect to live no more than a few years at best, could now look forward to nearly normal lives. In 1923 Banting and Macleod were awarded the Nobel Prize.

Plan of hormone regulation*

The two types of glands in the animal body are the exocrine and the endocrine. **Exocrine** glands are provided with ducts for discharging their secretions onto a free surface. **Endocrine** glands are ductless and their products are discharged and carried in the blood all over the body, but the hormones are picked out by some specific organ on which they exert a physiologic effect. Endocrine glands are similar to the exocrine glands, although their cells are usually arranged in cords or plates with abundant blood sinusoids (Fig. 33-14). The ductless glands derive their antecedents from the blood and transform them into their characteristic hormones, which are stored in cells or follicles until they are delivered back to the blood.

Secretin and other hormones of the alimentary canal are produced in the duodenal mucosa, which cannot be considered an endocrine gland in the strict meaning of the term. Some glands such as the pancreas have both exocrine and endocrine functions. The exocrine part elaborates the important digestive secretion, pancreatic juice, and the endocrine part furnishes insulin for carbohydrate metabolism.

The chemical substances called hormones act in very small quantities. Their total mass makes up only a small proportion of the organism. Their general mechanisms of action are slow and drawn out, although there are some exceptions to this principle; epinephrine acts with considerable speed because it is under direct autonomic nervous control; the slower hormones are secreted in response to hormonal stimulation.

The various hormones overlap each other in their actions. Their interrelations represent one of the most difficult problems in endocrinology. Removal of one kind of endocrine gland often affects other kinds, and some of the hormones are unable to function without the aid of others. Glands such as the adenohypophysis (anterior pituitary) influence practically every other endocrine gland in the body. This may indicate an evolutionary significance in hormonal integration similar to the dominance of the cerebral cortex over the nervous system.

What is the mechanism of hormone action, or how do they bring about physiologic changes? Proposed theoretical answers to this question involve hormone-enzyme interactions that control metabolic reactions, permeability changes of cell membranes by hormones resulting in an increase or decrease in cellular activity, or control by hormones of gene activity so that the DNA, through the genetic code mechanism, induces protein or enzyme synthesis that may produce physiologic changes. The latter view of hormone action at the nuclear level seems more in accord with our present-day conception, although all the aforementioned modes of action of hormones may be possible. There is some evidence for each of them.

On the basis of their control and influence over physiologic processes, hormones may be divided into four categories: (1) hormones concerned with metabolism, (2) hormones of digestion, (3) hormones that regulate growth and development, and (4) hormones that control reproduction.

Ectohormones and kinins

There has been described within recent years an exocrine endocrine reaction by which a special kind of hormone (**pheromone,** or **ectohormone**) is secreted by an exocrine gland to the exterior of an animal and influences in a specific way another member of the same species or of a different species. These ectohormones, or ectocrines, are known to be involved in such functions as colony formation in social insects, mating behavior, and alarm reactions. The endocrine system may be involved in the secretion of the pheromone by the producer organism, or it may control the physiologic response of the recipient. The mechanism is thought to play an important role in the social adjustment of animals and may be general, although investigations have been restricted to a few groups. The real

*Refer to Chapter 2, Principle 2.

nature of the specific chemical signs or substances involved are only partly known in the few cases studied.

Another class of hormones are the **kinins,** which have been discovered in recent years. These hormones are not produced by special glands, but are local hormones that are released near their places of action. They are quite evanescent and elusive, so their exact physiologic nature is not easily determined. They are small protein structures somewhat of the nature of a polypeptide with a restricted number of amino acids. They may be widespread in the animal kingdom. Although they were first discovered in mammalian blood plasma and urine, they have since been found in the venom of beestings and poisonous snakes. Although kinins cannot be detected in the bloodstream, they are released when the blood comes in contact with glass or with such agents as salt solutions and certain enzymes and chemicals. Apparently they are present in blood in an inactive form. The brevity of their existence at any one time is probably due to the counteracting effect of an enzyme.

What are their effects on the body? In many ways kinins resemble histamine in their bodily effects, but are usually more forceful in their action. Smooth muscle, especially, is very sensitive to them and reacts either by contraction or relaxation. When injected into the blood, kinins cause the smooth muscle of the walls of bronchioles to constrict and the muscular walls of blood vessels to relax. They also dilate capillaries and produce blisters on skin. In response to local needs, kinins are released in the blood from globulin by enzymatic action and are also inactivated by other enzymes. Their exact function is as yet unknown because their action parallels that of histamine. The common drug aspirin, however, has a specific and selective effect in counteracting the constrictive action of kinin but does not influence constriction produced by histamine or similar agents.

Endocrine glands in invertebrates

Much information about invertebrate endocrine glands has been obtained in recent years. There is reason to believe that hormones have an equally important role among these simpler forms.

In general, it is difficult to homologize the invertebrate endocrine glands with those in vertebrates, but many hormonal functions are analogous in the two groups. Most endocrine investigations among the invertebrates have been made in the arthropods, especially in crustaceans and insects. The chromatophores or pigment cells of shrimp and crabs are definitely known to be controlled by hormones from the sinus gland in the eyestalk or in regions close to the brain. When the eyestalk (and sinus gland) is removed or sinus gland extracts are injected, the effects on bodily coloration vary with different crustaceans; some darken and others pale under the experimental conditions. Migration or shifting of the retinal pigments of the arthropod compound eye for light adjustments is controlled by a hormone from the sinus gland. Ecdysis, or molting, in crustaceans and insects is also regulated by sinus gland extracts; the rather complicated process of insect metamorphosis (from larva to adult) involves a precise functioning of hormones from the brain and the corpus allatum of the head region. There is some evidence that secondary sex characteristics among invertebrates are under hormonal control. When parasitic castration by the parasite *Sacculina* occurs in male crayfish, sexual changes toward femaleness are known to occur.

Invertebrate endocrinology, however, presents many difficulties that vertebrate endocrinologists do not have to contend with. Endocrine structures in most invertebrates are extremely small, often involving only a few cells. A great deal of the invertebrate endocrine system is more or less restricted to neurosecretion that is associated with nerve cells. It is very difficult to localize the region of endocrine function because the anatomy of endocrine organs is hard to determine. Only small amounts of hormone material can usually be collected, which makes chemical analysis very difficult. Many hormones, moreover, may be concerned with a simple physiologic effect and it is very difficult to analyze the complexity of the interaction. At present it is very difficult to establish homology of endocrine functions between invertebrates and vertebrates.

Chemical structure of hormones

Endocrine organs are derived from all three germ layers. Those derived from ectoderm are the pituitary gland, urohypophysis, pineal body, and adrenal medulla; those from mesoderm are the adrenal cortex and gonads; and those from endoderm are the islets of Langerhans, thyroid gland, parathyroid, and thymus.

The mammalian hormones are usually divided into the following groups:

1. Hormones composed of modified amino acids, or simply amino acids, are represented by epinephrine

(Adrenalin) and the hormones of the neurohypophysis (oxytocin and vasopressin).

2. Steroid hormones are fat soluble compounds and are closely related to vitamin D, cholesterol, bile salts, and lipids in general. Cortisone, estrogen, and testosterone are examples of steroid hormones. They are all built around the steroid nucleus consisting of three 6-carbon rings and one 5-carbon ring (Fig. 33-15). By adding methyl, hydroxyl, and other radicals to one of the 19 carbons of the nucleus, it is possible to make the various steroid hormones. Cortical steroids of the adrenal cortex (interrenal) are concerned with regulating the electrolyte balance and the control of the body's utilization of water and minerals.

3. Protein hormones represent the largest group of hormones and are water soluble. Some are very simple (thyroxine). Sanger, who worked out the structure of the insulin molecule, found that it consisted of two chains, one of 21 and the other of 30 amino acids. The chains are joined together by sulfur linkages. Its molecular weight was given as about 6,000, although some of the protein hormones are much larger than this. Glucagon, the other hormone of the pancreatic islets that stimulates glycogenolysis, has a molecular weight of 3,500.

Endocrine glands in vertebrates

Hormones of pituitary gland (hypophysis). The **pituitary gland,** or **hypophysis,** produces many hormones that influence many parts of the body. For this reason it is often called the "master gland" of the body. It is well protected because it lies between the roof of the mouth and the floor of the brain in a depression of the sphenoid bone. The weight of the pituitary gland in man is about 0.5 gram. The pituitary is a duplex gland of double embryonic origin. The anterior lobe and intermediate lobe come from a pouch on the roof of the mouth; the posterior lobe arises from the brain (Fig. 33-16). The anterior lobe makes up about three fourths of the entire gland.

According to functional organization, the pituitary body is classified into the **adenohypophysis,** or portions that come from the mouth region, and the **neurohypophysis,** or portion from the brain. The **hypothalamus** of the brain controls the secretions of the tropic hormones of the pituitary (Fig. 33-17). It controls the secretions of the adenohypophysis through a hypophyseal portal system and the secretions of the neurohypophysis

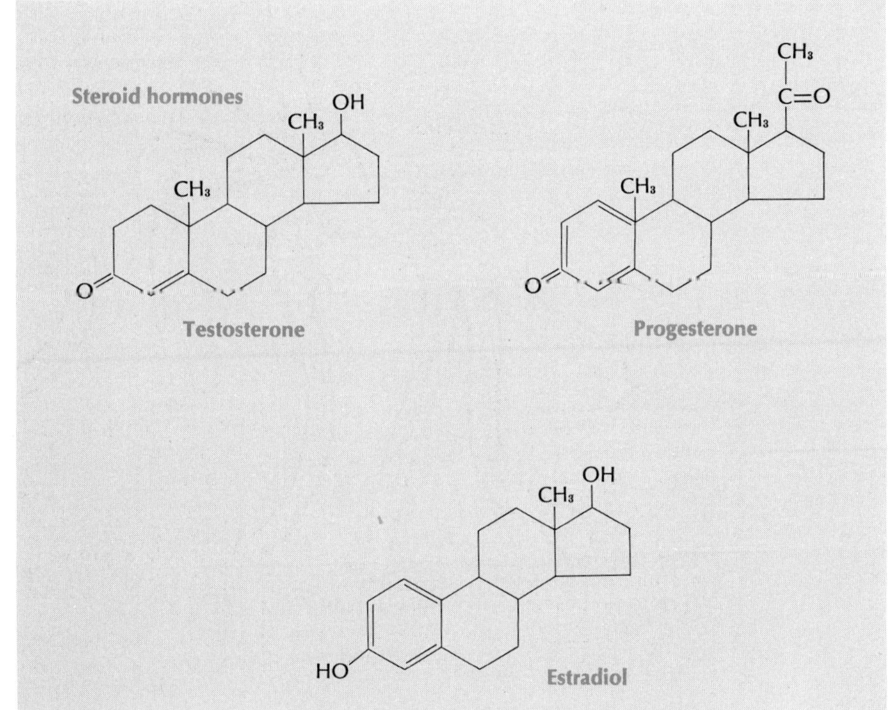

FIG. 33-15

These three sex hormones all show basic four-ring steroid structure. Note slight chemical differences in their molecular characteristics that depend on kinds and position of substances linked at carbon position. All steroid hormones have methyl group attached at position shown in third ring from left. Both estradiol (estrogen) in female and testosterone in male regulate secondary sex characteristics in the two sexes, respectively, but testosterone has two methyl (CH_3) radicals instead of one and =O instead of –OH in one of the rings. Some steroids given to animals are now known to increase strength and weight of muscles.

Posterior lobe
Anterior lobe
Intermediate lobe

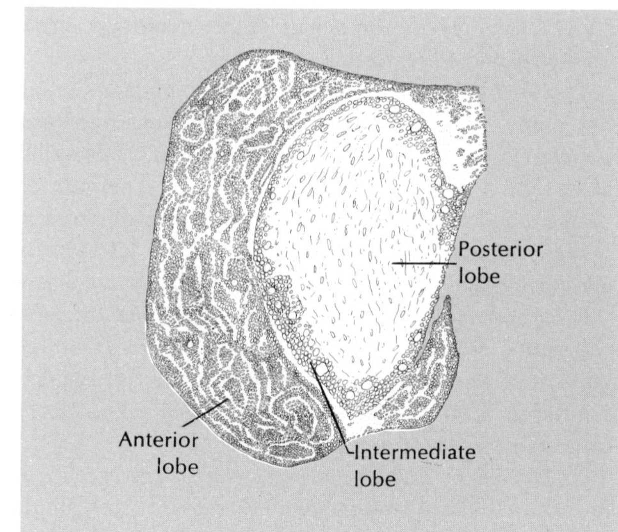

FIG. 33-16

Histologic section of pituitary gland.

FIG. 33-17

Relations of hypothalamus to pituitary gland showing varied functions and relations of complex. (Courtesy C. P. Hickman, Jr.)

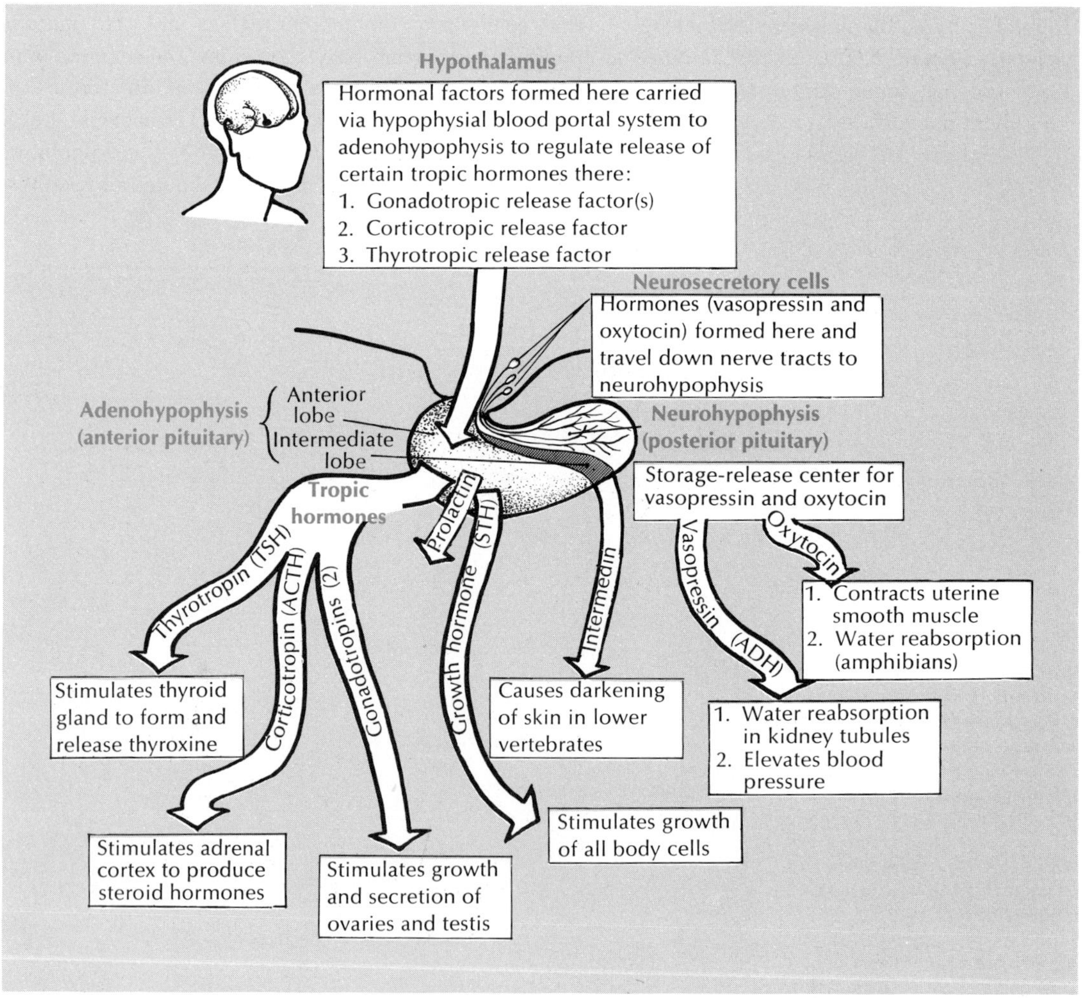

Hypothalamus
Hormonal factors formed here carried via hypophysial blood portal system to adenohypophysis to regulate release of certain tropic hormones there:
1. Gonadotropic release factor(s)
2. Corticotropic release factor
3. Thyrotropic release factor
Neurosecretory cells
Hormones (vasopressin and oxytocin) formed here and travel down nerve tracts to neurohypophysis
Adenohypophysis (anterior pituitary)
Anterior lobe
Intermediate lobe
Neurohypophysis (posterior pituitary)
Storage-release center for vasopressin and oxytocin
Tropic hormones
Prolactin
Growth hormone (STH)
Intermedin
Vasopressin (ADH)
Oxytocin
Thyrotropin (TSH)
Corticotropin (ACTH)
Gonadotropins (2)
1. Contracts uterine smooth muscle
2. Water reabsorption (amphibians)
Stimulates thyroid gland to form and release thyroxine
Causes darkening of skin in lower vertebrates
1. Water reabsorption in kidney tubules
2. Elevates blood pressure
Stimulates growth of all body cells
Stimulates adrenal cortex to produce steroid hormones
Stimulates growth and secretion of ovaries and testis

by direct nervous connections. The hypothalamus itself is controlled through nerves from higher nerve centers.

Except for the adrenal medulla, the **neurohypophysis** (posterior lobe) is the only gland receiving direct nervous connections. The hormones are formed in the lower hypothalamus and travel down nerves to be stored in the neurohypophysis. An extract from the entire lobe is known as **Pituitrin,** which is made up of more than one fraction. Two of these are **pitocin (oxytocin),** which contracts smooth muscle, especially of the uterus, and **Pitressin (vasopressin),** which constricts the smooth muscle of the gastrointestinal tract, urinary bladder, gallbladder, and arterioles. Pitressin is also responsible for the antidiuretic effect of the posterior lobe, since it stimulates the resorption of water in the renal tubules and reduces the volume of urine excreted. When vasopressin is deficient, diabetes insipidus occurs, in which an excessive amount of urine is excreted.

The **adenohypophysis** (anterior lobe) produces several hormones, all of which are proteins. One of these is the growth hormone (**somatotropin, STH**). Others stimulate the gonads (**gonadotropins**), the adrenal cortex (**adrenocorticotropin, ACTH**), the thyroid gland (**thyrotropin, TSH**), and the mammary glands (**prolactin**). The diabetogenic hormone is also produced here. Another hormone, **intermedin,** is produced in the intermediate part or, in animals that lack this part, in the anterior lobe. This hormone is a doubtful entity in man, but in many vertebrates it stimulates the expansion of the melanophores (pigmented cells) in the adjustment of body coloration to environmental conditions.

The **hypothalamus** elaborates three important tropic hormones—**gonadotropic release factor, corticotropic release factor,** and **thyrotropic release factor**—which are carried by the hypophyseal portal system or by the general circulation to the adenohypophysis, causing it to release its various tropic hormones. In return, these tropic hormones react back (**feedback**) and influence the functions of the nervous system. Thus this plan involves a three-stage hormonal system—releasing factors from the hypothalamus regulate tropic hormones from the adenohypophysis, which in turn regulate the hormone secretions of the respective target glands (gonads, thyroid, etc). This mechanism of feedback, whereby a target organ can influence its own production positively or negatively by sending back information to an early stage in its synthetic pathway, is not clear in all instances, but it is thought that whenever a feedback occurs it is mediated through the nervous system and reaches the pituitary by way of the hypothalamus. Apparently some pituitary hormones are not subject to feedback control and are secreted independently of the central nervous system. This general scheme shows that parts of the nervous system function as specialized endocrine organs.

Hormones of metabolism. Hormones that affect the metabolic activity of the individual are secreted by the thyroid, parathyroid, pancreas, and adrenal cortex.

Thyroid hormone (thyroxine). The thyroid is a double gland, with a lobe on each side of the trachea at the base of the larynx. The lobes may be joined by a connection, the isthmus. Embryologically, the thyroid starts out as an exocrine gland, secreting through the thyroglossal duct into the mouth; this duct is later lost. The thyroid is the largest of all the endocrine organs, weighing from 20 to 30 grams in the human being. The secreting part of the gland consists of tiny spheres (follicles) lined with cuboidal epithelium (Fig. 33-18).

FIG. 33-18

Histologic section of thyroid gland showing follicles filled with colloid. (Courtesy J. W. Bamberger.)

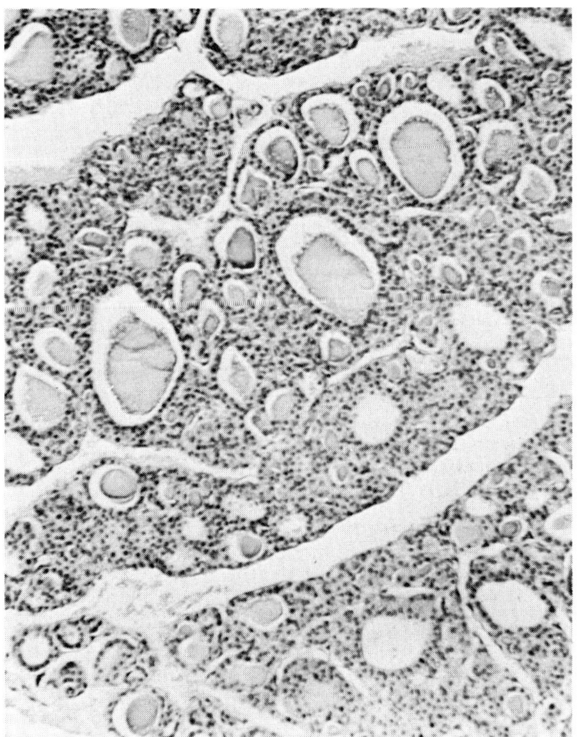

These follicles are filled with a colloid, which contains the thyroid hormone **thyroxine.** Its primary function is to regulate the metabolism of the body. A second and more universal function is the regulation of growth, development, and maturation (Fig. 33-19). In lower vertebrates (amphibians) it is necessary for metamorphosis. Hyperfunction of the gland speeds up the metabolic rate; hypofunction slows it down. Since iodine is the principal constituent of thyroxine, deficiency of this chemical in water or food will often produce disturbances in the gland. **Myxedema,** a disease characterized by a low metabolic rate and puffy skin, is caused by the secretion of too little thyroxine and represents a hypothyroid condition. Another hypothyroid condition, **endemic colloid goiter,** is caused by a deficiency of iodine in the diet and may result in a greatly enlarged thyroid gland. Certain types of goiter are now known to be linked to the inherited trait of an inability to taste phenylthiocarbamide (PTC), one of a group of chemical substances that block the synthesis of thyroxine. When hypothyroidism is present from birth, the condition is known as **cretinism.** Such children are stunted and of low intelligence. Administration of iodine or thyroxine is used in the treatment of hypothyroid conditions. Iodized salt is an effective preventive of endemic colloid goiter.

FIG. 33-19

Relation between thyroxine and thyrotropin.

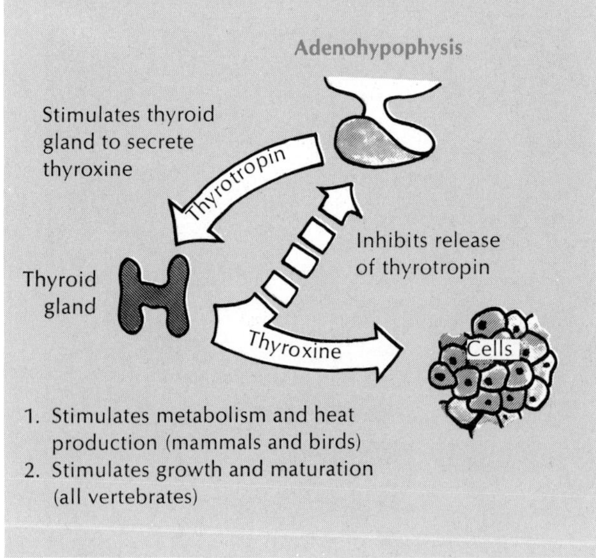

Hyperthyroidism involves an overactive gland and is characterized by a slight swelling of the gland and the production of a great amount of thyroxine. This causes a high metabolic rate, and it is often called **toxic goiter.** Other effects may be increase in blood pressure and heart rate, tremors and irritability, and protrusion of the eyeballs. Major treatments now used are (1) surgical removal, (2) use of drugs that inhibit thyroxine, and (3) administration of large doses of radioactive iodine that destroys most of the thyroid cells.

Iodine makes up about 65% of thyroxine, as indicated in the following structural formula:

$$HO-C_6H_2I_2-O-C_6H_2I_2-CH_2-CH(NH_2)-COOH$$

Thyroxine

Nearly 1 mg. of iodine is required in our diets each week to supply normal quantities of thyroxine. When stored in the follicles, thyroxine is combined with a globulin to form thyroglobulin, which releases thyroxine when the latter passes into the blood.

Parathyroid hormone (parathormone). Four **parathyroid** glands, all small, are located on the posterior surface of the lateral lobes of the thyroid gland. The hormone-secreting tissue is made up of cords of epithelioid cells closely related to the blood capillaries. The parathyroid gland produces two hormones for regulating the blood calcium and phosphorus. One of these, **parathyroid hormone,** is released when the blood calcium level is low and tends to elevate the level. The other, **calcitonin,** is released when the calcium level of the blood is high and lowers the blood calcium. The antagonistic action of the two hormones makes possible a precise control of blood calcium.

Hyperparathyroidism is produced by tumors on the glands and causes the calcium to be withdrawn from the bones, thus producing a high blood level of calcium. Under such conditions the bones may become soft and porous or have only localized areas of calcification. Vitamin D promotes the rate of calcium absorption from the intestine. From Fig. 33-20 it will be noted that bone cells withdraw calcium and phosphate from the blood for the production of bone, whereas parathyroid hormone (parathormone) draws the minerals from the bones. These two actions are antagonistic and tend to balance each other.

Insulin from islet cells of pancreas. The pancreas is both an exocrine and an endocrine gland. The exocrine portion produces the digestive secretion pancreatic juice. The **endocrine** part of the gland consists of the small islets of **Langerhans** that are very numerous and vary greatly in size (Fig. 33-21). They are made up of at least three different kinds of cells—alpha, beta, and delta cells. It is thought that the **beta cells** produce the hormone **insulin,** which is of great importance in the metabolism of fats and carbohydrates. Deficiency of insulin leads to excess sugar in the blood that is excreted in the urine. The hormone appears to be necessary for the storage of glucose as glycogen in the liver and for the oxidation of glucose. Many metabolic disturbances are brought about in **diabetes mellitus,** the disease caused by a lack of insulin. Much urine is excreted, the individual loses weight, and there is an accumulation of incompletely oxidized ketone bodies from fat oxidation. These latter substances are toxic and eventually lead to the death of the patient. The injection of insulin since its discovery in 1922 is very effective and removes all the symptoms for a short time. But repeated injections are necessary because insulin does not cure diabetes permanently. Too much insulin will produce convulsions by sweeping the sugar out of the blood. Another hormone, **glucagon** or the hyperglycemic factor, is produced by the alpha cells and possibly other tissues and causes a breakdown of liver glycogen into glucose.

Adrenal cortical hormones. The adrenal or suprarenal gland is a double endocrine organ and is made up of a **cortex** and a **medulla** (Fig. 33-22). Each of these has its own internal secretions, and each has developed differently embryologically. The adrenal cortex has arisen from the same origin (mesodermal) as that of the sex glands; the medulla has an ectodermal origin similar to that of the postganglionic fiber cells of the sympathetic nervous system.

The adrenal cortex is absolutely essential to life; when it is completely removed, most animals will live only a week or two. The cortex has several hormones and it ranks next to the anterior pituitary in endocrine importance. Structurally, the cortex is made up of parallel and looped cords of cells with numerous blood capillaries.

All the adrenocortical hormones are steroid com-

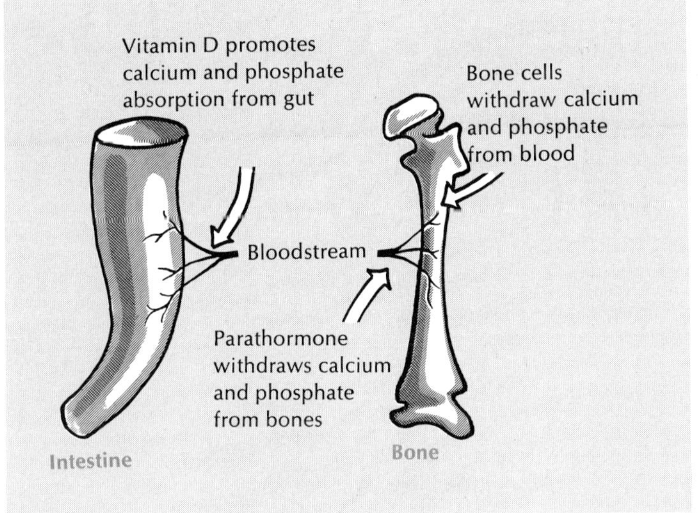

FIG. 33-20

Relation of parathormone (parathyrin) to calcium metabolism. Two hormones may be involved—one regulating excretion of phosphorus and the other deposition of calcium in tissues. When calcium level of blood becomes too high, another parathyroid hormone (calcitonin) lowers the blood calcium.

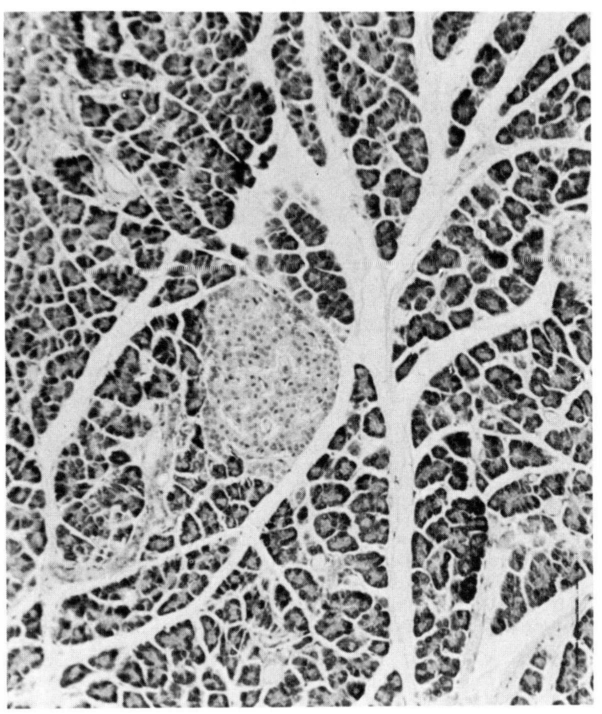

FIG. 33-21

Histologic section of mammalian pancreas showing one large (center) and some smaller islets of Langerhans. (Courtesy J. W. Bamberger.)

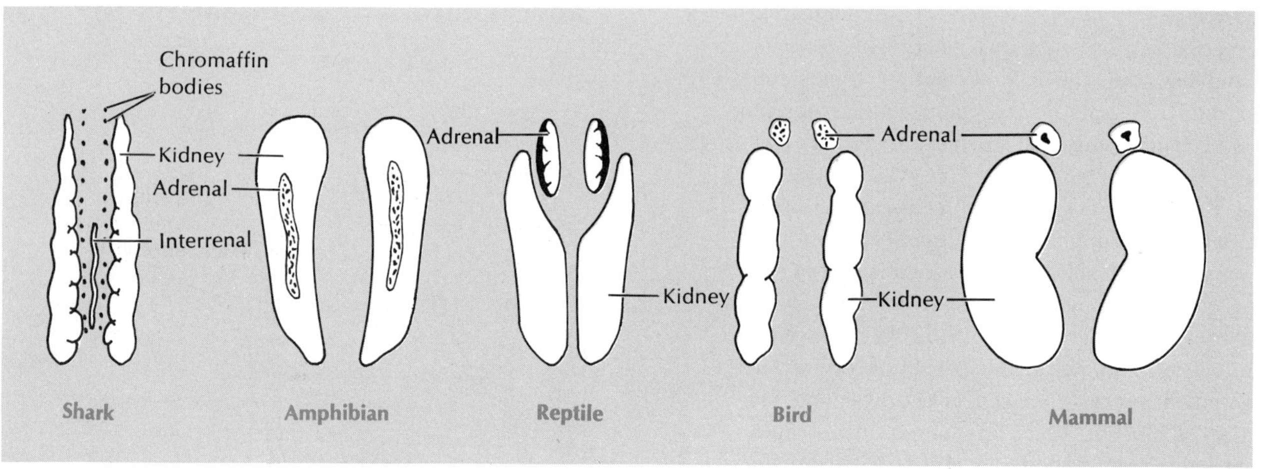

FIG. 33-22

Vertebrate adrenal glands. In shark (elasmobranch), chromaffin (medullary) tissue is separate from interrenal (cortical) tissue. In most amphibians, reptiles, and birds, chromaffin and interrenal tissues are interspersed. Some reptiles (lizards and some snakes) have chromaffin tissue (black) aggregated along one side of interrenal tissue. In most mammals, cortex (interrenal) entirely surrounds chromaffin tissue (medulla). (From several sources.)

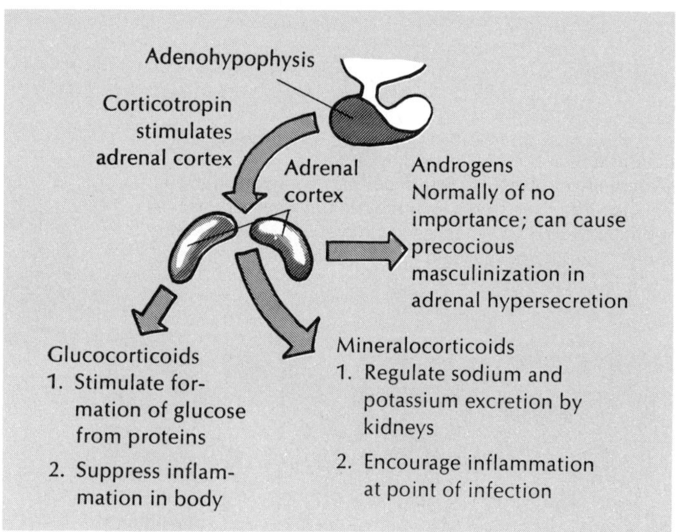

FIG. 33-23

Relations of adrenocortical hormones and their functions.

pounds and all are structurally similar. They can be divided into three groups: (1) **glucocorticoids** such as **cortisone** and **hydrocortisone,** which regulate food metabolism (glucose, proteins, fats); (2) **mineralocorticoids** such as **aldosterone** and **desoxycorticosterone,** which control the reabsorption of sodium by kidney tubules as well as the regulation of other salts; and (3) **sex hormones,** which have **androgenic** (chiefly) and **estrogenic** effects to a minor extent. All these hormones are controlled by the corticotropin hormone of the adenohypophysis (Fig. 33-23).

In Addison's disease the adrenal cortex degenerates, resulting in a complicated syndrome of altered fluid balance and a bronze pigmentation of the skin. In hyperfunction of the adrenal cortex, a condition that sometimes arises from tumors, male children may become sexually mature precociously, and females take on masculine characters such as a beard, deep voice, and oversized clitoris.

Adrenal medulla hormones. The cells of the adrenal medulla form the central core of the adrenal gland. Sympathetic fibers secrete at their terminals the hormones **epinephrine (Adrenalin)** and **norepinephrine (Levophed).** Epinephrine is one of the few hormones whose rate of secretion is affected by nervous stimulation. The general action of this hormone centers around emergency functions of the body, such as those of fear, fight, flight, rage, and work. During emotional states epinephrine is secreted in great amounts. Specifically, the hormone causes a rise in blood pressure, increase in heart rate, increase in blood sugar, inhibition of the gastrointestinal tract, decrease in liver glycogen, and hastening of blood coagulation. Norepinephrine of the adrenal medulla has a similar effect but has a wider vasoconstrictor influence. Most of these effects can also be produced by stimulating the sympathetic nervous

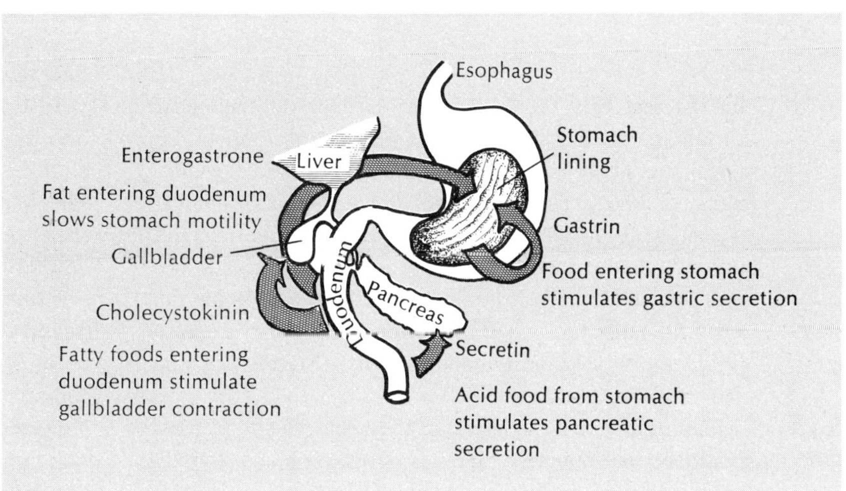

FIG. 33-24

Actions of gastrointestinal hormones. Under each hormone, stimulus for its secretion and specific action of hormone are indicated.

system. Epinephrine is one of the simplest hormones known and can be produced synthetically.

Hormones of digestion. Certain hormones influence the secretion and motility of the gastrointestinal tract.

Hormones of gastrointestinal mucosa. Several hormones are associated with the activities of the digestive tract. All of these hormones are produced in the mucosa lining. One of these is **gastrin,** produced in the pyloric wall (Fig. 33-24). When food enters the stomach, gastrin stimulates the gastric glands to secrete gastric juices. The active principle of this hormone appears to be histamine. The intestinal mucosa produces three hormones that are active in some phase of the digestive process. **Secretin** is formed when acid chyme from the stomach enters the upper intestine; it stimulates the secretion of pancreatic juice. **Cholecystokinin** is liberated from the intestinal mucosa by fatty foods and causes the gallbladder to empty. **Enterogastrone** is also liberated in the small intestine by fatty foods, and when carried by the blood to the stomach, it slows down the motility of the stomach. No deficiency diseases have been associated with the undersecretion of the gastrointestinal hormones, and some endocrinologists consider them of minor importance.

Hormones of growth and development. Every step in normal growth and development depends upon one or many hormones.

Pituitary growth hormone. **Somatotropin, STH,** from the anterior lobe of the pituitary, has a controlling influence over the rate of growth. In excess it produces **gigantism** in the young so that the period of skeletal and tissue growth is extended beyond the normal period. If this hormone is produced in excess after the person has completed his normal growth, **acromegaly** results. In this condition the bones are greatly thickened and the hands and feet are enlarged. Deficiency of the hormone causes **dwarfism** and the young mature as dwarfs. The growth hormone also has an "anti-insulin" effect, since it increases blood sugar.

Most of the major hormones influence growth and development in some manner. Deficiency in the production of thyroxine, insulin, adrenocortical hormones, parathyroid hormone, or sex hormones may cause stunted growth or improper development.

Hormones that control reproduction. Some male and female organs are endocrine-forming as well as gamete-forming (cytogenic) glands.

Male sex hormone. Reproduction is a process that involves the coordinated action of many hormones. Those hormones that promote male characteristics are called **androgens;** those that promote female characteristics are **estrogens.** The primary sex organs, testes and ovaries, not only produce sperm and eggs but they also serve as sources for important sex hormones that are concerned with the regulation and control of reproduction. The male sex hormone is called **testosterone** and is produced by the **interstitial** cells (Leydig) located between the seminiferous tubules that produce the sperm. Interstitial cells are not present during childhood but are found in the infant and after puberty. The production of testosterone is stimulated by such gonadotropins as the luteinizing (or the interstitial cell-stimulating) hormone. Testosterone is responsible for the secondary male sex characteristics such as the beard on the face and the distribution of hair on the body, the character of the voice, and the distribution of fat pads. It is also concerned with the growth and development of the accessory sex characters—penis, seminal vesicle, and prostate gland (Fig. 33-25). When injected into a female, secondary male sex characteristics are often developed. Testosterone is also responsible for the sex urge and for sexual behavior. Estrogens are also produced by the sustentacular cells (Sertoli) of the seminiferous tubules.

Castration, or the removal of the testes, has long been practiced on domestic animals. Such animals usually become fatter and more docile. If castration is performed on the young animal, the secondary sex characteristics and the accessory sex organs fail to develop; if performed on adults, they undergo retrograde changes. Castration in man (**eunuchism**) will cause the boy's voice to remain high pitched. Such a castrated boy will be neutral toward sex (without sex desire); if castration is done after puberty, sex urge and potency may remain, although reduced in intensity.

FIG. 33-25

Hormonal relations and functions of testosterone.

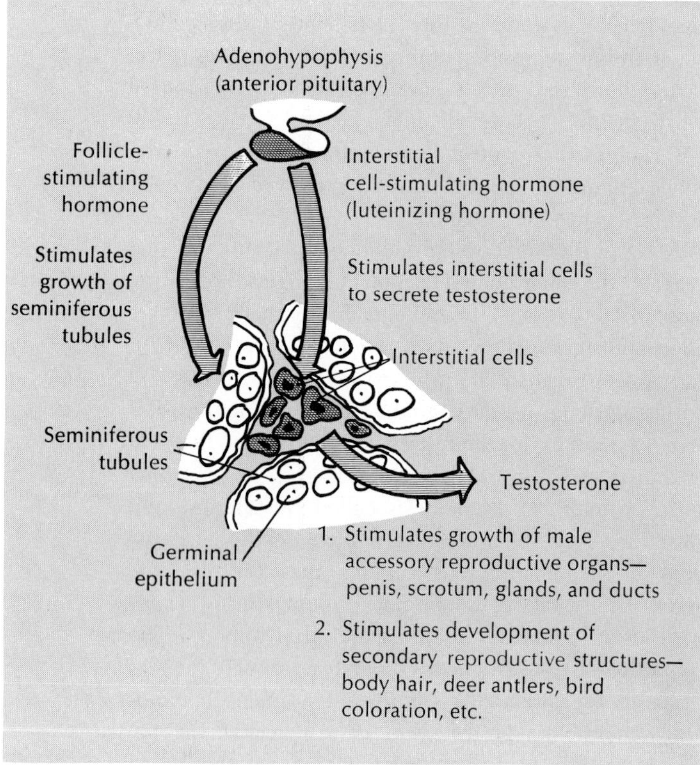

In the condition in which the testes fail to descend into the scrotal sac from the abdominal cavity (**cryptorchidism**), the higher temperature there destroys the sperm and the individual is sterile. However, the interstitial cells are not affected by the higher temperature and the male hormone is produced.

Female sex hormones. Two important hormones are involved in the cyclic sex changes of the female. One of these is **estradiol** (estrogen), which is produced by the cells of the developing graafian follicles of the ovary. One or more of these follicles enlarge each lunar month, burst open through fluid pressure, and release an ovum, or egg, by the process of **ovulation.** The egg passes into the oviduct where it may be fertilized if sperm are present, or else it goes on to the uterus where it degenerates. In the ruptured follicle the follicular cells increase and fill up the cavity left by the egg and follicular fluid. These cells are yellowish in color and the structure they form is called the yellow body, or **corpus luteum** (Fig. 33-26), which lasts only two or three weeks if the egg is unfertilized but throughout the first half of pregnancy if the egg is fertilized. This corpus luteum forms the second female hormone, **progesterone.**

The combined action of these two hormones accounts mainly for the reproductive cycle in the female. Estradiol, for instance, is responsible for the sex changes at puberty, the development of the accessory sex organs, the development of the secondary sex characters (breasts, pubic hair, voice quality, etc.), the initiation of the growth changes in the endometrium, vagina, and other organs, and the production of **estrus,** or heat. Progesterone carries on the growth of the endometrium, makes possible the implantation of the fertilized egg in the uterine wall, and stimulates the development of the mammary glands. Just as testosterone is produced by females as well as males, so the two female sex hormones are also found in the male. The chief commercial source of estradiol is the urine of stallions, male horses. The same hormone has also been obtained from sources outside the animal body, for example, from pussy willows. Another female sex hormone, **relaxin,** is produced by the corpus luteum and causes the pelvic ligaments to relax in childbirth.

ESTRUS CYCLE. The females of all mammals, with the possible exception of human beings, show certain cyclic or rhythmic changes in the intensity of the sex urge. Sexual reception at its height is called **estrus,** or heat, and usually the female will receive the male only during this period. Most mammals have only one estrus period each year, although there are several exceptions. Cats and dogs usually have two each year, whereas rabbits and rats have many. Estrus is closely correlated with the ripening and discharge of the ova. Some animals such as the cat and rabbit will ovulate only following copulation; others have spontaneous ovulation. Changes in the uterine lining occur in anticipation of the implantation of a fertilized ovum or ova and involve a thickening of the lining (endometrium) and an increase in the uterine glands and blood vessels. If fertilization of the egg does not occur, these changes revert to their original state. In this estrus cycle all stages are governed by the interplay of the female sex hormones and those of the anterior pituitary gland. The relation of these hormones to each other and to the rhythmic changes can best be shown by the menstrual cycle in the human being.

MENSTRUAL CYCLE. In primate animals, the estrus cycle is largely replaced by periods of bleeding called **menstruation.** This period on the average occurs every 28 days (in the human being), but it is far from regular. The actual menstrual, or bleeding, periods are of 3 to 5 days' duration. Menstruation is the sloughing off of the thickened endometrium, which has been developed under the influence of the female sex hormones. If the egg is fertilized and implanted, menstruation does not occur. The initiation of the menstrual flow is due to a marked decline in the hormones progesterone and estradiol. Ovulation occurs about 14 days after the beginning of the menstrual period. The following is a summary of the events that occur during a menstrual cycle and the relation of the various hormones to these events.

FIG. 33-26

Section of cat ovary showing corpus luteum (large, rounded mass of light-colored cells in lower center). (Courtesy J. W. Bamberger.)

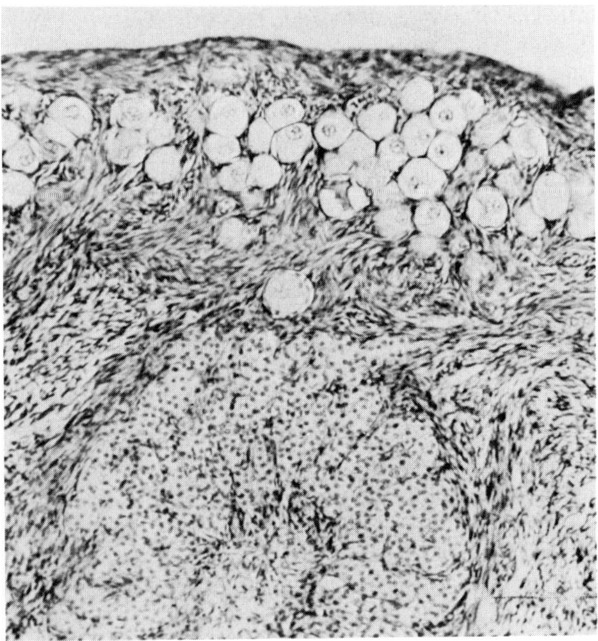

Just after the menses flow, most of the endometrium has been sloughed off and only a thin lining is left (Fig. 33-27). By means of a gonadotropic hormone (**follicle-stimulating hormone, FSH**) from the anterior pituitary, a follicle in the ovary is stimulated to grow. Then the follicular cells secrete estradiol that causes a thickening of the uterine lining but does not cause ovulation. This latter process appears to be due to a balance between the gonadotropic hormones of the pituitary. Estradiol has an inhibitory action on FSH so that no other follicles are developed. When ovulation occurs, the corpus luteum is formed in the ruptured follicle and becomes the source of the other female sex hormone, progesterone. The corpus luteum is also formed under the stimulating action of hormones from the anterior pituitary—the **luteinizing hormone (LH)** and **luteotropin (LTH, prolactin).** Progesterone continues the preparation of the uterine lining as well as the growth of the mammary glands. If the egg is not implanted in the uterine wall, the corpus luteum disappears and its hormone is no longer secreted. Since the endometrium depends on progesterone for its maintenance, when this hormone ceases to be secreted, the disintegration of the uterine lining with its characteristic flow begins.

The **placenta** must also be considered an endocrine organ. Actually, during the latter part of pregnancy most of the progesterone comes from the placenta because the corpus luteum is decreasing. Estradiol and progesterone are responsible mainly for the development of the mammary glands during the period of pregnancy. Lactation (milk secretion) is the result of another hormone, luteotropin or LTH (prolactin), from the anterior pituitary. This hormone is assisted by those adrenal cortex hormones that regulate carbohydrate metabolism. Milk is not secreted during pregnancy because the female sex hormones inhibit the production of prolactin by the pituitary; when the level of the sex hor-

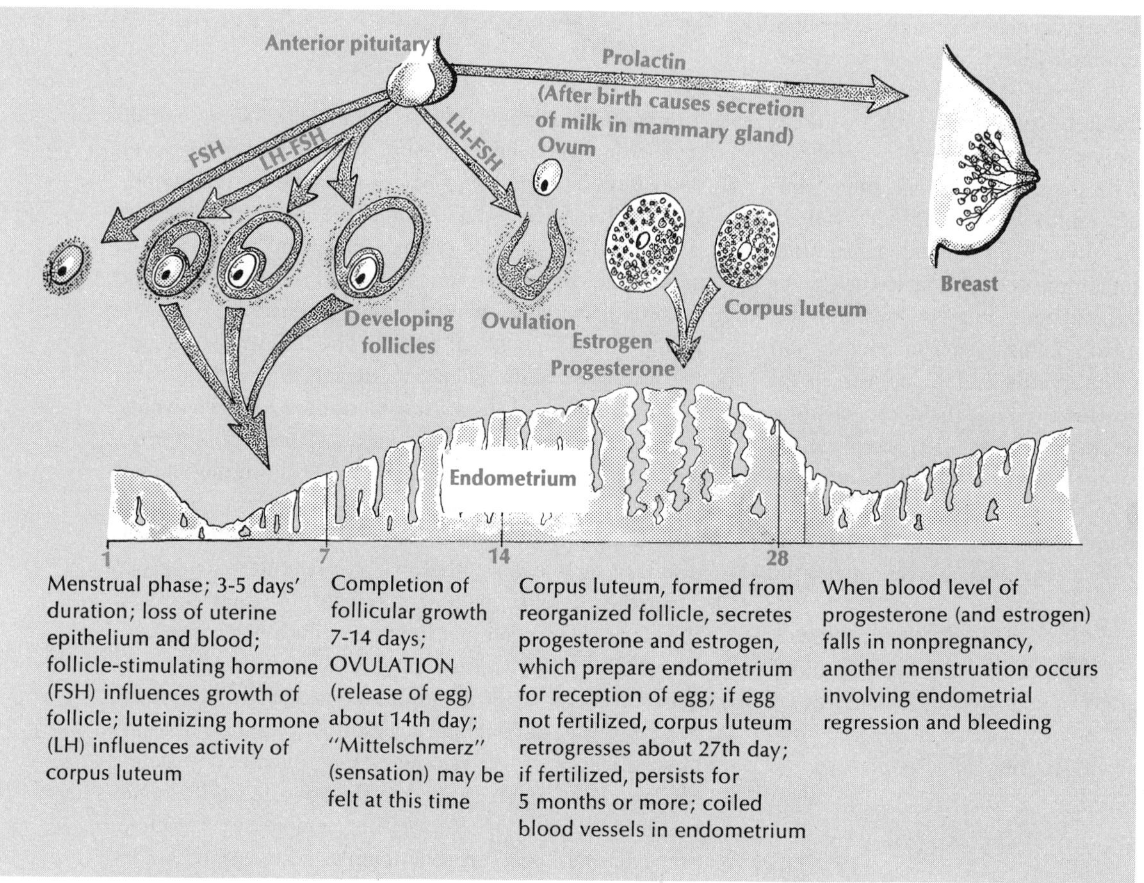

FIG. 33-27

Reproductive cycle in human female showing hormonal-ovarian-endometrial relationships. It will be noted that endometrium undergoes cyclical chain of events (thickness, congestion, etc.) under influence of hormones from ovary—estradiol (estrogen) and progestin (progesterone)—and from pituitary gland—FSH and LH. Another hormone, prolactin, stimulates secretion of milk.

mones falls, prolactin has an opportunity to act. The secretion of prolactin is also increased through nervous stimulation when the nipple is manipulated by sucking. During lactation the follicle-stimulating hormone of the pituitary is inhibited by prolactin so that follicle production and ovulation do not usually occur.

Other possible endocrine organs. Other organs are strongly suspected of having some hormonal function, although so far the evidence is not entirely conclusive.

Thymus. The thymus is a large mass of lymphoid tissue located in the upper part of the chest and covering the great vessels at the base of the heart. It reaches its maximum size during the second year of life, when it may weigh about 12 grams. After puberty it regresses, so that it is very small in later life. The organ contains lobules of lymphatic tissue which are separated by fibrous connective tissue. Lymphatic nodules and germinal centers, however, are absent, but it is divided into cortex and medulla regions. Recent work indicates that the thymus is the source of lymphoid cells that are liberated into the circulation and are responsible for the production of antibodies in the spleen and lymph nodes. It may also produce a humoral factor that confers immunologic properties on lymphoid cells wherever they are found.

Pineal body (epiphysis)

Many vertebrates have two fingerlike outgrowths of the thin roof of the diencephalon, known as the anterior **parietal body** and the posterior **epiphysis** or **pineal body** (Fig. 33-28) (an anterior paraphysis of unknown function may also occur). Only one or the other of these two bodies is found in most vertebrates, but certain cyclostomes have both. In certain extinct vertebrates,

TABLE 33-2

Important endocrine glands and their hormones

Gland	Hormone	Function
Gastric mucosa of stomach	Gastrin	Stimulates secretion of gastric juice
Intestinal mucosa of duodenum	Secretin	Stimulates secretion of pancreatic juice
	Enterogastrone	Decreases motility and secretion of stomach
	Cholecystokinin	Causes gallbladder to contract
Thyroid	Thyroxine (primary)	Controls rate of metabolism, growth, and maturation
	Triiodothyronine	Similar to thyroxine but more rapid in action
Parathyroid	Parathyroid hormone	Elevates blood calcium levels
	Calcitonin	Lowers blood calcium levels
Islets of Langerhans of pancreas	Insulin	Controls metabolism of glucose
	Glucagon	Controls glycogen breakdown in liver
Adrenal cortex	Glucocorticoids (hydrocortisone, cortisone)	Control food metabolism, suppress inflammation
	Mineralocorticoids (aldosterone, desoxycorticosterone)	Control salt and water excretion, promote inflammation
	Androgens (androsterone and others similar to testosterone)	Mimic action of testosterone
Adrenal medulla	Epinephrine (adrenine, Adrenalin) Norepinephrine	Raises blood pressure, increases sugar of blood, increases heart rate, mimics action of sympathetic nerves
Adenohypophysis (anterior pituitary, including pars intermedia)	Growth stimulator (STH)	Regulates somatic cell growth
	Follicle stimulator (FSH)	Regulates growth of follicles in female, spermatogenesis in male
	Interstitial cell–stimulating hormone (ICSH)	Same as FSH
	Luteinizing (LH)	Forms corpus luteum, interstitial cells
	Prolactin (LTH)	Stimulates lactation after alveolar growth, stimulates secretion of corpus luteum hormones
	Thyrotropic (TSH)	Controls thyroid gland
	Adrenocorticotropic (ACTH)	Controls adrenal cortex
	Intermedin	Chromatophore expansion in lower vertebrates
	Melanocyte-stimulating hormone (MSH)	
Neurohypophysis (posterior pituitary)	Vasopressin (Pitressin, antidiuretic hormone, ADH)	Stimulates smooth muscle, elevates blood pressure, decreases volume of urine
	Oxytocin (Pitocin)	Contracts uterine muscle
Testis (interstitial tissue)	Testosterone (primary) Androsterone	Controls secondary sex characteristics
Ovary (follicles) Placenta Testis (interstitial)	Estradiol (estrone, estrogen)	Controls secondary sex characteristics, menstrual cycle, mammary glands
Ovary (corpus luteum)	Progesterone	Regulates menses, mammary glands, pregnancy
Placenta	Chorionic gonadotropin	Regulates growth of corpus luteum during pregnancy
	Progesterone, estrogen	Supplements or replaces the functions of these ovarian hormones
	Relaxin	Relaxes pelvic ligaments at labor
Pineal	Melatonin	Slows down estrus and ovarian development
	Serotonin	Releases histamine?

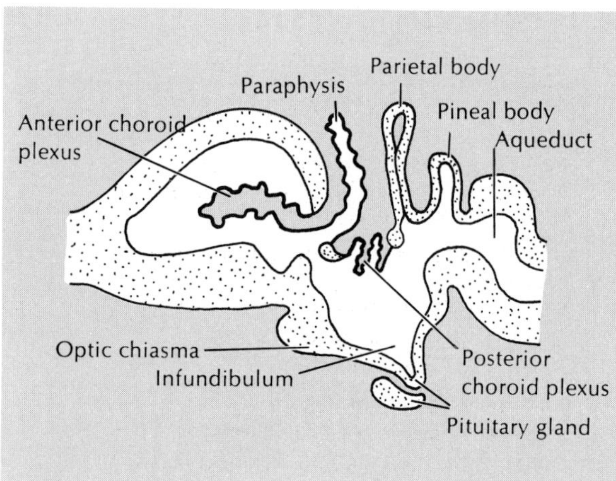

FIG. 33-28

Sagittal section through generalized vertebrate diencephalon showing median evaginations from roof of third ventricle. There is evolutionary evidence that ancestral vertebrates may have had one or two median dorsal eyes, in addition to bilateral eyes. Paraphysis (function unknown) usually disappears some time in life cycle. Anterior parietal body and posterior pineal body are both found in lampreys, some ganoid fishes, and some reptiles; in other vertebrates one or the other is suppressed.

FIG. 33-29

Section of pineal gland with brain sand. These calciferous encrustations are abundant in old glands.

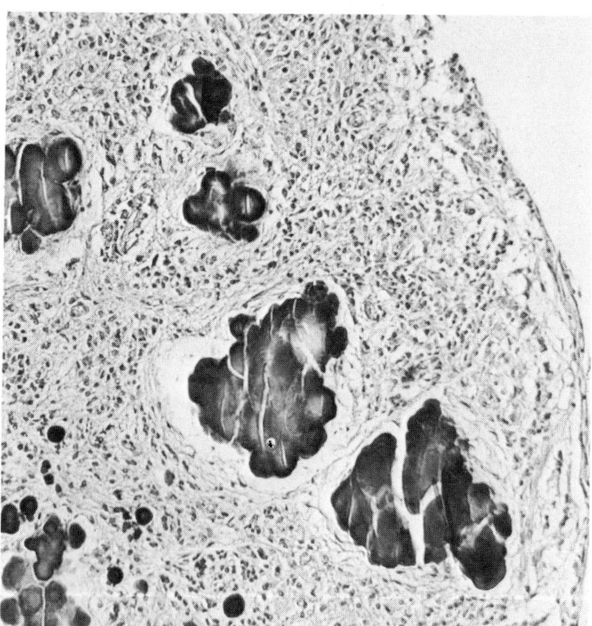

there may have been a fully developed median eye in this region, or there could have been a pair. In *Sphenodon*, the parietal body develops an eyelike organ with rudimentary retina and lens easily visible externally. In frogs and some other amphibians a rudimentary optic structure arises from the fused paraphysis and epiphysis (collectively a pineal body) and extend to the surface as the "brow spot" between the eyes. In some reptiles, birds, and mammals the pineal body has been considered a glandular organ.

The pineal body (epiphysis) in vertebrates, other than those mentioned above, cannot be seen externally, but lies under the skull on the upper surface of the brain between the two halves of the cerebral cortex and in front of the midbrain where it is attached by a stalk to the roof of the third ventricle. It is also covered by the pia mater of the meninges that divides the organ into lobules by septa. The pineal body contains certain characteristic cells and neuroglial cells for support. In older individuals it contains brain sand (**corpora arenacea**) that is composed of concretions of mineral salts (Fig. 33-29). The functions of this small body have been a mystery. Tumors in this region have been known to be associated with precocious sexual maturity or the reverse. Recent investigations on the rat indicate that the body is a biologic clock. The pineal gland contains two hormones, melatonin and serotonin, which undergo circadian rhythms in their content. When injected into rats, melatonin slows down the estrus cycle and causes the ovaries to lose weight. Continuous illumination blocks the production of the enzyme that helps form melatonin. This hormone may act directly on the gonads or on some other site. Its action appears to convert light energy of certain wavelengths into nervous impulses that are carried over nerves of the sympathetic system. The correlation between the reproductive cycle of mammals and the seasons of the years appear to be controlled by the pineal gland.

Table 33-2 summarizes the important endocrine glands and their hormonal action.

Annotated references

Barrington, E. J. W. 1964. Hormones and evolution. Princeton, D. Van Nostrand Co.

Carlisle, D. B., and F. Knowles. 1959. Endocrine control in crustaceans, Cambridge Monographs in Experimental Biology. London, Cambridge University Press.

Gorbman, A. (editor). 1959. Comparative endocrinology. New York, John Wiley & Sons, Inc. *This work is based upon an important symposium on comparative endocrinology held at Columbia University in 1958.*

It is an account of the work of many active investigators in this rapidly growing field of research.

Gorbman, A., and H. A. Bern. 1962. A textbook of comparative endocrinology. New York, John Wiley & Sons, Inc. *One of the best texts on this subject on the market.*

Gordon, M. S. (editor). 1968. Animal function: principles and adaptations. New York, The Macmillan Co.

Hall, P. F. 1959. The functions of the endocrine glands. Philadelphia, W. B. Saunders Co. *An account of our present knowledge about the physiology of endocrinology. It is not as heavy as some other works in this field but is concise and to the point. It is recommended to the advanced undergraduate student.*

Hanstrom, B. 1939. Hormones in invertebrates. New York, Oxford University Press. *One of the few works devoted to invertebrate hormones. Gives a full summary of the work done in this field up to the time of its publication.*

Kelly, G. F. 1967. Endocrine coordination in invertebrates. New York, Pageant Press. *An introductory summary.*

Turner, C. D. 1960. General endocrinology, ed. 3. Philadelphia, W. B. Saunders Co. *This work presents an excellent and concise summary of the main principles of endocrinology.*

Wilson, E. O. 1963. Pheromones. Sci. Amer. **208**:100-114 (May).

PART SIX

HOW LIFE CONTINUES

● Living systems have three important characteristics—reproduction of their kind, transmission of biochemical information to a succeeding generation, and the development of the individual animal into a functional unit. One of these is the ability to replace with new individuals those that die from a variety of causes. All living organisms are mortal, that is, their lives have a span of existence that will terminate. Thus every animal has the ability to reproduce its kind, to ensure the perpetuation of its species. This has been dealt with in Part V. The reproductive process varies from simple fission of cells among unicellular organisms to the complex processes of higher forms. Sex is associated with that type of reproduction in which specialized cells (gametes) are produced and when united form an entity that develops into a new individual. One kind is called the spermatozoan (male gamete) and the other the ovum (female gamete). The union of the two kinds of gametes forms the zygote. Differentiation into two sexes (male and female) is common among members of the animal kingdom and even is implied in the conjugation of the protozoans. Many lower forms have in the same individual two different kinds of cells that unite to form an individual. In higher forms the sexes are usually dimorphic and distinguishable by secondary sexual characteristics, as well as hormonal and other differences. Sex is an adaptive process by introducing genetic change into the offspring by combining genes from two parents.

Heredity is the transmission of biochemical information on structure and function from the parent to the offspring generation. This information is coded in a sequence of nucleotides in the genes of the chromosomes. By mutation of the genetic information and by sex whereby the genetic information from two parents are combined, variations occur so that evolutionary natural selection can provide for adaptation. The individual animal can function only as an interbreeding member of a population within the interactions of an ecosystem. In this way heredity can have adaptive value, for the animal must survive with what its hereditary potential has endowed it.

Development is a universal phenomenon among animals. Even in the less complex protozoa that reproduce either by binary fission or by budding, development occurs at some stage. Increase in size must occur. Structural specializations in the form of organelles must be provided. Some organelles are inherited equally or unequally by the daughter organisms that later complete their necessary equipment by producing new structures. All these are developmental changes that may be structural or physiologic in whatever animal in which they take place. Every animal must undergo morphogenesis or the development of the architectural features of an animal. In complex animals this is a complicated process and is made more complicated by different patterns in different groups of animals. But the greatest problem of all in development is how a single cell (the zygote) can differentiate into many different kinds of cells. Each cell inherits the same set of genes as the others, yet cell division occurs to form many cells and these cells become radically different to form the structures found in an individual animal.

CHAPTER 34

• PRINCIPLES OF DEVELOPMENT

● In Chapter 7 a brief survey of embryologic development was described. This chapter is concerned with some of the special aspects of development in the higher groups (amniotes) as well as an account of some concepts in experimental embryology. Certain embryologic facts and theories should be studied by the student to gain a comprehensive knowledge of the organism as a whole.* At this point it would be well for the student to review briefly the main points of embryologic development in Chapter 7.

HISTORIC BACKGROUND OF EMBRYOLOGY

How a one-cell fertilized egg is able to develop into a complete animal usually within a relatively short time has challenged investigators in nearly every field of biologic thought. Aristotle made extensive studies on the development of animals, and his description of the chick in the hen's egg has considerable accuracy. His belief that development was a gradual building up was somewhat in line with present-day concepts. The modern study of embryology really started in the early seventeenth century when the revival of learning was making itself felt in nearly all spheres of human activity and thought. In 1600 Fabricius of Aquapendente, an Italian, published the first embryologic treatise. His description of the hen's egg and the development of the chick has much of interest but contains the erroneous belief that the various parts of the organism appeared much sooner than is actually the case.

The idea of many early biologic students was that the young animal was preformed in the egg and development was an unfolding and growth of a miniature animal that they claimed could be seen in germ cells. This **preformation theory** was advocated by many naturalist-philosophers of the seventeenth and eighteenth centuries, notably by Bonnet and Haller. William Harvey, the great student of blood circulation, who published a treatise on embryology in his old age, was against the preformation theory, and his famous dictum, *ex ovo omnia* (all from the egg), was a fruitful concept for all future embryologists. The preformation theory, however, received its death blow in 1759 when the German Caspar Friedrich Wolff plainly showed that there were no little animals or plants in germ cells, but only undifferentiated tissue that gradually developed into germ layers and organs. His theory was called **epigenesis** (origin upon). This view is nearer the truth than preformation but errs in assuming that the formative substance that gives rise to the embryo is undifferentiated. It is now known that there are certain substances in germ cells that are predestined to guide the development of parts and are, in a restricted sense, preformed.

The discovery of the small mammalian egg by Karl Ernst von Baer in 1827 represents a great landmark in embryology, The eggs of the other classes of vertebrates as well as those of most invertebrates are large enough to be easily seen. In contrast, the mammalian egg is very small and microscopic, and its discovery brought the reproductive process of mammals in line with other animals. No other embryologist contributed as much to this field as did von Baer because he established the germ layer theory, made embryology comparative, discovered the notochord, and developed the **biogenetic law,** which states that the embryos of higher and lower forms tend to resemble each other more closely the farther one goes back in their development (Fig. 34-1). He gave the study of embryology an impetus that has led to the development of one of the greatest divisions of zoology.

IMPLANTATION (NIDATION) OF THE FERTILIZED OVUM

The problem of the implantation (nidation) of the fertilized ovum in mammals is very much of a mystery. After the egg is fertilized and the zygote formed, cleavage begins. Fertilization usually occurs in the uterine tube and the zygote must pass through this tube, while cleavage is taking place, to the uterus where implanta-

*Refer to Chapter 2, Principles 10, 14, 21, and 26.

tion is made in the endometrium, the lining of the uterus. Usually three or four days are required for this passage in most mammals, but the time varies with different species. In the dog and cat about 7 days is the the passage time; but in the opossum only 1 day is required. In the uterus the blastocyst, or developing embryo, remains free for a varying length of time, depending on the species. In the rabbit this is about four days and in the human about six days; but in the mouse and rat it is only 36 hours. In some mammals the implantation may be delayed several weeks.

The method of implantation varies greatly. In ungulates and carnivores the blastocyst may fill a large part of the uterus (central implantation). In rodents the small blastocyst becomes lodged in a fold of the uterus, where it implants itself (eccentric implantation). In man and some other animals the blastocyst passes through the uterine wall and is completely cut off from the lumen of the uterus (interstitial implantation). During the period of preimplantation, changes occur in the uterus under the influence of hormones from the adenohypophysis. Progesterone from the corpus luteum is influential in preparing the endometrium and for maintaining the blastocyst. The dominance of progesterone appears to be responsible for the physiologic status of the genital tract, the normal cleavage of the ova, and migration of the ova to the implantation sites. This period is later followed by the dominance of estrogen (estrogen surge) that brings about the release of histamine, the transformation of the stromal cells of the endometrium into decidual cells (thick endometrial lining), and tissue lysis (disintegration of cells). This activity makes possible the invasion of the blastocyst into the endometrium. Although the ovary may be the primary source of the estrogen surge, the blastocyst may also carry some estrogen. The process of implantation can be prevented by placing an object within the uterus, a method the Arabs performed by inserting pebbles into the uteri of their camels to prevent breeding.

EMBRYOLOGY OF AMNIOTES

Embryos that develop into land animals, such as reptiles, birds, and mammals (**amniotes,** or those that develop an amnion), are provided with **extraembryonic membranes.** These membranes are the yolk sac, amnion, allantois, and chorion. Of these, only the yolk sac is present in other vertebrates (fish and amphibians). These membranes, which are not a definite part of the developing embryo, afford a sort of aquarium for the embryo so that it may develop as its fish ancestors did before an aquatic life was abandoned for a land existence.

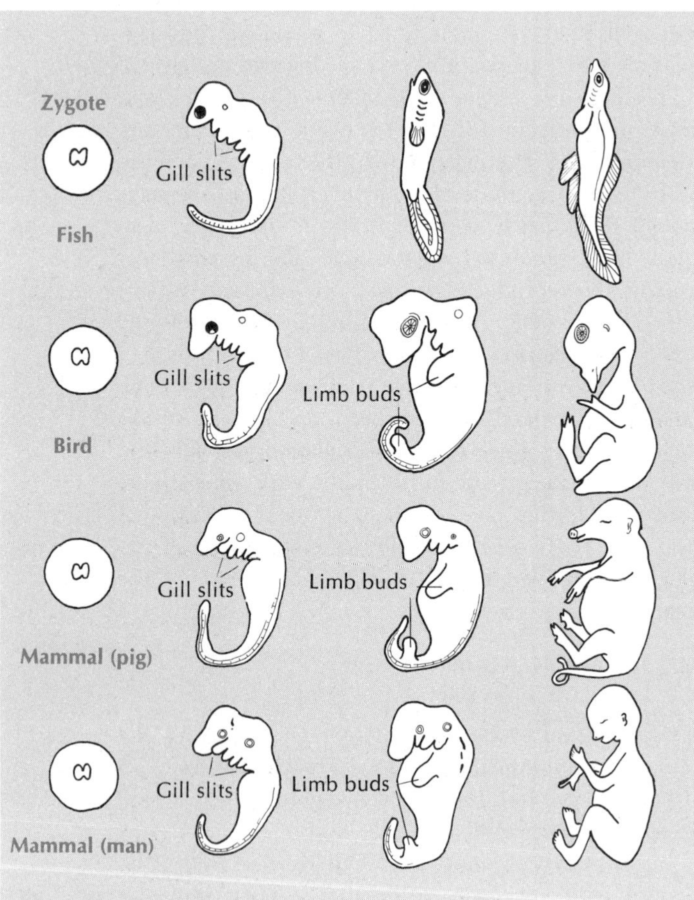

FIG. 34-1

Comparative series of four vertebrate embryos showing comparable stages of development. It will be noted that early stages of all four series look very much alike. Distinctive characteristics show up in later stages. Because of this pattern of similarity, Haeckel formulated his biogenetic law, which stated that "ontogeny (development of individual) recapitulates phylogeny (evolutionary history of group)." In its extreme form this view is no longer held, for all stages of ontogeny are modified in evolution. Von Baer's view that embryonic stages of higher form are like embryonic stages of lower animals but not like adults of those animals is considered to be more accurate.The pharyngula stage of the different vertebrates (second row from left) indicates the most marked resemblance of the embryos to each other.

The **yolk sac**, a protruding outgrowth of the primitive gut (Fig. 34-2), encloses the yolk mass. It is connected by a yolk stalk to the gut and is lined with endoderm and covered with mesoderm. Endodermal cells digest the yolk material, and the mesodermal blood capillaries absorb the digested material and carry it to the growing embryo. When the embryo hatches, the degenerating yolk sac is absorbed in the body cavity. Although best developed in the reptiles and birds, some of the sharks have large yolk sacs.

The **chorion** and **amnion** develop at the same time in reptiles and birds. A combined fold of ectoderm and mesoderm (the head of the amnion fold) appears at the anterior end and gradually extends backward over the surface of the embryo. A similar fold (the tail fold) appears posteriorly in the embryo, meets, and fuses with the head fold. Lateral folds of the amnion extend above and below the embryo and finally fuse over the top of the embryo, thus enclosing the amniotic chamber. The outer double layer is the chorion and the inner double layer is the amnion. Between the chorion and the amnion is the extraembryonic space. The amniotic cavity becomes filled with fluid and contains the developing embryo. The mesodermal muscle cells of the amnion contract rhythmically; this rocks the embryo in the amniotic fluid and prevents its adhesion to the surrounding wall.

The **allantois** grows out as a tube from the ventral wall of the hindgut and is formed in about the same way as the urinary bladder of amphibians. As it grows, its free end expands into the space between the amnion and yolk sac internally and the chorion externally. It fuses with the chorion to form the chorioallantoic membrane. This has been a favorite experimental site for the growth and differentiation of isolated parts of the developing embryo. Its mesoderm is supplied with blood vessels that pick up oxygen that diffuses through the porous shell and give off carbon dioxide in the opposite direction. Its function is primarily one of respiration, but some nitrogenous waste is also excreted into its cavity.

Reptiles and birds. The large amount of yolk in the eggs of reptiles and birds offers so much resistance to cell cleavage that the latter is confined only to the surface layer (**partial cleavage**). In such cases the yolk is a continuous mass. In the fertilized hen's egg (Fig. 34-3) the white albuminous matter and the shell are envelopes that surround the yolk or true zygote. The nucleus and its chromosomes are found in the small **germinal disk** on top of the yolk. Two spiral cords (**chalazae**) at the blunt and narrow ends of the egg represent the twisted dense mucin fibers of albumin formed by the rotation of the egg through the oviduct. When cleavage is initiated, the nucleus in the germinal disk divides repeatedly by meroblastic cleavage, cell membranes are formed, and a plate of cells result (**blastodisk**) on top of the yolk mass (Fig. 7-3), which is eventually used up in the nourishment of the embryo. When the center of the germinal disk pulls away from the yolk, a cavity is formed—the **blastocoel.** This stage corresponds to the blastula of other types of development and is called a **blastoderm.** The separation of the blastoderm into a superficial layer (**ectoderm**) and a deeper layer (**endoderm**) takes place by a process of delamination. A thickening of the ectoderm and endoderm occurs at the posterior part of the blastoderm to form the **primitive streak,** which is homologous to the dorsal lip of the blastopore of lower forms. It also marks the longitudinal axis of the future embryo. At the anterior end of the primitive streak a node that lays down the **notochord** is formed. **Mesoderm** is formed as a sheet of cells between the ectoderm and the endoderm at either side of the notochord. The mesoderm typically splits into two sheets that grow between the ectoderm and endoderm; one of these sheets is attached to the outer ectoderm and the other to the inner endoderm. The space between the two sheets is the **coelomic cavity.** On each side of the notochord somites or segments appear in the

FIG. 34-2

Amniote egg in early stage of development showing embryonic membranes. This type of egg made land existence possible, for it is protected against drying out by tough shell, embryonic membranes, and fluids that surround embryo. Other adaptive features of this egg are gaseous exchange (O_2 and CO_2) through porous shell and yolk nourishment for growing embryo until it hatches.

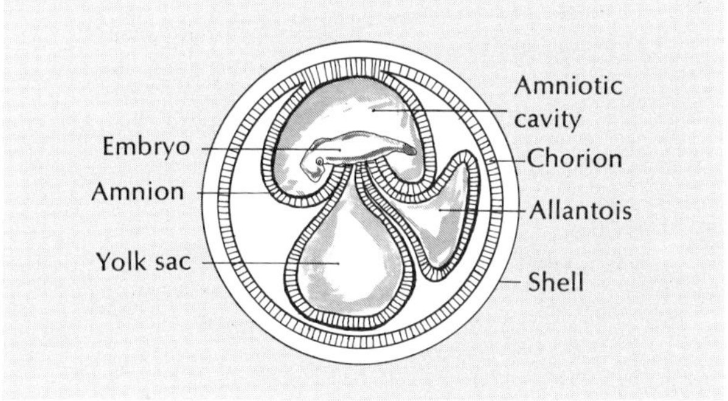

mesoderm; from these the main muscles of the trunk develop. Above the notochord the ectoderm thickens to form the **neural plate,** which later develops into the neural tube and finally the brain and spinal cord. Only the central part of the blastoderm develops into the embryo; the other portion develops into the four extra-embryonic membranes just described. Most other aspects of reptilian and bird development are similar to those of the mammal, to be described later.

EARLY DEVELOPMENT OF HUMAN EGG

The monotremes have eggs that resemble those of birds because they contain much yolk and are laid externally. Other mammals have very small eggs (the human egg is only 0.2 mm. in diameter) that contain very little yolk. The early cleavage of the human egg results in a spherical group of cells (**morula** stage) that becomes divided into two parts—an outer layer of cells and an inner mass of cells attached to the outer layer (Fig. 34-4). The outer part develops into the chorion, which is concerned with the nourishment of the embryo from the maternal wall of the uterus; the inner cell mass gives rise to the embryo and the other fetal membranes.

The formation of a gastrula from the inner cell mass is similar to that of other mammals, but unlike other vertebrates, there is no blastopore. Two cavities arise in this inner cell mass. The upper one is the **amniotic cavity** lined with ectoderm, and the lower is the **yolk sac** and the primitive gut lined with endoderm. Between the two cavities the embryo arises as a flat, two-layered plate (the embryonic disk). As development proceeds, the posterior end of the embryo becomes connected to the chorion by the **body stalk** (Fig. 34-5). After the gastrula stage the human embryo, as well as that of other mammals, undergoes a development similar to

FIG. 34-3

Longitudinal section of bird's egg. Adaptive structures of egg are as follows: (1) Limy shell is minutely porous for gas exchange and its double membrane lining encloses air bubble for young embryo. (2) Yolk is anchored by twisted cords of albumin (chalazae) and enclosed in sac (vitelline membrane). (3) Blastodisk, which gives rise to embryo, always turns uppermost to be nearest incubating bird and external air. (4) Lighter, semifluid yolk is collected nearest developing embryo for nourishment. (5) Albumin suspends egg and furnishes aqueous environment for it. Yolk is ovarian egg; albumin, shell membranes, and limy shell are secreted by wall of oviduct and by shell gland and are added as coatings to yolk. Such a telolecithal (megalecithal) egg restricts early cleavage stages to blastodisk (meroblastic cleavage).

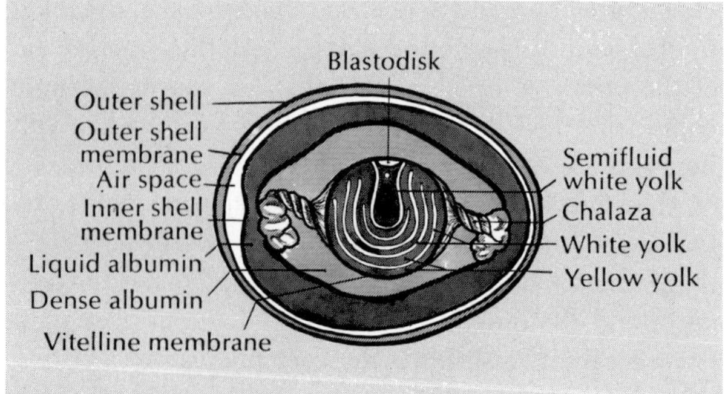

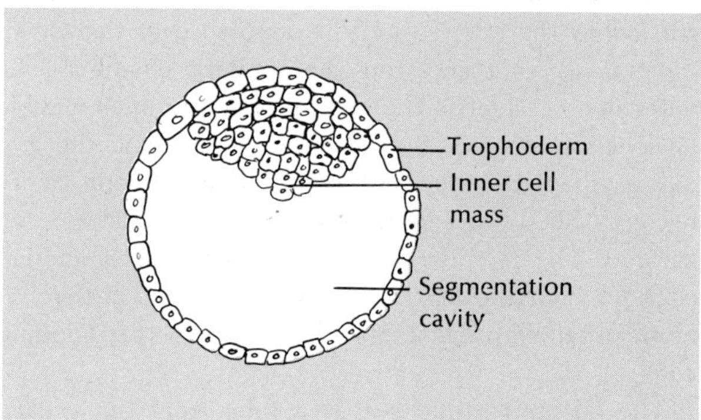

FIG. 34-4

Morula stage. Trophoderm becomes the chorion; inner cell mass gives rise to embryo and other fetal membranes.

FIG. 34-5

Early embryonic stage in man showing amniotic cavity and yolk sac.

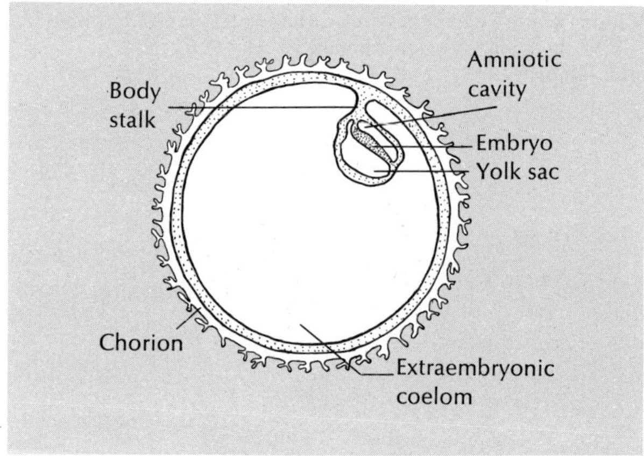

that of birds during its early embryology. Gill slits or depressions are plainly visible at an early stage but probably do not break through into the pharynx (Fig. 34-1).

PLACENTA AND UMBILICAL CORD

The embryo of mammals differs from that of reptiles and birds in having little or no food in the yolk sac for its nourishment and in having in its place a special device, the **placenta,** for obtaining its food from the mother (Fig. 34-6). The placenta is formed by processes, or **villi,** of the chorion embedded in the uterine wall close to the maternal blood vessels. These villi and the tissues of the uterus in which they are embedded form the combined structure known as the placenta. The placenta, therefore, has both an embryonic and a maternal part. Connecting the placenta with the ventral surface of the embryo's abdomen is the soft flexible **umbilical cord,** which encloses two arteries and a vein for carrying materials to and from the embryo. There is no direct connection between the embryonic and maternal circulations because there is no mixing of the bloods of the two, although the embryo's blood circulates in the chorionic villi in close contact with the mother's blood in the maternal part of the placenta. The relationship between the two is purely an osmotic one and all substances must diffuse through a membrane that separates the two systems. The placenta grows in size as the embryo develops; in the human being at birth it is about 7 inches in diameter and a little more than 1 inch thick.

The form of the placenta varies with different mammals. In man and rodents its shape is disklike (**discoidal**); in hogs (Fig. 34-7) and cattle it is called a **diffuse** placenta because the villi are scattered; and in cats and other carnivores the placenta is in the form of a

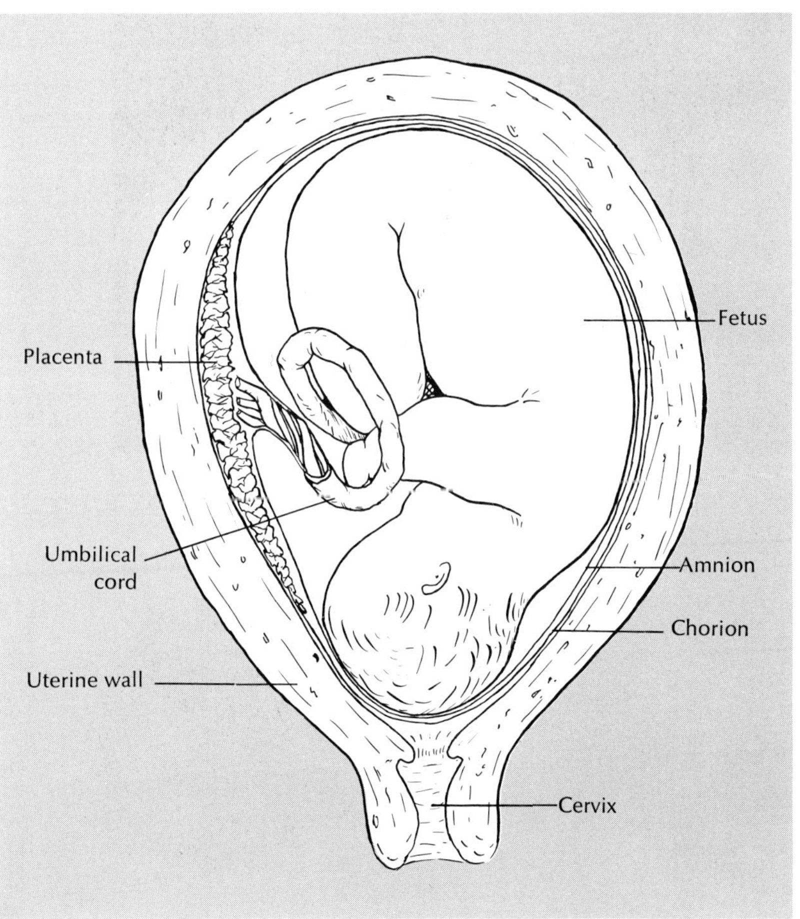

FIG. 34-6

Human fetus just prior to birth. Note discoidal placenta, in contrast to diffuse and zonary types shown in Figs. 34-7 and 34-8.

band and is called **zonary** (Fig. 34-8). At the time of birth the embryonic part of the placenta is expelled either with the young or shortly thereafter as the "afterbirth." Some mammals eat the placenta after the birth of their young.

DEVELOPMENT OF SYSTEMS AND ORGANS IN AMNIOTES

The **nervous system** is one of the first to form. Shortly after gastrulation the ectoderm thickens over the notochord to form a **neural plate.** The center of this plate becomes depressed by the more rapid growth of cells along its margin and the plate becomes a neural groove (Fig. 34-9). Then the outer ridges or folds come together at the top to form the hollow neural tube. The anterior end of this tube enlarges to form the brain, while the posterior part becomes the spinal cord. Nerve cells and nerves originate from the walls of the tube or from the neural crest along the sides.

Most of the **endoskeleton** arises as ossification of cartilage, but some of the cranial bones come from membrane. In man, some bones begin their ossification as early as the end of the second month of prenatal life.

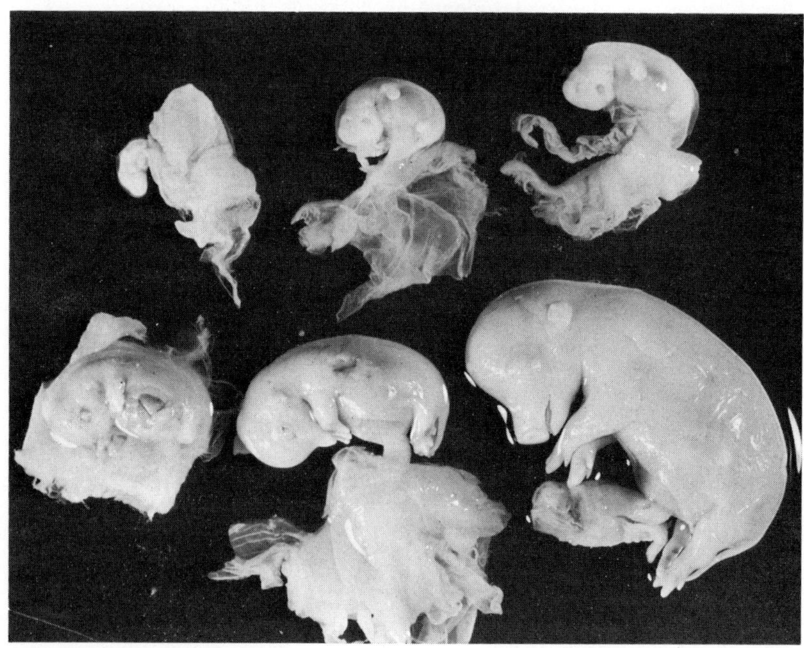

FIG. 34-7

Stages in embryonic development of pig. Stages range from 9 mm. (upper left) to 45 mm. (lower right). Pig has diffuse type of placenta.

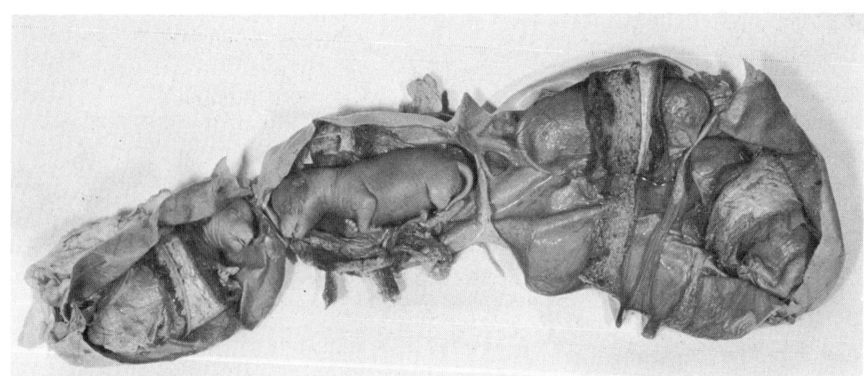

FIG. 34-8

Uterus of dog opened up to expose litter of four pups. Zonary placenta, which is band around body, is well shown. Three pups are still wholly or partially enclosed in their amniotic sacs; one has been exposed to show its umbilical cord.

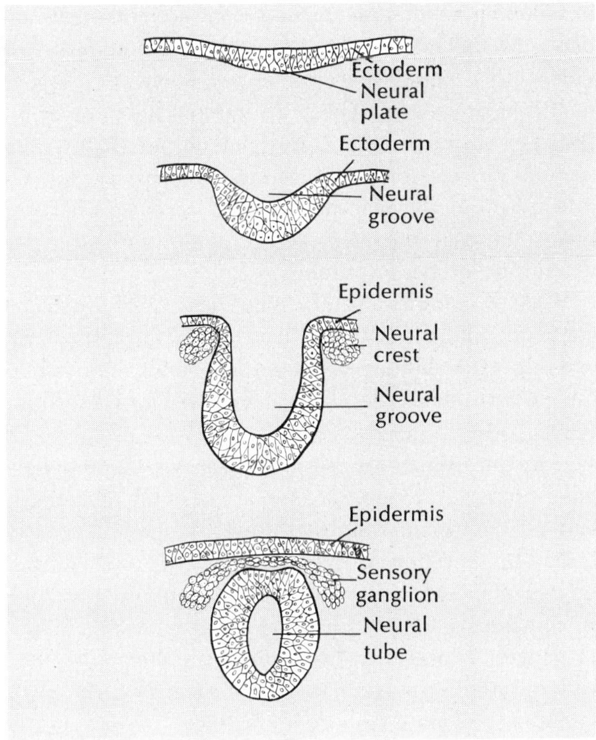

FIG. 34-9

Development of neural tube from neural plate of ectoderm (cross section).

FIG. 34-10

Embryo showing muscle somites.

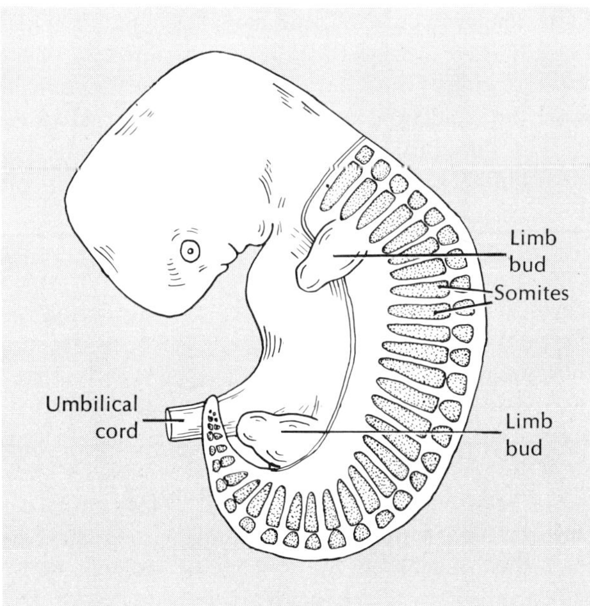

Large bones may have several centers of ossification, which is not complete until long after birth. In frogs the notochord buds off from the roof of the archenteron, but in amniotes it arises from the anterior end of the primitive streak. The **skin** has a double origin, the epidermis coming from ectoderm and the dermis, or corium, from the mesoderm.

Most **muscles** arise from the mesoderm along each side of the spinal cord (Fig. 34-10). This mesoderm divides into a linear series of somites (38 in man) that by splitting, fusion, and migration become the muscles of the body and axial parts of the skeleton. The **limbs** begin as buds from the side of the body. Projections of the limb buds develop into digits.

The **alimentary canal** is early folded off from the yolk sac by the growth and folding of the body wall (Fig. 34-11). The ends of the tube open to the exterior and are lined with ectoderm, whereas the rest of the tube is lined with endoderm. The **lungs, liver,** and **pancreas** arise from the foregut. At the anterior end of the body, crevices appear that in early vertebrates, such as fish, open directly into the pharyngeal part of the digestive system. These are the **gill clefts** associated with the gills of gill-breathing forms. In man these crevices never break through to form gill clefts, but they do suggest a fish stage in his ancestry. The transformation of the pharyngeal region in the land vertebrates is an interesting evolution. Since these forms breathe by means of lungs instead of gills, the gill pouches develop into other structures. The eustachian tube, for instance, comes from a remnant of the first gill pouch, whereas the palatine tonsils, the parathyroid, and the thymus come from certain of the other pouches.

The **heart, blood vessels,** and **red blood cells** are formed from the mesoderm. In its early condition the human heart is similar to the heart of lower vertebrates. Two tubes fuse for a part of their length into a single tube that divides into two cavities—the auricle and the ventricle. Later each of these subdivides, forming two auricles and two ventricles. This type of heart is characteristic of birds, mammals, and some of the reptiles.

The **urinary bladder** varies a great deal among the vertebrates, for in some it is entirely absent. In some fish the bladder is formed by the fusion of the lower parts of the wolffian ducts and a part of the cloaca. In other vertebrates it arises from the ventral wall of the

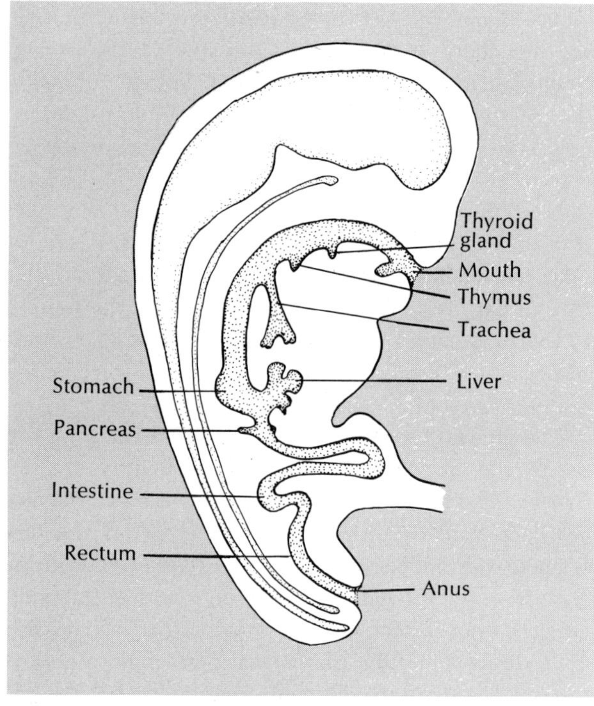

FIG. 34-11

Derivatives of alimentary canal.

cloaca. In higher vertebrates the base of the allantois helps in the formation of the bladder.

Both **testes** and ovaries of the **reproductive** system develop from the genital ridge, along the dorsal ridge of the coelom. The male cells, or sperm, develop in special seminiferous tubules of the testes, but the ova, or eggs, of the ovaries develop in special follicles and must break through the ovarian walls when mature. The higher vertebrates use wolffian, or mesonephric, ducts to carry the sperm and müllerian ducts to carry the eggs.

BIRTH OR PARTURITION

During the period of pregnancy, the placenta gradually takes over most of the functions of regulating the growth and development of the uterus and the embryo (fetus). As an endocrine gland it secretes estradiol and progesterone, which are secreted by the ovaries and corpus luteum in the early periods of pregnancy. The placenta also assumes the functioning of the pituitary in secreting a chorionic gonadotropin hormone that now performs the role of the LH and FSH pituitary hormones that cease their secretions about the second month of pregnancy. This gonadotropin hormone of the placenta maintains the corpus luteum so that it may secrete progesterone and estradiol necessary for the attachment of the placenta. In the later stages of pregnancy the placenta can manage affairs without either the corpus luteum or pituitary.

What stimulates birth? Why does not pregnancy continue indefinitely? What factors produce the onset of labor (the rhythmic contractions of the uterus)? So far, no satisfactory answer can be given to these questions. The real mechanism for parturition seems to reside in the uterus and placenta. Various theories have been proposed. Since the uterine-placental relationship is dependent mainly on the estradiol-progesterone ratio, it may be that labor is initiated by a high concentration of estradiol and a low concentration of progesterone. But mammals vary in their reactions to sex hormones. In general, progesterone cuts down uterine contractions and estradiol speeds them up. Injections of the latter hormone will cause abortion in mice but not in the human being. The mechanical effect of uterine muscle stretching (by the increased size of the fetus) may be a stimulus for labor.

The first major signs of labor or the beginning of parturition are the so-called labor pains that are caused by the rhythmic contractions of the uterine musculature. These are usually slight at first and occur at intervals of 15 to 30 minutes. They gradually become more intense, longer in duration, and more frequent. They may last anywhere from 6 to 24 hours, usually longer with the first child. The object of these contractions is to expel the child from the uterus and birth canal to the outside. Childbirth occurs in three stages. In the first stage the neck (cervix), or opening of the uterus into the vagina, is enlarged by the pressure of the child in its bag of amniotic fluid, which may be ruptured at this time; in the second stage the child is forced out of the uterus and through the vagina to the outside; and in the third stage the placenta, or afterbirth, is expelled from the mother's body. After birth, the umbilical cord that connects the child to the placenta is clamped off and cut. Usually within 10 minutes after the baby is born the placenta is expelled from the mother's body.

The fetal circulation (Fig. 34-12) differs in certain particulars from the postnatal circulation. In the fetal stage the placenta on the wall of the mother's uterus is concerned with the interchange of nutrients and

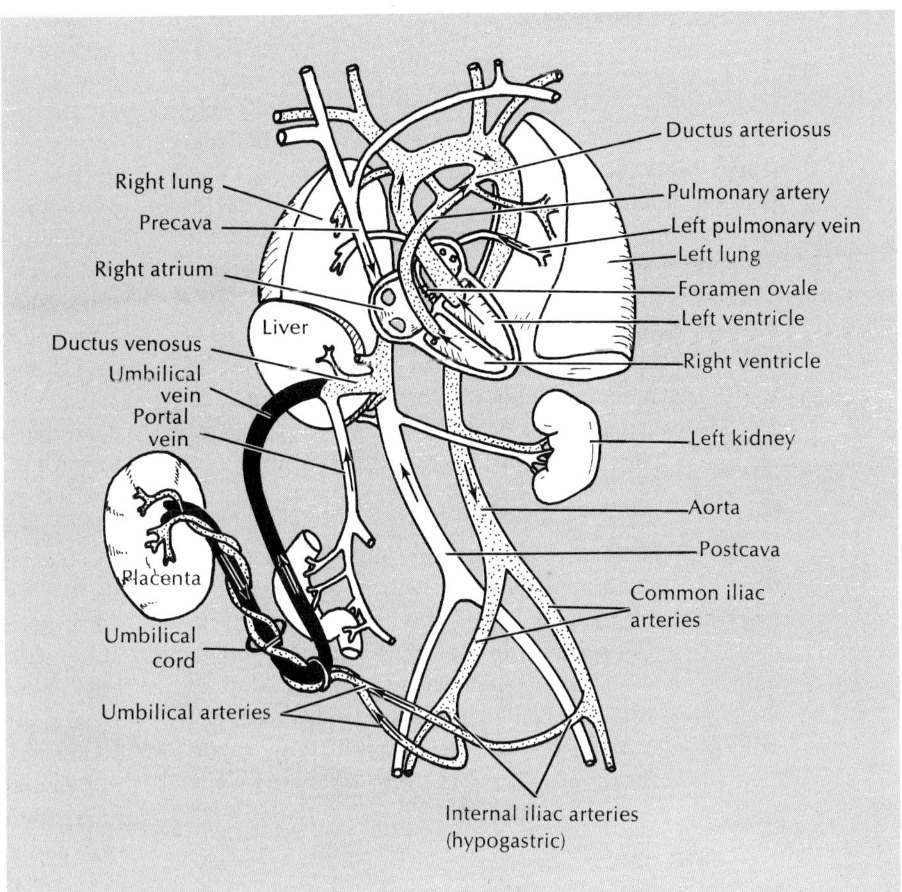

FIG. 34-12

Fetal circulation. Blood carrying food and oxygen from placenta is brought by umbilical vein to liver, is shunted through ductus venosus to vena cava where it mixes with deoxygenated blood returning from fetal tissues, and then is carried to right atrium. Two fetal shortcuts bypass nonfunctioning lungs. Some blood goes directly from right atrium to left atrium by an opening, the foramen ovale, and so enters systemic circulation. Some blood passes from pulmonary trunk into aorta by a temporary duct, the ductus arteriosus. At birth, placental exchange ceases; ductus venosus, foramen ovale, and ductus arteriosus all close; and regular postnatal pulmonary and systemic circuits take over.

waste and the oxygenation of the blood. By osmosis, nourishment and oxygen pass from the mother's blood in the placenta into the fetal blood, which in return gives up carbon dioxide and waste to the maternal blood. These substances are carried in the umbilical cord that is composed of one umbilical vein and two umbilical arteries. The umbilical vein, which carries oxygenated blood from the placenta, passes through the umbilical cord and then to the liver where it joins the portal vein. The blood is now shunted to the right atrium by the ductus venosus and the postcava. To avoid the nonfunctioning lungs the blood is shunted from the pulmonary system to the left side of the heart by the foramen ovale (a temporary opening between right and left atria) and by the ductus arteriosus that connects the pulmonary artery with the aorta. The two umbilical arteries from the internal iliac arteries return blood to the placenta. At birth the foramen ovale closes and the ductus arteriosus becomes the ligament of Botallo; the blood from the right side of the heart is thus forced into the lungs, and the adult circulation is established.

Many mammals give birth to more than one offspring at a time or to a litter, each member of which has come from a separate egg. Most higher mammals, however, have only one offspring at a time, although occasionally they may have plural young. The armadillo (*Dasypus*) is almost unique among mammals in giving birth to four young at one time—all from one egg and all members of a litter of the same sex, either male or female. Plural or multiple births occur with a certain regularity in the human being. Twins, triplets, quadruplets, and quintuplets are found in human populations. These may come from a single egg or there may be a separate egg for each offspring. Most human plural births are twins. If the two twins come from two eggs (**dizygotic**), they are called **fraternal twins;** if they come from a single egg (**monozygotic**), they are known as **identical twins** and are always of the same sex. Fraternal twins do not resemble each other more than other children born separately in the same family, but identical twins have striking resemblances. Embryologically, each member of fraternal twins has its own placenta, chorion, and amnion. Usually (but not always) identical twins share the same chorion and the same placenta, but each has its own amnion. Sometimes identical twins fail to separate completely and form Siamese twins, in which the organs of one may be a mirror image of the organs of the other. The ratio of the different plural births of man is interesting. The frequency of twin births to single births is 1 in 86, that of triplets 1 in 86^2, and that of quadruplets 1 in 86^3.

PROBLEM OF DIFFERENTIATION

Differentiation in biology is the formation, localization, and modification of cells, tissues, and organs in function and structure during the course of development. It is the biggest problem in biology and only a little is known about its fundamental nature. Most of the higher organisms originate from a fertilized egg cell (zygote) that has the potentiality to form an organism consisting of billions of cells with an infinite complexity of structures and function. The process of development involves a passage from simple to complex, from general to special, and from homogenesis to heterogenesis. Life thus begins as a single cell, which by successive cell divisions (cleavage) forms cells of many different kinds and functions in the makeup of a complex individual (Fig. 34-13). Some of the daughter cells in cleavage are destined to form muscle, others brain, and so on throughout the whole range of bodily structures. Can this differentiation be explained? For a long time embryologists were content to describe comparatively the embryologic histories of different animals, and a vast amount of accurate information about the development of animals resulted. But it was soon apparent to thoughtful investigators that mere description did not explain the underlying problems of development and that an experimental and analytical approach was necessary. From this new viewpoint there arose the science of experimental zoology, which has been in the forefront of biologic investigation for many years. Many able investigators have been active in this field, but two who have spearheaded causal embryology deserve special mention—W. Roux and H. Spemann. Experimental embryology emphasizes methods for artificially modifying normal development by such means as separating early cleavage blastomeres, by subjecting eggs and embryos to various external factors (temperature and chemicals), by transplanting grafts from one region of an embryo to another, by fusing eggs and embryos together, and by many other ways.

FIG. 34-13

Organization of recently fertilized egg of *Amphioxus* showing organ-forming areas that, when egg develops, will give rise to differentiations indicated on drawing. In cytoplasm of many chordate eggs there is found basic organization of definite areas that are predestined to develop into certain organs. Although these organization areas are visible, many morphogenetic organization patterns are invisible and their exact location in egg before development can only be guessed. It has been assumed that real morphologic ground substance of egg consists of enzymes, hormones, and other regulative materials. (Modified from Conklin.)

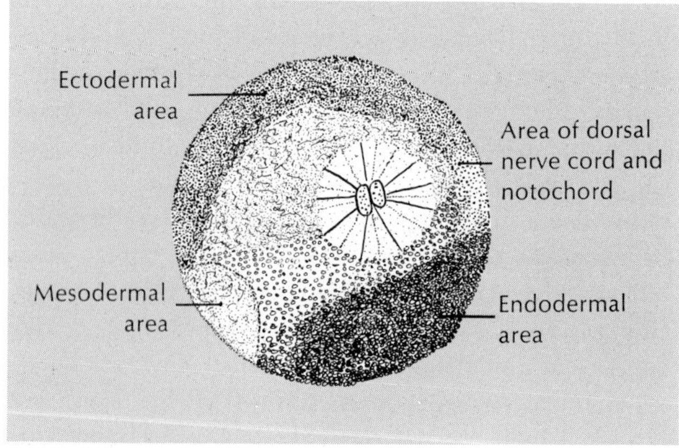

Modern embryologists have sought a middle ground between the theories of preformation and epigenesis, as previously described. Results indicate that neither the egg nor spermatozoan can be considered homogeneous and lacking in organization, but also they cannot be thought of as containing the embryos in miniature form. The germ cells are highly differentiated and possessed of certain potentialities localized more or less in the zygote, which develops under the influence of both external and internal factors. Descriptive embryology shows that certain structures in their earliest beginnings (anlagen or primordia) can be located or mapped in certain regions of the egg, and the exact organs they are going to give rise to can be followed with great accuracy.

Eggs of different species vary in their organization both before and after fertilization. It has been shown experimentally that, in certain forms, the blastomeres when separated from each other in early cleavage stages will each develop into a complete individual, whereas undisturbed they stay together and produce only one individual. In the frog's egg, for instance, if one of the blastomeres in the two-cell stage is killed by a hot needle, the intact blastomere will give rise to half an embryo; but when the two intact blastomeres are separated, each will form a whole embryo. In some eggs this power of separate blastomeres to form a complete embryo is possessed up to the four-cell stage. Such a condition is called **indeterminate** cleavage and is found in the regulative eggs of echinoderms, jellyfish, *Amphioxus*, and others (Fig. 34-14). On the other hand, there are eggs whose blastomeres when separated will give rise to only that part of the embryo that each blastomere would form in an intact egg. In such a case one may get a half or a quarter or some other part of an embryo, depending on the blastomeres that have been separated. This is called **determinate** cleavage or mosaic development. Examples of this type are the eggs of annelids, mollusks, ctenophores, and a few others.

The explanation behind these two types of cleavage and development seems to lie in the time of differentiation and organization of the egg. In those forms in which each of the early blastomeres will give rise to a complete embryo, or in which the blastomeres are totipotent, the formative substance is scattered through the egg and each blastomere receives a portion of all material necessary for a complete organism. The plane of cleavage gives an explanation of this type of totipotent blastomeres. Normally, the first divisions of the zygote cleave the egg along the axis of differentiation and each blastomere has a sample of the complete formative substance. Experimentally, if such an indeterminate egg is cleaved with a needle across the axis of differentiation, neither of the two halves will develop into normal embryos. Hoerstadius has shown, however, that this formative substance is of two types, both of which must be present for a blastomere to form an entire embryo. Thus the regulative power of these eggs have restrictions. In the determinate cleavage type the material is organized and localized so early that each blastomere receives a portion that is qualitatively different from that received by the others. It has been possible in some cases to map out the organization of some eggs (mosaic) to show that certain parts of the egg will give rise to only certain parts of the embryo. In this way certain regions can be determined in blastula and early gastrula stages that are presumptive for specific structures, such as the germ layers, notochord, and nervous system. From the evidence of identical twins, man apparently has the indeterminate type

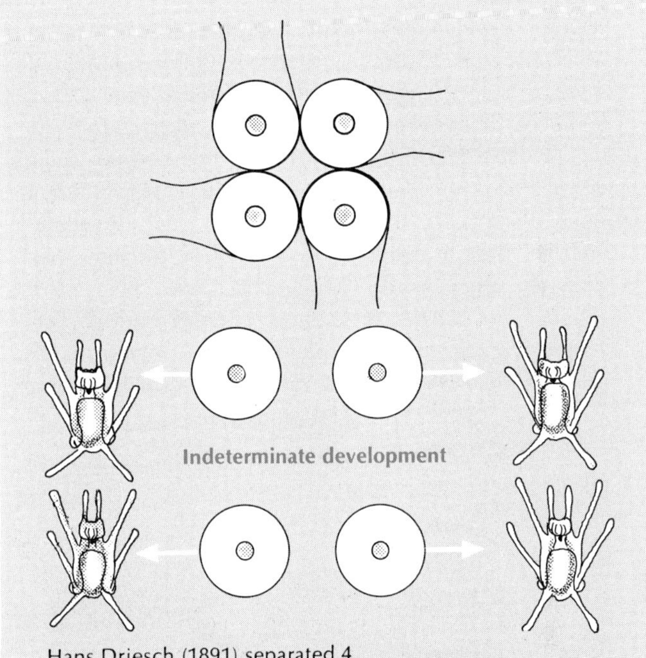

Hans Driesch (1891) separated 4 blastomeres of 4-cell stage of sea urchins and found that each blastomere gave rise to whole pluteus larva; early cleavage stages of other forms, including man, will behave in similar manner; such is called indeterminate development

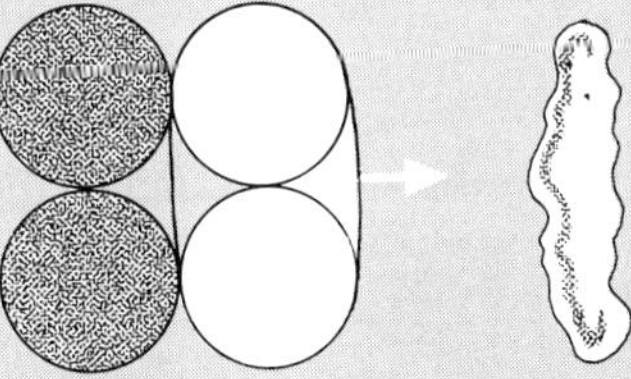

When 2 left blastomeres of 4-cell stage of Styela (tunicate) larva are killed with hot needle, right blastomeres will form only half of larva; early cleavage stages of annelids and mollusks are similar; each cell can produce only specific part of whole organism; this is called mosaic (determinate) development

FIG. 34-14

Determinate (mosaic) and indeterminate cleavage.

of cleavage, for identical twins come from the same zygote.

ROLE OF ORGANIZERS AND EMBRYONIC INDUCTORS

A method helpful in explaining the differentiation and development of the embryo is furnished by **embryonic induction.** Embryonic induction is a process by which a developing structure (inductor) stimulates another structure to become a specific differentiation. Induction is mediated by chemicals called evocators. It has been demonstrated by numerous investigators during the last 4 or 5 decades that, when certain groups of cells are transplanted from their normal position to some other parts of the body of the early developing embryo, they are profoundly altered in the new positions. In other words, the fate of these cells can be changed by placing them in a different location. Presumptive skin cells transplanted to a region of the brain to take the place of brain cells that have been removed become nerve cells rather than skin cells. These changes occur only when the transplantation is made during the early gastrula stage; if made later, the transplanted cells will remain the same. In early transplantation the region determines the nature of the growth, but older transplanted cells have already been determined and therefore do not change.

When pieces from the dorsal lip of the blastopore of the gastrula are transplanted beneath the ectoderm of another gastrula, a second embryo may be made to develop on the side of the host embryo (Fig. 34-15). The dorsal lip of the blastopore is known to be a center of organization (organizer) and is responsible for the formation of the brain, spinal cord, and notochord. There are many centers of organization in a developing embryo. Source centers such as the dorsal lip of the blastopore are known as **primary organizers** because they are concerned with the establishment of the basic axial organs of brain, spinal cord, etc. A secondary organizer is the optic vesicle that, transplanted to some region of the body other than the eye, will induce the formation of a lens in tissue that is normally destined for other roles. Many chemical substances (nu-

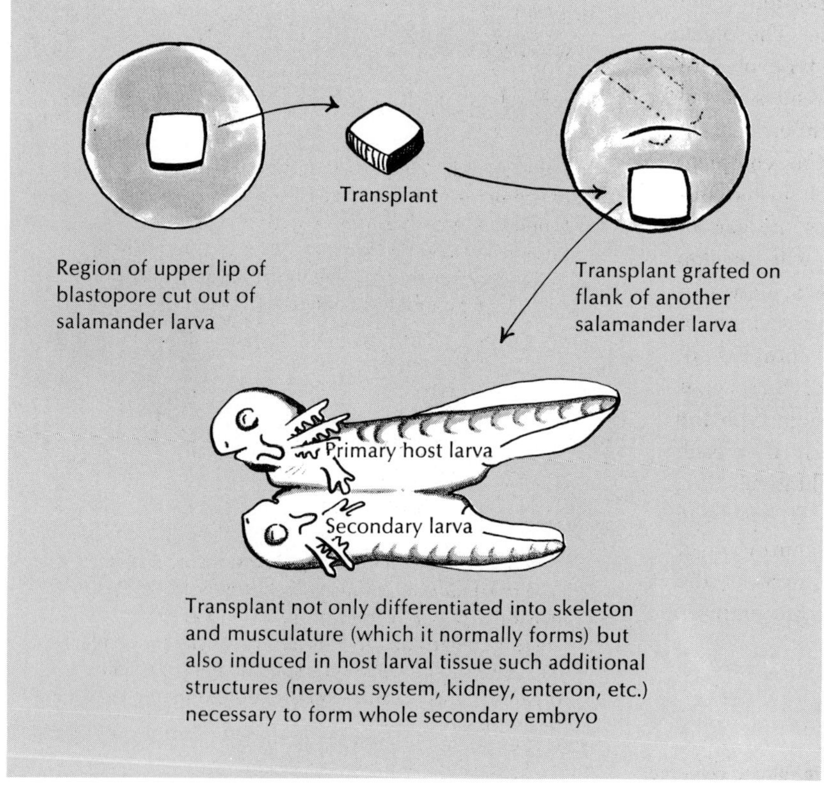

FIG. 34-15

Spemann's famous organizer experiment.

cleoproteins, steroids, various acids) will cause induction and there is some evidence to show that inductors can exert their influence on the reacting tissue at a distance by means of diffusible substances. Recently, from a region of the chick embryo spinal cord, a substance that causes cartilage to be formed in surrounding tissues has been isolated. Chemically the material may be a nucleoprotein because it contains nucleotide bases and amino acids.

SOME ASPECTS OF DIFFERENTIATION AND SPECIALIZATION*

Differentiation is determined by both external and internal factors. Most embryologists believe that internal activities exert the greater influence on morphogenesis. The belief commonly held is that the nuclei of an organism appear to be genetically uniform and that differentiation is a cytoplasmic phenomenon. According to this view the different cytoplasms can activate or inhibit the gene systems of the nuclei by chemical agents so that only certain genes can exert an influence within a particular morphogenetic field. However, in recent years there is some evidence (Briggs and King) to show that nuclei are not all the same, and their differences may play a part in determination or differentiation. These investigators found that the early cleavage nuclei were interchangeable and totipotent, but when these nuclei were transplanted from older donors, the resulting embryos showed abnormalities. There is much evidence that the developing embryo is divided into areas or morphogenetic fields that are different from each other with respect to their potencies to determine particular body structures (limbs, tail, heart, etc.) Each field has the power of self-differentiation and possesses all the requirements for specific specialization. In the early embryo, there is considerable regulative power and flexibility in the morphogenetic fields so that the organ primordia may undergo considerable alteration, such as duplication, under certain conditions. Later, the fields become rigidly fixed and lose their power of regulation. In their differentiation, cells are restricted by the potency of their particular morphogenetic field. There are no intermediate possibilities, for they must develop into bone, muscle, nerve, etc., or abnormal modifications thereof.

As a general rule, the hereditary pattern of the induced structure expresses itself in the character of the induced organ and not that of the inductor. Thus in Schotte's famous experiment in which he transplanted a small piece of flank skin of a frog embryo to the mouth region of a salamander embryo, he obtained the mouth character of a frog, although the presumptive flank skin was induced to become mouth tissue by the salamander inductor. In this case the induced cells from the frog followed their own genetic equipment. This method of differentiation is sometimes called the feedback theory because the character of the induced structure is controlled by the chemical feedback of its own genes.

Some external or environmental factors are very effective in producing cellular differentiation. Thus a single median or cyclopia eye will result when an embryo is exposed during a sensitive period to a solution of lithium salts. Another striking example is the experiment of Fell and Mallanby in which they exposed the epidermis of a chick embryo to vitamin A. Under normal conditions chick embryo epidermis forms keratinized squamous epithelium, but exposure to vitamin A converted it into ciliated, mucus-producing epithelium characteristic of the respiratory passageways. Such experiments might be explained on the basis that some cells and tissues have many synthetic codes and that certain environmental factors will activate one code and suppress others. In the vitamin A experiment it is interesting to note that the process is reversible because the ciliated, mucus-secreting epithelium is converted back into the normal squamous type when placed into a normal medium. Many such alterations do not change the essential nature of the cells but are merely modulations.

Some striking experiments of tissue synthesis from dissociated cells throw some light on the intrinsic nature of differentiation. The classic experiment of Wilson, who dissociated sponge cells by pressing live sponges through finely woven cloth and found that the cells collected together later to form complete sponges, has instigated many other similar experiments with such highly developed organisms as the amphibian, chick, and mouse embryos (Fig. 34-16). By separating with enzymes or other means the cells of a morphogenetic field, which is destined to form a specialized organ such as kidney or wing bud, it was found that these cells when cultured in a suitable medium would assemble together to form an organized organ like the original one. If cells from different organs were mixed

*Refer to Chapter 2, Principles 5 and 14.

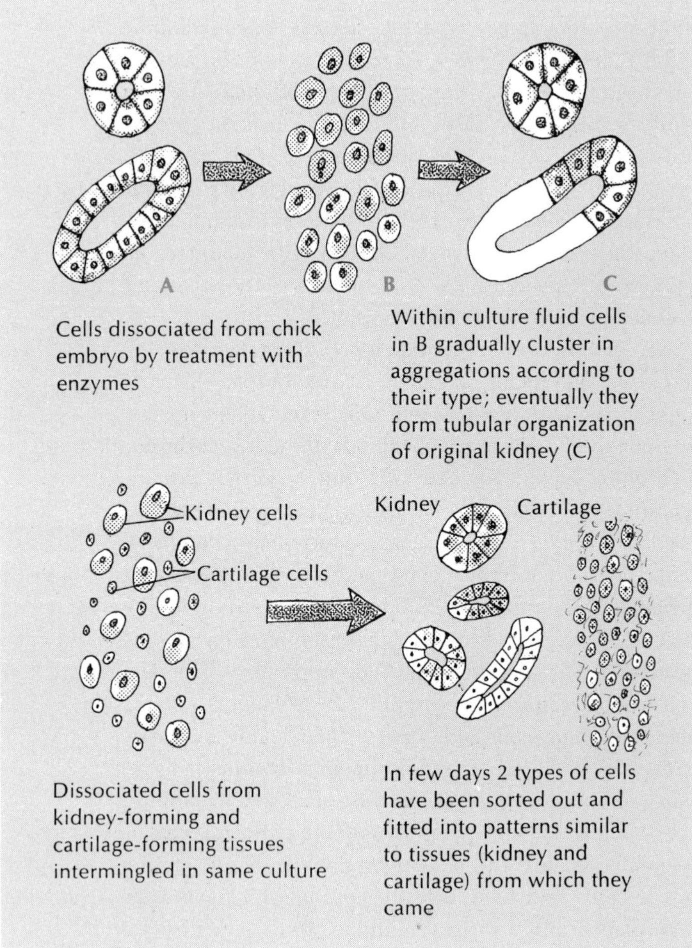

FIG. 34-16

Tissue synthesis from dissociated cells. Such experiments in time may make possible restoration of lost cells from vital organs by simple process of injecting suitable cell suspensions. Student should recall pioneer work of H. V. Wilson on regeneration of marine sponges.

together, the cells would selectively regroup themselves according to type and form the tissues from which they came, kidney cells forming kidneys, cartilage cells forming cartilage, etc. Something in the cells causes similar cells to associate together and dissimilar cells to separate.

How do the cells of a particular organ all differentiate at the same time? Some light on this problem has been thrown by recent electron microscope observations on germinal epithelium. Clusters of spermatids, for instance, are found joined together by intercellular connections or cytoplasmic bridges. These bridges are different from the connecting strands of spindle apparatus remnants in that the former contain the cytoplasmic elements of the regular cell. It is thought that this protoplasmic continuity represents open communication between the cells and is responsible for the synchronous coordination of differentiation within a particular group of spermatids. Similar bridges have been reported in clusters of cnidoblasts in the hydra.

Advances in molecular biology have also shed some light upon differentiation and development. It has long been known that certain hormones influence growth and development as well as nearly every type of physiologic function. The adenohypophysis, for instance, secretes several **tropic** hormones (thyrotropin, gonadotropin, etc.), which regulate the growth and activity of hormone-producing tissues, and **direct action hormones** (for example, somatotropin), which produce their effects without the mediation of other hormones. Somatotropin, or growth hormone, is responsible for dwarfism and gigantism. One hormone (somatotropin) may regulate the size of a tissue structure, while another (thyroxine) may stimulate the differentiation or maturation of the same tissue. Both hormones are thus necessary for a balanced development and growth. There are also other examples in which one growth-promoting hormone will produce a different effect from that of another growth-promoting hormone.

It was formerly thought that hormones produced their characteristic effects by modifying the activity of enzymes by direct interaction. The evidence now seems to indicate that hormones control gene activity, or an alteration in the amount of enzymes, rather than a direct modification of enzyme activity (see discussion of genetic code, pp. 727-731). Much of this evidence has been found in the way the action of the insect-molting and metamorphosis hormones are correlated with the "puffs" or gene activity regions, of giant chromosomes (see discussion of salivary gland chromosomes, p. 721). When a chromosome shows a "puff" or enlargement, it indicates that genes at that particular site are actively forming genetic material that will eventually lead to protein (enzyme) synthesis. It is also known that the puffing pattern of the chromosomes changes during the development and metamorphosis of the insect correlation with the action of the molting hormones. Injection of the molting hormones will also induce puffing. This theory would indicate that the specific action of a hormone would be determined by the particular genes it activates, which leads to the production of certain enzymes.

The great problem in differentiation and an understanding of the mechanism whereby it occurs involve, on the one hand, the genetic information that passes from the nucleus to the cytoplasm, and, on the other hand, the information that passes from the cytoplasm to the nucleus. Although all differentiated cells have basically the same chromosomal genetic information as coded on the DNA molecule, yet they acquire diverse biochemical properties. It may be that the quality of the information passing from the nucleus to the cytoplasm is modified during the process of differentiation. Such modified information could then determine in the cytoplasm the varied structures found in differentiated cells. But what changes the nuclear information? There must be a reciprocal action whereby the cytoplasm influences the nucleus. There are evidences to show that cytoplasm does have an effect on the nucleus. In many insect eggs, for instance, whichever nuclei migrate into a certain end of the egg become the gametes; if prevented, those nuclei, which normally migrate there to become gametes, never do so. At present it is impossible to state just what substances, or interactions, are involved in the progressive differentiation of embryonic tissues. Many biologically active substances and kinds of physical shock may induce differentiation. More and more, the nucleolus seems to be regarded as a mediator for the cytoplasm-to-nuclear differential information. Embryos lacking nucleoli often fail to differentiate. Nuclear RNA, which is mostly in the nucleolus, is regarded by some embryologists as the differential notebook of information made use of by the cell. It is generally agreed that whatever the mechanism of differentiation may be, both intrinsic and extrinsic factors are involved in the process.

REGENERATION

Problems of regeneration. One interesting aspect of experimental embryology is regeneration. Regeneration is the normal response of organisms to replace lost structures by cellular multiplication and differentiation. Most animals possess this power to a greater or lesser extent. The higher the animal in the scale of life, the more restricted this power is. Many lower forms, however, have this capacity to a marked degree. We have already seen that pieces of the flatworm *Planaria* are each able to produce complete flatworms. In higher forms the capacity for regeneration is shown by the formation of new tissue during wound healing. But there are many other examples in the body, for cells of various tissues, such as blood and skin, are being lost and replaced all the time.

All animals are in a stage of dynamic equilibrium throughout their life span. The chief difference between the lower and higher organisms in this respect is that the former retain more of the embryonic organization in their adult stages. This ability is extremely marked in the flatworms and coelenterates but is lessened in vertebrates. Vertebrates themselves show remarkable variations in regeneration. For instance, if the limb of a young salamander is amputated, a new limb will grow out from the cut stump in the course of a few weeks. This replacement will also include everything that was lost. Where a frog's limb is cut off, the skin heals over the cut stump without regeneration of the lost part. If all the skeletal parts of a salamander's limb are removed, but leaving all the other muscles, connective tissues, nerves, blood vessels, etc., in place, a normal limb will regenerate, with all the missing bones replaced in normal position. When the limb of a larval salamander is amputated, at the end of the cut stump, a region of small cells called **blastema** is formed. This blastema is apparently formed from dedifferentiated cells from skin, muscle, and bone that are found in that region. When the blastema has assumed a certain size, it begins the differentiation of the various tissues that go to make up the limb.

In these cases of regeneration the presence of nerves seems to be indispensable for the regeneration processes. If the nerves that supply a limb are cut before amputation, no regeneration will occur. In addition, when the nerve supply is lacking, complete regression of the limb will take place and it is resorbed so that no blastema is formed. If a blastema is allowed to form before the nerves are cut, regeneration will continue and a new limb is formed. Here the blastema is the controlling factor and no nervous control is necessary. If nerves are allowed to grow back into the limb during the period of degeneration, growth and differentiation will be resumed, which again shows the influence of nervous control.

Recent work indicates that the capacity of a limb to regenerate depends on the number of nerve fibers that run to it. If the number of nerves running to the limb of a salamander is reduced artificially, there will be no regeneration. In adult frogs it has been possible by operation to shift to an amputated forelimb the peripheral end of the sciatic nerve and its branches that run to the hind limb, thereby increasing the number of nerves in the forelimb. In such a case the amputated frog forelimb will regenerate. This experiment might indicate that regeneration of limbs in higher forms is lost because their nerve supplies are inadequate and that a certain minimum number is required for regeneration. This principle of regeneration presents a striking contrast to embryonic development, in which the evidence indicates that nervous innervation plays little or no role in the differentiation of organs. When nerves are prevented from entering the limb buds of amphibian and chick embryos, the buds differentiate into limbs in a normal manner.

When a frog's limb is cut off, the wound normally heals over without the formation of a blastema and consequently there is no regeneration. If the wound is prevented from healing by the application of a salt solution, a blastema is formed at the cut surface and a completely new limb will form. In a salamander, if the whole skin is pulled over the cut surface of the amputated stump, no regeneration occurs because apparently the presence of the skin blocks the formation of the blastema. The salt solution in the case of the frog limb prevents the migration of the skin over the wound surface so that a blastema has a chance to perform. These results would indicate that the power of regeneration of lost parts, apparently absent in some animals, is actually present but is halted by normal healing.

One aspect of regeneration that has received considerable attention is that of **axial gradients.** According to this theory, there is a metabolic differential from the head to the tail region. The head has the higher metabolic rate and more or less dominates the rest of the body, where the metabolic rate is lower. These gradients have thrown some interesting light upon regeneration, for the higher the metabolic rate, the more sensitive that region is to poisons. Abnormalities may be induced more easily in the head region than in posterior regions. Where they are located in the gradient determines the fate of the embryonic cells to a great extent. Gradients also help to explain how environmental conditions influence the development of organisms.

GROWTH*

Biologic growth is a complex physiologic process. It is a fundamental characteristic of protoplasmic systems and expresses itself in a hereditary pattern more or less specific for each kind of animal. It is not easy to define growth, for a mere increase in size may not be true growth. The accumulation of excess fat is not considered growth, since such a condition may be temporary. True growth involves a permanent increase in volume, especially during the stages of the development. Growth is mainly a synthesis of protein substances throughout the cell, a process known as an **intussusception.** This process can take place only when the cells are supplied with materials beyond their needs of metabolism. Anything additional can thus be used to construct new molecules. During the developmental period of the life cycle, both increase in cell numbers and increase in cell size play a part in growth.

Growth is not necessarily restricted to protoplasmic increase, however, because it is possible to have growth by the differentiation of nonliving substances, such as the extracellular fibers in connective tissue. In bone, for instance, there are many nonliving materials outside the bone-forming cells that are relatively undifferentiated. But cells can undergo differentiation within themselves, such as those of muscle and nerve and the more they are differentiated, the more they lose the capacity for growth. This may be one of the reasons why undifferentiated primitive tissues, connective and epithelial, are affected with abnormal growths (cancer) and why the differentiated muscle and nerve cells are free from them.

As complex animals get older, the growth rate slows down and may finally cease altogether. Growth curves have been worked out for many organisms. This may be done in various ways, but one common method is to plot weight against time. Many factors influence these curves. If animals are well nourished and develop under ideal conditions, the growth curve rises steeply almost in a straight line, but organisms developing under poor environmental conditions will give growth curves more or less S shaped (Fig. 34-17). What causes growth to decrease as the animal grows older? One reason is that more and more of the body becomes differentiated into nonliving substance such as fibers, sheaths, and mineral deposits, which do not grow. Another reason is that when cells become highly specialized, they cease to grow. The animal tends to reach

*Refer to Chapter 2, Principles 14 and 15.

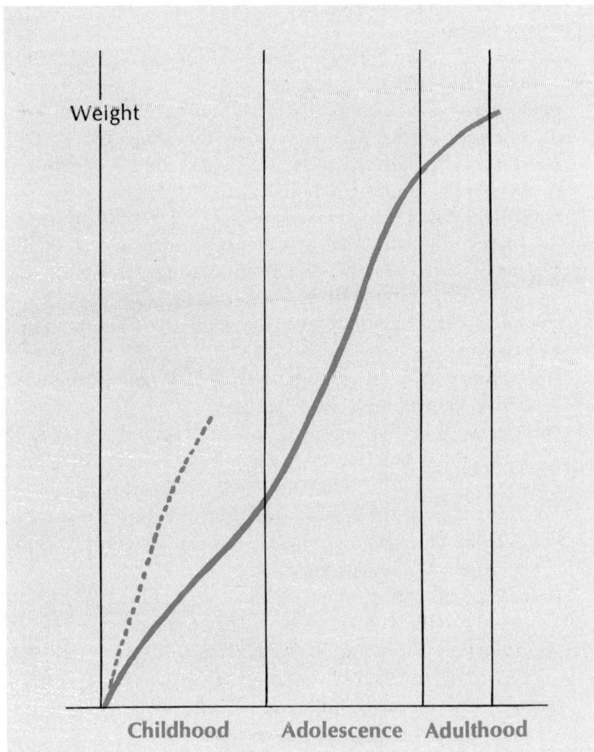

FIG. 34-17

Growth curve. Under ideal conditions, curve will follow dotted line.

a condition of adult stability or equilibrium. In aging, the body tissues may actually shrink (negative growth). These changes will all be expressed in the growth curve.

Terrestrial animals are more restricted in their growth than are aquatic forms. With most land forms, growth largely ceases when adulthood is reached, although reptiles and a few others will continue to grow. The reason for this is that increased body weight of a terrestrial form in an air medium necessitates greater adjustments to new environmental conditions, such as gravity forces, than those that are more or less of a constant mean size. With aquatic animals, a heavy weight receives support from the buoyant action of a water medium. The largest animal, the whale, is an aquatic form. Growth in many aquatic forms continues indefinitely, although at a decreasing rate that never quite reaches zero.

During the life history of all animals the change in form is caused by a differential growth of their various body parts. Some organs grow faster and some slower than the body as a whole. Differential growth rates of such organs alter the form of the body. Organs that grow at the same rate as the mean growth rate of the body have **isometric** growth; if they grow at a different rate from that of the body, they have **allometric** growth. If allometric growth is greater than the mean growth of the body, it is positive; if less, negative. Allometric growth is more pronounced in the developmental stages of an animal than in the adult stages. In sexual differentiation, for example, secondary or other sex characters in the young or juveniles may be about the same in both sexes. But allometric growth of these characters produces a male or a female at maturity, with marked differences in the size (and functions) of the distinguishing sex characters.

AGING AND DEATH

Aging and death are the terminal stages of the life cycle. Aging refers to the decline that occurs after the organism has reached the peak of its activity. This period naturally varies with different kinds of animals and also with different individuals. Animals with a short life span will be undergoing the aging process, while animals that live longer are still in the flush of activity. Likewise, the decline shows a great variation among individuals of the same species. Some men are as old at 50 years of age as others are at 70. The problem of aging has been studied in many animals with emphasis upon what occurs in individual cells and tissues of the organism as it declines. Do all animals exhibit aging? Professor Woodruff of Yale University carried one strain of paramecia through thousands of generations from 1907 to 1943 and found that they could multiply indefinitely by fission alone without conjugation and showed no evidence of decline. He found, however, that nuclear reorganization did occur periodically in these protozoans. Other strains of protozoans, however, do exhibit changes of senescence and old age. Among the metazoans, practically all forms studied have shown some signs of aging. Both anatomic and physiologic changes occur, but not all organs and tissues show equal degrees of decline. Degenerative changes in the heart and vascular system are important because of their effect on the life span.

The problem of old age has a practical importance in human populations as an increasing proportion of our population reaches old age. Many studies recently published indicate a great interest in the science of aging, or **geriatrics.**

Death may be considered the terminal sequence of the degenerative changes of old age. Death of the organism involves the death of cells, but not all of the cells die at once. Many cells of the body continue to live after the animal has been pronounced dead by certain conventional signs we associate with death. Among protozoans that reproduce by fission, death in the ordinary sense does not occur, since the body is shared by the daughter cells resulting from the division. Life spans are usually considered more or less definite for most species of animals, but it is very difficult to state with accuracy just how long these life spans are. Even in the case of man, whose life span is better known than that of any other animal, only general averages can be given. The average life expectancy has increased in man from about 50 years to around 70 years in the past half century (in the United States [1967] females, 73.8 years; males, 66.7 years) and further increases are expected under better medical and hygienic conditions. However, there is little indication that the upper limit of the life span of man has increased. So many factors influence the span in all animals that exact figures cannot be given in most cases. Natural death resulting from the degenerative changes of aging rarely occurs in animals other than man, for the debility produced by senescence makes them an easy prey for their enemies. Death, however, considered from any standpoint is a definite part of the hereditary pattern of animals. Specifically, death from whatever cause is due to the failure of one of the following: heart, blood, or nervous system. Death must occur whenever the vascular system fails to deliver oxygen, vitamins, hormones, and other vital substances. Failure of the nervous system may affect vital centers and quickly result in death.

Derivation and meaning of basic terminology

allantois (Gr. *allas,* sausage, + *eidos,* resemblance). Saclike outgrowth from embryonic gut of amniotes for respiration and excretion.

allometry (Gr. *allos,* other, + *metron,* measure). A study of relative growth or a change in proportion with increase in size.

amnion (Gr. *amnion,* bowl for sacrificial blood). Inner embryonic sac of amniotes.

anlage (Gr. *anlage,* foundation). Primordium.

archenteron (Gr. *arch,* primitive, + *enteron,* intestine). Primitive gut of gastrula stage and later becomes the digestive tract.

blastocoel (Gr. *blastos,* germ, + *koilos,* hollow). Cavity of blastula.

blastomere (Gr. *blastos,* germ, + *meros,* part). Early cleavage cells.

blastopore (Gr. *blastos,* germ, + *porus,* pore). External opening of the archenteron in the gastrula.

blastula (Gr. *blastos,* germ, + L. *ula,* dim.). Early embryologic stage of a hollow mass of cells.

centrolecithal (Gr. *kentron,* center, + *lekithos,* yolk). Insect egg with the yolk concentrated in the center.

chorion (Gr. *chorion,* membrane). Outer embryonic membrane in amniotes.

cleavage (OE. *cleofan,* to cut). Cell division in animal ovum.

embryology (Gr. *embryon,* embryo, + *logos,* science). Early development of organisms.

epigenesis (Gr. *epi,* upon, + *genesis,* origin). Theory of lack of organization of the zygote.

gastrula (Gr. *gaster,* stomach, + L. *ula,* dim.). Embryonic stage of double-layered cup.

holoblastic (Gr. *holos,* whole, + *blastos,* germ). Equal division of cleavage cells.

isolecithal (Gr. *isos,* equal, + *lekithos,* yolk). Zygote (or ovum) with yolk evenly distributed.

meroblastic (Gr. *meros,* part, + *blastos,* germ). Cleavage restricted to the blastoderm.

morula (L. *morus,* mulberry, + *ula,* dim.). Group of cells in early stage of segmentation.

placenta (Gr. *plakous,* flat cake). Vascular structure by which fetus is nourished.

telolecithal (Gr. *telos,* end, + *lekithos,* yolk). Yolk concentrated at one end of egg.

umbilical (L. *umbilicus,* navel). Refers to the umbilical, or navel, cord.

zygote (Gr. *zygotos,* yoked). The fertilized egg.

Annotated references

Abercrombie, M., and J. Brachet (editors). 1961. Advances in morphogenesis, vols. 1 and 2. New York, Academic Press, Inc. *An advance treatise on the integration of the many problems in this complicated field.*

Bonner, J. T. 1958. The evolution of development. New York, Cambridge University Press. *An evolutionary approach to development and how it helps explain the mechanisms of the developmental process.*

Ephrussi, B., and M. C. Weiss. 1969. Hybrid somatic cells. Sci. Amer. **220**:26-35 (April). *In cultures to fuse a cell, in which a particular enzyme is suppressed, with another type of cell that produces this enzyme affords a mechanism for determining the site of enzymatic regulation.*

Gilbert, M. S. 1939. Biography of the unborn. Baltimore, The Williams & Wilkins Co. *A brief yet fascinating summary of the main events in elementary human embryology. Can be read by all beginning biology students with profit.*

Gurdon, J. B. 1968. Transplanted nuclei and cell differentiation. Sci. Amer. **219**:24-35 (Dec.). *An extension* *of the work first successfully done by R. W. Briggs and T. J. King.*

Hadorn, E. 1968. Transdetermination of cells. Sci. Amer. **219**:110 120 (Nov.). *How cells of a fruit fly larva can change their predestined fate by being transplanted into an adult fly.*

Hayflick, L. 1968. Human cells and aging. Sci. Amer. **218**:32-37 (March). *Barring all disease agencies, many factors (aberrations of chromosomes, limitation of cell divisions, cell loss, loss of functional units, etc.) set a definite limit to the life span. The average life expectancy may allow more people to reach the upper limits of life, but does not prevent a finite life time of normal cells.*

McElroy, W. D., and H. B. Glass. 1958. A symposium on the chemical basis of development. Baltimore, The Johns Hopkins Press. *This work is based on a symposium held in 1958 and attempts to throw some light on growth and differentiation—one of the most difficult problems in biology.*

Nelsen, O. E. 1953. Comparative embryology of the vertebrates. New York, The Blakiston Co. *This treatise is a comprehensive study of the comparative morphology of the vertebrates and protochordates.*

Spemann, H. 1938. Embryonic development and induction. New Haven, Conn., Yale University Press. *An authoritative work by a pioneer in this aspect of embryology. Suitable for the advanced student.*

Spratt, N. T., Jr. 1964. Introduction to cell differentiation. New York. Reinhold Publishing Corp. *The problem of cell differentiation is one of the most difficult in biology, and in this concise account the author has described some of the methods of attack in trying to solve its problems.*

Thornton, C. S. (editor). 1959. Regeneration in vertebrates. Chicago, University of Chicago Press.

Waddington, C. H. 1962. New patterns in genetics and development. New York, Columbia University Press. *The author analyzes many of the difficult problems concerned with the nature and structural organization at the molecular level as well as at higher levels.*

Watterson, R. L. (editor). 1959. Endocrines in development. Chicago, University of Chicago Press. *A symposium on the influence of hormones on growth and development.*

CHAPTER 35

• PRINCIPLES OF INHERITANCE

MEANING OF HEREDITY*

● It was recognized long ago that heredity was one of the great stabilizing agencies in nature. Despite dissimilarities between offspring and parents in a particular generation, there was a sameness that ran from generation to generation through the same type of plant or animal. But variations appeared, and some were inherited and others disappeared with the generation in which they arose. The real causes behind these variations were of course unknown until the laws of genetics were worked out. These inherited characteristics, which may be like or unlike those of the parents, we now know to be due to the segregation of hereditary factors, and those that are not inherited, to be caused by environmental conditions.

Children are not duplicates of their parents. Some of their characteristics show resemblances to one or both parents, but they also demonstrate many not found in either parent. What is actually inherited by an offspring from its parents is a certain type of germinal organization (**genes**) that, under the influence of environmental factors, differentiates into the physical characteristics as we see them. Although development is orderly and progressive, many unpredictable environmental factors can alter the general outcome. The mechanism for the orderly distribution of the germinal substance through individual development and successive generations is now well known. We know, too, that heredity can be changed by altering the germ cells, either by changing the genetic constitution or by rearranging chromosome organization.

The inheritance of any characteristic depends on the interaction of many genes. This interaction is often complex, although the individual genes may behave as though they are independent of one another. There is a germinal basis for every characteristic that appears in the development of the organism, such as stature, color of eyes and hair, and intellectual capacity. The germinal organization sets the potential bounds of these and all other characteristics, but environmental factors of food, disease, etc., may greatly affect the physical expression of the characteristics so that their potentialities are never fully realized.

The pattern of heredity naturally depends on whether reproduction is unisexual or bisexual. In a unisexual organism, only one parent is involved, as in binary fission or sporulation. Unless there is mutation or other genetic variation, the offspring and parent are genetically alike. But in bisexual reproduction, two sets of genes are pooled together in the zygote, and the offspring shares genetic potentialities of both parents and can produce combinations of traits unlike either parent. Mutation also may play a part here in the alteration of genes.

CYTOLOGIC BACKGROUND OF HEREDITY

Heredity is a protoplasmic continuity between parents and offspring. In bisexual animals the gametes are responsible for establishing this continuity. Certain parts of the cell must represent the physical basis for inheritance. The basic laws of genetics were first worked out without much understanding of the physical mechanism that formed the real explanation of the whole process. Experiments and observations were made from visible traits. There could be no real scientific explanation of genetic principles until a study had been made of the germ cells and their behavior. This was really a case of working backward from certain visible results of inheritance to the mechanism responsible for such results. Considerable progress had already been made in cytology, or the science of cells, particularly germ cells, by the time the chief laws of genetics were announced. The nuclei of sex cells were early suspected of furnishing the real answer to the mechanism. This applied especially to certain constituents of the nuclei,

*Refer to Chapter 2, Principles 3 and 27.

the chromosomes, for they appeared to be the only entities passed on in equal quantities from parents to offspring.

When the rediscovery of Mendel's laws was announced in 1900 (a date that may be considered the beginning of modern genetics), the time was ripe to demonstrate the parallelism that existed between these fundamental laws of inheritance and the cytologic behavior of the chromosomes. In a series of brilliant experiments by Boveri, Sutton, McClung, and Wilson, the mechanism of heredity was definitely assigned to the chromosomes. Since that time, geneticists have been busy establishing the chromosome theory of heredity. The next problem was to find how chromosomes affected the hereditary pattern. This study led to an analysis of the chromosome structure and the idea of the gene as the physical basis of hereditary traits. The outstanding work of Thomas Hunt Morgan and his colleagues on the fruit fly (*Drosophila*) led to the mapping of chromosomes in which the location of genes was more or less definitely determined. Out of all this work there developed a new science, that of **cytogenetics.** In recent years the chromosome has been studied with renewed interest, as new techniques developed, with the main objective of finding and demonstrating the actual physical units or genes and their nature.

Nature of chromosomes

The important role played by chromosomes in heredity and development, their individualized structure, and the precision with which they are distributed at mitosis have made them of primary interest ever since cells were studied in detail. Every aspect of their physicochemical makeup is being closely scrutinized. Perhaps more has been learned about them in the past two decades than in all previous times, partly because of better techniques and partly because of more intensive study.

Chromosomes differ a great deal among the different organisms, although for a particular form they have in general a definite size and shape in each stage of their cycle (Figs. 35-1 and 35-2). Fixatives may alter them to some extent, and in certain stages of mitosis they are more clearly seen than in others. In the metaphase and anaphase stages their general morphology shows up most distinctly, whereas in other stages they appear as fine chromatin threads. Whatever their appearance, they are distinct structural entities and retain their individuality throughout all stages of the cell cycle. Each chromosome is made up of a central, spiral thread called a **chromonema** that bears beadlike enlargements, the **chromomeres.** The chromomeres were first thought to be identical with the **genes,** the chief hereditary factors, but many cytologists have more recently adopted the view that a chromomere may contain more than one gene, and some genes apparently are not

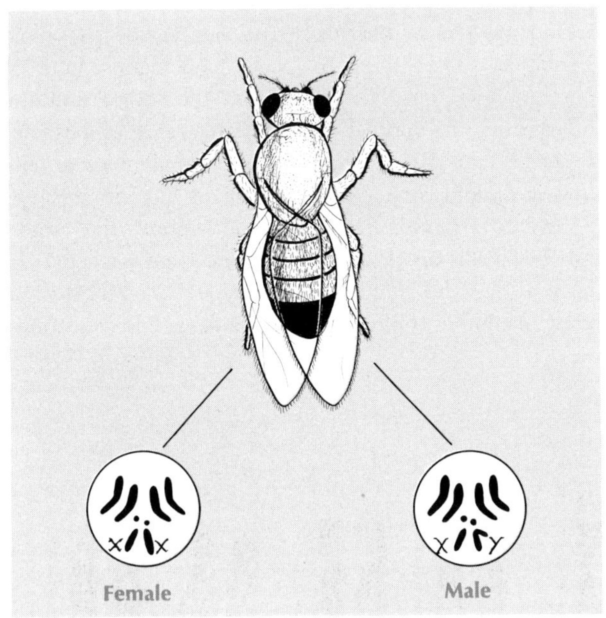

FIG. 35-1

Fruit fly (*Drosophila melanogaster)* and diploid set of chromosomes of each sex. Sex chromosomes X and Y are marked. Males have three black bands on abdomen, which is rounded at tip; females have five black bands, with pointed abdomen. Many genetic concepts have been developed from extensive investigations on this now classic animal.

FIG. 35-2

Diploid chromosomes of *Drosophila*.

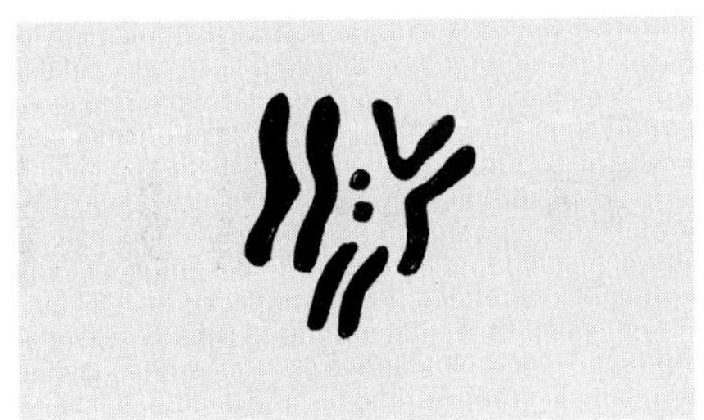

associated with chromomeres at all. The various chromomeres appear in regular and constant patterns in a particular chromosome.

Chromosomes constant for a species

Each somatic cell in a given organism contains the same number of chromosomes. Somatic chromosomes of diploid organisms are found in pairs, the members of each pair being alike in size, in position of spindle attachment, and in bearing genes relating to the same hereditary characters. In each homologous pair of chromosomes, one has come from the father and the other from the mother. The number of chromosomes found in the various species of animals varies. The lowest diploid number in the cell of any organism is 2, which is found in certain roundworms; the largest number (300 or more) is found in some protozoa. In most forms the number is between 12 and 40, the most common diploid number being 24. Naturally, many forms wholly unrelated have the same number of chromosomes and so the number is without significance because the nature of the genes is what differentiates different species of animals. In man the number is 46. Some chromosomes are as small as 0.25 μ in length and (with the exception of salivary chromosomes) some are as long as 50 μ. Within the haploid set of chromosomes of most species there are considerable differences in size and shape. In man, most chromosomes are 4 to 6 μ in length.

Mature germ cells have only one half as many chromosomes as somatic cells. Only one member of each homologous pair of chromosomes is found in a mature, functional gamete.

Chromosomes of man

The chromosomes of man have always presented many problems of analysis because the number is large and they are normally crowded close together on the spindle. Until 1956 their diploid number was supposed to be 48. Newer and improved techniques now employ cultures of white blood corpuscles that are induced to

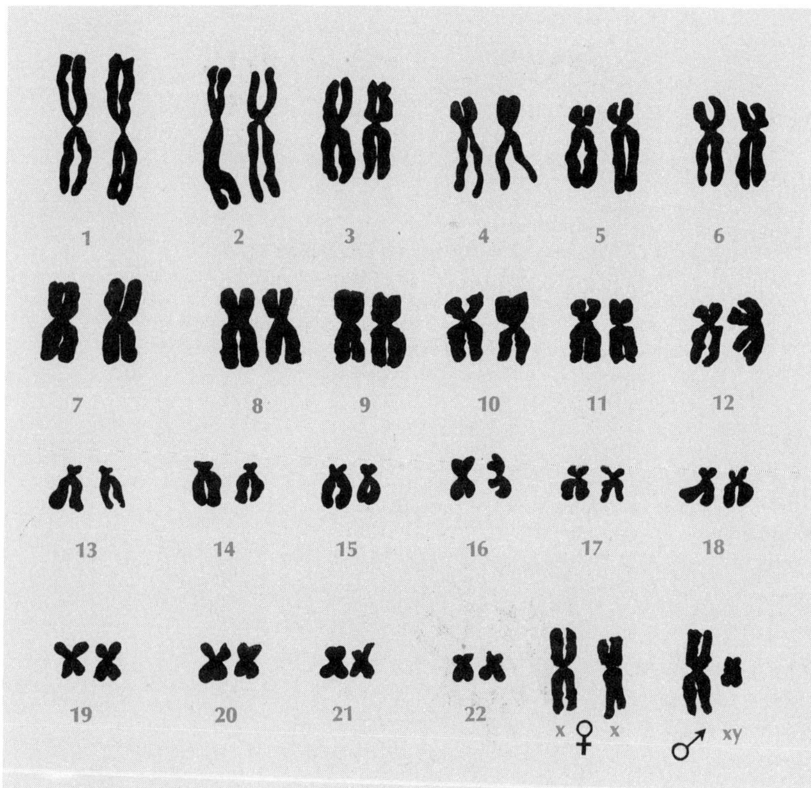

FIG. 35-3

Human chromosomes showing both male and female sex chromosomes. Diploid number is 46. Chromosomes are arranged according to standard pattern (karyotype) of homologous pairs. Chromosomes differ in size, shape, and position of centromeres; arrangement is based on these characteristics, two members of homologous pair (one from each parent) being identical except in case of XY sex chromosomes. Techniques for preparation of human cells for chromosome counting are based upon tissue cultures, biopsy material, and bone marrow studies. Procedures involve tissue exposure to trypsin and special growth media. During part of culture period, colchicine (which arrests cell division at metaphase) is added, and treatment with hypotonic salt solution swells and disperses chromosomes. Squash preparations are usually stained with acetocarmine or Feulgen reagent.
(Modified from several sources.)

divide by phytohemagglutinin (an extract of red kidney beans). Other tissue cells such as bone marrow have also been used. With colchicine for arresting mitosis in the metaphase stage and hypotonic solutions and centrifugation for dispersing the chromosomes, it has been possible to arrive at an accurate count of 46 chromosomes (Fig. 35-3). A standard arrangement of the chromosomes according to size and position of centromeres has been adopted. In the somatic cell, such as the white blood corpuscles, there is a pair of each type of chromosome, including 2 X chromosomes (female) and a pair of each type, with the exception of the X and Y chromosomes in the male. The Y chromosome is one of the smallest chromosomes, although there are some autosomes almost as small.

Significance of reduction division

In each body or somatic cell there is a pair of genes (except sex-linked genes) for each trait, one gene from each parent. Since these genes are in paired, homologous chromosomes, when these chromosomes separate at the reduction division of meiosis, the homologous genes must also separate, one gene going to each of the germ cells produced. Thus at the end of the maturation process each mature gamete (egg or sperm) contains one gene of every pair or a single set of every kind of gene instead of two genes for each character as in somatic cells. The haploid number of chromosomes found in the germ cells does not consist of just any half of the diploid somatic number but must include one of the members of each homologous pair of chromosomes. A particular germ cell does not necessarily contain all the chromosomes from one or the other parent of the individual producing that germ cell. It is a matter of chance in the reduction division whether the paternal chromosome of a homologous pair goes to one daughter cell or the other, and the same is true of the maternal chromosome.

The real significance of the reduction division for explaining the principles of heredity lies mainly in the segregation of the chromosomes and consequently the genes that the chromosomes carry. We have seen that there are two genes for each trait that develops in the individual, but in the mature germ cells there is only one gene for a trait. Of course, when the zygote is formed at fertilization, the homologous pairs of chromosomes (and genes) will be restored. It will be seen later that the factors of the genetic laws behave in a similar manner and were arrived at before the cytologic explanation was forthcoming.

Salivary gland chromosomes

Details about the structure of chromosomes have been difficult to obtain because of their small size in most animals. Since most chromosomes are only a few microns in length, and each one bears many genes, little hope was held for discovering the real nature of the physical units of heredity. About 1934 Professor Painter of the University of Texas and some German investigators independently discovered in the salivary glands of the larvae of *Drosophila* and other flies chromosomes many times as large as those of the ordinary somatic or germinal chromosomes of these forms. Actually, these giant chromosomes had been discovered

FIG. 35-4

Chromosomes from salivary gland of larval fruit fly *Drosophila*. These are among largest chromosomes found in animal cells. Bands of nucleoproteins may be loci of genes. Such chromosomes are sometimes called polytene because they appear to be made up of many chromonemata. These chromosomes are not confined to salivary glands but are also known to occur in other organs, such as gut and malpighian tubules of most dipteran insects. Technique for their study is simply to crush salivary glands between cover glass and slide in drop of acetocarmine so that chromosomes are set free from nuclei and are spread out as shown in photograph. (Courtesy General Biological Supply House, Inc., Chicago.)

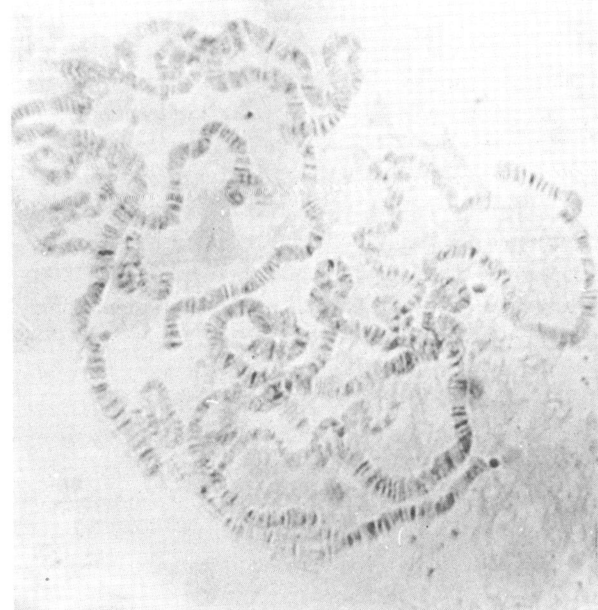

as early as 1881 by the Italian cytologist Balbiani in the larval forms of the midge fly *Chironomus*, but their real meaning was not detected until they were rediscovered. Their rediscovery marked a new era in the development of cytogenetics, for they afforded much new information about the structure and nature of chromosomes.

The salivary glands of the larval flies are a pair of club-shaped bodies attached to the pharynx and each is made up of about 100 cells. Salivary tissue grows by an increase in cell size and not by an increase in cell number. Each gland has attached to it a fat body that helps identify the gland. When the glands are stained with acetocarmine, the chromosomes can be seen more or less coiled up within the cells. When the cell membrane is disintegrated, the chromosomes are scattered out and can be easily studied. The giant chromosomes are elongated, ribbonlike bodies about 100 to 200 times longer than the ordinary chromosome (Fig. 35-4). In some flies they lie separated from each other; in *Drosophila* they are attached to a dark mass called the **chromocenter.**

What are these chromosomes and what do they show? The chromosomes are really somatic prophase chromosomes with the homologous chromosomes closely paired throughout their length. Such a pairing of somatic chromosomes is unusual, for such a feature is commonly restricted to meiosis. In favorable preparations these double chromosomes appear as six single strands instead of four because two pairs are attached to the chromocenter by their centers, thus producing four arms, and the other two pairs are connected to the chromocenter by their ends. One of their most striking characteristics is the transverse bands with which they are made. Another feature is the number of chromonemata they possess. In the ordinary somatic chromosome there may be only one or two of these gene strings, but in the salivary gland chromosomes there may be between 512 and 1,024 (*Drosophila*). This indicates that the chromonemata may have divided many times without being accompanied by the division of the whole chromosome; hence, they are often called **polytene** chromosomes. A polytene chromosome may be considered a typical mitotic chromosome that has uncoiled and undergone many repeated duplications that have remained together in the same nucleus.

The transverse bands appear to be made up of chromatic granules, the chromomeres. These bands result from the lateral apposition of the chromomeres on the adjacent fibrils or chromonemata. More than 6,000 of these bands have been found on the three large chromosomes of *Drosophila*. Of great genetic significance is the fact that the bands form a pattern that is constant for a given chromosome and that the bands

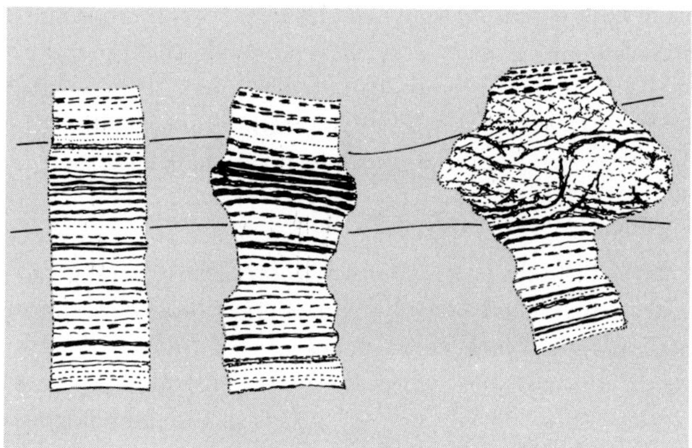

FIG. 35-5

Puffing in one of the bands of a salivary gland chromosome of a midge larva *(Chironomus)*. Swelling, or puff, indicates activity in a region where protein and RNA (and perhaps some DNA) are being produced, and may include single bands or adjacent ones. Puffs always include same bands that occur in a definite sequence during development of larva. (From several sources.)

FIG. 35-6

Small portion of a lampbrush chromosome showing two pairs of loops. These chromosomes are found in germinal vesicles (nuclei) of oocytes during diplotene phase of first meiotic division and may indicate synthesis of yolk. They appear to be largest in certain salamanders. Loops represent lateral extensions of chromatids, or half chromosomes. RNA is being transcribed along loop and (with protein formed there) gives a fuzzy appearance to loop. Central axis with closely coiled chromomeres is made up of DNA. Exact relation of loop to gene is not yet known. (Modified from J. G. Gall, 1956.)

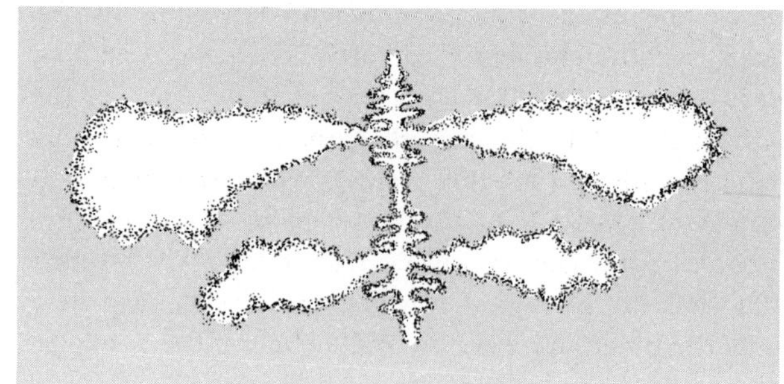

in one chromosome are identical with those in the homologous mate. On the basis of differences in the bands, it is possible to make out different regions of the various chromosomes and to assign the basis of certain characters to particular regions of the chromosomes. In this way it has been possible to construct chromosome maps.

The bands contain much DNA and each may be considered the equivalent of the conceptual gene. In the regions between the bands there is little DNA. Another aspect of giant chromosomes is the so-called "puffs" that are local and reversible enlargements in the bands (Fig. 35-5). Each "puff" may be due to the unfolding or uncoiling of the chromosomes in a band. The pattern of puffing may vary with different tissues and with different locations on the same chromosome. Its size may be large (Balbiani's rings) or small. In addition to the DNA of the band, the puff contains a great deal of RNA. The size of the puff is an indication of gene activity and the rate of RNA synthesis. Evidence seems to indicate that messenger RNA is produced at the puff, where it makes a complementary copy of a DNA strand. The RNA messenger is then carried to the ribosome, where it serves for the synthesis of proteins. (See discussion of genetic code, pp. 727-731.)

The even larger lampbrush chromosomes found in the oocytes of many vertebrates and some invertebrates are characterized by loops extending laterally that give them the appearance of a brush (Fig. 35-6). These chromosomes each appear to be composed of two chromatids that form loops (gene loci) when they are active but are coiled up within a chromomere when at rest. Both salivary and lampbrush chromosomes may shed more light on the genetic relations of genes in the course of future investigations.

GENE THEORY

The term **gene** was given by Johannsen in 1909 to the hereditary factors of Mendel (1865). Genes represent the material bases or chemical entities that are responsible for the hereditary pattern of an organism. No one perhaps has seen a definite gene and much is yet to be discovered about the nature of genes; yet by much investigation, direct and indirect, a great deal has been learned about them. It is known that they belong to chromosomes and go wherever chromosomes go. By long, patient genetic experiments, their relative positions (loci) on the chromosomes have been mapped in many cases. Evidence indicates that they are arranged in linear order on the chromosome-like beads on a string and in some cases (salivary gland chromosomes) are assigned to definite bands. Since chromosomes are few and genes are many in number, each chromosome must contain many genes (linkage group). It is not known how many genes there are in an organism. Estimates of 10,000 (*Drosophila*) to 90,000 (man) have been made.

Each zygote of sexual reproduction has two sets (diploid) of homologous chromosomes, one set from each parent; in other words, there are two of each kind of chromosomes, one from the father and the other from the mother. When the gametes are formed in meiosis, disjunction of the homologous chromosomes occurs so that each germ cell receives one or the other of the pair at random. Since the genes are a part of the chromosomes, their distribution will parallel that of the chromosomes. All the genes of a particular homologous chromosome, or **linkage group,** will go at meiosis into one gamete and all the genes of the other homologous mate will go into another gamete. If each gene occupies a specific locus in a specific chromosome, all the genes occupying this locus in a given pair of homologous chromosomes are called **alleles.** Just as members of a homologous pair of chromosomes are derived from separate parents, so does each member of a pair of alleles come from a different parent. In some cases a set of alleles may contain more than two members (maybe as many as 20) and such sets are called multiple alleles. But, normally, only two alleles for any one hereditary character may occur in a somatic cell and only one in a gamete.

The two members of a homologous pair of chromosomes often exchange corresponding segments or blocks of genes. This is called **crossing-over.** There is visible evidence of this physical exchange, for at the beginning of the first meiotic division the two members of each pair of chromosomes come into side-by-side contact (synapsis) and become twisted. When they separate they have exchanged parts. Naturally, the genes on the traded portions will be exchanged also. The new combinations so found are as stable as the original ones. Linkage groups are also altered by such rearrangements as the linear reversal of gene sequence in the **reversal of a chromosome segment,** by the shifting of a chromosome segment to another part of the same chromosome (**translocation**), by **polyploid changes** in chromosome number, etc.

Although genes can reproduce themselves exactly for many generations, they do occasionally undergo abrupt changes called **mutations.** A mutation involves a change in the chemical arrangement of a gene so that there is a difference in the structure and action of a gene that may result in a new character. In such cases the mutant gene now faithfully reproduces itself just as before. The natural mutation rate, which varies with different animals, is slow but can be speeded up artificially by agents such as radiation, which is cumulative in its effect, by temperature, by certain chemicals, and by other environmental agents. Mutations are called **random** because they are unpredictable and because they are unrelated to the needs of the organism, but some mutations are favored by tissue and environmental conditions. Many mutant genes are actually harmful because they may replace adaptive genes that have evolved in the long evolution of the organism. However, a minority of mutant genes are advantageous and have great significance in evolution. Some mutant genes are dominant genetically, but more are recessive and their effects are masked by normal dominant alleles. Mutation may be a reversible process, and the difference between the mutation of a gene in one direction and its mutation rate in the reverse direction is called its **mutation pressure.** Such reverse mutations indicate that true mutations are not gene losses. Gene mutations may occur in one direction more frequently than in others, and thus certain mutant alleles are far more common than others. Most mutations ordinarily occur in one gene at a time and thus are called **point mutations.** In the long evolution of any organism, all the genes it carries have had time to mutate and all its present genes are really mutants.

There is some evidence that some genetic variability is the result of self-duplicating, hereditary units in the cytoplasm. Such units are called **plasmagenes** and are apparently transmitted only by the cytoplasm. Two examples of this type of cytoplasmic inheritance are plant plastids and the "kappa" (killer) substances of *Paramecium.* In some cases the plasmagenes depend on the nuclear genes for their reproduction and maintenance. Plasmagenes can mutate and produce definite characters. They also have mendelian patterns of genetic behavior, but some are distributed more or less at random to daughter cells at cell division. Their exact role in the overall hereditary pattern of organisms is still obscure.

Genes perform a unique role in cellular economy. As the chief functional unit of genetic material, they determine the basic architecture of every cell, the nature and life of the cell, the specific protein syntheses, the enzyme formation, the self-reproduction of the cell, and, directly or indirectly, the entire metabolic function of the cell. By their property to mutate, to be assorted and shuffled around in different combinations, genes have become the basis for our modern interpretation of evolution. Genes are molecular patterns that can maintain their identities for many generations, can be self-duplicated in each generation, and can control cell processes by allowing their specificities to be copied. Genes thus have the properties of controlling protein specificities, of determining the specificities of new genes, and by changing their own specificities (mutation), of furnishing the materials for evolutionary advancements and adaptations. Specifically, genes are able to store information that they can transmit as needed for a basic pattern of life and its maintenance. What things the gene can do, or its varied properties, are intimately associated with its chemical structure. The nature of the gene substance has been the subject of intense biologic investigation during the past decade. It is now known that genes, like chromosomes, are made up chiefly of nucleoproteins that consist of nucleic acids and proteins (histones and protamines). Life as we know it really began with the first formation of nucleoproteins, because they have the properties of self-duplication and specificity. Nucleoproteins, so far as is known, are the only molecules with the power of self-duplication.

Viruses and bacteria have been helpful tools in understanding the nature of genetic materials and the mechanism of heredity. In the typical virus the DNA core is surrounded by a protein coat in the form of a capsule. When a virus enters a cell to reproduce, only the DNA core enters; the protein coat remains outside. In the phenomenon of transformation, extracts of the DNA core from one strain of bacteria may be transferred to a second strain of bacteria that incorporates some of the DNA material into its own genetic system. The recipient cells, as a result, produce new characters. A similar phenomenon is transduction, in which a bacteriophage (bacterial parasite) can transfer DNA from one host to another. The bacteriophage does this by disintegrating one kind of bacterium, picking up some of the DNA of the host bacterium, and transferring this genetic material to the next host of another strain. The latter may acquire new traits by this method. Groups of linked genes and not single genes appear to be transferred by this process. Both transformation and transduction represent a type of nonmendelian heredity, for sexual fusion of the bacterial cells is not involved.

The evidence indicates that the nucleic acid components are the essential parts that display the properties of genes because of (1) the constant amount of nucleic acid for each chromosome set of a given organism, (2) the transfer of the donor's genetic traits when a donor's nucleus is transplanted into a recipient cell, and (3) the ability of nucleic acid extracts from one kind of bacteria to produce hereditary transformation in another type of bacteria.

The nucleic acids are each chemically made up of a purine or pyrimidine base, a sugar, and phosphoric acid. On the basis of the kind of sugar (deoxyribose or ribose), the nucleic acids are divided into two main groups: **deoxyribonucleic acid (DNA)** and **ribonucleic acid (RNA)**. DNA occurs only in the nucleus, where it is the major structural component of genes; RNA is found throughout the cell, being especially abundant in nucleoli and in the cytoplasm. The nucleic acids may be broken down chemically or enzymatically into **nucleotides.** Thus a nucleic acid molecule is made up of many nucleotides joined to form long chains. Each nucleotide consists of phosphoric acid, either deoxyribose or ribose sugar, and a pyrimidine or purine base. The purine units are adenine and guanine; the pyrimidines are cytosine, thymine, and uracil. Five kinds of nucleotides are recognized on the basis of these purines and pyrimidines: (1) adenine-sugar-phosphate, (2) guanine-sugar-phosphate, (3) cytosine-sugar-phosphate, (4) thymine-sugar-phosphate, and (5) uracil-sugar-phosphate. The DNA molecule has the first four of these nucleotides (Fig. 35-7); the RNA has the first three and the last one. Although the phosphate-sugar part of the long chain of nucleotides is regular, the base attached to the sugar is not always the same, and the order of these bases is irregular and varies from one section to another of the nucleic acid molecule. Depending on the proportion and sequence of the nucleotides, there is an almost unlimited variety of nucleic acids.

Structure of DNA molecule (Watson-Crick model)

In 1953 J. D. Watson and F. H. Crick proposed a model of the structure of the DNA molecule that has been widely accepted. Based on the information then available about the molecule, such as the x-ray diffraction studies of M. H. F. Wilkins on the spatial arrange-

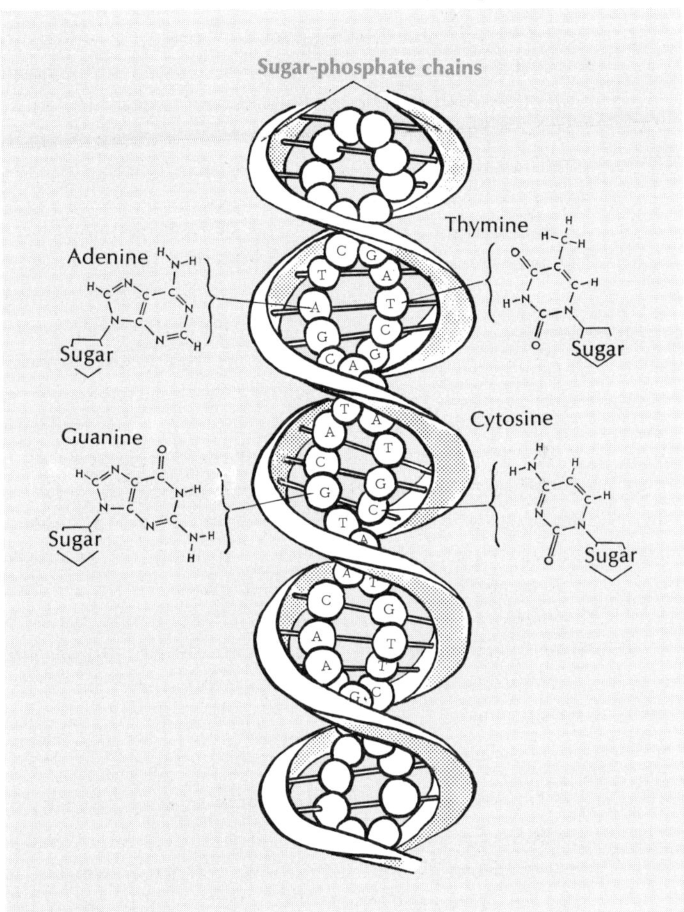

FIG. 35-7

Structure of DNA (deoxyribonucleic acid) molecule. Evidence at present indicates that molecule is formed by two interlocking helixes or chains of nucleotides. Each nucleotide is made up of deoxyribose sugar attached to phosphoric acid molecule on one side and to nitrogenous base on another side. Bases are of four kinds: adenine **(A)**, cytosine **(C)**, guanine **(G)**, and thymine **(T)**. It will be noted that adenine is always paired with thymine and guanine with cytosine. This pairing is necessary because in every pair only large base and small one will fill space available between parallel sugar-phosphate chains. Apparently nucleotides occur in great variety of sequences so that long double chains contain many combinations that confer specificity on given DNA molecule, just as many words are formed out of a few letters of alphabet. Since each spiral thread is complement of the other, this structure of DNA molecule provides basis for duplication, for either spiral chain can serve as template on which missing part of other spiral can reconstruct itself. Various sections (genes?) of long molecule may also serve as pattern codes for enzymes, proteins, and other kinds of molecules so necessary for living cell.

ment of molecules, the nucleotide composition of various DNA molecules, and the ratios of the purine and pyrimidine bases, they constructed a model that suggested plausible answers to such problems as (1) how specific directions are transmitted from one generation to another, (2) how DNA could control protein synthesis, and (3) how the DNA molecule could duplicate itself.

According to this model, the DNA molecule consists of two complementary polynucleotide chains helically wound around a central axis and cross-linked through specific hydrogen bonding between purine and pyrimidine bases. In this arrangement the phosphate and sugar groups are on the outside of the axis; the bases are inside and connected to each other by hydrogen bonds. For each complete turn of the double helix, there are about 10 nucleotides in each chain. The hydrogen bonding is such that, at any level where adenine is found on one chain, thymine appears on the other chain; and wherever guanine is placed on one chain, cytosine is its mate on the other chain. If one omits the sugar and phosphate components common to all four nucleotides, the pairing may be represented in the following way:

```
A—T—C—G
:  :  :  :
T—A—G—C
```

Only in the space available can such combinations fit. It will be noted that there are no restrictions on the sequence of nucleotides in the DNA double helix. The hydrogen bonds are represented by dots, and it will be noted also that A and T are joined by two hydrogen bonds and C and G by three bonds. A hydrogen bond takes place from the sharing of a single hydrogen atom by two atoms. Such bonds are weaker than ordinary chemical bonds. One of the atoms acts as a hydrogen donor and the other as a hydrogen acceptor. Donor atoms and acceptor atoms are found in each of the nitrogenous bases. The DNA molecule has a diameter of about 20 angstrom units (Å) (1 Å = 1/10,000,000 mm.). DNA chains have various lengths, but some are thought to be at least 200,000 nucleotide pairs long.

The Watson-Crick model suggests how a DNA molecule can replicate itself. Since each chain of the double helix is complementary to the other, each has the information to direct the synthesis of a partner. In some way not yet understood, the two chains separate or unwind, and each chain then serves as a template to synthesize another chain complementary to it. In the new chain free nucleotides from the surrounding medium are properly assembled and form hydrogen bonds with matching nucleotides of the original chain. That DNA replication occurs this way is indicated by two kinds of experiments. One of these methods is by the use of isotope-labeling, such as phosphorus 32, by which it is possible to distinguish the mother DNA strand from the daughter strand. The second method involves the growing of bacteria on a culture medium of heavy nitrogen 15. The DNA of such an organism had a molecular weight 1% greater than DNA of bacteria grown on nitrogen 14. This experiment indicated that the eight nitrogen atoms per pair of nucleotides had replaced their N^{14} with N^{15} in the experimental medium. Replication of DNA must occur at every cell division to ensure that each daughter cell has the same amount of DNA that the parent cell had. A second great function of DNA, in addition to its capacity for duplication, is its ability to transfer specific information contained in its sequence of nucleotides so that the cell can build enzymes or other specific proteins.

How DNA is arranged in a chromosome is not yet known. Chromosomes undergo duplications as though they were single DNA molecules. Some suggestions have been made as to the relationship, such as that the DNA runs the entire length of the chromosome or that a number of DNA molecules are attached end to end by "linkers" that allow flexibility at the joints of attachment.

Present concept of gene

The study of the finer structure of the gene has produced a new concept of the classical gene. A common definition of a gene is that it is a hereditary unit that can undergo mutation. As already mentioned, a mutation is any stable, inheritable change in genetic material. Mutations are either **chromosomal mutations** or **point mutations.** Chromosomal mutations may involve polyploidy (duplication), loss or addition of a chromosome, loss of part of a chromosome (deletion), transference of one part to another chromosome, inversion of a segment of a chromosome, etc. All of these produce visible changes in chromosome structure. Point mutations are stable changes in the structure of the gene and are not visible. It has been suggested that any change in the sequence of the nucleotides in the DNA molecule would also alter the sequence of the amino acids in a specific protein, thus producing a detectable mutation.

The newer concept of the gene indicates that the classic gene is no longer regarded as the indivisible minimal unit of heredity but that it consists of smaller functional subunits. The outstanding work of S. Benzer on mutations in bacteria explains how these subunits function. In genetics it has long been known that the alleles (already mentioned) for a particular locus may differ (in phenotypic expression) from each other only to a slight extent. Molecular genetics indicates that these small differences may be due to slight chemical differences brought about by small changes in the sequences of the nucleotides within a particular region of a DNA molecule. New alleles for a particular locus are produced by gene mutations. If the gene represents some section of a DNA molecule, it is conceivable that a mutation may affect only a small part of the nucleotides within a gene. According to Benzer's terminology, a **muton** is the smallest segment of a gene that can produce an altered trait by mutation. It may consist only of two to five nucleotide pairs, and a gene must have many mutons. Recombinations of subunits within genes may also occur and produce new genes. The smallest segment within a gene that is interchangeable but not divided by genetic recombination is called a **recon.** Recombinations can occur, therefore, not only between genes but also within genes. A recon may contain no more than two nucleotide pairs. Such recombinations could give rise to a hereditary unit composed of parts of two alleles. A larger subunit of the gene is the **cistron,** which refers to the smallest number of mutons or recons of a gene that must remain together on one chromosome to perform a biochemical or genetic function. If a series of consecutive mutons, for instance, are necessary for the synthesis of a certain protein and are located on the same chromosome (**cis** position), the whole gene functions normally. But if one part of the mutons are on one chromosome and the other part on the other chromosome (**trans** position), the protein synthesis will occur normally only if the two groups of mutons complement each other. However, if the trans arrangement does not produce complementation between the two groups of mutons, the synthesis of the protein does not occur. Only a few cistrons are found in a gene and each must be made up of many nucleotides. It has been suggested that recons and mutons may control the synthesis of individual amino acids, whereas cistrons control the formation of polypeptide (chains of amino acids).

Genetic code

The problem of gene action is mainly a problem of protein synthesis. The kinds of proteins in a cell determine the structure and function of that cell. All the different kinds of chemical transformations for biosynthesis and for the utilization of energy are dependent on organic catalysts or enzymes. In all cellular organisms there are thousands of enzymes, each being a specific catalytic protein. All of them have the same basic structure—large macromolecules consisting of polymers of some 20 amino acids joined to each other in peptide linkage (polypeptides). The highly specific nature of enzymes can be traced to the unique sequence of amino acids (their primary structure) and to their three-dimensional spatial structure that arises from the specific foldings of the amino acid chain and cross-linkages between certain pairs of amino acids in adjacent folds. This specific arrangement must be intact to ensure the biologic activity of the enzyme in question.

For many years it has been taught in classic genetics that the hereditary genes are arranged linearly along the chromosomes in the nucleus of the cell. It has also been known that chromosomes are composed largely of proteins and nucleic acids. Studies on microorganisms since 1944 indicate that genes are made up (chiefly, if not entirely) of deoxyribonucleic acid (DNA). (Certain viruses have RNA in place of DNA.) Earlier it had been demonstrated that genes control enzymes. Since amino acids are proteins, there must be some connection between the DNA of the gene and the amino acids of the proteins. In other words, how is information in the form of DNA molecules conveyed to sites of protein formation? The translation of genetic information has been the cause of the most exciting scientific quest in this century.

The Watson-Crick model suggested how new DNA may be made from old. The coding problem indicated that there must be some relation between the sequence of the four bases of DNA and the sequence of the 20 amino acids of proteins. The coding hypothesis had to account for the way these four bases (adenine, thymine, cytosine, guanine) must arrange themselves so that each permutation is the code for an amino acid. In the coding procedure it is obvious that there cannot be a 1:1 correlation between four bases and 20 amino acids. If the coding unit (often called a word, or codon) consists of two bases, only 16 words can be formed, which cannot account for 20 amino acids. Therefore, the protein code must consist of at least three bases or 3 letters because 64 possible words can be formed by four bases when taken as triplets. DNA must then be considered a language written in a 4-letter alphabet. The particular composition or sequence of amino acids in a given protein are thus specified by the particular sequence of nucleotide pairs in a specific DNA molecule. **But the information is coded in DNA of the nucleus, whereas protein synthesis occurs in the cytoplasm.** An intermediary of some kind between the two regions is necessary. This intermediary appears to be a special kind of RNA called **messenger RNA.** Messenger RNA is thought to be transcribed directly from DNA in the nucleus, each of the many messengers RNA being determined by a gene or a particular segment of DNA. (It will be recalled that RNA differs from DNA in having thymine [T] replaced by uracil [U] and in having a sugar residue of ribose instead of deoxyribose.) In this process of making a complementary copy of one strand or gene of DNA in the formation of messenger RNA, an enzyme, RNA-DNA polymerase, is needed. The messenger RNA contains a sequence of bases that complement the bases in one of the two DNA strands. Thus, A in DNA is replaced by U in messenger RNA; C is replaced by G; G is replaced by C; and T is replaced by A. It appears that only one of the two chains is used as the template for RNA synthesis, although either one could be so used. The reason why only one strand of the double-stranded DNA is a "coding strand" is that messenger RNA otherwise would always be formed in complementary pairs and enzymes also would be synthesized in matching pairs. The messenger RNA when formed is separated from the DNA and migrates through nuclear pores into the cytoplasm of the cell, where it becomes attached to a granular **ribosome** (Fig. 35-8), submicroscopic structures of protein, and a nonspecific RNA. Here the messenger RNA molecule serves as a template against which amino acids are lined up in a sequence according to the coded instructions in messenger RNA. (These amino acids are either obtained in the food supply or synthesized by the organism.)

While this is taking place, various amino acids are activated and enzymatically attached to a second type of RNA called **transfer RNA,** a small molecule of about 80 ribonucleotides and folded back on itself to form a double helix. This RNA molecule is probably synthesized on a DNA template. In a specific region of each transfer RNA, there is a coding sequence of three bases that have a complementary sequence on messenger RNA. Thus UUU on the messenger would furnish the complementary site for the coding sequence of AAA on a transfer RNA. A different transfer RNA molecule corresponds to each triplet code on messenger RNA. Each transfer RNA is specific for a particular amino acid. The coding sequence of three unpaired nucleotides is found in the region where the chain of the transfer RNA turns back on itself and, at a different place, a recognition site where the amino acid is attached. There must be 20 recognition sites, one for each amino acid. At the end to which the amino acid is attached, the base triplet ACC is always the same on all kinds of transfer RNA. The sequence of three nucleotides at the other end of transfer RNA represents a code that determines where transfer RNA fits into the template. More than one kind of transfer RNA is found for certain amino acids. By stepwise addition, the amino acids are guided by the coding sequence on transfer RNA, to which they are attached, and arranged in the correct order along messenger RNA to form a protein molecule (Fig. 35-9). Each gene codes for about 500 amino acids, which is the average of a polypeptide chain, and since the code triplets, or codons, are in groups of three nucleotides, there would be 1500 nucleotide pairs in a single gene. These figures naturally will vary with the protein or enzyme being coded.

The general scheme of the code may be abbreviated thus:

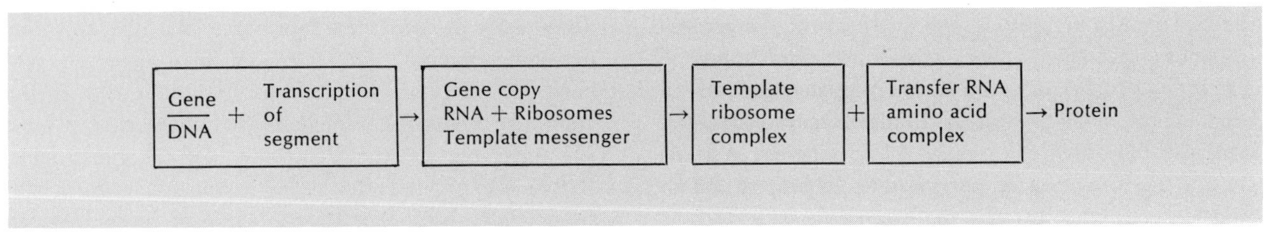

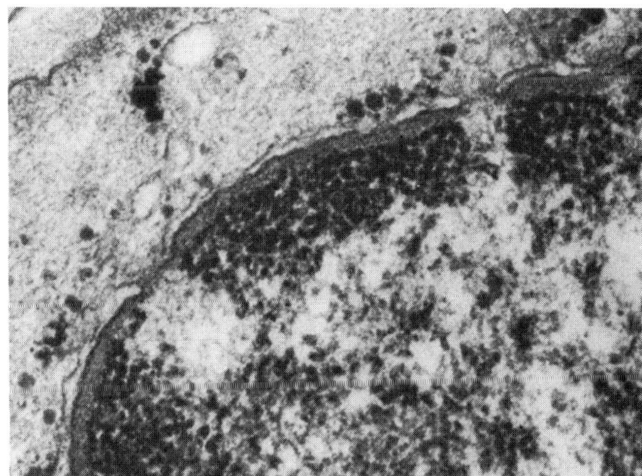

FIG. 35-8

Electron micrograph of smooth muscle cell of frog showing part of nucleus with nuclear pores and nuclear envelope. Two nuclear pores are seen. (×120,000.) (Courtesy G. E. Palade and National Academy of Sciences, Washington, D. C.)

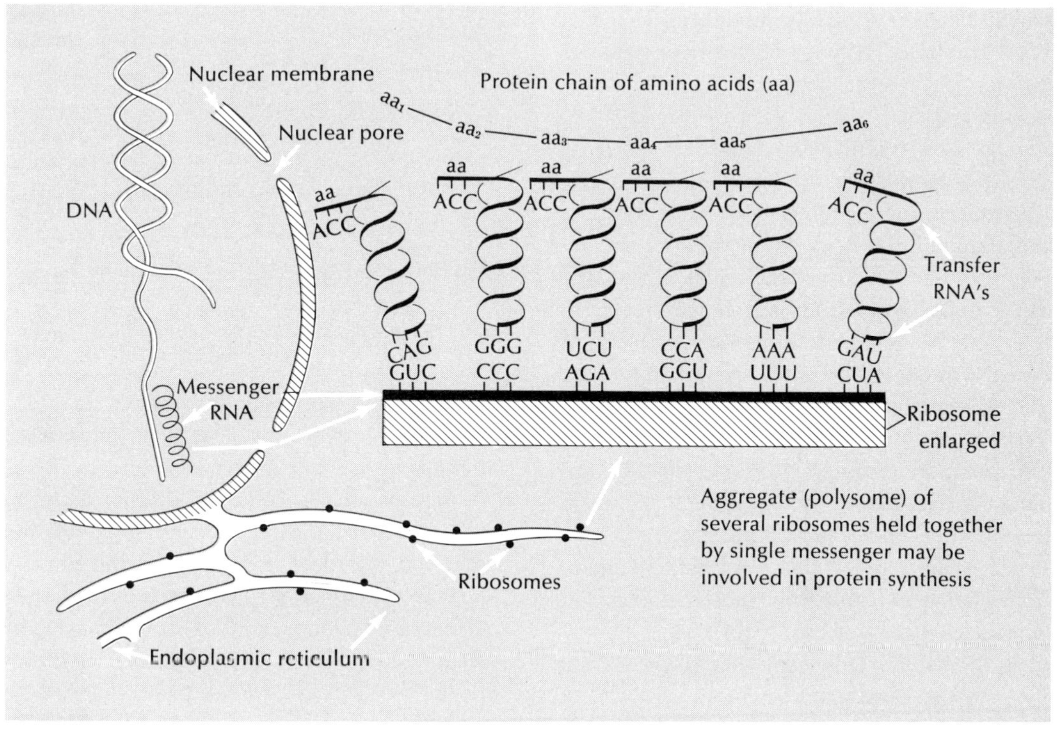

FIG. 35-9

Genetic code. Illustrates how genetic information may be passed from DNA molecule in nucleus by means of messenger RNA to ribosomes of endoplasmic reticulum where amino acids are arranged in proper sequence to form specific enzyme. Messenger RNA is thought to be synthesized from particular segment (gene?) of one of DNA chains serving as template. Messenger RNA, with its specific code from DNA, passes through nuclear pore to endoplasmic reticulum where it becomes attached to ribosome or ribosomes. Amino acids, obtained preformed in food supply or else synthesized by organism, are probably activated by specific enzyme for each of 20 or so amino acids. High-energy ATP may play a part in activation. Activated amino acid is then attached to specific transfer RNA molecule (s-RNA) at recognition site on folded double helix of molecule. Transfer RNA bearing specific amino acid is now lined up and brought into correct position by base pairing of triplet-code between transfer RNA and messenger RNA (C always pairs with G and A with U). Diagram shows some transfer RNA molecules, with their amino acids being transferred to form peptide or protein chain (aa_1, aa_2, etc.) as they are "read off" on template of messenger RNA. Each specific transfer RNA bears base triplet ACC at amino acid acceptor end.

The manner in which the peptide bonds link together adjacent amino acids is at present unknown. As soon as a specific transfer RNA delivers its amino acid to the proper place, it is released to pick up another activated amino acid. Radioactive techniques have shown that the protein molecules are synthesized unidirectionally, beginning with the free amino ends, and the amino acids are added in succession until the molecule is completed. Many details of the process are still lacking, but metabolic energy and enzymatic action are probably involved at each step.

The experiments of M. W. Nirenberg and J. H. Matthaei of the National Institutes of Health indicated first how the genetic code works. They discovered that if a synthetic RNA composed entirely of uracil nucleotides is substituted for the natural messenger RNA in a protein-synthesizing system, a polypeptide is formed solely of phenylalanine. This was the first time that synthetic RNA served as a template in protein synthesis. The code word, therefore, for the amino acid phenylalanine is UUU. Other investigations by these workers and by S. Ochoa showed that when various combinations of the other RNA nucleotides A, C, and G were used in addition to U, other amino acids were also produced in the synthetic polypeptide. By such means the code words for the other amino acids have been worked out. By using various proportions and combinations of nucleotides and comparing the proportions of different amino acids in the resulting polypeptides, the code words appeared to be made up of three letters. There may also be two or more code words for the same amino acid. The information in Table 35-1 must be regarded as tentative, and changes will no doubt occur as new information is available. This code deciphering was done mainly with the system of the intestinal bacteria *Escherichia coli,* but the few code words so far found in mammals are identical.

TABLE 35-1

Proposed codons (code triplets) between messenger RNA and specific amino acids

Codons	Amino acid
GCU, GCC, GCA, GCG	Alanine
CGU, CGC, CGA, CGG, AGA	Arginine
AAU, AAC	Asparagine
GAU, GAC	Aspartic acid
UGU, UGC	Cysteine
GAA, CAG	Glutamic acid
CAA, CAG	Glutamine
GGU, GGC, GGA, GGG	Glycine
CAU, CAC	Histidine
AUU, AUC, AUA	Isoleucine
CUU, CUC, CUA, CUG, UUA, UUG	Leucine
AAA, AAG	Lysine
AUG	Methionine
UUU, UUC	Phenylalanine
CCU, CCC, CCA, CCG	Proline
AGU, AGC, UCU, UCC, UCA, UCG	Serine
ACU, ACC, ACA, ACG	Threonine
UGG	Tryptophan
UAU, UAC	Tyrosine
GUU, GUC, GUA, GUG	Valine

Operon concept

The genetic code as given in the foregoing description simply explains how the code carried on the DNA molecules of the nucleus is transcribed into a definite protein or enzyme synthesized in the cytoplasm. It does not explain how genes are turned off and on as their products are needed by the cell. It does not explain why certain enzymes are not formed when they are not needed. If an enzyme-forming system lacks control, the whole economy of the cell would be affected adversely. Cells also require control as they differentiate different amounts of the same enzyme at different times. The rate of synthesis of a protein or enzyme must be controlled by two factors—partly by the genetic apparatus of the code and ribosome transcription, and partly by factors from the environment such as the amount of products accumulated. Thus there must be mechanisms in the cell for repressing the synthesis of enzymes when they are not needed and for inducing them when they are needed.

In 1960 the two French scientists, F. Jacob and J. Monod, proposed the **operon hypothesis,** or model, for explaining how repressions and inductions of protein synthesis might occur (Fig. 35-10). Although these investigators worked with bacteria, it seems highly probable that their hypothesis applies to all living beings. The gist of their hypothesis, for which they were awarded the Nobel Prize in 1965, may be stated in the following way:

1. There are two types of genes, **structural genes** and **regulator genes.** The structural genes contain the

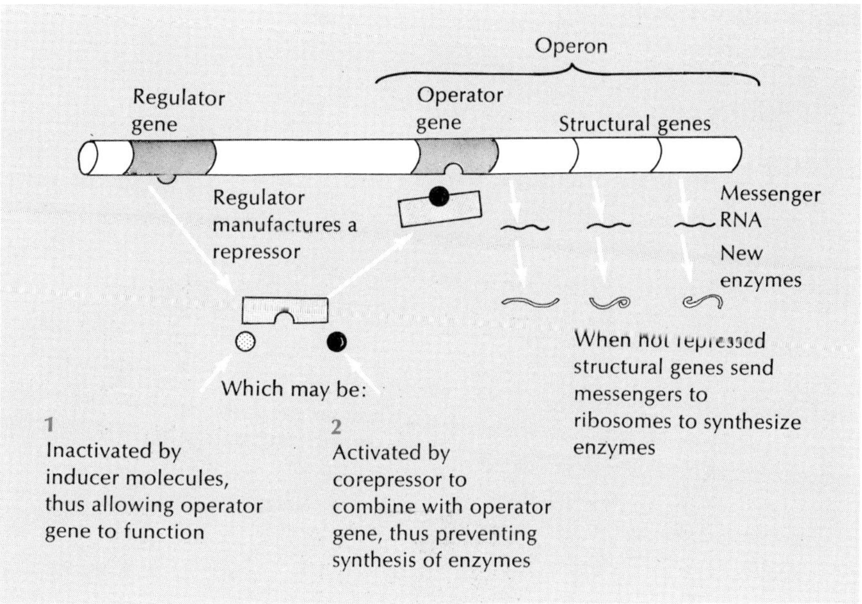

FIG. 35-10

Operon hypothesis. Regulator gene acts by way of a repressor on the operator gene. These regulator genes control rate of information sent to operator gene, either to induce more of a particular enzyme or to cut off (repress) additional amounts of unneeded enzymes. Repressor is a cytoplasmic factor, probably a macromolecule. When operator is "turned on," entire operon is active in synthesis of enzymes; when it is "off," operon is inactive. Inducer molecules modify regulator substance to prevent it from switching off operator; repressor molecules react with regulator substance and cause it to switch off operator (and genes that it controls). (From several authors.)

coded formulas for the synthesis of the primary structure of a protein, or enzyme, that are useful in cellular metabolism. The regulatory genes are concerned with the function of certain structural genes.

2. There are two kinds of regulator genes. One is the **operator** gene that determines whether or not the formula, or code, in a structural gene adjacent to it is to be transcribed into an enzyme. The other kind has the information for the structure of a cytoplasmic factor (the **repressor**) whose function is to turn the operator on and off.

3. The operon is that portion of a chromosome that regulates all the steps in the synthesis of an enzyme, or protein. Some operons may contain only one gene, or they may contain more. An operon consists of an operator gene and the segment of DNA it controls. The operator may control either a single structural gene to which it is adjacent or several structural genes of related function. Thus all the nine enzymes in the histidine pathway are controlled by a single operator.

4. The regulator genes produce a substance called the repressor that blocks the operator genes and thus prevents the structural gene from functioning normally. Repression occurs when the repressor substance combines with the operator gene and prevents the initiation of messenger RNA along the segment of DNA controlled by the operator gene. The operator is that part of the operon that is the receptor site for the repressor.

5. If the repressor substance reacts with an appropriate substance, it **derepresses** the repressor substance and permits the operator gene to act. This is called the **inducible system.** In other words, it renders the repressor incapable of turning the operator off.

6. In this way the two antagonistic systems, the inducible system and the repressor system, maintain a refinement in the amount and kind of enzymes necessary for the steady states of the cell. For instance, if there is a high concentration of a particular enzyme in the cell, this high concentration can act as a "feedback" through the repressor system to block the action of the operator gene so that the structural gene can no longer produce the enzymes. The repressor may be changed to an inactive form by a lower-than-normal concentration of the enzyme, or by a specific substance synthesized in the cytoplasm or from the environment (ions and amino acids) so that the operator gene is turned on to produce more of the enzyme. In this way the genes influence the cytoplasm and the cytoplasm exerts a "feedback" influence on the genes for turning on or off their action.

The operon model is still a hypothesis and may work in other ways, but more and more the above plan is being confirmed.

MENDEL'S INVESTIGATIONS

The first man to formulate the cardinal principles of heredity was Gregor Johann Mendel (1822-1884), who was connected with the Augustinian monastery at

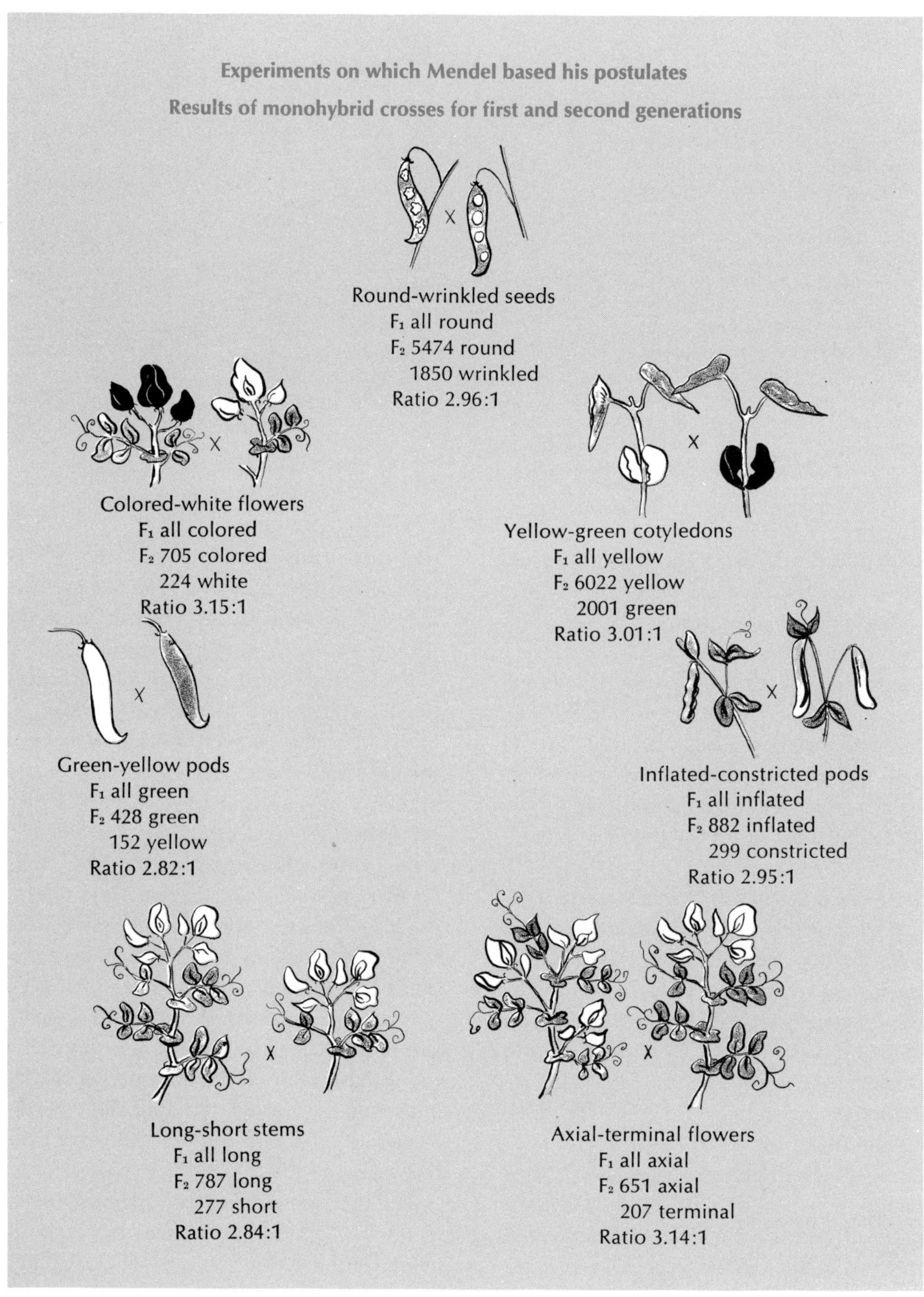

FIG. 35-11

Seven experiments of Mendel.

Bruenn, Moravia, then a part of Austria, later a part of Czechoslovakia. In the small monastery garden he conducted his experiments on hybridization, which resulted in two clear-cut laws that bear his name. In the conduction of these experiments from 1856 to 1864 he examined with great care and accuracy many thousands of plants. He worked with several kinds of plants, but his classic observations were made on the garden pea. In the first place, there are several distinct varieties of these plants that always bred true because gardeners over a long period by careful selection had produced pure strains. For example, some varieties were definitely dwarf and others were tall. A second reason for selecting peas was that they are self-fertilizing, but they are also capable of cross-fertilization as well. To simplify his problem he chose single characters and those that were sharply contrasted. Mere quantitative and intermediate characters he carefully avoided. Mendel selected seven pairs of these contrasting characters, such as tall plants and dwarf plants, smooth seeds and wrinkled seeds, green cotyledons and yellow cotyledons, inflated pods and constricted pods, yellow pods and green pods, axial position of flowers and terminal position of flowers, and transparent seed coats and brown seed coats (Fig. 35-11). Mendel crossed a plant having one of these characters with one having the contrasting character. He did this by removing the stamens from a flower so that self-fertilization could not occur, and then on the stigma of this flower he placed the pollen from the flower of another plant that had the contrasting character. He then prevented the experimental flowers from being pollinated from other sources, such as wind and insects. When the cross-fertilized flower bore seeds, he noted the kind of plants (hybrids) they produced when planted. His next step was to cross these hybrids among themselves and to see what happened. He made careful counts of his plants, repeated his experiments, and worked out certain ratios.

Among other experiments Mendel crossed pure tall plants with pure dwarf plants and found that the hybrids (F_1 or first filial generation) thus produced were all tall, just as tall as the tall parent that was involved in the cross. This result he found was always obtained whether the tall plant furnished the male germ cells or the female germ cells. Next, he crossed two of these hybrid tall plants together. From this cross he raised several hundred plants and found that both tall plants and dwarf plants were represented among them. He also noted that none of this generation (F_2 or second filial generation) were intermediate in size; they were either as tall or as short as the parents in the original cross. When he counted the actual number of tall and dwarf plants in the F_2 generation, he found there were three times as many tall plants as dwarf ones, or a ratio of 3:1. His next step was to self-pollinate the plants in the F_2 generation; that is, the stigma of a flower was fertilized by the pollen of the same flower. The results showed that self-pollinated F_2 dwarf plants produced only dwarf plants, whereas one third of the F_2 tall plants produced tall and the other two thirds produced both tall and dwarf in the ratio of 3:1, just as the F_1 plants had done. This experiment showed that the dwarf plants were pure because they at all times gave rise to short plants when self-pollinated; the tall plants contained both pure tall and hybrid tall. It also demonstrated that, although the dwarf character disappeared in the F_1 plants, which were all tall, the character for dwarfness appeared in the F_2 plants.

MENDEL'S LAWS

From the results of these and other experiments, Mendel formulated certain postulates. Mendel knew nothing about the cytologic background of heredity, for chromosomes and genes were unknown to him. Instead of using the term "genes" as we do today, he called his inheritance units factors. He reasoned that the factors for tallness and dwarfness were units that did not blend when they were together. The F_1 generation contained both these units or factors, but when these plants formed their germ cells, the factors separated out so that each germ cell had only one factor. In a pure plant both factors were alike; in a hybrid they were different. He concluded that individual germ cells are always pure with respect to a pair of contrasting factors, even though the germ cells are formed from hybrids in which the contrasting characters were mixed. This idea formed the basis for his first principle, the **law of segregation,** which states that whenever two factors are brought together in a hybrid, when that hybrid forms its germ cells, the factors segregate into separate gametes and each germ cell is pure with respect to that character. Thus in the gametes of the F_1 plants, half of the germ cells will bear the factor for tallness and half for dwarfness; no germ cell will contain both factors.

In the crosses involving the factors for tallness and dwarfness, in which the resulting hybrids were tall, Mendel called the tall factor **dominant** and the short

recessive. Similarly, the other pairs of characters that he studied showed dominance and recessiveness. Thus when plants with yellow unripe pods were crossed with green unripe pods, the hybrids all contained yellow pods. In the F_2 generation the expected ratio of 3 yellow to 1 green was obtained. Whenever a dominant factor (gene) is present, the recessive one cannot produce an effect. The recessive factor will show up only when both factors are recessive, or, in other words, a pure condition.

The law of segregation deals only with one pair of contrasting characters. Mendel also ascertained what would happen when a cross is made between plants differing in two pairs of contrasting characters. Thus when a tall plant with the yellow type of pod was crossed with a dwarf plant bearing green pods, the F_1 generation was all tall and yellow, for these factors are dominant. When the F_1 hybrids were crossed with each other, the result was 9 tall and yellow, 3 tall and green, 3 dwarf and yellow, and 1 dwarf and green. In this experiment each factor separated independently of the other and showed up in new combinations. This is Mendel's second law, or the **law of independent assortment,** which states that, whenever two or more pairs of contrasting characters are brought together in a hybrid, the factors of different pairs segregate independently of one another. Rarely do two organisms differ in only one pair of contrasting characters; nearly always they differ in many. The second law of Mendel therefore deals with two or more pairs of contrasting characters.

Crosses involving more than two pairs of characters result in still more complicated ratios of types of offspring. However, it is usually convenient to work with just one pair of contrasting characters, for each pair may be considered by itself. It may be stated here that Mendel's second law is true only when the factors for the different pairs of characters are located on different pairs of chromosomes. It happened that all seven pairs of characters Mendel worked with were on different pairs of chromosomes, but since his laws became known, many pairs of characters have been found on the same chromosome, which alters the original mendelian ratios. This modification does not detract, however, from the basic significance of his great laws.

Although Mendel published his observations on the principles of heredity in *The Proceedings of the Society of Natural Science of Brünn* in 1866, his experiments attracted no attention and apparently were forgotten. In 1900 three investigators, De Vries in Holland, Tschermak in Austria, and Correns in Germany, independently rediscovered his laws but found that the obscure priest had already published them 34 years before.

Although Darwin was a contemporary of Mendel and realized the importance of understanding heredity, Darwin knew nothing of Mendel's fundamental discoveries. Darwin had proposed a heredity theory of his own for explaining how heredity worked. His pangenesis theory suggested that each part of the body produced particles (pangenes) that were carried by the blood to the gonads where they were incorporated into the germ cells.

EXPLANATION OF MENDELIAN RATIOS

In representing his crosses Mendel used letters as symbols. For dominant characters he employed capitals and for recessives, corresponding small letters. Thus the factors, or genes, for pure tall plants might be represented by TT, the pure recessive by tt, and the hybrid of the two plants by Tt. In diagram form, one of Mendel's original crosses (tall plant and dwarf plant) could be represented in this manner:

	(tall)			(dwarf)
Parents	TT	×		tt
Gametes	all T			all t
F_1		Tt (hybrid tall)		
Crossing hybrids	Tt	×		Tt
Gametes	T,t			T,t
F_2	TT	Tt	tT	tt
		(3 tall to 1 dwarf)		

It is convenient in most mendelian crosses to use the checkerboard method devised by Punnett for representing the various combinations resulting from a cross. Thus in the previous F_2 cross, the following scheme would apply.

Sperm \ Eggs	T	t
T	TT (pure tall)	Tt (hybrid tall)
t	Tt (hybrid tall)	tt (pure dwarf)

Ratio: 3 tall to 1 dwarf.

Mendel's experiment involving two pairs of contrasting characters instead of one pair may be demonstrated in the diagram shown below.

In the cross between tall and dwarf it will be noted that there are two types of visible characters—**tall** and **dwarf.** These are called **phenotypes.** On the basis of genetic formulas there are three hereditary types, TT, Tt, and tt. These are called **genotypes.** In the cross involving two pairs of contrasting characters (**tall yellow** and **dwarf green**) there are in the F_2 generation four phenotypes: **tall yellow, tall green, dwarf yellow,** and **dwarf green.** The genotypes are nine in number: TTYY, TTYy, TtYY, TtYy, TTyy, Ttyy, ttYY, ttYy, and ttyy. The F_2 ratios in any cross involving more than one pair of contrasting pairs can be found by combining the ratios in the cross of one pair of factors. Thus the genotypes will be $(3)^n$ and the phenotypes $(3{:}1)^n$. To illustrate, in a cross of two pairs of factors the phenotypes will be in the ratio of $(3{:}1)^2 = 9{:}3{:}3{:}1$. The genotypes in such a cross will be $(3)^2 = 9$. If three pairs of characters are involved, the phenotypes will be $(3{:}1)^3 = 27$: 9:9:9:3:3:3:1. The genotypes will be $(3)^3 = 27$. Thus it is seen that the numerical ratio of the various phenotypes is a power of the binomial $(3 + 1)^n$ whose exponent (n) equals the number of pairs of heterozygous genes in F_2. This is true only when one member of each pair of genes is dominant. By experience, then, one may determine the ratios of phenotypes in a cross without using the checkerboard. In a dihybrid (9:3:3:1 ratio), for instance, it will be seen that those phenotypes that make up the dominants of each pair will be $\frac{9}{16}$ of the whole F_2; each of the $\frac{3}{16}$ phenotypes will consist of one dominant and one recessive; and the $\frac{1}{16}$ phenotype will consist of the two recessives.

LAWS OF PROBABILITY

When Mendel worked out the ratios for his various crosses, they were approximations and not certainties. In his 3 to 1 ratio of tall and short plants, for instance, the resulting phenotypes did not come out exactly 3 tall to 1 short. All genetic experiments are based on

	(tall, yellow)		(dwarf, green)
Parents	TTYY	×	ttyy
Gametes	all TY		all ty
F_1		TtYy (hybrid tall, hybrid yellow)	
Crossing hybrids	TtYy	×	TtYy
Gametes	TY, Ty, tY, ty		TY, Ty, tY, ty
F_2		(see checkerboard)	

	TY	Ty	tY	ty
TY	TTYY pure tall pure yellow	TTYy pure tall hybrid yellow	TtYY hybrid tall pure yellow	TtYy hybrid tall hybrid yellow
Ty	TTYy pure tall hybrid yellow	TTyy pure tall pure green	TtYy hybrid tall hybrid yellow	Ttyy hybrid tall pure green
tY	TtYY hybrid tall pure yellow	TtYy hybrid tall hybrid yellow	ttYY pure dwarf pure yellow	ttYy pure dwarf hybrid yellow
ty	TtYy hybrid tall hybrid yellow	Ttyy hybrid tall pure green	ttYy pure dwarf hybrid yellow	ttyy pure dwarf pure green

Ratio: 9 tall yellow to 3 tall green; 3 dwarf yellow to 1 dwarf green.

probability; that is, the outcome of the events is uncertain and there is an element of chance in the final results. Probability values are measures of expectations. Probabilities are expressed in fractions, or it is always a number between 0 and 1. This probability number (p) is found by dividing the number (m) of favorable cases (for example, a certain event) by the total number (n) of possible outcomes: $p = \frac{m}{n}$.

When there are two possible outcomes, such as in tossing a coin, the chance of getting heads is $p = \frac{1}{2}$, or 1 chance in 2.

The more often a particular event occurs, the more closely will the number of favorable cases approach the number predicted by the p value. Probability predictions are often unreliable when there are only a few occurrences.

The probability of independent events occurring together involves the **product rule,** which is simply the product of their individual probabilities. When two coins are tossed together, the probability of getting two heads is $\frac{1}{2} \times \frac{1}{2} = \frac{1}{4}$, or 1 chance in 4. Here, again, this prediction is most likely to occur if the coins are tossed a sufficient number of times.

The ratios of inheritance in a monohybrid cross of dominant and recessive genes can be explained by the product rule. In the gametes of the hybrids the sperm may carry either the dominant or the recessive gene; the same applies to the eggs. The probability that the sperm carries the dominant is $\frac{1}{2}$ and the probability of an egg carrying the dominant is also $\frac{1}{2}$. The probability of a zygote obtaining two dominant genes is $\frac{1}{2} \times \frac{1}{2}$, or $\frac{1}{4}$. Thus 25% of the offspring will probably be pure dominants. The same principle applies to the recessive gene, which will be pure for 25% of the offspring. The heterozygous gene combinations will be found by the sum of the two possible combinations—a sperm with a dominant gene and an egg with a recessive gene, and a sperm with a recessive gene and an egg with a dominant gene—which yields 50% heterozygotes. Thus we have the 1:2:1 ratio.

TERMINOLOGY OF GENETICS

Genetics, in common with other branches of science, has built up its own terminology. Some of the terms first proposed by Mendel have been replaced by those that seem more suitable in the light of present-day knowledge. These terms are all important to the student of heredity, because they are essential in understanding the analyses of genetic problems. Whenever a cross involves only one pair of contrasting characters, it is called a **monohybrid;** when the cross has two pairs, it is a **dihybrid;** when the cross has three pairs, it is a **trihybrid;** and when it has more than three pairs, it is a **polyhybrid.** Characters that show in the F_1 are **dominant;** those that are hidden are **recessive.** When a dominant always shows up in the phenotype, it is said to have **complete dominance;** when it sometimes fails to manifest itself it is called **incomplete dominance.** When two characters form a contrasting pair, they are called **alleles** or **allelomorphs.** The term **factor** that Mendel used so widely is replaced by **gene.** A **zygote** is the union of two gametes; whenever the two members of a pair of genes are alike in a zygote, the latter is **homozygous** for that particular character; when the genes are unlike for a given character, the zygote is **heterozygous.** A **hybrid,** for instance, is a heterozygote, and a **pure** character is a homozygote.

ADVANCES IN GENETICS SINCE MENDEL'S LAWS REDISCOVERED

The rediscovery of Mendel's laws in 1900 served as an enormous stimulus to the study of genetics. The basic contribution of Mendel was that hereditary characters behave as units. His principles have been abundantly verified by many investigators. Since his time, however, it has been necessary to modify and extend some of his conclusions. It has been found that his laws are not so simple and direct as he first proposed them. Many of the modifications advanced, however, served all the more to strengthen Mendel's concepts. It has already been pointed out that the principle of independent assortment applies only when the pairs of contrasting genes are in different chromosomes. Since his time, the phenomena of linkage and crossing-over make necessary a modification of the law. The principles of dominance and recessiveness are no longer stressed as much as formerly because they are not well marked in many crosses. The idea of unit character is no longer thought of as Mendel thought of it, for it is now known that many factors may enter into the development of a particular character. Adult characters as such are not found in germ cells, but only differentiation determines which cells cause a character to express itself in a certain way.

Although many significant investigations have been made in genetics since 1900, none have been more fruitful than those performed by Professor Thomas Hunt Morgan and his colleagues on the fruit fly *Drosophila*. This little fly, which is much smaller than the common housefly, is found on decaying fruit. It is ideal for genetic experimentation because it produces so many generations within a few weeks. Morgan started his work on these forms about 1910, and now the heredity of no animal is better known than this common fly. Many of its characters are easily recognized and followed, and several striking mutations have helped explain the more intricate mechanism of heredity. As many as 500 genes have been mapped on its four pairs of chromosomes. The principles of linkage and crossing-over have also been best explained in this form. In addition, the salivary gland chromosomes, which have yielded so much information about the nature of the gene, were also first discovered in this fly.

One of the greatest advancements in understanding the physical basis of heredity made since Mendel's laws were known is the parallelism between these laws and the behavior of the chromosomes (and genes) during the processes of maturation and fertilization. The Sutton-Boveri hypothesis has already been described earlier in this chapter. It may be regarded as the one basic concept of biology because Morgan's great work, as well as the more recent work on the salivary gland chromosome, has given striking confirmation of the principle.

TESTCROSS

The dominant characters in the offspring of a cross are all of the same phenotypes whether they are homozygous or heterozygous. For instance, in Mendel's experiment of tall and dwarf characters, it is impossible to determine the genetic constitution of the tall plants of the F_2 generation by mere inspection of the tall plants. Three fourths of this generation are tall, but which of them are heterozygous recessive dwarf? The test is to cross the F_2 generation (dominant hybrids) with pure recessives. If the tall plant is homozygous, all the plants in such a testcross will be tall, thus:

TT (tall) × tt (dwarf)
Tt (hybrid tall)

If, on the other hand, the tall plant is heterozygous, the offspring will be half tall and half dwarf, thus:

Tt × tt
Tt (tall) or tt (dwarf)

The testcross is often used in modern genetics for the analysis of the genetic constitution of the offspring as well as for a quick way to make homozygous desirable stocks of animals and plants.

INCOMPLETE DOMINANCE

A cross that always shows the heterozygotes as distinguished from the pure dominants is afforded by the four-o'clock flower *(Mirabilis)* (Fig. 35-12), discovered since Mendel's time. Whenever a red-flowered variety is crossed with a white-flowered variety, the hybrid (F_1), instead of being red or white according to whichever is dominant, is actually intermediate between the two and is pink. Thus the homozygotes are either red or white, but the heterozygotes are pink. The testcross is therefore unnecessary to determine the nature of the genotype.

In the F_2 generation, when pink flowers are crossed with pink flowers, one fourth will be red, one half pink, and one fourth white.

This cross may be represented in this fashion:

	(red flower)			(white flower)
Parents	RR	×		rr
Gametes	R,R			r,r
F_1		Rr (all pink)		
Crossing hybrids	Rr	×		Rr
Gametes	R,r			R,r
F_2	RR (red)	Rr (pink)	rR (pink)	rr (white)

FIG. 35-12

Cross between red and white four-o'clock flowers. Red and white are homozygous; pink is heterozygous (stippled).

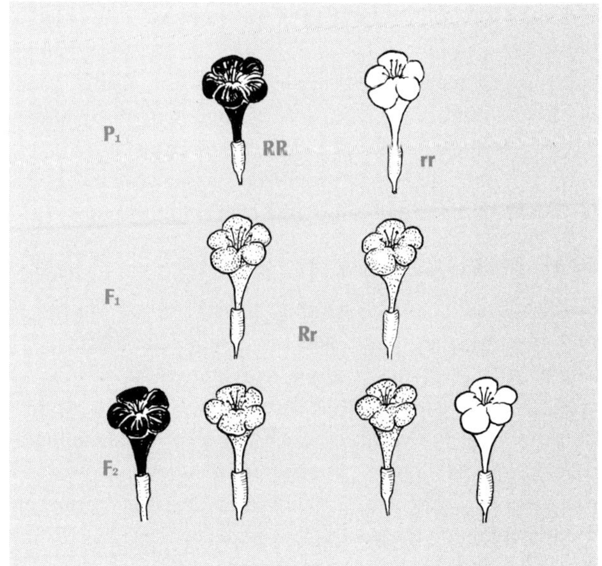

In this kind of cross neither of the genes demonstrates complete dominance; therefore, the heterozygote is a blending of both red and white characters. A similar phenomenon is found in the Blue Andalusian fowl in which a cross between black and white varieties produces a hybrid blue. In a cross between red and white cattle a roan hybrid is obtained. In both these cases of fowl and cattle a heterozygote always gives rise to blue or roan, respectively.

PENETRANCE AND EXPRESSIVITY

Penetrance refers to the percentage frequency with which a gene manifests phenotypic effect. If a dominant gene or a recessive gene in a homozygous state always produces a detectable effect, it is said to have **complete penetrance.** If dominant or homozygous recessive genes fail to show phenotypic expression in every case, it is called **incomplete** or **reduced penetrance.** Environmental factors may be responsible for the degree of penetrance because some genes may be more sensitive to such influences than are other genes. The genotype responsible for diabetes mellitus, for instance, may be present, but the disease does not always occur because of reduced penetrance. All of Mendel's experiments apparently had 100% penetrance.

The phenotypic variation in the expression of a gene is known as **expressivity.** For instance, a heritable allergy may cause more severe symptoms in one person than in another. Environmental factors may cause different degrees in the appearance of a phenotype. Lower temperatures permit expression of the genes for a black color in certain regions of the Siamese cat. Other genes in the hereditary constitution of one may also modify the expression of a trait. What is inherited is a certain genotype, but how it is expressed phenotypically is determined by environmental and other factors.

SOME SPECIAL FORMS OF HEREDITY

The types of crosses already described are simple in that the characters involved are due to the action of a single gene, but many cases are known in which the characters are the result of two or more genes. At first these more complex cases were thought to be nonmendelian, for they often produce unusual ratios. Most of these crosses, however, are now considered to be merely modifications of the mendelian expectations and do not invalidate the basic laws of Mendel. Mendel probably did not appreciate the real significance of the genotype as contrasted with the visible character—the phenotype. We now know that many different genotypes may be expressed as a single phenotype.

It is also known that many genes have more than a single effect. A gene for eye color, for instance, may be the ultimate cause for eye color, yet at the same time it may be responsible for influencing the development of other characters as well. Also, many unlike genes may occupy the same locus on a chromosome, but not, of course, all at one time. Thus more than two alternative characters may effect the same character. Such genes are called **multiple alleles** or factors. In the fruit fly (*Drosophila*) there are 18 alleles for eye color alone. Not more than two of these genes can be in any one individual and only one in a gamete. What is the reason for multiple alleles? The answer is that all genes can mutate in several different ways if given time and thus can give rise to several alternative conditions. In this way, many alleles for a particular locus on a chromosome may have evolved and added to the genetic pool of a population. Although it cannot be proved, it is thought that all genes present in an organism are mutants. In some cases dominance is lacking between two members of a set of multiple alleles, but usually one is dominant over the other. In *Drosophila* the gene for red eye color (wild type) is dominant over all other alleles of the eye color series; the gene for white eye is recessive to all the others.

Some of these unusual cases of inheritance are described in the following discussions on supplementary, complementary, cumulative, and lethal factors and pseudoalleles.

Supplementary factors. The variety of comb forms found in chickens illustrates the action of supplementary genes (Fig. 35-13). The common forms of comb are *rose, pea, walnut,* and *single.* Of these, the pea comb and the rose comb are dominant to the single comb. For example, when a pea comb is crossed with a single comb, all the F_1 are pea and the F_2 show a ratio of 3 pea to 1 single. When the two dominants, pea and rose, are crossed with each other, an entirely new kind of comb, walnut, is found in the F_1 generation. Each of these genes supplements the other in the production of a kind of comb different from each of the dominants. In the F_2 generation the ratio is 9 walnut, 3 rose, 3 pea, and 1 single. The walnut comb cannot thus be considered a unit character, but is merely the phenotype's expression of pea and rose when they act together.

Inspection of the ratio reveals that two pairs of genes

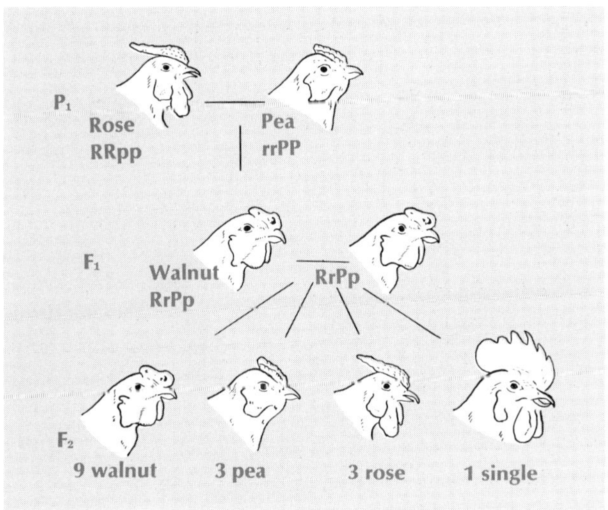

FIG. 35-13

Heredity of comb forms in chickens.

are involved. If P represents the gene for the pea comb and p its recessive allelomorph and if R represents the gene for the rose comb and r its recessive allelomorph, then the pea comb formula would be PPrr; and the one for rose comb, ppRR. Any individual having both dominant genes has a walnut comb. When no dominant gene is present, the comb is single. The cross may be diagrammed as follows:

Parents	PPrr (pea comb)	×	ppRR (rose comb)	
Gametes	all Pr		all pR	
F_1	PpRr (walnut)	×		PpRr (walnut)
Gametes	PR, Pr, pR, pr	×		PR, Pr, pR, pr

By the checkerboard method, the F_2 will show 9 walnut, 3 pea, 3 rose, and 1 single. It will be seen that genotypes with the combinations of PR will give walnut phenotypes; those with P, pea; those with R, rose; and those lacking in both P and R, single.

Complementary factors. When two genes produce a visible effect together, but each alone will show no visible effect, they are referred to as **complementary genes.** Some varieties of sweet peas can be used to illustrate this kind of cross. When two white-flowered varieties of these are crossed, the F_1 will show all colored (reddish or purplish) flowers. When these F_1's are self-fertilized, the F_2 will show a phenotypic ratio of 9 colored to 7 white flowers. This is really a ratio of 9:3:3:1, because the last three groups cannot be distinguished phenotypically. The explanation lies in the fact that in one of the white varieties of flowers there is a gene (C) for a colorless color base (chromogen) and in the other white variety a gene (E) for an enzyme that can change chromogen into a color. Only when chromogen and the enzyme are brought together is a colored flower produced. The cross may be diagrammed in this way:

Parents	CCee (white)	×	ccEE (white)	
Gametes	all Ce		all cE	
F_1	CcEe (colored)	×		CcEe (colored)
Gametes	CE, Ce, cE, ce			CE, Ce, cE, ce

By the checkerboard method, the F_2 phenotypes will be as follows:

9 colored (CCEE, CCEe, CcEE, or CcEe)—both chromogen and enzyme

7 { 3 white (CCee, or Ccee)—only chromogen
3 white (ccEE, or ccEe)—only enzyme
1 white (ccee)—no chromogen or enzyme }

Cumulative factors. Whenever several sets of alleles produce a cumulative effect on the same character, they are called **multiple genes** or factors. Several characteristics in man are influenced by multiple genes. In such cases the characters, instead of being sharply marked off, show continuous variation between two extremes. This is what is called **blending** or **quantitative inheritance.** In this kind of inheritance the children are more or less intermediate between the two parents. The best illustration of such a type is the degree of pigmentation in crosses between the Negro and the white race. The cumulative genes in such crosses have a quantitative expression. A pure-blooded Negro has two pairs of genes on separate chromosomes for pigmentation (AABB). On the other hand, a pure-blooded white will have the genes (aabb) for nonblack. In a mating between a homozygous Negro and a homozygous white, the mulatto (AaBb) will have a skin color intermediate between the black parent and the white. The genes for pigmentation in the cross show incomplete dominance. When such mulattoes are crossed (F_2), the children will show a variety of skin color, depending on the number of genes for pigmentation they inherit. Their skin color will range all the way from pure black (AABB) through dark brown (AABb or AaBB), half-colored (AAbb or AaBb or aaBB), light brown (Aabb or aaBb) to pure white (aabb). In the F_2 there will be the possibility of a child resembling the skin color of either grandparent, and the others will show intermediate grades. It is thus possible for parents heterozygous for skin color to produce children with darker colors and also with lighter colors than themselves.

The relationships can be seen in the following diagram:

Parents	AABB (black)	×	aabb (white)	
Gametes	AB		ab	
F_1	AaBb (mulatto)		×	AaBb (mulatto)
Gametes	AB, Ab, aB, ab			AB, Ab, aB, ab

By the checkerboard method, the F_2 will show this ratio:

1 pure black (AABB)
4 dark brown (AABb or aABB)
6 half-colored mulattoes (AaBb, AAbb, or aaBB)
4 light brown (Aabb, aaBb)
1 pure white (aabb)

The student should realize that when the term "pure white" is used in a cross involving mulattoes, it refers solely to skin color and not to other characteristics, for other racial characteristics are inherited independently. Thus in such a cross an individual may have pure white color (no genes for black) but could have other Negro characteristics.

Although skin color appears to depend on the distribution of two pairs of genes, there are many other traits in human inheritance that involve more than two pairs. These more complicated cases result in more varied ratios than in the simpler cases. When there are so many genes involved in the production of traits, the latter often take the form of distribution curves. One such trait is stature in man, where between a few extremely short and tall individuals, there are many in between these extremes.

Pseudoalleles. Some genes that have similar phenotypic effects may be so closely linked together that they are often considered as multiple alleles. Instead of being a single locus with multiple alleles, there are two or more closely linked loci with genes acting on the same trait. Such genes are called **pseudoalleles,** or **duplicate genes.** The only way in which a geneticist can be sure that pseudoalleles exist is by crossing-over, which is very rare because the genes are so close together. It is thought that pseudoalleles arose in the course of evolution as duplications of original genes and became slightly different in function by mutation. The fact that pseudoalleles act in a similar way indicates a common origin. The problem of pseudoalleles is complicated, and much investigation must be done to clarify it. The condition has been described in fruit flies and corn and affords some insight into the intricate evolution and nature of the gene.

Lethal factors. A lethal gene is one that, when present in a homozygous condition, will cause the death of the offspring. These have been found in both plants and animals, but the classic case is that found in mice. It has been known for a long time that the yellow race of the house mouse *(Mus musculus)* is heterozygous. Whenever two yellow mice are bred together, the progeny are always 2 yellow to 1 nonyellow. In such a case the expected ratio should be 1 pure yellow, 2 hybrid yellow, and 1 pure nonyellow. Examination of the pregnant yellow females shows that the homozygous yellow always dies as an embryo, which accounts for the unusual ratio of 2:1. What causes the lethal condition is not known. Some lethals bring about death in the early stages of the embryo, others in later stages. Some human defects are supposed to be caused by them. Although many lethal genes are recessive and produce their effects only when they are homozygous, there are other lethal genes that are dominant, causing nonlethal effects when heterozygous and lethal effects when homozygous. The creeper fowl, for instance, has very short legs in the heterozygous state; when homozygous, the chicks die before hatching.

SEX DETERMINATION

Before 1902 the cause of sex was variously ascribed to many different external and internal influences. Many of these early beliefs seem ridiculous to modern geneticists in the light of what is now known about sex determination. The first really scientific clue to its cause was discovered in 1902 by McClung, who found that in some species of bugs *(Hemiptera)* two kinds of sperm were formed in equal numbers. One kind contained among its regular set of chromosomes a so-called accessory chromosome that was lacking in the other kind of sperm. Since all the eggs of these species had the same number of haploid chromosomes, half the sperm would have the same number of chromosomes as the eggs and half of them would have one chromosome less. When an egg is fertilized by a spermatozoan carrying the accessory (sex) chromosome, the resulting offspring is a female; when fertilized by the spermatozoan without an accessory chromosome, the offspring is a male. There are, therefore, two kinds of chromosomes in every cell; X chromosomes determine sex (and sex-linked traits), and **autosomes** determine the other bodily traits. The particular type of sex determination just described is often called the XX-XO type, which indicates that the females have 2 X chromosomes and the male only 1 X chromosome (the O stands for its absence).

Later, other types of sex determination were discovered. In man and many other forms there are the same number of chromosomes in each sex, but the sex chromosomes (XX) are alike in the female but unlike (XY) in the male. Hence the human egg contains 22 autosomes + 1 X chromosome; the sperm are of two kinds: half will carry 22 autosomes + 1 X and half will bear 22 autosomes + 1 Y. The Y chromosomes in such cases are diminutive. At fertilization, when 2 X chromosomes come together, the offspring will be a girl; when XY, it will be a boy.

A third type of sex determination is found in birds, moths, and butterflies in which the male has 2 X (or sometimes called ZZ) chromosomes and the female an X and Y (or ZW). In this latter case the male is homozygous for sex and the female is heterozygous.

Whether or not sex in animals is solely determined by the sex chromosomes may well be doubted, notably in the case of *Drosophila*. In this form certain intersexes have been found that suggest that autosomes may play a part in the development of sex. Due to irregularity (**nondisjunction**) in meiosis, it is possible for a fly to have an extra set of autosomes in addition to the regular set. The female fly normally has 6 autosomes (expressed as 2 A) + 2 X chromosomes. If a fly has 3 A + 2 X, instead of being a female as expected from the sex chromosomes' composition, it actually is an intermediate between male and female. The extra autosomes have upset the genic balance, indicating that sex is determined by a quantitative relation between the X chromosomes and autosomes. Also, through irregularities of meiotic divisions, it is possible for a female to have a chromosome complex of 2 A + 3 X, in which case she is called a **superfemale.** A **supermale,** on the other hand, has 3 A + 1 X. In both these cases the sex characteristics are exaggerated toward femaleness or maleness, respectively. These experiments also show that the X chromosomes carry more genes for femaleness and the autosomes more genes for maleness. These abnormalities in sex determination do not invalidate the various types of sex determination described earlier in this section when there is a normal genic balance between the autosomes and the sex chromosomes. In man and the mouse (and perhaps in others), however, the Y chromosome primarily determines maleness. In *Drosophila* an XO individual is a male with abnormal sperm and an XXY fly is a functional female. In man the abnormal condition of an XXY is a sterile male; the XO is a sterile female.

Sex ratios in certain forms can also be influenced by environmental forces. When toad eggs are partially dried out, the proportion of females over males is thereby increased, and variations in diet are also known to upset the ratio between the sexes of some animals.

An interesting abnormality of sex is illustrated by the so-called **gynandromorphs** or **sex mosaics.** In such cases one part of the body shows male and the other female characteristics. It is due to the irregular distribution or loss of sex chromosomes during early development. Thus a zygote with 2 X chromosomes could lose one of the X's from one of the early blastomeres and all the descendants of that cell would have male characteristics; the 2 X cells would be female. Such abnormalities are found in insects in which the sex characteristics of the cell depend mainly on the sex chromosomes. They are also excellent examples for the confirmation of the chromosomal determination of sex.

FIG. 35-14

Cellular determination of sex. **A,** Squamous epithelial cell of human female showing Barr body, which is absent in male. **B,** White blood cell of human female showing accessory nuclear lobule ("drumstick"), which is mostly lacking in male.

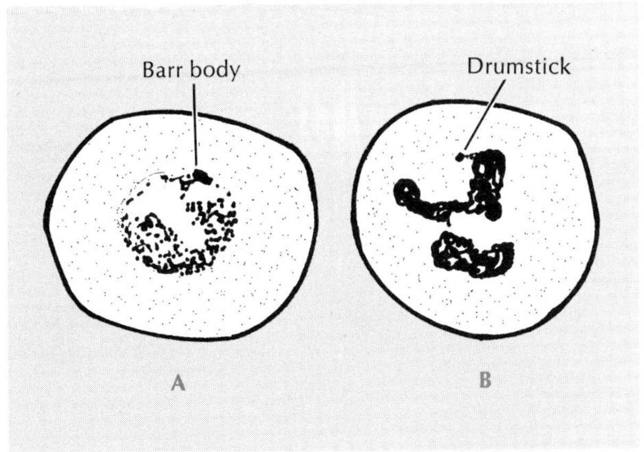

MICROSCOPIC DETERMINATION OF SEX

Sexual dimorphism in the nuclei was first discovered in 1949 by M. Barr and E. G. Bertram. These investigators discovered a chromatin mass in female nuclei that they identified as the heterochromatic parts of 2 X chromosomes in the interphase stage. Such a body, which is often called the nucleolar satellite, or the Barr body (Fig. 35-14, *A*), is found lying against the nuclear membrane. It is not found in the nuclei of the male because the male has only 1 X. Although first found in the cat, the sex chromatin has been found in other organisms including man. An oral smear of the oral epithelium is one of the simplest places in man for demonstrating the Barr body.

Another type of sexual dimorphism is found in the polymorphonuclear leukocyte of blood smears. An accessory nuclear lobule called the "drumstick" (Fig. 35-

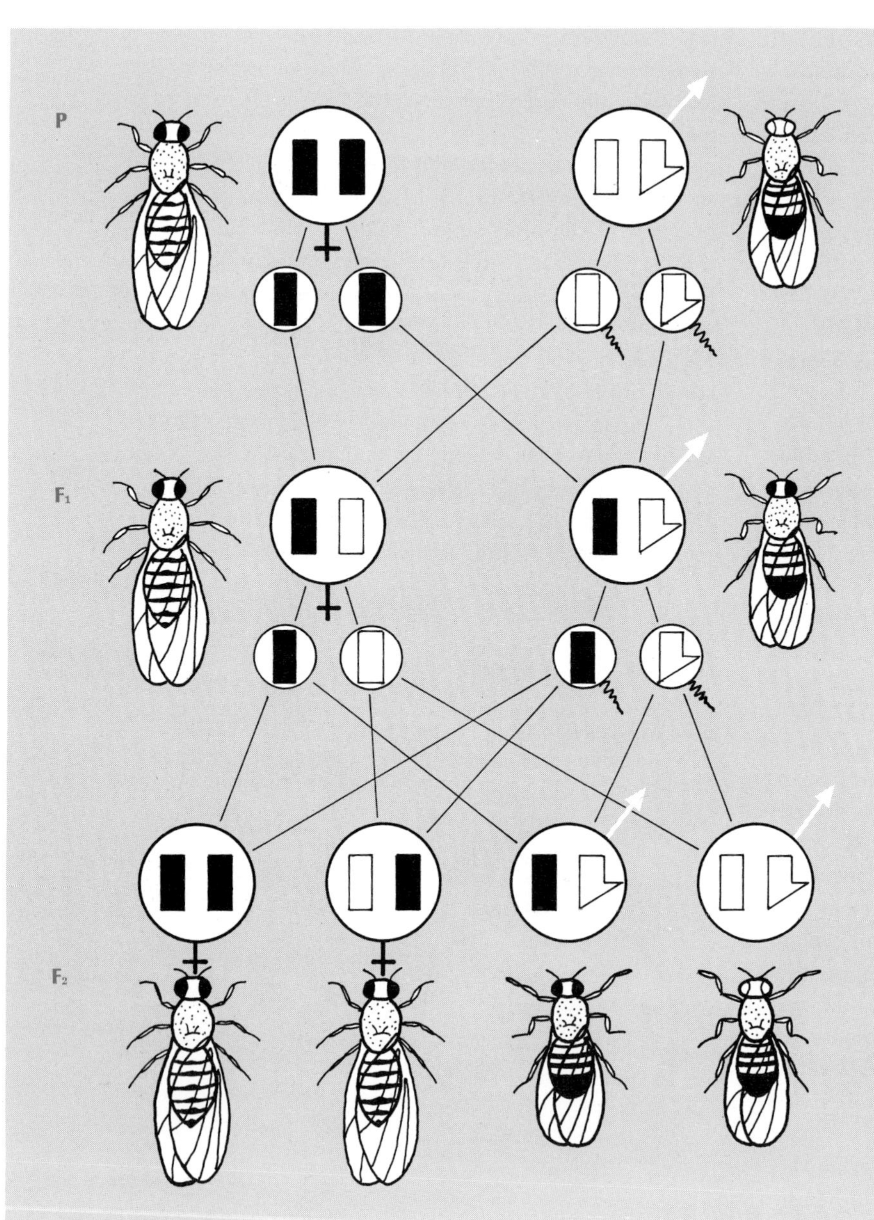

FIG. 35-15

Sex determination and sex-linked inheritance of eye color in fruit fly *(Drosophila)*. Normal red eye color is dominant to white eye color. If a homozygous red-eyed female and a white-eyed male are mated, all F_1 flies are red eyed. When F_1 flies are intercrossed, F_2 yields approximately 1 homozygous red-eyed female and one heterozygous red-eyed female to 1 red-eyed male and 1 white-eyed male. Genes for red eyes (black) and white eyes (white) are carried by sex (X) chromosomes; Y carries no genes for eye color.

14, *B*) is found in leukocytes from females but is lacking or else is very diminutive in males. Both drumsticks and Barr bodies indicate the presence of more than 1 X chromosome. In those abnormal sex chromosome cases, such as the XXX constitution, there may be two Barr bodies and two "drumsticks."

SEX-LINKED INHERITANCE

Sex-linked inheritance refers to the carrying of genes by the X chromosomes for body characters that have nothing to do with sex. The sex chromosomes, in addition to determining sex in an organism, also have genes for other body traits, and because of this the inheritance of these characters are linked with that of sex. The X chromosome is known to contain many such genes, the Y chromosome only a few because of its small size. Such sex-linked traits are not always limited to one sex but

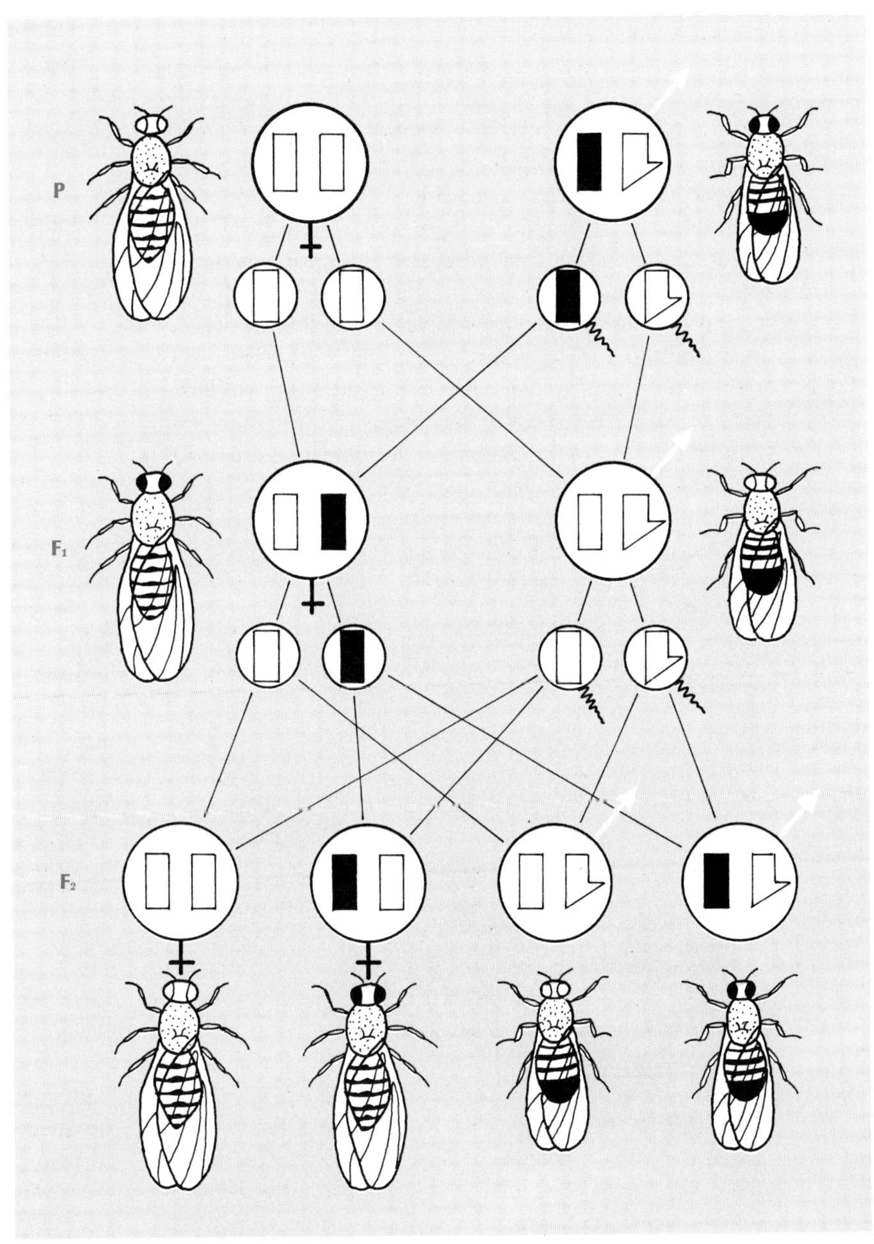

FIG. 35-16

In cross of a homozygous white-eyed female and a red-eyed male (reciprocal cross of Fig. 35-15), F_1 consists of white-eyed males and red-eyed females. In the F_2, there are equal numbers of red-eyed and white-eyed females and red-eyed and white-eyed males.

may be transmitted from the mother to her male offspring or from the father to his female offspring. One of the examples of a sex-linked character was discovered by Morgan in *Drosophila* (Fig. 35-15). The normal eye color of this fly is red, but mutations for white eyes do occur. The genes for eye color are known to be carried in the X chromosome. If a white-eyed male and a red-eyed female are crossed, all the F_1's are red eyed, because this trait is dominant. If these F_1's are interbred, all the females of F_2's will have red eyes and half the males will have red eyes and the other half white eyes. No white-eyed females are found in this generation; only the males have the recessive character (white eyes). The gene for white-eyed, being recessive, should appear in a homozygous condition. However, since the male has only 1 X chromosome (the Y does not carry a gene for eye color), white eyes will appear whenever the X chromosome carries the gene for this trait. If the reciprocal cross is made in which the females are white eyed and the males red eyed, all the F_1 females are red eyed and all the males are white eyed (Fig. 35-16). This is called **crisscross inheritance.** If these F_1's are interbred, the F_2 will show equal numbers of red-eyed and white-eyed males and females.

If the allele for red-eyed is represented by R and white-eyed by r, the following diagrams will show how this eye color inheritance works:

Parents	RR (red ♀)		×	rY (white ♂)
F_1	Rr (red ♀)		×	RY (red ♂)
Gametes	R,r			R,Y
F_2	RR red ♀	RY red ♂	rY white ♂	rR red ♀

Reciprocal cross

Parents	rr (white ♀)		×	RY (red ♂)
F_1	rR (red ♀)		×	rY (white ♂)
Gametes	r,R			r,Y
F_2	rr white ♀	rY white ♂	Rr red ♀	RY red ♂

Many sex-linked genes are known in man, such as bleeder's disease (hemophilia), night blindness, and color blindness. The latter is often used as one of the most striking cases of sex-linked inheritance in man. The particular form of color blindness involved is called daltonism, or the inability to distinguish between red and green. The defect is recessive and requires both genes with the defect in the female but only one defective gene in the male to acquire a visible defect. If the defective allele is represented by an asterisk (*), the following diagram will show the inheritance pattern:

Cross between color-blind male (X*Y) and homozygous normal female (XX)

	X*Y	×	XX
F_1	X*X	×	XY (all normal)
Gametes	X*,X		X,Y
F_2	X*X, X*Y, XX, XY (X*Y, color-blind individual)		

It will be seen from this cross that the color-blind father will transmit the defect to his daughters (who do not show it because each has only one defective gene), but these daughters transmit the defect to one half their sons (who show it because a sex-linked recessive gene in the male has a visible effect).

LINKAGE AND CROSSING-OVER

As has been pointed out previously, all of the pairs of contrasting characters Mendel worked with were in different or nonhomologous chromosomes. This fact formed the basis for his principle of random assortment. But the study of heredity since the discovery of his laws reveals that many traits are inherited together. Since the number of chromosomes in any animal is relatively few compared to the number of traits, it is evident that each chromosome bears many genes. All the genes contained in a chromosome tend to be inherited together and are therefore said to be **linked.** The sex-linked phenomena described in the previous section are examples of linkage; genes borne on chromosomes other than sex chromosomes form **autosomal linkage.** Genes, therefore, occur in linkage groups and there should be as many linkage groups as there are pairs of chromosomes. In *Drosophila,* in which this principle has been worked out most extensively, there are four linkage groups that correspond to the four pairs of chromosomes found in these flies. Small chromosomes have small linkage groups and large chromosomes have large groups. Five hundred genes have been mapped in the fruit fly and all these are distributed among the four pairs.

Linkage alters the expected mendelian ratios, which are based on free assortment. Linkage was first discovered in 1906 by Bateson and Punnett in sweet peas, when it was found that sweet peas with purple flowers had elongated pollen grains and those with red flowers had round pollen grains. How the mendelian ratios can be altered by linkage can best be illustrated by one of Morgan's experiments on *Drosophila.* When a wild-type fly with gray body and long wings is crossed with a fly bearing two recessive mutant characters of black body and vestigial wings, the dihybrids (F_1) all have gray bodies and long wings. If a male of one of the F_1's is testcrossed with a female with a black body and vestigial wings, the flies are all gray-long and black-vestigial. If there had been free assortment, that is, if the various characters had been carried on different chromosomes, the expected offspring would have been represented by four types of flies: gray-long, gray-vestigial, black-long, and black-vestigial. However, in this case gray-long and black-vestigial had entered the dihybrid cross together and stayed together, or linked.

Linkage, however, is usually only partial, for it is broken up frequently by what is known as **crossing-over.** In this phenomenon the characters usually separate with a certain frequency. How often two genes break their linkage, or their percentage of crossing-over, varies with different genes. In some cases this percentage of crossing-over is only 1% or less; with others it may be nearly 50%. The explanation for crossing-over lies in the synapsis of homologous chromosomes during the maturation division when two nonsister chromatids sometimes become intertwined and, before separating from each other, exchange homologous portions of the chromatids (and the genes they bear) (Fig. 35-17).

Cytologic proof for crossing-over was demonstrated by Stern in 1931. By using strains of fruit flies that had distinctive X chromosomes formed by translocation (in which a portion of one chromosome abnormally becomes attached to another chromosome), he followed certain sex-linked traits and chromosomal configurations through crosses. He was thus able to demonstrate that there was an actual visible exchange of chromosomal segments that agreed with genetic results. If the genes are arranged in a linear order on the chromosomes, the closer any two linked genes are, the less chance there is that they will break their linkage and go to different chromosomes; the greater the distance between any two genes, the more likely they will separate from each other. This crossing-over thus makes possible new combinations of linked genes.

FIG. 35-17

Simple case of crossing-over between two chromatids of homologous chromosomes. Block of genes shown in black is thus transferred to white and vice versa.

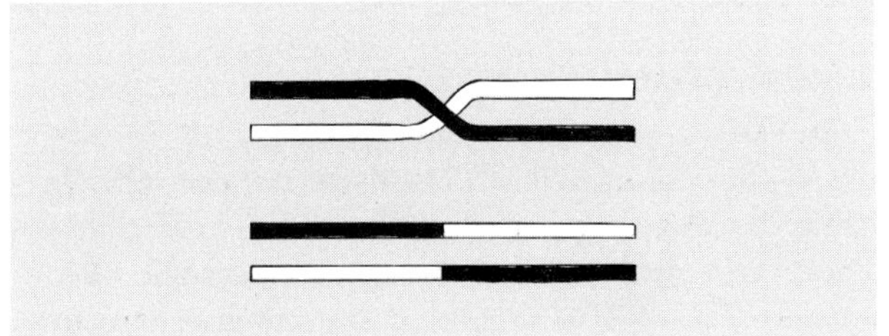

Crossing-over makes possible the construction of chromosome maps and proof that the genes lie in a linear order on the chromosomes. To illustrate how this is done one may take a hypothetical case of three genes (A, B, C) on the same chromosome. In the determination of their comparative linear position on the chromosome, it will first be necessary to find the crossing-over value between any two of these genes. If A and B have a crossing-over of 2% and B and C of 8%, then the crossing-over percentage between A and C should be either the sum $(2 + 8)$ or the difference $(8 - 2)$. If it is 10%, B lies between A and C; if 6%, A is between B and C. By laborious genetic experiments over many years, the famed chromosome maps in *Drosophila* were worked out in this manner (Fig. 35-18). Cytologic investigations on the giant chromosomes since these maps were made tend to prove the correctness of the linear order, if not the actual position, of the genes on the chromosomes. There is no evidence of crossing-over occurring in the giant chromosomes themselves, and it is also absent in the male *Drosophila*.

THE GENE AND MUTATION

Among the variations that appear in the makeup of animals, there are both hereditary and nonhereditary kinds. Nonhereditary variations are due to environmental changes such as nutrition, light, heat, and other factors that operate during the development of the animal. Such fluctuating variations occur in all animals and are not hereditary. The hereditary variations are due to changes in the genes or chromosomes and are referred to as **mutations.** Ordinarily, genes are very stable, but they are molecules and are subject to change under the influence of many kinds of factors. Some changes arise spontaneously, and others can be induced by artificial agencies. Undoubtedly many more mutations occur than are actually seen, but most of them are recessive and produce visible effects only when they are homozygous. Mutations happen in both somatic and germinal tissue, but only the latter ones are transmitted sexually. Moreover, many mutant genes are concerned with abnormalities or other defects and thus have little significance in the evolutionary development of animals. Oth-

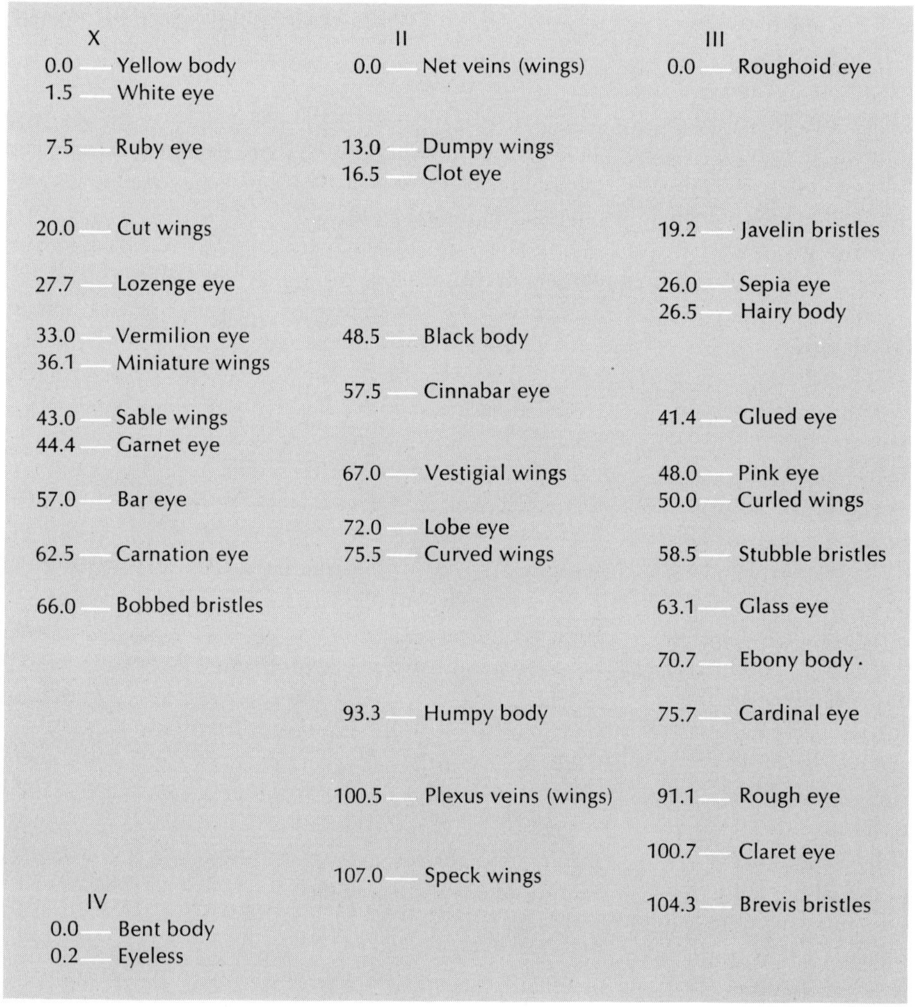

X		II		III	
0.0	Yellow body	0.0	Net veins (wings)	0.0	Roughoid eye
1.5	White eye				
7.5	Ruby eye	13.0	Dumpy wings		
		16.5	Clot eye		
20.0	Cut wings			19.2	Javelin bristles
27.7	Lozenge eye			26.0	Sepia eye
				26.5	Hairy body
33.0	Vermilion eye	48.5	Black body		
36.1	Miniature wings				
		57.5	Cinnabar eye		
43.0	Sable wings			41.4	Glued eye
44.4	Garnet eye				
		67.0	Vestigial wings	48.0	Pink eye
57.0	Bar eye			50.0	Curled wings
		72.0	Lobe eye		
62.5	Carnation eye	75.5	Curved wings	58.5	Stubble bristles
66.0	Bobbed bristles			63.1	Glass eye
				70.7	Ebony body
		93.3	Humpy body	75.7	Cardinal eye
		100.5	Plexus veins (wings)	91.1	Rough eye
				100.7	Claret eye
		107.0	Speck wings		
IV				104.3	Brevis bristles
0.0	Bent body				
0.2	Eyeless				

FIG. 35-18

Chromosome maps of certain representative genes in *Drosophila*. One chromosome of each pair is shown with figures, indicating relative positions of genes in crossover units from end of chromosome.

ers, however, have proved quite useful, such as hornless Hereford cattle. Also, the rate of mutation varies greatly in various animals and for different genes. Many genes are far more mutable than others. The gene for eye color in the fruit fly has at least 18 mutant forms that are variants of the normal red eye. Mutations to white and to vermilion eyes have occurred many times. This spontaneous mutation rate in *Drosophila* has been estimated to be from 1 in 100,000 to 1 in several billion per gene per generation. A mutation involves a change in a gene, not an actual loss of a gene. This is proved by the fact that a mutant gene may revert back to the original gene. Similar mutations, known as **parallel mutations,** may also occur in closely related species of animals. One significant fact about gene mutations is that usually only one gene mutates at a time; mass mutations are very rare.

In the past 25 years or so, many mutations have been induced by artificial methods such as x-rays, radium, and temperature. By such means it has been possible to increase the mutation rate more than a hundredfold. Many mutations so induced were similar to those that arose spontaneously and were heritable. Some of them were also lethal and harmful. These induced mutations were first discovered in *Drosophila* by Muller, but they have since been produced in bacteria, yeasts, and other forms.

CHROMOSOMAL CHANGES

The term "mutation" is usually restricted to alteration within the gene itself, but there are also other heritable variations associated with chromosomal changes. These are often referred to as chromosomal aberrations and involve variations in the number, structure, and arrangement of chromosomes. These are usually gross changes in the chromosomes and affect many genes at one time. The main types of chromosomal changes are loss of a part of a chromosome (**deletion**), shifting of a part of a chromosome over to another chromosome (**duplication**), rearrangement of parts of a chromosome so that a block of genes is inverted (**inversion**), and the gaining of a whole set or sets of chromosomes (**polyploidy**). This latter term refers to those conditions in which there are more than the diploid number so that triploids, tetraploids, and even higher combinations are formed. Such aberrant conditions arise through a duplication of the chromosome complement by nondisjunction in the reduction division of maturation. Such polyploids differ in characters from the original parent stock. Although most of such cases are found in plants, they are not unknown among animals, particularly some amphibians.

HYBRID VIGOR

Hybrid vigor, or **heterosis,** refers to the greater vitality and vigor manifested by the hybrids produced by crossing individuals of two pure races that differ from each other in a number of genes. Such hybrids are often bigger and more vigorous than either parent. What actually happens is that such crosses may bring together dominant genes for vigor in the hybrid, provided each of the pure line races carries a vigor gene lacking in the other. In this way it is conceivable that the hybrid may contain homozygous dominant vigor genes that would account for its more desirable traits. There is also the possibility that some genes in the heterozygous condition in the hybrid might produce more vigor than genes in the homozygous state found in the inbred race. Hybrid vigor, however, tends to be lost in succeeding generations when hybrids are crossed, because the desirable dominant genes may segregate out again and the undesirable recessives would again make their effects visible.

There are many examples of hybrid vigor in both plants and animals. Among the former is the valuable hybrid corn, which enabled the farmers of the United States to greatly increase their corn yield; among animals one of the best examples is the mule, which is the hybrid between a jackass and a mare and is stronger and sturdier than either parent. To overcome the infertility of inbred lines in hybrid corn production, the **double cross** method is employed. Four inbred lines (A, B, C, D) are intercrossed in pairs (A-B and C-D). The hybrids of these two crosses (AB and CD) are then crossed to produce the commercial seed of the farmer.

Many studies have been made on hybrid vigor in man. A study of history usually shows that great civilizations are preceded by a mixing of races. Race crossing, even among subgroups of one race, often results in exceptional vitality and vigor. The flowering of Greek culture a few centuries before the Christian era has been shown to be due to a preliminary close inbreeding of many independent political units, thus producing many types of gene pools, followed by a recombination of these genes in crosses (hybrid vigor) when political barriers were broken down in the later, larger city units. Close inbreeding in the human race usually results in reduced vitality, many defective traits, and a pronounced sterility of the stock.

CYTOPLASMIC INHERITANCE

All the genetic behavior so far considered has stressed the importance of the nuclear elements (chromosomes and genes) as the bearers of heredity. Does the cytoplasm bear any hereditary factors? Of course, the effects of the gene are carried out in the cytoplasm, such as growth, development, secretion, and enzymatic action, but are there self-duplicating genetic units in the cytoplasm itself? Organisms inherit the information both that specifies the types of substance synthesized in the cells and specifies the cell structure in which these substances act. The genetic code pattern considered earlier explains how the types of substances (proteins or enzymes) are inherited. At present it is not entirely clear whether or not the basic structures of cells can be attributed to nuclear genes. Evidence for cytoplasmic inheritance is often sought in reciprocal cross differences (for example, whether or not the genetic type is introduced into a cross by the father or the mother) because the egg (maternal contribution) contains most of the cytoplasm of the new organism, and the phenotype of the latter should follow that of the mother. A few cases of cytoplasmic inheritance seem well established. One of these is the chlorophyll-bearing plastids in the cytoplasm of certain plants. These are self-duplicating bodies and some of them are always maternal in character regardless of the kind introduced by the pollen in the cross. Another case is the cortical pattern of certain paramecia (T. M. Sonneborn) that has been explained by nonchromosomal inheritance. When two paramecia, one with a double cortical pattern and the other with a single cortical pattern, conjugate, it was occasionally found that one conjugant had received a piece of the cortex of the other and became intermediate in appearance between the other two types and thereafter reproduced true to this new intermediate type.

Mention has already been made in Chapter 10, Phylum Protozoa, of the kappa substance in the cytoplasm of certain strains of paramecia. This kappa substance produces paramecin that can kill sensitive strains containing no kappa substance. When individuals of killer clones conjugate with members of sensitive strains, the latter will become killers only when they receive some cytoplasm in the exchange, indicating that the cytoplasm carries the plasmagenes, which such cytoplasmic bodies are called. Kappa particles have many of the characteristics of genes, for they are self-duplicating and contain DNA. However, it has been shown that the maintenance of the kappa substance is actually dependent on a nuclear gene. Thus, in some cases at least, there is an interrelationship between plasmagenes and nuclear genes and some geneticists consider the former as replicas of nuclear genes that are released into cytoplasm. Plasmagenes have many resemblances to viruses, such as self-duplication, cytoplasmic location, and capability of transmissible mutations, but they do not cause diseases in the cells in which they are found. The demonstration of plasmagenes bids to shed some light upon the difficult problem of developmental differentiation.

Annotated references

See Chapter 36, pp. 757-758.

• APPLIED GENETICS; HUMAN HEREDITY

PRACTICAL APPLICATION OF GENETICS

● Although genetics as a science has developed within the last 50 years, many of the practical applications of heredity extend as far back as the dawn of civilization itself. The improvement of domestic plants and animals has always interested man. Has the discovery of the precise way by which the laws of heredity work helped him to make additional progress? It is not amiss for the zoology student to look at a few of the ways by which man has been able to use the principles of hereditary formulas to his own advantage.

Methods of increasing productivity in plants and animals. Plant and animal breeders have two main objectives—to produce strains that give greater productivity and to produce those that are pure in their pedigree. The latter enables the breeder to control and predict the outcome of his crosses. One of the first problems facing the breeder is to distinguish between environmental and heritable characters. This is not always easy because most characters can be influenced by environmental factors. Desirable hereditary qualities are carefully selected and propagated by breeding. Much effort is made to use pure lines to control the desired qualities. Plant geneticists make use of hybridization between different strains of plants. Often the production of pure lines is for the purpose of crossing with other strains to take advantage of hybrid vigor, a practice used by both plant and animal breeders. Practical application of Mendel's laws are freely used and form the basis for most plant and animal experiments, greatly simplifying the work in comparison with methods before Mendel's time. The testcross, for instance, is a common procedure in getting homozygous stocks.

The alert breeder takes advantage of new combinations and variations produced by crossing different strains, by mutations, and by crossovers.

Hybrid varieties. The production of hybrid corn was one of the great triumphs of genetics. In the 30 years since it was introduced, the yield of corn per acre has been increased 25% to 50%. Pure lines of corn were found to be of low fertility and gave scanty yields. When these pure strains were crossed, the hybrids showed a remarkable increase in both fertility and general yield. Only the seed of the first generation following a cross can be used, for later generation seed tends to produce segregation of undesirable traits, as explained under hybrid vigor, p. 747. This makes it necessary for the farmer to buy his seed each season. The principle of first-generation hybrids has been applied successfully to other plants such as squash, pine trees, and cucumbers.

Progeny selection. Selection, an effective tool in the hands of the breeder, may be done by **phenotypic selection** or by **progeny selection.** The first is based on the appearance of the desired trait or traits in the individual. This method has obvious disadvantages because the phenotypic appearance of the animal or plant is not necessarily an indication of its genotype. For this reason, prize-winning stock may not transmit desirable traits to its offspring. Progeny selection, however, is based on selecting those individuals that produce desirable offspring so that the genotype is the chief basis of selection. Many great successes have been scored this way, such as high milk-producing cattle, poultry with higher yield of eggs, and desirable strains of tobacco.

Disease-resistant strains. By careful selection and breeding, plant breeders produce varieties that do not become infected by common plant diseases. In this way it has been possible to develop wheat that is resistant to rust and corn to smut. However, many disease germs mutate, and some of the mutants may be able to attack plants that were formerly disease resistant. Constant vigilance is necessary to spot these changes and to introduce a new resistant gene into the genetic constitution of the stock.

Detection and control of lethal genes. Many cases of lethal genes, or genes that destroy the individual, are known among stock breeders. Some of these produce visible effects in the offspring, such as the peculiar "bulldog" calf (so-called because of its facial appearance) and the creeper fowl with unusually short appendages, and may not kill until a late stage of development, but others may destroy early without noticeable effects in the offspring. Some lethal genes produce their effects only in the homozygous condition and others when they are heterozygous. In the first case their detection is not always easy, for as long as the lethal gene is carried along with a normal one no harm is done. But there is always the possibility, especially in close inbreeding, that two lethal genes will be brought together. Stock breeders can by trial matings find these lethals and exclude such animals from breeding. Some plants are also known to bear hidden lethal genes.

Polyploidy. Many polyploids have been experimentally produced, such as tulips, roses, fruit trees, tomatoes, and even cotton, and represent an improvement over the original stock. In cases when polyploids cannot breed true, as in triploids, they may be propagated asexually.

Application of biochemical genetics. Another practical application of an unusual form is the use of molds, such as *Neurospora,* in determining the presence of certain vitamins and amino acids. When these molds are irradiated, some of their genes may be made to mutate so that they lose the power to synthesize specific vitamins and amino acids. Apparently this failure to synthesize is due to the loss of certain enzymes. Each enzyme is dependent on a single gene, and when this gene mutates, its enzyme suffers as a result. Strains of mold that lack the power to synthesize a particular amino acid will not grow in a medium deficient in this specific amino acid. It is thus possible to determine whether a culture contains or lacks specific vitamins or amino acids by ascertaining its ability to support certain such strains of mold.

HUMAN HEREDITY

The study of human inheritance is one of the most difficult fields in genetics. Experimental breeding, the key to most genetic studies, is impractical. It is also difficult to study man's heredity from a cytogenetic viewpoint because of the many chromosomes (46) that he possesses as compared with simpler forms. Moreover, man is a relatively slow-breeding animal, he is largely heterozygous in his hereditary makeup, and he is influenced in his development to a greater extent by an extremely complicated and varied environment. Despite these handicaps, however, a great deal of information is known about his heredity. There is every reason to suppose that man follows the same principles of genetics as those of other organisms. Many studies of human inheritance have stressed congenital defects because such traits can easily be followed through many generations and are easily recognized. Many of these defects are dominant, and their visible effects are not hidden as are recessive traits. Naturally much of the information about human inheritance is fragmentary and some of it is conflicting, but significant achievements are being made in the field.

Genetic diseases

The work of G. W. Beadle and E. L. Tatum on the mold *Neurospora,* by which it was shown that a single gene controlled the specificity of a particular enzyme, has helped explain many inherited human diseases. An English physician, A. E. Garrod, contended in 1908 that enzyme deficiencies were to blame for certain disorders that he described as "inborn errors of metabolism." Among such disorders is **alkaptonuria,** which is inherited as a recessive gene. In this disease the person is lacking in an enzyme that oxidizes homogentisic acid, an intermediate product in the metabolism of the two amino acids phenylalanine and tyrosine. Normally, homogentisic acid is oxidized to carbon dioxide and water, but when a certain oxidase enzyme is lacking, the homogentisic acid accumulates in the blood, is excreted by the kidneys, and turns black on exposure to the air. A more common and far more serious genetic disorder is phenylketonuria (PKU), which is produced by the absence of the enzyme phenylalanine hydroxylase carried by a recessive gene. A person afflicted with this disorder cannot convert phenylalanine into tyrosine. Some phenylalanine is converted into phenylpyruvic acid, which produces injury to the nervous system and mental deficiency. The disorder is detected by a simple test with blood or urine and can be controlled by restricting phenylalanine in the diet.

About one person in 20,000 has the condition known as albinism, which is characterized by the lack of the dark pigment melanin in the skin and hair. Albinism is caused by the absence of the enzyme tyrosine, which is necessary for the synthesis of melanin. Albinism is also inherited as a recessive gene, and an individual must be homozygous for the condition to show it.

Many other such genetic diseases have been uncovered in man in the past decade or so. Almost all traits are produced by a sequence of chemical reactions, each under the control of a specific enzyme. With the one-to-one relationship of gene and enzyme, it is easy to see that a change in one gene may influence the whole expression of the trait because of the lack of a single enzyme.

Some genetic disorders that are caused by recessive genes may show some effect in a heterozygous condition. One of these is the sickle cell mutant gene that produces the abnormal S-hemoglobin. This hemoglobin differs from normal hemoglobin in having a valine amino acid in place of the glutamic acid molecule in a chain of more than 300 amino acids. A person with one gene for normal hemoglobin and one gene for the abnormal S-hemoglobin will usually suffer a mild anemia. However, such persons have a better resistance to falciparum, or malignant malaria, which may account for the high prevalence of the heterozygotes in parts of Africa. A homozygous condition of S-hemoglobin is usually fatal.

Although most genetic diseases have selective disadvantages and natural selection tends to eliminate them whenever they appear in the population, recurrent mutations furnish fresh cases, usually with a definite frequency for each gene responsible. The examples already described are almost entirely recessive, and the expressed trait in the homozygous condition is of relative infrequency, although the hidden recessive gene may be present in fairly large numbers in the population as a whole. Albinism, for example, occurs in only one person among 20,000, but the recessive gene is found once in every 70 persons. Dominant genes would show up immediately if present.

Genetic defects are very common in the population and may be on the increase. Geneticists estimate that at least one person in every four or five of the population is born with a defective gene, which can bring about serious consequences to the population, depending on whether the genes are dominant or recessive. It is thought that one conception in every five results in a genetic defect that destroys the individual at some time before maturity. In addition, various types of abnormalities, not necessarily lethal, are caused by both dominant and recessive genes. These include sex-linked and nonsex-linked mutant genes as well as those caused by gross chromosomal abnormalities. The noted geneticist H. J. Muller estimates that each individual carries at least eight recessive lethal genes in his sex cells. These will cause death only in the homozygous condition, the possibilities of which can be increased by marriage of relatives.

Roles of heredity and environment

If the human organism is the product of both heredity and environment, which is the more important factor? This question has been asked many times, but no outright answer can be given at present. Even the naive know that no kind of environment can transform a monkey into a human being. Each kind of animal has something that makes it different from all other kinds, and this something we refer to as heredity. The genes determine the general pattern of development, but at every step of the way these genes must interact with environmental factors. Although the genic constitution within the nucleus remains essentially the same in all cells and tissues, the cytoplasm undergoes various changes under the joint influence of genes on the one hand and a constantly changing environment on the other. Both these factors are, therefore, important in the realization of the individual's possibilities.

Of the two factors, heredity is relatively stable, whereas the environment is constantly changing. Even during intrauterine existence, the important factors of nutrition are operating, as well as numerous hormones from the mother's body. Here there are interactions between the genes of the embryo and the environment of the uterus. After birth, additional factors, including complex social ones, have a marked effect in the final molding of the individual character. Genes direct the general course of development, but their potentiality can be expressed or suppressed by the environment.

Experiments have been made to determine the relative influence of environment and heredity on lower animals. Results are not always conclusive because of the complicated factors involved. Such work is restricted in the case of man, but attempts have been made to determine the relative influence of heredity and environment on identical twins. Identical twins come from one egg and have the same set of genes, so their hereditary patterns are alike. What differences they manifest in their expressed characters should therefore be due to environment. Studies made on twins reared in different homes and under different social and other environmental conditions show a remarkable similarity in height, weight, and other physical characteristics. However, their mental traits, I.Q., and general intelligence may show some differences as well as many cultural aspects of their characters. Such investigations indicate that hereditary factors dominate in influencing the general development and personality of the individual, although environment, such as education, does have a bearing upon the general intelligence level of the individual.

Hair and eye color

The color of the hair seems to be determined by several genes or several pairs of modifying factors, at least in certain cases. Often the pigmentation of hair and eye color are correlated, for the darker shades of hair are usually accompanied by darker eyes. In general, blond hair is recessive to the darker shades, but the presence of varying shades of blond and dark hair indicates a blending effect or the interaction of more than one pair of genes. Red hair is recessive to the other shades of hair. One may be homozygous for genes for red hair and have a darkish shade of red hair color because of the presence of genes for darker hair.

The color of the eyes is due to the presence and location of pigment in the iris. If the pigment is on the back of the iris, the eyes are blue; if the pigment is on both back and front of the iris, the eyes are of the darker shades. If pigment is lacking altogether (albinism), the eyes are pinkish because of the blood vessels. The pigment is actually dark and produces the varying eye colors by the reflection of light. Blue eyes are recessive to the other eye shades, and when the parents are blue eyed, the children are normally blue eyed. Blue-eyed children may appear also if parents are heterozygous for the darker eye colors. The manner in which eye color is inherited indicates that there are many kinds of genes, all variant forms of the gene for dark color, which behave in a simple mendelian way in their hereditary expression. In exceptional cases, environmental factors may prevent the full expression of eye pigment so that homozygous dark-eyed parents could have a blue-eyed child.

Blood group inheritance

The inheritance of blood groups follows Mendel's laws. This inheritance is based on three genes or allelomorphs, I^a, I^b, and i. I^a and I^b are antigens and are dominant, and they never appear in a child's blood unless present in at least one of the parents; i represents no antigen and is recessive to the antigens. Neither I^a nor I^b is dominant to each other, but each is dominant to i. The relationships of the blood groups and genotypes are as follows:

Blood groups	O	A	B	AB
Genotypes	ii	I^aI^a or I^ai	I^bI^b or I^bi	I^aI^b

If both parents belong to group O, a child must also belong to group O. On the other hand, if one parent belongs to group A and the other to B, the child could belong in any one of the four groups. The various possibilities of inheritance are shown in Table 36-1.

This pattern of heredity has some practical applications in medicolegal cases involving disputed parentage. From the possibilities given in Table 36-1, it is seen that, if a child in question has group A and the supposed parents group O, it is obvious that the child could not belong to them. On the other hand, if the parents belong to groups A and B, the blood tests would prove nothing, for the parents could have children of all groups.

Evolutionists have laid much stress on the geographic distribution of blood groups among the various racial populations. The frequencies of the blood groups O, A, B, and AB have been tabulated by investigators for most races all over the world, although data are scanty and incomplete in many instances. Among the interesting facts revealed by these studies is the absence of the allele B in the American Indians and Australian aborigines, the high frequency of B in Asia and India and its decline in Western Europe, and the high fre-

TABLE 36-1

Inheritance of blood groups

Parent groups	Possible children groups	Impossible children groups
O × O	O	A, B, AB
O × A	O, A	B, AB
O × B	O, B	A, AB
A × A	O, A	B, AB
A × B	O, A, B, AB	None
B × B	O, B	A, AB
O × AB	A, B	O, AB
A × AB	A, B, AB	O
B × AB	A, B, AB	O
AB × AB	A, B, AB	O

quency of group O in Ireland and Iceland. The distribution of the Rh factor also shows a varied pattern. Reasons for these varied distributions are obscure, but some explanations have been advanced, such as genetic drift involving small populations, natural selection, and migration and mixing of races.

Inheritance of Rh factor

As stated in a former section, about 85% of American people possess a dominant gene called **Rh,** which causes the formation of a special antigen in the blood. The remaining 15% have the recessive allele **rh** that cannot produce this antigen. Investigations have disclosed that there are many other alleles at this locus, thus greatly increasing the possible blood groups. Thus there are several kinds of Rh-positive and Rh-negative persons. At present at least eight different alleles are found in the series designated as R^1, R^2, R^0, R^z, r′, r″, r^y, r. The capital letters indicate those alleles that give an Rh-positive reaction; the small letters stand for the Rh-negative ones. Although all of these subtypes are inherited and produce antigens, it appears that the allele Rh^0 is mainly responsible for the clinical cases of erythroblastosis fetalis. The genetics of all these subtypes becomes involved when one considers all their possible combinations. They represent one of the most extensive groups of multiple alleles known. Other antigens are caused by factors independent of Rh, such as the so-called Kell antigen produced by an uncommon dominant gene that, in incompatibility cases, can cause serious hemolytic diseases.

Other antigens that do not react to form antibodies and are of no clinical significance are the M and N antigens. No allele for the absence of these antigens has been found. All persons are typed as M, N, or MN. In their inheritance pattern, two M-type parents will produce only M children; two N-type parents, only N children; and types M and N parents will give all these types of children in the ratio of 1M:2MN:1N.

Inheritance of mental characteristics

Mental traits, both good and bad, are known to be inherited, although because of environmental influences it is not always possible to appraise them genetically. Heredity is in general responsible for the basic patterns of intelligence and mental deficiencies, although environmental factors can and do influence the development of intellectual capacities. Intelligence is not a single hereditary unit; apparently many different genes are responsible for its expression. The field of inheritance affords many examples of both outstanding abilities and mental defects being handed down through long family histories. One is forced to conclude that hereditary factors have played a major part in the determination of these intellectual strengths or weaknesses. The best kind of environment in the world cannot make a superior intelligence out of one who has inherited a moron potentiality, and conversely, superior hereditary abilities may always remain mediocre unless stimulated by favorable environmental factors. Identical twins, for instance, with exactly the same genes for intelligence may show considerable difference in their I.Q.s when reared under different advantages of education and culture.

There are several million feebleminded persons in the United States, but only a small percent have come from feebleminded parents. The great majority of them are born of parents heterozygous for this trait. Such parents may be in all particulars normal for intelligence and carry the recessive gene for feeblemindedness. Recessive genes are hidden and may continue so until they become homozygous. That is why the sterilization of feebleminded persons to prevent them from reproducing their kind would eliminate only part of such defectives.

The inheritance of special abilities, such as that of music, has been thoroughly investigated, and the evidence indicates that talents for music may have a constitutional basis. The hereditary pattern, however, is very complex and probably involves a number of genes. It is not always possible either to distinguish between the influences of heredity and environment in musical families. Special talents may be to a considerable extent independent of general intelligence, for some individuals of marked ability along some lines may have a low I.Q.

Should first cousins be allowed to marry?

The marriage of near relatives such as first cousins would bring recessive genes together in a homozygous condition. It is logical that descendants from a near common ancestor are going to share his genes. The more remote the relationship, the less is this possibility. Inbreeding does intensify many kinds of defects such as feeblemindedness, congenital deafness, and albinism. For this reason, in most states marriage of first cousins is prohibited. Of course, inheritance can work both ways, for good as well as for bad. If there should be desirable genes in a family stock, marriage between cousins should bring these traits together and produce superior children. Laws, however, are made with reference to the prevention of undesirable traits instead of the promotion of favorable ones.

Inheritance of twinning

Fraternal twins, which are four or five times as common as identical ones, result from the independent fertilization of separate ova by separate sperm. They are simply conceived and born together, and genetically they have the same likeness and differences as ordinary brothers and sisters. They may be of the same or opposite sex. **Identical** twins come from a single zygote that has split during its early stages. They have the same genetic constitution and are always of the same sex. Identical twins show a remarkable similarity in their general characters, both physical and mental. When the halves of the zygote fail to separate completely, Siamese twins are the result.

The inheritance of twinning is very complex, but there seems to be a hereditary basis for many cases of twins. This hereditary tendency is found in domestic animals as well as in man. Sheep, especially, exhibit strains of twinning. Environmental factors may play a part in the production of multiple births, but what they are is largely unknown. Both father and mother seem to influence the heredity of twinning. It is not too difficult to see how the father could induce the formation of identical twins because something about his sperm might cause the zygote to split. It is more difficult to see how he could cause fraternal twins. Some biologists suggest that the female releases two eggs at ovulation, of which only one is normally fertilized. But if the sperm are unusually virile, both eggs could be fertilized. More puzzling still is the fact that older parents tend to have more twins than younger ones. There are also racial variations. Negroes have more twins than whites, but most Mongolian people have fewer than whites. The prenatal mortality rate of twins may be much higher than that of single conceptions, which would make a difference in the ratios.

Inheritance of certain physical traits in man

It is impossible to deal with man's heredity in a simple mendelian ratio. Information about his heredity must be acquired by inspection and analysis of family life histories, or pedigrees. Such a plan involves the formation of hypotheses to explain hereditary expression and careful checking of these hypotheses to determine whether they apply to the data obtained. The inheritance of many abnormal characters has been stressed in family pedigrees because they are easily followed.

Following are some of the more common traits, but their dominance or recessiveness is not always clear cut.

Dominant	Recessive
Curly hair	Straight hair
Dark hair	Light hair
Nonred hair	Red hair
Dark skin color	Light skin color
Hairy body	Normal hair
Skin pigmentation	Albinism (no pigment)
Brown eyes	Blue or gray eyes
Hazel eyes	Blue or gray eyes
Ichthyosis (scaly skin)	Normal skin
Near or farsightedness	Normal vision
Hereditary cataract	Normal vision
Astigmatism	Normal vision
Glaucoma	Normal vision
Normal hearing	Deaf-mutism
Normal color vision	Color blindness
Normal blood clotting	Hemophilia
Broad lips	Thin lips
Large eyes	Small eyes
Long eyelashes	Short eyelashes
Short stature	Tall stature
Polydactylism (extra fingers or toes)	Normal number of digits
Brachydactylism (short digits)	Normal length of digits
Syndactylism (webbed digits)	Normal digits
Normal muscles	Progressive muscular atrophy
Hypertension	Normal blood pressure
Diabetes insipidus	Normal excretory system
Enlarged colon	Normal colon
Tasters (of certain substances)	Nontasters
Huntington's chorea	Normal
Normal mentality	Schizophrenia
Nervous temperament	Phlegmatic temperament
Average intellect	Very great or very small
Normal intellect	Feeblemindedness
Migraine headache	Normal

Application of genetics to medical problems

Medical men realize that hereditary patterns have an important bearing on clinical problems. Disease germs are not carried through genes from one generation to another, but many authorities have found marked susceptibility to a particular disease running through families.

Some inherited traits have already been pointed out, such as color blindness, Rh factor, and deaf-mutism. Certain susceptibilities to cancer are inherited in both man and other animals. Children of parents who carry abnormal traits should be watched as they develop. For instance, hemolytic icterus, a condition in which the spleen is enlarged, is inherited as a dominant gene and about half of the offspring of a parent carrying this gene should be expected to have the defect. When such is known, it is the duty of the physician to check the suspected children frequently and detect the disorder in time to remove the spleen before serious damage is done. Some forms of hypertension have a hereditary basis, and children of such a parent should be trained to conform to conditions that will not aggravate the malady. It is possible for doctors to facilitate their diagnosis of obscure diseases by knowing whether the family and near relatives carry susceptibilities to them.

Many of our great universities have heredity clinics, such as California, Michigan, Ohio State, Oklahoma, Texas, Minnesota, and Tulane, where expertly trained geneticists give counseling and information on problems of heredity.

Influence of radiation on human heredity

Radiation and radioactive substances such as x-rays, radium rays, and ultraviolet light greatly increase the mutation rate of the gene. Most of these gene mutations are lethal and either destroy or else produce abnormalities of various types in the offspring of animals exposed under certain conditions to irradiation. Since the development and use of the atomic bomb in modern warfare, geneticists have been concerned about the possible genetic effect these could have on man. The explosion of an atom bomb releases large amounts of ionizing radiations that differ in their ability to penetrate tissues. Many other factors affect the amount of damage radiation can do, such as the intensity and duration of exposure, whether the exposure occurs immediately after the explosion or later, etc.

In the light of the fierce controversy that is raging over the possible effects of radiation in an atomic age, it may suffice to summarize certain generalizations that the data seem to substantiate:

1. All life is constantly exposed to high-energy radiations. Some of this radiation comes from natural sources, such as cosmic rays from outer space, radioactive elements (radium, thorium, radioactive isotopes of potassium), and atomic disintegration within the organism; some comes from the technologic use of radioactive substances in medicine and industry (x-rays, radium treatment, mustard gas); and some from the fallout of the explosion of atomic bombs.

2. High-energy radiations are definitely known to increase the rate of mutation in every organism tested.

3. Most mutations are harmful to the organism whether they are natural mutants or artificial ones induced by man. This harm is produced chiefly by the ionization effect by which electrons are removed from atoms and attached to other atoms so that positive and negative ion pairs are produced. Protoplasm is greatly injured by ionization because the molecular organizations of chromosomes especially is disrupted and mutations (mostly harmful) of the code result.

4. Mutations do not as a rule occur in more than one gene at a time, for a mutation is highly localized and may involve only one gene locus when the latter is struck by a quantum of radiation.

5. Radiations may affect any cell in the body, but only those changes that are produced in sex cells can be transmitted to the offspring.

6. Sensitivity to radiation effects vary from species to species. Mice are far more sensitive than fruit flies.

7. An atomic fallout occurs when atom bombs are exploded and refers to the unstable and radioactive isotopes of many elements that are hurled high into the air and carried about the earth by the winds, eventually settling down to earth on a large or small area, depending on circumstances. Some radioactive elements may settle out quickly and others may remain aloft for years.

8. Genetic radiations from whatever source are insidious because their effects seem to be cumulative, although this is denied by some authorities. Small exposures add up, and what really counts in the long run is the total amount of radiation one is exposed to during one's reproductive life. The rate of delivery of the radiation is of no consequence; the genetic effect is the same for low or high rate.

9. Some of the radioactive elements released in an atom bomb explosion decompose very slowly and have half-lives of many years, such as strontium 90 (half-life, 28 years). This means that the body may be exposed to these isotopes for a long time and can absorb a large amount of them.

10. The danger of radioactive substances is far greater

to future generations than to present ones because of the genetic implications referred to.

11. In addition to genetic effects of radiation, there are also physiologic or somatic effects. Some somatic effects are leukemia, cancer, and a syndrome of radiation illness, depending on the amount of exposure. Body tissues of rapidly dividing cells are especially prone to damage. If the exposure has not been excessive, many somatic effects may be healed by therapeutic measures, but healing does not apply to genetic damages.

Human chromosomal abnormalities

Since 1959 it has been found that certain disorders or diseases are associated with an abnormal number of chromosomes in man. Instead of the normal number of 46 chromosomes, a number of individuals have been reported who had one more or one less than the normal number. In mongolian idiocy, which is characterized by mental and physical retardation together with a mongolian type of eyelid fold, the individual has 47 chromosomes. This extra chromosome is thought to be due to nondisjunction of a pair of chromosomes (autosomes) during meiosis in the maternal ovum so that some of the eggs carry 24 chromosomes. Mongolian idiocy varies with the age of the mother. With mothers under 30 years of age, its frequency is about 15 in 10,000; in those 45 years of age or older, its frequency may be increased fiftyfold. Few mongolian idiots live to maturity, but those who have done so and had offspring produced mongolians and normal children in about equal proportions. The predisposition to have a mongolian child can be detected by an examination of tissue culture cells made from certain blood cells of the woman, where there is a likelihood that such a condition could occur.

Certain other conditions are associated with abnormalities of the sex chromosomes. Klinefelter's syndrome is produced by the presence of two X chromosomes plus a Y, or an XXY complex. Such an individual is a sterile male with undeveloped testes and a tendency toward female breasts (gynecomastia). That the person outwardly is a male indicates that the Y chromosome is male-determining, just as it is in mice (but not in *Drosophila*, in which the Y chromosome is more or less passive).

Turner's syndrome (45 chromosomes) is a condition in which the individual has only one X chromosome with no Y chromosome as a mate instead of the normal female (XX) or male (XY) state. In Turner's disease the XO (O = absence) constitution produces an external appearance of femaleness, although the person may lack ovaries or else have imperfect ones and so is sterile.

An XXX type of abnormal female (47 chromosomes) is also known, in which the person has underdeveloped reproductive organs and secondary sex characters, but may be fertile.

Both Klinefelter's and Turner's syndromes as well as the XXX type of female are caused by meiotic nondisjunction in the paternal or maternal germ lines. Since hormones are involved in regulative processes of sex, abnormalities in primary and secondary sex characters just mentioned may be due to hormonal imbalance produced by the faulty chromosome behavior.

In one or two instances a polyploid condition has been found in human beings. One case was that of a highly abnormal boy who had a total chromosome count of 69. The child appeared to have three haploid sets of chromosomes (triploidy). The sex chromosomes were XXY. Such a person could have developed from a zygote composed of either a normal haploid egg fertilized by an abnormal diploid sperm or an abnormal diploid egg fertilized by a normal haploid sperm. The XYY pattern of chromosomes appears to be the cause of antisocial tendencies among a high percentage of criminals examined.

Many cases of human abortions are probably caused by abnormal chromosome patterns, since many aborted fetuses have extra chromosomes.

Improvement of human race

The scientific improvement of the human race is called **eugenics.** Many organizations all over the world have been formed with the objective of promoting a superior stock of people, such as has been done with domestic animals and plants. Even before the laws of heredity were formulated, educators, sociologists, and others had pointed out the necessity of controlling or eradicating undesirable strains of human inheritance. They reasoned that if man was able to improve his domestic animals, why should not the same principles applied to his own inheritance promote desirable traits for the advancement of society as a whole. However, it is impossible to direct, control, and select the desirable human traits and eliminate the undesirable ones in the manner of animal and plant breeders. Man is a huge mixture of so many traits, both good and bad, that the task of selecting all good ones and eliminating poor ones would not be practical.

A large part of our population carries defective genes. The mental and physical capacity of millions of Americans is below normal and many of these people constitute a serious burden on society for their maintenance. Of course, not all physical and mental conditions are hereditary; some are due to environmental causes such as diseases and injuries. Subnormal people reveal only a part of the defective traits found in a population. Many defective genes are recessive and are carried by individuals who have normal phenotypes. Because of this, abnormal individuals are continually cropping out from the normal population as defective genes become homozygous.

Trained geneticists view with a critical eye many of the programs advocated by eugenists. The great emphasis on family pedigrees is considered unwarranted in the light of possible environmental factors. Many geneticists claim that, had the so-called degenerate stocks been provided with better social conditions, their showing would have been vastly improved. There is also the possibility that many eugenists have been influenced by racial or national prejudice. Geneticists are prone to recognize desirable traits in all races and believe that racial mixtures may have an invigorating influence. Hybrid vigor probably applies in man's case the same as it does with domestic stock and plants.

The eugenic movement, however, has helped institute some methods for control. Many states have sterilization laws for such defectives as feebleminded persons, imbeciles, and persons with certain forms of insanity. These statutes, however, are broad in their interpretation and make little attempt to distinguish between hereditary and environmental causes, and only a few states have made use of these laws to any extent. There is still much popular feeling against enforcing them.

On the constructive side, eugenists have advocated a greater birth rate among the upper and desirable stocks of people. There is no doubt that the lower socioeconomic groups have a higher birth rate, but whether there are marked genetic differences between the different levels of society is not known with certainty. Tests of intellectual abilities so far devised are not able to distinguish between native abilities of individuals who are of different socioeconomic levels. These tests too frequently take into consideration the environmental factors that influence the expression of mental traits, and these factors favor those of the higher social and economic classes. Therefore, under the present setup there seems to be a tendency for a drop in the average I.Q. among Americans from generation to generation. This decline, however, may be due largely to environmental conditions and not to a widespread increase in mediocre genes. In England the decline in average I.Q. varies from one to four points a generation according to geneticists.

Annotated references

Barry, J. M. 1964. Molecular biology: genes and the chemical control of living cells. Englewood Cliffs, N. J., Prentice-Hall, Inc. *An excellent review of the chemical foundations of genetics.*

Beadle, G. W. 1964. The new genetics: the threads of life. Chicago, Britannica Book of the Year, Encyclopaedia Britannica, Inc.

Benzer, S. 1962. Fine structure of the gene. Sci. Amer. **206**:70-84 (Jan.).

Cold Spring Harbor Symposia on Quantitative Biology. Genetics and twentieth century Darwinism, vol. 24, 1959. Cold Spring Harbor, N. Y., The Biological Laboratory. *An appraisal of the mechanisms of the evolutionary processes as developed from the study of population genetics ecology, paleontology, and other disciplines.*

Crow, J. F. 1963. Genetic notes, ed. 5. Minneapolis, Burgess Publishing Co. *An excellent summary of the principles of genetics.*

DeBusk, A. G. 1968. Molecular genetics. New York, The Macmillan Co. *An excellent account of genetic transcription and translation with clear diagrams. A recent and up-to-date account of molecular biology.*

Frisch, L. (editor). Cold Spring Harbor Symposia on Quantitative Biology. Cellular regulatory mechanisms, vol. 26, 1962. Cold Spring Harbor, N. Y., The Biological Laboratory. *A comprehensive analysis of biosynthetic catalytic units as understood at present. The live subjects of protein synthesis and the genetic code are especially stressed.*

Jukes, T. H. 1963. The genetic code. Amer. Sci. **51**:227-245 (March).

Knudson, A. G., Jr. 1965. Genetics and disease. New York, McGraw-Hill Book Co. *Along with the immense developments in biology in the past few decades, new relationships have been discovered between heredity and certain disorders of man.*

Levine, R. C. 1968. Genetics, ed. 2. New York, Rinehart & Winston, Inc. *A paperback that presents both the classic and molecular aspects of the principles of genetics.*

Peters, J. A. (editor). 1959. Classic papers in genetics. Englewood Cliffs, N. J., Prentice-Hall, Inc. *Here are the principal landmarks in the development of the science of genetics. All students of heredity should be familiar with these classic papers.*

Ravin, A. W. 1965. The evolution of genetics. (Paperback.) New York, Academic Press, Inc. *Shows the connection between the past and the present development of genetics.*

Roslansky, J. D. (editor). 1966. Genetics and the future of man. New York, Appleton-Century-Crofts. *A series of lectures given at the first Nobel Conference held at Gustavus Adolphus College in Minnesota. Among the participants were several Nobel Laureates. The lectures were built around the various aspects of genetics as they affect the destiny of man.*

Scheinfeld, A. 1950. The new you and heredity, ed. 2. Philadelphia, J. B. Lippincott Co. *A popular yet accurate account of human heredity. One of the best works for the beginning zoology student.*

Schull, W. J. (editor). 1962. Mutations. Ann Arbor, University of Michigan Press. *A report of a conference on genetics dealing with various aspects of mutations such as rate, mutagenesis, detection, and genetic loads. The give-and-take, informal method of presentation is revealing.*

Sturtevant, A. H. 1965. A history of genetics. New York, Harper & Row, Publishers. *An excellent concise history of genetics written by one of the members of the famous Morgan team that did so much in the development of classic genetics. Should be read by all students of genetics.*

Taylor, J. H. (editor). 1963. Molecular genetics. Part I. New York, Academic Press, Inc. *The background in the breaking of the genetic code, one of the most spectacular advances in modern science, is well described by many active workers in this field.*

Thomasz, A. 1969. Cellular factors in genetic transformation. Sci. Amer. **220**:38-44 (Jan.). *Shows how some bacteria are able to absorb genetic material from other sources with the aid of a giant molecule.*

Watson, J. D. 1968. The double helix. New York, Atheneum Press. *The exciting story of how the molecular model of DNA was worked out.*

PART SEVEN

THE EVOLUTION OF ANIMAL LIFE

● Evolution is the doctrine that the great variety of organisms now existing have arisen by modifications from preexisting species. Evolution is an orderly change from one condition to another and applies equally well to inanimate things as well as the living. For instance, the physical condition of this planet has undergone a change from its inception. This is called inorganic evolution in contrast to that of living matter or organic evolution. According to our present concept of the origin of life, the earliest organisms were formed in a primitive atmosphere, and by the abiotic synthesis of proteins and nucleic acids, simple self-replicating living systems gradually emerged. By the process of natural selection there was selection of favorable forms over less favorable ones so that in time more and more life forms emerged and became fitted for diverse ecologic niches.

The evidence for the evolutionary process is based to a great extent on the comparisons between the structures of present-day forms and those of fossils. Paleontology is the historic record and is to a great extent the best evidence for the process. Unfortunately, the fossil record is far from being complete and is nonexistent for some important groups. There are many other lines of evidence for evolution, but one of the most promising at present seems to be the homologies of polynucleotide sequences in the DNA molecules as indications of the degree of relationships between different animals, but little has been done so far along this line.

Evolution is concerned with populations that furnish the raw materials of inheritable variations on which evolutionary mechanisms work. A population is a gene pool in which the genes are freely intermingled among the interbreeding members of the population. Genetic systems of inheritable variations may arise in a population by sexual recombinations and mutations. Natural selection will determine what inheritable variations will survive and produce more offspring (differential reproduction). Naturally, those favored individuals will contribute more of their genes to the population than those that have fewer offspring. In this way particular genetic traits may become widespread in a population.

Man with his great capacities for culture, language, and rational and imaginative thought has interjected an entirely new dimension to evolution. He has not only become the dominant form of life, but has been able to control the destiny of all other forms of life. The pattern of evolution has been changed from a strictly organic one of millions of years duration into one that is assuming a cultural pattern.

CHAPTER 37

ORIGIN OF LIFE (BIOPOIESIS)*

Most biologists agree that life at its beginning arose naturally from nonliving matter. At the present time, however, life comes only from life. There is no evidence whatsoever that living organisms are now formed from nonliving matter. During the past decade or so many able biologists have proposed theories to account for the origin of life. Many disciplines (biochemistry, physical chemistry, astronomy, microbiology, geology, etc.) have been employed to obtain a knowledge of the early history of the earth and the chemical properties of living matter. Although the whole problem must always remain speculative, scientists have devised experiments demonstrating the conditions by which evolutionary events may have occurred. If the planet Earth in its primitive condition had certain chemicophysical properties, it is reasoned that, given enough time, life was an inevitable outcome. By means of orthodox scientific experiments students of this problem have proposed stages of increasing complexity, with each stage leading logically in order of time to the next stage. By proper checking of each stage with experimental evidence, it is argued that a logical outcome of life patterns could have been obtained.

The historic fossil record is incomplete and cannot give us the remotest idea of what the earliest life was like. The early organisms up to the Cambrian period were probably small and soft bodied and did not preserve as fossils. Precambrian animals were primarily motile; calcareous skeletons and hard parts appeared only when animals adopted a sessile or sluggish mode of existence (Brooke-Raymond theory). Some primitive fossils (algae) have been found in rocks at least 2.7 billion years old. The primitive conditions under which life first arose are not thought to be available at present; any of the simple organisms that first appeared would now be quickly destroyed by saprophytic bacteria and would have no chance to start an evolutionary pattern.

Many theories about the early origin of life, such as special creation, origin on other planets, or sudden creation from inorganic materials, either lack experimental investigation or are so improbable that they receive little consideration.

Charles Darwin thought that when life originated the conditions in the world may have been quite different from what they are at present. He proposed that amino acids could have survived outside the living organism and that mixed with phosphoric acid salts, ammonia, light, heat, etc., the amino acids might link together to form proteins. Furthermore, he added that it would be impossible for such matter to exist today under the impact of living creatures who would surely devour it. In the present century J. B. S. Haldane, the British biologist, proposed that the gases of the early atmosphere of the earth consisted of water, carbon dioxide, and ammonia. When ultraviolet light shines on such a gas mixture, many organic substances, such as sugars and possibly amino acids, are formed. Ultraviolet light must have been very intense before the appearance of oxygen (from plants) to form ozone (the 3-atom form of oxygen), which serves at present as a blanket to prevent ultraviolet rays from reaching the earth's surface. Haldane believes that the early formative substances could accumulate in the early oceans where synthesis of sugars, fats, proteins, and nucleic acids might occur. Recognizing the importance of the four elements carbon, hydrogen, oxygen, and nitrogen in the structure of living matter, Haldane could account for these four elements from his hypothetic early gas mixture.

However, one proposal has attracted the attention of scientists in recent years—that life arose spontaneously but gradually in the primitive ocean under the impact of certain favorable conditions that no longer exist. This theory stresses the presence of large quantities of or-

*Refer to Chapter 2, Principles 3, 23, and 28.

ganic compounds similar to those that are now found in living organisms. Although not a new theory by any means, forceful arguments in its favor have been advanced by Oparin, Haldane, Urey, and many others in a recent renewal of the hypothesis. Oparin, the Russian biochemist, through his book *The Origin of Life* (English translation, 1938) has mainly been responsible for this renewed interest. He argued that if the primitive ocean contained large quantities of organic compounds, in time these compounds would react with each other to form structures of increasing complexity. Eventually such a structure would reach a stage that could be called living. His belief was that a living system was gradually synthesized from nonbiologic compounds by logical and probable steps. Energy sources for the creation of the first organic compounds would come from ultraviolet light, electric discharges, localized areas of high temperature, such as volcanoes, and to some extent radioactivity. Since the necessary metabolites are already present in the environment to be used by the primitive organisms, such a metabolism is called heterotrophic. Other conditions necessary for such a scheme of spontaneous generation would be a sterile environment to prevent the destruction of primitive organisms by microorganisms such as exist today and a reducing atmosphere of such precursor compounds as water, methane (CH_4), ammonia (NH_3), and hydrogen instead of the present oxidizing atmosphere of carbon dioxide (CO_2), nitrogen, and oxygen.

Urey thinks that at low temperatures such substances as methane and ammonia would have been formed in the earth's early atmosphere and would have existed for some time during the early origination of life. As evidence for his theory, it has been discovered by spectroscopic analysis that the remote and large planets of Jupiter and Saturn have atmospheres (frozen) of methane and ammonia. This could have been the original atmosphere of the planet Earth. As a prerequisite to understanding conditions at the time of the origin of early life, one needs some knowledge of the early history of the earth and of the chemical properties of living matter.

ORIGIN OF THE EARTH

Of the many theories to account for the origin of our planet, the one that is most seriously considered at present states that the sun and the planets were formed together from a spherical cloud of cosmic dust, which by rotation and gravitation develop a sun at the center and a swirling belt of gas around it. In time the belt broke up into smaller clouds that condensed by gravity to form the planets. Free hydrogen atoms were the most abundant elements in the gas cloud and gravitated toward its center to create the sun, which is largely composed of hydrogen. If the early surface temperature of the earth was high, it should have cooled rapidly by convection and radiation and reached its present condition in the relatively short time of 25,000 years.

While the earth was in a more or less gaseous condition, the various atoms became sorted out according to weight, with the lighter elements (hydrogen, oxygen, carbon, and nitrogen) in the surface gas, and the heavier ones (silicon, aluminum, nickel, and iron) toward the center. At first many gases, such as hydrogen, helium, methane, water, and ammonia, escaped from the earth, but when the gaseous materials became dense enough, the gravitational field tended to prevent these gases from escaping into outer space. Jupiter and Saturn, which have much lower temperatures than Earth, have an atmosphere containing methane and ammonia at the present time.

If the earth's surface temperature was relatively high at first, molecules of atoms were slow in formation because heat disrupts the bonds that hold atoms together. As the earth cooled, stable bonds could be formed and free atoms began to disappear as molecules appeared. Since the lighter elements (hydrogen, oxygen, nitrogen, carbon) were the most abundant atoms on the earth's surface, these elements reacted to form the first molecules.

The present atmosphere of the earth is an oxidizing and not a reducing one as was the early atmosphere. Only simple organic molecules would be formed in the reducing atmosphere of the primitive earth. Its carbon would be in the form of methane or carbon monoxide (perhaps a little carbon dioxide), its nitrogen in the form of ammonia, most of the oxygen in the form of water, and there would be considerable hydrogen. These primitive molecules would, then, begin with the following:

```
   H                           H         H              H
   |                           |         |              |
H—O      O=C=O          H—C—H       N—H             H
                               |         |
                               H         H

 Water     Carbon       Methane   Ammonia    Hydrogen
 (H₂O)     dioxide      (CH₄)     (NH₃)      (H₂)
           (CO₂)
```

From these the complex biologic molecules would be formed later. Temperature conditions of the earth were such that these primitive compounds existed as gases and formed the early atmosphere. The key element in the formation of the molecules of the primitive atmosphere was undoubtedly hydrogen, for when it was present in large amounts, its great reactivity led to the formation of methane, ammonia, and water vapor. Conversion to the present oxidizing atmosphere must have taken long periods of time. By photochemical decomposition in the upper atmosphere, methane and ammonia were converted to carbon and nitrogen, and water was converted to oxygen and hydrogen. However, most of the oxygen (20+%) now present in the atmosphere may have come from photosynthesis. Carbon dioxide became dissolved in the ocean or reacted with silicates to form calcium carbonate.

STEPS IN CHEMICAL EVOLUTION

In any living system a great variety of molecules are found whose reactions are intimately involved in the process we call life. These molecules are commonly referred to as biomolecules. They may be divided into two groups: (1) molecules of relatively simple structure such as the sugars (disaccharides and polysaccharides), neutral fats, phospholipids, amino acids, and nucleotides and (2) macromolecules such as proteins, nucleic acids, nucleoproteins, and viruses. There had to be appropriate conditions that could produce a certain series of chemical reactions. In brief, free atoms formed simple molecules, which in turn formed larger and larger molecules, leading eventually to chance synthesis of macromolecules with the molecular patterns characteristic of the living organism.

In the long period of time when this chemical complexity was being built up, an abundance of carbon compounds must have been formed under the influence of thermodynamic and kinetic factors. Any chemical reaction is associated with thermodynamic changes that determine the direction of the reaction and its outcome.

If the early atmosphere contained methane, ammonia, water, and hydrogen, a mixture of these compounds would react only when energy was supplied in some form. Ordinarily, organic compounds are formed by organisms, but organisms were nonexistent in the early origin of life. As biochemists know today, the synthesis of organic compounds involves enzymatic action at every step. But enzymes are complex proteins and in any scheme for explaining early life their formation must be considered, not at the beginning, but well along in the process. Simpler compounds from early primordia must have come along before proteins. However, enzymes only hasten the reaction rate; reactions can occur slowly without them. At the present time the source of free energy to produce all energy directly or indirectly is the sun. This requires photosynthetic organisms, but photosynthesis is not thought to have been an early evolutionary development. Therefore, other sources of free energy must have been used.

Some light on this problem was added by the now classic experiment of S. L. Miller (1953) (Fig. 37-1). By circulating a mixture of water vapor, methane, ammonia, and hydrogen continuously for a week over an electric spark, he was able to get certain amino acids and some other products. It is possible, therefore, to have had various sources of energy in the early formation of organic compounds—ultraviolet light, electric discharges, radioactivity, etc. In Miller's experiment the mechanism of amino acid formation involved first the appearance of certain intermediate products such as aldehydes and hydrogen cyanide. The reaction of these compounds led to the synthesis of amino acids.

More recently other workers have varied Miller's experiments by irradiating gaseous mixtures of H_2O, H_2, and NH_3 with electrons, by heating aqueous solutions of hydrocyanic acid (HCN), and by exposing solutions of HCN and formaldehyde to ultraviolet irradiation. From such experiments many different molecules were obtained, such as several amino acids, formic acid, aldehydes, purine and pyrimidine bases, some complex polymers of amino acids and sugars, ribose, and deoxyribose. The high-energy adenosine triphosphate (ATP) has also been produced by the ultraviolet-irradiated solutions of adenine, ribose, and ethyl metaphosphate, using the Miller technique with an oxygen-free, artificial atmosphere.

The early atmosphere of the earth is supposed to have contained little or no free oxygen; all the oxygen was bound up in water or metal oxides. Carbon dioxide was also lacking, for carbon was mostly combined in metal carbides or hydrocarbons. This would indicate that the living organism has played an important part in the formation of the physical environment, such as the present atmosphere whose composition of oxygen and carbon dioxide was brought about by living organisms.

The formation of water deposits or oceans was no

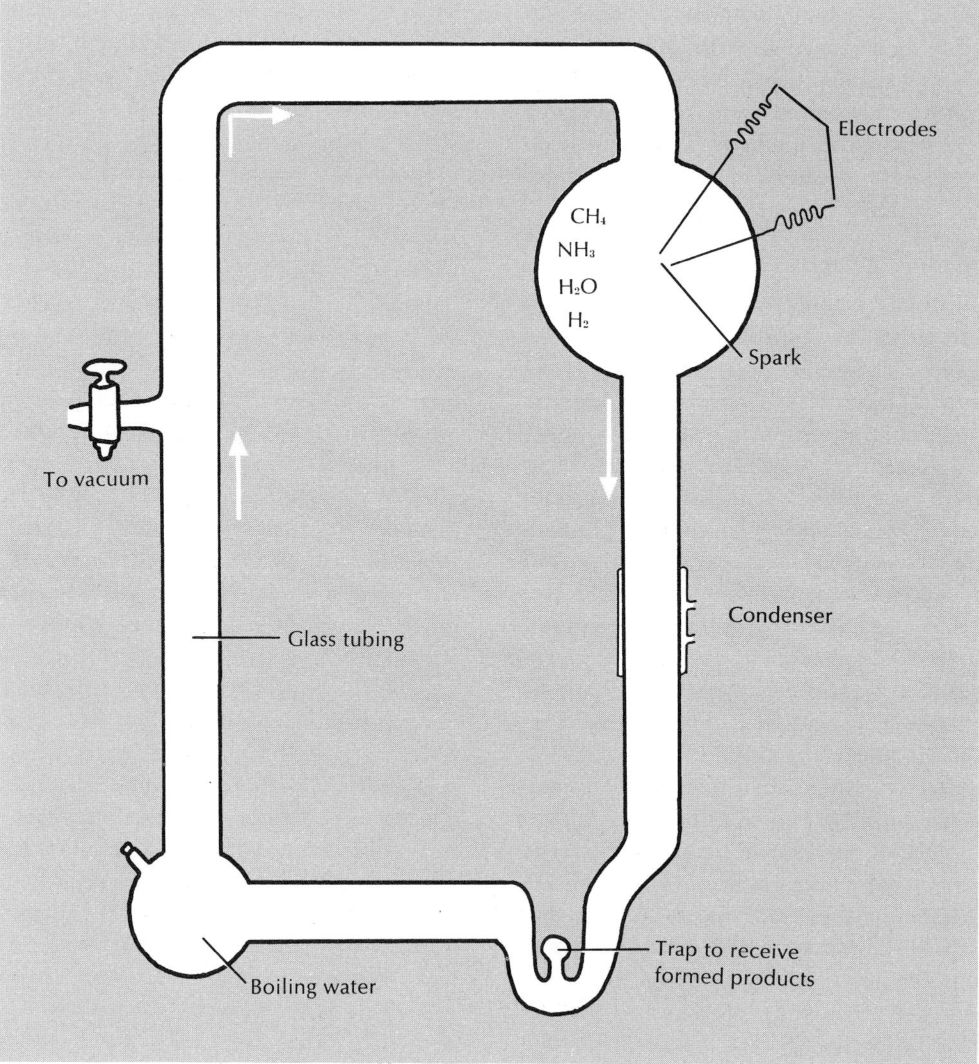

FIG. 37-1

Miller's classic experiment (1953) on synthesis of organic compounds under assumed primitive conditions of Earth's early atmosphere. Electric discharge through mixture of gases produced several amino acids and other organic substances. Variations of this experiment, making use of HCN (hydrocyanic acid), adenine, ribose, ethyl metaphosphate, etc. exposed to ultraviolet irradiation, have produced on RNA nucleotide, high-energy ATP, and a host of other organic molecules (aldehydes, purines, pyrimidines, fatty acids, etc.). ATP may have been abundant in early primordial oceans of reacting molecules and may have provided a ready source of energy for chemical reactions.

doubt due to the condensation of water vapor from the atmosphere, although another theory accounts for the origin of oceans by the escaping of water from the earth's interior during its cooling stage. Dissolved in ocean water were salts and minerals washed down from the continents as well as atmospheric ammonia and methane. Volcanoes may have also contributed some constituents to the ocean waters. The presence of water and these early dissolved substances may be considered the crucial conditions that led eventually to the origin of life. The main bulk of organic compounds accumulated in the oceans, and it was there that the chief processes in the formation of high-molecular compounds occurred. In this broth of dissolved organic compounds of great variety, the conversion of multimolecular systems into living systems took place. Before the advent of the organism, water, now the principal component of living substance, provided an ideal medium for the reactions of the organic molecules as they were formed. Methane (CH_4) was probably one of the first molecules to react, for the 4 H atoms could be replaced by other kinds of atoms, and thus many kinds of carbon-containing molecules could be formed. The versatility of the carbon atom, with its bonding capacity of 4, made possible an enormous complexity and variety of molecular structures.

Logical steps in chemical evolution would suggest that some of the earliest organic compounds formed would be the simple sugars, amino acids, fatty acids, pyrimidines, and purines. Each of these compounds represents a chain or ring of carbon atoms attached to various combinations of hydrogen, oxygen, and nitrogen. The sugars, or carbohydrates, and the fatty acids are formed entirely of carbon, hydrogen, and oxygen. The amino acids have, in addition to these elements, nitrogen, which occurs in an amino group (NH_2). Nitrogen could have been obtained in a reaction involving ammonia (NH_3) in which one of the hydrogen atoms was removed. The slow accumulation of the inorganically synthesized molecules was thus made possible by the primitive atmosphere of methane, ammonia, and water; by energy in the form of ultraviolet radiation, electric discharges, etc.; and by the absence of decay factors. The formation of the amino acids is especially significant because they represent the building blocks of proteins. Some of the amino acids are known to have long half-lives and have actually been isolated from fossils as far back as the Devonian period of more than 300 million years ago. This would suggest that amino acids could accumulate and exist over long geologic periods; this would afford plenty of time for proteins to be built from them.

The various reactions of these early compounds with each other and with inorganic molecules could have led to still more complex molecules. Simple sugars could form polysaccharides, and fatty acids could combine to produce fats. The appearance of proteins represented an important landmark because they are absolutely essential to living things. Proteins are made up of amino acids that are linked together in gigantic patterns to form complex and varied protein molecules. However, a mixture of amino acids would not form a protein unless other factors were involved.

How are proteins synthesized from amino acids? The experiment of Miller showed that it is rather easy to account for the amino acids, but the formation of these into the complex polypeptide chains is far more difficult. It is well to mention some of the exciting experiments along this line. In 1963 M. Calvin and others subjected a mixture of methane, ammonia, and water to a bombardment of electrons from the Berkeley cyclotron, and after an hour got adenine, 1 of the 4 bases of the DNA molecule. About a year later, S. W. Fox proposed that heat may have played an important part in the synthesis of organic compounds and heated a mixture of methane, ammonia, and water to 1,800° F. Of the many amino acids Fox obtained by this method, he found 14 of them involved in what is now known as the genetic code. He later demonstrated, by using more modest heat ranges (150° to 180° C.), that the 18 kinds of amino acids so treated together formed chains of polypeptides that could be digested by enzymes. By adding polyphosphate to his reaction mixture, he also found that such polypeptide chains could be formed 70° to 80° C. The high temperatures used by Fox could have been caused by hot meteorites in the early history of our planet. The most available energy source could have been ultraviolet light in the synthesis of the early organic compounds. Autocatalysis, or the products formed in a reaction, acting as a stimulus to the reactions from which they were formed, could have played a great part in the early synthesis.

Two compounds, hydrocyanic acid (HCN) and formaldehyde (CH_2O), are supposed to have performed key roles in the synthesis of organic compounds. Hydrogen peroxide appears to be a major product in first-step processes. When it and water are mixed and subjected to ultraviolet light, its products are adenine, guanine (two bases of DNA), and urea. Formaldehyde and water mixed together could be made to form ribose and deoxyribose (the sugars of RNA and DNA). Cyanide is found by spectroscopic analysis to be in the heads of comets, and when such bodies collided with the earth, they left carbon compounds.

The synthesis of hydrocyanic acid can be more easily explained by a new theory which emphasizes that the early atmosphere consisted of nitrogen, hydrogen, carbon monoxide, and carbon dioxide instead of the one described above. When this mixture is subjected to radiant energy, hydrocyanic acid is produced. When hydrocyanic acid is irradiated with ultraviolet light, amino acids are produced in abundance.

Adenosine triphosphate (ATP), the great energy molecule in life's processes, has also been synthesized under the conditions that may have existed in the early history of the earth.

Another important aspect of protein development was their role in acting as **enzymes.** The first catalysts were probably metal ions and were somewhat weak in their action, but the development of proteins as enzymes greatly accelerated reactions without increasing the temperature. The importance of enzymatic action cannot be overestimated, for each step of the living process is governed by teams of enzymes.

Other key organic molecules that developed from the purines and pyrimidines were the **nucleotides.** These contain a purine or pyrimidine base combined with a sugar and a phosphate. Combinations of many different nucleotide molecules produced the supermolecules known as nucleic acids. Some of the nucleotides are synthetically produced from ammonium cyanide, which in turn can be formed from methane and ammonia by electric discharges. The polymerization of ribonucleic and deoxyribonucleic acids could have been effected by enzymes or by mineral surfaces. The formation of the nucleic acids was of crucial importance in the development of a living organism. The combination of nucleic acid with a protein produced the nucleoproteins, which are the principal components of the cell nucleus and are intimately associated with the life process. It has been suggested by some investigators that they were the first proteins formed, but they do not mark the first beginning of life and should not be regarded as constituting the living system by themselves.

At the present time, speculations about the origin of life have not ceased because interest in the problem never abates. The National Aeronautics and Space Administration is always seeking demonstrations about how life could have originated extraterrestrially, and encouraging the development of life-detection devices that could be applied where potential life is possible. Exobiology, or the study of life elsewhere than on this planet, has loomed of great importance in this space age. Only by understanding how life could have originated on earth is it possible to evaluate what could happen on other planets.

FIRST ORGANISMS

It is very doubtful that the transition from the nonliving to the living was a sharp or abrupt process. From our present environment not much can be learned about the evolutionary steps leading to the first organism. The simplest system subject to evolution would be the replication of a nucleic acid, such as DNA, that would require complex nucleotide triphosphate for its synthesis. For making exact duplicate copies, it is necessary to have in abundance the component parts of nucleoproteins such as sugars, amino acids, purines, pyrimidines, and phosphorus. The formation of nucleoproteins is mainly dependent on what is already present. The first nucleoproteins served as models for the formation of more nucleoproteins. The Watson-Crick model of the structure of deoxyribonucleic acid shows how a molecule can act as a pattern to synthesize another molecule complementary to itself. The first living organism could have been strips of DNA or RNA that, with the necessary enzymes, could duplicate themselves. The sequence of the process may have occurred something like this: (1) A single strand of nucleic acid was formed, (2) nucleotides complementary to the bases in the first chain lined up, (3) the polymerization of the nucleotides to form the complementary strand occurred, (4) the original strand separated from the newly formed complementary strand, and (5) the final stage was the addition of cytoplasm and a membrane to the self-duplicating polynucleotides.

An alternative theory of the origin of the first organism is the coacervate theory of A. I. Oparin. According to this theory, coacervate aggregates, a special form of a colloidal solution in which one of the liquids of a hydrophilic sol appears as viscous drops (coacervates) instead of forming a continuous liquid phase, would absorb proteins and other materials from the environment, increase in size, and then divide (Fig. 37-2).

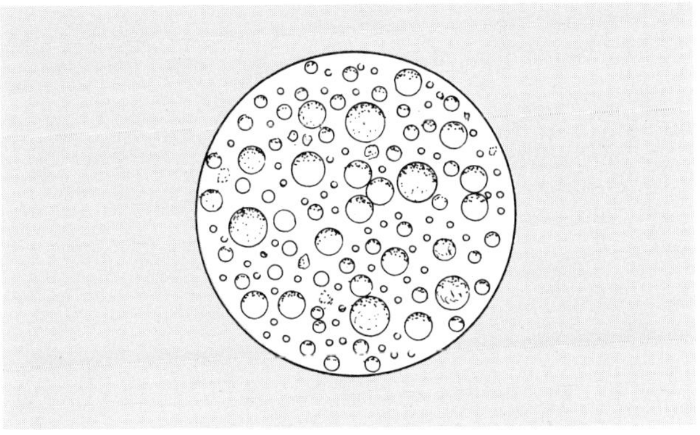

FIG. 37-2

Coacervate droplets in hydrophilic colloid. According to this theory of origin of first organisms, complex coacervates of different proteins made up a type of dilute "broth" in the ocean, and by intermolecular attraction large complex molecules were formed into colloidal aggregates. These colloidal aggregates could selectively concentrate materials from ocean "broth," and by unknown favorable internal organization, some aggregates would pick up molecules better than could others and would become dominant. Thus natural selection could operate at very early stage in origin of life. Coacervate particles would split into smaller particles when they had increased their size. A genetic mechanism for precise duplication would be incorporated in time into particle. (After Keosian, 1964.)

More accurate duplication of parts would evolve in time. Protoplasm, as now organized, has the structure of a complex coacervate.

There are logical reasons for believing that the early organisms were heterotrophic; that is, they got their energy from sources outside of themselves. They have fewer enzymes and specializations for metabolic processes than do autotrophics. The primitive oceans must have accumulated large quantities of compounds, and the first organisms used this reservoir of compounds for their evolution and expansion. When this reservoir of resources was used up, spontaneous generation could no longer occur and biogenesis became the only possible method of origin of organisms. By mutations, certain early organisms acquired the capacity to synthesize organic compounds from simpler ones. Natural selection could operate here to favor those organisms that could synthesize all the essential complex compounds, and competition became a rule of existence. Less successful forms would become extinct.

All organisms require free energy for their chemical reactions and for the synthesis of their body parts. If the early organisms were heterotrophic and anaerobic, the source of their energy must have come from fermentation processes. At the present time many microorganisms get their energy this way. Lactic acid bacteria get free energy from the breaking down of glucose into lactic acid, each molecule of glucose producing 2 molecules of the high-energy ATP. The yeast organisms produce ethyl alcohol and carbon dioxide instead of lactic acid. Most animals at present obtain their free energy from the oxidation of organic molecules by oxygen, and plants get their energy from light in the photosynthetic process (autotrophic). When early organisms used up the fermentable compounds of the ocean "broth," other sources of energy had to be utilized. About this time photosynthesis evolved and was made possible by the accumulation of atmospheric carbon dioxide produced by the metabolism of the early heterotrophs. Photosynthesis released oxygen to the atmosphere and established the conditions for aerobic respiration.

Another form of autotrophic nutrition is **chemosynthesis,** in which energy for forming carbohydrates is obtained from metallic or nonmetallic materials such as iron, sulfur, and nitrogen. By using bond energy from chemical reactions it was possible to combine CO_2 and water into carbohydrates. With the appearance of oxygen, an ozone (O_3) layer was formed in the higher atmosphere and it absorbed most of the sun's ultraviolet rays that had made life possible only in water. It is thought that all the present oxygen of the air can be renewed by photosynthetic processes every 2,000 years and that all the CO_2 molecules pass through photosynthesis every 300 years. Autotrophic forms, or those that could synthesize complex organic compounds from simple renewable resources, were now established. Mutational descendants of these autotrophs produced secondary heterotrophs that could now live on autotrophs. Thus the present scheme of living systems was initiated.

In the overall picture (Fig. 37-3) there were three major evolutionary directions in the formation of organisms. These directions are based on the three methods of nutrition found in the biologic world: (1) the photosynthetic processes, or producers of organic compounds, represented by plants; (2) the ingestion of producers, or consumers, represented by animals; and (3) the reduction, or decomposition, of the dead remains of both producers and consumers to an absorbable state represented by saprophytes, such as fungi and certain bacteria. Some organisms may fit into more than one of these nutritional categories.

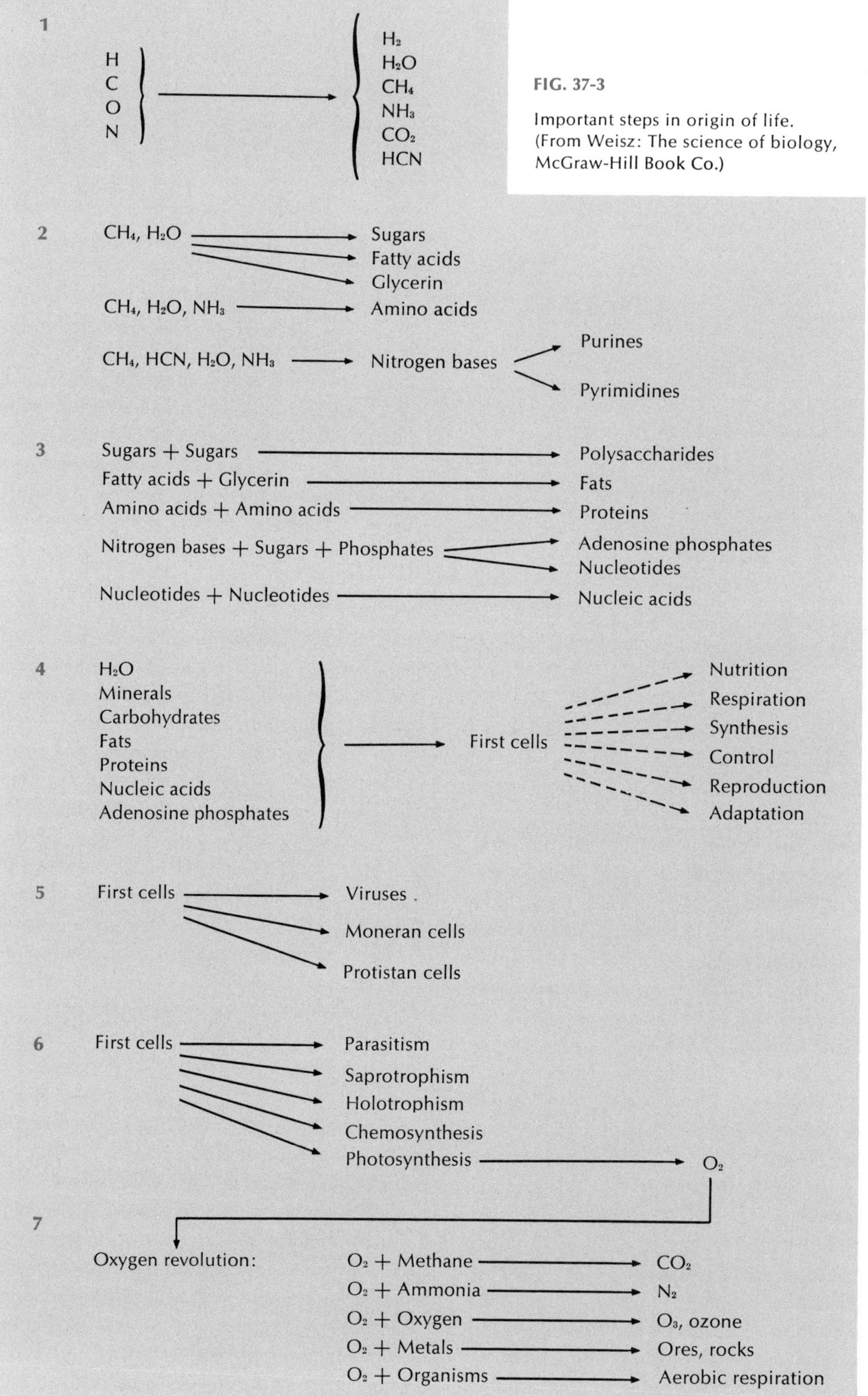

FIG. 37-3

Important steps in origin of life. (From Weisz: The science of biology, McGraw-Hill Book Co.)

The basic unit of living systems is the cell, and its formation must have represented a significant event in early evolution. A number of theories have been proposed to account for the origin of the cell. One theory stresses the aggregations or clumpings of nucleoproteins with nutrient shells around them. This arrangement could have been the start of more complex structures within which were incorporated the characteristic organelles of cells. An alternative theory suggests that cell-like structures were first formed from water droplets and accumulated organic materials in which chemical reactions could occur. In this way nucleoproteins could be formed. Such a scheme is not unlike the coacervate theory of Oparin. A cellular level of simple organization may thus have been attained in the early origin of heterotrophs.

In whatever way cells were formed, in time they could produce their own energy by their ability to decompose organic molecules and release the great bond energy through respiratory processes. They could also synthesize many organic substances such as nucleoproteins and other organic materials. Cells undoubtedly have had a long evolutionary development, which involved integration of cellular activity, adjustment to steady states, duplication of parts, and change (mutation).

SOME PRIMITIVE CELLS

No one knows what the earliest ancestral cells were like, but certain types of present-day cells may throw some light on this problem. Although viruses are not considered cells and are inert when not in the host cells, the relative simplicity of their genetic pattern and their capacity to shuffle nucleoproteins among true cells has assigned them a unique role in the evolution of the cell. Two kinds of present-day organisms, collectively called **Monera,** are considered to have some characteristics of the earliest cells. Bacteria (**phylum Schizophyta**) represent one of these two types of organisms. They are the smallest cells known, ranging in size from 0.2 to about 10 μ in length. (A micron is 1/25,000 inch.) They may occur as single cells or in clumps. They have a variety of metabolisms including heterotrophic, chemosynthetic, and photosynthetic. They lack nuclear membranes and their nucleoproteins are scattered in clumps through the cell. Reproduction is by rapid cell division and some undergo a sexual process by mating. They also appear to lack definite chromosomes. Bacteria, however, are not simple cells, and early cells were no doubt much simpler.

The other type of **Monera** are the blue-green algae (**phylum Cyanophyta**). They have no nuclear membrane and their nucleoproteins are arranged the same as are those in bacteria. In addition to certain characteristic pigments, most possess a form of chlorophyll that is dispersed in granules through the cell and not in chloroplasts as are found in higher plants. They carry on the same type of photosynthesis as the higher plants. They reproduce by cell division, but they have no sexual processes.

In some interpretations bacteria and viruses are considered degenerate secondary heterotrophs and not primitive patterns at all. It has been suggested on logical grounds that parasitism may account for the apparent simplicity of some of them.

ORGANIC MATTER FROM METEORITES

In recent years considerable interest has been aroused by the analysis of certain meteorites in which a variety of hydrocarbons has been found. The ones of greatest interest are those belonging to a large family of stony meteorites known as chondrites. These carbonaceous meteorites do not look at all like other meteorites. Fewer than twenty have been found to date. One of these, the Cold Bokkeveld meteorite from South Africa, was studied in 1953 by G. Mueller. He was able, with organic solvents (benzene and alcohol), to extract a brown, soft, resinous material of organic compounds that consisted of approximately oxygen, 49%; carbon, 24%; hydrogen, 17%; nitrogen, 4%; sulfur, 9%; chlorine, 5%; and an ash of iron oxide, etc. The extract contained no optically active compounds so characteristic of living organisms. The presence of these compounds might be interpreted as indicating life on those bodies from which they came, but Mueller believed that the meteorite organic material consisted of organic acids that originated abiogenetically by polymerization in a gaseous medium of nitrogen, chlorine, and sulfur.

In 1961 other investigators working on the Orgueil meteorite of the American Museum of Natural History reported that the hydrocarbons of the meteorite resembled the biogenetic hydrocarbons of the earth. By means of physicochemical tests these investigators have found that the extracts contained amino, carbonyl and other groups, and spectral wavelengths comparable to extracts of terrestrial oils. Some staining evidence even points to the possible presence of nucleic acid. In explanation of this evidence there is, however, the possibility of terrestrial contamination of the meteorites. The whole question of extraterrestrial origin of life is still much in doubt, but some scientists think that the nature of chondrites might at least throw some light on the primordial material of the solar system and the early origin of the earth.

Annotated references

Allen, J. M. (editor). 1963. The nature of biological diversity. New York, McGraw-Hill Book Co. *A stimulating book on the diversification of biologic systems, mostly at the cellular and subcellular levels. Every topic (by a noted authority) arouses the student's interest.*

Bernal, J. D. 1961. The problem of the carbonaceous meteorites. The Times Science Review, no. 40, pp. 3-4 (Summer).

Fox, S. W. 1960. How did life begin? Recent experiments suggest an integrated origin of anabolism, protein, and cell boundaries. Science **132**:200-208.

Keosian, J. 1968. The origin of life, ed. 2. New York, Reinhold Publishing Corp. *Summarizes the present status of this fascinating problem. A concise and readable account.*

Miller, S. L. 1953. A production of amino acids under possible primitive earth conditions. Science **117**:528-529.

Oparin, A. I. 1957. The origin of life, ed. 3. New York, Academic Press, Inc.

Urey, H. C. 1952. The planets. New Haven, Conn., Yale University Press.

CHAPTER 38

• BACKGROUND OF ORGANIC EVOLUTION

MEANING OF EVOLUTION*

● It is evident that animals and plants, as we see them, present an immense variety of different forms, ranging all the way from those of small size and low degree of complexity to those of large size and complicated structure. Moreover, organisms are found in nearly every kind of habitat that will support life at all and manifest every conceivable kind of adaptation to their surroundings. The thinking person must often ask himself when and how this abundance of life originated? Have these different species always existed this way? Are some more closely related than others? Is there a similar basic pattern throughout all life? What is the basis for grouping animals into certain taxonomic units? These and similar questions have posed real problems to scientists for centuries. One of the most important contributions of biology is the principle of evolution, which attempts to answer some of these questions.

Evolution is the doctrine that modern organisms have attained their diversity of form and behavior through hereditary modifications of preexisting lines of common ancestors. It means that all organisms are related to each other because of common descent, or that all organic life can be traced back to relatively simple common ancestral groups. It also implies the genetic changes populations undergo in their descent from ancestral populations. Basically, evolution is the change in the relative frequency of genes. This theory rejects the old traditional belief of the origin of life as expressed in the book of Genesis. Organic evolution is only one aspect of the larger view that the entire earth has undergone an amazing evolution of its own. The evolutionary principle has profoundly influenced every field of human thought and, one may add, no principle has been more disturbing to persons at certain stages of thinking. On the other hand, the grand concept of evolution arouses in all thoughtful individuals a feeling of awe and wonder, and one of inspiration, at the great drama that has been and is unfolding before their eyes.

Evolution is more than a change in the form and function of organisms; it is rather a change in their whole, integrated life as a part of nature. Evolution must account for all the conditions of life. That is why the population is the natural form of existence of all organisms. The evolution of any particular organism always involves its complex interrelations with the fellow members of its population and with its total environment. It is impossible to appreciate the concept of species—a focal point in all evolutionary theories—without understanding the mutual relations of organisms to one another in their natural population groups. The basic principle of evolution must, therefore, emphasize two vital points: (1) how the genotype changes and operates to perform its action in the body and (2) how the conditions of the environment influence the adjustments of an organism, its preservation, its variations, and its life history. The environment is thus the directive force in the evolutionary process. How the organism responds depends on its genotype or gene pool, its mutant genes, and its gene combinations. The adaptive value of the genotype must depend on the environment in which a species lives.

The study of evolution is a definite branch—perhaps the most important branch—of biologic science. Its problems must be treated in accordance with the principles of any empiric science, that is, studied by observation and experiment. However, evolutionary study has certain limitations in this respect, for evolution is an extremely slow process; most of it has occurred in the remote past and much of it must remain in the stage of a hypothesis because it is not easily testable in practice. The fossil record represents the most clear-cut and verifiable evidence that the evolutionary process has occurred, and population genetics also affords a certain amount of direct testable experiments of the process.

*Refer to Chapter 2, Principles 23, 25, and 28.

The student may well ask at this point the questions: Does evolution have a definite goal? What is the purpose of evolution anyway? Much of the evolutionary process does appear to be directional and shows specialization and advancement along certain definite lines. Many groups, especially vertebrates, show definite trends toward better organization patterns by which the animal is capable of a more efficient life and is more independent of the environment. All successful evolution is progressive. Change in the same direction may continue for long periods of time, as shown by the horse and many other forms. It is a popular belief that man has been the ultimate goal—the pinnacle toward which the evolutionary process has been pointed. But there is no evidence for such a view. Evolution has had many directions and many of them have been successful in a biologic sense. Man enjoys a superior position because he has evolved a type of genotype that enables him to profit from the transmission of cultural development. As Professor J. S. Huxley emphasizes, human evolution tends to become conscious and self-directing. But about the only purpose the student can see in this vast panorama of evolution is that organisms are striving for preservation and survival by means of more efficient adaptations. Man, along with other organisms, has been the outcome of the same forces of natural selection and environmental opportunity. Blessed with favorable mutant genes and gene combinations in his genotype, he has met the challenge of the environment with a greater degree of educability than have other species.

Evolution is a continuous process and is taking place today. At any point in time, any group of animals one may select is undergoing the process of evolution. Any diversity a group may possess, now or past, has been the product of prior evolution. The variability as expressed in structural and physiologic features of any form is the basis of evolution still to come. The chief effect of new features is to increase the variability of any population group. It is a very slow process but some striking evolutionary changes have taken place within historic times. Once it occurs, evolution seems to be irreversible except for small, minor reversals. A new pattern is always a modification of one that has existed. Many striking patterns of animal life, such as the dinosaurs, have been lost irretrievably.

Many viewpoints and hypotheses have been proposed to account for the evolutionary process, but within recent years there has been a fruitful attempt to converge or synthesize these various points of view into one unified and consistent picture of the whole process. Instead of many different processes, it is now thought that a single mechanism is involved in explaining evolution. This approximation of the various viewpoints is often referred to as the **modern synthesis of evolution.**

In the overall picture of evolution one may discern three important stages: (1) a period of evolution in which many different basic chemical patterns were evolved in the inorganic world, from which organic forms later arose; (2) the origin of the living systems from the nonliving through the gradual development and transformation of self-duplicating units into more complex units; and (3) the establishment of the organic systems as we know them from the fossil record and from existing forms. It is with the last stage that we are most concerned in our discussion of evolution.

Evolution is a complex process and many different evolutionary patterns are found. Although the evolution of every great group of organisms is more or less unique in its details, three basic kinds of organic evolution have been followed in producing the great diversity of life we know today. There is first a buildup within a population of a gene pool of specific characters of structure, function, or habit. From one generation to the next there is usually a change in the gene pool so that there is a gradual alteration in the range or kind of these characters. Variations in the environment may account for such changes because the genetic composition will develop in a different way under different environmental conditions, but changes in the genetic composition may also occur by mutation. Through successive generations, there will be a succession of different gene pools that will be expressed in different characters. This results in a change of the population as a whole and is not a splitting up of the population. This kind of evolution is usually restricted to a fairly stable organism-environment complex and is called **sequential** or **phyletic evolution** (Fig. 38-1, *A*). Such evolutionary changes may be slight if the environment is stable, but shifts of gene combinations in adaptive types may occur in response to a changing environment, thus producing distinguishably different forms (species). A rapid shift of a population into another and different adaptive zone where it is necessary for the organisms to adapt quickly results in a type of rapid evolution called **quantum evolution.** Quantum evolution is promoted by excessive mutation, relaxation of selective pressure, and such short cuts as paedomorphosis. It may produce taxa of

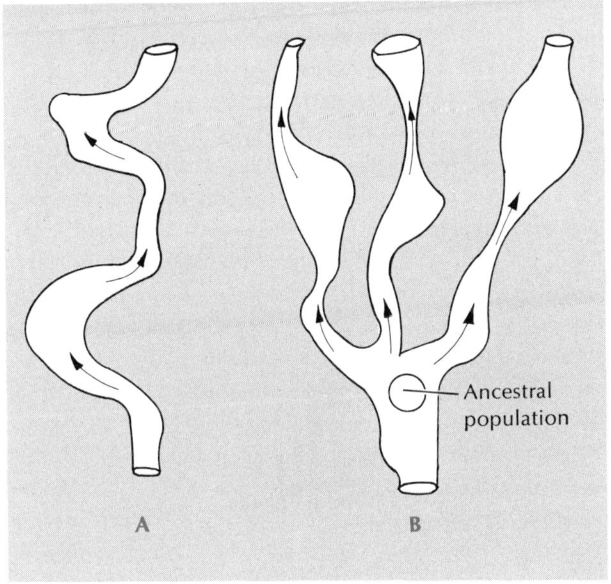

FIG. 38-1

Two basic patterns of evolution. **A,** Phyletic or sequential pattern. Phyletic evolution involves progressive, directional shift of average genotypes and phenotypes of population from one generation to another. Although population changes, there is no splitting up of population as it continues within zone of varying breadth, depending on fluctuations of characters at particular times. Differences may be great enough, however, for origin of new species. **B,** Divergent or cladogenesis pattern. This type involves splitting up of population into two or more separate lines, each of which may give rise to taxa of different ranks. It is well represented by adaptive radiation characteristic of most major groups. Both these patterns are usually found in any population over long periods of time.

all ranks but probably applies best to such taxonomic units as families, orders, and classes (Simpson).

Another type of evolution, **divergent evolution** or **cladogenesis** (Fig. 38-1, *B*), involves a splitting process in which new populations originate from old populations. It is the differentiation of two or more groups within a widespread population. It involves a complex of adaptations that are exploited in diverse ways by adaptive radiation into various ecologic niches if these are available (opportunism). Within each of the adaptive lines, more or less directional progress (phyletic evolution) occurs, with alternate stages of advancement and stability, and in some cases there is enough diversification within a line for the formation of taxonomic units of the rank of species or higher. In time, and on rare occasions, new adaptive complexes of further improvement may emerge in some or all of the original adaptive lines and a new cycle is initiated, upsetting the stable phases of no essential change. This process in a group may continue indefinitely or it may be cut short by extinction. Within most groups there have been an enormous diversity of rate, directness, stability, progress in complexity, and numbers of branches of phyletic lines.

Biologic evolution tends to produce types or patterns of life that can make use of more of the world's space and resources with greater efficiency. New types of metabolic systems must be evolved for this purpose. This can be expressed as a sort of feedback mechanism by which a metabolic novelty may offer an opportunity for exploitation by another metabolic novelty. Termites could evolve only when woody plants came into existence, thus providing them with ecologic niches. The complex life cycle of many parasitic flatworms indicates an evolutionary pattern by which the parasites have moved from one host to another as new groups of animals or metabolic novelties evolved, yet retaining at the same time the older hosts in their phylogeny. As a rule, new major groups have arisen to occupy new ecologic niches, not those already occupied by other groups. A metabolic novelty, or the evolution of a new form of life, may create other possibilities or new resources of further opportunities for new patterns of life. Thus each new step in evolution creates further steps for evolutionary expansion.

Nearly every branch of biology, as well as other sciences, has made contributions to our understanding of evolution, but the recent outlook has greatly emphasized the roles of genetics and ecology. The importance of the genotype and its composition explains the emphasis on genetics; the role of the environment in directing the course of evolution explains the emphasis on ecology. Evolutionary study involves direct experiments of breeding and artificial mutations, observation of biogeographic and ecologic factors of distribution, morphologic similarity of patterns and adaptations to different ways of life, a study of the fossil sequences in their relations to each other, and the statistical transformation of populations in terms of gene and chromosomal frequencies. It should be possible to demonstrate the elements of the evolutionary processes at the present day.

In an analysis of the modern synthesis of evolutionary processes, the following major causes are given priority rating—mutation rate, natural selection, chance or random genetic drift, and isolation and population structure.

Mutation rate. Mutation rate is the chance, random change of hereditary mechanisms. This and the subsequent reshuffling of the genes into various new combinations by bisexual reproduction make possible structural differences in populations. Gene mutations occur by chance in an unpredictable manner, but their rate can often be predicted. Mutations provide the basis for hereditary variations.

Natural selection. Natural selection is the real basic external factor that molds the development of a species. Selection determines which mutant genes survive and which ones are eliminated. It molds the genes into a coordinated whole, and although it cannot originate new characters, it can determine what sets of genes can be of immediate biologic usefulness to the species. It can produce rapid evolutionary transformation or it can stabilize the evolutionary trend.

Chance or random genetic drift. In small populations, random fluctuations or changes in gene frequency may have an important bearing on evolutionary trends. Some genes may be entirely lost and others may be greatly increased in frequency because certain mutant genes may not be included in gametes in the process of meiosis, or they may not be present at all or present with a greater frequency than they were in the original larger population. Close interbreeding in such populations would tend to make heterozygous genic pairs homozygous.

Isolation and population structure. This factor refers to those conditions in which groups of organisms are prevented from interbreeding or are divided into subunits with limited cross migration. This results in evolutionary divergence because an isolated population would not share its mutant genes with others and would develop its own unique evolution. This process could lead to the formation of a new species in each of the isolated groups by this chance accumulation of mutations.

How these four basic factors operate in the evolutionary process may be made clear by selecting a hypothetical species population of great extent and following it through its possible evolutionary fate. Suppose this population is found in a wide geographic area and exhibits the characteristics of a **cline;** that is, there is a gradual, continuous, gradient change in the members of the population because of adjustments to local conditions that show considerable variations in different parts of the cline. Thus in certain parts of the cline, climate conditions may be hot, in others cold; weather may vary from extreme moisture in some parts to very dry in others, etc.

Within a cline the species will be divided into smaller units of population (**demes**) that are more or less isolated from each other in accordance with the different habitats found within the range of a cline. The members of a deme may breed freely with each other but usually not with the members of other demes. Each deme more or less can develop an evolution of its own, for small hereditary differences (mutations) that occur in demes may be, to some extent, unique, and thus each deme in time becomes different from other demes. Natural selection will operate to select the better-adapted characters in each case and their possessors will increase in frequency. In most cases the variations or mutations are small and quantitative in effect (**micromutations**), but some may have larger effects (**macromutations**). Some of the mutations may confer only small advantages at first, but reshuffling of the genes at meiosis and further recombinations may increase their effects. Recessive mutants will spread slowly, dominant ones more rapidly. If the environmental conditions remain fairly stable, there is a slow successional evolution within the deme; readaptation to changing conditions, however, speeds up the evolutionary rate.

The demes within a cline will not all have the same fate. Some of them may come together (if interbreeding can occur) and fuse; others may differentiate far enough to prevent interbreeding and form true species. Whenever two demes fuse, each contributes its pool of genes to the future offspring, which thus acquire advantageous genes of both demes. Still other demes may become extinct in a large cline. Other degrees of demes may be found in a large species population. Adjacent demes may intergrade into each other. A common pattern of demes consists of many subspecies formed by divergent evolution in partially isolated demes. The time factor may cause these subspecies to differentiate into true species. Because of the smallness of some of the demes, genetic drift can operate to produce a marked differential in gene frequency. In this way chance may determine whether or not certain genes will be emphasized or neglected. It will thus be seen that whenever a population is subdivided into small subunits there is a strong possibility that there may be a rapid evolutionary process of a divergent nature, with results favorable to the formation of new species.

EARLY HISTORY OF EVOLUTIONARY IDEA

Although the development of the evolutionary theory has occurred chiefly during the past hundred or so years, many thinking men long before this time had ideas about the evolving of the various forms of life from one another. Some of the early Greek philosophers, Thales, Epicurus, Empedocles, and Aristotle, who lived from 500 to 300 B.C., thought a great deal on the evolution and the development of the different types of organisms. Many of their ideas were very crude in the light of present-day information, for they lacked the necessary data to test their observations. Their viewpoint was that all animal life had its origin by special creation or by spontaneous generation. Many puzzling problems were posed by the discovery of fossils that had remarkable resemblances to present-day forms and yet at the same time showed considerable differences. This evidence of former life was explained largely by the theory of **catastrophism,** which was the idea that animal life had suffered total destruction at times by some form of catastrophe and had been replaced by forms somewhat different from the previously existing ones.

Among modern zoologists who thought seriously about the idea of evolution was the French naturalist Buffon (1707-1788), who stressed the influence of environment on the modifications of animal types. In 1745 Maupertuis, a French philosopher, described many of the concepts of variation and the diversity of animal life. Another French zoologist, Lamarck (1744-1829), put his ideas into a more concrete form and elaborated a theory to account for the evolutionary changes of animal life by use and disuse of organs. Although the basic idea of his theory is no longer considered seriously by most biologists, the influence of Lamarck did stimulate serious thought about evolution. Erasmus Darwin (1731-1802), the grandfather of Charles Darwin, recognized that the various forms of organisms arose from each other and stressed the response of the animal to environmental changes as the basis for its modifications.

One development that helped foster sound thinking along evolutionary lines was the science of geology in the early nineteenth century. The geologist Sir Charles Lyell (1797-1875), in his *Principles of Geology* (1830), elaborated the theory of **uniformitarianism,** which stated that the causes that produced changes in the earth's surface in the past are the same that operate upon the earth's surface at present. Such forces over a long period of time could account for all the observed changes, including the formation of fossil-bearing rocks, and did not require catastrophes for an explanation of the geologic process. This concept of geology showed conclusively that the earth's age must be reckoned with in millions of years rather than in thousands. Charles Darwin was greatly stimulated by this important geologic work and was aided greatly by it in his own thinking on the processes of organic evolution.

No one has done more to stimulate interest and study in the field of evolution than the great Englishman Charles Darwin (1809-1882). His name, or rather his theory, is almost a synonym for evolution itself. Although the theory he proposed is now known to have many flaws, so forcibly did he present his ideas and his array of carefully collected scientific data that no one before or since can really challenge his preeminence in this field. He was thus the first to give a clear-cut idea of how evolution may have operated. Although the theory of natural selection was not entirely original with Darwin, no one else had proposed it with such clarity or supported it with such forcible arguments. *The Origin of Species,* published in 1859, has influenced biologists of every race and country, and many have extended the concept of organic evolution by valuable information. Darwin's theory and the many modifications of it will be mentioned later in this section.

PALEONTOLOGY: THE HISTORIC RECORD

The strongest and most direct evidence for evolution is the fossil record of the past because the study of paleontology, or the science of ancient life, shows how the ancestors of present-day forms lived in the past and how they became diversified. Incomplete as the record is—and many groups have left few or no fossils—more and more biologists rely on the discoveries of new fossils and their significance in the interpretation of the phylogeny and relationships of both plant and animal life. It would be difficult to make sense out of the evolutionary patterns or classification of organisms without the support of the fossil record. The documentary evidence for evolution as a general process, the progressive changes in life from one geologic era to another, the links between the one grade of taxon to another, the past distribution of lands and seas, and the environmental conditions of the past (paleoecology) are all dependent on what fossils teach us.

FIG. 38-2

Representative fossils. **A,** Fossil arthropod *Eurypterus,* which was abundant during upper Silurian period; related to modern scorpions. **B,** Some worm tubes. **C,** Bryozoan. **D,** Trilobite; related to king crab of today and one of most abundant of arthropod fossils. **E,** Cephalopod; chambered nautilus of today is little changed from this ancient fossil. **F,** Coral. **G,** Gastropod. **H,** Coelenterate strobila.

A fossil may be defined as any evidence of past life. It refers not only to complete remains (mammoths and amber insects), actual hard parts (teeth and bones), petrified skeletal parts that are infiltrated with silica or other minerals by water seepage (ostracoderms and mollusks), but also to molds, casts, impressions, and fossil excrement (coprolite). Skeletal parts are perhaps the most common of all and paleontologists have been very skillful in reconstructing the whole animal from only a few parts. Vertebrate animals and invertebrates with shells or other hard structures have left the best record (Fig. 38-2). But now and then a rare, chance discovery, such as the Burgess shale deposits of British Columbia and the Precambrian fossil bed of South Australia, reveal an enormous amount of information about soft-bodied organisms.

Fossils may be found in any part of the world, although certain regions, because of ideal conditions for their formation, may have a greater abundance than others, such as the tar pits of Rancho La Brea in Hancock Park, Los Angeles; the great dinosaur beds of Alberta, Canada, and Jensen, Utah; the Olduvai Gorge of South Africa; and many others. It is not always possible to analyze just what conditions are most favorable for the preservation of fossils. A common method of fossil formation is the burial of animals under the sediment deposited by large bodies of water. Climatic conditions must have also been a great factor, as well as the nature of the deposits. Many fossils are found in regions where there are excellent conditions for preservation, such as asphalt tar pits and cold places for refrigeration.

Most fossils are laid down in deposits that become stratified and, if undisturbed, the older strata are the deeper, lower ones. The five major rock strata were mainly formed by the accumulation of sand and mud at the bottoms of seas or lakes. However, strata are not always in the regular sequence by which they were laid down, for in many regions they have buckled and arched under pressure so that older strata may be shifted over more recent ones. Since various fossils are correlated with certain strata, they often serve as a means of identifying the strata of different regions. Fossils thus serve as a guide to any fossil-bearing rock and characterize the deposits in the geologic time scale. This has given rise to the geologic science of stratigraphy.

One of the most useful methods for determining the age of geologic formations and fossils is radioactivity. Radioactive elements are transformed into other elements at certain rates, independent of pressure and temperature. Uranium 238, for example, is slowly changed into lead 206 at the rate of 0.5 gram of lead for each gram of uranium in a period of 4.5 billion years, or the half-life of uranium.

The ratio of lead 206 to the amount of uranium 238 in a sample of rock formation should give a fair estimate of the age of the stratum from which the specimen is taken. By the use of similar techniques, the potassium-argon method is now considered to be even more precise. It is found that the radioactive isotope K^{40} decays into Ca^{40} (88%) and argon 40 (12%) at the rate of a half-life of 1.3 billion years. By knowing the amount of argon emitted (calcium is unreliable) from each unit of potassium in a unit of time, it has been possible to date the age of the rock and that of the fossil laid down in this rock. For fossils not over 50,000 years old, the radiocarbon method of Libby is very accurate. Radioactive carbon 14 has a half-life of 5,568 years and is slowly transformed into N^{14}. Its ratio to C^{12} in the living organisms is the same as that in the atmosphere. There is no exchange of carbon atoms after death, and by knowing the C^{14}/C^{12} ratio in a fossil, its age can be estimated.

The earth's crust has witnessed many striking revolutions. In some regions these changes have taken the form of mountain elevations, emergence of large areas from the sea, sinking of areas into the sea, and marked climatic changes. All these geologic changes involved changes in the distribution of animals and plants. Geologists have therefore divided the history of the sequence of the accumulated deposits or strata into eras, periods, and epochs. There is first the division into five eras, then each era into periods, and finally each period (in some cases) into epochs. These various divisions of the geologic time scale are closely correlated with the fossils they bear.

In recent years the science of **paleoecology** has been attracting widespread interest. The major aim of this discipline is to throw light on the kinds of environment under which sedimentary rocks of the past were accumulated. In this way it is possible to derive information about the physical environments in which fossil organisms lived and their relations to each other. Assemblages of fossils may show the nature of sea floors, the chemicophysical nature of water, and climatic conditions at the time of their existence. The problems of the paleoecologist are far more difficult than those of the present-

TABLE 38-1

Geologic time scale (younger ages toward top of chart; older ages toward bottom)

Era	Period	Epoch	Time at beginning of each period (millions of years ago)	Geologic events and climate	Biologic characteristics
Cenozoic (Age of Mammals)	Quaternary	Recent	0.025	End of fourth ice age; climate warmer	Dominance of modern man; modern species of animals and plants
		Pleistocene	0.6 to 1	Four ice ages with valley and sheet glaciers covering much of North America and Eurasia; continents in high relief; cold and mild climates	Modern species; extinction of giant mammals and many plants; development of man
	Tertiary	Pliocene	12	Continental elevation; volcanic activity; dry and cool climate	Modern genera of mammals; emergence of man from man-apes; peak of mammals; invertebrates similar to modern kinds
		Miocene	25	Development of plains and grasslands; moderate climates; sierra mountains renewed	Modern subfamilies rise; development of grazing mammals; first man-apes; temperate kind of plants; saber-toothed cat
		Oligocene	34	Mountain building; mild climates	Primitive apes and monkeys; whales; rise of most mammal families; temperate kind of plants; archaic mammals extinct
		Eocene	55	Land connection between North America and Europe during part of epoch; mountain erosion; heavy rainfall	Modern orders of mammals; adaptive radiation of placental mammals; subtropical forests; first horses
		Paleocene	75	Mountain building; temperate to subtropical climates	Dominance of archaic mammals; modern birds; dinosaurs all extinct; placental mammals; subtropical plants; first tarsiers and lemurs
Mesozoic (Age of Reptiles)	Cretaceous		130	Spread of inland seas and swamps; mountains (Andes, Himalayas, Rocky, etc.) formed; mild to cool climate	Extinction of giant land and marine reptiles; pouched and placental mammals rise; flowering plants; gymnosperms decline
	Jurassic		180	Continents with shallow seas; Sierra Nevada Mountains	Giant dinosaurs; reptiles dominant; first mammals; first toothed birds
	Triassic		230	Continents elevated; widespread deserts; red beds	First dinosaurs; marine reptiles; mammal-like reptiles; conifers dominant

TABLE 38-1

Geologic time scale—cont'd

Era	Period	Epoch	Time at beginning of each period (millions of years ago)	Geologic events and climate	Biologic characteristics
Paleozoic (Age of Amphibians)	Permian		260	Rise of continents; widespread mountains; Appalachians formed; cold, dry, and moist climate; glaciation; red beds	Adaptive radiation of reptiles which displace amphibians; many marine invertebrates extinct; modern insects; evergreens appear
	Pennsylvanian*		310	Shallow inland seas; glaciation in Southern Hemisphere; warm, moist climate; cool swamp-forests	Origin of reptiles; diversification in amphibians; gigantic insects
	Mississippian*		350	Inland seas; mountain formation; warm climates; hot swamp lands	Amphibian radiation; insects with wings; sharks and bony fish; crinoids
(Age of Fishes)	Devonian		400	Small inland seas; mountain formation; arid land; heavy rainfall	First amphibians; mostly freshwater fish; lungfish and sharks; forests and land plants; brachiopods; wingless insects; bryozoans and corals
	Silurian		425 to 430	Continental seas; relatively flat continents; mild climates; land rising; mountains in Europe	Eurypterids; fish with lower jaws; brachiopods; graptolites; invasions of land by arthropods and plants
(Age of Invertebrates)	Ordovician		475	Oceans greatly enlarge; submergence of land; warm mild climates into higher latitudes	Ostracoderms (first vertebrates); brachiopods; cephalopods; trilobites abundant; land plants; graptolites
	Cambrian		550	Lowlands; mild climates	Marine invertebrates and algae; all invertebrate phyla and many classes; abundant fossils; trilobites dominant
Proterozoic (Precambrian)			2,000	Volcanic activity; very old sedimentary rocks; mountain building; glaciations; erosions; climate warm moist to dry cold	Fossil algae 2.6 billion years old; sponge spicules; worm burrows; soft-bodied animals; autotrophism established
Archeozoic (Precambrian)			4,000 to 4,500	Lava flows; granite formation; sedimentary deposition; erosion	Origin of life; heterotrophism established

*The Pennsylvanian (Upper) and Mississippi (Lower) are often referred to as the Carboniferous period.

day ecologist. The fossil record is so incomplete and the almost entire absence of certain groups as fossils makes it impossible to determine with any degree of accuracy the nature of populations, communities, and other important ecologic concepts. Whatever is found, however, has been of great importance not only to an understanding of the biologic conditions of the past but also to geologic aspects of the ancient distribution of lands and seas.

The major characteristics of the geologic eras are indicated in Table 38-1. As far as the fossil record is concerned, the recorded history of life begins about the base of the Cambrian period of the Paleozoic era. The Cryptozoic eon, which includes the Archeozoic and Proterozoic eras, has been a great puzzle because of the lack of fossils. The chief evidences of life during this period were mostly the burrows of worms, sponge spicules, algae, and a few others. However, the Precambrian fossil deposits of South Australia, with many invertebrate forms, indicate that life had already evolved to a marked extent for perhaps as long as a billion years before the Cambrian period. There is also a great deal of carbon as a residue of organic matter in the sedimentary rocks of this time. As pointed out in a former section, there may have been a great diversity of life in the Precambrian seas, but it was not preserved because of the lack of shells or other hard parts.

Since the Cambrian period when all the major phyla (with one or two exceptions) were well established, it has been a matter of replacing primitive lines with better-adapted ones. Many of the vertebrate classes and orders appeared first in the Ordovician to Devonian periods. By the end of the Paleozoic era, some dominant groups became extinct and were replaced by the expansion of other groups (Fig. 38-3).

Evolution of elephant

Paleontology has afforded evidences for tracing the phylogeny of many groups of animals. Two classic examples are those of the elephant and the horse. Elephants have stressed two morphologic features in par-

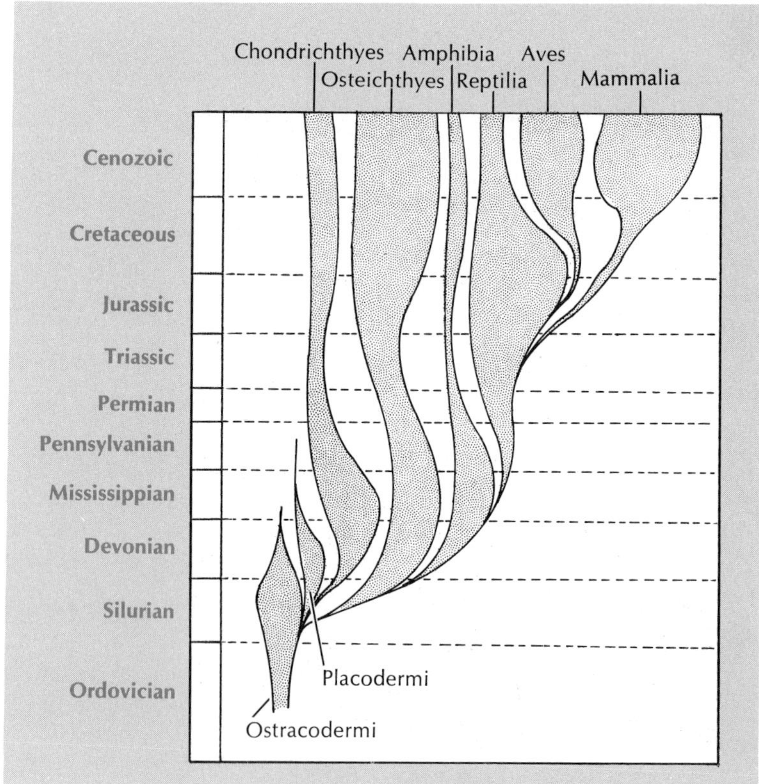

FIG. 38-3

Fossil record of vertebrates. Relative abundance of groups, as indicated by width of shaded areas, is based upon numbers of genera that have been identified. Note expansion and decline of reptiles. Osteichthyes, Aves, and Mammalia are dominant groups at present.

ticular—a prehensile proboscis and teeth. They originated in Africa (in the late Eocene epoch) and gradually spread to other continents. They appear to have evolved from types similar to *Moeritherium* and were about the size of a pig (Fig. 38-4). The second incisors of their upper and lower jaws were a little enlarged. By the Oligocene epoch, four tusks had developed from these incisors (*Palaeomastodon*) and the size had increased to that of a steer. From this type the larger Miocene and Pleistocene forms, lacking the lower tusks, emerged. Later, during the Pliocene epoch came elephants as large or larger than the modern types such as the wooly mammoths (Fig. 38-5). Of the many types of elephants that have appeared, only the African (*Loxodonta*) and Asiatic form (*Elephas*) exist now.

Evolution of horse

The fossil record affords us no more convincing or more complete evolutionary line of descent than that of the horse. The evolution of this form, which covers many millions of years, extends back to the Eocene epoch, and much of it took place in North America. This record seems to indicate that its evolution pro-

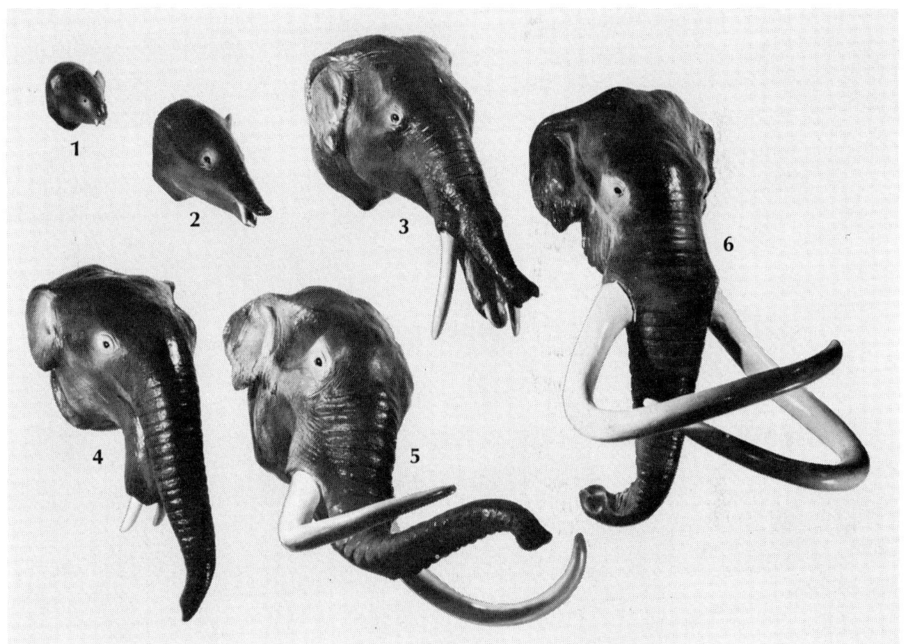

FIG. 38-4

Restoration of heads of fossil elephant-like animals. **1,** *Moeritherium*. **2,** *Palaeomastodon*. **3,** *Trilophodon*. **4,** *Dinotherium*. **5,** *Mastodon*. **6,** *Elephas*. (Courtesy Ward's Natural Science Establishment, Inc., Rochester, N. Y.)

FIG. 38-5

Mammoths. These have been found frozen in Siberia in a good state of preservation. (Courtesy Chicago Natural History Museum.)

ceeded in a definite direction, but it was far from being so. Our best paleontologists who have studied the problem of the horse's evolution consider the true history of the horse family to be made up of many lineages, that is, descent from many lines. Phylogeny of the horse is extensively branched, with most of the branches now extinct. There was not a gradual change in size and reduction of toes, but the change was highly irregular and sporadic. There were millions of years when little change occurred; there were other eras when changes took place relatively rapidly. No real change in the feet occurred during the Eocene epoch, but at least three types of feet developed later and were found in different groups during the late Cenozoic. Only one of these three types of feet is found today. There was extensive adaptative radiation throughout the horse's evolutionary history. Some of these feet became extinct through the operation of natural selection. In the evolution of the horse the morphologic changes of the limbs and teeth were of primary importance, along with a progressive increase in size of most of the types in the direct line of descent.

The first member of the horse phylogeny is considered to be *Hyracotherium*, about the size of a small dog. Its forefeet had four digits and a splint (Fig. 38-6); the hind limb had three well-developed toes and two splints that represented the first and fifth toes. The teeth, 44 in number, had short crowns and long roots, and the teeth in the cheek were specialized to some extent for grinding, since their upper surfaces possessed conical cusps that tended to fuse. The habitat of this form was mostly forest underbrush on which it grazed. The middle Eocene was represented by *Orohippus*, which had a further development of molar-like teeth.

The next type in the line of descent was *Mesohippus*, which flourished in the Oligocene epoch. This animal was taller than the others and had three digits on each foot. Of the three toes, the middle one was larger and better developed than the others. The cheek teeth especially tended to have their cusps united into ridges. *Miohippus*, which was also found in the Oligocene, was larger but definitely of the three-toed type. These horses as well as *Hyracotherium* were browsing forms.

The Miocene epoch was represented by two types, *Parahippus* and *Merychippus*, the latter arising in direct line from the former. *Merychippus* is considered

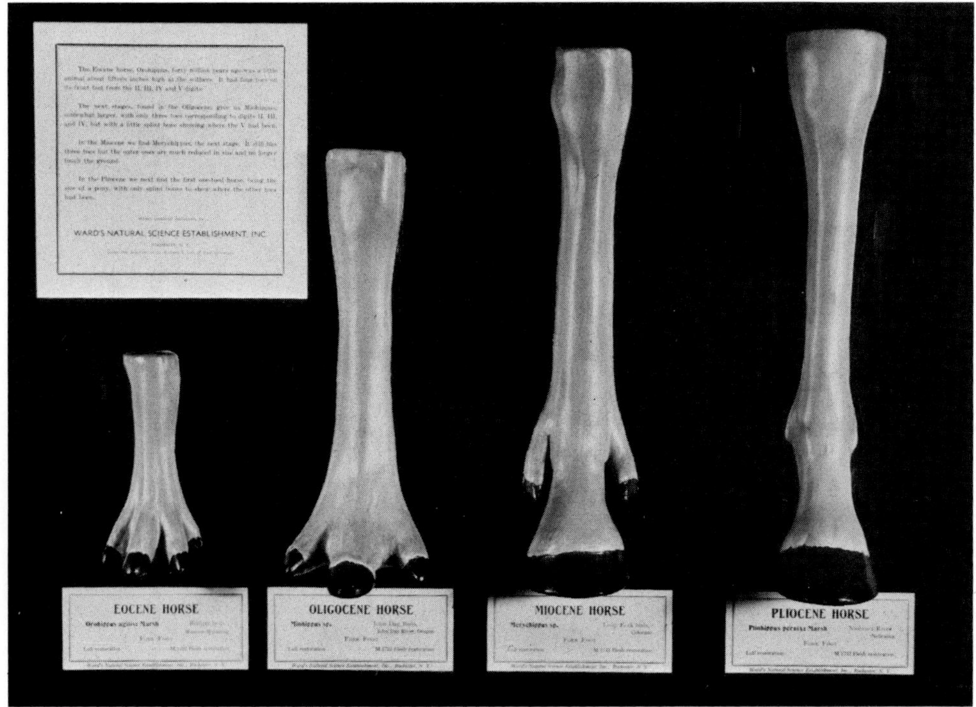

FIG. 38-6

Evolution of forefoot of horse as revealed by fossil record. (Courtesy Ward's Natural Science Establishment, Inc., Rochester, N. Y.)

the direct ancestor of the later horses. They were three toed, but the lateral toes were high above the ground. Thus the weight of the body was thrown upon the middle toe. The teeth were definitely high crowned, and the molar pattern was adapted as a flat grinding surface, with sharp ridges of enamel. The evidence indicates that *Merychippus* was associated with grass feeding. It also had a larger skull and heavier lower jaws than the preceding forms. This horse was between 3 and 4 feet high at the shoulders. *Merychippus* gave rise to a number of horse types, most of which became extinct by the end of the Tertiary period. One of these that persisted into the Pleistocene was *Pliohippus.* This type was the first one-toed horse, for the lateral toes had disappeared.

From *Pliohippus* the genus *Equus,* or modern horse, arose. *Equus* is supposed to have arisen in the Pleistocene epoch. It arose in North America and spread to most of the other continents. In time they came to be about 60 inches or more in height at the shoulders. They have only one toe on each foot, but the two splint bones are evidences of the former lateral toes. By the end of the Pleistocene epoch the horse had become extinct in North America, but migrant forms persisted in Eurasia to become the ancestors of the present-day horse. One or two wild types are still found in central Asia. After the discovery of America by Columbus, the horse was reintroduced by the early Spanish colonists, and many escaped to become wild on the great plains of our west and the pampas of South America.

It is impossible to appreciate the full significance of the horse's evolution without at the same time taking into consideration the geologic changes that went along with it. The development of this great animal from a small foxlike form was closely associated with the geologic development from a hilly, forested country to the great plains of the west. Thus the horse in its evolution represents a close parallelism between the development of an adaptive structural pattern on the one hand and a great geologic development of the earth's surface on the other.

EVIDENCES FOR EVOLUTION

The fossil record already presented represents the strongest and most convincing evidence for the fact of evolution because it is the direct and historic record. Unfortunately, the fossil record for any group is far from complete, and for some, it is practically nonexistent. But there are other biologic disciplines that afford

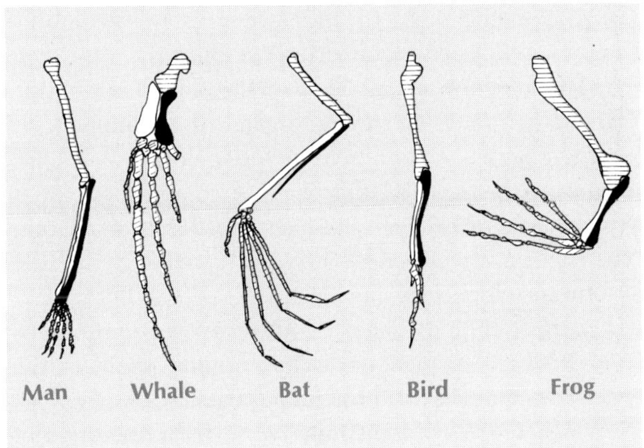

FIG. 38-7

Forelimbs of five vertebrates to show skeletal homologies. Cross-hatching = humerus; white = radius; black = ulna; diagonal hatching = wrist and phalanges. Most generalized or primitive limb is that of man—the feature that has been primary factor in man's evolution because of its wide adaptability. Various types of limbs have been structurally modified for adaptations to particular functions.

FIG. 38-8

Certain vestigial organs in man. **A,** Nictitating membrane in corner of eye, remnant of functional structure in lower forms; **B,** vermiform appendix; **C,** extrinsic muscles of ear, largely nonfunctional in man.

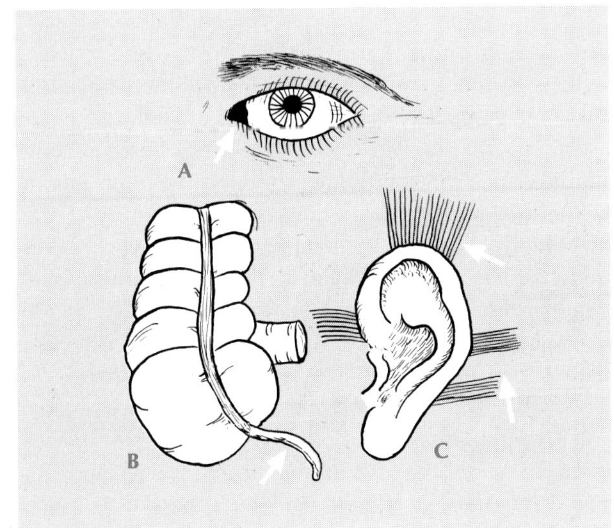

very convincing clues to and evidences for evolution. These may be briefly summarized as follows:

1. **Homologous resemblances.** Homology, you recall, refers to structurally similar organs or functions that become adapted for different environmental conditions. It is best explained on the basis of common ancestral types that have become modified into different adaptations. There are several kinds of homology, such as **structural,** which may be illustrated by the basic skeletal pattern of limb bones of all terrestrial vertebrates (Fig. 38-7); **vestigial,** or **useless organs,** such as the vermiform appendix and nictitating membrane (Fig. 38-8), which must represent inheritance from ancestors in which they were functional; **embryonic,** or the resemblance of early embryos that become unlike as they develop into the adults and that retain their resemblances longer the more closely they are related; **microscopic,** or the similar patterns of cell units, chromosomes, cell organelles, cell processes of mitosis and gamete formation, and histologic tissues that indicate a fundamental unity of organisms; and **physiologic** and **biochemical,** as represented by the similar basic structure of protoplasm, by similar metabolic processes, by the same classes of biochemical compounds, by the similar genetic code of the nucleic acids, by the same methods of biosynthesis and energy transfer, and by similar body fluids.

2. **Classification.** The present-day interpretation of taxonomy is based on the degree of natural relationship. The concept of evolution assumes that the various taxonomic categories have arisen by modification of species. Early life was represented by only a few species, perhaps by only one. Modifications within these early species built up a slow accumulation of different characteristics that resulted in the divergence found among the different groups of animals today. Evolution has in its course proceeded from the taxonomic groups of the lower ranks (species, genera, families) to the higher ranks (orders, classes, phyla). Thus within the animal kingdom the resemblance becomes more detailed as the lower taxonomic units are approached. Many intermediate organisms linking one group with another have been found among both living and fossil forms.

3. **Geographic distribution.** Whenever a new species arises by mutation in a center of origin, it tends to spread out until it is prevented by a barrier of some kind. The higher taxonomic units, such as families, orders, and classes, occupy larger areas than the lower ranks of species and genera. Evolution would explain this on the basis that the higher taxonomic ranks are older, have had a longer time for dispersal, and have had time to break up. Discontinuous distribution, when closely related animals are far apart, can often be explained by the fossil record in the gap between the groups of animals. The camel family, for instance, is represented by the true camels in Asia and the llamas in South America. However, the fossil record indicates that camels may have had their true center of origin in North America, spreading to the other regions. Thus a continuous range became discontinuous. Animals long isolated from each other also tend to show great differences from each other, such as those in Australia and oceanic islands in contrast to those that are near the mainland (continental).

4. **Experimental biology.** By carefully selecting and preserving desirable qualities, man has been able to produce numerous varieties of plants and animals. Although these varieties cannot be considered separate species, they are known to come from common ancestors and may give an inkling of what could be done by nature in the wild. Experimental induction of mutant forms by x-rays, radiation, etc. indicates ways by which speciation may occur in nature.

Within recent years, one of the most striking evidences for evolution is the rapid, man-influenced evolution of certain viruses, bacteria, and insects. Confronted with antibiotics and insecticides, these forms evolve within short periods a resistance to these drugs. These organisms have short generations, amazing reproduction, and high mutation rates. Such evolution is observable and its mechanism can be verified.

THEORIES TO ACCOUNT FOR METHODS OF EVOLUTION

In a field that lends itself to so many different interpretations, we should expect to find many theories. Many theories have some elements of truth in them; but the mistake, common enough in any field of inquiry, of considering a few logical and demonstrated facts as being the whole picture, is characteristic of most of them. The background of training of the biologist often has an important bearing on the theory of evolution he espouses. The paleontologist, for instance, leans strongly toward the orthogenetic interpretation of evolutionary mechanisms; the cytogeneticist, on the other hand, stresses the importance of gene transformations and behavior in mutational changes.

Although no one theory adequately explains the mechanism of evolution, biologists are gradually getting a clearer comprehension of the overall picture of evolution. Many fields of biologic study have made contributions toward its understanding. The difficulty of testing experimentally is a serious disadvantage to any line of scientific inquiry and explains the relative slowness in working out the mechanism of organic evolution.

Inheritance of acquired characters

One of the earliest evolutionary theories proposed was the one by Jean Baptiste de Lamarck (1744-1829), a French biologist. This theory is named after him and is commonly known as **lamarckianism.** He first published his theory in full in his *Philosophic zoologique* (1809). His theory was based on the concept of the use and disuse of organs in the adaptation of animals to their environment. His belief was that, whenever such an adaptation arose, it was definitely inherited from generation to generation—the inheritance of acquired characters. According to Lamarck, new organs arose in response to the demands of the environment. The size of an organ depended on its use and disuse. The limbless condition, for instance, of the snake he would explain by the handicap of legs in crawling through dense vegetation, and thus the loss of the legs through disuse. On the other hand, he would explain the long neck of the giraffe by its habit of reaching up into trees to browse. There is little or no evidence for Lamarck's theory, and it has never received much support from biologists.

The effects of use and disuse are restricted mainly to somatic tissues but genetics does not give support to the transmission of somatic characters. Many experiments have been performed to demonstrate the validity of the theory, but none are convincing. There can be no permanent change unless the germ cells themselves are altered, and experiments have shown conclusively that they are subject to little or no effect from the somatic or body cells and the environment.

Natural selection theory of Darwin

The first real mechanical explanation of evolution was the one proposed by Charles Darwin in his work *The Origin of Species* published in 1859. Another English scientist, Alfred Russell Wallace (1823-1913), should receive some credit for this theory of **natural selection.** Both Darwin and Wallace had arrived at the main conclusions of this theory independently, but the publication of *The Origin of Species* the year after Wallace had announced his conclusions in a brief essay really clinched Darwin's position and prestige.

Darwin's early training had afforded him an opportunity to accumulate data for his theory. As a young man he had spent five years (1831-1836) as a naturalist on board the *Beagle,* a vessel that had been commissioned to make oceanographic charts for the British admiralty. This vessel in the course of its voyage around the world spent much time in the harbors and coastal waters of South America and adjacent regions, and Darwin had ample time to make extensive collections and studies of the flora and fauna of those regions. He kept a detailed journal of his observations on the animal and plant life, an account that he later published. When he returned to England, he brought out a number of scientific papers based on the collections and observations he had made on this extensive voyage.

The idea of natural selection did not occur to him for some time after he had returned. He was especially puzzled over the fossils he found in Patagonia and elsewhere, because he noted the similarities and dissimilarities of these to existing forms of life. The bird life of the Galápagos Islands also intrigued him. After the idea of natural selection dawned on him, he spent the next 20 years accumulating data from all fields of biology to prove or disprove his theory. He made many experiments to test this and that point of natural selection and he evaluated all his work with a careful, scientific appraisal. Darwin, incidentally, obtained some of his clues for this theory from the *Essay on Population* by Malthus, especially the part on competition among people in an overpopulated world. Essentially, most of the concepts of the theory of natural selection were worked out by Darwin himself. So much evidence was brought forth and so forcible were the arguments advanced for natural selection by Darwin in his book, that one may safely say that a new era in thinking, not only in organic evolution but also in many related fields, dates from the publication of the book.

The essential steps in the theory of natural selection as advanced by Darwin include nature of variation, great rate of increase among offspring, struggle for survival, natural selection and variation, survival of the fittest, and formation of new species.

Nature of variation. No two individuals are exactly alike. There are variations in size, coloration, physiology, habits, and other characteristics. Darwin did not know the causes of these variations and was not always able to distinguish between those that were heritable and those that were not. Only the heritable ones are important in evolution, since those caused by environmental factors of temperature, food, etc., are not passed on to succeeding generations. He laid stress on artificial selection in domestic animals and plants and the role it played in the production of breeds and races of livestock and plants. He observed that man had been able to do this by carefully selecting and breeding those individuals with the desired modifications. Darwin thought that this idea of selective breeding under human planning and control could also be produced by agencies operating in the wild state. These agencies he sought to explain in his theory.

Great rate of increase among offspring. In every generation the young are far more numerous than the parents. Even in a slow-breeding form, such as the elephant, if all the offspring lived and produced offspring in turn, in a few hundred years the earth could not hold the elephants. Most of the offspring perish, because the population of most species remains fairly constant under natural conditions. Few animals or plants ever have the opportunity to increase within their theoretic possibilities. Placed in locations more favorable for their natural rate of increase, they may multiply with enormous rapidity, such as the rabbit in Australia. Usually natural checks of food, enemies, diseases, etc. keep the populations within bounds.

Struggle for survival. If more individuals are born than can survive, there must be a severe struggle for existence among them. This competition for food, shelter, breeding places, and other environmental factors results in the elimination of those that are not favorably suited to meet these requirements. There are many factors involved in this struggle for existence, many of them obscure and difficult to demonstrate.

Natural selection and variation. Individuals of the same species tend to be different through variations. Some of these variations make it easier for their possessors to survive in this struggle for existence; other variations are a handicap and result in the elimination of the unfit.

Survival of fittest. Out of the struggle for existence there results the survival of the fittest. Natural selection therefore determines that those individuals that have favorable variations will survive and will have a chance to breed and transmit their characteristics to their offspring. The less fit will naturally die without reproducing themselves. This process will operate anew on each succeeding generation so that the organisms will gradually become better and better adapted to their environment. With a change in the environment, there must also occur a change in those characters that have survival value, or else the animal will be eliminated by the new conditions.

Formation of new species. How does this result in new species? According to Darwin, whenever two parts of an animal or plant population are each faced with slightly different environmental conditions, they would diverge from each other and in the course of time become different enough from each other to form separate species. In this way two or more species may arise from a single ancestral species. Also a group of animals, through adaptation to a changed environment, may become different enough from their ancestors to be a separate species. In a similar manner, greater divergencies could arise in time and lead to the higher taxonomic ranks of genera, families, etc.

What happens to characters when they are nonadaptive or indifferent? Variations that are neither useful nor harmful will not be affected by natural selection and may be transmitted to succeeding generations as fluctuating variations. This explains many variations that have no significance from an evolutionary viewpoint.

Appraisal of theory of natural selection. Although Darwin's theory of natural selection has given in general a logical and satisfactory explanation of evolution, many parts of his theory have to be changed in the light of biologic knowledge and interpretation. Two weaknesses in his theory centered around the concepts of variation and inheritance. Darwin made little effort to distinguish between variations induced by the environment (physical or chemical) and those that involve alterations of the germ plasm or the chromosomal material. It is now known that many of the types of variations Darwin stressed are noninheritable and can have no significance in evolution. Only variations arising from changes in the genes (mutations) are inherited and furnish the material on which natural selection can act.

It will be recalled that the mechanism of genetics was not appreciated until 1900, long after Darwin's death. Darwin referred to sudden and radical variations as "sports" and considered them of little importance in evolution. Modern biology now considers mutations as the cornerstone of the evolutionary concept.

Darwin overemphasized the role of natural selection and failed to note its limitations. He thought that selection could operate indefinitely in promoting the development of a desirable variation. It is now known that, when the population becomes homozygous for the genes of a particular trait, natural selection can no longer operate, as shown from experiments in pure lines. Additional genic changes (mutations) must occur before selection can continue.

Darwin did not appreciate the real nature of isolation in the differentiation of new species. There are really three types of isolation involved—geographic, genetic, and ecologic. Darwin appreciated the fact that groups of animals cut off from each other by natural barriers, such as mountains, deserts, and water, were often quite different from each other. He noticed this in the Galápagos Islands and elsewhere. This **geographic** isolation accounts for the existence of many different species and subspecies of animals in rather small regions that are broken up effectively by natural barriers so that each taxonomic group has a chance to develop independently of the others. A small oceanic island, such as St. Helena, with many valleys separated by high mountains, has many species of snails that are effectively isolated from each other. The explanation for this is that whenever a group of individuals in the range of a given species are in slightly different environments, mutations that may arise within a particular group may enable that group to diverge from the others. If the groups are separated from each other long enough, they may become distinct species.

There may be several kinds of barriers that prevent interbreeding. The geographic ones that have been mentioned are often effective this way. But there are also cases in which mutations may occur in a species and result in a group of organisms that are infertile with the parent stock. This **genetic isolation** is as effective in isolating separate species as are the geographic ones. Although infertility is not always used as a criterion in distinguishing between species, there is no doubt that when two groups of animals are infertile with each other they are distinct species.

Ecologic isolation may be due to differences in habitats and ecologic niches that may tend to keep groups of animals away from each other during the breeding season. Or two groups of animals may actually intermingle but, because of a seasonal variation in their breeding habits, are effectively isolated from each other.

Natural selection seems to play its most important role in the later stages of the evolutionary process. It does not explain the origin of mutations that give a group of animals its unique characteristics. Natural selection may determine what mutations are adaptive and have survival merit. It operates on the whole organism and not merely on individual traits so that a particular trait in a successful species may be highly nonadaptive, yet not sufficiently injurious to upset the survival of the species. However, if the environment changes or the animal moves to a new environment, traits formerly of no use may now prove to be highly advantageous. Thus it is possible for an animal to be adapted in some way long before it actually meets an environment to which it is best suited. This theory of **preadaptation** may have played an important role in the evolutionary process. Ecologically, preadaptation may account for the remarkable way some animals have flourished in new surroundings.

Orthogenesis

Orthogenesis is the inherent tendency for a group of animals to continue to change in a definite direction. This is often referred to as **straight-line evolution,** and the idea involved is that certain structural changes once started may continue without deviation for an indefinite period unless checked by extinction. Some authorities have described such an evolutionary process as oriented evolution. Paleontology furnishes many classic examples, such as that of the horse already described, where certain structural trends, such as the increased size, the reduction in the number of toes, and the increased differentiation of the teeth, are very marked. In the case of the horse, the evolutionary trend has proved highly adaptive, but in others no such advantage is seen.

The theory of orthogenesis occupies a unique position in evolutionary study. The theory does not explain the underlying cause for the evolutionary change along a particular line. The theory also is connected with the idea of the irreversibility of evolution, or the view that an animal does not return toward a former condition. Blum, in his illuminating book *Time's Arrow and Evolution,* has stressed this viewpoint of the irreversibility of evolution through the operation of the second law of thermodynamics, which in some cases permits no exercise of natural selection in altering the direction of evolution. But this author shies away from the implication of an extraphysical force that early advocates of orthogenesis had in mind and thinks the term "orthogenesis" should be avoided altogether.

The random mutation of genes has undoubtedly produced many patterns, some of which have been eliminated by natural selection, leaving those that do have adaptive advantages. The sequence of the adaptive patterns gives the impression of direction and orientation, even though there have been many irregularities in the process. Paleontologists do not stress orthogenesis with all its implications as much as they formerly did, because they now recognize that most examples of it do not have direct, unbranched lines, but that there have been many side branches that have been eliminated by natural selection.

Mutation*

Little was known in Darwin's time about the behavior of chromosomes and their bearing on heredity. Soon after the principles of mendelism were rediscovered in 1900, the parallelism between the chromosomal behavior and mendelian segregation was worked out. It was some years later before the real significance of cytogenetics to the problems of evolution was appreciated. Hugo de Vries, a Dutch botanist, had stressed the importance of **mutations** in the evolutionary process. Working with the evening primrose, he had found certain types of this plant differing materially from the original wild plant and, more important, he found that these aberrant forms bred true thereafter. de Vries explained these mutant forms mainly on the basis of a recombination of chromosomes, but since his time, stress has been laid on genetic transformations. Mutations, as now understood, refer to sudden random changes in genes and chromosomes due to errors in self-copying, but it is precisely these errors that make evolutionary progress possible.

The work of Morgan and his colleagues in working out the theory of linkage of genes, the mapping of chromosomes, nondisjunction of chromosomes, etc. laid the basis for the modern understanding of the hereditary mechanism. The experimental production of mutations through radiation, x-rays, etc. and the discovery of the giant chromosomes in the salivary glands of certain larval insects have added to this understanding.

Natural selection is an important factor in evolution, but its chief role operates in a much later stage of evolution than Darwin had assigned it. Before a new species can evolve, there must be both mutation and natural selection. Mutations furnish many possibilities, natural selection determines which of them have survival merit, and the environment imposes a screening process that passes the fit and eliminates the unfit. Mutations are constantly producing new allelomorphs on which natural selection works.

Nature of mutations. Mutations may be harmful, beneficial, or neutral in their action. Perhaps the majority are harmful because most animals are already adapted and any new change would likely be disadvantageous, but some are distinctly beneficial. In *Drosophila,* in which they have been studied extensively, it has been found that the same mutation occurs with a certain frequency. Thus the red-eyed wild type can be expected to mutate to the white-eyed type ever so often. Moreover, the white-eyed type undergoes mutation, either changing back to the original red eyes or else to one of the other eye color allelomorphs. Mutant characters tend to be recessive in their hereditary patterns and may show up as a phenotype only when they are homozygous; when paired with normal or original allelomorphs, they usually show no effect. Some mutant characters are lethal, but here this action is expressed, as a usual thing, only in the homozygous condition. Since mutations ordinarily occur at random, it is not possible to predict the nature or time of their appearance. Nor is it possible to see a concerted action of mutants along a particular direction, for the genes appear to mutate independently of each other.

Mutations can also be divided into those that produce small changes (micromutations) and those that produce large changes (macromutations). Evolutionary changes produced by the action of the former are referred to as **microevolution;** those produced by the latter, as **macroevolution.** The great majority of evolutionists now favor small mutations as the more important in causing evolution. In this way they can also explain the many intermediate forms (races, subspecies, etc.) between the parent species and the new one. Those who hold to macroevolution explain such intermediate forms as being only geographic varieties of basic species (produced by big changes) that do not lead to definite taxonomic units. Some striking changes due to large mutations are the tailless manx cat and the bandy-legged Ancon sheep.

Most mutations are destined to a very short existence because competition in nature quickly eliminates them.

*Refer to Chapter 2, Principle 28.

There are cases, however, in which mutations may be harmful to an animal under one set of environmental conditions and decidedly helpful under a different set of conditions. If the environment should happen to change at about the same time as favorable mutations appear, then there could be adaptations along special lines and within restricted limits. Such an opportunism of evolution may help explain the evolution of the horse; otherwise it is very difficult to see how the unidirectional and highly specialized nature of its adaptation could occur except through a balance between changing environment and the adaptive mutations of the animal. For the environment to change without a simultaneous appearance of the right mutations would have little or no significance for evolution. The physical world has in its history provided many opportunities for animals with the right mutations, as evidenced by the numerous forms found in the animal kingdom today.

Types of mutations. There are two main types of mutations—gene mutations and chromosome mutations. A **gene mutation** is a chemicophysical change of a gene resulting in a visible alteration of the original character. Although the actual change in the gene is largely unknown, it is thought to be a rearrangement of the nucleotides within a region of the DNA molecule. Such changes cannot be detected under the microscope, for there are no visible alterations in the chromosomes bearing the genes in question. Many of this type of mutation have been found in *Drosophila* and other forms. Most gene mutations are point mutations, that is, the physical or chemical change of one gene.

Chromosome mutations involve either chromosome rearrangement during meiosis or an alteration in the number of chromosomes. The rearrangement of the chromosomes may involve inversion of the linear order of the genes, the deletion of blocks of genes, translocation of portions of chromosomes in which a part of one chromosome becomes attached to another nonhomologous chromosome, and some other irregular procedures. Such changes are usually detectable and often produce phenotypic changes that are inherited in the regular mendelian manner. Increase in number of chromosomes usually involves the formation of extra sets of chromosomes, sometimes a doubling or tripling of the diploid set, resulting in the condition called **polyploidy.** Polyploids are usually characterized by a larger size than the parent stock. Such mutations are far more common in plants than in animals. Among roses, for instance, there are found species with 14, 28, 42, and 56 diploid chromosomes, although the basic parent rose is thought to be one with 14 chromosomes. Such duplication of chromosome sets is due to an upsetting of the meiotic process so that through omission of the reduction division, germ cells are formed with the diploid number of chromosomes instead of the normal haploid number. Experimentally, polyploidy may be induced by the drug colchicine that prevents the division of cells but does not interfere with the duplication of the chromosomes. This results in gametes with the diploid number of chromosomes.

This variability gives natural selection something to work on in the production of a new species, for natural selection can eliminate the unfit characters and allow the adaptable ones to survive. Such variations come and go, dependent on such factors as the size of populations, degree of segregation and isolation, etc. Many mutant characters, therefore, never have a chance to become persistent characters in a population.

Causes and frequency of mutations. Different genes possess different frequencies of mutation rates because some genes are more stable than others. Mutation is also a reversible process and cases of back mutation are well known. Gene A, for instance, may mutate to gene a, and gene a may mutate back to gene A. This reversibility must be taken into account in mutation equilibrium, and the difference between the mutation rate in one direction and the mutation rate in the reverse direction constitutes **mutation pressure,** which is usually of a low magnitude. Mutation frequencies are best known in the fruit fly *Drosophila* and the corn plant. In corn, some genes are known to mutate much more frequently than others. Some plants may be expected to produce 10% of their offspring with at least one mutant gene. The widely known *Drosophila* is supposed to produce at least one new mutation in every 200 or so flies.

Mutation rates are higher in the human male as well as in the males of *Drosophila*. The spontaneous rate is relatively low in all forms studied, which indicates that genes must be very stable. Some loci are far more stable than others. It is also known that there are mutability genes that induce mutations in other loci. The mutation rate in *Drosophila* may be 1,000 times as high as that in the bacterium *Escherichia coli*. In higher vertebrates the average mutation rate per individual may be between 1 in 50,000 to 1 in 200,000 (Mayr).

Many mutations are not detected and estimates of their frequency are in many cases only guesses. Certain genes are also known to increase the mutation rate of other genes in the same organism.

So far as the causes of natural mutations are concerned, very little is known about the matter. Many mutations that were first found in laboratory stocks are now known to occur in the wild state. This contradicts the belief once common that most mutations happen under the influence of laboratory conditions. It is true that both gene and chromosome mutations can be produced artificially by the influence of x-rays, ultraviolet rays, chemicals, temperature, and other agencies. It has been suggested that cosmic rays may be responsible for the appearance of mutations in wild populations. There is also the possibility that spontaneous mutations may be caused by metabolic influences on the unstable genic molecules.

RATES OF EVOLUTION

Evolution has not always proceeded at the same rate among different types of organisms or within different geologic periods. Some groups of animals, such as the brachiopods, have undergone relatively little change since early geologic times. Others, such as the primates, have evolved rapidly. Evolution appears to be most rapid when a new species first appears and then slows down in the later development of the group. The nature of the geologic periods has had an important bearing on the rate of evolution. When there are geologic changes in surface, temperature, and water distribution, only those animals that have suitable variations for natural selection to operate on can adapt to these changes. On the other hand, periods of geologic uniformity and stability have usually been periods of slow evolutionary progress. Stability of environmental conditions is not conducive to rapid evolution of any form. The type of animal group is correlated to some extent with the rate of structural change and diversification. In general, vertebrates have tended to evolve faster than invertebrates, although there are some exceptions to this rule. We have seen that the opossum has changed little since the late Cretaceous period. Evolution seems to advance by spurts and rarely does it proceed in a steady, uniform manner.

Evolutionary rates have been computed for some taxonomic units. Such estimates show that it takes about 500,000 to 1,000,000 years for a new species to evolve among birds and mammals, 20,000 to 50,000 years for a subspecies in the same groups. Paleontology has given some revealing data on evolution rates. The horse required 45 to 50 million years to evolve to its present state and passed through some eight genera. Thus about 6 million years were required, on the average, for each genus. Some species, no doubt, have evolved faster than these rates; fossil records can neither affirm nor deny estimates about the evolutionary rate in most instances.

EVOLUTION AND ADAPTATION

The major aim of evolution is the adaptation of the organism to its environment. Throughout evolution the chief features of life are very much the same. All organisms share in common about the same biochemical compounds, the same kinds of biosynthesis and energy transfer, the same structural features of tissues, and the same metabolic mechanisms of growth, respiration, digestion, etc. These primordial processes of mutual adaptations were fashioned somewhere in the long evolutionary process and no explanation is at present adequate to account for them, although speculations are to be found in the current interest in the origin of life. All individual adaptations are shaped by evolution because maladjusted organisms simply do not survive to reproduce. Fitness to the environment must be found at all levels, from cellular ecology to that of populations. Adaptation, then, is fitting a biologic system to harmonize with the environmental factors of its existence. Also, the more strongly the adaptive features an animal has, the higher the level of taxonomic distinction. Thus the adaptive features of a mammal, such as hair and milk-feeding of the young, place them far above the species level of other vertebrates.

All adaptations are of evolutionary origin, brought about by variability and natural selection. No single adaptive mechanism fits all the conditions of the environment. The organism's adaptive nature is a developmental pattern, faithfully transmitted from generation to generation, and preserved because of its survival merit. The adaptive responses of any organism are prefitted by its evolutionary endowment. They are determined by and restricted to the range of environmental conditions the organism has had in its long evolutionary and phylogenetic experience. This means that there may be no adaptation at all to an entirely novel condition. Only the gross aspects of adaptation are predetermined; the individual must fill in the details to adjust to the conditions it meets in its existence. The limits of its adjustment are fixed by heredity.

No animal is perfectly adaptive to its environment; adaptation is relative because the adaptive endowment of an organism is never able to anticipate all the constantly occurring variations in its environment. There seems to be many characteristics, both anatomic and physiologic, that do their possessors little good. The successful adaptation of an organism is determined by the sum total of all its adaptations. This means that, although some of its adaptations may be highly favorable and others unfavorable, the animal survives. This is why many so-called adaptations, such as **protective coloration** and **sexual selection,** are now viewed with a critical eye.

Coloration is widespread throughout the animal kingdom and apparently serves many purposes, camouflage being one of the most common. In protective coloration the organism blends into its environment so that it can escape detection by enemies. A common example is the dark dorsal and lighter ventral side of fish and many birds. Their color blends with the sky to a potential enemy viewing them from underneath, and viewed from above, the darker shades blend with the darker shades and regions below. Many types of concealment blend the animal into its background; frogs and lizards have the added advantage of changing their color to suit their background. One of the most striking cases of protective camouflage is the *Kallima* butterfly that has a remarkable resemblance to a leaf with venation, imitation holes, and leaf-coloration patterns. For predators, concealing coloration enables them to approach their prey undetected. **Mimicry** adaptation is common among many forms in which harmless animals have found survival value by imitating other species that are well equipped with defensive or offensive weapons. Thus harmless snakes may have a resemblance to venomous ones, and some flies look very much like bees. There are also many examples of **warning** coloration, which advertises the presence of a well-protected animal, such as the white stripes of the skunk and the brilliant colors of the poisonous coral snake.

These adaptive resemblances, whether of protection, warning, or mimicry, have been subjected to experiments with the idea of determining their selective value. Conclusions from these experiments are often conflicting. Some biologists have gone as far as to deny the selective value of color altogether. The extensive investigations of McAtee on the stomach contents of birds indicated that protectively as well as nonprotectively colored insects were eaten by birds without discrimination, but the relative abundance of the protected and unprotected forms in nature must be carefully considered in such experiments. Other experiments seem to indicate that color patterns do play some useful role in survival selection. It has been suggested that some animals that are not protectively colored to the human eye are so protected when viewed by the type of vision of their enemies. Many experiments have also been performed in which predators had an opportunity to choose among prey bearing concealing, warning, or other color devices, and the results indicated that these color patterns do have selective value. These and other experiments emphasize the point that sweeping denunciations of the coloration concept are not warranted.

Darwin's idea of **sexual selection** has been more bitterly criticized than any other aspect of his natural selection theory. Darwin believed that the conspicuous patterns of pigmentation in the males of many species of birds could be accounted for on the basis that the females tend to select those males with the most brilliant colors and most ornamental devices. In this way only those males so attractively equipped would have a chance to leave descendants. Darwin also suggested that such structures as antlers and spurs could be accounted for by sexual selection. Stronger males in this respect could win out over less favored rivals, but often the female will select the vanquished. Sexual selection usually implies that there are more males than females or that polygamy is generally practiced. Polygamy is found among certain groups, such as the fur seals, but with them the females have no choice in the matter, for the strongest and most aggressive male simply takes over a number of females for his harem and fiercely defends them against the weaker males. Experiments to determine the role of ornamentation in the selection of their mates by females have not given very conclusive results, for courtship display may not occur until after pairing. So many factors are involved that it is difficult to state just what part sexual selection does play. It is generally agreed, however, that Darwin overemphasized its importance.

Annotated references

Boule, M., and H. V. Vallois. 1957. Fossil men. New York, The Dryden Press. *A revealing account of man's past history and keen appraisals of the many discoveries in the field of human paleontology.*

Cold Spring Harbor Symposia on Quantitative Biology. Origin and evolution of man, vol. 15. 1950. Cold Spring Harbor, N. Y., The Biological Laboratory. *While this excellent symposium stresses the latest evidence of man's ancestry, much attention is also given to fossil records and their interpretation. A work for the advanced student.*

Gregory, W. K. 1951. Evolution emerging. A survey of changing patterns from primeval life to man, 2 vols. New York, The Macmillan Co. *This excellent work emphasizes the major evolutionary trends in the emergence of animal life, but considerable attention is given to fossils and their significance throughout the work. Suitable for the specialist only.*

Hotton, N. 1968. The evidence of evolution. New York, American Heritage Publishing Co., Inc. *This is a work on evolution by paleontologists with an emphasis on the fossil record. An excellent geologic timetable and a concise account of the voyage of the Beagle are included.*

Leeper, G. W. (editor). 1962. The evolution of living organisms. Melbourne, Melbourne University Press. *This work is based on a symposium held in honor of Darwin's centenary year. Emphasis is placed on Australasian fauna, but the work as a whole gives a fine summary of many evolutionary problems.*

Mayr, E. 1963. Animal species and evolution. Cambridge, Mass., Harvard University Press. *This excellent synthesis and critical evaluation of the processes of evolution will be the "last word" for a long time to come.*

Moore, R. C. 1956. Introduction to historical geology, ed. 2. New York, McGraw-Hill Book Co. *Much stress is given to fossils and their formation. There is a great deal of interest in this work for the beginning student.*

Moore, R. C., C. G. Lalicker, and A. G. Fischer. 1952. Invertebrate fossils. New York, McGraw-Hill Book Co. *A well-balanced textbook, with abundant and revealing illustrations. Every group has a concise list of definitions that are very helpful in understanding the discussions of the different forms. There is an excellent chapter on the way fossils are formed and preserved.*

Romer, A. S. 1950. Vertebrate paleontology, ed. 2. Chicago, University of Chicago Press. *An advanced text and one of the best in the field. Of great interest to all students of fossils.*

Ross, H. H. 1960. A synthesis of evolutionary theory. Englewood Cliffs, N. J., Prentice-Hall, Inc. *An integration of the factors that attempt to explain the how and why of the evolutionary process. There is a short but interesting chapter on the effects of structural (geotectonic) geology on evolution.*

Simpson, G. G. 1953. Life of the past. New Haven, Conn., Yale University Press. *One of the best works on fossils for the beginning student. In a clearly written manner the author surveys the formation of fossils, their meaning, and how they fit into the evolutionary plan.*

Stirton, R. A. 1959. Time, life and man. The fossil record. New York, John Wiley & Sons, Inc. *An account of paleontology, its methods, and its principles. Among its many interesting chapters, the student will find especially revealing the ones dealing with the history of paleontology, the relation of the Foraminifera to oil deposits, and prehistoric men.*

Watson, D. M. S. 1951. Paleontology and modern biology. New Haven, Conn. Yale University Press. *The value of paleontology in the study of evolution cannot be overemphasized, and no one is better qualified to discuss this relationship than the greatest of English paleontologists.*

CHAPTER 39

• PRESENT CONCEPTS OF EVOLUTION—EVOLUTION OF MAN

MODERN SYNTHESIS OF EVOLUTION (NEO-DARWINISM)

● Our present interpretation of evolutionary processes began to take form about 1930. In the first 30 years of the present century there was gradually accumulated a great factual amount of information about the chromosomal and genic theory of heredity, the way mendelian heredity operated, and a more fundamental understanding of the mutation theory. All these branches of investigation had become more or less unified into what we now call cytogenetics. Under the influence of a brilliant group of biologic thinkers, such as J. S. Huxley, R. A. Fisher, and J. B. S. Haldane in England and Sewall Wright, H. J. Muller, and T. Dobzhansky in America, there has been a fruitful attempt to unify all the various theories and ideas of evolution into one underlying mechanism of organic evolution. The new outlook on evolutionary causes has pinpointed the genotype and its behavior in the organism as the focal point for understanding how evolution operates. Evolution has thus been found to be mainly a sequence of genic changes. These workers and many others have shown that changes in the genotype (mutations), with the recombination of genes through biparental reproduction under the influence of natural selection over long periods of time, can operate to produce evolution as we see it around us. How the major causes operate together to produce evolution has already been briefly summarized in a former section.

It remains to examine these evolutionary factors more in detail.

Population genetics and evolutionary processes

Evolution implies changes in the hereditary characteristics, and it is generally agreed that the best conditions for evolutionary changes occur in large populations that are broken up into small subdivisions. The population must be considered the natural form of existence of all species. Moreover, the materials with which evolution works are the genetic variations produced by mutation and recombination of genes. This is especially true of biparental populations in which the normal mechanisms, aside from mutations, of recombinations can operate to produce great variation. The gene pool of large populations must be enormous, for at observed mutation rates many mutant alleles can be expected at all gene loci. In some cases more than 40 alleles of the same gene have been demonstrated. Suppose there are two alleles present, A and a. Among the individuals of the population there will be three possible genotypes: AA, Aa, aa. When there are three alleles present, there are six possible genotypes. Increasing the number of alleles increases the possible genotypes. The reshuffling of genes at the reduction division of meiosis makes possible combinations of a gene at one locus, with any of several others at other loci.

Changes in uniparental populations occur by the addition and elimination of a mutation; in biparental populations the mutant gene may combine with all existing combinations and thus double the types. With only 10 alleles at each of 100 loci, the number of mating combinations would be 10^{100}. Genetic differences must therefore exist among the individuals of biparental populations. The student has seen in the discussion on genetics the many genotypes and phenotypes that can be produced when only a few pairs of genes are involved, but when an organism has thousands of pairs the amount of diversity is staggering. Even though many genes are found together on a single chromosome and tend to stay together in inheritance, this linkage is often broken by crossing-over. If no new mutations occurred, the shuffling of the old genes would produce an inconceivably great number of combinations. But this is not the whole story because genes exert different influences in the presence of other genes. Gene A may act differently in the presence of gene B than it does in the presence of gene C. The diversity produced by this interaction and the addition of new mutations now and then adds to the complication of population genetics. If this diversity is possible in a single population, suppose two different populations with different genes should mix by interbreeding. It is easy to see that many more combinations of genes and their phenotypic expression would occur. All this means that populations have enormous possibilities for variation.

What does this signify for evolution? It has already been stated that genetic variation produced in whatever manner is the material on which natural selection works to produce evolution. Natural selection does this by favoring beneficial variations and eliminating those that are not useful to the organism. Selective advantages of this type represents a very slow process, but on a geologic time scale they can bring about striking evolutionary changes represented by the various taxonomic units (species, genera, etc.), adaptive radiation groups, and the various kinds of adaptations. It must be stressed, however, that natural selection works on combinations of genic variations on the whole animal and not on single hereditary characteristics. The organism that possesses the most beneficial combination of characteristics or "hand of cards" is going to be selected over one not so favored. This concept helps explain some of those puzzling instances in which an animal may have certain characteristics that can be of no advantage to it or may actually be harmful, but in the overall picture it has a winning combination. In this way population genetics can create pools of variations on which natural selection can work to produce evolutionary change.

Why are most mutations recessive? If mutations represent the material for evolutionary change, would not dominant mutants be the most important in evolutionary processes? Why are most mutations recessive? In *Drosophila* only about 7% of the 600 or so mutant genes are dominant. Not all of the answers to these questions are known. We do know that the character of each organ in an organism is controlled by many genes, not by a single gene. The genotype, or all the genes of an animal or plant, controls the character of each organ. This interaction of genes or mutants on each other may be complex. One may inhibit the action of another or one may have no effect without the other, etc. Dominance and recessiveness can be altered in this manner also. Ordinarily, a recessive gene would express itself only in a homozygous condition that might require many generations, but there is some evidence to indicate, however, that new mutations may not be completely recessive and may make their presence felt at once in a heterozygous condition. It is thus possible that a heterozygous condition may give natural selection an opportunity to exercise its effect, for good or bad, over the homozygous condition. It is also possible for natural selection to change recessive genes into dominant ones, for it could spread more rapidly as a dominant.

Why are not recessive genes lost from the population? In an interbreeding population why does not the dominant gene gradually supplant the recessive one? It is a common belief that a character dependent on a dominant gene will increase in proportion because of its dominance. This, however, is not the case, for there is a tendency for genes to remain in equilibrium generation after generation. In this way a dominant gene will not change in frequency with respect to its allele. This important principle is based on a basic law of population genetics called the Hardy-Weinberg equilibrium. According to this law, gene frequencies and genotype ratios in large biparental populations will reach an equilibrium in one generation and will remain constant thereafter unless disturbed by new mutations, by natural selection, or by genetic drift (chance). The rule does not operate in small populations. A rare gene, according to this principle, will not disappear merely because it is rare. That is why certain rare traits, such as albinism, persist for endless generations. It is thus seen that variation is retained even though evolutionary processes are not in active operation. Whatever changes occur in a population—gene flow from other populations, mutations, and natural selection—involve the establishment of a new equilibrium with respect to the gene pool, and this new balance will be maintained until upset by disturbing factors.

The Hardy-Weinberg formula is a logical consequence of Mendel's first law of segregation and is really the tendency toward equilibrium inherent in mendelian heredity. Select a pair of alleles such as T and t. Represent the proportion of T genes by p and the proportion of t genes by q. Therefore, $p + q = 1$, since the genes must be either T or t. By knowing either p or q, it is possible to calculate the other. Of the male gametes formed, p will contain T and q will contain t, and the same will apply to the female gametes. (See checkerboard in Chapter 35.) As we know from Mendel's law, there will be three possible genotypic individuals, TT,

Tt, and tt, in the population. By expanding to the second power, the algebraic formula $p + q$ will be $(p + q)^2 = p^2 + 2pq + q^2$, in which the proportion of TT genotypes will be represented by p^2, Tt by $2pq$, and tt by q^2. Recall the 1:2:1 ratio of a mendelian monohybrid. The homozygotes TT and tt will produce only T and t gametes, whereas the heterozygotes Tt will produce equal numbers of T and t gametes. In the gene pool the frequencies of the T and t gametes will be as follows:

$$T = p^2 + \tfrac{1}{2}(2pq) = p^2 + pq = p(p + q) = p$$
$$t = q^2 + \tfrac{1}{2}(2pq) = q^2 + pq = q(q + p) = q$$

In all random mating the gene frequencies of p and q will remain constant in sexually reproducing populations (subject to sampling errors). It will be seen that the formula $p^2 + 2pq + q^2$ is the algebraic formula of the checkerboard diagram, and thus the formula can be used for calculating expectations without the aid of the checkerboard.

To illustrate how the Hardy-Weinberg formula applies, suppose a gene pool of a population consisted of 60% T genes and 40% t genes. Thus:

$$p = \text{frequency of T (60\% or 0.6)}$$
$$q = \text{frequency of t (40\% or 0.4)}$$

Substituting numerical values of gene frequency in the following,

$$p^2 + 2pq + q^2$$
$$(0.36 + 0.48 + 0.16)$$
$$\text{TT} \quad \text{Tt} \quad \text{tt}$$

the proportions of the various genotypes will be 36% pure dominants, 48% heterozygotes, and 16% pure recessives. The phenotypes, however, will be 84% (36 + 48) dominants and 16% recessives.

On the other hand, suppose 4% of a population is made up of a certain recessive trait, then:

$$q^2 = 4\% \text{ or } 0.04$$
$$q = \sqrt{0.04} = 0.2 \text{ or } 20\%$$

Thus 20% of the genes are recessive. Even though a recessive trait may be quite rare, it is amazing how common a recessive gene may be in a population. Only 1 person in 20,000 is an albino (a recessive trait); yet by the above formula, it is found that 1 person in every 70 carries the gene or is heterozygous for albinism.

How chance operates to upset the equilibrium of genes in a population. The Hardy-Weinberg equilibrium can be disturbed, as already stated, by mutation, by selection, and by chance or genetic drift. The term **genetic drift** (Wright) refers to changes in gene frequency resulting from purely random sampling fluctuations. By such means a new mutant gene may be able to spread through a small population until it becomes homozygous in all the organisms of a population (random fixation) or it may be lost altogether from a population (random extinction). Such a condition naturally would upset the gene frequency equilibrium mentioned in the previous section. It also affords a means by which small, isolated populations can originate characteristics that are of no use to the individuals of that population, such as the small differences between subspecies and even species. It has also been suggested that genetic drift may result in a new species being formed, or else contributing to the gene pool of the large, ancestral population under certain conditions.

How does the principle apply? Suppose a few individuals at random became isolated from a large general population. This could happen by some freakish accident of physical conditions, such as a flood carrying a small group of field mice to a remote habitat where they would have no opportunity to mix with the general population, or a disease epidemic could wipe out most of a population and produce the same effect. Suppose that in the general population individuals would be represented by both homozygotes, TT, for example, and heterozygotes, Tt. It might be possible for the small, isolated group to be made up only of TT individuals and the t gene would be lost altogether, or the reverse could happen. Also, when only a small number of offspring are produced, certain genes may, by sampling errors, be included in the germ cells and others not represented. It is possible in this way for heterozygous genes to become homozygous. In this way the new group may in time have gene pools quite different from the ancestral population.

We should note also that most breeding populations of animals are usually small. Most large and widespread populations are divided into more or less isolated groups by physical barriers of some kind. The home areas even of animals that can get around are amazingly small in many instances. A mere stream may be effective in separating two breeding populations. Thus, chance could lead to the presence or absence of genes without being directed at first by natural selection. In the long run, however, whether or not the trait has adaptive significance will depend on natural selection.

Genetic drift has been assigned as the cause of the

frequency of certain human traits such as blood groups. Among some American Indian tribes it is known that group B, for instance, is far rarer than it is among other races and may be due to small isolated mating units.

How effective genetic drift is in the evolutionary process is a controversial subject, and there are many who deny its importance. But it is generally agreed that in bisexually reproducing species evolution proceeds more rapidly when a population is broken up into isolated or partially isolated breeding communities, and the smaller the population the greater will be the importance of genetic drift.

What is natural selection? The concept of natural selection was Darwin's great contribution to evolution and is a key factor in most if not all theories of evolution. Most of us think of natural selection as the struggle for existence, survival of the fit, brutal competition, etc. But other factors that are less related to struggle and competition and that play a part in the natural selection concept are the ability to produce large numbers of viable offspring, ability to resist disease, speed of development, mutual cooperation, etc. In accordance with the evolutionary opportunity of an environment in which an organism is living, natural selection can stabilize, direct, or disrupt the whole evolutionary process of a particular form. Natural selection is a blind force without purpose and has often been called noncreative. But the newer evolutionary synthesis assigns it to a creative role, for natural selection can ensure the continuance of a favorable allele and the elimination of an unfit allele and can mold all the chromosomes and their genes into an integrated whole. Natural selection does not operate on an all-or-none basis but is a statistical phenomenon. It works on populations as a whole and not on definite fit and unfit types. Populations are made up of thousands of variable genes. Those individuals with the most favorable genes (a superior genotype) will survive and will tend to leave more offspring so that natural selection is the differential perpetuation of genotypes. Natural selection works only on those members of a population that are of reproductive age. This explains why disease and other ailments strike relatively soon after the period of reproduction because natural selection is not concerned with what happens in old age. The variations on which natural selection works are produced both by recombinations of genes and by mutations of genes. All phenotypic characters are variable because every individual differs genetically. Selection operates on the available variations (usually those around a mean) to produce the most efficient gene pool for adaptation and reproductive success. It is thus seen that two factors are required for effective natural selection—the choice of variations and reproductive individuals to carry on these variations to future generations.

Examples of speciation. Speciation refers to the splitting of one species into two or more other species. It implies the formation of two or more populations that do not exchange genes. Mutations, recombinations of genes, selection, and isolation operating together produce genetic diversification that is the essence of species formation. Although there may be several patterns in the diversification of organisms, it is thought that the sequence of geographic isolation, morphologic differences (mutations, etc.), and conditions that prevent future fusion of groups represents one of the most important and effective patterns of evolutionary progress. It is clear that whenever distinct forms interbreed, their genotypes will intermix and any differences between them will be lost. Any effective evolutionary pattern must prevent this interbreeding so that each group (species) can profit from its own independent evolution. Evolution seems to be most rapid when a group of organisms are presented with a new environment with many unoccupied ecologic niches of low competition and predation. By adaptive radiation many new types can evolve to fill these niches.

A striking illustration of isolation and adaptive radiation is afforded by Darwin's finches of the Galápagos Islands. These islands are found about 600 miles west of the South American mainland (Ecuador) and attracted the attention of Darwin when he visited them about 1835 during his famous voyage on the *Beagle.* Darwin was struck by the unusual animal and plant life on these islands as contrasted with that on the nearest mainland of South America. These volcanic islands have never had land connections with the mainland and such life as is found there had to be by accidental immigration. Darwin was particularly interested in the bird life of the islands, especially the finches.

In 1947 the English ecologist Lack published a book on these finches that has served to renew interest in their evolutionary development. All the different species of finches (family Geospizidae) found on these islands are supposed to have descended from a South American finch that reached the island. Their most interesting adaptive structures are their different beak modifications that permit them to exploit the food resources of the various ecologic habitats. The ancestral finch was probably a ground feeder, but as competition increased in this habitat, finches evolved that were adapted (or radiated out) to utilize food in other ecologic niches unavailable to the ancestral form. The ground feeders have thick, conical beaks for seed, the cactus ground finch has a long, curved beak for the nectar of cactus flowers, the vegetarian tree finch has a parrotlike beak for buds and fruit, and the woodpecker finch has a long, stout beak (and an improvised spine) for probing into bark. Some of the finches are vegetarian and some are insectivorous. Altogether, some 14 species (and some subgenera) of finches have evolved from the ancestral finch that first reached the islands. Moreover, each island of the group, because of geographic isolation, has had an effect on the evolution of the various species, although most of the islands have the same type of ecologic habitats.

An example of speciation in the making is the common laboratory frog *Rana pipiens*. For years herpetologists have puzzled over the status of this frog, which ranges from northern Canada to Panama and from the Atlantic coast to the edge of the Pacific states. Is it one species or is it divided into subspecies? Individuals from adjacent localities, such as those from New England and New Jersey, or those from Florida and Louisiana, can be crossed successfully and yield normal and viable embryos. Also, a frog of this species from New Jersey can be crossed with one from Louisiana and will produce normal embryos. But crosses between individuals from widely separated localities, such as a cross between one from Wisconsin and one from Florida, will produce abnormal and nonviable embryos. Evidently the genetic differences between the northern and southern forms are great enough to prevent normal hybrid development. Selection has produced different developmental physiologies in these types of frogs. Those in the north are adapted for rapid growth at low temperatures; those in the south, for slow growth at high temperatures. This genetic difference is sufficient, if one ignores the individuals from adjacent localities, to produce at least two distinct species—the northern form and the southern form. They certainly meet the chief criterion of separate species in not being able to interbreed.

It is very doubtful that hybridization plays a major role in the evolutionary process in animals. When two different species are crossed, especially those with different chromosome numbers, the offspring are generally sterile. Some fertile hybrids are known that do not reproduce in nature. Reference has already been made to polyploidy of plants in Chapter 36. This process has been an important mechanism in plant speciation.

Species populations or their subdivisions, separated from each other by natural barriers and thus occupying different territories, are called **allopatric.** Two or more species or populations inhabiting the same geographic range are called **sympatric.** Allopatric and sympatric populations may show different degrees of isolation. It is easy to see that effective barriers will produce complete isolation and prevent interbreeding between separate groups so that evolution may proceed in the isolated group without interference with other groups. In sympatric populations isolation may be seasonal (breeding at different times of the year) or behavioral (incompatibility of mating reactions); these are as effective as the geographic one. Whenever two closely related species occupy the same area, it is thought that they evolved in different ecosystems and later merged into one.

Concept of polymorphism

Many species including both plants and animals are represented in nature by two or more clearly distinguishable kinds of individuals. Such a condition is called **polymorphism.** This polymorphic variation may involve not only color but many other characters, physiologic as well as structural. The term has been used with many meanings, but the definition rules out seasonal and some other variations, such as the winter and summer pelage and plumage of certain mammals and birds. Polymorphism always refers to variability within a population and is restricted to genetic polymorphism. It results when there are several alleles or gene arrangements with discontinuous phenotypic or visible effects. It may be expressed by just two alternative types, such as male and female dimorphism, or there may be many morphologic types within the species. The genetic pattern is well exemplified by the ladybird beetle, *Adalia bipunctat*, studied by Timofeeff-Ressovsky. In this genus some of the individuals are red with black spots, whereas others are black with red spots. The black color behaves as a mendelian dominant and red as a recessive. The black and red forms live side by side and interbreed freely. Studies show that the black form is predominant from spring to autumn and the red form from autumn to spring. It is thought that the changes are produced by natural selection, which favors the black form during summer and the red during winter.

For instance, more black forms, produced by dominant genes, die out during winter, while the recessive red form survives. It is thus possible for the recessive gene, at least during part of the seasonal cycle, to be more common than its dominant allele.

Sometimes an advantageous gene may spread through a population and tend to replace its allele. Such an example is industrial melanism in moths in certain industrial regions of England. In this case a mutant gene (melanism) of rather low frequency has a selective advantage over the normal form when the environment becomes black from pollution. Two polymorphic forms may exist side by side because of a balance of selective forces (balanced polymorphism) or because one may have a selective advantage and gradually replace the other (transient polymorphism).

Polymorphism has adaptive value in that it adapts the species to different environmental conditions. Polymorphic populations are thus better able to adjust themselves to environmental changes and exploit more niches and habitats. Without a doubt, the potentialities of polymorphism are much greater than its realization because every population must have many allelic series that are never expressed in the visible phenotype. So far, there is no satisfactory explanation for the phenotypic uniformity of some species in contrast to the polymorphism of others.

Polymorphism is widespread throughout the animal kingdom, and often different forms have been mistaken for separate species. Some classic examples of polymorphism are the right-handed and left-handed coils of snails of the same species, the blood types of man and other animals (a biochemical distinction), sickle cell anemia in man, albinism in many animals, silver foxes in litters of gray foxes, and rufous and gray phases of screech owls in the same brood.

Neoteny as an evolutionary factor

The concept of neoteny is thought to play an important role in creating new patterns or types of animals. This concept emphasizes the retention of larval characteristics in the adult and the appearance of sexual maturity in a larval, or juvenile, condition. Mention has already been made in a former section of the axolotl form of the salamander, whose metamorphosis may have been suspended because the thyroid mechanism fails to operate normally. By such means it is possible for many new patterns of animal life to have evolved from generalized species. Some striking examples in evolution may occur when certain stages of the life history are simply dropped off. For instance, insects with six legs are supposed to have evolved from the myriapods with many segments and legs. At an early stage of their existence, myriapods have three pairs of legs and few segments. It would be easy for such a larval form to be transformed into an insect by the retention of the larval characteristics of the myriapods which already have some of the fundamental characteristics of insects (tracheae, malpighian tubules, antennae, etc.).

Many evolutionists believe that man himself is a neotenous form of a primitive apelike ancestor. This may account for the lack of hair that is a fetal characteristic in apes, but an adult trait in man. The flat face of man, the large brain (which in the embryos of all mammals is proportionally much larger than the rest of the body), the lack of pigmentation in certain races, etc. are really fetal characteristics.

IS IT POSSIBLE TO OBSERVE EVOLUTION IN ACTION TODAY?

Darwin in his time could not point to a single visible example of evolution in action. Some of his opponents were quick to point out that this lack was a major weakness in his arguments. However, in England during his lifetime, a striking case of evolution was actually taking place in nature before his eyes had his attention been directed to it. Such an example is industrial melanism in moths. Within the last century, certain moths, such as the peppered moth *(Biston)*, has undergone a coloration change from a light *(B. betularia)* to a dark melanic form *(B. carbonaria)*. This moth is active at night and rests on the trunks of trees during the day. The light form is especially well adapted to rest on the background of lichen-encrusted trees where it is largely invisible. In the industrial regions of England, however, there has been a change from lighter to darker tree trunk backgrounds because of the pollution from the fallout of smoke particles. Such pollution kills the light-colored lichens and blackens the vegetation. Against a dark background, light-colored moths are conspicuous and fall prey to predator birds. Natural selection would therefore, in the course of time, largely eliminate the moth, as numerous experiments have shown. However, by mutation the light-colored moth has given rise to a dark-colored melanic form that has a much better survival rate under such surroundings. Within a period of years in polluted areas, the dark species *(B. carbonaria)* has, to a great extent, replaced the light species (*B. betularia*). The mutation for industrial melanism appears to be controlled by a single dominant gene that is also known to occur in natural environments (not due to pollution) in which a dark color is a distinct advantage. Thus by mutation and natural selection a moth of a wholly different color and physiologic nature has emerged to confirm Darwin's mechanism of the evolution of a new species from another species.

EXPERIMENTAL PRODUCTION OF NEW SPECIES

In 1924 Karpechenko was able to produce a new species by hybridization. He crossed the radish (*Raphanus sativus*) with the cabbage (*Brassica oleracea*), each of which has 9 haploid chromosomes. In most cases the hybrids of two different species of unlike chromosomes (as these were) are unable to produce fertile offspring because unlike chromosomes cannot pair (synapsis) properly in the meiosis of their gametes. The 18-chromosome hybrids (9 chromosomes from each parent) in this cross were entirely sterile and could not produce offspring. However, a few of the hybrids by spontaneous allopolyploidy, or doubling of the chromosomes, had 36 chromosomes (18 radish chromosomes and 18 cabbage chromosomes). When these hybrids underwent meiosis to form their gametes, the homologous radish chromosomes could pair with each other and the homologous cabbage chromosomes could pair with each other so that each gamete had 9 radish and 9 cabbage chromosomes. The union of such eggs and sperm could produce a fertile plant of 36 chromosomes. This new plant, which had characteristics of both the radish and the cabbage, could not be crossed with either one of the original parents and was reproductively isolated. The new synthetic genus was called *Raphanobrassica* and was the first recorded instance of the artificial creation of a new species (Fig. 39-1).

Allopolyploidy has perhaps played an important role in plant evolution but very little in that of animals.

SOME EVOLUTIONARY GENERALIZATIONS

In evolution there are several generalizations that reveal certain trends in the evolutionary process. There are some exceptions to these rules, but they do reveal many interesting aspects that the student of evolution might overlook. Some of these, such as Gloger's, Bergmann's, and Allen's rules, represent geographic variation gradients correlated with adaptive morphologic structures and are the result of mutation and selection.

Dollo's law. Dollo's law applies to the irreversibility of evolution and was first stated by a paleontologist, Dollo. Recently the principle has been greatly emphasized by the American evolutionist Blum. Although minor reversals, such as back mutations, may occur,

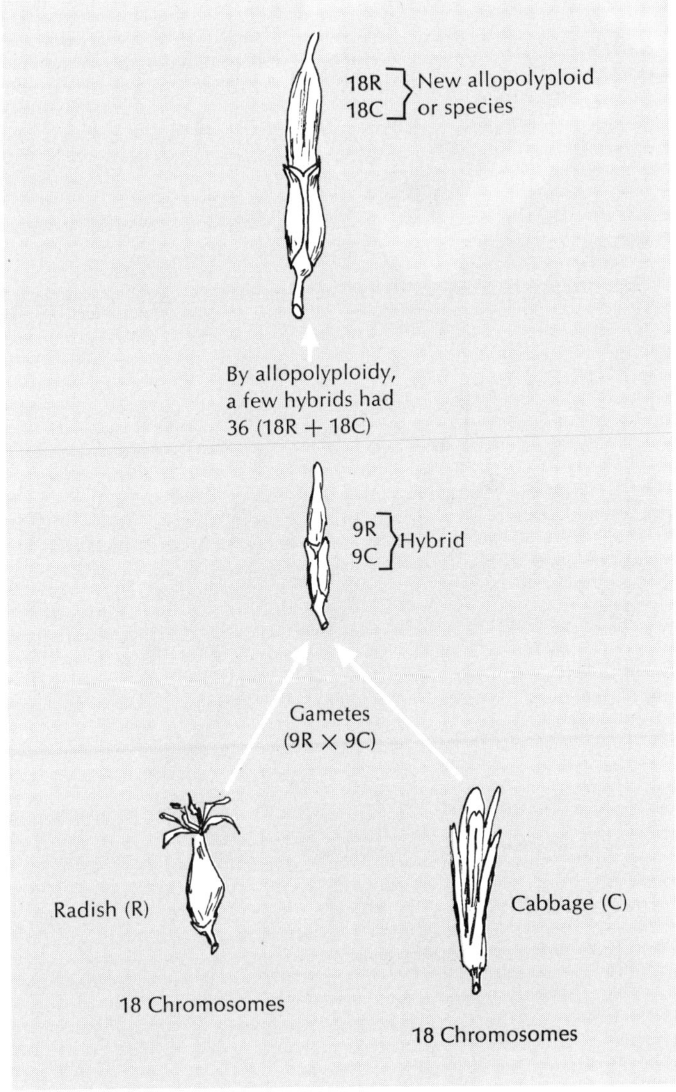

FIG. 39-1

Karpechenko's classic experiment of producing artificial species. Allopolyploidy is that form of polyploidy in which there is doubling of chromosomes in hybrid—in this case, result of cross between cabbage gamete of 9 chromosomes, **C**, and radish gamete of 9 chromosomes, **R**. (Modified from Karpechenko.)

there is no evidence to indicate that evolution is other than a one-way process.

Cope's law. This principle states that during the course of evolution there is a tendency for animals to increase in size until they become extinct. It was formulated by the American paleontologist Cope and is based on the overall increase in complexity of most evolutionary lines. The present horse, for example, evolved from a much smaller animal. Larger animals are probably more independent of their environments because they are more complex and are less affected by external changes. They can also store more food reserves and can usually move faster.

Gloger's rule. In the northern hemisphere, most species of birds and mammals living in a north-south range tend to be lighter colored (less melanin) in the north than races of the same species living in humid, warm climates. Darker colors are usually associated with greater humidities, and this factor, as well as temperature, may play a part in the application of the rule.

Bergmann's rule. According to this principle endothermal animals are usually larger in the colder parts and smaller in the warmer parts of their range (Fig. 39-2). It is based on the physiologic principle that a large body is correlated with a relatively smaller body surface and thus can conserve its heat better. There are many striking examples of this rule. Penguins are much larger on the Antarctic continent than they are on the islands off the coast of South America;

FIG. 39-2

Bergmann's rule, as illustrated by 3 of 17 species of penguins. Emperor penguin, even larger than king penguin, is restricted mainly to Antarctic continent. Rule is based upon principle that large body has smaller surface in proportion to mass (weight) than does small body and so is better able to maintain its heat. Other birds and mammals verify rule, for larger members are found in colder parts of their range, whether in northern or southern hemisphere.

bears are larger in Alaska than they are in the United States; and hares are much larger in Russia than they are in central Europe. There are some exceptions, however, to the rule.

Allen's rule. Most races of mammals and birds in cold regions have relatively shorter extremities than races of the same species from warmer regions. Arctic hares and foxes, for instance, have much shorter ears than closely related southern species of those animals. The rule has some experimental verification because mice reared at high temperatures have relatively longer ears and feet than those developed at lower temperatures. This is an adaptation against loss of heat and the possibility of freezing in cold climates. There is about a 25% exception to this rule.

Jordan's rule. This rule states that closely related species or subspecies are not found in the same range but in adjacent ones separated by some barrier. This generalization is verification of the role of geographic isolation in the evolution of species. There are some exceptions to the rule, for some closely related forms may be found in the same region but due to ecologic or other isolation do not interbreed.

Gause's rule. Two species with identical ecologic relations cannot occupy indefinitely the same ecologic niche in the same habitat. Usually one species exterminates or drives out the other. If the species have sparse populations, it is possible for the two groups to share similar ecologic niches, or one species could occupy peripheral regions and the other central areas of the same general habitat (centrifugal speciation). The study (1958) of R. H. McArthur on five species of warblers that are found together in coniferous forests and have in general the same insectivorous habits reveals a nice discrimination in the application of Gause's principle. Even though these species ate about the same kind of food, each species tended to avoid severe competition with the others by inhibiting overgrowth of its population through territorial behavior, by feeding in different positions or zones in the trees and thus being exposed to different types of food, by different nesting dates, etc. In this way the different species could be coexistent, even though there was some overlapping of their activities.

CONVERGENCE AND PARALLELISM

Two groups of animals not closely related may evolve similar structures because similar habitats have afforded them the same evolutionary opportunity. The two groups may be quite dissimilar in the beginning, or their ancestors may be entirely lacking in the common structures under consideration. The radiations of the two groups have been along lines of similar opportunities. Similar mutations are favored because of the possibilities of the environment. The ways of life are common to both groups and each has taken advantage of similar ecologic niches. Good examples of convergence are seen in the likenesses between the placental and marsupial types of animals (Fig. 29-1) and by the resemblance between the body forms of aquatic mammals and fishes.

When two groups are rather closely related to begin with, the evolutionary phenomenon is called parallelism. In this case, mutations are more likely to be similar in each group, and each will undergo evolutionary changes along similar lines, although the two are never completely identical. For instance, the enamel-crowned molars of the horse, rhinoceros, and elephant came from ancestral forms that lacked this characteristic.

MAN'S CLOSEST RELATIVES—PRIMATES

Man belongs to the order of mammals called Primates. This order is now commonly divided into two suborders—Prosimii and Anthropoidea. The Prosimii include the more primitive members, such as the tree shrews, the lemurs, the lorises, and the tarsiers. The suborder Anthropoidea is made up of the more advanced primates and is divided into two infraorders—Platyrrhini, or New World primates, and Catarrhini, or the more advanced anthropoids that include the Old World monkeys, apes, and man. The catarrhine infraorder is likewise separated into two groups (superfamilies)—Cercopithecoidea, or those anthropoids with tails, and Hominoidea, or the great apes and man. The superfamily Hominoidea is represented by three families—Hylobatidae, Pongidae, and Hominidae. The Hylobatidae contain the gibbon *(Hylobates)*; the Pongidae include the orangutan *(Pongo)*, the chimpanzee *(Pan)*, and the gorilla *(Gorilla)*; and the Hominidae include man *(Homo sapiens)*.

The basic adaptive features that have guided the evolution of this great mammalian order culminating in man have revolved mainly around the arboreal habits of the group. Some of the group, such as man, abandoned the brachiating habit (using the arms for swinging) and took up a terrestrial existence, but there are anatomic structures, such as the limbs, hands, and feet, which plainly indicate the basic ancestral traits for an arboreal life. The free rotation of limbs in their sockets, the movable digits on all four limbs, and the opposable thumbs are all modifications for grasping branches and swinging through trees. Omnivorous food habits have produced a characteristic dentition. Along with skeletal specializations, there are many correlated features that have evolved in primates, such as many muscular, neural, and sensory adaptations superior to those in other animals. Better vision and development of other sense organs, as well as the proper coordination of limb and finger muscles, have meant an enlargement of appropriate regions of the brain. Precise timing and judgments of distance were necessary concomitants of an arboreal life and required a larger cerebral cortex. Concurrent enlargement of the brain led to a level of intelligence and alertness of mind characteristic of the higher primates. The order as a whole is considered a very primitive group of placental mammals which have retained certain generalized features that have made possible a wider range of adaptations than is found in extremely specialized groups.

As mentioned elsewhere, mammals have arisen during the Triassic period from reptiles, when early in their adaptive radiation, certain mammal-like reptiles developed into several lines of mammals. Early in the Cenozoic era the basic radiation of primitive placental mammals began and continued until more than a score of orders arose and took over the niches formerly occupied by reptiles. The most primitive order was the Insectivora, familiar examples of which are the present terrestrial moles and shrews. But some members of this order, the tree shrews, took to living in trees and gave rise to the great order of primates. Living tree shrews in Asia thus may be considered a transition between the primitive insectivore ancestors and the primates. According to Romer, tree shrews may be placed in either the order Insectivora or the order Primates because their primitive and other features show definite relationships to the primates. Although tree-dwelling animals do not form fossils to any extent, fossil remains of shrewlike mammals have been found in the Paleocene epoch of 75 million years ago.

From a common, shrewlike, arboreal ancestor, the first distinct primate thus arose. These first primates, commonly called the early prosimians, were small nimble animals adapted for living in trees. Although they possessed good muscular coordination and sense organs, their intelligence was low; intelligence among modern primates is a later development in their evolution. As stated in the first part of this section, the living primitive primates are placed in the suborder Prosimii. Besides the tree shrews, the suborder includes the lemurs (mostly in Madagascar), the tarsiers of the East Indies, and the lorises of Asia and Africa. Some modern prosimians have many primitive characteristics, such as eyes on the side, long snouts, and long tails (lemurs); but in the tarsiers the large eyes have moved forward and the muzzle is short. Their larger brain and better-developed placenta also place the tarsiers nearer the anthropoids than the lemurs. Although tarsiers have all but vanished, many Paleocene and Eocene fossil genera have been found. Certain basic adaptations had to be developed by primates for a tree-dwelling existence. For security in treetops it was not only necessary to have grasping ability, such as the opposability of the thumb and great toe, but also stereoscopic vision and the ability to judge distance in swinging precariously from limb to limb.

Some of the tarsiers may have been ancestral to the higher primates, which include monkeys, apes, and man (suborder Anthropoidea). This suborder is divided into two groups—the New World monkeys and the other anthropoids. New World monkeys (family Cebidae) are the more primitive of the two groups. They are usually smaller than Old World monkeys, although they are similar in appearance. Their nostrils are far apart and they have long prehensile tails. The thumb is only slightly opposable to the other fingers. The fossil record (which is scanty) indicates that their radiation may have occurred during the Oligocene and Miocene epochs. The Old World monkeys (family Cercopithecidae) probably arose independently from tarsioid stock also. Their fossil material dates back to the Oligocene epoch (35 to 40 million years ago). The fossil *Parapithecus* of the lower Oligocene epoch in Egypt may be the link between the tarsioids and the Old World monkeys. A recent fossil has been named *Oligopithecus* and may indicate a connective link also. The Old World monkeys have their nostrils close together, and they do not use their tails as prehensile organs. They have a wide range of structure. Like the New World monkeys, they are four footed in terrestrial locomotion, walking on their palms and soles. Most are arboreal, but the short-tailed baboons show a tendency for ground dwelling.

The Old World monkeys cannot be considered ancestral to the anthropoid apes or man. The primitive, hominoid apes evolved independently from prosimian ancestors. They were small monkey-sized animals. Many of their fossils have been found in the Miocene and Pliocene deposits. Although they are apelike, they do not have the specializations of the modern apes. *Propliopithecus* from the Oligocene from the Fayum bed of Egypt is thought to be a generalized hominoid ancestor, or it may be the direct ancestor of the modern gibbon. A Miocene fossil, *Pliopithecus,* was also an early hominoid and was similar to the living gibbon but had forelimbs and hind limbs of about equal length, in contrast to the longer forearms of the gibbon.

In addition to the two hominoid fossils mentioned, the Miocene and Pliocene epochs have produced numerous other anthropoid fossils in Africa, Asia, and Europe. One of these was *Proconsul,* which left an abundance of skeletal remains in Africa and appears to be close to the ancestry of the higher apes (family Pongidae). Although they had some Old World monkey traits, some were as large as a gorilla. A similar but more widespread genus was *Dryopithecus,* which have been found in Europe and India as well as in Africa. Some authorities consider *Proconsul* and *Dryopithecus* as the same genus. In an Italian coal bed of the Pliocene epoch, the controversial fossil *Oreopithecus* was found in 1872. A recent specimen was discovered in 1958. It is so different from other hominoids that it may be placed in a family of its own or as an aberrant member of the Hominidae. It cannot be placed in either the stem leading to the higher apes or to that of man. Although these fossils are definitely apelike, they lack, in general, the specializations of the modern apes. Rather, they show many primitive characteristics similar to man. They lack especially the brachiating arms and simian shelf found in living apes. The evidence indicates that during the Miocene epoch (25 million years ago) the hominoid line branched into two sublines. One of these led to apes and the other to man or manlike types (hominids). The fossil evidence shows that both lines have undergone many changes since they branched off from the common ape-hominid stem. The common ancestor of the two branches must lack the brachiating specialization of the living apes because the long arms of the Pongidae were acquired after they had split off from the common ancestor. Two recent fossil forms, *Ramapithecus* and *Kenyapithecus,* are considered closest to the hominid line, or the ancestry of man. Although modern apes are more specialized than man for arboreal life and in other ways, the fossil record discovered in the past decade or so indicates that man and the higher apes have a very close affinity. The evidence for a common ancestry of the two groups is more and more convincing as new fossils are found.

Man is a product of evolution and is the descendent of apes of the Old World. He has a biologic nature, as indicated by his evolutionary history and by his condition today. Of all the animals, the great apes are anatomically most similar to man. Man and the apes have certain differences, often minor ones, in structure, but as knowledge has become more precise, new evidence about the closeness of the relationships, such as structure of hemoglobin, resemblance in serum proteins, shape of chromosomes, as well as other similarities has emerged. Without a doubt the common ancestor of apes and man was an ape. The evidence indicates that his actual ancestor was the common ancestor also of the gorilla and the chimpanzee after the latter animals had diverged from the other living apes (orangutan and gibbon).

Apes today are represented by the genera mentioned at the beginning of this section—gibbons, orangutans, chimpanzees, and gorillas (Fig. 39-3, *B*). They differ from man in a number of morphologic characters, but these differences are mainly quantitative. Apes have longer arms than legs, long trunk compared to lower limbs, curved legs with the knees turned outward, large canines, laterally compressed dental arch (not rounded), long protruding face, and a brain about one third as large as man's. Some modern apes have largely abandoned the arboreal way of life. Chimpanzees and gorillas are quite at home on the ground. A more or less erect posture is characteristic of many of them, although they may use their long arms for support while walking. More abundant food on the ground may have induced them to come down out of the trees.

When the hominids separated from the higher apes, they underwent a radiation of their own. Giving up a arboreal life was a necessary prelude to their amazing evolution. Climatic changes during certain geologic ages may have greatly reduced the forests and forced a ground existence. Increased body size may have been a factor also. Because of dangerous predators, selection pressure may have brought about evolution of feet and strong running muscles. The fossil record is very incomplete between the rather abundant ape fossils of the Miocene epoch and the hominid fossils of the Pleistocene epoch. In this period of more than 20 million years,

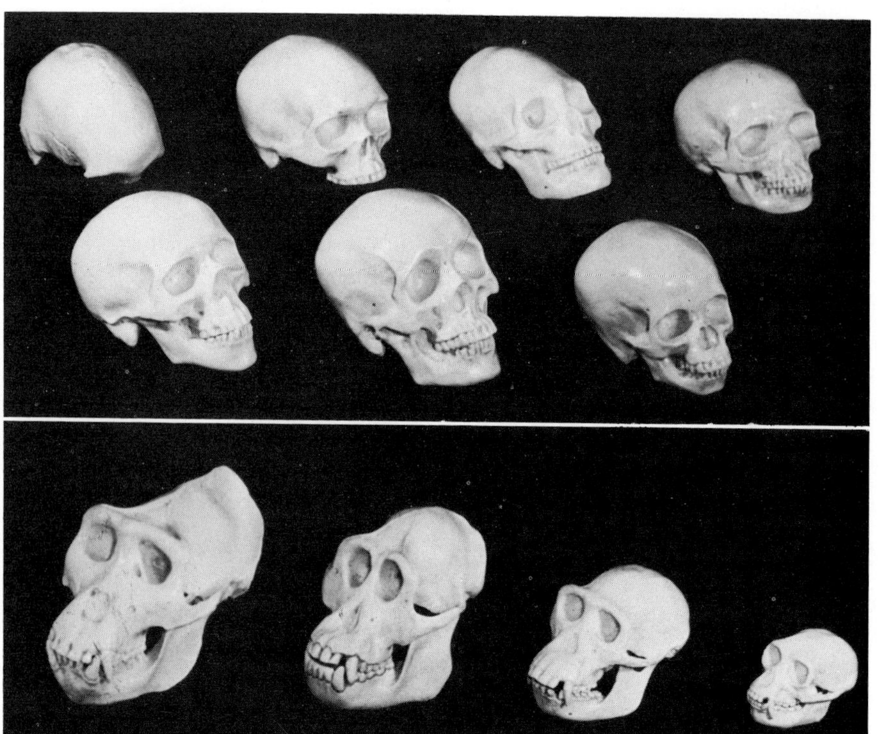

A

B

FIG. 39-3

Comparison of skulls of living races of man with those of living simians. **A,** Seven living races of man. **B,** Four living simians. (Courtesy Ward's Natural Science Establishment, Inc., Rochester, N. Y.)

little is known about the hominid line. The initial phases of hominid evolution are largely unknown. The fossil record indicates that the hominid radiation produced various lines of descent. It is not known just what the ancestral taxon that started this radiation is like. From its dentofacial features, *Ramapithecus,* as already stated, appears to be the most appropriate ancestral taxon. One of the chief problems of paleontologists is to find fossils that will close the gap between the differences of man from the higher apes. Although both groups have features in common and are obviously closely related, the much larger cranium and brain size with its correlated functions, the erect position, and the more adaptable opposable thumb in man as contrasted with the apes—all indicate a wide gulf between them. Much of this gulf between the two groups appears to have widened in a relatively short time, geologically speaking. This may have been due to the strong selection pressure for those characteristics that have enabled man to reach such a high level of dominance over his environment. The exciting discoveries found in Africa in the past few years have added much to our knowledge of man's emergence.

FOSSIL RECORD OF MAN

Apes and man do not form fossils easily. Important developments of their evolutionary history took place largely in the tropics where fossilization is not common and where fossils are difficult to find. Compared with other fossil animals, the populations of hominids were quite modest, and their natural ecologic relations did not favor the formation and preservation of fossils.

The hominids appear to date back to the early Pleistocene epoch and maybe earlier. The recent fossil *Zinjanthropus* found in Africa has been dated at 1,750,000 years old, which would place it in the late Pliocene epoch. Authorities are not agreed on the age of many fossils nor on the interpretations that are made about them. Hominid phylogeny is very difficult to analyze. The practice of assigning a new taxon to every fossil discovered and the attempt to place them in some kind of morphologic series without regard to the modern principles of speciation has complicated the whole problem. It is generally agreed that man is a polytypic species, that is, composed of several races, each with a different gene pool. The newer idea of speciation would consider the hominid fossils as samples of populations wherein there are many variations in type and form. There is a tendency today among certain paleontologists to lump together fossil taxa in the light of their distribution and geologic age, as well as homologous resemblances, etc. Many students think that perhaps only one or two fossil species of man existed at any one time. The problem of hominid phylogeny is in a state of flux and is subject to constant change. A survey of hominid evolution within the Pleistocene epoch when man was evolving from apelike to manlike individuals shows three well-marked stages. The transitions that occurred during this period may have been greatly influenced by the vast climatic changes induced by the advances and recessions of four north polar ice caps. The three stages were (1) the *Australopithecus* group of the basal Pleistocene in Africa, (2) the *Homo erectus* or *Pithecanthropus* forms of the middle Pleistocene, and (3) the *Homo sapiens* types of the late Pleistocene. Students may be interested in some of the famous fossil finds and evidences of their position in the phylogeny of the human race.

Separation of hominid lineage from ape lineage

Darwin probably knew only two types of important fossils for apes and man. One was *Dryopithecus* (fossil ape) and the other the Neanderthal (fossil man). Darwin in his *Descent of Man* stated his belief that the lineage of apes and monkey had separated by the late Miocene epoch, which began about 25 million years ago. From this time on apes and monkeys were common throughout Europe, Asia, and Africa. Some think that apes and monkeys separated in the Oligocene epoch several million years earlier. Since the earliest apes were ancestral to man, the divergence of the two groups must have occurred about the same time. The exact time when apes and man parted company has not yet been determined by paleontologists, but probably did not occur later than the Miocene epoch.

Mention has already been made to *Ramapithecus* (in India) and *Kenyapithecus* (in Africa), which are considered to be the most definite prehuman line yet discovered. Since only fragments of these fossils have been found, their exact status is unknown, although their age is put at about 10 million years.

Australopithecus (southern ape)

In 1925 the fossil brain cast of an immature anthropoid was discovered in South Africa by Professor R. Dart. This specimen had a mixture of both human and ape characters. Additional fossils of this and related types, including skeletons that were almost complete, have been found by a number of investigators since that time.

Two distinct groups were discovered, *Australopithecus (Paranthropus) robustus* and *Australopithecus africanus*. Both of the groups definitely belonged to the human family Hominidae. They showed some apelike characteristics along with more human ones. They are dated about 2 million years ago. The two groups coexisted for many years, but finally *A. robustus* became extinct, and *A. africanus* evolved into *Homo*.

Although various parts of Africa seem to be the basic home of this subfamily, similar fossils have been found as far away as Java. The volume of their brain casts varied from about 450 to 600 ml. and overlapped the range of the chimpanzee and gorilla. Certain bones, such as those in the pelvis, were hominid rather than pongid. They walked in an erect or semierect position, as attested to by the shape of the leg and foot bones. The face does not protrude as far as that of the chimpanzee. Their dentition was more human than apelike. From the evidences of primitive stone tools, these so-called man-apes were toolmakers and tool users. They may be regarded as the earliest type with distinct manlike characteristics, and they come close to the anatomical features expected in a "missing link." Their habitat was mainly terrestrial, which may have some significance.

Zinjanthropus

This fossil was discovered in 1959 by L. S. B. Leakey in the famous Olduvai gorge of Tanganyika, Africa, where so many significant paleontologic specimens have been found. It probably belongs to the *Paranthropus*, one of the genera of the australopithecines. Its age has been calculated by the potassium-argon method at 1,750,000 years. Although evidence of tools were found with the fossil, these tools could have been left by more recent members of the *Homo* type. In some ways this form seems to be closer to the Hominidae than any others of the australopithecines. They were generally less than 5 feet tall, walked almost erect, and had small brains. Some of their skull features (mastoid processes, occipital condyle, etc.) were similar to man's. Leakey has also found a tool-using hominid, which he called *Homo habilis*, in the same locality. This one seems to be even closer to *Homo*.

Pithecanthropus (Java man)

This famous fossil was discovered in eastern Java in 1891 by E. Dubois, a Dutch anatomist. Only a skullcap and thigh bone were first found, but better specimens have since been discovered (Fig. 39-4). This taxon is considered to be almost 500,000 years old (middle Pleistocene). Because so many of the anatomic features were so close to modern man's, Java man has been called *Homo erectus*. They walked fully erect, were over 5 feet tall, and had heavy projecting brow ridges. They may have had a spoken language and used stone tools. The brain capacity was at least 900 ml. and may have been more in certain races. This species was widespread, being found in various parts of Asia and Africa, as well as in Java. The Peking man (*Sinanthropus pekinensis* or *Homo erectus pekinensis*) is a northern race of the same species.

Heidelberg man (Homo heidelbergensis)

The evidence for the existence of the Heidelberg man rests on an almost perfect jaw discovered in a sand pit in 1907 near Heidelberg, Germany. It was found in a deposit of bones from the lower Pleistocene. Its general aspect is human, although it combines a very massive jaw with small humanlike teeth. Some authorities classify this man under the australopithecines, but it differs from the Asiatic type of that group.

FIG. 39-4

Restoration of prehistoric men. Left to right: Java man, Neanderthal man, and Cro-Magnon man. (Courtesy J. H. McGregor.)

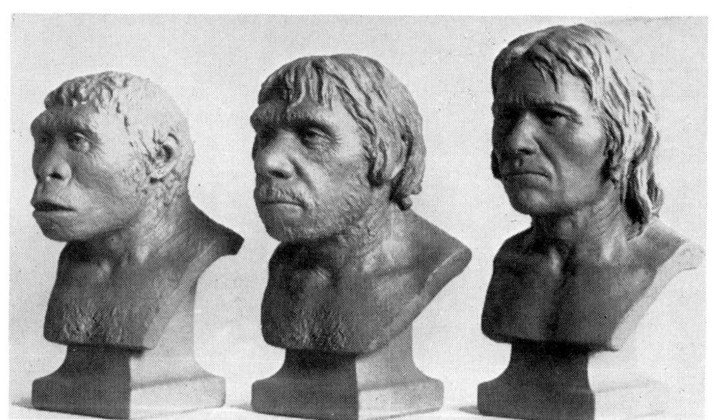

Swanscombe and Steinhelm skulls

Between the *Pithecanthropus* group and the establishment of the modern polytypic species of *Homo sapiens*, the hominid evolution has taken a complex course because of the long time span of several hundred thousands of years and the climatic changes that must have occurred during the interglacial periods. The earliest fossils that show clear-cut *Homo sapiens* features were the Swanscombe man in England and the Steinhelm man in Germany. These may have evolved from the pithecanthropines about 300,000 years ago. Both of these were found in the period of 1933 to 1935. Their skulls appear to be intermediate between *Pithecanthropus* and modern man. They had prominent eyebrow ridges and a brain capacity not far from that of modern *Homo*. Their chin was not well developed. They may be the earliest *Homo* that cannot clearly be differentiated from *Homo sapiens*. Leakey's recent (1961) discovery of the Chellean man at Olduvai gorge in East Africa has been dated at 250,000 years. This new find seems to mark a morphologic transition from *Pithecanthropus* to *Homo*, but further study is awaited. However, more recent fossils than those of the Olduvai gorge are known to occur. It appears that primitive australopithecines, near ape-men, and members of the first true men (*Homo*) were undergoing an evolution, with considerable overlapping of the different types in the period of the middle Pleistocene about 300,000 to 1,000,000 years ago.

Emergence of modern man

Modern man, or *Homo sapiens*, first appeared in the fossil record about 75,000 to 100,000 years ago in the form of Neanderthals. This race has left many fossils in West Central Europe (and some elsewhere) in the deposits of the third interglacial and the last glacial period. Selective pressure of this severe climatic condition may have been responsible for the development of the race. This taxon has been assigned the name of *Homo sapiens neanderthalensis* (Fig. 39-4). The first specimen was discovered near Düsseldorf, Germany, in 1856—the first hominid fossil to receive attention by competent scholars. He was short in stature, averaging little more than 5 feet in height. His brain capacity was about the same as modern man, and he had developed a crude form of paleolithic (mousterian) culture. He differed from modern *Homo sapiens* in having a flattened braincase, projecting jaws, recessive chin, large supraorbital bridges, and strong mandibles. Their populations dominated the scene in late Pleistocene times, from Europe to Africa and Asia. The race was not a uniform type (which has given rise to varied interpretations), but varied from place to place in response to local conditions or the intermixing of the different types. Of the various types of *Homo sapiens* that have arisen, there may be mentioned the Solo man (Japan), Rhodesian man (South Africa), and the Mt. Carmel man (Palestine). These fossil men shared the large supraorbital ridges, but differed in other respects from the European Neanderthal.

During the last interglacial period about 30,000 to 40,000 years ago, the Neanderthal race was replaced in Europe rather suddenly by the Cro-Magnon race, which emerged from an unknown source (Fig. 39-4). They may be descendants of early, generalized Neanderthals of Asia. They may have been responsible for the extermination of the Neanderthals. The Cro-Magnon was not homogeneous but was rather a mixture of people that showed considerable physical variations in different localities. They had a far superior culture (Perigordian) and left artistic paintings and carvings in their caves. They are considered ancestors of modern man and represent the modern type of man. They were about 6 feet tall, had a high forehead but no supraorbital ridges, a rather prominent chin, and a brain capacity as large as (or larger than) present-day man. Their physical characteristics are matched today by the Basques in northern Spain and certain Swedes in southern Sweden. Attempts to discern the characteristics of present-day races in early populations of *Homo sapiens* have not been successful. It is not known whether they were white, black, or brown.

The evolutionary course of modern man in his 30,000 to 40,000 years has exhibited the same pattern of divergence and extinction demonstrated by his forbears and that of other organisms. The essential characters of human phylogeny, such as man's superior brain and wide adaptability, can all be attributed to the strictly quantitative effects of mutations that could have happened at any evolutionary level. In other words, man has been the outcome of the basic factors of evolution that have directed the evolution of every organism from the time life first originated. Mutation, selection, population factors, genetic drift, and isolation—all the general processes of evolutionary progress have operated for man the same as for other animals.

The polytypic species of present-day man is divided into a number of races, the number of which varies with different authorities (Fig. 39-3, *A*). There has been a common evolution for all races, with their differentiation coming relatively late in the history of mankind. Although they differ in various morphologic characters, such as skin color, hair, shape, and body dimensions, it is very difficult to classify them on the basis of physiologic traits. Mankind has not speciated because of ecologic diversity, ability to occupy so many ecologic niches, or lack of isolating mechanisms for preventing the interchange of genes. Of the many types of man mentioned in the foregoing account, it is doubtful if there were more than two species coexisting at one time, and in most cases perhaps only one. A polytypic species such as man could have many types in a widespread population.

MAN'S UNIQUE POSITION

That man is an animal is attested by his evolutionary history and his present biologic condition. That he is just another animal is not believed by the thoughtful individuals who have studied man in relation to his place in nature and who have made a critical examination of his unique characteristics. He is a product of evolution, as we have seen, from primeval apelike creatures, which in turn have had millions of years of evolution behind them. But man has what no other animal has—a psychosocial evolution, or a directional cultural pattern that involves a constant feedback between past and future experience. Although human evolution has become increasingly cultural as opposed to genetic, he is still subjected to the same biologic forces and principles that regulate other animals.

When one considers all the factors involved in a comparison of man with other animals, he finds a broad gap between himself and the others. First of all, he is really the only animal that knows how to make and use tools effectively. His everwidening expansion in tool application, plus the tradition of tool using that he inherits culturally, has more than any other factor been responsible in giving man his dominant position. Another unique characteristic of man is his capacity for conceptual thought that is denied to other animals, except in the minutest degree. Man has a symbolic language of wide and specific expression. With words, he can carve concepts out of experience. This has resulted in cumulative experience that can be transmitted from one generation to another. In other animals, transmission never spans more than one generation. Man owes much to his arboreal ancestry. This early evolutionary development has resulted in a whole series of mutually reinforcing steps that have proved of the utmost value in man's evolutionary rise to dominance. This arboreal life promoted his binocular vision of precise judgement of distance, a fine visual-tactile discrimination, and manipulative skills in the use of his hands, which are provided with five fingers. If a horse (with one toe) had man's intellect and culture, could it accomplish what man has done? When did man's brain enlarge beyond that of the ape? Intelligence depends on the organization and size of the brain and fossils do not reveal its organization, although the cranial cavity does indicate in general its possible size.

Man is a definite and single species; a species is a continued population of interchanging genes by interbreeding. Man's population is commonly divided into races or populations that are genetically distinguished from others. A so-called race has certain genes or gene combinations that may be more or less unique, although races grade into each other and do not have definite boundaries. Pure races are nonexistent and there are no fixed number of races. Races are adaptations to local conditions. It is thought that as primitive men spread over geographic areas, they became adapted to certain regions, and natural selection stamped on them certain distinguishing features. Since Africa is thought to have been the original home of man, the Negro may be in that respect better adapted biologically to that region. Races at present are losing their biologic significance as human adaptation to environment is becoming largely cultural. Rapid mobility and quick communication and intercourse has shrunk the size of our planet so that isolation of races rarely exists. Genes can shift through human populations now with amazing speed. Racial intermixtures are far more common than formerly. Since all races have more or less unique potentialities, hybrid vigor could operate within racial interbreeding just as it does for other animals. Although man can never shed his animal nature, he has the power to evolve a widespread cultural adaptation that can become progressively more directional toward a varied excellence in all aspects of his behavior and relations.

Annotated references

Anfinsen, C. B. 1959. The molecular basis of evolution. New York, John Wiley & Sons, Inc. *This work attempts to pinpoint the evolutionary process insofar as genetics and protein chemistry reveal it.*

Barnett, S. A. (editor). 1958. A century of Darwin. Cambridge, Mass., Harvard University Press. *This book is made up of chapters contributed by eminent American and English authorities on the various aspects of Darwin's contributions to biology.*

Bates, M., and P. S. Humphrey. 1956. The Darwin reader. New York, Charles Scribner's Sons. *This book is made up of generous portions of Darwin's principal works and is a fine introduction for one who wishes to become acquainted with the works of the great master.*

Berrill, N. J. 1955. Man's emerging mind. New York, Dodd, Mead & Co. *The author thinks man still has possibilities of future brain improvement by refined differentiation of the brain man at present possesses; it is mainly a matter of exploiting the capacities of our existing state.*

Blum, H. F. 1955. Time's arrow and evolution, ed. 2. Princeton, N. J., Princeton University Press. *A work for the serious student on certain implications of evolution.*

Carpenter, G. D. H. 1933. Mimicry. London, Methuen & Co., Ltd. *A classic work on a subject of perennial interest—and also of perennial controversy.*

de Chardin, P. T. 1959. The phenomenon of man. New York, Harper & Brothers. *An evaluation of man's evolutionary position. Much of its thesis is in line with that of Sir Julian Huxley (writer of introduction to this work) who has long stressed the unique aspects of man's evolution in the biologic world.*

Conklin, E. G. 1943. Man: real and ideal. New York, Charles Scribner's Sons. *The author believes that there is no evidence that man has advanced in intellectual capacities since ancient time but that his future progress will be along the lines of cooperation and organization of social forces for his own welfare. Although evolution has taken many directions and has regressed as well as progressed, he thinks that there has been no permanent retreat in the evolution of man's intellect, reason, and ethics.*

Dobzhansky, T. 1951. Genetics and the origin of species, ed. 3. New York, Columbia University Press. *A treatise showing the bearing of modern genetic interpretation upon the problems of evolution. A work for the advanced student.*

Dobzhansky, T. 1955. Evolution, genetics, and man. New York, John Wiley & Sons, Inc. *A presentation of evolution in relation to genetics; written in an easy style.*

Dobzhansky, T. 1962. Mankind evolving. New Haven, Conn., Yale University Press. *Human evolution is considered as the interdependence of the biologic and cultural components. This has resulted in what the author calls the superorganic. An excellent appraisal of our present concept of man's evolution.*

Eiseley, L. 1958. Darwin's century. Evolution and the men who discovered it. New York, Doubleday & Co. *An excellent background of the evolutionary theory and the many conflicts between the divergent views of scholars in this field during the nineteenth century.*

Florkin, M. (editor). 1960. Aspects of the origin of life. New York, Pergamon Press, Inc. *A series of papers by many eminent authorities on the basic problems of the origin and development of life.*

Glass, B., O. Temkin, and W. L. Straus, Jr. (editors). 1959. Forerunners of Darwin: 1745-1859. Baltimore, The Johns Hopkins Press. *All scientific concepts have an extensive background and this work rightly assigns some credit for Darwin's great theory to some of the men that had been thinking along similar lines long before Darwin arrived at his basic conclusions. Among some of these forerunners were Maupertuis, Buffon, Kant, Lyell, Malthus, and Lamarck.*

Hardin, G. 1959. Nature and man's fate. New York, Rinehart & Co., Inc. *An excellent appraisal of man in relation to our present concept of evolutionary progress. Written in a lucid and popular style, this book is excellent supplementary reading for the general zoology student.*

Hoagland, H., and R. W. Burhoe (editors). 1962. Evolution and man's progress. New York, Columbia University Press. *Six eminent scientists attempt to integrate man's biologic and cultural evolutionary patterns and the implications of such patterns for future generations.*

Hooton, E. A. 1949. Up from the ape. New York, The Macmillan Co. *A fine study of the background of human evolution.*

Huxley, J. 1942. Evolution: the modern synthesis. New York, Harper & Brothers. *The modern interpretation of evolutionary advancement by one of the foremost students in the field. For the advanced student.*

Huxley, T. H. 1859. Darwin on the origin of species. The Times (London), Dec. 26, 1859. *This famous review of Darwin's epoch-making work was published a few weeks after The Origin of Species came from the press. It was unsigned, but, as Darwin surmised, there was only one man in all of England who could have written it, and Huxley was quickly identified as the author.*

Irvine, W. 1955. Apes, angels, and victorians. New York, McGraw-Hill Book Co. *By skillfully combining history and biography, the author has given a vivid account of the conflict that revolved around the theory of evolution when it was first announced and for many years thereafter.*

Lack, D. 1947. Darwin's finches. New York, Cambridge University Press. *Adaptive radiation is a highly interesting subject in evolutionary development, but no example has ever been found that illustrates this principle better than these finches Darwin studied in the early development of his evolutionary theory.*

Le Gros Clark, W. E. 1960. The antecedents of man. Chicago, Quadrangle Books, Inc. *This noted authority explains the evolution of man by first tracing the extensive background of the primate order. The chapter on the evolutionary radiations of the primates is especially revealing.*

Moody, P. A. 1968. Introduction to evolution, ed. 2. New York, Harper & Brothers. *There is no better introduction to evolution for the beginner.*

Savage, J. M. 1963. Evolution. New York, Holt, Rinehart & Winston, Inc. *A brief but finely written account of the major concepts in the evolutionary process.*

Simons, E. L. 1964. The early relatives of man. Sci. Amer. **211**:50-62 (July).

Simpson, G. G. 1951. Horses. New York, Oxford University Press. *A comprehensive account of the interesting evolution of the horse.*

Simpson, G. G. 1953. The major features of evolution. New York, Columbia University Press. *This is one of the most up-to-date accounts of evolution, written by one of the best authorities in the field.*

Symposia of the Society for Experimental Biology, 1953, no. VII: Evolution. New York, Academic Press, Inc. *This volume contains the papers delivered at a symposium at Oxford in 1952. They cover many concepts in the field of evolution. Among the many interesting papers in the volume, the one on "Regressive Evolution in Cave Animals" is especially revealing. Unfortunately, the volume is not indexed.*

Tax, S., and C. Callender (editors). 1960. Evolution after Darwin. Vol. I, The evolution of life; Vol. II, The evolution of man; Vol. III, Issues in evolution. Chicago, University of Chicago Press. *A collection of the papers given at the Darwin Centennial held at the University of Chicago in November, 1959. A monumental tribute to the great evolutionist and an epoch-making appraisal of evolution as it is understood at present.*

Washburn, L. L. (editor). 1963. Classification and human evolution. Chicago, Aldine Publishing Co. *Papers presented by specialists in paleontology and anthropology at a symposium held in 1961. An evaluation of the fossil record that bears on man's early evolution and his place in primate taxonomy.*

PART EIGHT

THE ANIMAL IN RELATION TO ITS ENVIRONMENT

● The ecosystem may be considered a community of populations of living organisms (both plants and animals) and the physical environment in which they exist. The ecosystem is the basic unit of the biosphere and represents the interdependence of organisms on environmental conditions. This interrelationship between living organisms and their environment is called ecology. The importance of this relationship cannot be overestimated. Life was created by environmental forces, and no organism is for an instant free from the requirements of the surroundings in which it lives. Diversity of life was made possible by the interactions between the plasticity of living organisms and the plasticity of the environmental conditions around them. Everything one does is dependent on conditions of his physical environment. The environment therefore refers to the totality of all extrinsic factors and conditions that in any way affects the life of an organism. In this way there is both a physical and a biotic environment.

Ecology is thus concerned with all kinds of environmental conditions, food chains, diverse aspects of populations, energy utilization, dynamics of populations, ecologic niches, physical conditions, and many others. The beginnings of ecology start with life itself, whenever that remote event occurred. No doubt its very comprehensiveness has been responsible for the lagging of its study as a scientific discipline. There are so many variable elements in its makeup that mathematical exactness in its study has been slow in appearing. Its development also depended on the development of other sciences that could in any way contribute to an understanding of ecologic principles. Man is just beginning to comprehend a little about his ecosystem and what he must do to correct the many mistakes he has made in its management. Right now ecology holds a primary position in man's thinking.

Animal behavior represents another important facet of the ecosystem. This study is important in the understanding of the life process and how the organism reacts to its environment. The interest in this subject has increased by leaps and bounds in the new revival of the biologic sciences, but has always attracted man as a necessary asset in his adjustments. It is a difficult and complicated subject because man has to rely on the external aspects of behavior. No one knows what goes on in the minds of other animals whose mechanisms of reactions are so different from those of man. Interpretations of their actions and motives often become anthropomorphic and thus unscientific. The new approach to an understanding of animal behavior stresses the levels of organization of the nervous system, the types of hereditary behavior, the experimental investigation of their responses to varied stimuli, and the mechanisms of the anatomic relationships between stimuli and reactions.

CHAPTER 40

• THE BIOSPHERE AND ANIMAL DISTRIBUTION*

● The **biosphere** refers to that part of our planet where animals and plants live. It was so named by J. Lamarck, the French naturalist of the nineteenth century, a foremost advocate of evolution during the first part of that century. It is the environment of living things; the place where living organisms have established themselves and find conditions in which they can live. It includes fresh and salt water, surface, depths below the surface, and air. The biosphere may be said to extend down in the ocean to more than 30,000 feet, below the land surface more than 1,000 feet, and vertically in the atmosphere to more than 40,000 feet. With the possible exception of certain arid regions, frozen mountain peaks, restricted toxic sea basins, and a few others, every place on earth is represented by some form of life. Most species are adapted to a particular type of environment that is restricted in size, resources of food, places to live (niches), and general conditions of living. The biosphere is the result of the complex interactions of so many factors that it is impossible to analyze their ecologic significance in all respects.

Inasmuch as living things depend on the conditions of their physical environment, they have in their long evolution become adjusted to it and depend on it for their continued existence. Every animal is affected by every physical factor in its environment. Weather and climate conditions, temperature, pressure, nature of substratum, physicochemical structure, constant change due to geologic, geochemical, meteorologic, and other factors—all are involved in forming a background to which animals must adjust to survive. The animal itself is part and parcel of the earth's substance, and its evolutionary diversity has been correlated with the changing earth at every level of its existence. As an open system, an animal is forever receiving and giving off materials and energy. Inorganic materials are obtained from the physical environment, either directly by producers, such as green plants, or indirectly by consumers, which return the inorganic substances to the environment by excretion or by the decay and disintegration of their bodies.

*Refer to Chapter 2, Principle 31.

Thus there is a constant cycle between the animal and its environment. The living form is a transient link that is built up out of environmental materials which are then returned to the environment to be used again in the re-creation of new life. Life, death, decay, and re-creation have been the cycle of existence since life began.

The biosphere may be conveniently divided into three major subdivisions—**hydrosphere, lithosphere,** and **atmosphere.** The hydrosphere refers to the aquatic portions of the biosphere, the streams, rivers, ponds, oceans, and wherever water may be found. The lithosphere is made up of the crust of the earth, especially the solid portions such as rocks. Surrounding the other two subdivisions is the atmosphere, which forms a gaseous envelope. Animals obtain inorganic metabolites from each of these subdivisions. From the hydrosphere, they get water that makes up about 75% of living material. The lithosphere furnishes the essential minerals and chemicals, whereas the atmosphere supplies oxygen, nitrogen, and carbon dioxide. These inorganic substances are needed in all living organisms.

HYDROSPHERE

About 72% of the earth's surface is water, which also forms part of the lithosphere and atmosphere. Not only is water the most abundant constituent of protoplasm, but it is also the source of hydrogen that is so fundamental to the metabolic reactions of all living substance. Water also serves as one of the sources of oxygen in the body of organisms.

Water is involved in a cycle that consists of evaporation to a gaseous state and a return to a liquid by condensation of the vapor at higher altitudes. Evaporation of water occurs both in the ocean and on the land. About five sixths of this evaporation is in the ocean. It is estimated that the oceans evaporate a quantity of water from its surface equal to about a depth of 1 meter. Part of the land evaporation of water is the transpiration of plants. An ecologic principle of great economic importance is that the precipitation of water on land exceeds the evaporation. This means that the difference in water between these two factors represents the annual runoff water from the continents, carrying off minerals, producing erosion, and wearing away the surface of the continents. This leveling off process, however, is offset by the geologic uplift, thus bringing marine sediments above sea level. Living things also carry water through their bodies in addition to what they need themselves and in doing so speed up the return of water to the atmosphere. The metabolism of organisms thus accelerates the cycle of water and may profoundly influence weather conditions, not only locally, but also over extensive areas such as the rank vegetation of jungles.

Displacement of water in the ocean is also cyclic in nature. The warm water of tropical seas comes to the surface and the cold polar water sinks so that shifts of currents between the equator and the pole are aided by the east-west displacements produced by the rotation of the earth. Ocean currents, such as the Gulf Stream, have enormous influences on climatic conditions in all parts of the world.

The very nature of water itself is of great significance. It is slow to heat or cool and stores great amounts of thermal energy. Heat radiation from water can produce favorable regions for land organisms in many places that otherwise would be too cold for their survival.

It is also unique in attaining its greatest density at 4° C., therefore ice floats because it is lighter than it is in the liquid condition. Except for very cold superficial pools, water never freezes throughout so that life can continue beneath the ice cover.

In the long overall picture, the cyclic changes of ice ages, of which at least four great glacial periods have occurred in the last million years, involve the advance or retreat of polar ice. Warm interglacial periods have actually freed the poles from ice. (Amphibian fossils have been discovered in the Antarctic.) Melting of polar ice during the present warm trend in temperature has gradually raised the level of ocean water and made possible a steady advance of biota toward the poles. Deserts are also on the march and localized glaciers are receding.

LITHOSPHERE

The lithosphere consists of a number of components. Below the loose soil and subsoil is the solid bedrock of sedimentary rock, such as limestone and sandstone, resting on a thicker base of igneous and metamorphic rocks. Below this layer is a thicker stratum composed mostly of basaltic rock. These two layers form the so-called crust of the earth. As far as life is concerned, only the more superficial part of the lithosphere is involved, although the tetonic movements of folding and breaking of the bedrock plus the rise of molten lava in volcanoes may bring additional minerals to the surface.

All the mineral metabolites of the animal are received from the lithosphere, which also forms the chief part of the soil mentioned above. The crust of the earth shows striking changes over long periods of time. Uplifting and buckling are always occurring, resulting in mountain building and shifting of land masses. Mountains produce profound changes in climate conditions such as the unequal distribution of thermal energy and moisture. Moisture-laden clouds may not be able to pass mountain barriers and dump their contents on one side alone so that this inequality results in favorable rainfall with fertility on one side and desert on the other. These factors influence the distribution of both vegetation and animals which must adapt to these different conditions to survive.

There is also a leveling process going on all the time as mentioned in a former section. A large part of rainfall is not evaporated and the excess water is run off from the land into the rivers and streams, eroding the land surface by carrying with it dissolved soluble mineral matter to the sea. Billions of tons of dissolved inorganic and organic matter as well as much undissolved matter are carried into the oceans each year. Many important chemicals such as phosphorus are lost to animal and plant life and the biosphere is unable to make good the losses, especially to terrestrial forms. Marine forms, on the other hand, may profit from such an economy. Some valuable minerals are replaced by the decay of animals and plants and in the long run by the upheaval of the sea floor to form new land. This last is a slow process and life could be greatly affected by the gradual decline of certain key minerals.

Many ecologists have been concerned about this decline, especially so from man's greater influence in the misuse of certain resources.

ATMOSPHERE

The gases present in the atmosphere are (by volume) oxygen about 21%; nitrogen, 78%; carbon dioxide, 0.03%; water vapor, in varying amounts; and small traces of inert gases (neon, helium, krypton, argon, ozone, and xenon). Each of these, except the inert gases, serve as metabolites in living substances. Carbon dioxide is a basic ingredient of the process of photosynthesis and ozone screens out ultraviolet rays. The percentage of gases remains very constant, except in a few places such as volcanoes, underground sources, or industrial plants. Carbon dioxide plays a unique role in the ecology of animals, although it makes up such a small percentage of atmosphere air. This gas enters water from the air, the ground, decay of organic matter, respiration of animals, and the action of acids on carbonates dissolved in water. Among its many functions are its action as a chemical buffer in the maintenance of neutrality in aquatic habitats, its role in photosynthesis, its regulation of, or influence on respiration, and its general influence on other essential biologic activities (raising the threshold availability of oxygen, developing of eggs, increasing or decreasing rate of egg cleavage, etc.). One of its useful aspects is its chemical combination with water to form the weak carbonic acid (H_2CO_3).

With the exception of anaerobic animals (which can carry on oxidative processes without free oxygen), oxygen is a necessary prerequisite for respiration in all animals. Its major function in cellular metabolism is its role in the final hydrogen acceptor resulting in the formation of water. Oxygen is dissolved in water, which makes possible aquatic life. All atmospheric gases dissolve in water in accordance to certain principles. Any gas soluble in water will dissolve in it until equilibrium is reached. Its solubility in water will depend on temperature and its partial pressure. In a mixture of gases each gas will exert a pressure proportional to its partial pressure in the moisture, and each gas will dissolve irrespective of the solution of other gases. Solubilities differ for different gases. The total pressure of a gas mixture is the sum of the partial pressures of the various gases. If atmospheric air of 760 mm. pressure (sea level) is exposed to distilled water at 0° C., at equilibrium the water will contain about 49 cc. of oxygen, 23 cc. of nitrogen, and 1,715 cc. of carbon dioxide. Oxygen is lost from water by the respiration of organisms, oxidation of organic matter and decay of dead bodies, consumption by bacteria, bubbling of other gases that carry oxygen with them, and the warming of the surface layer of water. The lack of dissolved oxygen in the water may be a severe limiting factor in the distribution of aquatic animals. Lakes in the high Andes have no fish because the partial pressure of oxygen is too low for the minimum amount to be dissolved in the water.

Nitrogen is a chemically inert gas, but nitrogen is one of the chief constituents of living matter. Atmospheric nitrogen is the ultimate source. It may be fixed as nitrites or nitrates by electric discharges and later washed to earth by rain or snow. In the nitrogen cycle, nitrogen-fixing bacteria living symbiotically with legumes form nitrites and nitrates by the reactions **ammonification** and **nitrification** and add them to the soil where plants can get their nitrogen supplies. Animals get their nitrogen from eating plants or one another.

The atmosphere has a low degree of buoyancy and cannot be used as a permanent habitat by organisms. It is used as a passageway by those forms that are specialized to use it as a medium. Most of the life found within it is restricted to its lower boundary. Much of the terrestrial surface of the earth cannot be used to any extent by animal life because of seasonal and climatic conditions. The scarcity of moisture in desert regions requires that activity be restricted to certain periods of the day by those forms adapted for living there.

The atmosphere presents other ecologic factors of great importance to life. The atmosphere is commonly divided into three great strata, the **troposphere, stratosphere,** and **ionosphere.** The troposphere is the layer nearest the earth and extends upwards from about six to ten miles above sea level. Above the troposphere is the stratosphere which extends to about fifty miles above the earth, and the ionosphere is the gradually thinning air still above the stratosphere. In the troposphere are the complex wind movements and currents that help produce the great climatic changes. As air masses warmed in the tropical regions rises and cooled polar air sinks, the rotation of the earth shifts the air masses laterally and produces the enormous currents of many types that profoundly influence the lives of both man and beast.

DISTRIBUTION OF ANIMALS (ZOOGEOGRAPHY)

Zoogeography tries to explain why animals are found where they are, their patterns of dispersal, and the factors responsible for their distribution. It is obvious that each type of animal is not found everywhere but is found in an area of distribution that may be widespread or very restricted. Those with wide ranges are called **eurytopic**; those with narrow boundaries, **stenotopic.** Dispersal of animals usually depends on two important factors: (1) their means of dispersal and (2) the presence of barriers of some kind that might limit their distribution. As a rule, members of a particular species or closely related species occupy **continuous** ranges, but there are exceptions. When the same taxonomic unit or group is found in different areas far apart, it is said to have **discontinuous** distribution. The strange arthropod *Peripatus* is found in both tropical Africa and tropical America as well as elsewhere. Marsupials are found in the Americas and Australia—regions far apart.

The fossil record plainly shows animals flourished in a region but are now no longer found there. Extinction has played a major role in such conditions, but many of these groups left descendants that migrated to other regions and survived. The evolutionary pattern has been one of increase in diversity by evolving different ecologic habits and by spreading into new environments. Camels probably originated in North America, where their fossils are found, but spread to Eurasia by way of Alaska (true camels) and to South America (llamas). Barriers are altered by geologic changes in the earth's surface and by climatic changes. Many places now occupied by land were once covered with seas; regions now plains were formerly mountain ranges; such cold regions as Greenland were once quite warm. Evolution has been responsible for both the historic geographic distribution of animals and their ecologic relationships. Historic processes have determined where animals are and what they do.

By adaptive radiation, animals tend to spread into regions where they are ecologically fitted. Distinct species found in the same general area are called **sympatric;** those living in different geographic areas are called **allopatric.** Although life is believed to have originated in the sea, terrestrial conditions favor a more varied and more rapid evolution. Although the land makes up only 29% of the earth's surface, 80% of the known species are terrestrial. The abundance of oxygen on land and its role in releasing chemical energy have made possible a more intensive life. There are also many other advantages of terrestrial life over an aquatic one, such as the low density of air and the possibility of flight, the variety of foods, and the development of a greater variety of adaptations.

Animals tend to spread from their center of origin because of competition for food, shelter, and breeding places. Changes in environment may force them to move elsewhere, although most great groups have spread to gain favorable conditions, not to avoid unfavorable ones. **Dispersal movements** that result in the dispersal of animals are unidirectional and one way. They involve emigration from one region and immigration into another. Such movements must be distinguished from seasonal migration, such as that of birds, where there is a regular to-and-fro movement between two regions. The chief deterrent to the spread of animals are barriers of various kinds, such as mountains, water, deserts, and climatic conditions.

Simpson has stressed three chief paths of faunal interchange—corridors, filters, and sweepstakes routes. A **corridor** may be a widespread, more or less open stretch of land that usually allows the free movement of animals from one region to another. A **filter route** is defined as one that allows some animals to pass into another area but keeps others from doing so. A mountain may act as a filter in which mollusks may be prevented from passing but affords fewer impediments to mammals or birds. Filters may also be narrow land bridges such as that of the Isthmus of Panama. A **sweepstakes route** is one that is highly improbable for animals to pass over, but some manage to do so by some fortuitous event. Such seems to have been the case of oceanic islands where crossing is long delayed. Sweepstakes routes may also explain the peculiar marsupial animals of Australia because they were the first mammals to reach that continent. In the case of the corridor and filter routes animals may spread in both directions, but in a sweepstakes route they usually pass in one direction only.

Faunal interchange between continents has occurred many times. This interchange is most likely to occur when regions afford potential ecologic niches to a migrating group. Newcomers to a particular region often had adaptations that did not clash with the groups already there. In this way the fauna of a continent could be greatly enriched and diversified, such as that of South America when North American types passed into that region in the Pleistocene epoch.

Geographic equivalents, or syngeographs, refer to species that occupy about the same general territory. In the eastern United States the widely distributed salamanders of the genus *Plethodon* afford an example of geographic equivalents. *P. glutinosis* and *P. cinereus* have the same general range, except that *P. glutinosis* extends farther south and *P. cinereus* farther north.

Man himself has played a major role in the spread of species, as in the introduction of the English sparrow into America and the rabbit into Australia. Convergent evolution may also account for two similar groups widely separated from each other. This could occur by the repetition of a mutation under similar environmental conditions in the two regions. Often, however, a better explanation in such cases is that the original range has been broken up by environmental changes so that the individuals of the two similar groups became isolated.

Krakatao as example of animal dispersion

Krakatao is a volcanic island off the Sundra Straits between Java and Sumatra in the East Indies. In 1883 this island was practically destroyed by one of the most terrific volcanic eruptions in modern times. Every living thing was reported to be destroyed, for what remained of the island was covered with many feet of hot volcanic ash. Several naturalists from the first have been interested in seeing when life would first reappear there. It thus served as an interesting case of animal distribution under direct observation. The position of the island between two great land masses and less than 40 miles from the nearest land made it specially favored for receiving a new stock of plants and animals.

Vegetation was the first to appear on the island and in a matter of some years completely covered the island. The first animals to appear were flying forms—birds and bats. It took more than 20 years for the first strictly terrestrial animals to gain a foothold. Rats, snakes, and lizards became common there. Insects, centipedes, millipedes, and spiders, especially those that travel by gossamer threads, had become common by 1921. Some of these had reached the island by driftwood, by currents of water, and by wind. There are few species but many individuals on the island, which may be due to the absence of natural enemies. Yet despite the favorable position of the island for receiving new animals, some forms have been slow in reaching the island and many have not reached there at all. This may indicate how long oceanic islands, far from the mainland, have been in acquiring their flora and fauna.

Lake Baikal as example of restricted dispersal

The large Lake Baikal in eastern Siberia is the deepest lake in the world, being more than a mile deep in some places. It is famed for its characteristic fauna, which is almost unique in the great number of peculiar or endemic species. Among certain groups up to 100% of the species are found nowhere else. Some groups, such as planarian worms, are represented by more species here than in all the rest of the world put together. Only groups such as protozoans and rotifers, which are easily transported from one region to another, are represented by nonendemic species to any extent. The distribution in the lake is also somewhat unique in that animal life is found at nearly all depths, perhaps because the water is well oxygenated throughout. All the evidence indicates that Lake Baikal has never had any connection with the sea but is strictly a freshwater formation. Whence came its unique fauna? Long geographic speciation through isolation, because this lake is very ancient, might account for some species. But the prevailing opinion is that the fauna of this lake mainly represents species that have evolved elsewhere in many ecologic habitats and have been washed into this lake by different river systems over long periods of time. Hence, the present fauna represents the accumulation and survival of ancient freshwater organisms (relicts) that were widely distributed at one time but are now found only here. Other deep freshwater lakes of ancient geologic history, such as Tanganyika and Nyasa in East Africa, also have unique faunas for the same reasons.

Major faunal realms

On the basis of animal distribution, numerous regions over the earth have distinctive animal populations. These divisions indicate the influence of land masses and their geologic history, as well as the corresponding evolutionary development of the various animal groups. These realms of distribution have developed and fluctuated during geologic times. The higher vertebrates mainly have been used in working out these broad faunal realms. There are many complications in dividing the earth into such realms in which all groups of animals are involved. Some animals have purely a local origin; others within the same realm show affinities with groups quite remote. To explain many of these discrepancies, it has been necessary to assume various land connections or bridges for which there are no geologic evidences. Such major faunal realms can thus have only a limited significance.

Sclater (1858) first proposed this scheme for birds, and later Wallace (1876) applied this pattern of distribution to vertebrates in general. There have been modifications of the plan by other workers, such as the one that grouped the six original regions into three major regions—Arctogaea (Holarctica, Ethiopian, Oriental), Neogaea (Neotropical), and Notogaea (Australasian).

Following is a discussion of the faunas of the major zoogeographic realms as they are now classified.

Australian. This realm includes Australia, New Zealand, New Guinea, and certain adjacent islands. Some of the most primitive mammals are found here, such as the monotremes (duckbill) and marsupials (kangaroo and Tasmanian wolf), but few placental mammals. Most of the birds are also different from those of other realms, such as the cassowary, emu, and brush turkey. The primitive lizard *Sphenodon* is found in New Zealand.

Neotropical. This realm includes South and Central America, part of Mexico, and the West Indies. Among its many animals are the llama, sloth, New World monkey, armadillo, anteater, vampire bat, anaconda, toucan, and rhea.

Ethiopian. This realm is made up of Africa south of the Sahara desert, Madagascar, and Arabia. It is the home of the higher apes, elephant, rhinoceros, lion, zebra, antelope, ostrich, secretary bird, and lungfish.

Oriental. This region includes Asia south of the Himalaya Mountains, India, Ceylon, Malay Peninsula, Southern China, Borneo, Sumatra, Java, and the Philippines. Its characteristic animals are the tiger, Indian elephant, certain apes, pheasant, jungle fowl, and king cobra.

Palearctic. This realm consists of Europe, Asia north of the Himalaya Mountains, Afghanistan, Iran, and North Africa. Its animals include the tiger, wild boar, camel, and hedgehog.

Nearctic. This region includes North America as far south as southern Mexico. Its most typical animals are the wolf, bear, caribou, mountain goat, beaver, elk, bison, lynx, bald eagle, and red-tailed hawk.

Annotated references

Andrewartha, H. G., and L. C. Birch. 1954. The distribution and abundance of animals. Chicago, University of Chicago Press. *An analysis of animal populations and the factors that influence their abundance and distribution.*

Berrill, N. J. 1951. The living tide. New York, Dodd, Mead & Co.

Buchsbaum, R. 1958. The life in the sea. Condon Lectures. Eugene, Ore., University of Oregon Press. *An excellent appraisal of man's exploration of the mysteries of the sea. Many fine illustrations.*

Carson, R. L. 1951. The sea around us. New York, Oxford University Press. *A popular account of the sea and its influence on animals, including man.*

Darlington, P. J. 1957. Zoogeography: the geographical distribution of animals. New York, John Wiley & Sons, Inc. *This is a book about animal distribution. It does not emphasize the ecologic approach, although it draws heavily on ecology and evolution for an explanation of its basic principles.*

Dietz, R. S. 1962. The sea's deep scattering layers. Sci. Amer. **207**:44-50 (Aug.).

Fairbridge, R. W. 1960. The changing level of the sea. Sci. Amer. **202**:70-79 (May).

Hardy, A. C. 1956. The open sea. Its natural history: The world of plankton. Boston, Houghton Mifflin Co. *This fine work shows the role of Protozoa and other forms in the natural history of plankton. Good descriptions are given of the Radiolaria and other protozoans in Chapter 6. Beautiful color illustrations.*

Henderson, L. J. 1913. The fitness of the environment. New York, The Macmillan Co. *Explains how conditions on our planet made life possible.*

Hubbs, C. L. 1958. Zoogeography. Washington, D. C., American Association for the Advancement of Science. *This includes the papers presented at two symposia at Stanford and Indianapolis. Part I deals with the Origin and Affinities of the Land and Freshwater Fauna of Western North America, and Part II deals with the Geographic Distribution of Contemporary Organisms.*

Howells, W. W. 1960. The distribution of man. Sci. Amer. **203**:113-127 (Sept.).

Hutchinson, G. E. 1957. A treatise on limnology, vol. I. Geography, physics, and chemistry, New York, John Wiley & Sons, Inc. *This is the first of a projected two-volume work on the rapidly growing science of limnology. It is an ambitious work that appeals to a variety of professional workers, such as limnologists, general biologists, and oceanographers.*

Kurten, B. 1969. Continental drift and evolution. Sci. Amer. **220**:54-64 (March). *Explains why mammals diversified faster than reptiles.*

Pettersson, H. 1954. The ocean floor. New Haven, Conn., Yale University Press. *The role the Forami-*

nifera and Radiolaria have placed in building up the sediment carpet of the ocean floor is vividly described in this little book. The author thinks the time of accumulation of deep sea deposits to be 2 billion years and the rate of sedimentation of Globigerina ooze to be 0.4 inch in 1,000 years.

Simpson, G. G. 1953. Evolution and geography. Eugene, Oregon State System of Higher Education. *An excellent appraisal of the main concepts of animal distribution by a great paleontologist.*

Sverdrup, H. U., M. W. Johnson, and R. H. Fleming. 1942. The oceans: their physics, chemistry and general biology. Englewood Cliffs, N. J., Prentice-Hall, Inc. *A standard work on this subject, although somewhat outdated in some particulars.*

CHAPTER 41

• ECOLOGY OF POPULATIONS AND COMMUNITIES*

BASIC REQUIREMENTS FOR EXISTENCE

● For life to exist, certain basic requirements make up what is known as the fitness of the environment. These essentials are suitable and available **food**, a place to live (**shelter**), and suitable conditions for **reproduction.** To meet these requirements, organisms are provided with adaptive structures of both form and function. If one requirement is lacking, the organism suffers even though the others are ideal. These basic needs vary; most plants require chlorophyll for photosynthesis, but animals get their food in a different way. Each animal is adapted for a particular combination of factors of food, shelter, and reproduction. An anteater would starve in the midst of plenty if there were no ant hills. A shelter may be suitable for some but not others. Favorable climate, weather, food, and shelter conditions are necessary for reproduction, a critical period in the life cycle. Basic needs may vary with different stages in a life cycle. Dormant animals need no food; a caterpillar's needs differ from those of an adult insect; amphibian young often require an aquatic habitat, whereas the adults may live on land.

These three requirements—nutrition, shelter, and reproduction—interact with each other as well as with other environmental factors to control the existence of an organism. The amount of available food often determines breeding activity. Many animals need special breeding places in which to raise their young. Meadowlarks nest in meadows and grasslands, not in forests or tilled fields. The food habits of some animals destroy the shelters of others. A flock of goats will clean out the shrubbery of a waste field and thus destroy the nesting sites of birds and meadow mice. Competition in meeting these requirements is found within the same species or between different species. This intense competition of many complex relations is called the **web of life.**

The ability of an organism to adjust readily to unfavorable conditions is called **vagility.** Many animals can adapt to a new food when their preference is unavailable. Grass-eating animals will often browse on shrubbery during severe winters. This adaptability is often the deciding factor in survival.

ENVIRONMENTAL FACTORS OF ECOLOGY

The nature of an organism is largely determined by the interaction of its heredity and environment. Heredity furnishes in the genes a basic type of germ plasm organization. But how these genes express themselves in the structure and functioning of an animal is conditioned by environmental factors. These include both the nonliving **physical** factors (temperature, moisture, light, etc.) and the living or **biotic** factors (other organisms). The environment, then, includes every external object or factor that influences the organism and determines its total economy in the general scheme. Organisms react toward their environment in characteristic ways, either by trying to avoid detrimental situations or by being able to adjust physiologically, within their genetic limits, to adverse factors.

How organisms are influenced by these physical and biotic factors is determined largely by the **law of tolerance.** The range of distribution of each species is determined by its range of tolerance to the variations in each factor. Animals vary greatly in range of tolerance. To describe a species with a narrow range of tolerance for a particular factor, we use the prefix **steno-;** for those with a wide range we use the prefix **eury-.** The terms **stenothermal** and **eurythermal** refer to temperature tolerance. A species will be most restricted by the factor for which it has the narrowest range of tolerance; those with the widest range for the most factors are likely to have the widest distribution. In this connection Liebig's "law of the minimum" may apply. According to this principle, an animal's ability to survive depends on those requirements that must be present in at least mini-

*Refer to Chapter 2, Principles 31 to 34.

mum amounts for the needs of the organism in question, even though all other conditions are fully met.

Any factor that limits the range of a species or an individual may be known as a **limiting** factor. Temperature is a limiting factor for the polar bear, whose thick insulation of fur and fat makes temperatures above freezing unsuitable. (The presence of polar bears in zoos is, of course, an unnatural distributional pattern.)

PHYSICAL FACTORS

Temperature. Temperature is an important factor in the animal's environment. Warm-blooded (homoiothermal or endothermal) animals are more independent of temperature changes than cold-blooded (poikilothermal or ectothermal) animals, although they are restricted by temperature extremes. Usually cold-blooded forms have body temperatures not much higher than that of their surroundings, although some active forms such as insects may have higher temperatures. Some forms can help regulate the body temperature to some extent by fanning their wings to create air currents and increase evaporation, or by living massed together as the bees do to conserve heat.

Many animals have an optimum temperature at which their body processes work best. For some protozoans this is between 24° and 28° C. Other forms have a wider range, usually with a lower limit of just above freezing and an upper limit of around 42° C. However, thermal limits are difficult to define because the temperature at which a degree of lethality occurs depends on duration of exposure, thermal history of the animal, nutrition, etc. Stenothermal animals have a very narrow range of temperature tolerance and have restricted distribution, whereas eurythermal animals are more widely distributed. An increase in temperature speeds up body metabolism so that cold-blooded animals, sluggish during cold spells, become more active as the temperature rises. Fluctuating temperatures will sometimes speed up metabolism faster than constant temperatures. The eggs of certain arthropods develop faster at optimum temperatures after they have been subjected to cold temperatures for part of their existence.

Many warm-blooded animals **hibernate** during winter months. Cold-blooded forms may retire deep underground or to other snug places to pass the winter. In some of the lower forms the adults die at the approach of winter and the species is maintained by larval forms or by eggs. Prolonged freezing or excessive heat is highly destructive to cold-blooded forms.

Habitats of animals are greatly influenced by temperature. Herbivorous forms are restricted by the amounts of grass and leaves available. Deer feed high on the mountains during the summer but in winter retreat to the valleys where they find better shelters and more food. Birds that live upon insects are forced to go elsewhere when their food is destroyed by cold weather. Temperature also plays a part in the rearing of the young and the hatching of eggs. Some eggs will not develop unless the temperature is fairly high.

Temperature changes are also known to effect structural changes. Experiments show that the common fruit fly *Drosophila* may undergo structural modifications at high temperatures. The vestigial wings of one of the mutants will develop into normal wings at high temperatures. Evolutionary changes in the same fly may be induced by temperature. Some of the changes induced by radiation in fruit flies can, to some extent, be duplicated by temperature effects. Color patterns in many insects can be induced or altered by regulating the temperature under which they develop. Many of the differences in the color phases of animals of the same species living in different environments may be thus explained.

A spot climate, or **microclimate,** near the surface of the ground, in contrast to the **macroclimate** of the higher air levels, may show striking gradients. Air at the 2-inch level, for instance, has a higher daytime and lower nocturnal temperature than the macroclimate. The gradient may be as great as 10° F. The microclimate also has a greater humidity as well as less wind disturbance. These factors may play an important part in the distribution of terrestrial animals.

Light. Light is an environmental factor toward which most animals react in a characteristic way. Many low forms express this reaction in the form of tropisms or taxes, either moving toward the light (positively phototactic) or away from it (negatively phototactic). The effect of different intensities and wavelengths of light varies greatly for different animals. Visible light represents only a small fraction of the radiation from the sun. Within the visible spectrum, heat energy is more common at the red end (longer rays) and photochemical influences are greater at the violet end (shorter rays). Those animals that are positively phototactic usually collect near the blue end of the spectrum when they have a choice; negatively phototactic forms collect at the red end.

Since plants depend on photosynthesis, which requires light, their distribution affects animal life, for directly or indirectly animals depend on plants as their ultimate source of food. Plankton, which is composed of small plants and animals in surface waters, is restricted to the upper strata of water because light rays cannot penetrate deeply. Only about 0.1% of light reaches a region 600 feet below the surface of most marine waters, and this depth is usually considered the lower level of the population gradient of plant life. The distribution of plants at the surface and at the margins of bodies of water determines the range of many aquatic animals. Certain regions of land, especially in northern climates, may lack sufficient light to support an extensive flora, thus affecting the distribution of animals there.

The color of animals is also influenced by light conditions. Pigment cells (melanophores) are affected by the amount of light that enters the eye in many of the lower vertebrates. Nerve impulses aroused in the eye may cause a contraction of the pigment cells and a lighter color in the animal; less light causes expansion of the pigment cells and a darker color. Many animals, such as flatfish, show this color adaptation to dark and light backgrounds.

Photoperiodicity, or the effect of light on the physiology and activities of organisms, is marked in some animals. A certain amount of light is necessary to activate the gonads and determine the breeding season in many forms. Ferrets and starlings become sexually active with lengthening days and can be induced to breed out of season when exposed experimentally to a great amount of light. It is thought that the seasonal northward migration of birds may be induced by the stimulation of their gonads by the greater light associated with longer days in the spring; the southward migration is caused by the regression of their glands by shorter days. In many other ways animals and plants are influenced by the length of the daylight (photoperiod), such as the diapause (resting period) in arthropods, excretion and other physiologic functions of animals, the seasonal coat changes of birds and mammals, and the growth of trees. These seasonal responses may be controlled by a photoreaction involving the anterior pituitary and certain hormones. Both day and night lengths may determine the response, but little is known of these factors. The parasitic filarial worm *(Wuchereria bancrofti)* lives by day in the deeper blood vessels but by night in skin vessels, where they can be picked up by mosquitoes.

Also structural changes may occur in some animals through the effect of light. Shull has shown that certain strains of aphids (plant lice) may be made to develop wings by exposing them alternately to light and darkness. Short periods of darkness followed by continuous light produced wingless forms.

Hydrogen ion concentration. The concentration of hydrogen ions is thought to have a limited importance in the distribution of animals. Although some animals prefer alkaline surroundings and others acid ones, many forms can endure a wide range of pH concentration. Tapeworms can live in concentrations of pH 4 to pH 11, or very acid to very alkaline. Some protozoans are limited to a very narrow alkaline medium, whereas others, such as certain species of *Euglena,* live and flourish in water that varies from pH 2 to pH 8. Some mosquito larvae are normally found in water with a pH of less than 5 and will not live in an alkaline medium. The pH of water has a very limited importance in the distribution of fish, which seem able to adjust to a wide range. Animals with calcium carbonate shells such as clams may be more sensitive to acid media because their shells are corroded by acids. Water with a pH of 6 or less contains few mollusks. The factors that regulate the hydrogen ion concentration of the water are numerous and complicated. Some of these are carbon dioxide and carbonates; and these factors, rather than the hydrogen ions, may be responsible for an animal's reactions in a particular medium. At present, hydrogen ion concentration seems of minor importance in the general distribution of animal life.

Substratum and water. The **substratum** is the medium on or in which an animal lives, such as the soil, air, water, and bodies of other animals. Many of the structural adaptations of animals determine the type of substratum they seek. The wings of bats, insects, and birds are fitted for the air (Fig. 41-1); the streamline form of fish and whales for the water (Fig. 41-2); the digging feet of moles and other mammals for the earth; and the hooks and suckers of parasites for the host. Many animals spend their entire life suspended in water; others spend a great deal of time in the air. Most organisms are found on a hard substratum on the land, at the bottom of a body of water, in the hole of a tree, etc. Many small forms, such as water striders, whirligig beetles, various larvae, and pulmonate snails, make use of the surface film of water either in locomotion or for clinging.

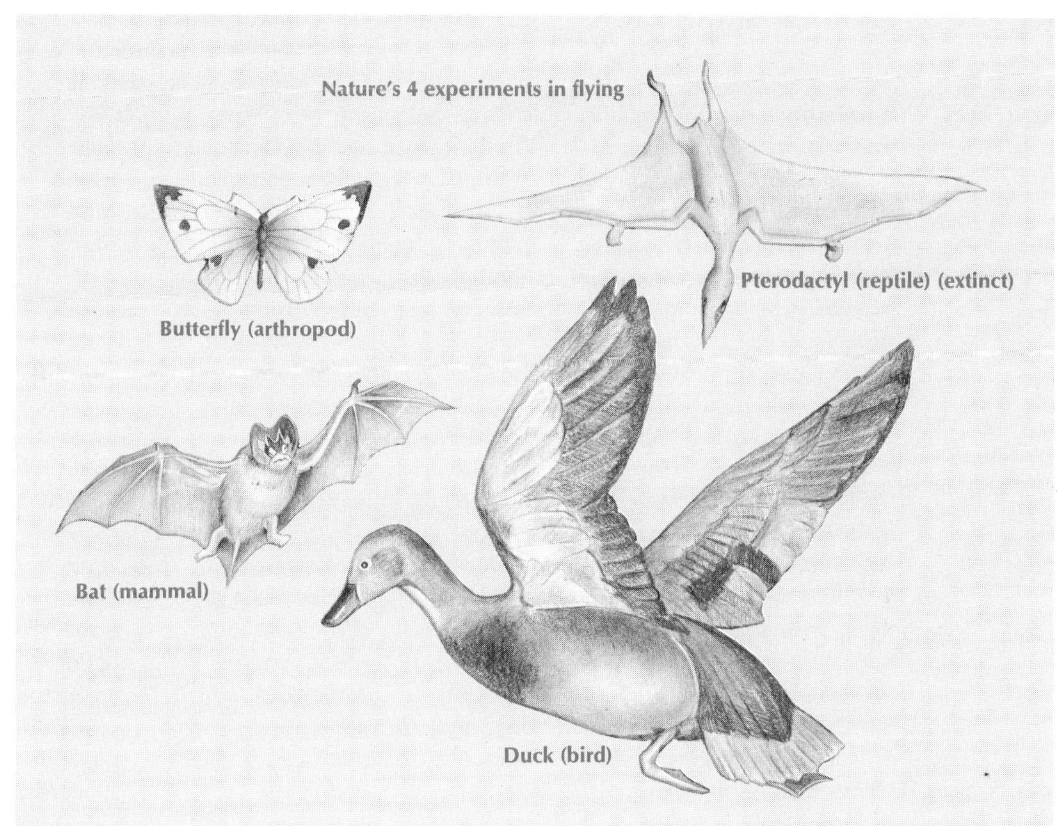

FIG. 41-1

Of four groups of animals that experimented with flying, only reptiles, as group, gave it up entirely.

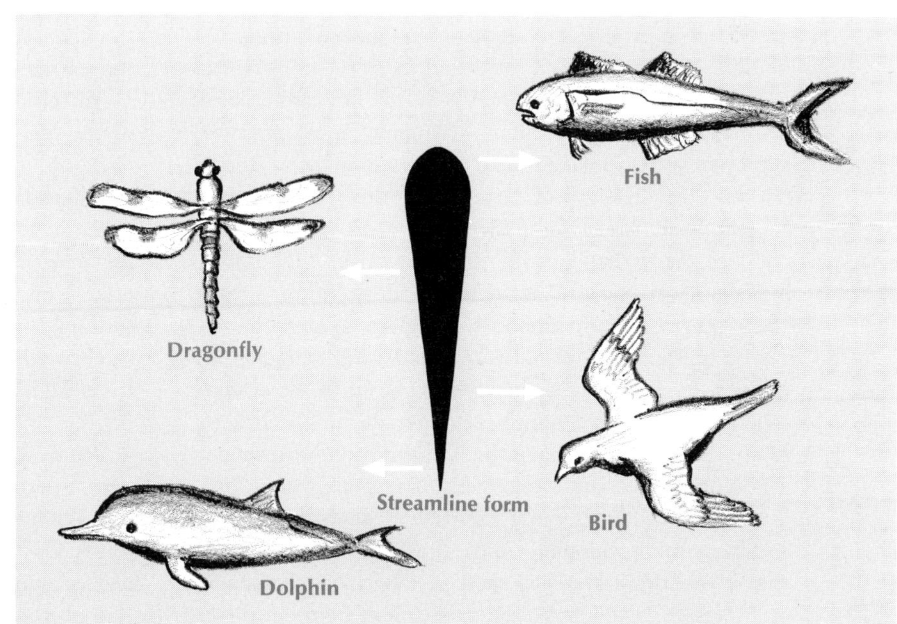

FIG. 41-2

Streamline form. This is one of most successful body forms for rapid locomotion through air and water. It is an elongated tapering form, somewhat rounded anteriorly and tapered posteriorly, and with its greatest diameter a short distance from anterior end. As animal moves through water, for instance, body anteriorly offers resistance, but return force of water against longer tapering posterior part more than offsets force used in pushing water aside in front and so aids locomotion. Same advantages accrue when body is stationary against moving water.

The soil supports an enormous population of animals, some fairly large, but the majority small, such as nematodes, crustaceans, insects, protozoans, and bacteria. The nature of the soil influences the distribution of forms. Earthworms prefer soil rich in humus. Whether the soil is acid or alkaline makes little difference if they have abundant food. Land snails are more common on soils rich in calcium because they need this mineral for their shells. Deer also depend on calcium for their antlers and bony skeleton. Many chemicals (cobalt, fluorine, iodine) in trace amounts in the soil are important to animals.

Animals have evolved interesting adaptations for burrowing. Moles and mole crickets have shovellike appendages and broad, sturdy bodies. Earthworms secrete mucus to line their burrows. The trap-door spider lines its burrow with silk and conceals the entrance with a trapdoor that it pops open to seize its prey (Fig. 19-6). Many forms live under stones and other objects on the surface of the soil. Termites and ants build mounds of soil in which they make tunneled passageways. Sometimes these mounds are elevated far above the surface and may consist of excavated material and excreta cemented together with their salivary secretions.

Some forms utilize burrows made by others. Many snakes, burrowing owls, American rabbits, and even insects take over abandoned burrows made by rodents or other forms. Many animals merely take advantage of natural crevices between rocks and debris.

A large part of any animal is water, for protoplasm consists of 70% to 92% water. All animals must preserve a proper water balance. The conservation of water is naturally more acute in terrestrial forms, for they are constantly in danger of desiccation. Most animals cannot lose more than one third of their water and live, but some can survive considerable desiccation. Protozoans secrete a cyst around themselves to prevent excessive desiccation; roundworms and rotifers may lose much water and then revive when placed in moist conditions. Water is a limiting factor for life in the desert. Many desert animals have thick, horny skins to prevent evaporation. During prolonged dry spells, some undergo **aestivation,** burying themselves deep in the soil and remaining dormant until the wet season comes again. Breathing systems, such as the tracheal systems of insects and the internal lungs of snails, help cut down the amount of water evaporated. The dry feces of birds and reptiles is another water-saving device. Nocturnal habits of many animals expose them to lower temperatures and relative humidity.

Many animals get most of the water they need from their food, especially such animals as jackrabbits, mountain goats, and certain mice. Carnivorous animals may get their water supplies from the blood of their prey. Water supplies play a vital role in the distribution of many animals, for in tropical countries some do not stray far from water holes. This determines the distribution of other animals that prey on those that must have water.

Water contains many salts and other substances that organisms use for the structure and functioning of their bodies. Organisms also must work out favorable water balances between their internal and external environments, as pointed out in a previous section. The salinity of marine water is rather constant in all oceans, being about 3.5%; the salinity of fresh water varies greatly, although its salts may be limiting factors in many instances. Some salt lakes may have a salinity of 25% to 30%, which greatly restricts the life in them. The freezing point of sea water is about $-1.9°$ C., which is an advantage to animals in colder regions. Water is heaviest at 4° C. so that ice at 0° C. can float; thus deep lakes and ponds do not have permanent ice on their bottoms. Although shallow lakes in high altitudes do remain frozen to the bottom in the winter, life can survive there. Water also has a very high heat capacity, which makes for a constancy in temperature during most of the year. Water makes up 71% of the earth's surface and represents the most extensive medium for animal life.

An important water relation is the relative humidity of the air. Animals in rain forests live only where the air is almost saturated with moisture (high humidity); desert forms live where the air is extremely dry (low humidity). There seems to be an optimum humidity for most animals and they are uncomfortable under other conditions. Amphibians are especially sensitive to humidity changes. Forests are important as shelters, food supplies, and hiding places, for the relative humidity is higher and evaporation much lower than in open fields.

Wind and general weather conditions. Air-borne eggs, spores, and adults (insects and snails) are often taken long distances by strong currents of air. Such forms may suddenly spring up in regions where they were not previously found. Ballooning spiders are carried on their gossamer threads to locations far away. So powerful are wind currents that animal life may be transported from continents to islands and other lands hundreds of miles away.

Where wind currents are prevalent, birds place their nests in sheltered places. Insects and other forms on wind-swept regions take advantage of cover to prevent being swept away. Many such insects are wingless; this may be adaptive, for wingless animals might stand less chance of being blown away. Forests afford many habitats that are protected against the force of winds. Wind is also an agency of erosion. In our western states the wind has shifted and carried away the topsoil for great distances, producing the well-known "dust bowl" of the West.

Animals in temperate climates face fluctuating weather conditions largely unknown in tropical countries. Seasonal changes influence habits and distribution of animals. Many of the physical factors, temperature, light, etc., already mentioned, are correlated with seasonal changes in weather. Some animals in the temperate zones can undergo enormous ranges in temperatures. Many, however, are killed near the freezing point of water, but the races are preserved by spores, eggs, and larval forms, which can withstand such rigorous conditions. The hazards of winter are met by animals in various ways—migration, hibernation, change of food habits, etc. Food chains in winter differ greatly from those in summer.

Shelters and breeding places. Many animals, such as fish, squids, deer, and antelopes, that are endowed with speed make limited use of shelters, but others must hide from danger. In rapid streams, where there is danger of being dislodged and washed away, some animals are flat for creeping under stones, others have suckers for attachment, and still others live in firmly attached cases. Vegetation creates shelter for both land and aquatic animals. Forest areas, grasslands, and shrubbery contain a variety of habitats for terrestrial animals; aquatic plants serve as cover for small fish, snails, crustaceans, and other forms. In many instances proper cover is a limiting factor.

The destruction of forests has brought a decline of large birds of prey because the birds have been unable to find suitable nesting sites. The disappearance of sandy beaches due to the growth of aquatic vegetation affects fish that require sandy bottoms in which to spawn. Salamanders are scarce in regions that lack streams or pools in which their young may be hatched and reared.

Other physical factors. Aquatic animals that live at great depths in water are subjected to enormous pressure (more than 14 pounds per square inch for each 33 feet of depth). Many vertebrates and invertebrates do live at such depths because their internal pressure is the same as the external pressure. Forms that normally do not live at high water pressures can withstand high pressures so that the latter is chiefly a limiting factor only when it is extreme. Fish without swim bladders are less sensitive to deep pressure than those with swim bladders because of gas tension complications; and most invertebrates are more resistant to pressure than vertebrates. Many marine animals (eurybathic) have wide vertical ranges, making diurnal movements of great amplitude, and can adjust themselves to a wide range of pressures.

Atmospheric pressure decreases with increased altitude and influences breathing, circulation, and general activity, but the ecologic significance of such pressure is not yet understood. At high altitudes other factors, such as temperature, humidity, and wind, may be the limiting factors.

Animal life may be lacking from the bottoms of deep bodies of water (Black Sea), where no dissolved oxygen is found. However, because of the currents of sinking cold water from the polar seas, some deeper waters of the sea may have more oxygen than regions near the surface. A certain amount of free oxygen must be available for aerobic animals. Lakes at high altitudes (Andes) cannot dissolve enough oxygen to support fish life. Atmospheric oxygen can thus be considered a limiting factor, for at altitudes of 18,000 to 20,000 feet, the barometric pressure is less than one half that at sea level, and the absolute amount (but not the percentage) of oxygen is correspondingly reduced. For man, and possibly for some other animals, oxygen requirements at high altitudes cannot be met by the oxygen available.

BIOTIC FACTORS

Nutrition. The presence of an animal in a particular region is determined to a great extent by the available food. Many animals such as man have a varied diet and can use the food that happens to be convenient (**omnivores**). Other animals are plant feeders (**herbivores**) or flesh feeders (**carnivores**). Within each of these main types, there are numerous subdivisions. Thus the beaver lives on the bark of willows and aspens, the crossbill lives upon pine cones, aphids suck plant juice, leeches suck blood, and the king cobra feeds on other snakes. Animals restricted to seasonal foods are sometimes forced either to starve or to migrate to more favorable regions. Aquatic animals depend less on vegetation than do terrestrial ones, for water plants are restricted to limited regions, such as the shorelines, shallow bottoms, and surface plankton.

The interrelations between animals in their food getting furnish interesting **food chains** (Fig. 41-3). Because plant life is the most abundant food in most localities, herbivorous animals form the basis of the animal community. These in turn serve as food for certain carnivorous forms, which also may serve as food for larger predators. Eventually in this food cycle an animal is found that does not serve as food for another animal. In a food chain the successive animals involved usually are larger in size but fewer in numbers. Animals at the end of the food chain are large and few, and usually one or two of them dominate a definite region, jealously keeping out all other members of that species. Many food chains could be used as examples. In a forest, for instance, there are many small insects, a lesser number of spiders and carnivorous insects that prey on the small insects, still fewer small birds that live on the spiders and carnivorous insects, and finally one or two hawks that live on the birds. Such an arrangement of populations in the food chain of a community is often called a **food pyramid** (Fig. 41-4); each successive level of the pyramid shows an increase in size and a decrease in number of animals. Food chains may be more complex than the one cited or may be very short, as, for example, the whale, which lives mainly on plankton which forms the base of that particular pyramid. In every food chain plants, which get their energy from the sun, form the basic energy for the chain. On account of this pyramid arrangement, one could expect very few large predatory animals within any region, for such a large pyramid of animals is required to support them. Only one grizzly bear can be found on the average of

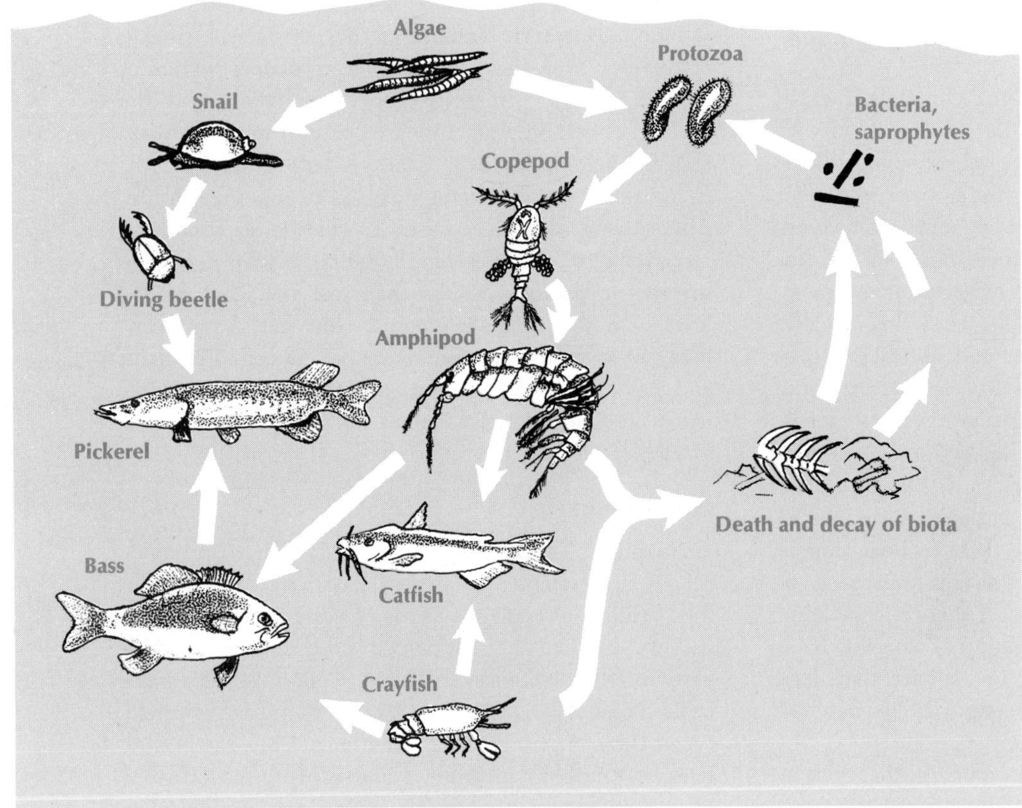

FIG. 41-3

Some interrelationships between food chains or webs of pond. Arrows point from prey to consumer. Chains have many side branches and are not always in linear order.

each 40 square miles of its territory; and in India, tigers are few in number for the same reason.

Besides the predator food chain just described there are two other types—the **parasitic** and the **detrital** food chains. The parasitic goes from larger to smaller organisms and the detrital from disintegrated bodies to microorganisms.

Another quantitative way of expressing the population of a step in a food chain is through the concept of the **biomass.** Biomass refers to the weight of a species population per unit of area. For instance, Juday (1938) found in a Wisconsin lake that there were 209 pounds of carp per acre (biomass). The biomass of a community would be the sum of the biomasses of the many species that make up the steps of the food pyramid. This might be called a **pyramid of biomass.** However, total biomasses obtained by sampling methods are not always reliable. So far, no complete biomass for a community has been obtained.

A better quantitative pyramid is the energy pyramid that expresses both the total amount and the rate of production of energy. It indicates the rate of the food mass as it moves through the food chain. Life on earth receives energy from the sun, the moon, cosmic radiation, meteors, and other sources, but mostly it is solar energy that amounts to about 13×10^{23} gram-calories annually. Some of this energy is lost by being reflected back to space and most of the rest is used on earth for purposes other than supporting life. To give some idea of how energy is expended in a food chain, this example by L. C. Cole (1958) explains the relationship.

FIG. 41-4

Simple food pyramid. Size of boxes does not correspond to relative abundance of forms.

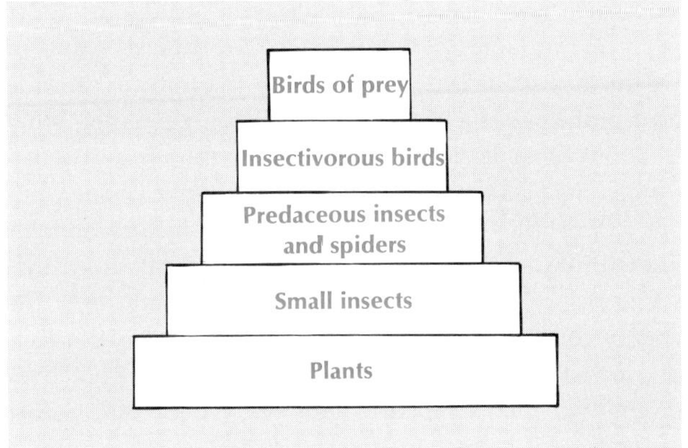

Out of each 1,000 calories stored by algae in Cayuga Lake, 150 calories can be converted to protoplasm in small aquatic animals, 30 calories by smelt in the next step of the food chain, 6 calories by trout that eat the smelt, and 1.2 calories by man who eats the trout. It is thus seen that passage through a food chain is very expensive as well as indicating that there is a definite limit to the amount of life this planet can support.

Food size is important in the arrangement of a community. Carnivorous animals, for instance, are unable to kill animals above a certain size, and many cannot live on forms below a certain size, for they cannot eat enough to furnish them the necessary amount of energy. A lion, for example, could not catch enough mice under ordinary circumstances to satisfy its food requirements. Elton showed that the tsetse fly *(Glossina palpalis)* can suck up the blood of only those animals whose blood corpuscles do not exceed 18 μ in diameter. Man, by his ingenuity, masters any food, regardless of size.

Some animals are able to change to a food they ordinarily do not eat. The fox, when pressed by winter scarcity, can subsist on dried-up berries and grapes. Many animals adjust their food requirements to the seasonal abundance of various types of food. Animals with a wide range of food habits are better fitted for survival. The robin is a good example because its diet includes seasonal items, such as cherries, raspberries, and other small fruits, in addition to insects and earthworms that form its staple diet.

Other biotic factors. In addition to food relations, other biotic factors play a part in the structure of an animal community. These involve social life within a group, cannibalism, mutual assistance, symbiotic relations, mating habits, predatory and parasitic relations, commensalism, mutual dependence of plants and animals, etc. These factors determine behavior patterns within animal communities and may be as important as any other factors.

Many animals are solitary in their habits, but others live together in colonies. Various degrees of social life are found among animals, from those that simply band together with no real division of labor (schools of fish and flocks of birds) to those that have worked out complicated patterns of social organization and division of labor (bees, termites, ants). Many predators (grizzly bears, mountain lions, tigers, hawks, owls) tend toward a solitary life and are rarely found together except for mating purposes. Many birds may be more or less solitary most of the year but quite gregarious during their migrations. Snakes are mainly solitary but hibernate together in numbers.

Many cases of **symbiotic relationship** could be mentioned, such as the small fish that obtains shelter in the cloaca of certain sea cucumbers, the tiny crab *Pinnotheres* commensal in the shells of oysters and scallops, or the flagellates that live in the gut of the termite and makes its digestion possible. Ants use the secretions of aphids for food and, in return, give protection and shelter to the aphids. The ant slavemaker *Polyergus* raids the colonies of other species of ants and carries away their larvae to be reared as slaves in its own colony. **Parasitism** is another common type of symbiosis. An interesting symbiotic association is the one involving a sea anemone, a hermit crab, and the snail shell (usually *Bucinnum*) in which the crab lives. The hermit crab *(Pagurus)* always lives in an empty gastropod shell to which the European anemone (*Adamsia* or *Calliactis*) is attached. The anemone protects the crab with its stinging tentacles and receives scraps of food from the crab's feeding. Investigations indicate that the anemone is attracted to the shell, whether occupied or empty, by a chemical factor in the shell (Ross and Sutton) and that the crab has no role in establishing the relationship. Some reef crabs of the tropics fasten an anemone in each claw and use them for protection. Many examples of **cleaning symbiosis** have been found by skin divers among marine organisms. This symbiosis involves the removal of debris or parasites from the teeth or body of one animal by another. Cleaners include many species of small fish, shrimp, and other forms and are usually conspicuous by color or behavior patterns. Cleansers may have stations to which the larger fish go to be cleaned. This is an interesting example of cooperation among animals.

Eat and be eaten is almost a universal rule in the animal kingdom. Most of the animals in a food chain are **predators,** preying on other animals. **Cannibalism** (eating members of one's own species) is not unusual among animals, both low and high. It is common among insects, especially ants and termites.

Many plants depend on insects for transferring their pollen. This is a mutual relation, for insects use nectar or pollen from the blossoms. The classic case of the delicate reciprocal relation between insect and plant in pollination is shown by the yucca moth and the yucca plant of the southwestern states. This moth collects some pollen from one plant and carries it to another, where it lays its eggs in the ovary of the yucca; after depositing an egg, the moth climbs to the top of the pistil and inserts the pollen into a stigmatic tube. This process is repeated for each egg laid (usually six). Each egg in its development requires a fertilized ovule, but enough ovules are left unmolested by the developing larvae to ensure seed for the plant.

ECOLOGIC ENERGETICS

Ecologic energetics is the study of energy transfer and energy transformations within ecosystems. Since all forms of energy can be converted completely to heat, the calorie, or kilogram-calorie, is considered the basic unit of measurement for comparative purposes. Food chains, as we have seen, can be very complex and different methods are employed in determining them. Direct observation may give some superficial insight, but this is not very reliable in the overall picture. Gut analysis is often used to determine what food a member of a food chain uses, but it is impossible to get a complete picture of the food relations unless there are hard parts as key identifying structures. A method of greater value is perhaps the "tagged-atom" method whereby radioactive isotopes (for example, phosphorus 32) were used to label (by spraying or otherwise) the suspected food source, and then later checking animals for the presence of the tagged atoms.

To get an impression of ecosystem energetics and the efficiency by which solar energy is converted or used in a food chain, it is necessary to ascertain the quantity of energy per unit area per unit time. The amount of solar energy per unit area per unit time available to plants varies with the geographic region. In Michigan the amount of solar energy available to plants is considered to be about 4.7×10^8 calories per square meter per year; in Georgia the figure is 6×10^8 cal./M.^{2}/yr. Of this energy at least 95% is lost in the form of sensible heat and heat of evaporation, and the remainder (that is, about 5% or less) is used in photosynthesis and transformed into the chemical energy of plant tissue. But not all of this stored energy is available to animals (heterotrophs) that eat plants, for the plant in synthesizing organic matter must perform work and gets the energy to do this from the oxidation of its organic supply in the process of respiration. The animal that lives directly on plants probably gets only about 80% to 90% of the total energy the plant first stored up.

ANIMAL POPULATIONS*

The term "population" is defined by some ecologists as a group of organisms of the same species that live at a given time in a particular area. Others broaden the term to include similar species. Genetically, the members of a population share in a common gene pool. A population has its own characteristics, such as population density, birth rate, death rate, reproductive potential, age distribution, population pressure, population cycles, and growth. In a broad sense the study of population is the study of biology with all of its implications. Ecologic units, such as communities, are made up of complex population groups and cannot be understood without a study of the interrelations of populations. Populations must adjust to the environment the same as individuals, although their environmental relations are far more complex. A population may live in a continuous small or large area; but the term does not usually include local populations of the same species that are isolated from one another.

Studies of animal populations in most habitats often reveal a large number of different species as well as of individuals in each species. In general the small forms are most numerous. An acre of rich humus soil may contain several hundred thousand earthworms and many million nematode worms. A quart of rich plankton water may have more than a million protozoans and other small forms. The number of insects of all kinds found on an acre of lush meadow in midsummer often reaches millions. On the other hand, there may be only two or three birds per acre and only one or two foxes per several hundred acres. Animals at the top of the food pyramid, having few or no enemies, often regulate their numbers by arbitrarily dividing their territory and keeping out all other members of their species. This avoids competition for food, nesting sites, and shelters.

The population of any species at a given time and place depends on its birth rate and its mortality or death rate. If more organisms are born than die, the species will increase. Shifting of members of a species from one habitat into an adjacent one (migration, etc.) would affect the local abundance of that species but not the general population of the species involved.

The biotic potential rate is the innate capacity of a population to increase under optimal surroundings and stable age ratios. What are the controlling factors for keeping populations in check? Ecologists now stress a study of these regulations. The concept of **density-dependent** factors indicates that animal populations are regulated automatically, to a certain extent, by such influences as density, increased mortality rate or reduced births, food supplies, infectious diseases, and territorial behavior. All these factors operate to produce a general overall effect of feedback, either negative or positive, as the case might warrant to keep the population within check. There are many complicated factors that play a role in population regulation and that are only partially understood. Examples of such are the dominance hierarchies (Chapter 43, Animal Behavior Patterns) and the fluctuating fecundity of populations in accordance with the degree of density. As density increases, for instance, fertility declines—a good example of feedback control of population growth.

What are the advantages of organized populations? Many species are so organized for survival value because grouping together is characteristic of primitive as well as highly specialized forms. Animal populations find safety in numbers against predators and opportunities for food getting. There are also advantages in social grouping for territorial possession and for reproductive activities. Organization represents a key behavioral aspect in sharing community life and in the development of social rank within a particular population. Social rank may be a form of division of labor and a trend toward specialization of function. The energy flow through a community is most efficient in well-organized populations in well-balanced relations with other populations.

The success of a population is reflected in its **density,** which is the number of individuals per unit area or volume. The unit of area used in measuring density varies. For small forms such as plankton, estimates may be made from forms found in a liter of water; for larger animals the acre or square mile may be the unit. The complete count of individuals in an area is called a **census.** Usually counts are made on sample plots, from which estimates are made. Small mammals, such as mice and chipmunks, may be trapped in live traps, tagged by clipping toes or ears, and then released. A recent method employs radioactive tagging, by which it has been possible experimentally to trace and recover small animals in the field with a Geiger-Müller counter. Suppose 100 animals are caught and tagged, and at a later date another lot of animals is caught in the same way on the same area. In the second sample the number of

*Refer to Chapter 2, Principles 17 and 34.

tagged animals is noted. If the second sample showed 5 tagged animals among 100 caught, then the total population (X) would be 100/X = 5/100, or X = 2,000. This assumes that animals caught in the first sample are just as likely to be caught in the second sample. If sample plots are carefully selected and possible sources of error carefully checked, this random sampling method of estimating the population density of the entire area is considered fairly reliable.

All populations undergo what is called **population dynamics,** which refers to the quantitative variations of growth, reproductive rates, mortality rates, fluctuations in numbers, age distribution, etc. The characteristic growth of a population is represented by a **population growth curve.** This is the mathematic expression of the growth of a population from its early beginning until it arrives at some stabilizing level of density. Such a curve or graph is produced by plotting the number of animals, or its logarithm, against the time factor. In the beginning, if there is no serious competition with other species and enemies and there is plenty of food, the population grows at about the rate of its potential increase and the curve grows steeply upward. Such curves, however, are rarely realized, except for brief periods, because of the increasing factors of competition, crowding, and higher mortality rates. These growth curves are very similar for all types and sizes of organisms. One usually starts out with a **lag phase** because it takes time for the few individuals to find each other and start mating. Then it proceeds at a rapid rate, so that a **logarithmic phase** of growth occurs when the population tends to double with each generation, and the curve is fairly straight. But because of more competition for food, losses to enemies, fewer places to live, and greater mortality rate, the growth rate slows down or levels off into the **stationary phase** (Fig. 41-5).

The logistic theory of population growth seems to be restricted to the population growth of animals with simple life histories, such as many kinds of protozoans, but does not apply closely to those animals that have complex life histories (many insects). Many complicated factors of an ecologic nature may greatly alter the conditions that produce the generalized logistic curve, as described originally by Verhulst (1839). There is a tendency for every population to reach a number at which it becomes stabilized (saturation level) with the resources of its environment.

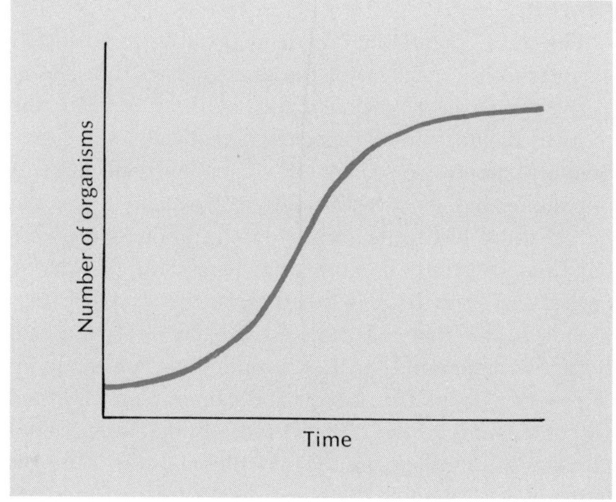

FIG. 41-5

Population growth curve.

The **birth** rate (natality) is the average number of offspring produced per unit of time. The theoretic or maximum birth rate is the potential rate of reproduction that could be produced under ideal conditions. This is never realized because not all females are equally fertile, many eggs do not hatch, not all the larva survive, and for many other reasons. **Mortality** rate is the opposite of birth rate and is measured by the number of organisms that die per unit time. **Minimum mortality** refers to those that die from old age. The actual mortality rate, however, is far different from the minimal one, for as the population increases, the mortality rate increases. Survival curves (made by plotting the number of survivors against the total life-span) vary among different species. Among many small organisms the mortality rate is very high early in life; others, such as man, have a higher survival rate at most levels. Man is unique in being able to change his life expectancy through better medical and regulative practices.

Both birth rates and mortality rates are influenced by the **age distribution** of a population. Age at which animals can reproduce varies. Asexual forms begin to multiply quite early; many sexual forms (insects, etc.) attain sexual maturity a few days after hatching; others may not become mature for several months or years. Reproductive capacity is usually highest in middle-age groups. Rapidly growing populations have many young members; stationary populations have a more even age distribution. The relative distribution of age groups in a population indicates trends toward stability or otherwise.

Fluctuation in members occurs in all animal populations. Some of these fluctuations are very irregular; others show only slight variations over long periods of time. Some annual seasonal changes are to be expected. There are more birds in early summer than at other times because of the crop of recently hatched members. Later, many of these birds are destroyed by the hazards of the environment, such as **population pressure.** Examples of cycle populations are the lemmings of the northern zones which become so abundant every three or four years that they migrate to the sea and drown; the snowshoe hares of Canada which have approximately a ten-year cycle of abundance (there is a close parallelism in cyclic abundance of the lynx, which feeds on the hare); and meadow mice which usually show a four-year cycle of abundance. A recent appraisal of the ten-year cycle (Keith, 1963) indicates that this periodicity is in a broad sense applicable to many animals (grouse, hare, lynx, fox, etc.), although there are exceptional fluctuations and peak irregularities. The cycle is generally restricted to the northern coniferous forests and tundra regions. Invasions of birds into regions where they are not normally found, such as crossbills and waxwings, have tended to follow a ten-year cycle in some instances in England. Irregular fluctuations are especially common in insects. Grasshoppers may appear suddenly in enormous numbers, but at other times they are very scarce. No satisfactory theory as yet accounts for cyclic fluctuations, although sunspots and climatic cycles have been suggested. Some irregular fluctuations can be explained by weather and climate changes. The great "dust bowl" of 1933 to 1936 must have affected every aspect of life in the stricken area.

The so-called **population turnover** refers to the movement of individuals into and out of populations, and it is caused by birth, death, and immigration into and emigration out of a given population. Some species have rapid turnovers, especially those that live only a single season or have more than one generation a year. However, even in species that live much longer, the turnover rate per year may be 70% or more.

BIOTIC COMMUNITIES

The community is a natural assemblage of plants and animals that are bound together by their requirement of the same environmental factors. Organisms in a community share the same physical factors and react to them in a similar way. The community and the nonliving environment together form the ecosystem described in a former section. Communities may be widely separated, but if the environmental factors are the same, similar kinds of animals will be found in them. Thus in any brook rapids community certain characteristic animals are likely to be found. There will, of course, be exceptions.

A **major community** is the smallest ecologic unit that is self-sustaining and self-regulating. It is made up of innumerable smaller **minor communities** that are not altogether self-sustaining. Forests and ponds are major communities; decaying logs and ant hills are minor communities. Members of a major community are relatively independent of other communities, provided they receive radiant energy from the sun. These members will show a similarity in their physiologic makeup, behavior, and mode of life. Communities do not have exact limits but tend to overlap each other. Animals frequently shift from one community to another because of seasonal or other variations. Some spend the day in one and the night in another.

Stratification is the division of the community into definite horizontal or vertical strata. In a forest community, for instance, there are animals that live on the forest floor, others on shrubbery and low vegetation, and still others in the treetops. Many forms shift from one stratum to another, especially in a diurnal manner. Many of the adjustments and requirements of a particular stratum are very similar in forests widely separated from each other in many parts of the world. The animals that occupy such similar strata, although geographically separated, are called **ecologic equivalents.** The pronghorn antelope of North America and the zebra of South Africa are equivalents.

Between two distinct communities there may be an intermediate transitional zone. This is called an **ecotone,** or tension zone. An example would be the marginal region between a forest and a pasture or open land.

Food relations are a basic aspect of all communities. In a self-sufficient community they follow a certain sequence. **Producer organisms,** such as green plants, make their own food; **primary consumers,** such as insects, larvae, and various other arthropods, feed on plants; **secondary consumers,** such as carnivores, live on the primary consumers, etc. Other organisms such as bacteria are called **decomposer organisms,** for they break down the dead organisms into simpler substances that can then be used by plants.

In every community some plants and animals exert a dominant influence because of their numbers, activities, and other reasons. Generally those organisms with the largest biomasses within their levels of feeding interrelations are the ones that exert a controlling interest. In land communities, plants are usually the **dominants,** and some communities are named from their dominant vegetation, such as beech-maple woods. In the ecologic cycle of a community the removal of a dominant usually causes serious disturbances.

A basic characteristic of community organization is **periodicity.** This refers to rhythmic patterns of organisms in their search for mates, food, and shelter. Some community periodicities are correlated with the daily rhythms of day and night, some are seasonal, and others represent tidal or lunar events. Periodic activities include the diurnal and nocturnal faunas that are specialized for day and night activities, respectively; seasonal cycles of growth, mating periods, hibernation, migration, etc.; and activities of swarming, spawning, etc., which are correlated with the lunar and tidal periodicity. There are also various intermediate activities, such as those that occur during the crepuscular period (twilight). Because of this community periodicity, more ecologic habitats are available and more ecologic relationships are established.

ECOLOGIC NICHE

The special place an organism has in a community with relation to its food and enemies is called an **ecologic niche.** In every community there are herbivorous animals of several types, some of which feed on one kind of plant and others on other plants. There are also in every community different types of carnivores that prey on different species of animals. Similar niches in different communities are occupied by forms that have similar food habits or similar enemies, although the species involved may be different in each case. For example, there is the niche in wooded regions occupied by hawks and owls that prey on field mice and shrews, but in regions close to homes this niche is taken over by cats. In this respect the birds of prey and cats occupy the same niche. The arctic fox and the African hyena are other examples. Both are scavengers; the arctic fox eats what the polar bear leaves; the African hyena eats leavings from the lion.

ECOLOGIC SUCCESSION

Communities are not static but are continually changing according to well-defined laws. This process, called biotic or **ecologic succession,** may be brought about by physiologic factors, such as the erosion of hills and mountains down to a base level, the filling up of lakes and streams, and the rise and fall of the earth's surface. All organisms die, decay, and become a part of the substratum; vegetation invades ponds and lakes; regions of the earth's surface become grasslands, forests, or deserts, according to physical factors of temperature and rainfall. These changes are often regular and directional and may be predicted. Communities are succeeded by other communities until a fairly stable end product is attained. Such a sequence of communities is called a **sere** and involves early pioneer communities, transient communities, and finally a **climax community,** which is more or less balanced with its environment.

The sequence of plants follows in a certain order during the evolution of a habitat. For instance, a small lake begins as a clear body of water with sandy bottom and shores more or less free from vegetation. As soil is washed into the lake by the surrounding streams, mud and vegetable muck gradually replace the sandy bottom. Vegetation grows up along the sides of the lake and begins a slow migration into the lake, resulting in a bog or marsh. The first plant life is aquatic or semiaquatic, consisting of filamentous algae on the surface and later of rooted plants, such as *Elodea,* bulrushes, and cattails. As the water recedes and the shore becomes firm, the marshy plants are succeeded by shrubs and trees, such as alders and larches and, later, beeches and maples. Eventually the lake may be replaced by a forest, especially if its sides and slopes are steep; if the sides have gentle slopes, a grassy region may replace the site of the lake. The terminal forest or grassland is a climax community (Fig. 41-6).

Along with the succession of plants, there will be a corresponding ecologic succession in the types of animal communities. In its beginning a lake may contain fish that use the gravelly or sandy bottoms for spawning. When the bottoms are replaced by muck, these fish will be replaced by others that spawn in aquatic vegetation. Eventually, no fish may be able to live in the habitat; but other forms, such as snails, crayfish, many kinds of insects, and birds, are able to live in

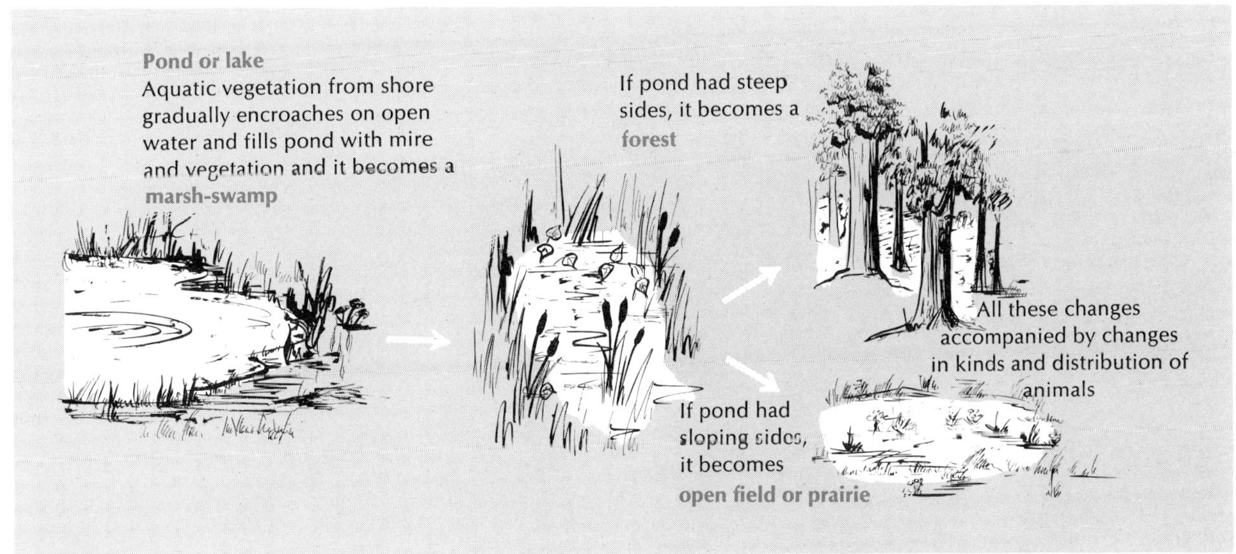

FIG. 41-6

Ecologic succession in pond or lake.

the swampy, boggy community. As the community becomes a forest or grassland, there will be other successions of animal life.

In general, it may be stated that communities in their development and evolution tend to go from a state of instability to one of stability, or climax. The term "stability," however, must be used in a relative sense, for changes are inevitable.

KINDS OF HABITAT

Habitats tend to be rather sharply defined from each other, each with its own set of physical and biotic factors. Transition zones between them are not common. An abundance of different habitats may be found in a small region if there is a diversity of physicochemical and other factors. A small lake or pond (Fig. 41-7) may have littoral or open water, cove, sandy or pebbly bottom, bulrush or other vegetation, drift, and other kinds of habitats. Within the relatively short range of a high mountain, there are many life zones, each of which may correspond to the latitudinal zones. The small altitudinal life zones of the mountain are similar to the large latitudinal zones of the earth's surface with respect to vegetation and, to some extent, to the distribution of animal life. On the other hand, there may be extensive regions, such as the surface of the open sea or a sandy desert, where there is no such diversity of habitats because ecologic conditions are more or less uniform throughout its extent.

The animals that are distributed among the various habitats may be classified into two groups: (1) exclusive or those that are not found outside a particular habitat (Fig. 41-8) and (2) characteristic, or those that are not confined to one habitat but occur in others. Examples of the first are crossbills, which, on account of their peculiar adaptation, are confined to the coniferous forests, and, of the second class, such forms as rabbits, which roam both woods and open fields.

Freshwater streams

Freshwater habitats are usually divided into those that are found in **running water** and those found in **standing water.** Freshwater streams naturally belong to the first type. They range from tiny intermittent brooks to rivers. Smaller streams are either intermittent ones that flow only at certain seasons, or spring-fed streams that usually flow all the time. Larger, permanent streams include the swift brooks and the rivers that have reached the level of permanent ground water. Water found in streams differs from marine water in having smaller volume, greater variations in temperature, lesser mineral content, greater light penetration, greater suspended material content, and greater plant growth. Many of the forms found in such habitats have organs of attachment, such as suckers and modified appendages, streamlined body shapes for withstanding currents, or shapes adapted for creeping under stones.

FIG. 41-7

Woodland pond affords excellent shelter and breeding places for many forms, such as amphibians, reptiles, and insects. (Courtesy C. Alender.)

FIG. 41-8

Tree hole habitat. Some arthropods found here are never or rarely found elsewhere. One of these groups is pselaphid beetles.

Various kinds of habitats are found in all streams. Some are found in the swiftly flowing regions where there may be rapids or cataracts, others are found in pools of sluggish waters. Usually the types of animals found in the two regions vary. In rapids (Fig. 41-9) characteristic forms are the black fly larvae (*Simulium*), caddis worms (*Hydropsyche*), snails (*Goniobasis*), darters of several species, water penny larvae (Fig. 41-10), miller's thumbs, and stone fly nymphs. All these forms have characteristic behavior patterns, such as positive rheotaxis, high oxygen requirements, and low temperature toleration. In the pool habitats of streams are found various minnows, mussels, certain snails, dragonfly nymphs, mayfly larvae, crayfish, flatworms, leeches, and water striders (Fig. 41-11). Many of the forms that dwell here partially bury themselves in the sandy or mucky bottoms.

Some of the larger streams and rivers may have considerable plankton, but this plankton has gotten into the rivers from lakes and backwaters and is not developed from the rivers, for their currents are too swift.

FIG. 41-9

Brook rapids habitat contains many different forms that have special adaptations for withstanding strong water currents.

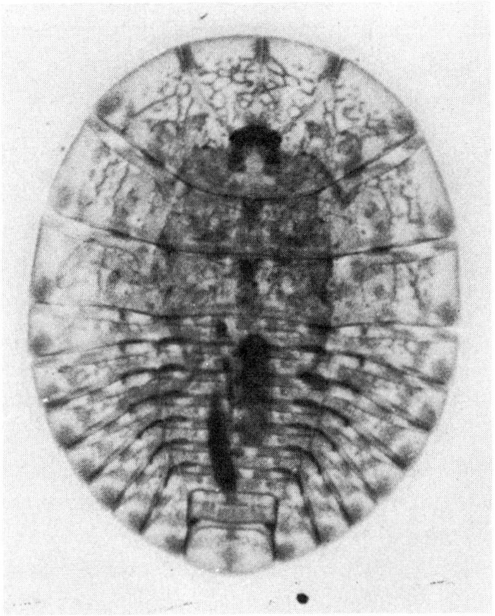

FIG. 41-10

Water penny, larva of riffle beetle *Psephenus*. This flat larva is adapted for clinging to lower surfaces of stones in swift brooks. (Size, ⅓ inch.)

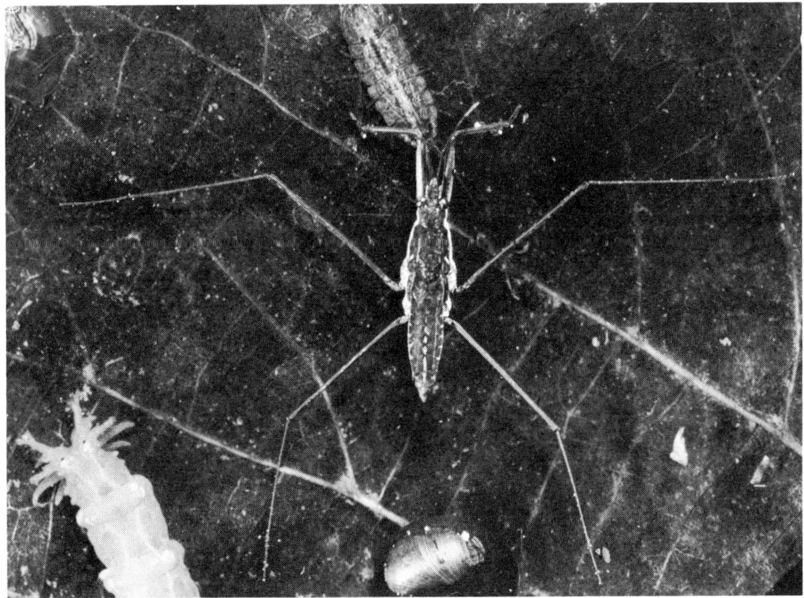

FIG. 41-11

Group of forms found in quiet pools of brooks. This shows water strider *Gerris*, small crustacean *Asellus* in upper center, head of crane fly larva in lower left, and water snail in lower center.

The study of fresh waters in all their aspects is called **limnology.**

Ponds

Unlike the streams, ponds have feeble currents or none at all. They vary, depending on their age and location. Most ponds contain a great deal of vegetation that tends to increase with the age of the pond. Many of them have very little open water in the center, for the vegetation, both rooted and floating types, has largely taken over. As ponds fill up, the higher plants become progressively more common. The bottoms of ponds vary all the way from sandy and rocky (young ponds) to deep mucky ones (old ponds). The water varies in depth from a few inches to 8 to 10 feet, although some may be deeper. Ponds are too shallow to be stratified, for the force of the wind is usually sufficient to keep the entire mass of water in circulation. Because of this, the gases (oxygen and carbon dioxide) are uniformly distributed through the water and the temperature is fairly uniform.

Animal communities of ponds are usually similar to those of bays in larger bodies of water (lakes). The large amount of vegetation and plant decomposition products affords an excellent habitat for many forms. Among the common forms found are varieties of snails and mussels, larvae of flies (Fig. 41-12), beetles, caddis flies, dragonflies, many kinds of crustaceans, midge larvae, and many species of frogs. Most of these live on the bottom or among the submerged vegetation and are called the **benthos.** Many swimming forms, called **nekton,** are also found in ponds and include many varieties of fish, turtles, water bugs, and beetles. Muskrats are usually found in the larger ponds, where they make their characteristic houses. Because of the abundance of food, many birds are usually found in and around ponds. These include herons, killdeers, ducks, grebes, and blackbirds. Most ponds also have plankton composed of microscopic plants and animals, such as protozoans, crustaceans, worms, rotifers, diatoms, and algae. Plankton floats on or near the surface and is shifted about passively by the winds.

Forms that live in ponds ordinarily require less oxygen that those found in streams or rapids (Fig. 41-13).

Lakes

The distinction between lakes and ponds is not sharply defined. Lakes are usually distinguished from

FIG. 41-12

Group of larval forms commonly found in ponds. **A,** Crane fly larva found in decaying debris along bank. Beside it is small crustacean, *Asellus.* **B,** Rat-tailed maggot *Tubifera.* This larva lives in water and gets its air when submerged by means of its caudal respiratory tube ("rat-tail"), which is in sections like telescope and can be extended to four times the length of body. **C,** Larval form of *Dytiscus,* giant diving beetle (shown in Fig. 21-32). Larva is equally as savage and predaceous as adult. These were all found in tiny midwestern woodland pond in early March.

ponds by having continuous and permanent water in their centers and by having some sandy shores. Lakes vary with respect to vegetation and other factors. Most of them have bays where there may be aquatic vegetation similar to that of ponds. The bottoms of lakes depend to a great extent on exposure to winds. Where waves are common, the bottoms are usually sandy, but protected areas may contain a great deal of deposited bottom muck. Sizes vary from oceanlike bodies of water to those only a few acres in extent. Naturally, there are differences associated with their size. There is less surface of water in proportion to the total volume of water in a lake than there is in a pond, for lakes are deeper. The depths vary too. In large lakes, such as the Great Lakes of America, the depth rarely exceeds

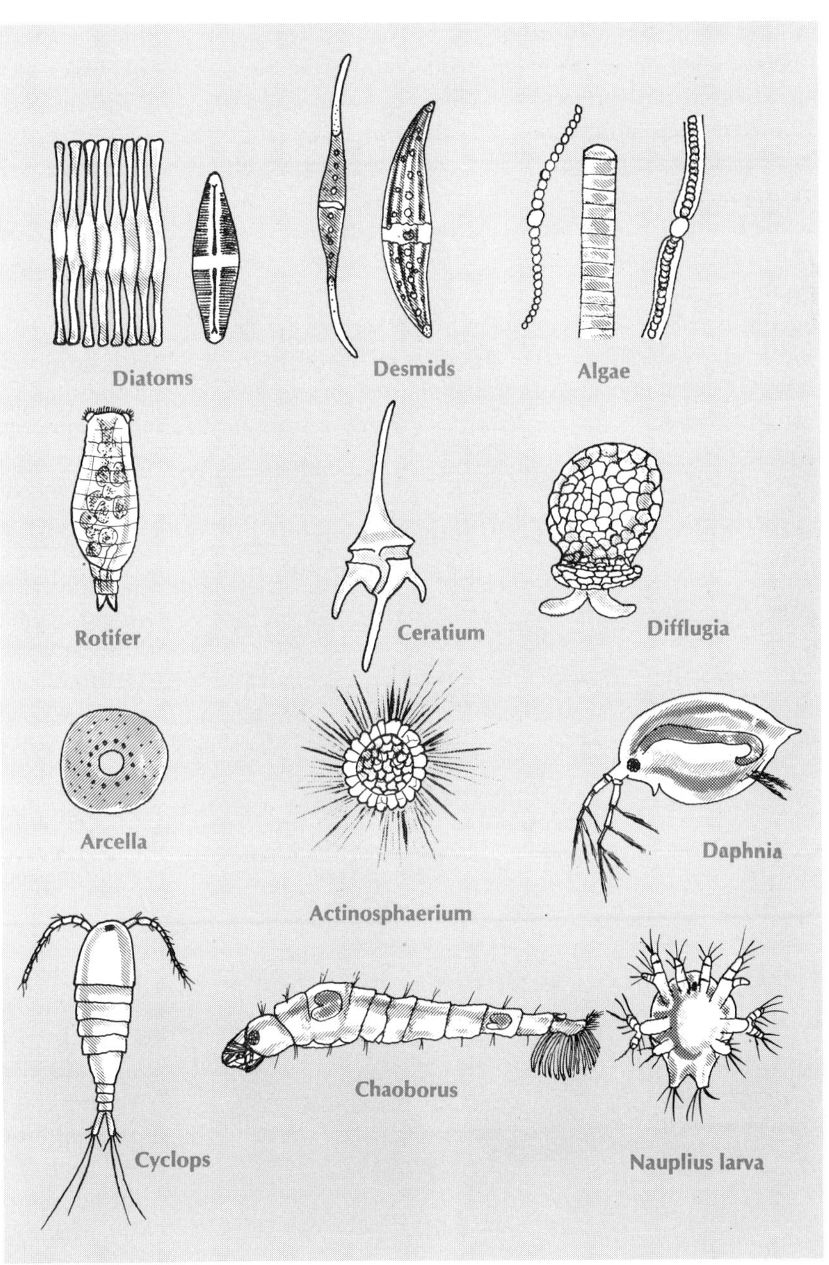

FIG. 41-13

Some typical forms found in pond plankton.

500 meters; in moderate-sized lakes the depth is much less. Many factors, therefore, influence the ecologic nature of a lake. Oxygen is scarcer in the deeper regions where there is little circulation. Light penetration depends on the sediment in water. Most of the light is absorbed by the first meter of surface water, and little penetrates beyond a few meters.

One factor of great importance is temperature. Water in lakes tends to become stratified, and only the surface layers are stirred up by wind action during the summer. Within this surface layer of water, usually about 10 meters deep in medium-sized lakes, the temperature is very uniform (about 20° to 25° C.). Below this the water becomes much colder (reaching 4° to 5° C. at the bottom) and is poorly oxygenated and stagnant. This level between the surface layer of uniform temperature and that stratum where the temperature falls rapidly is called the **thermocline.** In other words, the waters above the thermocline are agitated; below it they are still. The thermocline is shallow at midsummer and deeper in early autumn. In the autumn, when the surface water is colder, the wind agitates the water from surface to bottom and the thermocline disappears so that the temperature is about uniform throughout. In winter the surface water may freeze (0° C.), but the bottom remains at 4° to 5° C. Water at the latter temperature is heavier than ice, which accounts for the fact that ice remains at the surface. As the surface waters become warmer in the spring, there occurs another complete overturn through wind action. In early summer the thermocline is established again.

FIG. 41-14

Group of common land snails, largely various species of *Polygyra,* found on forest floor.

The thermocline is important ecologically, for it establishes the division between two animal communities. Several habitats are found in lakes, such as **terrigenous bottoms,** where the water is shallow and vegetation is absent; **cove,** which has a great deal of vegetation (emergent, submerged, and floating); and **open water,** which may contain some floating plants, especially algae. Characteristic organisms are found in each. Snails, caddis worms, and mayfly nymphs are found in the terrigenous bottom habitat; bryozoans, small crustaceans, snails, and some insects in the cove habitat; and plankton and nekton (fish, turtles, insects) in the open waters. The animals that live on the bottom (the **benthos**) are restricted to those that require no light and little or no oxygen (a few annelid worms, bivalves, and midge larvae).

Terrestrial

Land habitats are more varied than those of the water because there are more variable conditions on land. Physical differences in the air are expressed in such factors as humidity, temperature, pressure, and winds to which air-dwelling forms must adapt themselves, as well as types of soils and vegetation. Variations from profuse rainfall to none at all; topographic differences of mountains, plains, hills, and valleys; climatic differences from arctic conditions to those of the tropics; temperature variations from those in hot deserts to those of high altitudes and polar zones; and air and sunlight differences from those of daily variations to great storms—all these factors have influenced animal life and have been responsible for directing its evolutionary development.

Land forms have become specially adapted for living in the soil (subterranean), on the open ground, on the forest floor (Fig. 41-14), in vegetation, and in the air. Although more species of animals live on land than in water, there are fewer phyla among terrestrial forms. The chief land organisms are the mammals, birds, reptiles, amphibians, worms, protozoans, and arthropods.

Land habitats are classified on the basis of soil relations, climatic conditions, plant associations, and animal relations. Some of the more important habitats in North America will be considered here, together with a few of their characteristic animals.

Subterranean. Subterranean refers to regions within the soil or under the land surface. It includes such habitats as holes and crevices in or between rocks (Fig. 41-15), burrows in the soil, and caves and caverns. Many animals spend at least a part of their lives in the soil. Larval forms of many insects develop there. Ants, nematodes, earthworms, moles, and shrews either have their homes in the soil or spend a part of their time there. For abundance of forms, no other ecologic habitat can compare with the soil. Most cave animals originated on the surface and were adapted for existence in caves before they entered them. Caves are unique in having uniform darkness, high humidity, no green plants, and no rain or snow. Meager food supply restricts the number of animals living there. Cave animals are usually small, have little or no pigment, and have degenerate sense organs. Many are totally blind. Most true cave animals illustrate regressive evolution in that selection puts a premium on loss of internal stability, low basal metabolism, and low food requirements. Common examples of cave animals are springtails, mites, small crustaceans, fish, salamanders, and snails.

FIG. 41-15

Habitat of shelving and drift rock—excellent for many species of salamanders and lizards.

FIG. 41-16

Correspondence of life zones or biomes as correlated with latitudinal and altitudinal zones. This succession of biomes over extensive horizontal range from the tropics to polar regions is found in a condensed form within a few miles on a high mountain in the tropics and, to a slightly lesser extent, in temperate zone.

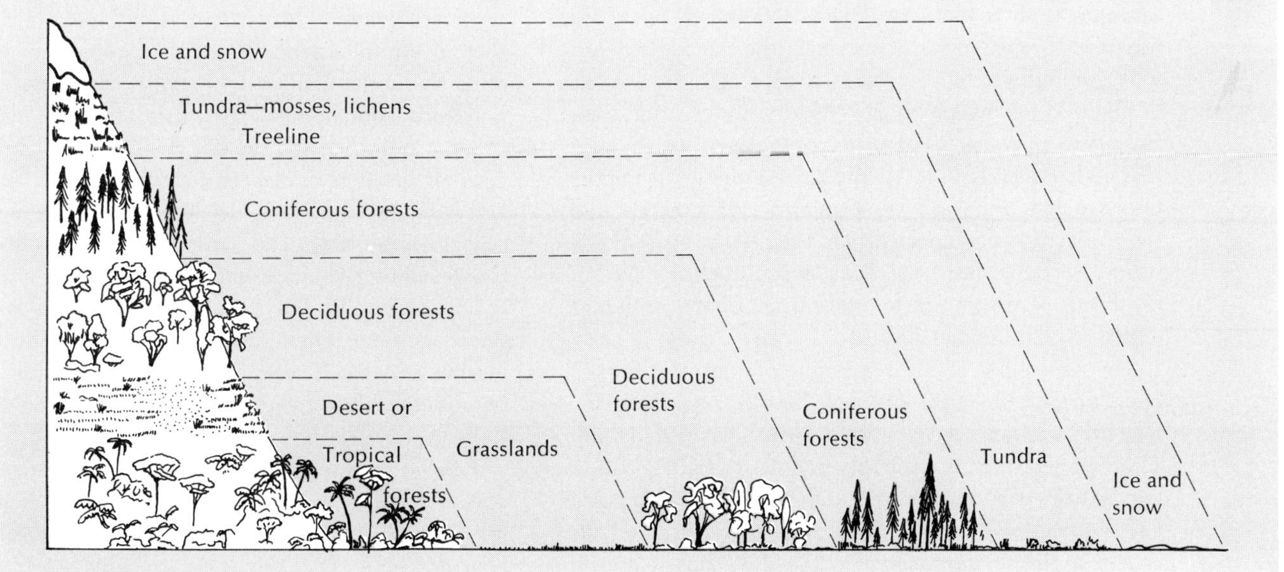

BIOMES

Biotic communities may also be aggregated into biomes, which are the largest ecologic units. In a biome the climax vegetation is of a uniform type, although many species of plants may be included. Each biome is the product of physical factors, such as the nature of the substratum, the amount of rainfall, light, temperature, etc. They are distributed over the surface of the earth as broad belts from the equator to the poles and each may or may not be continuous. Within each biome are many major communities. Biomes are not always sharply marked off from each other; there are often intermediate zones. Some six important terrestrial biomes are recognized: desert, grassland, equatorial forests, deciduous forests, coniferous forests, and tundra. This succession of biomes from the tropics to the poles may also be found in condensed form on the vertical zones of a high mountain (Fig. 41-16). The various oceans make up the so-called marine biome, a major community that may be subdivided into a number of minor communities.

Marine biome

To call the sea a single biome is perhaps too simple a description. The oceans have so many diversified physicochemical conditions that innumerable habitats are found in them.

The conditions of marine existence are many. Salt water makes up about 70% of the earth's surface. The average depth of the sea is about 10,000 feet, but there are much deeper regions; and along the shores its depth may grade down to a few feet. Its average salt content is about 3.5%, which makes its density greater than fresh water but not so great as protoplasm, for the animal body will sink in it. Its pressure in the great depths may reach a thousand atmospheres; yet animals live there and are not crushed, for their own body fluids have the same pressure. Mechanical disturbances in the forms of waves, tides, and currents have profound effects on the animal life.

The movement of the sea is one of the most important features of marine ecology. Besides tides and surface wave action, the sea is in continuous circulation. The currents are, in general, due to prevailing trade winds, caused by temperature differences between poles and equator, and due to the rotation of the earth, which can give rise to movements in the deep layers of the ocean as well as near the surface. The ice caps at the poles, particularly the South Pole, form glaciers that eventually melt in the sea and produce a cold but light current of dilute salt water that flows away toward the equator. A similar current of cooled water under the surface layer sinks and flows along the ocean floor, also toward the equator. Other currents of water flow toward the poles between the other two currents to take the place of the displaced waters. Off-shore winds push coastal waters away, and their place is taken by the upwelling of water from below. This upwelling brings to the surface water rich in phosphates and nitrates that influence the distribution of plankton.

The temperature of sea water varies with location and with the seasons. In the arctic regions it may go to below 0° C.; in the tropics the surface water may exceed 30° C. These regions may have a relatively uniform temperature the year round, but in the temperate zones there are seasonal variations in the temperature of surface waters that are more pronounced in landlocked bodies of the sea. Deep regions of the sea always contain cold water.

The penetration of light is restricted mainly to the upper 50 to 60 meters, although it can be detected at greater depths.

Oxygen varies in different parts of the sea. Where deep waters obtain their oxygen supply from cold currents from the polar regions (which can absorb more oxygen than warm water), the concentration of oxygen may be greater than at intermediate depths. Bottom drifts of such cold water may extend long distances. In deep sea water where there is no such replacement, there is a total absence of oxygen. Stagnated water with much hydrogen sulfide is found in many isolated bays and gulfs and supports few or no animals. Surface and shore waters contain a great deal of oxygen.

Plant life is restricted to certain regions. The surface layers contain plankton; sheltered regions may contain plants where they can take root; and seaweeds are found floating about in most seas.

Differences in environmental conditions have produced corresponding differences in the adaptations of marine animals. The animals that inhabit the sea may be divided into two main groups—pelagic and benthonic.

Pelagic group. The pelagic group, which lives in the open waters, includes (1) the **plankton,** small organisms (protozoans, crustaceans, mollusks, worms, etc.) that float on the surface of the water, and (2) the **nekton,**

composed of animals that swim by their own movements (fish, squids, turtles, whales, seals, birds, etc.)

Benthonic group. The benthonic group includes the bottom-dwelling forms, or those that cannot swim about continuously and need some support. This group can be subdivided according to the zones in which they are found.

1. The **littoral,** or lighted zone, is the shore region between the tidelines that is exposed alternately to air and water at each tide cycle. These forms are subjected to high oxygen content and much wave disturbance. In this region originated the ancestors of all aquatic fauna, both fresh water and salt water. It contains a very rich animal life, both in species and numbers of individuals. Some are adapted for crawling (worms, echinoderms, mollusks), some are adapted for burrowing (worms and mollusks), and some are attached, or **sessile** (crinoids, bryozoans, corals).

2. The **neritic** zone lies below the tide water on the continental shelf and has a depth of 500 to 600 feet. There is some wave action here, and the water is well oxygenated. Many forms, including fish, echinoderms, and protozoans, are found in this habitat.

3. The **bathyal** zone is a stratum of the deeper water from the neritic region down to 5,000 or more feet. It contains small crustaceans, arrowworms, medusae, and fish. Many of the animals in this region have luminescent organs, for this is a dark zone.

4. In the **abyssal** zone, or deeper parts of the oceans, the water is always cold and there is total darkness. Oxygen is scarce or absent, and only a few deep sea are found—certain specialized fish and crustaceans. Many of these are provided with light organs.

Terrestrial biomes

Tundra. The tundra is characteristic of severe, cold climates, especially that of the treeless arctic regions and high mountain tops. Plant life must adapt itself to a short growing season of about 60 days and to a soil that remains frozen for most of the year. Most tundra regions are covered with bogs, marshes, ponds, and a spongy mat of decayed vegetation, although high tundras may be covered only with lichens and grasses. Despite the thin soil and short growing season, the vegetation of dwarf woody plants, grasses, sedges, and lichens may be quite profuse. The plants of the alpine tundra of high mountains, such as the Rockies and Sierra Nevadas, may differ from the arctic tundra in some respects. Characteristic animals of the arctic tundra are the lemming, caribou, musk ox, arctic fox, arctic

hare, ptarmigan, and (during the summer) many migratory birds.

Grasslands. This biome includes prairies and open fields and has a wide distribution. It is subjected to all the variations of temperature in the temperate zones, from freezing to extremely hot temperatures. It undergoes all the vicissitudes of seasonal climatic factors of wind, rain, and snow. The animals that occupy this region vary with different localities. On the western prairies there will be jack rabbits, antelope, wolves, coyotes, skunks, gophers, prairie chickens, and insects. In the eastern parts of the country, some of these will be replaced by other forms.

Desert. Deserts are extremely arid regions where permanent or temporary flowing water is absent. The yearly amount of water is widely fluctuating, but when rain does come, it may do so with a terrific downpour. The skies are usually unclouded; the temperature becomes very hot during the day but cools off at night. There is some scattered vegetation that quickly revives after a rain. Some of the most characteristic plants are the cacti.

Desert faunas are varied and mostly active at night, so as to avoid the heat of the day. Most of them show adaptive coloration and the power of rapid locomotion. To conserve water they have physiologic devices for passing dry excretions. To the casual visitor the desert fauna may seem somewhat scanty, but actually the desert possesses representatives of many animal groups. Mammals found there include the white-tailed deer, peccary, cottontails, jack rabbit, kangaroo rat, pocket mouse, ground squirrel, badger, gray fox, skunk, etc. Birds include migrants and those that are quite typical to desert life, such as the roadrunner, cactus wren, turkey vulture, cactus woodpecker, burrowing owl, Gambel's quail, raven, hummingbird, and flicker. Reptiles are numerous, such as the horned lizard, Gila monster, race runner, collared lizard, chuckwalla, coral snake, rattlesnake, and bull snake. A few species of toads are also common. Arthropods include a great variety of scorpions, spiders, centipedes, and insects.

Coniferous forests (taiga). The coniferous forests are the evergreens—pines, firs, and spruces—found in various areas of the North American continent. They may occur in mountains or flat country. They bear leaves the year around and afford more cover than deciduous forests. They are often subject to fires that influence the animal habitats. Conditions within such forests depend on their location. On mountains and in northern regions they undergo severe winters with much snowfall; in southern regions they have milder conditions. A great deal of food—berries, nuts, and cones—is found in evergreen forests, and there is also a great variety of animal life. In the north there are martens, lynxes, foxes, moose, bears, many birds, some reptiles, amphibians, and many insects. Southern coniferous forests lack some of these forms but have more snakes, lizards, and amphibians. Many of these undergo extensive seasonal migrations.

Deciduous forests. Deciduous forests are more common east of the Mississippi river, and their distribution depends on moisture, soil, and temperature. The trees shed their leaves in the fall, leaving them bleak during the winter, especially in northern climates. There may be some low underbrush and vines. Some of these forests have scattered evergreen trees. They possess a varied animal life, including many burrowing forms. Among characteristic fauna of these forests are the deer, fox, bear, beaver, squirrel, flying squirrel, raccoon, skunk, wildcat, rattlesnake, copperhead, and various songbirds, birds of prey, and amphibians. Insects and other invertebrates are common, since decaying logs afford excellent shelters for them.

Tropical rain forests. Tropical rain forests are found in Central America. Vegetation is luxuriant and varied. The trees are mainly broad-leaved evergreens; also there are many vines. These forests have a copious rainfall and a constant high humidity. Because of their density, they have a reduced illumination. The forests are divided ecologically into a vertical series of strata, each of which is occupied by characteristic animals. These strata include the forest floor, the shrubs, small trees, lower treetops, and the upper forest canopy. The enormous amount of life found here is represented by monkeys, amphibians, insects, snails, leeches, centipedes, scorpions, termites, ants, reptiles, and birds.

FOOD CYCLE*

Animals are stores of potential energy that they transform into kinetic energy to be used in their life processes. All energy utilized by animals is derived ultimately from the sun. Plants utilize radiant energy from sunlight and the chlorophyll in their cells to produce carbohydrates from carbon dioxide and water. Plants can also form proteins and fats. Animals, with few exceptions, do not have this power and depend on the plants as sources for the basic food substances. Animals that do not live directly on plants live on animals that do; therefore, all their potential energy can be traced back to a plant origin.

In this energy cycle of transfer and transformation the laws of thermodynamics apply. When a plant transforms light into the potential energy of food by the process of photosynthesis, energy is being transformed into another form without being destroyed (first law of thermodynamics), but when this plant food is utilized or consumed by other organisms, although there is no loss in total energy, there is a decrease in amount of useful energy, for some energy is degraded or lost as heat in a dispersed form (second law of thermodynamics). Thus in every step in a food chain or pyramid there is a certain loss in useful energy. Energy is used only once by an organism or population, for it is then converted into heat and lost. On the other hand, the nonenergy materials, such as nitrogen, carbon, and water, may be used over and over again. Energy, therefore, is a one-way flow. When the sun's energy is exhausted, there will be no further photosynthesis and no more life.

All plants in their metabolism require certain elements, such as carbon, oxygen, nitrogen, hydrogen, and, to a lesser extent, potassium, magnesium, calcium, sulfur, iron, and a few others. All these are derived from the environment, where they are present in the air, soil, rock, or water. Animals require about the same elements, most of which they get from the plants. When plants and animals die and their bodies decay, or when organic substances are burned or oxidized, these elements are released and returned to the environment. Bacteria fulfill a useful role in decomposing the body wastes and the bodies of dead animals and plants. The elements that are involved in these processes, therefore, pass through cycles that involve relations to the environment, to plants, and to animals. Three or four of these important cycles will be pointed out here.

Carbon cycle (Fig. 41-17). Both animals and plants respire and give off carbon dioxide to the air. More is released in the bacterial decomposition of organic substances, such as dead plants and animals. Although the percentage of carbon dioxide in air is relatively small (0.04%) as compared with the other gases of air, this small amount is of great importance in nature's

*Refer to Chapter 2, Principle 18.

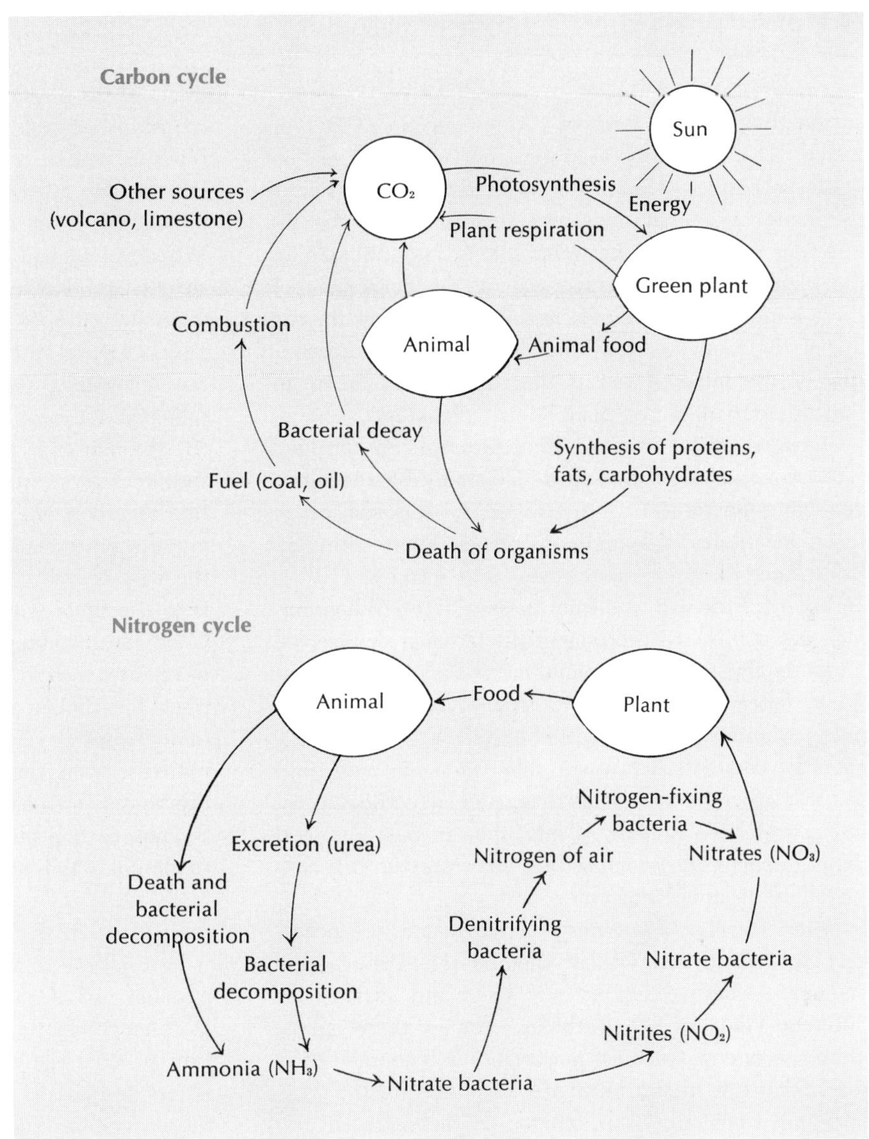

FIG. 41-17

Carbon and nitrogen cycles.

economy. Living green plants take carbon dioxide from the air or water and by **photosynthesis,** with the help of sunlight, carbohydrates are formed. This process is complicated but in a simple form may be expressed thus:

$$6H_2O + 6CO_2 \rightarrow C_6H_{12}O_6 + 6O_2$$

Carbon dioxide   Sugar   Oxygen

Carbohydrates thus formed, together with proteins and fats, compose the tissues of plants. Animals eat the plants and the carbon compounds become a part of animal tissue. Carnivorous animals get their carbon by eating herbivorous forms. In either case a certain amount of carbon dioxide is given off to the air in breathing (this also occurs in plants), and when the animal dies, a great deal of the gas is released to the air by bacterial decomposition. This cycle is called the carbon cycle. The importance of carbon in the organic world cannot be overestimated; for of all the chemical elements, it is the one that enters into the greatest number of chemical combinations.

Oxygen cycle. Animals get their oxygen from the air or from oxygen that is dissolved in water and utilize it in their oxidative reactions. They return it to their surroundings in the form of carbon dioxide (CO_2) or water (H_2O). Plants also give off some oxygen in photosynthesis, as seen in the formula on p. 843. Plants use some oxygen in their own respiration. In the interesting relationship between plants and animals in the plankton life of surface waters, the floral part of these populations gives off the oxygen necessary for the life of the faunal portion and determines the distribution of the latter. Light is the determining factor in the distribution of the plant life of plankton.

Nitrogen cycle (Fig. 41-17). Atmospheric nitrogen (78% of air) can be utilized directly only by the nitrogen-fixing bacteria that are found in the soil or in the root nodules of leguminous plants. These nitrogen-fixing bacteria combine nitrogen into nitrates (NO_3), and plants form proteins from these nitrates. When animals eat plants, the proteins of the latter are converted into animal proteins. In animal metabolism, nitrogenous waste (urea, etc.) is formed from the breakdown of proteins and is excreted. In the soil or water certain bacteria convert this waste into ammonia and into nitrites; other bacteria (nitrifying) change the nitrites into nitrates. Whenever plants and animals die and undergo bacterial decomposition, their proteins are converted into ammonium compounds.

Mineral cycle. Many inorganic substances are necessary for plant and animal metabolism. Usually the amount of these constituents is small and varies with different kinds of living things. Among these, phosphorus is one of the most important. It is found in the soil and water in the form of phosphoric oxides. It is taken up by plants, is passed on to the animals, and is eventually returned to the soil or water in the form of excreta or upon the decay of their bodies. Many think that phosphorus is the critical resource for the efficient functioning of ecosystems. The supply is very much limited and vast amounts are carried into the sea. Man has so disrupted the amount of phosphorus in his disturbance of the soil that erosion can readily carry it away. Phosphorus represents one of the most important ingredients of most fertilizers.

ECOLOGY AND CONSERVATION

Most aspects of ecologic study are related to the principles of conservation. Conservation may be defined as the most efficient and most beneficial utilization of natural resources (soil, forests, water, wildlife, minerals, etc.). This is a logical relation, for the basis of ecology is the ecosystem, or the combination of the biotic community and the physical environment. A great conservationist, Aldo Leopold, once stated that the biotic pyramid is really a symbol of land and its uses as a circuit of energy, which involves soils, plants, and animals. A study of ecology is necessary to understand these relations. Whenever a change occurs anywhere in this broad persistent circuit of energy, adjustments must be made to maintain a proper balance of nature.

Our natural resources are commonly divided into (1) the renewable, such as the biotic factors of flora and fauna and the physical factors of soil and water, and (2) the nonrenewable, such as minerals. The renewable resources form an intricate relationship and are closely tied together; one cannot be disturbed without disturbing the others. Able conservationists now believe that the wisest way to preserve renewable natural resources is to use them within the limits of continuous renewal. Good forest management, as many European countries have demonstrated, is to remove the less vigorous trees for timber and allow the others a chance for normal growth. Good game management involves regulated hunting seasons so that wildlife may stay within the bounds of food resources and optimum populations. In conservation planning it is not always the best policy to eliminate the inferior or less desirable plant or animal members of the ecosystem. Predators, for instance, have their place in the biotic pyramid.

In the final analysis, sound conservation is the best possible use of the available energy in an ecosystem. Without the biotic factors, energy from the sun is mostly lost on our planet, for sunlight energy is stored by plants and passed in food chains and food webs around the ecosystem. Soil is dependent on biotic factors that must be present or else there is the enormous problem of erosion waste.

Specifically, any adequate conservation program must include the natural resource background of soil, water, wildlife, vegetation, and natural topography. It should include the application of ecologic principles to the integration of those environmental factors. It should include methods for the most efficient use of the land for a growing population. Definite controls must be worked out to limit the wastage of land erosion, fires, flood, and water pollution. Effective controls involving both biologic and chemical methods must be employed to check insect pests, rodents, and disease-carrying animals. The program includes the dynamics of wildlife populations and the most efficient practices of hunting and fishing. Such a plan also provides recreational areas for the health and enjoyment of the people.

The ultimate success of a conservation program will depend mainly on an efficient system of education that teaches basic ecologic concepts throughout its curriculum. The development of this conservation attitude in the public will be slow and laborious. Leopold refers to this concept or attitude as a land ethic, which he regards as a product of social evolution based on intellectual and emotional processes and woven into the very pattern of the community's daily life.

Annotated references

Ecology

Ager, D. V. 1963. Principles of paleoecology. New York, McGraw-Hill Book Co. *The study of paleoecology is a very difficult subject and this work is one of the few that attempts an evaluation of investigations that have been performed in this field.*

Allee, W. C., A. E. Emerson, O. Park, T. Park, and K. P. Schmidt. 1949. Principles of animal ecology. Philadelphia, W. B. Saunders Co. *A comprehensive treatise. Nearly every aspect of the subject is covered in this masterly work.*

Boughey, A. S. 1968. Ecology of populations. New York, The Macmillan Co. *Deals with the requirements, population interactions, population evolution, food chains and community organization, and certain aspects of human ecology.*

Brower, L. P. 1969. Ecological chemistry. Sci. Amer. **220:** 22-29 (Feb.). *How insects make themselves unpalatable to bird predators.*

Buchsbaum, R., and M. Buchsbaum. 1957. Basic ecology. Pittsburgh, The Boxwood Press. *For the general student of biology, the basic concepts of ecology are presented with accuracy and clarity. Students interested in this field should read this little book before studying the more comprehensive treatises.*

Elton, C. S. 1927. Animal ecology. London, Sidgwick & Jackson, Ltd. *A concise statement of ecologic principles, well organized for ready comprehension.*

Elton, C. S. 1958. The ecology of invasions by animals and plants. New York, John Wiley & Sons, Inc. *The noted ecologist points out with graphic clearness how the invasion of fauna and flora pests (which he terms "ecological explosions") has altered the face of the earth, affected the welfare of man and beast, and posed problems for man to solve.*

Hedgpeth, J. W. (editor). 1957. Treatise on marine ecology and paleoecology. Vol. 1, Ecology; vol. 2, Paleoecology. New York, The Geological Society of America. *A pretentious treatise by many specialists on the many aspects of ecology both past and present. A work for the advanced student.*

Keith, L. B. 1963. Wildlife's ten-year cycle. Madison, University of Wisconsin Press. *An evaluation of the cyclic phenomena of wildlife populations. Although there are many variations and exceptions, the 10-year cycle is shown to be a useful description.*

Kevan, D. K. M. 1955. Soil zoology. London, Butterworth's Scientific Publications. *This is one of the few monographs that deals exclusively with the forms found in the soil. Their economic relation, ecology, methods for their control, and methods for sampling their populations are all dealt with in a thorough manner.*

Klopfer, P. H. 1962. Behavioral aspects of ecology. Englewood Cliffs, N. J., Prentice-Hall, Inc. *A study of some basic ecologic problems and their ethologic backgrounds. Animal behavior is one of the liveliest subjects in biology and many lines of investigation are being integrated to help explain it.*

Kormondy, E. J. (editor). 1965. Reading in ecology. Englewood Cliffs, N. J., Prentice-Hall, Inc. *Classic and fundamental studies of ecologic investigations.*

Ng, L. K. Y., and S. Mudd (editors). 1964. The population crisis. Bloomington, Indiana University Press. *A treatise by many authorities on the problems of population and their bearing on the food and other resources of the world.*

Odum, E. P. 1963. Ecology. New York, Holt, Rinehart & Winston, Inc. *The basic principles of ecology as they apply to man and his welfare are stressed throughout this concise ecologic treatise. An excellent background for the study of ecology.*

Reid, G. K. 1961. Ecology of inland waters and estuaries. New York, Reinhold Publishing Corp. *The estuarine environment is looming more and more in importance as an ecologic factor in the invasion and distribution of terrestrial forms; this work gives a detailed description of estuarine oceanography.*

Shelford, V. E. 1913. Animal communities in temperate America. Chicago, University of Chicago Press. *A classic work in ecologic study. Has had a profound influence on the direction of much ecologic work.*

Shelford, V. E. 1963. The ecology of North America. Urbana, University of Illinois Press. *A description and evaluation of the major biotic areas (vegetation and associated animals) of North America by the pioneer American ecologist.*

CHAPTER 42

• PROBLEMS OF MAN'S ECOSYSTEM*

Nothing in modern life is of more concern at present than is the problem of man's relation to his environment. This awareness has been slow in developing and its full impact is just now being realized. The explosive realization that we are faced with ecologic relationships that threaten to disrupt our whole cultural and social pattern has alarmed the civilized world.

The forces that have brought this state of affairs about are not new; they have been building up gradually ever since man became a dominant animal and assumed the power to create his own type of ecosystem. Civilization has been too busy with technologic advancements to stop to count the cost or to see just what was happening. The problems have accumulated in the meantime.

Primitive man was just another species that had to make adjustments to his environment as other animals had to do. He had few characteristics that were not found in other animals. His own claim to uniqueness lay in his highly specialized brain. Primitive man was a member of the biotic community and got along very well with it. He fitted into the balance of nature as he found it and he did little to change it.

But in the past few hundred years man has made enormous strides in nearly every aspect of his economic, physical, and social life. Most of his advancements in these fields were made as single objectives—that is, they promoted his welfare and he gave little attention to their impact on the overall environment. In agriculture he selected those crops he liked and did away with others. In medicine he aimed to control infectious, parasitic, and dietary diseases, mental disorders, degenerative disorders, and others. With many of these diseases he had marked success and has greatly increased the population. However, he has actually made possible an increase in genetic diseases by preserving those who will transmit bad genes. Man's most spectacular advances have been in technology, which has made more progress in the last hundred years than in all of his past existence. It has magnified his wealth and increased his living standards. This has encouraged him to think that everything about technology is an undiluted good.

However, we are now beginning to realize that all this advancement has been obtained at the cost of producing vast problems in environmental pollution, manifested in water pollution, smog pollution of the air, dwindling wild life, poisoning of the environment by pesticides, biologic hazards of radiation, unstable ecologic systems, misuse of natural resources, abnormal increase in human populations, the concentration of people in small crowded areas, a failure to comprehend the nature of the social and personal environment, and a general failure to understand the complex interactions between man and the environment in which he lives.

All these factors have made man the unwitting victim of these affronts to the environment. In his efforts to become independent of his environment, man has created a greater dependence on it. All this has called for a reassessment of how a favorable balance of nature can be regained. Our technologic skill must now be applied to ways and means of correcting what has been lost. To survive in the cultural and physical environment we have created, we must now formulate concepts and methods of providing an experimental and quantitative approach to every aspect of our environment.

Some of the major problems confronting us in the application of ecologic principles to our ecosystem are described in the following account. It will be seen that the solution to these problems will require all the skill we can muster.

PESTICIDE POLLUTION

One of the most pressing of problems with which we have to deal is the poisoning of our environment with agents used in the control of crops. One of man's

*Refer to Chapter 2, Principles 33 and 34.

greatest competitors in his environmental relations are the insects, which are highly destructive to food supplies. Control of insect pests has been used by man in some form from time immemorial, but in the past few decades new pesticides have been developed, and it was found that crop production would burgeon and acre yields could be greatly increased if pesticides were used. As new synthetic pesticides are manufactured each year the industry has steadily increased from approximately 124 million pounds of synthetic pesticides in 1947 to 637 million pounds in 1960. More than 500 different compounds are used in the 56,000 types of pesticides registered in the United States in 1965. All this is used to kill insects, weeds, and other agents inimical to man's interests without considering the contamination these same agents cause to our general environment (soil, water, food products, etc.). Such a narrow, irresponsible attitude takes no account of the subtle interrelationships and intricate webs of life that are broken up by this contamination.

Examples of pesticide pollutions have been accumulating almost daily. One of the greatest dangers of pesticides is that the poisonous chemicals are passed along food chains for long periods of time. DDT, a widely used pesticide, has appeared as residues in small animals as long as nine years after a single application of the chemical. This would indicate that cumulative residues from repeated applications would finally lead to the extinction of the animal. The same pesticide has been found in mice and voles from forests when a single pound of the pesticide was used per acre. Larger animals prey on these smaller forms and are likewise poisoned. Our large birds of prey, hawks and eagles, are at the end of food chains that are being poisoned. Already a serious decline has been noted in these birds. Of 27 carcasses of eagles tested a few years ago, 26 of them showed appreciable levels of DDT and other pesticides in their bodies.

A more striking example of pesticide poisoning is demonstrated by what is known as the "Mississippi fish kill" of 1960 to 1963 when the runoff of the highly poisonous pesticide endrin and other toxic pesticides from the northern farmlands carried the toxic substances into the Mississippi River. Several million fish, representing many species, were killed by the pesticides as revealed by chemical analysis. Another example is Clear Lake, California, where three spraying applications of DDT were used to rid the lake of gnats from 1949 to 1957. Of the 1,000 nesting pairs of grebes that formerly lived there, not a single young grebe was hatched from 1950 to 1961. Some of the grebes died from the effects of the pesticides as long as five years after the last application of the pesticide.

Experimental and testing evidence from many sources has demonstrated in convincing fashion how pesticides have produced a disruption of our wild life. But what happens to other animals may be of little concern to some persons. Man, however, is an animal and must conform to ecologic laws the same as other animals. His physiology, digestion, and cellular metabolism are quite similar to other forms. Pesticides leave residues on foods that man eats. The average American's body fat contains about 12 parts per million of DDT, according to a recent report. The poultry and meat we eat contains antibiotics and pesticides. Nitrogen compounds from fertilizers poison our food and water. Many crops, especially garden vegetables, contain high residues of nitrites that can be converted to nitrates by intestinal bacteria, especially in young children. Nitrates cause a severe form of anemia. There is also evidence that certain amino acids in the body may interact with pesticides to produce toxic substances. Milk has been condemned in many states because the pesticides used on crops were absorbed by cows and contaminated their milk. Two million gallons of milk were discarded recently in Maryland because of pesticide contamination.

The problem of pesticide contamination has not gone unchallenged by the chemical corporations who manufacture pesticides. They not only take the stand that the hazards of pesticides have been greatly exaggerated, but also that the publicity given to such hazards have produced a campaign of unjustified fear. They argue that the use of modern insecticides has been the key to increased crop yields and that any possible hazards in their use is worth the gamble because of the great returns we have received in preventing hunger which would otherwise exist.

AIR POLLUTION

The pollution of the air we breathe has become extremely acute in many urbanized regions and has aroused concern in the minds of the public and of health officials. The hazy smog that covers many of our great cities is caused by pollutants that get into the air from the exhaust of automobiles, trash burning, fuel burning, industrial plants, and other results of burning. Thermal inversion interrupts the normal cleansing of the air; a layer of warm air at high altitudes may trap a layer of cold air at the ground. Pollutants accumulate in this colder air and produce the smog so characteristic of Los Angeles and other great cities. Los Angeles has suffered more than most places because of its situation against a background of mountains, a very concentrated population, and an abnormal number of automobiles with the consequent emission of hydrocarbons. The Donova, Pennsylvania, disaster of 1948 was due to a thermal inversion; a blanket of smog hung over the locality for several days and caused the death of many people.

Automobiles give off hydrocarbons and nitrous oxides that, when exposed to the sunlight for a short time, yield ozone and other reactive compounds that become very irritating to the eyes. These substances are also conducive to bronchitis and emphysema and can eventually lead to cardiac failure; that is, an extra load is imposed on the heart because it must pump the same amount of blood through the greatly reduced air-sac lining of the lung. The rising incidence of these diseases has been very striking in smog-ridden communities.

There are also air contaminants other than those mentioned. Many natural substances, such as dust, bacteria, viruses, pollen, terpenes, and esters, are released into the air and add to its pollution. This fact, however, does not lessen the problem of air pollution in densely populated urbanized regions, which are definitely known to be caused by man himself.

The control of air contamination has made considerable headway in many places, but it is still a formidable problem. Many industries have been able to convert sulfur dioxide and other products of the flue gas into useful products and cars are now being processed that eliminate much of the exhaust fumes.

RADIATION POLLUTION

Concern about radioactive fallout and wastes has been in the forefront of potential hazards to health ever since the development of the atom bomb. Both the fallout and the wastes from nuclear reactors emit ionizing reactions, due especially to the gamma rays and subatomic particles emitted whenever radioactive substances decay. X-rays and particle accelerators as well as natural sources from the earth also produce ionizing radiation. Actually, man has been exposed to low levels of ionization since he came on the evolutionary scene. In this atomic age much more interest in the problem has arisen. At the present time it is thought that ionizing radiation has a damaging effect not only on man but also on his entire ecosystem. Forest ecosystems are known to be harmed, especially pine trees, which are very sensitive to the rays. At places where ionizing radiation has been heavy (for example, at the site of a nuclear reactor) and the vegetation has been killed over a particular area, the reproductive capacity is inhibited in surviving pines for considerable distances away from the lethal area.

But one of the major damages and hazards in the ecosystem is the fate of the unstable radioactive isotopes. After a bomb is exploded near the surface of the earth, the radioactive particles are scattered far and wide, carried around by winds, and eventually produce fallouts. Many of the radioactive particles have a half-life of many years. (A half-life is the length of time required for one-half of the element to decompose and lose its radioactivity.) The length of time for these particles to settle down to earth varies. Some of the particles have a half-life of twenty-eight years, for example, cesium 137 is about twenty-seven years. When these radioactive substances reach the earth they may enter the topsoil, vegetation, and even the bones of living animals. Cows feeding on contaminated grass pass the particles into their milk and thus contaminate man. Naturally water can be polluted, either directly or from runoffs from the soil. At the present time, the amount of such radioactive products is somewhat negligible when compared with radiation from natural and other sources. Testing has been underground in many cases and more control has been exercised.

It is still too early to evaluate precisely the overall status of the ionizing radiation hazards. In man it is known to be a powerful cause of mutations as is indicated by animal experimentation. Some geneticists think that successive exposures are cumulative as far as germ cells are concerned, and thus each exposure and the resultant damage is added on to that induced before. Others are not convinced that exposures behave this way.

INDUSTRIAL POLLUTION

Reports on our streams and rivers present a gloomy picture of their conditions. Many factors contribute to this state of affairs, but not the least of these has been the utter indifference of our extensive industrialization. The millions of tons of waste poured into our streams with little or no attempt to prevent or correct pollution have constituted such an abuse that many years will be needed before good, clean water will run in our principal streams again. Of course, industry is not wholly to blame, for pesticide runoffs, soil erosion, and ionizing radiation fallouts and waste have contributed their share to the wrongdoing. The destruction of aquatic life and damage to the seabeach at Santa Barbara along the Southern California coast in January, 1969, by petroleum oil from leakage of an offshore oil well is an example of pollution that will require years to remedy.

But water pollution is not the only source of industrial abuse. Air pollution in many regions is due mainly to the belching smoke of factories. The noxious gases, sulfur dioxide and others, have had devastating effects on our vegetation and on our respiratory systems. The smog of many industrial regions, as already mentioned, has been due to the smoke of factories. Attempts to correct these conditions, influenced by an aroused public opinion, have been successful in many places.

A recent report has been made on thermal pollution produced by factories discharging hot water waste into rivers. Along rivers where industries are concentrated, high water temperatures are transmitted for many miles along the course of a stream. Power plants that use huge quantities of natural water to cool condensers, etc. are mainly to blame. As nuclear power plants increase in number, the problem will become more acute unless other facilities are used to cool water before it is discharged into rivers. What are the general effects of thermal pollution? There is some evidence that fish may be killed directly, but there is more data that fish are driven away to find more favorable conditions. Evidence seems to indicate that new kinds of ecosystems are formed when high temperature water occurs permanently in a region of a stream. Plankton and algae may increase abnormally and oxygen may be depleted by respiration and decay. Certain plants may choke bays and places of stagnant water. Hydrogen sulfide and other noxious gases are enhanced by hot water temperatures. Most fish have optimal temperatures at which their general metabolism, feeding, growth, and reproduction function best. Young fish in particular are very sensitive to radical temperature changes. But the whole problem is one of a favorable balance in aquatic life—an aquatic ecosystem of basic plants, invertebrate life, and food chains that operate effectively for all the members within it.

POPULATION CRISIS

One of the greatest problems confronting man in his ecosystem is the rapid increase in his own numbers and the uneven distribution of his population. Some regions of this planet are literally swarming with humanity and others are practically empty. One half of the world's population is concentrated on only 5% of its land surface. The surface of our planet consists of about 72% water, and only about 25% of the land surface is suitable for human life. The greatest problem of all is to feed adequately whatever population we have, but there is a maximum intensity of production beyond which it is doubtful that science and technology can help much. Man's numbers in the final analysis will depend on the capacity of the earth to furnish the food necessary for the energy of life. If a large part of the world's population is now hungry and faced with the possibility of doubling within the next few generations, what is going to be the outcome? Granting that science and technology will make great advancements in the overall food production, there must be a breaking point before long.

A look at the population growth in the past few centuries may give some indication of the population problem. In 1650 it is estimated that the world population was about 500 million. By 1850, or in a span of two centuries, the population had reached about 1,000 million (or 1 billion). In 1930 the population had doubled to 2,000 million (or 2 billion). At the present time the world's population is estimated at over 3,000 million (or 3 billion). If the current rate of increase (50 to 60 million annually) remains unchanged, there will be another doubling about the beginning of the next century, or 6 billion.

What has caused this phenomenal rise in mankind? In the first place the birth rates and mortality rates do not balance. Medical science has made enormous gains in saving life whenever possible, but especially in the first year of life. The infant mortality rate (first year of life) in the United States for 1900 was 162 per 1,000 live births; in 1966, it was only 22. Undoubtedly, better infant and mother care accounted for much of this improvement. Tropical medicine has made immense strides in overcoming malaria, the most common worldwide disease. Since World War II, the World Health Organization has accomplished much along this line with other diseases. The amazing increase in population in Africa is due, not to an increased birthrate, but to better care of those who are born. Better standards of living have no doubt contributed to the population explosion, and of course by simple arithmetic progression the larger the population, the more infants are born.

The result of such a population explosion is going to aggravate still more the inequality of economic conditions, and famine and starvation, from which the world is not entirely free now, will operate with a vengeance. Many experts believe that man will revert in time to natural selection in the survival of his numbers, as is the case with other animals. Meanwhile, ill health results from poor food and contaminated water, and the end result is low economic status and general deterioration.

Experts on population have proposed many remedies, but none have been really put into effective use on a worldwide basis. One of the most effective would be simple and cheap contraceptives to cut down the birth rate, but many despair of persuading individuals to use them, especially the great masses of people who need such controls the most. Another suggestion is that vast regions of the tropics could be made suitable for much larger populations, if people could be persuaded to move there. Many deserts will be made suitable for living in the future, but such extra space would only postpone what must happen eventually—a stabilization of population.

OTHER PROBLEMS OF THE ECOSYSTEM

Man is responsible for many other problems in his ecosystem. Excessive soil erosion resulting from poor land use is an ever present problem. The amount of silt discharged at Boulder Dam, which has become an engineering problem within thirty years after the dam was formed, attests to the erosion effects of one river system. Domestic pollution of streams by sewage disposal is still a great problem even though there are widespread effective methods for treating sewage before it is discharged into streams.

Misuse of natural resources is a national disgrace in America. A large part of our resources that are used up are nonrenewable, such as coal, oil, gas, and minerals. The extensive amounts of these substances were perhaps responsible for the lack of conservation in preserving them. The renewable resources, such as forests, have often been destroyed with reckless abandon, resulting not only in the loss of a valuable product, but also paving the way for destructive erosion and floods. Destructive fires each year destroy thousands of acres of valuable forest land and disrupt the ecosystems of wild life. Our careless behavior often destroys the things we seek most—a productive environment.

Perhaps one of our most irresponsible acts has been the destruction of the ecosystems of other animals. Forests have been cut down, grasslands plowed up, swamps drained, and ponds and pools have been filled. Streams have been changed in their course, and microenvironments have been overturned.

Through the application of intelligent conservation methods, we must begin to ensure the preservation of major natural communities and maintain a balanced cycle of natural areas. Solving the ecologic problems of the present and future stands as a real challenge to the very finest talents in the social, scientific, and technologic fields.

Annotated references

Callison, C. H. (editor). 1957. America's natural resources. New York, The Ronald Press Co. *Each chapter in this small work has been written by a specialist and each author gives a brief summary of the main problems in his particular aspect of conservation. A good introduction to a study of this field; more comprehensive treatises can be followed up later.*

Carson, R. 1962. Silent spring. Boston, Houghton Mifflin Co. *A book that has aroused a fierce controversy over the use of pesticides.*

Clark, J. R. 1969. Thermal pollution and aquatic life. Sci. Amer. **220**:18-27 (March). *Discusses the ecologic problems of industrial discharge of heat into natural waters.*

Dasmann, R. F. 1959. Environmental conservation. New York, John Wiley & Sons, Inc. *An ecologic appraisal of conservation problems. To read this excellent book is to become a conservationist in spirit.*

Hardin, G. 1964. Population, evolution, birth control. San Francisco, W. H. Freeman & Co.

Hoover, H. 1968. The long-shadowed forest. New York, Thomas Y. Crowell Co. *A delightful account of wilderness ways and an appreciation of the ideal balance of nature.*

Huth, H. 1957. Nature and the American: three centuries of changing attitude. Berkeley, University of California Press. *Traces the development of the conservation movement. Shows how a love of natural scenery aroused an interest in the natural resources of America.*

Huxley, Sir J. (editor). 1959. The destiny of man. London, Hodder & Stoughton, Ltd.

Leopold, A. 1949. A sand county almanac. New York, Oxford University Press. *A great conservationist points out many of the problems that must be solved for any comprehensive conservation plan.*

Mountfort, G. 1958. Wild paradise. The story of the Coto Donana Expeditions. Boston, Houghton Mifflin Co. *Coto Donana is a wild, unspoiled wilderness in the southwestern part of Spain and is noted for its many varieties of wildlife.*

Panofsky, H. A. 1969. Air pollution meteorology. Amer. Sci. **57**:169-185 (Summer, 1969). *Explains the role of the atmosphere in the distribution of pollutants.*

Ritchie, J. 1920. The influence of man on animal life in Scotland. Cambridge, Cambridge University Press. *This work has had a marked influence on conservation problems the world over, for the author has traced the influences of man on the fauna of a restricted compass and has shown how this fauna has reacted to this influence. This treatise has served as a model for later similar works.*

Sears, P. B. 1935. Deserts on the march. Norman, University of Oklahoma Press. *An ecologic interpretation of the causes of the "dust bowl" regions.*

Sears, P. B. 1957. The ecology of man. Condon Lectures. Eugene, University of Oregon Press. *The eminent ecologist shows how man can apply his vast biologic knowledge to improving his ecologic relationships.*

Thomas, W. L. Jr. (editor). 1956. Man's role in changing the face of the earth. Chicago, University of Chicago Press. *This ponderous volume is the outcome of a symposium of the Wenner-Gren Foundation of Anthropological Research. More than 50 eminent authorities contributed to the work, which represents a far-flung picture of man's influence on the earth's resources and how this has affected man's cultural patterns.*

Wynne-Edwards, V. C. 1964. Population control in animals. Sci. Amer. **211**:68-74 (Aug.).

CHAPTER 43

• ANIMAL BEHAVIOR PATTERNS

SIGNIFICANCE OF BEHAVIOR*

● Every kind of organism has its characteristic pattern of response to changes in its environment. Even the simplest form has many responses often so complicated that no one has been able to puzzle out the stimulus-response processes involved. A given behavior pattern may start in response to a definite external change or stimulus, or it may originate from internal stimuli. Many animals may initiate a behavior pattern without any apparent reason at all. A response may take place immediately after an animal is disturbed, or it may be delayed for a considerable time after the stimulation. Levels of organization also complicate the problem. It is obvious that a vertebrate animal has a greater complexity of nervous and other systems involved in behavior than that of many low forms of life. Most animals also have social responses of behavior as well as individual ones. Anything that lives, moves, and has its being has some form of behavior, but the same can also be said of nonliving entities that have molecular patterns of action involving movements of atomic constituents. Larger components of the universe also show definite patterns of activity. In a mechanistic viewpoint it would be said that there is a unity of behavior plan for both living and nonliving matter, but this has not yet been demonstrated.

Some may well question the viewpoint that animal behavior is a genuine science at the present time. Science implies conceptual schemes of general principles with wide applications, and it is very doubtful that the study of behavior has progressed this far. The vigorous controversies that our leading behavior students have over even the simplest type of behavior indicate how observations and experiments must be extended before general laws and principles can be formulated. This does not in the least detract from the impressive work that has been done or is being done in the field of behavior.

Animal behavior can never become static because the animal is always in the process of adjustment to the environment, which is continually changing, often at an imperceptible rate. There are also pressures for more successful adjustment constantly confronting animals. Just as animals show morphologic evolutionary changes in time, so sequences of behavior patterns also occur. Not all aspects of behavior can be traced to a specific genetic code, but there is a certain flexibility of behavior under various circumstances. No genetic code can anticipate all adjustments that an animal must face in its life-span. The higher the animal in the levels of life, the more flexible are its adjustments; the lower the animal is, the more it is at the mercy of its environment. Evolution has tended to promote the control of their environment by animals. Animal behavior is complex because the ecologic relationships of organisms must be understood before one can appreciate how it is going to react. In addition one must also know the morphologic and physiologic equipment of the animal to appreciate its limitations and potentialities for meeting its adjustments.

HISTORIC BACKGROUND

Primitive people have not always distinguished sharply between themselves and other animals with regard to emotions, feelings, and understanding. According to the eminent American psychologist Schneirla, two views have developed regarding man's relations to the lower animals. One view emphasizes differences and ignores similarities between man and the so-called brute world; the other, which is more modern and is an outcome of evolutionary thought, analyzes in a comparative way both similarities and differences. In a strict scientific sense, Aristotle was one of the first to record descriptions of animal behavior in which he set off

*Refer to Chapter 2, Principles 24, 29, 33, and 34.

rather sharply man's reasoning powers against that of lower animals. Roman writers, such as Pliny and Plutarch, also recorded observations on the intelligence of animals. In more modern times, Erasmus Darwin, Lamarck, Herbert Spencer, Charles Darwin, and many others made important observations on animal instincts and intelligence.

Significant behavior studies were made only when animal activities were analyzed in objective terms. Anecdotal and anthropomorphic methods (for example, ascribing human attributes to other animals) were of little or no significance. Evolutionary development gave a great impetus to experimental testing and control methods of analyzing behavior. Two early investigations deserve special mention—the outstanding work of E. G. and G. W. Peckham on the instincts and habits of the solitary wasp and the work of C. O. Whitman on the behavior of pigeons. J. Loeb and C. Morgan did much to develop the study along the lines followed by present-day investigators. Morgan (1894) gave an important principle known as "Morgan's canon," which states that an animal's behavior pattern should be interpreted in terms of the simplest explanation that meets the facts involved. Loeb advanced his theory of forced movements (tropisms), or the reactions of an animal in response to a difference in stimulation on its two sides. Both these investigators tried to explain behavior, at least in part, on the basis of physicochemical principles. H. S. Jennings' theory of trial and error was in conflict with Loeb's tropism theory, and his study of the behavior of the lower organisms represents an important advance in this field. In the early part of the present century I. P. Pavlov demonstrated his famous conditioned reflexes, wherein he showed that basic physiologic functions and behavior of an animal could be modified by associated experience.

G. E. Coghill, who carefully traced throughout all stages of the developing vertebrate (salamander) embryo the emergence of correlated movements and nervous connections, laid the basis for a structural interpretation of behavior. He showed, among other things, how broad, general movements preceded the appearance of more specialized local reflexes because of the delay in the development of the nervous connections for the latter.

The marked revival of interest in animal behavior in recent years has been due mainly to the researches of two European investigators, K. Lorenz and N. Tinbergen. Their theory of instinctive and innate behavior has attracted attention everywhere because of their fresh outlook. In fact, they call their approach to behaviorism **ethology**, which is the comparative study of the physiologic basis of the organism's reaction to stimuli and its adaptations to its environment. They have tried to explain innate behavior by investigating the stimuli that control it and by studying the animal's internal conditions that are organized for particular patterns. Their studies have greatly stimulated other competent workers, such as D. S. Lehrman, T. C. Schneirla, and W. H. Thorpe, to undertake similar investigations, either in confirmation or in refutal of the theories Lorenz and Tinbergen have proposed. What these investigators did will be more apparent in the succeeding sections of this chapter.

METHODS OF STUDYING BEHAVIOR

Animal behavior is a difficult subject and its study requires techniques from many branches of science, such as neurology, genetics, physiology, ecology, embryology, and the physical sciences. It involves the activities of the whole organism with reference to the environment so that animal sociology or group relations must also be understood. Animal behavior work involves both laboratory experiments and field observations. Testing must conform to the standard scientific procedure of the control experiment in which conditions are kept as uniform as possible, except in the one environmental factor (stimulus, etc.) that is being studied. So many variable factors may enter into behavior studies, such as age, physiologic conditions, hormonal balance, insidious disturbances, individual difference of intelligence, and number of subjects studied, that one's conclusions are not valid enough for sweeping generalizations. The experimentalist must know the nature and normal responses of the animals being studied. A raccoon, for instance, is far more adept in manipulating its forelimbs than a cat, and experiments that involve the use of this limb must therefore take this into account. An animal can organize its behavior capacities only within the range of its abilities.

Since the nervous system is mainly responsible for the coordination of behavior, many investigations have been conducted to determine the neurologic basis of behavior. Several methods may be employed. Certain areas of the brain may be removed surgically or destroyed and the resulting functional deficiencies noted; electric stimulation of brain regions is effective in causing responses in muscles and other effectors; and it is possible to use the electroencephalogram (for detecting electric discharges) to find those parts of the nervous system that are functioning under a given condition. By such methods it has been possible to determine important nerve centers, such as the cocoon-spinning center (corpus pedunculatum) of caterpillars, the satiety center of mammals, motivation centers, and many others. Coghill's great work emphasizes the parallelism between the emergence of behavior patterns and the growth of nervous connections. Such a study combined both a physiologic method and a microanatomic method.

An exciting new development in understanding animals in their wild state is the method of **biotelemetry,** or radio-tracking. This technique involves the attachment of a transistorized radio transmitter to an animal and then recording the data given off by signals while the animal is undisturbed and freely functioning under its natural conditions. Many physiologic aspects can be obtained this way, such as body temperature, wing beats, and other activity states. The size of the transmitter naturally varies with the kind of animal and many technical problems are to be resolved. Radio-telemetry has been used successfully with ruffed grouse, grizzly bears, rabbits, reptiles, amphibians, etc. Factors of the animal's environment can also be studied by this method.

The greatest pitfall in all behavior studies is interpretation, for there is the tendency to attribute humanlike reasons for an animal's activities. Morgan's canon of using the simplest explanation for explaining animal activity may at times be wrong, but it has often been neglected when it could have proved useful. When another animal does something humanlike in nature, it does not mean that the animal is thinking like a man. It is reacting in accordance with its own basic behavior patterns, which in turn depend on the organization and degree of complexity of its own nervous system. A bird thinks like a bird, a dog like a dog, and an anthropomorphic interpretation in unjustified in either case. Another pitfall is the ascribing of purpose to an animal's reactions. It is true that many of its behavior patterns are adaptive, but this does not mean that animals perform these acts with an understanding of the end result or with the ability to anticipate what the end is to be. Such an interpretation would involve human reasoning.

LEVELS OF NERVOUS ORGANIZATION

The behavior patterns of an animal largely depend on its type of nervous system. Complex behavior is restricted to highly organized nervous systems and superior sensory reception. It is only when the brain has advanced to the role of an organizing center that it can truly be thought of as regulating and controlling behavior organization.

The trend of evolution in the nervous system beyond the protists is centralization. From this standpoint most animals fall into one of three major types of nervous systems—nerve net of coelenterates, nervous systems with beginnings of brains, and centralized nervous systems.

Nerve net of coelenterates. There is very little centralization in this type, for a reaction to a stimulus may spread over the entire net and cause the animal to act as a whole. This diffused type of conduction does allow some coordination, for a slight stimulus may cause only a single tentacle to react, whereas stronger ones may involve other tentacles or even the entire body.

Nervous systems with beginnings of brains. There are several kinds of this type of nervous system. Mollusks have paired masses of ganglia located in the head, foot, and viscera that are interconnected by nerves. In the cephalopods there is a definite concentration of ganglia in the head. Nematodes and nemerteans have ganglia in the head region with usually several longitudinal nerves. Planarians, with two longitudinal nerves running from paired ganglia (brain) in the head, have rather complex behavioral reactions and can be taught simple processes. The evolution of the nervous system in higher forms may be considered a modification and an elaboration of the planarian plan.

Centralized nervous systems. This type consists of a brain, or aggregation of ganglia in the head, from which runs a centralized nerve cord or cords (with ganglia) and includes the higher invertebrates (annelids and arthropods) and the vertebrates. There is a wide diversity of centralization and coordination in a range from the earthworm to mammal, but it is in such a type that we find the highest development of nervous coordination and behavior patterns.

In summary, it may be stated that the evolutionary trends that promote the capacity for organized behavior of increasing complexity are (1) the development of centralized control by means of concentrating the nerve cells (neurons) in dominant ganglia (brains) and in ganglia on or near a few nerve cords; (2) the differentiation of various kinds of neurons of more or less polarity (carrying impulses in one direction only), such as afferent, efferent, and association neurons, which are arranged to form a mechanism of coordination (reflex arc); (3) the variety and richness of nerve pathways, connections, and associations, which make an organization suitable for precision and variation of specialized behavior; and (4) the development of the sensory capacities, which depend upon many sense organs of great complexity, sensitivity, and range of response.

Students of animal behavior are often confronted with such questions as, are animals conscious of what they do? Do they have subjective awareness? Sir J. H. Huxley has recently pointed out that the major tendency in the evolution of mind is the trend toward a higher degree of awareness in animals, especially those of the dominant types. Since subjective experience is the primary reality, all deductions about what goes on in the minds of other animals, including man, can only be inferred from one's own subjective experience. One can detect experimentally the sensory limitations of others and from these draw conclusions about their restricted potentialities, but this tells little about their mind's processes. Huxley considers that self-awareness is a natural and gradual development of the potentiality that is found in the original substance of life. He considers the brain as a psychometabolic organ, similar to other physiologic metabolic systems, and whose functions have been to transform the raw materials of experience into special systems of organized awareness.

SIMPLE BEHAVIOR PATTERNS (TROPISMS AND TAXES)

The simplest form of organized behavior is one in which a specific stimulus gives rise to a specific response. This type belongs to what is called inherited behavior patterns and is best represented perhaps by the **tropisms** of plants and the **taxes** of animals. It is true that early embryos and perhaps sponges have a form of organized responses because they have poorly developed nervous systems or none at all. (Irritability, you may recall, is a property of all protoplasmic systems.) Plants illustrate this specific stimulus-response behavior, or tropism, for most of their behavior patterns are tropistic responses. A tropism, which literally means a "turning," refers to the bending movements of plants brought about by differences in the stimulation of the two sides of an organ (stem, root, etc.). Tropisms involve two aspects: a definite direction caused by a difference in stimulation intensity and a rigid hereditary pattern not subject to modification. Tropisms take their name from the stimulus involved, such as phototropism (light) and geotropism (gravity).

The term **taxis** is now employed by freely swimming organisms and is used by zoologists to describe the movements of forms, such as protozoans. Description of the various forms of taxes is given in Chapter 10, Phylum Protozoa.

In the early part of the century J. Loeb and his school tried to interpret all animal behavior, whether low or high, on the basis of tropisms (taxes). He attempted to show that the differences in stimulation intensity on the two sides of an animal toward light, current, etc., caused the animal to orient itself toward or away from the source. Specifically, he explained the orientation of multicellular animals to light as being due to differences in muscular movements brought about by a faster contraction of the less illuminated side (or eyes) so that the animal curves toward the source of light (forced movement). When the light intensity is the same on both eyes, the animal goes in a straight direction.

Loeb's theory has met with opposition from many sources. H. S. Jennings, in his now classic book *The Behavior of the Lower Organisms*, proposed a trial-and-error explanation in place of the tropistic theory. This is really a stimulus-response theory, for Jennings found that most environmental changes will produce a response. The avoiding reaction of paramecium is due not to unequal stimulation of its two sides but to a fixed orientation pattern that enables the animal to find a favorable escape channel. (See Chapter 10, Phylum Protozoa.) All organisms have the capacity for several different responses to the same external stimulus. As Jennings showed, a ciliate like *Stentor* will react in a highly variable way to a constant stimulus, such as carmine particles or ink—it will turn to one side, reverse its cilia, and finally retire into its protective tube. When *Stentor* emerges again from its tube and is subjected to the same stimuli, it contracts again into its tube immediately, as though it remembered its previous experience. Another valid objection to Loeb's theory is that the exhibition of a response pattern may be delayed until the animal has attained a certain degree of maturity. Its responses, therefore, at one stage of the life cycle may be different from that at another.

HEREDITY AND BEHAVIOR

Behavior patterns are the result of the interaction between hereditary factors and the environment. No behavior pattern is found as such in the zygote. It must develop out of certain potentialities (or genes) that physiologic influences act on and limit at each stage of development. The so-called inheritance of behavior thus falls into line with the modern concept of genetics that genes and somatic expression are not in a direct relationship. Behavior patterns involve many factors such as nervous integration, hormone balance, and muscular coordination. Many genes must therefore be responsible for even the simplest activity of an animal. It is often difficult to determine whether heredity or learning experience is more involved.

Some types of activity are rather definitely triggered. Each species of bird builds its typical nest without being taught; the parasitic cowbird raised in a warbler's nest never tries to mate with a warbler but only of its own kind; a spider weaves its web without learned modification; a stickleback fish always performs its courtship ritual the same way; etc. The influence of hereditary factors seem to be much more pronounced in lower than in higher animals. Many of the basic patterns of adaptive behavior in them do not seem to change much but are rigidly stereotyped. It must not be forgotten that the sensory, muscular, and other mechanisms that limit and define behavior can be controlled or affected by heredity. Behavior patterns can also be influenced by the kind of endocrine system an animal inherits. Certain forms of dwarfism are caused by a mutant gene that produces an underactive pituitary gland. The pituitary is known to control growth.

Some behavior traits of vertebrates segregate in accordance with mendelian heredity. In a cross between the wild gray rat and the docile white rat the progeny will be of the dominant, wild, savage type. Other cases of cross-breeding involving behavior traits show the same effect, but it is not always possible to rule out environmental effects. Much more work in this field needs to be done before definite generalizations can be made.

TAXONOMY AND BEHAVIOR

In recent years emphasis has been placed on the relationship between behavior patterns and taxonomic units at all levels. Evolutionary relationships are clearly expressed by behavior similarities and differences that are correlated with taxonomic subdivisions. It is thus possible to study species differences on the basis of behavior characteristics. H. S. Barber was able to separate many species of fireflies on the basis of differences in characteristic flashes emitted by flies of different populations. Most revealing of all was the work of B. B. Fulton on field crickets, in which he found four different populations (supposedly one species) that would not interbreed (a behavior trait) in the laboratory, thus indicating the divergence and formation of four new species. Behavior patterns of *Drosophila* have also been shown to conform to the accepted taxonomy of the various species, and in some cases taxonomic revision has been made on a behavior basis.

WHAT IS AN INSTINCT?

The concept of the term "instinct" formerly meant any form of innate behavior that arose independently of the animal's environment, that was distinct from learned behavior, and that followed an inherited pattern of definite responses. At one time there was thought to be a sharp line between instinct and learned experience, and any action of an organism was either instinctive or learned. In the evolutionary process instinct was supposed to be the primitive plan of behavior patterns; intelligence and the learning process came later. Psychologists at present believe that most behavior must be interpreted in terms of both innate traits and learning. Few behaviorists are willing to concede that a particular activity is wholly instinctive or is wholly learned.

Some behaviorists rightly argue that behavior cannot be inherited through the genes of the chromosomes but must develop under the influence of environment. Certain types of behavior, it is true, can be modified more than other types. Nest building among birds is unlearned, yet older robins build better nests than younger robins (Allee). Some birds reared away from their parents will still sing the song characteristic of their species; other kinds of birds when raised with members of another species will sing the song of that species rather than their own.

Many students who have studied the habits of web building in spiders, the nest building of solitary wasps, as well as the behavior of higher forms have found behavior very flexible and adapted to daily variations depending on the circumstances to which they were exposed. Many acts that have been considered purely instinctive have been modified under the impact of unusual circumstances, such as the repair of a disrupted nest or web, decisions involving the choice of two or more alternatives, etc. So-called instinctive behavior appears to have both fixity and plasticity (W. H. Thorpe).

Lorenz and Tinbergen, the well-known European investigators, have stressed instinctive behavior as a stereotyped action that follows a definite pattern of expression. They believe that there are at least three components involved in an instinct. First, there is an **appetitive behavior,** which may be regarded as a buildup of readiness for the instinctive act. An appetite for the act is generated in the organism so that it gets into a situation in which the instinct can be released. The animal is very restless until the instinct is released. This phase is goal directed, concerned only with the actual performance of the act. Second, an **innate releasing mechanism** is activated. This may be due to something in the environment or to an inner bodily condition. It refers to the removal of any inhibition for the performance of the instinctive behavior. Third, the **final consummatory act,** which might be considered the relief of the animal's tension by the actual discharge of the activity. This pattern of instinctive behavior might be illustrated simply by the reactions of a hungry young bird in a nest when something is waved before it. The bird is in a condition for response (appetitive); the movement of the object activates the release mechanism; and the lunge and gaping that follow is the consummatory act.

This theory has been subjected to critical analysis by able American behavior students who believe that some of its concepts are too preconceived and lack experimental verification and that it is based too much on preformed, inherited behavior.

Perhaps in our present state of knowledge the best way to regard an instinct is that it is concerned with activities that depend mainly or wholly on an animal's organic equipment in reaction with the environment, with learning playing a minor role or else being entirely absent in the process.

INSTINCTIVE BEHAVIOR PATTERNS

An instinct is usually considered to differ from a taxis or tropism in being more complicated and involving more separate phases in the performance of the act. However, the two types of behavior may overlap. Both involve reflex action, but a taxis or tropism is less flexible and is based more on a rigidly inherited plan. Another way of expressing the difference is to state that a taxis is more innate, is based more on a specific neural mechanism, and is less modifiable in its expression. In studying any instinctive behavior it is necessary to determine the stimuli that control the behavior, to appraise the internal conditions that prepare the organism for the reaction, and to seek out the neural mechanism responsible for the integration of the whole basic pattern of behavior. No instinctive action can be explained without knowing the organic circumstances under which it occurs and the role environment has played. The organic factors that may be involved in instincts are the sensory equipment, endocrine system, neuromuscular system, etc. Another important influence on instinctive behavior is maturation, or the development of behavior patterns, as correlated with the age and growth of animals. The innate behavior of young animals for a particular act may be quite different from that of an adult, as Coghill so well demonstrated. To a certain extent this can be explained by the development of new types of connection in the nervous mechanism.

Most instincts are adaptive in nature and can contribute much to the success of a group, as shown by the arthropods in which innate behavior of great variety predominates over learning. However, one cannot attribute purpose in their performance, for instincts are triggered by definite stimuli and will occur when certain stimuli act on an inherited organic equipment, producing thereby a more or less predictable outcome. In some cases the act may be far from adaptive. The life cycle of the schistosome cercariae, which produce swimmer's itch in man, is terminated by the death of the cercariae when they penetrate man's skin.

Striking examples of automatic behavior are perhaps best shown by the web spinning of spiders, the communication of honeybees, and the cocoon spinning of caterpillars. The animal involved performs its act with mechanical regularity step by step. Each stage of performance seems to serve as a stimulus for the succeeding stage. Environmental influences for a characteristic behavior to appear is demonstrated by the experiment of D. Lack on the European robin. He discovered that a male robin during its breeding season and when holding its territory will attack even a bundle of red feathers (which simulate the red breast of an actual male robin) but will do so only under the conditions mentioned. The same experiment also shows the effect of what is called **"sign stimuli,"** for Lack found that a tuft of red feathers would provoke an attack, whereas a stuffed young robin with a brown breast would not. In this case the red breast is the effective stimulus. A somewhat similar case of sign stimuli is the reaction of the herring gull chicks. These chicks beg food by pecking at the tip of the parent's beak where there is a little red spot. When this spot is painted out or painted some other color there is no releasing stimulus, and the chicks are confused.

MOTIVATION AND BEHAVIOR

Why do animals perform characteristic patterns of activity? What is the motive behind their behavior? Why do they act at all? A simple answer for many forms of activity is the stimulus-response theory that may involve some change in the environment. But not all behavior can be answered as simply as this, for some are related to internal conditions that are not easy to appraise. One of the basic principles of life is the maintenance of stable internal conditions (recall the principle of homeostasis). Hunger, for instance, is accompanied by a low blood glucose level, an imbalance of fluids, etc. Such internal changes stimulate characteristic behavior patterns. A hungry hydra will behave differently from a satiated one. It is very difficult to understand many of the complex mechanisms of internal stimulation because they vary greatly.

The basic motivating force behind most behavior is a reward or punishment factor. Animals perform acts that either give them pleasure, or else prevent pain or unpleasant conditions. They make their adjustments to these conditions perhaps wholly unconscious of the end results (this certainly would be true of the lower forms). This concept, as the student can see, is in line with the maintenance of internal stability as already described. The appetitive phase of instincts that Lorenz and Tinbergen stressed is supposed to furnish the chief source of motivation. According to their theory, animals actively seek out those stimuli that trigger their instinctive acts. Failure to find such outlets is supposed to create intense emotion in animals.

A clear understanding of these instinctive acts is furnished by the rather modern concept of **biologic drives.** A biologic drive may be defined as a motive for stabilizing the organism. Examples of such drives are hunger, which arises from the nervous impulses of an empty, contracting stomach; thirst, which may be due to sensations from a drying pharyngeal mucosa; and sex, which is caused by a release of hormones from sex glands. All of these upset internal stability, and restoration of this stability is a reward or motive. Most drives are also characterized by rhythm patterns, in which the drive fluctuates up and down in a periodic manner, such as the estrous cycle of the female mammal. Some drives are not as clear-cut, but a certain nervous pattern has to be satisfied, as, for instance, the weaving of a net by a spider.

In recent years great strides have been made in locating brain centers associated with motivation of particular kinds. W. R. Hess, a Swiss psychologist, was able to fasten fine metal electrodes into specific parts of the brain (by inserting them through the skull), and when the wound healed, the ordinary activities of an animal (rat) could be studied by giving electric shocks through these electrodes. By such means it has been possible to explore the brain and locate specific seats of emotions, such as pleasure, pain, sex, eating, and satiety. For instance, when an electrode was placed in a certain part of the hypothalamus and a rat had learned to stimulate itself by manipulating a lever (as in a Skinner box), it would press on the lever with great frequency. The conclusion was that this particular spot was a pleasure center. Other regions have been found in which stimulation is avoided by the experimental animal. Evidence from these and other experiments indicates that the hypothalamus is the chief center for many sensations and is where various drives lie. Whatever action is found here, however, is controlled and influenced by the higher centers of the cerebral cortex. The consummatory phase of an act, the way in which motivation is expressed, is controlled by the cerebral cortex.

REFLEX ACTION

A simple reflex act (reflex arc or circuit) is a ready-made behavior response in which a specialized receptor, when stimulated, transmits impulses to a specialized motor cell that arouses an effector (muscle or gland) to act. Most reflexes, at least in the higher forms, are more involved and include an association neuron, and the impulse must pass through a number of synapses. A reflex act may or may not involve a conscious sensation. Reflex acts are built into the body mechanism and control the automatic working of the internal organs. Most reflex arcs have the possibility of modification because there may be more than one channel of discharge. A complicated act may involve a chain of reflex acts.

Among lower invertebrates a reflex action has a local makeup and does not necessarily involve a more central or general control. The tube foot of a sea star, when severed from the body, will continue to react for some time, but there is central coordination of tube feet in such activities as locomotion or feeding.

Reflexes are less elaborate than instinctive actions. The latter also have a wider range of adaptability and variability. However, as Lorenz stresses, the releasing mechanism that triggers instinctive acts involves reflex action in its pattern. The idea that an instinct is a chain of reflexes is not rigidly held because of the varying intensity of instinctive behavior patterns.

Lorenz has also stressed the adaptive nature of all aspects of behavior, no matter how trivial they may seem. An animal's pattern of action, involving emotional displays of snarling, threats, courtship rituals, postures, symbolic gestures, etc., is the result of a long evolutionary integration of great effectiveness in adaptive functions. This concept is the very core of the science of ethology as propounded by Lorenz and his school.

LEARNED BEHAVIOR

Conditioned or learned behavior differs from inherited instinctive behavior in being acquired or modified from experience. Even the simplest animals are capable of learning. The distinction between unlearned and learned behavior is not easy. Behavior is never exactly predictable. The concept of learning must then have a variety of meanings. Ordinarily it refers to changes in behavior that are brought about by past experience and that involve more or less permanent modifications of the neural basis of behavior.

A particular kind of behavior cannot occur unless there is an established nerve channel for it. Learning implies multiplicity of responses so that if an organism is frustrated in one response it can try another. This requires adequate nervous interconnections and dominant nerve centers. In many invertebrates the brain is an efficient transmitter rather than an organizing center. When the principal nerve centers can override local reflex patterns, so characteristic of lower organisms, more diverse types of behavior can occur. The capacity for learning depends, then, on the anatomic and physiologic capacities possessed by each group of animals.

To what extent can learning be determined in the animal kingdom? With what accuracy can one say that this particular animal is capable or incapable of such and such a learning process? How valid are the conclusions of the almost endless experimentation that has been done on this problem? One of the greatest difficulties encountered in this field is the impossibility of supplementing objective behavior observations with subjective knowledge. The experimenter must depend on the use of stimuli and the way animals react to them for his knowledge of their behavior. By using controlled experiment, observation, physical analysis of the environment, discriminatory learning, etc., the investigator tries to ferret out just what the learning capacity is for a particular animal.

An animal's sensitivity determines how it reacts to its environment. Many animals are blind; others live below the surface of the ground in total darkness. Ants live in a world of odors, just as other animals live primarily in a world of light and shade. Honeybees are unresponsive to red colors when mixed with gray series but can be taught to distinguish most other colors of the spectrum when interspersed among shades of gray. Cats and dogs are insensitive to colors or hues. Bats emit and react to supersonic vibrations (inaudible to human ears). Male moths are attracted to female odors a mile away. Scores of other examples could be given to indicate that animals have many different sensory abilities, some greater and some less than that found in man.

Certain basic factors also influence behavior patterns. Among these factors are the animal's external environment, both past and present, its present physiologic states, its anatomy and physiology, its sensory mechanism, its level of nervous system, and its system of effectors (muscles, endocrine glands, etc.). Any investigation that has little relationship to the biology and natural history of the animal being studied will in general have little significance.

The factors that have done most in the evolution of learning ability are orientation, sensory perception, and skill in manipulation of materials.

Some of the most important varieties or types of learning are conditioned reflexes or associative learning, selective learning, insight learning, and imprinting.

Conditioned reflexes or associative learning. A conditioned reflex is substituting one stimulus for another in bringing about a type of response. It is often considered the simplest form of learning and involves a new stimulus-response connection. We owe this concept mainly to the Russian physiologist I. P. Pavlov, who noted that hungry dogs (and other animals) secrete copious amounts of saliva at the sight or odor of food. By ringing a bell (the conditioned stimulus) at the same time they saw food (unconditioned stimulus), it was possible in time for the conditioned stimulus alone to elicit the response of salivation. There was a definite limit to the number of factors to which an animal could be conditioned for a single response. Animals with higher nervous systems can handle more (and more complex) factors of conditioning, which is far more prominent among mammals and some birds. The application of the conditioned reflex concept to human behavior may explain many aspects of our reactions. No doubt many of our likes and dislikes, prejudices and interests, as well as our habits, are produced by associations of this kind.

Selective learning (trial and error). Selective learning is a higher type of learning and is rarely found below the arthropods. It has nothing to do with an unconditioned stimulus and involves rewards and punishments. With this type the animal does not learn something new but selects a random response on the basis of a reward or punishment. A dog, for instance, finds that a problem box containing food can be opened by pulling on a lever. To get to the food, the animal at first makes many random, useless movements (trial and error), but when it finally succeeds, trials later become fewer until it learns to open the box when confronted with the situation the first time. It has thus mastered a habit of appropriate response. Animals vary greatly in mastering problem boxes. Some do so with few trials; others require many.

Mazes and labyrinths are frequently used in selective learning in which a reward or punishment is involved with the right or wrong choice. The maze is often Y or T shaped. When the animal chooses the wrong passage, it confronts a blind end, which may involve punishment, or else it fails to achieve a reward, which it receives by choosing the right one. Even ants and earthworms can master this type of labyrinth after many trials, but some mammals can master the trick with very few attempts. It is a good test to determine an animal's capacity to use acquired behavior in new situations. The widely used Skinner box is based on a reward of food when the animal presses the right lever (Fig. 43-1).

Insight learning. Insight learning may be considered a modified form of trial and error. When a process is slowly learned by an animal, it is often called trial and error; when learned rapidly, it is insight, often called "abridged learning." It involves a solution to a problem after an initial survey of the elements involved, getting the idea on the first trial. The facility with which this is done often depends on previous experience with similar situations. Many cases of selective learning in which animals solve problems after a few trials may involve a test situation not entirely new to the animal and it profits from previous experience. The capacity for short-cut solutions is rare among most invertebrates

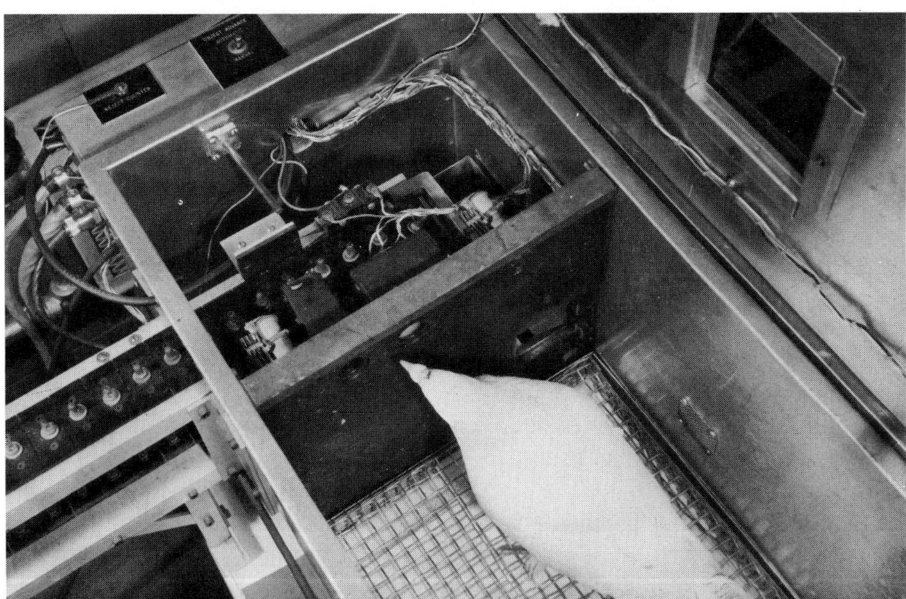

FIG. 43-1

Pigeon taught to do work of man. This bird has been taught to sort out, for drug company, inadequately coated capsules by pecking proper keys for acceptable or nonacceptable capsules as they are brought automatically into view through a tiny window. Birds are trained for this inspection by rewards of food whenever they spot defective capsule. Birds vary in length of time required for training, but most become expert inspectors in 60 to 80 hours and can easily detect minor flaws overlooked by human inspectors. Principle employed is that of Skinner method, which has been used for many species of animals. (Courtesy T. Verhave, Eli Lilly & Co., Indianapolis.)

but is common in higher mammals. A form of insight learning in birds has been illustrated in recent years in England. There, great tits have rather suddenly acquired the habit of opening milk bottles left on the doorsteps of households and feeding on the milk. The widespread nature of the practice poses the question as to how such a habit could be picked up by so many of them in a relatively short time.

The concept of latent learning overlaps that of insight learning, and some authorities do not make much distinction between the two. Latent learning refers to learning without definite motivation, such as the random exploration of the immediate surroundings by an animal without the motive of an immediate reward. Later, this learned experience can be used by the organism in its adjustments to specific needs. It is thus a form of transfer training. Birds and mammals probably best display latent learning.

Imprinting. This concept was formulated by O. Heinroth (1910) and refers to a very special type of learning in birds. In the first hours after hatching, a duck or goose is attracted to the first large object it sees and thereafter will follow that object (man, dog, or inanimate object) to the exclusion of all others; such birds show no recognition of their parents. When once accomplished, the behavior pattern is very stable and may be irreversible in some cases. Other species of birds may show imprinting. Some psychologists think the type of bird song young hatched birds acquire when exposed to members of different species may be of this nature. The process indicates how learning may be restricted to a critical period of the life cycle. According to Lorenz, when a young bird is imprinted to a member of another species, the imprinted bird will adjust its own functional cycles to that of its adopted parent. Other psychologists, however, think that imprinting is merely a strong early habit and that its socialization to another species is very restricted.

BASIS OF MEMORY AND LEARNING

The most difficult of nervous functions, especially that of the brain, are memory and learning. Little is known about these processes and how they occur. Capacities for memory and learning are associated in general with the development of large regions of the cerebral cortex. Experimentally there seems to be two processes associated with learning and memory. One of these operates within a brief time after an experience; the other is more delayed and involves an assimilation of the experience to some degree. The first process can be blocked by agents such as anesthesia, shock, and various drugs; the other is immune to such disruptions.

The activity of certain networks of synapses involved in sensory input with conscious attention may effect some long lasting effect in their functional efficiency. Memories that occur long after the original experience may be caused by the reestablishing of the original circuit of impulses. The continued passage of impulses across the synapses of a given circuit may cause a decrease in the resistance of those synapses, and thus facilitate succeeding nerve impulses that pass over that pathway. In this way a neural pathway, repeatedly used, might lead to a learning process.

In recent years, it is thought that RNA might be stimulated to code transmitter-receptor systems at certain junctions. It may be possible that specific memories are coded in the central nervous system by specific sequences of nucleotides in RNA. There is some evidence that the synthesis of RNA is increased in cells involved in conditioned responses, and some investigators have reported that they may have transferred learning by taking RNA from trained animals and having untrained ones eat it. Not enough evidence has been accumulated to confirm these results, or what is actually taking place if such stimulation of memory is possible.

The outstanding work of the neurologist W. Penfield, on the cortex of epileptic patients, gives some insight into the sites of certain types of memory; he was able to localize highly specific and detailed memories in certain areas of the temporal cortex. The study of a simple nervous system in some animal suitable for investigation, such as that of the primitive nervous system of a planarian, has not given very satisfactory results. Some positive results have been obtained on the way drugs alter RNA metabolism. Much further investigation will have to be done before the biochemical and physiologic basis of memory is clarified.

NATURE OF ADAPTATIONS*

Nearly everything about an organism is an adaptation of some kind, for adaptations may be structural, physiologic, or behavioral. Although we often are amazed at some gross spectacular adaptation of an

*Refer to Chapter 2, Principles 16 and 31.

unusual nature, the adaptive nature of bodily processes, such as the precision of chromosome behavior in mitosis, the interrelations of hormonal balance, the teamwork of enzymes in metabolic processes, the intricate pattern of nervous integration, and many others should elicit our wonder still more. The entire living system is adaptive throughout its organization. All adaptations, from simple to complex, have been due to the operation of natural selection on favorable mutations through long periods of time. By such processes, even the intricate mechanism of a sense organ such as the eye has been gradually evolved, provided each step of formation has conferred some advantage to the organism and resulted in differential reproductive success.

Adaptations may be classified in various ways. Narrow adaptations are associated with highly specialized and restricted habits, such as the tongue of an anteater. Broad adaptations are those shared with many other groups, such as hair and constant body temperature, which are found in all mammals as well as in anteaters. Evolutionary change and biologic progress have been due mainly to improvements of adaptations, as in the evolution of the nervous system throughout the animal kingdom from lower forms to man. Such improvements have led to better knowledge of the environment and to better adjusted behavior to a greater variety of ecologic niches. It is meaningless to state that an organism is well adapted or poorly adapted unless the kind of environment is specified. In general the criterion for good adaptation is the ability to perform a biologic function with the least expenditure of energy. Evolutionary progress in an organism is any change that reduced the energy requirements for meeting a specified adjustment.

Although animals have similar objectives in their living processes, they have different ways of attaining these ends. Often within the same group of animals and among closely related species there are strikingly different ways or adaptive methods for meeting the problems of life. How they meet these adaptations depends on their organization levels and the potentials they possess for evolutionary novelties. All organisms are restricted in reaching a new adaptive level by the basic patterns of their ancestors. Many of the adaptations described in this section are interesting not only because they are striking and somewhat unique in their patterns but also because many of them have been extensively studied by observational and experimental methods for the purpose of discovering their basic mechanisms.

TOOL USING AMONG ANIMALS

The ability to use tools is often considered one of the major achievements of man toward the high evolutionary rank he now holds. Tool using among animals below man is very restricted. Yerkes found that chimpanzees manipulated certain tools in a manner that indicated they had a clear perception of what the tools were for and that their use of them was not a chance trial-and-error method. Many animals rather low in the scale of evolution display amazing feats of craftsmanship, but this usually involves manipulating the materials with bodily parts, beaks, feet, and jaws. In the relatively few cases known among animals the behavior is of an instinctive pattern and no high degree of intelligence need be assigned it. Its action appears to be stereotyped, fixed, and of great antiquity.

One of the early observations of tool using by animals is recorded by the Peckhams in their famous monograph on the solitary wasps. *Ammophila,* a sphegid wasp, seizes a small pebble in her jaws and pounds down (as with a hammer) the earth with which she closes up her burrow. P. and N. Rau reported the same behavior in different species of the same group. In some cases a stone is only used occasionally; more commonly they use only their head and jaws to tramp down the sand.

A widely publicized case of tool using among birds is one of Darwin's finches of the Galápagos Islands. Among these finches, which so well illustrate adaptive radiation, one has the habits of a woodpecker in probing into crevices of bark and trees. To overcome the handicap of a short beak the bird holds a stick or thorn in its beak to pry out its prey. The bower bird of Australia paints the walls of its bower with charcoal and saliva that is applied with a crude brush of fibers. This habit is only one aspect of the elaborate courtship ritual of these unusual birds.

A fascinating account of unique tool using has been found in Malay, where a certain red ant (*Oecophylla*) builds its home in leaves. Although the larva of this ant does not weave a cocoon, it does produce silk, an advantage the adults use when they weave leaves together in building or repairing their homes. Some of the workers hold the edges of the leaves together whereas others hold the larvae in their jaws and pass them back and forth like shuttles from one edge to another, thus closing the gap with a sheet of silk that is secreted by the larvae during the sewing process. A very recent example of tool using was discovered in the Egyptian vulture (*Neophron percnopterus*). This raven-sized bird breaks open ostrich eggs, which are too big to be seized by its beak, by casting stones at the eggs. Many stones may be thrown before a vulture attains the desired effect.

COMMUNICATION AMONG ANIMALS

The idea of communication as applied to animals is not the same as language that involves the symbolic use of certain activities for influencing other members of the group. Every social group of animals has some way for maintaining contact between its members. Communication is simply the influencing of one individual by the behavior of another. This may take the form of bodily contacts (rubbing antennae in bees), scents from glands (mammals at mating season), voice effects (warning cries of birds and mammals), and hosts of others. In some cases, among the higher nonhuman mammals, distinctions between communication and language cannot be rigidly drawn. Yerkes observed in his chimpanzees many sounds and signs that seem to be understood by other members in specific or symbolic ways. Many animal behaviorists believe that animals have meaningful systems of communication that are not understood by man at all. However, it has been impossible to teach any nonhuman animal a true symbolic language with meaningful association. The reproduction of words and phrases by parrots and mynas has no significant meaning to the birds themselves. A simple form of symbolism of definite meaning is shown whenever a dog assumes a threatening attitude by baring its fangs or raising the hair on its back.

Communication in birds has been extensively studied, and revealing data have been discovered. Bird sounds of a particular species often show a great deal of differentiation. Many of these are thought to be meaningful calls of distress, hunger, warning, etc. W. H. Thorpe, the English investigator, thinks that the sound of birds is to arouse emotional states of warning and courtship and to convey precise information. It is now known since Howard's work that the bird song is actually a warning cry to others of territorial rights. Thorpe has shown that the common English chaffinch has two kinds of warning notes under different circumstances. When mobbing a predator bird, chaffinches utter sharp, low-pitched sounds ("chinks") that advertise the presence of a predator. Against a predator on the wing, they utter a high-pitched, thin note ("seeet") that is difficult to locate so that the hawk or owl has no positional clues of the small birds hiding in the foliage. It is thought that the varied songs of birds are an integration of both innate and learned song patterns and that they sing both for communication and for pleasure.

Bird reactions to calls of various kinds are partly learned and partly inborn. When American crows have been exposed only to the signals of their own group, they will not react to the alarm and assembly calls of French crows; when they have mingled with other groups of their own or different species, they learn to respond to the signals of the other groups, as though they had learned the meaning of crow calls regardless of species or group differences.

It has been known from the experience of underwater-sound men during World War II that fish and other marine forms make a variety of noises within the sea. Much investigation has been conducted to determine the nature of these sounds in supposedly silent animals. Fish and many other marine forms have no vocal organs but manage to produce a great variety of noises in diverse ways. The chief noisemakers are the toadfish, squirrelfish, sea robin, and triggerfish. Many of them use their air bladders to produce sounds. The toadfish and sea robin cause vibrations in their air bladders by muscle contraction; the triggerfish uses its pectoral fins for beating on a membrane of the air bladder near the body surface; and some, like the squirrelfish, grind together teeth in the back of their mouths and this sound is amplified by the air bladder. Their noises have been recorded on tape for study. Investigators think some of the sounds are made for communication. It is known that fish give different sounds under different physiologic states. During spawning, their sounds are different from those made at other times.

HOW HONEYBEES COMMUNICATE LOCATION OF FOOD

It has long been suspected that the sensory mechanisms of insects are extremely baffling in comparison with man's sensory equipment. Among the most interesting of these complicated behavior patterns is the power many insects have of finding their directions and of communicating such to others. It seems as if they had a kind of language for conveying information to each other.

One of the most striking behavior patterns is the ability of honeybees to inform others about the location of a source of food. The experiments conducted in recent years by Professor Karl von Frisch have given some clues to this interesting problem. By using glass observation hives and marked bees, he was able to observe with considerable accuracy just what occurs when bees report back to the hive the presence of a source of honey. Whenever a foraging bee finds a source of honey, she returns to the hive and performs a peculiar dancing movement that conveys to others in the hive in what direction and how far they must go to find the nectar. The pattern of this dance depends on how far the food is from the hive. If the food is more than 100 meters away, she performs a characteristic waggle dance (Fig. 43-2). This dance is roughly in the pattern of a figure eight that she makes against the vertical side of the comb. In the performance of this act she waggles her abdomen from side to side in a characteristic manner. She repeats this dance over and over, the number of dances decreasing per unit of time the farther away the source is. The direction of the food source is also indicated by the direction of the waggle dance in relation to the position of the sun. When the waggle dance is upward on the comb, the source of food is toward the sun. A waggle run downward on the comb indicates that the food is opposite to the position of the sun. If the food source is at an angle to the sun, the direction of the waggle dance is at a corresponding angle. During a dance other bees keep in contact with the scout bee with their antennae, and each performance results in several bees taking off in search of the food. When they return with the food, they also perform the dance if there is still food there. When the source of food is less than 100 meters from the hive, the pattern of dance is less complex. In this case the scout bee simply turns around in a circle first to the right and then to the left, a performance she repeats several times (Fig. 43-3). She is able in this way to convey to the other bees the information to seek around the hive food of the same odor she bears. One other interesting phenomenon is the ability of bees to determine the direction of the sun when only a small area of the sky is visible. They seem to be able to do this by the pattern of polarization in the light from that part of the sky that is still visible. When the waggle dance is performed on a horizontal

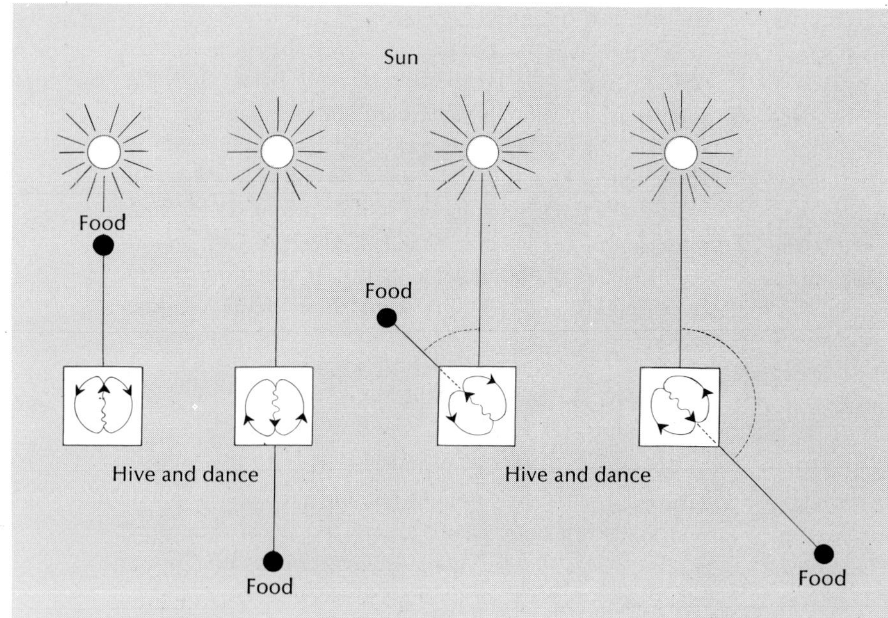

FIG. 43-2

Waggling dance of honeybee to indicate direction of food sources far from hive. Four possible directions of food from hive and direction of appropriate dance in each case are given. Dance is usually conducted on vertical side of hive.

FIG. 43-3

Round dance of honeybee. Whenever food supply is within 100 yards or so of hive, scout bee circles first one way and then the other to convey information of food source.

surface outside the hive, the bee goes through the dance in the actual direction of the food and not in relation to the sun.

In addition to the dance movements, it is now known that scout bees produce a sound during the straight run of the dance. This sound seems to be produced by wing vibration and is picked up by other bees through sense organs on their legs and antennae. The message conveyed by variations in the sound may give information about the nature of the food source. The "language of the bees" is still a fruitful subject for investigation.

BIOLOGIC CLOCKS*

Nearly all aspects of the behavior and physiology of organisms are rhythmic in nature; that is, there are cycles of recurring activities that make up the major part of their existence. Organisms and their body organs do not function at the same rate throughout the day, but they display rhythms of varied events that occur at similar intervals and in definite order. Thus there are periods when the organism is dormant or sleeping, alternating with periods of wakefulness. There are daily rhythms of high and lower temperatures, reproductive cycles, cyclic variations in color, and seasonal rhythms for different activities. Some animals are more active at night (nocturnal), others in daylight (diurnal), and still others in dim light (crepuscular). Some marine animals feed in the littoral zone at high tides, and others only feed at low tides. Some marine organisms spawn with reference to specific moon phases.

*Refer to Chapter 2, Principle 16.

The human female has a menstrual cycle every lunar month. In plants, there are flowering periods and seed-bearing periods. Basal metabolic rhythms occur in both plants and animals. These are only a few of the examples that could be cited. Because many rhythms are on a daily or 24-hour periodic basis, they are often called **circadian rhythms** (L. *circum,* about, + *diem,* day).

These circadian rhythms of animals and plants are based on the rhythmic changes of the physical environment to which living entities are constantly exposed. It is logical that organisms must have their activities geared to the rhythmic cycles of the physical world to exist. The external physical environment of organisms displays such patterns as the solar day of 24 hours, the lunar day of 24 hours and 50 minutes, the annual changes of light and temperature, the cycle of the tides in the oceans, the revolving of the earth about the sun, the cycles of weather, and even the patterns of atomic and molecular structure of matter. Nature can be stable only when there are such periodic patterns of changes. In all animals studied, endogenous rhythms of metabolic fluctuations corresponding to the geophysical frequencies are present. Many such rhythmic patterns of organisms are so firmly entrenched that they are not easily altered by prolonged exposure to external agencies, such as temperature differences and drugs, that are known to influence the ordinary metabolic chemical reactions of the body. In general these rhythmic patterns do not follow the common physiologic mechanisms known to be basic to the living process, but they represent an exceptional physiologic phenomenon.

Because many circadian rhythms, by which organisms adapt themselves to repetitive changes in the environment, have so many characteristics of timing mechanisms, many investigators in this field have for some time believed that organisms have the power to measure periods of time with great exactness by means of internal clocks. In other words, living forms possess an independent complex of rhythms that occur at select times of the day and are adapted to the complex of changes in the external physical environment. This system of biologic clocks can have new forms of behavior impressed upon it, and thereafter it keeps repeating this pattern until a new pattern replaces the old.

Although the concept of biologic clocks as now recognized is relatively new, it has long been known that plants and animals have been responsive to varying diurnal cycles and regulate their behavior accordingly. What is more striking is that many organisms that have rhythms coordinated with environmental changes will also have these same rhythms independent of the stimuli from the physical environment. For instance, plants kept in constant darkness will show the same periodic leaf movements as when they are exposed to the daily light-dark alternation. Plants that tend to droop their leaves by night and raise them by day will also do the same when the external conditions are constant. Fiddler crabs have darkened skin during daylight and lighter ones at night, but when placed in constant darkness for long periods of time, they will undergo the same cycle of color changes as if they were in a natural day-night environment. However, biologic clocks can be reset in various ways so that their cycles are quite different from the normal ones. For instance, placing the crabs (with normal cycles) on ice for six hours will set back the phases of their cycle the same length of time so that they now darken and blanch six hours earlier. The amazing fish called the grunion on the California coast will swarm ashore at spring tide (the highest tide produced by the conjunction of the sun and moon) and lay their eggs and sperm in pits dug in wet sand just beyond reach of the tide. Here, the young develop and enter the sea at the next monthly spring tide, timing their departure with great nicety (when the spring tides occur in April and June). Tidal and lunar rhythms are very common phenomena among marine animals.

Another interesting aspect of biologic clocks is the ability of some animals to find compass directions with the aid of the sun and to retain the same compass direction by making allowance for the changing position of the sun during the day. This behavior has been observed in bees, birds, arthropods, etc. Such animals are able to change their angle to the sun correctly at any time of the day and find their way to a desired position. (See discussion of bird migration, p. 867.)

Biologic clocks serve organisms in many useful ways. They enable plants and animals to adapt to the best advantage their own rhythms to the rhythms of the physical environment. In this way their activities can occur at the time of day when their physiologic adjustments are best served. Biologic clocks pose many problems to the many able investigators in this field. Where are these clocks located within the organisms? Are they localized in a particular tissue (for example, nervous system), or do they involve the total organization of the animal? Their level of organization is known to be as low as the cell because they have been found in protistan organisms. Evidence indicates that they are endogenous and innate. However, an alternative theory argues that, despite all precautions to exclude organisms from environmental forces, they do continuously receive information about the geophysical cycles from their external environment and to which they regulate their activities. Another problem is what is the mechanism whereby light-dark cycles (photoperiodism) entrain or mediate circadian rhythms within organisms? These and many other problems are far from being resolved.

MIGRATION

Birds. The term "migration," as used with reference to birds, signifies the regular seasonal shift birds make from one region to another. It does not mean the occupation of a new territory by birds so that they extend their ranges, although this may sometimes occur. For instance, there is the well-authenticated example of the mass migration of the crossbills from northern Europe into Ireland in the latter part of the nineteenth century, as a result of which many of them became permanent residents of Ireland.

Homing is the ability of an animal to return to a familiar region when the animal has been removed to some other region. Homing may depend to some extent on topographic memory of landmarks, which could explain certain forms of migration. However, it could not explain the ability of some young birds to migrate without their parents to wholly unknown places.

Most bird migrations are **latitudinal,** that is, the birds move into the northern zones during the summer and return south for the winter. In the southern hemisphere, where the seasons are reversed, there is a similar but more restricted migration of certain forms. Some birds are permanent residents the year round; others shift from regions far in the northern hemisphere to those deep in the southern hemisphere. Some birds in mountainous regions undergo a regular **altitudinal** or vertical migration from the lower to higher levels in the summer and the reverse for the winter. Some birds move only short distances in the winter from their regular homes, often into the deep woods, and are back early in the spring. Food and climatic conditions are also known to cause sporadic and irregular migrations of birds, such as the appearance of the snowy owl, an arctic form, in regions south of the Canadian border.

What are the advantages of migration? No doubt, one of the principal advantages is that the bird can live in a favorable climate all the time. This not only ensures it an adequate supply of food but also provides the optimum conditions for the rearing of its young. Waterfowl can avoid frozen waters by retiring to the south. The shortened hours of daylight in northern climates would also restrict the ability of birds to get enough food. The factors of low temperatures and severe winter conditions are probably minor ones, for most birds are able to withstand such, if they have sufficient food. However, many birds leave their breeding grounds while food supplies are still abundant.

Migration has become so firmly established in the behavior of birds that it has long since become a hereditary instinct. One theory tries to account for the movement by assuming that birds spread over the northern hemisphere when the latter was warm and food conditions were favorable all through the year. When the glacial era came and forced the birds to go south for survival, they came back in the spring when the ice age receded, only to be forced south again in winter because of the sharp establishment of the winter and summer seasons. This led in time to the firm establishment of the habit. Another theory centers around the view that the ancestral home of birds was in the tropics and some went north to avoid congestion and competition during the breeding season. After raising their young, they then returned.

Much geologic and paleontologic evidence in recent years has been advanced to support a modified view of A. L. Wegener's theory of continental drift (1912), which showed how large lateral displacements of the earth's crust could force the continents to be driven apart to positions where they are today. This theory presupposes two original land masses, a northern one (Laurasia) and a southern one (Gondwanaland). These two great land masses were at times in contact, and birds that had their original home on Gondwanaland drifted into Laurasia for better conditions to rear their young and to avoid overcrowding, returning to Gondwanaland at other times. As these two great land masses drifted apart and broke up into continents as we now know them, this habit of going from one land mass to the other persisted. This theory of migration is supposed to account for some of the strange, circuitous routes of certain migratory birds such as the turnstone, Arctic tern, and golden plover.

The annual stimulus for bird migration has been analyzed experimentally. Professor Rowan in Alberta, Canada, performed pioneer investigations on this problem as early as 1925. He kept juncos and crows in outdoor aviaries during the fall and winter at cold temperatures but exposed them to artificial lighting, thus simulating spring conditions. He concluded that this increased the exercise or wakefulness of the bird so that gonads were stimulated to enlarge and undergo reproductive activity. When released, some of the birds tended to migrate northward in winter. Some bird species, however, will not react this way to light. It has been proposed in recent years that the migratory urge may be due to a favorable energy balance and improvement in metabolism because the increased photoperiod makes fewer demands on temperature regulation, thus releasing more energy for gonad activity.

The direction-finding or orientation of birds has been much investigated in the past decade, for a solution of this problem would get at the very heart of homing and migration. Griffin, who released gannets many miles from their nesting sites and followed their wanderings in an airplane, concluded that the birds wandered aimlessly or in circles at first until they picked up visual clues; then they headed straight for home. Such an explanation could hardly apply to a shearwater that was released in America after being removed from its home in Wales and was back home a few days later. In recent years Kramer has shown that starlings and pigeons can orient themselves by the sun's position. In specially covered cages provided with six windows, these birds were trained to find food in a definite compass direction at a certain time of day. When tested at another time of day when the sun's position had changed, they compensated for the sun's motion and immediately went to the right window by keeping track of the time of day. Although this interesting experiment does not explain nocturnal migration (very common among birds), some theories have been proposed to account for direction finding at night, Sauer, a German investigator, has recently advanced evidence that birds (warblers) could orient themselves in a particular geographic position in a planetarium when the stars coincide with the night sky in Germany. By changing the synthetic constellations about, the birds were able, with their amazing time sense, to take that direction which would enable them to reach the point normally taken when they start their migration. These experiments involving the apparent effect of visible celestial bodies on migration may explain the ability of shearwaters to return thousands of miles directly to their home. Birds may also orient themselves to the magnetic fields.

Many species of migratory birds have well-established routes that they follow on schedule. Some use different routes in the fall and spring. Some of them complete their migratory routes in a very short time; this appears to be the case with certain aquatic species. Many, however, make the trip in a leisurely manner, often stopping here and there to feed. Some of the warblers are known to take 50 to 60 days to migrate from their winter quarters in Central America to their summer ones in Canada. Not all members of a species perform their migrations at the same time; there is a great deal of straggling so that some members do not reach the summer breeding grounds until after others are well along with their nesting. Many of the smaller species migrate at night and feed by day; others migrate chiefly in the daytime; and many swimming and wading birds, either by day or night. The height at which they fly varies greatly. Some apparently keep fairly close to the earth, and others are known to fly as high as 4,000 to 5,000 feet. Many birds are known to follow landmarks, such as rivers and coastlines; but others do not hesitate to fly directly over large bodies of water in their routes. The routes of any two species rarely coincide, for there is almost infinite variety in the routes covered. Some birds have very wide migration lanes, and others, such as certain sandpipers, are restricted to very narrow ones, keeping well to the coastlines because of their food requirements. Since birds have a tendency to follow the major topographic features of the earth's surface, many of their routes are in a north-and-south direction; but there are many exceptions to this rule. Some species, including the scarlet tanager, have a wide breeding ground in the United States, but as they migrate in the fall, their migratory lines tend to converge toward their winter quarters in Central America.

Some species are known for their long-distance migrations. The arctic tern (Fig. 43-4), for example,

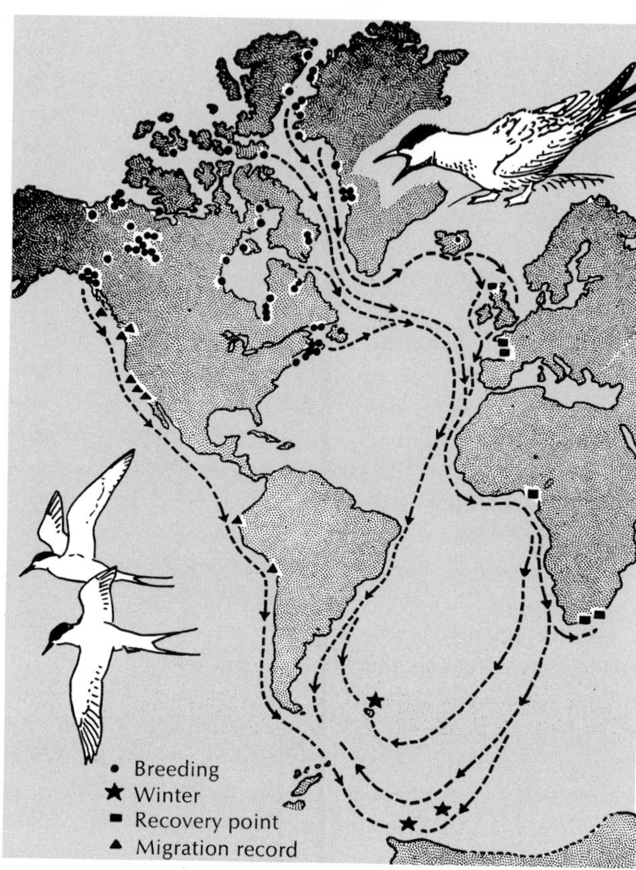

FIG. 43-4

Map showing migration of arctic tern. Enormous route covered by this bird in one year is probably 25,000 miles. (From drawing by R. W. Hines, U. S. Fish and Wildlife Service.)

breeds north of the Arctic Circle and in winter is found in the antarctic regions, 11,000 miles away. This species is also known to take a circuitous route in migrations from North America, passing over to the coastlines of Europe and Africa and thence to their winter quarters. Other birds that breed in Alaska follow a more direct line down the Pacific coast of North and South America.

Some birds with restricted food habits are still very much of a mystery as far as their migration is concerned. Some hummingbirds in tropical America are known to feed solely on one flower that is in bloom only for a month during the year; it is not known where they spend the rest of the year.

How precise are the arrivals of birds at their northern homes in the spring? This time of arrival varies greatly among different species. Some of their arrivals can only be predicted within a wide range. Other birds, such as the purple martins and catbirds, return to a certain locality on almost the same day of the month each season. Records of catbirds kept in a certain eastern state reveal that the birds arrived in the particular locality about the middle of April and did not vary more than a day in a period of 5 years. Many observations also revealed that the same individual bird returns not only to the same locality but also to the same territory that it occupied in previous seasons.

Eels. For centuries naturalists had been puzzled about the breeding and development of the common eel. It was known that the adults spent most of their life in freshwater streams in both North America and Europe, but where they spawned or where they underwent their development was not known until the patient work of Dr. Johannes Schmidt brought to light most of the facts in the case.

There are two common species of eels: the European form (*Anguilla vulgaris*) has a backbone of 114 vertebrae; the American species (*Anguilla rostrata*) has only 107 vertebrae in its backbone. (The number may vary slightly in each species.) The spawning grounds of both species are in the sea northeast of Puerto Rico, although in general the breeding grounds of the two species do not overlap. The eggs hatch into pelagic larval forms less than ¼ inch long and are called **leptocephalia.** The adults die immediately after spawning. A year later, the American species, now about 3 inches long, reach the American coasts, where the females distribute themselves through the freshwater streams and rivers; the males usually remain behind in the brackish waters near the coast. It takes from eight to fifteen years for them to grow to maturity. Eventually each female goes down the stream to the sea and joins a male; they go together to their breeding grounds. At this time they have changed their yellow color for a silver one, and their digestive system is undergoing degeneration. Their rate of travel through the sea is only about ½ mile an hour. It has been estimated that it takes them about 1 to 2 months to reach the place of spawning, although no adult eels have ever been taken in the open ocean. The European species has a much greater distance to travel, and its larval forms take three years to reach the European coast, where the females also ascend the rivers and streams and the males remain behind near the coast. Eventually they, too, return across the Atlantic to the spawning grounds, although they are about 6 months on the voyage.

A recent theory suggests that both American and European eels belong to the same species and that the adult European forms all die before reaching the spawning grounds. All eggs are laid by American eels, but when hatched the larvae in the northern part of the spawning grounds will be carried by currents to Europe; those in the southern part will be carried toward the American coast. The larger number of vertebrae in the European eel could be explained on the basis of Jordan's law, which states that fish in colder waters have more vertebrae than those in warmer temperatures.

The larvae, or elvers, are flat, ribbonlike, and transparent, but by the time they ascend the freshwater streams they have assumed the cylindric shape of the adults. At maturity the females are about 3 feet long; the males about 1½ feet. In their spawning grounds of the Sargasso Sea, the adults descend to depths of a thousand feet below the surface to spawn. Among the interesting and mysterious aspects of this strange migratory phenomenon is how the tiny elver without its parents is able to find its way across the sea, and why the elvers of the two species that are hatched in practically the same region do not mix to some extent. Yet each apparently reaches its respective home in America or Europe. Two other species of eels, *Anguilla japonica* and *Anguilla dieffenbachi,* are found in Japan and Australia, respectively.

Salmon. The salmon lives far out at sea and returns to the headwaters of streams to spawn. Both the Atlantic (one species) and Pacific (five species) forms have this practice, but there are some differences between the two. After spending three to four years at their feeding grounds at sea, the salmon return and ascend the freshwater streams (Fig. 43-5), both sexes making the journey together. After spawning, the Pacific species die, but some of the Atlantic species survive, go out to sea again, and are able to spawn a second or third time. From the time they return to fresh water until they spawn, the salmon lives on its reserve food, which it has accumulated in its body in the form of fat. After hatching in the shallow gravel pits, the larval fish live for some time in the streams before going out to sea. Some species stay only a few weeks, but others may remain for months. Hoar found that young salmon could not return to the sea until their salt-secreting cells had developed. Extensive studies by Hoar, Huntsman, and others seem to indicate

FIG. 43-5

Salmon jumping falls. (Courtesy G. B. Kelez, U. S. Fish and Wildlife Service.)

that migratory behavior in both adults and juveniles is not due to any special hormone regulation other than that which influences their general metabolism. Changes in their bodily states and behavior may cause them to be exposed to different environmental conditions to which they react in specific ways, such as traveling up freshwater streams by adults or downstream by juveniles. In the ocean they grow much faster because of abundant food there.

All sorts of theories have been proposed to account for the marvelous way in which salmon are able to return to the very place where they hatched. Some authorities think the fish have an extremely sensitive chemical sense that enables them to perform this feat. Another theory links the accelerated metabolism at spawning time with the need for more oxygen, which increases in amount the farther one ascends the headwaters of a stream. Still another idea stresses the importance of a carbon dioxide gradient in the water as being the determining factor. The research of Hasler and Larson favors very strongly the theory that the sense of smell is the determining factor in precision of homing, for different streams have different odors.

• • •

Besides the fish already mentioned, others are known to make extensive journeys from one locality to another. Although some of these movements are sporadic, definite seasonal migrations occur among the tunny (*Thunnus*) in the Mediterranean Sea, the mackerel (*Scomber*) on the coasts of the North Atlantic, the herring (*Clupea*) in the colder parts of the Atlantic, etc.

One of the shark group, the spiny dogfish (*Squalus acanthias*), makes a round-trip migration of 2,500 miles each year along the Atlantic coast. This shark spends the winter in the Carolina-Virginia coastal waters and the summer in northern coastal regions as far as Labrador (W. N. Hess). Fertilization appears to occur in their southern localities (where the pups are also born) and their internal embryonic development, or period of gestation, is unusually long (22 months). In their northern migration the larger and stronger females arrive ahead of the males. Other fish, however, may establish restricted territories and home ranges, where they will return when displaced and for which they will fight to keep possession (S. D. Gerking).

Butterflies. A number of the larger and stronger winged insects apparently are able to make long flights, such as the monarch butterfly (*Danaüs plexippus*) of North America. In early autumn immense swarms of these butterflies gather in the northern part of the United States and eastern Canada and make southward flights that may take them 2,000 miles or more to warmer regions, around the Gulf of Mexico and South America. Some of them are known to leave the mainland and journey as far as the Hawaiian Islands. Many observers have seen swarms of these butterflies far at sea. The northward flight in the spring is not so well known but appears to take place. The actual flight of these forms is not as directional as that of birds; they are carried more by wind currents; this may account for their sporadic appearance in places in which they ordinarily do not resort. Recent work (Tilden and Duncan) seems to indicate that most of the adult monarchs that drift southward in the fall have developed during the preceding summer. Those that go northward in the spring reproduce on milkweeds along the way and give rise to the fall migrants.

LIGHT PRODUCTION

The production of light by living organisms (bioluminescence) is widespread, but usually only scattered representatives are found within a particular phylum. There are more examples among the coelenterates than are found in any other phylum. Altogether, light production has been found in more than 300 genera. The forms that do possess it are largely marine or terrestrial, for no luminous freshwater forms have yet been discovered, except an aquatic glowworm. It may be for sex signalling, for kin recognition, for frightening enemies, for allurement, or for a lamp to guide the animal's movement. It is also possible that it has no significance for the organism, especially in those forms whose light is produced by symbiotic bacteria.

For light production, animals may be divided into two groups—those that produce their own light (self-luminous) and those whose light is produced by symbiotic bacteria. The self-luminous forms will emit light only when they are stimulated. This accounts for the luminescence of the sea at night when a boat is passing by. Many of the self-luminous organisms have rather complicated organs for the production of light. These light organs usually consist of a group of photogenic cells for producing the light, a transparent lenslike structure for directing the light, a layer of cells behind the photogenic tissue for reflecting the light, and surrounding most of the organ, a pigmented layer of cells for shielding the animal's own tissues from the possibly injurious effects of its own light. The luminescence of this type of luminous animal is due to the interaction of two substances—**luciferin** (Fig. 43-6), which is oxidized in the presence of an enzyme, **luciferase.** Oxygen is therefore necessary for light production also. It is now known that there are several different kinds of luciferins in different organisms, and some luciferins have been obtained in pure form. In the firefly the mechanism of light production also involves ATP and magnesium. The stimulation for light production may be merely mechanical, or nervous, as it appears to be in higher organisms. In those whose light is produced by symbiotic bacteria, light is given off continuously, although some of the forms have devices for concealing and showing the light intermittently. The light transmitted may differ with different animals depending on the difference of the wavelength in the visible spectrum and on the chemical makeup of luciferin.

Four or five classic examples of luminescence will give the student some idea of this interesting adaptation.

Among the protozoans, *Noctiluca* is the most striking example of bioluminescence. This flagellate is sphere shaped and about 1 mm. in diameter. It will give off light only when stimulated. Its luminescence originates from small granules scattered over the periphery and other parts of the cell. These animals will flash vividly whenever they are disturbed by a passing boat. They can also be stimulated by mechanical, chemical, and other agencies. Luciferin and luciferase cannot be demonstrated in these forms. In the absence of oxygen, *Noctiluca* will not produce light. *Noctiluca* often collects in enormous numbers at the surface of the sea; its display of color in the wake of a passing vessel on a dark night is wonderful to behold.

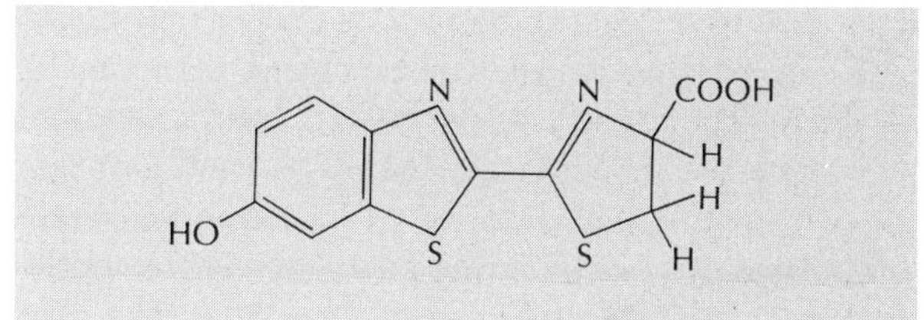

FIG. 43-6

Structure of luciferin in firefly. In bioluminescence, light is produced by a biochemical mechanism that involves oxygen, ATP, luciferin, luciferase, water, and inorganic ions. In presence of oxygen, ions, and enzyme luciferase, luciferin-ATP complex is converted to oxyluciferin with liberation of light. Luciferin and luciferase differ in composition in different species.

FIG. 43-7

Glowworm. Luminous organs represented on last segment.

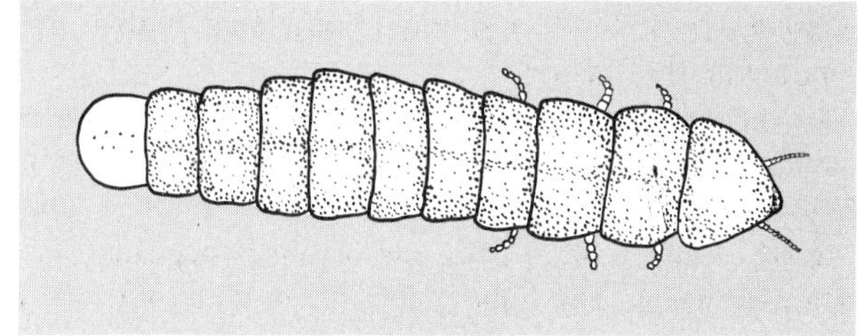

The famed glowworm (Fig. 43-7) of literature is usually the wingless female of the lampyrid beetle *(Photinus),* although some are larval forms. Most of them are terrestrial, although one or two live in fresh water. The luminous organs are found on the ventral side of the posterior segments. The light they emit is rather bluish green in appearance. Experiments show that the light rays are restricted to a very narrow range of the spectrum, as compared with other luminous animals, and that they give a very high degree of luminous efficiency. In the glowworm, perhaps more than in most luminous animals, the problem of producing light without heat is solved to a great extent. Its light, as well as that of all forms that have bioluminescence, is really "cold light."

The best known of all light-producing organisms is the firefly. These beetles have a wide distribution, and many genera and species are found. Most of them are tropical, but two genera are very common in temperate North America (*Lampyris* and *Photinus*). These are the familiar "lightning bugs" known to everyone. The light organ of the male is located on the ventral surface of the posterior segments of the abdomen. It is made up of a dorsal mass of small cells (the reflector) and a ventral mass of large cells (the photogenic tissue). Many branches of the tracheal system pass into the organ and subdivide into tracheoles that are connected with tracheal end cells to ensure an ample supply of oxygen, so necessary for the light. The organ is also supplied with nerves that control the rhythmic flashing. The function of the reflector is to scatter the light produced by the photogenic cells. In the female the light organ is confined to a single abdominal segment. The flashing of fireflies is rhythmic and may be single or double, depending on the species.

In the tropics, the synchronous flashing of fireflies is common; thousands of individuals flash together with great regularity. Often these displays are made in and around certain trees, where one of the insects may act as a pacemaker. The light is considered a mating signal in the American forms. During the day the fireflies lie hidden under vegetation, but they emerge at dusk. The males do most of the flying, for the females of some species are wingless or have very short wings and usually remain on the ground or on low vegetation. When the males flash, the females respond and they eventually find each other.

All the foregoing examples of bioluminescence are self-luminous. One of the most striking examples of luminous symbiosis is that of certain East Indian fish (*Photoblepharon* and *Anomalops*). In these forms, under each eye there are large luminous organs; these give off light continuously, day and night. The organs are made up of a series of tubes having an abundant supply of blood vessels. These tubes contain luminous bacteria that give off the light. Like the other type of light organ, these are sensitive to lack of oxygen and will quickly cease to give off light if the oxygen supply fails. Although the bacteria give off a continuous light, the fish can conceal the organ at will by drawing a fold of black tissue over it like an eyelid (or by some other device). This is an example of true symbiosis, for the fish is dependent on the bacteria for light and the bacteria depend on the fish for nourishment and shelter. Many other cases have been described in which luminous bacteria are considered the responsible agents for light production in animals.

ELECTRIC ORGANS

The power to produce strong electric shocks is confined to two groups—teleosts and elasmobranchs. The actual forms that have this adaptation are the electric eels *Electrophorus* and *Gymnotus,* the electric ray *Torpedo,* the stargazer *Astroscopus,* and the electric catfish, *Malapterurus.* The electric organs in all these forms are modified from skeletal muscles, with the possible exception of *Malapterurus,* in which they have developed from skin muscles. The organs are composed of flattened plates arranged one above another like the alternating layers in a storage battery. Each plate, of which there are thousands, is innervated by a nerve fiber. In some forms more than 200 to 300 volts of electricity have been recorded. The position of the organs varies greatly with the different forms; this indicates that the various organs have arisen independently. Since active muscle normally generates some electricity, it is logical that such electric organs should have arisen from muscles.

The most familiar example of an electric fish along the Atlantic coast is the *Torpedo,* or electric ray (Fig. 43-8). In these forms, the organs are present, one on either side of the head in the large, flat, expanded pectoral fins. One of the most interesting and also one of the most powerful of fish possessing electric batteries is the electric eel *Electrophorus,* which is found in parts of Brazil, Venezuela, and other South American countries. It is an elongated, eel-like fish 3 to 7 feet long, with a continuous midventral fin extending from the head to a point near the tail. The electric organs in this fish are three pairs in number and occupy the greater part of the posterior body cavity, for the visceral organs are shoved forward to the region just behind the head. The paired organs are not of equal size; this may account for the ability of the animal to regulate the intensity of its shock. This form is the only electric fish capable of doing this.

It is thought that the largest of the paired organs delivers the strongest shocks and the smallest organs, lesser ones. The smaller shocks serve as a warning to possible enemies and the strong shocks are used for killing prey or enemies. The discharge is determined by the will of

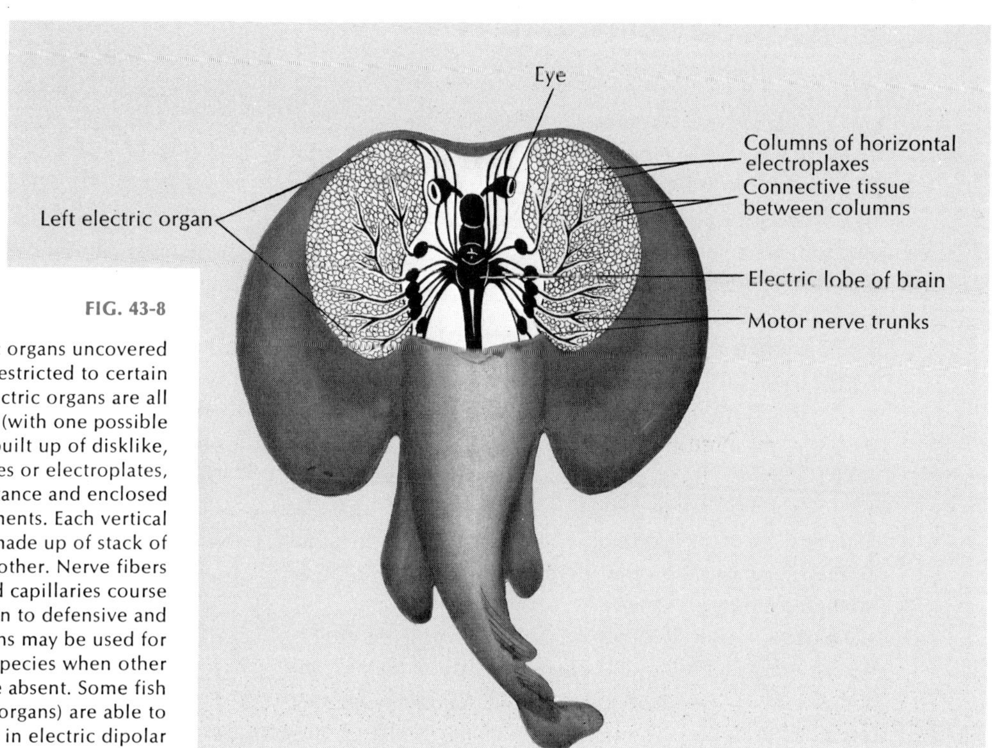

FIG. 43-8

Electric ray *Torpedo* with electric organs uncovered from above. Electric organs are restricted to certain teleost and elasmobranch fish. Electric organs are all modified from striated muscle (with one possible exception). Organs are built up of disklike, multinucleated cells called electroplaxes or electroplates, which are embedded in jellylike substance and enclosed within connective tissue compartments. Each vertical column in electric ray is made up of stack of electroplaxes piled on top of each other. Nerve fibers run to electroplaxes and blood capillaries course through jelly layer. In addition to defensive and offensive purposes, electric organs may be used for recognition among members of species when other methods of communication are absent. Some fish (especially those with weak electric organs) are able to detect disturbances made by object in electric dipolar field they form around their bodies, and thus keep informed about their environment.

the fish, for sometimes it will shock when touched and will not at other times. It is not necessary for an animal to come into contact with the eel to receive a shock, for the electric discharge carries through the water. How effective these shocks are in killing animals is a matter of controversy. There seems to be authentic records of the death of men and horses killed by the larger electric eels. In general, most of the victims of the fish are paralyzed and eventually recover, except for those caught and eaten by the creature.

ECHOLOCATION IN ANIMALS

Echolocation is a method of orientation whereby animals make use of a sonar system to detect objects at a distance. First worked out precisely in certain bats (by Griffin and Galambos), the method is now known to be employed by a number of other animals. Bats, such as *Myotis* and *Eptesicus*, emit chirps about ten times per second while cruising in the open. These sounds have high frequencies (about 40 to 80 kilocycles) and are inaudible to human ears (ultrasonic), which cannot detect sounds much above 20 kilocycles. Ultrasonic sounds can be picked up by man with a microphone, or sonic detector, and are heard as a series of clicks or buzzes. These sounds are bounced off objects while the bat is chasing its prey or avoiding obstacles and are reflected back to its sensitive ears. The large fruit-eating bats or flying foxes depend on vision or smell for finding their way about and do not have the echolocation method.

Echolocation has been described in whirligig beetles *(Gyrinus)*, oil birds *(Steatornis)* that make sounds audible to the human ear, porpoises, etc., and may be widespread in the animal kingdom.

SOCIAL BEHAVIOR AMONG ANIMALS

Social behavior refers to groups of animals (usually of the same species) living together and exhibiting activity patterns different from what the members would display when living as separate individuals. In this sense, animals are social when their behavior is modified by living together and when they influence and are influenced by other members of the group. There are many kinds and degrees of social organization and no single definition will apply to all. Mere aggregations of animals, such as those in an animal community, cannot be called social groups. Animals aggregate for many reasons. They may be attracted by some common favorable environmental factor (for example, light, shade, moisture) and form natural aggregations. Moths may be attracted to a light or barnacles to a common float. Such animals do not aid each other, but they have a social toleration toward each other and do not prevent others from sharing the same conditions. Some aggregations are the result of more positive reactions to others like themselves, such as schools of fish, flocks of birds roosting together, and migratory gregarious habits of many birds. Many types of aggregations also have a survival value and, to a certain extent, may be said to serve a social function. The protective circle of giraffe, musk ox, and other herds against predators is an example of this.

The sexes have division of labor that varies in degree from a mere shedding of gametes into the water by the two parents to the elaborate mating reactions and sex functions of higher forms. Among many kinds of animals, the parents and their offsprings may form a closely knit social group while the young are developing; in a wolf pack this family relationship may be more or less permanent. Social relationships may involve only two or three individuals or it may include a whole class of individuals.

Whether a social instinct is transmitted by inheritance from generation to generation is not yet certain. Social organization seems to be the result of the interaction between an inherited behavior pattern and learned experience. Perhaps among invertebrates, such as bees, ants, and termites, the inherited pattern would be the dominant factor. Social drives or appetites are usually less intense than those of hunger or sex (which may be considered a form of social behavior), although anyone who has watched schools of small squid in an aquarium and the quick recovery of their organization pattern when broken up is impressed with the force of this social behavior drive. In this connection, the **schooling of fish** represents a social organization in which the members form a constant orientation with respect to each other to produce a mass that behaves as a whole unit. Although controlled by internal factors, a school of fish is built up gradually from small numbers by the orientation of the members through visual attraction, by lateral line perception, by pressure waves, and in some cases, by sounds made by the fish. The adaptive nature of schooling may be the protection afforded in the evolution of fish by such patterns when they left the security of shore rock crevices and plants and took to the open sea. Many fish, however, do not form schools.

A definite relationship between structural complexity and levels of social integration is shown by insects that are at the peak of arthropod evolution and of social organization. The roles of the various members of ant and termite societies are determined by structural differences that result in an inflexible division of labor. Such societies have a long evolutionary history and are so integrated that a member has little chance of survival when separated from its society. Survival here depends on the fate of the group in meeting the requirements of the environment.

How has social organization arisen? What factors have determined its organization and complexity? No animal lives to itself but is knit to others in some way. Natural selection has operated here as elsewhere in the evolutionary pattern of social aggregations. Various types of societies have arisen, flourished, or become extinct, often without any relation to each other. Parallel evolution has been common. Many social organization patterns have followed similar lines, because their members have followed similar lines of evolution. Social organization has reached its climax with the arthropods and the mammals. Each of these groups is at the peak of the two main lines of evolution—the annelid-mollusk-arthropod line and the echinoderm-vertebrate line. The social development of these lines has been separately evolved and is not due to common ancestral stock. Each arose from a family unit rather than from aggregation of individuals. Most species of ants, for instance, start a colony by the queen laying eggs that differentiate into the various caste members of workers, soldiers, sexes, etc. Caste determination may be quite complicated and no single plan is followed. In some bees and ants the males develop from haploid (unfertilized) eggs and the other members from diploid eggs. Among termites the males are diploid and the females haploid. Food differences are also determining factors in some cases. Many mammal societies start from the family unit, such as the wolf pack and the societies of the great apes.

According to Allee, a great student of social behavior, vertebrate animal groups have organized their social behavior in accordance with three general principles. These are territorial rights, dominance-subordinance hierarchies, and leadership-followership relations. Much of our knowledge about **territorial rights** dates from Howard's work on birds (1920). This concept involves a restricted area that is taken over, usually by a male, and vigorously defended against trespass by members of the same species. The birds sing mainly to proclaim ownership; when a bird's domain is invaded, he will fight against the trespasser. Territories may be staked out before or after mating, and there are many variations of behavior among different species. Biologic values of such behavior are obvious, for population densities, accessible food supplies, and well-spaced aggregations are promoted to the best advantage. Other groups of animals, including fish, reptiles, and mammals, are known to follow similar territorial rights patterns.

Another pattern of territorial behavior is illustrated by the arena and bowerbirds of South America, New Guinea, and elsewhere. The basis of this behavior pattern is the establishment of mating stations by the males. Each male takes over a small arena during the breeding season and displays himself to the occasional females that happen to wander into the territory where the individual arenas are located. By some sign or other, the females select the males with which they desire to mate. The famous bowerbirds of Australia and New Guinea go even further in their courtship display. The males of some species build elaborate bowers of sticks and grass and decorate them often in an elaborate fashion, with snail shells, charcoal, dead insects, flowers, and brightly shining objects. Students of these birds (Gilliard and Marshall) believe that bower-building behavior has been evolved because sexual selection has been transferred from morphologic patterns of plumage displayed by the male to external objects, which become a kind of secondary sexual characteristic.

The concept of **dominance-subordinance** refers to a type of social behavior in a group in which one animal is dominant over others. We owe much of this concept to the Norwegian scientist T. Schjelderup-Ebbe, who in 1922 observed that in poultry flocks one hen was dominant over the others and exerted the right to peck other members without being pecked in return. Further study revealed that flocks were organized on the basis of social hierarchies; that is, there was a whole series of social levels in which members of the higher levels had peck rights over those of lower levels, etc. The hen of the lowest level is pecked by all the others but does not peck back. Just how many there could be in a peck order has never been ascertained, but these pecking organizations are based largely upon the ability of birds to recognize the members of a flock as individuals. If the population is too large, pecking orders may not exist. New members added to a flock, as well as those that are absent from the flock for any length of time, are usually assigned to lower levels. When dominance is once won (usually by fighting), it is relatively permanent. However, it is possible for a lower ranking member to advance to a higher level when its victories are greater than its defeats in challenging the social ranking. A given individual may maintain her social position in many flocks at the same time, although she may occupy a different rank in each flock.

Social hierarchy also exists among the males. One of the best examples of this male dominance is found in the sage grouse of the western American plains. During the breeding season early in spring each male establishes a dominance relation with the other males. The most dominant or master cock takes his position in an area and the less dominant cocks form a guard ring around him. Hens are admitted in the ring, but others are driven away. About 75% of all mating is performed by the master cocks, which comprise about 1% of all the males. Dominance hierarchies have been found in all classes of vertebrates, including fish, lizards, mice, and primates. Some arthropods show dominance behavior patterns to a limited extent, but ordinarily the innate, stereotyped behavior of arthropods does not fit into this place of learned behavior.

Leadership behavior refers to the tendency of the members of a group to follow a certain member. It usually involves the selection of an experienced member that stabilizes the other members of the group and holds them together when they are on the move (sheep and deer). Leadership has definite values for the group as a whole and not merely for an individual. The behavior pattern is especially valuable in times of emergency. In some cases the leader may be the dominant member of the group; more often it is an old, experienced female that has the right because of the larger number of offspring that have acquired the habit of following her when they were young. Males, except during the breeding season, are away from the flock, whereas the females are always around.

The relationship between the leader and the followers is different from that of dominance and subordinance. Being the leader does not confer special social privileges, but there is a mutual dependence on each other of both leader and followers. Besides mammals, certain types of leadership are known to exist among fish, lizards, and birds. In the invertebrates, the arthropods show the behavior here and there. One of the most careful studies ever made on the leadership-followership concept was done by F. F. Darling on Scottish herds of red deer, which he describes vividly in his now classic book *A Herd of Red Deer* (1937). His observations show the important role of the female (hind) as a leader of a herd and the extreme care she exerts in looking after its welfare. He states that Landseer was a faulty observer in depicting the stag as the "Monarch of the Glen," in his famous picture, for the social system of red deer is definitely matriarchal. Stags form their own companies at times other than the breeding season, but such groups are extremely loose organizations with no apparent leader.

It is apparent that in nearly all groups of animals that show social relations the female is the primary influence in leadership and the center of family life. The aggressive males tend to break up social behavior patterns, and nature, to offset this tendency, either produces males in limited numbers (as in many insects) or the males are kept more or less to themselves except during the breeding season. A notable exception is the termite organization in which males play a role almost as prominent as that of the females.

● Annotated references

Bertin, L. 1957. Eels: A biological study. New York, Philosophical Library, Inc. *The puzzling migration of the freshwater eel has intrigued biologists for 2,000 years. Although Schmidt solved the main problem when he discovered its spawning grounds in the Sargasso Sea, there is still much to learn about the life cycle of this mysterious animal.*

Breland, O. P. 1957. Animal friends and foes. New York, Harper & Brothers. *A popular account of the ways animals affect man's welfare and also each other. The topic headings pose questions that are often asked by the layman (and sometimes by professional zoologists). General zoology students will find much of interest in the book.*

Bünning, E. 1964. The physiological clock. New York, Academic Press, Inc. *A concise, up-to-date account of the physiologic mechanisms animals and plants have for the timing order of their environments.*

Carthy, J. D. 1958. An introduction to the behavior of invertebrates. New York, The Macmillan Co. *In this work the author stresses the functions of the sensory patterns of invertebrates and their reactions to the various categories of stimuli.*

Darling, F. F. 1937. A herd of red deer. A study in animal behavior. Oxford, Oxford University Press. *This is a notable contribution to animal behavior and represents a careful and penetrating analysis of the movement, population, reproduction, and other aspects of an interesting group of animals.*

Eibl-Eibesfeldt, I. 1961. The fighting behavior of animals. Sci. Amer. **205**:112-122 (Dec.).

Frisch, K. von. 1950. Bees. Their vision, chemical senses, and language. Ithaca, N. Y., Cornell University Press. *A striking account of the classic experiments of this investigator in the determination of the ways bees convey information about food location.*

Gilliard, E. T. 1963. The evolution of bowerbirds. Sci. Amer. **209**:38-46 (Aug.).

Griffin, D. R. 1958. Listening in the dark. New Haven, Conn., Yale University Press. *The author subtitles this revealing work, "The Acoustic Orientation of Bats and Men," but other forms are also considered. The author's contribution to the concept of echolocation has fitted him to summarize the mechanisms of acoustic orientation wherever it is found in the animal kingdom, but the major portion of the present treatise is about bats. A bibliography of nearly 500 titles is included.*

Harvey, E. N. 1952. Bioluminescence. New York, Academic Press, Inc. *The authoritative work on this fascinating subject.*

Hasler, A. D., and J. A. Larson. 1955. The homing salmon. Sci. Amer. **193**:72-77 (Aug.).

Hess, E. H. 1958. Imprinting in animals. Sci. Amer. **198**:81-90 (March).

Hess, W. N. 1964. Long journey of the dogfish. Natural History **73**:32-35.

Peckham, G. W., and E. G. Peckham. 1905. Wasps, social and solitary. New York, Houghton-Mifflin Co. *The careful observations made on an interesting group of insects by these investigators represent a classic study in animal behavior. One of the most revealing observations was the action of some wasps in using pebbles as hammers in pounding down the entrance to their burrows.*

Sauer, E. G. F. 1958. Celestial navigation by birds. Sci. Amer. **199**:42-47 (Aug.).

Shaw, E. 1962. The schooling of fishes. Sci. Amer. **206**: 128-138 (June).

Thorpe, W. H. 1956. Learning and instinct in animals. Cambridge, Mass., Harvard University Press. *Of the many works on animal behavior in recent years, this book is an excellent synthesis of the behavior concepts and learning processes of animals from protozoans to mammals.*

Watson, J. B. 1930. Behaviorism, rev. ed. Chicago, University of Chicago Press. *A classic psychologic work that has exerted a great influence on the modern interpretation of behavior patterns.*

Wenner, A. M. 1964. Sound communication in honeybees. Sci. Amer. **210**:116-124 (April).

Wilson, J. T. 1963. Continental drift. Sci. Amer. **208**: 86-100 (April).

PART NINE

DEVELOPMENT OF ZOOLOGY

Man in his long evolution has had many motives for the study of animal life. In the first place, life with all its implications must have aroused the curiosity of those who gave any thought at all to the nature of things. From his experience, many objectives afforded man motivation for understanding as much as he could learn at his cultural level about the life process that he shared with other animals. These motives increased in number as he discovered facts relating to the structure and functioning of animal life and his relations to the animal kingdom. Man was concerned with the economic aspects of improving his domestic stock, with ecologic control of the animals around him, with medical treatment against disease agents and abnormalities of body disorders, with using animals for clothing and food, and in many other ways. But one of man's greatest motives has been his innate desire to learn, to satisfy his curiosity, and to increase his general comprehension of life. This has led in time to the formation of many generalizations in the discipline of zoologic study.

No generalization in the life sciences is advanced without being challenged. Since there are so many variables in all aspects of life, conclusions have to be formulated with extreme caution, for so many factors can be faulty. Before widespread statements can be made, many investigations have to be made for checking and rechecking the phenomena of life. But like a snowball, discoveries pile on each other as new breakthroughs appear. Often a biologic study may reach a dead end until a fundamental discovery opens the way for new advancements. As man realizes more and more the basic unity of all sciences, other disciplines and new techniques aid in the understanding of the basic nature of life.

It is very difficult to appraise the historic development of any field of study. Discoveries are usually due to the cooperation and investigation of many minds. It is not unusual for several workers to arrive at virtually the same conclusions independently because they have been studying on the same frontier of some particular aspect. One investigator often gets the credit for an important discovery, whereas many others should share in the prestige. No one individual has a monopoly of ideas, and advances in science are built on the results of many causes and the work of many minds. However, certain important generalizations have been aptly phrased by some one worker who crystalizes the thought on that particular aspect of study.

Certain key discoveries have greatly influenced the progress along certain lines. This part aims to give some of the major landmarks in the development of biology and the individuals whose names are commonly associated with these key discoveries. In this brief outline the student may be able to see some relation between one discovery and another so that the discoveries do not appear completely isolated. It will be noted that fundamental discoveries in a particular branch of biology tend to be grouped fairly close together chronologically because that interest may have dominated the thought of biologic investigators at that time.

CHAPTER 44

• ORIGIN OF BASIC CONCEPTS AND KEY DISCOVERIES IN BIOLOGY, INCLUDING BOOKS THAT HAVE INFLUENCED ZOOLOGY

384-322 B.C.: *Aristotle. The foundation of zoology as a science.*

Although this great pioneer zoologist and philosopher cannot be appraised by modern standards, there is scarcely a major subdivision of zoology to which he did not make some contribution. He was a true scientist, for he emphasized the observational and experimental method. Despite his lack of scientific background, he was one of the greatest scientists of all time.

130-200 A.D.: *Galen. Development of anatomy and physiology.*

This Roman investigator has been praised for his clear concept of scientific methods and blamed for passing down to others for centuries certain glaring errors. His influence was so great that for centuries after his period students considered him the final authority on anatomic and physiologic subjects.

1347: *William of Occam. Occam's razor.*

This principle of logic has received its name from the fact that it is supposed to cut out unnecessary and irrelevant hypotheses in the explanation of phenomena. The gist of the principle is that, of several possible explanations, the one that is simplest, has the fewest assumptions, and is most consistent with the data at hand is the most probable one.

1543: *Vesalius, Andreas. First modern interpretation of anatomic structures.*

With his insight into fundamental structure. Vesalius ushered in the dawn of modern biologic investigation. Many aspects of his interpretation of anatomy are just now beginning to be appreciated.

1603: *Platter, F. First description of Diphyllobothrium latum.*

This first published account of the broad tapeworm of man represents an early beginning in the field of parasitology.

1616-1628: *Harvey, William. First accurate description of blood circulation.*

Harvey's classic demonstration of blood circulation was the key experiment that laid the foundation of modern physiology. He explained bodily processes in physical terms, cleared away much of the mental rubbish of mystic interpretation, and gave an auspicious start to experimental physiology.

1627: *Aselli, G. First demonstration of lacteal vessels.*

This discovery, coming at the same time as Harvey's great work, supplemented the discovery of circulation. His name was given to a group of lymph nodes in the mesenteries of mammals, the **pancreas of Aselli.**

1649: *Descartes, R. Early concept of reflex action.*

Descartes did not know the functions of the dorsal and ventral roots of the spinal nerves, but he did postulate the idea that impulses originating at the receptors of the body were carried to the central nervous system where they activated muscles and glands by what he called "reflection."

1651: *Harvey, William. Aphorism of Harvey: Omne vivum ex ovo (all life from the egg).*

Although Harvey's work as an embryologist is overshadowed by his demonstration of blood circulation, his *De Generatione Animalium*, published in 1651, contains many sound observations on embryologic processes. He was opposed to the preformation theory that was held by many biologists of his and later times.

1652: *Bartholin, Thomas. Discovery of lymphatic system.*

The significance of the thoracic duct in its relation to the circulation was determined in this investigation.

Bartholin performed his classic demonstrations mainly on human bodies, material not usually available in his time.

1658: *Swammerdam, Jan. Description of red blood corpuscles.*

This discovery, together with his observations on the valves of the lymphatics and the alterations in shape of muscles during contraction, represented early advancements in the microscopic study of bodily structures.

1660: *Malpighi, Marcello. Demonstration of capillary circulation.*

By demonstrating the capillaries in the lung of a frog, Malpighi was able to complete the scheme of blood circulation because Harvey never saw capillaries and thus never included them in his description. His name has been given to the malpighian corpuscles of the kidney and to the deeper portion of the epidermis of the skin.

1665: *Hooke, Robert. Discovery of the cell.*

This was an insignificant discovery at the time and was so regarded for a long time, but how important the cell loomed in the early nineteenth century! Hooke's investigations were made with cork and the term "cell" fits cork much better than it does to animal cells, but by tradition the misnomer has stuck.

1672: *Graaf, R. de. Description of ovarian follicles.*

de Graaf's name is given to the mature ovarian follicle, but he thought that the follicles were the actual ova, an error later corrected by von Baer.

1675-1680: *Leeuwenhoek, Anthony van. Discovery of protozoa.*

The discoveries of this eccentric Dutch microscopist revealed a whole new world of biology.

1693: *Ray, J. Concept of species.*

Although Ray's work on classification was later overshadowed by Linnaeus, Ray was really the first to make the species concept apply to a particular kind of organism and to point out the variations that exist among the members of a species.

1733: *Hales, Stephen. First measurement of blood pressure.*

This was further proof that the bodily processes could be measured quantitatively—more than a century after Harvey's momentous demonstration.

1734: *Borelli, A. Analysis of fish locomotion.*

The nature of fish propulsion has been the subject of many investigations from Aristotle down to the present. Borelli was really the first to demonstrate that the vibration of the tail, and not the fins, is the chief propulsive agency in fish movement. Fresh insights into this problem have been furnished in recent years by J. Gray, R. Bainbridge, E. Kramer, and J. R. Nursall.

1744: *Trembley, A. Observations on the structure of Hydra.*

Trembley worked out with considerable detail and accuracy the nature of this interesting little animal species.

1745: *Bonnet, Charles. Discovery of natural parthenogenesis.*

Although somewhat unusual in nature, this phenomenon has yielded much information about meiosis and other cytologic problems. It is of special importance in its relation to artificial parthenogenesis, a subject of perennial interest.

1745: *Maupertuis, P. M. Early concept of evolutionary process.*

Although Maupertuis' ideas are speculative and not based on experimental observation, he foretold many of the concepts of variation and natural selection that Darwin was to demonstrate with convincing evidence.

1753: *Réaumur, R. A. F. de. Experiments on digestion.*

This was the first recorded account of any note on the nature of the basic principle of nutrition and paved the way for the extensive studies of Beaumont, Pavlov, and Cannon.

1758: *Linnaeus, Carolus. Development of binomial nomenclature system of taxonomy.*

So important is this work in taxonomy that 1758 is regarded as the starting point in the determination of the generic and specific names of animals. Besides the value of his binomial system, Linnaeus gave taxonomists a valuable working model of conciseness and clearness that has never been surpassed.

1759: *Wolff, C. F. Embryologic theory of epigenesis.*

This embryologist, the greatest before von Baer, did much to overthrow the grotesque preformation theory then in vogue, and, despite many shortcomings, laid the basis for the modern interpretation of embryology. The wolffian ducts are named after him.

1760: *Hunter, John. Development of comparative investigations of animal structure.*

This vigorous eighteenth century anatomist gave a powerful impetus not only to anatomic observations but also to the establishment of natural history museums.

1763: *Adanson, M. Concept of empiric taxonomy.*

This botanist proposed a scheme of classification that grouped individuals into taxa according to shared characters. A species would have the maximum number of shared characters according to this scheme. The concept has been revived recently by exponents of numerical taxonomy. It lacks the evaluation of the evolutionary concept and has been criticized on this account.

1763: *Koelreuter, J. G. Discovery of quantitative inheritance (multiple genes).*

Koelreuter, a pioneer in plant hybridization, found that certain plant hybrids had characters more or less intermediate between the parents in the F_1 generation, but in the F_2 there were many gradations from one extreme to the other. An explanation was not forthcoming until after Mendel's laws were discovered, when it was shown that it was due to the effect of multiple genes.

1768-1779: *Cook, James. Influence of geographic exploration on biologic development.*

This famous sea captain made possible a greater range of biologic knowledge because of the able naturalists whom he took on his voyages of discovery. Captain Cook must also be remembered for the practical way he solved the ancient scourge of scurvy.

1772: *Priestley, J., and J. Ingenhousz. Concept of photosynthesis.*

These investigators first pointed out some of the major aspects of this important phenomena, such as the use of light energy for converting carbon dioxide and water into released oxygen and the retention of carbon. This was an early start in understanding a biologic mechanism that has intrigued researchers ever since.

1774: *Priestley, Joseph. Discovery of oxygen.*

The discovery of this element is of great biologic interest because it helped in determining the nature of oxidation and the exact role of respiration in organisms.

1778: *Lavoisier, Antoine L. Nature of animal respiration demonstrated.*

A basis for the chemical interpretation of the life process was given a great impetus by the careful quantitative studies of the changes during breathing made by this great investigator. His work also meant the final overthrow of the mystic phlogiston theory that had held sway for so long.

1781: *Abildgaard, P. First experimental life cycle of a tapeworm.*

Life cycles of parasites may be very complicated, involving several hosts. This early achievement was followed by many others less than a century later.

1781: *Fontana, F. Description of the nucleolus.*

Fontana discovered this organelle in the slime from the skin of an eel, and until recently its function has been a subject of controversy. Although its functions are not yet completely understood, it is known that it is involved in protein synthesis and has centers for ribose nucleoproteins.

1791: *Smith, W. Correlation between fossils and geologic strata.*

By observing that certain types of fossils were peculiar to particular strata, Smith was able to work out a method for estimating geologic age. He laid the basis of stratigraphic geology. His conclusion that fossils constituted a stratified series with unvarying arrangement prepared the way for Cuvier and Lyell.

1792: *Galvani, L. Animal electricity.*

The lively controversy between Galvani and Volta over the twitching of frog legs has led to extensive investigation of precise methods of measuring the various electrical phenomena of animals.

1796: *Cuvier, G. Development of vertebrate paleontology.*

Cuvier compared the structure of fossil forms with that of living ones and concluded that there had been a succession of organisms which had become extinct and were succeeded by the creation of new ones. To account for this extinction, Cuvier held to the theory of catastrophism, or the simultaneous extinction of animal populations by natural cataclysms. His colleague Lamarck, working with the fossils of invertebrates, believed that all populations did not cease at one time but that there was a continuation, with modifications, of life into succeeding geologic eras.

1797: *Goethe, J. W. von. Concept of archetypes of animals.*

In this theory, Goethe tried to formulate ideal forms that best fitted animals for their conditions of existence. Although his views were somewhat vaguely expressed, modern biology recognizes the importance of the concept in the way contemporary organisms can best fit into the varied ecologic niches of the animal kingdom, such as the basic adaptive features of the major groups.

1800: *Bichat, M. F. X. Analysis of body tissues.*

Bichat's studies on body tissues formed the basis of modern histology. He classified the tissues into 21 different types, but his failure to use the microscope prevented him from correctly appraising the true minute structure of tissues as we now know them.

1801: *Lamarck, J. B. Evolutionary concept of use and disuse.*

Lamarck gave the first clear-cut expression of a theory to account for organic evolution. His assumption that acquired characters were inherited has been the subject of fierce controversy ever since it was proposed, and although, in general, most evolutionists have refuted this part of the theory, nearly every generation sees a revival of it in some way or other.

1802: *Young, T. Theory of trichromatic color vision.*

Young's theory suggested that the retina contained three kinds of light-sensitive substances, each having a maximum sensitivity in a different region of the spectrum and each being transmitted separately to the brain. The three substances combined produced the colors of the environment. The three pigments responsible are located in three kinds of cones. Young's theory has been modified in certain details by other investigators.

1810: *Gall, F. J. Localization of brain functions.*

That different areas of the brain do have different functions has been verified by experimental work, a fact that Gall foreshadowed by his crude experiments on skull contours. He should not be blamed for phrenology, which quacks quickly developed. His name is recalled by the column of Gall, one of the nerve pathways of the spinal cord.

1814: *Kirchhoff, G. Demonstration of catalytic action.*

Kirchhoff's discovery that starch treated with an extract of barley malt was converted into glucose was the crude beginning of extensive investigations that have been fruitful in understanding the metabolic activities of living protoplasm.

1817: *Pander, C. First description of three germ layers.*

The description of the three germ layers was first made on the chick, and later the concept was extended by von Baer to include all vertebrates.

1822: *Bell, C., and F. Magendie. Discovery of the functions of dorsal and ventral roots of spinal nerves.*

This demonstration was a starting point for an anatomic and functional investigation of the most complex system in the body. The Bell-Magendie law appears simple when compared with other aspects of nervous behavior, but it showed that something could be done to unravel the complexity of this system.

1823: *Knight, T. Concept of dominance and recessiveness.*

Although this investigator worked with the same pea with which Mendel made his classic discoveries, he was unable to formulate clear-cut laws about the mechanism of heredity, but his information about the breeding of peas gave Mendel something to work with later.

1824: *Prévost, P., and J. B. A. Dumas. Cell division first described.*

The description of the cleavage of the frog egg before the arrival of the cell theory meant that the true significance of cleavage could not be appreciated at that time. The same observers also showed the true role of the spermatozoan in fertilization.

1825: *Raspail, F. V. Beginning of histochemistry.*

Raspail devised the iodine test for starch as well as many other histochemical tests for plant and animal tissues. Histochemistry has yielded much information on the location and chemical nature of various cell constituents such as minerals and enzymes.

1826: *Serres, E. R. A. Discovery of the urohypophysis of fishes.*

The presence of large neurosecretory cells at the posterior end of the spinal cord was found first in teleosts. A vascular plexus carries away the neurosecretions from the secretory neurons that bear axons with bulbous endings. U. Dahlgren (1914) and C. C. Speidel (1919) found similar neurosecretory cells in certain elasmobranchs. The concept of a caudal neurosecretory system has been studied and extended in recent years (M. Enami). The hormone or hormones produced by the urohypophysis may regulate the sodium ions into or out of the organism in osmoregulatory coordination.

1827: *Baer, Karl von. Discovery of mammalian ovum.*

The very tiny ova of mammals escaped de Graaf's eyes, but von Baer brought mammalian reproduction into line with that of other animals by detecting them and their true relation to the follicles. One of the first achievements of the greatest embryologist of all time was this important discovery.

1828: *Brown, Robert. Brownian movement first described.*

This interesting phenomenon is characteristic of living protoplasm and sheds some light on the structure of protoplasm.

1828: *Thompson, J. V. Nature of plankton.*

Thompson's collections of these small forms with a tow net, together with his published descriptions, are the first records of the vast community of planktonic animals. He was also the first to work out the true nature of barnacles.

1828: *Wöhler, F. First to synthesize an organic compound.*

Wöhler succeeded in making urea (a compound formed in the body) from the inorganic substance of ammonium cyanate, thus $NH_4OCN \rightarrow NH_2CONH_2$. This success in producing an organic substance synthetically was the stimulus that resulted in the preparation of thousands of compounds.

1829: *Vauguelin, N. L. Discovery of carotin.*

This important pigment, so widely distributed through the plant and animal kingdoms, has been the source of many investigations to determine its true significance. It is now known to be associated with vitamin A and to have many biologic activities. The carotinoids are a complex of many kinds of pigments of similar properties.

1830: *Amici, G. B. Discovery of fertilization in plants.*

Amici was able to demonstrate the tube given off by the pollen grain and to follow it to the micropyle of the ovule through the style of the ovary. Later it was established that a sperm nucleus of the pollen makes contact and union with the nucleus of the egg.

1830: *Baer, Karl von. Biogenetic law formulated.*

von Baer's conception of this law was conservative and sounder in its implication than has been the case with many other biologists (Haeckel, for instance), for von Baer stated that embryos of higher and lower forms resemble each other more the earlier they are compared in their development, and **not** that the embryos of higher forms resemble the adults of lower organisms. This viewpoint of von Baer has gradually come to prevail among most modern biologists.

1830: *Lyell, C. Modern concept of geology.*

The influence of this concept not only did away with the catastrophic theory but also gave a logical interpretation of fossil life and the correlation between the formation of rock strata and the animal life that existed at the time these formations were laid down. Lyell's great work *The Principles of Geology* influenced Darwin and his development of the evolutionary concept.

1831: *Brown, Robert. First description of cell nucleus.*

Others had seen nuclei, but Brown was the first to name the structure and to regard the nucleus as a general phenomenon. This description was an important preliminary to the formulation of the cell theory a few years later, for Schleiden acknowledged the importance of the nucleus in the development of the cell concept.

1833: *Hall, M. Concept of reflex action.*

Although Hall describes the method by which a stimulus can produce a response independently of sensation or volition, it remained for the outstanding work of the great Sir Charles Sherrington in this century to explain much of the complex nature of reflexes.

1833: *Purkinje, J. E. Discovery of sweat glands.*

This discovery was an important step in histologic development. It opened up a new field of investigation into problems of the skin and its structure that have not yet been resolved.

1835: *Bassi, Agostino. First demonstration of a microorganism as an infective agent.*

Bassi's discovery that a certain disease of silkworms was due to a small fungus represents the beginning of the germ theory of disease that was to prove so fruitful in the hands of Pasteur and other able investigators.

1835: *Dujardin, Felix. Description of living matter (protoplasm).*

Dujardin associated the jellylike substance that he found in protozoa and that he called "sarcode" with the life process. This substance was later to be called protoplasm, and the sarcode idea may be considered a significant landmark in the development of the protoplasm concept.

1835: *Owen, R. Discovery of Trichinella.*

This versatile investigator is chiefly remembered for his researches in anatomy, but his discovery of this most common parasite in the American people is an important landmark in the history of parasitology.

1837: *Berzelius, J. J. Formulation of the catalytic concept.*

Berzelius called substances that caused chemical conversions by their mere presence catalytic in contrast to analytic; this term described the real chemical affinity between substances in a chemical reaction. The concept was a cornerstone in the development of chemical science and paved the way for an understanding of biocatalysts or enzymes.

1838: *Liebig, Justus. Foundation of biochemistry.*

The idea that vital activity could be explained by chemicophysical factors has given biologic investigators their greatest method of attacking the nature of life problems. Liebig's chemical methods of organic analysis have borne fruit, as attested by the important role biochemistry has assumed in present-day investigation.

1838-1839: *Schleiden, M. J., and T. Schwann. Formulation of the cell theory.*

The cell doctrine, with its basic idea that all plants and animals were made up of similar units, represents one of the truly great landmarks in biologic progress. The theory opened up a new understanding of the life process, for it gave biologists a starting point for studying the structures and functions of the organisms. It must be remembered, however, that the concept of the cell was due to many workers and not merely to the men whose names are commonly associated with its establishment. Many biologists think the work of Schleiden and Schwann has been rated much higher than it deserves in the light of what others did to develop the cell concept. R. Dutrochet (1824) and H. von Mohl (1831) had described all tissues as being composed of cells.

1839: *Mulder, J. Concept of the nature of proteins.*

Mulder proposed the name "protein" for the basic constituents of protoplasmic materials because he considered them of first or primary importance in the structure of living matter. All subsequent investigation has proved the correct etymology of this name. It was Verworn who stated that living matter might be defined as the material in which protein metabolism occurs.

1839-1846: *Purkinje, J. E., and Hugo von Mohl. Concept of protoplasm established.*

Purkinje proposed the name protoplasm for living matter, and von Mohl did extensive work on its nature, but it remained for Max Schultze (1861) to give a clear-cut concept of the relations of protoplasm to cells and its essential unity in all organisms. Purkinje's name is perpetuated by the large basket cells of the cerebellum.

1839: *Verhulst, P. F. Logistic theory of population growth.*

According to this theory, animal populations have a slow initial growth rate that gradually speeds up until it reaches a maximum and then slows down to a state of equilibrium. By plotting the logarithm of the total number of individuals against time, an S-shaped curve results that is somewhat similar for all populations. Pearl (1920) revived the concept. The principle applies best to population growth of animals with simple life histories.

1840: *Liebig, J., and F. F. Blackman. The law of minimum requirements.*

Liebig interpreted plant growth as being dependent on essential requirements that are present in minimum quantity; some substances, even in minute quantities, were needed for normal growth. Later Blackman discovered that the rate of photosynthesis is restricted by the factor that operates at a limiting intensity (for example, light or temperature). The concept has been modified in various ways since it was formulated. It is now known that a factor interaction other than the minimum ones plays a part. The interaction of all environmental factors may be the final determiner of potential growth and development. The law, therefore, is best seen when certain common minimum requirements are considered.

1840: *Miller, H. Appraisal of geologic formation, Old Red Sandstone.*

These Devonian deposits in Scotland and parts of England represent one of the most important vertebrate-bearing sediments ever discovered. From them much knowledge about early vertebrates, such as ostracoderms, placoderms, and bony fish, has been obtained. Similar sediments in other parts of the world have also been found rich in fossils (Spitzbergen, Germany, Wyoming, etc.)

1840: *Müller, J. Theory of specific nerve energies.*

This theory states that the kind of sensation experienced depends on the nature of the sense organ with which the stimulated nerve is connected. The optic nerve, for instance, conveys the impression of vision however it is stimulated. This concept has been the focal point for many investigations.

1841: *Remak, Robert. Description of direct cell division.*

Remak first described direct cell division, or amitosis, in the red blood corpuscles of the chick embryo. The process appears restricted to fully differentiated or senescent tissue cells. Remak's name is carried by the unmyelinated sympathetic nerve fibers.

1842: *Bowman, William. Histologic structure of the nephron (kidney unit).*

Bowman's accurate description of the nephron afforded physiologists an opportunity to attack the problem of how the kidney separates waste from the blood, a problem not yet fully solved. His name is given to the capsule surrounding the renal capsule.

1842: *Steenstrup, J. Alternation of generations described.*

Metagenesis, or alternation of sexual and asexual reproduction in the life cycle, exists in many animals and plants. The concept had been introduced before this time by L. A. de Chamisso (1819).

1843: *Owen, Richard. Concepts of homology and analogy.*

Homology, as commonly understood, refers to similarity in embryonic origin and development, whereas analogy is the likeness between two organs in their functioning. Owen's concept of homology was merely that of the same organ in different animals under all varieties of form and function. Since his time the concept has been broadened to include evolutionary relationships. The concept has been widely used to establish the common ancestry of animals.

1844: *Ludwig, C. Filtration theory of renal excretion.*

About the same time that Bowman described the malpighian corpuscle, Ludwig showed that the corpuscle functions as a passive filter and that the filtrate which passes through it from the blood carries into the urinary tubules the waste products that are concentrated by the resorption of water as the filtrate moves down the tubules. Other investigators, Cushny, Starling, and Richards, have confirmed the theory by actual demonstration. This theory has been modified some since the discovery of tubular excretion, especially in the aglomerular marine fish, and the countercurrent multiplier system concept.

1845: *Helmholtz, H., and J. R. Mayer. The formulation of the law of conservation of energy.*

This landmark in man's thinking showed that in any system, living or nonliving, the power to perform mechanical work always tends to decrease unless energy is added from without. Physiologic investigation could now advance on the theory that the living organism is an energy machine and obeyed the laws of the science of energetics.

1848: *Hofmeister, W. Discovery of chromosomes.*

This investigator made sketches of bodies, later known to be chromosomes, in the nuclei of pollen mother cells (*Tradescantia*). Schneider further described these elements in 1873, and Waldeyer named them in 1888.

1848: *Siebold, C. T. E. von. Establishment of the status of protozoa.*

Siebold emphasized the unicellular nature of protozoa, fitted them into the recently developed cell theory, and established them as the basic phylum of the animal kingdom. F. Dujardin had earlier (1835) considered the protozoan body to be composed of a unit mass (sarcode), now known as protoplasm.

1849: *Berthold, A. A. Transplantation of the testis.*

Since progress in endocrinology depends so much on experimental modification of animals, such as organ transplantation, Berthold's experiment gave workers in this science one of their most important tools of research.

1850: *Bernard, C. Independent irritability of muscle.*

By using the drug curare, which blocks motor impulses through the myoneural junction, Bernard found that the muscle would still respond to direct stimulation, thus proving that the muscle is independently irritable. This curare experiment has had wide applications in physiology.

1851: *Bernard, C. Discovery of the vasomotor system.*

Bernard showed how the amount of blood distributed to the various tissues by the small arterioles was regulated by vasomotor nerves of the sympathetic nervous system, as he demonstrated in the ear of a white rabbit.

1851: *Waller, A. V. Importance of the nucleus in regeneration.*

When nerve fibers are cut, the parts of the fibers peripheral to the cut degenerate in a characteristic fashion. This wallerian degeneration enables one to trace the course of fibers through the nervous system. In the regeneration process the nerve cell body (with its nucleus) is necessary for the downgrowth of the fiber from the proximal segment.

1852: *Helmholtz, Herman von. Determination of rate of nervous impulse.*

This landmark in nerve physiology showed that the difficult phenomena of nervous activity could be expressed numerically.

1852: *Kölliker, Albrecht von. Establishment of histology as a science.*

Many histologic structures were described with marvelous insight by this great investigator, starting with the publication of the first text in histology (*Handbuch der Gewebelehre*). He was far ahead of his time in anticipating the modern trends in molecular biology. His influence in the development of histology cannot be overestimated.

1852: *Stannius, H. F. Stannius' experiment on the heart.*

By tying a ligature as a constriction between the sinus venosus and the atrium in the frog and also one around the atrioventricular groove, Stannius was able to demonstrate that the muscle tissues of the atria and ventricles have independent and spontaneous rhythm. His observations also indicated that the sinus is the pacemaker of the heartbeat. These experiments started many investigations on the nature of the heartbeat.

1854: *Newport, G. Discovery of the entrance of spermatozoan into frog's egg.*

This was a significant step in cellular embryology, although its real meaning was not revealed until the concept of fertilization as the union of two pronuclei was formulated about 20 years later (Hertwig, 1875).

1854: *Vogt, C. Experimental infestation of man by pork tapeworm.*

A common experiment among parasitologists is to infect a suspected host to determine a life history.

A little later, the great parasitologist R. Leuckart was able to infect a calf with the cysticerci of the beef tapeworm *Taenia saginata.*

1855: *Addison, T. Discovery of adrenal disease.*

The importance of the adrenals in maintaining normal body functions was shown when Addison described a syndrome of general disorders associated with the pathology of this gland. The discovery is a landmark as a first detection of a disease associated with the endocrine system.

1856: *Discovery of Neanderthal fossil man (Homo neanderthalensis).*

Many specimens of this type of fossil man have been discovered (Europe, Asia, Africa) since the first one was found near Düsseldorf, Germany. His culture was Mousterian, and although of short stature his cranial capacity was as large or larger than that of modern man. Supposed to have lived during the third interglacial stage in late Pleistocene times, he may have been exterminated by the Cro-Magnon man.

1856: *Perkin, W. H. Discovery of the first coal-tar dye.*

The first coal-tar dye, called aniline violet, was formed by oxidizing aniline with potassium bichromate. Rapid development of dyes, many synthetically, followed; their use in microscopic preparations brought rapid strides in cytologic and bacteriologic investigations.

1857: *Bernard, Claude. Formation of glycogen by the liver.*

Bernard's demonstration that the liver forms glycogen from substances brought to it by the blood showed that the body can build up complex substances as well as tear them down.

1858: *Sclater, P. L. Distribution of animals on basis of zoologic regions.*

This was the first serious attempt to study the geographic distribution of organisms, a study that eventually led to the present science of zoogeography. A. R. Wallace worked along similar lines.

1858: *Virchow, Rudolf. Aphorism of Virchow: Omnis cellula e cellula (every cell from a cell).*

1858: *Virchow, Rudolf. Formulation of the concept of disease from the viewpoint of cell structure.*

He laid the basis of modern pathology by stressing the role of the cell in diseased tissue.

1859: *Darwin, Charles. The concept of natural selection as a factor in evolution.*

Although Darwin did not originate the concept of organic evolution, no one has been more influential in the development of evolutionary thought. The publication of *The Origin of Species* represents the greatest single landmark in the history of biology.

1859: *Mauthner, L. Concept of the mauthnerian apparatus.*

Two giant cells or neurons with cell bodies located in the medulla and with axons running to the tip of the spinal cord are found in many fish and amphibians. These giant cells have functional significance in those animals that have lateral line systems and use the tail in swimming. Evidence indicates that they represent a system of connections between static centers of the lateral line and motor centers of the tail muscle that operates in swimming. Many teleosteans and all selachians lack them. Tadpoles of anurans appear to have them at some stage.

1860: *Bernard, Claude. Concept of the constancy of the internal environment (homeostasis).*

This important concept has influenced physiologic thinking, for it shows how organisms in their long evolutionary development have been mainly concerned in preserving their stability against environmental forces.

1860: *Pasteur, Louis. Aphorism of Pasteur: Omne vivum e vivo (every living thing from the living).*

We do not doubt the significance of this concept at present, but from what source did life originate?

1860: *Pasteur, Louis. Refutation of spontaneous generation.*

Pasteur's experiment with the open **S**-shaped flask proved conclusively that fermentation or putrefaction resulted from microbes, thus ending the long-standing controversy regarding spontaneous generation.

1860: *Wallace, A. R. The Wallace line of faunal delimitation.*

As originally proposed by Wallace, there was a sharp boundary between the Australian and Oriental faunal regions so that a geographic line drawn between certain islands, of the Malay Archipelago, through the Makassar Strait between Borneo and Celebes, and between the Philippines and the Sanghir Islands separated two distinct and contrasting zoologic regions. On one side Australian forms predominated; on the other, Oriental ones. The validity of this division has been questioned by zoogeographers in the light of more extensive knowledge of the faunas of the two regions.

1861: *Claparede, E. Discovery of giant nerve axons of annelids.*

These large nerve fibers were first found and described by Ehrenberg (1836) in the Crustacea. As new microscopic techniques were developed, many investigations have been made on the structure and functions of these unique nerve cells. Their chief function is in escape mechanisms involving widespread and synchronous muscular contractions.

1861: *Graham, Thomas. Colloidal states of matter.*

This work on colloidal solutions has resulted in one of the most fruitful concepts regarding protoplasmic systems. Most aspects of cell physiology involve colloidal interpretation in some form or other.

1862: *Bates, H. W. Concept of mimicry.*

Mimicry refers to the advantageous resemblance of one species to another for protection against predators. It involves palatable or edible species that imitate dangerous or inedible species that enjoy immunity because of warning coloration against potential enemies. Thus the mimics profit by deceiving the prey. Mimicry seems to be most common in insects such as butterflies and moths. Biologists have given varied explanations as to how the principle works.

1862: *Bert, P. Parabiosis technique.*

The grafting of one animal to another has been an active research tool in problems of hormonal transmission, pituitary-gonad relations, immunity, skin grafting, etc.

1864: *Haeckel, E. Modern zoologic classification.*

The broad features of zoologic classification as we know it today were outlined by Haeckel and others, especially R. R. Lankester, in the third quarter of the nineteenth century. B. Hatschek is another zoologist who deserves much credit for the modern scheme, which is constantly undergoing revision. Other schemes of classification in the early nineteenth century did much to resolve the difficult problem of classification, such as those of Cuvier, Lamarck, Leuckart, Ehrenberg, Vogt, Gegenbauer, and Schimkevitch. More recently, L. H. Hyman has done invaluable service in the arrangement of animal taxonomy.

1864: *Schultze, Max. Protoplasmic bridges between cells.*

The connection of one cell to another by means of protoplasmic bridges has been demonstrated in both plants and animals, but the concept has never been settled to the satisfaction of histologists. These intercellular connections have been described in many epithelial tissues, where some investigators believe them to be artefacts. The concept that cells are definitely separated from each other has been very well established, at least for nervous and muscular tissues.

1865: *Kekulé, F. A. Concept of the benzene ring.*

The concept of the benzene ring established the later development of synthetic chemistry; it also aided in understanding the basic structure of life that is so dependent on the capacity of carbon atoms to form rings and chains.

1866: *Haeckel, E. Nuclear control of inheritance.*

At the time the hypothesis was formed, the view that the nucleus transmitted the inheritance of an animal had no evidence to substantiate it. This lucky guess no doubt focused the attention of biologists on the nucleus for an explanation of heredity.

1866: *Kowalevsky, A. Taxonomic position of tunicates.*

The great Russian embryologist showed in the early stages of development the similarity between *Amphioxus* and the tunicates and how the latter could be considered a degenerate branch of the phylum Chordata. This was a confirmation of the evolutionary theory from an embryologic standpoint and must be considered a great landmark in understanding the development of animals.

1866: *Mendel, Gregor. Formulation of the first two laws of heredity.*

These first clear-cut statements of inheritance made possible an analysis of hereditary patterns with mathematical precision. When Mendel published his great laws they were unnoticed by students of heredity because they were looking for an explanation of heredity from a wholly different viewpoint and could not appreciate his findings. Rediscovered in 1900, his paper confirmed the experimental data geneticists had found at that time. Since that time mendelism has been considered the chief cornerstone of hereditary investigation.

1866: *Schiff, H. The Schiff reaction for aldehydes.*

The Schiff reagent of fuchsin sulfurous acid is the

colorless derivative produced by the action of sulfur dioxide in water on basic fuchsin or related dyes. There are many variant forms of this reagent, which is the basis of the Feulgen reaction for the nucleic acid DNA. Schiff's reagent has been widely used by investigators in cytochemical techniques for the study of nucleic acids and polysaccharides.

1866: *Schultze, Max. Histologic analysis of the retina.*

Schultze's fundamental discovery that the retina contained two types of visual cells, rods and cones, helped to explain the differences in physiologic vision of high and low intensities of light.

1867: *Kowalevsky, A. Germ layers of invertebrates.*

The concept of the primary germ layers laid down by Pander and von Baer was extended to invertebrates by this investigator. He found that the same three germ layers arose in the same fashion as those in vertebrates. Thus an important embryologic unity was established for the whole animal kingdom.

1867: *Traube, I. Concept of the semipermeable membrane.*

The nature and role of living membranes in biologic systems have been extensively studied in cellular physiology, for the characteristics of the membrane determine the osmotic behavior of cells and the exchanges cells make with their surroundings. Although Traube worked with nonliving membranes, he formulated many principles that have helped in understanding living ones.

1869: *Langerhans, P. Discovery of islet cells in pancreas.*

These islets were first found in the rabbit and since their discovery they have been one of the most investigated tissues in animals. Ever since endocrine functions have been assigned to them, many theories have been proposed to account for their origin. The theory that they have come from the transformation of pancreatic acinus cells has now given way to the theory that they have originated from the embryonic tubules of the pancreatic duct.

1869: *Miescher, F. Isolation of nucleoprotein.*

From pus cells, a pathologic product, Miescher was able to demonstrate in the nuclei certain phosphorus-rich substances, nucleic acids, which are bound to proteins to form nucleoproteins. In recent years these complex molecules have been the focal point of significant biochemical investigations on the chemical properties of genes, with the wider implications of a better understanding of growth, heredity, and evolution.

1871: *Bowditch, H. P. Discovery of the "all-or-none" law of heart muscle.*

This law states that a minimal stimulus will produce a maximal contraction of the heart musculature. A single skeletal fiber also obeys the law the same as cardiac muscle, but the latter is a continuous protoplasmic mass and an impulse that causes contraction in one part spreads also to other parts. This does not mean, however, that stimulation of any part of the heart will necessarily lead to contraction of the whole heart, for backward conduction in the conduction system (Purkinje) does not always occur.

1871: *Quetelet, L. A. Foundations of biometry.*

The applications of statistics to biologic problems is called biometry. By working out the distribution curve of the height of soldiers. Quetelet showed biologists how the systematic study of the relationships of numerical data could become a powerful tool for analyzing data in evolution, genetics, and other biologic fields.

1872-1876: *Challenger expedition.*

Not only did this expedition establish the science of oceanography, but a vast amount of material was collected that greatly extended the knowledge of the variety and range of animal life. No similar expedition has ever equaled this one.

1872: *Dohrn, Anton. Establishment of Naples Biological Station.*

The establishment of this famous station marked the first of the great biologic stations, and it rapidly attained international importance as a center of biologic investigation. Many of our greatest American investigators conducted studies here, especially toward the end of the nineteenth century and the beginning of the twentieth.

1872: *Ludwig, K., and E. F. W. Pflüger. Gas exchange of the blood.*

By means of the mercurial blood pump, these investigators separated the gases from the blood and thereby threw much light on the nature of gaseous exchange and the place where oxidation occurred (in the tissues).

1873: *Agassiz, L. Establishment of first American marine laboratory.*

Although short-lived, this laboratory on the island of Penikese near Cape Cod was instrumental in the training of an influential group of American biologists and in the establishment of a scientific tradition that gave a great impetus to biologic investigation.

1873: *Schneider, Anton. Description of nuclear filaments (chromosomes).*

In his description of cell division, Schneider showed nuclear structures that he termed "nuclear filaments," the first recorded description of what are now known as chromosomes. It was not until several years later that they were actually called chromosomes (colored bodies) by Waldeyer in 1888.

1874: *Haeckel, E. Taxonomic position of phylum Chordata.*

The great German evolutionist based many of his conclusions on the work of the Russian embryologist Kowalevsky, who in 1866 showed that the tunicates as well as amphioxus had vertebrate affinities. The embryologist von Baer had considered such animals to be molluscan forms.

1874: *Haeckel, E. H. Gastrea theory of metazoan ancestry.*

According to this theory, the hypothetic ancestor of all the Metazoa consisted of two layers (ectoderm and entoderm) similar to the gastrula stage in embryonic development, and the entoderm arose as an invagination of the blastula composed of a single layer of flagellate cells. Thus the diploblastic stage of ontogeny was to be considered as the repetition of this ancestral form. This theory has had wide acceptance but has been criticized on the grounds that the endoderm is not always formed by invagination, such as the inwandering of ectodermal cells in certain forms.

1875: *Heidenhain, R. Zymogen granules as enzyme precursors.*

Heidenhain concluded that the disappearance of intracellular bodies (zymogen granules) in the pancreas coincided with the appearance of proteolytic enzymes, and that such granules represented a temporary storage of digestive enzymes. His observations have received further clarification from molecular biology studies.

1875: *Hertwig, O. Concept of fertilization as the conjugation of two sex cells.*

The fusion of the pronuclei of the two gametes in the process of fertilization paved the way for the concept that the nuclei contained the hereditary factors and that both maternal and paternal factors are brought together in the zygote.

1875: *Strasburger, Eduard. Description of indirect cell division.*

The accurate description of the processes of cell division that Strasburger made in plants represents a great pioneer work in the rapid development of cytology during the last quarter of the nineteenth century.

1876: *Boll, F. Discovery of the visual pigment rhodopsin.*

This red substance, which bleaches in the light and regenerates its color in the dark, is now known to form part of a cycle of reactions of great importance in basic visual phenomena and is the source of rod vision sensitivity. The pigment was first discovered in the retina of the frog and was named by W. Kühne, the German physiologist.

1876: *Cohn, F. Significance of the bacterial spore.*

Spore formation among bacteria is restricted mainly to the bacilli. It is an oval body formed within the bacterial cell, and certain environmental conditions favor its formation within a particular kind of bacteria. It may be considered a normal stage in the life history of spore-forming bacteria and an adaptation to harsh survival conditions. Spore-forming bacteria were no doubt responsible for prolonging the belief in spontaneous generation.

1876: *Pasteur, L. The Pasteur effect.*

This metabolic regulation of the oxidative process refers to the release of energy by cells without the use of oxygen, other than that supplied by the metabolites involved. Under anaerobic conditions, Pasteur showed that yeasts and molds cause the fermentation of sugar to alcohol and CO_2. Oxygen suppresses fermentation and the products of anaerobic metabolism, and thus spares carbohydrate utilization. The study of metabolic pathways has focused much attention on the process in recent years.

1877: *Ehrlich, P. Discovery of mast cells.*

Mast cells are granular cells of connective tissue and are associated with inflammatory processes and new growth. They are known also to be the site of the concentration and release of histamine in hypersensitive reactions.

1877: *Lakes, A., O. Lucas, and W. Reed. Discovery of dinosaur fossils.*

The relatively late discovery of these fossil bones in Colorado and Wyoming is the more amazing because dinosaur bones are large and usually abundant wherever they are found. A dinosaur bone may weigh as much as 800 pounds and a skull much more than this.

1877: *Manson, P. First report of an arthropod vector.*

In working out the life cycle of *Wuchereria bancrofti*, Manson established the role of the mosquito in carrying the larval parasite. The arthropod vector has assumed great importance in the transmission of diseases and parasites.

1877: *Pfeffer, W. Concept of osmosis and osmotic pressure.*

Pfeffer's experiments on osmotic pressure and the determination of the pressure in different concentrations laid the foundation for an understanding of a general phenomenon in all organisms.

1878: *Balfour, F. M. Relationship of the adrenal medulla to the sympathetic nervous system.*

By showing that the adrenal medulla has the same origin as the sympathetic nervous system, Balfour really laid the foundation for the interesting concept of the similarity in the action of epinephrine and sympathetic nervous mediation. Out of this has developed the emergency theory of Cannon and others.

1878: *Brandt, K. Demonstration of vital coloring.*

The belief that only dead cells could be stained was long held by histologists, but Brandt was able to stain the lipid droplets in the cytoplasm of living *Actinosphaerium* (Heliozoa) with the dye Bismark brown and observe the process during the vital staining. Trembley had described vital staining, after a fashion, in the eighteenth century. An important research tool since Brandt's discovery, vital staining is now used less because of the development of phase-contrast and interference microscopy.

1878: *Kühne, W. Nature of enzymes.*

The study of the action of chemical catalysts in an understanding of the fundamental nature of life has steadily increased with biologic advancement and now represents one of the most interesting aspects of biochemistry.

1879: *Flemming, W. Chromatin described and named.*

Flemming shares with a few others the description of the details of indirect cell division. The part of the nucleus that stains deeply he called **chromatin** (colored) which gives rise to the chromosomes. This term, as well as certain other ones introduced by the same observer, has been universally accepted by all biologists.

1879: *Fol, Hermann. Penetration of ovum by a spermatozoan described.*

Fol was the first to describe a thin conelike body extending outward from the egg to meet the sperm. Compare Dan's acrosome reaction (1954).

1879: *Kossel, A. Isolation of nucleoprotein.*

Nucleoproteins were isolated in the heads of fish sperm; they make up the major part of chromatin. They are combinations of proteins with nucleic acids, and this study was one of the first of the investigations that interest biochemists at the present time.

Nobel Laureate (1910).

1880: *Laveran, C. L. A. Protozoa as pathogenic agents.*

This French investigator first demonstrated that the causative organism for malaria is a protozoan. This discovery led to other investigations that revealed the role the protozoans play in causing diseases such as sleeping sickness and kala azar. It remained for Sir Roland Ross to discover the role of mosquitoes in spreading malaria.

Nobel Laureate (1906).

1880: *Ringer, S. Influence of blood ions on heart contraction.*

The pioneer work of this investigator determined the inorganic ions necessary for contraction of frog hearts and made possible an evaluation of heart metabolism and the replacement of body fluids.

1881: *Zacharias, E. Distribution and nature of nucleic acids.*

In a pioneer cytochemical study involving the use of enzyme pepsin, he found that the nucleus of the frog erythrocyte and the macronuclei of *Vorticella* and *Paramecium* remained when the other parts of the cell were digested by the enzyme. Other investigators since, such as P. Mazia (1941), have used similar methods and added basic knowledge about these cell constituents of such interest in molecular biology today.

1882: *Flemming, W. First accurate counts of nuclear filaments (chromosomes) made.*

1882: *Flemming, W. Mitosis and spireme named.*

1882: *Metchnikoff, Élie. Role of phagocytosis in immunity.*

The theory that microbes are ingested and destroyed by certain white corpuscles (phagocytes) shares with the theory of chemical bodies (antibodies) the chief explanation for the body's natural immunity.

Nobel Laureate (1908).

1882: *Pfitzner, W. Discovery of chromomeres.*

The discrete granules that make up a large part of chromosomes are of especial interest because they are supposed to correspond to the loci of the genes. Some cytologists have even thought that chromomeres correspond to genes, but most agree that each chromomere has more than one gene.

1882: *Strasburger, E. Cytoplasm and nucleoplasm named.*

1882-1924: *The Albatross of the Fish Commission.*

This vessel, under the direction of the U. S. Fish Commission, was second only to the famed *Challenger* in advancing scientific knowledge about oceanography. Actually, in her long service the collections and investigations made greatly surpassed those of the earlier and better-known *Challenger* expedition.

1883: *Golgi, Camillo, and R. Cajal. Silver nitrate technique for nervous elements.*

The development and refinement of this technique gave a completely new picture of the intricate relationships of neurons. Modifications of this method have given valuable information concerning the cellular element—the Golgi apparatus.

Nobel Laureates (1906).

1883: *Hertwig, O. Origin of term mesenchyme.*

This important tissue, which is restricted to young embryos, may arise from all three germ layers, but chiefly from the mesoderm. It is a protoplasmic network whose meshes are filled with a fluid intercellular substance. Mesenchyme gives rise to a great variety of tissues and both its cells and intercellular substance may be variously modified; its most common derivative is connective tissue. In the transformation from embryonic mesenchyme to its adult derivatives, changes must be looked for in the nucleus and in the intercellular substance. Epithelium and mesenchyme may be regarded as the primary tissues of the body.

1883: *Leuckart, R., and A. P. Thomas. Life history of sheep liver flukes.*

This investigation is noteworthy in parasitology, for it represents the first time a complete life cycle was worked out for a trematode involving more than one host.

1883: *Roux, W. Allocation of hereditary functions to chromosomes.*

This theory could not be much more than a guess when Roux made it, but how fruitful was the idea in the light of the enormous amount of evidence since accumulated!

1884: *Flemming, W., E. Strasburger, and E. Van Beneden. Demonstration that nuclear filaments (chromosomes) double in number by longitudinal division.*

This concept represented a further step in understanding the precise process in indirect cell division.

1884: *Kollman, J. Concept of neoteny.*

Neoteny refers to the retention of larval characters and retardation of somatic growth after the gonads have become sexually mature. In most cases it implies acceleration of sexual maturity (pedogenesis). It was first described in the axolotl larval form of the Mexican newt *Ambystoma.*

1884: *Rubner, Max. Quantitative determinations of the energy value of foods.*

Although Liebig and others had estimated calorie values of foods, the investigations of Rubner put their determinations on a sound basis. His work made possible a scientific explanation for metabolism and a basis for the study of comparative nutrition. He also gave a working basis for the relation of basal metabolism to the surface area of the body, a standard of measurement that E. F. DuBois and other workers have greatly refined.

1884: *Strasburger, E. Prophase, metaphase, and anaphase named.*

1885: *Dubois, R. Nature of light production in animals.*

By his work on luminous clams, Dubois was able to show how a chemical substance, luciferin, could be oxidized with the aid of an enzyme, luciferase, with the production of light. Since this basic discovery, additional work has been done on the nature of the luciferin molecule.

1885: *Hertwig, O., and E. Strasburger. Concept of the nucleus as the basis of heredity.*

The development of this idea occurred before Mendel's laws of heredity were rediscovered in 1900, but it anticipates the important role the nucleus with its chromosomes was to assume in hereditary transmission.

1885: *Rabl, Karl. Concept of the individuality of the chromosomes.*

The view that the chromosomes retain their individuality through all stages of the cell cycle is accepted by all cytologists, and much evidence has accumulated in proof of the theory. However, it has been virtually impossible to demonstrate the chromosome's individuality through all stages. Rabl's suggestion was purely theoretic at the time he made it.

1885: *Roux, W. Mosaic theory of development.*

In the early development of the frog's egg, Roux showed that the determinants for differentiation were segregated in the early cleavage stages and that each cell or groups of cells would form only certain parts of the developing embryo (mosaic or determinate development). Later, other investigators showed that in many forms blastomeres, separated early, would give rise to whole embryos (indeterminate development).

1885: *Weismann, August. Formulation of germ plasm theory.*

Weismann's great theory of the germ plasm stresses the idea that there are two types of protoplasm—germ plasm, which gives rise to the reproductive cells or gametes, and somatoplasm, which furnishes all the other cells. Germ plasm, according to the theory, is continuous from generation to generation, whereas the somatoplasm dies with each generation and does not influence the germ plasm. It is not necessary to point out the influence of the germ plasm theory on biologic thought, both in the fields of evolution and heredity.

1886: *Establishment of Woods Hole Biological Station.*

This station is by all odds the greatest center of its kind in the world. Here most of the biologists in America have studied and the station has increasingly attracted investigators from many other countries as well. The influence of Woods Hole on the progress of biology cannot be overestimated. Here research is conducted the year round, but during the summer the concentration of biologists is greatly multiplied. Certain courses are offered for the benefit of undergraduates and others who are just beginning active biologic study.

1886: *MacMunn, C. A. Discovery of cytochrome.*

This iron-bearing compound was rediscovered in 1925 by D. Keilin and has been demonstrated in most types of cells. Its importance in cellular oxidation and the metabolic pathway has made possible a workable theory of cell respiration and has stimulated the study of intracellular localization of enzymes and how they behave in metabolic processes.

1887: *Fischer, Emil. Structural patterns of proteins.*

The importance of proteins in biologic systems has made their study the central theme of all modern biochemical work. The life process in a large measure revolves around the activities and relations of these complex substances.

Nobel Laureate (1902).

1887: *Haeckel, E. H. Concept of organic form and symmetry.*

Symmetry refers to the spatial relations and arrangements of parts in such a way as to form geometric designs. Although many others before Haeckel's time had studied and described types of animal form, Haeckel has given us our present concepts of organic symmetry, as revealed in his monograph on radiolarians collected on the *Challenger* expedition.

1887: *Van Beneden, E. Chromosome constancy within a species.*

The number of chromosomes is characteristic for each species, usually within the range of 2 to 200. There are minor exceptions to this rule, as in the case of spontaneous polyploidy.

1887: *Van Beneden, E. Demonstration of chromosome reduction during maturation.*

Weismann had predicted this important event before it was actually demonstrated. Only by this method can the constancy of chromosome numbers be maintained.

1887: *Weismann, August. Prediction of the reduction division.*

Weismann formulated the hypothesis that the separation of undivided whole chromosomes must take place in one of the maturation divisions (reduction division), or else the number of chromosomes would double in each generation *(reductio ad absurdum).* He predicted this on theoretic grounds, but the hypothesis was later proved true in all particulars and led to an explanation of Mendel's laws of heredity.

1888: *Helriegel, H., and H. Wilfarth. Discovery of nitrogen cycle.*

The description of the course of nitrogen in nature as it is used by plants and animals represents one of the most significant aspects of biologic economics.

1888: *Waldeyer, W. Chromosome named.*

1889: *Hertwig, R., and E. Maupas. True nature of conjugation in paramecium.*

The process of conjugation had been described (even by Leeuwenhoek) many times and its sexual significance interpreted, but these two investigators independently showed the details of pregamic divisions and the mutual exchange of the micronuclei during the process.

1889: *Maupas, E. Discovery of protozoan mating types.*

His observation that in certain species of ciliates *(Loxophyllum, Stylonychia, etc.)* conjugation was restricted to members of two clones of different origin and did not occur among those of a single clone was the beginning of a research problem that has proved fruitful in the hands of Sonneborn.

1889: *Mering, J. von, and O. Minkowski. Effect of pancreatectomy.*

The classic experiment of removing the pancreas stimulated research that led to the isolation of the pancreatic hormone insulin by Banting (1922).

1890: *Smith, T. Role of an arthropod in disease transmission.*

The transmission of the sporozoan *Babasia,* which is the active agent in causing Texas cattle fever by the tick *Boophilus,* represents one of the first demonstrations of the important role of arthropods as vectors of disease.

1891: *Driesch, H. Discovery of totipotent cleavage.*

The discovery that each of the first several blastomeres, if separated from each other in the early cleavage of the fertilized egg, would develop into a complete embryo stimulated investigation on totipotent and other types of development.

1891: *Dubois, Eugene. Discovery of the fossil man Pithecanthropus erectus.*

Although not the first fossil man to be found, the Java man represents one of the first significant primitive men that have been discovered.

1892: *Ivanovski, D. Discovery of the nature of viruses.*

This discovery was the start of the many investigations on the nature of these important biologic agents. It is still too early to appraise the exact role of viruses in the plan of biologic life, but they represent one of the most baffling problems with which biologists have to contend.

1893: *Dollo, I. Concept of the irreversibility of evolution.*

In general, the overall evolutionary process is one way and irreversible insofar as a whole complex genetic system is concerned, although back mutations and restricted variations may reoccur. The principle has been stressed by many evolutionsts (for example, Blum).

1893: *Haacke, W. Concept of evolutionary orthogenesis.*

This is the principle that stresses the evolutionary idea that groups of animals tend to evolve in one direction without deviation. It is the belief that there is an inherent trend for evolution to proceed in straight lines (rectilinear evolution). The concept has had different meanings and various interpretations, but in its original sense, it is considered to be restricted to certain levels of evolution in which there is slight selective pressure.

1893: *His, W. Anatomy and physiology of the auriculoventricular node and bundle.*

The specialized conducting tissue of the heart has given rise to many investigations, not the least of which were those of His, whose name was given to the intricate system of branches that are reflected over the inner surface of the ventricles.

1894: *Driesch, H. Constancy of nuclear potentiality.*

Driesch's view was that all nuclei of an organism were equipotential but that the activity of nuclei varied with different cells in accordance with the differentiation of tissues. That all genetic factors are present in all cells is supported by the constancy of DNA for each set of chromosomes and the similarity of histone proteins in the different somatic cells of an organism. This theory, however, is being challenged in the much investigated problems of differentiation and growth, and there has been some evidence to show that nuclear potentialities do vary with different stages in development.

1894: *Merriam, C. H. Concept of life zones in North America.*

This scheme is based on temperature criteria and the importance of temperature in the distribution of plants and animals. According to this concept, animals and plants are restricted in their northward distribution by the total quantity of heat during the season of growth and reproduction, and their southward distribution is restricted by the mean temperature during the hottest part of the year. Although students of birds and mammals have found the concept useful, most biologists at present regard it as oversimplified and believe that biotic distribution should be on the basis of plants and animals.

1894: *Morgan, C. L. Concept of animal behavior.*

The modern interpretation of animal behavior really dates from certain basic principles laid down by this psychologist. Among these principles was the one in which he stated that the actions of an animal should be interpreted in terms of the simplest mental processes (Morgan's canon). He did much to remove the study of animal activities from an anthropomorphic interpretation and place it on an objective basis.

1894: *Oliver, G., and E. A. Sharpey-Schaefer. Demonstration of the action of a hormone.*

The first recorded action of a specific hormone was the demonstration of the effect of an extract of the suprarenal (adrenal) gland upon blood vessels and muscle contraction.

1895: *Bruce, D. Life cycle of protozoan blood parasite (Trypanosoma).*

The relation of this parasite to the tsetse fly and to wild and domestic animal infection in Africa is an early demonstration of the role of arthropods as vectors of disease. This masterly work also threw light on other protozoan diseases and represents a distinct link between protozoology and medicine.

1895: *Lombroso, C. Physiologic accompaniment of emotional experience.*

Emotional responses may be accompanied by many physiologically detectable responses, such as breathing rates, heart rates, skin temperatures, salivation changes, and others, all of which are under the involuntary control of the autonomic nervous system. Many other investigators have refined methods for measuring such physiologic changes such as those leading to the polygraph for the detection of deception.

1895: *Nuttal, G. H. F., and H. Thierfelder. Sterile culture of animals (gnotobiotics).*

The technique of rearing animals in a germ-free environment has been revived in recent years and promises to be a useful tool in determining the complex roles microbiota may play in their hosts. The solution of technical problems has made it possible to apply the method to all animals, large or small. J. A. Reyniers and P. C. Trexler have been leaders in the new revival of interest in this field.

1895: *Pinkus, F. Discovery of terminal cranial nerve (O).*

This nerve (nervus terminalis) was discovered after the other cranial nerves had been named and numbered. It is sensory and runs from the olfactory membrane to the olfactory lobe of the brain. Its exact significance is unknown. It was first found in the African lungfish *Protopterus,* but has since been found in all vertebrate classes except birds, although it may be a temporary structure in some. It lies along the anterior border of the olfactory nerve.

1895: *Roentgen, W. Discovery of x-rays.*

This great discovery was quickly followed by its application in the interpretation of bodily structures and processes and represents one of the greatest tools in biologic research.

Nobel Laureate (1901).

1896: *Baldwin, J. M. Baldwin evolutionary effect.*

It is the belief that genetic selection of genotypes will be channeled or canalized in the same direction as the adaptive modifications that were formerly nonhereditary. Nonhereditary adaptive modifications are supposed to keep a racial strain in an environmental channel, where mutations producing similar phenotypes will be selected. The Baldwin effect emphasizes the genetic assimilation of the originally acquired adaptive characters resulting from reactions with environmental agents. The theory seems to be of limited application but has been revived by evolutionists in recent years.

1896: *Becquerel, A. H. Discovery of spontaneous radioactivity.*

His discovery of the rays emitted by uranium, together with the work of the Curies on high-energy particles, elucidated the process of radioactivity, which led in time to the isotope concept of so fruitful application to biologic phenomena.

Nobel Laureate (1903).

1896: *Russian Hydrographic Survey. Biology of Lake Baikal.*

This lake in Siberia is more than 500 miles long, 50 miles wide, and has an extreme depth of more than a mile (the deepest lake in the world). Its unique fauna is a striking example of evolutionary results from long-continued isolation. Up to 100% of the species in certain groups are endemic (found nowhere else). This remarkable fauna represents the survival of ancient freshwater animals that have become extinct in surrounding areas. The lake has been a fertile field for the study of various groups of animals by specialists for the past 75 years.

Lakes Tanganyika and Nyasa in Africa are similar lakes and likewise have unique faunas.

1897: *Abel, J. J., and A. C. Crawford. Isolation of the first hormone (adrenaline).*

The purification and isolation of one of the active principles of the suprarenal medulla led to its chemical nature and naming by J. Takamine (1901) and its synthesis by F. Stolz (1904).

1897: *Born, G. Heteroplastic grafting.*

By joining together parts of embryos of different species, such as frog and toad, Born was able to produce viable individuals that continued to develop as chimaeras. Other investigators, such as Harrison and Spemann, also performed many similar experiments, and the method has been put to practical use by plant workers.

1897: *Braun, F. Invention of the cathode-ray oscillograph.*

This instrument has been one of the most useful tools ever invented for measuring electrical events in excitable tissues.

Nobel Laureate (1909).

1897: *Buchner, E. Discovery of zymase.*

Buchner's discovery that an enzyme (a nonliving substance) manufactured by yeast cells was responsible for fermentation resolved many problems that had baffled Pasteur and other investigators. Zymase is now known to consist of a number of enzymes.

Nobel Laureate (1907).

1897: *Canadian Geological Survey. Dinosaur fauna of Alberta, Canada.*

In the rich fossil beds along the Red Deer River in Alberta there was found the fauna of the Upper Cretaceous time, and a whole new revelation of the dinosaur world has been made from the study of these fossils. The fossils reveal that the dinosaurs had reached the peak of their adaptive radiation at this time and had evolved into many types of diverse morphology and habits. This discovery must rank as one of the most important in the whole field of vertebrate paleontology.

1897: *Eijkman, C. Discovery of the cause of a dietary deficiency disease.*

Eijkman's pioneer work on the causes of beriberi led to the isolation of the antineuritic vitamin (thiamine). This work may be called the key discovery that resulted in the development of the important vitamin concept.

Nobel Laureate (1929).

1897: *Garnier, C. Discovery of the ergastoplasm organelle.*

This term was originally applied to those diffused or discrete cytoplasmic masses of fibrillar materials (especially in gland cells) that stain with basic dyes just as the nuclear chromatin, hence the basophilic part of the cytoplasm. The electron microscope has shown that this material is the same as the rough-surfaced endoplasmic reticulum because of the dense granules of RNA (ribosomes, or the classic microsomes).

1897: *Hertwig, O. Influence of yolk on patterns of egg segmentation.*

The mechanical effect of yolk is mainly responsible for the great variety of segmentation types of eggs, a concept that was proved by Hertwig by experimental procedures.

1897: *Huot, A. Discovery of the aglomerular fish kidney.*

This discovery in the angler fish (*Lophius*) and later in the toadfish and others proved to renal physiologists that renal tubules of kidneys could excrete as well as resorb substances. By using such a kidney as a test organ, it has been possible to ascertain what things can and cannot be excreted by the kidney tubules, and thus a better understanding of many renal functions has been acquired.

1897: *Ross, Ronald. Life history of malarian parasite (Plasmodium).*

This notable achievement represents a great landmark in the field of parasitology and the climax of the work of many investigators on the problem. It also marks the important role arthropod vectors play in the transmission of disease.

Nobel Laureate (1902).

1897: *Sherrington, C. S. Concept of the synapse in the nervous system.*

If the nervous system is composed of discrete units or neurons, functional connections must exist between these units. Sherrington showed how individual nerve cells could exert integrative influences on other nerve cells by graded excitatory or inhibitory synaptic actions. The electron microscope has in recent years added much to a knowledge of the synaptic structure.

Nobel Laureate (1932).

1898: *Benda, C., and C. Golgi. Discovery of mitochondria and the Golgi apparatus.*

These interesting cytoplasmic inclusions were actually seen by various observers before this date, but they were both named in 1898 and the real study of them began at this time. Flemming and R. Altmann first demonstrated mitochondria. The Golgi apparatus was demonstrated by V. St. George (1867) and G. Platner (1885), but Camillo Golgi, with his silver nitrate impregnation method, gave the first clear description of the apparatus in nerve cells. Mitochondria are now known to play an important role in the synthesis of enzymes in cellular metabolism.

1898: *Osborn, H. F. Concept of adaptive radiation in evolution.*

This concept states that, starting from a common ancestral type, many different forms of evolutionary adaptations may occur. In this way evolutionary divergence can take place, and the occupation of many ecologic niches is made possible, according to the adaptive nature of the invading species. The concept has been very fruitful in the interpretation of evolutionary progress, and many examples are often cited as evidences for its correctness, such as Darwin's finches of the Galápagos Islands, the varied limb structure of mammals, and Australian marsupials.

1899: *Bayless, W. H., and E. H. Starling. Law of the intestine.*

As originally formulated, the law stated that the movement of food down the alimentary canal is accomplished by a wave of muscular contraction above the bolus of food and a dilation below it. It is doubtful that there is an inhibition of the muscle below the bolus, but the dilation is simply due to the general opening of the gut by the contraction of the longitudinal muscles.

1899: *Hardy, W. A. Appraisal of conventional fixation methods.*

This investigation showed that the common preservatives used in killing and fixing cells produced either fibrous networks or fine emulsions and that the method of fixation determined which of these states is produced (artefacts). Thus it is impossible to appraise the structure of dead protoplasm, revealed by such methods, as a true index of the condition of living protoplasm, and the structures found in stained cells needed confirmation by other methods because the fibrillar, reticular, and other appearances of protoplasm are artefacts due to the type of fixation and staining employed.

1900: *Chamberlain, T. C. Theory of the freshwater origin of vertebrates.*

The evidence for this theory as first proposed was based mainly on the fact that early vertebrate fossils were found in sediments of freshwater origin, such as Old Red Sandstone, and were largely absent from marine deposits. Much of these freshwater deposits were supposed to have been laid down in rivers that drained the higher ranges of the continents. Other lines of evidence have also been presented, such as the adaption of the vertebrate morphologic pattern for currents of water and the evolution of the glomerular kidney. The theory has in general been widely accepted by paleontologists.

1900: *Correns, K. E., E. Tschermak, and Hugo de Vries. Rediscovery of Mendel's laws of heredity.*

These three investigators independently in their genetic experiments on plants obtained results similar to Mendel's, and in their survey of the literature found that Mendel had published his now famous laws in 1866. A few years later, W. Bateson and others found that the same laws applied to animals also. The impetus given to genetic study by this rediscovery has resulted in some of the most important contributions in biology.

1900: *Discovery of fossil beds in Fayum Lake province of Egypt.*

The work of C. F. Andrews and others on these fossils has shown how important Africa has been in the evolution of mammals. The many new types that evolved here may have been due to geographic isolation and inbreeding.

1900: *Landsteiner, Karl. Discovery of blood groups.*

This fundamental discovery made possible successful blood transfusions as well as initiated the tremendous amount of work on the biochemistry of blood, an investigation that is more active now than ever before.

Nobel Laureate (1930).

1900: *Loeb, J. Discovery of artificial parthenogenesis.*

The possibility of getting eggs that normally undergo fertilization to develop by chemical and mechanical methods has been accomplished in a number of different animals from the sea urchin and frog eggs (Loeb, 1900) to the rabbit egg (Pincus, 1936). The phenomenon has some importance in experimental cytology. As a matter of record, O. Hertwig had mentioned the possibility of parthenogenesis in one of his works many years before.

1901: *Montgomery, T. H. Homologous pairing of maternal and paternal chromosomes in the zygote.*

Sutton, also, showed that in synapsis before the reduction division each pair is made up of a maternal and a paternal chromosome. This phenomenon is of fundamental importance in the segregation of hereditary factors (genes).

1901: *Vries, Hugo de. Mutation theory of evolution.*

de Vries concluded from his study of the evening primrose *Oenothera lamarckiana* that new characters appear suddenly and are inheritable. Although the variations in *Oenothera* were probably not mutations at all since many of them represented hybrid combinations, yet the evidence for the theory from other sources has steadily mounted until now the theory affords the most plausible explanation for evolutionary progress.

1902: *Kropotkin, P. Mutual aid as a factor in evolution.*

This concept is not new by any means, but Kropotkin elaborated on the importance of social life at all levels of animal life in the survival patterns of the evolutionary process. Population studies in many groups show an underlying element of automatic mutual aid, and many students of animal behavior have stressed the principle since Kropotkin's time.

1902: *Lillie, F. R. Differentiation without cleavage.*

By placing eggs (fertilized or unfertilized) of the annelid worm *Chaetopterus* in sea water containing potassium chloride, Lillie found that the egg would undergo development and differentiation without cleavage. Differentiation is thus not dependent on uninucleate compartments.

1902: *McClung, C. E. Discovery of sex chromosomes.*

The discovery in the grasshopper that a certain chromosome (X) had a mate (Y) different in appearance or else lacked a mate altogether gave rise to the theory that certain chromosomes determined sex. H. Henking actually discovered the X chromosome in 1891.

1903: *Bayliss, W. M., and E. H. Starling. Discovery of the first hormone, secretin.*

The isolation of a substance from the mucosa of the duodenum that had a powerful effect on stimulating the secretion of pancreatic juice was a key experiment in the development of the great science of endocrinology.

1903: *Boveri, T., and W. S. Sutton. Parallelism between chromosome behavior and mendelian segregation.*

This theory states that synaptic mates in meiosis correspond to the mendelian alternative characters and that the formula of character inheritance of Mendel could be explained by the behavior of the chromosomes during maturation. This is therefore a cytologic demonstration of mendelism.

1903: *Sutton, W. S. Constitution of the diploid group of chromosomes.*

The diploid group of chromosomes is made up of two chromosomes of each recognizable size, one member of which is paternal and the other maternal in origin.

1904: *Cannon, W. B. Mechanics of digestion by x-rays.*

The clever application of x-rays to a study of the movements and other aspects of the digestive system has revealed an enormous amount of information on the physiology of the alimentary canal. Cannon first used this technique in 1898.

1904: *Carlson, A. J. Pacemaking activity of neurogenic hearts.*

Heartbeats may originate in muscle (myogenic hearts) or in ganglion cells (neurogenic hearts). Carlson showed that in the arthropod (*Limulus*) the pacemaker was located in certain ganglia on the dorsal surface of the heart and that experimental alterations of these ganglia by temperature or other means altered the heart rate. Neurogenic hearts are restricted to certain invertebrates.

1904: *Jennings, H. S. Behavior patterns in Protozoa.*

The careful investigations of this lifelong student of the behavior of these lower organisms lead to concepts such as the trial-and-error behavior and many of our important beliefs about the various forms of tropisms and taxes.

1904: *Macallum, A. B. Similarity of blood salts to sea salts.*

The relative concentration and proportions of the salts (potassium, sodium, calcium) in the blood of most vertebrates is similar to that found in sea water and is considered to be evidence of the origin of animals in the sea. The higher concentration of salts in the sea today, as compared with the Cambrian period when land forms are supposed to have arisen, is explained by the constant addition of salt from continental streams.

This hypothesis has been subjected to critical analysis in recent years on the basis that the salt concentration of vertebrate extracellular fluid is proportionally much smaller than the salt concentration of the Cambrian period and that the magnesium content of extracellular fluid is proportionally much smaller than that in the Cambrian seas.

1904: *Nuttall, G. H. F. Serologic relationships of animals.*

This method of determining animal relationships is striking evidence of evolution. It has been used in recent years to establish the taxonomic position of animals whose classification has not been determined by other methods.

1905: *Haldane, J. S., and J. G. Priestley. Role of carbon dioxide in the regulation of breathing.*

By their clever technique of obtaining samples of air from the lung alveoli, these investigators showed how the constancy of carbon dioxide concentration in the alveoli and its relation to the concentration in the blood was the chief regulator of the mechanism of respiration.

1905: *Huber, G. C. Dissection of the nephron.*

The isolation of a complete mammalian kidney nephron by maceration and teasing is a landmark in renal histology, for it revealed for the first time the structure of the different parts of the tubule in relation to each other, as shown in the sequence of a gross morphologic preparation.

1905: *Zsigmondy, R. Application of ultracentrifuge to colloids.*

This has made possible a study of colloidal particles and the finer details of protoplasmic systems.

Nobel Laureate (1925).

1906: *Bateson, W., and R. C. Punnett. Discovery of linkage of hereditary units.*

Although first discovered in sweet peas, it was Morgan and associates who gave the real meaning to this great genetic concept. All seven pairs of Mendel's alternative characters were in separate chromosomes, a fact that simplified his problem.

1906: *Einthoven, W. Mechanism of the electrocardiogram.*

The invention of the string galvanometer (1903) by Einthoven supplied a precise tool for measuring the bioelectric activity of the heart and quickly led to the electrocardiogram, which gives accurate information about disturbances of the heart's rhythm. That the heart generates an electric current at each systole was discovered by A. Kolliker and J. Muller.

Nobel Laureate (1924).

1906: *Hopkins, F. G. Analysis of dietary deficiency.*

Hopkins tried to explain dietary deficiency by a biochemical investigation of the lack of essential amino acids in the diet—an approach that has led to many important investigations in nutritional requirements.

Nobel Laureate (1929).

1906: *Tswett, M. Principle of chromatography.*

This is the separation of chemical components in a mixture by differential migration of materials according to structural properties within a special porous sorptive medium. The technique, which may involve the flow of either solvent or gas, is widely used in the purification and isolation of many substances and in other applications.

1907: *Boltwood, B. B. Use of uranium-lead method for dating geologic periods.*

A stable end product of the disintegration of uranium is a lead isotope, with the emission of helium, which remains in the rock formations along with the remainder of the uranium. Uranium has a half-life of about 4.5 billion years and the age of the rock can be estimated by comparison of the proportions of undecayed uranium and of lead present in the rock. The method can be applied only to igneous rocks that have uranium and that are at least 50 million years old.

1907: *Boveri, T. Qualitative differences of chromosomes.*

Boveri showed in his classic experiment with sea urchin eggs that chromosomes have qualitatively different effects on development. He found that only those cells developed into larva that had one of each kind of chromosome; those cells that did not have representatives of each kind of chromosome failed to develop.

1907: *Discovery of the Heidelberg fossil man (Homo heidelbergensis).*

This fossil consisted of a lower jaw with all its teeth. The jaw shows many simian characteristics, but the teeth show patterns of primitive men. This type is supposed to have existed during mid-Pleistocene times and is more or less intermediate between the Java man and modern man.

1907: *Hopkins, F. G. Relationship of lactic acid to muscular contraction.*

Hopkins showed that, after being formed in muscular contraction, a part of the lactic acid is oxidized to furnish energy for the resynthesis of the remaining lactic acid into glycogen. This discovery did much to clarify part of the cyclic reactions involved in the complicated process of muscular contraction.

Nobel Laureate (1929).

1907: *Keith, A., and M. J. Flack. Discovery of the sinoauricular (S-A) node.*

The ancestory of this node is the sinus tissue of the primitive heart of cold-blooded animals. In mammals this node is embedded in the muscle of the right auricle near the openings of the superior and inferior venae cavae and initiates the beat and sets the pace (pacemaker) for the mammalian heart.

The atrioventricular (A-V) node, which lies in the septum of the atria near the A-V valves, was discovered in 1906 by Tawara.

1907: *Wilson, H. V. Reorganization of sponge cells.*

In this classic experiment, Wilson showed that the disaggregation of sponges, by squeezing them through fine silk bolting cloth so that they are separated into minute cell clumps, resulted in the surviving cells coming together and organizing themselves into small sponges when they were in sea water. Some cells other than those of sponges have since been found to have the same ability. It is also possible for cells from different species of sponges to reorganize together in the formation of a new sponge.

1908: *Hardy, G. H., and W. Weinberg. Hardy-Weinberg population formula.*

This important theorem states that, in the absence of factors (mutation, selection, etc.) causing change in genes, the proportion of genes in any large population will reach an equilibrium in one generation and thereafter will remain stable regardless of whether the genes are dominant or recessive. Its mathematic expression forms the basis for the calculations of population genetics.

1909: *Arrhenius, S., and S. P. L. Sörensen. Determination of hydrogen ion concentration (pH).*

The sensitivity of most biologic systems to acid and alkaline conditions has made pH values of the utmost importance in biologic research.

Arrhenius, Nobel Laureate (1903).

1909: *Bataillon, E. Discovery of the pseudogamy concept.*

Pseudogamy is the activation of an unfertilized egg by a sperm without the participation of the male chromosomes of the sperm in the hereditary pattern of the resulting developed egg. The sperm may be from a male of the same species or from a different species. Interest in the peculiar process has been revived in recent years by the discovery of a naturally occurring all-female species of poeciliid fish *(Poecilia formosa)* whose eggs develop parthenogenetically when activated by the sperm from either of two related sympatric species. Many evolutionary implications are raised by this phenomenon.

1909: *Castle, W. E., and J. C. Philips. The inviolability of germ cells to somatic cell influences.*

That germ cells are relatively free from somatic cell influences was shown by the substitution of a black guinea pig ovary in a white guinea pig that gave rise to black offspring when mated to a black male.

1909: *Doublass, E. Discovery of dinosaur fossil bed.*

Dinosaur fossils have been found in various parts of the world, such as the deposits in Alberta, Canada, and those in Tendaguru, East Africa, but few have equaled the dinosaur bed near Jensen, Utah. Here one may see the dinosaur skeletons preserved in the rocks just as they were laid down millions of years ago. More than 12 species of dinosaurs have been identified from this bed, including the *Diplodocus* that grew almost 90 feet long. This region is a national monument, and a large dinosaur museum is now being prepared there.

1909: *Janssens, F. A. Chiasmatype theory.*

When homologous chromosomes are paired before the reduction division, they or their chromatids form visible crosslike figures or chiasmata, which Janssens interpreted as the visible exchange of parts of two homologous chromatids, although he could not actually prove this point. More than 20 years elapsed before the theory in substance was put on a demonstrable cytologic basis. This phenomenon of crossing-over is the key to the genetic mapping of chromosomes so extensively worked out by Morgan and his school with *Drosophila.*

1909: *Johannsen, W. Gene, genotype, and phenotype named.*

1909: *Johannsen, W. Limitations of natural selection on pure lines.*

This investigator found that when a hereditary group of characters becomes homogeneous, natural selection cannot change the genetic constitution with regard to these characters. Selection was shown to be something that could not create and was effective only in isolating genotypes already present in the group; it therefore could not effect evolutionary changes directly.

1909: *Nicolle, C. J. H. Body louse as vector of typhus fever.*

The demonstration that typhus fever was transmitted from patient to patient by the bite of the body louse paved the way for the control of this dreaded epidemic disorder by delousing populations with DDT.

Nobel Laureate (1928).

1910: *Dale, H. H. Nature of histamine.*

Dale and colleagues found that an extract from ergot had the properties of histamine (β-imidazolyl ethylamine), which can be produced synthetically by splitting off carbon dioxide from the amino acid histidine. It is also a constituent of all tissue cells, from which it may be released by injuries or other causes. The pronounced effect of histamine in dilating small blood vessels, contracting smooth muscle, and stimulating glands has caused it to be associated with many physiologic phenomena, such as anaphylaxis, shock, and allergies. Although histamine has been the focal point of many investigations, its exact role in bodily processes is still far from being resolved.

Nobel Laureate (1936).

1910: *Ehrlich, Paul. Chemotherapy in the treatment of disease.*

The discovery of salvarsan as a cure for syphilis represents the first great discovery in this field. Another was the dye sulfanilamide, discovered by Domagk in 1935. These chemicals, which are more or less harmful to the body, have been generally superseded by the more effective and less harmful antibiotics.

Nobel Laureate (1908).

1910: *Heinroth, O. Concept of imprinting as a type of behavior.*

This is a special type of learning that is demonstrated by birds (and possibly other animals). It is based on the fact that a goose or bird is attracted to the first large object it sees just after hatching and thereafter will follow that object to the exclusion of all others. Although the behavior pattern appears to be strongly fixed, there is some doubt about its irreversibility.

D. Spalding (1872) had observed and described this behavior also.

1910: *Herrick, J. B. Discovery of sickle cell anemia.*

In this inherited condition, red blood cells have an abnormal sickle shape and do not function normally. Investigation has shown that the S hemoglobin found in this type of anemia differs from the normal A hemoglobin in the protein component but not in the heme component. Glutamic acid, one of the 300 amino acids in the molecule of normal hemoglobin, is replaced by valine in the sickle cell hemoglobin. The inheritance is supposed to involve a single gene.

1910: *Morgan, T. H. Discovery of sex linkage.*

Morgan and colleagues discovered that the results of a cross between a white-eyed male with a red-eyed female in *Drosophila* were different from those obtained from the reciprocal cross of a red-eyed male with a white-eyed female. This was a crucial experiment, for it showed for the first time that how a trait behaved in heredity depended on the sex of the parent, in contrast to most mendelian characters, which behave genetically the same way whether introduced by a male or female parent.

1910-1920: *Morgan, T. H. Establishment of the theory of the gene.*

The extensive work of Morgan and associates on the localization of hereditary factors (by genetic experiments) on the chromosomes of the fruit fly (*Drosophila*) represents the most significant work ever performed in the field of heredity. The next step is to actually see the physical entity known as the gene, and there has been progress along this line.

Nobel Laureate (1933).

1910: *Murray, J., and J. Hjort. Deep sea expedition of the Michael Sars.*

Of the many expeditions for exploring the depths of the oceans, the *Michael Sars* expedition, made in the North Atlantic regions, must rank among the foremost. The expedition yielded an immense amount of information about deep sea animals, as well as many important concepts regarding the ecologic pattern of animal distribution in the sea. This expedition first demonstrated that the ocean was divided vertically and horizontally into many different kinds of environments, each with its characteristic animal population.

1910: *Pavlov, I. P. Concept of the conditioned reflex.*

The idea that acquired reflexes play an important role in the nervous reaction patterns of animals has greatly influenced the development of modern psychology.

Nobel Laureate (1904).

1911: *Child, C. M. Axial gradient theory.*

This theory attempts to explain the pattern of metabolism from the standpoint of localized regional differences along the axes of organisms. The differences in the metabolic rate of different areas has made possible an understanding of certain aspects of regeneration, development, and growth.

1911: *Cuénot, L. The preadaptation concept.*

Preadaptation refers to a morphologic or physiologic character that may be indifferent or of minor importance in the environment in which it first occurs, but that may be suited to take advantage of a certain type of environment should the latter arise. This favorable conjunction of characters and suitable environment is considered to be an important factor in progressive evolution (opportunistic evolution).

1911: *Dobell, C. C. The acellular status of the protist.*

It is the belief of some zoologists that a protistan cell is not homologous with the metazoan cell because one is a whole organism and the other only a part of an organism. Arguments pro and con have been advanced in the controversy. It may be stated that a valid interpretation might be advanced considering the relative homologues in the two types of cells.

1911: *Funk, C. Vitamin hypothesis.*

Vitamin deficiency diseases are commonly called avitaminoses and refer to those diseases in which causes can be definitely traced to the lack of some essential constituent of the diet. Thus beriberi is caused by an insufficient amount of thiamine, scurvy by a lack of vitamin C, etc.

Funk is also credited with the name vitamin(e). He also formed a crude preparation of the antiberiberi substance (thiamine), which was finally synthesized in 1936 by R. R. Williams.

1911: *Harvey, E. B. Cortical changes in the egg during fertilization.*

In the mature egg, cortical granules gather at the surface of the egg, but on activation of the egg these granules, beginning at the point of sperm contact, disappear in a wavelike manner around the egg. These granules by their breakdown are supposed to release material that helps form the ensuing fertilization membrane. This phenomenon may be considered the first visible change in the egg after fertilization.

1911: *Rutherford, E. Concept of the atomic nucleus.*

This cornerstone of modern physics must be of equal interest to the biologist in the light of the rapid advances of molecular biology. Rutherford also discovered (1920) the proton, one of the charged particles in the atomic nucleus.

Nobel Laureate (1908).

1911: *Walcott, C. D. Discovery of Burgess shale fossils.*

The discovery of a great assemblage of beautifully preserved invertebrates in the Burgess shale of British Columbia and their careful study by an American paleontologist represent a landmark in the fossil record of invertebrates. These fossils date from the middle Cambrian age and include the striking *Aysheaia,* which has a resemblance to the extant *Peripatus.*

1912: *Carrel, A. Technique of tissue culture.*

The culturing of living tissues in vitro, that is, outside of the body, has given biologists an important tool for studying tissue structure and growth. Many facts about cell division and its rate and the processes of senescence and rejuvenation in tissues have been found by this method. R. Harrison in 1907 had found that parts of living tissues in suitable media under suitable conditions could live and multiply.

Nobel Laureate (1912).

1912: *Gudernatsch, J. F. Role of the thyroid gland in the metamorphosis of frogs.*

This investigator found that the removal of the thyroid gland of tadpoles prevented metamorphosis into frogs, and also that the feeding of thyroid extracts to tadpoles induced precocious metamorphosis. In 1919 W. W. Swingle also showed that the presence and absence of inorganic iodine would produce the same results. These and other investigations did much to clarify the function of an important endocrine gland.

1912: *Kite, G. L. Micrurgic study of cell structures.*

The use of micromanipulators for the microdissection of living cells has greatly enriched our knowledge of the finer microscopic details of protoplasm, chromosomes, cell division, and many other phenomena of cells. The development of the method has been due to many workers, such as H. D. Schmidt (1859), M. A. Barber (1904), and W. Seifriz (1921), but R. Chambers has perhaps done more to refine its use and to employ it in experimental cell research.

1912: *Wegener, A. L. Concept of continental drift theory.*

This theory postulates that the continents were originally joined together in one or two large masses that gradually broke up during geologic time, and the fragments drifted apart to form the current land masses. The theory has been revived recently on the basis of the geologic shifting of paleomagnetism convection currents in the earth and definite biologic evidence, for example, the finding of an amphibian fossil in Antarctic regions.

1913: *Federley, H. Explanation of hybrid sterility.*

The failure of chromosome pairing in meiosis when different species of moths were crossed was shown to be the primary cause of sterility in hybrids. In such cases the gene arrangement in the chromosomes of different species is so disarranged that homologous loci between pairs no longer exist. Many other cases have since been described.

1913: *Michaelis, L., and M. Menton. Enzyme-substrate complex.*

On theoretic and mathematic grounds these investigators showed that an enzyme formed an intermediate compound with its substrate (the enzyme-substrate complex) which subsequently decomposes to release the free enzyme and the reaction products. Some progress has been made in recent years in demonstrating the nature of this intermediate compound that is extremely evanescent. D. Keilin of Cambridge University and B. Chance of the University of Pennsylvania have demonstrated the presence of such a complex by color changes and measurements of its rate of formation and breakdown that agree with theoretic predictions. Its clear-cut demonstration will yield further information on the amazing role of enzymes in the life process.

1913: *Miyairi, K., and M. Suzuki. First complete life cycle of a schistosome.*

This work was done with *Schistosoma japonicum,* one of the three common species of blood flukes.

1913: *Reck, H. Discovery of Olduvai Gorge fossil deposits.*

This region in East Africa has yielded an immense amount of early mammalian fossils as well as the tools of the Stone Age man, such as stone axes. Among the interesting fossils discovered were elephants with lower jaw tusks, horses with three toes, and the odd ungulate (chalicothere) with claws on the toes.

1913: *Shelford, V. E. Law of ecologic tolerance.*

This law states that the potential success of an organism in a specific environment depends on how it can adjust within the range of its toleration to the various factors to which the organism is exposed. The complex nature of the different factors for normal existence has been the subject of intense investigation in ecologic population studies.

1913: *Sturtevant, A. H. Formation of first chromosome map.*

By the method of crossover percentages it has been possible to locate the genes in their relative positions on chromosomes—one of the most fruitful discoveries in genetics, for it led to the extensive mapping of the chromosome in *Drosophila.*

1913: *Tashiro, S. Metabolic activity of propagated nerve impulse.*

The detection of slight increases in carbon dioxide production in stimulated nerves, as compared with inactive ones, was evidence that conduction in nerves is a chemical change. Later (1926), A. V. Hill was able to measure the heat given off during the passage of an impulse. Oxygen consumption has also been measured in excited nerves.

1914: *Kendall, E. C. Isolation of thyroxine.*

The isolation of thyroxine in crystalline form was a landmark in endocrinology. Its artificial synthesis was done by Harington in 1927.

1914: *Lillie, F. R. Role of fertilizin in fertilization.*

According to this theory, the jelly coat of eggs contains a substance, fertilizin, which combines with the antifertilizin on the surface of sperm and causes the sperm to clump together. Although this theory received little acceptance when first proposed, biologists have in recent years revived the idea and have added new interpretations to it.

1914: *Sharp, R. Discovery of the neuromotor apparatus of ciliates.*

This demonstration of a system of neurofibrils connected to a motor mass in the anterior part of the organism (*Epidinium*), which was concerned in the coordination of cilia and other motor organelles of the cystostomial region, has been extended to other ciliates and may be considered a universal structural feature of this group.

1914: *Shull, G. H. Concept of heterosis.*

When two standardized strains or races are crossed, the resulting hybrid generation may be markedly superior to both parents as shown by greater vigor, vitality, and resistance to unfavorable environmental conditions. First worked out in corn (maize), such hybrid vigor may also be manifested by other kinds of hybrids. Although its exact nature is still obscure, the phenomenon may be due to the bringing together in the hybrid of many dominant genes of growth and vigor that were scattered among the two inbred parents, or it may be due to the complementary reinforcing action of genes when brought together. It was first studied in artificial plant hybrids by J. G. Koelreuter in 1763. The concept is an example of the practical utilization of modern genetics.

1914: *Williston, S. W. Concept of Williston's law of evolutionary simplification.*

This principle stresses the structural simplification of bodily parts in evolutionary development, wherein the parts are reduced in number but become more specialized. For instance, ancient crustaceans (trilobites) had many similar somites and legs in comparison with the fewer ones of modern crustaceans. The principle is mainly restricted to those parts of an animal that perform the same or closely related functions, such as the teeth of vertebrates.

1915: *Mathew, W. D. Dispersal pattern of biota.*

According to this concept, the primitive types of a group are arranged in the peripheral zones of a distribution pattern, whereas highly evolved or specialized types are found near the center. This horizontal stratification is due in part to the inability of primitive forms to compete successfully with the better adjusted members in the center zones.

1916: *Bridges, C. B. Discovery of nondisjunction.*

Bridges explained an aberrant genetic result by a suggested formula that later he was able to confirm by cytologic examination of the failure of a pair of chromosomes to disjoin at the reduction division so that both chromosomes passed into the same cell. It was definite proof that genes are located on the chromosomes.

1916: *Lillie, F. R. Theory of freemartin.*

The sexually abnormal female calf when it is born as a twin to a normal male had been a baffling problem for centuries until Lillie demonstrated in convincing fashion that hormones from the earlier developing gonads of the male circulate into the blood of the female and alter the sex differentiation of the latter. As a result the gonads of the freemartin never reach maturity and so she remains sterile. Lillie's theory has done much to stimulate investigation into the nature of sex differentiation, especially the role of sex hormones in the process.

1916: *Winkler, H. Concept of heteroploidy.*

Deviations from the normal diploid number of chromosomes are known to occur spontaneously in both plants and animals. It has also been known for some time that heteroploidy can be induced by artificial means. Intensive investigation of the phenomenon has yielded a great deal of information concerning its relation to such matters as correlation of cell size with number of chromosomes, the viability of organisms possessing abnormal number of chromosomes, and nucleoplasmatic ratio.

1917: *Bloch, N. Discovery of dopa reaction for melanin.*

This selective stain for the dendritic melanoblast cells of the skin is based on the presence of an enzyme (dopa oxidase) in melanoblasts that converts dopa (dihydroxyphenyalanine) into a dark brown or black pigment. Such cells are called dopa positive and are to be distinguished from dopa-negative melanophores. The method has clinical application.

1917: *Broili, F. Discovery of amphibian-reptilian fossil, Seymouria.*

This interesting fossil found near Seymour, Texas, has characteristics of both amphibians and reptiles and thus throws some light on the relations between the two great vertebrate classes.

1917: *Grinnell, J. Concept of the ecologic niche.*

This is the spatial unit occupied by a taxon (species or subspecies) to which it is adapted morphologically and physiologically with reference to physical and biotic factors. Elton has done much to develop the concept and simplified its meaning to an animal's place in the biotic environment with respect to food and enemies.

1917: *McCollum, E. V. Discovery of vitamin A.*

This vitamin is derived from carotin, the yellow pigment of carrots, green vegetables, and liver oils of many fish.

1917: *Papanicolaou, G. N., and C. R. Stockard. Smear technique of vaginal contents.*

By this technique the reproductive cycle could be followed accurately in the living animal. The technique has had other applications such as the "Pap" test for uterine cancer.

1918: *Haecker, V. Genic control of development.*

This process, called phenogenetics, involved a method of following a mutant phenotype back in development to the point at which it cannot be distinguished from the normal phenotype. Experimental methods have largely supplanted this morphologic method and have led to the modern concept of genic control of specific enzymes, as demonstrated in the revealing work of Tatum and Beadle.

1918: *King, H. D. Modified sex ratios by genetic selection.*

By close inbreeding and careful selection in rats, she was able to split in 25 generations a strain with a secondary sex ratio of 110 (110♂:108♀) into two substrains with sex ratios of 124 and 82. This classic experiment may give some insight into those cases of unexpected sex ratios.

1918: *Krogh, A. Regulation of the motor mechanism of capillaries.*

The mechanism of the differential distribution of blood to the various tissues has posed many problems from the days of Harvey and Malpighi, but Krogh showed that capillaries were not merely passive in this distribution but that they had the power to actively contract or dilate, according to the needs of the tissues. Both nervous and chemical controls are involved.

Nobel Laureate (1920).

1918: *Starling, E. The law of the heart.*

Within physiologic limits, the more the ventricles are filled with incoming blood, the greater is the force of their contraction at systole. This is an adaptive mechanism for supplying more blood to tissues when it is needed. This important principle has many implications and relationships to cardiac functions and throws some light on the nature of muscular action, for both skeletal and cardiac muscle fibers contract with maximal force when they are slightly stretched at the beginning of contraction.

1918: *Szymanski, J. S. Demonstration of time-measuring mechanism of animals.*

Szymanski showed that animals had some means of measuring time independently of such physical factors as light and temperature, for he discovered that 24-hour activity patterns were synchronized with the day-night cycle when animals were kept in constant darkness and temperature. This work has led to the concept (demonstrated by many investigations) that animals have some kind of internal clock whereby they can measure certain cycles independent of external factors.

1918: *Vavilov, N. I. Biologic centers of origin as reservoirs of desirable genes.*

The Russian botanist and plant geographer stressed the importance of tracing strains of cultivated plants to the locale of their original cultivation, where inferior plants (by present standards) may contain valuable genes already selected by natural selection. Such a pool of genes, he maintained, could by selection and intercrossing afford genetic banks for constructing new and superior genotypes.

1919: *Aston, F. W. Discovery of isotopes.*

Radioactive isotopes have proved of the utmost value in biologic research because of the possibility of tracing the course of various elements in living organisms.

Nobel Laureate (1922).

1919: *Meyerhof, O. Formation of lactic acid during muscular contraction.*

The discovery that the glycogen content decreases as lactic acid increases was a key discovery in understanding the nature of muscular contraction, a problem that has not yet been solved. Meyerhof also showed that about four fifths of the lactic acid is resynthesized to glycogen by the energy furnished by the oxidation of the other one fifth of lactic acid. The relation of lactic acid to muscular fatigue and to oxygen debt was explained also by this discovery.

1920: *Allard, H. A., and W. W. Garner. Concept of photoperiodism.*

This concept refers to the day length-regulated responses of plants in such matters as flowering, bud formation, and leaf and fruit coloration. Seasonal responses of plants are often timed to the duration of light and darkness; for example, short-day or long-night plants usually bloom in the early spring or early fall. Some plants (day-neutral) are independent of the daily duration of light and darkness. The principle has practical application for greenhouse crops and in the ecologic explanation of plant distribution.

1920: *Howard, H. E. Territorial patterns of bird behavior.*

A mating pair of birds establishes and defends a specific territory against others of the same species. Usually the male asserts his claim by singing at points close to the boundaries of his staked-out claim. The concept has been confirmed for many species by numerous investigators.

1921: *Hopkins, F. G. Isolation of glutathione.*

The discovery of this sulfur compound gave a great impetus to the study of the complicated nature of cellular oxidation and metabolism, a process far from being solved at present.

Nobel Laureate (1929).

1921: *Langley, J. N. Concept of the functional autonomic nervous system.*

Langley's concept of the functional aspects of the autonomic system dealt mainly with the mammalian type, but the fundamental principles of the system have been applied with modification to other groups as well. Two divisions—sympathetic and parasympathetic—are recognized in the functional interpretation of excitation and inhibition in the antagonistic nature of the two divisions.

1921: *Loewi, O., and H. H. Dale. Isolation of acetylcholine.*

This key demonstration has led to the neurohumoral concept of the transmission of nerve impulses to muscles.

Nobel Laureates (1936).

1921: *Pearl, R. Analysis of population cycles.*

Through experimental population studies, Pearl analyzed such factors as population growth, density, and longevity, and expressed the results in quantitative terms. This started a series of similar investigations by many competent scientists on varied aspects of the subject. The concept of the population is important in such fields as speciation, evolution, and animal behavior.

1921: *Richards, A. N. Collection and analysis of glomerular filtrate of the kidney.*

This experiment was direct evidence of the role of the glomeruli as mechanical filters of cell-free and protein-free fluid from the blood and was striking confirmation of the Ludwig-Cushny theory of kidney excretion.

1921: *Spemann, Hans. Organizer concept in embryology.*

The idea that certain parts of the developing embryo known as organizers have a determining influence on the developmental patterns of the organism has completely revolutionized the field of experimental embryology and has afforded many clues into the nature of morphogenesis.

Nobel Laureate (1935).

1922: *Banting, F. Extraction of insulin.*

The great success of this hormone in relieving a distressful disease, diabetes mellitus, and the dramatic way in which active extracts were obtained have made the isolation of this hormone the best known in the field of endocrinology.

Nobel Laureate (1923).

1922: *Bridges, C. B. Genic balance theory of sex.*

Bridges found in *Drosophila* that sex is determined by autosomes as well as by X chromosomes. By crossing triploid (3n) females with diploid (2n) males, he found that the X chromosome carries more genes for femaleness and the autosomes more genes for maleness. What determines the sex is the ratio between the number of X chromosomes and the sets of autosomes in the zygote.

1922: *Erlanger, J., and H. S. Gasser. Differential conduction of nerve impulses.*

By using the cathode-ray oscillograph, these investigators found that there were several different types of mammal nerve fibers that could be distinguished structurally and that had different rates of conducting nervous impulses, according to the thickness of the nerve sheaths (most rapid in the thicker ones).

Nobel Laureates (1944).

1922: *Kopec, S. Concept of the hypothalamo-hypophyseal and neurosecretory systems.*

This concept has emerged from the work of many investigators. R. Cajalin (1899) discovered that the nerve fibers to the neurohypophysis are extensions of the neurons of the hypothalamus. Kopec found that the substance responsible for metamorphosis in the larva of moths originated in the brain where certain cerebral ganglia served as glands of internal secretion. The outstanding work of B. Scharrer, E. Scharrer, S. Zuckerman, I. Assenmacher, and others have greatly extended the scope of neuroendocrine studies in recent years.

1922: *Kopec, S. Demonstration of hormonal factors in invertebrate physiology.*

This investigation showed that the brain was necessary for insect metamorphosis, for when the brain was removed from the last instar larva of a certain moth, pupation failed to occur; when the brain was grafted into the abdomen, pupation was resumed.

1922: *Schiefferdecker, P. Distinction between eccrine and apocrine sweat glands.*

In mammals certain large sweat glands that develop in connection with the hair follicles in localized regions respond to stresses, such as fear, pain and sex. This concept has stimulated investigation on the histology and physiology of the glandular activity of the skin. Apocrine glands have been described as early as 1846 by W. E. Horner, an English investigator.

1922: *Schjelderup-Ebbe, T. Social dominance-subordinance hierarchies.*

This observer found certain types of social hierarchies among birds in which higher ranking individuals could peck those of lower rank without being pecked in return.

Those of the first rank dominated those of the second rank, who dominated those of the third, etc. Such an organization, once formed, may be permanent. Dominance orders have also been found in other vertebrate classes as well as in some arthropods. The concept has thrown much light on the social organization of animals.

1922: *Schmidt, Johannes. Life history of the freshwater eel.*

The long, patient work of this oceanographer in solving the mystery of eel migration from the freshwater streams of Europe to their spawning grounds in the Sargasso Sea near the Bermudas represents one of the most romantic achievements in natural history.

1923: *Andrews, R. C. Discovery of dinosaur eggs.*

The discovery of these fossilized eggs in Mongolia added to information about these reptiles that appeal so much to our imagination.

1923: *Hevesy, G. First isotopic tracer method.*

Tracer methodology has proved especially useful in biochemistry and physiology. For instance, it has been possible by the use of these labeled units to determine the fate of a particular molecule in all steps of a metabolic process and the nature of many enzymatic reactions. The exact locations of many elements in the body have been traced by this method. In physiology this method has been helpful in determining absorption phenomena, blood volume, the nature of permeability, and many others.

Nobel Laureate (1943).

1923: *Taylor, C. V. Isolation of micronucleus in Ciliophora.*

By micromanipulation Taylor removed the micronucleus of Euplotes and discovered that this organelle was necessary for the existence of the organism.

1923: *Warburg, Otto. Manometric methods for studying metabolism of living cells.*

The Warburg apparatus has been useful in measuring the gaseous exchange and other metabolic processes of living tissues. It has proved of great value in the study of enzymatic reactions in living systems and is a standard tool in many biochemical laboratories.

Nobel Laureate (1931).

1924: *Cleveland, L. R. Symbiotic relationships between termites and intestinal flagellates.*

This study was made on one of the most remarkable examples of evolutionary mutualism known in the animal kingdom. Equally important were the observations this investigator and others found in the symbiosis between the wood-roach *(Cryptocercus)* and its intestinal Protozoa. This work put such studies on an analytic basis and gave a great impetus to further investigation.

1924: *Feulgen, R. Test for nucleoprotein.*

This microchemical test is widely used by cytologists and biochemists to demonstrate the presence of DNA (deoxyribonucleic acid), one of the two major types of nucleic acids.

1924: *Houssay, B. A. Role of the pituitary gland in regulation of carbohydrate metabolism.*

This investigator showed that when a dog had been made diabetic by pancreatectomy, the resulting hyperglycemia and glucosuria could be abolished by removing the anterior pituitary gland. This work threw additional light on the complex cycle of carbohydrate metabolism and the interrelationships of the endocrine system.

Nobel Laureate (1946).

1924: *Karpechenko, G. D. Experimental synthesis of a new species.*

This investigator crossed the radish *(Raphanus sativus)* with the cabbage *(Brassica oleracea)*, each of which has a haploid number of 9. The hybrid had 18 chromosomes, but at meiosis its chromosomes did not pair and the gametes were sterile. But allopolyploidy arose spontaneously in a few, producing egg and sperm nuclei, each with 9 cabbage and 9 radish chromosomes. This kind of hybrid had 18 synapsed pairs and bred true, but could not breed with either of the original parents, thus giving rise to a new species *(Raphanobrassica)*.

1925: *Baltzer, F. Sex determination in Bonellia.*

This classic discovery of the influence of environmental factors on sex determination, with all the potentialities of sex intergrades that it demonstrates, has formed the basis for another theory of the development of sex.

1925: *Barcroft, J. Function of the spleen.*

Barcroft and associates showed that the spleen served as a blood reservoir that in time of stress adds new corpuscles to the circulation. The spleen reservoir is especially important in hemorrhage and shock. This action is effected mainly by the smooth muscle fibers in the elastic capsule that contracts and squeezes out quantities of red corpuscles. The spleen also destroys old and worn-out red cells.

1925: *Dart, Raymond. Discovery of Australopithecus africanus.*

This important fossil is commonly referred to as the ape-man or the "missing link." This led to the finding of many related ape-men. With many human characteristics and a brain capacity only slightly greater than the higher apes, they have shed a great deal of light on the evolution of the higher primates, since they are placed on or near the main branch of human ancestry.

1925: *Lacassagne, A., J. Lattes, and J. Lavedan. Discovery of the technique of radioautography.*

Sections containing radioactive material and coated with photographic emulsion when exposed in the dark and developed by photographic methods will reveal a darkened effect where the radioactive substances are located. Refinements of this technique have had wide applications in locating tissue components.

1925: *Mast, S. O. Nature of ameboid movement.*

By studying the reversible sol-gel transformation in the protoplasm of an ameba, the author not only gave a logical interpretation of amoeboid movement, but also initiated many fruitful concepts about the contractile nature of protoplasmic gel systems, such as the furrowing movements (cytokinesis) in all divisions.

1925: *Minot, G. R., M. W. P. Murphy, and G. H. Whipple. Liver treatment of pernicious anemia.*

That the feeding of raw liver had a pronounced effect in the treatment of pernicious anemia (a serious blood disorder) was discovered by these investigators. Much later investigation by numerous workers has led to some understanding of the antipernicious factor or vitamin B_{12} whose chemical name is cyanocobalamin. This complex vitamin contains among other components porphyrin that has a cobalt atom instead of iron or magnesium at its center.

Nobel Laureates (1934).

1925: *Rowan, W. Gonadal hypothesis of bird migration.*

By increasing the hours of light by artificial illumination, Rowan demonstrated that birds subjected to such conditions in winter increased the size of their gonads and showed a marked tendency to migrate out of season. In the development of his theory he laid emphasis on the role of the pituitary gland as well as other aspects of physiologic function. The exact relationship of this hypothesis to bird migration is still largely speculative, but Rowan's experiments greatly stimulated investigation in this field.

1926: *Fujii, K. Finer analysis of the chromosome.*

With the development of the smear and squash techniques, it was possible with the light microscope to demonstrate the internal structure of a chromosome, which formerly was described as a rod-shaped body. The newer version emphasizes a coiled filament (chromonema) that runs through the matrix of the chromosome and bears the genes. In certain stages of cell division two such threads are spirally coiled around each other so compactly that they appear as one thread. The extensive research on the detailed nature of the chromosome, has given rise to many and varied interpretations.

1926: *Hill, A. V. Measurement of heat production in nerve.*

By applying the principle of the thermocouple, which Helmholtz had used to detect the heat of contracting muscle, Hill and other workers were able to measure the different phases of heat release, such as initial heat and recovery heat. The values of heat production in nervous tissue are extremely small when compared with readings of muscle heat.

Nobel Laureate (1922).

1926: *Kutscher, F., and D. Ackerman. Distribution of the phosphagens arginine and creatine.*

Creatine phosphate was found in chordate skeletal muscle and arginine phosphate in the muscle of invertebrates. These high-energy substances serve as a source of energy for muscular work, and their distribution was supposed to explain vertebrate ancestry. The sharpness of this distinction is not as marked as formerly supposed, for tunicates have arginine instead of creatine and some invertebrates have no arginine at all. Hemichordates appear to have both phosphagens.

1926: *Moore, C. The thermoregulatory function of the scrotum.*

Since the body temperature of most mammals prevents spermatogenesis, experimental work has demonstrated that scrotal temperature may be 5° C. below rectal temperature and that higher temperatures than this often produce abnormal spermatogenesis. On this basis the external position of the scrotum is explained. However, the concept is controversial because some mammals (Cetacea, Edentata, Proboscidea, etc.) and the birds have internal testes, and some authorities believe that the scrotal sac is a visual sexual signal of selective value during mating.

1926: *Sumner, J. B. Isolation of enzyme urease.*

The isolation of the first enzyme in crystalline form was a key discovery to be followed by others that have helped unravel the complex nature of these important biologic substances.

Nobel Laureate (1946).

1926: *Warburg, O. Discovery of the respiratory enzyme cytochrome oxidase.*

This enzyme catalyzes the oxidation of cytochromes by oxygen, for in the presence of free oxygen and cytochrome oxidase, cytochrome gives up its hydrogen to the oxygen with the formation of water. In this process, cytochrome is a hydrogen acceptor and functions in the union of hydrogen and oxygen.

1927: *Bozler, E. Analysis of nerve net components.*

Bozler's demonstration that the nerve net of coelenterates was made up of separate cells and contained synaptic junctions resolved the old problem of whether or not the plexus in this group of animals was an actual network. Recent work indicates that coelenterates have both a continuous and discontinuous nerve net.

1927: *Coghill, G. E. Innate behavior patterns of Amphibia.*

Coghill's studies on the origin and growth of the behavior patterns of salamanders by following the sequence of the emergence of coordinated movements and nervous connections through all stages of embryonic development have represented one of the most fruitful investigations in animal behavior. He showed how broad, general movements preceded local reflexes and how the probable phylogenetic appearance of behavior patterns originated.

1927: *Eggleton, P., G. P. Eggleton, C. H. Friske, and Y. Subbarow. Role of phosphagen (phosphocreatine) in muscular contraction.*

The demonstration that phosphagen is broken down during muscular contraction into creatine and phosphoric acid and then resynthesized during recovery gave an entirely new concept of the initial energy necessary for the contraction process. Confirmation of this discovery received a great impetus from the discovery of E. Lungsgaard (1930) that muscles poisoned with monoiodoacetic acid, which inhibits the production of lactic acid from glycogen, would still contract and that the amount of phosphocreatine broken down was proportional to the energy liberated.

1927: *Heymans, C. Role of carotid and aortic reflexes in respiratory control.*

The carotid sinus and aortic areas contain pressoreceptors and chemoreceptors, the former responding to mechanical stimulation, such as blood pressure, and the latter to oxygen lack. When the pressoreceptors are stimulated, respiration is inhibited; when the chemoreceptors are stimulated, the respiratory rate is increased. These reflexes are of great physiologic interest, although their adaptive nature is not as apparent as the vascular control initiated from the same regions.

Nobel Laureate (1938).

1927: *Muller, H. J. Artificial induction of mutations.*

By subjecting fruit flies *(Drosophila)* to mild doses of x-rays, Muller found that the rate of mutation could be increased 150 times over the normal rate. This key demonstration has led to an extensive investigation of other forms by these methods and to many fruitful results, such as the biochemical mutations of Beadle and Tatum.

Nobel Laureate (1946).

1927: *Stensio, E. A. Appraisal of the Cephalaspida (Ostracoderm) fish fossil.*

The replacement of *Amphioxus* as a prototype of vertebrate ancestry by the ammocoetes lamprey larva, currently of great interest, has been due to a great extent to this careful fossil reconstruction. It is generally believed that living Agnatha (lamprey and hagfish) are descended from these ancient forms. The best fossils were obtained from Spitsbergen of the Ordovician period.

1928: *Garstang, W. Theory of the ascidian ancestry of chordates.*

According to this theory, primitive chordates were sessile, filter-feeding marine organisms very similar to present-day ascidians that have evolved from pterobranch (Hemichordata) ancestors. The actively swimming prevertebrate was considered a later stage in chordate evolution. The tadpole ascidian larva, with its basic organization of a vertebrate, had evolved within the group by progressive evolution; and by neoteny became sexually mature, ceased to metamorphose into a sessile, mature ascidian, and through adaptation to freshwater conditions became the true vertebrate. The theory has had added support in recent years, notably from the investigations of Berrill.

1928: *Griffith, F. Discovery of the transforming principle (DNA) in bacteria (genetic transduction).*

By injecting living nonencapsulated bacteria and dead encapsulated bacteria of the *Pneumococcus* strain into mice, it was found that the former acquired the ability to grow a capsule and that this ability was transmitted to succeeding generations. This active agent or transforming principle (from the encapsulated type) was isolated by other workers later and was found to consist of DNA. This is excellent evidence that the gene involved is the nucleic acid deoxyribonucleic acid (DNA).

Sanfelice (1893) had actually found the same principle when he discovered that nonpathogenic bacilli grown in a culture medium containing the metabolic products of true tetanus bacilli would also produce toxins and would do so for many generations. This was the first demonstration that a definite chemical substance had hereditary properties.

1928: *Koller, G., and E. B. Perkins. Hormonal control of color changes in crustaceans.*

These investigators found out independently that the chromatophores of crustaceans were regulated by a substance that originated in the eyestalk and was carried by the blood. Before this time, the common belief was that nerves served as the principal control. This early investigation has stimulated an enormous research in this field since that time and has led not only to a better knowledge of the role of endocrine glands in the animal kingdom but has also thrown much light on such problems as insect molting and metamorphosis.

1928: *Wieland, H., and A. Windaus. Structure of the cholesterol molecule.*

Sterol chemistry has been one of the chief focal points in the investigation of such biologic products as vitamins, sex hormones, and cortisone. The real role of cholesterol, which is universally present in tissues, has not yet been determined, but it may serve as the precursor for the many forms of steroids whose use is definitely known. Animals make their own steroids but cannot absorb those of plants.

Nobel Laureates (1927, 1928).

1929: *Berger, Hans. Demonstration of brain waves.*

The science of electroencephalography, or the electrical recording of brain activity, is in its infancy because of the complexity of the subject, but much has been revealed about both the healthy and the diseased brain by this technique. More refinements in technique and better interpretations will no doubt yield more information in this field.

1929: *Butenandt, A., and E. A. Doisy. Isolation of estrone.*

This discovery was the first isolation of a sex hormone and was arrived at independently by these two investigators. Estrone was found to be the urinary and transformed product of estradiol, the actual hormone. The male hormone testosterone was synthesized by Butenandt and L. Ruzicka in 1931. The second female hormone, progesterone, was isolated from the corpora lutea of sow ovaries in 1934.

Doisy, Nobel Laureate (1943).

1929: *Castle, W. B. Discovery of the antianemic factor.*

Castle and associates showed that the gastric juice contained an enzymelike substance (intrinsic factor) that reacts with a dietary factor (extrinsic) to produce the antianemic principle. The latter is stored in the liver of healthy individuals and is drawn on for the maintenance of activity in bone marrow (erythropoietic tissue), that is, the formation of red blood cells. If the intrinsic factor is missing from gastric juice, pernicious anemia occurs. At present, it is thought that vitamin B_{12} is both the extrinsic factor as well as the antianemic principle (erythrocyte-maturing factor).

1929: *Fleming, A. Discovery of penicillin.*

The chance discovery of this drug from molds and its development by H. Florey a few years later gave us the first of a notable line of antibiotics that have revolutionized medicine. Penicillin, however, still remains the most effective and safest of all.

Nobel Laureate (1945).

1929: *Heymans, C. Discovery of the role of the carotid sinus in regulating the respiratory center and arterial blood pressure.*

It was found that the carotid bodies and similar structures on the aorta were chemosensitive to the concentration of oxygen in the blood, and by means of nerve fibers of the IX and X nerves an afferent limb of the reflex is formed. The sensitivity of these bodies is also influenced by the carbon dioxide concentration of the blood. The sensory apparatus of chemoreceptors within the sinus is also affected directly by blood hypertension to produce a reflex slowing of the heart rate and a reflex vasodilation of blood vessels, whereas a blood hypotension increases heartbeat and vasoconstriction of blood vessels.

Nobel Laureate (1938).

1929: *Lohmann, K. Discovery of ATP.*

The discovery of ATP (adenosine triphosphate) culminated a long search for the energy sources in biochemical reactions of many varieties, such as muscular contraction, vitamin action, and many enzymatic systems. Its nature and functions are the focal point of many present-day investigations.

1930: *Fisher, R. A. Statistical analysis of evolutionary variations.*

With Sewall Wright and J. S. B. Haldane, Fisher has analyzed mathematically the interrelationships of the factors of mutation rates, population sizes, selection values, and others in the evolutionary process. Although many of their theories are in the empiric stage, evolutionists in general agree that they have great significance in evolutionary interpretation.

1930: *Giersberg, H., and G. H. Parker. Neurohumoral theory of color control.*

This theory, which was largely developed by Parker, states that the terminations of the neurons, which supply the chromatophores, produce chemical substances (neurohumors) that activate the pigment cells. One type of fiber secretes a neurohumor that causes pigment dispersal; another type of fiber gives rise to a neurohumor that causes pigment aggregation. One of the neurohumors appears to be acetylcholine (dispersion effect chiefly) and the other neurohumor is similar to adrenaline or sympathin (aggregation effect). A third neurohumor (selachine) is found in the dogfish *Mustelus* and has the same effect as adrenaline. The neurohumors are supposed to be the same as those involved in the functioning of the autonomic nervous system.

1930: *Lawrence, E. O. Invention of the cyclotron.*

The importance of artificial radioactive isotopes, the synthesis of which is made possible by this invention, to biologic research cannot be overestimated. Not only have tagged atoms been of inestimable value in learning about the structure and functioning of the body, but many also have been put to medical use.

Nobel Laureate (1939).

1930: *Northrop, J. H. Crystallization of the enzymes pepsin and trypsin.*

This was a further step in the elucidation of the nature of enzymes that form the core of biochemical processes.

Nobel Laureate (1946).

1930: *Papa, G. T., and U. Fielding. Hypophyseal portal vessels.*

First discovered in mammals, these vessels are constant in all vertebrates from Anura to primates. Similar in cyclostomes, fishes, and salamanders, the hypothalamus can influence adenohypophyseal activities through humoral effects carried by these vessels.

1931: *Lewis, W. H. Concept of pinocytosis.*

This refers to a discontinuous process of fluid engulfment by cells, in contrast to diffusion. Many types apparently exist, but often the process involves membranous pseudopodia that enclose droplets of surrounding fluid. These vesicles are then pinched off and sucked into the interior of the cell. The phenomenon may also be concerned with the uptake and transport of substances by cells. Electron microscope studies have done much to resolve the process.

1931: *Lorenz, K., and N. Tinbergen. Theory of instinctive behavior.*

The upsurge of interest (second only to molecular biology) in animal behavior within recent years has been due to the investigations of these men and their school concerning the problems of instinct and instinctive behavior. The interest they have aroused has been a result of their attempt to determine the physiologic basis of the animal's reactions to stimuli by focusing attention on the instinctive behavior pattern that controls innate behavior, by studying the internal conditions of the animal that are organized for particular patterns, and by showing the neural mechanisms that are correlated with these patterns.

1931: *Stern, C., H. Creighton, and B. McClintock. Cytologic demonstration of crossing-over.*

Proof that crossing-over in genes is correlated with exchange of material by homologous chromosomes was independently proved by Stern in *Drosophila* and by Creighton and McClintock in corn. By using crosses of strains that had homologous chromosomes distinguishable individually, it was definitely demonstrated cytologically that genetic crossing-over was accompanied by chromosomal exchange.

1932: *Bethe, A. Concept of the ectohormone (pheromone).*

These substances are secreted to the outside of the body by an organism; another member of the same species may react to the substance in some behavioral or developmental way. These substances have been demonstrated in insects, where they may function in trail-making, sex attraction, development control, etc. (Gr. *pherein,* to carry, + *hormon,* to excite.)

1932: *Danish scientific expedition. Discovery of fossil amphibians (ichthyostegids).*

These fossils were found in the upper Devonian sediments in east Greenland and appear to be intermediate between advanced crossopterygians *(Osteolepis)* and early amphibians. They are the oldest known forms that can be considered amphibians. Many of their characters show primitive amphibian conditions. Only the skulls were found, and these apparently belonged to animals of considerable size.

1932: *Roughton, F. J. W. Discovery of enzyme carbonic anhydrase.*

This enzyme speeds up the reaction of CO_2 with water to form carbonic acid or the reverse reaction. The enzyme is found in red blood corpuscles and contains zinc in its structure. The enzyme plays an important role in the respiratory process.

1932: *Wright, S. Genetic drift as a factor in evolution.*

In small populations the Hardy-Weinberg formula of gene frequency may not apply because chance may determine the presence or absence of certain genes and this tendency will be expressed in the gene frequency of the new population, which may be quite different from the original large population.

1932: *Zondek, B., and H. Krohn. Effect of intermedin on melanophores.*

This hormone (now called the melanocyte-stimulating hormone, or MSH) is known to effect pigment dispersion in amphibians and other lower vertebrates, but its role in higher vertebrates is debatable. The pars intermedia of the pituitary is commonly considered to be its site of origin.

1933: *Collander, R., and H. Bärlund. Measurement of cell permeability.*

Their quantitative measurements of cell membranes made possible testable hypotheses and critical analyses of experimental data of the important biologic principle of permeability. This investigation made more meaningful E. Overton's (1895) classic experiments on the permeability of organic substances.

1933: *Gerard, R. W., and H. K. Hartline. Respiration in nerve.*

With rather simple apparatus, these workers were able to measure the amount of oxygen consumed per gram of nerve tissue during active and inactive conditions. This work shows definitely that nervous activity is a metabolic process. At present, it appears that nerve conduction involves energy-rich phosphate bonds the same as does muscular contraction.

1933: *Goldblatt, M., and U. S. von Euler. Discovery of prostaglandins.*

These fatty acid derivative compounds have been isolated from many mammalian tissues (seminal plasma, pancreas, seminal vesicle, brain, kidney, etc.). Their biologic activities are obscure because many compounds of different functions are involved, but pharmacologic evidence indicates that they stimulate smooth muscle contractions and relaxation, lower blood pressure, inhibit enzymes and hormones, etc.

1933, 1938: *Haldane, J. B. S., and A. I. Oparin. Heterotroph theory of the origin of life.*

This theory is based on the idea that life was generated from nonliving matter under the conditions that existed before the appearance of life and which have not been duplicated since. The theory stresses the idea that living systems at present make it impossible for any incipient life to gain a foothold as primordial life was able to do. That complex organic molecules may arise from nonliving substances under proper conditions has been shown by such experimenters as Urey and Miller (1953), who were able to produce certain amino acids. This theory, with variations, has aroused much interest and speculation among biologists.

1933: *Holtfreter, J. Chemical nature of embryologic inductors.*

Holtfreter and others found that the amphibian organizer retains its capacity to induce a nervous system (after the organizer has been killed by artificial agents) by transplanting fragments of the dead inductor into the blastocoel before gastrulation. They also found that embryonic tissues that cannot induce when alive can do so after they are killed. The agent that induces nerve tube formation seems to be widespread in the embryo and is released by the dead tissue. The great variety of chemical substances that will induce nerve tube formation makes it impossible at present to determine the exact nature of the inducing substance.

1933: *Painter, T. S., E. Heitz, and H. Bauer. Rediscovery of giant salivary chromosomes.*

These interesting chromosomes were first described by Balbiani in 1881, but their true significance was not realized until these investigators rediscovered them. It has been possible in a large measure to establish the chromosome theory of inheritance by comparing the actual cytologic chromosome maps of salivary chromosomes with the linkage maps obtained by genetic experimentation.

1933: *Wald, G. Discovery of vitamin A in the retina.*

The discovery that vitamin A is a part of the visual purple molecule of the rods not only gave a better understanding of an important vitamin but also showed how night blindness can occur whenever there is a deficiency of this vitamin in the diet.

Nobel Laureate (1967).

1934: *Bensley, R. R., and N. L. Hoerr. Isolation and analysis of mitochondria.*

This demonstration has suggested an explanation for the behavior and possible functions of these mysterious bodies that have intrigued cytologists for a generation, and much has been learned about them in recent years.

1934: *Dam, H., and E. A. Doisy. Identification of vitamin K.*

The isolation and synthesis of this vitamin is important not merely because of its practical value in certain forms of hemorrhage but also because of the light it throws on the physiologic mechanism of blood clotting.

Nobel Laureates (1943).

1934: *Danielli, J. F. Concept of the cell (plasma) membrane.*

Danielli had proposed a hypothesis that cell membranes consist of two layers of lipid molecules surrounded on the inner and outer surfaces by a layer of protein molecules. The electron microscope reveals the plasma membrane of a thickness of 75 to 100 Å, consisting of two dark (protein) membranes (25 to 30 Å thick) separated by a light (lipid) interval membrane of 25 to 30 Å thickness. The exact relationship of the protein and lipid constituents has never been resolved.

1934: *Urey, H. Discovery of heavy water (deuterium).*

Water, the most common constituent of protoplasm, has properties that are still not understood. It is not a single substance but is made up of at least 33 substances. Deuterium has furnished the basis for much biologic investigation on the structure of water in relation to its role in biologic systems.

Nobel Laureate (1934).

1934: *Wigglesworth, V. B. Role of the corpus allatum gland in insect metamorphosis.*

This small gland lies close to the brain of an insect, and it has been shown that during the larval stage this gland secretes a juvenile hormone that causes the larval characters to be retained. Metamorphosis occurs when the gland no longer secretes the hormone. Removal of the gland causes the larva to undergo precocious metamorphosis; grafting the gland into a mature larva will cause the latter to grow into a giant larval form. The gland was first described by A. Nabert in 1913.

1935: *DuShane, G. P. Role of the neural crest in pigment cell formation.*

DuShane's discovery that pigment cells in amphibians originated from the neural crest was quickly followed by other investigations that showed that other groups (fish, birds, mammals) had the same pattern of pigment formation. The current interest in the relation of the pigment cell to certain malignant growths (melanoblastomas), which may be considered immature pigment cells induced by some metabolic error, has been focused on all possible aspects of the pigment cell.

1935: *Hanstrom, B. Discovery of the x organ in crustaceans.*

This organ, together with the related sinus gland, constitutes an anatomic complex that has proved of great interest in understanding crustacean endocrinology. One view holds that neurosecretory cells in the x organ and the brain produce a molt-preventing hormone that is stored in the sinus gland of the eyestalk; other theories postulate a molt-accelerating hormone produced in a y organ. The interrelations of these two hormones may be responsible for the molting process.

1935-1936: *Kendall, E. C., and P. S. Hench. Discovery of cortisone.*

Kendall had first isolated from the adrenal glands this substance that he called compound E. Its final stages were prepared by Hench later and involved a long tedious chemical process. A similar hormone, as far as its effects are concerned, was isolated in 1943 from the pituitary and called ACTH (adrenocorticotropic hormone). These hormones are not merely of interest because of their promise in relieving certain diseases, but their relations are of great importance in the development of endocrinology. The use of cortisone in the treatment of arthritis was developed first by Hench of the Mayo Clinic.

Nobel Laureates (1950).

1935: *Needham, J., and C. H. Waddington. Chemical nature of the organizer region in embryology.*

The major effect of the organizer region described by Spemann and others was really due to the production by that region of a specific evocator substance closely related to the sterols and other chemical compounds.

1935: *Stanley, W. M. Isolation of a virus in crystalline form.*

This achievement of isolating a virus (tobacco mosaic disease) is not merely noteworthy in giving information about these small agencies responsible for many diseases but also in affording much speculation on the differences between the living and the nonliving. The viruses appear to be a transition stage between the animate and the inanimate.

Nobel Laureate (1946).

1935: *Tansley, A. G. Concept of the ecosystem.*

The relatively recent science of ecology has added many new terms, but the ecosystem is considered the basic functional unit in ecology, for it best expresses the environmental relations of organisms in their entirety. It includes both the biotic and abiotic factors, and the concept under different terminology had been used by others in the early development of ecology.

1935: *Timofeeff-Ressovsky, N. W. Target theory of induction of gene mutations.*

Timofeeff-Ressovsky's discovery that mutation can be induced in a gene if a single electron is detached by high-energy radiation gave rise to one of the two prevailing theories of how radiation affects mutation rate. The target theory (Treffertheorie) has tried to pinpoint the genetic effect to a certain sensitive volume of matter that is affected by a single ionization or atomic excitation.

1936: *Demerec, M., and M. E. Hoover. Correspondence between salivary gland chromosome bands and normal chromosome maps.*

By means of three stocks of *Drosophila,* each with a different deficiency at one end of the x chromosome, these investigators were able to find approximately on the giant chromosomes the location of the same genes found on the normal chromosome maps constructed by the percent of crossing-over.

1936: *Stern, C. Discovery of mitotic crossing-over.*

Although common in meiosis, crossing-over in somatic mitosis occasionally occurs. Crossing-over in mitosis takes place after the chromosomes have split, and the crossing-over usually takes place near the centromere in *Drosophila* where the process was originally found. Mitotic crossing-over may result in the production of sister cells homozygous for genes that were heterozygous in the original cell.

1936: *Young, J. Z. Demonstration of giant fibers in squid.*

These giant fibers are formed by the fusion of the axons of many neurons whose cell bodies are found in a ganglion near the head. Each fiber is really a tube, more than 1 mm. wide, consisting of an external sheath filled with liquid axoplasm. These giant fibers control the contraction of the characteristic mantle that surrounds these animals. Much information about nervous impulses has been obtained by a study of these fibers.

1937: *Blakeslee, A. F. Artificial production of polyploidy.*

By applying the drug colchicine to dividing cells, it was found that cell division in plants is blocked after the chromosomes have divided (metaphase), and thus the cell has double the normal number of chromosomes. When applied to hybrid plants, it has been possible to produce new plants.

1937: *Findlay, G. W. M., and F. O. MacCullum. Discovery of interferon.*

These protein substances, produced by cells in response to viruses and other foreign substances, inhibit selectively virus replication. Their potential as antiviral agents is still in the experimental stage. They may be considered another factor in intracellular regulation.

1937: *Krebs, H. A. Citric acid (tricarboxylic) cycle.*

This theory of aerobic carbohydrate oxidation (through stages involving citric acid), which is supposed to occur in most living cells, involves a cycle of linked reactions under the influence of many enzymes (mainly from mitochondria). The scheme consists of many intermediary stages and aims to show how pyruvic acid (a derivative of carbohydrate oxidation) is converted to carbon dioxide and water. The cycle is thought to be the final common path for the oxidation of fatty acids, amino acids, and carbohydrates and represents the chief source of chemical energy in the body. The cycle has been the chief focal point in the study of cellular metabolism.

Nobel Laureate (1953).

1937: *Sonneborn, T. M. Discovery of mating types in paramecium.*

Sonneborn's discovery that only individuals of complimentary physiologic classes (mating types) would conjugate opened up a new era of protozoan investigation that bids to shed new light on the problems of species concept and evolution.

1937: *Werle, E., W. Gotze, and A. Keppler. Discovery of kinins.*

Kinins are local hormones produced in blood or tissues that bring about dilation of blood vessels and other changes. They are also found in wasp venoms. They have no connection with special glands, are peptides in nature, are very evanescent, perform their functions rapidly, and are then quickly inactivated by enzymes. They also have powerful effects on smooth muscle wherever it is found.

1938-1950: *Cohn, E. J. Blood fractionation.*

Dr. Cohn and associates have separated more than a score of fractions from plasma, and their investigations have not only yielded medical value but also have furnished much physiologic information on the diversified roles of the blood.

1938: *Kozlowski, R. Analysis of the relationship of fossil graptolites to the pterobranchs.*

Carefully studying graptolites by transmitted light and by serial sections, this investigator found that the skeleton and other features of these wholly extinct forms corresponded with those of *Rhabdopleura,* one of the pterobranchs, which belong to the phylum Hemichordata. Since the hemichordates represent a stock close to vertebrates, this analysis throws additional light on the early ancestry of vertebrates. Formerly classified with the coelenterates or bryozoans, graptolites are now considered an extinct division under Hemichordata.

1938: *Remane, A. Discovery of the new phylum Gnathostomulida.*

This marine phylum was first described by P. Ax in 1956, and its taxonomic position is still under appraisement. The members of the phylum are small wormlike forms (about ½ mm. long) and show great diversity among the different species. One of their major characteristics is their complicated jaws provided with teeth. They live in sandy substrata and are worldwide in distribution. They show some relationships to the Turbellaria, Gastrotricha, and Rotatoria.

1938: *Schoenheimer, R. Use of radioactive isotopes to demonstrate synthesis of bodily constituents.*

By labeling amino acids, fats, carbohydrates, etc., with radioactive isotopes, it was possible to show how these were incorporated into the various constituents of the body. Such experiments demonstrated that parts of the cell were constantly being synthesized and broken down and that the body must be considered a dynamic equilibrium.

1938: *Skinner, B. F. Measurement of motivation in animal behavior.*

Skinner worked out a technique for measuring the rewarding effect of a stimulus, or the effects of learning on voluntary behavior. His experimental animals (rats) were placed in a special box (Skinner's box) containing a lever that the animal could manipulate. When the rat presses the lever, small pellets of food may or may not be released, according to the experimental conditions. He found that the frequency with which the lever is pressed by the rat is correlated with the frequency of the reward. Many variant experiments can be done with this box.

1938: *Svedberg, T. Development of ultracentrifuge.*

In biologic and medical investigation this instrument has been widely used for the purification of substances, the determination of particle sizes in colloidal systems, the relative densities of materials in living cells, the production of abnormal development, and the study of many problems concerned with electrolytes.

Nobel Laureate (1926).

1939: *Brown, F. A., Jr., and O. Cunningham. Demonstration of molt-preventing hormone in eyestalk of crustaceans.*

Although C. Zeleny (1905) and others had shown that eyestalk removal shortened the intermolt period in crustaceans, Brown and Cunningham were the first to present evidence to explain the effect as being due to a molt-preventing hormone present in the sinus gland. This key discovery has thrown considerable light upon a problem that has been extensively studied but has not yet been resolved.

1939: *Discovery of coelacanth fish.*

The collection of a living specimen of this ancient fish (*Latimeria*), followed later by other specimens, has brought about a complete reappraisal of this "living fossil" with reference to its ancestry of the amphibians and land forms.

1939: *Hoerstadius, S. Analysis of the basic pattern of regulative and mosaic eggs in development.*

The masterful work of this investigator has done much to resolve the differences in the early development of regulative eggs (in which each of the early blastomeres can give rise to a whole embryo) and mosaic eggs (in which isolated blastomeres produce only fragments of an embryo). Regulative eggs were shown to have two kinds of substances and both were necessary in proper ratios to produce normal embryos. Each of the early blastomeres has this proper ratio and thus can develop into a complete embryo; in mosaic eggs the regulative power is restricted to a much earlier time scale in development (before cleavage), and thus each isolated blastomere will give rise only to a fragment.

1939: *Huxley, J. Concept of the cline in evolutionary variation.*

This concept refers to the gradual and continuous variation in character over an extensive area because of adjustments to changing conditions. This idea of character gradients has proved a very fruitful one in the analysis of the mechanism of evolutionary processes, for such a variability helps to explain the initial stages in the transformation of species.

1939: *Pincus, G. Artificial parthenogenesis of the mammalian egg.*

This experiment of producing a normal, fatherless rabbit showed that Loeb's classic method could be made to apply to the eggs of the highest group of animals, and that the primary physiologic process of fertilization is the activation of the egg.

1940: *DDT as a biologic control agent.*

DDT, or dichlor-diphenyl-trichlormethylmethane, was synthesized in 1874 by Othmar Leidler but was not put to practical use until the last decade or two. Its value in controlling certain insect pests, such as lice, mosquitoes, and potato bugs, has been amply demonstrated. Other agents of more or less selective toxicity have been developed as insecticides. Just how these control agents are going to fit into the biologic balances of nature is at present a matter of surmise. DDT is now known to be harmful to man when ingested in any form.

1940: *Kunitz, M. Crystallization of ribonuclease.*

This important enzyme made possible a better understanding of ribonucleic acid—the focal point of protein synthesis.

1940: *Landsteiner, Karl, and A. S. Wiener. Discovery of Rh-blood factor.*

Not only was a knowledge of the Rh factor of importance in solving a fatal infant's disease but it has also yielded a great deal of information about relationships of human races.

Landsteiner, Nobel Laureate (1930).

1940: *Timofeeff-Ressovsky, N. W. Cyclic changes in genetics in populations of species.*

Red and black elytral color patterns of a certain beetle (*Adalia*) differed by a single mendelian gene. The black gene had a greater selective value during the summer, whereas the red had a greater survival during hibernation. This seasonal inequality in population phases has been found in a number of wild species and is an example of polymorphism.

1941: *Beadle, G. W., and E. L. Tatum. Biochemical mutation.*

By subjecting the bread mold *Neurospora* to x-ray irradiation, it was found that genes responsible for the synthesis of certain vitamins and amino acids were inactivated (mutated) so that a strain of this mold carrying the mutant genes could no longer grow unless these particular vitamins and amino acids were added to the medium on which the mold was growing. This outstanding discovery has revealed as never before the precise way in which a single gene controls the specificity of a particular enzyme and has greatly stimulated similar research on other simple forms of life such as bacteria and viruses.

Nobel Laureates (1958).

1941: *Cori, C. F., and G. T. Cori. Lactic acid metabolic cycle.*

The regeneration of muscle glycogen reserves in mammals involves the passage of lactic acid from the muscles through the blood to the liver, the conversion of lactic acid there to glycogen, the production of blood glucose from the liver glycogen, and the synthesis of muscle glycogen from the blood glucose.

Nobel Laureates (1947).

1941: *Martin, A. J. P., and R. L. M. Synge. Practical application of chromatography.*

This simple method has proved to be the one of choice in the direct isolation of amino acids instead of the more tedious ones based on slight differences in solubilities and pH values of the various amino acids. The method has wide applications in present-day biologic investigations.

The method was first discovered by M. Tswett in 1906.

1941: *Szent-Györgyi, Albert von. Role of ATP in muscular contraction.*

The demonstration showing that muscles get their energy for contraction from ATP (adenosine triphosphate) has done much to explain many aspects of the puzzling problem of muscle physiology and has been responsible in stimulating research in this and allied fields.

Nobel Laureate (1937).

1942: *Lindemann, R. L. Concept of the trophic-dynamic aspect of ecologic communities.*

The measurement of the rate of energy transfer in ecosystems has proved a focal point of interest to ecologists because of its insight into the functional structure of communities—one of the most significant aspects of ecology.

1942: *McClean, D., and I. M. Rowlands. Discovery of the enzyme hyaluronidase in mammalian sperm.*

This enzyme dissolves the cement substance of the follicle cells that surround the mammalian egg and facilitates the passage of the sperm to the egg. This discovery not only aided in resolving some of the difficult problems of the fertilization process but also offers a logical explanation of cases of infertility in which too few sperm may not carry enough of the enzyme to afford a passage through the inhibiting follicle cells.

1943: *Claude, A. Isolation of cell constituents.*

By differential centrifugation, Claude found it possible to separate, in relatively pure form, particulate components, such as mitochondria, microsomes, and nuclei. These investigations led immediately to a more precise knowledge of the chemical nature of these cell constituents and aided the elucidation of the structure and physiology of the mitochondria—one of the great triumphs in the biochemistry of the cell.

1943: *Holtfreter, J. Tissue synthesis from dissociated cells.*

By dissociating the cells of embryonic tissues of amphibians (by dissolving with enzymes or other agents the intercellular cement that holds the cells together) and heaping them in a mass, it was found that the cells in time coalesced and formed the type of tissue from which they had come. This is an application to vertebrates of the discovery of Wilson with sponge cells. Many variant aspects of the experiment have been performed by numerous investigators, such as mixing together dissociated cells from different tissues and also tissue cells from different organisms. In all cases there was a selective regrouping of cells according to tissue types. There are obvious implications from such experiments to the problems of morphogenesis.

1943: *Sonneborn, T. M. Extranuclear inheritance.*

The view that in paramecia cytoplasmic determiners (plasmagenes) that are self-reproducing and capable of mutation can produce genetic variability has thrown additional light on the role of the cytoplasm in hereditary patterns.

1944: *Avery, O. T. C., C. M. MacLeod, and M. McCarty. Agent responsible for bacterial transformation.*

These workers were able to show that the bacterial transformation of nonencapsulated bacteria to encapsulated cells was really due to the DNA fraction of debris from disrupted encapsulated cells to which the nonencapsulated cells were exposed. This key demonstration showed for the first time that proteins cannot be the basic structure of hereditary transmission but that this role is taken by nucleic acids. More direct evidence of this came through the work of Chase and Hershey (1952).

1944: *Robinow, C. F. Discovery of nuclei in bacteria.*

The genetic mechanism of bacteria appears to be similar to those of higher forms, and this discovery has given a great impetus to genetic study of these common organisms. Much of this study has been focused on mutations and the possibility of transforming strains of bacteria by introducing specific hereditary characteristics from another strain. The power to transform bacteria was first demonstrated by the English investigator F. Griffith in 1928, and numerous workers since have realized the significance of such investigation as a laboratory tool in genetics and in the appraisal of the gene.

1944: *Waksman, S. A. Discovery of streptomycin.*

This antibiotic ranks next to penicillin in importance and represents a triumph of carefully planned investigation.

Nobel Laureate (1952).

1945: *Cori, Carl. Hormone influence on enzyme activity.*

The delicate balance insulin and the diabetogenic hormone of the pituitary exercise over the activity of the enzyme hexokinase in carbohydrate metabolism has opened up a whole new field of the regulative action of hormones on enzymes.

Nobel Laureate (1947).

1945: *Griffin, D., and R. Galambos. Development of the concept of echolocation.*

Echolocation refers to a type of perception of objects at a distance by which echoes of sound are reflected back from obstacles and detected acoustically. These investigators found that bats generated their own ultrasonic sounds that were reflected back to their own ears so that they were able to avoid obstacles in their flight without the aid of vision. Their work climaxed an interesting series of experiments inaugurated as early as 1793 by Spallanzani, who believed that bats avoided obstacles in the dark by reflection of sound waves to their ears. Others who laid the groundwork for the novel concept were C. Jurine (1794), who proved that ears were the all-important organs in the perception; H. S. Maxim (1912), who advanced the idea that the bat made use of sounds of low frequency inaudible to human ears; and H. Hartridge (1920) who proposed the hypothesis that bats emitted sounds of high frequencies and short wavelengths (ultrasonic sounds).

1945: *Lipmann, F. Discovery of coenzyme A.*

The discovery of this important catalyst made possible a better understanding of the breaking down of fatty acid chains and furnished an important link in the reactions of the Krebs metabolic cycle.

Nobel Laureate (1953).

1945: *Porter, K. R. Description of the endoplasmic reticulum.*

The endoplasmic reticulum is a very complex cytoplasmic structure consisting of a lacelike network of irregular anastomosing tubules and vesicular expansions within the cytoplasmic matrix. Associated with the reticulum complex are small dense granules of ribonucleoprotein and other granules known as microsomes that are fragments of the endoplasmic reticulum. The reticulum complex is supposed to play an important role in the synthesis of proteins and RNA.

1946: *Auerbach, C., and J. M. Robson. The chemical production of mutations.*

Besides radiation effects (Muller, 1927), many inorganic and organic compounds (mustard gas, oils, alkaloids, phenols, etc.) are now known to have mutagenic effects such as chromosome breakage. It is thought that such agents disrupt the nucleic acid metabolism responsible for protein synthesis and reduplication.

1946: *Lederberg, J., and E. L. Tatum. Sexual recombination in bacteria.*

These investigators found that two different strains of bacteria (*Escherichia coli*) could undergo conjugation and exchange genetic material, thereby producing a hereditary strain with characteristics of the two parent strains. W. Hayes (1952) found that recombination still occurred after one parent strain was killed.

Nobel Laureates (1958).

1946: *Libby, W. F. Radiocarbon dating of fossils.*

The radiocarbon age determination is based on the fact that carbon 14 in the dead organism disintegrates at the rate of one half in 5,560 years, one half of the remainder in the next 5,560 years, etc. This is on the assumption that the isotope is mixed equally through all living matter and that the cosmic rays (which form the isotopes) have not varied much in periods of many thousands of years. The limitation of the method is around 30,000 years.

Nobel Laureate (1960).

1946: *White, E. I. Discovery of primitive chordate fossil, Jamoytius.*

The discovery of this fossil in the freshwater deposits of Silurian rock in Scotland bids to throw some light on the early ancestry of vertebrates, for this form seems to be intermediate between *Amphioxus* or *Ammocoetes* larva and the oldest known vertebrates, the ostracoderms. Morphologically, *Jamoytius* represents the most primitive chordate yet discovered. It could well serve as an ancestor of such forms as *Amphioxus* and the jawless ostracoderms.

1947: *Bonner, J. T. Discovery of acrasin.*

In slime mold cells a chemotactic substance of unknown composition was discovered that had the power to attract amebas to growing aggregation centers to form a lump of spores or reproductive bodies. This agent helps explain one of the ways by which cells are organized into tissues.

1947: *Holtz, P. Discovery of norepinephrine (noradrenaline).*

This hormone (vasoconstriction effects) has since been found in most vertebrates and shares with epinephrine (metabolic effects) the functions of the chromaffin part of the adrenal gland.

1947: *Sprigg, R. C. Discovery of Precambrian fossil bed.*

The discovery of a rich deposit of Precambrian fossils in the Ediacara Hills of South Australia has been of particular interest because the scarcity of such fossils in the past has given rise to vague and uncertain explanations about Precambrian life. It was all the more remarkable that the fossils discovered were those of soft-bodied forms, such as jellyfish, soft corals, and segmented worms, including the amazing *Spriggina* that shows relationship to the trilobites. The fossils are prearthropod, but are not preannelid.

1947: *Szent-Györgyi, A. Concept of the contractile substance, actomyosin.*

This protein complex consists of the two components, actin and myosin, and is considered the source of muscular contraction when triggered by ATP. Neither actin nor myosin singly will contract.

1948: *Frisch, Karl von. Communication patterns of honeybees.*

Climaxing 40 years of patient work on bees, von Frisch has been able to unravel some of the amazing patterns of behavior bees possess in conveying information to each other about the distance, direction, and sources of food supplies—an outstanding demonstration of animal behavior.

1948: *Hess, W. R. Localization of instinctive impulse patterns in the brain.*

By inserting electrodes through the skull, fixing them in position, and allowing such holders to heal in place, it was possible to study the brain of an animal in its ordinary activities. When the rat could automatically and at will stimulate itself by pressing a lever, it did so frequently when the electrode was inserted in the hypothalamus region of the brain, indicating a pleasure center. In this way, by placing electrodes at different centers, rats can be made to gratify such drives as thirst, sex, and hunger.

Nobel Laureate (1949).

1948: *Hogeboom, G. H., W. C. Schneider, and G. E. Palade. Separation of mitochondria from the cell.*

This was an important discovery in unraveling the amazing enzymatic activity of the mitochondria in the Krebs cycle. The role mitochondria play in the energy transfer of the cell has earned for these rod-shaped bodies of the appellation of the "powerhouse" of the cell.

1948: *Johnson, M. W. Relation between echo-sounding and the deep-scattering layer of marine waters.*

The development of a sound transmitter and a receiver coupled with a timing mechanism for recording the time between an outgoing sound impulse and the echo of its return has made possible an accurate method for determining depths in the ocean. By means of this device a deep-scattering layer far above the floor of the ocean was discovered that scattered the sound waves and sent back echoes. This scattering layer tends to rise toward the surface at night and sink to a depth of many hundred meters by day. Johnson saw a marked parallelism between the shifting of this scattering layer and the diurnal vertical migration of plankton or pelagic animals. The nature and cause of this layer has been the subject of intense investigation during the past decade and has not yet been fully resolved, although fish and their swim bladders have entered more and more into the picture.

1949: *Barr, M. L., and E. G. Bertram. Sex differences in nuclear morphology—nucleolar satellite.*

The discovery that an intranuclear body (nucleolar satellite) was far better developed in the female mammalian cell has aroused the interesting possibility of detecting the genetic sex of an individual by microscopic examination. The body, which is about 1 μ in diameter, appears as a satellite to the large nucleolus of the female nucleus. The present explanation is that the two X chromosomes of the female are responsible for the nucleolus. The male satellite (with one X chromosome), if present, is too small to see. Some cells in the body show the phenomenon better than others.

1949: *de Duve, C. Discovery of the lysosome organelle.*

These small particles were first identified chemically, and later (1955) morphologically with the electron microscope. They are supposed to provide the enzymes for digestion of materials taken into the cell by pinocytosis and phagocytosis and for the digestion of the cell's own cytoplasm. When the cell dies, their enzymes are also released and digest the cell (autolysis).

1949: *Enders, J. F., F. C. Robbins, and T. H. Weller. Cell culture of animal viruses.*

These investigators found that poliomyelitis virus could be grown in ordinary tissue cultures of nonnervous tissue instead of being restricted to host systems of laboratory animals or embryonated chick eggs. Their work made possible the mass production of viruses and vaccines.

Nobel Laureates (1954).

1949: *Pauling, L. Genic control of protein structure.*

Pauling and his colleagues demonstrated a direct connection between specific chemical differences in protein molecules and alterations in genotypes. Making use of the hemoglobin of patients with sickle cell anemia (which is caused by a homozygous condition of an abnormal gene), he was able by the method of electrophoresis to show a marked difference in the behavior of this hemoglobin in an electric field compared with that from a heterozygote or from a normal person.

Nobel Laureate (1954).

1949: *Selye, H. Concept of the stress syndrome.*

In 1937 Selye began his experiments, which led to what he called the "alarm reaction" that involved the chain reactions of many hormones, such as cortisone and ACTH, in meeting stress conditions faced by an organism. Whenever the stress experience exceeds the limitations of these body defenses, serious degenerative disorders may result.

1950: *Callan, H. G., and S. G. Tomlin. The bilamellar organization of the nuclear envelope.*

By means of the electron microscope, these investigators were the first to show that the nuclear envelope was composed of two membranes that are interrupted by discontinuities. This and many other investigations with the powerful electron microscope have revealed many exciting discoveries about the new concept of the cell and its constituents. The classic cytologist Flemming had suggested in 1882 that the nuclear envelope was bilamellar.

1950: *Caspersson, T. Biosynthesis of proteins.*

Investigations to solve the vital problem of protein synthesis from free amino acids have been under way since Fischer's outstanding work on protein structure. Many competent research workers, such as Bergmann, Lipmann, and Schoenheimer, have made contributions to an understanding of protein synthesis, but Caspersson and Brachet were the first to point out the significant role of ribonucleic acid (RNA) in the process—and most biochemical investigations on the problem since that time have been directed along this line.

1950: *Chargaff, E. Base composition of DNA.*

The discovery that the amount of purines was equal to the amount of pyrimidines in DNA, the amount of adenine was equal to that of thymine, and the amount of cytosine was equal to that of guanine paved the way for the DNA model of Watson and Crick. The two major functions of DNA are replication and information storage.

1950: *Hadzi, J. Theory of the origin of metazoans.*

The resemblance between multinucleate ciliates and acoelous flatworms has formed the basis of this theory, which was proposed by Sedgwick many years ago and was largely ignored by contemporary zoologists. It has been studied for 50 years by Hadzi, who has brought forth many logical reasons in its support. This new point of view supports the early views of Lankester and Metschnikoff, that the original diploblastic ancestor was solid rather than hollow and that the formation of the archenteron is a secondary process.

1950: *Simpson, M., and C. H. Li. Coordination of hormones for balanced development of a tissue.*

One hormone may control the size of an organ or tissue and a different hormone may be responsible for its maturation. Thus the growth hormone of the adenohypophysis may cause a bone to grow in length, but thyroxine from the thyroid is necessary for a fully differentiated bone. The same effect is strikingly shown in insect metamorphosis where the presence of both the molting hormone (ecdyson) and the juvenile hormone results in a larger and larger larva at each molt until the juvenile hormone disappears, when the pupa is able to appear.

1951: *Lewis, E. B. Concept of pseudoallelism in genetics.*

On the basis of a series of mutations in *Drosophila,* Lewis concluded that certain adjacent loci were closely linked, affected the same trait, and probably arose from a common ancestral gene instead of being a single locus with multiple genes.

1952: *Beermann, W. Concept of the chromosomal puff.*

Puffs are local and reversible enlargements in the

bands or loci of giant chromosomes. It is thought that puffs are related to the synthesis of genetic substance such as RNA. Puffing may indicate a correlation between hormonal action and larval development in insect metamorphosis, in which the phenomenon was first discovered.

1952: *Briggs, R., and T. J. King. Demonstration of possible differentiated nuclear genotypes.*

The belief that all cells of a particular organism have the same genetic endowment has been questioned as the result of the work of these investigators, who transplanted nuclei of different ages and sources from blastulas and early gastrulas into enucleated zygotes and got varied abnormal developmental results. This pioneer work promises to enlighten the difficult problem of cell localization and differentiation.

1952: *Chase, M., and A. D. Hershey. DNA as the basis of gene structure.*

By using radioactive isotopes, it was shown that when a bacterium is infected by a bacterial virus only the viral DNA enters the host cell, the protein coat remaining behind. Compare with H. Fraenkel-Conrat and R. C. Williams (1955) who were able to separate the protein coat from the RNA core in tobacco mosaic virus.

1952: *Danish Galathea Expedition. Discovery of primitive mollusks.*

The discovery of these interesting forms (class or order Monoplacophora) off the coast of Mexico in deep water represents the most important "living fossils" since the discovery of *Latimeria*. With a round, limpetlike shell and definite segments, this type may represent an intermediate form between the ancestors of annelids and that of mollusks. Its exact status has not been appraised.

1952: *Kramer, G. Orientation of birds to positional changes of sun.*

This discovery showed that birds (starlings and pigeons) can be trained to find food in accordance with the position of the sun. It was found that the general orientation of the birds shifted at a rate (when exposed to a constant artificial sun) that could be predicted on the basis of the birds' correcting for the normal rotation of the earth. Birds were able to orient themselves in a definite direction with reference to the sun, whether the light of the sun reached them directly or was reflected by mirrors. They were capable also of finding food at any time of day, thus indicating an ability to compensate for the sun's motion across the sky.

1952: *Palade, G. E. Analysis of the finer structure of the mitochondrion.*

The important role of mitochondria in the enzymatic systems and cellular metabolism has focused much investigation on the structure of these cytoplasmic inclusions. Each mitochondrion is bounded by two membranes; the outer is smooth and the inner is thrown into small folds or cristae that project into a homogenous matrix in the interior. Some modifications of this pattern are found.

1952: *Tuzet, O., R. Loubatieres, and M. Pavans de Ceccatty. Discovery of nerve cells in sponges.*

Bipolar and multipolar cells with long processes have been described on histologic and staining grounds in a variety of sponges. The processes connect choanocytes and contractile cells and apparently function in the coordination of pore size and water intake. Although more physiologic verification is needed, this finding indicates that sponges must have some integration.

1952: *Zinder, N., and J. Lederberg. Discovery of the transduction principle.*

Transduction is the transfer of DNA from one bacterial cell to another by means of a phage. It occurs when an infective phage picks up from its disintegrated host a small fragment of the host's DNA and carries it to a new host where it becomes a part of the genetic equipment of the new bacterial cell.

Lederberg, Nobel Laureate (1958).

1953: *Crick, F. H. C., and J. D. Watson. Chemical structure of DNA.*

Crick and Watson formulated the hypothesis that the DNA molecule was made up of two chains twisted around each other in a helical structure and cross-linked by pairs of bases—adenine and thymine or guanine and cytosine. Genes are considered to be segments of these molecules. Each of these complementary strands act as a model or template to form a new strand. The hypothesis has been widely accepted and affords a clue to the chemical structure of inheritance and the way chromosomes duplicate themselves.

Nobel Laureates (1962).

1953: *Lwoff, A. Concept of the prophage.*

When a bacterial virus enters a bacterial cell, it may enter a vegetative state and produce more phage, or it may become a property of the bacterial cell and become incorporated into the genetic material of its host. The bacterial cell can then reproduce itself and the phage through many generations. The term prophage is the hereditary ability to produce bacteriophage under such conditions.

Nobel Laureate (1965).

1953: *Palade, G. E. Discovery of cytoplasmic ribosomes.*

The discovery of ribonucleic acid–rich granules (usually on the endoplasmic reticulum) represents one of the key links in the unraveling of the genetic code. The ribosomes (about 250 Å in diameter) serve as the site of protein synthesis; the number of ribosomes (polysomes) involved in the synthesis of a protein depends on the length of messenger RNA and the protein being synthesized.

1953: *Urey, H., and S. Miller. Demonstration of the possible primordia of life.*

By exposing a mixture of water vapor, ammonia, methane, and hydrogen gas to electric discharge (to simulate lightning) for several days, these investigators found that several complex organic substances, such as the amino acids glycine and alanine, were formed when the water vapor was condensed into water. This demonstration offered a very plausible theory to explain how the early beginnings of life substances could have started by the formation of organic substances from inorganic ones.

1954: *Dan, J. C. Acrosome reaction.*

In echinoderms, annelids, and mollusks it has been shown that the acrosome region of the spermatozoan forms a filament and releases an unknown substance at the time of fertilization. Evidence seems to indicate that the filament is associated with the formation of the fertilization cone. Other observers had described similar filaments before Dan made his detailed descriptions. The filament (about 25 μ long) may play an important role in the entrance of the sperm into the cytoplasm.

1954: *Du Vigneaud, V. Synthesis of pituitary hormones.*

This investigator isolated the posterior pituitary hormones, oxytocin and vasopressin. Both were found to be polypeptides of amino acids, and oxytocin was the first polypeptide hormone to be produced artificially. Oxytocin contracts the uterus during childbirth and releases the mother's milk; vasopressin raises blood pressure and decreases urine production.

1954: *Huxley, H. E., A. F. Huxley, and J. Hanson. Theory of muscular contraction.*

By means of electron microscopic studies and x-ray diffraction studies these investigators showed that the proteins actin and myosin were found as separate filaments that apparently produced contraction by a sliding reaction in the presence of ATP. The concept currently has been widely accepted.

A. F. Huxley, Nobel Laureate (1963).

1954: *Loomis, W. F. Sexual differentiation in Hydra.*

By discovering that high pressures of free carbon dioxide and reduced aeration in stagnant water (and not temperature as formerly supposed) induces sexuality in *Hydra,* an explanation was found for the large number of sexual forms found in the fall when many individuals crowd together and build up gas pressure generated by their respiration. This work has suggested new methods of attack on some of the problems of growth and differentiation.

1954: *Sanger, F. Structure of the insulin molecule.*

Insulin is the important hormone used in the treatment of diabetes. The discovery of its structure was the first complete description of a protein molecule. The molecule was found to be made up of 17 different amino acids in 51 amino acid units. Although one of the smallest proteins, its formula contains 777 atoms. This achievement has given encouragement for investigating the structure of other protein molecules.

Nobel Laureate (1958).

1955: *Fraenkel-Conrat, H., and R. C. Williams. Analysis of the chemical nature of a virus.*

In tobacco mosaic virus these workers were able to separate the protein, which makes up the outer cylinder of the virus, from the nucleic acid, the inner core of the cylinder. Neither the protein fraction nor the nucleic acid by itself was able to grow or infect tobacco, but when the two fractions were recombined, the resulting particles behaved like the original virus. Hybrids were also produced by combining the protein of one strain with nucleic acid of a different strain. In the case of hybrids, the progeny assume the properties of the virus from which the nucleic acid came. Such investigations throw additional light upon the organization of biologically active material as well as upon certain aspects of inheritance.

1955-1957: *Kornberg, A., and S. Ochoa. Biologic synthesis of nucleic acids.*

By mixing the enzyme polymerase, extracted from the bacterium *Escherichia coli,* with a mixture of nucleotides and a tiny amount of DNA, Kornberg was able to produce synthetic DNA. Ochoa obtained the synthesis of RNA in a similar manner by using the enzyme polynucleotide phosphorylase from the bacterium *Azo-*

tobacter vinelandii. This significant work reveals more insight into the mechanism of nucleic acid duplication in the cell.

Nobel Laureates (1959).

1956: *Bekesy, G. von. The traveling wave theory of hearing.*

Helmholtz (1868) had proposed the resonance theory of hearing on the basis that each cross fiber of the basilar membrane, which increases in width from the base to the apex of the cochlea, resonates at a different frequency; von Bekesy showed that a traveling wave of vibration is set up in the basilar membrane and reaches a maximal vibration in that part of the membrane appropriate for that frequency.

Nobel Laureate (1961).

1956: *Borsook, H., and P. C. Zamecnik. Site of protein synthesis.*

By injecting radioactive amino acids into an animal, it was found that the ribosome of the endoplasmic reticulum is the place where proteins are formed. This discovery represents an important landmark in the structure of molecular biology and the genetic code.

1956: *Casper, D. L. D., and R. Franklin. The basic structure of a virus.*

These investigators showed that the essential structure of a virus consisted of a core of nucleic acid surrounded by a protein shell on the outside. The nucleic acid may be RNA or DNA, depending on the virus. Virus research has done much to unravel certain aspects of hereditary and other patterns.

1956: *Ingram, V. M. Nature of a mutation.*

By tracing the change in one amino acid unit out of more than 300 units that make up the protein hemoglobin, Ingram was able to pinpoint the difference between normal hemoglobin and the mutant form of hemoglobin that causes sickle cell anemia. This experiment is of great significance in determining the effect of a single genetic mutation on the molecular structure of body materials as well as in throwing some light on the exact mechanism of heredity.

1956: *Peart, W. S., and D. F. Elliot. Isolation of angiotensin.*

Ever since Volhard in 1928 suggested that a substance in the kidney might be responsible for certain cases of hypertension, investigators have been trying to identify this substance. Among the landmarks in the development of the concept were the Goldblatt clamp (an artificial constriction of the renal artery) that caused something in the kidney to elevate blood pressure; the discovery of the enzyme renin by Page and others; the action of this enzyme on a blood protein (renin substrate) to form an inactive substance (angiotensin I); and finally the conversion of the inactive form into the active angiotensin II by means of a converting enzyme. Although a protective mechanism for the body in times of stress, prolonged release of angiotensin caused by repeated stress could result in types of chronic hypertension.

1956: *Tjio, J. H., and A. Levan. Revision of human chromosome count.*

The time-honored number of chromosomes in man, 48 (diploid), was found by careful cytologic technique to be 46 instead. This investigation is of considerable interest because it throws some light on the difficulties of accurate chromosome counts, especially when the number is great or the chromosomes are highly irregular in shape and size.

1957: *Benzer, S. Concept of the cistron.*

The newer view of the gene has greatly changed the classic concept of the gene as an entity that controlled mutation, hereditary recombination, and function. There are actually several subunits, of which the cistron, the unit of function, is the largest. Many units of recombination may be found in a single cistron. The mutation unit (muton) is variable but usually consists of two to five nucleotides.

1957: *Calvin, M. Chemical pathways in photosynthesis.*

By using radioactive carbon 14, Calvin and colleagues were able to analyze step by step the incorporation of carbon dioxide and the identity of each intermediate product involved in the formation of carbohydrates and proteins by plants.

Nobel Laureate (1961).

1957: *Holley, R. W. The role of tRNA in protein synthesis.*

Nucleotides of tRNAs differ from each other only in their bases. Holley also devised methods that precisely established the tRNAs that were used in the transfer of certain amino acids to the site of protein synthesis.

Nobel Laureate (1968).

1957: *Ivanov, A. V. Analysis of phylum Pogonophora (beard worms).*

Specimens of this phylum were collected in 1900 and represent the most recent phylum to be discovered and evaluated in the animal kingdom. Collections have been made in the waters of Indonesia, the Okhotsk Sea, the

Bering Sea, and the Pacific Ocean. They are found mostly in the abyssal depths. They belong to the Deuterostomia division and appear to be related to the Hemichordata. At present 80 species divided into two orders have been described.

1957: *Perutz, M. F., and J. C. Kendrew. Structure of hemoglobin.*

The mapping of a complex globular protein molecule of 600 amino acids and 10,000 atoms arranged in a three-dimensional pattern represented one of the great triumphs in biochemistry. Myoglobin of muscle, which acts as a storehouse for oxygen and contains only one heme group instead of four (hemoglobin), was found to contain 150 amino acids.

Nobel Laureates (1962).

1957: *Sauer, F. Celestial navigation by birds.*

By subjecting old world warblers to various synthetic night skies of star settings in a planetarium, Sauer was able to demonstrate that the birds made use of the stars to guide them in their migrations. The birds used were hand raised and had never traveled under a natural sky, yet they were able with their precise time sense to adjust their orientation to the geography of the earth and its relation to the heavenly constellations, even when the synthetic conditions of the latter were vastly different from their surroundings.

1957: *Taylor, J. H., P. S. Woods, and W. L. Hughes. Application of the tracer method to organization and replication of chromosomes.*

By using radioactive materials as markers, these investigators were able to show that each new chromosome consists of one half of old material and one half of newly synthesized substances. This was confirmation of the Crick-Watson model of the nucleic acid molecule that is supposed to divide or unwind into two single threads, and each half reduplicates itself to form a complete double strand.

1958: *Hall, D. A., and others. Discovery of cellulose in human skin.*

The upsurge of interest in connective tissue in the past few years has been due partly to the many unsolved problems of the structure and chemistry of this tissue and partly to the relation of connective tissue to the pathology of atherosclerosis and other disorders. The possibility that the different fibers are interconvertible has been one of the many challenges of this versatile tissue, and the discovery of cellulose in man's skin recalls similar structures in the tunic of ascidians. Cellulose is more common in the aged, which may indicate a return to a primitive condition.

1958: *Lerner, A. B. Discovery of melatonin in the pineal gland.*

Although in an experimental stage, this substance has been assigned the role of a biologic clock in regulating gonadal functions by a neurosecretory mechanism. This discovery represented a breakthrough in understanding the function of the pineal gland.

1958: *Meselson, M., and F. W. Stahl. Confirmation "in vivo" of the duplicating mechanism in DNA.*

This was really confirmation of the self-copying of DNA in accordance with Watson and Crick's scheme of the structure of DNA. These investigators found that after producing a culture of bacterial cells labeled with heavy nitrogen 15 and then transferring these bacteria to a cultural medium of light nitrogen 14, the resulting bacteria had a DNA density intermediate between heavy and light as would be expected on the basis of the Watson-Crick hypothesis.

1959: *Ford, C. E., P. A. Jacobs, and J. H. Tjio. Chromosomal basis of sex determination in man.*

By discovering that certain genetic defects were associated with an abnormal somatic chromosomal constitution, it was possible to determine that the male-determining genes in man were located on the Y chromosome. Thus a combination of XXY (47 instead of the normal 46 diploid number) produced sterile males (Klinefelter's syndrome), and those with XO combinations (45 diploid number) gave rise to Turner's disease or immature females.

1959: *Leakey, L. S. B. Discovery of Zinjanthropus fossil man.*

This fossil is represented by a skull that shows the morphologic characters of a man and is thought to be in direct line of human ancestry. It seems to be definitely more advanced than its fossil relative Australopithecus and was a toolmaker. It was found in the Olduval Gorge, Tanganyika, South Africa.

1959: *LeJeune, J., M. Gautier, and R. Turpin. Abnormal chromosome pattern in man.*

The discovery of the presence of an extra chromosome (autosome) in the tissue cultures obtained from mongolian children has aroused much interest in the human cytogenetic pattern in its relation to disease states. This was the first clear-cut case of such an etiologic mechanism in the explanation of a disease and has stimulated many investigations of clinical interest along similar lines. Such a condition of an extra chromosome is called **trisomy;** a condition of one less chromosome is called **monosomy.**

1960: *Barski, G., S. Sorieul, and F. Cornefert. Hybrid somatic cell technique.*

When two different cultures of mouse-cancer cells were mixed together, in the course of time some cells of a new type containing the chromosomes of both parents in a single nucleus appeared. These hybrid cells had arisen from the fusion of pairs of cells of the two different types. J. F. Watkins and H. Harris (1965), English investigators, showed that a virus killed by exposure to ultraviolet light could be used to fuse together cells from mouse and man, thus producing artificial man-mouse hybrid cells. The study of hybrid cells may throw some light on the difficult problem of differentiation and the genetic analysis of enzyme syntheses.

1960: *Hurwitz, J., A. Stevens, and S. Weiss. Enzymatic synthesis of messenger RNA.*

The exciting development in the coding system between DNA and the site of protein synthesis (ribosomes) was further elucidated when it was discovered that an enzyme, RNA polymerase, was responsible for the synthesis of RNA from a template pattern of DNA. This form of RNA provides a direct transcription of the DNA genetic code. In 1962 two other forms of RNA, ribosomal RNA and transfer RNA (also from DNA), were found to be involved in the specific linking of amino acids in the protein chain.

1960: *Jacob, F., and J. Monod. The operon hypothesis.*

The operon hypothesis is a postulated model of how enzyme synthesis is regulated in the cell. The model proposes that refinement in regulation involves an inducible system for allowing structural genes to synthesize needed enzymes and a repressible system that cuts off the synthesis of unneeded enzymes.

Nobel Laureates (1965).

1960: *Strell, M., and R. B. Woodward. Synthesis of chlorophyll a.*

Strell and Woodward with the aid of many co-workers finally solved this problem that had been the goal of organic chemists for many generations. Since all biologic life depends on this important pigment, this achievement in molecular biology must have wide implications.

Woodward, Nobel Laureate (1965).

1960: *Towne, C. Development of the laser.*

The development of coherent light of light waves of finite wavelength and frequency has given biologists and workers in other disciplines a potential tool whose uses are just now emerging.

Nobel Laureate (1964).

1960: *Zalokar, M. Pattern of protein synthesis.*

By means of radioactive isotope of hydrogen (H_3) this investigator was able to trace uracil from its incorporation in RNA in the nucleus to the ribosomes of the cytoplasm, thus giving strong confirmation of the role of messenger RNA as outlined by the hypothesis of Jacob and Monod.

1961: *Hurwitz, J., A. Stevens, and S. B. Weiss. Confirmation of messenger RNA.*

This factor in the genetic code process has been suspected by many workers in molecular biology from their investigations. Messenger RNA transcribes directly the genetic message of the nuclear DNA and moves to the cytoplasm where it becomes associated with a number of ribosomes or submicroscopic particles containing protein and nonspecific structural RNA. Here the messenger RNA molecules serve as templates against which amino acids are arranged in the sequence corresponding to the coded instructions carried by messenger RNA.

1961: *Jacob, F., and J. Monod. The role of messenger RNA in the genetic code.*

The transmission of information from the DNA code in the genes to the ribosomes represents an important step in the unraveling of the genetic code, and these investigators proposed certain deductions for confirmation of the hypothesis, which in general has been established by many researchers.

Nobel Laureates (1965).

1961: *Miller, J. F. A. Function of the thymus gland.*

Long known as a transitory organ that persists during the early growth period of animals, the thymus is now recognized as the source of the first antibody-producing cells. Later these cells migrate to the lymph nodes and other places, where they continue the production of antibodies as needed.

1961: *Nirenberg, M. W., and J. H. Matthaei. The role of DNA-directed RNA in protein synthesis.*

By adding a synthetic RNA composed entirely of uracil nucleotides to a mixture of amino acids, these investigators obtained a polypeptide made up solely of a single amino acid, phenylalanine. On the basis of a triplet code, it was concluded that the RNA code word for phenylalanine was UUU and its DNA complement was AAA. This was the beginning of coding the various amino acids and represents a key demonstration for understanding the genetic code.

Nirenberg, Nobel Laureate (1968).

1962: *Perry, R. P. Cellular sites of synthesis of RNA.*

By using different labeled RNA precursors and other cytochemical techniques, this investigator concluded that messenger RNA and transfer RNA are produced by the chromosomes of the cell; the ribosomal RNA of greater molecular weight is produced in the nucleolus.

1963: *Cairns, J. Confirmation of the manner of replication of the DNA molecule.*

By using autoradiography, Cairns was able to follow step-by-step the duplication of the daughter strands in the circular two-stranded DNA molecule of the single chromosome of *Escherichia coli.* The preciseness of the time and manner of the unwinding of the original strands and the formation of the daughter strands gives this demonstration much significance.

1963: *Wells, J. W. Concept of the fossil coral clock.*

By means of daily striations within the annual bands of calcium carbonate deposits found in certain fossil coral material, it has been possible to ascertain the difference between the length of day in geologic times and that of the present, based on the deceleration of 2 seconds per 100,000 years in the earth's rotation about its axis (424 days for a year in Cambrian time).

1964: *Hoyer, B. H., B. J. McCarthy, and E. T. Bolton. Phylogeny and DNA sequence.*

These investigators presented evidence that certain homologies exist among the polynucleotide sequences in the DNA sequence of such different forms as fish and man. Such sequences may represent genes that have been retained with little change throughout vertebrate history. Possible phenotypic expressions may be bilateral symmetry, notochord, hemoglobin, etc.

1966: *Khorana, H. G. Proof of code assignments in the genetic code.*

By using alternating codons (CUC and UCU) in an artificial RNA chain, it was possible to synthesize a polypeptide of alternating amino acids (leucine and serine) for which these codons respectively stood.

Nobel Laureate (1968).

● Books and publications that have greatly influenced development of zoology

Aristotle. 336-323 B.C. De anima, historia animalium, de partibus animalium, de generatione animalium. *These biologic works of the Greek thinker have exerted an enormous influence on biologic thinking for centuries.*

Vesalius, Andreas. 1543. De fabrica corporis humani. *This work is the foundation of modern anatomy and represents a break with the Galen tradition. His representations of anatomic subjects, such as the muscles, have never been surpassed. Moreover, he treated anatomy as a living whole, a viewpoint present-day anatomists are beginning to copy.*

Fabricius of Aquapendente. 1600-1621. De formato foetu and de formatione ovi pulli. *This was the first illustrated work on embryology and may be said to be the beginning of the modern study of development.*

Harvey, William. 1628. Anatomical dissertation concerning the motion of the heart and blood. *This great work represents one of the first accurate explanations in physical terms of an important physiologic process. It initiated an experimental method of observation that gave an impetus to research in all fields of biology.*

Descartes, Rene. 1637. Discourse on method. *The physiologic section of this book gave a great stimulus to a mechanistic interpretation of biologic phenomena.*

Buffon, Georges. 1749-1804. Histoire naturelle. *This extensive work of many volumes collected together natural history facts in a popular and pleasing style. It had a great influence in stimulating a study of nature. Many eminent biologic thinkers, such as Erasmus Darwin and Lamarck, were influenced by its generalizations, which here and there suggest an idea of evolution in a crude form.*

Linnaeus, Carolus. 1758. Systema naturae. *In this work there is laid the basis for the classification of animals and plants. With few modifications, the taxonomic principles outlined therein have been universally adopted by biologists.*

Wolff, Caspar Friedrich. 1759. Theoria generationis. *The theory of epigenesis was here set forth for the first time in opposition to the preformation theory of development so widely held up to the time of Wolff's work.*

Haller, Albrecht von. 1760. Elementa physiologiae. *An extensive summary of various aspects of physiology that greatly influenced physiologic thinking for many years. Some of the basic concepts therein laid down are still considered valid, especially those on the nervous system.*

Malthus, T. R. 1798. Essay on population. *This work stimulated evolutionary thinking among such men as Darwin and Wallace.*

Lamarck, Jean Baptiste. 1809. Philosophie zoologique. *This publication was of great importance in focusing the attention of biologists upon the problem of the role of the environment as a factor in evolution. Lamarck's belief that all species came from other species represented one of the first clear-cut statements on the mutability of species, even though his method of use and disuse has not been accepted by most biologists.*

Cuvier, Georges. 1817. Le règne animal. *A comprehensive biologic work that dealt with classification and a comparative study of animal structures. Its plates are still of value, but the general plan of the work was marred by a disbelief in evolution and a faith in the doctrine of geologic catastrophes. The book, however, exerted an enormous influence upon contemporary zoologic thought.*

Baer, Karl Ernst von. 1828-1837. Entwickelungsgeschichte der Thiere. *In this important work are laid down the fundamental principles of germ layer formation and the similarity of corresponding stages in the development of embryos that have proved to be the foundation studies of modern embryology.*

Audubon, John J. 1828-1838. The birds of America. *The greatest of all ornithologic works, it has served as the model for all monographs dealing with a specific group of animals. The plates, the work of a master artist, have never been surpassed in the field of biologic achievement.*

Lyell, Charles. 1830-1833. Principles of geology. *From a biologic viewpoint this great work exerted a profound influence on biologic thinking, for it did away with the theory of catastrophism and prepared the way for an evolutionary interpretation of fossils and the forms that arose from them.*

Beaumont, William. 1833. Experiments and observations on the gastric juice and the physiology of digestion. *In this classic work the observations Beaumont made on various functions of the stomach and digestion were so thorough that only a few details have been added by subsequent research. This book paved the way for the brilliant investigations of Pavlov, Cannon, and Carlson of later generations.*

Müller, Johannes. 1834-1840. Handbook of physiology. *The principles set down in this work by the greatest of all physiologists have set the pattern for the development of the science of physiology.*

Darwin, Charles. 1839. Journal of researches (Voyage of the *Beagle*). *This book reveals the training and development of the naturalist and the material that led to the formulation of Darwin's concept of organic evolution.*

Schwann, Theodor. 1839. Mikroskopische Untersuchungen über die Uebereinstimmung in der Struktur und dem Wachstum der Thiere und Pflanzen. *The basic principles concerning the cell doctrine are laid down in this classic work.*

Kölliker, Albrecht. 1852. Mikroskopische Anatomie. *This was the first textbook in histology and contains contributions of the greatest importance in this field. Many of the histologic descriptions Kölliker made have never needed correction. In many of his biologic views he was far ahead of his time.*

Maury, M. F. 1855. The physical geography of the sea. *This work has often been called the first textbook on oceanography. This pioneer treatise stressed the integration of such knowledge as was then available about tides, winds, currents, depths, circulation, and such matters. Maury's work represents a real starting point in the fascinating study of the oceans and has had a great influence in stimulating investigations in this field.*

Virchow, Rudolf. 1858. Cellularpathologie. *In this work Virchow made the first clear distinction between normal and diseased tissues and demonstrated the real nature of pathologic cells. The work also represents the death knell to the old humoral pathology which has held sway for so long.*

Darwin, Charles. 1859. The origin of species. *One of the most influential books ever published in biology. Although built around the theme that natural selection is the most important factor in evolution, the great influence of the book has been due to the great array of evolutionary evidence it presented. It also stimulated constructive thinking on a subject that had been vague and confusing before Darwin's time.*

Marsh, G. P. 1864. Man and nature: physical geography as modified by human action. *A work that had an early and important influence on the conservation movement in America.*

Owen, Richard. 1866. Anatomy and physiology of the vertebrates. *This work contains an enormous amount of personal observation on the structure and physiology of animals, and some of the basic concepts of structure and function, such as homologue and analogue, are here defined for the first time.*

Brehm, A. E. 1869. Tierleben. *The many editions of this work over many years have indicated its importance as a general natural history.*

Bronn, H. G. (editor). 1873. Klassen und Ordnungen des Tier-Reichs. *This great work is made up of exhaustive treatises on the various groups of animals by numerous authorities. Its growth extends over many years. and is one of the most valuable works ever published in zoology.*

Balfour, Francis M. 1880. Comparative embryology. *This is a comprehensive summary of embryologic work on both vertebrates and invertebrates up to the time it was published. This work is often considered the beginning of modern embryology.*

Semper, K. 1881. Animal life as affected by the natural conditions of existence. *This work first pointed out the modern ecologic point of view and laid the basis for many ecologic concepts of existence that have proved important in the further development of this field of study.*

Butschli, O. 1889. Protozoen (Bronn's Klassen und Ordnungen des Tier-Reichs). *This monograph has been of the utmost importance to students of Protozoa. No other work on a like scale has ever been produced in this field of study.*

Hertwig, R. 1892. Lehrbuch der Zoologie. *A text that has proved to be an invaluable source of material for many generations of zoologists. Its illustrations have been widely used in many other textbooks.*

Weismann, A. 1892. Das Keimplasma. *Weismann predicted from purely theoretic considerations the necessity of meiosis or reduction of the chromosomes in the germ cell cycle—a postulate that was quickly confirmed cytologically by others.*

Hertwig, O. 1893. Zelle und Gewebe. *In this work a clear distinction is made between histology as the science of tissues and cytology as the science of cell structure and function. Cytology as a study in its own right really dates from this time.*

Korschelt, E., and K. Heider. 1893. Lehrbuch der vergleichender Entwicklungsgeschichte der wirbellosen Thiere, 4 vols. *A treatise that has been a valuable tool for all workers in the difficult field of invertebrate embryology.*

Wilson, Edmund B. 1896. The cell in development and heredity. *This and subsequent editions represented the most outstanding work of its kind in the English language. Its influence in directing the development of cytogenetics cannot be overestimated, and in summarizing the many investigations in cytology, the book has served as one of the most useful tools in the field.*

Pavlov, Ivan. 1897. Le travail des glands digestives. *This work marks a great landmark in the study of the digestive system, for it describes many of the now classic experiments that Pavlov conducted, such as the gastric pouch technique and the rate of gastric secretions.*

de Vries, Hugo. 1901. Mutationslehre. *The belief that evolution is due to sudden changes or mutations is advanced by one who is commonly credited with the initiation of this line of investigation into the causes of evoluton.*

Sherrington, Sir Charles. 1906. The integrative action of the nervous system. *The basic concepts of neurophysiology laid down in this book have been little altered since its publication. Much of the work done in this field has served to confirm the nervous mechanism he here outlines.*

Garrod, A. 1909. Inborn errors of metabolism. *This pioneer book showed that certain congenital diseases were caused by defective genes that failed to produce the proper enzymes for normal functioning. It laid the basis for biochemical genetics, which later received a great impetus from the work of Beadle and Tatum.*

Henderson, L. J. 1913. The fitness of the environment. *This book has pointed out in a specific way the reciprocity that exists between living and nonliving nature and how organic matter is fitted to the inorganic environment. It has exerted a considerable influence on ecologic aspects of adaptation.*

Shelford, V. E. 1913. Animal communities in temperate America. *This work was a pioneer in the field of biotic community ecology and has exerted a great influence on ecologic study.*

Bayliss, W. M. 1915. Principles of general physiology. *If a classic book must meet the requirements of masterly analysis and synthesis of what is known in a particular discipline, then this great work must be called one.*

Mathew, W. D. 1915. Climate and evolution. *This book has stimulated much thinking on the importance of climate in the evolutionary process.*

Morgan, T. H., A. H. Sturtevant, C. B. Bridges, and H. J. Muller. 1915. The mechanism of mendelian heredity. *This book gave an analysis and synthesis of mendelian inheritance as formulated from the epoch-making investigations of the authors. This classic work will always stand as a cornerstone of our modern interpretation of heredity.*

Doflein, F. 1916. Lehrbuch der Protozoenkunde, ed. 6 (revised by E. Reichenow, 1949). *A standard treatise on Protozoa. Its many editions have proved helpful to all workers in this field.*

Thompson, D. W. 1917. Growth and form. *This pioneer work deals with the problems of growth and form in relation to physical and mathematical principles. It has thrown much light upon these difficult subjects.*

Kukenthal, W., and T. Krumbach. 1923. Handbuch der Zoologie. *An extensive modern treatise on zoology that covers all phyla. The work has been an invaluable tool for all zoologists who are interested in the study of a particular group.*

Fisher, R. A. 1930. Genetical basis of natural selection. *This work has exerted an enormous influence on the newer synthesis of evolutionary mechanisms so much in vogue at present.*

Barcroft, J. 1934. Features in the architecture of physiological function. *This is a remarkable book of physiologic principles dealing with the integration of certain bodily functions and their significance to the organism as a whole. Such a work gives the student a bearing and an attitude that he rarely gleans in the ordinary physiologic text.*

Dobzhansky, T. 1937. Genetics and the origin of species. *The vast change in the explanation of the mechanism of evolution, which emerged about 1930, is well analyzed in this work by a master evolutionist. Other syntheses of this new biologic approach to the evolutionary problems have appeared since this work was published, but none of them has surpassed the clarity and fine integration of Dobzhansky's work.*

Spemann, H. 1938. Embryonic development and induction. *In this work the author summarizes his pioneer investigations that have proved so fruitful in experimental embryology.*

Schrodinger, E. 1945. What is life? *The emphasis placed on the physical explanation of life gave a new point of view of biologic phenomena so well expressed in the current molecular biologic revolution.*

Grassé, P. P. (editor). 1948. Traité de zoologie. *This is a series of many treatises by various specialists on both invertebrates and vertebrates. Since it is both recent and comprehensive, the work is invaluable to all students who desire detailed information on the various groups.*

Allee, W. C., A. E. Emerson, O. Park, T. Park, and K. P. Schmidt. 1949. Principles of animal ecology. *Ecology is rapidly becoming a major field of biologic study and the basic principles laid down in this comprehensive work will never be outdated.*

Leopold, A. 1949. A sand county almanac. *In the current emphasis on conservation and ecology this work gives an evaluation of the awareness and gist of the problems that society must face to work out an effective ecosystem.*

Blum, H. F. 1951. Time's arrow and evolution. *In this thought-provoking book Blum explores the relation between the second law of thermodynamics (time's arrow) and organic evolution and recognizes that mutation and natural selection have been restricted to certain channels in accordance with the law, even though these two factors appear to controvert the principle of pointing the direction of events in time.*

• GLOSSARY

aboral (ab-o′ral) (L. *ab,* from, + *os,* mouth). A region opposite the mouth.

Acanthocephala (a-kan′tho-sef″a-la) (Gr. *akantha,* spine, thorn, + *kephale,* head). A phylum composed of spinyheaded worms that are pseudocoelomate parasites.

Acipenser (as′i-pen″ser) (L. sturgeon). A genus of sturgeon fish.

acoelomate (a-se′lo-mate) (Gr. *a,* not, + *koilos,* cavity). Without a coelom, such as flatworms and proboscis worms.

Actinopterygii (ak′ti-nop′ter-yj″e-i) (Gr. *aktino,* ray, + *pterygion,* fin or small wing). One of the two main groups of bony fish, or the ray-finned fish.

adenine (ad′e-nen) (Gr. *aden,* gland, + *ine,* suffix). A component of nucleotides and nucleic acids.

adenosine (a-den′o-sen) ***(di-, tri-) phosphate*** (ADP and ATP). Certain phosphorylated compounds that function in the energy cycle of cells.

adipose (ad′i-pos) (L. *adipis,* fat). Fatty tissue.

adrenaline (ad-ren′al-in) (L. *ad,* to, + *renalis,* kidney). A hormone produced by the adrenal, or suprarenal, gland.

aerobic (a′er-o″bik) (Gr. *aeros,* air, + *bios,* life). Oxygen-dependent form of respiration.

afferent (af′er-ent) (L. *ad,* to, + *ferre,* to bear). A structure (blood vessel, nerve, etc.) leading toward some point.

Agnatha (ag′na-tha) (Gr. *a,* not, + *gnathos,* jaw). A class of vertebrates that includes the modern lampreys and hagfish and the extinct ostracoderms.

allantois (a-lan′to-is) (Gr. *allas,* sausage, + *eidos,* form). One of the extraembryonic membranes of the amniotes.

allele (al-lel′) (Gr. *allelon,* of one another). One of a pair, or series, of genes that are alternative to each other in heredity and are situated at the same locus in homologous chromosomes. Allele genes may consist of a dominant and its correlated recessive, or two correlated dominants, or two correlated recessives.

alula (al′u-la) (L. dim. of *ala,* wing). The first digit or thumb of a bird's wing, much reduced in size.

alveolus (al-ve′o-lus) (L. dim. of *alveus,* hollow). A small cavity or pit, such as a microscopic air sac of the lungs, terminal part of an alveolar gland, or bony socket of a tooth.

amino acid (a-me′no) (amine, an organic compound). An organic acid with an amino radical (NH_2). Makes up the structure of proteins.

amitosis (am′i-to″sis) (Gr. *a,* not, + *mitos,* thread). A form of cell division in which mitotic nuclear changes do not occur; cleavage without separation of daughter chromosomes.

amnion (am′ni-on) (Gr. *caul,* probably from dim. of *amnos,* lamb). One of the extraembryonic membranes forming a sac around the embryo in amniotes.

amylase (am′i-las) (L. *amylum,* starch, + *ase,* suffix meaning enzyme). An enzyme that breaks down carbohydrates into smaller units.

anaerobic (an-a′er-o″bik) (Gr. *an,* not, + *aeros,* air, + *bios,* life). Not dependent on oxygen for respiration.

androgen (an′dro-jen) (Gr. *andros,* man, + *genes,* born). Any of a group of male sex hormones.

anhydrase (an-hi′dras) (Gr. *an,* not, + *hydor,* water, + *ase,* enzyme suffix). An enzyme involved in the removal of water from a compound. Carbonic anhydrase promotes the conversion of carbonic acid into water and carbon dioxide.

aperture (ap′er-tur) (L. *aperire,* to uncover). An opening; the slight entrance and exit of certain mollusk shells; longer passages are called siphons.

arboreal (ar-bor′e-al) (L. *arbor,* tree). Living in trees.

archenteron (ar-ken′ter-on) (Gr. *archein,* first, + *enteron,* gut). The central cavity of a gastrula that is lined with endoderm, representing the future digestive cavity.

autosome (aw″to-som) (Gr. *autos,* self, + *soma,* body). Any chromosome that is not a sex chromosome.

autotomy (aw-tot′o-my) (Gr. *autos,* self, + *tomos,* a cutting). The automatic breaking off of a part of the body.

autotroph (aw′to-trof″) (Gr. *autos,* self, + *trophos,* feeder). An organism that makes its organic nutrients from inorganic raw materials.

benthos (ben′thos) (Gr. depth of the sea). Those organisms that live along the bottom of seas and lakes.

biogenesis (bi′o-gen″e-sis) (Gr. *bios,* life, + *genesis,* birth). The doctrine that life originates only from preexisting life.

biomass (bi′o-mas) (Gr. *bios,* life, + *maza,* lump or mass). The weight of a species population per unit of area.

biome (bi-om) (Gr. *bios,* life, + *ome,* group). Complex of communities characterized by climatic and soil conditions; the largest ecologic unit.

blastopore (blas'to-por) (Gr. *blastos,* germ, + *poros,* passage). Opening into archenteron of the gastrula; future mouth in some, future anus in others.

blepharoplast (blef'ah-ro-plast") (Gr. *blepharon,* eyelid). A granule at the base of a flagellum or cilium; a kinetosome.

buffer (buf'er). Any substance or chemical compound that tends to keep pH constant when acids or bases are added.

caenogenesis (see'no-jen"i-sis) (Gr. *kainos,* new, + *genesis,* birth). In the development of an organism, the new stages that have arisen in adaptive response to the embryonic mode of life, such as the fetal membranes of amniotes.

carboxyl (kar-bok'sil) (carbon + oxygen + yl). The acid group of organic molecules —COOH.

carotene (kar'o-ten) (L. *carota,* carrot). A red, orange, or yellow pigment belonging to the group of carotenoids; precursor of vitamin A.

catalyst (cat'a-lyst) (Gr. *kata,* down, + *lysis,* a loosening). A substance that accelerates a chemical reaction but does not become a part of the end product.

cecum (se'kum) (L. *caecus,* blind). A blind pouch at the beginning of the large intestine, or any similar pouch.

Cenozoic (se'no-zo"ik) (Gr. *kainos,* recent, + *zoe,* life). The geologic era from the Mesozoic to the present (about 75 million years).

centriole (sen'tre-ol) (Gr. dim. of *kentron,* center of a circle). A minute granule, usually found in the centrosome and considered to be the active division center of the cell.

centromere (sen'tro-mere) (Gr. *kentron,* center, + *meros,* part). A small body or constriction on the chromosome where it is attached to a spindle fiber.

Chaetognatha (ke-tog'nath-a) (Gr. chaite, bristle, hair, + *gnathos,* jaw). Small marine worms, often called arrowworms, with curved bristles on each side of mouth; an enterocoelomate phylum.

chelicera (ke-lis'e-ra) (Gr. *chele,* claw). Pincerlike head appendage on the members of the subphylum Chelicerata.

cholinergic (ko'li-ner-jik). Type of nerve fiber that releases acetylcholine from axon terminal.

chorion (ko're-on) (Gr. membrane). The outer of the double membrane that surrounds the embryo of the amniotes; in mammals it helps form the placenta.

chromatid (kro'ma-tid) (Gr. *chromat,* color, + *id,* daughter). A half chromosome between early prophase and metaphase in mitosis; a half chromosome between synapsis and second metaphase in meiosis; at the anaphase stage each chromatid is known as a daughter chromosome.

chromomere (kro'mo-mer) (Gr. *chroma,* color, + *meros,* part). The chromatin granules of characteristic size on the chromosome; may be identical with genes or clusters of genes.

circadian (cir"ca-de'an) (L. *circa,* around, + *dies,* day). A period of about 24 hours.

climax (cli'max) (Gr. *klimax,* ladder). A state of dynamic equilibrium; a culmination of the succession in the biota of a community.

clone (Gr. *klon,* twig). A group of animals produced by asexual reproduction from a single individual.

coelogastrula (se'lo-gas"tru-la) (Gr. *koilos,* hollow, + *gaster,* stomach). The typical gastrula derived from a coeloblastula; a two- or three-layered stage in embryology.

coelom (se'lum) (Gr. *koilos,* hollow). The body cavity in triploblastic animals, lined with mesoderm.

coenzyme (ko-en'zim) (Gr. *koinos,* common, + *en,* in, + *zyme,* leaven). A required substance in the activation of an enzyme.

commensalism (ko-men'sal-iz"m) (L. *cum,* together, + *mensa,* table). A symbiotic relationship in which one benefits and the other is unharmed.

community (com-mu'ni-ty) (L. *communitas,* common). An assemblage of organisms that are associated together in a common environment and interact with each other in a self-sustaining and self-regulating relation.

cotylosaur (kot"i-lo-sor') (Gr. *kotyle,* hollow, + *sarous,* lizard). A primitive group of fossil reptiles that arose from the labyrinthodont amphibians and became the ancestral stem of all other reptiles.

Ctenophora (te-nof'o-ra) (Gr. *ktenos,* comb, + *phoros,* bearing). A small phylum of marine animals consisting of three germ layers and eight rows of comb plates by which they move.

cytochrome (si"to-krom') (Gr. *kytos,* vessel, + *chroma,* color). One of the hydrogen carriers in aerobic respiration.

deoxyribose (de-ok"se-ri'bos) (*deoxy,* loss of oxygen, + *ribose,* pentose sugar). A 5-carbon sugar having 1 oxygen atom less than ribose; a component of deoxyribose nucleic acid (DNA).

diploid (dip'loid) (Gr. *diploos,* double, + *eidos,* form). The somatic number of chromosomes, or twice the number characteristic of a gamete of a given species.

DPN Abbreviation of diphosphopyridine nucleotide, a hydrogen carrier in respiration. Now called NAD, nicotinamide adenine dinucleotide.

Echiuroidea (ek'i-u-roi"de-a) (Gr. *echis,* adder, + *oura,* tail, + *eidos,* form, + *ea,* pl. suffix). A phylum of wormlike animals that inhabit marine coastal mud flats.

ecologic equivalence Ecologic types of the same requirements, which are in similar but geographically separated environments.

ecologic niche The status of an organism in a community with reference to its responses and behavior patterns.

ecosystem (ek'o-sys-tem) (Gr. *ek,* out of, + system). An ecologic unit consisting of both biotic communities and the nonliving (abiotic) environment that interact to produce a stable system.

ecotone (ek'o-ton) (Gr. *oikos,* home, + *tonos,* stress). The transition zone between two adjacent communities.

ectohormone (ek'to-hor"mone) (Gr. *ektos,* outside, + *hormon,* excite). A pheromone; a substance secreted externally by an organism to influence the behavior of other organisms; an ectocrine.

ectoplasm (ec"to-plaz'm) (Gr. *ektos,* outside, + *plasma,* form). The cortex of a cell or that part of cytoplasm just under the cell surface; contrasts with endoplasm.

emulsion (e-mul'shun) (L. *emulsus,* milked out). A colloidal system in which both phases are liquids.

endergonic (end'er-go"nik) (Gr. *endon,* within, + *egron,* work). A chemical reaction that requires energy.

endocrine (en'do-krin) (Gr. *endon,* within, + *krinein,* to separate). Refers to a gland that is without a duct and that releases its product directly into the blood or lymph.

endoplasm (en"do-plaz'm) (Gr. *endon,* within, + *plasma,* form). That portion of cytoplasm that immediately surrounds the nucleus.

endoplasmic reticulum (en"do-plas'mic) (Gr. *endon,* within, + *plasma,* mold or form). The cytoplasmic double membrane with ribosomes (rough) or without ribosomes (smooth).

endostyle (en"do-stil') (Gr. *endon,* within, + *stylos,* column). A ciliated groove in the floor of the pharynx of tunicates, amphioxus, and ammocoetes, used for getting food; may be homologous to the thyroid gland of higher forms.

enterocoel (en"ter-o-sel') (Gr. *enteron,* gut, + *koilos,* hollow). A type of coelom that is formed by the outpouching of a mesodermal sac from the endoderm of the primitive gut.

enterocoelomate (en'ter-o-sel"o-mate) (Gr. *enteron,* gut, + *koilos,* hollow, + *ate,* state of). Those that have an enterocoel, such as the echinoderms and the vertebrates.

Entoprocta (en'to-prok"ta) (Gr. *entos,* within, + *proktos,* anus). A phylum of sessile animals that have the anus enclosed in the ring of ciliated tentacles.

enzyme (en'zym) (Gr. *en,* in, + *zyme,* leaven). A protein substance produced by living cells that is capable of speeding up specific chemical transformations, such as hydrolysis, oxidation, or reduction, but is unaltered itself in the process; a biological catalyst.

epididymis (ep'i-did"i-mis) (Gr. *epi,* over, + *didymos,* testicle). That part of the sperm duct that is coiled and lying near the testis.

epigenesis (ep'i-jen"e-sis) (Gr. *epi,* over, + *genesis,* birth). The embryologic view that an embryo is a new creation that develops and differentiates step by step from an initial stage; the progressive production of new parts that were nonexistent as such in the original zygote.

epigenetics (ep'i-je-net"iks) (Gr. *epi,* over, + *genesis,* birth). That study of the mechanisms by which the genes produce phenotypic effects.

estrogen (es'tro-jen) (Gr. *oistros,* frenzy, + *genes,* born). An estrus-producing hormone; one of a group of female sex hormones.

eurytopic (yu're-top"ic) (Gr. *eurys,* broad, + *topos,* place). Refers to an organism with a wide range of distribution.

exergonic (ek'ser-go"nik) (Gr. *exo,* outside of, + *ergon,* work). An energy-yielding reaction.

exocrine (ek'so-krin) (Gr. *exo,* outside, + *krinein,* to separate). That type of gland that releases its secretion through a duct.

exteroceptor (ek"ster-o-sep'ter) (L. *exterus,* outward, + *capere,* to take). A sense organ near the skin or mucous membrane that receives stimuli from the external world.

FAD Abbreviation for flavine adenine dinucleotide, a hydrogen acceptor in the respiratory chain.

fermentation (fur'men-ta"shun) (L. *fermentum,* ferment). The conversion of organic substances into simpler substances under the influence of enzymes, with little or no oxygen involved (anaerobic respiration).

fiber, fibril (L. *fibra,* thread). These two terms are often confused. Fiber is a strand of protoplasmic material produced or secreted by a cell and lying outside the cell, or a fiberlike cell. Fibril is a strand of protoplasm produced by a cell and lying within the cell.

Foraminifera (fo-ram'i-nif"er-a) (L. *foramen,* hole, + *ferre,* to bear). An order of sarcodine protozoans with slender branched pseudopodia (myxopodia) that are extruded through holes in their calcareous shells.

gamete (ga'mete) (Gr. *gamos,* marriage). A mature germ cell, either male or female.

Gastropoda (gas-trop'o-da) (Gr. *gaster,* stomach, + *podos,* foot). A class of mollusks consisting of slugs and snails.

Gastrotricha (gas-trot'ri-ka) (Gr. *gaster,* stomach, + *trichos,* hair). A class of aquatic pseudocoelomate animals with cilia or bristles on the body.

gel (jel) (L. *gelare,* to freeze). That state of a colloidal system in which the solid particles form the continuous phase and the fluid medium the discontinuous phase.

gene (jen) (Gr. *genes,* born). That part of a chromosome that is the hereditary determiner and is transmitted from one generation to another. It occupies a fixed chromosomal locus and can best be defined only in a physiologic or operational sense.

genome (jen'om) (Gr. *genos,* race). The total number of genes in a haploid set of chromosomes.

genotype (jen'o-typ) (Gr. *genos,* race, + *typos,* form). The genetic constitution, expressed and latent, of an organism; the particular set of genes present in the cells of an organism; opposed to phenotype.

genus (pl., genera) (je'nus) (L. *genus,* race). A taxonomic rank between family and species.

germ layer In the animal embryo, one of three basic

layers (ectoderm, endoderm, mesoderm) from which the various organs and tissues arise in the multicellular animal.

germ plasm. The germ cells of an organism, as seen from the somatoplasm.

gestation (jes-ta'shun) (L. *gestare,* to bear). The period in which offspring are carried in the uterus.

Golgi body (gol'je) (after Golgi, Italian histologist). A cytoplasmic component that may play a role in certain cell secretions or may represent a region where high-energy compounds from the mitochondria collect.

habitat (hab'i-tat) (L. *habitare,* to dwell). The place where an organism normally lives or where individuals of a population live.

haploid (hap'loid) (Gr. *haploos,* single). The reduced number of chromosomes typical of gametes, as opposed to the diploid number of somatic cells.

Hemichordata (hem'i-kor-da"ta) (Gr. *hemi,* half, + L. *chorda,* cord). A phylum of wormlike animals with close affinities to the chordates; body of proboscis, collar, and trunk, with stomochord or rudimentary notochord.

hermaphrodite (hur-maf'ro-dit) (Gr. *Hermaphroditos,* containing both sexes; from Greek mythology, son of Hermes and Aphrodite). An organism with both male and female organs. Hermaphroditism commonly refers to an abnormal condition in which male and female organs are found in the same animal; monoecious is a normal condition for the species.

heterotroph (het"er-o-trof') (Gr. *heteros,* another, + *trophos,* feeder). An organism that obtains both organic and inorganic raw materials from the environment in order to live.

heterozygote (het'er-o-zi"got) (Gr. *heteros,* another, + *zygotos,* yolked). An organism in which the pair of alleles for a trait is composed of different genes (usually dominant and recessive); derived from a zygote formed by the union of gametes of dissimilar genetic constitution.

homology (ho-mol'o-ji) (Gr. *homologia,* similarity). Similarity in embryonic origin and adult structure, based on descent from a common ancestor.

homozygote (ho'mo-zi"got) (Gr. *homos,* same, + *zygotos,* yolked). An organism in which the pair of alleles for a trait is composed of the same genes (either dominant or recessive but not both).

humoral (hu'mer-al) (L. *humor,* a fluid). Pertaining to a body fluid such as blood or lymph.

hydrolysis (hi-drol'i-sis) (Gr. *hydor,* water, + *lysis,* a loosening). The decomposition of a chemical compound by the addition of water; the splitting of a molecule into its groupings so that the split products acquire hydrogen and hydroxyl groups.

hydroxyl (hi-drok'sil) (Gr. *hydor,* water, + oxygen, + yl). Containing an OH— group, a negatively charged ion formed by alkalies in water.

hypertonic (hi'per-ton"ik) (Gr. *hyper,* over, + *tonos,* tension). Refers to a solution whose osmotic pressure is greater than that of another solution with which it is compared; contains a greater concentration of particles and gains water through a semipermeable membrane from a solution containing fewer particles.

hypothalamus (hi'po-thal"a-mus) (Gr. *hypo,* under, + *thalamos,* inner chamber). A ventral part of the forebrain beneath the thalamus; one of the centers of the autonomic nervous system.

hypotonic (hi'po-ton"ik) (Gr. *hypo,* under, + *tonos,* tension). Refers to a solution whose osmotic pressure is less than that of another solution with which it is compared or taken as standard; contains a lesser concentration of particles and loses water during osmosis.

inductor (in-duk'tor) (L. *inducere,* to introduce). In embryology a tissue or organ that causes the differentiation of another tissue or organ.

invagination (in-vaj'i-na"shun) (L. *in,* in, + *vagina,* sheath). An infolding of a layer of tissue to form a saclike structure.

isotope (i'so-top) (Gr. *isos,* equal, + *topos,* place). One of several different forms of a chemical element, differing from each other physically but not chemically.

keratin (ker'a-tin) (Gr. *keratos,* horn). A protein found in epidermal tissues and modified into hard structures such as horns, hair, and nails.

kinetosome (ki-net'o-som) (Gr. *kinetos,* moving, + *soma,* body). The granule at the base of the flagellum or cilium; similar to centriole.

kinin (kin'in) (Gr. *kinetos,* moving). A type of local hormone that is released near its site of origin.

Kinorhyncha (kin'o-ring"cha) (Gr. *kineo,* move, + *rhynchos,* beak). A class of pseudocoelomate animals belonging to the phylum Aschelminthes (Hyman). Same as Echinodera.

labyrinthodont (lab'i-rin"tho-dont) (Gr. *labyrinthos,* labyrinth, + *odontos,* tooth). A group of fossil stem amphibians from which most amphibians later arose. They date from the late Paleozoic.

lacteal (lak'te-al) (L. *lactis,* milk). Refers to one of the lymph vessels in the villus of the intestine.

lagena (la-je'na) (L. large flask). Portion of the primitive ear in which sound is translated into nerve impulses; evolutionary beginning of cochlea.

leukocyte (lu'ko-site) (Gr. *leukos,* white, + *kytos,* cell). A common type of white blood cell with beaded nucleus.

lipase (li'pas) (Gr. *lipos,* fat, + *ase,* enzyme suffix). An enzyme that converts fatty acids and glycerin; it may also promote the reverse reaction.

lipid, lipoid (lip'id) (Gr. *lipos,* fat). Pertains to certain fattylike substances that often contain other groups such as phosphoric acid.

lithosphere (lith'o-sfer) (Gr. *lithos,* rock). The rocky component of the earth's surface layers.

littoral (lit'o-ral) (L. *litus,* seashore). The floor of the sea from the shore to the edge of the continental shelf.

lophophore (lo'fo-for) (Gr. *lophos,* crest, + *phoros,* bearing). Tentacle-bearing ridge or arm that is an extension of the coelomic cavity in lophophorate animals.

luciferase (lu-sif′er-ase) (L. *lux,* light, + *ferre,* to bear). An enzyme involved in light production in organisms.

macronucleus (mak′ro-nu″kle-us) (Gr. *makros,* large, + *nucleus,* nut). The larger of the two kinds of nuclei in ciliate protozoa; controls all cell functions except reproduction.

marsupial (mar-su′pi-al) (Gr. *marsypion,* pouch). One of the pouched mammals of the subclass Metatheria.

Mastigophora (mas′ti-gof″o-ra) (Gr. *mastix,* whip, + *phoros,* bearing). A protozoan class whose members have flagella for locomotion; sometimes called flagellates.

matrix (ma′trix) (L. *mater,* mother). The intercellular substance of a tissue, or that part of a tissue into which an organ or process is set.

maxilla (mak-sil′a) (L. jaw). One of the upper jawbones in vertebrates; one of the head appendages in arthropods.

maxilliped (mak-sil′i-ped) (L. *maxilla,* jaw, + *pedis,* foot). One of the three pairs of head appendages located just posterior to the maxilla in crustaceans.

medulla (me-dul′a) (L. marrow). The inner portion of an organ in contrast to the cortex or outer portion; hindbrain.

medusa (me-du′sa) (Greek mythology, female monster with snake-entwined hair). A jellyfish, or the free-swimming stage in the life cycle of coelenterates.

meiosis (mi-o′sis) (Gr. *meioun,* to make small). That nuclear change by which the chromosomes are reduced from the diploid to the haploid number.

menopause (men′o-poz) (Gr. *menos,* month, + *pauein,* to cease). In the human female that time when reproduction ceases; cessation of the menstrual cycle.

menstruation (men′stru-a″shun) (L. *mensis,* month). The discharge of blood and uterine tissue from the vagina at the end of a menstrual cycle.

mesoglea (mes′o-gle″a) (Gr. *mesos,* middle, + *gloios,* glutinous substance). The jellylike gelatinous filling between the ectoderm and endoderm of certain coelenterates and comb jellies.

metabolism (me-tab″o-liz′m) (Gr. *metabole,* change). A group of processes that includes nutrition, production of energy (respiration), and synthesis of more protoplasm; the sum of the constructive (anabolism) and destructive (catabolism) processes.

metamorphosis (met′a-mor″fo-sis) (Gr. *meta,* beyond, + *morphe,* form). A sudden change in structure after the completion of embryonic development.

micron (μ) (mi′kron) (Gr. *mikros,* small). One one-thousandth of a millimeter; about 1/25,000 of an inch.

micronucleus (mi′kro-nu″kle-us). A small nucleus found in ciliate protozoa; controls the reproductive functions of these organisms.

microsome (mi′kro-som) (Gr. *soma,* body). A constituent of cytoplasm that contains RNA and is the site of protein synthesis.

miracidium (mi′ra-sid″e-um) (Gr. *meirakidion,* youthful person). A minute ciliated larval stage in the life of flukes.

mitochondria (mit′o-kon″dre-a) (Gr. *mitos,* a thread, + *chondros,* a small roundish mass). Minute granules, rods, or threads in the cytoplasm and the seat of important cellular enzymes.

Mollusca, mollusk (mol-lus′ka, mol′usk) (L. *molluscus,* soft). Mollusca is a major phylum of schizocoelomate animals; body typically of visceral mass, foot, and shell; comprises snails, clams, squids, and others.

monosaccharide (mo′no-sak″a-rid) (Gr. *monos,* one, + *sakcharon,* sugar). A simple sugar that cannot be decomposed into smaller sugar molecules; contains five or six carbon atoms.

morphogenesis (mor′fo-jen″e-sis) (Gr. *morphe,* form, + *genes,* born). Development of the architectural features of organisms.

morphology (mor-fol′o-ji) (Gr. *morphe,* form, + *logos,* study). The science of structure. Includes cytology, or the study of cell structure; histology, or the study of tissue structure; and anatomy, or the study of gross structure.

mutation (mu-ta′shun) (L. *mutare,* to change). A stable and abrupt change of a gene; the heritable modification of a character.

myofibril (mi′o-fi″bril) (Gr. *myos,* muscle, + L. *fibra,* thread). A contractile filament within muscle or muscular fiber.

myosin (mi′o-sin) (Gr. *myos,* muscle). A protein found in muscle; important component in the contraction of muscle.

myxedema (mik′se-de″ma) (Gr. *myxa,* slime, + *oidema,* a swelling). A disease that results from thyroid deficiency in the adult; characterized by swellings under the skin.

nekton (nek′ton) (Gr. *nektos,* swimming). Term for the actively swimming organisms in the ocean.

Nematomorpha (nem′a-to-mor″fa) (Gr. *nematos,* thread, + *morphe,* form). Hairworms, a pseudocoelomate class of phylum Aschelminthes.

notochord (no′to-kord) (Gr. *noton,* back, + *chorda,* cord). A rod-shaped cellular body along the median plane and ventral to the central nervous system in chordates.

nucleic acid (nu-kle′ik) (L. *nucleus,* nut). One of a class of molecules composed of joined nucleotides; chief types are deoxyribonucleic acid (DNA), found only in cell nuclei (chromosomes), and ribonucleic acid (RNA), found both in cell nuclei (chromosomes and nucleoli) and in cytoplasm (microsomes).

nucleolus (nu-kle′o-lus) (dim. of nucleus). A deeply staining body within the nucleus of a cell and containing RNA.

nucleoprotein (nu′kle-o-pro″tein). A molecule composed of nucleic acid and protein; occurs in two types, depending on whether the nucleic acid portion is DNA or RNA.

nucleotide (nu″kle-o-tid′). A molecule consisting of phosphate, 5-carbon sugar (ribose or deoxyribose), and a purine or a pyrimidine; the purines are adenine and guanine, and the pyrimidines are cytosine, thymine, and uracil.

nymph (nimf) (L. *nympha,* a young woman). The immature form of an insect that undergoes a gradual metamorphosis.

ontogeny (on-toj′e-ni) (Gr. *ontos,* being, + *gennao,* bring forth). The development of an individual from egg to senescence.

operculum (o-pur′ku-lum) (L. cover). The gill cover in bony fish.

organism (or″gan-iz′m). An individual plant or animal, either unicellular or multicellular.

osmosis (os-mo′sis) (Gr. *osmos,* impulse). The process in which water migrates through a semipermeable membrane, from a side containing a lesser concentration to the side containing a greater concentration of particles. The diffusion of a solvent (usually water) through a semipermeable membrane.

Osteichthyes (os′te-ik″thy-ez) (Gr. *osteon,* bone, + *ichthys,* fish). A class of vertebrates comprising the bony fish.

ostium (os′te-um) (L. mouth). A mouthlike opening.

oviparity, oviparous (o′vi-par″i-ti, o-vip′a-rus) (L. *ovum,* egg, + *parere,* to bring forth). Reproduction in which eggs are released by the female; development of offspring occurs outside the maternal body.

ovoviviparity, ovoviviparous (o′vo-viv′i-par″i-ti, o′vo-vivip″a-rus) (L. *ovum,* egg, + *vivere,* to live, + *parere,* to bring forth). Reproduction in which eggs develop within the maternal body without nutrition by the female parent.

oxidation (ok′si-da″shun) (Gr. *oxys,* acid). Rearrangement of a molecule to create a high-energy bond; a chemical change in which a molecule loses one or more electrons.

Paleozoic (pa′le-o-zo″ik) (Gr. *palaios,* old, + *zoe,* life). The geologic era between the Precambrian and the Mesozoic, approximately from 550 to 200 million years ago.

palingenesis (pal′in-gen″e-sis) (Gr. *palin,* backward, + *genesis,* birth). The stages in the development or ontogeny of an animal that are inherited from ancestral species, such as gill slits in the unborn of mammals.

papilla (pa-pil′a) (L. nipple). A small nipplelike projection.

parapodia (par′a-po″di-a) (Gr. *para,* beside, + *podos,* foot). The segmental appendages in polychaete worms that serve in breathing, locomotion, and creation of water currents.

parasympathetic (par′a-sim′pa-thet″ik) (Gr. *para,* bedside, + *sympathes,* sympathetic). One of the subdivisions of the autonomic nervous system, whose centers are located in the brain, anterior part of the spinal cord, and posterior part of the spinal cord.

parthenogenesis (par′the-no-jen″e-sis) (Gr. *parthenos,* virgin, + *genesis,* birth). The development of an unfertilized egg; a type of sexual reproduction.

pathogenic (path′o-jen″ic) (Gr. *pathos,* disease, + *gennao,* produce). Producing a disease.

pedogenesis (pe′do-jen″e-sis) (Gr. *pais,* child, + *genes,* born). Reproduction by young or larval forms, especially parthenogenesis.

peduncle (pe-dung′kl) (L. dim. of *pedis,* foot). A stalk; a band of white matter joining different parts of the brain.

pelagic (pe-laj′ik) (Gr. *pelagos,* the open sea). Pertaining to the open ocean.

Pelecypoda (pel′e-sip″o-da) (Gr. *pelekus,* hatchet, + *podos,* foot). A class of the phylum Mollusca comprising clams, mussels, and oysters.

pentadactyl (pen′ta-dak″til) (Gr. *pente,* five, + *daktylos,* finger). With five digits.

peptidase (pep′ti-das) (Gr. *peptein,* to digest, + *ase,* enzyme suffix). An enzyme that breaks down amino acids from a peptide.

peristalsis (per′i-stal″sis) (Gr. *peri,* around, + *stalsis,* contraction). The series of alternate relaxations and contractions by which food is forced through the alimentary canal.

peritoneum (per′i-to-ne″um) (Gr. *peri,* around, + *teinein,* to stretch). The membrane that lines the abdominal cavity and covers the viscera.

petrifaction (pet′ri-fak″shun) (L. *petra,* stone, + *facere,* to make). The changing of organic matter into stone.

pH A symbol of the relative concentration of hydrogen ions in a solution; pH values are from 0 to 14, and the lower the value, the more acid or hydrogen ions in the solution.

phagocyte (fag′o-sit) (Gr. *phagein,* to eat, + *kytos,* cell). A white blood cell of the body, that devours and destroys microorganisms or other harmful substances.

phenotype (fe′no-tip) (Gr. *phainein,* to show). The visible characters; opposed to genotype of the hereditary constitution.

Phoronida (fo-ron′i-da) (Gr. *phoros,* bearing, + L. *nidus,* nest). A phylum of wormlike, marine, tube-dwelling, schizocoelomate animals.

phosphagen (fos′fa-jen) (phosphate + glycogen). A term for creatine-phosphate and arginine-phosphate, which store and may be sources of high-energy phosphates.

phosphorylation (fos′fo-ri-la″shun). The addition of a phosphate group, such as H_2PO_3, to a compound.

phylogeny (fi-loj′e-ni) (Gr. *phylon,* tribe, + *gennao,* bring forth). The evolutionary history of a group of organisms.

phylum (pl., phyla) (fi′lum) (Gr. *phylon,* race, tribe). A chief category of taxonomic classification into which living things are divided.

pinocytosis (pi″-no-cy-tosis) (Gr. *pinein,* to drink, + *kytos,* cell, + *osis,* condition). A process of cell drinking.

placenta (pla-sen′ta) (L. flat cake; from Gr. *plax, plakos,* anything flat and broad). The vascular structure, embryonic and maternal, through which the embryo and fetus are nourished while in the uterus.

plankton (plangk'ton) (Gr. *planktos,* wandering). The floating animal and plant life of a body of water.

plasma membrane (plazma) (Gr. *plasma,* formed). The thin membrane that surrounds the cytosome; considered a part of the cytoplasm.

plastid (plas'tid) (Gr. *plastes,* one who forms, + *id,* daughter). A small body in the cytoplasm that often contains pigment.

Platyhelminthes (plat'y-hel-min"thes) (Gr. *platys,* flat, + *helmins,* worm). Flatworms; a phylum of acoelomate animals; consists of planarians, flukes, and tapeworms.

pleopod (ple'o-pod) (Gr. *plein,* to swim, + *podos,* foot). One of the swimming feet on the abdomen of a crustacean.

plesiosaur (ple"si-o-sor') (Gr. *plesios,* near, + *sauros,* lizard). A long-necked, marine reptile of Mesozoic times.

pleura (ploor'a) (Gr. side). The membrane that lines each half of the thorax and covers the lungs.

plexus (plek'sus) (L. braid). A network, especially of nerves or of blood vessels.

polarization (po'ler-i-za"shun) (L. *polaris,* pole). The arrangement of positive electric charges on one side of a surface membrane and negative electric charges on the other side (in nerves and muscles).

polymorphism (pol'i-mor"fizm) (Gr. *polys,* many, + *morphe,* form). The presence in a species of more than one type of individual.

polyp (pol'ip) (L. *polypus,* many-footed). The sessile stage in the life cycle of coelenterates.

polypeptide (pol'i-pep"tid) (Gr. *polys,* many, + *peptein,* to digest). A molecule consisting of many joined amino acids, not as complex as a protein.

polyphyletic (pol'i-fi-let"ik) (Gr. *polys,* many, + *phylon,* tribe). Derived from more than one ancestral type; contrasts with monophyletic, or from one ancestor.

polysaccharide (pol'i-sak"a-rid) (Gr. *polys,* many, + *sakcharon,* sugar). A carbohydrate composed of many monosaccharide units, such as glycogen, starch, and cellulose.

Porifera (po-rif'e-ra) (L. *porus,* pore, + *ferre,* to bear). The phylum of sponges.

Priapulida (pri'a-pu"li-da) (Gr. *priapos,* phallus, + *ida,* pl. suffix). A small phylum of pseudocoelomate animals.

progesterone (pro-jes'ter-on) (L. *pro,* before, + *gestare,* to carry). Hormone secreted by the corpus luteum and the placenta; prepares the uterus for the fertilized egg and maintains the capacity of the uterus to hold the embryo and fetus.

prothrombin (pro-throm'bin) (L. *pro,* before, + *thrombus,* clot). A constituent of blood plasma that is changed to thrombin by thombokinase in the presence of calcium ions; involved in blood clotting.

pterosaur (ter'o-sor) (Gr. *pteron,* feather, + *sauros,* lizard). An extinct flying reptile that flourished during the Mesozoic.

puff The pattern of swelling of specific bands or gene loci on giant chromosomes during the larval and imaginal stages of flies.

pylorus (pi-lo'rus) (Gr. *pyle,* gate, + *ouros,* watcher). The opening between the stomach and duodenum which is guarded by a valve.

pyrenoid (pi're-noid) (Gr. *pyren,* fruit stone, + *eidos,* form). A protein body in the chloroplasts of certain organisms that serves as a center for starch formation.

Radiolaria (ra'de-o-la"re-a) (L. dim. of radius). A group of sarcodine protozoa, characterized by silicon-containing shells.

redia (re'de-a) (from Redi, Italian biologist). A larval stage in the life cycle of flukes; it is produced by a sporocyst larva, and in turn gives rise to many cercariae.

retina (ret'i-na) (L. *rete,* a net). The sensitive, nervous layer of the eye.

rhabdocoel (rab'do-sel) (Gr. *rhabdos,* rod, + *koilos,* a hollow). A member of a group of free-living flatworms possessing a straight, unbranched digestive cavity.

rostrum (ros'trum) (L. ship's beak). A snoutlike projection on the head.

Rotifera (ro-tif'er-a) (L. *rota,* wheel, + *ferre,* to bear). A class of microscopic pseudocoelomate animals belonging to the phylum Aschelminthes.

Sarcodina (sar'ko-di"na) (Gr. *sarkos,* flesh). A class of Protozoa; includes *Amoeba,* Foraminifera, Radiolaria, etc.; characterized by pseudopodia.

sarcolemma (sar'ko-lem"a) (Gr. *sarkos,* flesh, + *lemma,* rind). The thin noncellular membrane of striated muscle fiber or cell.

schizocoel, schizocoelomate (skiz'o-sel) (Gr. *schizein,* to split). Schizocoel is a coelum formed by a splitting of embryonic mesoderm. Schizocoelomate is an animal with a schizocoel, such as an arthropod or mollusk.

sclerotic (skle-rot'ik) (Gr. *skleros,* hard). The tough outer coat of the eyeball.

scrotum (skro'tum) (L. bag). The pouch that contains the testes and accessory organs in most mammals.

seminiferous (sem'i-nif"er-us) (L. *semen,* semen, + *ferre,* to bear). Pertains to the tubules that produce or carry semen in the testes.

semipermeable (sem'i-pur"me-a-bl') (L. *semi,* half, + *permeabilis,* capable of being passed through). Permeable to small particles, such as water and certain inorganic ions, but not to colloids, etc.

septum (sep'tum) (L. fence). A wall between two cavities.

sere (ser) (L. *serere,* to join). The sequence or series of communities that develop in a given situation from pioneer to terminal climax communities during ecologic succession.

serum (ser'um) (L. whey). The plasma of blood that separates on clotting; the liquid that separates from the blood when a clot is formed.

simian (sim'e-an) (L. *simia,* ape). Pertains to monkeys.

Sipunculida (si-pun-kyu″li-da) (L. *sipunculus*, small siphon). A phylum of wormlike schizocoelomate animals.

soma (so′ma) (Gr. body). The body of an organism in contrast to the germ cells (germ plasm).

somatic (so-mat′ik) (Gr. *soma*, body). Refers to the body, such as somatic cells in contrast to germ cells.

speciation (spe′shi-a″shun) (L. *species*, kind). The evolving of two or more species by the splitting of one ancestral species.

spermatheca (spurm′a-the″ka) (Gr. *sperma*, seed, + *theke*, a case). A sac in the female reproductive organs for the storage of sperm.

sphincter (sfingk′ter) (Gr. *sphingein*, to bind tight). A ring-shaped muscle capable of closing a tubular opening by constriction.

sporocyst (spo′ro-sist) (Gr. *sporos*, seed, + *kystis*, pouch). A larval stage in the life cycle of flukes; it originates from a miracidium.

Sporozoa (spo′ro-zo″a) (Gr. *sporos*, seed, + *zoon*, animal). A class of parasitic Protozoa.

sporozoite (spo′ro-zo″it) (Gr. *sporos*, seed, + *zoon*, animal, + *ite*, offspring, dim.). A motile spore formed from the zygote in many Sporozoa.

stenotopic (sten′o-top″ic) (Gr. *stenos*, narrow, + *topos*, place). Refers to an organism with restricted range.

stereogastrula (ste′re-o-gas″tru-la) (Gr. *stereos*, solid, + *gaster*, stomach). A solid type of gastrula, such as the planula of coelenterates.

sterol, steroid (ste′rol, ste′roid) (Gr. *stereos*, solid, + *ol* [L. *oleum*, oil]). One of a class of organic compounds containing a molecular skeleton of four fused carbon rings; it contains cholesterol, sex hormones, adrenocortical hormones, and vitamin D.

stoma (sto′ma) (Gr. mouth). A mouthlike opening.

stratum (L. *stratum*, covering). A horizontal layer or division of a biologic community that exhibits stratification of habitats (ecologic).

substrate (sub′strat) (L. *substratus*, strewn under). A substance that is acted upon by an enzyme.

symbiosis (sim′be-o″sis) (Gr. *sym*, with, + *bios*, life). The living together of two different species in an intimate relationship; includes mutualism, commensalism, and parasitism.

synapse (si-naps′) (Gr. *synapsis*, union). The place at which a nerve impulse passes from an axon of one nerve cell to a dendrite of another nerve cell.

syncytium (sin-sish′i-um) (Gr. *syn*, together, + *kytos*, cell). A mass of protoplasm containing many nuclei and not divided into cells.

tagma (tag′ma) (Gr. arrangement). Body division of an arthropod, containing two or more segments.

taiga (ti′ga) (Russ.). Habitat zone characterized by large tracts of coniferous forests, long, cold winters, and short summers; most typical in Canada and Siberia.

telencephalon (tel′en-sef″a-lon′) (Gr. *telos*, end, + *encephalon*, brain). The most anterior vesicle of the brain.

teleology (te′le-ol″o-ji) (Gr. *telos*, end, + *logos*, study). The philosophic view that natural events are goal directed and are preordained; contrasts with scientific view of causalism.

template (tem′plet). A pattern or mold guiding the formation of a duplicate; often used with reference to gene duplication.

tentaculocyst (ten-tak″u-lo-syst′) (L. *tentaculum*, feeler, + Gr. *kystis*, pouch). A sense organ of several parts along the margin of medusae and derived from a modified tentacle; sometimes called rhopalium.

tetrapoda (te-trap′o-da) (Gr. four-footed ones). Four-legged vertebrates; the group includes amphibians, reptiles, birds, and mammals.

therapsid (the-rap′sid) (Gr. *theraps*, an attendant). Extinct Mesozoic mammal-like reptile, from which true mammals evolved.

thrombokinase (throm′bo-kin″as) (Gr. *thrombos*, lump, + *kinein*, to move, + *ase*, enzyme suffix). Enzyme released from blood platelets that initiates the process of clotting; transforms prothrombin into thrombin in presence of calcium ions; thromboplastin.

trachea (tra′ke-a) (ML. windpipe, trachea). The windpipe; any of the air tubes of insects.

transduction (trans-duk′shun) (L. *trans*, across, + *ducere*, to lead). Transfer of genetic material from one bacterium to another through the agency of virus.

trochophore (trok″o-for′) (Gr. *trochos*, wheel, + *phoros*, bearing). A free-swimming ciliated marine larva characteristic of schizocoelomate animals; common to many phyla.

trophallaxis (trof′al-lak″sis) (Gr. *trophos*, feeder, + *allaxis*, exchange). Exchange of food between young and adults, especially among those of certain social insects.

trophozoite (trof′o-zo″it) (Gr. *trephein*, to nourish, + *zoon*, animal, + *ite*, offspring, dim.). That stage in the life cycle of a sporozoan in which it is actively absorbing nourishment from the host.

tundra (toon′dra) (Russ.). Terrestrial habitat zone, between taiga in south and polar region in north; characterized by absence of trees, short growing season, and mostly frozen soil during much of the year.

typhlosole (tif′lo-sol) (Gr. *typhlos*, blind, + *solen*, channel). A longitudinal fold projecting into the intestine in certain invertebrates such as the earthworm.

urethra (u-re′thra) (Gr. *ourethra*, urethra). The tube from the urinary bladder to the exterior in both sexes.

uriniferous tubule (u′ri-nif″er-us) (L. *urina*, urine, + *ferre*, to bear). One of the tubules in the kidney extending from a malpighian body to the collecting tubule.

Urochordata (u′ro-kor-da″ta) (Gr. *oura*, tail, + L. *chorda*, cord). A subphylum of chordates; often called the Tunicata.

utricle (u′tri-kl) (L. *utriculus*, little bag). That part of the inner ear containing the receptors for dynamic body balance; the semicircular canals lead from and to the utricle.

vacuole (vak'u-ol) (L. *vacuus,* empty, + *ole,* dim.). A fluid-filled space in a cell.

vagility (va-jil'i-ty) (L. *vagus,* wandering). Ability to tolerate environmental variation or the ability to cross ecologic barriers. Example: Birds have high and mollusks very low vagility.

vestige (ves'tij) (L. *vestigium,* footprint). A rudimentary structure that is well developed in some other species or in the embryo.

villus (vil'us) (L. tuft of hair). A small fingerlike process on the wall of the small intestine and on the embryonic portion of the placenta.

virus (vi'rus) (L. slimy liquid poison). A submicroscopic noncellular particle, composed of a nucleoprotein core and a protein shell; parasitic and will grow and reproduce in a host cell.

viscera (vis'er-a) (L., pl. of *viscus,* internal organ). Internal organs in the body cavity.

vitalism (vi'tal-iz'm) (L. *vita,* life). The view that natural processes are controlled by supernatural forces and cannot be explained through the laws of physics and chemistry alone; contrasts with mechanism.

vitamin (vi'ta-min) (L. *vita,* life). An organic substance contributing to the formation or action of cellular enzymes; essential for the maintenance of life.

vitelline membrane (vi-tel'in) (L. *vitellus,* yolk of an egg). The noncellular membrane that encloses the egg cell.

viviparity, viviparous (viv'i-par"i-ti, vi-vip'a-rus) (L. *vivus,* alive, + *parere,* to bring forth). Reproduction in which eggs develop within the female body, with nutritional aid of maternal parent; offspring are born as juveniles.

xanthophyll (zan'tho-fil) (Gr. *xanthos,* yellow, + *phyllon,* leaf). One of a group of yellow pigments found widely among plants and animals; the xanthophylls are members of the carotenoid group of pigments.

zygote (zi'got) (Gr. *zygotos,* yoked). The cell formed by the union of a male and a female gamete; the fertilized egg.

• INDEX

B

D

H

I

J

M

Q

R

U